D1208704

Teacher's Edition

Discovering Advanced Algebra

An Investigative Approach

Jerald Murdock

Ellen Kamischke

Eric Kamischke

DISCOVERING

MATHEMATICS™

Project Editor
Joan Lewis

Project Administrator
Erin Gray

Consulting Editors
Christian Aviles-Scott, Heather Dever, Ladie Malek, Josephine Noah

Mathematics Consultant and Writer
Larry Copes

Teacher Consultant
Jennifer North Morris

Teacher Reviewer
William Putnam

Multicultural Reviewer
Swapna Mukhopadhyay

Accuracy Checkers
Dudley Brooks, Monica Johnston, Abby Tanenbaum

Production Director
Diana Jean Ray

Editorial Production Manager
Deborah Cogan

Production Editor
Christine Osborne

Copyeditor
Mary Roybal

Production Coordinator
Ann Rothenbuhler

Cover Designer
Jill Kongabel

Text Designer
Marilyn Perry

Art Editor
Jason Luz

Photo Editor
Margee Robinson

Illustrators
Robert Arnow, Pamela Hobbs, William Pasini, Sue Todd

Technical Art
Matt Perry, Jason Luz

Compositor and Prepress
TSI Graphics

Printing
Von Hoffmann Press

Executive Editor
Casey FitzSimons

Publisher
Steven Rasmussen

This material is based upon work supported by the National Science Foundation under award number MDR9154410. Any opinions, findings, and conclusions or recommendations expressed in this publication are those of the authors and do not necessarily reflect the views of the National Science Foundation.

Key Curriculum Press
1150 65th Street
Emeryville, CA 94608
510-595-7000
editorial@keypress.com
www.keypress.com

Printed in the United States of America

10 9 8 7 6 5 4   10 09 08 07 06

ISBN 13: 978-1-55953-940-1
ISBN 10: 1-55953-940-2

Key Curriculum Press Texas Consultants

(in alphabetical order)

Amy Gaskins, EdD

Math Specialist

AIMS PreK-16, NSF Grant

Del Mar College, Corpus Christi, Texas

Reviewer of Texas Support Materials: *Discovering Algebra, Discovering Geometry, Discovering Advanced Algebra*

TEXTEAMS Leader

Pamela Weber Harris

Independent Consultant

Content Reviewer: *Discovering Algebra*

Reviewer of Texas Support Materials: *Discovering Algebra, Discovering Geometry, Discovering Advanced Algebra*

TEXTEAMS

Co-author: Algebra II/Precalculus Institute, *Rethinking Middle School Mathematics:* Algebraic Reasoning, *Rethinking High School Mathematics:* Algebraic and Geometric Modeling

Author: *Algebra 1: 2000 and Beyond*

Reviewer: *Elementary Assessments,* High School Mathematics from an Advanced Perspective Institute

Contributing author for Agile Mind Algebra II

Co-author: *Mathematics TEKS Refinement Project*

Editor and writer: T^3 (Teachers Teaching with Technology) *Algebra Institute*

T^3 National Instructor

TEXTEAMS Leader

Garland Linkenhoger

Independent Consultant

Content Reviewer: *Discovering Algebra*

Writer of Texas Lesson Plans, Scope and Sequence: *Discovering Algebra*

Reviewer of Texas Support Materials: *Discovering Algebra, Discovering Geometry, Discovering Advanced Algebra*

TEXTEAMS Leader

Kelli Mallory

Coordinator of Secondary Mathematics, Frisco ISD

Reviewer of Texas Support Materials: *Discovering Algebra, Discovering Geometry, Discovering Advanced Algebra*

TEXTEAMS

Reviewer: *Algebra 1 Assessments and the Geometry Assessments*

TEXTEAMS Leader

Susan May

Charles A. Dana Center, University of Texas at Austin

Writer of Texas Lesson Plans, Scope and Sequence: *Discovering Geometry*

Content Reviewer: *Discovering Geometry*

Reviewer of Texas Support Materials: *Discovering Algebra, Discovering Geometry, Discovering Advanced Algebra*

TEXTEAMS

Co-author: Algebra II/Precalculus, *Geometry Across the TEKS,* Geometry, Foundation of Functions

Author: Training module for *Geometry Assessments* and *Algebra II Assessments*

Co-author: *Advanced Placement™ Mathematics Vertical Teams Toolkit*

Contributing author and developmental editor for Agile Mind Geometry, Algebra II, Precalculus, and Calculus

TEXTEAMS Leader

Anne Papakonstantinou, EdD

Clinical Assistant Professor of Mathematics, Wiess School of Natural Sciences, Rice University

Director, Rice University School Mathematics Project

Content Reviewer: *Discovering Algebra*

Richard Parr

Director of Secondary Education and Educational Technology, Rice University School Mathematics Project

Content Reviewer: *Discovering Algebra*

Tim Pope

Key Curriculum Press

Charles A. Dana Center, University of Texas at Austin

Writer of Texas Lesson Plans, Scope and Sequence: *Discovering Advanced Algebra*

Reviewer of Texas Support Materials: *Discovering Algebra, Discovering Geometry, Discovering Advanced Algebra*

Key Resources for Texas Teachers

This teacher's edition will help you use *Discovering Advanced Algebra* in ways that will best support your Texas students. The essay on "Teaching with *Discovering Advanced Algebra*" (pages xxix–xxxvi) contains valuable information about a discovery classroom, including the benefits of cooperative learning and how to implement it in your classroom, and tips about assessment, planning, and structuring the class period. You will also find helpful suggestions on how to promote inquiry.

The Teaching Resources package includes additional instructional support and many practice and assessment tools. You'll also find effective assistance with technology. Many investigations in *Discovering Advanced Algebra* make use of graphing calculators, and some use data collection devices, such as motion sensors. Separate calculator notes provide step-by-step instructions for several models of calculators. *Discovering Advanced Algebra Demonstrations with Fathom and The Geometer's Sketchpad* contains activities that use Fathom Dynamic Data™ and The Geometer's Sketchpad®. These and other teaching resources are available online.

Texas Edition

The Texas Scope and Sequence (pages T4–T13 or online at www.keypress.com/texas as an editable Excel worksheet) associates each important algebra concept (and the time you will need to teach that concept) with lessons from *Discovering Advanced Algebra,* Texas Essential Knowledge and Skills statements, Texas Assessment of Knowledge and Skills objectives, a summary of big ideas, and Dana Center resources. The TEKS standards and TAKS objectives are written out the first time. The list of technology resources on pages T14–T15 shows how to integrate The Geometer's Sketchpad, Fathom, and data-collection devices.

Texas Lesson Plans

Web resources for Texas Teachers at www.keypress.com/texas include a Lesson Plan for each lesson from the scope and sequence as a printable PDF or an editable Word document. The sample lesson plan on the opposite page shows that each plan includes lesson objectives, materials needed, a lesson outline, the algebra TEKS and previous TEKS reviewed, LEP suggestions, strategies for students requiring extra study, and suggestions for homework. The second lesson-plan page lists Texas resources that apply to the lesson; additional technology resources available from Key Curriculum Press; a TEKS discussion guide with guiding questions, and a blank space for your notes.

Other Texas Resources

Additional resources in the *Discovering Advanced Algebra Texas Implementation Guide* include a pacing guide that will enable you to cover the required topics prior to Texas standardized tests. If you have time to teach additional lessons for enrichment, or if you teach on a block schedule, you might refer to the Pacing Options chart on pages xxxvii–xli for additional pacing alternatives.

The supplemental lessons in the implementation guide provide extra practice on the few Texas standards that are not emphasized in the textbook. These extra Texas lessons are included on the Scope and Sequence. The guide also contains a technology resource chart that will let you easily see all the technology that can enhance a chapter.

The guide also gives instructions for installing the *Discovering Advanced Algebra TestCheck™: Test Generator and Worksheet Builder* software so that test and practice items are correlated to the TEKS. Once installed with the Texas standards, you will be able to create multiple-choice or free-response practice problems on specific TEKS.

For Texas teachers, we offer additional test preparation. The *Discovering Mathematics Texas Test Preparation* book includes quizzes and tests designed to help students prepare for the ninth-, tenth-, and eleventh-grade TAKS test. You can use the quizzes and tests most appropriate for your students' grade levels.

Discovering Advanced Alebra Online and Keymath.com

Teachers who have registered at www.keyonline.com can make available to their students an electronic version of the *Discovering Advanced Algebra* textbook. Additional Key resources for students and their parents and tutors can be found at www.keymath.com/DA. Students will find Dynamic Algebra® Explorations that allow them to manipulate dynamic algebraic sketches. The site also contains Web links arranged by lesson, and downloadable *More Practice Your Skills* worksheets and *Calculator Notes,* arranged by chapter. Additional resources for parents and tutors include *Condensed Lessons* available both in English and Spanish.

Sample Lesson Plan

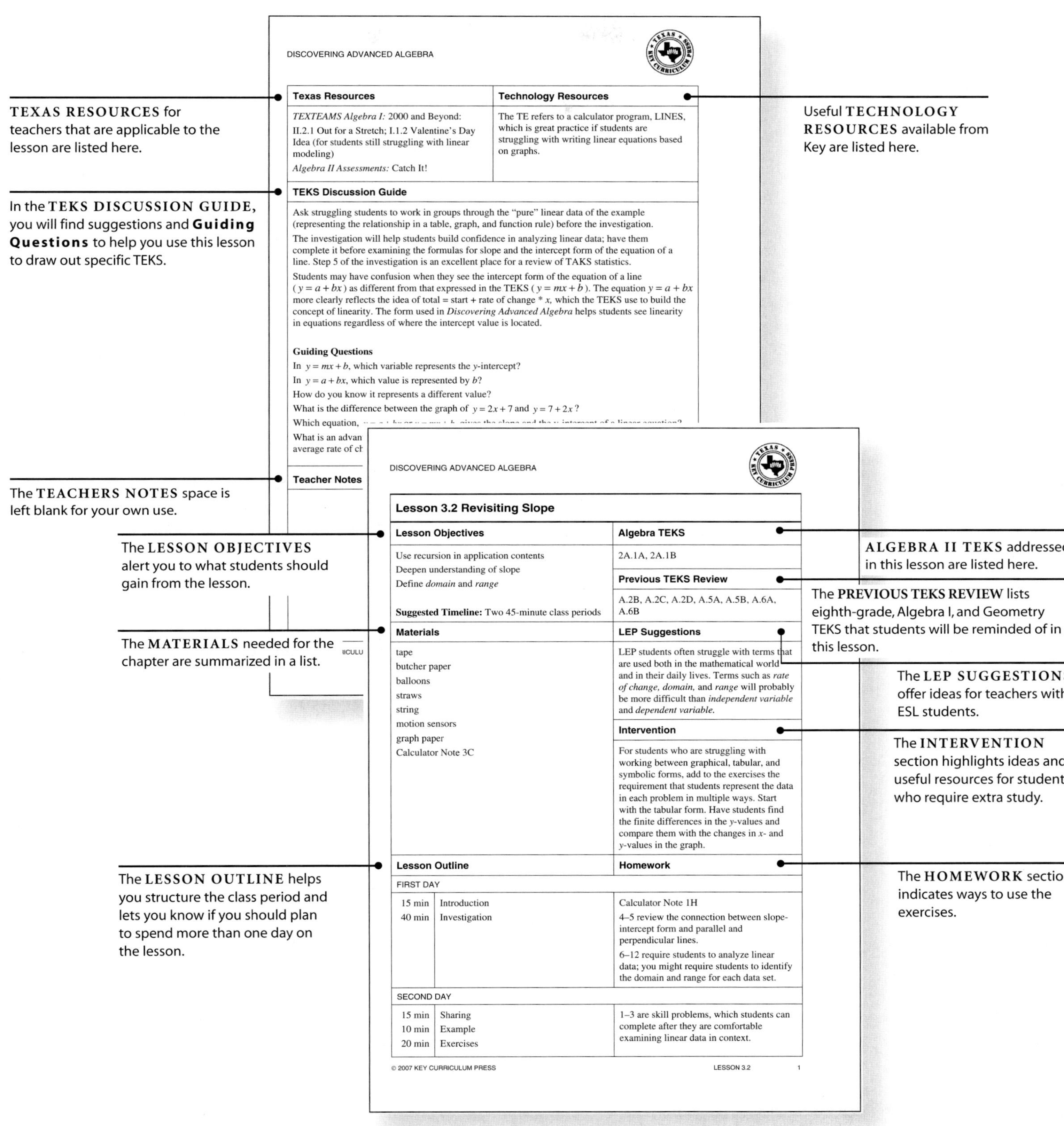

TEXAS RESOURCES for teachers that are applicable to the lesson are listed here.

In the **TEKS DISCUSSION GUIDE**, you will find suggestions and **Guiding Questions** to help you use this lesson to draw out specific TEKS.

The **TEACHERS NOTES** space is left blank for your own use.

Useful **TECHNOLOGY RESOURCES** available from Key are listed here.

DISCOVERING ADVANCED ALGEBRA

Texas Resources	Technology Resources
TEXTEAMS Algebra I: 2000 and Beyond: II.2.1 Out for a Stretch; I.1.2 Valentine's Day Idea (for students still struggling with linear modeling) *Algebra II Assessments:* Catch It!	The TE refers to a calculator program, LINES, which is great practice if students are struggling with writing linear equations based on graphs.

TEKS Discussion Guide

Ask struggling students to work in groups through the "pure" linear data of the example (representing the relationship in a table, graph, and function rule) before the investigation.

The investigation will help students build confidence in analyzing linear data; have them complete it before examining the formulas for slope and the intercept form of the equation of a line. Step 5 of the investigation is an excellent place for a review of TAKS statistics.

Students may have confusion when they see the intercept form of the equation of a line ($y = a + bx$) as different from that expressed in the TEKS ($y = mx + b$). The equation $y = a + bx$ more clearly reflects the idea of total = start + rate of change * *x*, which the TEKS use to build the concept of linearity. The form used in *Discovering Advanced Algebra* helps students see linearity in equations regardless of where the intercept value is located.

Guiding Questions

In $y = mx + b$, which variable represents the *y*-intercept?

In $y = a + bx$, which value is represented by *b*?

How do you know it represents a different value?

What is the difference between the graph of $y = 2x + 7$ and $y = 7 + 2x$?

Which equation,

What is an advan

average rate of ch

Teacher Notes

The **LESSON OBJECTIVES** alert you to what students should gain from the lesson.

The **MATERIALS** needed for the chapter are summarized in a list.

The **LESSON OUTLINE** helps you structure the class period and lets you know if you should plan to spend more than one day on the lesson.

ALGEBRA II TEKS addressed in this lesson are listed here.

The **PREVIOUS TEKS REVIEW** lists eighth-grade, Algebra I, and Geometry TEKS that students will be reminded of in this lesson.

The **LEP SUGGESTIONS** offer ideas for teachers with ESL students.

The **INTERVENTION** section highlights ideas and useful resources for students who require extra study.

The **HOMEWORK** section indicates ways to use the exercises.

DISCOVERING ADVANCED ALGEBRA

Lesson 3.2 Revisiting Slope

Lesson Objectives	Algebra TEKS
Use recursion in application contents Deepen understanding of slope Define *domain* and *range* **Suggested Timeline:** Two 45-minute class periods	2A.1A, 2A.1B **Previous TEKS Review** A.2B, A.2C, A.2D, A.5A, A.5B, A.6A, A.6B

Materials	LEP Suggestions
tape butcher paper balloons straws string motion sensors graph paper Calculator Note 3C	LEP students often struggle with terms that are used both in the mathematical world and in their daily lives. Terms such as *rate of change, domain,* and *range* will probably be more difficult than *independent variable* and *dependent variable.* **Intervention** For students who are struggling with working between graphical, tabular, and symbolic forms, add to the exercises the requirement that students represent the data in each problem in multiple ways. Start with the tabular form. Have students find the finite differences in the *y*-values and compare them with the changes in *x*- and *y*-values in the graph.

Lesson Outline		Homework
FIRST DAY		
15 min 40 min	Introduction Investigation	Calculator Note 1H 4–5 review the connection between slope-intercept form and parallel and perpendicular lines. 6–12 require students to analyze linear data; you might require students to identify the domain and range for each data set.
SECOND DAY		
15 min 10 min 20 min	Sharing Example Exercises	1–3 are skill problems, which students can complete after they are comfortable examining linear data in context.

© 2007 KEY CURRICULUM PRESS LESSON 3.2 1

Concept (Suggested Time)	*Discovering Advanced Algebra* Lessons	Texas Standards
		Knowledge and Skills Statements (Performance Descriptors)
Foundations for Functions (7 weeks)		
Introduction to functions (1 week)	**4.1** Interpreting Graphs **4.2** Function Notation	**2A.1 Foundations for functions.** The student uses properties and attributes of functions and applies functions to problem situations. (2A.1B) **2A.6 Quadratic and square root functions.** The student understands that quadratic functions can be represented in different ways and translates among their various representations. (2A.6A)
Parent functions and transformations on parent functions (4 weeks)	**3.2** Revisiting Slope **3.3** Fitting a Line to Data **4.3** Lines in Motion **4.4** Translations and the Quadratic Family **4.5** Reflections and the Square Root Family **4.6** Stretches and Shrinks and the Absolute Value Family	**2A.1** (2A.1A, 2A.1B) **2A.2 Foundations for functions.** The student understands the importance of the skills required to manipulate symbols in order to solve problems and uses the necessary algebraic skills required to simplify symbolic expressions and solve equations and inequalities in problem situations. **2A.4 Algebra and geometry.** The student connects algebraic and geometric representations of functions. (2A.4A, 2A.4B) **2A.7 Quadratic and square root functions.** The student interprets and describes the effects of changes in the parameters of quadratic functions in applied and mathematical situations. (2A.7B) **2A.9 Quadratic and square root functions.** The student formulates equations and inequalities based on square root functions, uses a variety of methods to solve them, and analyzes the solutions in terms of the situation. (2A.9A, 2A.9B)

Big Ideas	TAKS	Dana Center Resources	
	Texas Assessment of Knowledge and Skills	**Algebra I and Algebra II Assessments**	**TEXTEAMS Institutes and Teacher Quality Modules**
Students should be able to distinguish between an equation, a relation, and a function. Students will associate these definitions with the correct notation.	**Objective 6:** The student will demonstrate an understanding of geometric relationships and spatial reasoning.	*Algebra II* A Matter of Representation	*Algebra I: 2000 and Beyond:* 3.1 Interpreting Distance versus Time Graphs
Students should collect data, investigate domain and range, represent the data in multiple ways, and connect the multiple representations: (graph, table, symbolic function rule). Students should look at patterns (including analyzing rate of change) and use what they know about quadratic, exponential, and linear functions from Algebra I as a springboard to a more formal list of parent functions (linear, inverse, log, exponential, quadratic, and square root). Students perform transformations graphically, numerically, and symbolically and connect the different representations.	**Objective 5:** The student will demonstrate an understanding of quadratic and other nonlinear functions. **Objective 6** **Objective 2:** The student will demonstrate an understanding of the properties and attributes of functions.	*Algebra II* Catch It!; Hit the Wall Introducing Investigating the Effect of a, h, and k on $y = a\sqrt{(x - h)} + k$; A Matter of Representation Walk the Yo-Yo; Data Dilemma; Slip Sliding Away; Move the Monster; Transformations; *Algebra I* Summer Money; The Run; The Walk	*Part 1, Algebra II/ Precalculus:* I.1.1 Transformations; I.2.1. Matching Parent Functions *Algebra I: 2000 and Beyond:* 2.1 Out for a Stretch; 1.2 Valentine's Day Idea *Algebra II Institute:* Transformation Practices I and II *TQM Algebra I Module:* I.1.6 From Functions to Graphs

Concept (Suggested Time)	*Discovering Advanced Algebra* Topics	Texas Standards	
		Knowledge and Skills Statements (Performance Descriptors)	
Foundations for Functions (7 weeks)			
Inverse relationships (1.5 weeks)	**5.5** Building Inverses of Functions	**2A.4** (2A.4C) **2A.9** (2A.9G)	
Introduction to systems	**3.6** Linear Systems **3.7** Substitution and Elimination	**2A.3 Foundations for functions.** The student formulates systems of equations and inequalities from problem situations, uses a variety of methods to solve them, and analyzes the solutions in terms of the situations. (2A.3A, 2A.3B, 2A.3C)	
Exponential and Logarithmic Functions (6–7 weeks)			
Connecting linear and exponential functions (1 week)	**1.1** Recursively Defined Sequences **1.2** Modeling Growth and Decay **1.5** Loans and Investments	**2A.1** (2A.1B) **2A.4** (2A.4A) **2A.11 Exponential and logarithmic functions.** The student formulates equations and inequalities based on exponential and logarithmic functions, uses a variety of methods to solve them, and analyzes the solutions in terms of the situation. (2A.11F)	
Collecting and modeling data with exponential functions (1–1.5 weeks)	**5.1** Exponential Functions **5.2** Properties of Exponents and Power Functions **5.4** Applications of Exponential and Power Equations	**2A.2** (2A.2A) **2A.11** (2A.11B, 2A.11C, 2A.11D, 2A.11F) **2A.1** (2A.1A, 2A.1B) **2A.4** (2A.4A, 2A.4B)	

	Big Ideas	TAKS	Dana Center Resources	
		Texas Assessment of Knowledge and Skills	**Algebra I and Algebra II Assessments**	**TEXTEAMS Institutes and Teacher Quality Modules**
	Students show inverse connections among parent functions geometrically and numerically.	**Objective 1:** The student will describe functional relationships in a variety of ways. **Objective 2** **Objective 3:** The student will demonstrate an understanding of linear functions. **Objective 5** **Objective 9:** The student will demonstrate an understanding of percents, proportional relationships, probability, and statistics in application problems. **Objective 10:** The student will demonstrate an understanding of the mathematical processes and tools used in problem solving.		*Part 1, Algebra II/ Precalculus:* I.3.1 Inverses
	Systems are introduced graphically and numerically with connections back to these two approaches for solving linear systems in Algebra I; extend the ideas from Algebra I to nonlinear functions.	**Objective 1** **Objective 2**		*Algebra I: 2000 and Beyond:* 3.4 Systems of Linear Equations and Inequalities
	Students make the connection between linear and exponential functions numerically—as repeated addition versus repeated multiplication—as well as graphically.	**Objective 1** **Objective 2** **Objective 3** **Objective 5** **Objective 9** **Objective 10**	*Algebra II* Saving Money, Making Money	*Algebra I: 2000 and Beyond:* I.1.2 Valentine's Day Idea; III.3.1 Exponential Relationships; III.3.2 Exponential Growth and Decay
	Students confirm the appropriateness of the model from patterns in the data and then use transformations on the parent function to fit the chosen model to the data.		*Algebra II* A Graduation Present; Saving Money, Making Money *Algebra I* Summer Money; The Run; The Walk	*Part 1, Algebra II/ Precalculus:* II.1.1 Bacteria Growth; II.1.2 Exponential Decay *TQM Algebra I Module:* 1.1.6 From Functions to Graphs

Concept (Suggested Time)	*Discovering Advanced Algebra* Topics	Texas Standards
		Knowledge and Skills Statements (Performance Descriptors)
Exponential and Logarithmic Functions (6–7 weeks)		
The inverse of the exponential function (1 week)	**5.6** Logarithmic Functions	**2A.4** (2A.4A, 2A.4B, 2A.4C) **2A.11** (2A.11A, 2A.11B, 2A.11C, 2A.11D)
Collecting and modeling data with logarithmic functions (1–1.5 weeks)	**5.8** Applications of Logarithms	**2A.2** (2A.2A) **2A.11** (2A.11B, 2A.11C, 2A.11D) **2A.1** (2A.1B)
Solving exponential and logarithmic equations (1 week)	**5.3** Rational Exponents and Roots **5.6** Logarithmic Functions **5.7** Properties of Logarithms **SL 1** Exponential and Logarithmic Applications **SL 2** Exponential and Logarithmic Inequalities	**2A.1** (2A.1B) **2A.2** (2A.2A) **2A.10 Rational functions.** The student formulates equations and inequalities based on rational functions, uses a variety of methods to solve them, and analyzes the solutions in terms of the situation. (2A.10F) **2A.11** (2A.11A, 2A.11B, 2A.11C, 2A.11D, 2A.11E, 2A.11F) **2A.4** (2A.4A, 2A.4B, 2A.4C)
Quadratic Functions (7–8 weeks)		
Collecting and modeling data with quadratic functions (3–3.5 weeks)	**7.1** Polynomial Degree and Finite Differences **7.2** Equivalent Quadratic Forms **7.4** The Quadratic Formula	**2A.6** (2A.6B, 2A.6C) **2A.7** (2A.7A) **2A.8 Quadratic and square root functions.** The student formulates equations and inequalities based on quadratic functions, uses a variety of methods to solve them, and analyzes the solutions in terms of the situation. (2A.8A, 2A.8B, 2A.8D) **2A.2** (2A.2A)
Connecting symbolic representations (1 week)	**7.2** Equivalent Quadratic Forms **7.3** Completing the Square	**2A.6** (2A.6B, 2A.6C) **2A.7** (2A.7A) **2A.8** (2A.8A, 2A.8C) **2A.2** (2A.2A) **2A.5** (2A.5E)

	Big Ideas	TAKS	Dana Center Resources	
		Texas Assessment of Knowledge and Skills	**Algebra I and Algebra II Assessments**	**TEXTEAMS Institutes and Teacher Quality Modules**
			Algebra II Comparing an Exponential Function and Its Inverse	
	Students confirm the appropriateness of the model from patterns in the data and then use transformations on the parent function to fit the chosen model to the data.		*Algebra II* Desert Bighorn Sheep; A Graduation Present	*Part 1, Algebra II/ Precalculus:* II.2.1 The Energy of Earthquakes
		Objective 1 **Objective 2** **Objective 3** **Objective 5** **Objective 9** **Objective 10**	*Algebra II* Desert Bighorn Sheep; A Graduation Present; Saving Money, Making Money; Comparing an Exponential Function and Its Inverse	*Algebra I: 2000 and Beyond:* III.3.1 Exponential Relationships; III.3.2 Exponential Growth and Decay; III.3.3 Exponential Models *Algebra II Institute:* Using Logarithmic Functions
	Students confirm the appropriateness of the model from patterns in the data and then use transformations on the parent function to fit the chosen model to the data.	**Objective 1** **Objective 2** **Objective 5**	*Algebra II* Fixed Perimeter Rectangles; Fixed Area Rectangles	
		Objective 1 **Objective 2** **Objective 5**	*Algebra II* Fixed Perimeter Rectangles; Fixed Area Rectangles	

Concept (Suggested Time)	*Discovering Advanced Algebra* Topics	Texas Standards	
		Knowledge and Skills Statements (Performance Descriptors)	
Quadratic Functions (7–8 weeks)			
Solving quadratic equations and inequalities (3–3.5 weeks)	**7.2** Equivalent Quadratic Forms **7.3** Completing the Square **7.4** The Quadratic Formula **7.5** Complex Numbers **SL 3** Quadratic Inequalities	**2A.2** (2A.2A, 2A.2B) **2A.5 Algebra and geometry.** The student knows the relationship between the geometric and algebraic descriptions of conic sections. (2A.5E) **2A.6** (2A.6A, 2A.6B, 2A.6C) **2A.7** (2A.7A) **2A.8** (2A.8A, 2A.8B, 2A.8C, 2A.8D)	
Square Root Functions (2–3 weeks)			
The inverse of a quadratic function (0.5–1 week)	**SL 4** Square Root Functions	**2A.9 Quadratic and square root functions.** The student formulates equations and inequalities based on square root functions, uses a variety of methods to solve them, and analyzes the solutions in terms of the situation. (2A.9A, 2A.9C) **2A.1** (2A, 1A, 2A, 2A)	
Modeling situations with square root functions (0.5–1 week)	**SL 5** More Square Root Functions	**2A.9** (2A.9B, 2A.9C, 2A.9D, 2A.9E, 2A.9F)	
Solving square root equations and inequalities (0.5–1 week)	**SL 5** More Square Root Functions	**2A.9** (2A.9B, 2A.9C, 2A.9D, 2A.9E, 2A.9F)	
Rational Functions (3 weeks)			
Modeling situations with rational functions (0.5–1 week)	**9.6** Introduction to Rational Functions **9.7** Graphs of Rational Functions	**2A.10** (2A.10A, 2A.10B, 2A.10C) **2A.2** (2A.2A)	
Short- and long-run behavior of rational functions (0.5–1 week)	**9.6** Introduction to Rational Functions **9.7** Graphs of Rational Functions	**2A.10** (2A.10A, 2A.10B, 2A.10C) **2A.2** (2A.2A)	

	Big Ideas	TAKS	Dana Center Resources	
		Texas Assessment of Knowledge and Skills	**Algebra I and Algebra II Assessments**	**TEXTEAMS Institutes and Teacher Quality Modules**
		Objective 1 **Objective 2** **Objective 4:** The student will formulate and use linear equations and inequalities. **Objective 5**	*Algebra II* Basketball Throw; Motion Under Gravity; Parabolic Paths; Toricelli's Law; Doing What Mathematicians Do; Fixed Area Rectangles; Fixed Perimeter Rectangles; Pizza Wars; Triangle Solutions	
		Objective 1 **Objective 2** **Objective 5**	*Algebra II* I Can See Forever; I Was Going How Fast?; Tic Toc	
			Algebra II I Can See Forever; Investigating the Effect of a, h, and k on $y = a\sqrt{x-h} + k$; I Was Going How Fast?; Tic Toc	
		Objective 1 **Objective 2** **Objective 5** **Objective 8:** The student will demonstrate an understanding of the concepts and uses of measurement and similarity. **Objective 10**	*Algebra II* I Can See Forever; I Was Going How Fast?; Tic Toc	
		Objective 1 **Objective 2** **Objective 5**	*Algebra II* Pizza Wars, Part 2; Saline Solution; What's My Equation?; You're Toast, Dude	*Part 1, Algebra II Institute:* III.2.2 The Long and the Short of It
		Objective 1 **Objective 2** **Objective 5**	*Algebra II* Pizza Wars, Part 2; What's My Education?; You're Toast, Dude; Saline Solution	*Part 1, Algebra II Institute:* III.2.2 The Long and the Short of It

Concept (Suggested Time)	*Discovering Advanced Algebra* Topics	Texas Standards
		Knowledge and Skills Statements (Performance Descriptors)
Rational Functions (3 weeks)		
Solving rational equations and inequalities (0.5 week)	**9.8** Operations with Rational Expressions **SL 6** Rational Inequalities	**2A.2** (2A.2A) **2A.10** (2A.10A 2A.10C, 2A.10D, 2A.10E, 2A.10F)
Analyzing, Formulating, and Solving Systems (3–5 weeks)		
Solving systems of inequalities with two unknowns (1–1.5 weeks)	**6.5** Systems of Linear Inequalities **6.6** Linear Programming	**2A.3** (2A.3A, 2A.3B, 2A.3C)
Solving systems of equations with two or more unknowns (1–1.5 weeks)	**6.1** Matrix Representations **6.2** Matrix Operations **6.3** Row Reduction Method **6.4** Solving Systems with Inverse Matrices	**2A.3** (2A.3A, 2A.3B, 2A.3C) **2A.5** (2A.5B)
Conics (4–5 weeks)		
Intersections of a plane and a cone (1.5–2 weeks)	**9.1** Using the Distance Formula **9.2** Circles and Ellipses **9.3** Parabolas **9.4** Hyperbolas	**2A.5** (2A.5A, 2A.5B, 2A.5C, 2A.5D) **2A.2** (2A.2A)
Graphs of conic sections (1.5–2 weeks)	**9.2** Circles and Ellipses **9.3** Parabolas **9.4** Hyperbolas **9.5** The General Quadratic	**2A.5** (2A.5A, 2A.5B, 2A.5C, 2A.5D, 2A.5E) **2A.2** (2A.2A)
Symmetries of conic sections (1 week)	**9.4** Hyperbolas	**2A.5** (2A.5A, 2A.5B, 2A.5C, 2A.5D) **2A.2** (2A.2A)

	Big Ideas	TAKS	Dana Center Resources	
		Texas Assessment of Knowledge and Skills	**Algebra I and Algebra II Assessments**	**TEXTEAMS Institutes and Teacher Quality Modules**
			Algebra II Pizza Wars, Part 2; You're Toast, Dude; Paintings on a Wall	
	Students will solve these systems graphically.		*Algebra II* A Linear Programming; Problem: Parking at the Mall	
	Students will solve these systems using substitution, linear combination, and matrices. With the linear combination method on three equations and three unknowns, students will make the geometric connection of intersecting planes that is analagous to that of intersecting lines with two equations and two unknowns.		*Algebra II* The Mild and Wild Amusement Park	
	Students will investigate the intersections symbolically (to connect from solving systems) and geometrically.		*Algebra II* Contemplating Comets; Lost in Space; Kalotonic Kaper	*Part 2, Algebra II/ Precalculus: Algebra II:* IV.1.1 The Cone and the Intersecting Plane
			Algebra II Contemplating Comets; Kalotonic Kaper; Lost in Space	*Part 2, Algebra II/ Precalculus:* IV.1.1 The Cone and the Intersecting Plane
			Algebra II Kalotonic Kaper	

Technology Resources

This technology index shows the technology available for the lessons covered by the Scope and Sequence (pages T4–T13). Use it as you plan. Many other calculator, data collection device, The Geometer's Sketchpad, and Fathom activities are in lessons not included on the Texas Scope and Sequence. You will have time to use many of them. The Lesson Plans, available to Texas teachers at www.keypress.com/texas show the technology resources on each individual lesson plan.

Technology	*Discovering Advanced Algebra* Lesson			
	Chapter 1	**Chapter 3**	**Chapter 4**	**Chapter 5**
Calculator				
Calculator Notes	1.1, 1.2, 1.5	3.2, 3.6, 3.7	4.2, 4.3, 4.4, 4.5, 4.6	5.1, 5.2, 5.3, 5.5, 5.6, 5.7, 5.8
Data-collection device investigation	1.2	3.2	4.3	5.8
Fathom Dynamic Data				
Demonstrations with Fathom and The Geometer's Sketchpad		3.3		5.8
Teaching Mathematics with Fathom		3.3	4.3, 4.4, 4.5, 4.6	5.1, 5.4, 5.8
Fathom investigation				
The Geometer's Sketchpad				
Exercises and Explorations with The Geometer's Sketchpad			4.4	5.1
Demonstrations with Fathom and The Geometer's Sketchpad			4.3, 4.4, 4.5, 4.6	5.2, 5.3, 5.5, 5.6
Dynamic Algebra Explorations at www.keymath.com/DAA/			4.4	

	Discovering Advanced Algebra Lesson			
	Chapter 6	**Chapter 7**	**Chapter 9**	**Additional Lessons**
	6.1, 6.2, 6.3, 6.4, 6.5	7.1, 7.2, 7.4, 7.5	9.1, 9.5, 9.6, 9.8	SL 6 Rational Inequalities
		7.1, 7.2	9.4	
		7.1		
				SL 4 Square Root Functions
				SL 1 Exponential and Logarithmic Applications
			9.1, 9.5, 9.6	
	6.6	7.4	9.2, 9.3, 9.4, 9.5, 9.6	
		7.2	9.2, 9.3, 9.4	

Acknowledgments

Advanced Algebra Through Data Exploration

Consultants and Writers

Karen Wootton (assessment writer), Terre Haute, Indiana

Bill Medigovich (consultant), Redwood High School, Larkspur, California

Judy Cubillo (solutions writer), Northgate High School, Walnut Creek, California

Multicultural and Equity Reviewers

Edward D. Castillo, Sonoma State University, Rohnert Park, California

Robert Hamada, Los Angeles Unified School District, Los Angeles, California

Marva O. Wilkins, Richmond, California

Claudia Zaslavsky, New York, New York

Mathematical Reviewers

Mary Barnes, Cremorne, New South Wales, Australia

Tim Erickson, Epistemological Engineering, Oakland, California

Warren Page, Mathematical Association of America, Brooklyn, New York

James W. Wilson, University of Georgia, Athens, Georgia

Scientific Content Reviewer

Art Fortgang, Mills High School, Millbrae, California

Field Testers

Margaret A. Bambrick and Candace H. Fernandez, Atlantic High School, Port Orange, Florida

Deborah Berry, Linda A. Jones, and Andrea L. Sukow, Hillsboro High School, Nashville, Tennessee

Barbara Bredel, Crandon High School, Crandon, Wisconsin

Bruce Budzynski, Ludington High School, Ludington, Michigan

Susan H. Burgess, H. H. Dow High School, Midland, Michigan

John Crotty, Career High School, New Haven, Connecticut

Judy Cubillo, Northgate High School, Walnut Creek, California

Carol H. DeCuzzi, Audubon High School, Audubon, New Jersey

Bob Drake and Salvador Quezada, Jr., Roosevelt High School, Los Angeles, California

Steve Eckert, Robert H. Kosztowny, and Michele Mitchell, Fremont High School, Fremont, Michigan

Fred Gerhardt, Kingston High School, Kingston, Michigan

Elizabeth Hales, New School for the Arts, Scottsdale, Arizona

Jane E. Halverson, Grand Canyon High School, Grand Canyon, Arizona

Judy Hicks, Standley Lake High School, Westminster, Colorado

Jane Housman Jones, Du Pont Manual High School, Louisville, Kentucky

Carolyn S. Jordan, Franklin High School, Stockton, California

Jan Kledzik, Centerville High School, Centerville, Ohio

Kimberly E. Landeck, Lakeshore Public Schools, Stevensville, Michigan

Harry M. Lykens, Mary Institute and Saint Louis Country Day School, St. Louis, Missouri

Harry E. Mann, Scottsdale School District, Scottsdale, Arizona

Diane L. Martling, Illinois Math and Science Academy, Aurora, Illinois

Grant McMicken, San Juan High School, Citrus Heights, California

Bill Medigovich, Redwood High School, Larkspur, California

Denny Miller, Cheshire High School, Cheshire, Connecticut

Jeanette N. Mueller, Traverse City Senior High School, Traverse City, Michigan

Jennifer North Morris, West Hills High School, Santee, California

Marilyn J. Peak, Spencer County High School, Taylorsville, Kentucky

Gary Preto, Folsom High School, Cameron Park, California

Tara S. Rickart, Nonnewaug High School, Woodbury, Connecticut

Judith L. Simpfer, Alba Public Schools, Alba, Michigan

Lana Taylor, Siena Heights College, Adrian, Michigan

Tim Trapp, Mountain View High School, Mesa, Arizona

Hugo Trepte, Interlochen Arts Academy, Interlochen, Michigan

Frederick P. Wright, Lakeside School, Seattle, Washington

Author Acknowledgments

Creating a textbook and its supplementary materials is a team effort involving many individuals and groups. We are especially grateful to thousands of *Advanced Algebra Through Data Exploration* and *Discovering Algebra* teachers and students, to teachers who participated in the summer institutes and workshops, and to manuscript readers, all of whom provided suggestions, reviewed material, located errors, and most of all, encouraged us to continue with the project.

Our students, their parents, and our administrators at Interlochen Arts Academy have played an important part in the development of this book. Most importantly, we wish to thank Carol Murdock, our parents, and our children for their love, encouragement, and support.

As authors we are grateful to the National Science Foundation for supporting our initial technology-and-writing project that led to the 1998 publication of *Advanced Algebra Through Data Exploration. Discovering Advanced Algebra* has been developed and shaped by what we learned during the writing and publication of both *Advanced Algebra Through Data Exploration* and *Discovering Algebra,* and our work with so many students, parents, and teachers who were searching for a more meaningful algebra curriculum.

Over the course of our careers, many individuals and groups have been instrumental in our development as teachers and authors. The Woodrow Wilson National Fellowship Foundation provided the initial impetus for involvement in leading workshops. Publications and conferences produced by the National Council of Teachers of Mathematics and Teachers Teaching with Technology have guided the development of this curriculum. Individuals such as Ron Carlson, Helen Compton, Frank Demana, Arne Engebretsen, Paul Foerster, Christian Hirsch, Glenda Lappan, Richard Odell, Heinz-Otto Peitgen, James Sandefur, James Schultz, Dan Teague, Charles VonderEmbse, Bert Waits, and Mary Jean Winter have inspired us.

The development and production of *Discovering Advanced Algebra* has been a collaborative effort between the authors and the staff at Key Curriculum Press. We truly appreciate the cooperation and valuable contributions offered by the Editorial and Production Departments at Key Curriculum Press. Finally, a special thanks to Key's president, Steven Rasmussen, for encouraging and publishing a technology-enhanced *Discovering Mathematics* series that offers groundbreaking content and learning opportunities.

Jerald Murdock
Ellen Kamischke
Eric Kamischke

A Note from the Publisher

The algebra you find in this book won't look quite like the algebra you may have seen in older textbooks. The mathematics we learn and teach in school has to change continually to reflect changes in our world. Our workplaces are changing, and technology is present everywhere, fundamentally changing the work we do. There are some new topics that are now possible to explore with technology, and some standard topics that can be approached in new ways. As the National Council of Teachers of Mathematics (NCTM) Technology Principle says, "When technological tools are available, students can focus on decision making, reflection, reasoning, and problem solving." This has been the focus of the authors and the Key Curriculum Press editorial team in the creation of *Discovering Advanced Algebra: An Investigative Approach.* As you progress through this book, you'll see that graphing calculators and other technologies are used to explore patterns and to make, test, and generalize conjectures.

When Key Curriculum Press published the first version of this text, *Advanced Algebra Through Data Exploration: A Graphing Calculator Approach,* in 1998, few books were available that had a similar foundation in technology. In this revision, you'll see that that foundation has been enriched with projects, explorations, and exercises that utilize not only graphing calculators, but also the powerful analysis tools The Geometer's Sketchpad® and Fathom Dynamic Statistics™. Based on feedback from users and reviewers, this revision is reorganized and easier to read. *Discovering Advanced Algebra* also completes the fully updated *Discovering Mathematics* series. All of the features that make *Discovering Algebra* and *Discovering Geometry* innovative and exciting are now incorporated into this book as well, to make a coherent and streamlined series.

Investigations are at the heart of each book. Through the investigations, you'll explore interesting problems and generalize concepts. And if you, as a student, forget a concept, formula, or procedure, you can always re-create it—because you developed it yourself the first time! You'll find that this approach allows you to form a deep and conceptual understanding of advanced algebra topics.

As Glenda Lappan, mathematics professor at Michigan State University and former NCTM president, said about the first edition of this book, "Students coming out of a year with this text . . . will know the mathematics they know in deeper, more flexible ways. They will have developed a set of mathematical habits of mind that will serve them very well as students or users of mathematics. They will emerge with a sense of mathematics as a search for regularity that allows prediction."

If you are a student, we hope that what you learn this year will serve you well in life. If you are a parent, we hope you will enjoy watching your student develop mathematical confidence. And if you are a teacher, we hope *Discovering Advanced Algebra* greatly enriches your classroom. The professional team at Key Curriculum Press wishes you success and joy in the lifetime of mathematics ahead of you. We look forward to hearing about your experiences.

Steven Rasmussen, President
Key Curriculum Press

Contents

A Note to Teachers from the Authors

Jerald Murdock

Ellen Kamischke

Eric Kamischke

Discovering Advanced Algebra offers you and your students an experience rich in mathematical investigations and applications that encourage the exploration of ideas, data, patterns, and algebraic relationships. This *Teacher's Edition* can help you guide and encourage better learning of important mathematics—mathematics that students can immediately make sense of and use.

The teaching-learning model actively engages students in both guided and open-ended mathematical explorations that help them make sense of their experiences. This model requires active participants, not spectators. The course is advanced algebra, but students will frequently consider and represent patterns that blend advanced algebra, geometry, data analysis, discrete mathematics, statistics, and trigonometry.

Students will approach each new concept and challenge with mathematical tools that support their particular learning strengths—be they algebraic, numerical, graphical, or verbal. They will have ample experience with pencil-and-paper, mental, and technology-assisted calculations. The curriculum has been written and organized to incorporate appropriate uses of technology, especially graphing calculators, allowing your students to model more closely the way mathematics is applied in the real world.

Discovering Advanced Algebra will help close the gap between the mechanics of what has been taught for decades and the algebra required to empower students mathematically so that they can participate in our technological world as creative, productive citizens.

This curriculum has been influenced by research on the best teaching practices and the learning of mathematics, insights of contemporary curriculum leaders, the National Council of Teachers of Mathematics (NCTM) *Principles and Standards for School Mathematics,* and recent projects funded by the National Science Foundation (NSF). It has been influenced most of all by our classroom experiences with our students.

Discovering Advanced Algebra has been developed and shaped by what we learned as we wrote and used *Advanced Algebra Through Data Exploration* and *Discovering Algebra.* We have incorporated teacher feedback and suggestions and the advice of educational consultants.

Interlochen's 1991–1995 NSF-supported Graphing Calculator Enhanced Algebra Project (GCEAP) proposed a major reevaluation of both algebra content and instructional strategies to reflect the way people do mathematics with technology. Since 1993, we have had the good fortune of working with Key Curriculum Press, the leading-edge publisher of *Advanced Algebra Through Data Exploration,* the *Discovering Mathematics* series, and other materials that meet needs not satisfied by traditional publishers.

Jerald Murdock
Ellen Kamischke
Eric Kamischke

A Note to Students from the Authors

The goal of this stage of your mathematical journey is to develop advanced algebraic tools and the mathematical power that will help you participate fully as a productive citizen in a changing world. On this journey you will make connections between algebra and the world around you.

Important decision-making situations will confront you in life, and your ability to use mathematics and algebra can help you make informed decisions. You'll need skills that can evolve and be adapted to new situations. You'll need to interpret numerical information and use it as a basis for making decisions. And you'll need to find ways to solve problems that arise in real life, not just in textbooks. Success in algebra is also a recognized gateway to many varied career opportunities.

You've already found out that learning algebra is more than memorizing facts, theories, and procedures. With your teacher as a guide, you'll learn algebra by doing mathematics. You'll make sense of important algebraic concepts, learn essential skills, and discover how to use algebra. This requires a far bigger commitment than just "waiting for the teacher to show you" or studying worked-out examples.

Your personal involvement is critical to successful group work during **Investigations.** Keep your measurements, data, and calculations neat and accurate to make your work easier and the concepts clearer in the long run. Talk about algebra, share ideas, and learn from and with your fellow group members. Work and communicate with your teammates to strengthen your understanding of the mathematical concepts. To enjoy and gain respect in your role as a team player, honor differences among group members, listen carefully when others are sharing, stay focused during the process, be responsible and respectful, and share your own ideas and suggestions.

The right technology can help you explore new ideas and answer questions that come up along the way. Using a graphing calculator, you will be able to manipulate large amounts of data quickly so that you can see the overall picture. Throughout the text you can refer to **Calculator Notes** for information that will help you use this tool. Technology is likely to play an important role in your life and future career. Learning to use your graphing calculator efficiently today, and being able to interpret its output, will prepare you to use other technologies successfully in situations to come.

The book itself will be a guide, leading you to explore ideas and ponder questions. Read it carefully—with paper, pencil, and calculator close at hand—and take good notes. Concepts and problems you have encountered before can help you solve new problems. Work through the **Examples** and answer the questions that are asked along the way. Some **Exercises** require a great deal of thought. Don't give up. Make a solid attempt at each problem that is assigned. Sometimes you'll make corrections and fill in details later, after you discuss a problem in class. Features called **Project, Improving Your . . . Skills,** and **Take Another Look** will challenge you to extend your learning and to apply it in creative ways.

Just as this book is your guide, your notebook can be a log of your travels through advanced algebra. In it you will record your notes and your work. You may also want to keep a journal of your personal impressions along the way. And just as every trip results in a photo album, you can place some of your especially notable accomplishments in a portfolio that highlights your trip. Collect pieces of work in your portfolio as you go, and refine the contents as you make progress on your journey. Each chapter ends with **Assessing What You've Learned.** This feature suggests ways to review your progress and prepare for what comes next: organizing your notebook, writing in your journal, updating your portfolio, and other ways to reflect on what you have learned.

You should expect struggles, hard work, and occasional frustration. Yet, as you gain more algebra skills, you'll overcome obstacles and be rewarded with a deeper understanding of mathematics, an increased confidence in your own problem-solving abilities, and the opportunity to be creative. From time to time, look back to reflect on where you have been. We hope that your journey through *Discovering Advanced Algebra* will be a meaningful and rewarding experience.

And now it is time to begin. You are about to discover some pretty fascinating things.

Jerald Murdock
Ellen Kamischke
Eric Kamischke

Features of the Student Edition

Investigations promote responsibility for learning and lead to important insights. Investigations, whether carried out in groups or demonstrated with students, provide rich discussion opportunities for whole-class participation.

Opening text orients students to the content sequence and often relates the lesson topic to real-world experience.

Interesting **quotations** introduce some lessons.

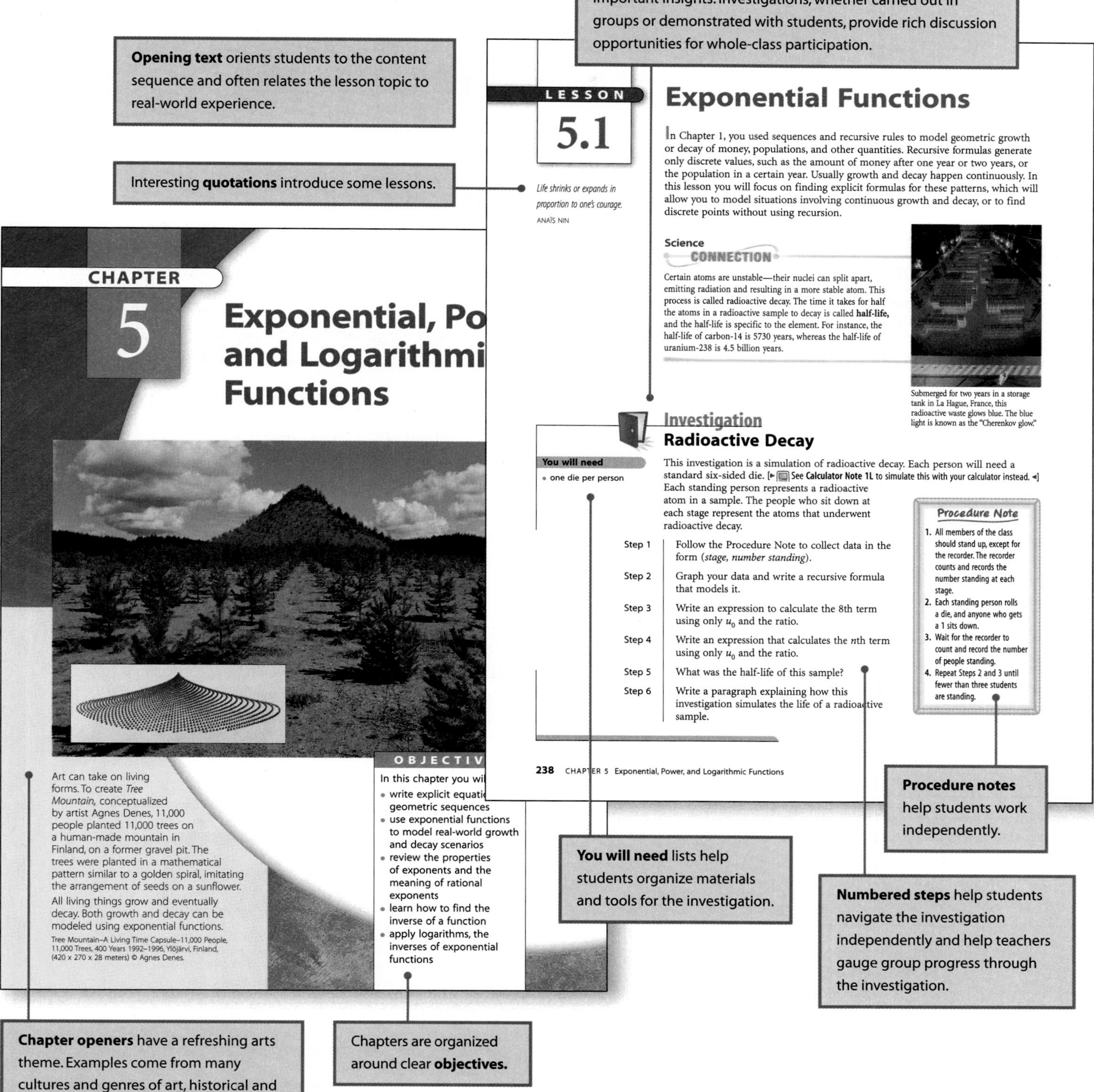

Procedure notes help students work independently.

You will need lists help students organize materials and tools for the investigation.

Numbered steps help students navigate the investigation independently and help teachers gauge group progress through the investigation.

Chapter openers have a refreshing arts theme. Examples come from many cultures and genres of art, historical and contemporary. A caption connects the opening image with the chapter content.

Chapters are organized around clear **objectives.**

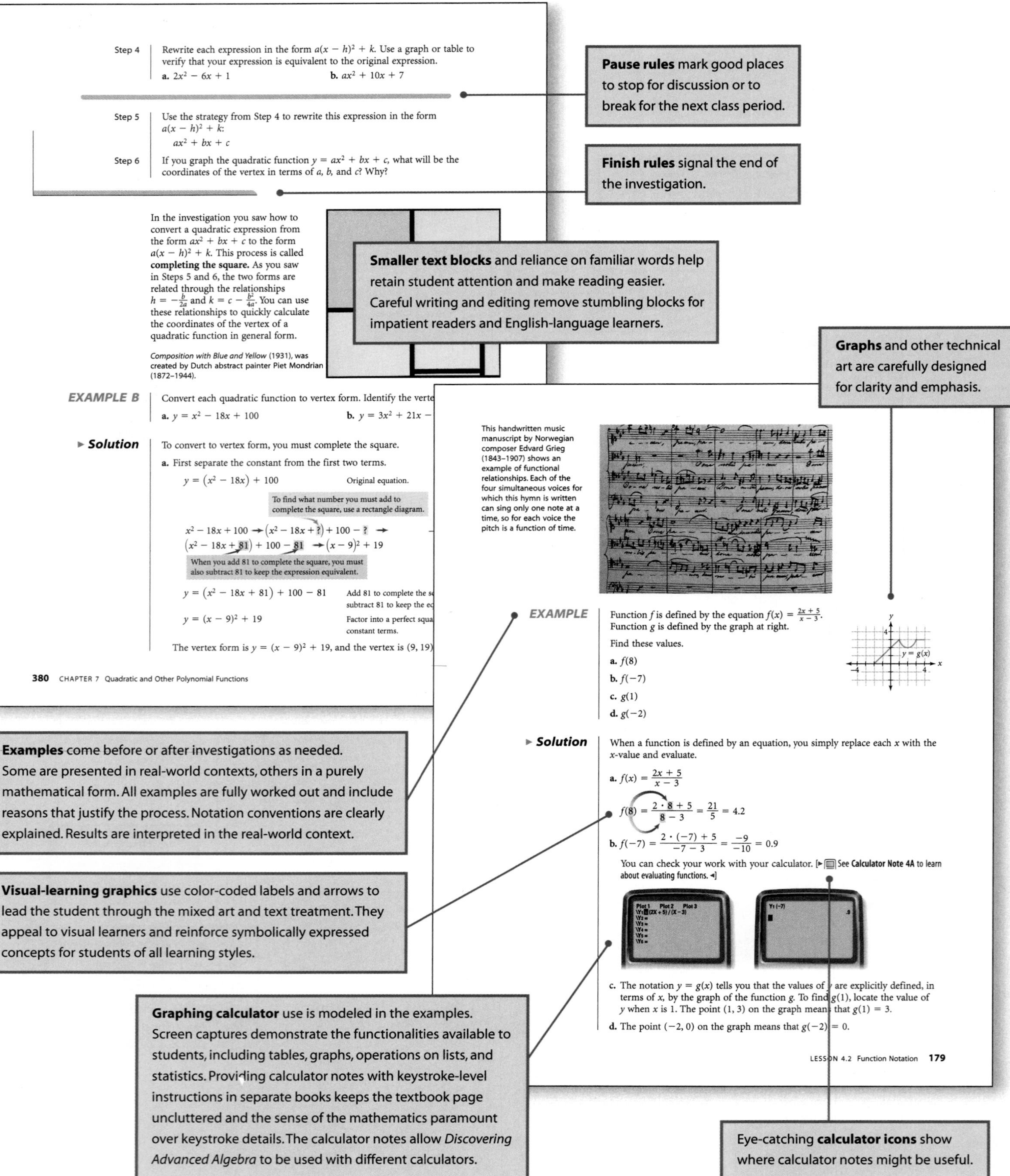

Step 4 | Rewrite each expression in the form $a(x - h)^2 + k$. Use a graph or table to verify that your expression is equivalent to the original expression.

a. $2x^2 - 6x + 1$ **b.** $ax^2 + 10x + 7$

Step 5 | Use the strategy from Step 4 to rewrite this expression in the form $a(x - h)^2 + k$:

$ax^2 + bx + c$

Step 6 | If you graph the quadratic function $y = ax^2 + bx + c$, what will be the coordinates of the vertex in terms of a, b, and c? Why?

In the investigation you saw how to convert a quadratic expression from the form $ax^2 + bx + c$ to the form $a(x - h)^2 + k$. This process is called **completing the square.** As you saw in Steps 5 and 6, the two forms are related through the relationships $h = -\frac{b}{2a}$ and $k = c - \frac{b^2}{4a}$. You can use these relationships to quickly calculate the coordinates of the vertex of a quadratic function in general form.

Composition with Blue and Yellow (1931), was created by Dutch abstract painter Piet Mondrian (1872–1944).

EXAMPLE B | Convert each quadratic function to vertex form. Identify the verte

a. $y = x^2 - 18x + 100$ **b.** $y = 3x^2 + 21x -$

▸ Solution | To convert to vertex form, you must complete the square.

a. First separate the constant from the first two terms.

$y = (x^2 - 18x) + 100$ Original equation.

To find what number you must add to complete the square, use a rectangle diagram.

$x^2 - 18x + 100 \rightarrow (x^2 - 18x + ?) + 100 - ? \rightarrow$

$(x^2 - 18x + 81) + 100 - 81 \rightarrow (x - 9)^2 + 19$

When you add 81 to complete the square, you must also subtract 81 to keep the expression equivalent.

$y = (x^2 - 18x + 81) + 100 - 81$ Add 81 to complete the s[…] subtract 81 to keep the ec[…]

$y = (x - 9)^2 + 19$ Factor into a perfect squa[…] constant terms.

The vertex form is $y = (x - 9)^2 + 19$, and the vertex is $(9, 19)$

380 CHAPTER 7 Quadratic and Other Polynomial Functions

This handwritten music manuscript by Norwegian composer Edvard Grieg (1843–1907) shows an example of functional relationships. Each of the four simultaneous voices for which this hymn is written can sing only one note at a time, so for each voice the pitch is a function of time.

EXAMPLE | Function f is defined by the equation $f(x) = \frac{2x+5}{x-3}$. Function g is defined by the graph at right.

Find these values.

a. $f(8)$

b. $f(-7)$

c. $g(1)$

d. $g(-2)$

▸ Solution | When a function is defined by an equation, you simply replace each x with the x-value and evaluate.

a. $f(x) = \frac{2x + 5}{x - 3}$

$f(8) = \frac{2 \cdot 8 + 5}{8 - 3} = \frac{21}{5} = 4.2$

b. $f(-7) = \frac{2 \cdot (-7) + 5}{-7 - 3} = \frac{-9}{-10} = 0.9$

You can check your work with your calculator. [▸ See **Calculator Note 4A** to learn about evaluating functions. ◂]

c. The notation $y = g(x)$ tells you that the values of y are explicitly defined, in terms of x, by the graph of the function g. To find $g(1)$, locate the value of y when x is 1. The point $(1, 3)$ on the graph means that $g(1) = 3$.

d. The point $(-2, 0)$ on the graph means that $g(-2) = 0$.

LESSON 4.2 Function Notation 179

Pause rules mark good places to stop for discussion or to break for the next class period.

Finish rules signal the end of the investigation.

Smaller text blocks and reliance on familiar words help retain student attention and make reading easier. Careful writing and editing remove stumbling blocks for impatient readers and English-language learners.

Graphs and other technical art are carefully designed for clarity and emphasis.

Examples come before or after investigations as needed. Some are presented in real-world contexts, others in a purely mathematical form. All examples are fully worked out and include reasons that justify the process. Notation conventions are clearly explained. Results are interpreted in the real-world context.

Visual-learning graphics use color-coded labels and arrows to lead the student through the mixed art and text treatment. They appeal to visual learners and reinforce symbolically expressed concepts for students of all learning styles.

Graphing calculator use is modeled in the examples. Screen captures demonstrate the functionalities available to students, including tables, graphs, operations on lists, and statistics. Providing calculator notes with keystroke-level instructions in separate books keeps the textbook page uncluttered and the sense of the mathematics paramount over keystroke details. The calculator notes allow *Discovering Advanced Algebra* to be used with different calculators.

Eye-catching **calculator icons** show where calculator notes might be useful.

Explorations give students a chance to apply what they know to new topics, extend their understanding, and use initiative in a technological environment.

EXPLORATION

Recursion in Geometry

In this chapter you have used recursive rules to produce sequences of numbers. In geometry, you may have used recursive rules to produce fractals or other geometric shapes. In this exploration you will explore two geometric designs that follow recursive rules.

The shell of the chambered nautilus, a relative of the octopus, reflects the Fibonacci sequence. It is only one of many occurrences of Fibonacci numbers in nature.

In Part 1, you will use The Geometer's Sketchpad® to create a Fibonacci spiral. In Part 2, you will construct a golden rectangle spiral, then compare the two constructions. You can learn more about mathematical spirals by visiting the Internet links at www.keymath.com/DAA .

Web markers to www.keymath.com/DAA lead students to more resources.

Activity
Two Spirals

Part 1: The Fibonacci Spiral

In his book *Liber abaci* (1202), Italian mathematician Le[...] (ca. 1170–1240) posed this question:

> How many pairs of rabbits will be produced in a year, beginning with a single pair, if every month each pair bears a new pair which becomes productive one month later?

You can model this scenario with the sequence 1, 1, 2, 3, 5, 8, 13, ...

Can you describe, in words, the rules of this sequence? Can you write a recursive formula that generates this sequence? (*Hint:* In a sequence, u_n need not depend only on u_{n-1}.) Interestingly, the Fibonacci sequence has applications in mathematics and life science. The sequence models such things as honeybee populations, the seed patterns in the middle of a sunflower, and the number of branches on a tree as it grows.

EXPLORATION Recursion in Geometry **59**

Connections highlight how the mathematics applies to students' lives—in the workplace or in the fields of science, history, technology, and the arts.

[...]mon ratio as the whole, 1, plus or minus [...]rite $(1 + p)$ or $(1 - p)$. The car example [...]mmon ratio could be written as $(1 - 0.20)$. [...]on ratio of 0.75, which you can write as [...]se are examples of decay, or geometric [...]e is one of growth, or a geometric

EXAMPLE B Gloria depos[its] $2000 into a bank account that pays 7% annual interest compounde[d] annually. This means the bank pays her 7% of her account balance as interest at the end of each year, and she leaves the original amount and the interest in th[e] account. When will the original deposit double in value?

Economics CONNECTION

Interest is a charge that you pay for borrowing money, or that the bank pays you for letting them invest the money you keep in your bank account. Simple interest is a percentage paid on the **principal**, or initial balance, over a period of time. If you leave the interest in the account, then in the next time period you receive interest on both the principal and the interest that were in your account. This is called **compound interest** because you are receiving interest on the interest.

▸ **Solution** The balance starts at $2000 and increases by 7% each year.

$u_0 = 2000$

$u_n = (1 + 0.07)u_{n-1}$ where $n \geq 1$ The recursive rule that represents 7% growth.

Use your calculator to compute year-end balances recursively.

The 11th term, u_{11}, is 4209.70, so the investment balance will more than double in 11 years.

2000
Ans*(1+0.07)
2000
2140
2289.8
2450.086
2621.59202
2805.103461
3001.460704
3211.562953
3436.37236
3676.918425
3934.302715
4209.703905 — u_{11}

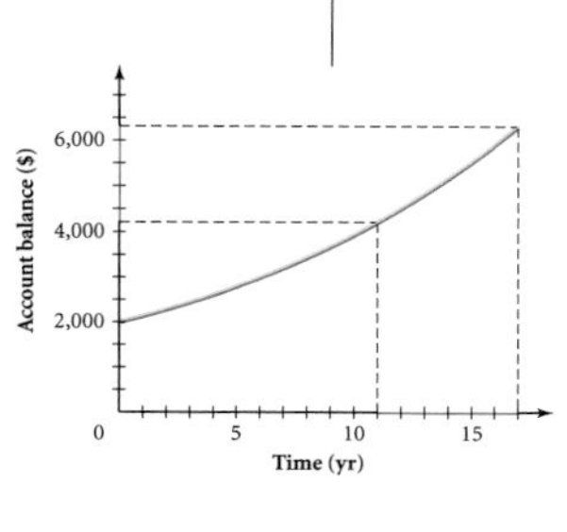

Compound interest has many applications in everyday life. The interest on both savin[gs] and loans is almost always compounded, often lead[...] This graph shows the account [...] example.

Leaving just $2000 in the bank [...] 11 years can double your mon[ey...] money will triple.

40 CHAPTER 1 Patterns and Recursion

As they read about and investigate patterns, students will learn to move easily between **multiple representations:** tables, graphs, recursive routines, equations, and words.

a. $x^5 = 3418$ b. $(x - 5.1)^4 = 256$ [...]14.4 = 69.4

Project

INCOME BY GENDER

The median annual incomes of year-round full-time workers in the United States, ages 25 and above, are listed in this table. Examine different relationships, such as data in the form *(time, men)*, *(time, women)*, *(women, men)*, *(time, men − women)*, *(time, men/women)*, and so on. Find best-fit models for those relationships that seem meaningful. Write an article in which you interpret some of your models and make predictions about the future. Research some recent data to see if your predictions are accurate so far.

Year	Men	Women
1970	$9,521	$5,616
1972	$11,148	$6,331
1974	$12,786	$7,370
1976	$14,732	$8,728
1978	$16,882	$10,121
1980	$20,297	$12,156
1982	$22,857	$14,477
1984	$25,497	$16,169
1986	$27,335	$17,675

(1990 Statistical Abstract of the United States)

Your project should include

- ▸ Your article, including relevant graphs, models, and predictions.
- ▸ More recent data (remember to cite your source).
- ▸ An analysis of how well the recent data fit your predictions.

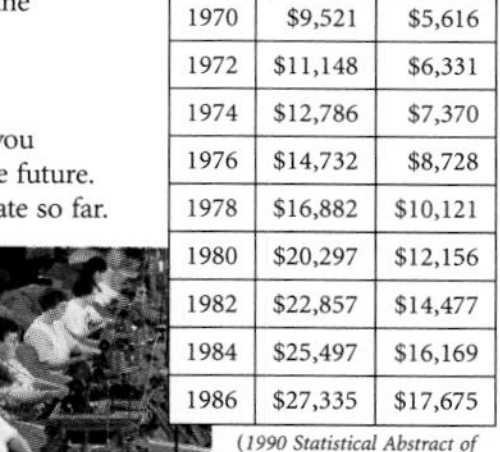

"Women constitute half the world's population, perform nearly two-thirds of its work hours, receive one-tenth of the world's income, and own less than one-hundredth of the world's property." (United Nations report, 1980)

292 CHAPTER 5 Exponential, Power, and Logarithmic Functions

Projects are practical, cultural, and mathematical extensions that engage individuals and groups in research and presentation activities. Some provide special technology opportunities.

Exercise sets are designed for optimal topic coverage and practice of recently acquired skills.

EXERCISES

Practice Your Skills

Exercise sets are developmental and begin with opportunities for students to practice new material in **Practice Your Skills.** These first exercises involve direct application of what students have learned through their investigation and the examples.

1. How should you divide the following sets into three groups for the median-median line method?
   a. Set of 51 elements b. Set of 50 elements c. Set of 47 elements d. Set of 38 elements

2. Find an equation in point-slope form of the line passing through
   a. (8.1, 15.7) and (17.3, 9.5) b. (3, 47) and (18, 84)

3. Find an equation in point-slope form of the line parallel to $y = -12.2 + 0.75x$ that passes through the point (14.4, 0.9).

4. Find an equation of the line one-third of the way from $y = -1.8x + 74.1$ to $y = -1.8x + 70.5$. (Hint: The first line came from two points in a median-median procedure, and the other line came from the third point.)

5. Find the equation of the line one-third of the way from the line $y = 2.8 + 4.7x$ to the point (12.8, 64).

Reason and Apply

Reason and Apply problems are more challenging, developing reasoning and the transfer of knowledge. These problems often include several steps that build on each other. They may also require students to combine information from earlier chapters with what they have just learned.

6. APPLICATION Follow these steps to find the equation for the median-median line for the data on life expectancy at birth for males in the United States for different years in the 20th century. Let x represent the year, and let y represent the male life expectancy in years.
   a. How many points are there in each of the three groups?
   b. What are the three representative points for these data? Graph these points.
   c. Draw the line through the first and third points. What is the slope of this line? What is the real-world meaning of the slope?
   d. Write the equation of the line through the first and third points. Rewrite this equation in intercept form.
   e. Draw the line parallel to the line in 6d passing through the second point. What is the equation of this line? Rewrite this equation in intercept form.
   f. Find the mean of the y-intercepts and write the equation of the median-median line. Graph this line. Remember to use the intercepts of all three lines.
   g. The year 1978 is missing from the table. Using your model, what would you predict the life expectancy at birth to be for males born in 1978?
   h. Use your model to predict the life expectancy at birth for m
   i. Using this model, when would you predict the life expectan in the United States to exceed 80 years?

Year of birth	Male life expectancy (years)
1920	53.6
1925	56.3
1930	58.1
1935	59.4
1940	60.8
1945	62.8

Review

Review keeps previous learning current.

13. APPLICATION Suppose a company offers a new employee a starting salary of $18,150 with annual raises of $1,000, or a starting salary of $17,900 with a raise of $500 every six months. At what point is one choice better than the other? Explain.

14. Suppose that you add 300 mL of water to an evaporating dish at the start of each day, and each day 40% of the water in the dish evaporates.
    a. Write and solve an equation that computes the long-run water level in
    b. Will a 1 L dish do the job? Explain why or why not.

Applications help students practice newly acquired skills in a realistic context.

15. APPLICATION Five stores in Tulsa, Oklahoma, sell the same model of a gra calculator for $89.95, $93.49, $109.39, $93.49, and $97.69.
    a. What are the median price, the mean price, and the standard deviation?
    b. If these stores are representative of all stores in the Tulsa area, of what is it to a consumer to know the median, mean, and standard deviation probably more helpful, the median or the mean?

Answers or **hints** for most odd-numbered exercises can be found in the back of the student book.

16. *Technology* Use statistics software to make a histogram of this data set: 44, 28, 46, 34, 19.
    a. Based on the histogram, predict what a box plot of the data will look l
    b. Use the software to create a box plot of the data. Were your prediction

Optional **technology** exercises allow students to explore algebra properties and make discoveries quickly, using dynamic software.

IMPROVING YOUR REASONING SKILLS

Sequential Slopes

Here's a sequence that generates coordinate points. What is the slope between any two points of this sequence?

$(x_0, y_0) = (0, 0)$

$(x_n, y_n) = (x_{n-1} + 2, y_{n-1} + 3)$ where $n \geq 1$

Now match each of these recursive rules to the slope between points.

a. $(x_n, y_n) = (x_{n-1} + 2, y_{n-1} + 2)$ b. $(x_n, y_n) = (x_{n-1} + 1, y_{n-1} + 3)$
c. $(x_n, y_n) = (x_{n-1} + 3, y_{n-1} - 4)$ d. $(x_n, y_n) = (x_{n-1} - 2, y_{n-1} + 10)$
e. $(x_n, y_n) = (x_{n-1} + 1, y_{n-1})$ f. $(x_n, y_n) = (x_{n-1} + 9, y$

A. 0 B. 1 C. 3 D. −5 E. $\frac{1}{3}$

In general, how do these recursive rules determine the slope between points?

Improving Your Skills features are puzzles that diverge from the topic under study and approach critical thinking from different points of view.

120 CHAPTER 3 Linear Models and Systems

The **Chapter Review** begins with a summary of the new mathematical ideas. The exercises are similar to those in the lessons and those that will appear on the chapter test. A more extensive **Mixed Review** is provided every three or four chapters.

CHAPTER 4 REVIEW

This chapter introduced the concept of a **function** and reviewed **function notation.** You saw real-world situations represented by rules, sets, functions, graphs, and most importantly, equations. You learned to distinguish between functions and other **relations** by using either the definition of a function—at most one y-value per x-value—or the vertical line test.

This chapter also introduced several **transformations,** including **translations, reflections,** and vertical and horizontal **stretches** and **shrinks.** You learned how to transform the graphs of **parent functions** to investigate several families of functions—linear, quadratic, square root, absolute value, and semicircle. For example, if you stretch the graph of the parent function $y = x^2$ by a factor of 3 vertically and by a factor of 2 horizontally, and translate it right 1 unit and up 4 units, then you get the graph of the function $y = 3\left(\frac{x-1}{2}\right)^2 + 4$.

Finally, you looked at the **composition** of functions. Many times, solving a problem involves two or more related functions. You can find the value of a composition of functions by using algebraic or numeric methods or by graphing.

Cameos of pictures that appeared earlier in the chapter remind students where an idea was first presented.

Boldface terms can be found in the glossary at the back of the student text.

EXERCISES

1. Sketch a graph that shows the relationship between the time in seconds after you start microwaving a bag of popcorn and the number of pops per second. Describe in words what your graph shows.

each coordinate ...

d. Find a quadratic function that models these data. Use your model to find
   i. the revenue if the fare is \$2.00.
   ii. the fare(s) that make no revenue (\$0).

$h(x + 2) - 3$
$h(f(-1))$
$h(f(a))$

TAKE ANOTHER LOOK

1. Some functions can be described as even or odd. An **even function** has the y-axis as a line of symmetry. If the function f is an even function, then $f(-x) = f(x)$ for all values of x in the domain. Which parent functions that you've seen are even functions? Now graph $y = x^3$, $y = \frac{1}{x}$, and $y = \sqrt[3]{x}$, all of which are **odd functions.** Describe the symmetry displayed by these odd functions. How would you define an odd function in terms of $f(x)$? Can you give an example of a function that is neither even nor odd?

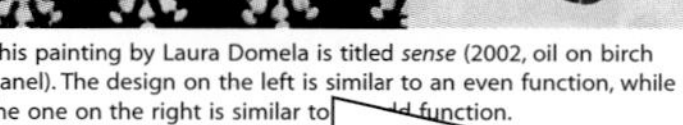
This painting by Laura Domela is titled *sense* (2002, oil on birch panel). The design on the left is similar to an even function, while the one on the right is similar to ... function.

2. A line of reflection does not have to be the x- or y-axis. Draw the graph ... and then draw its image when reflected across several different horizontal ... lines. Write the equation of each image. Try this with several different fun... general, if the graph of $y = f(x)$ is reflected across the vertical line $x = a$ ... equation of the image? If the graph of $y = f(x)$ is reflected across the hor... $y = b$, what is the equation of the image?

Assessing What You've Learned helps students capture their learning experiences and identify gaps in understanding. It introduces students to portfolios, journals, notebooks, presentations, and performance assessment as ways to assume responsibility for their own learning. Students will find chapter-specific suggestions to help them recognize their strengths and stay on top of their weaknesses.

Choose two functions $f(x)$ and $g(x)$. Use web graphs to find $f(g(x))$ ... values of x. Why does this method work?

Assessing What You've Learned

ORGANIZE YOUR NOTEBOOK Organize your notes on each type of parent function and each type of transformation you have learned about. Review how each transformation affects the graph of a function or relation and how the equation of the function or relation changes. You might want to create a large chart with rows for each type of transformation and columns for each type of parent function; don't forget to include a column for the general function, $y = f(x)$.

UPDATE YOUR PORTFOLIO Choose one piece of work that illustrates each transformation you have studied in this chapter. Try to select pieces that illustrate different parent functions. Add these to your portfolio. Describe each piece in a cover sheet, giving the objective, the result, and what you might have done differently.

WRITE TEST ITEMS Two important skills from this chapter are the ability to use transformations to write and graph equations. Write at least two test items that assess these skills. If you work with a group, identify other key ideas from this chapter and work together to write an entire test.

Take Another Look gives students a chance to approach concepts from a different perspective by giving a visual slant or by calling out connections between mathematical ideas.

Features of the Teacher's Edition

An **overview** of the chapter contents appears first in the teaching notes that open each chapter of the Teacher's Edition.

CHAPTER 5

Exponential, Power, and Logarithmic Functions

Overview

Exponential functions are introduced in **Lesson 5.1** to model growth and decay. In **Lesson 5.2,** students review properties of exponents as they become familiar with the power function $y = ax^n$ and are introduced to rational exponents. In **Lesson 5.3,** rational exponents $(x^{1/n})$ are related to root notation $(\sqrt[n]{x})$. Students then use the point-ratio form, $y = y_1 b^{x-x_1}$, to find an exponential equation through two points. Real-world applications are presented in **Lesson 5.4. Lesson 5.5** introduces inverses of functions and applications of inverses. Students learn to solve logarithmic functions in **Lesson 5.6,** and they also see why the inverse of an exponential function is a logarithmic function. Students increase their understanding of logarithms in **Lesson 5.7,** where they learn to work with logarithms of any base by changing to a common base; they also learn how a slide rule works. In **Lesson 5.8,** students use logarithms as a tool to solve problems with the variable in the exponent. The **exploration** on the transcendental number *e* introduces students to the natural logarithm function.

The Mathematics

Exponents and Exponential Functions

Exponents, or powers, represent repeated multiplication. Exponent properties such as $b^m b^n = b^{m+n}$ and $\frac{b^m}{b^n} = b^{m-n}$ can be understood for positive integer exponents through multiplication and division. We define other rational exponents in a way that extends the same properties to them. For example, because it is known that $\sqrt[3]{b}$ is the number whose cube is b, $b^{1/3}$ is defined to be $\sqrt[3]{b}$ so that $(b^{1/3})^3$ equals b.

But we have to be careful with rational exponents. If we use them carelessly, we can get statements like

$$1 = 1^{1/2} = \left((-1)^6\right)^{1/2} = (-1)^{6/2} = (-1)^3 = -1$$

implying that $1 = -1$. The student book applies rational exponents only to positive numbers, so that $(-1)^{6/2}$ is meaningless. This restriction is relaxed when the base is a variable, as it is for power functions; $y = x^{1/3}$ can be evaluated and graphed even when x is less than 0.

The book also makes the assumption that when a rational exponent is applied to a positive base, the result is positive. Because of this assumption, using rational exponents to solve equations may not produce all solutions. For example, the equation $x^2 = 4$ has two solutions, ± 2. However, if we raise both sides of the equation to the power of $\frac{1}{2}$, we get $x = 4^{1/2}$, which must be positive.

Exponential functions of the form $y = ab^x$ are characterized by the fact that any two pairs of x-values the same distance apart correspond to pairs of y-values with the same ratio, in contrast to linear functions, for which any two pairs of x-values the same distance apart correspond to pairs of y-values with the same difference. One consequence of this property of exponential functions is that every vertical stretch of the graph of an exponential function is the same as some horizontal translation. Another consequence is that the amount of increase in x required to double or halve the value of y is always the same, no matter what the starting value of y. For decreasing exponential functions, this time is called the *half-life;* for increasing exponential functions, it's called the *doubling time.*

Logarithms and Logarithmic Functions

The constant-ratio characteristic of exponential functions also implies that the product of any two values of $y = b^x$ is the image of the sum of the related x-values. That is, $b^{x_1}b^{x_2}$ equals $b^{x_1+x_2}$. This fact is behind the notion of logarithms. The logarithm to base b of a number x is the exponent put on b to get x. Before the days of electronic calculators, logarithms were used to calculate products and roots of very large or very small numbers. These methods underlie the design of slide rules.

The student book includes two modern uses of logarithms. It gives several ways of solving equations

CHAPTER 5 INTERLEAF 23

The **Mathematics** surveys the chapter contents, places the mathematics in context, and discusses topics in greater depth or at a higher level than is presented in the student book.

Using This Chapter suggests which lessons to emphasize and which may be optional for your algebra curriculum.

Materials needed for the entire chapter are summarized in a list.

for exponents, and it considers transformations. A vertical logarithmic transformation of the plane is like a vertical stretch and shrink, but by uneven amounts so that the graph of an exponential function becomes a straight line. Algebraically, the exponential equation $y = ab^x$ becomes the equation $\log y = \log a + x \log b$; that this equation is linear is seen by rewriting it as $z = c + dx$. This linearizing technique is especially useful when you are trying to find exponential functions that fit real-world data.

Inverse Functions

If points (x, y) are related by the exponential function $y = b^x$, then points (y, x) are related by the logarithmic function $x = \log_b y$. That is, the exponential and logarithmic functions are inverses of each other. In general, functions $f(x)$ and $g(x)$ are inverses if the ordered pairs of one are the ordered pairs of the other but in reverse order; that is, the x's and y's are interchanged. Equivalently, $f(g(x)) = g(f(x)) = x$.

Using This Chapter

To save time, you might combine Lessons 5.1 and 5.2 for students familiar with the topics. Lesson 5.7 can be shortened, but you should at least review the properties of logarithms before you go to the exercises. Most of Lesson 5.8 is not essential, but teach solving equations by taking the logarithm of each side, perhaps with Lesson 5.7.

Resources

Discovering Advanced Algebra Resources

Teaching and Worksheet Masters
Lessons 5.1, 5.2, 5.4, 5.5, 5.7, 5.8

Calculator Notes 1L, 1M, 3B, 3D, 4C, 4D, 5A–5E

Sketchpad Demonstrations
Lessons 5.2, 5.3, 5.5, 5.6

Fathom Demonstration
Lesson 5.8

Assessment Resources A and B
Quiz 1 (Lessons 5.1–5.3)
Quiz 2 (Lessons 5.4, 5.5)
Quiz 3 (Lessons 5.6–5.8)
Chapter 5 Test
Chapter 5 Constructive Assessment Options

More Practice Your Skills for Chapter 5

Condensed Lessons for Chapter 5

Other Resources

Powers of Ten film by Charles and Ray Eames.

Powers of Ten: A Book About the Relative Size of Things in the Universe and the Effect of Adding Another Zero by Philip and Phylis Morrison.

Historical Topics for the Mathematics Classroom from NCTM.

For complete references to these and other resources see www.keypress.com/DAA.

Materials

- dice (1 die per person)
- patty paper, *optional*
- rulers (2 per group)
- temperature probes
- cup of hot water

Pacing Guide

	day 1	day 2	day 3	day 4	day 5	day 6	day 7	day 8	day 9	day 10
standard	5.1	5.2	5.3	quiz, 5.4	5.5	quiz, 5.6	5.6	5.7	5.8	5.8
enriched	5.1, project	5.2	5.3, project	quiz, 5.4	5.5	quiz, 5.6	5.7	5.8	5.8, project	quiz, exploration
block	5.1, 5.2	5.3, quiz, 5.4	5.5, quiz, 5.6	5.6, 5.7	5.8, quiz	exploration, review	TAL, assessment			

	day 11	day 12	day 13
standard	quiz, review	review	assessment
enriched	review, project	review, TAL	assessment

237B CHAPTER 5 INTERLEAF Exponential, Power, and Logarithmic Functions

The **Pacing Guide** lets you see at a glance which lessons will require two days and when you might use a quiz or enrich your curriculum with a project.

The publisher **website** offers you links to more resources that you can use in your classroom.

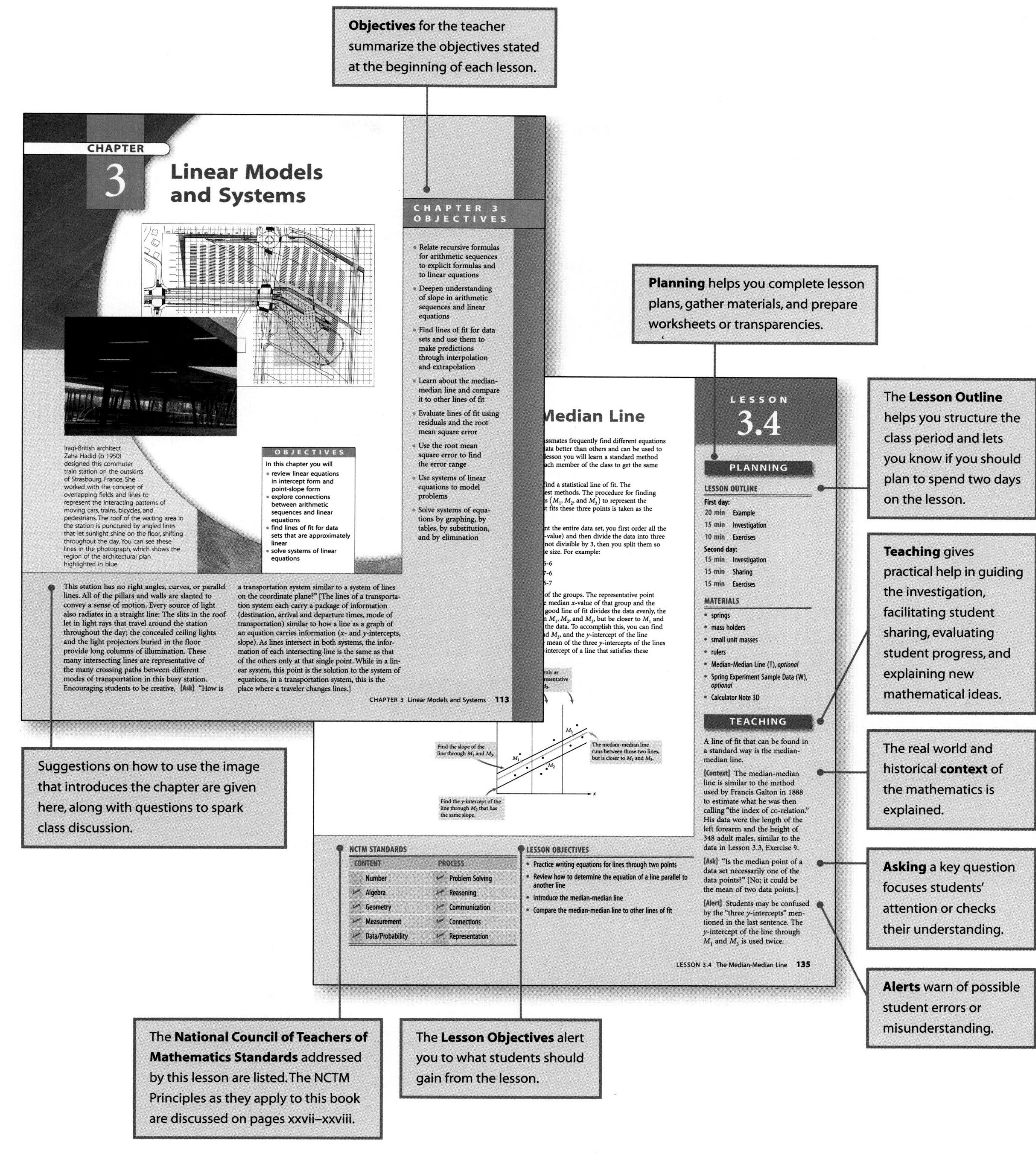

Objectives for the teacher summarize the objectives stated at the beginning of each lesson.
Planning helps you complete lesson plans, gather materials, and prepare worksheets or transparencies.
The **Lesson Outline** helps you structure the class period and lets you know if you should plan to spend two days on the lesson.
Teaching gives practical help in guiding the investigation, facilitating student sharing, evaluating student progress, and explaining new mathematical ideas.
The real world and historical **context** of the mathematics is explained.
Asking a key question focuses students' attention or checks their understanding.
Alerts warn of possible student errors or misunderstanding.
Suggestions on how to use the image that introduces the chapter are given here, along with questions to spark class discussion.
The **National Council of Teachers of Mathematics Standards** addressed by this lesson are listed. The NCTM Principles as they apply to this book are discussed on pages xxvii–xxviii.
The **Lesson Objectives** alert you to what students should gain from the lesson.
CHAPTER 3
Linear Models and Systems
CHAPTER 3 OBJECTIVES
Relate recursive formulas for arithmetic sequences to explicit formulas and to linear equations
Deepen understanding of slope in arithmetic sequences and linear equations
Find lines of fit for data sets and use them to make predictions through interpolation and extrapolation
Learn about the median-median line and compare it to other lines of fit
Evaluate lines of fit using residuals and the root mean square error
Use the root mean square error to find the error range
Use systems of linear equations to model problems
Solve systems of equations by graphing, by tables, by substitution, and by elimination
Iraqi-British architect Zaha Hadid (b 1950) designed this commuter train station on the outskirts of Strasbourg, France. She worked with the concept of overlapping fields and lines to represent the interacting patterns of moving cars, trains, bicycles, and pedestrians. The roof of the waiting area in the station is punctured by angled lines that let sunlight shine on the floor, shifting throughout the day. You can see these lines in the photograph, which shows the region of the architectural plan highlighted in blue.
OBJECTIVES
In this chapter you will
review linear equations in intercept form and point-slope form
explore connections between arithmetic sequences and linear equations
find lines of fit for data sets that are approximately linear
solve systems of linear equations
This station has no right angles, curves, or parallel lines. All of the pillars and walls are slanted to convey a sense of motion. Every source of light also radiates in a straight line: The slits in the roof let in light rays that travel around the station throughout the day; the concealed ceiling lights and the light projectors buried in the floor provide long columns of illumination. These many intersecting lines are representative of the many crossing paths between different modes of transportation in this busy station. Encouraging students to be creative, [Ask] "How is a transportation system similar to a system of lines on the coordinate plane?" [The lines of a transportation system each carry a package of information (destination, arrival and departure times, mode of transportation) similar to how a line as a graph of an equation carries information (x- and y-intercepts, slope). As lines intersect in both systems, the information of each intersecting line is the same as that of the others only at that single point. While in a linear system, this point is the solution to the system of equations, in a transportation system, this is the place where a traveler changes lines.]
CHAPTER 3 Linear Models and Systems 113
LESSON 3.4
PLANNING
LESSON OUTLINE
First day:
20 min Example
15 min Investigation
10 min Exercises
Second day:
15 min Investigation
15 min Sharing
15 min Exercises
MATERIALS
springs
mass holders
small unit masses
rulers
Median-Median Line (T), optional
Spring Experiment Sample Data (W), optional
Calculator Note 3D
TEACHING
A line of fit that can be found in a standard way is the median-median line.
[Context] The median-median line is similar to the method used by Francis Galton in 1888 to estimate what he was then calling "the index of co-relation." His data were the length of the left forearm and the height of 348 adult males, similar to the data in Lesson 3.3, Exercise 9.
[Ask] "Is the median point of a data set necessarily one of the data points?" [No; it could be the mean of two data points.]
[Alert] Students may be confused by the "three y-intercepts" mentioned in the last sentence. The y-intercept of the line through M_1 and M_3 is used twice.
Median Line
Find the slope of the line through M_1 and M_3.
The median-median line runs between those two lines, but is closer to M_1 and M_3.
Find the y-intercept of the line through M_2 that has the same slope.
NCTM STANDARDS
CONTENT: Number, Algebra, Geometry, Measurement, Data/Probability
PROCESS: Problem Solving, Reasoning, Communication, Connections, Representation
LESSON OBJECTIVES
Practice writing equations for lines through two points
Review how to determine the equation of a line parallel to another line
Introduce the median-median line
Compare the median-median line to other lines of fit
LESSON 3.4 The Median-Median Line 135

Teaching suggestions are keyed to the **steps** of the investigation.

Eminently readable feature-by-feature lesson commentary appears in the wrap-around space near the point where it is most relevant to help you with planning, teaching, and guiding students as they build understanding.

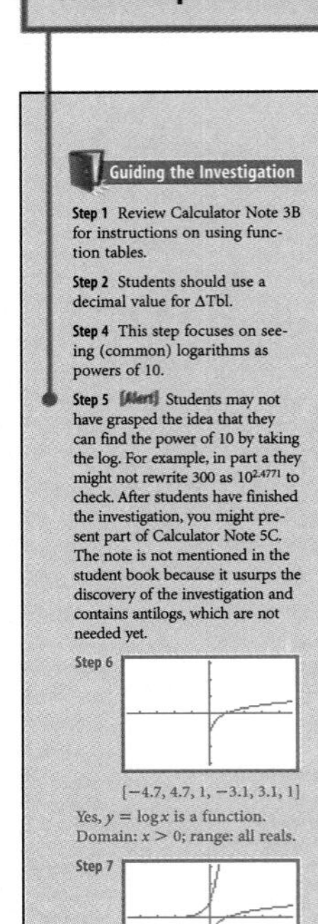

Guiding the Investigation

Step 1 Review Calculator Note 3B for instructions on using function tables.

Step 2 Students should use a decimal value for ΔTbl.

Step 4 This step focuses on seeing (common) logarithms as powers of 10.

Step 5 [Alert] Students may not have grasped the idea that they can find the power of 10 by taking the log. For example, in part a they might not rewrite 300 as $10^{2.4771}$ to check. After students have finished the investigation, you might present part of Calculator Note 5C. The note is not mentioned in the student book because it usurps the discovery of the investigation and contains antilogs, which are not needed yet.

Step 6

[−4.7, 4.7, 1, −3.1, 3.1, 1]

Yes, $y = \log x$ is a function. Domain: $x > 0$; range: all reals.

Step 7

[−4.7, 4.7, 1, −3.1, 3.1, 1]

$y = 10^x$ and $y = \log x$ are inverses.

▸ EXAMPLE A

The symbol $\log_{10}$ is the same as the symbol log used in the investigation. The answer, $x \approx 3.0654$, is given to five significant figures because that is the number of decimal places you need so that when you substitute back in for x the solution will check.

Step 5a $\log 300 = x$; $x \approx 2.4771$; $10^{2.4771} \approx 300$

Step 5b $\log 47 = x$; $x \approx 1.6721$; $10^{1.6721} \approx 47$

Step 5c $\log 0.01 = x$; $x = -2$; $10^{-2} = 0.01$

Step 5d $\log y = x$

Step 8 $f^{-1}(x) = \log x$; $f(f^{-1}(x)) = x$; $f^{-1}(f(x)) = x$

Step 5 Use logarithms to solve each equation for x. Check your answers.

a. $300 = 10^x$ **b.** $47 = 10^x$ **c.** $0.01 = 10^x$ **d.** $y = 10^x$

Step 6 Use a friendly window with a factor of 1 to investigate the graph of $y = \log x$. Is $y = \log x$ a function? What are the domain and range of $y = \log x$?

Step 7 Graph $y = 10^x$ and draw its inverse on the same set of axes. Now graph $y = \log x$. What observations can you make?

Step 8 If $f(x) = 10^x$, then what is $f^{-1}(x)$? What is $f(f^{-1}(x))$?

The expression $\log x$ is another way of expressing x as an exponent on the base 10. Ten is the common base for logarithms, so $\log x$ is called a **common logarithm** and is shorthand for writing $\log_{10} x$. You read this as "the logarithm base 10 of x." $\log x$ is the exponent you put on 10 to get x.

The spiral shape of this computer-generated shell was created by a logarithmic function.

EXAMPLE A Solve $4 \cdot 10^x = 4650$.

▸ Solution

$4 \cdot 10^x = 4650$	Original equation.
$10^x = 1162.5$	Divide both sides by 4.
$x = \log_{10} 1162.5$	The logarithm base 10 of 1162.5 is the exponent you place on 10 to get 1162.5.
$x \approx 3.0654$	Use the log key on your calculator to evaluate.

The general **logarithmic function** is an exponent-producing function. The logarithm base b of x is the exponent you put on b to get x.

Definition

For $a > 0$ a

The general lo expression. Th exponential eq

EXAMPLE B Solve $4^x =$

One Step

Pose the first part of Exercise 7: "Assume the Uni States national debt can be estimated with the m $y = 0.051517(1.1306727)^x$, where x represents th number of years since 1900 and y represents the in billions of dollars. According to the model, wh did the debt pass \$1 trillion?" Ask students how represent 1 trillion. Students from some countrie think of 1 trillion as 1 billion billion, but in the U States it's defined as 1000 billion. Students can so

One Step is an open-ended alternative to the more guided several-step investigation and is intended for classes experienced in mathematical investigation.

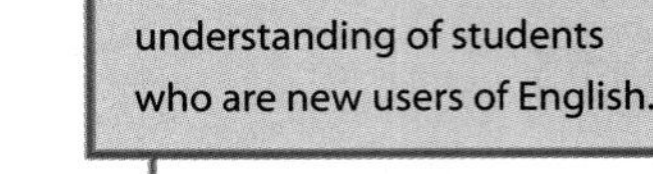

ESL prompts help boost the understanding of students who are new users of English.

b. As an alternative to completing the square for $y = 3x^2 + 21x - 35$, you can use the formulas for h and k. First, identify the coefficients, a, b, and c.

$$y = 3x^2 + 21x - 35$$

$a = 3$ $b = 21$ $c = -35$

Substitute the values of a, b, and c into the formulas for h and k.

$$h = -\frac{b}{2a} \qquad k = c - \frac{b^2}{4a}$$

$$h = -\frac{21}{2(3)} = -3.5 \qquad k = -35 - \frac{21^2}{4(3)} = -71.75$$

The vertex is $(-3.5, -71.75)$, and the vertex form is $y = 3(x + 3.5)^2 - 71.75$. Remember to include the value of a in the vertex form.

You may find that using the formulas for h and k is often simpler than completing the square. Both methods will allow you to find the vertex of a quadratic equation and write the equation in vertex form. However, the procedure of completing the square will be used again in your work with ellipses and other geometric shapes, so you should become comfortable using it.

EXAMPLE C Nora hits a softball straight up at a speed of 120 ft/s. If her bat contacts the ball at a height of 3 ft above the ground, how high does the ball travel? When does the ball reach its maximum height?

1999 U.S. Olympic Softball Team player Kim Maher at bat

▸ Solution Using the projectile motion function, you know that the height of the object at time x is represented by the equation $y = ax^2 + v_0x + s_0$. The initial velocity, v_0, is 120 ft/s, and the initial height, s_0, is 3 ft. Because the distance is measured in feet, the approximate leading coefficient is −16. Thus, the function is $y = -16x^2 + 120x + 3$. To find the maximum height, locate the vertex.

$y = -16x^2 + 120x + 3$	Original equation. Identify the coefficients, $a = -16$, $b = 120$, and $c = 3$.
$h = -\frac{b}{2a} = -\frac{120}{2(-16)} = 3.75$	Use the formula for h to find the x-coordinate of the vertex.
$k = c - \frac{b^2}{4a} = 3 - \frac{120^2}{4(-16)} = 228$	Use the formula for k to find the y-coordinate of the vertex.

The softball reaches a maximum height of 228 ft at 3.75 s.

You now have several strategies for finding the vertex of a quadratic function. You can convert from general form to vertex form by completing the square or by using the formulas for h and k.

▸ EXAMPLE C

[ESL] "How high" is asking for the greatest height of the ball, not just any height the ball reaches.

[Language] *Velocity* means "speed in a specific direction." The velocity of 120 ft/s in this example is a speed (rate of change of distance in feet for each second) of 120 ft/s in the upward direction. A negative velocity is downward. For example, a negative initial velocity would indicate that something was being thrown down.

Students may point out that a softball normally doesn't travel straight up and down. Even if the motion has a horizontal component, the projectile motion function describes the vertical component.

As an alternative approach to finding k, once students find that the x-coordinate of the vertex is $h = 3.75$, they could substitute that value for x into the equation $y = -16x^2 + 120x + 3$ and get a height of 228 ft.

SHARING IDEAS

As students discuss ideas, ask why they'd ever need to find the coordinates of a parabola's vertex. [Its coordinates give a maximum or minimum value in a real-world situation.]

[Ask] "Is there an alternative to remembering the formulas for h and k?" [The values can always be rederived by completing the square.]

[Ask] "Does it make sense that the expression $a\left(x + \frac{b}{2a}\right)^2 + \left(c - \frac{b^2}{4a}\right)$ has an optimum value at $\left(-\frac{b}{2a}, c - \frac{b^2}{4a}\right)$?" One way to make sense of this is to think of the first term as being added to (or subtracted from) the second. The square of the binomial is never negative, so the sum or difference will be optimized when this square is 0, which is when $x = -\frac{b}{2a}$. The optimum

Sharing Ideas (continued)

value will be the second term, with 0 being added or subtracted.

Let students know that completing the square to find an optimum value is a method that applies only to quadratics. Other methods are needed for other polynomials. [Link] Calculus provides a general method that applies to all polynomials and most other common functions.

If you have time, you might prepare students for Exercise 14 and foreshadow Chapter 9 by reminding them that the equation $x^2 + y^2 = 16$ represents a circle centered at the origin and having radius 4. Then [Ask] "What might the equation $x^2 - 6x + y^2 = 16$ represent?" [Completing the square gives $x^2 + 6x + 9 + y^2 = 25$, which is equivalent to $(x - 3)^2 + y^2 = 5^2$, representing a translation and dilation of the unit circle to a circled centered at the point (3, 0) and having radius 5.]

Vocabulary and other **language** points are explained.

Suggestions help you guide students as they **share** and discuss investigation results.

Links are made to other areas of mathematics.

Assessing Progress helps you to gauge how much students are retaining from previous lessons.

Closing the Lesson connects the new mathematical ideas of the lesson to students' experiences.

Building Understanding suggests how you might assign exercises and how you can anticipate difficulties and offer help.

The **Assigning Homework** chart indicates ways to use the exercises.

Helping with the Exercises indicates errors to watch for or ways to help students who are having difficulty with an exercise.

Sharing Ideas (continued)

[Ask] "If you view a circle from more and more of an angle, does the shape remain an ellipse?" [It eventually becomes a line segment.]

Assessing Progress

You can check how well students understand how equations are affected by stretching their graphs in the directions of the axes.

Closing the Lesson

Note the main point of this lesson: Stretching the graph of the unit circle in one direction or stretching it in both directions by different factors gives an **ellipse.** The equation of an ellipse is $\frac{x^2}{a^2} + \frac{y^2}{b^2} = 1$. You might also summarize the relationships between transformed graphs and equations given on this page.

BUILDING UNDERSTANDING

The exercises focus on the semicircle function but also include all the transformations and parent functions introduced in the chapter. The review exercises are quite lengthy; choose carefully which ones to assign.

ASSIGNING HOMEWORK

Essential	1–5
Performance assessment	6–9
Portfolio	9
Group	9
Review	10–15

MATERIALS

- Calculator Notes 2D, 4H, *optional*

Helping with the Exercises

Exercise 1 As needed, encourage students to verify their ideas by graphing on their calculators. A friendly window with a factor of 2 works well.

You have now learned to translate, reflect, stretch, and shrink functions and relations. These transformations are the same for all equations.

Transformations of Functions and Relations

Translations

The graph of $y = k + f(x - h)$ translates the graph of $y = f(x)$ h units horizontally and k units vertically.

or

Replacing x with $(x - h)$ translates the graph h units horizontally. Replacing y with $(y - k)$ translates the graph k units vertically.

Reflections

The graph of $y = f(-x)$ is a reflection of the graph of $y = f(x)$ across the y-axis. The graph of $y = -f(x)$ is a reflection the graph of $y = f(x)$ across the x-axis.

or

Replacing x with $-x$ reflects the graph across the y-axis. Replacing y with $-y$ reflects the graph across the x-axis.

Stretches and Shrinks

The graph of $y = af\left(\frac{x}{b}\right)$ is a stretch or shrink of the graph of $y = f(x)$ by a vertical scale factor of a and by a horizontal scale factor of b.

or

Replacing x with $\frac{x}{b}$ stretches or shrinks the graph by a horizontal scale factor of b. Replacing y with $\frac{y}{a}$ stretches or shrinks the graph by a vertical scale factor of a.

Exercises

Practice Your Skills

1. Each equation represents a s

Equation	Transfor (translation, stretch,
$y + 3 = x^2$	Transl
$-y = \lvert x\rvert$	Reflec
$y = \sqrt{\frac{x}{4}}$	Stret
$\frac{y}{0.4} = x^2$	Shri
$y = \lvert x - 2\rvert$	Transl
$y = \sqrt{-x}$	Reflec

220 CHAPTER 4 Functions, Relations, and Transformations

12.

13. $\begin{cases} x \geq 2 \\ y \leq 5 \\ x + y \geq 3 \\ 2x - y \leq 9 \end{cases}$

Exercise 14 This exercise depends on Lesson 6.3, so assign it only if your students completed that lesson.

14a. $\left[\begin{array}{cc|c} 2 & -1 & \frac{1}{2} \\ 5 & -2 & -5 \end{array}\right]$

14b. $\left[\begin{array}{cc|c} 1 & 0 & -6 \\ 0 & 1 & -12.5 \end{array}\right]$; $(-6, -12.5)$

14c. $-12.5 = 2(-6) - 0.5$; $5(-6) - 2(-12.5) + 5 = 0$

EXTENSIONS

A. Use Take Another Look activity 3 on page 357.

B. To extend Exercise 10, ask students to research shipping restrictions on package size and to draw feasibility regions for package sizes with different carriers. Students should find out what types of restrictions there are, whether different companies have different restrictions on size, and whether certain things cannot be mailed because of their size.

Review

6.4 **11.** Solve each of these systems in at least two different ways.

a. $\begin{cases} 8x + 3y = 41 \\ 9x + 2y = 25 \end{cases}$ $x = -\frac{7}{11}, y = \frac{169}{11}$

b. $\begin{cases} 2x + y - 2z = 5 \\ 6x + 2y - 4z = 3 \\ 4x - y + 3z = 5 \end{cases}$ $x = -3.5, y = 74, z = 31$

6.5 **12.** Sketch a graph of the feasible region described by this system of inequalities:

$\begin{cases} y \geq (x - 3)^2 + 5 \\ y \leq -\lvert x - 2\rvert + 10 \end{cases}$

6.5 **13.** Give the system of inequalities whose solution set is the polygon at right.

6.3 **14.** Consider this system of equations:

$\begin{cases} y = 2x - \frac{1}{2} \\ 5x - 2y + 5 = 0 \end{cases}$

a. Write the augmented matrix for this system.

b. Reduce the augmented matrix to row-echelon form. Write the solution as an ordered pair of coordinates.

c. Check your solution values for x and y by substituting them into the original equations.

4.6 **15.** Find the equation of the parabola at right.

$y = -\left(\frac{x}{2}\right)^2 - \frac{3}{2}$ or $y = -\frac{1}{4}x^2 - \frac{3}{2}$

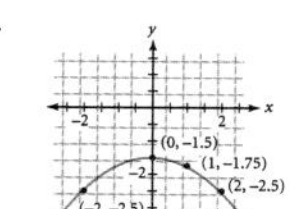

Project

NUTRITIONAL ELEMENTS

Write and solve your own linear programming problem similar to the cracker-and-yogurt snack combination problem in this lesson. Choose two food items from your home or a grocery store, and decide on your constraints and what you wish to minimize or maximize. Record the necessary information. Then write inequalities, and find the feasible region and optimum value for your problem. Your project should include

- Your linear programming problem
- A complete solution, including a graph of the feasible region
- An explanation of your process

Supporting the Project

Encourage students to explore problems in which they want to maximize nutrition, perhaps while keeping cost below a certain amount. If students choose criteria that produce no feasible region, they should revise their criteria and include in their write-ups a description of why the criteria were unworkable.

OUTCOMES

- The report includes a clearly written problem statement with at least two constraints in addition to the commonsense constraints.
- A complete solution is given, including a graph of the feasible region and the values that optimize the given function.
- The explanation of the process of writing and solving the problem is clear and complete and explains any difficulties.
- The problem statement includes four or more constraints.
- The student includes further information on linear programming, such as a description of a linear programming problem with more than two variables.

350 CHAPTER 6 Matrices and Linear Systems

Annotations that appear in magenta on the student page and in wrap-around text, or at the back of the book, give answers or possible answers.

Additional questions, challenges, or research topics are suggested. Brief answers are often included. You will find complete answers in the *Solutions Manual.*

The number printed in blue before each review exercise tells you which lesson is being reviewed. Review exercises with no numbers review beginning algebra or geometry.

A short introduction gives you more information about the **project.** Outcomes at two levels are listed. Outcomes you should expect of all projects are indicated with triangular bullets. Outcomes indicated with round bullets will be found only in the best presentations, those that have gone beyond the requirements of the project.

Answers are included for **Take Another Look** activities, which offer new perspectives on the concepts introduced in the chapter.

Take Another Look

1. The area of the tables generates a sequence proportional to 1, 2, 3, ...

The perimeters of the nested squares generate the sequence 4, 8, 12, 16, ... The growth is arithmetic; $u_1 = 4$ and $u_n = u_{n-1} + 4$ where $n \geq 2$. The areas of the nested squares generate the sequence 1, 4, 9, 16, ... The growth is neither arithmetic nor geometric; students probably won't be able to write the recursive rule $u_n = u_{n-1} + 2n - 1$, but they may write $u_n = n^2$ where $n \geq 1$. The heights generate the sequence 1, 2, 3, 4, ... The growth is arithmetic; $u_1 = 1$ and $u_n = u_{n-1} + 1$ where $n \geq 2$.

The perimeters of the other nested polygons generate the sequence 3, 4, 5, 6, ... The growth is arithmetic; $u_1 = 3$ and $u_n = u_{n-1} + 1$ where $n \geq 2$.

Using $s = 1$ and $A = \frac{ns^2}{4\tan\left(\frac{360°}{n}\right)}$, their areas generate the sequence $\frac{\sqrt{3}}{4}, 1, \frac{5}{4\tan 72°}, \frac{3}{2\tan 60°}, \ldots$, which generalizes to $u_n = \frac{n}{4\tan\left(\frac{360°}{n}\right)}$ where $n \geq 3$.

The growth is neither arithmetic nor geometric.

Invented geometric patterns will vary.

TAKE ANOTHER LOOK

1. In Lesson 1.1, Example A, you saw an arithmetic sequence that generates from a geometric pattern: the number of seats around a linear arrangement of square tables is 4, 6, 8, ... Notice that the sequence comes from the increase in the perimeter of the arrangement. What sequence comes from the increase in area?

4 6 8

Use these geometric patterns to generate recursive sequences using perimeter, area, height, or other attributes, and give their recursive formulas. Which sequences exhibit arithmetic growth? Geometric growth? Are there sequences you cannot define as arithmetic or geometric?

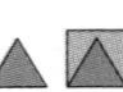

Invent a geometric pattern of your own. Look for and define different sequences.

2. Here's a strategy an algebra student discovered for finding the monthly payment you would need to make to pay off a loan. First, specify the loan amount, the annual interest rate, and the term (length) of the loan. Choose trial monthly payment amounts that form a sequence, say, \$0, \$1, \$2, \$3. Record the final balance remaining at the end of the term for each payment. Next, explore the differences in the final balances and find a pattern. Finally, use the pattern to find a monthly payment that results in a zero final balance. Tell how you know that your payment amount is correct. How many trial payment amounts do you need in order to determine the monthly payment? Try this strategy for one of the exercises in Lesson 1.5.

3. Imagine a target for a dart game that consists of a bull's-eye and three additional circles. If it is certain that a dart will land within the target but is otherwise random, what sequence of radii gives a set of probabilities that form an arithmetic sequence? A geometric sequence? Sketch what the targets look like.

4. As you probably realized in Lesson 1.5, your graphing calculator is a useful tool for solving loan and investment problems. With the added help of a special program, your calculator will instantly tell you information such as the monthly payment necessary for a home mortgage. [► See Calculator Note 1M to learn how to use your calculator's financial-solver program. ◄] Try using this program to solve some of the exercises in Lesson 1.5 or a problem of your own design.

2. Consider a loan of \$32,000 to be paid off in 60 months at 7.9% annual interest, compounded monthly ($u_0 = 32{,}000$).

Monthly payment	Final balance	Difference
\$0	\$47,438.84	
\$1	\$47,365.56	\$73.28
\$2	\$47,292.27	\$73.29
\$3	\$47,218.99	\$73.28

Each difference is approximately \$73.28, so the final balances form an arithmetic sequence with a common difference of about \$73.28. You can divide \$47,438.84 by \$73.28 to determine how many times you must repeat the sequence for the final balance to be 0 $\left(\frac{47438.84}{73.28} \approx 647.36\right)$. Hence the monthly payment should be about \$647.36. (Actually, because the differences are not exactly \$73.28, the closest we can get to 0 after 60 months is with a monthly payment of \$647.31.)

IMPROVING YOUR REASONING SKILLS

Coding and Decoding

One of the uses of matrices is in the mathematical field of cryptography, the science of enciphering and deciphering encoded messages. Here's one way that a matrix can be used to make a secret code:

Imagine encoding the word "CODE." First you convert each letter to a numerical value, based on its location in the alphabet. For example, C = 3 because it is the third letter in the alphabet. So, CODE = 3, 15, 4, 5. Arrange these numbers in a 2 × 2 matrix: $\begin{bmatrix} 3 & 15 \\ 4 & 5 \end{bmatrix}$.

Now multiply by an encoding matrix.

Let's use $[E] = \begin{bmatrix} 1 & -1 \\ -1 & 2 \end{bmatrix}$, so $\begin{bmatrix} 3 & 15 \\ 4 & 5 \end{bmatrix}[E] = \begin{bmatrix} -12 & 27 \\ -1 & 6 \end{bmatrix}$.

Now you have to convert back to letters. Notice that three of these numbers are outside of the numbers 1–26 that represent A–Z. To convert other numbers, simply add or subtract 26 to make them fall within the range of 1 to 26, like this:

$$\begin{bmatrix} -12 & 27 \\ -1 & 6 \end{bmatrix} \rightarrow \begin{bmatrix} 14 & 1 \\ 25 & 6 \end{bmatrix} \rightarrow \begin{bmatrix} N & A \\ Y & F \end{bmatrix}$$

Now, to *decode* the encoded message "NAYF," you convert back to numbers and multiply by the inverse of the coding matrix, and then you convert each number back into the corresponding letter in the alphabet:

$$\begin{bmatrix} 14 & 1 \\ 25 & 6 \end{bmatrix}[E]^{-1} = \begin{bmatrix} 29 & 15 \\ 56 & 31 \end{bmatrix} = \begin{bmatrix} C & O \\ D & E \end{bmatrix}$$

See if you can decode this Navajo saying. Begin by taking out the spaces and breaking the letters into groups of four letters each.

CC FSLG GTQN YP OPIIY UCB DKIC BYF BEQQ WW URQLPRE.

Language CONNECTION

The Navajo language was used in coding messages by the U.S. Marines in World War II, because it is a complex unwritten language that is unintelligible to anyone without extensive training. Navajo code talkers could encode, transmit, and decode three-line English messages in 20 seconds, whereas machines of the time required 30 minutes to perform the same job. Navajo recruits developed the code, including a dictionary and numerous words for military terms. Learn more about Navajo code talkers by using the links at www.keymath.com/DAA .

Navajo recruits, like these two shown in the Pacific Island of Bougainville in 1943, shared their complex language with U.S. Marines to communicate in code during World War II.

MAKING THE CONNECTION

The Navajo are Native Americans from the southwestern United States, mainly Arizona, Utah, and New Mexico. Their native language is part of the Athapaskan language family, which includes indigenous languages from Alaska to New Mexico. Navajo is one of the most widely spoken Native American languages, with some 100,000 speakers. Like most other indigenous languages, though, the Navajo language is in danger of disappearing. Because Native American children rarely learn their indigenous languages, 149 of the 187 surviving Native American languages are expected to vanish within a generation.

IMPROVING REASONING SKILLS

This coded message uses the same coding matrix $[E]$, so to decode you use the inverse, $\begin{bmatrix} 2 & 1 \\ 1 & 1 \end{bmatrix}$.
The message says, "If eyes have no tears the soul can have no rainbow."

[Language] *Enciphering* and *encoding* mean "writing in code." *Deciphering* means "determining what a coded message says." A system of secret writing is also called a *cipher*, a *cryptogram*, or a *cryptograph*.

Making the Connection allows you to share more information with your students about the connections found in their book. These are often good discussion topics.

Both approaches and answers are given to each **Improving Your Skills** problem.

NCTM Principles and Standards 2000

As part of the Key Curriculum Press *Discovering Mathematics* series, *Discovering Advanced Algebra* exemplifies the *Principles and Standards for School Mathematics* set forth by the National Council of Teachers of Mathematics (NCTM) in 2000.

The Equity Principle

Excellence in mathematics education requires equity—high expectations and strong support for all students. (*Principles and Standards for School Mathematics.* Reston, Virginia: National Council of Teachers of Mathematics, 2000, page 12.)

Discovering Advanced Algebra grew out of the belief that all students—not only a gifted few—are capable of learning mathematics. The approach promotes deeper learning for all students, including those who have succeeded at rote learning.

Different students need different experiences. Some need extra skills practice. *Discovering Advanced Algebra* provides that practice. Others learn from puzzles and different perspectives. *Discovering Advanced Algebra* sections such as Improving Your Reasoning Skills and Improving Your Visual Thinking Skills offer such challenges. Other students face learning disabilities or language barriers or have gaps in their past mathematical learning. The *Discovering Advanced Algebra Teacher's Edition* offers advice for accommodating such differences through **[Alert]**, **[Language]**, and **[ESL]** prompts as well as through **[Ask]** prompts that can help clarify and push students to explain why. Some students learn quickly and need more challenges. Projects, extension problems, and Take Another Look activities will keep such students challenged.

Research suggests that most students learn best when they are actively engaged. That's why *Discovering Advanced Algebra* includes investigations and activities. Through these experiences, students—including those who have difficulty memorizing formulas or doing calculations—come to understand algebra concepts more deeply.

The Curriculum Principle

A curriculum is more than a collection of activities: it must be coherent, focused on important mathematics, and well articulated across the grades. (NCTM *Principles and Standards,* page 14.)

The investigations and activities in *Discovering Advanced Algebra* are coherently organized and carefully crafted. They promote an intuitive understanding of algebra concepts, and their ideas are related. Students' introduction to symbols is accompanied by hands-on experience with the ideas; only then do students practice mechanics and problem solving.

Each lesson focuses on one or two important mathematical ideas. To help you emphasize these ideas, they are summarized in the lesson's Closing section of the *Discovering Advanced Algebra Teacher's Edition.*

This algebra course does not stand alone. *Discovering Advanced Algebra* is part of the Key Curriculum Press *Discovering Mathematics* series, which articulates a three-year high-school curriculum that includes the most important ideas of algebra and geometry.

As part of this series, *Discovering Advanced Algebra* ties algebra to other mathematical topics. It approaches many algebra topics through data analysis; reviews geometric ideas in algebraic and trigonometric contexts; ties algebra to statistics, combinatorics, and probability; and strengthens inductive and deductive reasoning skills.

The *Principles* state (page 15), "... teachers also need to be able to adjust [the curriculum] and take advantage of opportunities to move lessons in unanticipated directions." To help you maintain this flexibility, the *Discovering Advanced Algebra Teacher's Edition* includes advice of the form "If students ask ... then you might ... ."

The Teaching Principle

Effective mathematics teaching requires understanding what students know and need to learn and then challenging and supporting them to learn it well. (NCTM *Principles and Standards,* page 16.)

To help you challenge and support your students' learning, the *Discovering Advanced Algebra Teacher's Edition* assumes that you are a creative professional and wouldn't simply follow a script. It also supports the four primary aspects of professional teaching outlined in the *Principles*:

To **deepen your own mathematical understanding,** each chapter of the *Discovering Advanced Algebra Teacher's Edition* is introduced by an essay titled The Mathematics. These essays summarize the mathematics in the chapter, place it in historical context, and relate new material to what your students already know.

Throughout the *Discovering Advanced Algebra Teacher's Edition,* you can find advice that helps you **create a supportive learning environment.** Later in this introduction you'll find tested ideas about how to promote inquiry through cooperative learning.

While **interacting with students,** you might encounter confusion or questions that hint at a misunderstanding. The commentary in the *Discovering Advanced Algebra Teacher's Edition* alerts you to comprehension issues, suggests reasons why they arise, and proposes questions (with an **[Ask]** prompt) and alternative representations that you might use to alleviate them.

The *Discovering Advanced Algebra Teacher's Edition* offers advice about the important activities of **analyzing and reflecting** on your teaching. It also offers suggestions for adapting the text to what your school or district expects students to know.

The Learning Principle

Students must learn mathematics with understanding, actively building new knowledge from experience and prior knowledge. (NCTM *Principles and Standards,* page 20.)

We want our students to gain factual knowledge, become proficient at procedures, improve at learning on their own, and become better at applying their learning in this changing, technological world. Research indicates that these four outcomes will follow if we achieve one underlying goal: conceptual understanding. Moreover, by emphasizing conceptual understanding, you can motivate a large part of that diverse group of students who are not able to remember facts and procedures unless they understand them.

Each student's conceptual understanding comes from interacting with ideas—encountering them independent of their names or formulas and connecting them to past experience. The investigations in *Discovering Advanced Algebra* that are contextually based lead students to experiment with concepts before related terminology and formulas are introduced. They facilitate a cooperative classroom climate that encourages students to make connections as they work with their peers.

In pursuit of the specific goal of helping students become accomplished at applying their learning, *Discovering Advanced Algebra* takes students beyond learning algebra. They also learn to be open to new ideas as they solve problems, examine alternatives, think critically, and use initiative. Moreover, the investigations empower students to communicate by asking them to record their reactions, make conjectures (perhaps with the help of technology), or test hypotheses.

The Technology Principle

Technology is essential in teaching and learning mathematics; it influences the mathematics that is taught and enhances students' learning. (NCTM *Principles and Standards,* page 24.)

Technological tools can be useful in deepening conceptual understanding, because they allow students to surmount algorithmic barriers and focus on concepts. The predecessor to *Discovering Advanced Algebra,* then called *Advanced Algebra Through Data Exploration,* was the first textbook to integrate graphing calculators into the algebra curriculum. The present edition now also incorporates projects, exercises, and extensions that can be explored with Fathom Dynamic Statistics software and with The Geometer's Sketchpad Dynamic Geometry software. The Teaching Resources package includes Sketchpad and Fathom demonstrations that can help students visualize concepts and changing relationships.

Students receive ample help as they learn to use technology. Calculator notes, which include keystrokes and screen grabs linked to a specific lesson, and extra worksheets fill in procedural details for students who need more guidance with dynamic software than the student book can supply. Students quickly gain the facility they need and begin to ask "What if . . . " questions. The tools also allow students to focus on decision making, reflection, reasoning, and problem solving, and they erase artificial lines separating algebra, geometry, data analysis, and calculus.

To help a variety of students make connections, *Discovering Advanced Algebra* includes numerous exercises depicting situations all over the world. Links at www.keymath.com/DAA lead students to web pages related to those topics.

The Assessment Principle

Assessment should support the learning of important mathematics and furnish useful information to both teachers and students. (NCTM *Principles and Standards,* page 22.)

Often the focus of teaching is on final assessment: quizzes and tests with right or wrong answers. Also important, however, is ongoing assessment of how students are thinking so that they can see how well they're learning and you can modify your teaching to accommodate individuals. *Discovering Advanced Algebra* supports both kinds of assessment.

In the *Discovering Advanced Algebra Teacher's Edition,* each lesson includes a section that lists what you can assess as you observe students while they work or present ideas. The list includes mathematical concepts and abilities from earlier lessons, as well as skill at visualization, problem solving, and cooperative learning. Later in this introduction you will find detailed advice on assessing group work.

Teaching resources include many assessment options: quizzes and tests (with answers) for skill assessment, and constructive assessments (with rubrics) to assess conceptual understanding. These items and hundreds more are part of the *Test Generator and Worksheet Builder.* Students can learn from self-assessment as well. Ideas for self-assessment appear at the end of each chapter of the student book.

The Content and Process Standards

Each lesson addresses many of the NCTM content and process standards. At the beginning of each lesson, the *Discovering Advanced Algebra Teacher's Edition* lists the relevant content standards.

Teaching with *Discovering Advanced Algebra*

Discovering Advanced Algebra: An Investigative Approach is adapted from *Advanced Algebra Through Data Exploration: A Graphing Calculator Approach,* which since its publication in 1998, has gained a reputation as a leading textbook using graphing calculators to help students learn through doing. This new edition has been reformatted and renamed to become part of the *Discovering Mathematics* series.

Revised using feedback from teachers, *Discovering Advanced Algebra* continues to emphasize cooperative-group activities that help students make sense of algebra ideas as they improve their reasoning skills. It continues to incorporate graphing calculators so students can explore real data and its often-messy numbers. In addition, this revision includes the opportunity to use more technology. Activities that incorporate The Geometer's Sketchpad Dynamic Geometry software and Fathom Dynamic Statistics software give students an opportunity to explore functions and data in dynamic learning environments. Internet links through the student and parent website, www.keymath.com/DAA, help students pursue connections and extensions more fully. The website also gives students access to extra practice.

One important requirement of traditional algebra courses is skill at symbol manipulation. *Discovering Advanced Algebra* and its teaching resources include many opportunities for students to practice skills such as multiplying and factoring polynomials and solving many kinds of equations. In a traditional curriculum, students do not learn these skills in the context of the world around them. As a result, only a small percentage of students master effective symbol manipulation. Modern research indicates that students will learn to manipulate symbols effectively if they understand the operations conceptually. You can help students achieve this conceptual understanding by guiding them to explore situations and data that interest them.

The investigations in *Discovering Advanced Algebra* are designed to engage students so that learning becomes important to them. As you teach, keep in mind that you are addressing the need for students to be able to manipulate symbols not through developing automatic responses to stimuli, but rather through motivating students' understanding of the reasons for the operations and the meanings behind them.

In today's technological world all students need to be problem solvers who are not afraid to ask and answer questions about the mathematics they use to understand and model their world. Students using *Discovering Advanced Algebra* are not told how to solve every problem, so they make connections and develop techniques that are meaningful to them. And they learn how to deal with problems for which they have not been told one right way to solve. Their minds are engaged, and by sharing their results they see interesting alternative approaches. *Discovering Advanced Algebra* emphasizes reasoning about mathematics in the context of an experiment or real-world data.

Teaching with *Discovering Advanced Algebra* changes the rules for what is expected of students and what they should expect of their teachers. You become the guide, helping students make meaning of the algebraic and statistical relationships they explore. Your success depends on your conviction that students will learn more deeply by exploring and discovering concepts than by you simply telling them what to do. We feel confident that you'll be happy with your students' results, the classroom atmosphere, and your own teaching satisfaction as you implement *Discovering Advanced Algebra.*

Cooperative Learning

Students with a wide range of backgrounds flourish in a course that catches their interest. *Discovering Advanced Algebra*'s investigations attract students' attention. Using technology also piques their interest. The most dramatic way to engage students, however, is to have them work in cooperative groups.

If you haven't already experienced the power of teaching with cooperative groups, you might have several questions: Why use groups? How big should groups be? How do I decide group membership? How often do groups change? Do they require working at tables? How do I teach group cooperation skills?

Why use groups? Cooperative learning has many benefits:

- Students learn and practice the essential life skill of working with others. In a cooperative learning environment, the groups' cooperative skills are an integral part of the curriculum.
- Students are exposed to more ideas for how to solve problems. In solving challenging problems, two heads are indeed better than one.
- Students who are good in social situations can gain confidence in their mathematical abilities, even if they have previously been unsuccessful in mathematics.
- Students understand an idea more deeply if they have to articulate it for someone else.
- Students learn to solve more complex problems than they could if they didn't have other members of a group to contribute different areas of expertise.
- Groups working in a supportive atmosphere can give quicker feedback on ideas than a single teacher could offer.
- Some students will be more willing to risk contributing to a small group than to a full class, thus getting more opportunities to practice oral communication skills.

How big should groups be? Most investigations are appropriate for groups of three or four. If students are new to group work, you might want to start with pairs.

What about membership and change in groups? You might at first assign students to groups randomly. As you get to know the students, think about who works well with whom. Mixing abilities is best, but putting the strongest and weakest students together can frustrate both. Keep student groups together long enough for group members to get to know one another, but change group assignment every four to six weeks for variety and for a healthy dynamic.

Do groups need to work at tables? Tables are best for giving students plenty of work space, but desks are okay, too, and have the advantage of flexibility on exam days. If you use desks, bring the desktops together to form an area as close to a single surface as possible—and to have students facing one another.

How can you teach cooperative skills? One way is to make clear to the class your reasons for preferring group work. Directly counter some students' ideas that learning is competitive, that a course is about delivering information that only the teacher knows, or that stronger students will be graded lower because they are working with weaker students. Let students know that they are developing important life skills that they will apply in the working world, where people often work in groups, consult with others, and rely on others to complete part of a large project.

Develop with your students some specific guidelines to follow for productive work. These might include being considerate, listening without interrupting, asking questions when needed, helping others in the group, and making sure everyone in the group understands the ideas well enough to present them to the class. A poster listing the guidelines is helpful.

Hold each group fully accountable. End most group sessions with presentations to the class. You won't have time for all groups to present each time, but each student should be prepared.

Hold individuals responsible for group participation. As you move around the room, sometimes carry a copy of the roll and record points or a plus or minus for individual contributions to the group. Make these marks part of each student's participation grade. As the course progresses, you might extend your observation sheet to include items such as contributing ideas, asking questions, giving directions, actively listening, expressing support, encouraging members to participate, summarizing, talking through problems, and justifying viewpoints. Let your students know when you are looking for specific contribution skills so that they learn from the assessment.

Most important, trust the group process. Allow plenty of time for the group to correct mistakes. If a student asks you a question, turn it back to the group. If some students are causing behavior problems, try to facilitate a group solution by reviewing the guidelines with the group or by helping students clarify their roles. In some cases you will need to call a student aside for a discussion of poor group behavior. When you do so, also talk with the other group members individually about your expectations. Sometimes it helps to point out that the groups will change and that students will have a chance to work with a different set of classmates soon.

Promoting Inquiry

Various investigations in *Discovering Advanced Algebra* encourage students to inquire about relevant ideas and issues beyond the bounds of the course. Students have legitimate opportunities to experiment, hypothesize, measure, analyze, test, talk, write, explain, and justify their ideas. In short, they engage in real mathematics.

Inquiry-based classes go beyond engaging students in activities—they place students in the role of researchers. The quality of students' investigations is linked to the quality of their own inquiries. Students' motivation for pursuing answers to their own questions is very strong. In fact, it conforms to the old educational maxim "Don't answer questions that students haven't asked."

The flexibility required to implement an inquiry-based classroom presents new opportunities for both you and your students:

- It challenges everyone to develop skills for posing problems as well as solving them. Encourage the posing of new problems during Sharing and as you close the lesson. You can foster problem posing by using question openers such as those listed in the box.
- It challenges you to develop a list of inquiry questions that includes some questions specific to the next lesson. Use the questions suggested in this *Teacher's Edition* for that lesson as well as questions based on the section The Mathematics in the teaching notes before each chapter. What questions does each lesson answer? Where did these questions arise in previous lessons?
- Students are challenged to take responsibility for their own learning and to recognize that learning is an active, not a passive, process. *Discovering Advanced Algebra*'s cooperative investigations are chosen for their value as vehicles to promote activity and to help students construct their own knowledge. The interaction, discussion, questions, suggestions, and ideas that students offer while working in their groups can benefit all group members. Some students will need emotional support in learning this independence; it may not be the way they have been conditioned to respond. Remind them that a work environment requires both independent thinking and teamwork. Emphasize your point by making their grades in the course, like their evaluations in the workplace, take into account how well they're contributing to a team, not just the content of their contribution.
- An inquiry-based classroom allows you to play the role of an experienced co-researcher rather than of someone with all the answers. Don't give too many hints. Offer encouragement for good thinking, not just for right answers. Treat answers, right and wrong, as discussion topics until the class—the research team—reaches consensus. Often your labeling an answer "right" shuts off thinking about that problem, even if students don't understand the answer. If you present answers and explanations too quickly, students will continue to depend on you rather than take responsibility for their own learning.
- Students will be spurred to move beyond their conception of mathematics as a collection of facts and procedures. Many mathematical investigations, such as those in *Discovering Advanced Algebra,* have more than one answer, and rarely is there only one valid approach to a solution. Justifying ideas and problem solving become more important than the actual solutions. The goal is for students to experience mathematics as a process of finding and connecting ideas. Let students know that the thinking and problem-solving skills they develop can serve them in all aspects of their lives. They are learning more than algebra.
- An inquiry-based classroom demands flexibility in responding to students' ideas. Spend planning time thinking of how students might address the problem under investigation. This *Teacher's Edition* points out places where students might need help and suggests questions you can ask to keep students thinking.

Inquiry Question Openers

Why . . . ?	What's the largest/smallest . . . ?
What if not . . . ?	What are the properties of . . . ?
What happens if . . . ?	What other . . . ?
How many . . . ?	How do you know . . . ?
In general, . . . ?	Is it always true that . . . ?
What do we mean by . . . ?	Is it possible . . . ?
Is there a relationship . . . ?	How can you . . . ?
Under what conditions . . . ?	Is there a similarity between . . . ?

Teaching with Cooperative Groups

Now's your chance to become a leader in problem solving. You will constantly be making professional judgments in response to student contributions.

One basis for those judgments lies in how you see your role shifting from telling students mathematical ideas to helping investigation teams function well. Well-functioning groups working on tested investigations such as those in *Discovering Advanced Algebra* will gain conceptual understanding as you function as a facilitator rather than the person with all the answers.

How does this work in practice? Once you have introduced the lesson to the class, students begin group work. Give groups a few minutes to settle down and get started on the investigation (this is a good time to take attendance). Then move among groups, observing carefully, and encouraging as necessary but trying not to turn attention toward yourself. Sit down if an empty seat is available nearby. If students ask you a mathematical question, reflect it back to the group. Don't be too quick to jump in and correct errors. If the students in the group don't catch a common error, make a note to have someone from that group present that error later so the entire class can learn from its correction.

Take special notice of any groups that don't seem to be on task. If your joining them doesn't refocus them, ask about their progress. If they think they've finished the task, look at their work, ask questions, and challenge them to extend their results, perhaps by taking another approach. If they say they're stuck, ask one group member to describe what they've done, and ask other members for their ideas about it. If they're not cooperating, remind them of the group process guidelines. Praise good group work and good thinking, even if the group does not yet seem to be on a productive track mathematically.

As you listen to functioning groups, plan the Sharing time. Who should present what and in what order? What questions should be asked and what points raised? Consider an example: The group that actually constructed the next stage of a fractal design and counted areas should be chosen to display its picture first. Group members should come forward together, because two of them haven't presented recently. If no student asks if there's an easier way, you might. Then a student who used the area formula for triangles could describe that formula. Someone will raise a question about patterns. Finally a group could show the pattern they found. The group members may not have good calculation skills, but their creativity in problem solving can be an inspiration. You also want to praise the teamwork of another group, even though there's no reason to have them present today.

During student presentations to the class, sit down and watch. Keep in mind that if you take the stage or answer a question many students will stop thinking about that question. You can ask questions to help clarify points, and you might wonder aloud about possible relationships and extensions (following suggestions in this *Teacher's Edition*)—but wait for students to do so first.

One warning: It's tempting to assume that an emphasis on process over product means that "anything goes," but sloppy thinking is no more acceptable now than it ever was. Indeed, you want students to be convinced that everything in mathematics can be justified logically and that conflicts between intuition and logic can be resolved by logic. On the other hand, coming to understanding can be a messy process, requiring lots of approximations. In an open atmosphere, small groups and the class will be largely self-correcting. Even if they don't catch errors, students will learn the lessons of reasoning and cooperation better if you ask for clarification rather than simply saying "That's wrong."

At first glance, if your class is engaged in group work you may feel out of control. Students conferring with one another make more noise than do students sitting passively or working alone. When you realize, though, that every student in your class is actively engaged in doing good mathematics—thanks to the climate you have established—you can delight in the learning and in your professionalism as a teacher.

Structuring the Class Period

The order of events in a class period will vary with the lesson, with your class's growing experience in independent learning, with the need for variety, and with the class response. If students are lethargic, for example, have them act out the investigation. If they're overly excited, channel the energy into their inquiry. If you are short on equipment or time, run the investigation as a demonstration.

For most lessons, the *Discovering Advanced Algebra Teacher's Edition* includes **One Step,** which offers an alternative to the several-step investigation and to some examples. You can use the one-step approach for classes that are experienced in investigating. It is based on the philosophy of having the mathematical ideas grow out of students' work on a problem you have not already told them how to solve. Even if your class needs more guidance at the beginning of the course, read through these alternative investigations to keep in view your goal of helping your students become more independent investigators. This practice will help you become better at finding "teachable moments" as you interact with your students.

If you do not start with the one-step investigation, you can follow the order suggested in the Lesson Outline. Though an introduction is not mentioned in the outline, it is assumed that you will spend a few minutes opening each lesson.

For one-step lessons, here's a suggested schedule:

Introduction (5–10 minutes). Respond to homework questions and set the context for the investigation. Pose the problem and be sure the terms are clear. Resist the temptation to tell students how to do the investigation; they will learn in part from making mistakes. Sometimes you'll want to go over an example of a concept before students begin the investigation.

Investigation (15–50 minutes). Students work in groups while you observe, encourage, and craft plans for the rest of the class period. (The longer time applies to lessons for which the Pacing Guide recommends spending two days. The section Using This Chapter in the teaching notes that begin each chapter of the *Teacher's Edition* will help you decide which lessons you can skip, depending on the requirements of your curriculum, in order to give more time to other lessons.)

Sharing (10–20 minutes). Selected students or groups report to the class. As needed, you introduce terminology and notation and help the class reach consensus about how to articulate definitions and procedures. Ask questions that help clarify or lead to further thought about the ideas that have arisen. Praise good teamwork. As appropriate, facilitate the study of examples in the text that can deepen understanding of the main concepts of the lesson. Lead students in posing problems that motivate later lessons.

Closing (5 minutes). Remind students of the main mathematical ideas and where they arose in the lesson. If cooperative learning is new to your students, you might lead a short discussion on how the groups are functioning, what areas they can improve in, and what they are doing well. Or you might ask students to write briefly about what they learned or what they're confused about.

Exercises (5–10 minutes). Assign and begin work on the exercises.

Communicating

Over the last decade, teachers and researchers have learned that the ability to read mathematics and other technical material and to communicate ideas orally and in writing not only improves students' other language abilities but also enhances their conceptual understanding of mathematics.

The authors and editors have taken care to make *Discovering Advanced Algebra* readable. Students will read the steps of an investigation, the contexts of the applications, and other parts of the student book. Ideally, you won't tell them things they can read in the book, and you'll point out that they can use the book as a resource.

As you embark on teaching the course, be sensitive to students' inexperience with reading mathematics and, perhaps, with English. You can take steps to help them. If you ask one student in the class or a group to read an instruction or a problem aloud, the others (especially auditory learners) might benefit from hearing it. To avoid embarrassment on the part of the student, you probably shouldn't ask them to read aloud anything they haven't first read silently. You might, for example, request that all students read through some instructions silently and then ask a student in each group to read them aloud. You might also suggest that a group rotate readers to be sure everyone gets a chance to read aloud.

Asking students to paraphrase is also helpful. After one student reads aloud, ask another student to restate the instruction or problem in different words. After they have read a passage, help struggling students by emphasizing the main ideas and relating the ideas to what the students have learned previously.

(continued)

Assessing

Assessment is your way of getting feedback about how well your students are learning. Students want to know how well they are doing, too. The materials accompanying *Discovering Advanced Algebra* support a variety of methods for assessing both processes and results.

As you circulate among groups or watch students' presentations, engage in informal assessment of students' previous learning. Assessing Progress sections in the *Discovering Advanced Algebra Teacher's Edition* provide ideas about what students should have learned. Also, during class, note how effectively the lesson is proceeding, and make adjustments as you go. Throughout the *Teacher's Edition,* you can find suggestions for what to look for. You can also assess group process skills as described in the Cooperative Learning section in these teaching notes. Because *Discovering Advanced Algebra* emphasizes conceptual understanding, journal entries describing how individual students are making sense of the ideas can be especially useful assessment tools.

You will also use more intentionally focused activities to evaluate students' learning. *Discovering Advanced Algebra Assessment Resources A* and *B* include two versions of quizzes, tests, and Constructive Assessment Options for each chapter, as well as unit exams and a final exam. The Test Generator contains all the test and constructive assessment items as well as other questions, both free response and multiple choice. If you believe that in-class examinations don't allow you to evaluate students' understanding to the depth you desire, you can use the projects in *Discovering Advanced Algebra* for assessment. You might also have students prepare portfolios of their best work. This *Teacher's Edition* lists exercises you might assign for inclusion in a portfolio. At the end of each chapter of the student book, the section Assessing What You've Learned contains suggestions for student self-assessment that will give both you and your students additional feedback on students' learning.

You can find more details about assessment in the front matter of *Assessment Resources A* and in the book *Discovering Mathematics: A Guide for Teachers.*

(Communicating—continued)

The real-life context of much of the material in *Discovering Advanced Algebra* will help promote student reading and enhance critical thinking skills as students solve problems that they can relate to familiar situations. If students are having difficulty understanding an exercise they read, refer them back to the mathematical concepts involved in solving the problems. It is crucial that students recognize the underlying mathematical concepts in order to apply them to specific situations.

Students can often deepen their comprehension of a chapter by writing in their notebooks, outlining the chapter and listing the objectives and the main ideas. Writing is also an important tool for clarifying ideas. Encourage students not to turn in their scratch paper as a homework assignment but rather to write up a careful presentation of their answers and their justifications. The same holds true for careful speaking. Cultivate in your students the habit of reflecting on what they are saying and writing. When you grade homework or critique a presentation, ask students for clarification of vague expressions or murky logic.

Encourage students to use graphics in communicating, both orally and in writing. They can create freehand diagrams, use computer graphics programs, or use geometry or statistical software to incorporate graphical illustrations into oral presentations and written reports.

Planning

The *Discovering Advanced Algebra Teacher's Edition* includes many ideas for planning. For each chapter and lesson, it lists objectives and materials and also outlines how to spend class time. The commentary on the lesson includes alerts, based on teachers' experiences, to difficulties students might have (but not be able to articulate) and suggestions about how you might respond to them. But every class is different. As a professional, you'll want to think about each chapter and lesson with your own students and schedule in mind.

Planning a Course

Use the curriculum guidelines for your school, the Pacing Guides, and the teaching notes sections Using This Chapter to outline your year. Think about what topics students must learn and what explorations or projects you want them to experience. Leave blank days in your schedule for the unexpected, and plan for some extra days when you will concentrate on homework questions or catch up on investigations and Sharing.

Planning a Chapter

To allow flexibility to meet your class's needs, each chapter of *Discovering Advanced Algebra* contains more material than most classes will have time to cover. While all the investigations are valuable, you probably won't be able to include all of them in depth. Complete for yourself those investigations you want to do in class. Then decide whether to work through them as a whole class, assign them to groups, or even occasionally omit an investigation because of time constraints. Ask yourself, "What do my own students need at this time?" The section Using This Chapter in the teaching notes before each chapter can help you decide what you might skip.

Part of planning involves deepening your own understanding of the mathematics. You might think that because students are to figure out the mathematics themselves you yourself don't need to know the mathematics very well. Such a belief doesn't take into account the intellectual level of an investigation-based classroom. Students working collaboratively in groups will find themselves on many paths that you haven't explored before. Students using software or graphing calculators may raise "What if . . ." questions that astound you. As a coresearcher, you will sometimes say "I don't know." Even though your role is no longer to offer answers, you need to keep encouraging and challenging students. To do so requires a deep understanding of the mathematical ideas, even though your most effective teaching strategy at times might be to hide it. Reading the section The Mathematics on the teaching notes pages will help you.

Planning a Lesson

You also need to think about your students' strengths and weaknesses when you plan individual lessons. Work through the investigation and ask yourself how your students might respond to it and how you can facilitate. If you have time, ask friends and colleagues to think out loud about how they would do the investigation.

While planning lessons, keep in mind that the approach of this course is different from what you might be used to. Instead of telling students everything they need to know before they embark on an investigation (and then retelling them as they work), you should aim to have students first encounter the mathematical ideas during the investigation. Later, during Sharing, those ideas can be formalized with a name and a definition. Remember that your role is to help students discover mathematics—in both the processes and the content of the journey.

Although careful planning is necessary, don't let it get in the way of your teaching. Planning should not mean preparing a script you have to follow. What students do with technology-enhanced investigations can be different from what you anticipated. Each day you'll need to adjust your plans for the next few days. The farther you can see ahead, the better you'll be able to decide how to balance allowing students to explore and answer their own questions with getting the class through the course.

The Lesson Outline suggests pacing for each lesson over one or two class periods. These outlines are only guidelines. You might want to add time to answer homework questions. You should also prepare to move faster or more slowly according to how well your class is learning.

Planning Assignments

In planning homework assignments, be aware that *Discovering Advanced Algebra* contains many more exercises than most students will have time to work on. Select those you think can generate interest among your own students and satisfy your curriculum goals. At times you might want to assign different exercises to different groups or individuals and follow with classroom presentations. The Assigning Homework chart offers guidance about the appropriateness of the exercises for particular goals. When hardworking students return to class with questions, consider asking them to continue working on the assignment and turn it in the following day.

Pacing Options

The Pacing Options chart indicates the days per lesson for several schedules:

- a block schedule, in which there are fewer, longer class periods each week
- a standard one-year advanced algebra course, covering all the essential lessons
- an enriched course, in which students cover all the topics and the projects

Pacing Guide for Block Schedules

Chapter	day 1	day 2	day 3	day 4	day 5	day 6	day 7	day 8	day 9
0	0.1	0.2, 0.3	review, TAL	assessment					
1	1.1, 1.2	1.2, quiz 1.3	1.4, exploration	exploration, 1.5	quiz, exploration	review, TAL	assessment		
2	2.1, 2.2	quiz, 2.3	quiz, exploration	review, TAL, assessment					
3	3.1, 3.2	3.2	3.3, quiz, 3.4	3.5, quiz	exploration, 3.6	3.7, quiz, review, TAL	assessment, mixed review	exam	
4	4.1, 4.2	quiz, 4.3, 4.4	4.5, 4.6	quiz, 4.6, 4.7	4.8	quiz, review	TAL, assessment		
5	5.1, 5.2	5.3, quiz, 5.4	5.5, quiz, 5.6	5.6, 5.7	5.8, quiz	exploration, review	TAL, assessment		
6	6.1, 6.2	quiz, 6.3	6.4, 6.5	quiz, 6.6, project	quiz, review	TAL, assessment	review, exam		
7	7.1, 7.2	7.3	quiz, 7.4, 7.5	quiz, 7.6, 7.7	7.8	quiz, review	TAL, assessment		
8	8.1, 8.2	quiz, 8.3	exploration	8.4	project, 8.5	quiz, 8.6, 8.7	quiz, review, project	TAL, assessment	
9	9.1, 9.2	quiz, 9.3, 9.4	9.4, exploration	9.5, exploration	quiz, 9.6	9.7, project, 9.8	quiz, review, TAL	assessment, review	exam
10	10.1, 10.2	quiz, 10.3, 10.4	10.5, projects	quiz, 10.6	10.7, exploration	quiz, review	TAL, assessment		
11	11.1, 11.2	quiz, 11.3, exploration	quiz, TAL, review	TAL, assessment					

Pacing Options

Pacing Guide for Block Schedules (continued)

Chapter									
	day 1	**day 2**	**day 3**	**day 4**	**day 5**	**day 6**	**day 7**	**day 8**	
12	12.1, exploration	12.2	exploration, 12.3	quiz, 12.4	12.5, 12.5	quiz,12.7	quiz, review, TAL	TAL, assessment	
	day 1	**day 2**	**day 3**	**day 4**	**day 5**	**day 6**	**day 7**	**day 8**	**day 9**
13	13.1, 13.2	exploration, quiz, 13.3	13.4	exploration, quiz, 13.5	13.6, 13.7	13.7, quiz, review	TAL, assessment, review	exam, review	review, final exam

Pacing Guide for a Standard Class

Chapter										
	day 1	**day 2**	**day 3**	**day 4**	**day 5**	**day 6**				
0	0.1	0.1	0.2	0.3	review	assessment				
	day 1	**day 2**	**day 3**	**day 4**	**day 5**	**day 6**	**day 7**	**day 8**	**day 9**	
1	1.1	1.2	quiz, 1.3	1.4	exploration	1.5	quiz, review	review	assessment	
	day 1	**day 2**	**day 3**	**day 4**	**day 5**	**day 6**				
2	2.1	2.2	quiz, 2.3	2.3	quiz, review	assessment				
	day 1	**day 2**	**day 3**	**day 4**	**day 5**	**day 6**	**day 7**	**day 8**	**day 9**	**day 10**
3	3.1	3.2	3.2	3.3	quiz, 3.4	3.4	3.5	3.5	quiz, 3.6	3.7
	day 11	**day 12**	**day 13**	**day 14**						
	quiz, review	assessment	mixed review	exam						
	day 1	**day 2**	**day 3**	**day 4**	**day 5**	**day 6**	**day 7**	**day 8**	**day 9**	**day 10**
4	4.1	4.2	quiz, 4.3	4.4	4.4	quiz, 4.6	4.6	4.7	4.8	4.8
	day 11	**day 12**								
	quiz, review	assessment								
	day 1	**day 2**	**day 3**	**day 4**	**day 5**	**day 6**	**day 7**	**day 8**	**day 9**	**day 10**
5	5.1	5.2	5.3	quiz, 5.4	5.5	quiz, 5.6	5.6	5.7	5.8	5.8
	day 11	**day 12**	**day 13**							
	quiz, review	review	assessment							
	day 1	**day 2**	**day 3**	**day 4**	**day 5**	**day 6**	**day 7**	**day 8**	**day 9**	**day 10**
6	6.1	6.2	quiz, 6.3	6.3	6.4	quiz, 6.5	6.5, 6.6	6.6	quiz, review	review
	day 11	**day 12**	**day 13**							
	assessment	review	exam							

Pacing Guide for a Standard Class (continued)

Chapter										
7	day 1	day 2	day 3	day 4	day 5	day 6	day 7	day 8	day 9	day 10
	7.1	7.2	7.3	7.3	quiz, 7.4	7.5	quiz, 7.6	7.7	7.7	7.8
	day 11	day 12	day 13	day 14						
	7.8	quiz, review	review	assessment						
8	day 1	day 2	day 3	day 4	day 5	day 6	day 7	day 8	day 9	day 10
	8.1	8.2	quiz, 8.3	8.3	8.4	8.4	8.5	quiz, 8.6	8.7	quiz, review
	day 11									
	assessment									
9	day 1	day 2	day 3	day 4	day 5	day 6	day 7	day 8	day 9	day 10
	9.1	9.2	quiz, 9.3	9.4	9.4	9.5	9.5	quiz, 9.6	9.7	9.8
	day 11	day 12	day 13	day 14						
	quiz, review	assessment	review	exam						
10	day 1	day 2	day 3	day 4	day 5	day 6	day 7	day 8	day 9	day 10
	10.1	10.2	quiz, 10.3	10.4	10.5	quiz, 10.6	10.7	quiz, exploration	review	review
	day 11									
	assessment									
11	day 1	day 2	day 3	day 4	day 5	day 6				
	11.1	quiz, 11.2	11.3	quiz, review	review	assessment				
12	day 1	day 2	day 3	day 4	day 5	day 6	day 7	day 8	day 9	day 10
	12.1	exploration	12.2	12.2	12.3	quiz, 12.4	12.5	quiz, 12.6	12.7	quiz, review
	day 11	day 12								
	review	assessment								
13	day 1	day 2	day 3	day 4	day 5	day 6	day 7	day 8	day 9	day 10
	13.1	13.2	quiz, 13.3	13.4	13.4	quiz, 13.5	13.6	13.7	13.7	quiz, review
	day 11	day 12	day 13	day 14	day 15					
	assessment	review	exam	review	final exam					

Pacing Options

Pacing Guide for an Enriched Class

Chapter										
0	**day 1**	**day 2**	**day 3**	**day 4**	**day 5**	**day 6**				
	0.1	0.1	0.2, project	0.3	review, TAL	assessment				
1	**day 1**	**day 2**	**day 3**	**day 4**	**day 5**	**day 6**	**day 7**	**day 8**	**day 9**	
	1.1	1.2	quiz, 1.3	1.4	exploration	1.5	quiz, exploration	review, TAL	assessment	
2	**day 1**	**day 2**	**day 3**	**day 4**	**day 5**	**day 6**				
	2.1	2.2	quiz, 2.3, project	quiz, exploration	review, TAL	assessment				
3	**day 1**	**day 2**	**day 3**	**day 4**	**day 5**	**day 6**	**day 7**	**day 8**	**day 9**	**day 10**
	3.1	3.2	3.2	3.3, project	quiz, 3.4	3.5	3.5	exploration	quiz, 3.6	3.7
	day 11	**day 12**	**day 13**	**day 14**						
	quiz, review, TAL	assessment	mixed review	exam						
4	**day 1**	**day 2**	**day 3**	**day 4**	**day 5**	**day 6**	**day 7**	**day 8**	**day 9**	**day 10**
	4.1	4.2, project	quiz, 4.3	4.4, 4.5	quiz, exploration	4.6	4.7	4.8	4.8, project	quiz, review
	day 11									
	TAL, assessment									
5	**day 1**	**day 2**	**day 3**	**day 4**	**day 5**	**day 6**	**day 7**	**day 8**	**day 9**	**day 10**
	5.1, project	5.2	5.3, project	quiz, 5.4	5.5	quiz, 5.6	5.7	5.8	5.8, project	quiz, exploration
	day 11	**day 12**	**day 13**							
	review, project	review, TAL	assessment							
6	**day 1**	**day 2**	**day 3**	**day 4**	**day 5**	**day 6**	**day 7**	**day 8**	**day 9**	**day 10**
	6.1	6.2	quiz, 6.3	6.3	6.4	quiz, 6.5	6.6	project	quiz, review	review, TAL
	day 11	**day 12**	**day 13**							
	assessment	review	exam							
7	**day 1**	**day 2**	**day 3**	**day 4**	**day 5**	**day 6**	**day 7**	**day 8**	**day 9**	**day 10**
	7.1	7.2	7.3	7.3	quiz, 7.4, project	7.5, project	quiz, 7.6	7.7	7.8	quiz, review
	day 11	**day 12**								
	review, TAL	assessment								

Pacing Guide for an Enriched Class (continued)

Chapter										
8	**day 1**	**day 2**	**day 3**	**day 4**	**day 5**	**day 6**	**day 7**	**day 8**	**day 9**	**day 10**
	8.1	8.2	quiz, 8.3	exploration	8.4	8.4, project	quiz, 8.5, project	8.6	8.7, project	quiz, TAL, review
	day 11									
	assessment									
9	**day 1**	**day 2**	**day 3**	**day 4**	**day 5**	**day 6**	**day 7**	**day 8**	**day 9**	**day 10**
	9.1	9.2	quiz, 9.3	9.4	9.4	exploration, 9.5	9.5	exploration	quiz, 9.6	9.7, project
	day 11	**day 12**	**day 13**	**day 14**	**day 15**					
	9.8	quiz, review, TAL	assessment	review	exam					
10	**day 1**	**day 2**	**day 3**	**day 4**	**day 5**	**day 6**	**day 7**	**day 8**	**day 9**	**day 10**
	10.1	10.2	quiz, 10.3, 10.4	10.4, project	10.5, project	quiz, 10.6	10.7	quiz, exploration	review, TAL	review
	day 11									
	assessment									
11	**day 1**	**day 2**	**day 3**	**day 4**	**day 5**	**day 6**				
	11.1	quiz, 11.2	11.3	quiz, exploration	TAL, review	assessment				
12	**day 1**	**day 2**	**day 3**	**day 4**	**day 5**	**day 6**	**day 7**	**day 8**	**day 9**	**day 10**
	12.1	exploration	12.2	exploration	12.3	quiz, 12.4	12.5	quiz, 12.6	12.7	quiz, review
	day 11	**day 12**								
	review, TAL	assessment								
13	**day 1**	**day 2**	**day 3**	**day 4**	**day 5**	**day 6**	**day 7**	**day 8**	**day 9**	**day 10**
	13.1, project	13.2, exploration	quiz, 13.3	13.4	exploration	quiz, 13.5, project	13.6	13.7	13.7, project	quiz, review, TAL
	day 11	**day 12**	**day 13**	**day 14**	**day 15**					
	assessment	review	exam	review	final exam					

Materials List

Materials	Quantity	Chapters
algebra tiles, *optional*	1 set per group	0, 7
balloons	2 per group	3
basketball, soccer ball, or handball	1 per group	1
books	2–4 per group	2
bowls	1 per group	1
butcher (or heavy) paper	about 2 sq ft per group	3
calculator-based sensor with microphone probe	1 per group	10
cardboard or pad of paper	1 per group	2
centimeter graph paper		7, 9
centimeter rulers	2 per group	2, 3, 7, 8, 9, 12, 13
coins (pennies, nickels, dimes, quarters)	1 each per group	12
compass or circle template	1 per student	9, 10
cup of hot water		5
decimal rulers	2 per group	5
dice	1 die per person	5, 12
dry spaghetti	1 box	9
dynamic statistics software		
empty coffee cans or poster tubes	1 per group	7
flashlights	1 per group	9
food coloring		1, 13
geometry software		1, 4
graph paper		0, 3, 4, 6, 7, 8, 9, 10, 13
graphing calculators	1 per student	all chapters
long tables		7
masking tape		2, 8
mass holders (such as film canisters)	1 per group	3, 9
masses of 50–100 g	1 set per group	10

Materials	Quantity	Chapters
measuring cups	1 per group	1
measuring tapes or metersticks	1 per group	2, 4, 8, 13
model cube, *optional*	1	12
motion sensors	1 per group	1, 3, 4, 7, 8, 9, 10
musical instruments, *optional*	1 per group	10
patty paper or tracing paper		9
pencils		13
pieces of rope	1 per group	13
plastic water containers	1 per group	13
protractors	1 per student	8, 9
rubber bands	2 per group	2
scissors	1 per group	7
sets of five distinct objects	1 set per group	12
small mirrors	1 per group	4
small pillows or other soft objects	1 per group	7
small weights	1 set per group	3, 4, 9
springs	1 per group	3, 10
stopwatches	1 per group	2, 3, 4
straws		3
string		3, 4, 9, 10
support stands, *optional*	1 per group	10
tape		3, 9, 13
temperature sensors	1 per group	5
tuning forks	2 per group	10
washers	1 per group	10
waste buckets	1 per group	1
water		1, 13

CHAPTER

0

Problem Solving

Overview

In the context of problem solving, Chapter 0 reviews important concepts from beginning algebra, including finding slope, representing binomials geometrically, solving linear systems, using the distributive property, simplifying expressions, and using exponents. The problem-solving focus of **Lesson 0.1** uses sketches, graphs, and diagrams. **Lesson 0.2** focuses on representing English sentences with algebraic symbols. Strategies for organizing information are presented in **Lesson 0.3.**

The Mathematics

Problem Solving

It's often said that problem solving is the essence of mathematics. To some this means applying a given algorithm to solve "drill problems." Others prefer to use the term "problem" for challenges that can't be met by following a single algorithm.

George Pólya's *How to Solve It,* perhaps the most influential discourse on mathematical problem solving, referred to problems in the latter sense. In this 1945 work, Pólya laid out a four-step outline for solving problems:

- Understand the problem
- Devise a plan
- Carry out the plan
- Look back

These steps are too general to provide a method for solving all problems. Rather, they describe an art that requires more than following formulas. This chapter concentrates on the first three steps and touches on looking back as far as checking the solution in the original problem.

This chapter offers problems grouped according to three problem-solving techniques: Draw a diagram, use symbolic representation, and organize information. (Students see a longer list of techniques in the Chapter 0 Review.) Students may be reluctant to draw. Reassure them that artistic drawings are not necessary, or even helpful, and that they need only sketch diagrams and graphs, consisting of a few lines. Similarly, students who are intimidated by letters representing variables might be calmed if you assure them that thinking about the variables without using letters can solve many problems. (This *Teacher's Edition* provides many nonsymbolic solutions.) Algebra is about variables and constants, not necessarily the letters representing them; thinking about variables, with or without letters, is algebraic thinking.

Pólya's fourth step, "look back," meant more than check your work. He suggested asking questions such as "Does the answer make sense?"; "Could I have solved this problem in a different, perhaps better, way?"; "Can I use the result or method for some other problem?"; and "What other questions does the solution raise?" By pursuing such questions, students not only improve as problem solvers, but they also deepen their understanding of mathematical ideas and discover exciting and beautiful aspects of mathematics.

It's up to you to get students to ask those questions. You're not just teaching problem solving; you're using problems to teach some facts of mathematical life: Solving problems is an art, and therefore is sometimes messy. Students sometimes learn most from trying things that don't work. There's a real thrill to solving a challenging problem. There are many ways of solving most problems, even exercises. Some solutions are better than others—more efficient, more elegant, or more insightful. Thinking back—making sense of answers, creating new problems by changing aspects of the original problem, finding similarities and differences among problems—can lead to finding powerful mathematical relationships.

Measurement

This chapter uses quite a few measurements, so you might be aware of two kinds. A few measurements can be made *directly:* distance, angle measure, time, temperature, mass, current, and light intensity. Other measurements are *derived* from these, so precision and rounding issues arise. For example, speed is calculated as distance traveled divided by time. If the distance is measured to two significant figures and the time to five significant figures, then the calculated velocity is accurate only to the lesser of these—two significant figures.

In general, the book uses the metric system for technical measurements and the common measurement system in the United States for some less-technical problems.

Using This Chapter

You might consider Chapter 0 to be a pretest of basic algebra skills before starting into advanced algebra content. This chapter is optional because the concepts reviewed here can be refreshed as new concepts are introduced in future chapters. However, the investigations give you an excellent means to introduce cooperative learning into your classroom while your class lists are stabilizing. They also can give students experience with looking at problems in various ways and thinking independently. Students can learn to appreciate that the process and the written record of the work are as important as the solution.

If your students are experienced investigators, you might use the one-step problems in place of the more guided investigations. These problems allow students to construct mathematical knowledge in the context of one rich problem. They can be used before the examples. Then you might discuss the examples when you feel they would be useful.

This book does not review calculator skills, relying instead on the calculator notes. A few exercises mention how students can use the calculator notes for Chapter 0 to review basic operations.

Resources

Discovering Advanced Algebra Resources

Teaching and Worksheet Masters
Lessons 0.1, 0.3

Calculator Notes 0A, 0B

Sketchpad Demonstrations
Lesson 0.1

Assessment Resources A and B
Chapter 0 Test
Chapter 0 Constructive Assessment Options

More Practice Your Skills for Chapter 0

Condensed Lessons for Chapter 0

Other Resources

How to Solve It by George Pólya.

Problem Solving Strategies: Crossing the River with Dogs by Ken Johnson and Ted Herr.

For complete references to these and other resources see www.keypress.com/DAA.

Materials

- graphing calculators (assumed for all lessons)
- graph paper
- algebra tiles, *optional*

Pacing Guide

	day 1	day 2	day 3	day 4	day 5	day 6
standard	0.1	0.1	0.2	0.3	review	assessment
enriched	0.1	0.1	0.2, project	0.3	review, TAL	assessment
block	0.1	0.2, 0.3	review, TAL	assessment		

CHAPTER

0 Problem Solving

The Art of the Motorcycle, an exhibit at the Guggenheim Museum Las Vegas, required several very different problem-solving strategies. Architect Rem Koolhaas used diagrams and models to design a building that can house one large exhibit or several small galleries. Frank O. Gehry designed this installation as a visual representation of the materials and craftsmanship of the motorcycles. The organizers of the exhibit had to organize, schedule, and budget to bring the exhibit together as a whole.

OBJECTIVES

In this chapter you will

- solve problems both on your own and as a member of a group
- use pictures and graphs as problem-solving tools
- learn a four-step process for solving problems with symbolic algebra
- practice strategies for organizing information before you solve a problem

CHAPTER 0 OBJECTIVES

- Introduce a four-step outline for solving problems
- Use pictures, diagrams, and graphs as problem-solving tools
- Find the slope of a line from a graph and from coordinates of two points
- Translate English phrases into algebraic symbols
- Encounter absolute-value notation
- Review solving equations and solving systems of equations
- Learn good ways to organize information
- Practice using dimensional analysis and unit conversion
- Solve logic problems
- Practice working in a cooperative group

This motorcycle exhibition displays the history of motorcycle engineering and includes photographs displaying the history of motorcycles in American pop culture and the media. The design of this museum was chosen for its flexibility in displaying different types of art. The floor can be opened to reveal smaller galleries, and a large skylight can be opened or closed to control the lighting in the gallery. The design of the building also conceals a 35-ton crane used to install large works of art. The designers of the exhibit used problem solving as they coordinated the multimedia components.

[Ask] "What other elements of this museum or this particular exhibit require problem solving?" [budgeting, getting everything to fit in the space, redesigning the exhibit to work in a variety of locations, lighting the exhibit correctly] "What math might have been used in designing this exhibit?" [ratios and proportions, area, similarity, visualization in three dimensions, finance]

Students can learn more about this exhibit at the Guggenheim Museum Las Vegas through links at www.keymath.com.

LESSON
0.1

PLANNING

LESSON OUTLINE

First day:

10 min Example A

30 min Investigation

5 min Exercises

Second day:

10 min Example B

15 min Sharing

5 min Closing

15 min Exercises

MATERIALS

- graph paper
- Sketchpad demonstration Multiplying Binomials, *optional*

TEACHING

These problems can be solved in many ways. Encourage students to use diagrams, but commend those who find alternate techniques.

One Step

If your students are experienced investigators, give groups the problem of the investigation before looking over Example A. As you circulate, encourage students to draw a diagram. If students ask you if their answers are right or how to solve the problem, refer the question back to the group. Observe how different groups solve the problem, and plan the order of presentations for Sharing so that students will see a variety of approaches. After Sharing, continue with the examples if you think they'll be useful.

For students who need more structure, you can work through the examples and investigation in order.

LESSON
0.1 Pictures, Graphs, and Diagrams

A whole essay might be written on the danger of thinking without images.

SAMUEL COLERIDGE

In this textbook there are many problems that ask you to look at situations in new and different ways. This chapter offers some strategies to approach these problems. Although some of the problems in this chapter are fictitious, they give you a chance to practice skills that you will use throughout the book and throughout life.

This first lesson focuses on using a sketch, graph, or diagram to help you find a solution.

EXAMPLE A

Allyndreth needs to mix some lawn fertilizer with 7 liters of water. She has two buckets that hold exactly 3 liters and 8 liters, respectively. Describe or illustrate a procedure that will give exactly 7 liters of water in the 8-liter bucket.

▶ Solution

There is more than one solution to this problem. The picture sequence below shows one solution.

A written description of the solution to Example A might be complex and hard to understand. Yet the pictures help you keep track of the amount of water at each step of the solution. You also see how the water is poured into and out of the buckets. Can you think of a different solution? Does your solution take more or fewer steps?

Using pictures is one way to visualize a problem. Sometimes it helps if you actually use objects and act out the problem. For instance, in Example A you could use paper cups to represent the buckets and label each cup with the amount of water at each step of the solution. When you act out a problem, it helps to record positions and quantities on paper as you solve the problem so that you can recall your own steps.

Problem solving often requires a group effort. Different people have different approaches to solving problems, so working in a group gives you the opportunity to hear and see different strategies. Sometimes group members can divide the work based on each person's strengths and expertise, and other times it helps if everyone does the same task and then compares results. Each time you work in a group, decide how to share tasks so that each person has a productive role.

▶ EXAMPLE A

This example provides a review of ratios while illustrating diagrams as a problem-solving technique. If you would like students to try this problem on their own, ask them to keep their books closed.

[Language] As needed, remind students that a *proportion* is an equation stating that two ratios are equal. A *liter* (L) is a unit of liquid metric measurement equal to 1.0567 U.S. quarts. **[ESL]** Some English-language learners might need help with other words: *Fertilizer* is material that is applied to plant life to promote growth. To *visualize* is to imagine or see an image in one's mind.

A verbal solution is not given. You might ask students to verbalize what is happening in each step and to compare the number of words to the number of pictures.

Students may also want to find alternative solutions or discuss practical solutions (for example, fill the 3-liter bucket twice and then estimate $\frac{1}{3}$ of the 3-liter bucket).

The following investigation will give you an opportunity to work in a group and an opportunity to practice some problem-solving strategies.

Investigation
Camel Crossing the Desert

A camel rests by a pile of 3000 bananas at the edge of a 1000-mile-wide desert. He plans to travel across the desert, transporting as many bananas as possible to the other side. He can carry up to 1000 bananas at any given time, but he must eat one banana at every mile.

What is the maximum number of bananas the camel can transport across the desert? How does he do it? Work as a group and prepare a written or visual solution.

Pictures are useful problem-solving tools in mathematics but are not limited to diagrams like those in Example A. Coordinate graphs are some of the most important problem-solving pictures in mathematics.

EXAMPLE B A line passes through the point (4, 7) and has slope $\frac{3}{5}$. Find another point on the same line.

▶ Solution You *could* use a formula for slope and solve for an unknown point. But a graph may be a simpler way to find a solution.

Plot the point (4, 7). Recall that slope is $\frac{\text{change in } y}{\text{change in } x}$ and move from (4, 7) according to the slope, $\frac{3}{5}$. One possible point, (9, 10), is shown.

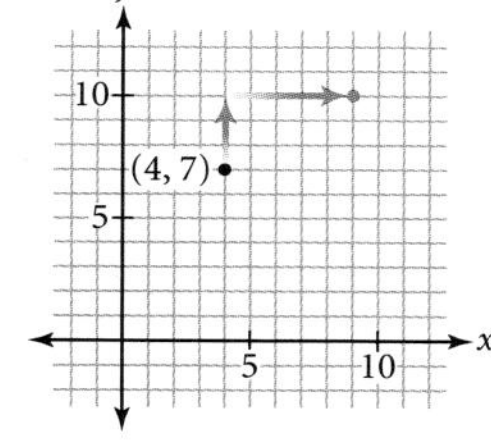

René Descartes

Mathematics CONNECTION

Coordinate graphs are also called Cartesian graphs, named after the French mathematician and philosopher René Descartes (1596–1650). Descartes was not the first to use coordinate graphs, but he was the first to publish his work using two-dimensional graphs with a horizontal axis, a vertical axis, and an origin. Descartes's goal was to apply algebra to geometry, which is today called analytic geometry. Analytic geometry in turn laid the foundations of modern mathematics, including calculus.

NCTM STANDARDS

CONTENT		PROCESS	
	Number	✓	Problem Solving
✓	Algebra	✓	Reasoning
✓	Geometry	✓	Communication
✓	Measurement	✓	Connections
	Data/Probability	✓	Representation

LESSON OBJECTIVES

- Introduce a four-step outline for solving problems
- Use pictures, diagrams, and graphs as problem-solving tools
- Find the slope of a line from a graph
- Find the slope of a line through a pair of points
- Learn to work in a cooperative group

Guiding the Investigation

[ESL] A *desert* is a dry environment with sparse plant growth and little animal life. To *transport* is to move, relocate, or carry.

Students could spend the entire class period, or even several days, on this investigation, so be aware of the time. The primary purpose is for students to learn to work cooperatively in a group. Try not to put much emphasis on a correct answer. Instead, listen to the groups' discussions and evaluate how they work together.

[Alert] Students might forget the camel must eat bananas in both directions. If the camel doesn't have a banana, he won't move.

If students are struggling, **[Ask]** "What's the difficulty?" Help students realize that the camel has to eat one banana for each mile he walks, so if he goes straight there he will eat all 1000 bananas he can carry and will deliver none. **[Ask]** "Is there a way around the difficulty?" [Have a drop-off point.] "Ideally, how many bananas should the camel get to the drop before making his trip from the drop to the end?" [1000, the most he can carry] "How can the camel get 1000 bananas to the drop?" [Make two trips from the start to the drop, each beginning with 1000 bananas.] "How many will he eat while it's carrying those 3000 bananas?" [2000] "How far should the drop be from the start?" [400 miles, for 5 legs] "How many bananas will be delivered?" [1000 − 600 = 400] "How might the camel do better?" Repeat the questions as needed, working backward to see that ideally there should be 1000 bananas at the last drop and 2000 at the previous drop, meaning that there should be just two drops. A symbolic approach with two drops is given

See page 875 for answer to the investigation.

Guiding the Investigation (continued) in the answer on page 875, but don't expect students to find this solution. Other results based on diagrams or guess-and-check are equally valid. If students don't find an answer of 533 bananas, use the given answer to satisfy your own curiosity, but don't present it to the class.

As you circulate, plan which students will share which ideas on the second day of the lesson.

▶ EXAMPLE B

This example reviews coordinate graphing as a problem-solving technique. **[Language]** As the need arises, review terminology such as *coordinate graph, Cartesian graph/plane, axis/axes, x-axis/horizontal axis, y-axis/vertical axis,* and *coordinates* (of a point). Also **[Ask]** "What does slope mean?" $\left[\frac{rise}{run} \text{ or } \frac{\text{vertical change}}{\text{horizontal change}}\right]$ Commend students who remember a formula for slope, such as $\frac{y_2 - y_1}{x_2 - x_1}$, but focus more on understanding through diagrams than on formulas. Help students see that if they begin at (4, 7) and move to the right 5 (the change in x) and up 3 (the change in y), they will arrive at (9, 10).

SHARING IDEAS

On the second day, you might give groups a chance to meet and share further insights before you ask groups to share their results with the entire class.

After all presentations, ask which approach is best. Don't worry if no group has found the best one. **[Ask]** "Do you believe you've found the best solution?" Bring out the point that most mathematics problems can be solved in a variety of ways; some methods are more efficient, some are better for understanding, some are easier to remember.

Point out that some of the approaches used diagrams whereas others were symbolic.

Although pictures and diagrams have been the focus of this lesson, problem solving requires that you use a variety of strategies. As you work on the exercises, don't limit yourself. You are always welcome to use any and all of the strategies that you know.

History CONNECTION

George Pólya (1887–1985) was a Hungarian-American mathematician often recognized for his contribution to the study of problem solving. In his 1945 book, *How to Solve It,* he describes a four-step problem-solving process:

- Understand the problem
- Devise a plan
- Carry out the plan
- Look back

You might want to practice this four-step process as you work through the problems in this chapter.

You can learn more about Pólya and his contributions to mathematics and problem solving by using the Internet links at www.keymath.com/DAA .

EXERCISES

Practice Your Skills

1. The pictures below show the first and last steps of bucket problems similar to Example A. Write a statement for each problem.

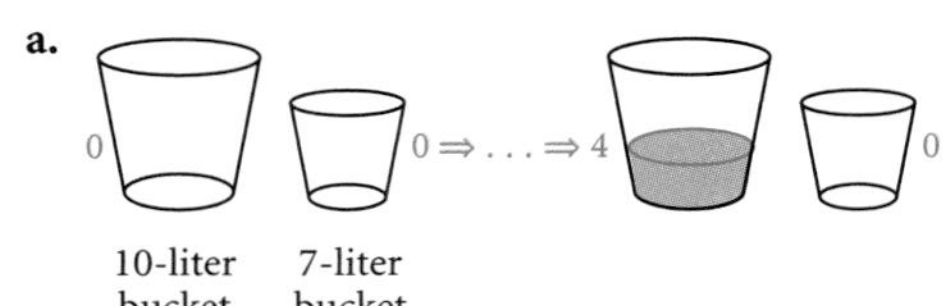

2. Find the slope of each line.

a. $-\frac{2}{5}$

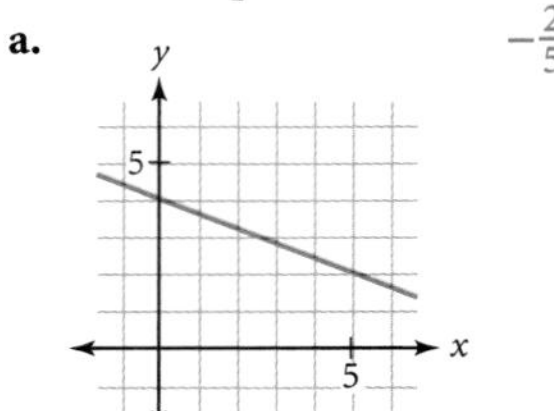

b. $\frac{3}{2}$

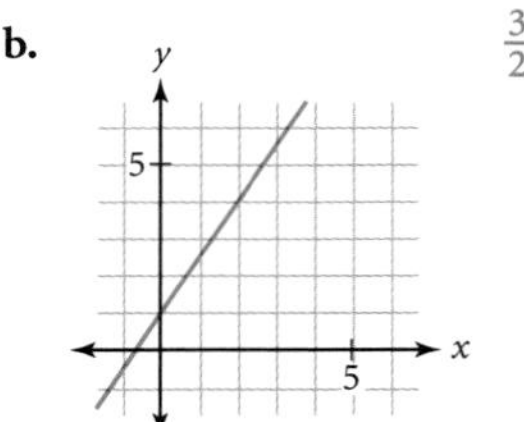

3. A line passes through the point (4, 7) and has slope $\frac{3}{5}$. Find two more points on the line other than (9, 10), which was found in Example B. possible answer: (14, 13) and (−1, 4)

[Language] A *symbolic* representation uses mathematical symbols.

You might ask the class what went well and what needs improvement in their group work. As needed, discuss the benefits of cooperative groups, norms for group work, and ways to work collaboratively. (See Cooperative Learning on page xxx.)

Assessing Progress

As you watch students work and present, you can assess informally their understanding of mathematical ideas, mastery of terminology, use of techniques, and comfort with inquiry. Also note how well they work with groups, how willing they are to take intellectual risks, and how critically they think.

Closing the Lesson

Reiterate, with students' help, the major mathematical ideas of this lesson: Using diagrams is one of several useful techniques for problem solving and every problem can be solved in various ways.

4. Explain how this graph helps you solve these proportion problems. Then solve each proportion.

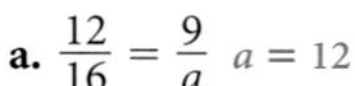

a. $\frac{12}{16} = \frac{9}{a}$ $a = 12$ **b.** $\frac{12}{16} = \frac{b}{10}$ $b = 7.5$

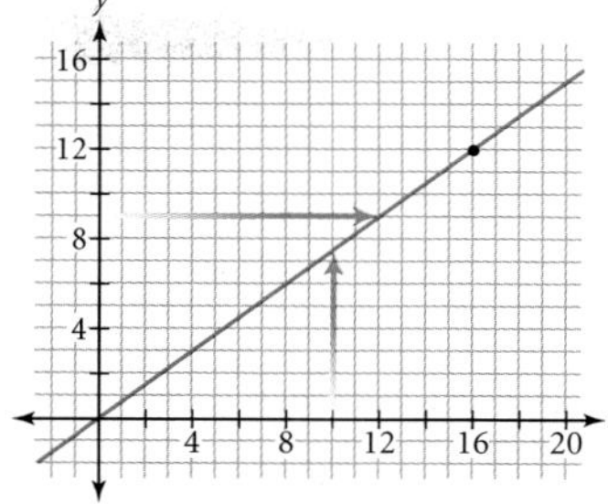

5. The following problem appears in *Problems for the Quickening of the Mind,* a collection of problems compiled by the Anglo-Saxon scholar Alcuin of York (ca. 735–804 C.E.). Describe a strategy for solving this problem. Do not actually solve the problem.

A wolf, a goat, and a cabbage must be moved across a river in a boat holding only one besides the ferryman. How can he carry them across so that the goat shall not eat the cabbage, nor the wolf the goat? Sample answer: Use three coins to represent the wolf, the goat, and the cabbage. Draw both banks of the river on paper and use an index card as a boat. Act out the problem trying to never leave the wolf and the goat together or the goat and the cabbage together.

Reason and Apply

6. Find the slope of the line that passes through each pair of points.

a. (2, 5) and (7, 10) 1 **b.** (3, −1) and (8, 7) $\frac{8}{5}$ or 1.6

c. (−2, 3) and (2, −6) $-\frac{9}{4}$ or −2.25 **d.** (3, 3) and (−5, −2) $\frac{5}{8}$ or 0.625

7. For each scenario, draw and label a diagram. Do not actually solve the problem.

a. A 25 ft ladder leans against the wall of a building with the foot of the ladder 10 ft from the wall. How high does the ladder reach?

b. A cylindrical tank that has diameter 60 cm and length 150 cm rests on its side. The fluid in the tank leaks out from a valve on one base that is 20 cm off the ground. When no more fluid leaks out, what is the volume of the remaining fluid?

c. Five sales representatives e-mail each of the others exactly once. How many e-mail messages do they send?

8. Use this graph to estimate these conversions between grams (g) and ounces (oz).

a. 11 oz ≈ _?_ g 312 g **b.** 350 g ≈ _?_ oz 12.5 oz

c. 15.5 oz ≈ _?_ g 437 g **d.** 180 g ≈ _?_ oz 6.2 oz

e. What is the slope of this line? Explain the real-world meaning of the slope. Using the approximate point (15, 425) and the definite point (0, 0), the slope is $\frac{85}{3}$. There are about 28.3 grams in an ounce.

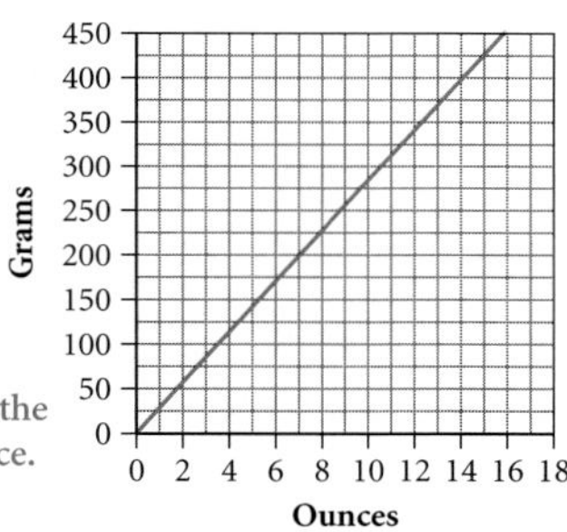

History CONNECTION

The unit of measure today called the pound comes from the Roman unit *libra,* abbreviated "lb," a weight of around 5000 grains (a very small unit of weight). It was subdivided into ounces, or *onzas,* abbreviated "oz." In England the Saxon pound was based on a standard weight of 5400 grains kept in the Tower of London. This nonstandard system eventually became so confusing that many countries adopted the Système Internationale (SI), or metric system, as the standard form of measurement.

BUILDING UNDERSTANDING

As the opportunity arises, ask the class for alternative approaches to an exercise.

MATERIALS

- Coordinate Axes (T), *optional*
- Exercise 11 (T), *optional*
- Algebra Tiles (W), *optional*
- Calculator Note 0B, *optional*

ASSIGNING HOMEWORK

Essential	1–6
Performance assessment	7, 8, 10–12
Portfolio	9
Journal	4, 5, 9, 10
Group	7, 9, 12
Review	13–16

Helping with the Exercises

Exercise 1 The problems students write might have a context, like the fertilizer of Example A.

1a. Begin with a 10-liter bucket and a 7-liter bucket. Find a way to get exactly 4 liters in the 10-liter bucket.

1b. Begin with a 10-liter bucket and a 7-liter bucket. Find a way to get exactly 2 liters in the 10-liter bucket.

Exercises 2–4 You might use the Coordinate Axes transparency as you discuss these and other exercises.

Exercise 3 Students might use a formula. Commend variety, but encourage all students to draw diagrams from which they can find the points.

4. The line has slope $\frac{12}{16}$. The slope from (0, 0) to any point (x, y) on the line will be $\frac{y}{x}$.

See page 875 for answer to Exercise 7.

Exercise 5 [Context] Alcuin was born in England but later moved to France to become a mathematician in Charlemagne's court. **[ESL]** A *strategy* is a plan. Students may need to solve the problem before they can articulate a strategy by reflecting back on what they did. As needed, remind them that acting out the situation (as with coins) is a strategy.

Exercise 6 Different students will attack this exercise differently. Some will use a graph, some will recall the slope formula, and others will mentally visualize the change in y and the change in x. Having students share their solutions helps demonstrate that there is more than one way to attack a problem.

Exercise 8 Using ratios of units as fractions is called *dimensional analysis* or *unit conversion.* Using the graph, students will be able only to estimate conversions. For your information, not the students', the actual conversion factors are 0.0353 g = 1 oz and 28.35 oz = 1 g.

Exercise 9 A picture diagram for 9a should show the chlorine levels: 0-0, 0-7, 7-0, 7-7, 10-4, 0-4, 4-0. A picture diagram for 9b should show these levels: 0-0, 10-0, 3-7, 3-0, 0-3, 10-3, 6-7, 6-0, 0-6, 10-6, 9-7, 9-0, 2-7, 2-0.

Exercise 10 Rectangle diagrams will show up again in Chapter 7. Students who studied *Discovering Algebra* may also recall the use of rectangles for completing the square. You might use the Sketchpad demonstration Multiplying Binomials as you talk about this exercise.

[Context] René Descartes was the first mathematician to use the notation x^2 to indicate the squaring of a variable.

Exercise 11 Drawing rectangle diagrams is sufficient, but you might have algebra tiles available if students wish to use them to model these situations. If you don't have commercial tiles, you might copy the Algebra Tiles worksheet on heavy paper or make geometry software available. You might use the Exercise 11 transparency as you discuss this exercise. Students can either subtract from a larger rectangle or add a negative in 11d.

Exercises 14, 15 You may need to remind students how to convert from fractions to decimals on a calculator. To convert decimals to fractions, students might use Calculator Note 0B: Fractions.

Exercise 16 As needed, review the Pythagorean Theorem: The sum of the squares of the two legs of a right triangle equals the square of the hypotenuse. Students may recognize 16a as a 3-4-5 right triangle and 16c as having two Pythagorean triples and not need to use the theorem directly.

See page 875 for answers to Exercises 9–13.

9. APPLICATION Kyle has a summer job cleaning pools. He needs to measure exact amounts of chlorine but has only a 10-liter bucket and a 7-liter bucket. Assuming an unlimited supply of chlorine, describe or illustrate a procedure that will

a. Give exactly 4 liters of chlorine in the 10-liter bucket.

b. Give exactly 2 liters of chlorine in the 10-liter bucket.

Pool on a Cloudy Day with Rain (1978) by David Hockney (b 1937)

10. You can use diagrams to represent algebraic expressions. Explain how this rectangle diagram demonstrates that $(x + 2)(x + 3)$ is equivalent to $x^2 + 2x + 3x + 6$.

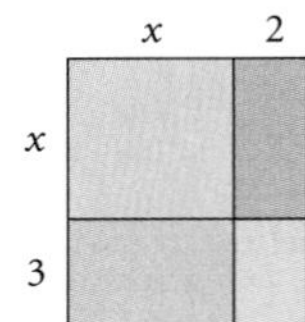

11. Draw a rectangle diagram to represent each product. Use the diagrams to expand each product.

a. $(x + 4)(x + 7)$ b. $(x + 5)^2$ c. $(x + 2)(y + 6)$ d. $(x + 3)(x - 1)$

12. Solve the problem in Exercise 5. Explain your solution.

Review

13. Translate each verbal statement to a symbolic expression or an equation.

a. Three more than a number

b. Venus is 24.3 million miles farther from the Sun than Mercury.

c. Seth owns twice as many CDs as his sister Erin.

14. Convert these fractions to decimal form.

a. $\frac{3}{8}$ 0.375 b. $\frac{13}{9}$ $1.\overline{4}$ c. $\frac{16}{25}$ 0.64 d. $\frac{5}{14}$ $0.3\overline{571428}$

15. Convert these decimal values to fraction form.

a. 0.375 $\frac{375}{1000} = \frac{3}{8}$ b. 1.42 $\frac{142}{100} = \frac{71}{50} = 1\frac{21}{50}$ c. $0.\overline{2}$ $\frac{2}{9}$ d. $0.\overline{35}$ $\frac{35}{99}$

16. Use the Pythagorean Theorem to find each missing length.

a.

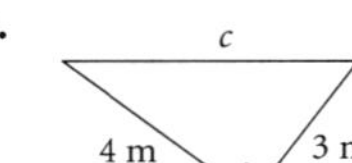

$c = 5$ m

b.

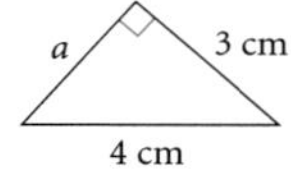

$a = \sqrt{7}$ cm ≈ 2.6 cm

c.

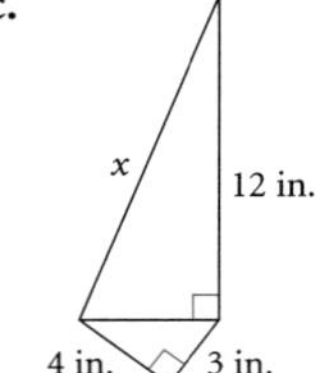

$x = 13$ in.

EXTENSIONS

A. If the chlorine levels in the two buckets in Exercise 9 are plotted as ordered pairs (0, 0), (0, 7), (7, 0), (7, 7), . . . , and sequential points are connected, students will find an interesting pattern of line segments. Wonder aloud if the pattern can be described well enough to find a solution using only the graph. As students see that the segments are horizontal or vertical or have slope 1 or −1, help them focus on the endpoints of the segments and to phrase the problem as getting from (0, 0) to (4, 0) (9a) or to (2, 0) (9b). They might keep appending line segments until they get to (0, 7), thus creating a graphic they can trace in either direction to see how to measure any amount into either container. Students might use a picture like this for 9b:

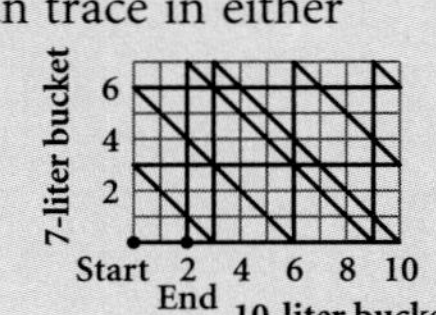

B. Use Take Another Look activities 1 and 3 on pages 25 and 26.

LESSON 0.2

Symbolic Representation

The customer service team had planned to double the number of calls answered the second day, but they exceeded that by three dozen. Seventy-five dozen customer service calls in two days set a new record.

You can translate the paragraph above into an algebraic equation. Although you don't know how many calls were answered each day, an equation will help you figure it out.

For many years, problems like this were solved without writing equations. Then, around the 17th century, the development of symbolic algebra made writing equations and finding solutions much simpler. Verbal statements could then be translated into symbols by representing unknown quantities with letters, called variables, and converting the rest of the sentence into numbers and operations. (You will actually translate this telephone call problem into algebraic notation when you do the exercises.)

History CONNECTION

Muhammad ibn Mūsā al-Khwārizmī (ca. 780–850 C.E.), an Iraqi mathematician, wrote the first algebra treatise. The word *algebra* comes from the treatise's title, *Kitāb al-jabr wa'al-muqābalah,* which translates to *The Science of Completion and Balancing.* Al-Khwārizmī wanted the algebra in this treatise to address real-world problems that affected the everyday lives of the people, such as measuring land and doing trade. You can learn more about Al-Khwārizmī and the history of algebra by using the links at www.keymath.com/DAA .

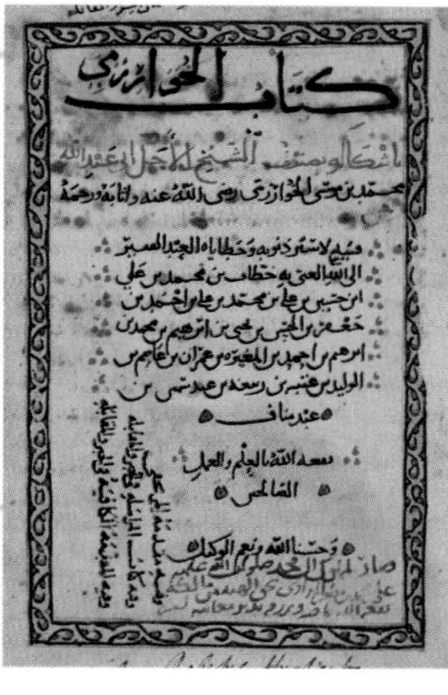

The postage stamp above depicts al-Khwārizmī and was issued in the former Soviet Union. At left is the title page of al-Khwārizmī's treatise on algebra.

Language is very complex and subtle, designed for general descriptions and qualitative communication. For quantitative communication, translating words into symbols can be a very helpful problem-solving skill. The symbols stand for numbers that vary or remain constant, that are given in the problem, or that are unknown. In applications, the numbers quantify data such as time, weight, or position.

NCTM STANDARDS

CONTENT		PROCESS	
	Number	✓	Problem Solving
✓	Algebra	✓	Reasoning
✓	Geometry	✓	Communication
	Measurement		Connections
	Data/Probability	✓	Representation

LESSON OBJECTIVES

- Translate English phrases into algebraic symbols assigning a variable to each unknown quantity
- Encounter absolute-value notation
- Review solving equations and solving systems of equations

LESSON 0.2

PLANNING

LESSON OUTLINE

One day:

15 min	Examples
15 min	Investigation
10 min	Sharing and Closing
5 min	Exercises

MATERIALS

none

TEACHING

Following the problem-solving technique of drawing a diagram, we move to the technique of symbolic representation.

[ESL] A *symbol* is a sign or character used to represent a number or an operation. **[Language]** The adjective *subtle* means difficult to comprehend or master; multifaceted; understated. The adjective *qualitative* refers to quality, such as color, texture, or other descriptive characteristics. The adjective *quantitative* refers to quantity, such as volume or height, often a measured amount. *Symbolic algebra* is a notational convention, and *algebra* is a system of thinking and solving problems.

Some algebra books make a distinction between *unknowns* and *variables.* For example, because x has a definite value in the equation $x + 2 = 3$, it could be called an *unknown.* In the equation $y = x$, however, x could take on any value, so it is a *variable.* The equation $distance = rate \cdot time$ contains three variables. This book will use *variable* to mean any letter or word that represents one or more numbers.

One Step

Ask students to work on Problem 3 of the investigation. As you circulate, encourage the use of symbolic algebra, but don't be too quick to discourage diagrams or fractional reasoning without variables. Students may find diagrams useful in making meaning of the fractions. Plan the Sharing time to take advantage of the variety of approaches students use. During Sharing, introduce and use the terms *symbolic algebra* and *variable.*

► *EXAMPLE A*

This example reviews the symbolic notation for absolute value and inequality. As needed, remind students that $| \; |$ means absolute value. **[Ask]** "Why does $|a - 10|$ indicate how close a is to 10?" Absolute value is often used for distance because neither absolute value nor distance is ever negative.

[Alert] Students might be confused because the problem says the numbers are "closer to 10" but the inequality uses the symbol for "greater than." Ask students to explain why the number on the right of this inequality is less than the number on the left.

A few students might be satisfied saying that there is clearly no solution even without considering symbolic algebra. Rather than insist that they use symbols at this point, commend their creative thinking even as you ask for careful justification in words.

Students may come up with a solution that doesn't depend on wordplay: Put 5 pigs into pen 1, 8 pigs into pen 2, 11 pigs into pen 3, and 5 pigs *and pen 1* into pen 4 so that pen 4 actually has 10 pigs in it.

[Ask] "Do you know of other puzzles that use similar tricks?"

EXAMPLE A

Twenty-nine pigs are to be placed into four pens arranged in a circle. As you move clockwise around the circle, each pen should have closer to 10 pigs than the previous pen. How should you divide the 29 pigs?

► *Solution*

To represent this problem with symbolic algebra, you need to first determine which quantities are unknown. In this case, the number of pigs in each pen is unknown. Use the variables a, b, c, and d for these quantities.

How close each number is to 10 is expressed as

$$|a - 10|, \; |b - 10|, \; |c - 10|, \text{ and } |d - 10|$$

If each pen has a number of pigs closer to 10 pigs than the previous pen, then this inequality must be true:

$$|a - 10| > |b - 10| > |c - 10| > |d - 10| > |a - 10|$$

However, this doesn't make sense! It says that $|a - 10|$ must be greater than $|a - 10|$, and that is impossible.

So you might be tempted to say there is no solution.

However, consider placing 7 pigs in the first pen, 12 pigs in the second pen, 10 pigs in the third pen, and no pigs in the last pen. Then, starting at the pen with 7 pigs, you see that 12 is closer to 10 than 7, 10 is closer to 10 than 12, "nothing" is closer to 10 than 10, and 7 is closer to 10 than 0.

You may claim, "Unfair!" after reading the answer to Example A, yet it is a solution. The solution lies in the multiple meanings of words. "Nothing" is used to mean something that does not exist *and* to mean the quantity of 0. Although symbolic algebra seems to have failed in Example A, it did help you recognize that no mathematical answer existed. If a problem does have a mathematical answer, there is usually a way to get it with symbolic algebra. Therefore, as you approach problems of a descriptive nature, it is often helpful to translate the problem into variables, expressions, and equations.

mù
tree

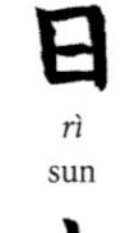

rì
sun

森

shēn
forest

dōng
east

Cultural CONNECTION

Some cultures use systems of writing based on ideograms—symbols that represent an idea or a thing. The traditional Chinese system of writing, called *hànzì,* is one example. The complete system contains thousands of symbols, some of which look like the objects they represent. For example, the symbol for *mù,* or "tree," looks similar to a tree.

Hànzì characters are also combined to create symbols with more complex meanings. The symbol for *shēn,* or "forest," shows many trees. The symbol for *dōng,* or "east," combines two symbols to show a sun rising behind a tree.

MAKING THE CONNECTION

Algebraic symbols are often simple but are combined to create larger, more complex expressions and equations in the same way that simple *hànzì* symbols are combined to form complex words and sentences.

EXAMPLE B

Three friends went to the gym to work out. None of the friends would tell how much he or she could leg-press, but each hinted at their friends' leg-press amount. Chen said that Juanita and Lou averaged 87 pounds. Juanita said that Chen leg-pressed 6 pounds more than Lou. Lou said that eight times Juanita's amount equals seven times Chen's amount. Find how much each friend could leg-press.

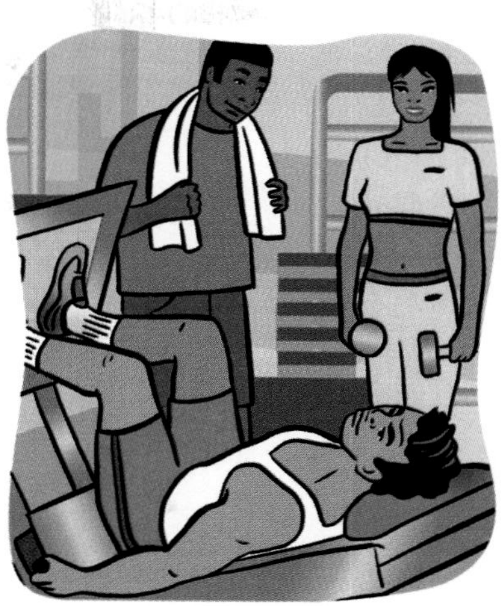

▶ Solution

First, list the unknown quantities and assign a variable to each.

Let C represent Chen's leg-press weight in pounds.
Let J represent Juanita's leg-press weight in pounds.
Let L represent Lou's leg-press weight in pounds.

Second, write equations from the problem.

$$\begin{cases} \dfrac{J+L}{2} = 87 \\ C - L = 6 \\ 8J = 7C \end{cases}$$

Chen's statement translated into an algebraic equation. Call this Equation 1.
Juanita's statement as Equation 2.
Lou's statement as Equation 3.

Third, solve the equations to find values for the variables.

$J + L = 174$	Multiply both sides of Equation 1 by 2.
$C - L = 6$	Equation 2.
$J + C = 180$	Add the equations.
$7J + 7C = 1260$	Multiply both sides of the sum by 7.
$7J + 8J = 1260$	Equation 3 allows you to substitute $8J$ for $7C$.
$15J = 1260$	Add like terms.
$J = 84$	Divide both sides by 15.
$8(84) = 7C$	Substitute 84 for J in Equation 3.
$C = 96$	Solve for C.
$96 - L = 6$	Substitute 96 for C in Equation 2.
$L = 90$	Solve for L.

Last, interpret your solution. Chen leg-presses 96 pounds, Juanita leg-presses 84 pounds, and Lou leg-presses 90 pounds.

▶ EXAMPLE B

This example is good for reviewing how to solve systems of equations by elimination. The sequence of the given solution by elimination is only one possible sequence. Ask students to explain other approaches they might try. You may want to ask them to solve the system with substitution as well, for review purposes. The key concept for this example is to write algebraic expressions for the problem.

Assessing Progress

Depending on how much you have students work on the examples before reading the book, you have opportunities in this lesson to assess understanding of absolute value, ability to solve systems of equations, comfort with ratios and fractions, ability to represent situations with variables and solve linear equations, and facility at analyzing multistep problems.

You may notice that Example B used a four-step solution process. The investigation will give you a chance to try these four steps on your own or with a group.

Investigation
Problems, Problems, Problems

Select one or more of the problems below, and use these four steps to find a solution.

Step 1 List the unknown quantities, and assign a variable to each.

Step 2 Write one or more equations that relate the unknown quantities to conditions of the problem.

Step 3 Solve the equations to find a value for each variable.

Step 4 Interpret your solution according to the context of the problem.

When you finish, write a paragraph answering this question: Which of the four problem-solving steps was hardest for you? Why?

Problem 1

When Adam and his sister Megan arrive at a party, they see that there is 1 adult chaperone for every 4 kids. Right behind them come 30 more boys, and Megan notices that the ratio is now 2 boys to 1 girl. However, behind the extra boys come 30 more girls, and Adam notices that there are now 4 girls for every 3 boys. What is the final ratio of adult chaperones to kids?

Step 4 The final ratio of adults to kids is 1 adult for every 14 kids.

Problem 2

Abdul, Billy, and Celia agree to meet and can tomatoes from their neighborhood garden. Abdul picks 50 pounds of tomatoes from his plot of land. Billy picks 30 pounds of tomatoes from his plot. Unfortunately, Celia's plants did not get enough sun, and she cannot pick any tomatoes from her plot.

They spend the day canning, and each has 36 quarts of tomatoes to take home. Wanting to pay Abdul and Billy for the tomatoes they gave to her, Celia finds \$8 in her wallet. How should Celia divide the money between her two friends?

Step 4 Abdul should get \$7 and Billy should get \$1.

Problem 3

A caterer claims that a birthday cake will serve either 20 children or 15 adults. Tina's party presently has 12 children and 7 adults. Is there enough cake?

Step 4 The current party is equivalent to 16 adults, so no, there is not enough cake.

The four problem-solving steps in the investigation help you organize information, work through an algebraic solution, and interpret the final answer. As you do the exercises in this lesson, refer back to these four steps and practice using them.

Guiding the Investigation

You may have each group work on all three problems, or assign each group a different problem to present to the whole class. (In making such an assignment, bear in mind that the problems are listed in order from most difficult to least difficult for most students.) If each group is assigned all three problems, you will need to allot more time to the investigation.

Problem 1

[ESL] A *chaperone* is a person responsible for the safety and well-being of another person, like a teacher or parent on a field trip.

If students are struggling, suggest that it's often helpful to focus first on what you want to know and what you need to find out in order to know it. After students decide they need to know the number of kids and adults at the end, ask (if needed) what they need to find out to know the number of adults. As they realize that they must find the number of kids at the beginning—for which they must find the initial numbers of boys and girls—you might mention that in complicated problems like this it's often helpful to use letters to represent the unknowns and set up equations.

In Step 2, students may misrepresent "4 girls for every 3 boys" with the equation 4(*number of girls*) = 3(*number of boys*). Correcting them without discussing the inadequacies of their approach gives the message that math is arbitrary, not logical, and teacher-dependent. Instead, suggest that a good habit to get into is to check equations like this with numbers. **[Ask]** "Three girls and 4 boys satisfies the equation. Does that give 4 girls for every 3 boys?" If students get very confused with discrepant results, ask whether there are more boys or girls and what equation with a fraction might represent the situation accurately. [*number of girls* $= \frac{4}{3}$(*number of boys*)]

Problem 2

[ESL] To *can* is a verb meaning to preserve food in jars or cans.

Many students believe that the solution is simple: Because Abdul contributed $\frac{5}{8}$ of the tomatoes, he should get $\frac{5}{8}$ of the money and Billy should get the other $\frac{3}{8}$. If nobody in a group questions this approach, you might ask for careful justification, working in the question "So, you're saying that Abdul contributes $\frac{5}{8}$ of the tomatoes Celia actually takes home?" If students answer yes, claiming that the tomatoes are well mixed up, express skepticism by pointing out that Abdul and Billy also get some tomatoes and asking for a symbolic argument (Steps 2 and 3).

Problem 3

If students have worked on Problem 2, they may not be sure whether to write $20c = 15a$ or $20a = 15c$. Remind them to try out numbers for the variables.

See page 876 for complete answers to Problems 1–3.

EXERCISES

You will need

Geometry software for Exercise 16

Practice Your Skills

1. Explain what you would do to change the first equation to the second.

a. $a + 12 = 47$ → $a = 35$ On both sides: subtract 12

b. $5b = 24$ → $b = 4.8$ divide by 5

c. $-18 + c = 28$ → $c = 46$ add 18

d. $\frac{d}{-15} = 4.5$ → $d = -67.5$ multiply by -15

2. Which equation would help you solve the following problem?

Each member of the committee made three copies of the letter to the senator. Adding these to the 5 original letters, there are now a total of 32 letters. How large is the committee? C

A. $5 + c = 32$ **B.** $3 + 5c = 32$ **C.** $5 + 3c = 32$

3. Solve each equation.

a. $5 + c = 32$ $c = 27$ **b.** $3 + 5c = 32$ $c = 5.8$ **c.** $5 + 3c = 32$ $c = 9$

4. Which equation would help you solve this problem? What does x represent? B; x represents the number of dozens of calls.

The customer service team had planned to double the number of calls answered the second day, but they exceeded that by three dozen. Seventy-five dozen customer service calls in two days set a new record.

A. $x + 3 = 75$ **B.** $x + 2x + 3 = 75$ **C.** $2x + 3 = 75$

5. Solve each equation.

a. $x + 3 = 75$ $x = 72$ **b.** $x + 2x + 3 = 75$ $x = 24$ **c.** $2x + 3 = 75$ $x = 36$

Reason and Apply

6. Here is a problem and three related equations.

Anita buys 6 large beads and 20 small beads to make a necklace. Ivan buys 4 large and 25 small beads for his necklace. Jill selects 8 large and 16 small beads to make an ankle bracelet. Without tax, Anita pays \$2.70, and Ivan pays \$2.85. How much will Jill pay?

$$\begin{cases} 6L + 20S = 270 & \text{(Equation 1)} \\ 4L + 25S = 285 & \text{(Equation 2)} \\ 8L + 16S = J & \text{(Equation 3)} \end{cases}$$

a. What do the variables L, S, and J represent?

b. What are the units of L, S, and J? cents

c. What does Equation 1 represent?

6a. L represents the cost of a single large bead. S represents the cost of a single small bead. J represents the amount that Jill will pay for her purchase.

6c. Anita's purchase of 6 large beads and 20 small beads for \$2.70

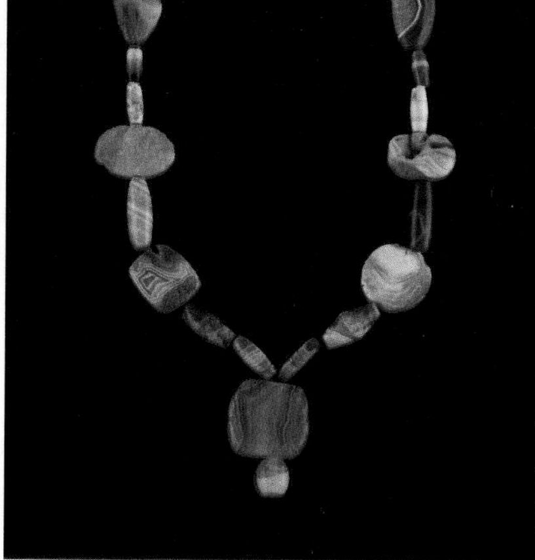

This necklace was crafted around the 3rd to 2nd millennium B.C.E. in the southwest Asian country of Bactria (now in Afghanistan).

Helping with the Exercises

Encourage students to use any method of problem solving, including symbolic representation, pictures, diagrams, or acting out.

Exercise 2 If needed, **[Ask]** "How do the proposed equations seem to represent the size of the committee? What happens to get from that number up to 32?"

Exercise 4 If students are struggling, **[Ask]** "What might the x in the proposed equations represent? In which equation does there seem to be doubling and adding 3?"

Guiding the Investigation (continued)

When students reach Step 4 of the problem-solving process, **[Ask]** "How many people need to skip cake so that there is enough for everyone else?" [either one adult or two children]

Students may argue, without using variables, that the children together would eat $\frac{12}{20}$ of the cake, the adults would eat $\frac{7}{15}$ of the cake, and that $\frac{12}{20} + \frac{7}{15} = \frac{16}{15} > 1$ cake. Praise this good understanding of fractions, and ask if the students can find another way to solve the problem, using variables. Make a note to have the class compare the approaches during Sharing.

SHARING IDEAS

You might have students present the problems in reverse order. If they arrived at different answers, try to have the full range presented. Savor different answers as an opportunity to deepen understanding as the class sorts out, with your help, the different ways the concepts are being used.

Students' ideas about Problem 1 may give you insight into different depths of understanding. It's not the case that "either students understand it or they don't." Each student understands concepts in different ways, to different depths.

After students present Problem 2, **[Ask]** "Is there any unnecessary information?" [the number of quarts of tomatoes after canning] If students perceive the problem to be very open-ended, they could assert that the time spent picking or the time spent canning should be factored into the division of compensation. Encourage such critical thinking.

Closing the Lesson

Reiterate the main point of this lesson: Symbolic notation (variables and equations and inequalities) can be useful in solving problems.

BUILDING UNDERSTANDING

The exercises provide review of solving linear equations as well as problems that can be solved with symbolic algebra.

MATERIALS

- Calculator Note 0A, *optional*

ASSIGNING HOMEWORK

Essential	1–6, 10
Performance assessment	7–10
Portfolio	10
Journal	6
Group	8–10
Review	11–15

Helping with the Exercises

Exercises 6, 7 The problem can be solved by reasoning without algebraic symbols: If Ivan had gotten 1.5 times as much as he did, he would have had the same number of large beads as Anita, but would have had 17.5 more small beads, for which he would have paid \$1.575 more. So each small bead must cost 9 cents. From either Anita's or Ivan's total, you can find that each large bead cost 15 cents, making Jill's total \$2.64. Commend this reasoning, and point out how it reflects the symbolic solution of a system of equations.

Exercise 8 [Language] A *denarius* (plural *denarii*) was the monetary unit of Rome. **[ESL]** *Fivefold* means five times as much.

Exercise 10 [ESL] A *will* specifies who is to get the money and possessions when someone dies. Be sensitive to students who may have had loved ones recently pass away or to whom the concept of a will may be foreign.

See page 876 for answers to Exercises 10 and 11.

7. Follow these steps to solve Exercise 6.

a. Multiply Equation 1 by negative two. $-12L - 40S = -540$

b. Multiply Equation 2 by three. $12L + 75S = 855$

c. Add the resulting equations from 7a and b. $35S = 315$

d. Solve the equation in 7c for S. Interpret the real-world meaning of this solution. $S = 9$. The small beads cost 9¢ each.

e. Use the value of S to find the value of L. Interpret the real-world meaning of the value of L. $L = 15$. The large beads cost 15¢ each.

f. Use the values of S and L to find the value of J. Interpret this solution. $J = 264$. Jill will pay \$2.64 for her beads.

8. The following problem appears in *Liber abaci* (1202), or *Book of Calculations,* by the Italian mathematician Leonardo Fibonacci (ca. 1170–1240).

If A gets 7 denarii from B, then A's sum is fivefold B's. If B gets 5 denarii from A, then B's sum is sevenfold A's. How much has each?

$$\begin{cases} a + 7 = 5(b - 7) & \text{(Equation 1)} \\ b + 5 = 7(a - 5) & \text{(Equation 2)} \end{cases}$$

a. What does a represent?
b. What does b represent?
c. Explain Equation 1 with words.
d. Explain Equation 2 with words.

9. Use Equations 1 and 2 from Exercise 8.

a. Explain how to get
$$b + 5 = 7((5b - 42) - 5)$$

b. Solve the equation in 9a for b. $b = \frac{167}{17}$

c. Use your answer from 9b to find the value of a. $a = \frac{121}{17}$

d. Use the context of Exercise 8 to interpret the values of a and b.

10. According to Mrs. Randolph's will, each of her great-grandchildren living in Georgia received \$700 more than each of her great-grandchildren living in Florida. In all, \$206,100 was divided between 36 great-grandchildren. The Georgian great-grandchildren decide that the will wasn't really fair, so they each contribute \$175 to be divided among the Floridian great-grandchildren. If all great-grandchildren now have an equal share, how many great-grandchildren live in Georgia?

a. List the unknown quantities and assign a variable to each.

b. Write one or more equations that relate the variables to conditions of the problem.

c. Solve the equations to find a value for each variable.

d. Interpret the value of each variable according to the context of the problem.

Review

11. **APPLICATION** A 30°-60°-90° triangle and a 45°-45°-90° triangle are two drafting tools used by people in careers such as engineering, architecture, and drafting. The angles in both triangle tools are combined to make a variety of angle measures in hand-drawn technical drawings, such as blueprints. Describe or illustrate a procedure that will give the following angle measures.

a. 15° **b.** 75° **c.** 105°

Exercise 11 With both a 30°-60°-90° triangle and a 45°-45°-90° triangle, it is possible to draw any angle that is a multiple of 15°. **[Ask]** "Is there more than one way to find each measurement?" You may want to have students compare alternative approaches. Another possibility for 11a is to draw a 60° angle and subtract a 45° angle. Another possibility for 11c is to draw a 90° angle, add a 45° angle, and then subtract a 30° angle.

8a. a represents the number of denarii that A has.

8b. b represents the number of denarii that B has.

8c. If you take 7 denarii from B and give them to A, then A's new amount equals five times B's new amount.

8d. If you take 5 denarii from A and give them to B, then B's new amount equals seven times A's new amount.

9a. Solve Equation 1 for a. Substitute the result, $5b - 42$, for a in Equation 2 to get $b + 5 = 7((5b - 42) - 5)$.

9d. A has $\frac{121}{17}$ or about 7 denarii, and B has $\frac{167}{17}$ or about 10 denarii.

12. Rewrite each expression without parentheses.

a. $3(x + 7)$ $3x + 21$ b. $-2(6 - n)$ $-12 + 2n$ c. $x(4 - x)$ $4x - x^2$

13. Substitute the given value of the variable(s) in each expression and evaluate.

a. $47 + 3x$ when $x = 17$ 98

b. $29 - 34n + 14m$ when $n = -1$ and $m = -24$ -273

14. Find the slope of the line that passes through each pair of points.

a. (4, 7) and (8, 7) 0 b. (2, 5) and (−6, 3) $\frac{1}{4}$ or 0.25

15. Rudy is renting a cabin on Lake Tahoe. He wants to make a recipe for hot chocolate that calls for 1 cup of milk. Unfortunately, the cabin is not well stocked, and he has only a 1-gallon container of milk, a 4-cup saucepan, and an empty 12-ounce soda can. Describe or illustrate a process that Rudy can use to measure exactly 1 cup of milk. (There are 8 ounces per cup and 16 cups per gallon.)

16. ***Technology*** Use geometry software to construct a line through two points. Measure the coordinates of the points and use them to calculate the slope. Observe how the value of the slope changes as you move one of the points. What is the slope when the line is horizontal? Vertical? What other observations can you make?

Project

CREATE YOUR OWN COMPUTER ICON

Many computers use an operating system with a desktop interface. A small picture, or icon, typically represents items on the desktop, such as folders, disk drives, and files. Many of these computer icons are specifically designed to be symbolic representations. A word processing file might look like a piece of paper. Other icons are designed to symbolically convey more abstract ideas. For example, a group of programs that work cooperatively might be represented by puzzle pieces that appear to connect to each other. Even within computer programs, symbolic icons are used for commands, such as a picture of a disk to represent the "save" command.

Try to create a computer icon of your own. Select a type of file, computer program, or command, and design an icon that helps the user symbolically understand the icon.

Your project should include

- A full-color drawing of your icon.
- A description of the item or command represented by your icon.
- An explanation of how and why you chose your design. (What elements of your design help a computer user interpret your icon?)

Exercise 12 [Language] This exercise gives you the opportunity to review the term *distributive property.*

Exercise 13 As needed, review the order of operations. Calculator Note 0A: Order of Operations explains how the calculator uses the order of operations.

15. Fill the 4-cup pan with milk; pour from the pan to the soda can, completely filling the 12-ounce $\left(1\frac{1}{2}\text{ cup}\right)$ can and leaving $2\frac{1}{2}$ cups in the pan; empty the soda can; pour from the pan to the soda can again, this time leaving 1 cup in the pan.

Exercise 16 In The Geometer's Sketchpad a vertical line is given the slope ∞.

16. A horizontal line has slope 0. A vertical line has undefined slope. A line that increases from left to right has positive slope. A line that decreases from left to right has negative slope.

EXTENSION

Use Take Another Look activity 4 on page 26.

Supporting the Project

To broaden the project, you could discuss icons used throughout the Internet or those used by other types of technology (such as graphing calculators, synthesizers, or personal organizers). Students may find it interesting to research copyright issues surrounding icons used in software.

OUTCOMES

- Student has designed an icon.
- There is a clear explanation of what the icon represents and how it helps a user recognize its function.
- Student creates more than one icon, possibly creating a suite of icons for an entire program or variations on the icon for different word-processing programs.
- Student embellishes the written explanations by comparing and contrasting the new icon with icons in existing software or operating systems—explaining how his or her icon is unique or better.
- Student attaches the icon to an actual computer file or software.

LESSON

0.3

PLANNING

LESSON OUTLINE

One day:

15 min Examples

15 min Investigation

10 min Sharing

5 min Exercises

MATERIALS

none

TEACHING

Organizing information is a third problem-solving technique. You might use two days for this lesson if your students lack experience with problems like these. You can save some time by using the problem in Example C in place of the investigation.

One Step

Without preamble, have students read the problem of the investigation or pose the problem in Example C with books closed. As you circulate, suggest as needed that students organize the information into categories (for the investigation: house color, car, pet, plant/crop, newspaper) and make a table. During Sharing, have students read the examples and look for commonalities. From their observations, elicit the idea of organizing information.

► *EXAMPLE A*

This example illustrates organizing information through units, or dimensions. If your students don't remember dimensional analysis, this example may take 15 minutes.

LESSON 0.3

Organizing Information

If one and a half chickens lay one and a half eggs in one and a half days, then how long does it take six monkeys to make nine omelets?

Everybody gets so much information all day long that they lose their common sense.
GERTRUDE STEIN

What sort of problem-solving strategy can you apply to the silly problem above? You could draw a picture or make a diagram. You could assign variables to all sorts of unknown quantities. But do you really have enough information to solve the problem? Sometimes the best strategy is to begin by organizing what you know and what you want to know. With the information organized, you may then find a way to get to the solution.

There are different methods of organizing information. One valuable technique uses the units in the problem to help you see how the information fits together.

EXAMPLE A

To qualify for the Interlochen 470 auto race, each driver must complete two laps of the track at an average speed of 100 miles per hour (mi/h). Due to some problems at the start, Naomi averages only 50 mi/h on her first lap. How fast must she go on the second lap to qualify for the race?

► *Solution*

Sort the information into two categories: what you know and what you might need to know. Assign variables to the quantities that you don't know.

Know	Need to know
Speed of first lap: 50 mi/h	Speed of second lap (in mi/h): s
Average speed for both laps: 100 mi/h	Length of each lap (in mi): l
	Time for first lap (in h): t_1
	Time for second lap (in h): t_2

LESSON OBJECTIVES

- Learn good ways to organize information
- Practice using dimensional analysis and unit conversion
- Solve logic problems
- Improve at working cooperatively

NCTM STANDARDS

CONTENT		PROCESS	
	Number	✓	Problem Solving
✓	Algebra	✓	Reasoning
	Geometry	✓	Communication
✓	Measurement		Connections
	Data/Probability		Representation

Next, look at the units to find connections between the pieces of information. Speed is measured in miles per hour and therefore calculated by dividing distance by time, so you can write these equations:

$$\begin{cases} 50 \text{ mi/h} = \dfrac{l \text{ mi}}{t_1 \text{ h}} & \text{The speed, distance, and time for the first lap.} \\ s \text{ mi/h} = \dfrac{l \text{ mi}}{t_2 \text{ h}} & \text{The second lap.} \\ 100 \text{ mi/h} = \dfrac{2l \text{ mi}}{(t_1 + t_2) \text{ h}} & \text{The average speed needed for both laps to qualify.} \end{cases}$$

You can write the first and third equations as

$$t_1 \text{ h} = \frac{l \text{ mi}}{50 \text{ mi/h}} = \frac{l}{50} \text{ h} \qquad (t_1 + t_2) \text{ h} = \frac{2l \text{ mi}}{100 \text{ mi/h}} = \frac{l}{50} \text{ h}$$

This means that the time for the first lap, t_1, and the time for both laps together $(t_1 + t_2)$, are the same and $t_2 = 0$. There is no time at all to complete the second lap.

It is not possible for Naomi to qualify for the race.

In Example A, it was easy to find relationships between the known and unknown quantities because the units were miles, hours, or miles per hour. Sometimes you will need to use common knowledge to make the intermediate connections between the units.

EXAMPLE B

How many seconds are in a calendar year?

▶ Solution

First, identify what you know and what you want to know.

Know	Need to know
1 year	Number of seconds

It may seem like you don't have enough information, but consider these commonly known facts:

1 year = 365 days (non–leap-year)
1 day = 24 hours
1 hour = 60 minutes
1 minute = 60 seconds

This fragment of an ancient Roman calendar shows months, days, and special events. You can learn how to read Roman calendars, or *fasti,* with an Internet link at www.keymath.com/DAA .

You can write each equality as a fraction and multiply the chain of fractions such that the units reduce to leave seconds.

$$1 \cancel{\text{year}} \cdot \frac{365 \cancel{\text{days}}}{1 \cancel{\text{year}}} \cdot \frac{24 \cancel{\text{hours}}}{1 \cancel{\text{day}}} \cdot \frac{60 \cancel{\text{minutes}}}{1 \cancel{\text{hour}}} \cdot \frac{60 \text{ seconds}}{1 \cancel{\text{minute}}} = 31{,}536{,}000 \text{ seconds}$$

There are 31,536,000 seconds in a non–leap-year calendar year.

Example A (continued)

[Ask] "What is the advantage of using subscripts?" [A t can be used for both times.] "Why does miles divided by miles per hour equal hours?" [Ratios of units follow the rules of fraction operations: $\frac{\text{mi}}{\text{mi/h}} = \cancel{\text{mi}} \cdot \frac{\text{h}}{\cancel{\text{mi}}} = \text{h}$.]

[Alert] Students often think that they can find the average speed by averaging the two speeds. In that case, the answer would be 150 mi/h because $\frac{50 + 150}{2} = 100$. If students don't mention this idea, raise the alternative approach and ask why the answer differs from that of the student book. You might ask for justification of the 150, based on some assumed lap distance, such as 5 miles. Keep pressing until the students see that Naomi took $\frac{1}{10}$ hour for the first lap, and at 150 mi/h would take $\frac{1}{30}$ hour for the second lap, so her total time for the two laps would be $\frac{2}{15}$ hour, making her average speed over two laps $\frac{10 \text{ mi}}{\frac{2}{15} \text{ h}} = 75$ mi/h.

This kind of mistake gives you a chance to mention that doing mathematics often involves the interplay between intuition and logic. If there's no error in logic, then the intuition is open to improvement. Students may feel uncomfortable when their intuition, a part of their identity, is challenged. You can show them how to improve their intuition by asking good questions such as "Why can't you just average averages?" [Averages, like other fractions, can be added (or averaged) only if they have a common denominator. In this case of speed, although the numerators (lap distances) are the same, the denominators must be different times, so the average of averages is meaningless. The total time and total distance must be taken into account when finding average speed.]

▶ EXAMPLE B

This example also illustrates the usefulness of dimensional analysis in problem solving. The given solution uses an intuitive approach; no variable is assigned to the unknown quantity. You could, however, assign a variable, say x, to the number of seconds in one year, and write the equation 1 year = x seconds.

[Alert] If students are confused about why they are multiplying by factors such as $\frac{365 \text{ days}}{1 \text{ year}}$, you can point out that they are multiplying by 1. You might introduce the term *multiplicative identity.* The number 1 is the multiplicative identity because any number times 1 equals the original number. Algebraically, $n \cdot 1 = n$.

[Language] A fraction equivalent to 1 is often called a *unit fraction.* (*Unit* in this term means 1, not a unit of measure.)

▶ EXAMPLE C

[Language] A *flask* is a glass container that is often used in laboratory experiments. An *Erlenmeyer flask* is a flat-bottomed, conical flask.

Students are not asked to solve this problem at this time. They need to organize the information and determine if any information is not needed, a key step in the problem-solving process.

For one way of organizing the information see Take Another Look activity 2, page 25, and make available the Exercise 8 worksheet for students who want to use a chart.

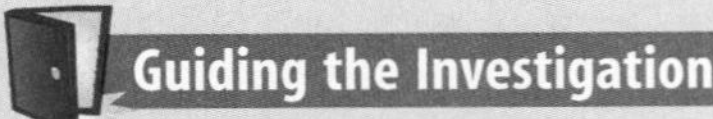

Guiding the Investigation

Acknowledge to students that this is a silly context, but emphasize that it lets them practice organizing information and solving problems without serious consequences.

Assure students that there is no one right way to solve logic problems like those in Example C and the investigation. One way is to make a grid with the houses along one side and the different alternatives for each category along the other side. Mark off all the things the clues eliminate. You will need grids to compare pairs of categories and a way of combining the information from the various grids. Some students find that the guess-and-check method works best for them.

[Ask] "How many different variables are in this problem?" [five: house color, car, pet, plant/crop, newspaper]

This zebra problem was an "Elementary Problem of the Week" on the popular Math Forum website; for a link to the Math Forum, go to www.keypress.com/DAA.

Some problems overwhelm you with lots of information. Identifying and categorizing what you know is always a good way to start organizing information.

EXAMPLE C

Lab assistant Jerry Anderson has just finished cleaning a messy lab table and is putting the equipment back on the table when he reads a note telling him *not* to disturb the positions of three water samples. Not knowing the correct order of the three samples, he finds these facts in the lab notes.

- The water that is highest in sulfur was on one end.
- The water that is highest in iron is in the Erlenmeyer flask.
- The water taken from the spring is not next to the water in the bottle.
- The water that is highest in calcium is left of the water taken from the lake.
- The water in the Erlenmeyer flask, the water taken from the well, and the water that is highest in sulfur are three distinct samples.
- The water in the round flask is not highest in calcium.

Organize the facts into categories. (This is the first step in actually determining which sample goes where. You will finish the problem when you do the exercises.)

▶ Solution

Information is given about the types of containers, the sources of the water, the elements found in the samples, and the positions of the samples on the table. You can find three options for each category.

Containers: round flask, Erlenmeyer flask, bottle

Sources: spring, lake, well

Elements: sulfur, iron, calcium

Positions: left, center, right

Now that the information is organized and categorized, you need to see where it leads. You will finish this problem in Exercise 8.

Science CONNECTION

Piecing together clues in order to understand a bigger picture is a major problem-solving strategy of the Human Genome Project. Since 1990, researchers from around the world have been working cooperatively to map and sequence the human genome—the complete set of more than 3 billion human DNA base pairs. By 2000, despite an overwhelming amount of information to organize, researchers were able to sequence roughly 90% of the human genome. By understanding the organization and function of human DNA, the researchers hope to improve human health and create guidelines for the ethical use of genetic knowledge.

This is one of the computers used in the Human Genome Project.

SHARING IDEAS

Ask if students can think of other ways to solve the problem of Example A. One way is to assume a convenient lap length (say 5 miles) and look at the units. To find the miles, multiply the rate (speed) by the time: $\frac{\text{mi}}{\text{h}} \cdot \text{h} = \text{mi}$. The hours reduce or cancel to make both sides miles. The arrangement could lead to three equations:

First lap	$50t_1 = 5$	$t_1 = 0.1$ h
Second lap	$st_2 = 5$	$t_2 = \frac{5}{s}$ h
Both laps	$100(t_1 + t_2) = 10$	$t_1 + t_2 = 0.1$ h

Combining this information into one equation gives $0.1 + \frac{5}{s} = 0.1$ h. But there is no solution to this equation. A different value for the length of a lap would yield the same result.

Use this investigation as an opportunity to practice categorizing and organizing information as you did in Example C.

Investigation
Who Owns the Zebra?

There are five houses along one side of Birch Street, each of a unique color. The home-owners each drive a different car, and each has a different pet. The owners all read a different newspaper and plant only one thing in their garden.

- The family with the station wagon lives in the red house.
- The owner of the SUV has a dog.
- The family with the van reads the *Gazette.*
- The green house is immediately to the left of the white house.
- The *Chronicle* is delivered to the green house.
- The man who plants zucchini has birds.
- In the yellow house they plant corn.
- In the middle house they read the *Times.*
- The compact car parks at the first house.
- The family that plants eggplant lives in the house next to the house with cats.
- In the house next to the house where they have a horse, they plant corn.
- The woman who plants beets receives the *Daily News.*
- The owner of the sports car plants okra.
- The family with the compact car lives next to the blue house.
- They read the *Bulletin* in the house next to the house where they plant eggplant.

Who owns the zebra?

Organizing the known information and clarifying what you need to find out is a very useful strategy. Whether it involves simply keeping track of units or sorting out masses of information, organizing your data and making a plan are essential to finding a solution efficiently.

Position	1 (left)	2	3	4	5 (right)
House color	Yellow	Blue	Red	Green	White
Car	Compact	Van	Station wagon	Sports car	SUV
Newspaper	*Bulletin*	*Gazette*	*Times*	*Chronicle*	*Daily News*
Plant	Corn	Eggplant	Zucchini	Okra	Beets
Pet	Cats	Horse	Birds	Zebra	Dog

The family in the green house owns the zebra.

Sharing Ideas (continued)

Encourage creativity by asking if students can solve the problem of Example B by thinking "outside the box." Because the word *second* has multiple definitions, students could answer 12: January second, February second, March second, ... Or they might answer 24, including the twenty-second of each month as well.

Assessing Progress

As you watch students at work, you can assess their organizational skills and their abilities to read carefully. If they worked on Examples A and B, you can check their comfort with dimensional analysis and their understanding of average speed.

Closing the Lesson

Reiterate the main point of this lesson: Organizing information systematically, through a study of units or tables, is an important problem-solving technique.

BUILDING UNDERSTANDING

The exercises let students practice organizing information through units, averages, and rates. As you work with students, look for evidence that they are following the four-step process: understand the problem, devise a plan, carry out the plan, look back.

ASSIGNING HOMEWORK

Essential	1–3, 9
Performance assessment	6, 7, 9, 10
Portfolio	8, 10
Group	8
Review	4, 5, 11–14

MATERIALS

- Graph paper
- Exercise 8 (W), *optional*
- Calculator Note 0A, *optional*

Helping with the Exercises

Exercise 1 Students may want to convert units on their calculators. Calculator Note 0A: Order of Operations may be helpful.

Exercise 2 Students might give a nonsymbolic solution like this: If they'd worked at the same rates twice as long on Monday as they actually did, then Alejandro would have worked 2 hours, the same as he did on Tuesday. Emily would have worked 4 hours more than she did on Tuesday, and they would have solved 278 problems, which is 148 more than they actually solved on Tuesday. So Emily must be working $\frac{148}{4} = 37$ problems per hour. Therefore the first day she worked $3 \cdot 37 = 111$ problems, leaving 28 for Alejandro to have worked in 1 hour.

In 2d, points i and ii satisfy the first equation. Points ii and iii satisfy the second equation. The last point doesn't work in either equation.

Malaysian-American architect and artist Daniel Castor (b 1966) created this pencil drawing of the Amsterdam Stock Exchange. Castor's work—which he calls "jellyfish" drawings—organizes lots of information and several perspectives into one drawing. He describes his art as "[capturing], in two dimensions, the physical power of the spaces yielded by [the] design process, a power that cannot be adequately described by word or photograph."

EXERCISES

Practice Your Skills

1. Use units to help you find the missing information.
   a. How many seconds would it take to travel 15 feet at 3.5 feet per second? approximately 4.3 s
   b. How many centimeters are in 25 feet? (There are 2.54 centimeters per inch and 12 inches per foot.) 762 cm
   c. How many miles could you drive with 15 gallons of gasoline at 32 miles per gallon? 480 mi

2. Emily and Alejandro are part of a math marathon team on which they take turns solving math problems for 4 hours each day. On Monday Emily worked for 3 hours and Alejandro for 1 hour. Then on Tuesday Emily worked for 2 hours and Alejandro for 2 hours. On Monday they collectively solved 139 problems and on Tuesday they solved 130 problems. Find the average problem-solving rate for Emily and for Alejandro.
   a. Identify the unknown quantities and assign variables. What are the units for each variable?
   b. What does the equation $3e + 1a = 139$ represent?
   c. Write an equation for Tuesday. $2e + 2a = 130$
   d. Which of these ordered pairs (e, a) is a solution for the problem? ii
      i. (34, 37) **ii.** (37, 28) **iii.** (30, 35) **iv.** (27, 23)
   e. Interpret the solution from 2d according to the context of the problem.
      Emily averages 37 problems per hour and Alejandro averages 28 problems per hour.

2a. Let e represent the average problem-solving rate in problems per hour for Emily, and let a represent the average rate in problems per hour for Alejandro.

2b. This is the equation for Monday. 3 hours times e problems per hour plus 1 hour times a problems per hour is equal to 139 problems.

3. To qualify for the Interlochen 470 auto race, each driver must complete two laps of the track at an average speed of 100 mi/h. Benjamin averages only 75 mi/h on his first lap. How fast must he go on the second lap to qualify for the race? 150 mi/h

4. Use the distributive property to expand and combine like terms when possible.

a. $7.5(a - 3)$ $7.5a - 22.5$

b. $12 + 4.7(b + 6)$ $40.2 + 4.7b$

c. $5c - 2(c - 12)$ $3c + 24$

d. $8.4(35 - d) + 12.6d$ $294 + 4.2d$

5. Solve each equation.

a. $4.5(a - 7) = 26.1$ $a = 12.8$

b. $9 + 2.7(b + 3) = 20.7$ $b = \frac{4}{3} = 1.\overline{3}$

c. $8c - 2(c - 5) = 70$ $c = 10$

d. $8.4(35 - d) + 12.6d = 327.6$ $d = 8$

Reason and Apply

6. **APPLICATION** Alyse earns \$15.40 per hour, and she earns time and a half for working past 8:00 P.M. Last week she worked 35 hours and earned \$600.60. How many hours did she work past 8:00 P.M.? Alyse worked 8 hours past 8:00 P.M.

7. The dimensions used to measure length, area, and volume are related by multiplication and division. Find the information about the following rectangular boxes. Include the units in your solution.

a. A box has volume 486 in.^{3} and height 9 in. Find the area of the base. $\frac{486 \text{ in.}^3}{9 \text{ in.}} = 54 \text{ in.}^2$

b. A box has base area 3.60 m^2 and height 0.40 m. Find the volume. $3.60 \text{ m}^2 \cdot 0.40 \text{ m} = 1.44 \text{ m}^3$

c. A box has base area 2.40 ft^2 and volume 2.88 ft^3. Find the height. $\frac{2.88 \text{ ft}^3}{2.40 \text{ ft}^2} = 1.20 \text{ ft}$

d. A box has volume 12,960 cm^3, height 18 cm, and length 30 cm. Find the width. $\frac{12960 \text{ cm}^3}{(18 \text{ cm} \cdot 30 \text{ cm})} = 24 \text{ cm}$

Nicaraguan artist Federico Nordalm (b 1949) created this painting, titled *Box of Apples.*

8. Lab assistant Jerry Anderson has just finished cleaning a messy lab table and is putting the equipment back on the table when he reads a note telling him *not* to disturb the positions of three water samples. Not knowing the correct order of the three samples, he finds these facts in the lab notes.

- The water that is highest in sulfur was on one end.
- The water that is highest in iron is in the Erlenmeyer flask.
- The water taken from the spring is not next to the water in the bottle.
- The water that is highest in calcium is left of the water taken from the lake.
- The water in the Erlenmeyer flask, the water taken from the well, and the water that is highest in sulfur are three distinct samples.
- The water in the round flask is not highest in calcium.

Determine which water sample goes where. Identify each sample by its container, source, element, and position.

8.

Container	Bottle	Erlenmeyer flask	Round flask
Source	Well	Lake	Spring
Element	Calcium	Iron	Sulfur
Position	Left	Center	Right

Exercise 3 This exercise can be solved by any of the approaches to Example A described on pages 14 and 15.

Exercise 4 [Language] As needed, review the meanings of the terms *distributive property, expand,* and *combine like terms.*

Exercise 5 Students may use a variety of approaches to solve these problems: guess-and-check, undoing, and balancing. Encourage students to use whatever methods make sense to them so that they don't believe they can't solve a problem just because they "can't remember the right method."

Exercise 6 [Language] *Time and a half* is the wage that a worker often earns for working overtime; it is equal to one and a half times the worker's normal wage. A nonsymbolic approach might calculate the total that Alyse would earn over 35 hours at the regular rate (\$539) and realize that the extra (\$61.60) must have come from the extra half pay (\$7.70) picked up from late hours. That implies that she worked 8 of the hours after 8:00 P.M.

Exercise 7 As needed, review that the volume of a box equals the area of the base times the height, and wonder aloud if dimensional analysis would help.

Exercise 8 If students are struggling, you might suggest that they make a chart. One such chart appears on the Exercise 8 worksheet. Students might number the clues and use those numbers as they fill out the chart. Be open to other approaches, though; some students are successful at using guess-and-check.

Exercise 9 Students' intuition may lead them to average the two times. Because 17.5 does not satisfy any of the three equations, the students may be confused. This is the good kind of confusion that can lead to deeper understanding. **[Ask]** "Does the average of 17.5 make sense?" Most students will realize that two people working together can finish the job in less time than either working alone. You might then say that you find it helpful to think of what part of the job each of the workers can do in a minute, and then calculate what part they can do together in a minute.

9a. Equation iii. The area painted is calculated by multiplying painting rate by time. Equation iii represents the sum of Paul's area and China's area equaling the whole area, or $\frac{96\text{ ft}^2}{15\text{ min}} \cdot t\text{ min} + \frac{96\text{ ft}^2}{20\text{ min}} \cdot t\text{ min} = 96\text{ ft}^2$.

9b. i. $t = \frac{1}{35} \approx 0.03$

ii. $t = \frac{96}{3360} \approx 0.03$

iii. $t = \frac{60}{7} \approx 8.57$

Exercise 10 If you or your students are interested in the source of any cartoons or photos, they are listed in the photo credits at the end of the book.

Career CONNECTION

Event planners make a career organizing information. To plan a New Year's Eve celebration, for example, an event planner considers variables such as location, decorations, food and beverages, number of people, and staff. For the celebration of the year 2000, event planners around the world worked independently and cooperatively to organize unique events for each city or country and to coordinate recording and televising of the events, which occurred in every time zone. Problem-solving strategies that were taught in this lesson may have been used to coordinate these global events.

Berlin, Germany (left), and Seattle, Washington (right), celebrate the new millennium at midnight, January 1, 2000.

9. APPLICATION Paul can paint the area of a 12-by-8 ft wall in 15 min. China can paint the same area in 20 min.

a. In which equation does t represent how long it would take Paul and China to paint the area of a 12-by-8 ft wall together? Explain your choice.

i. $\frac{15t}{96} + \frac{20t}{96} = \frac{1}{96}$ **ii.** $(96)15t + (96)20t = 96$ **iii.** $\frac{96t}{15} + \frac{96t}{20} = 96$

b. Solve all three equations in 9a.

c. How long would it take Paul and China to paint the wall together?
It would take approximately 9 minutes.

10. Kiane has a photograph of her four cats sitting in a row. The cats are different ages, and each cat has its own favorite toy and favorite sleeping spot.

- Rocky and the 10-year-old cat would never sit next to each other for a photo.
- The cat that sleeps in the blue chair and the cat that plays with the rubber mouse are the two oldest cats.
- The cat that plays with the silk rose is the third cat in the photo.
- Sadie and the cat on Sadie's left in the photo don't sleep on the furniture.
- The 8-year-old cat sleeps on the floor.
- The cat that sleeps on the sofa eats the same food as the 13-year-old cat.
- Pascal likes to chase the 5-year-old cat.
- If you add the ages of the cat that sleeps in a box and the one that plays with a stuffed toy, you get the age of Winks.
- The cat that sleeps on the blue chair likes to hide the catnip ball, which belongs to one of the cats sitting next to it in the photo.

Who plays with the catnip-filled ball?

10.

Position	1 (left)	2	3	4 (right)
Name	Rocky	Sadie	Winks	Pascal
Age	8	5	13	10
Sleeps	Floor	Box	Chair	Sofa
Toy	Stuffed toy	Catnip ball	Silk rose	Rubber mouse

Sadie plays with the catnip-filled ball.

Review

11. Rewrite each expression using the properties of exponents so that the variable appears only once.

a. $(r^5)(r^7)$ r^{12} **b.** $\frac{2s^6}{6s^2}$ $\frac{s^4}{3}$ **c.** $\frac{(t)(t^3)}{t^8}$ t^{-4} or $\frac{1}{t^4}$ **d.** $3(2u^2)^4$ $48u^8$

12. Joel is 16 years old. His cousin Rachel is 12.

a. What is the difference in their ages? 4 years

b. What is the ratio of Joel's age to Rachel's age? $\frac{16}{12} = \frac{4}{3} = 1.\overline{3}$

c. In eight years, what will be the difference in their ages? 4 years

d. In eight years, what will be the ratio of Joel's age to Rachel's age? $\frac{24}{20} = \frac{6}{5} = 1.2$

13. Draw a rectangle diagram to represent each product. Use the diagrams to expand each product.

a. $(x + 1)(x + 5)$ **b.** $(x + 3)^2$ **c.** $(x + 3)(x - 3)$

14. APPLICATION Iwanda sells African bead necklaces through a consignment shop. At the end of May, the shop paid her $100 from the sale of 8 necklaces. At the end of June, she was paid $187.50 from the sale of 15 necklaces. Assume that the consignment shop pays Iwanda the same amount of money for each necklace sold.

a. Make a linear graph showing the relationship between the number of necklaces sold and the amount of money Iwanda gets.

b. Use your graph to estimate how much money Iwanda will get if the shop sells only 6 of her necklaces in July. $75

c. How much does the consignment shop pay Iwanda from the sale of each necklace? $12.50 per necklace

IMPROVING YOUR REASONING SKILLS

Internet Access

A nationwide Internet service provider advertises "1000 hours free for 45 days" for new customers. How many hours per day do you need to be online to use 1000 hours in 45 days? Do you think it is reasonable for the Internet service provider to make this offer?

IMPROVING REASONING SKILLS

This problem gives more practice using dimensional analysis. 1000 hours in 45 days would require someone to be online for more than 22 hours per day. Because there are only 24 hours per day, students probably will argue that the advertisement is unreasonable because the average human needs to sleep more than 2 hours per day. You might **[Ask]** "Why doesn't the company advertise unlimited service for 45 days?" [1000 is more eye-catching than unlimited; unlimited implies that you never have to stop, whereas 1000 signifies a cut-off point; 1000 is a rounder number than 1080, the actual number of hours in 45 days.] **[Context]** This slogan was actually used by America Online during late 2001 and early 2002.

Exercise 11 If you need to review the properties of exponents, be sure to go beyond formulas to show why the formulas make sense. For example, $(r^5)(r^2) = (r \cdot r \cdot r \cdot r \cdot r)(r \cdot r) = r^7$. You might also review negative exponents. **[Ask]** "How would you write $\frac{1}{x^2}$ without using a fraction?" [x^{-2}]

Exercise 12 Most students will realize upon reflection that the differences in ages remain the same, but they may need to try out some numbers to see that the ratios change. You might use symbols to ask if there are any values of n for which $\frac{a}{b} = \frac{a+n}{b+n}$.

Exercise 13 13c could be drawn using dotted lines to show a negative.

	x	-3
x	x^2	$-3x$
3	$3x$	-9

Exercise 14 Students can use graph paper to make an accurate graph. Rather than use their graph to solve 14b, students might recognize the direct variation and divide 100 by 8 (or 187.50 by 15) and multiply the result by 6: $12.50 \cdot 6 = 75$. Or they might reason that the $87.50 more she was paid in June than in May was for 7 extra necklaces, so she must have been paid $\frac{87.50}{7} = 12.50$ dollars each. This is good linear thinking. **[Ask]** "How much does the consignment shop sell the necklaces for?" [There is not enough information to answer this.] **[Language]** A *linear graph* is the graph of a straight line. A *consignment shop* is a store that allows people to sell their goods for a percentage of the sale.

EXTENSION

See Take Another Look activity 2 on page 25.

See pages 876–877 for answers to Exercises 13 and 14a.

PLANNING

LESSON OUTLINE

One day:

10 min	Reviewing
25 min	Exercises
10 min	Student self-assessment

REVIEWING

The problem-solving steps given in the Chapter Review opener are largely condensed from Johnson and Herr's *Problem Solving Strategies: Crossing the River with Dogs,* which follows suggestions given in Pólya's *How to Solve It.* You might have a class discussion about other strategies students use.

To begin the review, you might pose a single problem that is amenable to a variety of approaches. For example, "If you fit a steel belt tightly around Earth's equator, and then lengthen it by 40 feet and make it stand out equally around the equator, how high is it from Earth?" (The radius of Earth is about 4000 miles.) A diagram can be useful for solving this problem, as can symbolic algebra and generating some data to organize. It's also an example of a problem whose algebraic result $\left(\frac{40}{2\pi}\right.$, or about 6 feet$\left.\right)$ is counterintuitive.

[Language] A *manipulative* is an object that can be used to represent a mathematical idea. Seeing relationships using manipulatives can aid in understanding the mathematical idea.

See page 877 for answers to Exercises 1 and 2.

CHAPTER 0 REVIEW

There is no single way to solve a problem. Different people prefer to use different problem-solving strategies, yet not all strategies can be applied to all problems. In this chapter you practiced only a few specific strategies. You may have also used some strategies that you remember from other courses. The next paragraph gives you a longer list of problem-solving strategies to choose from.

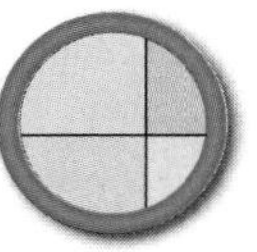

Organize the information that is given, or that you figure out in the course of your work, in a list or table. **Draw a picture,** graph, or diagram, and label it to illustrate information you are given *and* what you are trying to find. There are also special types of diagrams that help you organize information, such as tree diagrams and Venn diagrams. **Make a physical representation** of the problem. That is, act it out, make a model, or use manipulatives. **Look for a pattern** in numbers or units of measure. Be sure all your measures use the same system of units and that you compare quantities with *the same* unit. **Eliminate some possibilities.** If you know what the answer cannot be, you are partway there. **Solve subproblems** that present themselves as part of the problem context, or **solve a simpler problem** by substituting easier numbers or looking at a special case. Don't forget to **use algebra**! Assign variables to unknown quantities and write expressions for related quantities. Translate verbal statements into equations, and solve the equations. **Work backward** from the solution to the problem. For instance, you can solve equations by undoing operations. **Use guess-and-check,** adjusting each successive guess by the result of your previous guess. Finally, but most importantly, **read the problem**! Be sure you know what is being asked.

EXERCISES

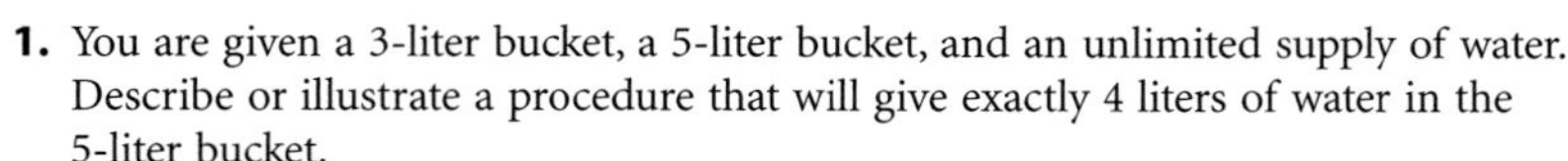

1. You are given a 3-liter bucket, a 5-liter bucket, and an unlimited supply of water. Describe or illustrate a procedure that will give exactly 4 liters of water in the 5-liter bucket.

2. Draw a rectangle diagram to represent each product. Use the diagrams to expand each product.

a. $(x + 3)(x + 4)$ **b.** $(2x)(x + 3)$ **c.** $(x + 6)(x - 2)$ **d.** $(x - 4)(2x - 1)$

3. Use the Pythagorean Theorem to find each missing length.

a. $x = \sqrt{18}$ cm $= 3\sqrt{2}$ cm ≈ 4.2 cm

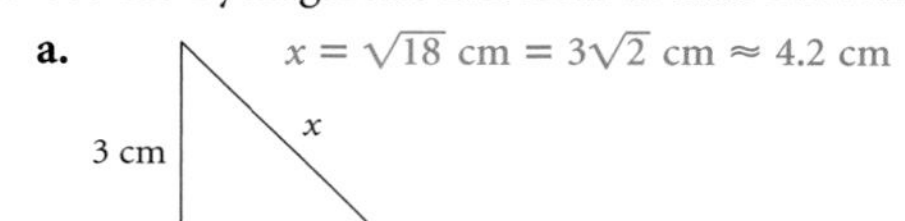

b. $y = \sqrt{25}$ in. $= 5$ in.

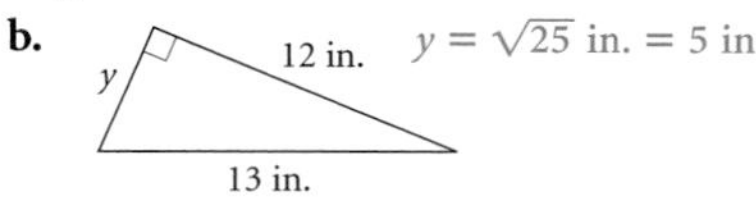

ASSIGNING HOMEWORK

These exercises review Chapter 0, as well as some topics from algebra and geometry. You might use Exercises 1–14 as a pretest of algebra knowledge. If students struggle with one or more topics, spend time reviewing those fundamental skills.

Helping with the Exercises

Exercise 2 This exercise is the first of this type in which x does not have a coefficient of 1. As needed, wonder aloud if $2x$ can be written as a sum, because the rectangle diagrams seem to use sums.

Exercise 3 This exercise reviews the Pythagorean Theorem and side lengths of special triangles. Students may recognize the isosceles right triangle or the 5-12-13 right triangle and not use the Pythagorean Theorem directly.

4. This graph shows the relationship between distance driven and gasoline consumed for two cars going 60 mi/h.

a. How far can Car A drive on 7 gallons (gal) of gasoline? 168 mi

b. How much gasoline is needed for Car B to drive 342 mi? 9.5 gal

c. Which car can drive farther on 8.5 gal of gas? How much farther? Car B can go 102 miles farther than Car A.

d. What is the slope of each line? Explain the real-world meaning of each slope.

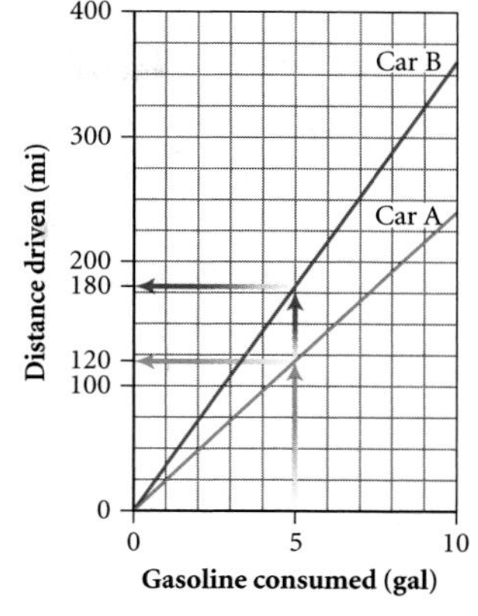

Consumer CONNECTION

The U.S. Environmental Protection Agency (EPA) obtains fuel economy estimates each year on car manufacturers' new models. In a controlled laboratory setting, professional drivers test the cars on a treadmill-type machine with engines and temperature conditions that simulate highway and city driving. Hybrid cars—a cross between gasoline-powered cars and electric cars—are some of the highest-rated vehicles for fuel economy.

This diagram illustrates the components of a parallel hybrid car.

Engine
Electric motor
Battery
Fuel
Transmission

5. Solve each equation. Check each answer by substituting into the original equation.

a. $3(x - 5) + 2 = 26$ $x = 13$

b. $3.75 - 1.5(y + 4.5) = 0.75$ $y = -2.5$

6. In 6a and b, translate each verbal statement to a symbolic expression. Combine the expressions to solve 6c. Let n represent the unknown number.

a. Six more than twice a number $2n + 6$

b. Five times three less than a number $5(n - 3)$

c. Six more than twice a number is five times three less than the number. Find the number. $2n + 6 = 5(n - 3)$; $n = 7$

7. APPLICATION Keisha and her family are moving to a new apartment 12 miles from their old one. You-Do-It Truck Rental rents a small truck for $19.95 per day plus $0.35 per mile. Keisha's family hopes they can complete the move with five loads all on the same day. She estimates that she will drive the truck another 10 miles for pickup and return.

a. Write an expression that represents the cost of a one-day rental with any number of miles. $c = 19.95 + 0.35m$

b. How much will Keisha pay if she does complete the move with five loads? possible answer: $61.25

c. How much can Keisha save if she completes the move with four loads? $8.40

Exercise 4 This exercise reviews ratio and proportion. The exact answers given use the ratios $\frac{120 \text{ mi}}{5 \text{ gal}}$ for Car A and $\frac{180 \text{ mi}}{5 \text{ gal}}$ for Car B. If students approximate each answer from the graph, instead of using proportions, their answers will vary slightly.

4d. For Car A the slope is $\frac{120}{5} = 24$, which means the car can drive 24 miles per gallon of gasoline. For Car B the slope is $\frac{180}{5} = 36$, which means the car can drive 36 miles per gallon.

Exercise 5 Encourage students to use whatever methods they feel comfortable with. You might ask them to justify each step of their solutions with reasons such as "Add 13 to both sides" or "Undo addition of 3.75" or "Trace either graph to find the x-value of the point of intersection" or "Use the distributive property." Checking answers is an important habit.

Exercise 6 Be sure students distinguish between expressions (as in 6a and b) and equations (as in 6c). Students who prefer the undoing method of solving equations will find that it doesn't work for equations like this, which contain more than one occurrence of the variable. Encourage them to try other methods. To deepen their understanding of solutions to equations, suggest guess-and-check or maybe graphing. Otherwise, suggest balancing.

Exercise 7 This exercise requires linear reasoning. If Keisha makes five trips, she will drive the twelve-mile distance only nine times (not ten times), because she doesn't need to go back to the old apartment after the fifth time. Students may, however, argue that she needs to go back to clean or return keys, in which case $65.45 is an acceptable answer to 7b.

7. Let m represent the number of miles driven, and let c represent the total cost in dollars of renting the truck.

8. Toby has only a balance scale, a single 40 g mass, and a stack of both white and red blocks. (Assume that all white blocks have the same mass and all red blocks have the same mass.) Toby discovers that four white blocks and one red block balance two white blocks, two red blocks, and the 40 g mass. He also finds that five white blocks and two red blocks balance one white block and five red blocks.

a. List the unknown quantities and assign a variable to each.

b. Translate Toby's discoveries into equations. $4w + r = 2w + 2r + 40$; $5w + 2r = w + 5r$

c. Solve the equations to find a value for each variable. $w = 60$; $r = 80$

d. Interpret the solution according to the context of the problem. The mass of a white block is 60 g, and the mass of a red block is 80 g.

Science CONNECTION

Calculating how much food a human being needs and planning how much food can be carried are critical factors for space travel. Weight and volume of food must be limited, trash must be minimized, and nutritional value and variety must be provided. Current U.S. space shuttle flights can carry 3.8 pounds of food per person per day, providing 3 meals a day for up to 14 days.

Astronaut Linda Godwin handles food supplies aboard the space shuttle *Endeavor* in December 2001.

9. Amy says that it is her birthday and that six times her age five years ago is twice as much as twice her age next year. How old is Amy? 17 years old

10. Scott has 47 coins totaling \$5.02. He notices that the number of pennies is the same as the number of quarters and that the sum of the number of pennies and quarters is one more than the sum of the number of nickels and dimes. How many of each coin does Scott have? 12 pennies, 8 nickels, 15 dimes, 12 quarters

11. The height of a golf ball in flight is given by the equation $h = -16t^2 + 48t$, where h represents the height in feet above the ground and t represents the time in seconds since the ball was hit. Find h and interpret the real-world meaning of the result when

a. $t = 0$ b. $t = 2$ c. $t = 3$

12. Rewrite each expression using the properties of exponents so that the variable appears only once.

a. $(4x^{-2})(x)$ $4x^{-1}$ or $\frac{4}{x}$ b. $\frac{4x^2}{8x^3}$ $\frac{1}{2}x^{-1}$ or $\frac{1}{2x}$ c. $(x^3)^5$ x^{15}

13. Consider the equation $y = 2^x$.

a. Find y when $x = 0$. $y = 2^0 = 1$

b. Find y when $x = 3$. $y = 2^3 = 8$

c. Find y when $x = -2$. $y = 2^{-2} = \frac{1}{2^2} = \frac{1}{4}$

d. Find x when $y = 32$. $x = 5$

14. Use units to help you find the missing information.

a. How many ounces are in 5 gallons? (There are 8 ounces per cup, 4 cups per quart, and 4 quarts per gallon.) $5 \text{ gal} \cdot \frac{4 \text{ qt}}{1 \text{ gal}} \cdot \frac{4 \text{ c}}{1 \text{ qt}} \cdot \frac{8 \text{ oz}}{1 \text{ c}} = 640 \text{ oz}$

b. How many meters are in 1 mile? (There are 2.54 centimeters per inch, 12 inches per foot, 5280 feet per mile, and 100 centimeters per meter.)

Exercise 8 Instead of using symbolic variables and equations, students may want to manipulate (or think of manipulating) blocks on a balance scale. If they begin with the first situation and remove 2 white blocks and 1 red from each side, they'll see that 2 whites balance with 1 red plus 40 kg. In the second situation, they can remove 1 white and 2 reds from both sides to see that 4 whites balance with 3 reds. They can conclude that they should double the weights on each side of the first situation, to have 4 whites balancing with 2 reds and 80 kg. Replacing those 4 whites with the equivalent 3 reds from the second situation, and removing 2 reds from both sides, balances 1 red with 80 kg. Commend reasoning like this, and have the students represent it in symbols, tracking how it reflects the balancing approach to solving a linear equation.

Exercise 9 An answer of 3 indicates that students missed the double doubling in the second condition. Students might solve this puzzle by guess-and-check; it will help if they realize that the product of 6 and her age 5 years ago must be divisible by 4. An approach that doesn't use symbolic variables is to realize that the 6 years from 5 years ago to next year represent $\frac{1}{4} - \frac{1}{6} = \frac{1}{12}$ of the large number, which must therefore be 72. So her age next year is $\frac{1}{4}$ of 72, meaning that she's currently 17.

Exercise 10 Students may reason that the odd number 47 is the sum of the number of nickels and the number of dimes added to the same sum plus 1. The number of nickels plus the number of dimes must be 23, and the number of pennies plus the number of quarters must be 24. The fact that there is the same number of pennies as quarters implies that there are 12 of both. Subtracting the value of these two coins, \$3.12, reveals that the value of the nickels and dimes together is \$1.90. If they were all nickels, there would be 38 of them; but there are only 23 of these coins, so 15 of them must be dimes.

Exercise 11 This exercise helps assess students' ability to evaluate and make meaning of expressions, not to solve quadratic equations, which appear in Chapter 7.

Exercise 12 If necessary, **[Ask]** "How would you write x^{-1} with a positive exponent?" $\left[\frac{1}{x}\right]$ "Does the negative sign affect the way you apply the properties of exponents?" [no]

Exercise 13 In this exercise, students evaluate expressions and review exponents. Students do not need to know what *exponential function* means at this point. Exponential functions will be studied in depth in Chapter 5. This is a good opportunity to demonstrate how to enter exponents on the calculator using the ^ key.

See page 877 for answers to Exercises 8a, 11, and 14b.

15. Bethany Rogers temps as a sales assistant. She learns that all three sales representatives have important meetings with clients, but she only uncovers these clues.

- Mr. Bell is a sales representative although he is not meeting with Mr. Green.
- Ms. Hunt is the client who will be meeting in the lunch room.
- Mr. Green is the client with a 9:00 A.M. appointment.
- Mr. Mendoza is the sales representative meeting in the conference room.
- Ms. Phoung is a client, but she will not be in the 3:00 P.M. meeting.
- Mrs. Plum is a sales representative, but not the one meeting at 12:00 noon.
- The client with the 9:00 A.M. appointment is not meeting in the convention hall.

Help Bethany figure out which sales representative is meeting with which client, where, and when.

TAKE ANOTHER LOOK

1. You have seen that the multiplication expression $(x + 2)(x + 3)$ can be represented with a rectangle diagram in which the length and width of the rectangle represent the factors and the area represents the product. Find a way to represent the multiplication of three factors, such as $(x + 2)(x + 3)(x + 4)$. Explain how the geometry of the diagram represents the product.

2. Recall Jerry Anderson's problem with the water samples (Exercise 8 in Lesson 0.3). Notice that the table below has six subsections that each compare two of the characteristics. Each statement given in the problem translates into yeses (Y) or noes (N) in the cells of the table. When you have two noes in the same row or column of one subsection, the third cell must be a yes. And when you have a yes in any cell of a subsection, the other four cells in the same row and column must be noes. The table will eventually show you how the characteristics match up. Use this table to solve Jerry's problem.

	Erlenmeyer flask	Round flask	Bottle	Calcium	Sulfur	Iron	Lake	Well	Spring
Left	n	n	y				N	y	n
Center	y	n	N		N		y		N
Right		y	n	N					y
Lake									
Well	N				N				
Spring									
Calcium	n	N	y						
Sulfur	N	y	n						
Iron	Y	n	n						

If students have access to geometry software such as The Geometer's Sketchpad, they can accurately draw volume models with parallel lines and segments in proper ratio, and even create dynamic models that will change size and shape based on parameters or sliders.

2. Tables like these are sometimes called *matrix logic tables.* See *Problem Solving Strategies: Crossing the River with Dogs* for a detailed presentation of this strategy and for other problems.

The sample answers in the chart are marked with capital letters when the relationship comes directly from the clues and lower case when they are deduced from other relationships. Once all bottles are determined no more cells are filled in. See page 19 for a table of answers.

3. The distributive property can be used to multiply any two binomials. For example:

$$\begin{aligned}(x + 2)(x + 3) &= (x + 2)(x) + (x + 2)(3)\\ &= (x \cdot x + 2 \cdot x) + (x \cdot 3 + 2 \cdot 3)\\ &= x^2 + 2x + 3x + 6\end{aligned}$$

Exercise 15 A chart similar to the one used in Take Another Look activity 2 may be used to solve this problem.

Take Another Look

You can use the Take Another Look activities to review and extend the content of the lesson. Students might use any one of the Take Another Look activities to deepen their understanding of something that particularly interests them. Or you might assign some of the activities to individuals or cooperative groups.

1. A classic model for the multiplication of three binomials is a volume model, in which the length, width, and height each represent a factor, and the volume represents the product. The volume model has 8 different sections. This volume model represents $x^3 + 4x^2 + 3x^2 + 2x^2 + 8x + 6x + 12x + 24$.

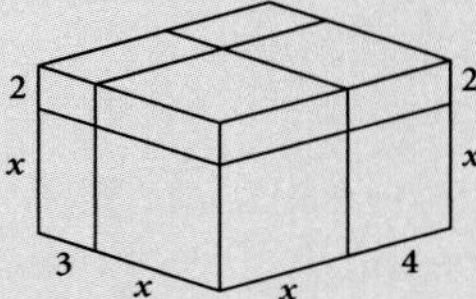

After students have devised a workable diagram (be it a volume model or not), you may want to have them write a few exercises to share with a classmate. The exercises can go both ways: converting an expression into a diagram and converting a diagram into an expression.

As an extension, challenge students to think of a model for four factors. How is the fourth dimension represented?

See page 877 for answers to Exercise 15.

Take Another Look (continued)
Using the distributive property is equivalent to using the rectangle method. The logic, however, is a little different. Instead of multiplying each term of the first factor by each term of the second factor (sometimes called *FOIL—First Outside Inside Last*), you multiply the entire first factor by each term of the second factor, and then use the distributive property again. The distributive property method has advantages over FOIL, because it is not limited by the number of terms in each factor. FOIL is not sufficient to multiply $(x + y + 7)(x + y + z + 3)$, but a student could distribute the first factor over each of the four terms of the second factor. Another advantage of the distributive property is that students practice "chunking," treating a string of symbols as a single entity. You may want to have students write a paragraph generalizing the distributive property method for any two polynomial factors. Students can then exchange papers and critique each other's explanation.

4. A nicely organized summary might characterize the direction and steepness of lines according to slopes less than -1 (steep and decreasing), between -1 and 0 (flatter and decreasing), equal to 0 (horizontal), between 0 and $+1$ (increasing), and greater than $+1$ (steeper and increasing). Students should also recognize that a slope of 1 or -1 creates a line at a 45° angle on a square coordinate grid. Students may remember some key slope values from beginning algebra (0 for horizontal, undefined for vertical, positive for increasing, negative for decreasing).

The Geometer's Sketchpad is a useful tool for this activity. Students can create a square coordinate grid, construct any line or line segment, and measure the slope. If the line or segment is constructed without any anchors, students can simply drag one of the endpoints to rotate the line and see how the slope changes.

3. Find a way to use the distributive property to rewrite $(x + 2)(x + 3)$ without parentheses. Compare and contrast this method to the rectangle diagram method. Look back at Exercise 11 in Lesson 0.1, and explain how you could use the distributive property for each multiplication.

4. Use your graphing calculator or geometry software to explore the slopes of lines. What is the slope of a horizontal line? Of a vertical line? What slopes create a diagonal line at a 45° angle from the x-axis? For which slopes does the line increase from left to right? For which slopes does it decrease? Can you estimate a line's slope simply by looking at a graph? Write a short paper summarizing your findings.

Assessing What You've Learned

WRITE IN YOUR JOURNAL Recording your thoughts about the mathematics you are learning, as well as about areas of confusion or frustration, help point out when you should seek assistance from your teacher and what questions you could ask. Keeping a journal is a good way to collect these informal notes, and if you write in it regularly, you'll track the progress of your understanding throughout the course. Your journal can also remind you of interesting contributions to make in class or prompt questions to ask during a review period.

Here are some questions you might start writing about.

- How has your idea about what algebra is changed since you finished your first-year course in algebra? Do you have particular expectations about what you will learn in advanced algebra? If so, what are they?
- What are your strengths and weaknesses as a problem-solver? Do you consider yourself well organized? Do you have a systematic approach? Give an everyday example of problem solving that reminds you of work you did in this chapter.

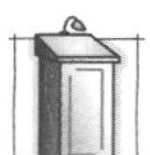

GIVE A PRESENTATION In the working world, most people will need to give a presentation once in a while or contribute thoughts and opinions at meetings. Making a presentation to your class gives you practice in planning, conveying your ideas clearly, and adapting to the needs of an audience.

Choose an investigation or a problem from this chapter, and describe the problem-solving strategies you and your group used to solve it. Here are some suggestions to plan your presentation. (Even planning a presentation requires problem solving!)

- Work with a partner or team. Divide tasks equally. Your role should use skills that are well established, as well as stretch your abilities in new areas.
- Discuss the topic thoroughly. Connect the work you did on the problem with the objectives of the chapter.
- Outline your talk, and decide what details to mention for each point and what charts, graphs, or pictures would clarify the presentation.
- Speak clearly and loudly. Reveal your interest in the topic you chose by making eye contact with listeners.

ASSESSING

There are tests for this chapter, but you may decide not to give a test or to use review Exercises 1–15 as a pretest that will not affect students' grades. Another good written assessment option is to use one or two constructive assessment items.

FACILITATING SELF-ASSESSMENT

It is often helpful to understand students' conceptions of algebra or their views of themselves as problem solvers. Read and comment on some of the writing students do so that they see you are interested in their thinking and that you think their writing is important.

CHAPTER

1

Patterns and Recursion

Overview

Recursive formulas introduced in this chapter will be used throughout *Discovering Advanced Algebra.* Recursive formulas for arithmetic sequences are emphasized in **Lesson 1.1. Lesson 1.2** explores geometric sequences that model growth and decay. **Lesson 1.3** introduces shifted geometric sequences and talks about long-run values that approach a limit. Sequences can be represented in tables, as recursive formulas, and as graphs; graphs are the emphasis of **Lesson 1.4.** Concepts that students have learned in geometry are applied to the golden ratio in the first **exploration,** to interest in **Lesson 1.5,** and to population growth and marketing a product in the **exploration** that ends the chapter.

The Mathematics

Sequences

A sequence of numbers is a list, an ordering. The order may follow some rule, but it may also be random. In mathematics a series is a summation of terms, so avoid the common use of the word *series* in place of *sequence.*

Traditionally, mathematics courses have emphasized finding an expression into which you can substitute any number n to get the nth term of the sequence. For example, the nth term of the sequence of nonnegative even numbers is given by $2n$. This is called a *closed form* expression. Generating the sequence of nonnegative even numbers by repeatedly substituting the counting numbers for the variable in the expression $2n$ is an iterative approach.

A different approach, called *recursive,* emphasizes how each term is generated from the previous term and thus helps students understand growth. A recursive formula for the sequence of nonnegative even numbers consists of two equations: $u_0 = 0$ and $u_n = u_{n-1} + 2$ where $n \geq 1$. The sequence is generated recursively by starting with 0 and repeatedly adding 2 to the previous result.

Any sequence generated recursively by adding a constant in this manner is an arithmetic sequence (pronounced "ar-ith-'me-tik" when used as an adjective). In general, $u_n = u_{n-1} + b$ where b is a constant specifying the growth, or the difference between each pair of consecutive terms of the sequence.

Sequences in which consecutive terms have the same ratio rather than the same difference are called *geometric sequences.* These are commonly used to model decay and growth. In general, $u_n = u_{n-1}r$, for the common ratio r. If $-1 < r < 1$, the terms of the geometric sequence get closer and closer to 0; we say 0 is the limit of such a sequence. Often r is written as $1 + p$ or $1 - p$ to make clear whether the sequence is increasing or decreasing; p is the growth rate.

Both arithmetic and geometric sequences are special cases of the shifted geometric sequence $u_n = u_{n-1}r + b$. As with geometric sequences, shifted geometric sequences in which $-1 < r < 1$ converge to a limit; the limit won't be 0, however, unless b is 0.

Calculator roundoff error can indicate that a sequence reaches its limit when in fact it doesn't. The shifted geometric sequence reaches its limit only if $r = 1$ and $b = 0$, that is, when the terms are all equal.

Models

A mathematical model of a situation is a mathematical object—such as a diagram, table, equation, or sequence—representing the situation. If the model is good, a problem about the real-life situation can be translated into a problem about the model whose solution translates back into a good solution to the original problem.

Even a good mathematical model has limitations. For example, a sequence modeling the temperature of a cooling cup of coffee approaches a limit it never reaches. But real coffee does stabilize in temperature, because it consists of discrete molecules.

Population Models

Shifted geometric sequences begin to approximate population growth, but populations don't always grow in environments with unlimited resources. Generally, any environment will support a population only up to some maximum carrying capacity. This logistic growth is modeled by a recursive formula in which the growth rate p is modified: $u_n = u_{n-1}\left(1 + p\left(1 - \frac{u_{n-1}}{L}\right)\right)$ where L is the carrying capacity. When u_{n-1} is very small, p is multiplied by a number very close to 1, so $r = 1 + p$ isn't much different from exponential growth. When u_{n-1} is very close to L, p is multiplied by a number close to 0, so r is close to 1 and the function is almost constant.

Using This Chapter

Chapter 1 is important for establishing a major theme for this course because patterns and recursion will be used throughout the course. Even though sequences are an optional topic in many books, this chapter should not be skipped. If you find that you do not have time for all the investigations, you can skip the investigation in Lesson 1.4 and perhaps assign it for homework. The exercises provide more than enough practice for the concepts in this chapter. You do not need to assign every problem to ensure understanding. The exploration on logistic growth is an excellent extension of recursion. It is not critical to the advanced algebra curriculum of this book, but students need to realize that most growth that starts off as exponential is actually logistic.

Resources

Discovering Advanced Algebra Resources

Teaching and Worksheet Masters
- Lesson 1.2
- Exploration: Recursion in Geometry
- Exploration: Refining the Growth Model

Calculator Notes 1A–1M

Sketchpad Demonstrations
- Lesson 1.4
- Exploration: Recursion in Geometry

Assessment Resources A and B
- Quiz 1 (Lessons 1.1, 1.2)
- Quiz 2 (Lessons 1.3–1.5)
- Chapter 1 Test
- Chapter 1 Constructive Assessment Options

More Practice Your Skills for Chapter 1

Condensed Lessons for Chapter 1

Other Resources

"How Good Can We Get?" by Jonas Mureika.

"Drugs and Pollution in the Algebra Class" by James Sandefur.

For complete references to these and other resources see www.keypress.com/DAA.

Materials

- basketball, soccer ball, or handball
- motion sensor or metersticks
- bowls
- water
- food coloring
- measuring cups
- waste buckets
- graph paper
- geometry software

Pacing Guide

	day 1	day 2	day 3	day 4	day 5	day 6	day 7	day 8	day 9	
standard	1.1	1.2	quiz, 1.3	1.4	exploration	1.5	quiz, review	review	assessment	
enriched	1.1	1.2	quiz, 1.3	1.4	exploration	1.5	quiz, exploration	review, TAL	assessment	
block	1.1, 1.2	1.2, quiz, 1.3	1.4, exploration	exploration, 1.5	quiz, exploration	review, TAL	assessment			

CHAPTER

1

Patterns and Recursion

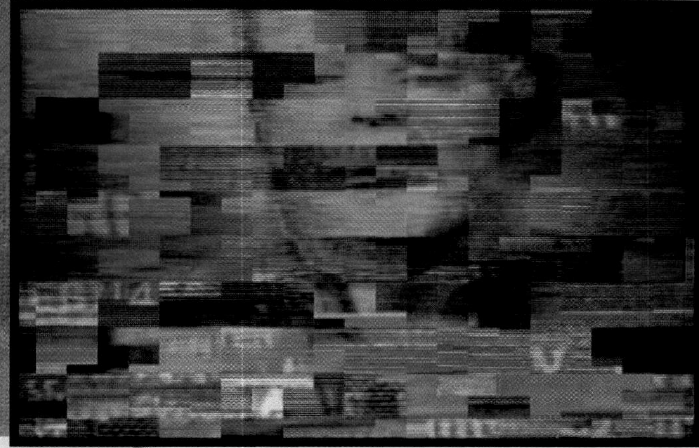

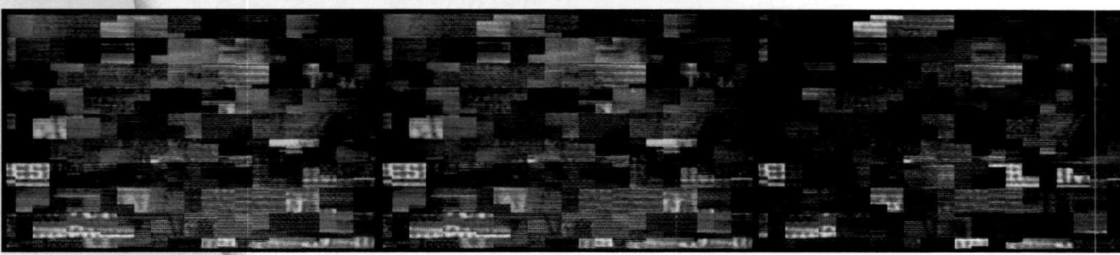

To create the video piece *Residual Light,* experimental video artist Anthony Discenza (American, b 1967) recorded 3 hours of commercial television by filming the TV screen while continuously channel surfing. This 3-hour sample was then compressed in stages by recording and re-recording the material on analog and digital tape while controlling the speed of the playback. Through this recursive process, the original 3 hours was gradually reduced to just 3 minutes. This 3-minute sequence was then slowed back down, resulting in a 20-minute loop.

OBJECTIVES

In this chapter you will

- Recognize and visualize mathematical patterns called sequences
- Write recursive definitions for sequences
- Display sequences with graphs
- Investigate what happens to sequences in the long run

CHAPTER 1 OBJECTIVES

- Use recursive formulas for generating arithmetic, geometric, and shifted geometric sequences
- Recognize arithmetic and geometric sequences from their graphs
- Use geometric sequences to model growth and decay
- Explore long-run values of geometric and shifted geometric sequences
- Use graphs to check whether a recursive formula is a good model for data
- See an example of recursion in geometry
- Use shifted geometric sequences to model loans and investments
- Use a logistic function to model growth that has a maximum capacity

Video artist Anthony Discenza feels that people are constantly bombarded by mediated images in their everyday lives. These images fly by people so quickly and steadily that ultimately the images become invisible. In his artwork, he manipulates pieces of video, often taped off of television, to depict an exaggerated representation of how these fabricated images look to people in real life.

[Ask] "What do you see in these images? Is there anything recognizable in these frames of the video?" [It is very difficult to make out any specific objects. It is possible to see some characteristics of a face in the top image, but the images get more and more blurred, and even the colors start to fade to black.] "What do you think these images say about recursion?" [They show how a recursive process results in the original objects being distorted as they repeatedly undergo an expansion that becomes too much for our eyes and minds to make sense of.]

LESSON

1.1

PLANNING

LESSON OUTLINE

One day:

15 min Examples

15 min Investigation

15 min Exercises

MATERIALS

- Calculator Notes 1A–1C

TEACHING

This lesson studies how arithmetic and geometric sequences can be defined recursively.

One Step

Read, or have students read, this problem, taken from the investigation: "Heater King, Inc., has purchased the parts to make 2000 water heaters. Each day, the workers assemble 50 water heaters from the available parts. The company has agreed to supply MegaDepot with 40 water heaters per day and Smalle Shoppe with 10 water heaters per day. MegaDepot currently has 470 water heaters in stock, and Smalle Shoppe has none. The assembly-line machinery malfunctions the first day that MegaDepot has a number of water heaters greater than twice the number of unmade water heaters. How many water heaters does Smalle Shoppe have the day assembly stops?" Encourage a variety of approaches, especially making tables by hand or using a calculator or spreadsheet. Students may want to draw graphs or work with formulas. During Sharing, ask what this situation has in common with those in the examples; bring out the idea of sequences, especially of arithmetic versus geometric sequences.

LESSON 1.1

Recursively Defined Sequences

For every pattern that appears, a mathematician feels he ought to know why it appears.

W. W. SAWYER

Look around! You are surrounded by patterns and influenced by how you perceive them. You have learned to recognize visual patterns in floor tiles, window panes, tree leaves, and flower petals. In every discipline, people discover, observe, re-create, explain, generalize, and use patterns. Artists and architects use patterns that are attractive or practical. Scientists and manufacturing engineers follow patterns and predictable processes that ensure quality, accuracy, and uniformity. Mathematicians frequently encounter patterns in numbers and shapes.

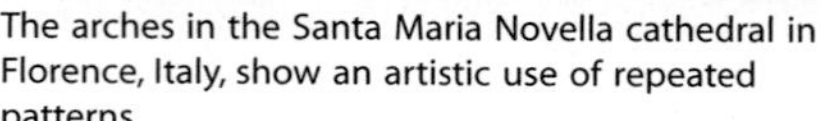

The arches in the Santa Maria Novella cathedral in Florence, Italy, show an artistic use of repeated patterns.

Scientists use patterns and repetition to conduct experiments, gather data, and analyze results.

You can discover and explain many mathematical patterns by thinking about recursion. **Recursion** is a process in which each step of a pattern is dependent on the step or steps that come before it. It is often easy to define a pattern recursively, and a recursive definition reveals a lot about the properties of the pattern.

EXAMPLE A

A square table seats 4 people. Two square tables pushed together seat 6 people. Three tables pushed together seat 8 people. How many people can sit at 10 tables arranged in a straight line? How many tables are needed to seat 32 people? Write a recursive definition to find the number of people who can sit at any linear arrangement of square tables.

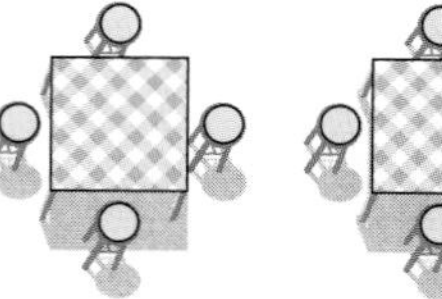

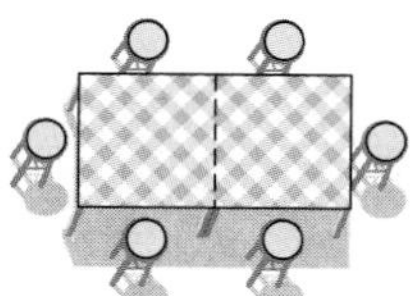

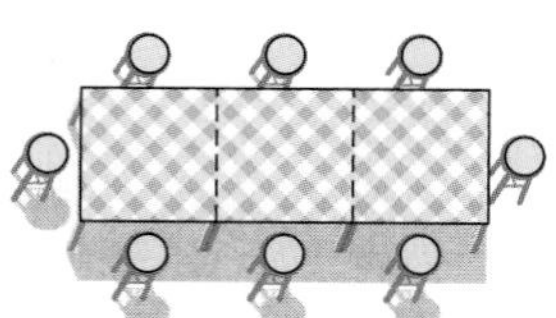

LESSON OBJECTIVES

- Introduce recursive formulas for sequences
- Explore arithmetic sequences
- Practice using recursive notation
- Define and use geometric sequences
- Use recursively defined sequences to model applications

NCTM STANDARDS

CONTENT		PROCESS	
✓	Number	✓	Problem Solving
✓	Algebra	✓	Reasoning
✓	Geometry	✓	Communication
	Measurement	✓	Connections
	Data/Probability	✓	Representation

▶ ***Solution***

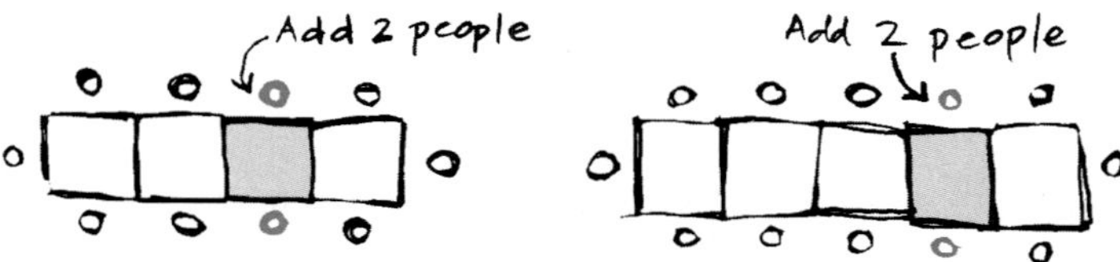

If you sketch the arrangements of four tables and five tables, you notice that when you add another table, you seat two more people than in the previous arrangement. You can put this information into a table, and that reveals a clear pattern. You can continue the pattern to find that 10 tables seat 22 people.

Tables	1	2	3	4	5	6	7	8	9	10
People	4	6	8	10	12	14	16	18	20	22

This graph shows the same information by plotting the points (1, 4), (2, 6), (3, 8), and so on. The graph also reveals a clear pattern. You can extend the graph to find that 15 tables are needed for 32 people.

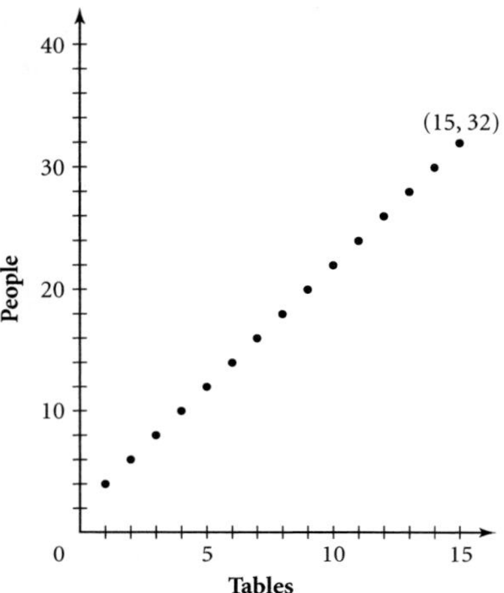

You can use recursion—repeatedly adding 2 to the previous number of people—to find more numbers in the pattern or more points on the graph. A recursive definition tells the starting value and the mathematical operations that are required to find each subsequent value. For this example you could write

number of people at 1 table = 4

number of people at n tables = number of people at $(n - 1)$ tables + 2

This definition summarizes how to use recursion to find the number of people who can sit at any linear arrangement of tables. For example, to find how many people can sit at 10 tables, you take the number of people at 9 tables and add 2, or $20 + 2 = 22$.

A **sequence** is an ordered list of numbers. The table and graph in Example A represent the sequence

4, 6, 8, 10, 12, . . .

Each number in the sequence is called a **term.** The first term, u_1 (pronounced "u sub one"), is 4. The second term, u_2, is 6, and so on.

The nth term, u_n, is called the **general term** of the sequence. A **recursive formula,** the formula that defines a sequence, must specify one (or more) starting terms and a **recursive rule** that defines the nth term in relation to a previous term (or terms).

▶ ***EXAMPLE A***

This example introduces (or reviews) the notion of recursion, in the context of a sequence of numbers.

[Alert] Students might be confused by the word *table* being used for both the table to sit at and the data table.

[Ask] "Why aren't the data points connected with a line?" [You can have only whole numbers of tables.]

[Ask] "What's behind the pattern?" Mathematics isn't about only seeing patterns, but also explaining them. Elicit the idea that we can imagine, as a new table is inserted, two new people can sit down, one on each side.

A recursive formula states two things: the rule and the starting value. You might want to show how the sequence generated by the rule in this example changes according to the starting numbers.

If the symbolic formula confuses students, suggest that they use the words *next* in place of u_n and *previous* in place of u_{n-1}.

[Alert] Students might think that in an ordered list the terms are in increasing or decreasing order. Actually, a sequence might not be generated by any rule.

▶ EXAMPLE B

[Ask] "Is there a difference between u_{n-1} and $u_n - 1$?" [Yes; a term is not necessarily 1 less than the previous term.]

As before, students may be more comfortable with the words *next* and *previous* than with the symbols u_n and u_{n-1}. Another way to counter notation difficulties is to use home-screen recursion on graphing calculators. See Calculator Note 1B. If graphing calculators are new to your students, also give them copies of Calculator Notes 1A and 1C.

You generate the sequence 4, 6, 8, 10, 12, . . . with this recursive formula:

$$u_1 = 4$$
$$u_n = u_{n-1} + 2 \quad \text{where } n \geq 2$$

Because the starting value is $u_1 = 4$, the recursive rule $u_n = u_{n-1} + 2$ is first used to find u_2. This is clarified by saying that n must be greater than or equal to 2 to use the recursive rule.

This means *the first term is 4* and *each subsequent term is equal to the previous term plus 2.* Notice that each term, u_n, is defined in relation to the previous term, u_{n-1}. For example, the 10th term relies on the 9th term, or $u_{10} = u_9 + 2$.

EXAMPLE B

A concert hall has 59 seats in Row 1, 63 seats in Row 2, 67 seats in Row 3, and so on. The concert hall has 35 rows of seats. Write a recursive formula to find the number of seats in each row. How many seats are in Row 4? Which row has 95 seats?

An opera house in Sumter, South Carolina.

▶ Solution

First, it helps to organize the information in a table.

Row	1	2	3	4	. . .
Seats	59	63	67		. . .

Every recursive formula requires a starting term. Here the starting term is 59, the number of seats in Row 1. That is, $u_1 = 59$.

This sequence also appears to have a common difference between successive terms: 63 is 4 more than 59, and 67 is 4 more than 63. Use this information to write the recursive rule for the nth term, $u_n = u_{n-1} + 4$.

Therefore, this recursive formula generates the sequence representing the number of seats in each row:

$$u_1 = 59$$
$$u_n = u_{n-1} + 4 \quad \text{where } n \geq 2$$

You can use this recursive formula to calculate how many seats are in each row. [▶ See **Calculator Note 1B** to learn how to do recursion on your calculator. ◀]

$u_1 = 59$ — The starting term is 59.

$u_2 = u_1 + 4 = 59 + 4 = 63$ — Substitute 59 for u_1.

$u_3 = u_2 + 4 = 63 + 4 = 67$ — Substitute 63 for u_2.

$u_4 = u_3 + 4 = 67 + 4 = 71$ — Continue using recursion.

$\vdots$

Because $u_4 = 71$, there are 71 seats in Row 4. If you continue the recursion process, you will find that $u_{10} = 95$, or that Row 10 has 95 seats.

In Example B, the terms of the sequence are related by a **common difference.** This type of sequence is called an **arithmetic sequence.**

Arithmetic Sequence

An **arithmetic sequence** is a sequence in which each term is equal to the previous term plus a constant. This constant is called the **common difference.** If d is the common difference, the recursive rule for the sequence has the form

$$u_n = u_{n-1} + d$$

The key to identifying an arithmetic sequence is recognizing the common difference. If you are given a few terms and need to write a recursive formula, first try subtracting consecutive terms. If $u_n - u_{n-1}$ is constant for each pair of terms, then you know your recursive rule must be a rule for an arithmetic sequence.

Investigation
Monitoring Inventory

Heater King, Inc., has purchased the parts to make 2000 water heaters. Each day, the workers assemble 50 water heaters from the available parts. The company has agreed to supply MegaDepot with 40 water heaters per day and Smalle Shoppe with 10 water heaters per day. MegaDepot currently has 470 water heaters in stock, and Smalle Shoppe has none. The management team at Heater King, Inc., needs a way to monitor inventory and demand.

Step 1 As a group, model what happens to the number of unmade water heaters, the inventory at MegaDepot, and the inventory at Smalle Shoppe. Keep track of your daily results in a table like this one. [▶ See **Calculator Note 1B** for different ways to do recursion on your calculator. ◀]

Day	Unmade water heaters	MegaDepot	Smalle Shoppe
1	2000	470	0
2	1950	510	10

Step 1

Day	Unmade water heaters	MegaDepot	Smalle Shoppe
3	1900	550	20
...	...	...	...
n	$u_{n-1} - 50$	$v_{n-1} + 40$	$w_{n-1} + 10$

The three sequences have terms called u_n, v_n, and w_n.

Arithmetic Sequence

[Language] Even though it's spelled the same as the noun *arithmetic,* the adjective is pronounced "ar-ith-'me-tik."

Guiding the Investigation

Students do not need any prior knowledge of recursion to work on this investigation. If they didn't work on Chapter 0, you may need to talk about the fundamentals of group work.

Step 1 You may want to specify how many days students are to track.

Step 2 Encourage a variety of approaches to these problems. For example, students might continue the table, use recursion, or draw a graph.

SHARING IDEAS

Choose a few students to present a variety of approaches to Step 2 of the investigation.

[Ask] "What are the differences between the terms *previous* and u_{n-1} (and, if students worked on calculators, the term *Ans*)?" [They all refer to the same thing.]

[Ask] "How are arithmetic and geometric sequences alike and different?" [They're both sequences; arithmetic sequences are generated by adding, and geometric sequences by multiplying.]

Students may recognize the natural connection between arithmetic sequences and linear functions. The connection between recursive and explicit formulas will be addressed in Chapter 3. They may also see a connection between geometric sequences and exponential functions. If students are impatient with the recursive approach, mention that it is more useful than closed-form formulas for studying growth. You might also mention that there are many levels of understanding, and you're trying to deepen their understanding.

Sharing Ideas (continued)

[Ask] "A difference is the result of subtracting. Why is a common difference being added here?" Elicit the idea that the difference results from subtracting each term from the next term of the sequence. If that difference is added back onto a term, the result is the next term.

[Ask] "Is the same thing going on with multiplying by a common ratio, even though *ratio* refers to division?" [Yes; it's the ratio of a term to the previous term.]

[Ask] "The arithmetic sequence 5, 2, −1, −4, and so on is decreasing. We seem to be subtracting rather than adding. What's happening?" [We're adding a negative common difference.]

[Ask] "What generalizations can you make for geometric sequences?" [If the common ratio is between 0 and 1, the sequence is decreasing. If the common ratio is negative, the terms alternate between positive and negative.]

▶ *EXAMPLE C*

[Language] This triangle is sometimes called the *Sierpiński gasket.* If extended for infinitely many steps, it's an example of a fractal, having fractional dimension.

The initial figure is called Stage 0 because no change has occurred. Thus it is appropriate to refer to 1 as the zero term in the sequence listing the number of triangles at each stage.

[Language] *Common ratio* should be defined specifically here. Emphasize that it is the number, which can be a fraction, that each term is multiplied by to get the next.

[Ask] "What is the common ratio for the sequence in Example C?" [3] "What would be the common ratio for the sequence if the terms in the series were reversed?" $\left[\frac{1}{3}\right]$

Step 2a On Day 18 MegaDepot has 1150 water heaters and there are 1150 unmade water heaters.

Step 2b On Day 27 MegaDepot has 1510 water heaters, there are 700 unmade, and Smalle Shoppe has 260. (On Day 26 MegaDepot had 1470 and there were 750 unmade.)

Step 3 Answers will vary.

Step 2 Use your table from Step 1 to answer these questions:

a. How many days will it be until MegaDepot has an equal number or a greater number of water heaters than the number of water heaters left unmade?

b. The assembly-line machinery malfunctions the first day that MegaDepot has a number of water heaters greater than twice the number of unmade water heaters. How many water heaters does Smalle Shoppe have on the day that assembly stops?

Step 3 Write a short summary of how you modeled inventory and how you found the answers to the questions in Step 2. Compare your methods to the methods of other groups.

Career CONNECTION

Economics is the study of how goods and services are produced, distributed, and consumed. Economists in corporations, universities, and government agencies are concerned with the best way to meet human needs with limited resources. Professional economists use mathematics to study and model factors such as supply of resources, manufacturing costs, and selling price.

The sequences in Example A, Example B, and the investigation are arithmetic sequences. Example C introduces a different kind of sequence that is still defined recursively.

EXAMPLE C

The geometric pattern below is created recursively. If you continue the pattern endlessly, you create a **fractal** called the Sierpiński triangle. How many red triangles are there at Stage 20?

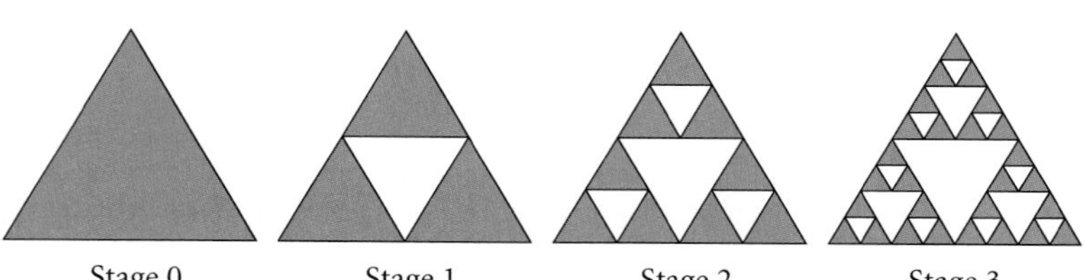

This stamp, part of Poland's 1982 "Mathematicians" series, portrays Waclaw Sierpiński.

Mathematics CONNECTION

The Sierpiński triangle is named after the Polish mathematician Waclaw Sierpiński (1882–1969). He was most interested in number theory, set theory, and topology, three branches of mathematics that study the relations and properties of sets of numbers or points. Sierpiński was highly involved in the development of mathematics in Poland between World War I and World War II. He published 724 papers and 50 books in his lifetime. He introduced his famous triangle pattern in a 1915 paper.

Sierpiński Triangle

Many different sequences can be studied based on the Sierpiński triangle. **[Ask]** "If the area of Stage 0 is 1 unit, what sequence represents the areas of the triangles at successive stages?" $\left[1, \frac{3}{4}, \frac{9}{16}, \frac{27}{64}, \ldots\right]$ "What is the recursive formula for the sequence of areas?" $\left[u_0 = 1, u_n = \frac{3}{4}u_{n-1} \text{ where } n \geq 1\right]$ "If the length of each side in the Stage 0 figure is 1, what sequence represents the perimeter (total distance around all red triangles at a particular stage)?" $\left[3, 4\frac{1}{2}, 6\frac{3}{4}, 10\frac{1}{8}, \ldots\right]$ "What is the recursive formula for the sequence of perimeters?" $\left[u_0 = 3, u_n = 1.5u_{n-1} \text{ where } n \geq 1\right]$

▸ Solution

Count the number of red triangles at each stage and write a sequence.

1, 3, 9, 27, . . .

The starting term, 1, represents the number of triangles at Stage 0. You can define the starting term as a zero term, or u_0. In this case, $u_0 = 1$.

Starting with the second term, each term of the sequence multiplies the previous term by 3, so that 3 is 3 times 1, 9 is 3 times 3, and 27 is 3 times 9. Use this information to write the recursive rule and complete your recursive formula.

$u_0 = 1$

$u_n = 3 \cdot u_{n-1}$ where $n \geq 1$

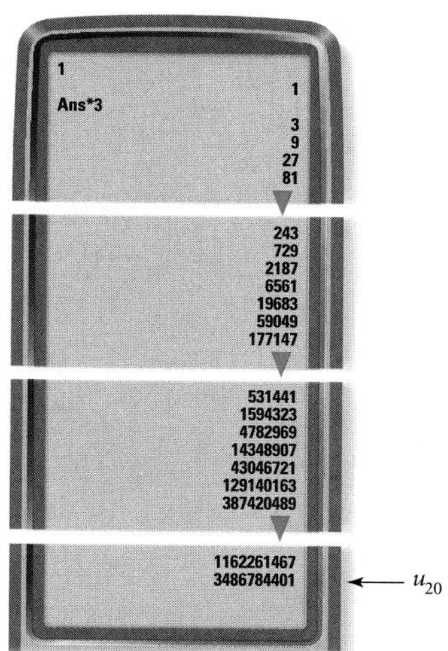

Using the recursive rule 20 times, you find that $u_{20} = 3{,}486{,}784{,}401$. There are over 3 billion triangles at Stage 20!

In Example C, consecutive terms of the sequence are related by a **common ratio.** This type of sequence is called a **geometric sequence.**

Geometric Sequence

A **geometric sequence** is a sequence in which each term is equal to the previous term multiplied by a constant. This constant is called the **common ratio.** If r is the common ratio, the recursive rule for the sequence has the form

$u_n = r \cdot u_{n-1}$

You identify a geometric sequence by dividing consecutive terms. If $\frac{u_n}{u_{n-1}}$ is constant for each pair of terms, then you know the sequence is geometric.

Arithmetic and geometric sequences are the most basic sequences because their recursive rules use only one operation: addition in the case of arithmetic sequences, and multiplication in the case of geometric sequences. Recognizing these basic operations will help you easily identify sequences and write recursive formulas.

Guitar feedback is a real-world example of recursion. When the amplifier is turned up loud enough, the sound is picked up by the guitar and amplified again and again, creating a feedback loop. Jimi Hendrix (1942–1970), a pioneer in the use of feedback and distortion in rock music, remains one of the most legendary guitar players of the 1960s.

Assessing Progress

As students work and present, you can assess their ability to collect data systematically, to work together in groups, and to write about their approach. You can also see how well they understand "greater number" and "twice the number of" and check their skill at arithmetic calculations.

Closing the Lesson

Reiterate the main points of the lesson: Every **arithmetic sequence** is defined **recursively** by one equation giving the starting value and another showing how a common difference is added to each term to get the next. A **geometric sequence** is defined the same way, except it is defined by multiplication by a common ratio instead of addition of a common difference.

Guitar Feedback

Some students will recognize feedback as the loud whine a microphone sometimes makes. Explain that this occurs when the output of the speakers becomes the input to the microphone. The feedback is the result of the system being unable to handle this recursive process.

Additional Examples

Copy these tables on the board. Students should silently determine the missing entries and take turns entering them into the class chart.

1	2	3	4	. . .	10	u_n
8	2	−4	−10	. . .		

$[u_{10} = -46;\ u_n = u_{n-1} - 6]$

0	1	2	3	. . .	10	u_n
−3	−1	$-\frac{1}{3}$		. . .		

$\left[u_{10} = \frac{1}{19683};\ u_n = \frac{1}{3}u_{n-1}\right]$

1	2	3	4	. . .	10	u_n
12	18	27		. . .		

$\left[u_{10} = \frac{59049}{128};\ u_n = \frac{3}{2}u_{n-1}\right]$

BUILDING UNDERSTANDING

The exercises emphasize arithmetic sequences. Geometric sequences will receive more attention in later lessons.

ASSIGNING HOMEWORK

Essential	1–6
Performance assessment	7–12
Journal	12
Group	8, 10
Review	13–17

Helping with the Exercises

Exercises 4, 5 Students may use either recursive sequences or home-screen recursion on their calculators to find the terms of these sequences.

5a. $u_1 = 2$ and $u_n = u_{n-1} + 4$ where $n \geq 2$; $u_{15} = 58$

5b. $u_1 = 10$ and $u_n = u_{n-1} - 5$ where $n \geq 2$; $u_{12} = -45$

5c. $u_1 = 0.4$ and $u_n = 0.1 \cdot u_{n-1}$ where $n \geq 2$; $u_{10} = 0.0000000004$

5d. $u_1 = -2$ and $u_n = u_{n-1} - 6$ where $n \geq 2$; $u_{30} = -176$

5e. $u_1 = 1.56$ and $u_n = u_{n-1} + 3.29$ where $n \geq 2$; $u_{14} = 44.33$

5f. $u_1 = -6.24$ and $u_n = u_{n-1} + 2.21$ where $n \geq 2$; $u_{20} = 35.75$

Exercise 6 Students might have difficulty making the transition from single numbers to ordered pairs (and points in a two-dimensional space). To help, **[Ask]** "What is the first coordinate in each pair?" [1, 2, 3, . . . ; the term numbers] "The second coordinate?" [4, 9, 14, . . . ; the terms of the sequence]

EXERCISES

You will need

Geometry software for Exercise 13

Practice Your Skills

1. Write the first 4 terms of each sequence.

a. $u_1 = 20$
$u_n = u_{n-1} + 6$ where $n \geq 2$ 20, 26, 32, 38

b. $u_1 = 47$
$u_n = u_{n-1} - 3$ where $n \geq 2$ 47, 44, 41, 38

c. $u_0 = 32$
$u_n = 1.5 \cdot u_{n-1}$ where $n \geq 1$ 32, 48, 72, 108

d. $u_1 = -18$
$u_n = u_{n-1} + 4.3$ where $n \geq 2$ −18, −13.7, −9.4, −5.1

2. Identify each sequence in Exercise 1 as arithmetic or geometric. State the common difference or the common ratio for each.

2a. arithmetic; $d = 6$
2b. arithmetic; $d = -3$
2c. geometric; $r = 1.5$
2d. arithmetic; $d = 4.3$

3. Write a recursive formula and use it to find the missing table values.

n	1	2	3	4	5	. . .	9
u_n	40	36.55	33.1	29.65	26.2	. . .	12.4

$u_1 = 40$ and $u_n = u_{n-1} - 3.45$ where $n \geq 2$

4. Write a recursive formula to generate an arithmetic sequence with a first term 6 and a common difference 3.2. Find the 10th term. $u_1 = 6$ and $u_n = u_{n-1} + 3.2$ where $n \geq 2$; $u_{10} = 34.8$

5. Write a recursive formula to generate each sequence. Then find the indicated term.

a. 2, 6, 10, 14, . . . Find the 15th term.
b. 10, 5, 0, −5, . . . Find the 12th term.
c. 0.4, 0.04, 0.004, 0.0004, . . . Find the 10th term.
d. −2, −8, −14, −20, −26, . . . Find the 30th term.
e. 1.56, 4.85, 8.14, 11.43, . . . Find the 14th term.
f. −6.24, −4.03, −1.82, 0.39, . . . Find the 20th term.

History CONNECTION

Hungarian mathematician Rózsa Péter (1905–1977) was the first person to propose the study of recursion in its own right. In an interview she described recursion in this way:

> The Latin technical term "recursion" refers to a certain kind of *stepping backwards* in the sequence of natural numbers, which necessarily ends after a finite number of steps. With the use of such recursions the values of even the most complicated functions used in number theory can be calculated in a finite number of steps.

In her book *Recursive Functions in Computer Theory,* Péter describes the important connections between recursion and computer languages.

Rózsa Péter

6. Write a recursive formula for the sequence graphed at right. Find the 46th term.
$u_1 = 4$ and $u_n = u_{n-1} + 5$ where $n \geq 2$; $u_{46} = 229$

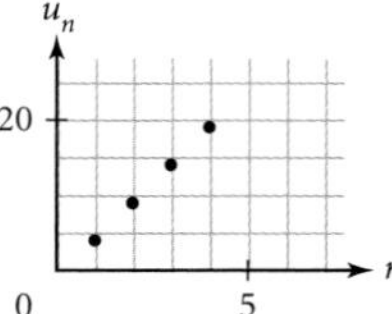

MAKING THE CONNECTION

Péter's interest in communicating mathematics to nonmathematicians led her to write *Playing with Infinity: Mathematical Explorations and Excursions.* Another of her books, *Recursive Functions in Computer Theory,* describes the connections between recursion and computer language. She saw recursion as stepping backward to the beginning of a sequence rather than as moving forward from the first term.

Reason and Apply

7. Write a recursive formula that you can use to find the number of segments, u_n, for Figure n of this geometric pattern. Use your formula to complete the table. $u_1 = 4$ and $u_n = u_{n-1} + 6$ where $n \geq 2$

Figure 1 Figure 2 Figure 3 Figure 4

Figure	1	2	3	4	5	. . .	12	. . .	32
Segments	4	10	16	22	28	. . .	70	. . .	190

8. A 50-gallon (gal) bathtub contains 20 gal of water and is filling at a rate of 2.4 gal/min. You check the tub every minute on the minute.

a. Suppose that the drain is closed. When will you discover that the water is flowing over the top? 13 min

b. Now suppose that the bathtub contains 20 gal of water and is filling at a rate of 2.4 gal/min, but the drain is open and water drains at a rate of 3.1 gal/min. When will you discover that the tub is empty? 29 min

c. Write a recursive formula that you can use to find the water level at any minute due to both the rate of filling and the rate of draining. $u_0 = 20$ and $u_n = u_{n-1} - 0.7$ where $n \geq 1$

9. A car leaves town heading west at 57 km/h.

a. How far will the car travel in 7 h? 399 km

b. A second car leaves town 2 h after the first car, but it is traveling at 72 km/h. To the nearest hour, when will the second car pass the first? 10 hours after the first car starts, or 8 hours after the second car starts

10. **APPLICATION** Inspector 47 at the Zap battery plant keeps a record of which AA batteries she finds defective. Although the battery numbers at right do not make an exact sequence, she estimates an arithmetic sequence.

a. Write a recursive formula for an arithmetic sequence that estimates which batteries are defective. Explain your reasoning.

b. Predict the numbers of the next five defective batteries.

c. How many batteries in 100,000 will be defective?

Exercise 9 This exercise does not require that students use recursion. For example, they might use the concept of closing speed. As needed, **[Ask]** "How can you model this problem recursively?"

10a. The differences are 245, 273, 225, 229, 283, 211, and 289. The average is about 250, so a recursive formula is $u_1 = 250$ and $u_n = u_{n-1} + 250$ where $n \geq 2$.

10b. $u_9 = 2250$, $u_{10} = 2500$, $u_{11} = 2750$, $u_{12} = 3000$, $u_{13} = 3250$

10c. $u_{400} = 100000$. There will be approximately 400 defective batteries in 100,000.

Exercise 11 Students might use the recursive rule $u_n = u_{n-1} - 0.25u_{n-1}$ or, equivalently, $u_n = 0.75u_{n-1}$. This exercise foreshadows Lesson 1.2, Example A.

12a. 3.2; $\frac{51-35}{5} = 3.2$

12b. 25.4, 28.6, 31.8, . . . , 38.2, 41.4, 44.6, 47.8, . . . , 54.2

13. Sample answer: Construct two lines that intersect, $\overleftrightarrow{AB}$ and $\overleftrightarrow{BC}$. On one line, $\overleftrightarrow{AB}$, use congruent circles to mark off ten equally spaced points. Construct lines perpendicular to $\overleftrightarrow{AB}$ through each point. The segments between $\overleftrightarrow{AB}$ and $\overleftrightarrow{BC}$ represent an arithmetic sequence.

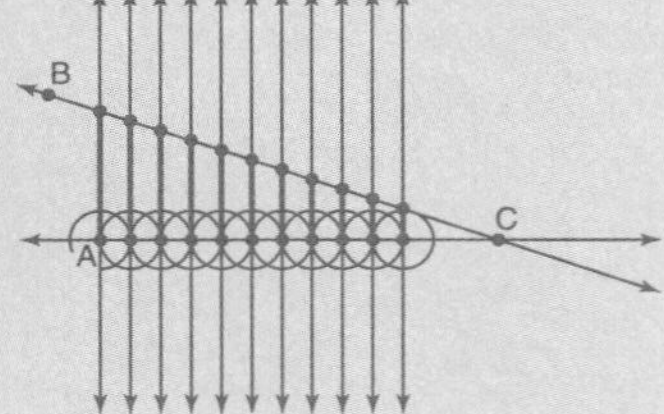

Exercise 14 **[Language]** A motion sensor is a device used to measure the distance of an object from the device. If students are confused about this concept, the problem can be solved using the word *stool* in place of *motion sensor.*

11. The week of February 14, the owner of Nickel's Appliances stocks hundreds of red, heart-shaped vacuum cleaners. The next week, he still has hundreds of red, heart-shaped vacuum cleaners. He tells the manager, "Discount the price 25 percent each week until they are gone."

a. On February 14, the vacuums are priced at $80. What is the price of a vacuum during the second week? $60

b. What is the price during the fourth week? $33.75

c. When will the vacuum sell for less than $10? during the ninth week

12. Taoufik picks up his homework paper from the puddle it has fallen in. Sadly he reads the first problem and finds that the arithmetic sequence is a blur except for two terms.

a. What is the common difference? How did you find it?

b. What are the missing terms?

c. What is the answer to Taoufik's homework problem? 172.6

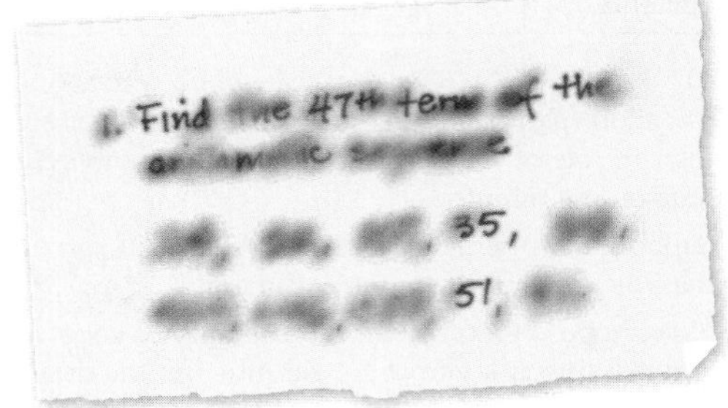

13. *Technology* Use geometry software to construct 10 segments whose lengths represent the first 10 terms of a sequence. Describe how you constructed the segments, and explain whether your sequence is arithmetic or geometric.

Review

14. Ayaunna starts 2.0 m from a motion sensor. She walks away from the sensor at a rate of 1.0 m/s for 3.0 s and then walks toward the sensor at a rate of 0.5 m/s for 4.0 s.

a. Create a table of values for Ayaunna's distance from the motion sensor at 1-second intervals.

b. Sketch a time-distance graph of Ayaunna's walk.

14a.

Elapsed time (s)	Distance from motion sensor (m)
0.0	2.0
1.0	3.0
2.0	4.0
3.0	5.0
4.0	4.5
5.0	4.0
6.0	3.5
7.0	3.0

14b. Distance (m) 0 3 6; Time (s) 0 4 8

15. Write each question as a proportion and then find the unknown number.

a. 70% of 65 is what number?

b. 115% of 37 is what number?

c. 110 is what percent of 90?

d. What percent of 18 is 0.5?

16. Find the area of this triangle using two different strategies. Describe your strategies.

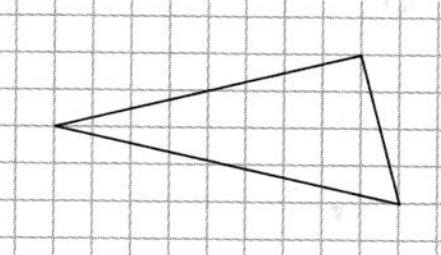

17. APPLICATION Sherez is currently earning \$390 per week as a store clerk and part-time manager. She is offered either a 7% increase or an additional \$25 per week. Which offer should she accept? the 7% offer at \$417.30 per week

IMPROVING YOUR REASONING SKILLS

Fibonacci and the Rabbits

Suppose a newborn pair of rabbits, one male and one female, is put in a field. Assume that rabbits are able to mate at the age of one month, so at the end of its second month a female can produce another pair of rabbits. Suppose that each female who is old enough produces one new pair of rabbits (one male, one female) every month and that none of the rabbits die. Write the first few terms of a sequence that shows how many pairs there will be at the end of each month. Then write a recursive formula for the sequence.

This sequence is called the **Fibonacci sequence** after Italian mathematician Leonardo Fibonacci (ca. 1170–1240), who asked a similar problem in his book *Liber abaci* (1202). How is the Fibonacci sequence unique compared to the other sequences you have studied?

Two arctic hares blend with the white tundra in Ellesmere Island National Park in northern Canada.

Exercise 15 Students might know easier and quicker ways to solve these problems without using proportions. Using proportions can reinforce the notion of percent as "per hundred." To tie percents to decimals and fractions, you might say that *percent* is "hundredths."

15a. $\frac{70}{100} = \frac{a}{65}$; $a = 45.5$

15b. $\frac{115}{100} = \frac{b}{37}$; $b = 42.55$

15c. $\frac{c}{100} = \frac{110}{90}$; $c \approx 122.2\%$

15d. $\frac{d}{100} = \frac{0.5}{18}$; $d \approx 2.78\%$

16. 17 square units; Sample answer: Enclose the triangle in a rectangle and subtract the areas of the right triangles on the outside; or label the triangle ABC with $\angle B$ the largest and notice that $AB \perp BC$, find their lengths using the distance formula, and use the formula $A = \frac{1}{2}(AB)(BC)$.

EXTENSION

Use Take Another Look activities 1 and 3 on page 74.

IMPROVING REASONING SKILLS

1, 1, 2, 3, 5, 8, 13, 21, 34, 55, 89, 144, . . . ; $u_1 = 1$, $u_2 = 1$, and $u_n = u_{n-1} + u_{n-2}$ where $n \geq 3$. Thus the recursive rule for the Fibonacci sequence is defined by two preceding terms.

Rabbits do actually have a gestation period (from conception, or *breeding,* to birth, or *kindling*) of one month. However, in real life, rabbits usually have to be six to nine months old before breeding, and they usually are not able to breed again immediately after kindling. The Fibonacci sequence, which is related to the golden ratio, has many applications in biology.

Fibonacci is credited with informing Europeans about the number system developed by the Hindus and Arabs.

This problem foreshadows the exploration on page 59. If you plan to do that exploration, you might use this puzzle as an introduction.

LESSON

1.2

PLANNING

LESSON OUTLINE

One day:

30 min Investigation

5 min Examples

5 min Sharing

5 min Exercises

MATERIALS

- balls (basketballs or handballs work well)
- motion sensors or metersticks
- Sample of a Lab Report (W), *optional*
- Calculator Notes 1F–1J

TEACHING

This lesson gives more experience with geometric sequences, both decreasing and increasing.

One Step

Give the instructions for the investigation (perhaps by pointing out the Procedure Note) and pose this problem: "What's a recursive formula for the height of the ball at the top of each bounce?" After students gather data, some will look for an additive formula (an arithmetic sequence) and others for a multiplicative formula (a geometric sequence). Ask them all to check their formulas against their actual data and adjust their formulas accordingly. If some groups stick to additive models, have them present first and be sure that the difference between approaches comes out. You might even have students discuss which models are best, based on differences between predicted and actual data. Ask students what the examples have in common with the investigation, bringing out the notions of decay and growth.

LESSON 1.2

Modeling Growth and Decay

Each sequence you generated in Lesson 1.1 was either an arithmetic sequence with a recursive rule in the form $u_n = u_{n-1} + d$ or a geometric sequence with a recursive rule in the form $u_n = r \cdot u_{n-1}$. You compared consecutive terms to decide whether the sequence required a common difference or a common ratio.

In most cases you have used u_1 as the starting term of each sequence. In some situations (like the one in the next investigation), it is more meaningful to treat the starting term as a zero term, or u_0. The zero term represents the starting value before any change occurs. You can decide whether it would be better to begin at u_0 or u_1.

EXAMPLE A

An automobile depreciates, or loses value, as it gets older. Suppose that a particular automobile loses one-fifth of its value each year. Write a recursive formula to find the value of this car when it is 6 years old, if it cost $23,999 when it was new.

Consumer CONNECTION

The *Kelley Blue Book,* first compiled in 1926 by Les Kelley, annually publishes standard values of every vehicle on the market. Many people who want to know the value of an automobile will ask what its "Blue Book" value is. The *Kelley Blue Book* calculates the value of a car by accounting for its make, model, year, mileage, location, and condition.

▶ Solution

Each year, the car will be worth $\frac{4}{5}$ of what it was worth the previous year, so the recursive sequence is geometric. It is convenient to start with $u_0 = 23999$ to represent the value of the car when it was new so that u_1 will represent the value after one year, and so on. The recursive formula that generates the sequence of annual values is

$u_0 = 23999$ — Starting value.

$u_n = 0.8 \cdot u_{n-1}$ where $n \geq 1$ — $\frac{4}{5}$ is 0.8.

Use this rule to find the 6th term.

After 6 years, the car is worth $6,291.19.

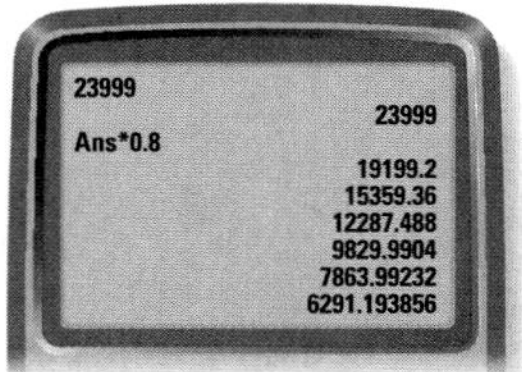

In situations like the problem in Example A, it's easier to write a recursive formula than an equation using x and y.

▶ EXAMPLE A

If students are having difficulty with recursion and the notation, you might want to start this example with a table, asking students to calculate the first few values. The table will help students make the connection to Lesson 1.1. See Sharing Ideas on page 40 for more ideas on using this example.

LESSON OBJECTIVES

- Use geometric sequences to model decay
- Analyze data from a motion sensor
- Use geometric sequences to model growth

Investigation
Looking for the Rebound

You will need

- a ball
- a motion sensor

When you drop a ball, the rebound height becomes smaller after each bounce. In this investigation you will write a recursive formula for the height of a real ball as it bounces.

Procedure Note

Collecting Data

1. Hold the motion sensor above the ball.
2. Press the trigger, then release the ball.
3. If the ball drifts, try to follow it and maintain the same height with the motion sensor.
4. If you do not capture at least 6 good consecutive bounces, repeat the procedure.

Step 1 Set up your calculator and motion sensor and follow the Procedure Note to collect bouncing-ball data. [▶ **See Calculator Note 1F** for calculator instructions on how to gather data. ◀]

Step 2 The data transferred to your calculator are in the form (x, y), where x is the time since you pressed the trigger, and y is the height of the ball. Trace the data graphed by your calculator to find the starting height and the rebound height after each bounce. Record your data in a table.

Step 3 Graph a scatter plot of points in the form (*bounce number, rebound height*). [▶ See **Calculator Notes 1G, 1H, 1I, and 1J** to learn how to enter, graph, trace, and share data. ◀]

Step 4 Sample answer: 0.7, 0.63, 0.64, . . .

Step 4 Compute the rebound ratio for consecutive bounces.

$$\textit{rebound ratio} = \frac{\textit{rebound height}}{\textit{previous rebound height}}$$

Step 5 $u_0 = 1.00$ and $u_n = 0.64 \cdot u_{n-1}$ where $n \geq 1$. 1.00, 0.64, 0.41, 0.26, 0.17, 0.11

Step 5 Decide on a single value that best represents the rebound ratio for your ball. Use this ratio to write a recursive formula that models your sequence of *rebound height* data, and use it to generate the first six terms.

The initial reading is likely to be inaccurate, resulting in the first ratio being far off. Discuss the feasibility of disregarding this figure in determining the best value for the ratio.

Step 6 Compare your experimental data to the terms generated by your recursive formula. How close are they? Describe some of the factors that might affect this experiment. For example, how might the formula change if you use a different kind of ball? Answers will vary.

NCTM STANDARDS

CONTENT	PROCESS
✓ Number	✓ Problem Solving
✓ Algebra	✓ Reasoning
Geometry	✓ Communication
✓ Measurement	✓ Connections
✓ Data/Probability	✓ Representation

Step 5 Students will probably find the average value for their common ratio; however, some groups may decide to throw out the initial value or any unusual data before choosing their single value. As needed, remind students to include the first equation (starting value) in their recursive formulas.

Step 6 You might want students to write up the experiment using suggestions from the Sample of a Lab Report worksheet.

Guiding the Investigation

You might refer to this book's cover photo of the bouncing ball.

If you do not have motion sensors, you can videotape a bouncing ball against a stationary meterstick, then use the pause button to read off the height of each bounce. Alternatively, students can design strategies for collecting data by hand, eye, and meterstick. In this case, they should run the experiment several times and average the heights of the rebounds.

Step 1 With the motion sensor it is not necessary to start from a great height. Small bounces work fine. If students are collecting data by hand, it is better to have an initial height of about 2 meters.

Step 1 Sample answer:

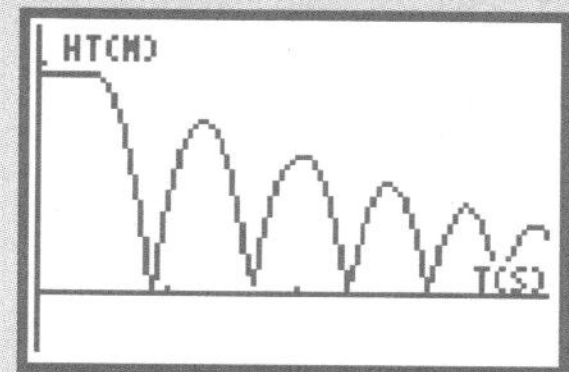

Step 2 **[Ask]** "What units do you want to record for x and y?" [bounce number has no units, height is in meters] **[Alert]** Students might be confused because the motion sensor is sending time units to the calculator for x-values.

Step 3 Students should plot only the bounce heights.

Step 4 Let students be the judge of what amount of error in the data is acceptable. Even with good bounces, the initial height reading can be inaccurate (sometimes due to the student's hand passing in front of the sensor in releasing the ball). If the sensor does not remain at a constant height over the ball, the transferred graph bounces will not extend to the x-axis.

See page 877 for answers to Steps 2 and 3.

▶ **EXAMPLE B**

This example concerns an increasing geometric sequence, similar to that in Lesson 1.1, Example C.

[Language] In the context of interest rates, *annual* means "once a year"; *semiannual* means "twice a year"; *quarterly* means "four times a year"; *monthly* means "twelve times a year"; *biweekly* means "26 times a year"; *weekly* means "52 times a year"; *daily* means "360 times a year" (not 365; each month is given 30 days).

SHARING IDEAS

Choose student presentations to include a variety of decimal places in the results. Question which number of decimals is most appropriate. [The height measurements are to two decimal places at most, so ratios wouldn't include more than two significant figures, though students may argue that reporting one or two more digits can be appropriate as they look for patterns.]

[Ask] "Could we use the first or second rebound height as u_0?" [Yes; starting the sequence from the second height would produce an identical set of subsequent bounces.]

[Ask] "What kind of sequences are these?" [geometric] Remind students of the Sierpiński triangle from Lesson 1.1 and ask how its sequence differed from that of this investigation. The bouncing ball, like Example A, gives a decreasing geometric sequence, called *decay;* the Sierpiński triangle, like Example B, gives an increasing geometric sequence, called *growth.*

With respect to Example A, **[Ask]** "Why can we find a 20% depreciation by multiplying by $\frac{4}{5}$?" If students can't explain why, suggest that they think about specific numbers, such as $100.

To motivate Exercise 5, point out that Example A seems to be claiming that $23{,}999 - (0.2)23{,}999 = 23{,}999(0.8)$. To encourage critical thinking, ask if that reasoning is justified. You might generalize to $u_{n-1} - (0.2)u_{n-1} = u_{n-1}(1 - 0.2) = u_{n-1}(0.8)$ as you review factoring.

You may find it easier to think of the common ratio as the whole, 1, plus or minus a percent change. In place of r you can write $(1 + p)$ or $(1 - p)$. The car example involved a 20% (one-fifth) loss, so the common ratio could be written as $(1 - 0.20)$. Your bouncing ball may have had a common ratio of 0.75, which you can write as $(1 - 0.25)$ or a 25% loss per bounce. These are examples of decay, or geometric sequences that decrease. The next example is one of growth, or a geometric sequence that increases.

EXAMPLE B Gloria deposits $2000 into a bank account that pays 7% annual interest compounded annually. This means the bank pays her 7% of her account balance as interest at the end of each year, and she leaves the original amount and the interest in the account. When will the original deposit double in value?

Economics CONNECTION

Interest is a charge that you pay for borrowing money, or that the bank pays you for letting them invest the money you keep in your bank account. Simple interest is a percentage paid on the **principal,** or initial balance, over a period of time. If you leave the interest in the account, then in the next time period you receive interest on both the principal and the interest that were in your account. This is called **compound interest** because you are receiving interest on the interest.

▶ **Solution**

The balance starts at $2000 and increases by 7% each year.

$$u_0 = 2000$$
$$u_n = (1 + 0.07)u_{n-1} \quad \text{where } n \geq 1$$

The recursive rule that represents 7% growth.

Use your calculator to compute year-end balances recursively.

The 11th term, u_{11}, is 4209.70, so the investment balance will more than double in 11 years.

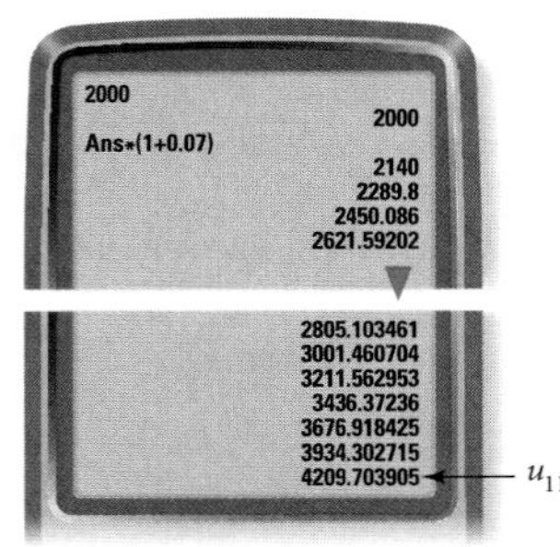

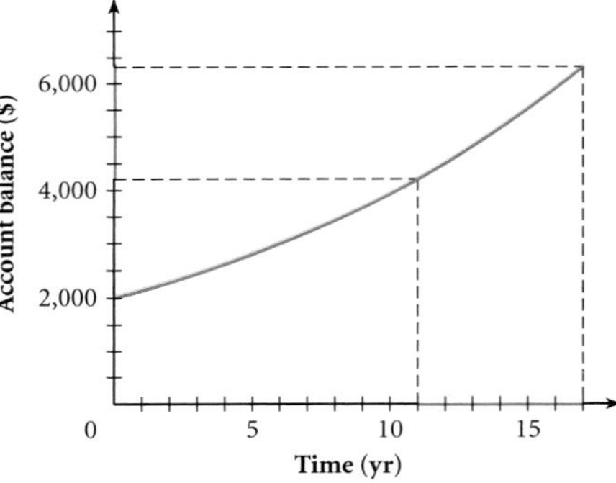

Compound interest has many applications in everyday life. The interest on both savings and loans is almost always compounded, often leading to surprising results. This graph shows the account balance in the previous example.

Leaving just $2000 in the bank at a good interest rate for 11 years can double your money. In another 6 years, the money will triple.

Referring to Example B, mention that interest might be compounded quarterly, monthly, daily, or even continuously. Each method produces a slightly different yield, so the interest is often stated in the equivalent annual percentage yield (APY).

You might discuss the difference between *nominal* and *effective interest rates.* If a 6.5% annual interest rate is compounded monthly, 6.5% is the nominal interest rate and $\left(1 + \frac{0.065}{12}\right)^{12}$ is the effective annual interest rate. After compounding, the effective interest rate is more than 6.5%, so 6.5% is the interest rate in name only. The use of formulas like $\left(1 + \frac{0.065}{12}\right)^{12}$ will arise in discussion of explicit formulas.

You might **[Ask]** "When is writing a formula that multiplies by $(1 - 0.15)$ preferable to writing one that multiplies by 0.85?" [The 0.15 shows the decay rate.]

Some banks will compound the interest monthly. You can write the common ratio as $\left(1 + \frac{0.07}{12}\right)$ to represent one-twelfth of the interest, compounding monthly. When you do this, n represents months instead of years. How would you change the rule to show that the interest is compounded 52 times per year? What would n represent in this situation? $\left(1 + \frac{0.07}{52}\right)$; n would represent the number of weeks.

EXERCISES

Practice Your Skills

1. Find the common ratio for each sequence.

a. 100, 150, 225, 337.5, 506.25 . . . 1.5

b. 73.4375, 29.375, 11.75, 4.7, 1.88 . . . 0.4

c. 80.00, 82.40, 84.87, 87.42, 90.04 . . . 1.03

d. 208.00, 191.36, 176.05, 161.97 . . . 0.92

2. Identify each sequence in Exercise 1 as growth or decay. Give the percent change for each.

3. Write a recursive formula for each sequence in Exercise 1 and find the 10th term. Use u_1 for the first term given.

4. Match each recursive rule to a graph. Explain your reasoning.

A. $u_1 = 10$
$u_n = (1 - 0.25) \cdot u_{n-1}$ where $n \geq 2$ ii. decay

B. $u_1 = 10$
$u_n = (1 + 0.25) \cdot u_{n-1}$ where $n \geq 2$ i. growth

C. $u_1 = 10$
$u_n = 1 \cdot u_{n-1}$ where $n \geq 2$ iii. constant

Films quickly display a sequence of photographs, creating an illusion of motion.

i.

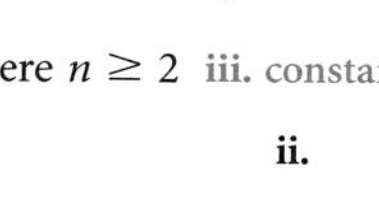

ii.

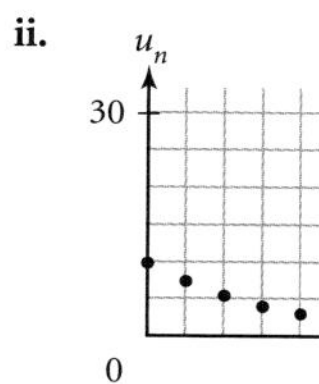

iii.

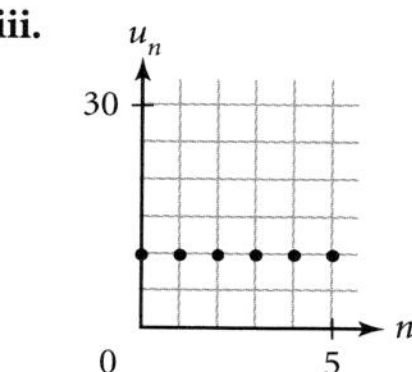

5. Factor these expressions so that the variable appears only once.

a. $u_{n-1} + 0.07u_{n-1}$ $(1 + 0.07)u_{n-1}$ or $1.07u_{n-1}$

b. $A - 0.18A$ $(1 - 0.18)A$ or $0.82A$

c. $x + 0.08125x$ $(1 + 0.08125)x$ or $1.08125x$

d. $2u_{n-1} - 0.85u_{n-1}$ $(2 - 0.85)u_{n-1}$ or $1.15u_{n-1}$

Reason and Apply

6. Suppose the initial height from which a rubber ball drops is 100 in. The rebound heights to the nearest inch are 80, 64, 51, 41, . . .

a. What is the rebound ratio for this ball? 0.8

b. What is the height of the tenth rebound? 11 in.

c. After how many bounces will the ball rebound less than 1 in.? Less than 0.1 in.? 21 bounces; 31 bounces

BUILDING UNDERSTANDING

The exercises focus on geometric sequences and their application to growth and decay.

ASSIGNING HOMEWORK

Essential	1–3, 8, 9
Performance assessment	4, 6, 7, 10–15
Portfolio	14
Journal	8, 11
Group	10, 11
Review	5, 16–20

Helping with the Exercises

Exercise 2 [Alert] Students might offer the common ratio as the percent change.

2a. growth; 50% increase

2b. decay; 60% decrease

2c. growth; 3% increase

2d. decay; 8% decrease

3a. $u_1 = 100$ and $u_n = 1.5u_{n-1}$ where $n \geq 2$; $u_{10} = 3844.3$

3b. $u_1 = 73.4375$ and $u_n = 0.4u_{n-1}$ where $n \geq 2$; $u_{10} = 0.020$

3c. $u_1 = 80$ and $u_n = 1.03u_{n-1}$ where $n \geq 2$; $u_{10} = 104.38$

3d. $u_1 = 208$ and $u_n = 0.92u_{n-1}$ where $n \geq 2$; $u_{10} = 98.21$

Exercise 5 Factoring is reviewed here. If you skipped Chapter 0, students may need some review of factoring.

Exercises 6, 7 These exercises are related to the investigation. Students who missed the investigation may need assistance visualizing the graph of the data.

Assessing Progress

As students work and present, you can assess their understanding of geometric sequences and their common ratios. You can also check their familiarity with motion sensors and their ability to calculate ratios, follow directions, work with groups, and use calculators.

Additional Example

Ask students to create a word problem that would be solved using this recursive formula $u_0 = 10000$ and $u_n = u_{n-1}\left(1 + \frac{0.07}{365}\right)$ where $n \geq 1$. Then have them find u_{10}. [Word problems will vary; $u_{10} = 10019.19$]

Closing the Lesson

The key points are that geometric sequences can be either decreasing, in which case they represent **decay,** or increasing, representing **growth.**

Exercises 7, 8 If students have difficulty understanding the recursive formulas because they are printed on one line, suggest that they write them out as they've seen them before.

7. 100 is the initial height, but the units are unknown. 0.20 is the percent loss, so the ball loses 20% of its height with each rebound.

Exercise 8 Because n is related to the year 2003, students will probably conclude that the interest rate is annual. Be open to multiple interpretations: 0.025 could be $\frac{1}{12}$ of 30% compounded monthly or $\frac{1}{4}$ of 10% compounded quarterly. With these two options n would need to change to represent months or quarters.

Exercise 9 Discourage students from answering with fractions of people.

9a. number of new hires for next five years: 2, 3, 3 (or 4), 4, and 5

7. Suppose the recursive forumula $u_0 = 100$ and $u_n = (1 - 0.20)u_{n-1}$ where $n \geq 1$ models a bouncing ball. Give real-world meanings for the numbers 100 and 0.20.

8. Suppose the recursive formula $u_{2003} = 250000$ and $u_n = (1 + 0.025)u_{n-1}$ where $n \geq 2004$ describes an investment made in the year 2003. Give real-world meanings for the numbers 250,000 and 0.025. $250,000 was invested at 2.5% annual interest in 2003.

9. **APPLICATION** A small company with 12 employees is growing at a rate of 20% per year. It will need to hire more employees to keep up with the growth, assuming its business keeps growing at the same rate.

a. How many people should the company plan to hire in each of the next five years?

b. How many employees will it have in five years? about 30 employees

Economics CONNECTION

To manage the financial demands of a company's growth, forecasters use the substantial growth rate model. This rate, represented by the variable g^*, is the annual percentage increase in sales that a company can maintain while keeping its capital stable. If a company grows at a rate faster than g^*, it may not have the means to finance its growth. If it grows slowly, its capital will grow at a pace that will reduce debt and increase investments. Using g^* allows a business to project its financial ability to grow.

10. **APPLICATION** The table below shows investment balances over time.

Elapsed time (yr)	0	1	2	3	...
Balance ($)	2000	2170	2354.45	2554.58	...

a. Write a recursive formula that generates the balances in the table. $u_0 = 2000$, $u_n = (1 + 0.085)u_{n-1}$ where $n \geq 1$

b. What is the annual interest rate? 8.5%

c. How many years will it take before the original deposit triples in value? 14 years ($6266.81)

11. **APPLICATION** Carbon dating is used to find the age of ancient remains of once-living things. Carbon-14 is found naturally in all living things, and it decays slowly after death. About 11.45% of it decays in each 1000-year period of time.

Let 100%, or 1, be the beginning amount of carbon-14. At what point will less than 5% remain? Write the recursive formula you used.

$u_0 = 1$ and $u_n = 0.8855u_{n-1}$ where $n \geq 1$

$u_{25} = 0.048$, or 4.8%. It would take about 25,000 years to reduce to 5%.

At an excavation site in Alberta, Canada, these scientists uncover the remains of an Albertosaurus (a relative of the Tyrannosaurus) about 65–70 million years old.

12. Suppose Jill's biological family tree looks like the diagram at right. You can model recursively the number of people in each generation.

Mom's mom | Mom's dad | Dad's mom | Dad's dad
Her mom | Her dad
Jill

a. Make a table showing the number of Jill's ancestors in each of the past five generations. Use u_0 to represent Jill's generation. See below.

b. Look in your table at the sequence of the number of ancestors. Describe how to find u_n if you know u_{n-1}. Write a recursive formula.

c. Find the number of the term of this sequence that is closest to 1 billion. What is the real-world meaning of this answer? u_{30}; 30 generations ago, Jill had 1 billion living ancestors.

d. If a new generation is born every 25 years, approximately when did Jill have 1 billion living ancestors in the same generation? 750 years ago

e. Your answer to 12c assumes there are no duplicates, that is, no common ancestors on Jill's mom's and Jill's dad's sides of the family. Look up Earth's population for the year you found in 12d. You will find helpful links at **www.keymath.com/DAA**. Write a few sentences describing any problems you notice with the assumption of no common ancestors. The population of the planet at that time was less than 1 billion. Jill must have some common ancestors.

Cultural CONNECTION

Family trees are lists of family descendants and are used in the practice of genealogy. People who research genealogy may want to trace their family's medical history or national origin, discover important dates, or simply enjoy it as a hobby. Alex Haley's 1976 genealogical book, *Roots: The Saga of an American Family,* told the powerful history of his family's prolonged slavery and decades of discrimination. The book, along with the 1977 television miniseries, inspired many people to trace their family lineage.

Alex Haley (1921–1992)

13. **APPLICATION** Suppose \$500 is deposited into an account that earns 6.5% annual interest and no more deposits or withdrawals are made.

a. If the interest is compounded monthly, what is the monthly rate? $\frac{6.5}{12} \approx 0.542\%$

b. What is the balance after 1 month? \$502.71

c. What is the balance after 1 year? \$533.49

d. What is the balance after 29 months? \$584.80

14. **APPLICATION** Between 1970 and 2000, the population of Grand Traverse County in Michigan grew from 39,175 to 77,654.

a. Find the percent increase over the 30-year period. 98.22%

b. What do you think the *annual* growth rate was during this period?

c. Check your answer to 14b by using a recursive formula. Do you get 77,654 people after 30 years? Explain why your recursive formula may not work.

d. Use guess-and-check to find a growth rate, to the nearest 0.1% (or 0.001), that comes closest to producing the 30-year growth experienced. 2.3%

e. Use your answer to 14d to estimate the population in 1985. How does this compare with the average of the populations of 1970 and 2000? Why is that?

Exercise 12 Encourage students to critique their answer in 12c and to compare it with their answer in 12d.

12b. Start with 1 and recursively multiply by 2; $u_0 = 1$ and $u_n = 2u_{n-1}$ where $n \geq 1$.

14b. Students might guess $\frac{0.9822}{30} = 3.27\%$. If they realize growth is not linear, they might guess 3% or less.

14c. Using $u_{1970} = 39175$ and $u_n = (1 + 0.0327)u_{n-1}$ where $n \geq 1971$ yields $u_{2000} = 102857$. Explanations will vary.

Exercise 14e After solving this problem and realizing that averaging is accurate only for linear growth, students may wonder why the average $\frac{r}{12}$ is used in calculating compound interest, which is also exponential. Indeed, if you multiply an amount by $1 + \frac{r}{12}$, you don't get $\frac{1}{12}$ of the total increase, $\left(1 + \frac{r}{12}\right)^{12}$, that you'd get compounding over 12 months. It is by convention that we say the annual interest rate is r; in actuality, the interest compounded monthly at a rate of $\frac{r}{12}$ is larger than the result of a one-time application of rate r.

14e. Using $u_{1970} = 39175$ and $u_n = (1 + 0.023)u_{n-1}$ where $n \geq 1971$ yields $u_{1985} = 55099$. The average is 58414.5. The mean only works if the growth is arithmetic.

12a.

Generations back n	0	1	2	3	4	5
Ancestors in the generation u_n	1	2	4	8	16	32

15a. 3; $\frac{162}{18} = 9, 3^2 = 9$

15b. 2, 6, . . . , 54, . . . , 486, 1458, . . . , 13122

18a. $u_1 = 180$ and $u_n = u_{n-1} - 7$ where $n \geq 2$

Exercise 19 Be open to nonbalancing methods of solving these equations, such as undoing, graphing, or guess-and-check.

EXTENSION

Pose this problem: "In Example B, how long would it take the original deposit to double if the 7% interest were compounded monthly or daily?" [By guess-and-check, perhaps coupled with the "rule of 70" (divide 70 by the interest rate to get the approximate number of years required for doubling), $\left(1 + \frac{0.07}{12}\right)^n$ first exceeds 2 when $n = 120$ months, or 10 years. $\left(1 + \frac{0.07}{360}\right)^n$ first exceeds 2 when $n = 3566$, about a month less than 10 years.]

Logarithms aren't necessary here, but you might ask if there's a direct way to solve an equation for an exponent, to lay groundwork for the study of logarithms in Chapter 5. **[Link]** In fact, to calculate the result of compounding interest continually, we use exponential growth based on *e*, the base of the natural logarithm.

15. Taoufik looks at the second problem of his wet homework that had fallen in a puddle.

a. What is the common ratio? How did you find it?

b. What are the missing terms?

c. What is the answer he needs to find? 118,098

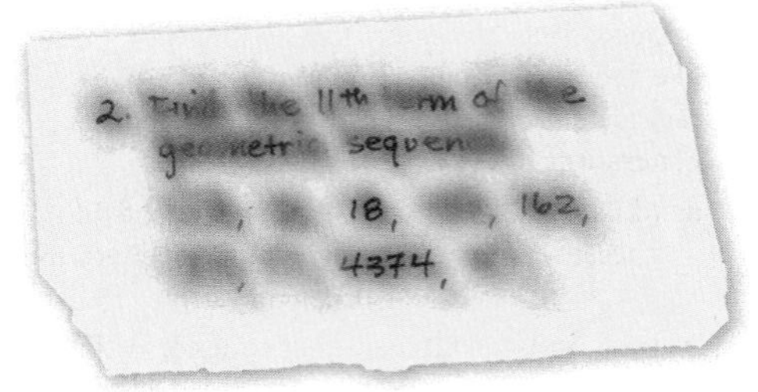

Review

16. The population of the United States grew 13.20% from 1990 to 2000. The population reported in the 2000 census was 281.4 million. What population was reported in 1990? Explain how you found this number. 248.6 million; $(1 + 0.132)x = 281.4$

17. An elevator travels at a nearly constant speed from the ground to an observation deck at 160 m. This trip takes 40 s. The trip back down is also at this same constant speed.

a. What is the elevator's speed in meters per second? 4 m/s

b. How long does it take the elevator to reach the restaurants, located 40 m above ground level? 10 s

c. Graph the height of the elevator as it moves from ground level to the observation deck.

d. Graph the height of the elevator as it moves from the restaurant level, at 40 m, to the observation deck.

e. Graph the height of the elevator as it moves from the deck to ground level.

The CN Tower in Toronto is one of Canada's landmark structures and one of the world's tallest buildings. Built in 1976, it has six glass-fronted elevators that allow you to view the landscape as you rise above it at 15 mi/h. At 1136 ft, you can either brace against the wind on the outdoor observation deck or test your nerves by walking across a 256 ft² glass floor with a view straight down.

1.1 **18.** Consider the sequence 180, 173, 166, 159, ...

a. Write a recursive formula. Use $u_1 = 180$.

b. What is u_{10}? $u_{10} = 117$

c. What is the first term with a negative value? $u_{27} = -2$

19. Solve each equation.

a. $-151.7 + 3.5x = 0$ $x \approx 43.34$

b. $0.88x + 599.72 = 0$ $x = -681.5$

c. $18.75x - 16 = 0$ $x \approx 0.853$

d. $0.5 \cdot 16 + x = 16$ $x = 8$

20. For the equation $y = 47 + 8x$, find the value of y when

a. $x = 0$ $y = 47$

b. $x = 1$ $y = 55$

c. $x = 5$ $y = 87$

d. $x = -8$ $y = -17$

17c.

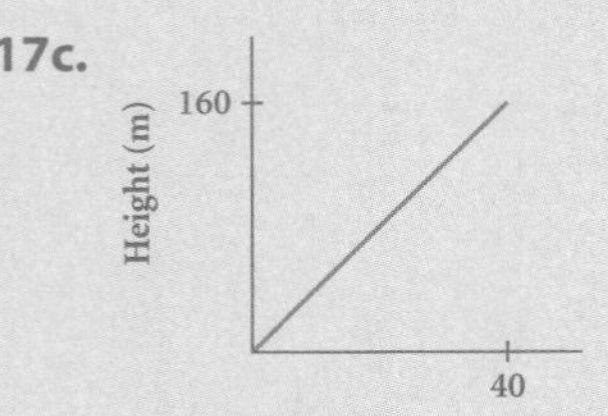

17d.

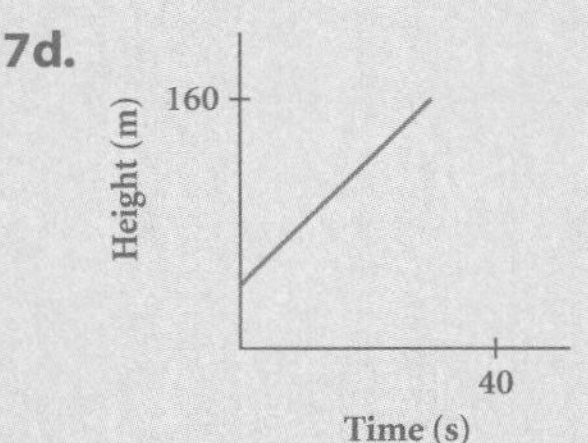

17e.

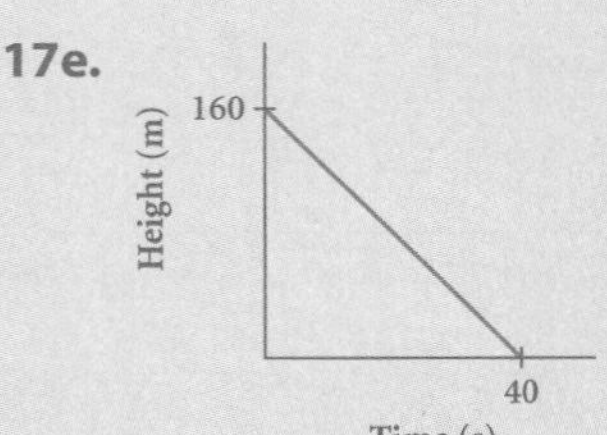

LESSON 1.3 A First Look at Limits

A Mathematician is a machine for turning coffee into theorems.
PAUL ERDÖS

Increasing arithmetic and geometric sequences, such as the number of new triangles at each stage in a Sierpiński triangle or the balance of money earning interest in the bank, have terms that get larger and larger. But can a tree continue to grow larger year after year? Can people continue to build taller buildings, run faster, and jump higher, or is there a limit to any of these?

The women's world record for the fastest time in the 100 m dash has decreased by about 3 s in 66 yr. Marie Mejzlíková (Czechoslovakia) set the record at 13.6 s in 1922, and Florence Griffith-Joyner (USA), shown at right, set it at 10.49 s in 1988. In the 1998 article "How Good Can We Get?" Jonas Mureika predicts that the ultimate performance for a woman in the 100 m dash will be 10.15 s.

How large can a tree grow? It depends partly on environmental factors such as disease and climate. Trees have mechanisms that slow their growth as they age, similar to human growth. (Unlike humans, however, a tree may not reach maturity until 100 yr after it starts growing.) This giant sequoia, the General Sherman Tree in Sequoia National Park, California, is considered to be the world's largest living thing. The volume of its trunk is over 52,500 ft^3.

Decreasing sequences may also have a limit. For example, the temperature of a cup of hot cocoa as it cools, taken at one-minute intervals, produces a sequence that approaches the temperature of the room. In the long run, the hot cocoa will be at room temperature.

In the next investigation you will explore what happens to a sequence in the long run.

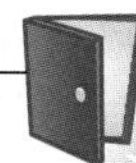

Investigation
Doses of Medicine

You will need

- a bowl
- a supply of water
- a supply of tinted liquid
- measuring cups, graduated in milliliters
- a sink or waste bucket

Our kidneys continuously filter our blood, removing impurities. Doctors take this into account when prescribing the dosage and frequency of medicine.

In this investigation you will simulate what happens in the body when a patient takes medicine. To represent the blood in a patient's body, use a bowl containing a total of 1 liter (L) of liquid. Start with 16 milliliters (mL) of tinted liquid to represent a dose of medicine in the blood, and use clear water for the rest.

LESSON 1.3

PLANNING

LESSON OUTLINE

One day:

25 min	Investigation
5 min	Example
5 min	Sharing
10 min	Exercises

MATERIALS

- bowls
- water
- food coloring
- measuring cups (in milliliters)
- waste buckets or sink
- Calculator Notes 1D, 1E, *optional*

TEACHING

This lesson is the first of several on limits. Don't expect students to understand the theoretical nature of limits very deeply yet. The term *long-run value* is used interchangeably with *limit.*

[ESL] To *approach* means to "get closer and closer."

[Language] The everyday meaning of *limit* is as a cutoff value (for example, *speed limit*). The mathematical meaning is more theoretical, describing a number that is approached eventually within any specified margin of error. A mathematical sequence may or may not ever take on the value of the limit.

NCTM STANDARDS

CONTENT		PROCESS	
	Number	✓	Problem Solving
✓	Algebra	✓	Reasoning
	Geometry	✓	Communication
✓	Measurement	✓	Connections
✓	Data/Probability	✓	Representation

LESSON OBJECTIVES

- Explore long-run values
- Begin to understand the concept of *limit*
- Investigate shifted geometric sequences

One Step

Pose this problem: "A doctor prescribes a daily dose of 16 mL of medicine for each liter of blood in a patient's body. Each day, the patient's kidneys filter 25% of the medicine out of the blood. Use recursion and graphs to determine the amount of medicine in 1 L of blood over many days." Have available the materials of the investigation for students to experiment with as they desire.

Guiding the Investigation

Students need no prior knowledge of limits to complete this investigation, which is based on an article by James Sandefur, "Drugs and Pollution in the Algebra Class," from the February 1992 issue of *Mathematics Teacher.*

[ESL] A *dosage* is an amount or quantity, especially of medicine. *Frequency* is the rate of occurrence of an event or the number of times an event takes place.

Step 1 You might do this step as a class demonstration. One student can be the patient, who will hold the container that represents the kidney and remove 250 mL. Another student can be the nurse who will add the 250 mL of water. As a class, students should figure out the first few entries in the chart and then move on to finish the project in groups.

[Ask] "Why does removing 250 mL of 'blood' remove 25% of the 'medicine'?" [If the medicine is evenly distributed, $\frac{1}{4}$ of the blood contains $\frac{1}{4}$ of the medicine.]

Step 2 Be open to a variety of equivalent forms of the equations. Plan to have these presented during Sharing for comparison.

See pages 877–878 for answers to Steps 5 and 6.

Step 1 Suppose a patient's kidneys filter out 25% of this medicine each day. To simulate this, remove $\frac{1}{4}$, or 250 mL of the mixture from the bowl and replace it with 250 mL of clear water to represent filtered blood. Make a table like the one below, and record the amount of medicine in the blood over several days. Repeat the simulation for each day.

Day	Amount of medicine (mL)
0	16
1	12
2	9
3	6.75

Step 2 Write a recursive formula that generates the sequence in your table.

Step 2 $u_0 = 16$ and $u_n = (1 - 0.25)u_{n-1}$ where $n \geq 1$

Step 3 How many days will pass before there is less than 1 mL of medicine in the blood?

Step 3 10 days

Step 4 Is the medicine ever completely removed from the blood? Why or why not?

Step 4 Because there is only a percent of the medicine removed each day, there will be a trace of medicine left until the long-run value is reached as that trace becomes smaller than one molecule.

Step 5 Sketch a graph and describe what happens in the long run.

A single dose of medicine is often not enough. Doctors prescribe regular doses to produce and maintain a high enough level of medicine in the body. Next you will modify your simulation to look at what happens when a patient takes medicine daily over a period of time.

Step 6 Start over with 1 L of liquid. Again, all of the liquid is clear water, representing the blood, except for 16 mL of tinted liquid to represent the initial dose of medicine. Each day, 250 mL of liquid is removed and replaced with 234 mL of clear water and 16 mL of tinted liquid to represent a new dose of medicine. Complete another table like the one in Step 1, recording the amount of medicine in the blood over several days.

Step 7 Write a recursive formula that generates this sequence.

Step 8 Do the contents of the bowl ever turn into pure medicine? Why or why not?

Step 8 No, there is always pure water added at each step. The amount of medicine levels off.

Step 9 Sketch a graph and explain what happens to the level of medicine in the blood after many days.

Step 4 These sequences appear to reach a particular value only because of rounding.

Step 6 Students may wonder why taking 16 mL of medicine doesn't increase the total amount of blood to more than 1 L. In order to make predictions, this model ignores the natural variation in the volume of human blood due to fluid intake, perspiration, and elimination.

Step 7 $u_0 = 16$ and $u_n = (1 - 0.25)u_{n-1} + 16$ where $n \geq 1$

Step 9

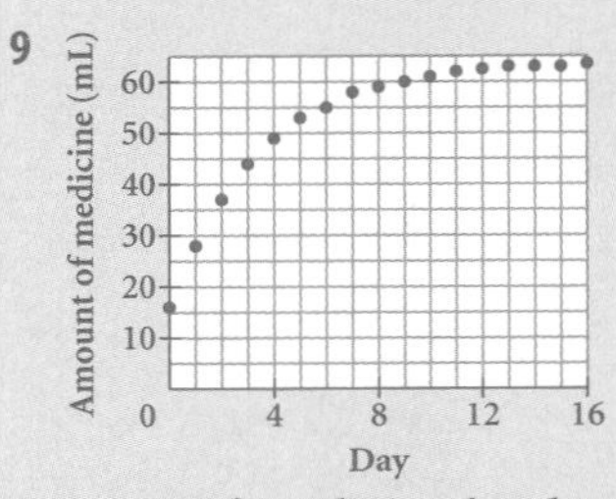

The amount of medicine levels off at 64 mL. Using a calculator to generate the sequence, it gets very close to 64 mL within 10 days and appears to reach 64 mL after 12 days.

Medicine and its elimination from the human body is a real-world example of a dynamic, or changing, system. A contaminated lake and its cleanup processes is another real-world example. Dynamic systems often reach a point of stability in the long run. The quantity associated with that stability, such as the number of milliliters of medicine, is called a **limit.** Mathematically, we say that the sequence of numbers associated with the system approaches that limit. Being able to predict limits is very important for analyzing these situations. The long-run value helps you estimate limits.

Environmental CONNECTION

The Cuyahoga River in Cleveland, Ohio, caught fire several times during the 1950s and 1960s because its water was so polluted with volatile chemicals. The events inspired several clean water acts in the 1970s and the creation of the federal Environmental Protection Agency. After testing the toxic chemicals present in the water and locating possible sources of contamination, environmental engineers established pollution control levels and set standards for monitoring waste from local industries. In the end, the private and corporate sectors of Cleveland managed to clean up the waterways, preserve the wildlife areas that relied on them, and provide a number of parks for recreational use.

This photograph shows a fire on the Cuyahoga River in 1952.

Each of the sequences in the investigation approached different long-run values. The first sequence approached zero. The second sequence was shifted and it approached a nonzero value. A **shifted geometric sequence** includes an added term in the recursive rule. Let's look at another example of a shifted geometric sequence.

EXAMPLE

Antonio and Deanna are working at the community pool for the summer. They need to provide a "shock" treatment of 450 grams (g) of dry chlorine to prevent the growth of algae in the pool, then they add 45 g of chlorine each day after the initial treatment. Each day, the sun burns off 15% of the chlorine. Find the amount of chlorine after 1 day, 2 days, and 3 days. Create a graph that shows the chlorine level after several days and in the long run.

▶ Solution

The starting value is given as 450. This amount decays by 15% a day, but 45 g is also added each day. The amount remaining after each day is generated by the rule $u_n = (1 - 0.15)u_{n-1} + 45$, or $u_n = 0.85u_{n-1} + 45$. Use this rule to find the chlorine level in the long run.

$u_0 = 450$	The initial shock treatment.
$u_1 = 0.85(450) + 45 = 427.5$	The amount after 1 day.
$u_2 = 0.85(427.5) + 45 \approx 408.4$	The amount after 2 days.
$u_3 = 0.85(408.4) + 45 \approx 392.1$	The amount after 3 days.

▶ EXAMPLE

This example gives another case of a shifted geometric sequence.

[Alert] Students might need help in solving an equation for a variable that appears on both sides.

[Ask] "Will the value ever stop changing? We solve for it, but will the input value ever equal 300?" [In theory, the input value would grow to 300 only in an infinite length of time.]

[Ask] "From the investigation and this example, can you make a conjecture about the limit of a shifted geometric sequence with the recursive rule $u_n = au_{n-1} + b$?" $\left[\frac{b}{1-a}\right.$, assuming that $\left.0 < a < 1\right]$

SHARING IDEAS

As students present their ideas about Step 9 of the investigation, **[Ask]** "Does the sequence actually reach this limit?" [The geometric sequence does not reach its limit of 64, though eventually the calculator doesn't have enough decimal places to represent the difference from 64.] Physically, the concentration of medicine will actually reach the long-run value when it becomes less than one molecule away from it.

[Ask] "Why do you think this sequence is called a shifted geometric sequence?" [The "geometric" part comes from the multiplier; a graph of the sequence is "shifted" up or down from that of the geometric sequence, so the limit might not be 0.]

In chemistry, the leveling off is called *reaching equilibrium.* At this point, a dynamic system reaches *stasis* (stability).

[Ask] "Do all geometric sequences have limits?" [If the common ratio is more than 1, they become large without bound. Because infinity isn't considered a number, they have no limits. If the common ratio is between 0 and 1, they approach a

Sharing Ideas (continued)

limit of 0.] "Does any geometric sequence reach its limit?" [yes; if the common ratio is 1, so that all the terms are the same, or 0, so that all terms after the first term are 0] "If the limit of nonconstant geometric sequences can only be 0, how can the sequence of the investigation have a limit of 64?" [It's not a geometric sequence, but rather a shifted geometric sequence.]

[Ask] "Can an arithmetic sequence have a limit?" [Only if the common difference is 0, so that all terms are the same.]

If you would like to introduce Sequence mode on the calculator, you might use Calculator Notes 1D and 1E at this point. Though Sequence mode may be difficult initially, it will become a powerful tool for exploring graphs, finding specific sequence values, and finding monthly payments.

Assessing Progress
You can assess students' understanding of geometric sequences and their skill at following instructions.

Closing the Lesson

A number is the **limit,** or **long-run value,** of a sequence if the sequence gets closer and closer to the number, perhaps even reaching it. The only arithmetic sequences with limits are constant. The only nonconstant geometric sequences with limits have common ratios less than 1 (in absolute value), and their limits are 0. **Shifted geometric sequences,** whose recursive formulas involve addition as well as multiplication, might have nonzero limits.

BUILDING UNDERSTANDING

ASSIGNING HOMEWORK

Essential	1, 3, 4
Performance assessment	5, 6, 7, 9
Portfolio	8, 11
Journal	5, 10
Group	10, 12
Review	2, 13–15

Helping with the Exercises

Exercise 2c Students may not have seen an equation that has no solution. If this equation were a true statement, then 210 would equal 0.

Exercise 3 Students might find the long-run value in many ways: by recursion, by looking at the graph, or by solving explicitly.

To find the long-run value of the amount of chlorine, you can continue evaluating terms until the value stops changing, or see where the graph levels off. From the graph, the long-run value appears to be 300 g of chlorine.

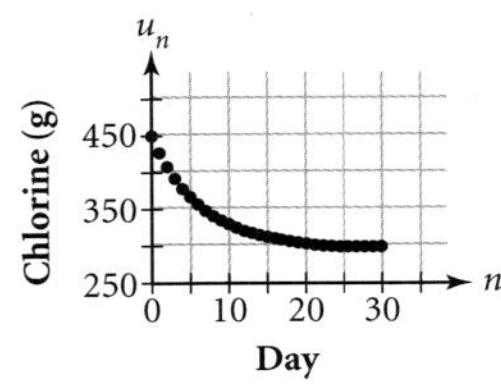

You can also use algebra to find the value of the terms as they level off. If you assume that terms stop changing, then you can set the value of the next term equal to the value of the previous term and solve the equation.

$u_n = 0.85u_{n-1} + 45$	Recursive rule.
$c = 0.85c + 45$	Assign the same variable to u_n and u_{n-1}.
$0.15c = 45$	Subtract $0.85c$ from both sides.
$c = 300$	Divide both sides by 0.15.

The amount of chlorine will level off at 300 g, which agrees with the long-run value estimated from the graph.

The study of limits is an important part of calculus, the mathematics of change. Understanding limits mathematically will give you a chance to work with other real-world applications in biology, chemistry, physics, and social science.

EXERCISES

Practice Your Skills

1. Find the value of u_1, u_2, and u_3. Identify the type of sequence (arithmetic, geometric, or shifted geometric) and tell whether it is increasing or decreasing.

a. $u_0 = 16$
$u_n = (1 - 0.05)u_{n-1} + 16$ where $n \geq 1$

b. $u_0 = 800$
$u_n = (1 - 0.05)u_{n-1} + 16$ where $n \geq 1$

c. $u_0 = 50$
$u_n = (1 - 0.10)u_{n-1}$ where $n \geq 1$

d. $u_0 = 40$
$u_n = (1 - 0.50)u_{n-1} + 20$ where $n \geq 1$

2. Solve each equation.

a. $a = 210 + 0.75a$ $a = 840$

b. $b = 0.75b + 300$ $b = 1200$

c. $c = 210 + c$ no solution

d. $d = 0.75d$ $d = 0$

3. Find the long-run value for each sequence in Exercise 1.
a. 320; **b.** 320; **c.** 0; **d.** 40

4. Write a recursive formula for each sequence.

a. 200.00, 216.00, 233.28, 251.94 . . .

b. 0, 10, 15, 17.5, 18.75 . . .

1a. 31.2, 45.64, 59.358; shifted geometric, increasing

1b. 776, 753.2, 731.54; shifted geometric, decreasing

1c. 45, 40.5, 36.45; geometric, decreasing

1d. 40, 40, 40; arithmetic or shifted geometric, neither increasing nor decreasing

4a. $u_0 = 200$ and $u_n = 1.08u_{n-1}$ where $n \geq 1$

4b. $u_0 = 0$ and $u_n = 0.5u_{n-1} + 10$ where $n \geq 1$

Reason and Apply

5. The Osbornes have a small pool and are doing a chlorine treatment. The recursive formula below gives the pool's daily amount of chlorine in grams.

$u_0 = 300$

$u_n = (1 - 0.15)u_{n-1} + 30 \quad \text{where } n \geq 1$

a. Explain the real-world meanings of the values 300, 0.15, and 30 in this formula.

b. Describe what happens to the chlorine level in the long run. It levels off at 200 g.

6. APPLICATION On October 1, 2002, Sal invested $24,000 in a bank account earning 3.4% annually, compounded monthly. A month later, he withdrew $100 and continued to withdraw $100 on the first of every month thereafter.

a. Write a recursive formula for this problem.

b. List the first five terms of this sequence of balances, starting with the initial investment. 24,000; 23,968; 23,935.91; 23,903.73; 23,871.45

c. What is the meaning of the value of u_4? After 4 months the account balance is $23,871.45.

d. What is the balance on October 2, 2003? On October 2, 2005? $u_{12} = \$23{,}609.96$, $u_{36} = \$22{,}789.00$

7. APPLICATION Consider the bank account in Exercise 6.

a. What happens to the balance if the same interest and withdrawal patterns continue for a long time? Does the balance ever level off?

b. What monthly withdrawal amount would maintain a constant balance of $24,000 in the long run? $68

8. APPLICATION The Forever Green Nursery owns 7000 white pine trees. Each year, the nursery plans to sell 12% of its trees and plant 600 new ones.

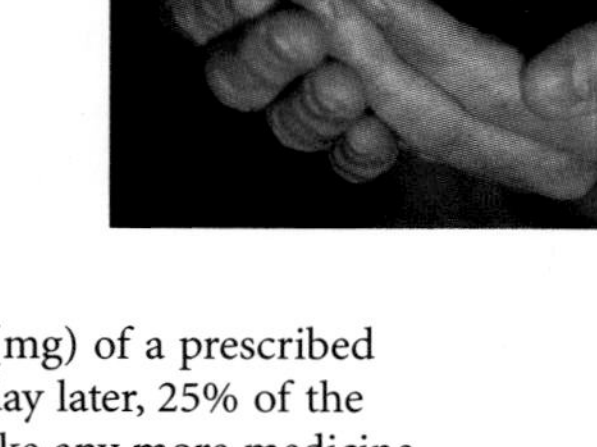

a. Find the number of pine trees owned by the nursery after 10 years. 5557 trees

b. Find the number of pine trees owned by the nursery after many years, and explain what is occurring.

c. What equation can you solve to find the number of trees in the long run? $c = 0.88c + 600$

d. Try different starting totals in place of the 7000 trees. Describe any changes to the long-run value.

e. In the fifth year, a disease destroys many of the nursery's trees. How does the long-run value change?

9. APPLICATION Jack takes a capsule containing 20 milligrams (mg) of a prescribed allergy medicine early in the morning. By the same time a day later, 25% of the medicine has been eliminated from his body. Jack doesn't take any more medicine, and his body continues to eliminate 25% of the remaining medicine each day. Write a recursive formula for the daily amount of this medicine in Jack's body. When will there be less than 1 mg of the medicine remaining in his body?

10. Consider the last part of the Investigation Doses of Medicine. If you double the amount of medicine taken each time from 16 mL to 32 mL, but continue to filter only 250 mL of liquid, will the limit of the concentration be doubled? Explain.

9. $u_0 = 20$ and $u_n = (1 - 0.25)u_{n-1}$ where $n \geq 1$; 11 days $(u_{11} \approx 0.84 \text{ mg})$

10. Yes, the long-run value was $\frac{16}{0.25}$, or 64 mL, and it is now $\frac{32}{0.25}$, or 128 mL.

5a. The first day, 300 grams of chlorine were added. Each day, 15% disappears, and 30 more grams are added.

Exercise 6 Students may not realize that this is a shifted geometric sequence, because a constant amount is subtracted, rather than added, each month.

6a. $u_0 = 24000$ and $u_n = \left(1 + \frac{0.034}{12}\right)u_{n-1} - 100$ where $n \geq 1$

Exercise 7a As needed, encourage use of recursive sequences or home-screen recursion on a graphing calculator. Eventually, there will be no money left in the account. Theoretically, the balance will become negative and keep decreasing.

7a. The account balance will continue to decrease (slowly at first, but faster after a while). It does not level off, but it eventually reaches 0 and stops decreasing.

Exercise 8 As appropriate, **[Ask]** "How is this situation different from that in the previous exercises, in which the amount decreased to 0?" [Although the nursery begins by selling more trees than it plants, 12% of smaller numbers becomes smaller than the 600 planted.] Highlight any expressions of surprise that the limit doesn't depend on the starting value.

8b. 5000 trees; The number of trees sold will be exactly equal to the number planted.

8d. Answers will vary. Initial values greater than 5000 decrease, and initial values less than 5000 increase. Regardless of the initial value, all stop changing at 5000.

8e. The long-run value will be the same as long as the nursery continues to sell and plant at the same rate.

11. APPLICATION An anti-asthmatic drug has a half-life of about 9 hours. This means that 9 hours is the length of time it takes for the amount of drug present in a person's blood to decrease to half that amount.

a. Explain what this means about the amount of this drug in a person's bloodstream that starts out with a drug concentration of 16 mg/L.

b. Create a graph of points in the form (*elapsed time, drug concentration*) using 9-hour increments on the time axis.

c. What dosage of this drug should a person take every 9 hours to maintain a balance of at least 16 mg/L? 8 mg

12. Suppose square *ABCD* with side length 8 in. is cut from paper. Another square, *EFGH,* is placed with its corners at the midpoints of *ABCD,* as shown. A third square is placed with its corners at midpoints of *EFGH,* and so on.

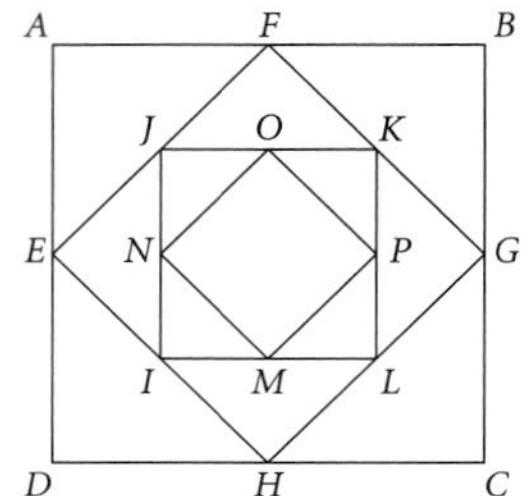

a. What is the perimeter of the ninth square? 2 in.

b. What is the area of the ninth square? 0.25 in.^{2}

c. What happens to the ratio of perimeter to area as the squares get smaller? The ratio gets larger and larger without limit.

Review

1.1 **13.** Assume two terms of a sequence are $u_3 = 16$ and $u_4 = 128$.

a. Find u_2 and u_5 if the sequence is arithmetic. $u_2 = -96, u_5 = 240$

b. Find u_2 and u_5 if the sequence is geometric. $u_2 = 2, u_5 = 1024$

1.1 **14.** A park biologist estimates the moose population in a national park over a four-year period of mild winters. She makes this table.

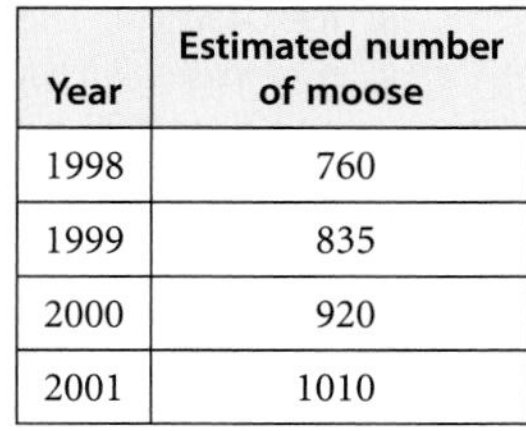

Year	Estimated number of moose
1998	760
1999	835
2000	920
2001	1010

a. Write a recursive formula that approximately models the growth in the moose population for this four-year period.

b. The winter of 2002 was particularly severe, and the park biologist has predicted a decline of 10% to 15% in the moose herd. What is the range of moose population she predicts for 2002? between 859 and 909

1.2 **15.** If a rubber ball rebounds to 97% of its height with each bounce, how many times will it bounce before it rebounds to half its original height? 23 times

IMPROVING YOUR VISUAL THINKING SKILLS

Think Pink

You have two 1-gallon cans. One contains 1 gallon of white paint, and the other contains 3 quarts (qt) of red paint. (There are 4 quarts per gallon.) You pour 1 qt of white paint into the red, mix it, and then pour 1 qt of the mixture back into the can of white paint. What is the red-white content of each can now? If you continually repeat the process, when will the two cans be the same shade of pink?

Exercise 11 [ESL] An anti-asthmatic drug is one that treats the lung disease asthma.

11a. Sample answer: After 9 hours there are only 8 mg, after 18 hours there are 4 mg, after 27 hours there are still 2 mg left.

11b.

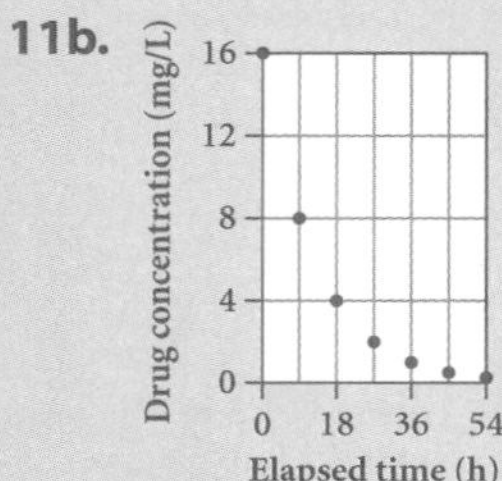

Exercise 12 Encourage a variety of approaches. In 12a, for example, students might use the Pythagorean Theorem or remember its consequence that in an isosceles right triangle the length of the hypotenuse is $\sqrt{2}$ times the length of a leg. They might extend the pattern that the perimeter of the third square is half the perimeter of the first square.

Exercise 14a If graphed, the data look somewhat linear. A good linear formula is $u_0 = 760$, $u_n = u_{n-1} + 83.5$. As needed, point out that multiplicative models are often better for population growth.

14a. $u_{1998} = 760$ and $u_n = (1 + 0.1)u_{n-1}$ where $n \geq 1999$

EXTENSIONS

A. Some people buy or lease a new car every two years. Have students research and compare the costs of buying versus leasing. Which is more economical? They will need to consider things such as the down payment, the interest paid, and the depreciated value of the car after two years.

B. Use Take Another Look activity 2 on page 74.

IMPROVING VISUAL THINKING SKILLS

Students might be surprised that at each step the same amount of red paint is in the white as there is white paint in the red. For example, after the first mixing, the "white" can contains 0.75 qt of red paint and 3.25 qt of white paint; the "red" can contains 0.75 qt of white paint and 2.25 qt of red paint. With numerous repetitions, the two cans will get closer and closer to the same shade of pink, but theoretically they will never be exactly the same.

This problem has the nice feature of a nonzero limit. In one can the limit (say, the amount of red paint in the mixture) is approached from below, and in the other it is approached from above.

LESSON

1.4

Graphing Sequences

By looking for numerical patterns, you can write a recursive formula that generates a sequence of numbers quickly and efficiently. You can also use graphs to help you identify patterns in a sequence.

Investigation
Match Them Up

Below are 18 different representations of sequences. Match each table with a recursive formula and a graph that represent the same sequence. As you do the matching, think about similarities and differences between the sequences and how those similarities and differences affect the tables, formulas, and graphs.

1.

n	u_n
0	8
1	4
3	1
6	0.125
9	0.015625

2.

n	u_n
0	0.5
1	1
2	2
3	4
4	8

3.

n	u_n
0	−2
1	1
2	2.5
4	3.625
5	3.8125

4.

n	u_n
0	−2
2	2
5	8
7	12
10	18

5.

n	u_n
0	8
1	6
3	2
5	−2
7	−6

6.

n	u_n
0	−4
1	−4
2	−4
4	−4
8	−4

A. $u_0 = 8$
$u_n = u_{n-1} - 2$ where $n \geq 1$

B. $u_0 = 8$
$u_n = 0.5u_{n-1}$ where $n \geq 1$

C. $u_0 = 0.5$
$u_n = 2u_{n-1}$ where $n \geq 1$

D. $u_0 = -2$
$u_n = u_{n-1} + 2$ where $n \geq 1$

E. $u_0 = -4$
$u_n = u_{n-1}$ where $n \geq 1$

F. $u_0 = -2$
$u_n = 0.5u_{n-1} + 2$ where $n \geq 1$

i.
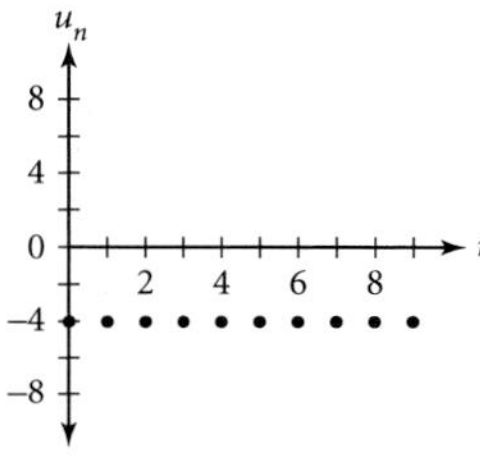

ii.
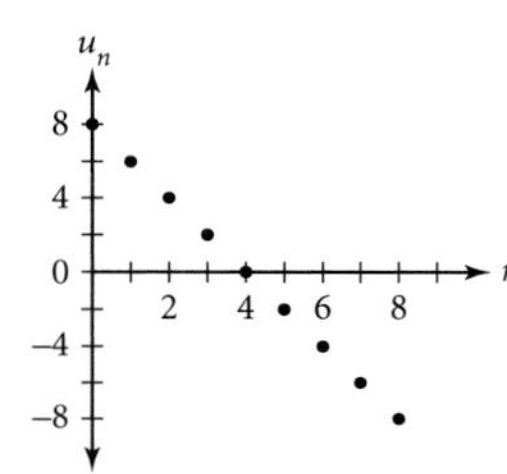

iii.
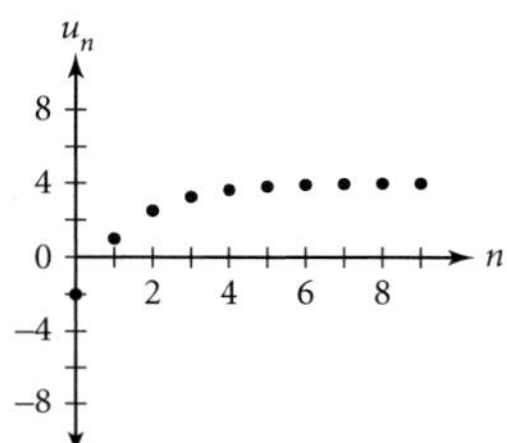

iv.
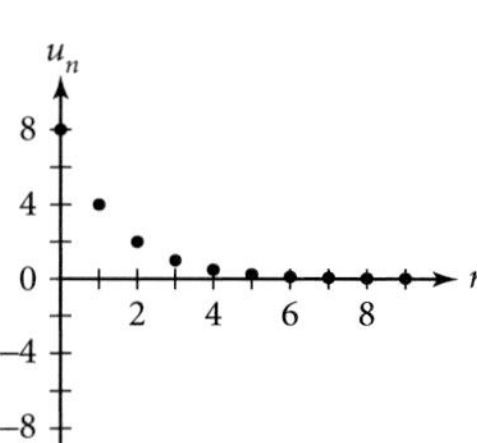

v.
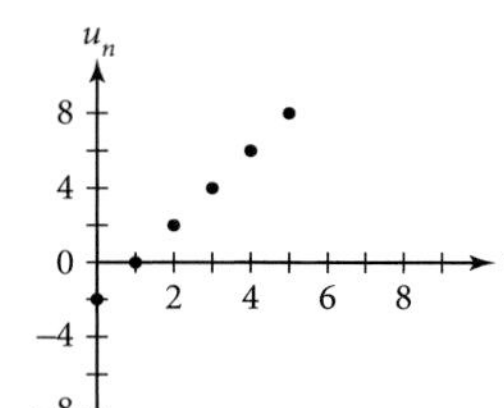

vi.
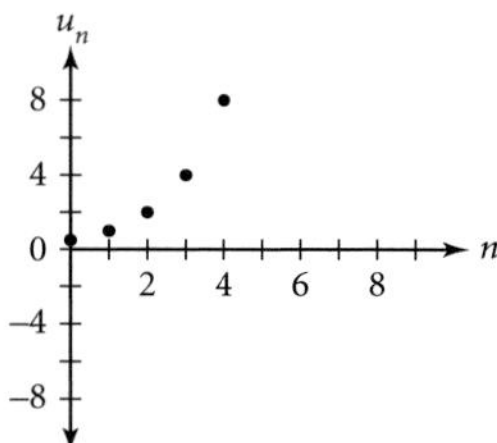

NCTM STANDARDS

CONTENT		PROCESS	
	Number	✓	Problem Solving
✓	Algebra	✓	Reasoning
	Geometry	✓	Communication
✓	Measurement	✓	Connections
✓	Data/Probability	✓	Representation

LESSON OBJECTIVES

- Recognize arithmetic and geometric sequences from their graphs
- Use graphs to check whether a recursive formula is a good model for data

LESSON 1.4

PLANNING

LESSON OUTLINE

One day:

15 min Investigation
10 min Example
5 min Sharing
15 min Exercises

MATERIALS

- Calculator Notes 1D, 1E, 1G, 1H, 1K
- Sketchpad demonstration Recursive Sequences, *optional*

TEACHING

Sequences can be described by tables, recursive formulas, or graphs. The one-step investigation is on page 52.

Guiding the Investigation

This investigation connects the previous lessons by tying together graphs, equations, and sequences. If you skip this investigation, find some alternative way to be sure students understand that the general shape of graphs of arithmetic sequences is linear and the general shape of graphs of geometric sequences is curved.

[Alert] Students may miss the fact that the values given for n are consecutive only in table 2.

If students have trouble writing the paragraph summarizing their findings, suggest that they organize their observations by type of sequence: arithmetic, geometric, or shifted geometric.

1. B. iv.; 2. C. vi.; 3. F. iii.; 4. D. v.; 5. A. ii.; 6. E. i.

Written paragraphs will vary, but may include the following points:

- Arithmetic sequences have linear graphs.
- Geometric sequences have curved graphs.
- When the common difference of an arithmetic sequence is positive, the linear shape slopes upward from left to right.
- When the common difference of an arithmetic sequence is negative, the linear shape slopes downward from left to right.
- When the common ratio of a geometric sequence is greater than 1, the curved shape increases from left to right.
- When the common ratio of a geometric sequence is between 0 and 1, the curved shape decreases from left to right approaching the n-axis.
- Shifted geometric sequences level off to a nonzero value.

One Step

Give this assignment: "Each group write two arithmetic sequences, two geometric sequences, and two shifted geometric sequences, trying to make sequences that no other group in the room will be making. On one sheet of paper, generate a table of values for each sequence; on another sheet, make a graph for each sequence, not identifying the sequences. Give your graphs to another group and see how many of the graphs they can label correctly as arithmetic, geometric, or shifted geometric sequences." As appropriate, use Calculator Notes 1D and 1E to show students how to use the Sequence mode on the calculator to save some time.

Write a paragraph that summarizes the relationships between different types of sequences, different types of recursive formulas, and different types of graphs. What generalizations can you make? What do you notice about the shapes of the graphs created from arithmetic and geometric sequences?

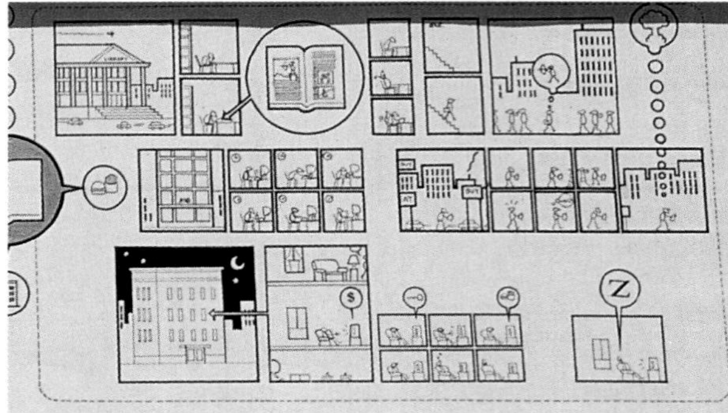

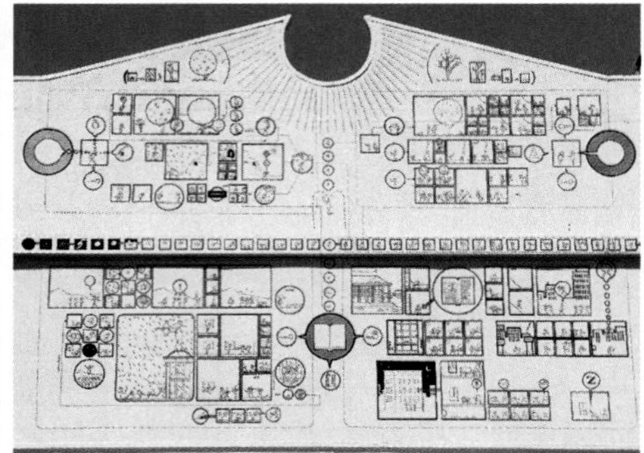

Many cartoons and comic strips show a sequence of events in linear order. The artwork of American artist Chris Ware (b 1967) breaks the convention by showing many sequences intertwined. This complex mural by Ware, at 826 Valencia Street in San Francisco, depicts human development of written and spoken communication.

The general shape of the graph of a sequence's terms gives you an indication of the type of sequence necessary to generate the terms.

The graph at right is a visual representation of the first five terms of the arithmetic sequence generated by the recursive formula

$$u_1 = 1$$
$$u_n = u_{n-1} + 2 \quad \text{where } n \geq 2$$

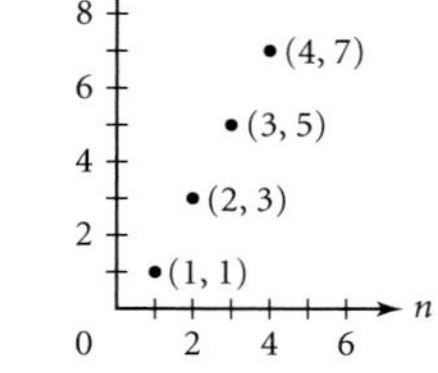

This graph, in particular, appears to be **linear,** that is, the points appear to lie on a line. The common difference, $d = 2$, makes each new point rise 2 units above the previous point.

Graphs of sequences are examples of **discrete graphs,** or graphs made of isolated points. It is incorrect to connect those isolated points with a continuous line or curve because the term number, n, must be a whole number.

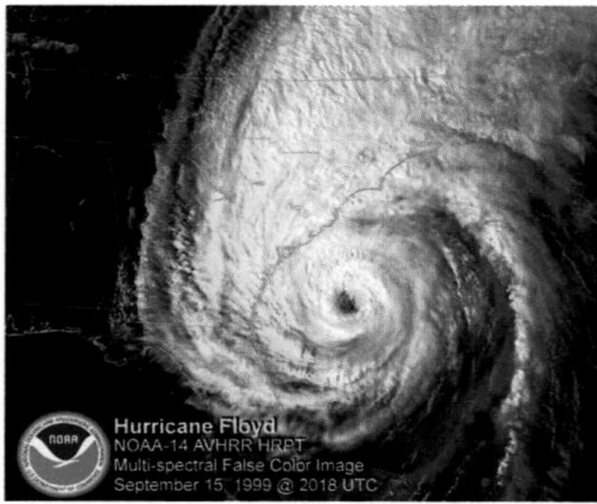

The general shape of the graph of a sequence allows you to recognize whether the sequence is arithmetic or geometric. Even if the graph represents data that are not generated by a sequence, you may be able to find a sequence that is a **model,** or a close fit, for the data. The more details you can identify from the graph, the better you will be at fitting a model.

Weather forecasting is one career that relies on mathematical modeling. Forecasters use computers and sophisticated models to monitor changes in the atmosphere. Trends in the data can help predict the trajectory and severity of an impending storm, such as a hurricane.

EXAMPLE

In deep water, divers find that their surroundings become darker the deeper they go. The data here give the percent of surface light intensity that remains at depth n ft in a particular body of water.

Depth (ft)	0	10	20	30	40	50	60	70
Percent of surface light	100	78	60	47	36	28	22	17

Find a sequence model that approximately fits these data.

Science CONNECTION

Marine life near the ocean's surface relies on organisms that use the sun for photosynthesis. But lifeforms at the bottom of the ocean, where sunlight is virtually absent, feed on waste material or microorganisms that create energy from chemicals released from the Earth's crust, a process called chemosynthesis. Squat lobsters and galatheid crabs are among many deep sea lifeforms that thrive near hydrothermal vents, where the Earth's crust releases chemical compounds.

▶ Solution

A graph of the data shows a decreasing, curved pattern. It is not linear, so an arithmetic sequence is not a good model. A geometric sequence with a long-run value of 0 will be a better choice.

The starting value at depth 0 ft is 100% light intensity, so use $u_0 = 100$. The recursive rule should have the form $u_n = (1 - p)u_{n-1}$, but the data are not given for every foot so you cannot immediately find a common ratio. The ratios between the given values are all approximately 0.77, or $(1 - 0.23)$. Because the light intensity decreases at a rate of 0.23 every 10 feet, it must decrease at a smaller rate every foot. A starting guess of 0.02 gives the model

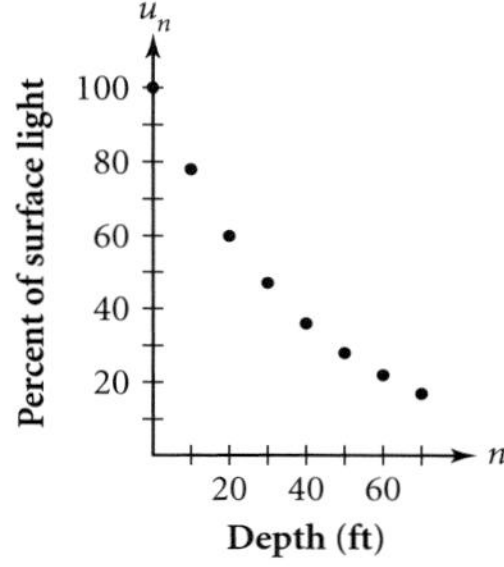

$$u_0 = 100$$
$$u_n = (1 - 0.02)u_{n-1} \quad \text{where } n \geq 1$$

Check this model by graphing the original data and the sequence on your calculator. The graph shows that this model fits only one data point—it does not decay fast enough. [▶ See **Calculator Note 1D** to learn about sequences on your calculator and **Calculator Note 1E** to learn about graphing sequences. ◀]

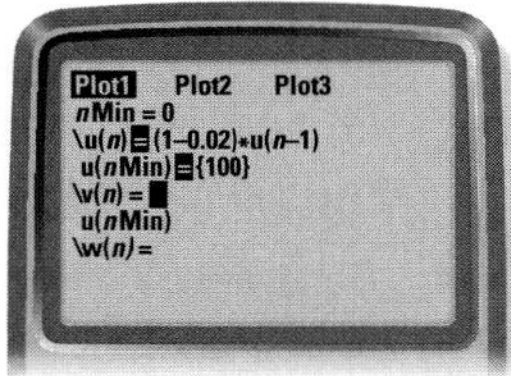

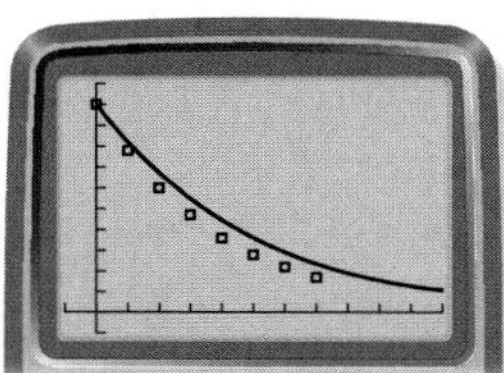

[−10, 110, 10, −10, 110, 10]

▶ EXAMPLE

If students did not do the Investigation Looking for the Rebound in Lesson 1.2, they may need to review Calculator Notes 1G and 1H in order to enter data into lists and make a scatter plot. These are in addition to Calculator Notes 1D and 1E, mentioned in the example.

The starting guess of 2% could be arrived at by linear interpolation and rounding down. However, dividing 0.23 by 10 to get a decrease of 0.023 between terms would impose a linear model on data that are really exponential. You might show how the linear model results in a sequence that does not match the data. Encourage students to guess their own rates of decay and have them explain why they came up with their guess. This will encourage students to use the guess-and-check method throughout the course.

As questions arise, point out that some calculators put subscripts in parentheses and that $u(5)$ does not mean u times 5.

Another way to check how well the model fits the data is to create a scatter plot of the original data (see Calculator Note 1H) and simultaneously graph the sequence (see Calculator Note 1E). You might show this method on a calculator display panel.

MAKING THE CONNECTION

[Ask] "What factors might influence surface light intensity?" [Wavelengths of visible light are absorbed as light travels through water; substances in the water, such as waste and vegetation, block light; light intensity decreases with the square of the distance from the source.]

Hydrothermal vents are found 2–5 km below the ocean's surface. Although no sunlight reaches this depth of the sea, the temperature heats up to 300–400°C because of volcanic activity.

For more information on chemosynthetic organisms, which live around hydrothermal vents in the ocean's floor, students can follow a link from www.keymath.com/DAA.

SHARING IDEAS

[Ask] "If arithmetic sequences give straight-line graphs, can we tell the slope of the line from the formula?" [It's the common difference, the amount of change in y for each unit change in x.]

Referring to the formula in part e of the investigation, **[Ask]** "Is this sequence arithmetic or geometric?" [The matching graph is a straight line, so the sequence is arithmetic, with common difference 0. On the other hand, the formula fits the definition of a geometric sequence, with common ratio 1. Thus the sequence is both arithmetic and geometric.]

[Ask] "Is a shifted geometric sequence a special kind of geometric sequence?" [Not necessarily, because it may not have a common ratio between consecutive terms. On the other hand, every geometric sequence is a shifted geometric sequence, with 0 being added. And every arithmetic sequence is a shifted geometric sequence, with 1 being multiplied.]

To show the relationship between the three types of sequences, you might use the Sketchpad demonstration Recursive Sequences with its sliders that control r and d.

Ask if the graph of a sequence is a continuous curve, as it appears on the calculator. If the points were connected, the function being graphed would be defined at all real numbers. But sequences are discrete functions defined on the term numbers, n, which are nonnegative integers, so their graphs shouldn't be connected. On a calculator, if the horizontal axis goes from -10 to 110, the discrete points are bunched together and look continuous. If students trace the sequence, they will see that the spider (trace cursor) jumps along discrete points. If students change Xmax to 10, they can see the first ten discrete points of the sequence graph.

Experiment by increasing the rate of decay. With some trial and error, you can find a model that fits the data better.

$$u_0 = 100$$
$$u_n = (1 - 0.025)u_{n-1} \quad \text{where } n \geq 1$$

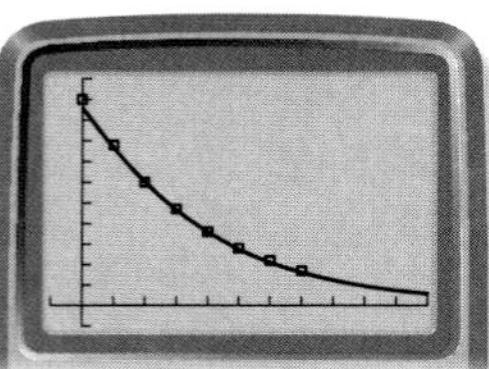

$[-10, 110, 10, -10, 110, 10]$

Once you have a good sequence model, you can use your calculator to find specific terms or make a table of terms [► See **Calculator Note 1K** to learn how to make a table of sequence values. ◄]. For example, the value of u_{43} means that at depth 43 ft approximately 34% of surface light intensity remains.

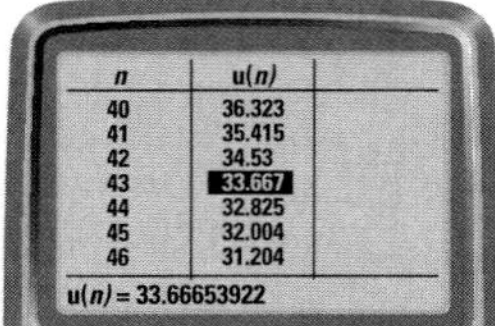

As you see in the calculator screens in the previous example, some calculators use $u(0), u(1), u(2), \ldots, u(n-1)$, and $u(n)$ instead of the subscripted notation $u_0, u_1, u_2, \ldots, u_{n-1}$, and u_n. Be aware that $u(5)$ means u_5, not u multiplied by 5. You may also see other variables, such as a_n or v_n, used for recursive formulas in other textbooks. It is important that you are able to make sense of these equivalent mathematical notations and be flexible in reading other people's work.

Being alert also pays off when working with graphs. Graphs help you understand and explain situations, and visualize the mathematics of a situation. When you make a graph or look at a graph, try to find connections between the graph and the mathematics used to create the graph. Consider what variables and units were used on each axis and what the smallest and largest values were for those variables. Sometimes this will be clear and obvious, and sometimes you will need to look at the graph in a new way to see the connections.

EXERCISES

Practice Your Skills

1. Suppose you are going to graph the specified terms of these four sequences. For each sequence, what minimum and maximum values of n and u_n would you use on the axes to get a good graph?

a.

n	0	1	2	3	4	5	6	7	8	9
u_n	2.5	4	5.5	7	8.5	10	11.5	13	14.5	16

0 to 9 for n and 0 to 16 for u_n

b. The first 20 terms of the sequence generated by

$$u_0 = 400$$
$$u_n = (1 - 0.18)u_{n-1} \quad \text{where } n \geq 1$$

0 to 19 for n and 0 to 400 for u_n

Assessing Progress

This is a good activity for assessing students' understanding of tables, recursive formulas, and graphs.

Closing the Lesson

From a table, recursive formula, or graph of a sequence, the other **representations of the sequence** can be derived. In particular, the graph of an arithmetic sequence is linear, and the graphs of geometric and shifted geometric sequences are curved.

c. The first 30 terms of the sequence generated by

$u_0 = 25$
$u_n = u_{n-1} - 7$ where $n \geq 1$ 0 to 29 for n and -178 to 25 for u_n

d. The first 70 terms of the sequence generated by

$u_0 = 15$
$u_n = (1 + 0.08)u_{n-1}$ where $n \geq 1$ 0 to 69 for n and 0 to 3037 for u_n

2. Identify each graph as a representation of an arithmetic sequence, a geometric sequence, or a shifted geometric sequence. Use an informed guess to write a recursive formula for each.

a.

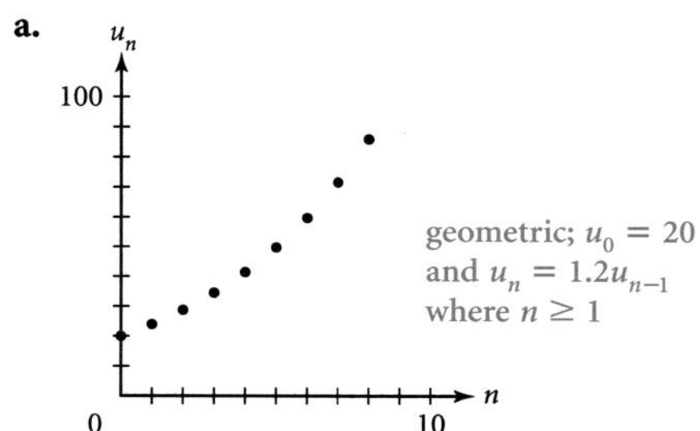

geometric; $u_0 = 20$ and $u_n = 1.2u_{n-1}$ where $n \geq 1$

b.

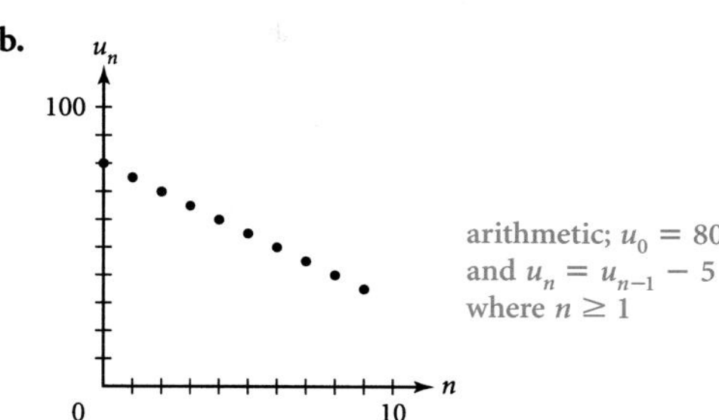

arithmetic; $u_0 = 80$ and $u_n = u_{n-1} - 5$ where $n \geq 1$

c.

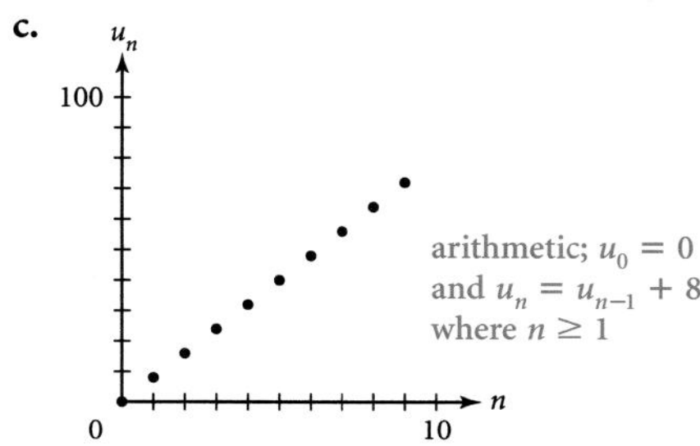

arithmetic; $u_0 = 0$ and $u_n = u_{n-1} + 8$ where $n \geq 1$

d.

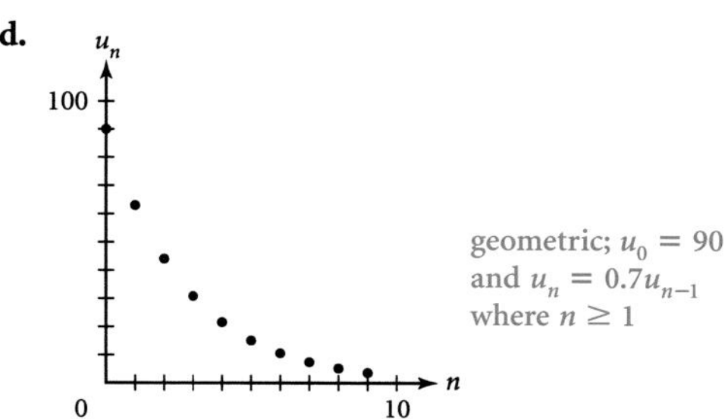

geometric; $u_0 = 90$ and $u_n = 0.7u_{n-1}$ where $n \geq 1$

3. Imagine the graphs of the sequences generated by these recursive formulas. Describe each graph using exactly three of these terms: arithmetic, decreasing, geometric, increasing, linear, nonlinear, shifted geometric.

a. $u_0 = 450$ geometric, nonlinear, decreasing
$u_n = a \cdot u_{n-1}$ where $n \geq 1$ and $0 < a < 1$

b. $u_0 = 450$ arithmetic, linear, decreasing
$u_n = b + u_{n-1}$ where $n \geq 1$ and $b < 0$

c. $u_0 = 450$ geometric, nonlinear, increasing
$u_n = u_{n-1} \cdot c$ where $n \geq 1$ and $c > 1$

d. $u_0 = 450$ arithmetic, linear, increasing
$u_n = u_{n-1} + d$ where $n \geq 1$ and $d > 0$

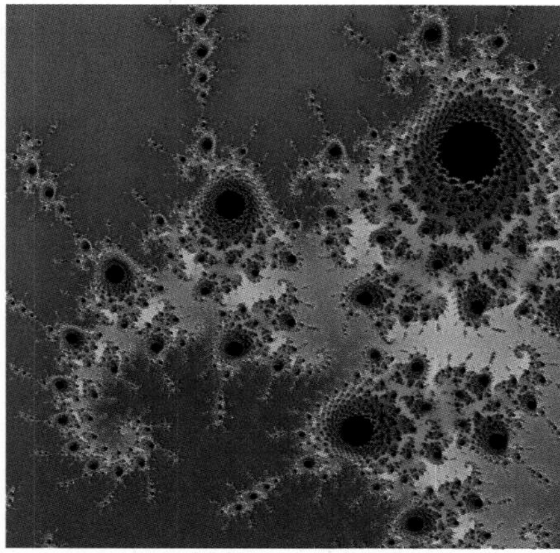

This complex fractal was created by plotting points generated by recursive formulas.

BUILDING UNDERSTANDING

If students are not learning how to use Sequence mode or home-screen recursion on the calculator, these problems will take significantly longer to solve.

ASSIGNING HOMEWORK

Essential	2, 3, 5
Performance assessment	1, 6, 7–12
Portfolio	4
Journal	4, 5, 7, 8
Group	11, 12
Review	13–15

Helping with the Exercises

Exercise 3 If students are having difficulty with the notation, suggest that they make up numbers for *a, b, c,* and *d* that satisfy the conditions.

Computer-Generated Fractals
To generate fractals like the one shown, we can use a recursive formula on the coordinates for each point (on the complex number plane). As the formula is applied over and over again, the value at a point either gets larger without limit (*escapes*) or it reaches a constant value. Each point that escapes is given a color determined by how fast it escapes. Points that approach a limit as the recursive process is applied are colored black. Students will work with another computer-generated fractal when they study complex numbers. That project, The Mandelbrot Set, is on page 397.

Exercise 4 Students may wonder what starting value to use. Suggest that they try several different ones and look for patterns. They might find the long-run value by calculating the individual terms or by using Sequence mode or home-screen recursion on the calculator. They may be surprised to find that the limit is the same for all starting values. **[Ask]** "Why doesn't the starting value affect the limit?" [Intuitively, multiplying repeatedly by 0.75 tends to move the values toward 0, no matter where they started; adding 210 compensates for this movement.]

Exercise 5 Graph i apparently approaches a nonzero limit; the only possible formula is the shifted geometric sequence in 5c, and then with $r < 1$. Graph ii is a curve that doesn't approach a limit, implying that $r > 1$ in 5b.

5i. C. The graph has a nonzero limit, so it must represent a shifted geometric sequence.

5ii. B. The graph of a nonshifted geometric sequence will increase indefinitely or have a limit of zero.

5iii. A. The graph of an arithmetic sequence is linear.

Exercise 6b This sequence can be graphed easily on a calculator.

7. The graph of an arithmetic sequence is always linear. The graph increases when the common difference is positive and decreases when the common difference is negative. The steepness of the graph relates to the common difference.

Reason and Apply

4. Consider the recursive rule $u_n = 0.75u_{n-1} + 210$.

a. What is the long-run value of any shifted geometric sequence that is generated by this recursive rule? 840

b. Sketch the graph of a sequence that is generated by this recursive rule and has a starting value See below.

i. Below the long-run value
ii. Above the long-run value
iii. At the long-run value

c. Write a short paragraph describing how the long-run value and starting value of each shifted geometric sequence in 4b influence the appearance of the graph. See below.

5. Match each recursive formula with the graph of the same sequence. Give your reason for each choice.

A. $u_0 = 20$
$u_n = u_{n-1} + d \quad \text{where } n \geq 1$

B. $u_0 = 20$
$u_n = r \cdot u_{n-1} \quad \text{where } n \geq 1$

C. $u_0 = 20$
$u_n = r \cdot u_{n-1} + d \quad \text{where } n \geq 1$

i.

ii.

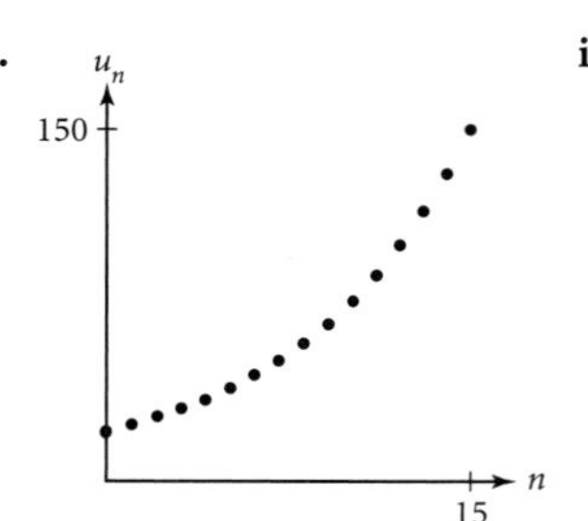

iii.

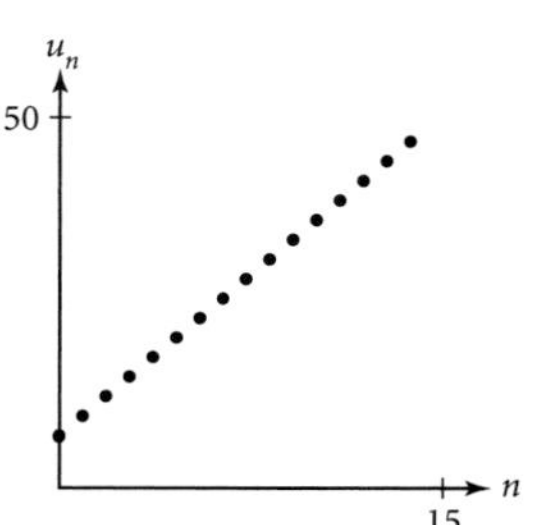

6. Consider the geometric sequence 18, −13.5, 10.125, −7.59375, ...

a. Write a recursive formula that generates this sequence. $u_0 = 18$ and $u_n = -0.75u_{n-1}$ where $n \geq 1$

b. Sketch a graph of the sequence. Describe how the graph is similar to other graphs that you have seen and also how it is unique.

c. What is the long-run value? 0

7. Your friend calls on the phone and the conversation goes like this:

Friend: What does the graph of an arithmetic sequence look like?

You: Be more specific.

Friend: Why? Don't they all look the same?

You: Yes and no.

Explain for your friend how the graphs of arithmetic sequences are similar and how they vary.

4b. i. sample answer: $u_0 = 200$

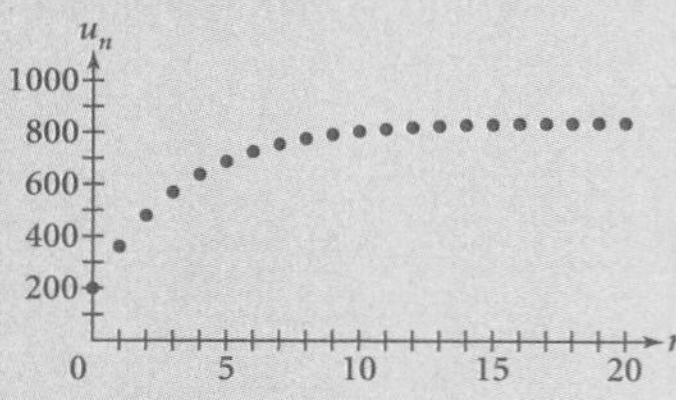

4b. ii. sample answer: $u_0 = 1000$

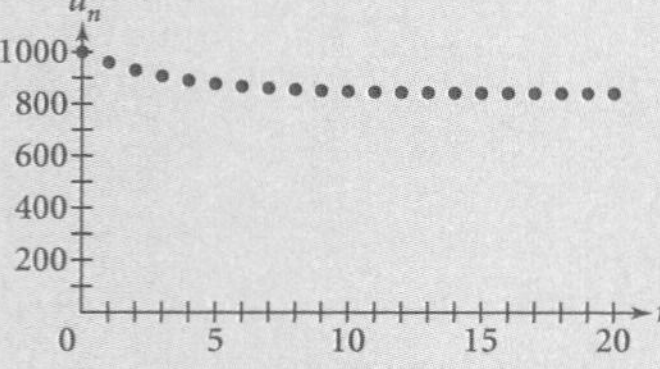

4b. iii. $u_0 = 840$

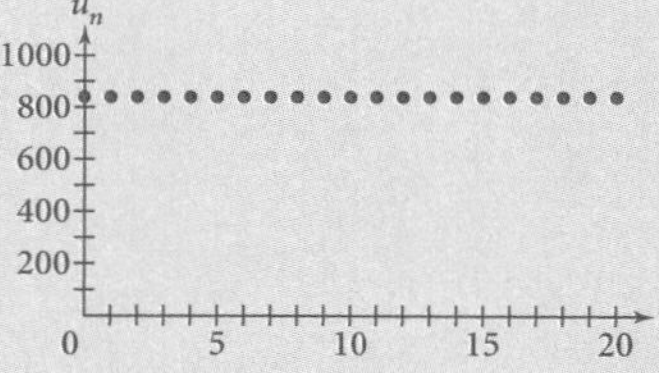

4c. When the starting value is below the long-run value, the graph increases toward the long-run value. When the starting value is above the long-run value, the graph decreases toward the long-run value. When the starting value is the long-run value, the graph is a constant, horizontal, linear pattern at the long-run value.

See page 878 for answer to Exercise 6b.

8. Your friend calls back and asks about geometric sequences. Explain how the graphs of geometric sequences are similar and how they vary.

9. APPLICATION The Forever Green Nursery has 7000 white pine trees. Each year, the nursery plans to sell 12% of its trees and plant 600 new ones.

a. Make a graph that shows the number of trees at the nursery over the next 20 years.

b. Use the graph to estimate the number of trees in the long run. How does your estimate compare to the long-run value you found in Exercise 8b in Lesson 1.3?

10. APPLICATION The Bayside Community Water District has decided to add fluoride to the drinking water. Board member Evelyn King does research and finds that the ideal concentration of fluoride in drinking water is between 1.00 mg/L and 2.00 mg/L. If the concentration gets higher than 4.00 mg/L, people may suffer health problems, such as bone disease or damage to developing teeth. If the concentration is less than 1.00 mg/L, it is too low to promote dental health. Ms. King supposes 15% of the fluoride present in the water supply is consumed during a period of one day. Create a graph to help her analyze each of these scenarios.

A water treatment plant

a. If the fluoride content begins at 3.00 mg/L and no additional fluoride is added, how long will it be before the concentration is too low to promote dental health?

b. If the fluoride content begins at 3.00 mg/L and 0.50 mg/L is added daily, will the concentration increase or decrease? What is the long-run value? Explain your reasoning.

c. Suppose the fluoride content begins at 3.00 mg/L and 0.10 mg/L is added daily. Describe what happens.

d. The Water District board members vote that there should be an initial treatment of 3.00 mg/L, but that the long-run fluoride content should be 1.50 mg/L. How much fluoride needs to be added daily for the fluoride content to stabilize at 1.50 mg/L?

11. APPLICATION As the air temperature gets warmer, snowy tree crickets chirp faster. You can actually use a snowy tree cricket's rate of chirping per minute to determine the approximate temperature in degrees Fahrenheit. Use a graph to find a sequence model that approximately fits these data.

Snowy Tree Crickets' Rate of Chirping

Temperature (°F)	50	55	60	65	70	75	80
Rate (chirps/min)	40	60	80	100	120	140	160

Snowy tree crickets are about 0.7 in. long, pale green, and live in shrubs and bushes. Only male crickets chirp, and they have different chirps for different activities, such as mating and fighting. All species of crickets chirp by rubbing their wings together.

Exercise 8 This exercise builds on the previous exercise. If $u_0 = 0$ or $r = 1$, the graph of the geometric sequence will be horizontal, so the geometric sequence will also be arithmetic.

8. The graph of a geometric sequence is usually nonlinear and usually approaches the n-axis or recedes more and more quickly from it. The graph increases when the common ratio is greater than 1 and decreases when the ratio is between 0 and 1. The change in steepness of the curve is related to the common ratio.

9a.

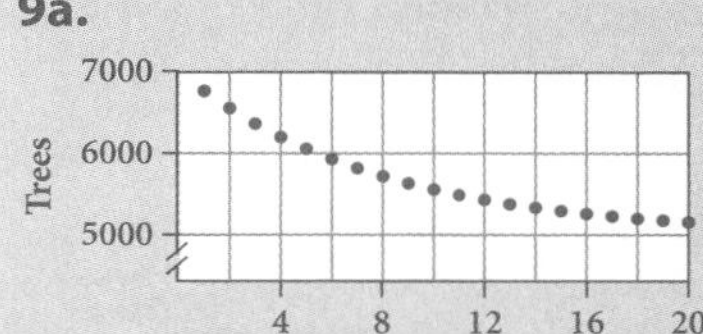

9b. The graph appears to have a long-run value of 5000 trees, which agrees with the long-run value found in Exercise 8b in Lesson 1.3.

Exercise 10 **[Context]** One mg/L is equivalent to one part per million (ppm). The Environmental Protection Agency has set the maximum level for fluoride in drinking water at 4 ppm.

In 10d, **[ESL]** *stabilize* means "become stable or fixed." If students are not using the Sequence mode on the calculator, this part will take some time. Students might need Calculator Note 1D. Sequence mode will allow students to graph and change the sequence quickly.

Exercise 11 **[Context]** The snow tree cricket, *Oecanthus fultoni,* is one of many subspecies of crickets. Every subspecies of cricket has a unique chirp; the snow tree cricket has the highest-pitched chirp.

If students write the recursive formula starting with $u_0 = -160$ for a temperature of 0, you might wonder aloud if crickets can chirp a negative amount.

11. possible answer: $u_{50} = 40$ and $u_n = u_{n-1} + 4$ where $n \geq 51$

See page 878 for answers to Exercise 10.

Exercise 12 These data were reported in Appendix A of the 2000 U.S. Census. Different sources may give slightly different population data. Students should understand that any measure of population is an estimate because it is impossible to count every person in any sizable country.

12. possible answer: $u_{1950} = 7.6$ and $u_n = (1 + 0.026)u_{n-1}$ where $n \geq 1951$

Exercise 13 This exercise uses shifted geometric sequences. It also reviews undoing operations (as taught through number tricks in *Discovering Algebra*). Students can also visualize the "undoing" sequence as a new sequence in the reverse order.

Exercise 15 It might help students if you are explicit about the patterns elicited in 15a–c. **[Ask]** "How does the change in the constant term relate to the change in the long-run value?" [In general, the limit of the sequence generated by $u_n = r \cdot u_{n-1} + (m \cdot d)$ will be m times the limit of the sequence generated by $u_n = r \cdot u_{n-1} + d$.]

EXTENSION

Extend Exercise 4 by challenging students to explore whether all shifted geometric sequences behave the way $u_n = 0.75u_{n-1} + 210$ behaves or whether there are exceptions. [When the multiplier is greater than 1, the sequence does not approach a limit.]

12. APPLICATION This table gives the estimated population of Peru from 1950 to 2000. Use a graph to find a sequence model that approximately fits these data.

Population of Peru

Year	Population (millions)
1950	7.6
1960	9.9
1970	13.2
1980	17.3
1990	22.0
1996	25.1
2000	27.0

(U.S. Bureau of the Census, International Data Base)

This painting, *Corpus Christi 1982,* by Antonio Huillca Huallpa shows a scene in Cuzco, Peru.

Review

1.1 **13.** Consider the recursive formula

$u_0 = 450$
$u_n = 0.75u_{n-1} + 210 \quad \text{where } n \geq 1$

a. Find u_1, u_2, u_3, u_4, and u_5. 547.5, 620.6, 675.5, 716.6, 747.5

b. How can you calculate backward from the value of u_1 to u_0, or 450? In general, what operations can you perform to any term in order to find the value of the previous term? $\frac{547.5 - 210}{0.75} = 450$; subtract 210 and divide the difference by 0.75.

c. Write a recursive formula that generates the values of u_5 to u_0 backward. $u_0 = 747.5$ and $u_n = \frac{u_{n-1} - 210}{0.75}$ where $n \geq 1$

14. Find the value of a that makes each equation true.

a. $47{,}500{,}000 = 4.75 \times 10^a$ 7 **b.** $0.0461 = a \times 10^{-2}$ 4.61 **c.** $3.48 \times 10^{-1} = a$ 0.348

1.3 **15.** *Mini-Investigation* For a–c, find the long-run value of the sequence generated by the recursive formula.

a. $u_0 = 50$
$u_n = (1 - 0.30)u_{n-1} + 10 \quad \text{where } n \geq 1$ $33\frac{1}{3}$

b. $u_0 = 50$
$u_n = (1 - 0.30)u_{n-1} + 20 \quad \text{where } n \geq 1$ $66\frac{2}{3}$

c. $u_0 = 50$
$u_n = (1 - 0.30)u_{n-1} + 30 \quad \text{where } n \geq 1$ 100

d. Generalize any patterns you notice in your answers to 15a–c. Use your generalizations to find the long-run value of the sequence generated by

$u_0 = 50$
$u_n = (1 - 0.30)u_{n-1} + 70 \quad \text{where } n \geq 1$

The long-run value grows in proportion to the added constant. $7 \cdot 33\frac{1}{3} = 233\frac{1}{3}$

E X P L O R A T I O N

Recursion in Geometry

In this chapter you have used recursive rules to produce sequences of numbers. In geometry, you may have used recursive rules to produce fractals or other geometric shapes. In this exploration you will explore two geometric designs that follow recursive rules.

The shell of the chambered nautilus, a relative of the octopus, reflects the Fibonacci sequence. It is only one of many occurrences of Fibonacci numbers in nature.

In Part 1, you will use The Geometer's Sketchpad® to create a Fibonacci spiral. In Part 2, you will construct a golden rectangle spiral, then compare the two constructions. You can learn more about mathematical spirals by visiting the Internet links at www.keymath.com/DAA .

Activity

Two Spirals

Part 1: The Fibonacci Spiral

In his book *Liber abaci* (1202), Italian mathematician Leonardo Fibonacci (ca. 1170–1240) posed this question:

> How many pairs of rabbits will be produced in a year, beginning with a single pair, if every month each pair bears a new pair which becomes productive one month later?

You can model this scenario with the sequence 1, 1, 2, 3, 5, 8, 13, ...

Can you describe, in words, the rules of this sequence? Can you write a recursive formula that generates this sequence? (*Hint:* In a sequence, u_n need not depend only on u_{n-1}.) Interestingly, the Fibonacci sequence has applications in mathematics and life science. The sequence models such things as honeybee populations, the seed patterns in the middle of a sunflower, and the number of branches on a tree as it grows.

NCTM STANDARDS

CONTENT		PROCESS	
✓	Number	✓	Problem Solving
✓	Algebra	✓	Reasoning
✓	Geometry	✓	Communication
	Measurement	✓	Connections
	Data/Probability	✓	Representation

LESSON OBJECTIVES

- Explore the Fibonacci sequence
- Understand the relationship between the Fibonacci sequence and the golden ratio
- See an example of recursion in geometry

EXPLORATION

PLANNING

LESSON OUTLINE

One day:

35 min Activity

10 min Sharing

MATERIALS

- The Geometer's Sketchpad
- Two Spirals (W), *optional*
- Sketchpad Demonstration Two Spirals, *optional*

TEACHING

In this exploration, students see recursion in geometry and review self-similarity. If only one computer is available, you might use the Sketchpad demonstration.

If your students have not used The Geometer's Sketchpad, you might want to spend a day on Sketchpad basics. Students need to know how to construct an arc on a circle, measure a distance, translate segments or construct perpendiculars, rotate points, and use the **Iterate** command. Students new to Sketchpad can use the more detailed notes on the Two Spirals worksheets.

The Fibonacci sequence is first explored in Lesson 1.1, Improving Your Reasoning Skills. You may want to assign that problem before doing this exploration.

Guiding the Activity

The exploration lends itself well to the jigsaw method of cooperative learning. Half the class can do Part 1, the other half Part 2. Then students can compare their spirals to answer the questions. Suggest that students set Sketchpad preferences so that points are named as they are created.

Guiding the Activity (continued)
Part 1
Step 4 Students might ask what "this process" is; suggest that they read the rest of the sentence carefully.

Step 5 The measured side of each successive square produces the Fibonacci sequence.

Step 6 The side of each new square spans the sides of the two previous squares laid end-to-end, and each square contains a 90° arc. The side of each square is the sum of the sides of the two previous squares, just as each term in the Fibonacci sequence is the sum of the two previous terms.

Part 2
[Language] The Greek letter ϕ (phi) is pronounced "fī."

[Language] The word *spiral* is derived from the Greek word *speira* meaning "coil, twist."

Procedure Note, 5 Students might construct the fourth vertex of the rectangle by translating point B' along vector AD. Or they might construct lines perpendicular or parallel to the other sides of the rectangle. If they do the latter, encourage them to hide the perpendicular lines used to create the rectangle before continuing to 6.

[Ask] "Why does the construction in the Procedure Note produce a golden rectangle?" [If $AB = 1$ unit, the distance $CB = \sqrt{1^2 + \left(\frac{1}{2}\right)^2} = \frac{\sqrt{5}}{2}$. So $B'E = \frac{1}{2} + \frac{\sqrt{5}}{2}$, or $\frac{1+\sqrt{5}}{2}$.]

SHARING IDEAS

You might **[Ask]** "Are the spirals self-similar?" The iterations of the golden rectangle are similar to each other, so the complete, unbounded spiral (after infinitely many steps) has the same self-similarity characteristic that fractals have. That is, if you cut it off at any point, the remaining unbounded part is similar to the original spiral. The Fibonacci spiral is not quite self-similar, as can be seen from the fact that the successive rectangles are not similar.

The Procedure Note in Part 1 uses a custom tool, while the one in Part 2 uses **Iterate.** Iteration is quicker, but a custom tool is necessary in Part 1 due to the discontinuity between the first and second iterations. Students may want to take on the challenge of creating an iteration that will perform the same function as the custom tool they've created.

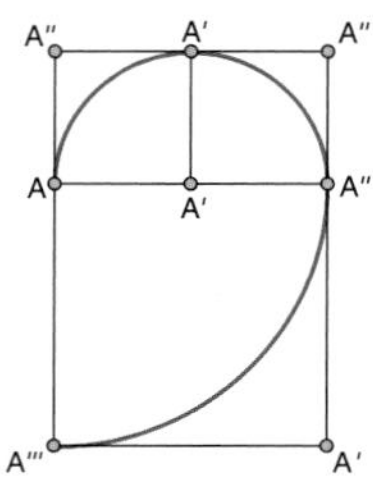

The first three stages of the Fibonacci spiral.

Procedure Note

Creating a Measured Square Tool with an Arc

1. In a new sketch, construct two points, A and B.
2. Rotate point B about point A by 90°. Then, rotate point A about point B' by 90°. Select, in order, A, B, A', and B'. Choose **Segments** from the Construct menu to create square $ABA'B'$.
3. Using the circle tool, construct a circle with point B as its center through point A. Construct the minor arc, $\overset{\frown}{A'A}$, then hide the circle.
4. Measure the distance between points A and B. Deselect all objects. Select, in order, points A and B, then choose **Select All** from the Edit menu.
5. Click and hold the **Custom Tool** icon and choose **Create New Tool . . .** from the pop-up menu. Name the tool Measured Square.

Step 1 Follow the Procedure Note to create the Measured Square tool. Then open a new sketch.

Step 2 Construct point A. Translate point A a distance of 1 cm at 0°.

Step 3 Using the Measured Square tool, select point A then point A'.

Step 4 Now select the new point A' created by your tool, followed by the original point A'. Next select the new point A'' followed by the original point A. Continue this process, creating larger and larger squares, always choosing the point at the end of the new arc first, followed by the other endpoint of the longest side.

Step 5 The spiral you have created is the Fibonacci spiral. What do you notice about the design?

Step 6 Describe the process that creates the Fibonacci spiral. How does this relate to the Fibonacci sequence?

Part 2: The Golden Rectangle Spiral

If you remove a square from a golden rectangle, you're left with another golden rectangle.

The **golden ratio** is a number, often represented with the Greek letter ϕ (lowercase phi). One definition of phi is that to square it you just add one to it, or

$$\phi^2 = \phi + 1$$

You can rearrange this equation and use the quadratic formula to solve for ϕ.

$$\phi = \frac{1 \pm \sqrt{5}}{2}$$

The positive root, which is approximately 1.618, is the golden ratio.

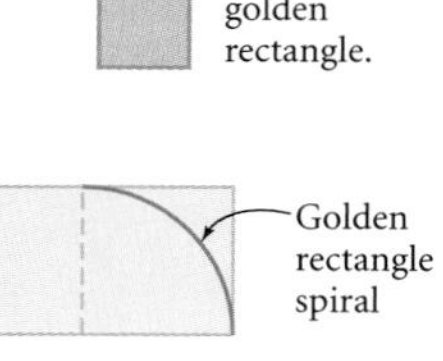

The **golden rectangle** is a rectangle whose length is ϕ times its width. The golden rectangle spiral is produced by drawing a segment to create a square inside the golden rectangle and constructing a 90° arc to span the corners of that square. A golden rectangle is unique because the smaller rectangle that remains is also a golden rectangle, so the process can be repeated.

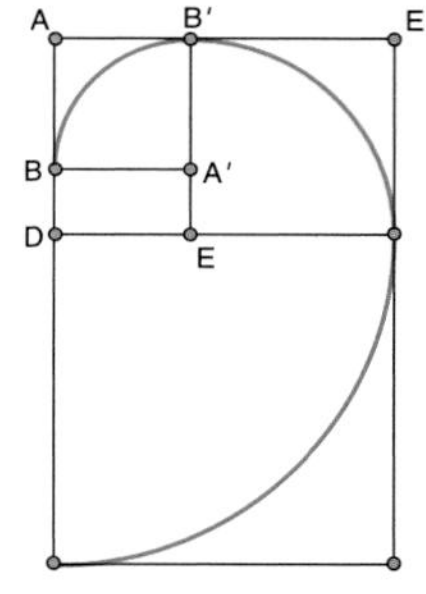

The first three stages of the golden rectangle spiral.

Procedure Note

Golden Rectangle Spiral

1. In a new sketch, construct two points, *A* and *B*.
2. Rotate point *B* around point *A* by 90°. Then, rotate point *A* around point *B′* by 90°. Select, in order, *A, B, A′*, and *B′*. Choose **Segments** from the Construct menu to create square *ABA′B′*.
3. Construct the midpoint *C* of side *AB*. Construct a circle centered at point *C* through point *A′*.
4. Construct a ray, $\overrightarrow{AB}$. Mark the intersection of the ray and the circle point *D*. Hide the circle, the ray, and point *C*.
5. Construct a rectangle with *D, A*, and *B′* as three of its vertices. Label the fourth vertex *E*. Hide any construction lines.
6. Construct a circle centered at point *A′* and containing points *B′* and *B*. Construct the minor arc, $\overset{\frown}{BB'}$, then hide the circle.
7. Rotate point *E* about point *B′* by 90° to create point *E′*. Select points *A* and *B* and choose **Iterate** from the Transform menu. Map point *A* to point *E′* and point *B* to point *B′*.

Step 1 Use the Procedure Note to create a golden rectangle spiral.

Step 2 Choose **Select All** from the Edit menu. Use the "+" key on your keyboard to add iterations to your sketch.

Step 3 The spiral you have created is the golden rectangle spiral. What is the ratio of length to width in each rectangle?

Step 4 Are all the rectangles in your design similar? Why or why not?

Step 3 approximately 1.618, or ϕ

Step 4 Yes. They all have the same angle measures and the same proportions, so they are all similar.

Questions

1. Print out each of your sketches so that you can compare them by laying one over the other. (When printing, you should select the Scale to Fit Page option in the Print Preview dialog box.) Is there a resemblance between the golden rectangle spiral and the Fibonacci spiral? How are they different?
2. Write the sequence of length-to-width ratios for the outermost rectangle at each stage of your golden rectangle spiral. Write the sequence of the length-to-width ratios for the outermost rectangle at each stage of your Fibonacci spiral. How are these sequences related?
3. How is recursion in geometry related to recursion in algebra?
Possible answer: A recursive rule in geometry usually produces a geometric design. The measurements of the shapes at each stage of the recursion process produce sequences that can be expressed with an algebraic recursive rule.

1. They are very nearly the same, except near the center and at the edge of the spiral. The center of the Fibonacci spiral breaks down into two congruent squares, but the golden rectangle spiral potentially continues inward indefinitely. Both spirals potentially continue outward indefinitely. This construction of the golden rectangle spiral starts with a finite outside edge (though the reverse process of adding a square to the longer side could always be carried out to continue expanding it outward).

2. golden spiral ratios: 1.618, 1.618, 1.618, 1.618, 1.618, . . .

Fibonacci spiral ratios: 1, 2, 1.5, 1.667, 1.6, 1.625, 1.615, 1.619, 1.618, . . .

The sequence of ratios for the Fibonacci spiral approaches the golden ratio in the long run.

Assessing Progress
As students work and discuss, you can assess their facility with Sketchpad and their understanding of similarity.

Closing the Lesson

The **Fibonacci spiral** is built from rectangles whose lengths are numbers in the Fibonacci sequence: 1, 1, 2, 3, 5, 8, 13, ... The ratios of consecutive terms approach the **golden ratio, ϕ**, whose square is one more than itself. The golden rectangle spiral is built from rectangles whose side lengths have ratio ϕ. If a square is extended by attaching a golden rectangle along one edge, the result is a larger golden rectangle.

▶ Helping with the Questions

Question 1 The spirals look very much alike, though there are slight differences at the beginning. **[Ask]** "Why do the spirals look the same when printed?" [Both spirals are generated by squares, each of which (after the second) has length equal to the sum of the lengths of the two previous squares. Moreover, the ratios of the lengths of consecutive sides are very close.]

Question 2 The length-to-width ratio of each rectangle in the golden spiral is ϕ. The corresponding ratio for the outermost rectangle of the Fibonacci spiral drawn will be close to ϕ, because these ratios approach ϕ.

Question 3 *Recursion* means constructing each stage (or term of a sequence) from the previous stage. You might discuss the difference between recursion and iteration. For example, you can generate the sequence of even numbers by iteration by just taking $2 \cdot 1, 2 \cdot 2, 2 \cdot 3$, and so on. Or you can generate it by recursion by starting with 2 and then adding 2, then adding 2 to the result, adding 2 to that result, and so on.

LESSON 1.5

PLANNING

LESSON OUTLINE

One day:

15 min Investigation

10 min Example

5 min Sharing

15 min Exercises

MATERIALS

- Calculator Note 1M, *optional*

TEACHING

In this lesson, students explore how shifted geometric sequences can describe loans and investments, with regular payments or deposits of a fixed amount. **[Ask]** "What kind of sequence does the recursive rule generate?" [shifted geometric, of which arithmetic and geometric sequences are special cases]

One Step

Pose the problem from Step 3 of the investigation: "You plan to borrow $22,000 over 5 years (60 months) to purchase a new car. The bank charges interest at an annual rate of 7.9%, compounded monthly. What monthly payment allows you to pay off the principal and interest on the loan in exactly 60 months?" As students work, remind them as necessary how to generate recursive sequences on the graphing calculator.

LESSON 1.5 Loans and Investments

. . . so little stress is ever laid on the pleasure of becoming an educated person, the enormous interest it adds to life.

EDITH HAMILTON

In life you will face many financial situations, which may include car loans, checking accounts, credit cards, long-term investments, life insurance, retirement accounts, and home mortgages. You will need to make intelligent choices about your money and whom you can trust. Fortunately, much of the mathematics is no more complicated than the recursive rule $u_n = r \cdot u_{n-1} + d$.

Investigation
Life's Big Expenditures

In this investigation you will use recursion to explore loan balances and payment options. Your calculator will be a helpful tool for trying different sequence models.

Part 1

You plan to borrow $22,000 to purchase a new car. The investment must be paid off in 5 years (60 months). The bank charges interest at an annual rate of 7.9%, compounded monthly. Part of each monthly payment is applied to the interest, and the remainder reduces the starting balance, or principal.

Step 1 What is the *monthly* interest rate? What is the first month's interest on the $22,000? If you make a payment of $300 at the end of the first month, then what is the remaining balance?

Step 1 $\frac{7.9\%}{12} = 0.658\overline{3}\%$; $144.83; $21,844.83

Step 2 Record the balances for the first 6 months with monthly payments of $300. How many months would it take to pay off the loan?

Step 2 $21,844.83, $21,688.65, $21,531.43, $21,373.18, $21,213.88, $21,053.54; 101 months

Step 3 Experiment with other values for the monthly payment. What monthly payment allows you to pay off the loan in exactly 60 months?

Step 3 Monthly payments of $445.03 give an overpayment of $0.11 with the 60th payment.

Step 4 How much do you actually pay for the car using the monthly payment you found in Step 3? (*Hint:* The last payment should be a little less than the other 59 payments.)

Step 4 59($445.03) + ($444.92) = $26,701.69

Part 2

Use the techniques that you discovered in Part 1 to find the monthly payment for a 30-year home mortgage of $146,000 with an annual interest rate of 7.25%, compounded monthly. How much do you actually pay for the house?

Monthly payments of $995.98 give an overpayment of $3.37 with the 360th payment; you actually pay $358,549.43.

Guiding the Investigation

Part 1

Step 2 Home-screen recursion on a calculator can easily give the figures for six months, but to answer the other question it's easier to use Sequence mode.

Step 3 Students can make an informal guess about the monthly payment by first calculating the interest that accrues in the first month. The minimum payment must be greater than the interest for the balance to decrease. You may want to encourage groups to pick different payments, find which is the closest, and then narrow it down from there.

You can use Finance mode (Calculator Note 1M) to check answers and explore scenarios. You might introduce Calculator Note 1M after you have assessed students' ability to calculate by hand.

Part 2

When needed, remind students that payments are made monthly, so there are a total of 360 payments. This question has two parts: Find the monthly payment, and find the total amount of money spent on the house.

[ESL] *Mortgage* means "loan," and it is generally applied to loans to buy homes.

Consumer
CONNECTION

In the last quarter of the year 2000, the National Association of Home Builders reported that the median price for a home in the United States was $151,000. Mortgage lenders usually require monthly payments to be no more than 29% of a family's monthly income, which means that less than 60% of families could afford to buy a home in 2000. The most affordable place to buy a house was Des Moines, Iowa, (median home price of $107,000) where people with median incomes could afford 88.9% of the homes sold. In contrast, the least affordable houses were in San Francisco, California, where the median home price was $530,000, and people earning the median income could afford only 6.1% of the homes sold.

Investments are mathematically similar to loans. With an investment, deposits are added on a regular basis so that your balance increases.

EXAMPLE Gwen's employer offers an investment plan that invests a portion of each paycheck before taxes are deducted. Gwen gets paid every week. The plan has a fixed annual interest rate of 4.75%, compounded weekly, and she decides to contribute $10 each week. What will Gwen's balance be in 5 years?

▸ Solution Gwen's starting balance is $10. Each week, the previous balance is multiplied by $\left(1+\frac{0.0475}{52}\right)$ and Gwen adds another $10. A recursive formula that generates the balance is

$$u_0 = 10$$
$$u_n = \left(1+\frac{0.0475}{52}\right)u_{n-1} + 10 \quad \text{where } n \geq 1$$

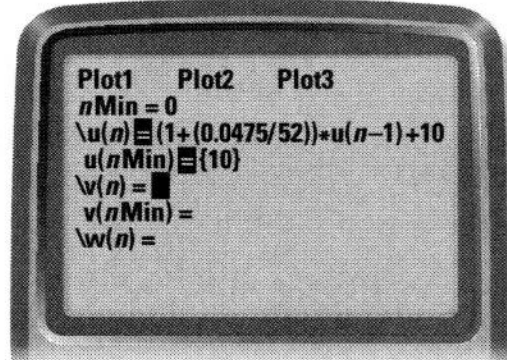

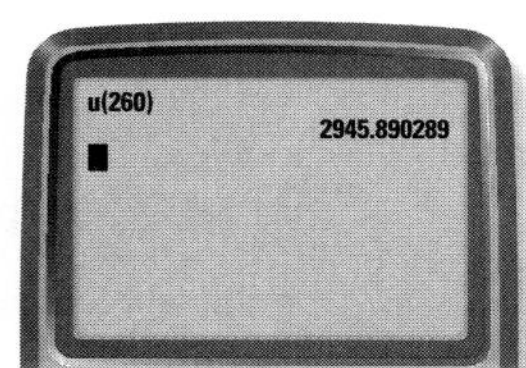

There are 52 weeks in a year and 260 weeks in 5 years. The value of u_{260} shows that the balance after 5 years is $2945.89.

As you work on each exercise, look for these important pieces of information: the principal, the deposit or payment amount, the annual interest rate, and the frequency with which interest is compounded. You will be able to solve many financial problems with these values using recursion.

NCTM STANDARDS

CONTENT		PROCESS	
✓	Number	✓	Problem Solving
✓	Algebra	✓	Reasoning
	Geometry	✓	Communication
	Measurement	✓	Connections
✓	Data/Probability	✓	Representation

LESSON OBJECTIVES

- Use a recursive formula to model a loan
- Use a recursive formula to model an investment

MAKING THE CONNECTION

[Ask] "Based on the information in the connection, what would your monthly income need to be to qualify for the home mortgage in Part 2?" $\left[\frac{29}{100} = \frac{\$995.98}{x}\right.$, or $0.29x = \$995.98;\ x \approx \$3434.41\left.\right]$

▸ EXAMPLE

This type of investment is called *tax deferred.* 401(k) plans are common tax-deferred investments; however, these moneys might be invested in the stock market and would not have a fixed annual interest rate.

Students should note that Gwen deposited $2600 and earned $345.89 in interest.

Additional Example
You invest $3000 with a nominal annual interest rate of 5.5%. Compare the time it takes to double your money with interest compounded daily, weekly, and monthly. [daily: 12.60363869 yr, or 12 yr 7 mo 8 d; weekly: 12.60933971 yr, or 12 yr 7 mo 2 wk; monthly: 12.63153513 yr, or 12 yr 8 mo]

SHARING IDEAS

The paragraph before the Example says that investments are similar to loans. Ask how. [Both can be described by a shifted geometric sequence, with a recursive rule $u_n = r \cdot u_{n-1} + d$. For a loan, d is negative; for an investment, d is positive.]

[Ask] "Should monthly interest be accrued right before or right after a monthly payment?" [You pay less interest on a loan if interest is calculated after the payment and receive more interest on an investment if interest is calculated after the payment.]

In Step 2 of the investigation, the calculator rounds the balances to many decimal places. In the real world, each bank balance is rounded to the nearest cent, and this rounded figure is then used to calculate the following month's interest. This rounding

Sharing Ideas (continued)
discrepancy may result in the balances differing by a few cents. As a challenge, **[Ask]** "How could you create a recursive formula that produces rounded answers?" $\left[u_0 = 22000 \text{ and } u_n = \text{round}\left((1 + (0.079/12)) \cdot u_{n-1} - 1000, 2\right) \text{ where } n \geq 1.\right]$ "By the time the loan is paid off, what is the cumulative difference between the rounded model and the unrounded model?"

[Ask] "On a loan, will you be paying the same amount of interest each month?" [No; a smaller portion of the payment goes to pay interest each time, because the interest is calculated on a smaller amount of principal.]

Assessing Progress
You can assess students' ability to generate recursive sequences on the calculator, their understanding of a multiplier to calculate percent increase, and their knowledge of how to calculate a monthly interest rate from an annual rate.

BUILDING UNDERSTANDING

Students practice working with loans and investments.

ASSIGNING HOMEWORK

Essential	1–7
Performance assessment	8–11
Portfolio	11
Journal	8
Group	11
Review	12–15

EXERCISES

Practice Your Skills

1. Assume the sequence generated by $u_0 = 450$ and $u_n = (1 + 0.039)u_{n-1} + 50$ where $n \geq 1$ represents a financial situation and n is measured in years.

a. Is this a loan or an investment? Explain your reasoning.

b. What is the principal? $450

c. What is the deposit or payment amount? $50

d. What is the annual interest rate? 3.9%

e. What is the frequency with which interest is compounded? annually (once a year)

2. Answer the questions in Exercise 1a–e for the sequence generated by $u_0 = 500$ and $u_n = \left(1 + \frac{0.04}{4}\right)u_{n-1} - 25$ where $n \geq 1$. Let n be measured in quarter-years.

3. Find the first month's interest on a $32,000 loan at an annual interest rate of

a. 4.9% $130.67 **b.** 5.9% $157.33 **c.** 6.9% $184.00 **d.** 7.9% $210.67

4. Write a recursive formula for each financial situation.

a. You borrow $10,000 at an annual interest rate of 10%, compounded monthly, and each payment is $300.

b. You buy $7000 worth of furniture on a credit card with an annual interest rate of 18.75%, compounded monthly. You plan to pay $250 each month.

c. You invest $8000 at 6%, compounded quarterly, and you deposit $500 every three months. (Quarterly means four times per year.)

d. You enroll in an investment plan that deducts $100 from your monthly paycheck and deposits it into an account with an annual interest rate of 7%, compounded monthly.

Reason and Apply

5. APPLICATION Find the balance after 5 years if $500 is deposited into an account with an annual interest rate of 3.25%, compounded monthly. $588.09

6. APPLICATION Consider a $1000 investment at an annual interest rate of 6.5%, compounded quarterly. Find the balance after

a. 10 years $1905.56 **b.** 20 years $3631.15 **c.** 30 years $6919.38

7. ***Mini-Investigation*** Find the balance of a $1000 investment, after 10 years, at an annual interest rate of 6.5% when compounded

a. Annually $1877.14

b. Monthly $1912.18

c. Daily (In financial practice, daily means 360 times per year, not 365.) $1915.43

d. After the same length of time, how will the balances compare from investments that are compounded annually, monthly, or daily?

Helping with the Exercises

Exercise 1d, e The exercise states that n is measured in years, so the interest rate is annual.

Exercise 3 If students forget to divide the interest rate by 12, ask them how their result compares to results in the investigation and example. Try to help students obtain the experience they need for an intelligent check of reasonableness.

Exercise 7c The calculator Sequence mode will help students complete this problem in a finite amount of time.

Closing the Lesson

For both **loans** and **investments,** with regular payments or deposits of a fixed amount the sequence of balances is generated by the recursive rule $u_n = r \cdot u_{n-1} + d$. The value of r is 1 more than the interest rate being calculated at that time. For loans, d is negative; for investments, d is positive. The principal, or initial amount of the loan or investment, is given by u_0.

See page 878 for answers to Exercises 1a, 2, 4, and 7d.

8. APPLICATION Beau and Shaleah each get a $1000 bonus at work and decide to invest it. Beau puts his money into an account that earns an annual interest rate of 6.5%, compounded yearly. He also decides to deposit $1200 each year. Shaleah finds an account that earns 6.5%, compounded monthly, and decides to deposit $100 each month.

a. Compare the amounts of money that Beau and Shaleah deposit each year. Describe any differences or similarities.

b. Compare the balances of Beau's and Shaleah's accounts over several years. Describe any differences or similarities.

9. APPLICATION Regis deposits $5000 into an account for his 10-year-old child. The account has an annual interest rate of 8.5%, compounded monthly.

a. What regular monthly deposit amount is needed to make the account worth $1 million by the time the child is 55 years old? $123.98

b. Make a graph of the increasing balances.

10. APPLICATION Cici purchased $2000 worth of merchandise with her credit card this past month. Then she was unexpectedly laid off from her job. She decided to make no more purchases with the card and to make only the minimum payment of $40 each month. Her annual interest rate is 18%, compounded monthly.

a. Find the balance on the credit card over the next six months.

b. When will Cici pay off the total balance on her credit card?

c. What is the total amount paid for the $2000 worth of merchandise? $3724.41

11. APPLICATION Megan Flanigan is a loan officer with L. B. Mortgage Company. She offers a loan of $60,000 to a borrower at 9.6% annual interest, compounded monthly.

a. What should she tell the borrower the monthly payment will be if the loan must be paid off in 25 years? $528.39

b. Make a graph that shows the unpaid balance over time.

Review

1.3 **12.** A mixture of nitric oxide (NO, a colorless gas) and dinitric oxide (N_2O_2, a red-brown gas) exists in equilibrium. A mixture of 20 mL of NO and 220 mL of N_2O_2 is heated. At the new temperature, 10% of the NO changes to N_2O_2 each second and 5% of the N_2O_2 changes to NO each second.

A model of a molecule of nitric oxide

a. Calculate the amount of NO that was changed into N_2O_2 during the first second. 2 mL

b. Calculate the amount of N_2O_2 that was changed into NO during the first second. 11 mL

c. Assume the container is sealed and will always contain 240 mL of gas. From your answers to 12a and b, find the amount of NO after 1 second. 29 mL

d. How much of the gas is N_2O_2 after 1 second? 211 mL

e. What will be the amounts of NO and N_2O_2 after 3 seconds? 10 seconds? What will happen in the long run?

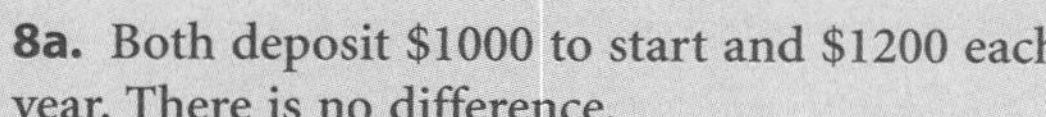

8a. Both deposit $1000 to start and $1200 each year. There is no difference.

8b.

Year	0	1	2	3	...
Beau	$1000.00	$2265.00	$3612.23	$5047.02	...
Shaleah	$1000.00	$2303.38	$3694.04	$5177.84	...

Shaleah's account always has a higher balance. The difference between Beau's and Shaleah's balances gets greater over time.

Exercise 9 This exercise is similar to the investigation.

9b. for $u_0 = 5000$ and $u_n = \left(1 + \frac{0.085}{12}\right)u_{n-1} + 123.98$ where $n \geq 1$

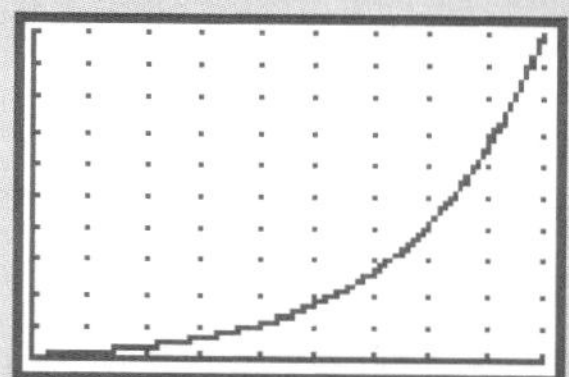

[0, 540, 60, 0, 900000, 100000]

10a. $1990, $1979.85, $1969.55, $1959.09, $1948.48, $1937.70

10b. 94 months, or 7 years 10 months

Exercise 11b Students can use Calculator Note 1M to learn more about the finance application. **[Ask]** "How does this graph compare to the graph in Exercise 9?"

11b. for $u_0 = 60000$ and $u_n = \left(1 + \frac{0.096}{12}\right)u_{n-1} - 528.39$ where $n \geq 1$

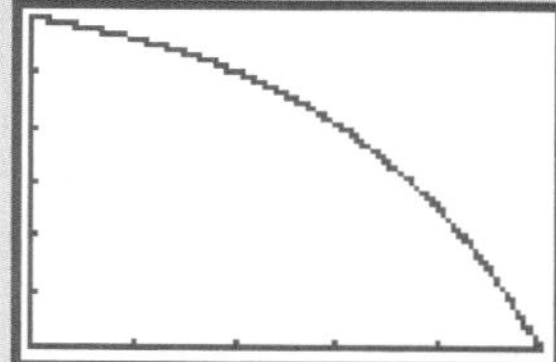

[0, 300, 60, 0, 60000, 10000]

Exercise 12 A real-world scientist would need to use much more precision than is represented by 5%. Students can assume that the 5% is measured very precisely so their answers can have as many as four significant digits. **[Context]** In chemistry, *equilibrium* is a state of balance in which two opposing reversible chemical reactions proceed at constant equal rates with no net change in the system.

12e. After 3 seconds: 43.2 mL of NO and 196.8 mL of N_2O_2. After 10 seconds: 68.2 mL of NO and 171.8 mL of N_2O_2. In the long run: 80 mL of NO and 160 mL of N_2O_2.

Exercise 13 If students are having difficulty, you might suggest that they assume it's a shifted geometric sequence, substitute two pairs of sequence terms, and solve the two equations for the multiplier and adder. Then they can see whether the same values generate other terms of the sequence.

Exercise 15c Students can avoid cross multiplying, which is often meaningless to them, by inverting both sides and then multiplying by the denominator of the right side. If students do use cross multiplication, make sure they understand that they are multiplying both sides of the equation by the product of the denominators.

EXTENSIONS

A. Have students investigate the interest rates at several banks and answer these questions: Is the interest rate compounded daily, monthly, or annually? How do the interest rates for loans and investments differ? Is interest added to the balance before or after an additional payment/investment is made?

B. Use Take Another Look activity 4 on page 74.

C. Present this problem: "You are offered similar jobs in California and Michigan. The salary in California will be $58,000, but homes cost $220,000. The salary in Michigan will be $47,000, but homes cost $175,000. Which job can you afford? If your parents live in California and will loan you $7,500 interest free, which is the better choice?

1.3 **13.** Is this sequence arithmetic, geometric, shifted geometric, or something else? something else

$\frac{1}{1}, \frac{1}{2}, \frac{1}{3}, \frac{1}{4}, \ldots$

1.2 **14.** Consider the geometric sequence generated by

$u_0 = 4$

$u_n = 0.7u_{n-1}$ where $n \geq 1$

a. What is the long-run value? 0

b. What is the long-run value if the common ratio is changed to 1.3? **14b.** There is no long-run value. The sequence increases faster and faster.

c. What is the long-run value if the common ratio is changed to 1? 4

15. Find the value of n in each proportion.

a. $\frac{2.54 \text{ cm}}{1 \text{ in.}} = \frac{n}{12 \text{ in.}}$ 30.48 cm **b.** $\frac{1 \text{ km}}{0.625 \text{ mi}} = \frac{n}{200 \text{ mi}}$ 320 km **c.** $\frac{1 \text{ yd}}{0.926 \text{ m}} = \frac{140 \text{ yd}}{n}$ 129.64 m

Project

THE PYRAMID INVESTMENT PLAN

Have you ever received a chain letter offering you prizes or great riches? The letters ask you to follow the simple instructions and not break the chain. Actually, chain-letter schemes are illegal, even though they continue to be quite common.

Suppose you have just received this letter, along with several quotes from "ordinary people" who have already become millionaires. How many rounds have already taken place? How many more rounds have to take place before you become a millionaire?

Your project should include

- A written analysis of this plan.
- Your conclusion about whether or not you will become a millionaire.
- An answer to the question, "Why do you think chain letter schemes and pyramid plans are illegal?"

Join the Pyramid Investment Plan (PIP)!

Become a millionaire! Send only $20 now, and return it with this letter to PIP. PIP will send $5 to the name at the top of the list below. Then the second person will move up to the top of the list, and your name will be added to the bottom of the list. You will receive a new letter and a set of 200 names and addresses. Your name will be in position #6. Make 200 copies of the letter, mail them, and **wait to get rich!**

Each time a recipient of one of your letters joins PIP, your name advances toward the top of the list. When your name reaches the top, each of the thousands of people who receive that letter will be sending money to PIP, and you will receive your share. **A conservative marketing return of 6% projects that you will earn over $1.2 million!**

1. *Chris*
2. *Katie*
3. *Josh*
4. *Kanako*
5. *Dave*
6. *Miranda*

Supporting the Project

[Ask] What happens to the other $15? How much have the initiators of the chain letter made in six rounds with a 6% return? [The initiators receive $15 from each respondent; 2,985,984 in six rounds is nearly $45 million.]

OUTCOMES

- The report includes statistics on a 6% return. See page 878 for table. In seven rounds, about 54,290,000 households are reached.
- Students show the estimated return is $1,244,160. But they indicate that before one more person comes to the top of the list, more households than exist in the United States will have been convinced to respond.
- Pyramid schemes may work for those who start them, but they quickly consume all potential gullible households. Most people lose their $20.

EXPLORATION

Refining the Growth Model

Until now you have assumed that the rate of growth or decay remains constant over time. The terms generated by the recursive formulas you have used to model arithmetic or geometric growth increase infinitely in the long run.

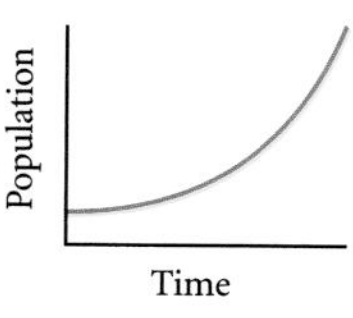

Geometric growth

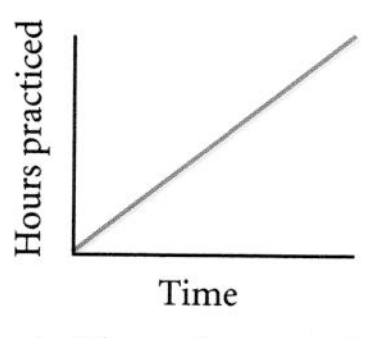

Arithmetic growth

However, environmental factors rarely support unlimited growth. Because of space and resource limitations, or competition among individuals or species, an environment usually supports a population only up to a limiting value.

The graph at right shows a **logistic function** with the population leveling off at the maximum capacity. If a population's growth is modeled by a logistic function, the growth rate isn't a constant value, but rather changes as the population changes.

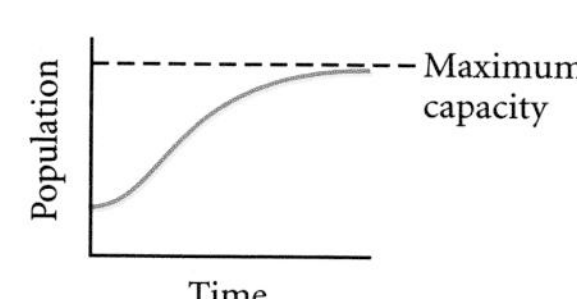

Logistic functions are used to model more than just population. Researchers in many fields apply logistic functions to study things such as the spread of disease or consumer buying patterns. In this exploration you will see an example of logistic growth.

Environmental CONNECTION

Some desert cities in the United States have growing populations and little supply of natural resources. Large populations need, for example, a plentiful water supply for drinking and sewage systems, as well as for luxuries such as watering lawns and filling swimming pools. Population growth reduces groundwater supply, which in turn activates old earthquake faults and surface fissures, and damages buildings. Using logistic functions to model population growth can help government agencies monitor natural resources and avoid environmental catastrophies.

The Hoover Dam, located on the border of Nevada and Arizona, helps supply water to desert cities such as Las Vegas.

EXPLORATION

PLANNING

LESSON OUTLINE

One day:

20 min	Activity
10 min	Example
5 min	Sharing
10 min	Questions

MATERIALS

- graph paper
- Sample Market Data (W), *optional*
- Calculator Note 1L

TEACHING

This exploration, in which students study the effect of a maximum potential population, is especially appropriate for an advanced class.

Most populations can't exceed a maximum (also known as *carrying capacity*) due to limited resources. Even if the current population is far below the maximum, the limited resources will cause a growth rate somewhat lower than the growth rate if resources were unlimited.

MAKING THE CONNECTION

Areas that have encountered land subsidence related to overuse of their water systems include Phoenix, Arizona; Los Angeles, California; and Venice, Italy.

NCTM STANDARDS

CONTENT		PROCESS	
	Number	✓	Problem Solving
✓	Algebra	✓	Reasoning
	Geometry	✓	Communication
	Measurement	✓	Connections
✓	Data/Probability	✓	Representation

LESSON OBJECTIVES

- Use a logistic function to model growth that has a maximum capacity
- Understand how marketing a product is an example of logistic growth

Guiding the Activity

This activity is intended to be done with the entire class. Though you might use the Sample Market Data worksheet, begin to gather data with the class so students can see how the scenario works.

If students have access to spreadsheets, you might use them instead of calculators, both for variety and for the ease of automatic calculation in Step 3.

[ESL] Here *gadget* means a useful or fun new product.

Step 1 Using 25 to 30 I.D. numbers works well. If your class has fewer than 25 students, some students can be assigned more than one I.D. number. Randomly choose one student to start. Ask the students who have the gadget to stand up. Build suspense. Help students see how difficult it is to add a person to the list as they get closer to the last step.

Step 2

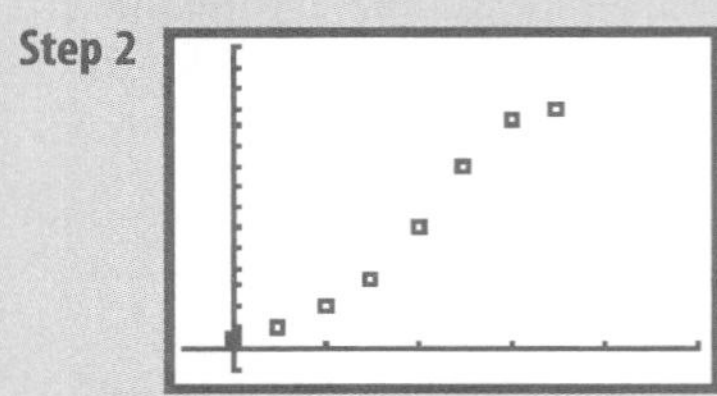

[0, 10, 2, 0, 16, 1]

The number of people who own the gadget does not always double because you occasionally tell someone about the gadget who already owns the gadget.

Step 3 Students may want to know how to make a list of ratios of consecutive terms of another list. One way on the TI-83 is to put the list of terms into list L2 and enter this formula for L3: seq(L2(A + 1)/L2(A), A, 1, DIM(L2) − 1).

Activity

Cornering the Market

A company has invented a new gadget, and everyone who hears about it wants one! The company hasn't started advertising the new gadget yet, but the news is spreading fast. Simulate this situation with your class to see what happens when a popular new product enters the market.

Each person in your class will be assigned an I.D. number. At time zero, only one person has bought the gadget, and at the end of every time period, each person who has one tells another person about it, and they go out and buy one (unless they already have one).

Step 1 For about 10 time periods each person who knows about the gadget generates a random I.D. number and tells that person, who immediately goes out and buys one. [► See **Calculator Note 1L** to learn how to generate random numbers. ◄] Create a table like the one at right, and record the total number of people who have the gadget.

Time period	Number of people who own the gadget
0	1
1	2
2	4
3	7

Step 2 Enter your data into lists L1 and L2. Make a scatter plot of your data. Describe your scatter plot. Explain why the number of people who own the gadget doesn't always double for each time period.

Step 3 Divide each term in list L2 by the previous term and enter these ratios in list L3. These ratios show you the rate at which the number of people who own the gadget grows during each time period.

Step 4 In this activity the growth rate depends on the number of people who own the gadget. Shorten list L1 and list L2 by deleting the last value in each list so that all three lists are the same length. Turn off the scatter plot from Step 2 and make a new scatter plot of (L2, L3). What happens to the growth rate as the number of people who own the gadget increases?

The net growth at each step depends on the previous population size u_{n-1}. So the net growth is a function of the population. This changes the simple growth model of $u_n = u_{n-1}(1 + p)$, in which the rate, p, is a constant, to a growth model in which the growth rate changes depending upon the population.

$$u_n = u_{n-1}\left(1 + p \cdot \left(1 - \frac{u_{n-1}}{L}\right)\right)$$

where p is the unrestricted growth rate, L is the limiting capacity or maximum population, and $p \cdot \left(1 - \frac{u_{n-1}}{L}\right)$ is the net growth rate.

Step 3

L1	L2	L3 3
0	1	2
1	2	2
2	4	1.75
3	7	1.7143
4	12	1.5
5	18	1.2778
6	23	1.0435

L3(1)=2

Step 4

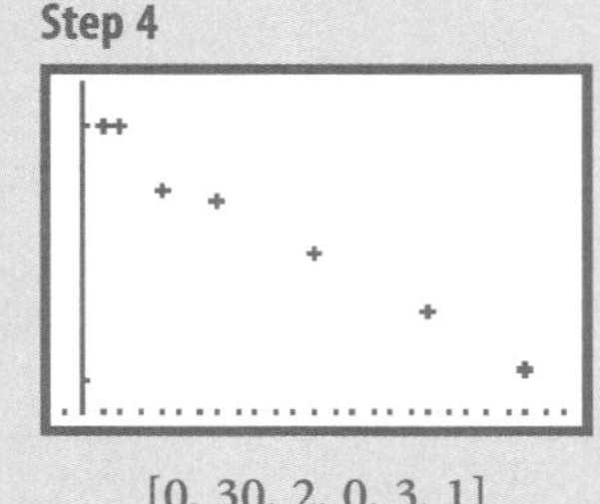

[0, 30, 2, 0, 3, 1]

The growth rate decreases almost linearly. There is a limit to the number of people who can own the gadget. The next value, u_n, depends on the fraction of people who already own the gadget. This rate is near 1 initially and decreases as the number of owners gets closer to the total population.

Step 5 What is the maximum population, L, for the gadget-buying scenario? What is u_0? What is the unrestricted growth rate, p? What does $\frac{u_{n-1}}{L}$ represent? Write the recursive formula for this logistic function.

Step 6 Create list L4, defined as $1 + p \cdot \left(1 - \frac{L2}{L}\right)$, using p and L from Step 5. Plot (L2, L4) and (L2, L3).

Step 7 Turn off the scatter plots from Step 6 and check how well your recursive formula from Step 5 models your original data (L1, L2).

History
CONNECTION

At the end of the 18th century, data on population growth were not available, and social scientists generally agreed with English economist Thomas Malthus (1766–1834) that a population always increases exponentially, eventually leading to a catastrophic overpopulation. In the 19th century, Belgian mathematician Pierre François Verhulst (1804–1849) and Belgian social statistician Adolphe Quételet (1796–1874) formulated the net growth rate expression $p \cdot \left(1 - \frac{u_{n-1}}{L}\right)$ for a population model. Quételet believed that limitations on population growth needed to be accounted for in a more systematic manner than Malthus described. Verhulst was able to incorporate the changes in growth rate in a mathematical model.

A "closed" environment creates clear limitations on space and resources and calls for a logistic function model.

EXAMPLE

Suppose the unrestricted growth rate of a deer population on a small island is 12% annually, but the island's maximum capacity is 2000 deer. The current deer population is 300.

a. What net growth rate can you expect for next year?

b. What will the deer population be in one year?

c. Graph the deer population over the next 50 years.

► ***Solution***

a. There is a maximum capacity, so the population can be modeled with a logistic function. The net growth rate is $p\left(1 - \frac{u_{n-1}}{L}\right)$, where p is the unrestricted growth rate and L is the limiting value, in this case, the island's maximum capacity. Because $p = 12\%$ and $L = 2000$ deer, the net growth rate will be

$$0.12\left(1 - \frac{u_{n-1}}{2000}\right)$$

Using $u_0 = 300$, this gives a growth rate of $0.12\left(1 - \frac{300}{2000}\right) = 0.102$, or 10.2%, for the first year.

Step 5 Until now, students have written $u_n = (1 + p)u_{n-1}$. Remind students that, by the commutative property of multiplication, this equation is equivalent to $u_n = u_{n-1}(1 + p)$, which is more easily modified for the logistic function.

Step 5 $L = 25$; $u_0 = 1$; $p = 1$ (if unrestricted, the growth would double, or be 100%); the fraction of the class that has bought the gadget; $u_0 = 1$ and $u_n = u_{n-1}\left(1 + 1\left(1 - \frac{u_{n-1}}{25}\right)\right)$ where $n \geq 1$ or $u_0 = 1$ and $u_n = u_{n-1}\left(2 - \frac{u_{n-1}}{25}\right)$ where $n \geq 1$

Step 6

L2	L3	L4
1	2	1.96
2	2	1.92
4	1.75	1.84
7	1.7143	1.72
12	1.5	1.52
18	1.2778	1.28
23	1.0435	1.08

L4(1)=1.96

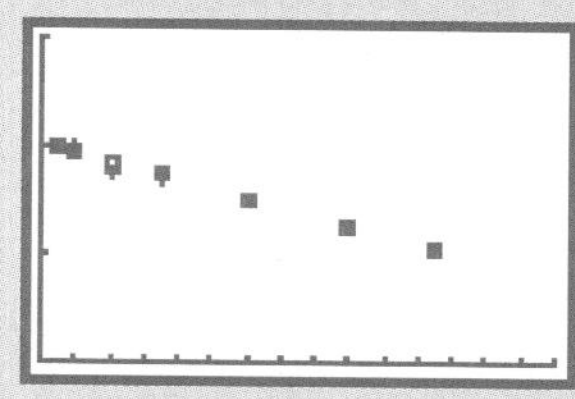

[0, 30, 2, 0, 3, 1]

Step 7

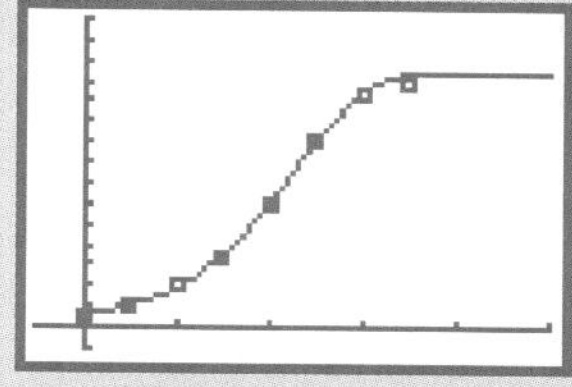

[−1, 10, 2, −2, 30, 2]

MAKING THE CONNECTION

Quételet is pronounced "ke-te-'la."

Assessing Progress

During the activity, you can assess students' ability to gather data systematically, to enter data into the calculator, and to make scatter plots.

► ***EXAMPLE***

Ask if the growth rate in part a makes sense. Try to elicit the question of why the growth rate is restricted at all (to 10.2% from 12%) when the actual population (300) is far from the maximum population (2000). Logistic growth is a mathematical model that predicts population growth, but the actual behavior of a population may vary from the model.

Some population growth models take into account the interaction of predator and prey such as these two equations.

$$new\ rabbit = rabbit(1 + 0.04 - 0.002fox)$$

$$new\ fox = fox(1 + 0.001rabbit - 0.03)$$

Interested students might research this model, called the Lotka–Volterra predator-prey model, or variations on this model that reflect additional assumptions about the situation.

SHARING IDEAS

[Ask] "How is it that the recursive rule for the standard shifted geometric sequence is modified for logistic growth?" [The growth rate p is multiplied by a number. When u_{n-1} is close to 0, that multiplier is close to 1 and does not change the growth rate much; when u_{n-1} is close to L, the multiplier reduces the growth rate to almost 0.]

[Ask] "How does the model compare to the real market?" [The students represent the subset of the population that is likely to buy the product. In real life, not everyone will buy it.]

The activity is a good opportunity to talk about consumerism, to help motivate critical thinking.

[Ask] "Do people 'go out and buy one' because everyone else seems to be doing so? What makes a product a 'must-have'? At some point the market starts to get saturated. What do companies do when the growth rate starts to decrease?" [They know they have reached half the potential sales and plan to reduce production accordingly.] "How do companies and marketing people ensure that sales will continue to grow?" [by developing new features, marketing to a different audience—frequently, a younger audience—and convincing you that you need a new one]

[Ask] "What other variables might be considered in developing a mathematical model for population?" [possible answers: predators, death rates, changes in climate]

Closing the Lesson

When resources are limited, population growth may be approximated by a **logistic** model, based on the recursion rule $u_n = u_{n-1}\left(1 + p\left(1 - \frac{u_{n-1}}{L}\right)\right)$. Here the initial growth rate p is modified according to how close the population u_{n-1} is to the maximum population L.

b. The recursive rule for this logistic function is $u_n = u_{n-1}\left(1 + 0.12\left(1 - \frac{u_{n-1}}{2000}\right)\right)$

Using $u_0 = 300$,

$$u_1 = 300\left(1 + 0.12\left(1 - \frac{300}{2000}\right)\right)$$
$$= 300(1 + 0.102)$$
$$= 330.6$$

So the deer population after 1 year will be around 331.

c. The graph shows the population as it grows toward the maximum capacity of 2000 deer.

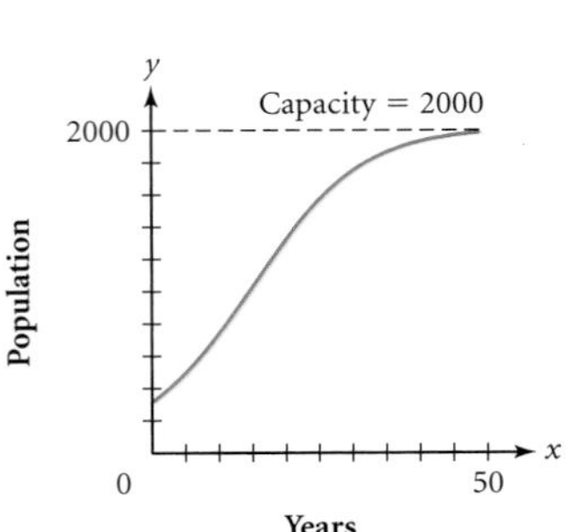

Now try your hand at applying logistic function models with these questions.

Questions

These eastern gray kangaroos mingle with tourists on Pebbly Beach in Murramarang National Park, Australia. When humans inhabit areas previously dominated by animals, population growth may be adversely affected.

1. Bacteria grown in a culture dish are provided with plenty of food but a limited amount of growing space. Eventually the population will become overcrowded, even though there is plenty of food. The bacteria grow at an unrestricted rate of 125% per week initially. The starting population is 50, and the capacity of the dish is 5000. Find the net growth rate and the population at the end of each week for 7 weeks. 124%, 122%, 119%, 111%, 96%, 69%, 30%; 112, 249, 544, 1150, 2260, 3800, 4940

2. A large field provides enough food to feed 500 healthy rabbits. When food and space are unlimited, the population growth rate of the rabbits is 20%, or 0.20. The population that can be supported is 500 rabbits. Complete each statement using the choices less than 0, greater than 0, 0, or close to 0.20.

a. When the population is less than 500, the net growth rate will be __?__.

b. When the population is more than 500, the net growth rate will be __?__.

c. When the population is very small, the net growth rate will be __?__.

d. When the population is 500, the net growth rate will be __?__. 0

3. Suppose the recursive rule $d_n = d_{n-1}\left(1 + 0.35\left(1 - \frac{d_{n-1}}{750}\right)\right)$ will give the number of daisies growing in the median strip of a highway each year. Presently there are about 100 daisies. Write a paragraph or two explaining what will happen. Explain and support your reasoning. Sample answer: The population begins at 100 and grows to 750. The growth rate starts near 35% and shrinks to 0%. It takes about 6 years to get halfway to the maximum and about 13 years to pass 700 daisies.

▶ Helping with the Questions

Question 1 [Language] A *culture dish,* also known as a *petri dish,* is a small glass or plastic dish used to grow or experiment on bacteria, microorganisms, or tissues.

[Ask] "At what time will the bacteria outgrow the culture dish?" [They won't; the growth will be logistic.]

Question 2 You might suggest that students look at the graph of this logistic function to answer the questions.

2a. greater than 0; **2b.** less than 0; **2c.** close to 0.20

Question 3 [Ask] "Do 0.35 and 750 have real-world meanings? What does d_{n-1} represent?" [0.35 is the initial growth rate; 750 is the maximum capacity; and d_{n-1} represents the number of daisies that grew the previous year.]

CHAPTER 1 REVIEW

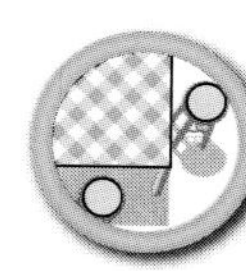

A **sequence** is an ordered list of numbers. In this chapter you used **recursion** to define sequences. A **recursive formula** specifies one or more starting terms and a **recursive rule** that generates the nth term by using the previous term or terms. You learned to calculate the terms of a sequence by hand and by using recursion and sequences on your calculator.

There are two special types of sequences—arithmetic and geometric. **Arithmetic sequences** are generated by always adding the same number, called the **common difference,** to get the next term. Your salary for a job on which you are paid by the hour is modeled by an arithmetic sequence. **Geometric sequences** are generated by always multiplying by the same number, called the **common ratio,** to get the next term. The growth of money in a savings account is modeled by a geometric sequence. For some **growth** and **decay** scenarios, it helps to write the common ratio as a percent change, $(1 + p)$ or $(1 - p)$. Some real-world situations, such as medicine levels, are modeled by **shifted geometric sequences** that use a recursive rule with both multiplication and addition.

Many sequences have a long-run value after many, many terms. Looking at a graph of the sequence may help you see the long-run value. Graphs also help you recognize whether the data are best modeled by an arithmetic or geometric sequence. The graph of an arithmetic sequence is **linear** whereas the graph of a geometric sequence is curved.

EXERCISES

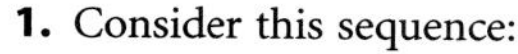

1. Consider this sequence:

256, 192, 144, 108, . . .

a. Is this sequence arithmetic or geometric? geometric

b. Write a recursive formula that generates the sequence. Use u_1 for the starting term.

c. What is the 8th term? $u_8 \approx 34.2$

d. Which term is the first to have a value less than 20? $u_{10} \approx 19.2$

e. Find u_{17}. $u_{17} \approx 2.57$

2. Consider this sequence:

3, 7, 11, 15, . . .

a. Is this sequence arithmetic or geometric? arithmetic

b. Write a recursive formula that generates the sequence. Use u_1 for the starting term.

c. What is the 128th term? $u_{128} = 511$

d. Which term has the value 159? $u_{40} = 159$

e. Find u_{20}. $u_{20} = 79$

1b. $u_1 = 256$ and $u_n = 0.75u_{n-1}$ where $n \geq 2$

2b. $u_1 = 3$ and $u_n = u_{n-1} + 4$ where $n \geq 2$

CHAPTER REVIEW 1

PLANNING

LESSON OUTLINE

One day:

15 min Reviewing

20 min Exercises

10 min Student self-assessment

MATERIALS

- Calculator Note 1M, *optional*

REVIEWING

You might pose this review problem: "Under what conditions is the shifted geometric sequence generated by $u_n = ru_{n-1} + d$ geometric?" [when $d = 0$] "Arithmetic?" [when $r = 1$] Stress the utility of looking at the graph of the sequence when determining what type of recursion is happening. Remind students of the difference between a common ratio and a common difference and their relationships to the graphs.

If students did the Exploration Refining the Growth Model, you might also **[Ask]** "Under what conditions is the logistic sequence generated by $u_n = u_{n-1}\left(1 + p\left(1 - \frac{u_{n-1}}{L}\right)\right)$ nearly geometric?" $\left[\text{when } \frac{u_{n-1}}{L} \text{ is very small}\right]$

ASSIGNING HOMEWORK

You might assign the exercises as homework and then use them to review in class those concepts the class is weakest in.

Helping with the Exercises

3a. −3, −1.5, 0, 1.5, 3; 0 to 6 for n and −4 to 4 for u_n

3b. 2, 4, 10, 28, 82; 0 to 6 for n and 0 to 100 for u_n

Exercise 4 Climbers don't actually do the calculation while climbing; they simply look up the pressure in a table. Many other factors also influence atmospheric pressure, so the rule stated in this problem is not universal.

4a. $u_0 = 14.7$ and $u_n = (1 - 0.20)u_{n-1}$ where $n \geq 1$

4b.

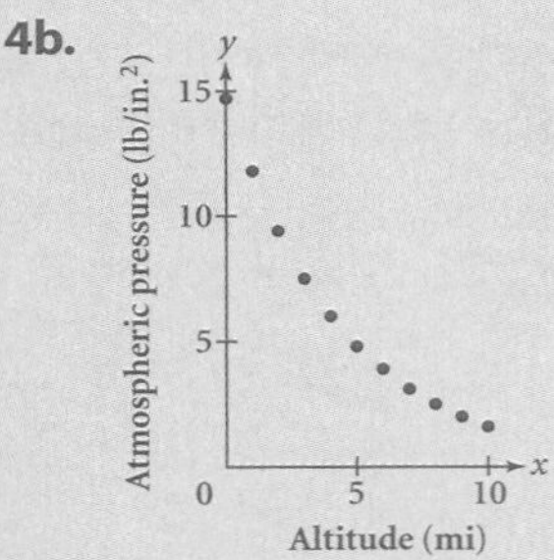

5. i. C. The recursive formula is that of a decaying geometric sequence, so the graph must be decreasing and curved.

5. ii. D. The recursive formula is that of a decreasing arithmetic sequence, so the graph must be decreasing and linear.

5. iii. B. The recursive formula is that of a growing geometric sequence, so the graph must be increasing and curved.

5. iv. A. The recursive formula is that of an increasing arithmetic sequence, so the graph must be increasing and linear.

3. List the first five terms of each sequence. For each set of terms, what minimum and maximum values of n and u_n would you use on the axes to make a good graph?

a. $u_1 = -3$
$u_n = u_{n-1} + 1.5$ where $n \geq 2$

b. $u_1 = 2$
$u_n = 3u_{n-1} - 2$ where $n \geq 2$

4. APPLICATION Atmospheric pressure is 14.7 pounds per square inch (lb/in.^{2}) at sea level. An increase in altitude of 1 mi produces a 20% decrease in the atmospheric pressure. Mountain climbers use this relationship to determine whether or not they can safely climb a mountain and to periodically calculate their altitude after they begin climbing.

a. Write a recursive formula that generates a sequence that represents the atmospheric pressure at different altitudes.

b. Sketch a graph that shows the relationship between altitude and atmospheric pressure.

c. What is the atmospheric pressure when the altitude is 7 mi? approximately 3.1 lb/in.^{2}

d. At what altitude does the atmospheric pressure drop below 1.5 lb/in.^{2}? 11 mi

These mountaineers climbed to an altitude of 11,522 feet to reach the top of Mt. Clark in Yosemite National Park, California.

Environmental CONNECTION

Humans of any age or physical condition can become ill when they experience extreme changes in atmospheric pressure in a short span of time. Atmospheric pressure changes the amount of oxygen a person is able to inhale which, in turn, causes the buildup of fluid in the lungs or brain. Someone who travels from a low-altitude city like Akron, Ohio, to a high-altitude city like Aspen, Colorado, and immediately ascends a mountain to ski, could get a headache, become nauseated, or even become seriously ill.

5. Match each recursive formula with the graph of the same sequence. Give your reason for each choice.

A. $u_0 = 5$
$u_n = u_{n-1} + 1$ where $n \geq 1$

B. $u_0 = 1$
$u_n = (1 + 0.5)u_{n-1}$ where $n \geq 1$

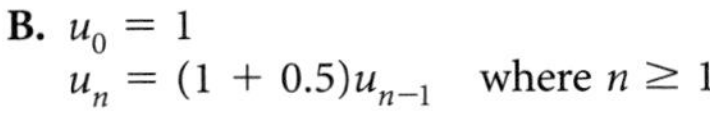

C. $u_0 = 5$
$u_n = (1 - 0.5)u_{n-1}$ where $n \geq 1$

D. $u_0 = 5$
$u_n = u_{n-1} - 1$ where $n \geq 1$

i.
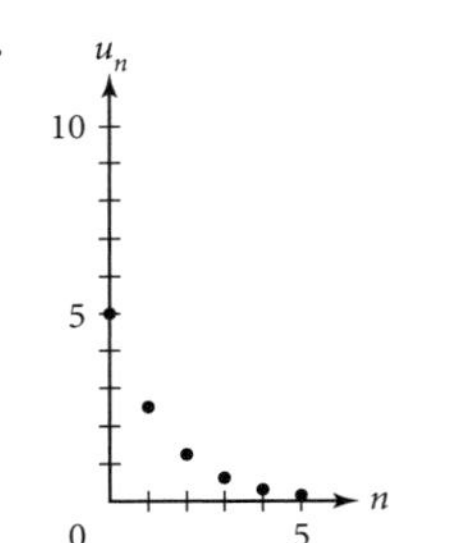

ii.
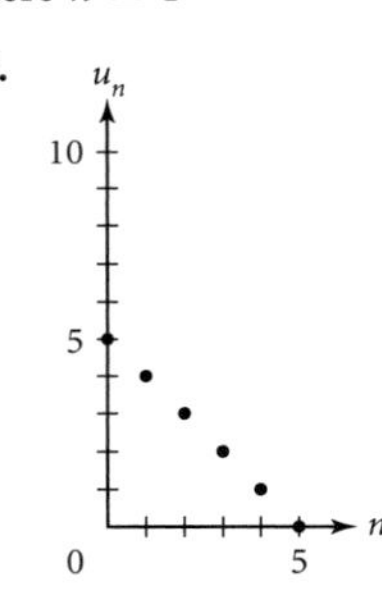

iii. **iv.**
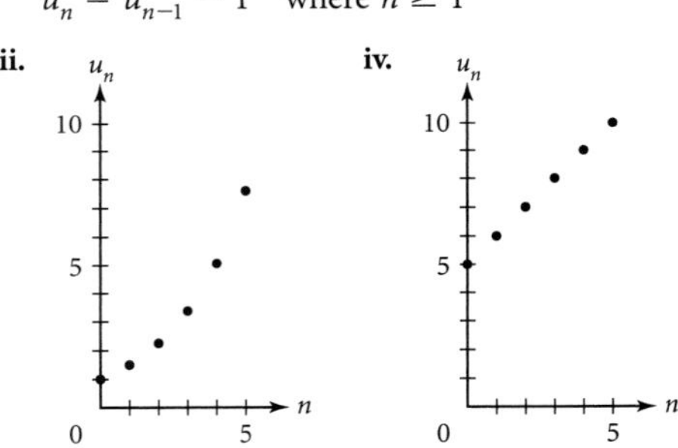

MAKING THE CONNECTION

Mountain climbers take steps to acclimate their bodies gradually to higher altitudes and prevent altitude sickness. Hence their bodies adapt better to the decrease in oxygen. Atmospheric pressure is also a concern for airplane flight. Commercial jets have pressurized cabins so that travelers don't suffer the effects of abrupt changes in air pressure.

6. A large barrel contains 12.4 gal of oil 18 min after its drain is opened. How many gallons of oil were in the barrel to start, if it drains at a rate of 4.2 gal/min? 88 gal

7. APPLICATION The enrollment at a college is currently 5678. From now on, the board of administrators estimates that each year the school will graduate 24% of its students and admit 1250 new students. What will the enrollment be during the sixth year? What will the enrollment be in the long run? Sketch a graph of the enrollment over 15 years.

8. APPLICATION You deposit $500 into a bank account that has an annual interest rate of 5.5%, compounded quarterly.

a. How much money will you have after 5 yr if you never deposit more money? $657.03

b. How much money will you have after 5 yr if you deposit an additional $150 every 3 mo after the initial $500? $4083.21

9. APPLICATION This table gives the consumer price index for medical care from 1970 to 2000. Use a graph to find a sequence model that approximately fits these data.
$u_{1970} = 34$ and $u_n = (1 + 0.075)u_{n-1}$ where $n \geq 1971$

Economics CONNECTION

The consumer price index (CPI) is a measure of the change over time in the prices paid by consumers for goods and services, such as food, clothing, and health care. The Bureau of Labor Statistics obtains price information for 80,000 items in order to adjust the index. The price of specific items in 1982–1984 is assigned an index of 100 and the index for all subsequent years is given in relation to this reference period. For example, an index of 130 means the price of an item increased 30% from the price during 1982–1984. Learn more about the CPI with the links at www.keymath.com/DAA

U.S. Consumer Price Index for Medical Care

Year	Consumer price index
1970	34.0
1975	47.5
1980	74.9
1985	113.5
1990	162.8
1995	220.5
2000	260.8

(U.S. Department of Labor, Bureau of Labor Statistics)

10. APPLICATION Oliver wants to buy a cabin and needs to borrow $80,000. What monthly payment is necessary to pay off the mortgage in 30 years if the annual interest rate is 8.9%, compounded monthly?
$637.95

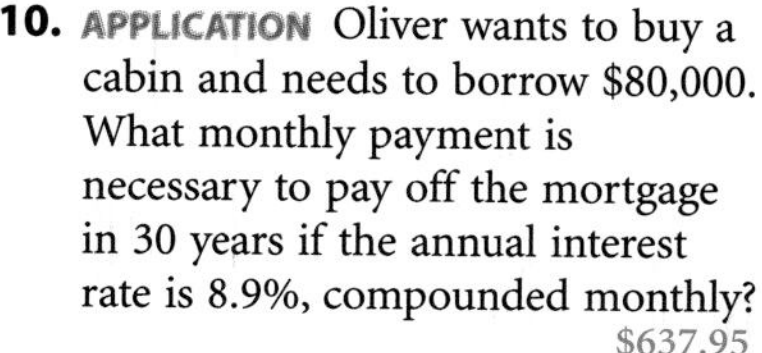

7. approximately 5300; approximately 5200; $u_0 = 5678$ and $u_n = (1 - 0.24)u_{n-1} + 1250$ where $n \geq 1$

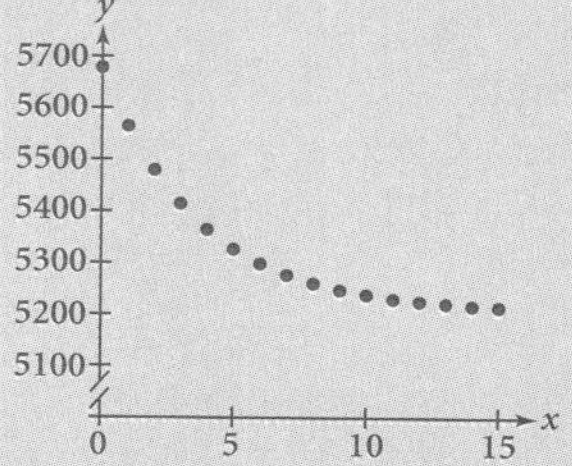

Exercise 9 On a graph, the consumer price index (CPI) data may appear to be linear. However, differences between terms five years apart are not constant. In fact the differences keep increasing, implying that the data are exponential and should be modeled with a geometric sequence.

Unlike the data in the example in Lesson 1.4, these data cannot be fitted closely with a sequence model; the data point (2000, 260.8) is especially problematic, because it doesn't fit the general pattern of the previous years. The ratio students use might vary from the ratio (1 + 0.075) given in the answer. (Though the calculator's built-in regression functions shouldn't be used at this stage, students who invoke an exponential regression function on a calculator will get a value of about 1.0737.)

As an extension to Exercise 9, have students research data on the CPI for medical care for every year between 1970 and 2000, or even every month, and see how well the sequence model fits their more extensive set of data. Research can be done through the links at www.keymath.com/DAA. **[Ask]** "How well does the sequence model the data set?" [Many real-world factors influence prices and inflation and hence the CPI; so the data are more complex than can be modeled by a simple recursive formula. In some areas the data are not recursive; the price of health care in 2000 is not necessarily related to the price of health care in 1999.]

Take Another Look

1. The area of the tables generates a sequence proportional to 1, 2, 3, ...

The perimeters of the nested squares generate the sequence 4, 8, 12, 16, ... The growth is arithmetic; $u_1 = 4$ and $u_n = u_{n-1} + 4$ where $n \geq 2$. The areas of the nested squares generate the sequence 1, 4, 9, 16, ... The growth is neither arithmetic nor geometric; students probably won't be able to write the recursive rule $u_n = u_{n-1} + 2n - 1$, but they may write $u_n = n^2$ where $n \geq 1$. The heights generate the sequence 1, 2, 3, 4, ... The growth is arithmetic; $u_1 = 1$ and $u_n = u_{n-1} + 1$ where $n \geq 2$.

The perimeters of the other nested polygons generate the sequence 3, 4, 5, 6, ... The growth is arithmetic; $u_1 = 3$ and $u_n = u_{n-1} + 1$ where $n \geq 2$.

Using $s = 1$ and $A = \dfrac{ns^2}{4\tan\left(\frac{360°}{n}\right)}$,

their areas generate the sequence $\dfrac{\sqrt{3}}{4}, 1, \dfrac{5}{4\tan 72°}, \dfrac{3}{2\tan 60°}, \ldots,$ which generalizes to

$u_n = \dfrac{n}{4\tan\left(\frac{360°}{n}\right)}$ where $n \geq 3$.

The growth is neither arithmetic nor geometric.

Invented geometric patterns will vary.

TAKE ANOTHER LOOK

1. In Lesson 1.1, Example A, you saw an arithmetic sequence that generates from a geometric pattern: the number of seats around a linear arrangement of square tables is 4, 6, 8, ... Notice that the sequence comes from the increase in the perimeter of the arrangement. What sequence comes from the increase in area?

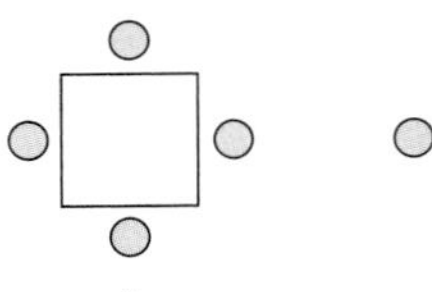
4

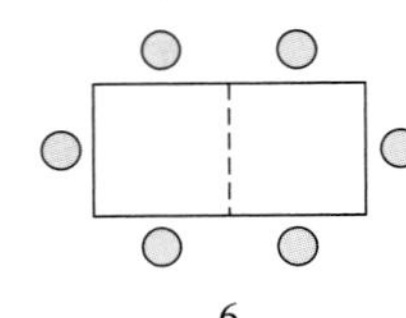
6

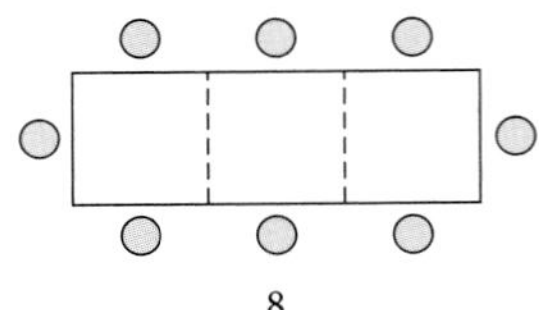
8

Use these geometric patterns to generate recursive sequences using perimeter, area, height, or other attributes, and give their recursive formulas. Which sequences exhibit arithmetic growth? Geometric growth? Are there sequences you cannot define as arithmetic or geometric?

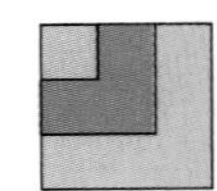
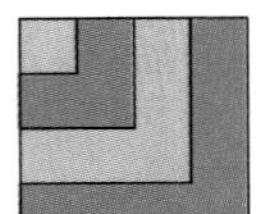
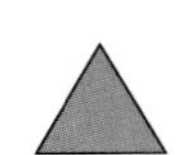
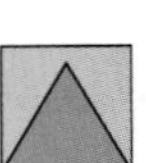
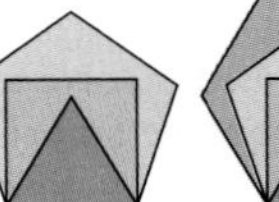

Invent a geometric pattern of your own. Look for and define different sequences.

2. Here's a strategy an algebra student discovered for finding the monthly payment you would need to make to pay off a loan. First, specify the loan amount, the annual interest rate, and the term (length) of the loan. Choose trial monthly payment amounts that form a sequence, say, \$0, \$1, \$2, \$3. Record the final balance remaining at the end of the term for each payment. Next, explore the differences in the final balances and find a pattern. Finally, use the pattern to find a monthly payment that results in a zero final balance. Tell how you know that your payment amount is correct. How many trial payment amounts do you need in order to determine the monthly payment? Try this strategy for one of the exercises in Lesson 1.5.

3. Imagine a target for a dart game that consists of a bull's-eye and three additional circles. If it is certain that a dart will land within the target but is otherwise random, what sequence of radii gives a set of probabilities that form an arithmetic sequence? A geometric sequence? Sketch what the targets look like.

4. As you probably realized in Lesson 1.5, your graphing calculator is a useful tool for solving loan and investment problems. With the added help of a special program, your calculator will instantly tell you information such as the monthly payment necessary for a home mortgage. [► See **Calculator Note 1M** to learn how to use your calculator's financial-solver program. ◄] Try using this program to solve some of the exercises in Lesson 1.5 or a problem of your own design.

2. Consider a loan of \$32,000 to be paid off in 60 months at 7.9% annual interest, compounded monthly ($u_0 = 32{,}000$).

Monthly payment	Final balance	Difference
\$0	\$47,438.84	
\$1	\$47,365.56	\$73.28
\$2	\$47,292.27	\$73.29
\$3	\$47,218.99	\$73.28

Each difference is approximately \$73.28, so the final balances form an arithmetic sequence with a common difference of about \$73.28. You can divide \$47,438.84 by \$73.28 to determine how many times you must repeat the sequence for the final balance to be 0 $\left(\frac{47438.84}{73.28} \approx 647.36\right)$. Hence the monthly payment should be about \$647.36. (Actually, because the differences are not exactly \$73.28, the closest we can get to 0 after 60 months is with a monthly payment of \$647.31.)

Assessing What You've Learned

ORGANIZE YOUR NOTEBOOK Wouldn't you like to have a record of what you've learned and just what you are expected to know in this algebra course? Your own notebook can be that record if you enter significant information and examples into it on a regular basis. It is a good place for new vocabulary, definitions and distinctions, and worked-out examples that illustrate mathematics that's new to you. On the other hand, if it is simply a stack of returned homework, undated class notes, and scratch-paper computations and graphs, it is too disorganized to perform that service for you.

Before you get very far along in the course, take time to go through your notebook. Here are some suggestions:

- Put papers into chronological order. If your work is undated, use the table of contents in this book to help you reconstruct the sequence in which you produced the items in your notebook. You can number pages to help keep them in order.
- Go through the book pages of Chapter 0 and Chapter 1, and see whether you have a good record of how you spent class time—what you learned from investigations and homework. Fill in notes where you need them while information is fresh in your mind. Circle questions that you need to have cleared up before going on.
- Reflect on the main ideas of this chapter. Organize your notes by type of sequence, and make sure you have examples of recursive formulas that produce different types of graphs. Be sure you can identify the starting value and the common difference or common ratio for each type of sequence, and that you know how to use the information to find a later term in the sequence.

PERFORMANCE ASSESSMENT It's important to know how well you are progressing in this course so that you're encouraged by your gains. Assessing what you've learned also alerts you to get help before you're confused about important ideas that you'll have to build on later in the course.

One way to tell whether or not you understand something is to try to explain it to someone else. Choose one of the modeling problems in Lesson 1.4, such as the population of Peru in Exercise 12, and present it orally to a classmate, a relative, or your teacher. Here are some steps to follow:

- Explain the problem context, and give the listener some background on what the problem calls for mathematically.
- Be sure the listener knows what you mean by finding a model. Then describe how you find the model, using the given information, and how you express mathematically what the model is.
- Comment on how well the model fits the original data.
- Show the listener how to use the model. For example, ask a question about the future population of Peru, and show the listener how to use the model to answer the question. Show at least one way to check that your result is reasonable. Don't forget to interpret the mathematical result in terms of the problem's real-world context.

ASSESSING

You can now use a chapter test from the Assessment Resources or you might choose to combine some short test items with one or two constructive assessment items for your chapter test.

FACILITATING SELF-ASSESSMENT

Assessing What You've Learned gives students ideas on organizing their notebooks. To encourage them to keep an orderly notebook, you might allow students to use their notebooks, but not their books, while taking tests.

A good way to check students' understanding is to have them explain a concept to other students. You might encourage this kind of performance assessment by assigning it as part of the chapter review. Allow time for students to present explanations to each other in pairs.

Take Another Look

3. Sample arithmetic probability sequence is shown in first table below.

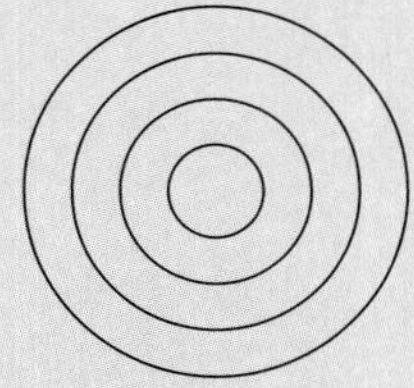

Radius	Circle area	Annulus area	Probability
1	π	π	$\frac{1}{16}$
2	4π	3π	$\frac{3}{16}$
3	9π	5π	$\frac{5}{16}$
4	16π	7π	$\frac{7}{16}$
	Totals	16π	1

Sample geometric probability sequence is shown in the second table below. Begin with areas of bull's-eyes and annuluses as a geometric sequence and work backward through the area formula.

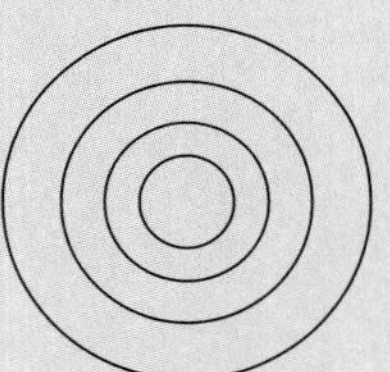

Radius	Circle area	Annulus area	Probability
1	π	π	$\frac{1}{15}$
$\sqrt{3}$	3π	2π	$\frac{2}{15}$
$\sqrt{7}$	7π	4π	$\frac{4}{15}$
$\sqrt{15}$	15π	8π	$\frac{8}{15}$
	Totals	15π	1

4. Answers will vary.

CHAPTER

2

Describing Data

Overview

Students begin to learn how to describe one-variable data in **Lesson 2.1** with measures of central tendency and box plots and their related five-number summaries based on the median. In **Lesson 2.2,** students look first at standard deviation as a measure of spread based on the mean and then at interquartile range as a measure of spread based on the median. **Lesson 2.3** focuses on the shape of the data in a data set and introduces the idea of percentile. The Fathom **exploration** gives students the opportunity to make conjectures about a set of microdata from a census and to check those conjectures using statistics and graphs.

The Mathematics

Chapter 2 focuses exclusively on describing one-variable data through statistics and graphs. Students will begin to analyze two-variable data in Chapter 3.

Statistics

One use of statistics is to draw conclusions about a large data set by looking at a small subset of the data. The larger set is called a population, and the smaller set is called a sample. A sample that reflects the population accurately is said to be representative; otherwise, it's biased. One way to obtain a representative sample is to choose its elements randomly from the population.

In some cases, the distinction between samples and populations is confusing. If a die is rolled 1000 times, the results comprise a random sample taken from an infinite population. In contrast the set of points a basketball player has scored in one season, though smaller, is an entire population. Chapter 13 contains a more rigorous discussion of sampling.

In general, data sets have three attributes: distribution (shape), central tendency, and dispersion (variability or spread). It's possible for two data sets to be alike in any two of these three attributes but differ in the third.

In this chapter, **shape** is described using only the terms *symmetric* and *skewed* (right or left). The definition of *skewed* is also left vague by using the term *center* without naming a particular measure of center. Later chapters introduce more refinements, such as normal (Chapter 13) and binomial (Chapter 12) distributions.

Measures of **central tendency,** often called averages, are the mean, median, and mode(s). Although the median and modes are useful for some purposes, their methods of derivation makes them less useful for calculations than the mean. In this chapter, the mean is defined using the Σ (sigma) notation that is so useful in working with series (sums of terms of a sequence), the topic of Chapter 11.

This chapter considers several measures of **spread.** Spread is measured relative to the median by the range and the interquartile range (*IQR*). These statistics are based on very few data points. Though useful in describing a data set, they often can't be extended very accurately from a sample to a population. When studying a sample to learn about a larger population, measures of spread relative to the mean are more useful. A measure of spread that appears natural to many students is the mean of distances of data points from the mean. This statistic is called the mean deviation. Its main disadvantage is that absolute values are difficult to add algebraically. Easier to manipulate is the variance, the sum of squares of these distances. Variance, however, exaggerates the importance of points far from the mean, or outliers. The square root of the variance—the standard deviation—has the same units as the data.

For each problem, encourage students to think about how the statistics they calculate could be used to analyze the data. What questions about the data does the statistic answer? What characteristics of the data are lost?

Rounding

Most calculations of statistics result in decimal numbers, so attention must be paid to rounding. The answers in this book were generated following the rules on the next page.

- The mean and median, if not whole numbers, are rounded to one decimal place more than the original data.
- The standard deviation is calculated using the mean to as many decimal places as are available, but the result is rounded to one decimal place more than the original data.
- All statistics for any problem are rounded to the same number of decimal places except for any statistic that's exact and has fewer decimal places.

If you ask your students to follow these rules, you may make exceptions for students planning to take an AP statistics test, which may follow other rules. Currently standard deviations must be stated to at least three decimal places if the original data include any decimal places.

Using This Chapter

If students recall many of the statistical ideas from *Discovering Algebra* (measures of central tendency, range, *IQR,* five-number summaries, outliers, and histograms) and you do not do the exploration, this chapter might take only four class days, including review and a short test on the last day. New material not covered in *Discovering Algebra* includes samples and populations, sigma notation, spread (variability), shape, deviation, standard deviation, and percentiles. If most of the material in this chapter is new to your students, the chapter might take eight days. The investigation in Lesson 2.3 can easily extend to a second day or be revisited after Chapter 3 for simultaneous analysis of two nutritional elements.

Resources

Discovering Advanced Algebra Resources

Teaching and Worksheet Masters
Lessons 2.1–2.3

Calculator Notes 1G, 2A–2D

Fathom Demonstrations
Lesson 2.3
Exploration: Census Microdata

Assessment Resources A and B
Quiz 1 (Lessons 2.1, 2.2)
Quiz 2 (Lesson 2.3)
Chapter 2 Test
Chapter 2 Constructive Assessment Options

More Practice Your Skills for Chapter 2

Condensed Lessons for Chapter 2

Other Resources

Data in Depth by Tim Erickson.

For complete references to this and other resources see www.keypress.com/DAA.

Materials

- watches or clocks with second hands
- rubber bands
- rulers
- measuring tapes or metersticks
- books
- cardboard or pads of paper
- masking tape

Pacing Guide

	day 1	day 2	day 3	day 4	day 5	day 6
standard	2.1	2.2	quiz, 2.3	2.3	quiz, review	assessment
enriched	2.1	2.2	quiz, 2.3, project	quiz, exploration	review, TAL	assessment
block	2.1, 2.2	quiz, 2.3	quiz, exploration,	review, TAL, assessment		

CHAPTER 2

Describing Data

CHAPTER 2 OBJECTIVES

- Review or learn measures of central tendency (mean, median, and mode)
- Learn about quartiles and five-number summaries and connect them to box plots
- Describe the shape and spread of a data set from box plots
- Develop a concept of spread (variability)
- Find variance and standard deviation by formula and by calculator
- Distinguish measures of spread relative to the mean (variance, standard deviation) from measures of spread relative to the median (range, *IQR*)
- Construct a data set having various statistics
- Understand and apply definitions of *outlier*
- Distinguish bar graphs from histograms
- Find the approximate number of data items, the range, and the median by studying a histogram
- Understand the effects of different bin widths in histograms
- Create histograms and box plots to analyze data
- Determine the percentile rank of a data item from raw data or a histogram
- Connect percentile rank and standard deviation

Contemporary German artist Andreas Gursky (b 1955) digitally manipulated this photograph so objects in the background appear as clearly as objects in the foreground. The resulting work of art, *99 Cent* (1999), conveys the vast amount of information that surrounds you in a supermarket. What data about the inventory of this store is helpful to you as a customer? What data is helpful to the management of the store? How would you describe and summarize that data with graphs or numbers?

OBJECTIVES

In this chapter you will

- create, interpret, and compare graphs of data sets
- calculate numerical measures that help you understand and interpret a data set
- make conclusions about a data set and compare it with other data sets based on graphs and numerical values

This 7-by-11-foot photograph was digitally manipulated to place the foreground and the background in the same visual plane, eliminating some sense of perspective. **[Ask]** "How does the photograph's size and the manipulation of the perspective affect your interpretation?" [The size and the repetitious nature make it difficult to focus on any one item. Individual elements, including the people, get lost. The manipulation makes the picture look somewhat abstract, so the viewer sees a normal situation from a new point of view.]

In a store it is important to keep accurate records of data; mistakes can be costly. **[Ask]** "What does this photograph tell us about organizing data into sets and graphs in order to draw conclusions?" [Everything is so spread out and repetitive that it is difficult to focus on any patterns.] "What data might you want to collect in this store situation?" [quantity, weight, size, cost, and frequency of purchase of each item; patterns of purchase in different areas of the store]

LESSON

2.1

Measures of Central Tendency and Box Plots

That is what learning is. You suddenly understand something you've understood all your life, but in a new way.

DORIS LESSING

Newspapers, magazines, the evening news, commercials, government bulletins, and sports publications bombard you daily with data and statistics. As an informed citizen, you need to be able to interpret this information in order to make intelligent decisions.

In this chapter you will graph data sets in several different ways. You'll also study some numerical measures that help you better understand what a data set tells you. Each numerical measure can be called a **statistic.** A collection of measures, or the mathematical study of data collection and analysis, is called **statistics.** Studying statistics helps you learn how to collect, organize, analyze, and interpret data.

EXAMPLE A

Owen is a member of the student council and wants to present data about backpack safety to the school board. He collects these data on the weights of backpacks of 30 randomly chosen students. How much does the typical backpack weigh at Owen's school?

Student	Grade	Weight of backpack (lb)
1	Junior	10
2	Senior	20
3	Junior	9
4	Junior	17
5	Junior	3
6	Junior	10
7	Senior	15
8	Junior	15
9	Senior	7
10	Senior	10

Student	Grade	Weight of backpack (lb)
11	Junior	9
12	Senior	10
13	Senior	9
14	Junior	7
15	Senior	4
16	Senior	6
17	Senior	7
18	Senior	9
19	Junior	13
20	Junior	10

Student	Grade	Weight of backpack (lb)
21	Senior	8
22	Senior	7
23	Senior	4
24	Senior	4
25	Junior	8
26	Junior	33
27	Senior	10
28	Senior	9
29	Senior	7
30	Junior	16

LESSON

2.1

PLANNING

LESSON OUTLINE

One day:

10 min Examples
20 min Investigation
10 min Sharing
5 min Exercises

MATERIALS

- watches or clocks with second hands
- Backpacks (W) for One Step
- Box Plot (T), *optional*
- Spread (T), *optional*
- Human Box Plot (T), *optional*
- Calculator Notes 1G, 2A–2C

TEACHING

A data set can be described in part by various measures of central tendency. If students have used *Discovering Algebra,* this lesson will be mostly review. If the ideas are new to your students, plan to spend two days on the lesson. The one-step investigation is on page 79; if you plan to use it, begin with it.

[Language] The word *data* is used in the book as a plural noun. In everyday language, the word *data* is sometimes used to describe a single piece of information (though the correct singular form is *datum*).

[ESL] *Collect* means "gather," *organize* means "arrange" or "put in order," *analyze* means "look at carefully," and *interpret* means "make conclusions based on observations."

NCTM STANDARDS

CONTENT		PROCESS	
	Number	✓	Problem Solving
✓	Algebra	✓	Reasoning
✓	Geometry	✓	Communication
✓	Measurement	✓	Connections
✓	Data/Probability	✓	Representation

LESSON OBJECTIVES

- Review mean, median, and mode
- Learn sigma notation for summation
- Create box plots from five-number summaries; conversely, read five-number summaries from box plots
- Describe the shape and spread of a data set from box plots
- Use box plots to compare the centers, shapes, and spreads of data sets
- Construct a data set having various statistics

▶ EXAMPLE A

You might take a moment to discuss *ergonomics*, the science of designing and arranging things so that people and those things interact most efficiently and safely. **[Ask]** "How might an ergonomist [ər-'gä-nə-mist] use Owen's data?"

As you discuss the measures of central tendency, mention that a set may have no mode, one mode, or more than one mode. If a set has several data values that appear most frequently, you might decide either that these values are all modes (if the set also has many other values) or that the set has no mode.

If students are new to graphing calculators, you might provide copies of the calculator notes mentioned in the student book and Calculator Note 2A, which gives more information about lists.

[Ask] "How much would a typical student need to weigh for the mean, the median, and the mode to be a safe backpack weight?" [102 lb; 90 lb; 100 lb]

As you discuss what statistic Owen might use, also **[Ask]** "Which statistic would you use if you were a school nurse?" [the mean] "If you were a textbook publisher?" [the median, to minimize assertions that books are too heavy] "If you were a backpack manufacturer?" [the mean, to demonstrate how much a backpack can hold]

[Language] The mean defined here is more properly called the *arithmetic* [ar-ith-'me-tik] *mean.* You might define *geometric mean* when your students work on Improving Your Geometry Skills on page 84.

Bring out the idea that a sample like this is usually taken to obtain information about a population—in this case, the entire school. A sample of backpack data might be biased if it comes from volunteers who want to complain or boast about the load they carry. A biased sample might not represent the entire population.

Choosing a representative sample can be complex. Students might already have an idea of what constitutes a random sample. In this situation, a random sample could be obtained by numbering all the students and using a random number generator to select the sample; all the individuals would have an equal chance of being selected.

[Language] Gottfried Achenwall, a German professor, coined the word *statistics* ("state arithmetic") in 1749 to describe government counting and analyzing, such as the census. Karl Pearson (1857–1936), a mathematician at University College in London, introduced the term *mode* in 1895, writing "I have found it convenient to use the term *mode* for the abscissa corresponding to the ordinate of maximum frequency."

▶ Solution

There are three statistics you could use to describe a typical item from a list of numerical data: the mean, the median, or the mode.

The **mean** is 10.2 lb, the sum of all data values, 306 lb, divided by the number of values, 30.

The **median** is 9 lb, the middle value when the data are arranged in order.

3, 4, 4, 4, 6, 7, 7, 7, 7, 7, 8, 8, 9, 9, 9, 9, 9, 9, 10, 10, 10, 10, 10, 10, 13, 15, 15, 16, 17, 20, 33

$$\frac{9+9}{2} = 9$$

Because there is an even number of values, the median is the mean of the two middle values.

The **mode** is 10 lb, the weight that occurs most frequently.

[▶ See **Calculator Note 1G** to learn how to enter these data into your calculator. See **Calculator Note 2B** to calculate the mean and median. ◀]

You can justify using any of these three statistics as a typical weight. If Owen wants to present a statistic that implies backpacks are too heavy, he might want to use the mean because it is higher than the median or mode due to one very large data value. When a data set has one or more values that are far from the rest, the median often is more representative of the data than the mean.

Health CONNECTION

The weight of a backpack, if carried improperly, can cause physical injuries. The American Chiropractic Association recommends that the items inside a backpack weigh no more than 10% of the person's body weight. To prevent muscle aches, fatigue, and pain in the shoulders, neck, and back, use straps on both shoulders, and adjust the straps so that the backpack falls below the shoulders and rests on the hips.

The data set in Example A did not include every student in the school, so it may or may not tell much about all student backpack weights. If Owen took his sample from the first 30 students who arrived to a single class, then the data set might be biased, or unfair: it could represent students who hurry to class because their backpacks are too heavy. How might the information be biased if Owen took the sample from the first 30 volunteers?

If you assume Owen's data are from a **random sample** of *all* students, then you can make some general conclusions about all backpacks at his school. The three values commonly used to describe a typical data value—the mean, the median, and the mode—are called **measures of central tendency.**

In statistics, the mean is often referred to by the symbol $\bar{x}$ (pronounced "*x* bar"). Another symbol, Σ (capital *sigma*), is used to indicate the sum of the data values. For example, $\sum_{i=1}^{5} x_i$ means $x_1 + x_2 + x_3 + x_4 + x_5$, where x_1, x_2, x_3, x_4, and x_5 are the individual data values. So the mean of n data values is given by

$$\bar{x} = \frac{\sum_{i=1}^{n} x_i}{n}$$

The sum of all data values.

The number of data values.

Summarizing a data set with a single "typical" number or statistic is an incomplete picture. Sharing the entire data set is not usually informative either. A good description of the data set includes not only a measure of central tendency but the spread and distribution of the data as well. This is often done with a set of summary values or a graph.

The **box plot** (or **box-and-whisker plot**) provides a visual tool for analyzing information about a data set. This is the box plot of the backpack data from Example A. [▶ See **Calculator Note 2C** to learn how to create a box plot on your calculator. ◀]

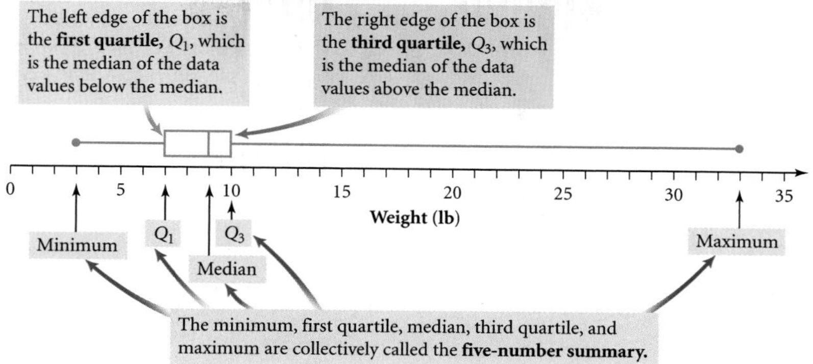

The lines extending from the "box" are called "whiskers." They identify the minimum and maximum values of the data. The difference between the maximum and minimum is the **range** of the data.

EXAMPLE B

Use the box plot above to analyze the backpack data.

a. What percentage of the data values is represented by the lower whisker?

b. What are the values for the first quartile, the median, and the third quartile?

c. What is the five-number summary for this data set?

▶ ***Solution***

Read the data values from the box plot at the five-number summary points, and use the definition of quartile.

a. One-quarter, or 25%, of the data values are represented by the lower whisker. As a matter of fact, one-quarter of the data values are represented by the upper whisker, one-quarter are represented by the upper part of the box, and one-quarter are represented by the lower part of the box as well.

b. There are 30 values, so after arranging them in order, the first quartile is the eighth value, or 7 lb; the median is the mean of the fifteenth and sixteenth values, or 9 lb; and the third quartile is the twenty-third value, or 10 lb.

c. The five-number summary is 3, 7, 9, 10, 33.

History CONNECTION

One early large-scale statistical survey was that of the 16th-century Hawaiian king, Umi. According to legend, he collected all of his people on a small plain, afterward called the Plain of Numbering, and asked each person to deposit a stone in an area encircling the temple on that plain. The stones were placed in piles according to district, and the piles were located in the direction of the districts. The result showed the relative sizes of the districts' populations.

One Step

Hand out copies of the Backpacks worksheet and present this problem, similar to that presented in Example A: "Owen is a member of the student council and wants to present to the school board data about backpack use in his school. He collects these data on the weights of the backpacks of 30 randomly chosen students. What conclusions can he draw for the school board?"

Some students will probably begin talking about averages. Others might think about the representativeness of the data. Encourage debate to the extent that it keeps students engaged. During Sharing, bring out the idea of statistics, the different kinds of measures of central tendency and the uses of each, the notions of sample and population, and the ideas of biased and random samples. Although students were chosen at random for the survey, they include only juniors and seniors, so the sample still might not be representative of the entire population.

Ask students whether they can represent the data graphically, and be sure someone draws a box plot of the backpack data after deriving the median and the quartiles.

MAKING THE CONNECTION

[ESL] A *plain* is a large, flat piece of land, as in the Great Plains of the United States.

Assessing Progress

As students work and present, you can assess their skill at collecting and organizing data and their familiarity with statistics from earlier experiences.

▶ ***EXAMPLE B***

You might use the Box Plot transparency as you discuss this example. Refer back to Example A to identify Q_1 and Q_3 from the ordered data. As with the median, when there is an odd number of values above or below the median, Q_1 or Q_3 is the middle value; when there is an even number, Q_1 or Q_3 is the mean of the two middle values. **[Language]** The median could be thought of as the second quartile (Q_2). The minimum would be Q_0, and the maximum Q_4. The first quartile is sometimes called the *lower quartile.* The third quartile is sometimes called the *upper quartile.*

Skew

[Language] The word *skew* is used differently in geometry (lines in space that do not intersect and are not parallel) than in statistics (nonsymmetric data); *symmetric* has the same meaning in both, though symmetric data seldom conform to the stricter definition of *symmetry* in geometry.

Have students look back at the box plot of the backpack data to see how it is skewed right. The data points to the right of the center are more spread out than those to the left.

Steps 1, 2 Before beginning, **[Ask]** "Do you think the pulse rates will be skewed left or right, or will they be symmetric?"

If your students need more practice with measures of central tendency, have them calculate these for their pulse rates. **[Ask]** "For what reason would you use each of the three measures of central tendency? Which would you say best describes the typical pulse rate of the students in the class?"

Step 4

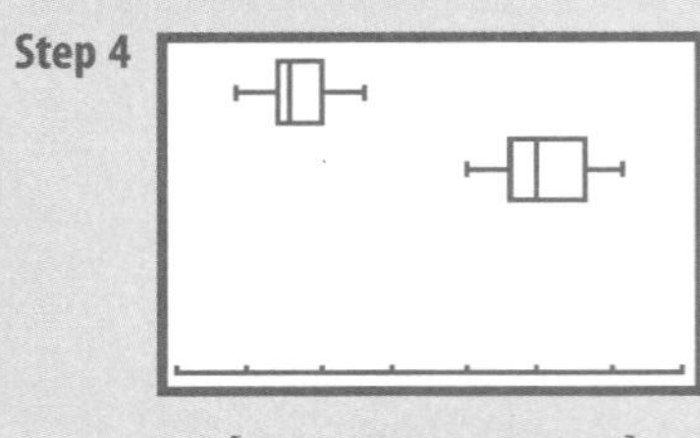

[40, 180, 20, 0, 1, 1]

Step 5 Students might believe it would be valuable to separate the data into subcategories of males and females or athletes and non-athletes. Encourage a discussion of the advantages and disadvantages of using these subcategories.

SHARING IDEAS

Ask why the mean is defined using sigma notation. An alternative for defining the mean of n numbers is to write $\bar{x} = \frac{x_1 + x_2 + \cdots + x_n}{n}$, but this expression might be misinterpreted. If $n = 2$, for example, would $\bar{x} = \frac{x_1 + x_2 + x_2}{2}$? Sigma notation is generally more compact as well as less misleading. Don't strive at this point for complete student understanding of sigma notation; students will encounter the idea throughout the course.

You might ask whether the shape and central tendency of a data set are enough to predict how spread out the data are. Two box plots with the same median and the same shape but different spreads appear on the Spread transparency. **[Ask]** "How might you describe the spread in order to distinguish between the two data sets?" [The range, the quartiles, and the five-number summary might help.]

[Ask] "How many numbers are needed to calculate the range?" [2] "How likely is it that the five-number summary of a population is the same as that of a sample?" [not very likely if the population is much larger than the sample]

See page 879 for answer to Step 5.

Statisticians often talk about the shape of a data set. **Shape** describes how the data are distributed relative to the center. A **symmetric** data set is balanced, or nearly so, at the center. Note that it does not have to be exactly equal on both sides to be called symmetric. **Skewed** data are spread out more on one side of the center than on the other side. The backpack data is an example of skewed data. You will learn more about spread in the next lesson. For now, a box plot can be a good indicator of shape because the median is clearly visible as the center.

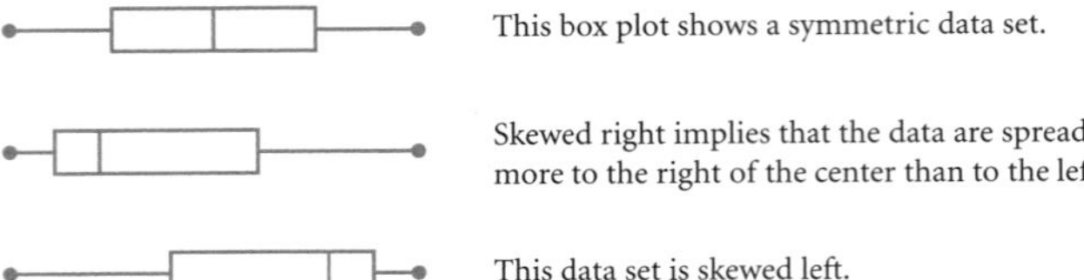

Investigation
Pulse Rates

You will need

- a watch or clock with a second hand

Pulse rate is often used as a measure of whether or not a person is in good physical condition. In this investigation you will practice making box plots, compare box plots, and draw some conclusions about pulse rates.

Step 1 Sample resting data: {68, 76, 84, 80, 76, 72, 60, 68, 68, 80, 68, 80, 64, 64, 72, 76, 72, 68, 56, 88, 80, 76, 68, 56, 64, 60, 92, 72, 84, 72}

Step 2 Sample exercise data: {148, 136, 157, 151, 121, 139, 137, 129, 127, 129, 155, 141, 133, 153, 161, 153, 127, 135, 144, 146, 136, 131, 133, 159, 127, 142, 133, 150, 164, 161}

Step 3 Summaries for sample data:
Resting: 56, 68, 72, 80, 92
Exercise: 121, 133, 140, 153, 164

Step 1 Measure and record your resting pulse for 15 s. Multiply this value by 4 to get the number of beats per minute. Pool data from the entire class.

Step 2 Exercise for 2 min by doing jumping jacks or by running in place. Afterward, measure and record your exercise pulse rate. Pool your data.

Step 3 Order each set of data. Calculate the five-number summaries for your class's resting pulse rates and for your exercise pulse rates.

Step 4 Prepare a box plot of the resting pulse rates and a box plot of the exercise pulse rates. Determine a range suitable for displaying both of these graphs on a single axis.

Step 5 Draw conclusions about pulse rates by comparing these two graphs. Be sure to compare not only centers but also spreads and shapes. How could a physician or a personal trainer use your results to determine whether a client is in good physical condition?

Box plots are a convenient way to compare two data sets. Not only can you readily compare the medians, but you can also see if the two sets are distributed in the same manner.

EXERCISES

Practice Your Skills

1. Find the mean, median, and mode for each data set.

a. Time for pizza delivery (min): {28, 31, 26, 35, 26}

b. Yearly rainfall (cm): {11.5, 17.4, 20.3, 18.5, 17.4, 19.0}

c. Cost of a small popcorn at movie theaters ($): {2.75, 3.00, 2.50, 1.50, 1.75, 2.00, 2.25, 3.25}

d. Number of pets per household: {3, 2, 1, 0, 3, 4, 1}

2. A data set has a mean of 12 days, the median is 14 days, and there are three values in the data set.

a. What is the sum of all three data values? 36 days

b. What is the one value you know? The middle value is 14 days.

c. Create a data set that has the statistics given. Is there more than one data set that could have these statistics? Possible answer: {7, 14, 15}. Yes, there are several data sets with the same statistics.

3. Approximate the values of the five-number summary for this box plot. Give the full name for each value. minimum: 1.25 days; first quartile: 2.5 days; median: 3.25 days; third quartile: 4 days; maximum: 4.75 days

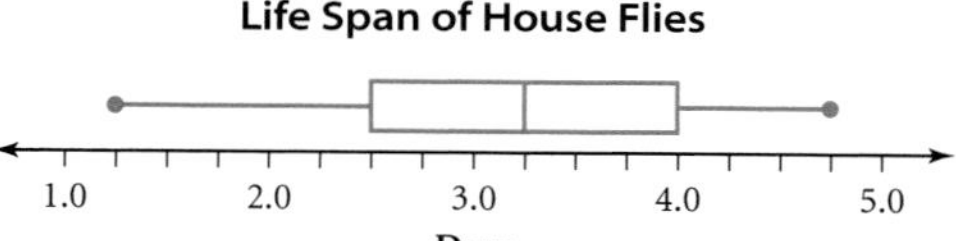

4. Match this data set to one of the four box plots. Licks to the center of a lollipop: {470, 510, 547, 558, 561, 574, 593} B

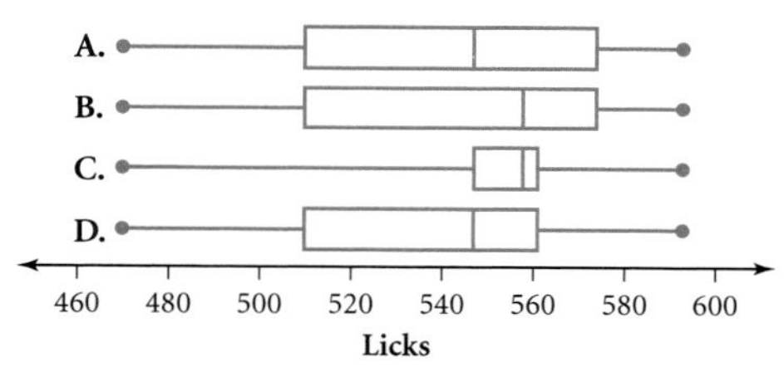

5. Match this box plot to one of the data sets for the number of minutes on the phone spent by 13 customer service representatives in a given hour. D

A. {36, 37, 38, 39, 40, 41, 42, 43, 44, 46, 48, 50, 52}

B. {37, 40, 42, 50, 51, 51, 51, 51, 51, 51, 51, 51, 51}

C. {36, 37, 40, 40, 40, 42, 42, 43, 44, 50, 50, 51, 52}

D. {37, 39, 40, 40, 40, 41, 42, 43, 44, 49, 51, 51, 51}

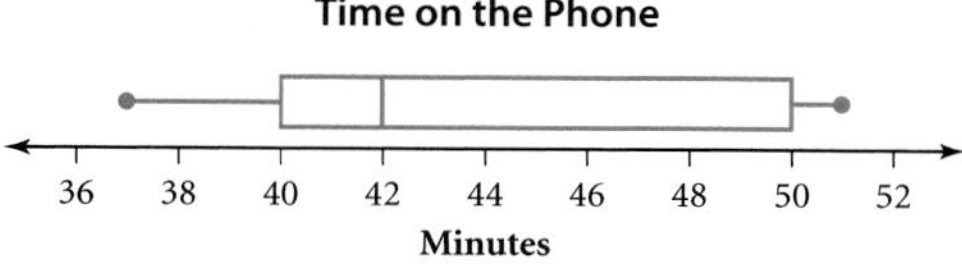

Closing the Lesson

Bring out the main points of the lesson: **Statistics** are used to summarize a data set, often a **sample** of a **population.** Statistics of **unbiased** samples, perhaps **random,** are closer to the corresponding measures of the entire population. Commonly used statistics are averages, or **measures of central tendency:** the (arithmetic) **mean,** the **median,** and **modes.** The mean can be defined using **sigma** notation. A **box plot** uses **quartiles** and the **range** to represent the data set graphically, indicating its **shape** and **spread.** If about the same number of data points are on each side of the center, the shape is **symmetric;** otherwise, it's **skewed.**

To motivate the next lesson, ask students whether they can devise a statistic that is more likely than the range or the five-number summary to predict the spread of a population from the spread of a sample.

BUILDING UNDERSTANDING

In the exercises, students practice calculating and making sense of measures of central tendency—especially the mean and the median—and shape (that is, box plots and quartiles). In Exercise 9, they encounter a definition of interquartile range, a statistic that is used later.

ASSIGNING HOMEWORK

Essential	1, 3–5, 9
Performance assessment	2, 6, 8–15
Portfolio	7
Journal	6, 7, 14
Group	11, 12
Review	16–19

Helping with the Exercises

Exercise 1 1c shows a data set with no mode; 1d shows a data set with more than one mode.

1a. mean: 29.2 min; median: 28 min; mode: 26 min

1b. mean: 17.35 cm; median: 17.95 cm; mode: 17.4 cm

1c. mean: $2.38; median: $2.38; mode: none

1d. mean: 2; median: 2; modes: 1 and 3

Exercise 2 [Alert] Even though students might know how to find the mean, they might not realize that the sum of the data values is the mean times the number of data values. Students might also miss the fact that, because there are three numbers in the data set, the median is one of those numbers. (If there were an even number of data values, the median might not be an element of the data set.)

6. The means and the medians for each student are the same, 84. Neither the mean nor the median reveals the larger variation of Oscar's scores.

7. Answers will vary. The bottom box plot is longer because it reflects the wider range of Oscar's scores. There is no left whisker for the top box plot because the first quarter of Connie's scores is made up of a single repeated score. The median isn't in the center of the top box because the second quarter of Connie's scores is spread over a larger interval than the third quarter of her scores. There is a bigger range for the first quarter of Oscar's scores than for the fourth quarter, so the left whisker is longer than the right one in the bottom box plot.

Exercise 8 Five-number summaries will often be stated without units. Students should understand that the unit of each individual number in the summary is the same as the unit of each data value.

8a.

20 30 40 50 60 70
Home runs

MAKING THE CONNECTION

[Ask] "Is the ERA a mean?" [Yes; the ERA is the mean number of earned runs scored on a pitcher in nine innings.]

Exercise 9 Don't skip this problem because the *IQR*, which is defined here, is essential for understanding outliers in Lesson 2.2.
[Ask] "How does the interquartile range compare with the range? Can the *IQR* and the range ever be the same value?" [In data sets with several equal data values, the maximum and minimum might be the same value as Q_3 and Q_1.] Also ask what conclusions students can draw from these statistics. A larger *IQR* indicates more variability in performance.

Reason and Apply

6. Here are the scores on semester assignments for two students.

Connie: {82, 86, 82, 84, 85, 84, 85}
Oscar: {72, 94, 76, 96, 90, 76, 84}

Find the mean and median for each set of scores, and explain why they do not tell the whole story about the differences between Connie's and Oscar's scores.

7. These box plots represent Connie's and Oscar's scores from Exercise 6.

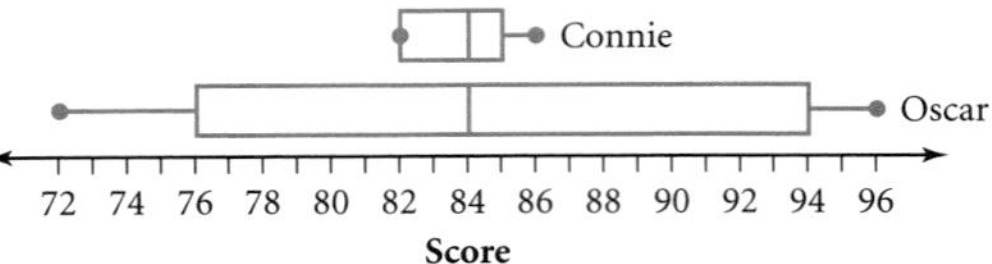

Write a paragraph describing the information pictured in the box plots. Use the box plots to help you draw some statistical conclusions. In your description, include answers to such questions as What does it mean that the second box plot is longer? Where is the left whisker of the top box plot? What does it mean when the median isn't in the middle of the box? What does it mean when the left whisker is longer than the right whisker?

8. Homer Mueller has played in the minor leagues for 11 years. His home run totals, in order, for those years are 56, 62, 49, 65, 58, 52, 68, 72, 25, 51, and 64.

a. Construct a box plot showing Homer's data.

b. Give the five-number summary. 25, 51, 58, 65, 72

c. Find $\bar{x}$. $\bar{x} \approx 57$ home runs

d. How many home runs would Homer need to hit next season to have a 12-year mean of 60? 98 home runs

Sports CONNECTION

Baseball fans thrive on the "stats" of their favorite players. For example, earned run average (ERA) is a statistic calculated for pitchers. You calculate ERA by taking the number of earned runs scored on the pitcher and dividing it by one-ninth the total number of innings pitched.

Pedro Martínez pitches for the Boston Red Sox.

9. The **interquartile range** (***IQR***) is the difference between the first and third quartiles, or the length of the box in a box plot.

a. Look at the box plots in Exercise 7. What are the range and interquartile range for Connie? For Oscar? Connie: *range* = 4, *IQR* = 3; Oscar: *range* = 24, *IQR* = 18

b. Find the range and interquartile range for your box plot from Exercise 8. *range* = 47; *IQR* = 14

10. Invent a data set with seven distinct values and a mean of 12. possible answer: {9, 10, 11, 12, 13, 14, 15}

11. Invent a data set with seven values and a mode of 70 and a median of 65.

Exercise 10 The answer is more interesting if not all of the values are 12. Values must sum to 84.

11. possible answer: {62, 63, 64, 65, 70, 70, 70}

12. Invent a data set with seven values that creates this box plot. possible answer: {33, 50, 60, 70, 80, 83, 91}

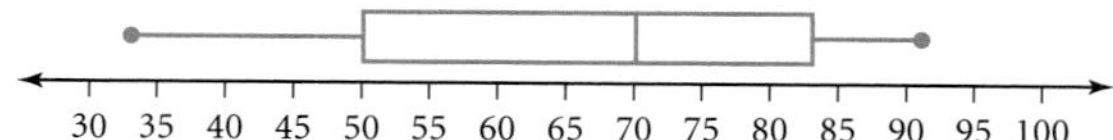

13. Refer to the backpack data listed in Example A. Separate the data by grade level.

a. Compute the mean weight for the juniors and for the seniors. juniors: $\bar{x} \approx 12.3$ lb; seniors: $\bar{x} \approx 8.6$ lb

b. Calculate the median for each grade level. juniors: *median* = 10 lb; seniors: *median* = 8 lb

c. Compare the mean and median values for each grade level. Which is the greater value, mean or median, in each set? Each mean is greater than the corresponding median.

14. Use the backpack data separated by grade level from Exercise 13.

a. Create a box plot for each grade level. Put both box plots on the same axis.

b. Based on the information in your box plots, write a brief statement analyzing these two groups. Use the vocabulary developed in this lesson in your statement.

c. Based on your box plots, explain why the means or medians may have been greater in 13c. The means are greater because both data sets are skewed right.

15. **APPLICATION** Lord Rayleigh was one of the early pioneers in studying the density of nitrogen. (Read the Science Connection below.) The following are data that he collected. Lord Rayleigh's measurements first appeared in *Proceedings of the Royal Society of London* (London, vol. 55, 1894). Each piece of data is the mass in grams of nitrogen filling a certain flask under a specified temperature and pressure.

Mass of Nitrogen Produced from Chemical Compounds (g)		
2.30143	2.29890	2.29816
2.30182	2.29869	2.29940
2.29849	2.29889	2.30074
2.30054		

Mass of Nitrogen Produced from the Atmosphere (g)		
2.31017	2.30986	2.31010
2.31001	2.31024	2.31010
2.31028	2.31163	2.30956

a. Calculate the five-number summary for each set of data.

b. On the same axis, create a box plot for each set of data.

c. Describe any similarities and differences in the shapes of the box plots. Do the box plots support Lord Rayleigh's conjecture?

Science CONNECTION

One of the earliest persons to study the density of nitrogen was the English scientist Lord Rayleigh (1842–1919, born John William Strutt). Working with fairly small samples, he noticed that the density of nitrogen produced from chemical compounds was different from the density of nitrogen produced from the atmosphere. On the supposition that the air-derived gas was heavier than the "chemical" nitrogen, he conjectured the existence in the atmosphere of an unknown ingredient. In 1894, Lord Rayleigh isolated the unknown ingredient, the colorless, tasteless, and odorless gas called argon. In 1904, Lord Rayleigh was awarded the Nobel Prize in physics for his discovery. You can learn more about Rayleigh's work by using the links at www.keymath.com/DAA .

Lord Rayleigh

Exercise 12 The five-number summary values are fixed, so only the 60 and the 80 given in the possible answer might vary in student answers.

14a.

Five-number summaries: juniors 3, 8.5, 10, 15.5, 33; seniors 4, 6.5, 8, 10, 20

14b. Sample answer: The juniors carry more weight in general. The juniors have a greater spread of weights. Both data sets are skewed right.

Exercise 15 [Context] Rayleigh's work in 1894 was done with Sir William Ramsay. Ramsay was also awarded a Nobel Prize in chemistry for discovering noble gases.

15a. chemical: 2.29816, 2.29869, 2.29915, 2.30074, 2.30182; atmospheric: 2.30956, 2.309935, 2.31010, 2.31026, 2.31163

15b.

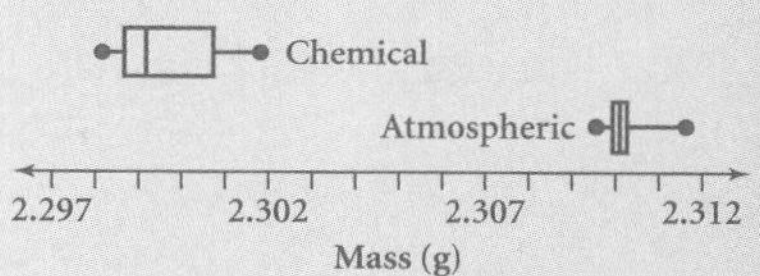

15c. Sample answer: Both graphs are skewed right. There is a significant difference in the range and *IQR* for the two sets of data. The mass of the nitrogen produced from the atmosphere is heavier than the mass of the nitrogen produced from chemical compounds, so the box plots support Rayleigh's conjecture.

EXTENSIONS

A. Have students create five different data sets for each of Exercises 10–12 or five different sequences for each set of terms in Exercise 16.

B. Use Take Another Look activity 1 or 2 on page 111.

C. As a class create a human box plot as described in the Human Box Plot transparency. The visual representation will help them remember how the values are found. Put cards at equal intervals on the floor numbered 15 cm to 30 cm, and ask students to line up parallel to these cards. As you find students that represent the key points on the box plot, if a median or quartile is the mean of two measures, choose one student to represent that value and step forward on, or between, the correct card(s).

D. Extend the problem in Improving Your Geometry Skills by challenging students to generalize the problem to any rectangle, any parallelogram, any rhombus, any triangle, or any other polygon.

Exercise 16 Infinitely many sequences start with the three terms. If students suggest a sequence such as 42, 45, 48, 45, 42, 45, 48, 45, 42, 45, . . . for 16a, for example, be open to their creativity but try to be sure they could also generate a linear sequence.

Exercise 17 **[Alert]** You might need to review how to evaluate roots. **[Language]** *Radical form* refers to a form that has a square root symbol (radical). It may also be written so that there are no perfect squares as factors of numbers under the radical.

18. On credit, Rebecca will have paid for the drum set after 11 months. Her total cost will be \$430.01. With savings, she could buy the drum set after 10 months. Sample advice: If it's worth it to Rebecca to pay \$30 extra to have the drum set now, she should buy it on credit; otherwise, she should wait.

Exercise 19 Students might solve these equations by undoing, graphing, guess-and-check, or balancing. Whatever beginning algebra methods they review will help prepare them for solving linear equations in Chapter 4.

Review

1.2 **16.** Find the next three terms in each sequence and write a recursive formula.

a. 42, 45, 48 . . .
51, 54, 57; $u_1 = 42$ and $u_n = u_{n-1} + 3$ where $n \geq 2$

b. 16, 40, 100, . . .
250, 625, 1562.5; $u_1 = 16$ and $u_n = u_{n-1} \cdot 2.5$ where $n \geq 2$

17. Evaluate each expression. Write your answers both in radical form and in decimal form rounded to one decimal place.

a. $\sqrt{\dfrac{432}{6}}$ $6\sqrt{2} \approx 8.5$

b. $\sqrt{\dfrac{782 + 1354}{24}}$ $\sqrt{89} \approx 9.4$

c. $\sqrt{\dfrac{49 + 121 + 16 + 81 + 100}{4}}$ $\dfrac{\sqrt{367}}{2} \approx 9.6$

1.5 **18.** APPLICATION Rebecca wants to buy a used drum set that costs \$400. Either she can buy it now on credit and pay an annual interest rate of 15%, compounded monthly, on the unpaid balance, or she can wait until she has saved the money in her bank account which earns an annual interest rate of 5% compounded monthly. Either way she can contribute \$40 each month from her weekend job. How long will it take to pay for the drum set if she buys it on credit? How long would she have to save to buy it? Give Rebecca advice.

19. Solve.

a. $x + 8 = 15$ $x = 7$

b. $3x = 15$ $x = 5$

c. $3x + 8 = 15$ $x = \frac{7}{3} = 2.\overline{3}$

IMPROVING YOUR GEOMETRY SKILLS

Dissecting a Square

Square $ABCD$ is divided into four regions by drawing $\overline{AC}$ and $\overline{BE}$, where E is the midpoint of $\overline{CD}$. Compare the areas of regions I, II, III, and IV.

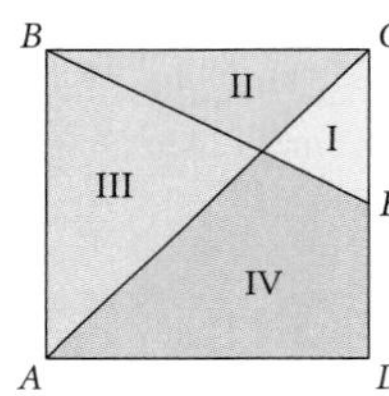

IMPROVING GEOMETRY SKILLS

Because this problem does not specify what is meant by *compare,* you can make it easier by asking for the relative areas of the regions: area I < area II < area III < area IV. A more mathematical answer uses ratios to compare areas. This answer can be approached either abstractly (comparing the geometry of regions) or concretely (assigning a length to each side of the square and calculating an actual area for each region). The ratio of area I to area II to area III to area IV is 1 : 2 : 4 : 5.

You might use this problem to introduce the *geometric mean,* or *mean proportional.* For two positive numbers a and b the geometric mean is the number x such that $\frac{a}{x} = \frac{x}{b}$. In this geometric example, the area of region II is the geometric mean of the areas of regions I and III, because $\frac{1}{2} = \frac{2}{4}$. Algebraically, the geometric mean of positive numbers a and b is $\sqrt{ab}$. The geometric mean of n positive numbers is the nth root of their product.

LESSON

2.2

Measures of Spread

Out on the edge you see all kinds of things you can't see from the center.

KURT VONNEGUT

If you ask several people to estimate the number of people in a crowd, their estimates will usually differ. The mean or median would measure the central tendency of the estimates, but neither of these statistics tell how widely people's estimates differ. Measuring variability, or **spread,** in numerical data allows a more complete description than just stating a measure of central tendency. In this lesson you will investigate different ways to measure and describe variability.

On August 28, 1963, about 250,000 people gathered at the Lincoln Memorial to support civil rights legislation. It was here that Martin Luther King, Jr., gave his "I Have a Dream" speech. The March on Washington was the largest gathering of people anywhere to that date.

Investigation
A Good Design

You will need

- a rubber band
- a ruler
- a measuring tape or metersticks
- paper
- books
- a pad of paper or cardboard

In a well-designed experiment, you should be able to follow a specific procedure and get very similar results every time you perform the experiment. In this investigation, you will attempt to control the setup of an experiment in order to limit the variability of your results.

Select and perform one of these experiments. Make complete and careful notes about the setup of your experiment.

Experiment 1: Rubber Band Launch

In this experiment you'll use a ruler to launch a rubber band. Select the height and angle of your launch and the length of your stretch, and determine any other factors that might affect your results. Launch the rubber band into an area clear of obstructions. Record the horizontal distance of the flight. Repeat this procedure as precisely as you can with the same rubber band, the same launch setup, and the same stretch another seven or eight times.

LESSON

2.2

PLANNING

LESSON OUTLINE

One day:

20 min	Investigation
10 min	Sharing
5 min	Example
10 min	Exercises

MATERIALS

- rubber bands
- rulers
- measuring tapes
- books
- cardboard or pads of paper
- masking tape
- Experiments 1 and 2 Sample Data (W), *optional*
- Calculator Notes 2B, 2C

TEACHING

In this lesson, students study statistics that describe the spread of data relative to the mean. For an alternative to the guided investigation, use the one-step investigation found on page 87.

Guiding the Investigation

Sample data are provided on the Experiments 1 and 2 Sample Data worksheet and on the Calculator Programs and Data CD. Though students might find Experiment 1 more exciting than Experiment 2, it could be hazardous for large classes. Make sure students follow safety guidelines. Students should wear protective goggles. Launch areas need to be clearly defined and groups sufficiently far apart so that no rubber bands are launched toward students.

NCTM STANDARDS

CONTENT		PROCESS	
	Number		Problem Solving
✓	Algebra	✓	Reasoning
	Geometry	✓	Communication
✓	Measurement	✓	Connections
✓	Data/Probability	✓	Representation

LESSON OBJECTIVES

- Develop a concept of spread (variability)
- Use a calculator to find standard deviation
- Derive formulas for standard deviation and variance; find standard deviation by hand
- Understand deviation from the mean
- Distinguish measures of spread relative to the mean (variance, standard deviation) from measures of spread relative to the median (range, *IQR*)
- Understand and apply definitions of *outlier*

Guiding the Investigation (continued)
In Experiment 1, be sure students are considering the amount of stretch.

In Experiment 2, a good ramp can be made from a piece of cardboard or a pad of paper propped up against a stack of books. Students might tape the bottom edge of the cardboard or pad to the desk to maintain the same ramp slope.

Step 1 [Language] *Trial* means one execution of an experiment.

Step 1 Rubber band launch sample data (cm): {182.2, 135.9, 187.6, 162.5, 150.0, 186.5, 180.0}; rolling ball sample data (cm): {17.3, 24.4, 28.7, 19.2, 36.8, 30.8, 41.6}. Rubber band launch: $\bar{x} \approx 169.24$ cm; rolling ball: $\bar{x} = 28.40$ cm.

Step 2 [ESL] *Variability* refers to how consistent the measurements are. That is, are they close together or far apart?

If students are worried about the amount of freedom they're given, reassure them that there is no best statistic. Encourage creativity. If students are tending to limit themselves to the measures of Lesson 2.1 (range, *IQR*), you might want to suggest to one or two groups that they consider using the mean rather than the median as a reference point.

Step 2 Students should realize that a better-controlled experiment will have less variability. Students will likely find different ways to calculate a single value that tells how accurate their group was.

Step 3 For sample data: rubber band launch: $s \approx 20.19$ cm rolling ball: $s \approx 8.89$ cm

Experiment 2: Rolling Ball

In this experiment you'll roll a ball of paper down a ramp and off the edge of your desk. Build your ramp from books, notebooks, or a pad of paper. Select the height and slope of your ramp and the distance from the edge of your desk, and determine any other factors that might affect your results. Make a ball by crumpling a piece of paper, and roll it down the ramp. Record the horizontal distance to the place where the ball hits the floor. Repeat this procedure with the same ball, the same ramp setup, and the same release another seven or eight times.

Step 1 Use your data from Experiment 1 or 2. Calculate the mean distance for your trials.

Step 2 On average, how much do your data values differ from the mean? How does the variability in your results relate to how controlled your setup was? Determine a way to calculate a *single* value that tells how accurate your group was at repeating the procedure. Write a formula to calculate your statistic.

Step 3 There is a value known as the **standard deviation** that helps measure the spread of data away from the mean. Use your calculator to find this value for your data. [► See **Calculator Note 2B** to learn how to calculate the standard deviation using your calculator. ◄]

Step 4 See if you can find a formula or procedure that allows you to calculate the value of the standard deviation by hand. (Hints: A **deviation** is the difference between a data value and the mean of the data set. Standard deviation involves both squaring and taking a square root.)

Step 5 Repeat the experiment and collect another set of data from seven or eight trials. Calculate your statistic and the standard deviation for your new set of data. How do the results of your experiments compare? Write a report explaining your procedures and conclusions. In your report, explain some things that you could do differently in order to minimize the standard deviation.

Step 4 Even with the hints, students might not be able to devise the formula; they might look ahead in the book to find where the formula is defined. Be sensitive to students' frustration level on this step and let them know not to worry if they can't figure out the formula. You might want to use Step 4 as a point at which to come together as a class for large-group discussion, but avoid telling students the formula. The text will lead them through a derivation.

Step 4 Answers will vary. The actual formula is on page 88.

Step 5 You might encourage students to try to minimize their standard deviation through careful control of the experiment. If time permits, the class might come up with a standard procedure. Using this procedure, students could then try to minimize their standard deviation not only within their groups but also as an entire class.

Step 5 Answers will vary. Students should be able to describe each experiment as more-controlled or less-controlled based on the standard deviation.

If you want to measure the spread of data, it is typical to start by finding the mean. Next you find the **deviation,** or directed distance, from each data value to the mean. When you compare the results from two groups in the previous investigation, you may find that one group's mean is 200 cm and another group's mean is 300 cm. However, if their deviations are similar, then they performed the experiment equally well. The deviations let you compare the spread independent of the mean.

Consider two groups that each do the rubber band launch seven times.

Group A distance (cm): {182, 186, 182, 184, 185, 184, 185}

Group B distance (cm): {152, 194, 166, 216, 200, 176, 184}

The mean for each group is 184. The individual deviations, $x_i - \bar{x}$, for each data value, x_i, are in the table below.

Group A			Group B		
Data value	Distance	Deviation	Data value	Distance	Deviation
x_1	182	182 − 184 = **−2**	x_1	152	152 − 184 = **−32**
x_2	186	186 − 184 = **2**	x_2	194	194 − 184 = **10**
x_3	182	182 − 184 = **−2**	x_3	166	166 − 184 = **−18**
x_4	184	184 − 184 = **0**	x_4	216	216 − 184 = **32**
x_5	185	185 − 184 = **1**	x_5	200	200 − 184 = **16**
x_6	184	184 − 184 = **0**	x_6	176	176 − 184 = **−8**
x_7	185	185 − 184 = **1**	x_7	184	184 − 184 = **0**

These deviations show more variation in Group B's distances than in Group A's distances. That might imply Group B's experiment was not designed well enough to give consistent results.

Begun in 1992 by Lorraine Serena and Elena Siff, *Women Beyond Borders* is a worldwide art project in which women artists are given identical wooden boxes and asked to transform them. If you consider the original box to be the mean, some of the resulting artworks have large deviations.

From left: **1.** The original pine box; **2.** Darlene Nguyen-Ely, USA, Vietnam, *Journey #17;* **3.** Madoka Hirata, Japan, *The Distance from Time #1;* **4.** Elena Mary Siff, USA, *Narcissism;* **5.** Cirenaica Moreira Diaz, Cuba, *Untitled;* **6.** Alejandra Mastro Sesenna, Guatemala, *Eva's Last Wish;* **7.** Gordana Kaljalovic Odanovic, Yugoslavia, *Model of Intimacy;* **8.** Lilian Nabulime, Kenya, *My Self.* On the web at *www.womenbeyondborders.org.*

One Step

Give students the data set $\{-1, -1, 0, 0, 1, 2, 2, 3, 3\}$. Help the class see how to use calculators to find the *population* standard deviation (σx on TI calculators). Then ask them to experiment with the data to determine what formula the calculators are using to find this measurement of the amount of spread relative to the mean.

As you circulate, encourage students to change data values systematically and to keep careful records. As needed, suggest that they try to find a formula for the square of the standard deviation.

Encourage debate. Students who at first are unsure of an approach or struggle to understand a method will learn. The more students struggle and debate, the more neural connections they are making in their brains. Thus they will learn more deeply and will more easily be able to use what they learn in new situations.

During Sharing (or perhaps with any groups that work quickly), ask students to find what formula the calculator is using for the sample standard deviation (s). Discuss why the formulas differ, and bring out the advantages of the standard deviation over other measures of spread.

Measuring Spread

[Language] The *directed distance* is the distance, including a positive or negative sign, that shows in which direction the data point lies relative to the mean.

You might want students to calculate both means to verify that they are 184. **[Ask]** "Does the equality of the means tell us that the groups did equally well?" [Group B's data were much more widely spread, indicating that its experiment was not as closely controlled as that of Group A.]

Measuring Spread (continued)

[Ask] "Why is the sum of the deviations not a good measure of spread?" [This sum is always 0.] Students might suggest taking the sum of absolute values of the deviations (or just "make them all positive"). When the sum of the absolute values of the deviations is divided by the number of data values, the statistic is called the *mean deviation;* this is the subject of Take Another Look activity 4 on page 112. Its main advantage is that it doesn't emphasize outliers as much as standard deviation does in squaring the deviations. The main disadvantage of the mean deviation is that it is difficult to add absolute values algebraically to derive other formulas.

[Link] If students are confused about why they are dividing by $(n - 1)$ to find the standard deviation, you can tell them that statisticians do not all agree on a reason, though there's little disagreement about the formula. Some students will be more attracted to mathematics if they realize that it contains controversy and requires judgment. Some statisticians give the reason in the book but use the term *degrees of freedom.* Others give various reasons why dividing by $(n - 1)$ makes the sample standard deviation closer to the standard deviation of the population than does dividing by n. Still others cite the way more advanced formulas are simplified. A similar discussion shows up in the formula for calculating root mean square error with two-variable data in Chapter 3.

How can you combine the deviations into a single value that reflects the spread in a data set? Finding the sum is a natural choice. However, if you think of the mean as a balance point in a data set, then the directed distances above and below the mean should balance out. Hence, the deviation sum for both Group A and Group B is zero.

Group A's deviation sum: $-2 + 2 + -2 + 0 + 1 + 0 + 1 = 0$

Group B's deviation sum: $-32 + 10 + -18 + 32 + 16 + -8 + 0 = 0$

In order for the sum of the deviations to be useful, you need to eliminate the effect of the different signs. Squaring each deviation is one way to do this.

	Group A			Group B	
Distance	Deviation	(Deviation)^2	Distance	Deviation	(Deviation)^2
182	−2	**4**	152	−32	**1024**
186	2	**4**	194	10	**100**
182	−2	**4**	166	−18	**324**
184	0	**0**	216	32	**1024**
185	1	**1**	200	16	**256**
184	0	**0**	176	−8	**64**
185	1	**1**	184	0	**0**
	sum = **14**			*sum* = **2792**	
Variance →	$\frac{sum}{6} = \mathbf{2.\overline{3}}$			$\frac{sum}{6} = \mathbf{465.\overline{3}}$	
Standard deviation →	$\sqrt{\frac{sum}{6}} \approx \mathbf{1.5}$			$\sqrt{\frac{sum}{6}} \approx \mathbf{21.6}$	

When you sum the squares of the deviations, the sum is no longer zero. The sum of the squares of the deviations, divided by one less than the number of values, is called the **variance** of the data. The square root of the variance is called the **standard deviation** of the data. The standard deviation provides one way to judge the "average difference" between data values and the mean. It is a measure of how the data are spread around the *mean.*

Standard Deviation

The **standard deviation,** s, is a measure of the spread of a data set.

$$s = \sqrt{\frac{\sum_{i=1}^{n}(x_i - \bar{x})^2}{n - 1}}$$

where x_i represents the individual data values, n is the number of values, and $\bar{x}$ is the mean. The standard deviation has the same units as the data.

The larger standard deviation for Group B indicates that their distances generally lie much farther from the mean than do Group A's. A large value for the standard deviation tells you that the data values are not as tightly packed around the mean. As a general rule, a set with more data near the mean will have less spread and a smaller standard deviation.

You may wonder why you divide by $(n - 1)$ when calculating standard deviation. As you know, the sum of the deviations is zero. So, if you know all but one of the deviations, you can calculate the last deviation by making sure the sum will be zero. The last deviation depends on the rest, so the set of deviations contains only $(n - 1)$ independent pieces of data.

When you make a box plot, you have a visual representation of how data are spread around the *median*. The range (the distance between the whisker endpoints) and the interquartile range (the length of the box) are measures of spread around the median. **Outliers** are data values that differ significantly from the majority of the data. The exact definition of an outlier may vary according to different textbooks. Some statisticians identify outliers from a box plot as values that are more than $1.5 \cdot IQR$ from either end of the box.

[Language] *Interquartile range* was defined in Lesson 2.1, Exercise 9. Review the definition so students can understand the definition of *outlier* based on the *IQR*.

Expressed as inequalities, $outlier > Q_3 + 1.5 \cdot IQR$ or $outlier < Q_1 - 1.5 \cdot IQR$.

The National Geophysical Data Center created this map of human settlements, based on composite data from many satellites about sources of nighttime light. You could consider isolated points of light to be outliers because they are far removed from dense concentrations of light.

EXAMPLE

This table gives the student-to-teacher ratios for public elementary and secondary schools in the United States.

Student-to-Teacher Ratios for Public Elementary and Secondary Schools (2000–2001 School Year)

State	AK	AL	AR	AZ	CA	CO	CT	DE	FL	GA	HI	IA	ID
Ratio	16.9	15.4	14.1	19.8	20.6	17.3	13.7	15.3	18.4	15.9	16.9	14.3	17.9

State	IL	IN	KS	KY	LA	MA	MD	ME	MI	MN	MO	MS	MT
Ratio	16.1	16.7	14.4	16.8	14.9	14.5	16.3	12.5	18.0	16.0	14.1	16.1	14.9

State	NC	ND	NE	NH	NJ	NM	NV	NY	OH	OK	OR	PA	RI
Ratio	15.5	13.4	13.6	14.5	13.1	15.2	18.6	13.9	15.5	15.1	19.4	15.5	14.8

State	SC	SD	TN	TX	UT	VA	VT	WA	WI	WV	WY
Ratio	14.9	13.7	14.9	14.8	21.9	12.5	12.1	19.7	14.1	13.7	13.3

(U.S. Department of Education, National Center for Education Statistics)

a. Calculate the mean and the standard deviation. What do the statistics tell you about the spread of the student-to-teacher ratios?

b. Make a box plot of the data and identify any outliers.

EXAMPLE

Students might use their calculators to verify the answers in the example.

Tell students that the entire U.S. student population was 46,467,465 and the teacher population was 2,906,878, giving a U.S. student-to-teacher ratio of 15.99. Yet the mean of the ratios is 15.60. [Ask] "Why are the mean of the ratios and the mean different?" [The ratios were not all based on the same number of teachers; thus they did not have a common denominator and can't be used to determine the student-to-teacher ratio for the country.]

SHARING IDEAS

Choose presentations to include a variety of results. **[Ask]** "Why do results of the same experiment vary?" [One reason might be that different groups used different measuring procedures, measuring to an edge or to the middle of the rubber band or paper.]

[Ask] "If groups got different results because they used different procedures, are the statistics useless?" [The standard deviations can still tell how well controlled the experiments were.]

[Ask] "Why does the formula for the standard deviation use a square root?" Students might say that it's to compensate for squaring. Ask if the square root of the sum of squares is the same as the sum of the numbers; that is, does $\sqrt{a^2 + b^2}$ equal $a + b$? The compensation comes only in the units; if the data values are in cm, for example, the variance will be in cm^2, but the standard deviation will be in cm.

[Ask] "How are variance and standard deviation different, as measures of spread, from range and *IQR*?" [The *IQR*, based on quartiles, measures spread relative to the median rather than to the mean. More important, the range and the *IQR* are based on very few numbers in a sample, so, depending on the situation, they may be less likely to give good information about the whole population than the variance and the standard deviation, which use all the numbers in the sample.]

1b. −6, 8, 1, −3

2b. −18.4, −0.4, 10.6, 5.6, 8.6, −10.4, 8.6, 9.6, −13.4

► ***Solution***

a. The mean student-to-teacher ratio is approximately 15.63. The standard deviation is approximately 2.18. So, many of the data values are within 2.18 units of the mean of 15.63.

b. The five-number summary is 12.1, 14.1, 15.15, 16.8, 21.9.

Student-to-Teacher Ratios

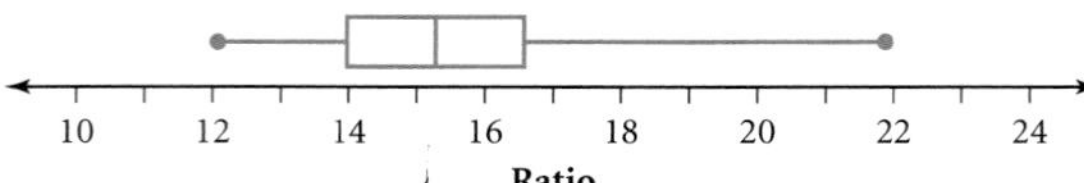

The interquartile range is 2.7. To be an outlier, a data value must be $1.5 \cdot 2.7$, or 4.05, away from an end of the box. That means it must be less than $14.1 - 4.05$, or 10.05, or more than $16.8 + 4.05$, or 20.85. There is one ratio, 21.9 (UT), that meets this condition, so it is an outlier. [► Revisit **Calculator Note 2C** to learn how to make a box plot that shows outliers. ◄]

As you work the exercises, you may notice that finding a measure of central tendency is usually an integral step of measuring the spread. In order to calculate the standard deviation you first need to calculate the mean. The interquartile range relies on the first and third quartiles, which in turn rely on the median.

EXERCISES

Practice Your Skills

1. Given the data set {41, 55, 48, 44}:

a. Find the mean. 47.0

b. Find the deviation from the mean for each value.

c. Find the standard deviation of the data set. 6.1

2. The lengths in minutes of nine music CDs are 45, 63, 74, 69, 72, 53, 72, 73, and 50.

a. Find the mean. 63.4

b. Find the deviation from the mean for each value.

c. Find the standard deviation of the data set. 11.2

d. What are the units of the mean, the deviations from the mean, and the standard deviation? minutes

3. In a classroom experiment, 11 bean plants were grown from seeds. After two weeks, the heights in centimeters of the plants were 9, 10, 10, 13, 13, 14, 15, 16, 17, 19, and 21.

a. Find the five-number summary. 9, 10, 14, 17, 21

b. Find the range and interquartile range. *range* = 12; *IQR* = 7

c. What are the units of the range and interquartile range? centimeters

Assessing Progress

As students work and present, you can check their ability to work in groups, to collect data systematically, to follow instructions, to make accurate measurements, and to present coherently. You can also assess their understanding of the mean.

Closing the Lesson

Measures of spread relative to the median are based on only a few data points. Predictors from the **deviations** from the mean are based on all the data points. The sum of squares of these deviations is the **variance,** and the square root of the variance is the **standard deviation. Outliers,** defined as data values having a distance from the median of more than 1.5 times the *IQR,* strongly affect the variance and the standard deviation.

4. In order to monitor weight, a cookie manufacturer samples jumbo chocolate chip cookies as they come off the production line. The weights in grams of 11 cookies are 22, 30, 27, 35, 32, 28, 18, 22, 25, 30, and 28.

   a. Find the five-number summary. 18, 22, 28, 30, 35

   b. Find the range and interquartile range. *range* = 17; *IQR* = 8

   c. What are the units of the range and interquartile range? grams

5. Invent a data set with seven data values such that the mean and the median are both 84, the range is 23, and the interquartile range is 12. possible answer: {71, 79, 80, 84, 89, 91, 94}

Reason and Apply

6. **APPLICATION** The mean diameter of a Purdy Goode Compact Disc is 12.0 cm, with a standard deviation of 0.012 cm. No CDs can be shipped that are more than one standard deviation from the mean. How would the company's quality control engineer use those statistics? She would not let CDs be shipped that measure more than 12.012 cm or less than 11.988 cm.

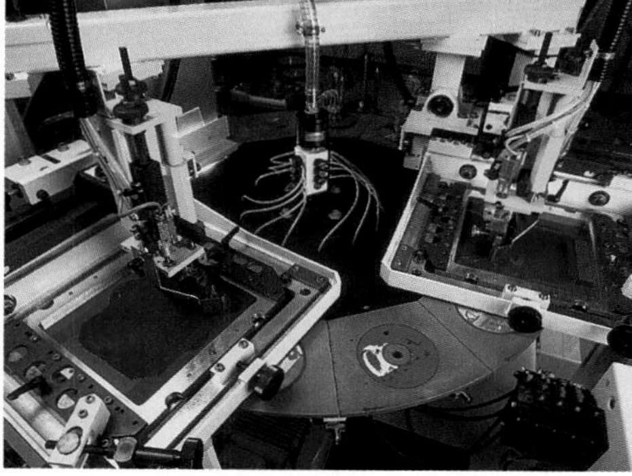
This automated machine paints labels on compact discs.

7. Some statisticians identify outliers as data values that are more than two standard deviations, or $2s$, from the mean. Use this method to identify any outliers in the student-to-teacher ratios from the example on page 89. How do the outliers found by standard deviation compare to the outliers found by interquartile range? 20.8 and 22.1. These are the same outliers found by the interquartile range.

8. Find the standard deviation and interquartile range of the backpack data from Example A in Lesson 2.1. Which of these two values is larger? Will this value always be larger? Explain your reasoning and find or create another data set that supports your answer. $s \approx 5.9$ lb; *IQR* = 3.0 lb; the standard deviation is larger here but not always. The data set given in the possible answer for Exercise 5 is a counterexample; $s = 8.0$; *IQR* = 12.

9. Two data sets have the same range and interquartile range but the first is symmetric and the second is skewed left.

   a. Sketch two box plots that satisfy the conditions for the two sets.

   b. Would you guess that the standard deviation of the skewed data set is less than, more than, or the same as the first? Explain your reasoning.

   c. Invent two data sets of seven values each that satisfy the conditions.

   d. Find the standard deviation for the two data sets. Do the standard deviations support your answer to 9b? Symmetric: 18.5; skewed left: 19.4. These support the answer to 9b.

10. Students collected eight length measurements during a mathematics lab. The mean measurement was 46.3 cm, and the deviations of *seven* individual measurements were 0.8 cm, −0.4 cm, 1.6 cm, 1.1 cm, −1.2 cm, −0.3 cm, and −1.0 cm.

    a. What were the original eight measurements collected? 47.1, 45.9, 47.9, 47.4, 45.1, 46.0, 45.3, and 45.7 cm

    b. Find the standard deviation of the original measurements. 1.03 cm

    c. Which measurements are more than one standard deviation above or below the mean? below: 45.1 cm; above: 47.9 cm and 47.4 cm

BUILDING UNDERSTANDING

The exercises allow students to develop skill with and make meaning of outliers and measures of spread.

ASSIGNING HOMEWORK

Essential	1–4
Performance assessment	5, 6, 9–13, 15
Portfolio	13, 14
Journal	7, 8
Group	5, 15
Review	16–18

Helping with the Exercises

Exercise 1c For this simple data set, you might ask students to calculate the standard deviation without using calculators.

Exercises 3, 4 Ask what conclusions students can draw from these statistics. Conclusions might be about the variability in the sample or about the entire population.

9a. possible answer:

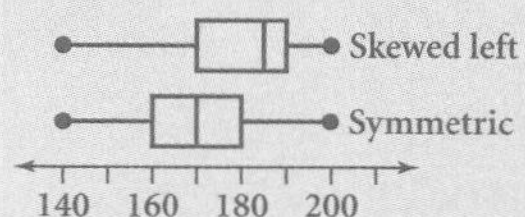

9b. The skewed data set will have a greater standard deviation because the data to the left (below the median) will be spread farther from the mean.

9c. possible answer: symmetric: {140, 160, 165, 170, 175, 180, 200}; skewed left: {140, 170, 180, 185, 187, 190, 200}

Exercise 10 Students should recall that the deviations will sum to 0. They can find the sum of the seven deviations and determine that the eighth deviation is −0.6 cm.

Exercise 11 [Ask] "Does it matter how many students are in each class?" In 11a, it is possible that one of the other classes had one extreme outlier that greatly increased the standard deviation. In 11b, although the students in sixth period are likely to have the fastest pulse rates, if their data are skewed left and those of some other period are skewed right, it could be that students in that other class have the fastest pulse rates.

11a. First period appears to have pulse rates most alike because that class had the smallest standard deviation.

12a. Juneau: $\bar{x} = 40.5$°F; $s \approx 11.5$°F. New York: $\bar{x} \approx 53.8$°F; $s \approx 16.2$°F.

12b. Juneau: *median* = 41°F; *IQR* = 21°F. New York: *median* = 54°F; *IQR* = 29.5°F.

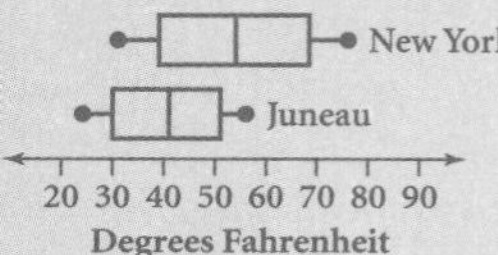

five-number summaries:
New York: 31, 39, 54, 68.5, 76;
Juneau: 24, 30, 41, 51, 56

12c. Juneau has a smaller spread of temperatures based on either the standard deviation or the interquartile range.

Exercise 13 To extend this exercise, have students suggest how the club members could use these statistics to plan for next year's sale. As needed, **[Ask]** "Would it be best to plan next year's sale using the mean and the standard deviation or using the median and the interquartile range? Would you include or exclude outliers? Would it be reasonable to forecast a minimum or maximum number of packages per student? How many packages should the club purchase for next year's sale, stated as either packages per student or total packages based on this year's enrollment?"

11. APPLICATION The students in four classes recorded their resting pulse rates in beats per minute. The class means and standard deviations are given at right.

a. Which class has students with pulse rates most alike? How can you tell?

b. Can you tell which class has the students with the fastest pulse rates? Why or why not? Sixth period might have the fastest pulse rates because that class has both the highest mean and the greatest standard deviation.

Resting Pulse Rates (beats/min)

Class	Mean	Standard deviation
First period	79.4	3.2
Third period	74.6	5.6
Fifth period	78.2	4.1
Sixth period	80.2	7.6

12. Here are the mean daily temperatures in degrees Fahrenheit for two cities.

a. Find the mean and standard deviation for each city.

b. Draw a box plot for each city. Find each median and interquartile range.

c. Which city has the smaller spread of temperatures? Justify your conclusion.

d. Does the interquartile range or the standard deviation give a better measure of the spread? Justify your conclusion. Because both data sets are symmetric, the standard deviation and the interquartile range do an equally good job of describing the spread.

Mean Temperatures (°F)

Month	Juneau, Alaska	New York, New York
January	24	31
February	28	33
March	33	41
April	40	51
May	47	60
June	53	69
July	56	76
August	55	75
September	49	68
October	42	57
November	32	47
December	27	37

13. Members of the school mathematics club sold packages of hot chocolate mix to raise funds for their club activities. The numbers of packages sold by individual members are given at right.

65	76	100	67	44
147	82	94	92	79
158	77	62	85	71
69	88	80	63	75
62	68	71	73	74

a. Find the median and interquartile range for this data set.

b. Find the mean and standard deviation.

c. Draw a box plot for this data set. Use the 1.5 · *IQR* definition to name any numbers that are outliers.

d. Remove the outliers from the data set and draw another box plot.

e. With the outliers removed, recalculate the median and interquartile range and the mean and the standard deviation.

f. Which is more affected by outliers, the mean or the median? The standard deviation or the interquartile range? Explain why you think this is so. The mean and standard deviation are calculated from all data values, so outliers affect these statistics significantly. The median and *IQR*, in contrast, are defined by position and not greatly affected by outliers.

13a. *median* = 75 packages; *IQR* = 19 packages

13b. $\bar{x} \approx 80.9$ packages; $s \approx 24.6$ packages

13c.

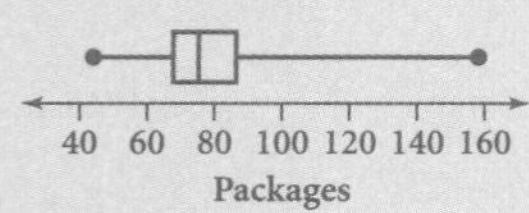

five-number summary: 44, 67.5, 75, 86.5, 158; outliers: 147, 158

13d.

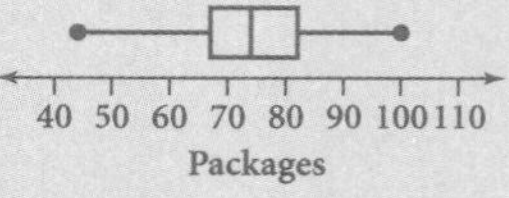

five-number summary: 44, 67, 74, 82, 100

13e. *median* = 74 packages; *IQR* = 15 packages; $\bar{x} \approx 74.7$ packages; $s \approx 12.4$ packages

14. Refer to the data in Exercise 13.

a. Suppose each package of hot chocolate yields a net profit of 28¢. Draw a box plot for the profit each club member generates. Find the median and interquartile range, and the mean and standard deviation for the profits. Compare your profit statistics with the original statistics describing the numbers of packages sold. How are the two sets of statistics and the graphs related?

b. Use your findings from 14a to predict the net profit statistics if the net profit per package is 35¢. *median* = \$26.25; *IQR* = \$6.65; $\bar{x} \approx$ \$28.32; $s \approx$ \$8.61

c. Suppose the school audit finds that each individual member actually sold 20 packages fewer than originally reported. Find the median and interquartile range, and the mean and standard deviation. Describe a process you could use to find the corrected results for all of the information requested in Exercise 13.

d. Use your findings from 14c to predict the statistical results if instead there were 10 packages fewer per member than originally reported.

15. **APPLICATION** Matt Decovsky wants to buy a 160W CD player for his car at an online auction site. Before bidding, he decides to do some research on the selling price of recently sold CD players. His search comes up with these 20 prices.

\$74.00	\$102.50	\$64.57	\$74.00
\$82.87	\$73.01	\$77.00	\$71.00
\$71.01	\$112.50	\$86.00	\$102.50
\$76.00	\$56.00	\$135.50	\$66.00
\$71.00	\$76.00	\$51.00	\$88.00

a. Find the mean, median, and mode.

b. Draw a box plot of the data. Describe its shape.

c. Find the interquartile range and determine whether there are any outliers. *IQR* = \$16; outliers: \$112.50 and \$135.50

d. While looking over the items' descriptions, Matt realizes that the outlier CD players contain features that don't interest him. If he removes the outliers, will the mean or the median be less affected? Explain.

e. Sketch a new box plot with the outliers removed. How does this help you support your answer in 15d?

f. If you were Matt, what might you set as a target price in your bidding? Explain your reasoning. Sample answer: Based on the box plot without outliers, Matt could start with a first bid of \$51.00 (the minimum for the CD player), but set his maximum bid at \$82.87. That way, he may exceed the median price, but he still will pay less than six of the previous selling prices he researched.

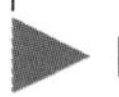

Review

1.1 16. Celia lives 2.4 km from school. She misses the school bus and starts walking at 1.3 m/s. She has 20 min before school starts. Write a recursive formula and use it to find out whether or not she gets to school on time.

17. Solve.

a. $\dfrac{x+5}{4} + 3 = 19$ $x = 59$

b. $\dfrac{3(y-4)+6}{6} - 2 = 7$ $y = 20$

2.1 18. These data sets give the weights in pounds of the offensive and defensive teams of the 2002 Super Bowl Champion New England Patriots. (*www.nfl.com*)

Offensive players' weights (lb): {190, 305, 310, 320, 315, 322, 255, 190, 220, 245, 230}
Defensive players' weights (lb): {280, 305, 280, 270, 250, 253, 245, 199, 196, 207, 218}

a. Find the mean and median weights of each team.

b. Prepare a box plot of each data set. Use the box plots to make general observations about the differences between the two teams.

Exercise 14 Remind students to use the statistics from 13a and b, not 13e. Because the mean and the standard deviation are rounded in Exercise 13b, students might get answers for 14a that are not exactly 0.28 times as large. The answers here are calculated from the formulas, not by multiplying the statistics by 0.28. The answers for 14b are calculated by multiplying the statistics from Exercise 13b by 0.35; using a calculator might yield slightly different results from those calculated from the formulas for mean and standard deviation.

14a. Hot Chocolate Mix

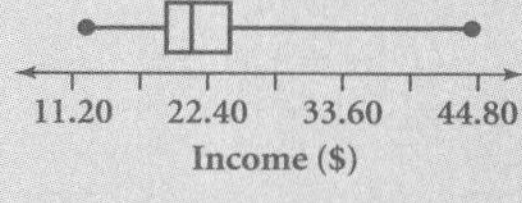

median = \$21.00; *IQR* = \$5.32; $\bar{x} \approx$ \$22.65; $s \approx$ \$6.90. Each of the original statistics is multiplied by 0.28.

14c. *median* = 55; *IQR* = 19; $\bar{x} \approx 60.9$; $s \approx 24.6$. Subtract 20 from each original statistic except those that measure spread (*IQR* and standard deviation).

14d. *median* = 65 packages; *IQR* = 19 packages; $\bar{x} \approx 70.9$ packages; $s \approx 24.6$ packages

15a. mean: \$80.52; median: \$75.00; modes: \$71.00, \$74.00, \$76.00, \$102.50

15b. CD Players

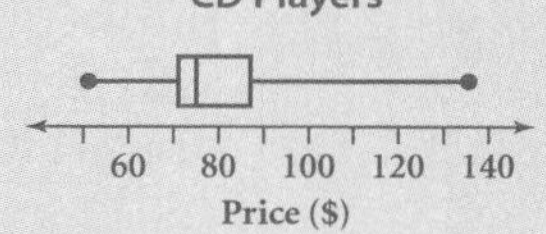

five-number summary: 51, 71, 75, 87, 135.5

The box plot is skewed right.

15d. The median will be less affected because the relative positions of the middle numbers will be changed less than the sum of the numbers.

Exercise 15e The mean of the new data set is 75.692, which is about 4.8 lower than the mean of the original data set.

15e. CD Players

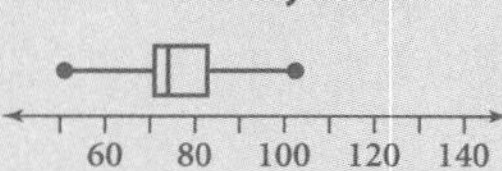

five-number summary: 51, 71, 74, 82.87, 102.5 The median of the new data set is \$74.00 and is relatively unchanged.

16. Sample answer: $u_0 = 2400$ and $u_n = u_{n-1} - 1.3 \cdot 60$ where $n \geq 1$. After 20 minutes, she is still 840 meters from school ($u_{20} = 840$).

EXTENSIONS

A. Use Take Another Look activity 4 on page 112.

B. Have the class decide on a common procedure for one investigation and then follow that procedure to try to minimize the standard deviation.

See page 879 for answers to Exercise 18.

LESSON
2.3

PLANNING

LESSON OUTLINE

First day:

15 min Examples

30 min Investigation

Second day:

10 min Investigation

20 min Sharing

15 min Exercises

MATERIALS

- Metropolitan Growth (T), *optional*
- Percentile Rank (T), *optional*
- Calculator Note 2D
- Fathom demonstration Metropolitan Growth, *optional*
- Fathom demonstration Eating on the Run, *optional*

TEACHING

This lesson focuses on two other ways to analyze the shape and spread of a data set: histograms and percentile ranks. It assumes that students are familiar with bar graphs.

One Step

Point out the data set in Example A and the accompanying histograms. Without saying how a histogram is made, ask each group to choose a column of the table in the investigation on page 99 and to make a histogram for those data. Also ask them to make a box plot on a separate sheet of paper and to calculate the mean, median, standard deviation, and interquartile range for the same nutritional element. Then ask groups to exchange just their histograms with another group and, without consulting the original data, see what other statistics they can construct describing those data.

LESSON 2.3

Histograms and Percentile Ranks

You miss 100 percent of the shots you never take.

WAYNE GRETZKY

A box plot gives you an idea of the overall distribution of a data set, but in some cases you might want to see other information and details that a box plot doesn't show. A **histogram** is a graphical representation of a data set, with columns to show how the data are distributed across different intervals of values. Histograms give vivid pictures of distribution features, such as clusters of values, or gaps in data.

The columns of a histogram are called **bins** and should not be confused with the bars of a bar graph. The bars of a bar graph indicate categories—how many data items either have the same value or share a characteristic. The bins of a histogram indicate how many numerical data values fall within a certain interval. You would use a bar graph to show how many people in your class have various eye colors, but a histogram to show how many people's heights fall within various intervals.

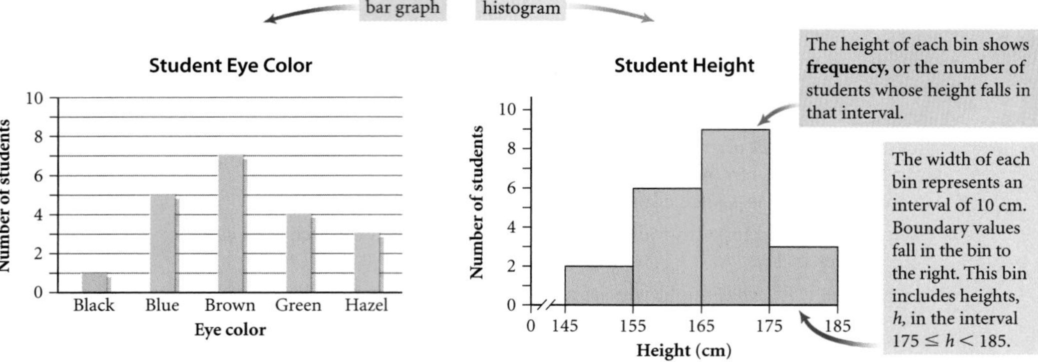

Histograms are a good way to display information from large data sets. Although you can't see individual data values, you can see the shape of the data and how the values are distributed throughout the range. As you will see in Example A, bin width depends on how much detail you want to show, but all the bins should have the same width.

Some stereo equalizers have spectrum displays that resemble histograms. These displays are similar to histograms because they show the output frequencies by intervals, or bands. They are different because the bands may not represent equal intervals.

If students ask you questions, try to redirect their questions back to the group. During Sharing, bring out the fact that they can determine the intervals of the five numbers in the five-number summary and of data in other percentiles, but not the mean or statistics based on the mean.

[Language] *Distribution* refers to the general shape of the data. *A cluster in the data* refers to a grouping of data. *Gaps* in the data are intervals with no data.

[Language] Karl Pearson introduced the term *histogram* in 1895 to describe "a common form of graphical representation, that is, by columns marking as areas the frequency corresponding to the range of their base."

EXAMPLE A | Both Graph A and Graph B were constructed from the data set in the table.

The 25 Fastest-Growing Metropolitan Areas in the United States (1990–2000)

Metropolitan area	1990 Population	2000 Population	Percent Population change
Las Vegas, NV	852,737	1,563,282	83.3
Naples, FL	152,099	251,377	65.3
Yuma, AZ	106,895	160,026	49.7
McAllen, TX	383,545	569,463	48.5
Austin, TX	846,227	1,249,763	47.7
Fayetteville, AR	210,908	311,121	47.5
Boise City, ID	295,851	432,345	46.1
Phoenix, AZ	2,238,480	3,251,876	45.3
Laredo, TX	133,239	193,117	44.9
Provo, UT	263,590	368,536	39.8
Atlanta, GA	2,959,950	4,112,198	38.9
Raleigh, NC	855,545	1,187,941	38.9
Myrtle Beach, SC	144,053	196,629	36.5
Wilmington, NC	171,269	233,450	36.3
Fort Collins, CO	186,136	251,494	35.1
Orlando, FL	1,224,852	1,644,561	34.3
Reno, NV	254,667	339,486	33.3
Ocala, FL	194,833	258,916	32.9
Auburn, AL	87,146	115,092	32.1
Fort Myers, FL	335,113	440,888	31.6
West Palm Beach, FL	863,518	1,131,184	31.0
Bellingham, WA	127,780	166,814	30.5
Denver, CO	1,980,140	2,581,506	30.4
Colorado Springs, CO	397,014	516,929	30.2
Dallas, TX	4,037,282	5,221,801	29.3

(U.S. Census Bureau)

Graph A
Fastest-Growing Metropolitan Areas

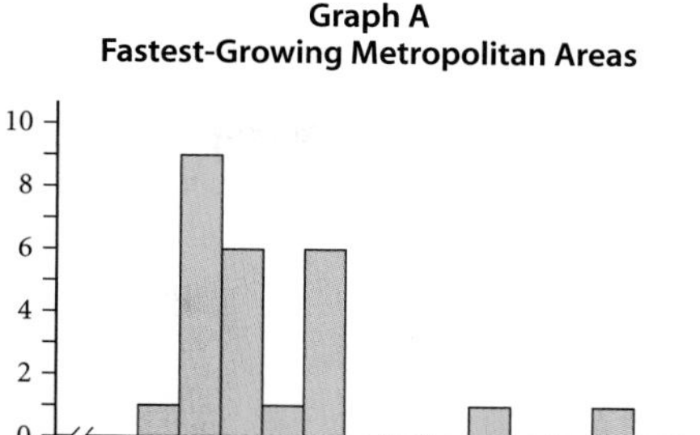

Graph B
Fastest-Growing Metropolitan Areas

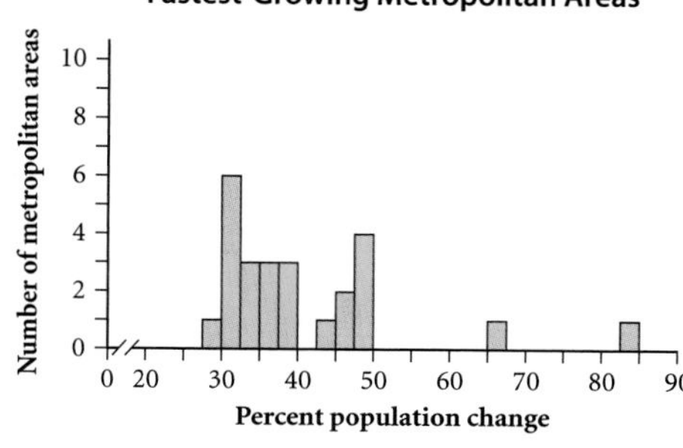

a. What is the range of the data?

b. What is the bin width of each graph?

c. Use the information in the table to create the same graphs on your calculator.

d. How can you know if the graph accounts for all 25 metropolitan areas?

e. Why are the columns shorter in Graph B?

▶ EXAMPLE A

You might use the Fathom demonstration Metropolitan Growth or the Metropolitan Growth transparency as you discuss this example. **[Language]** A *metropolitan area* includes a city and its suburbs as defined by the U.S. Office of Management and Budget.

These data are from the U.S. Census Bureau's website, which you and your students can find through links at www.keymath.com.

The height of each bin gives the frequency, that is, the number of cities whose growth is in the interval of the x-axis on which the bin sits. Thus frequency is plotted on the histogram's y-axis. Histograms can also be drawn so that the labels on the y-axis denote the percentages of the total rather than the actual numbers; such histograms are called *relative frequency histograms.*

The questions asked in parts a–i are the kinds of questions people should ask themselves as they interpret graphs to learn about data sets that are not available to look at directly.

[Ask] "Which graph is better and for what purpose? At a national conference of mayors discussing the need for more state support for social services, which graph is better if you are the mayor of Laredo, TX? Ocala, FL?"

NCTM STANDARDS

CONTENT		PROCESS	
	Number		Problem Solving
✓	Algebra	✓	Reasoning
	Geometry	✓	Communication
✓	Measurement	✓	Connections
✓	Data/Probability	✓	Representation

LESSON OBJECTIVES

- Distinguish bar graphs from histograms
- Find the approximate number of data items, the range, and the median by studying a histogram
- Understand the effects of different bin widths in histograms
- Create box plots and histograms in order to analyze specific characteristics of a data set
- Determine the percentile rank of a data item either from raw data or from a histogram
- Connect percentile rank and standard deviation

f. Describe how each graph illustrates clusters and gaps in the data.

g. How many of these metropolitan areas grew between 35% and 40%? How can you tell this from each graph?

h. In what interval of Graph A is the median growth rate? If you use Graph B to answer the question, can your answer be more accurate?

i. What percentage of these metropolitan areas had population changes less than 35%?

This photo of a housing development in Las Vegas conveys the city's rapid growth.

► *Solution*

a. Population changes for these metropolitan areas range from 29.3% for Dallas, TX, to 83.3% for Las Vegas, NV. The range is 54%.

b. The width of each bin is 5% in Graph A and 2.5% in Graph B.

c. The range and the bin width are important pieces of information that you need in order to duplicate these graphs. [► See **Calculator Note 2D** to learn how to make histograms on your calculator. ◄]

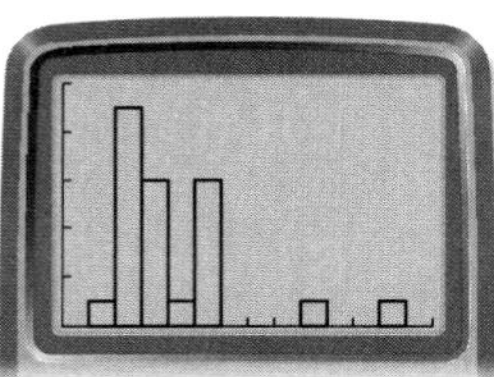

[20, 90, 5, 0, 10, 2]

[20, 90, 2.5, 0, 10, 2]

d. Add the bin frequencies in either histogram to verify that they sum to 25.

e. The bin width of Graph B is half the bin width of Graph A. So the data values represented by each bin in Graph A get split into two bins in Graph B, making the bins generally shorter.

Part e You might point out that dividing the bin width in half does not necessarily mean that each new bin contains half the data values of the original bin.

f. The gap between 50% and 65% in either graph means no metropolitan area had a population change between 50% and 65%. With Graph B, you also see gaps between 40% and 42.5%, and between 67.5% and 82.5%. The cluster of bins on the left side of either graph shows that most of these metropolitan areas grew between 25% and 50%.

g. Six metropolitan areas grew between 35% and 40%. In Graph A, you read the frequency of the bin in the 35-to-40 interval. In Graph B, you add the frequencies of the 35-to-37.5 bin and the 37.5-to-40 bin.

h. Each graph represents 25 metropolitan areas. You find the median, which is the "middle city" or the 13th data value, by adding the frequencies of each bin from the left until you get to 13. With Graph A, the median is between 35% and 40%. With Graph B, you can narrow down the interval—the median is between 35% and 37.5%.

i. Add the bin frequencies to the left of 35%. You find that 10 of these 25 metropolitan areas, or 40%, had population changes less than 35%.

Part h From a histogram it is not usually possible to find the exact value of the median, only what bin it's in. Students must use the original data set to find the median exactly.

[Context] Francis Galton originated the term *percentile* around 1885, saying "The value that is un-reached by *n* per cent of any large group of measurements, and surpassed by 100 − *n* of them, is called the *nth percentile.*"

The **percentile rank** of a data value in a large distribution gives the percentage of data values that are below the given value. In the previous example, Fort Collins, CO, has a percentile rank of about 40 among this group, because its population change exceeds that of 40% of the metropolitan areas in this group, as you found in part i.

Suppose a large number of students take a standardized test, such as the SAT. There are so many individual scores that it would be impractical to look at all of the actual numbers. A percentile rank gives a good indication of how one person's score compares to other scores across the country.

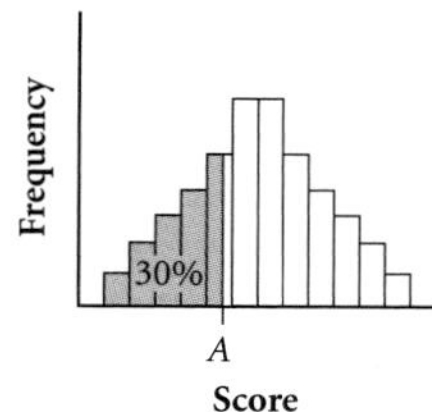

Students with score *A* are at the 30th percentile, because their score is better than the scores of 30% of the tested students.

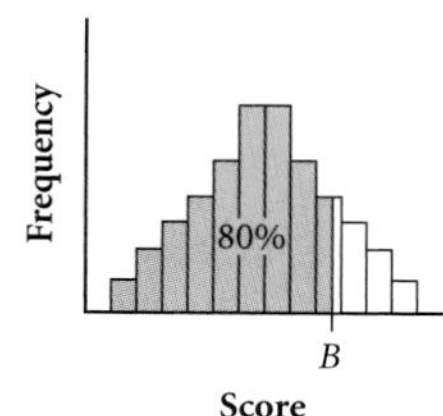

Likewise, students with score *B* are at the 80th percentile, because 80% of the tested students have scores that are lower.

Cultural CONNECTION

During the 15th and 16th centuries, the Inca used *quipus,* a system of knotted cords, to record numerical information, such as population. The number of knots, the number of strings, and variations in color and thickness combined to create a sophisticated method for keeping data and statistics, which scholars have yet to fully decipher.

The illustration at left, from a 17th-century letter by Felipe Guáman Poma de Ayala, shows an Incan treasurer holding a *quipu.* The photo shows an actual Incan *quipu.*

MAKING THE CONNECTION

The Incan Empire spanned about 2000 miles in western South America from the 1200s until the Spanish conquered them in 1532. Their official language was Quechua, which is still spoken by over 10 million people in South America. Some words that have come to English from Quechua are *condor, jerky, lima* [bean], *llama,* and *puma.*

▶ *EXAMPLE B*

You might use the Percentile Rank transparency as you discuss this example.

Part a Though all values less than 63 would be less than two standard deviations above the mean, you cannot be sure that any value in the bin 60–65 fits this condition. You therefore consider only those values you know to be less than 60. Although the calculation gives 92.5%, percentiles are generally given as whole numbers, so the answer is rounded to the 93rd percentile.

Guiding the Investigation

This open-ended investigation allows a review of the ideas of this chapter. Students can download the data to their calculators from the Calculator Programs and Data CD. Or, if students have access to computers with Fathom, they can start with the data in the Fathom demonstration Eating on the Run, which is designed as a way to review the chapter. If you replace this investigation with the Fathom demonstration Eating on the Run, concentrate on the last question.

You can decide the extent and caliber of work you expect and guide students appropriately. For a short investigation expect groups to make a box plot or histogram for one nutritional element and calculate the mean, median, standard deviation, and interquartile range. For a more involved investigation suggest that students reexamine the data without outliers or have them divide the data by type of sandwich and make cross-comparisons, possibly graphing several box plots on the same axis.

EXAMPLE B

The data used in this histogram have a mean of 34.05 and a standard deviation of 14.68.

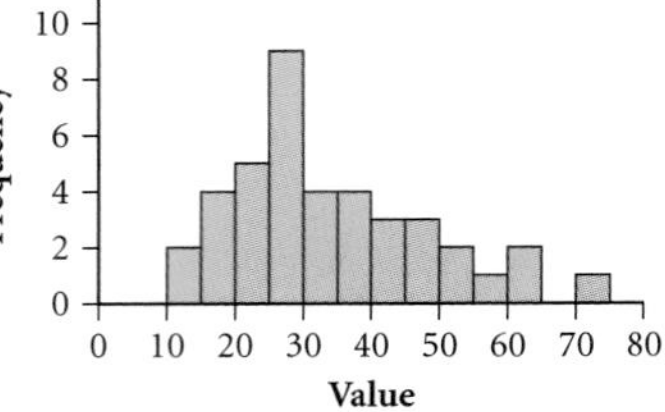

a. Approximate the percentile rank of a value two standard deviations above the mean.

b. Approximately what percentage of the data values are within one standard deviation of the mean?

▶ ***Solution***

Add the bin frequencies to find that there are 40 data values in all.

a. The value of two standard deviations above the mean is $34.05 + 2 \cdot 14.68$, or 63.41. All of the data values in the ten bins up to the value of 60 are less than 63.41. Adding the bin frequencies up to 60 gives 37. Therefore $\frac{37}{40}$, or approximately 92.5%, of the data lies below 63.41. So 63.41 is approximately the 93rd percentile.

b. One standard deviation above the mean is 48.73, and one standard deviation below the mean is 19.37. This interval includes at least those values in the bins from 20 to 45. So $\frac{25}{40}$, or approximately 62.5%, of the data lie within one standard deviation of the mean.

Combining what you know about measures of central tendency and spread with different displays of data enables you to provide a complete picture of a data set. The following investigation gives you an opportunity to analyze data using all of the statistics and graphs you have learned about.

Investigation
Eating on the Run

Teenagers require about 2200 to 3000 calories per day, depending on their growth rate and level of activity. The food you consume as part of your 2200- to 3000-calorie diet should include a high level of protein, moderate levels of carbohydrates and fat, and as little sodium, saturated fat, and cholesterol as possible. The table shows the minimum amount of protein and the maximum amount of other nutrients in a healthy 2500-calorie diet.

Nutrition Recommendations for a 2500-Calorie Diet

Nutrient	Amount
Fat	80 g
Cholesterol	300 mg
Sodium	2400 mg
Carbohydrate	375 g
Protein	65 g

(U.S. Food and Drug Administration and International Food Information Council)

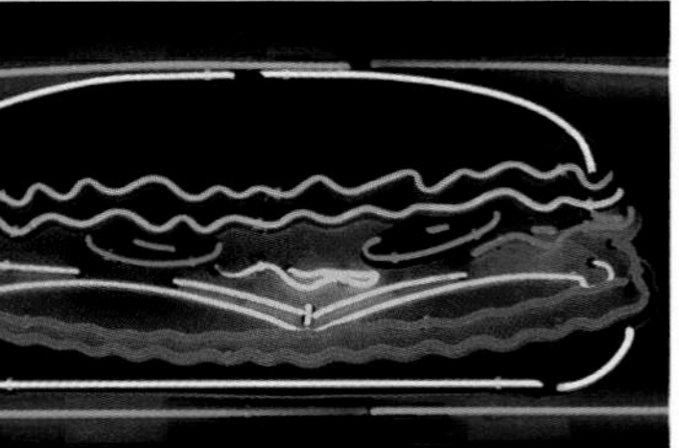

So, how does fast food fit into a healthy diet? Examine the information below about the nutritional content of fast-food sandwiches. With your group, study one of the nutritional components (total calories, total fat, cholesterol, sodium, carbohydrates, or protein). Use box plots, histograms, and the measures of central tendency and spread to compare the amount of that component in the sandwiches. You may even want to divide your data so that you can make

[Ask] "In which percentile or quartile of each box plot does the recommended amount fall?" For an even deeper investigation, you might have students compare the shape of the data for more than one nutritional element. **[Ask]** "Which elements have more spread?" [Fat, where the range is 14 times the minimum, and cholesterol, where the range is almost 3.5 times the minimum, have the greatest spread. Because the units for each nutritional element is different, they can't be compared directly.] "Why might the spread be so large for fat and cholesterol?" [Sample answer: Fat and cholesterol are the nutritional elements that consumers pay the most attention to, so some companies try hard to lower them, which brings down the minimum.]

These recommendations are based on 2002 guidelines. Students might investigate whether these recommendations have changed.

comparisons between types of sandwiches (burger, chicken, or fish) or between restaurants. As you do your statistical analysis, discuss how these fast-food items would affect a healthy diet. Prepare a short report or class presentation discussing your conclusions.

Fast food is a popular choice today because it is quick and convenient. Despite being high in fat, calories, sodium, and cholesterol, fast food is not bad, nutritionists say, but should be consumed in moderation with an otherwise healthy diet. Many fast-food restaurants have responded to America's new health consciousness and now offer low-calorie menu items such as salads, lean meats, and chili.

Fast Food Nutrition Facts

Sandwich	Total calories	Total Fat (g)	Cholesterol (mg)	Sodium (mg)	Carbohydrate (g)	Protein (g)
Burger King "Whopper Jr."	400	24	55	530	28	19
Carl's Jr. "Jr. Hamburger"	330	13	45	480	34	18
Dairy Queen "Hamburger"	310	13	45	580	29	17
Hardee's "Hamburger"	270	11	35	550	29	13
Jack in the Box "Hamburger"	280	12	30	490	30	12
McDonald's "Hamburger"	270	8	30	600	35	13
Wendy's "Single Hamburger"	420	20	70	920	37	25
Whataburger "Whataburger Jr."	322	13	42	603	35	16
Burger King "BK Broiler"	530	26	105	1060	45	29
Carl's Jr. "Barbecue Chicken"	280	3	60	830	37	25
Dairy Queen "Grilled Chicken Fillet"	300	8	50	800	33	25
Hardee's "Chicken Fillet"	480	23	55	1190	44	24
Jack in the Box "Chicken Sandwich"	420	23	40	950	39	16
McDonald's "Crispy Chicken"	550	27	54	1180	54	23
Wendy's "Grilled Chicken"	310	8	65	790	35	27
Whataburger "Grilled Chicken"	442	14	48	1103	66	34
Burger King "BK Big Fish"	720	43	80	1180	59	23
Carl's Jr. "Carl's Catch"	510	27	80	1030	50	18
Dairy Queen "Fish Fillet"	370	16	45	630	39	16
Hardee's "Fisherman's Fillet"	530	28	75	1280	45	25
McDonald's "Filet-O-Fish"	470	26	50	890	45	15
Whataburger "Whatacatch"	467	25	33	636	43	18

(*The NutriBase Complete Book of Food Counts,* 2001)

To preview Chapter 3, you might have advanced groups create a scatter plot comparing two nutritional elements. For example, plot (*saturated fat, calories*). (Students might recall two-variable data analysis from *Discovering Algebra.*) Or you might want to revisit this investigation after completing Chapter 3.

SHARING IDEAS

Ask students if they think it's typical for 93% of data to lie below two standard deviations above the mean, as in Example B. If data fit under a "bell-shaped curve," as do SAT scores, someone performing at two standard deviations above the mean is above the 97th percentile. About 68% of students lie within one standard deviation above or below the mean, 95% lie within two standard deviations of the mean, and 99.7% lie within three standard deviations of the mean. The percentile ranks will be higher, because they include all points below the mean.

Assessing Progress

Students' work on the investigation gives you an opportunity to assess their understanding of the ideas of the entire chapter: descriptions of shape, measures of central tendency, and measures of spread.

Closing the Lesson

Histograms give a visual idea of the shape and spread of a data set, and **percentile ranks** help identify where particular data points lie relative to the whole set.

BUILDING UNDERSTANDING

In the exercises, students encounter histograms and percentile ranks.

ASSIGNING HOMEWORK

Essential	1–4
Performance assessment	3–8, 10
Portfolio	9
Journal	2, 6, 8
Group	9
Review	11–13

Helping with the Exercises

Exercise 2 Two of the graphs require the person reading the graph to compute the interval at the left end of the graph. **[Ask]** "What is the minimum student height that could be represented on each graph?" [i. 90 cm; ii. 85 cm; iii. 60 cm; iv. 75 cm] "If three of the histograms are made from the same set of data, what was the minimum student height?" [90 cm]

In order to provide a complete statistical analysis of a data set, statisticians often need to use several different measurements and graphs. Throughout this course you will learn about more statistics that help you make accurate predictions and conclusions from data.

EXERCISES

Practice Your Skills

1. The histogram at right shows a set of data of backpack weights.

a. How many values are between 2 kg and 3 kg? 2

b. How many values are in the data set? 9

c. Make up a set of data measured to the nearest tenth of a kilogram that creates this histogram.
possible answer: {2.3, 2.7, 3.5, 5.7, 6.2, 6.2, 6.6, 6.8, 7.4}

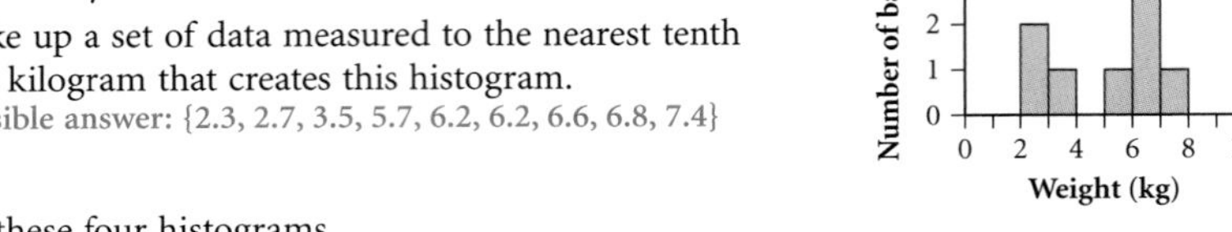

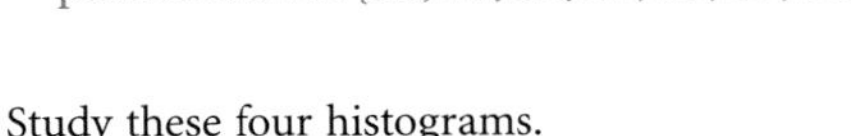

Weight of Students' Backpacks

2. Study these four histograms.

i.

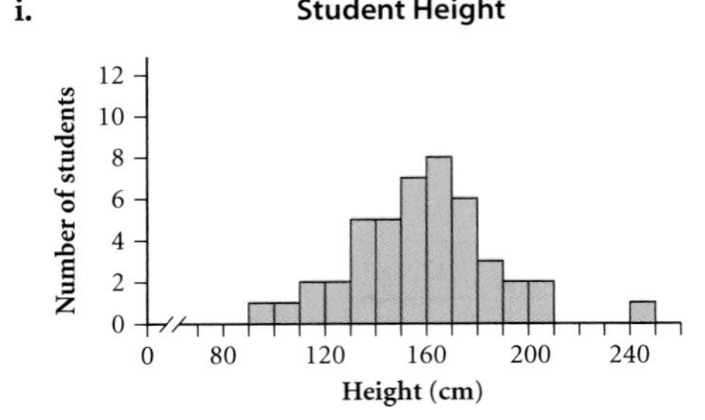

ii.

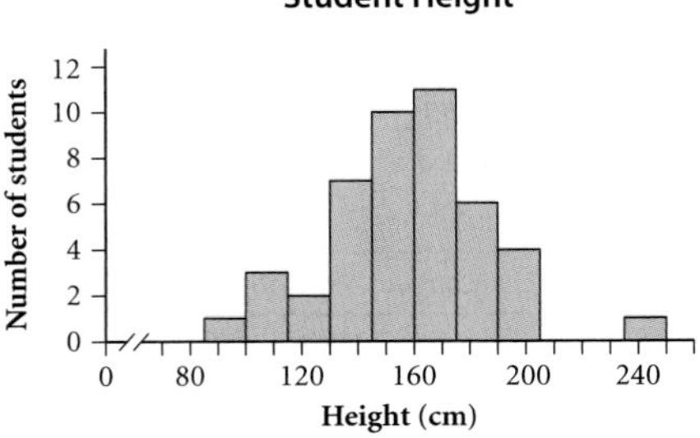

iii.

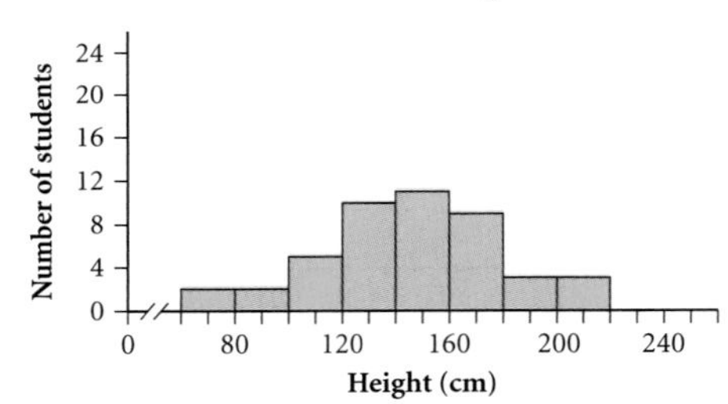

iv.

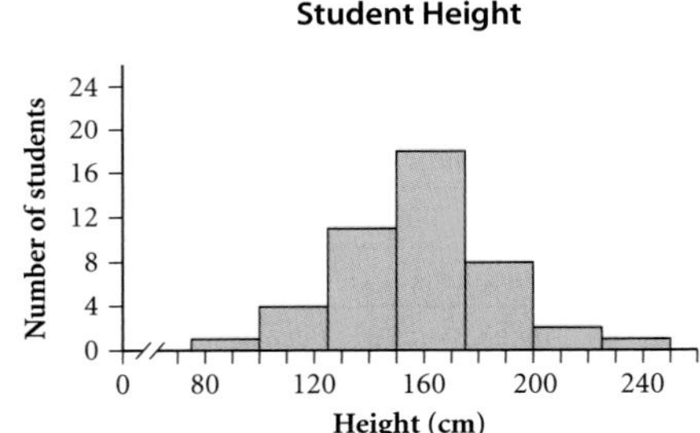

a. What is the bin width of each histogram above? i. 10; ii. 15; iii. 20; iv. 25

b. Which histogram could not come from the same data set as the other three? Explain why. Histogram iii is missing the value around 240 cm.

3. These data are the head circumferences in centimeters of 20 newborn girls:

{31, 32, 33, 33, 33, 34, 34, 34, 34, 34, 35, 35, 35, 35, 35, 36, 36, 36, 37, 38}

a. How many values are below 34 cm?

b. What is the percentile rank of 34 cm?

c. What is the percentile rank of 38 cm?

Growth charts, such as the one shown at right, often give a range of data divided into percentiles. This chart shows the 5th, 10th, 25th, 50th, 75th, 90th, and 95th percentiles.

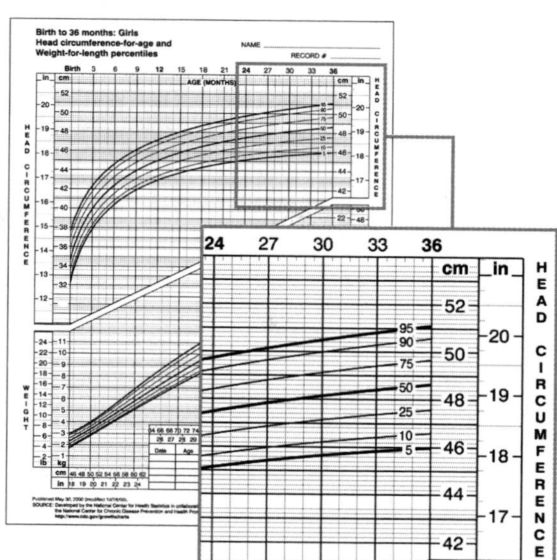

3a. 5 values

3b. 25th percentile

3c. 95th percentile

Reason and Apply

4. Carl and Bethany roll a pair of dice 1000 times and keep track of the sum on the two dice. The frequency of each sum is listed below and shown in the histogram.

Sum	Frequency
2	26
3	56
4	83
5	110
6	145
7	162
8	149
9	114
10	73
11	61
12	21

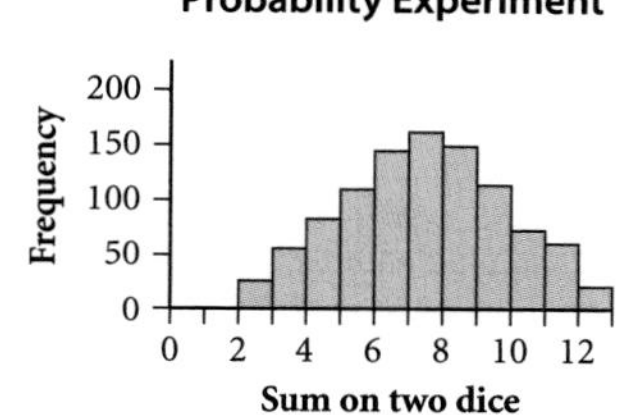

a. Graph this histogram on your calculator. List the window values needed for it to look like the histogram above.

b. Explain why the histogram is mound-shaped.

c. Describe how to find the mean sum and the median sum for this data set.

4a.

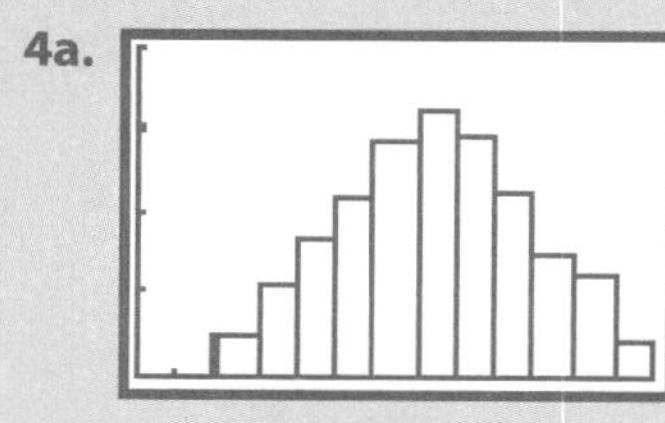

[0, 13, 1, 0, 200, 50]

4b. It is mound-shaped because 7 is the most likely sum when rolling a pair of dice, then 6 and 8, then 5 and 9, and so on.

4c. You can find the mean by summing the products of *sum* · *frequency* and dividing by 1000.

$$\frac{2(26) + 3(56) + \cdots + 12(21)}{1000} \approx 7.0$$

You can find the median by identifying the bin containing the 500th and 501st values. Both values are in the 7 bin, so the median is 7.

5. Rita and Noah survey 95 farmers in their county to see how many acres of sweet corn each farmer has planted. They summarize their results in a histogram.

Sweet Corn Crops

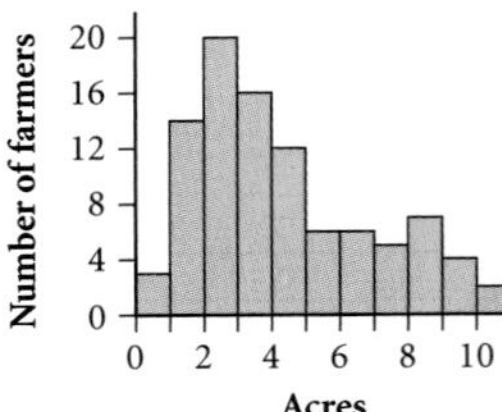

A harvesting vehicle at work in a corn field.

a. The distribution is skewed right. Explain what this means in terms of the data set.

b. Graph the histogram on your calculator.

c. Describe what you think a box plot of this information would look like, and then check your conjecture with your calculator.

6. Describe a situation and sketch a histogram to reflect each condition named below.

a. mound-shaped and symmetric

b. skewed left

c. skewed right

d. rectangular

7. Ignacio kept a log of the amount of time he spent doing homework and watching television during 20 school days.

Day	1	2	3	4	5	6	7	8	9	10
Homework (min)	4	10	40	11	55	46	46	23	57	28
Television (min)	78	30	15	72	25	30	90	40	35	56

Day	11	12	13	14	15	16	17	18	19	20
Homework (min)	65	58	52	38	38	39	45	27	41	44
Television (min)	12	5	95	27	38	50	10	42	60	34

a. Draw two box plots, one showing the amount of time spent doing homework, and one showing the amount of time watching television. Which distribution has the greater spread? See page 103.

b. Make an educated guess about the shape of a histogram for each set of data. Will either be skewed? Mound-shaped? Check your guess by drawing each histogram. See page 103.

c. Calculate the median and interquartile range, and the mean and standard deviation, for both homework and television. Which measure of spread best represents the data? See page 103.
Homework: *median* = 40.5 min; *IQR* = 21.5 min; $\bar{x} \approx 38.4$ min; $s \approx 16.7$ min.
Television: *median* = 36.5 min; *IQR* = 32 min; $\bar{x} = 42.2$ min; $s \approx 26.0$ min. Answers will vary.

▶Helping with the Exercises

5a. The numbers of acres planted by farmers who plant more than the median number of acres vary more than the numbers of acres planted by farmers who plant fewer than the median number of acres.

Exercise 5b To graph the histogram, students will need to enter data. They can enter whole numbers of acres or make up fractional numbers of acres.

5b.

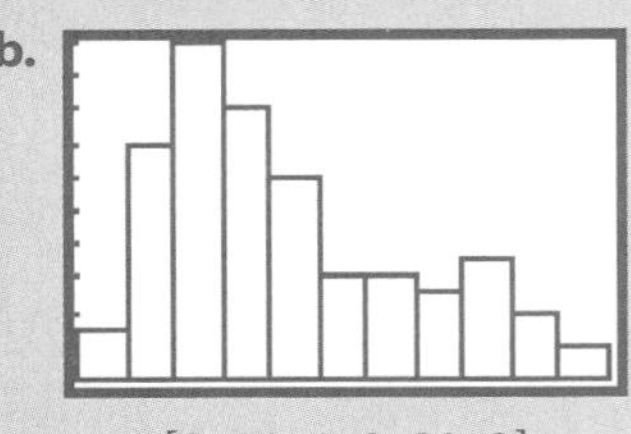

[0, 11, 1, 0, 20, 2]

5c. In a box plot, the part of the box to the left of the median would be smaller than the part to the right because there are more values close to 3 on the left than on the right.

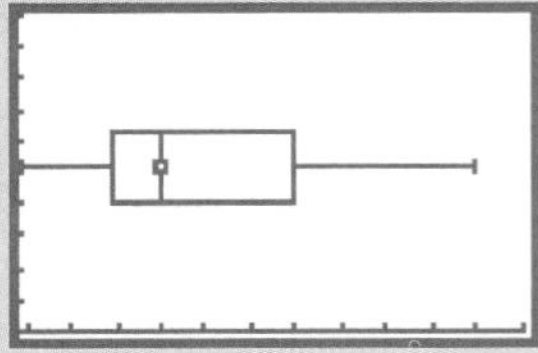

[0, 11, 1, 0, 20, 2]

6. possible answers:

6a. SAT scores for all students in one year

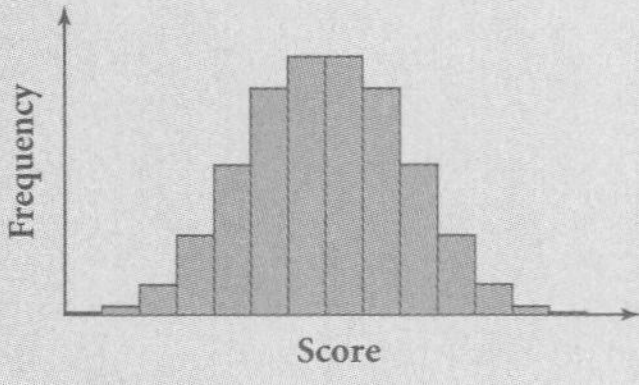

6b. number of good photos developed from a roll

Number of Good Photos

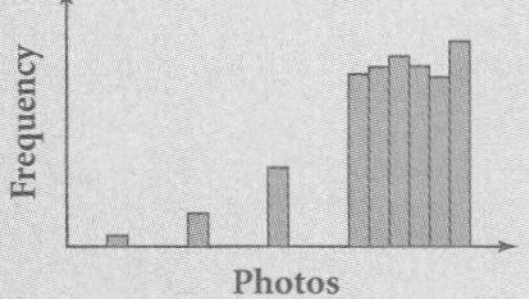

6c. number of pets owned by students in the class

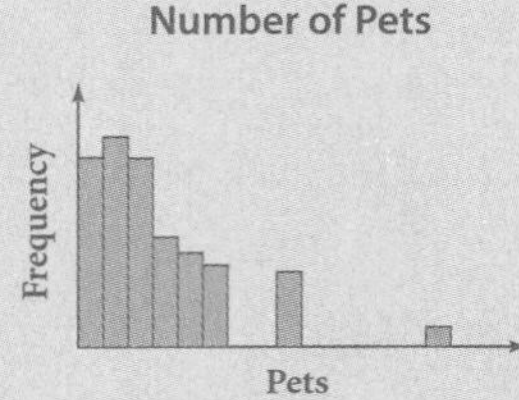

6d. number rolled on a standard die

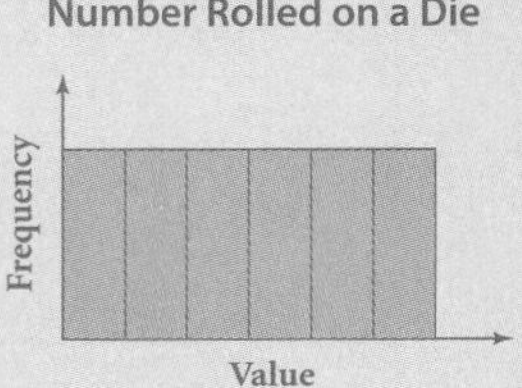

Exercise 6d [Language] A *rectangular histogram* is one with equal or nearly equal frequencies throughout the entire range.

Exercise 7 [Ask] "Does your answer to 7c support your answer to 7a?"

8. At a large university, 1500 students took a final exam in chemistry.

a. Frank learns that his score of 76 (out of 100) places him at the 88th percentile. How many students scored lower than Frank? How many scored higher?

b. Mary scored 82, which placed her at the 95th percentile. Describe how Mary's performance compares to that of others in the class.

c. The highest score on the exam was 91. What percentile rank is associated with this score? 99th percentile

d. Every student who scored above the 90th percentile received an A. How many students earned this grade? about 150 students

e. Explain the difference between a percent score and a percentile rank. In your opinion, should you be evaluated based on percent or percentile? Why?

Science CONNECTION

How are speed limits determined? Radar checks are performed at selected locations on the roadway to collect data about drivers' speeds under ideal driving conditions. A statistical analysis is then done to determine the 85th percentile speed. Studies suggest that posting limits at the 85th percentile minimizes accidents and traffic jams and that drivers are more likely to comply with the speed limit. You can learn more about how speed limits are determined by using the links at www.keymath.com/DAA .

9. **APPLICATION** Traffic studies have shown that the best speed limit to post on a given road is the 85th percentile speed.

Assume a road engineer collects these data to determine the speed limit on a local street.

a. Draw a histogram for these data.

b. Find the 85th percentile speed.

c. What speed limit would you recommend based on this traffic study? possible answer: 35 mi/h

d. What other factors should be considered in determining a speed limit?

Speed (mi/h)	Number of Cars (frequency)	Speed (mi/h)	Number of Cars (frequency)
13–15	1	31–33	17
16–18	2	34–36	13
19–21	5	37–39	7
22–24	11	40–42	6
25–27	15	43–45	1
28–30	21	46–48	1

(*Iowa Traffic Control Devices and Pavement Markings: A Manual for Cities and Counties,* Center of Transportation Research and Education, 2001)

10. **APPLICATION** A road engineer studies a rural two-lane highway and presents this histogram to the County Department of Highways.

a. For how many cars was data collected? 118 cars

b. What is the 85th percentile speed?

c. What speed limit would you recommend for this highway? possible answer: 60 mi/h

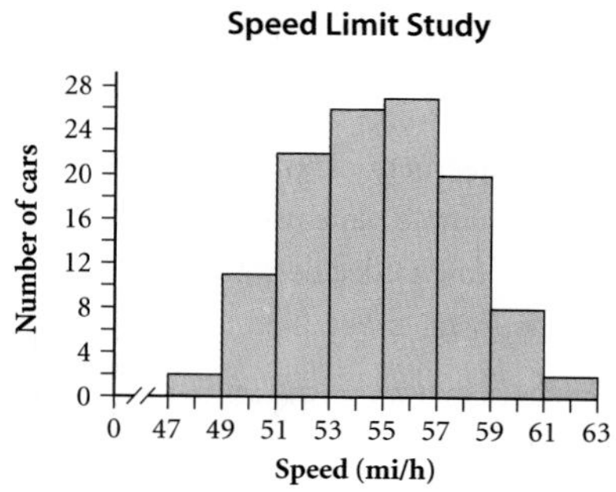

Exercise 9c Highway engineers round up to the nearest 5 mi/h.

9d. sample answers: road type and surface (such as curve or hill), location and type of access points (such as intersections or entrances), existing traffic control devices (such as signs or signals), accident history, traffic volume

10b. between 57 mi/h and 59 mi/h

Exercise 10c If students have not done Exercise 9, refer them to the guidelines stated there.

7a.

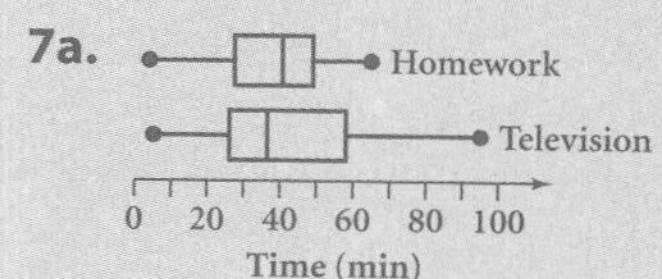

five-number summaries:
homework: 4, 27.5, 40.5, 49, 65
television: 5, 26, 36.5, 58, 95
Television has the greater spread.

7b. Television will be skewed right. Neither will be mound-shaped.

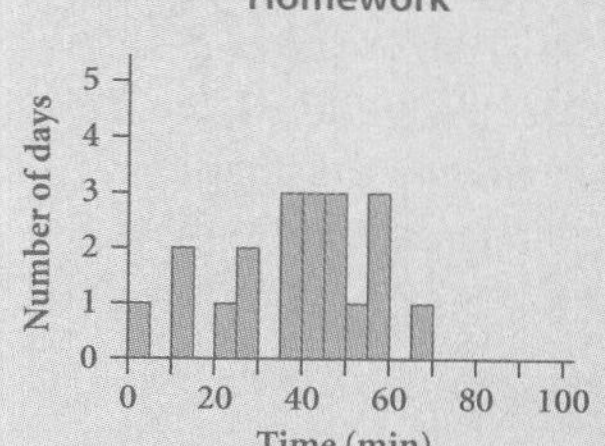

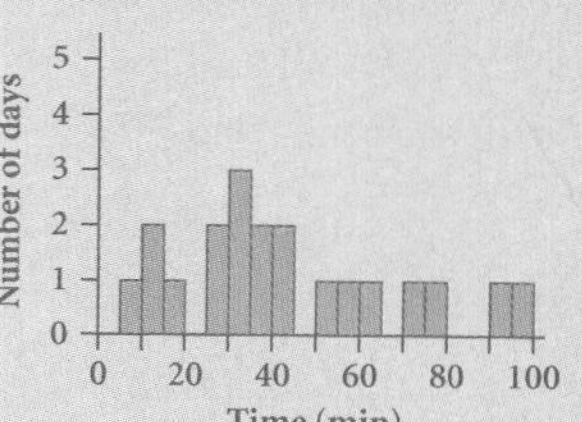

8a. About 1320 students scored lower. About 180 students scored higher.

8b. Mary scored higher than 95% of the students in the class.

Exercise 8c [Ask] "Why wouldn't you say the 100th percentile?" [100% of the data set can't be below a data value, because that data value is in the data set.]

8e. A percent score expresses number correct (presumably indicating percentage of content mastered), whereas a percentile rank compares one score relative to others. Opinions will vary.

9a.

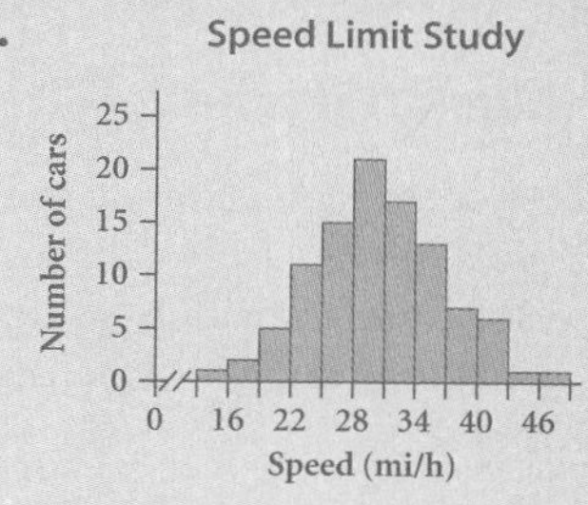

9b. between 37 mi/h and 39 mi/h

11a. The sum of the deviations is 13, not 0.

11c. i. {747, 707, 669, 676, 767, 783, 789, 838}; $s \approx 59.1$; $median = 757$; $IQR = 94.5$

ii. {850, 810, 772, 779, 870, 886, 892, 941}; $s \approx 59.1$; $median = 860$; $IQR = 94.5$

Exercise 11d [Link] You might make an analogy to translating functions. Translating a function does not change the shape of its graph, only the location of its points. Likewise, translating data does not change the shape or spread of the data, only the actual values.

11d. Translating the data doesn't change the standard deviation or the interquartile range. The measures of spread are not dependent on the mean or median, only on the way the data are distributed.

EXTENSIONS

A. Use Take Another Look activity 3 on page 111.

B. Students might collect data and summarize the data using the vocabulary of this chapter.

Review

2.2 **11.** Penny calculates that the deviations from the mean for a data set of eight values are 0, −40, −78, −71, 33, 36, 42, and 91.

a. How do you know that at least one of the deviations is incorrect?

b. If it turns out that 33 is the only incorrect deviation, what should the correct deviation be? 20

c. Use the corrected deviations to find the actual data values, the standard deviation, the median, and the interquartile range if the mean is

i. 747 **ii.** 850

d. Write your observations from 11a–c.

1.1 **12.** At Piccolo Pizza Parlor, a large cheese pizza sells for \$8.99. Each topping costs an additional \$0.50.

a. How much will a four-topping pizza cost? \$10.99

b. The Piccolo Extra Special has eight toppings and costs \$12.47. How much do you save by ordering this special combination instead of ordering eight toppings of your own choosing? \$0.52

13. Courtney can run 100 m in 12.3 s. Marissa can run 100 yd in 11.2 s. Who runs faster? (There are 2.54 centimeters per inch, 12 inches per foot, and 3 feet per yard.) Marissa runs faster.

Project

STEM-AND-LEAF PLOTS

John Tukey introduced **stem-and-leaf plots** in 1972 as a form for one-variable data that is appropriately compact and easy to look over.

Something like a sideways histogram, the stem-and-leaf plot is more detailed because individual data values can be found in the graph. Here are Connie's and Oscar's scores from Exercise 6 in Lesson 2.1 displayed in a stem-and-leaf plot.

Connie		Oscar
	7	2 6 6
	•	
6 5 5 4 4 2 2	8	4
	•	
	9	0 4 6

Key

	7	2 = 72

How do you think a stem-and-leaf plot works and why do you need a key? Read about stem-and-leaf plots in a high school or college statistics book and prepare a research project.

Your project should include

- Instructions to make a stem-and-leaf plot from data.
- Sample plots using data from this chapter. Include variations of stem-and-leaf plots.
- How to decide what level of accuracy is needed to communicate the data usefully.
- Insights obtained from your stem-and-leaf plots.

Supporting the Project

After students have created stem-and-leaf plots, **[Ask]** "How does a stem-and-leaf plot compare with a histogram? In what situations might one be preferred over the other?"

OUTCOMES

- The student's instructions are clear and easy to follow.
- At least two samples of stem-and-leaf plots are given.
- Criteria for selecting a type of stem-and-leaf plot for a given set of data are explained.
- Some conclusions based on the samples are given.
- A variety of stem-and-leaf plots are explained, including basic, back-to-back, and plots that use fractional stems.

EXPLORATION

Census Microdata

Since the establishment of the United States, the Constitution has required a nationwide population count, or census. The first U.S. census was conducted in 1790, less than a year after George Washington was inaugurated. A full census has been conducted every 10 years since.

The first censuses were primarily concerned with the number of people so that the federal government could make decisions about representation and taxation. Today, however, the U.S. Census Bureau collects a wide variety of data, including age, sex, race, national origin, marital status, and education. You can learn more about the history of the U.S. Census by visiting the Internet links at www.keymath.com/DAA .

The most detailed information published by the U.S. Census Bureau is called microdata—data about individuals. This microdata is originally published as an array of numbers, as shown below. You can see that microdata, by itself, would not be very useful to someone trying to make decisions.

Collecting data is only the first part of the U.S. Census Bureau's job. The Bureau also analyzes these data and publishes reports that help federal, state, and local governments, organizations, businesses, and citizens make decisions. In this exploration you'll use Fathom Dynamic Statistics™ software to analyze a set of census microdata. You'll make some conjectures about the data set and use what you've learned about statistics in this chapter to support or refute your conjectures.

A census taker gathers data at a New York City home in 1930.

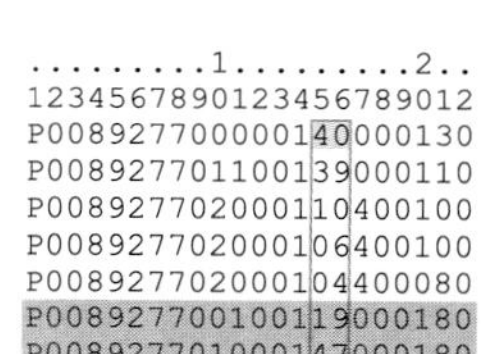

```
.........1.........2..
1234567890123456789012
P00892770000014000013O
P008927701100139000110
P008927702000110400100
P008927702000106400100
P008927702000104400080
P008927700100119000180
P008927701000147000180
```

This table shows 1990 U.S. Census microdata about people living around Berkeley, California. Each row represents one individual. Shaded and unshaded rows group individuals that live in the same household. Columns represent specific information about each individual. For example, columns 15–16 indicate age. In the first row the person is 40 years old.

Social Science CONNECTION

In theory, the census counts every person living in the United States. In actuality, despite outreach programs that attempt to count everyone, including people without housing and people who are not able to read or complete the census, the 2000 U.S. Census is estimated to have excluded up to 3.4 million people. Furthermore, the U.S. Census Bureau today uses both a short form and a long form, such that some questions are only asked to a small sample (5% to 20%) of the population, and the results are statistically applied to the whole population. Some statisticians believe that a census founded entirely on random sampling, but conducted more thoroughly by tracking down every single person in that sample, may be more beneficial in the future.

NCTM STANDARDS

CONTENT		PROCESS	
	Number		Problem Solving
✓	Algebra	✓	Reasoning
	Geometry	✓	Communication
✓	Measurement	✓	Connections
✓	Data/Probability	✓	Representation

LESSON OBJECTIVES

- Use statistics software to make and read box plots and histograms
- Use statistics software to calculate mean and median
- Make conjectures, and use statistics to support or refute a conjecture

EXPLORATION

PLANNING

LESSON OUTLINE

One day:

30 min Activity

15 min Sharing

MATERIALS

- Fathom
- Fathom demonstration Different Ways to Analyze Data, *optional*

TEACHING

This computer activity is most effective if students work in pairs. Students do not need any prior experience with Fathom. If computer access is limited, you might show the Fathom demonstration Different Ways to Analyze Data.

[Language] A *census* is an official counting of the population. A *conjecture* is a guess or speculation that is based on some information but not enough to ensure the truth of the guess. *Microdata* are data with lots of detail.

MAKING THE CONNECTION

The U.S. Census has been criticized for its exclusion of many people. In the 1790 U.S. Census, only three-fifths of African-American slaves were counted; people were classified as white males, white females, and "other free persons." Today the census is criticized for neglecting minorities such as the homeless, persons with insufficient education to complete the questionnaire, and migrant workers. Shortly after the 2000 U.S. Census, Congress debated allowing the U.S. Census Bureau to account for the missing 3.4 million people by using sampling, but the legislation was defeated.

Guiding the Activity

Step 1 The microdata census files for 1990 can be found in the Fathom program folder **Sample Documents.** You might want to create a shortcut/alias to the Fathom program folder on the desktop. Students might choose any of the census data files. Each Fathom census file contains 500 names randomly chosen from samples of 100,000 published by the U.S. Census Bureau. You might assign a different census file to each student pair. Students might be most interested in a geographic region near their hometown or one where they have friends or family.

Dragging one corner can extend any Fathom window, including the collection window. When extended, the collection window will change from a box of gold balls to a collection of individual gold balls (or another icon chosen by the user). Extending windows too far can cause difficulty in dragging items from one window to another.

Step 2 **[Ask]** "Which attributes are numerical?" [age, eduCode, income] "Which are categorical? [all others] Can an attribute be both numerical and categorical?" [No, but a characteristic might be listed as two attributes; education is listed both by eduCode, years completed, and eduText, highest degree.]

Step 3 **[Language]** To *refute* a conjecture means to prove it false.

Step 4 To find statistics for an attribute, you can select the attribute name and drag it to either of the two arrows in the summary table. To display two attributes, drag one to the vertical arrow and the other to the horizontal arrow. Fathom will not display more than one attribute at a time horizontally or vertically.

The basic statistics are displayed in the order in which they appear in the list at the bottom of the summary table. The notation stdDev stands for standard deviation. **[Alert]** If students attempt to calculate the statistics on categorical data, such as marital status, Fathom will display an argument error.

Step 5 Have students click on different areas of their box plots and case table to see what happens in other windows. Students might find that they can graph two-variable data using a scatter plot. They will study two-variable relationships beginning in the next chapter.

Step 6 To display more than one box plot, students drag a categorical attribute to the y-axis. Students can change the scale on either axis (including bin width on the x-axis) by moving the cursor to the axis until it changes to a hand and then dragging. If students construct box plots and histograms in separate windows, they can see how parts of one are highlighted when they highlight the corresponding parts of the other.

To delete any selected window that has no close box, choose **Delete** from the Edit menu.

Activity

Different Ways to Analyze Data

Step 1 Start Fathom. From the File menu choose **Open.** Open one of the census data files in the **Sample Documents** folder. You'll see a box of gold balls, called a collection, that holds data about several individuals, or cases.

Step 2 Click on the collection and then choose **Case Table** from the Insert menu. You now have a table of your microdata. Scroll through the data. How many people are there? What specific data, or attributes, were collected about each person?

Step 2 500 people; sex, age, race, Hispanic (ancestry), ancestry, marital status, education (coded by years and highest degree), income, industry, and job

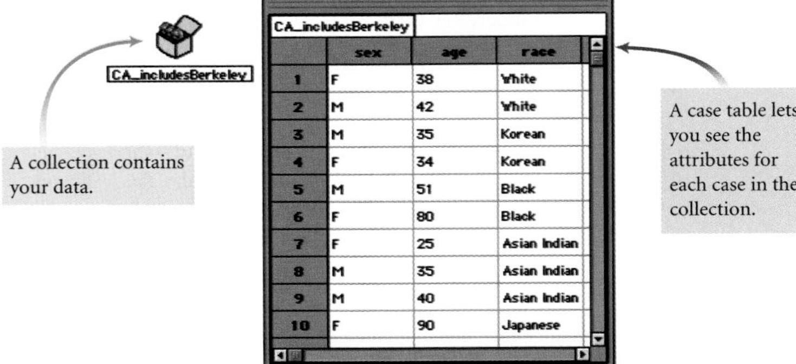

CA_includesBerkeley

	sex	age	race
1	F	38	White
2	M	42	White
3	M	35	Korean
4	F	34	Korean
5	M	51	Black
6	F	80	Black
7	F	25	Asian Indian
8	M	35	Asian Indian
9	M	40	Asian Indian
10	F	90	Japanese

Step 3 Make a conjecture about the people in your data set. Your conjecture can be about just one attribute, such as "The majority of people have some education beyond high school," or it can be about a combination of attributes, such as "The males are older than the females." Your conjecture should be something that you can test and, therefore, support or refute with statistics.

Step 3 Sample answer: The men (males) are older than the women (females).

Step 4 Begin testing your conjecture by calculating summary statistics, such as the mean, median, standard deviation, and interquartile range. Choose **Summary Table** from the Insert menu, and then drag and drop attributes from your case table. From the Summary menu choose **Add Basic Statistics** to see some of the statistics that you have studied in this chapter. Based on these statistics, does your conjecture seem to be true? Why or why not?

Step 4 The mean age of women is higher than the mean age of men which would refute the conjecture. The median age of men, however, is higher than the median age of women, so that could support the conjecture. Students may further use the standard deviation and interquartile range to support or refute their conjectures, or they may find that it is inconclusive based on these statistics alone.

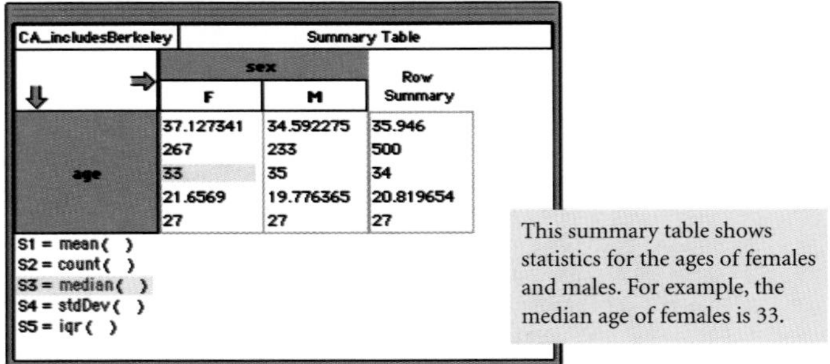

CA_includesBerkeley — Summary Table

	sex: F	sex: M	Row Summary
age	37.127341	34.592275	35.946
	267	233	500
	33	35	34
	21.6569	19.776365	20.819654
	27	27	27

S1 = mean( )
S2 = count( )
S3 = median( )
S4 = stdDev( )
S5 = iqr( )

Step 5 The box plot for the ages of men is almost identical to the box plot for the ages of women; the median age for men is slightly higher, but that is the only noticeable difference. The box plots do not seem to support the conjecture.

Step 6 The histograms seem to refute the conjecture that men are older than women.

Step 7 Answers will vary.

Step 5 Graphs are another way to test your conjecture. Choose **Graph** from the Insert menu. Drag and drop attributes into your graph and then choose **Box Plot** from the pull-down menu in the corner of the graph window. Do box plots help you support or refute your conjecture?

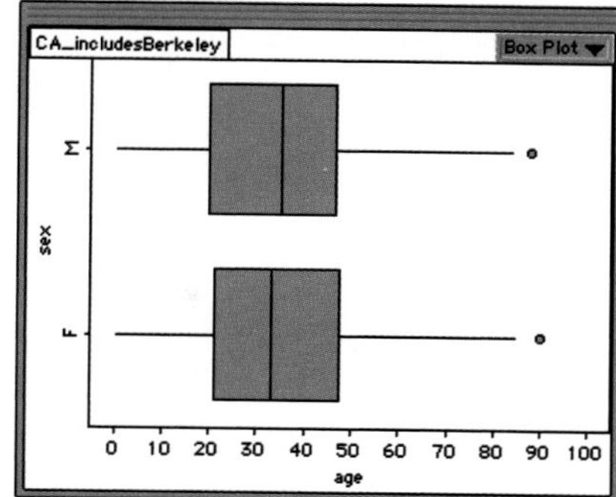

Step 6 Now create histograms to test your conjecture. You can either follow the process in Step 5 to create a new graph or you can simply use the pull-down menu to change your box plots to histograms. What new information do the histograms give you? Do histograms help support your conjecture? Do the histograms better support your conjecture if you change the bin width?

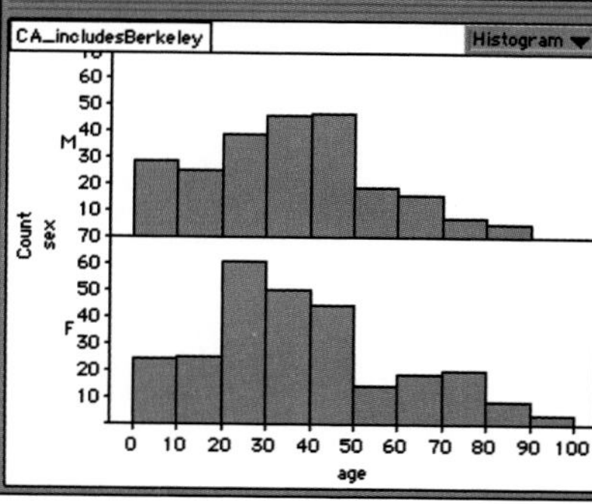

Step 7 Look at all of your analyses, including the summary statistics and graphs. Do you think your conjecture is true? If you aren't sure, you might want to modify your conjecture, or think about factors that might also be at work. Write a short paragraph explaining your findings. Think about these questions as you write: What factors might affect your analysis? Can you explain any outliers in your data? Which statistic or graph revealed the most about these data? In what ways might citizens or governments use these data to make informed decisions?

Questions

1. In this exploration, you've seen some ways to determine whether or not a conjecture is true. Is it possible for a conjecture to appear to be true or false, depending on what statistic or graph you select? Make a new conjecture for your microdata and try to find one statistic or graph that supports the conjecture and one that refutes the conjecture.
2. State and federal decision-makers often have to compare data from different regions to make sure they are meeting everyone's needs. Use Fathom to compare microdata for two different geographic regions. Make and test a few conjectures about how the regions compare and contrast. Describe at least one way in which these communities could use your graphs to make decisions.

SHARING IDEAS

Ask students whether the relationships they found indicate that one attribute causes another. For example, students might have found statistics and graphs that support the conjecture "People with college degrees earn more money." Does this mean that getting more education results in higher earnings? Not necessarily; correlations cannot always be extended to causation. For example, perhaps people with college degrees might have more connections, or are more persistent and thus can obtain or advance to jobs that pay more. Both attributes are the result of some other attribute.

▶Helping with the Questions

Students can include their conjecture and the answer to each question as text in their Fathom document. (Use **Text** under the Insert menu.) You can check student work on the screen or let them print it or e-mail it to you.

Question 1 This question will help students be skeptical about the data and statistics they encounter. Frequently, two conflicting conjectures can be supported in some way with the same set of data, depending on what is being emphasized and what is being ignored.

Question 2 Students can explore this question with their partner, or they can team up with another pair to compare and contrast data. If time is limited, comparisons can be made using the entire class's data.

One way to compare two communities is to keep the collections of microdata in separate files. It is also possible to combine the cases in one file.

Question 2 (continued)
To do the latter, first create a new attribute within each collection that contains the name of the region; then copy and paste both collections into a new collection.

This gives one collection with 1000 cases from which side-by-side graphs can be created.

EXTENSIONS

A. For a more complete, deeper exploration of census microdata with Fathom, you might use any of the activities in Chapter 1, "Come to Your Census," of *Data in Depth* by Tim Erickson.

B. Fathom can be used to test conjectures about any data. You might have students collect their own data or find data that interest them and then make some conjectures and use Fathom to help test those conjectures. Data can be typed in or imported from existing documents, such as spreadsheets and Internet tables.

See page 879 for answers to Questions 1 and 2.

CHAPTER REVIEW 2

PLANNING

LESSON OUTLINE

One day:

15 min Reviewing

20 min Exercises

10 min Student self-assessment

MATERIALS

- Fathom demonstration Eating on the Run, *optional*

REVIEWING

Use the investigation of Lesson 2.3 as a springboard to the chapter review. Ask each group to answer these questions about each of two attributes: What are the mean, median, mode, spread, quartiles, *IQR,* variance, and standard deviation of the data? Which of the central tendency and spread statistics could you find from a box plot and a histogram? How can you determine the shape of the data from a box plot and a histogram? From the measures of central tendency? How does the five-number summary relate to the box plot and the histogram? In what bin of the histogram does the data point at the 90th percentile lie?

Students could use Fathom to help them answer these questions. Or you can use the Fathom demonstration Eating on the Run, concentrating on the first six questions.

ASSIGNING HOMEWORK

You might assign the even-numbered exercises for homework and ask students to work in groups on the others.

CHAPTER 2 REVIEW

Sets of data, such as temperatures, the sugar content of breakfast cereals, and the number of hours of television you watch daily, can be analyzed and pictured using tools that you learned about in this chapter. The **mean** and the **median** are **measures of central tendency.** They tell you about a typical value for the data set. But a measure of central tendency alone does not tell the whole story. You also need to look at the **spread** of the data values. The **standard deviation** helps you determine spread about the mean, and the **interquartile range** helps you determine spread about the median. These measures of spread are also frequently used to identify **outliers** in the data set.

To display a data set visually, you can use a box plot or a histogram. A **box plot** shows the median of the data set, the **range** of the entire set, and the interquartile range between the **first quartile** and the **third quartile.** A **histogram** uses **bins** to show how the data are spread throughout the entire range. By changing the width of the bins, you can get a different perspective on the distribution. Neither a box plot nor a histogram shows individual data values, but both help you see whether the data set is **symmetric** or **skewed.**

Percentile ranks are useful to show how one data value compares to the data set as a whole. The percentile rank of one data value tells you the percentage of values that are less than the given data value. Percentile ranks are not the same as percent scores.

By using a combination of **statistics** and graphs, you can better understand the meaning and implications of a data set. A careful analysis of a data set helps you make general conclusions about the past and predictions for the future.

EXERCISES

1. Which box plot has the greater standard deviation? Explain your reasoning.
Plot B has the greater standard deviation, because the data have more spread.

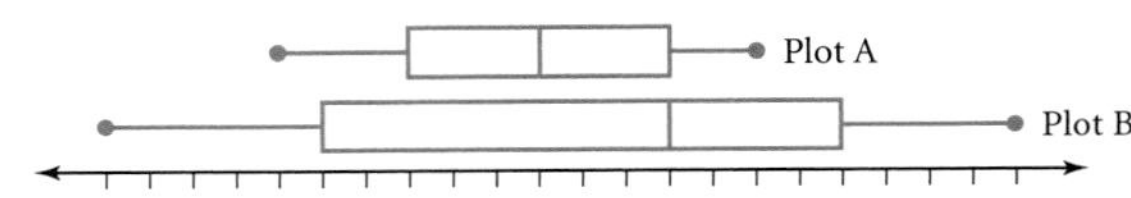

2. Consider these box plots. Group A conducted the rubber band launch experiment 30 times, and Group B conducted the experiment 25 times.

a. How many data values are represented in each whisker of each box plot?

b. Which data set has the greater standard deviation? Explain how you know.

c. Draw two histograms that might represent the information pictured in these two box plots.

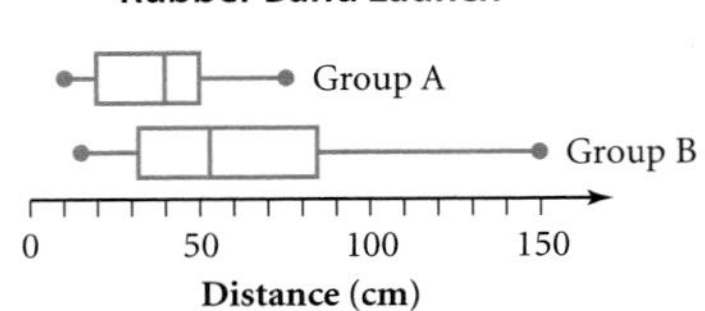

Helping with the Exercises

Exercise 1 This exercise might seem odd to some students because a box plot uses the median as the measure of central tendency but standard deviation is a measure of spread relative to the mean. The larger concept in this problem is how spread translates into standard deviation.

Exercise 2 This exercise refers to Experiment 1 in the investigation of Lesson 2.2. If you skipped that investigation, you might want to explain the activity briefly.

2a. Seven values are represented in each whisker of Group A. Six values are represented in each whisker of Group B.

2b. Group B has the greater standard deviation, because the data have more spread.

2c. See page 109.

3. The Los Angeles Lakers won the 2002 National Basketball Association Championship. This table gives the total points scored by each player during that season.

Total Points Scored by Los Angeles Lakers Players (2001–2002 Season)

Player	Points	Player	Points	Player	Points
Kobe Bryant	2019	Robert Horry	550	Shaquille O'Neal	1822
Joseph Crispin	10	Lindsey Hunter	473	Mike Penberthy	5
Derek Fisher	786	Mark Madsen	167	Mitch Richmond	260
Rick Fox	645	Jelani McCoy	26	Brian Shaw	169
Devean George	581	Stanislav Medvedenko	331	Samaki Walker	460

(*www.nba.com*)

a. Find the mean, median, and mode for this data set.

b. Find the five-number summary. 5, 167, 460, 645, 2019

c. Draw a box plot of the data. Describe the shape of the data set.

d. Calculate the interquartile range. 478 points

e. Identify any outliers. Use the $1.5 \cdot IQR$ definition for outliers.

Derek Fisher

4. Invent two data sets, each with seven values, such that Set A has the greater standard deviation and Set B has the greater interquartile range.

5. The table below contains the recorded extreme temperatures, in degrees Fahrenheit, for each of the seven continents.

Highest and Lowest Recorded Temperatures

Continent	High (°F)	Low (°F)
Africa	136	−11
Antarctica	59	−129
Asia	129	−90
Australia	128	−9
Europe	122	−67
North America	134	−87
South America	120	−27

(*www.infoplease.com*)

a. Find the mean and standard deviation of the high temperatures. $\bar{x} \approx 118.3$°F; $s \approx 26.8$°F

b. Find the mean and standard deviation of the low temperatures. $\bar{x} = -60.0$°F; $s \approx 45.7$°F

c. Which temperatures, if any, are outliers in each set of data? Use the $2s$ definition for outliers.

2c. possible answer:

Group A

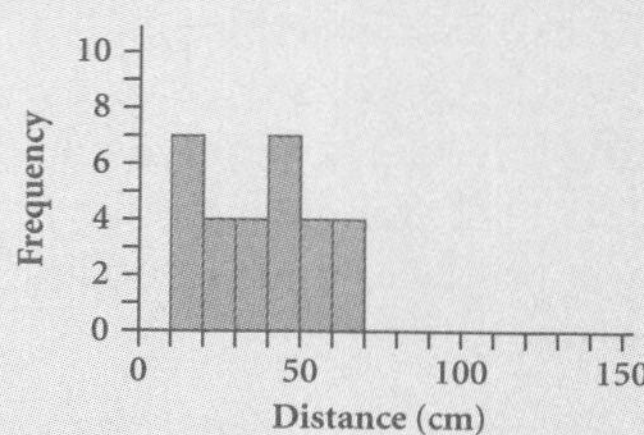

Group B

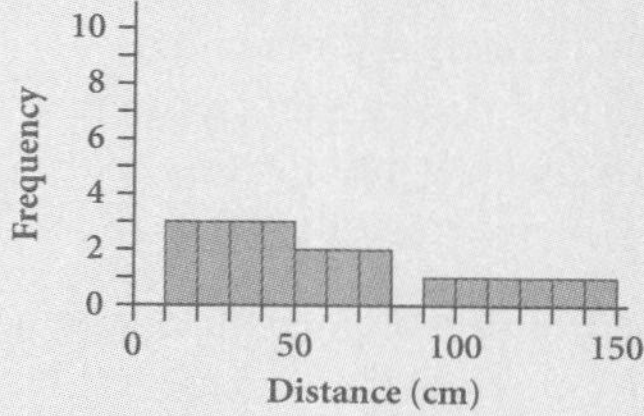

Exercise 3 **[Ask]** "How might the statistics be used?" [They could be valuable in comparing the Lakers to other teams, especially after eliminating outliers.]

3a. mean: 553.6 points; median: 460 points; mode: none

3c.

Points Scored by Los Angeles Lakers Players (2001–2002 Season)

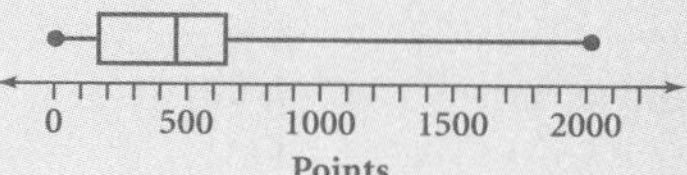

skewed right

3e. Kobe Bryant (2019 points) and Shaquille O'Neal (1822 points)

4. One strategy is to make Set A skewed and Set B symmetric. Possible answer: Set A: {1, 2, 3, 4, 5, 6, 47}; $s \approx 16.5$; $IQR = 4$. Set B: {1, 5, 7, 9, 11, 13, 17}; $s \approx 5.3$; $IQR = 8$.

Exercise 5 Ask what use the statistics might have. Students might propose that they tell something about the world's temperatures. Encourage them to critique this idea. Because the values are record highs and lows, all the data are outliers. Also, in order to determine something about the world's temperatures, factors such as land area, latitude, and altitude should probably be considered.

5c. Antarctica (59°F) is an outlier for the high temperatures. There are no outliers for the low temperatures.

Exercise 6 Students might want to use Fathom for this and similar problems. As an extension, students could research the data for all Academy Award winners from 1928 to 2002 and see if the larger data set produces drastically different results.

The box plots in 6c clearly show that women are younger when they win. **[Ask]** "What are some of the reasons the mean age is younger for women?" [more roles for younger women, fewer roles for women over 40]

In 6e the Best Actress data have a greater standard deviation. **[Ask]** "In what ways are the Best Actress data grouped more tightly than the Best Actor data?" [smaller *IQR*] "Which group has more outliers?" [women 3, men 1]

6c. Academy Awards Winners

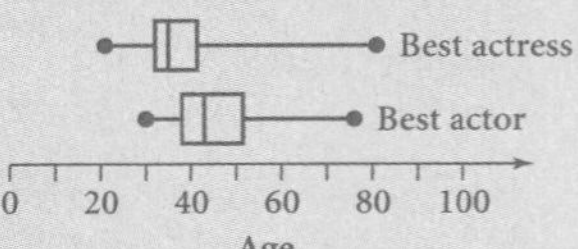

five-number summaries:
best actress: 21, 32.5, 35, 41.5, 81;
best actor: 30, 38, 43, 51.5, 76

6d.

Best Actress Winners

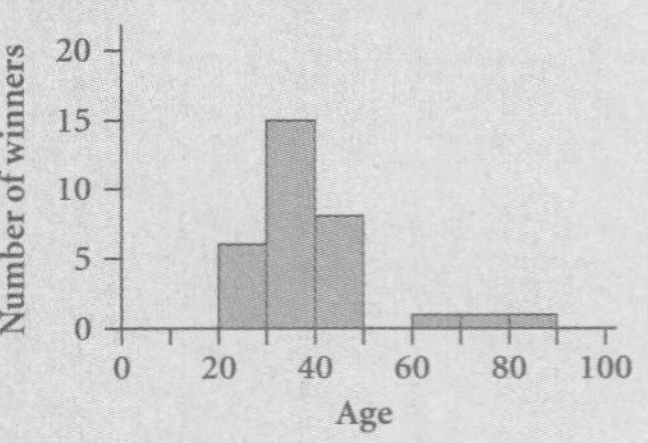

Best Actor Winners

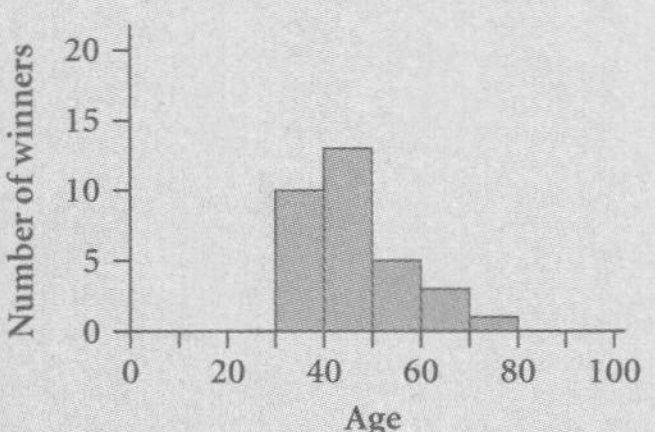

6. Below is a list of Academy Award winners in the Best Actress and Best Actor categories and each person's age when he or she received the award.

Academy Award Winners 1970–2001

Year	Best actress in a leading role, Age	Best actor in a leading role, Age	Year	Best actress in a leading role, Age	Best actor in a leading role, Age
1970	Glenda Jackson, 34	George C. Scott, 43	1986	Marlee Matlin, 21	Paul Newman, 62
1971	Jane Fonda, 34	Gene Hackman, 42	1987	Cher, 41	Michael Douglas, 43
1972	Liza Minnelli, 26	Marlon Brando, 48	1988	Jodie Foster, 26	Dustin Hoffman, 51
1973	Glenda Jackson, 37	Jack Lemmon, 49	1989	Jessica Tandy, 81	Daniel Day-Lewis, 32
1974	Ellen Burstyn, 42	Art Carney, 56	1990	Kathy Bates, 42	Jeremy Irons, 42
1975	Louise Fletcher, 41	Jack Nicholson, 38	1991	Jodie Foster, 29	Anthony Hopkins, 54
1976	Faye Dunaway, 36	Peter Finch, 60	1992	Emma Thompson, 33	Al Pacino, 52
1977	Diane Keaton, 32	Richard Dreyfuss, 30	1993	Holly Hunter, 36	Tom Hanks, 37
1978	Jane Fonda, 41	Jon Voight, 40	1994	Jessica Lange, 45	Tom Hanks, 38
1979	Sally Field, 33	Dustin Hoffman, 42	1995	Susan Sarandon, 49	Nicolas Cage, 31
1980	Sissy Spacek, 31	Robert De Niro, 37	1996	Frances McDormand, 39	Geoffrey Rush, 45
1981	Katharine Hepburn, 74	Henry Fonda, 76	1997	Helen Hunt, 34	Jack Nicholson, 60
1982	Meryl Streep, 33	Ben Kingsley, 39	1998	Gwyneth Paltrow, 26	Roberto Benigni, 46
1983	Shirley MacLaine, 49	Robert Duvall, 53	1999	Hilary Swank, 25	Kevin Spacey, 40
1984	Sally Field, 38	F. Murray Abraham, 45	2000	Julia Roberts, 33	Russell Crowe, 36
1985	Geraldine Page, 61	William Hurt, 36	2001	Halle Berry, 33	Denzel Washington, 47

(*www.imdb.com*)

a. Find the mean age and the median age for the Best Actress winners. *$\bar{x} \approx 38.6$; median = 35*

b. Find the mean age and the median age for the Best Actor winners. *$\bar{x} \approx 45.3$; median = 43*

c. On the same axis, draw two box plots, one for the age of Best Actress winners and the other for the age of Best Actor winners.

d. Draw two histograms, one each for Best Actress and Best Actor.

e. Use your graphs from 6c and 6d to predict which data set has the greater standard deviation. Explain your reasoning. Then calculate the standard deviations to check your prediction.

f. Julia Roberts was 33 years old when she won Best Actress in 2000. What is her percentile rank among all Best Actress winners from 1970 to 2001? Explain what this percentile rank tells you.

At the 74th annual Academy Awards, Halle Berry was the first African-American to win Best Actress. Denzel Washington was the second African-American to win Best Actor.

6e. The Best Actress data set should have the greater standard deviation because it has more spread. Best Actress: $s \approx 13.0$; Best Actor: $s \approx 10.1$.

6f. 25th percentile. 25% of the Best Actress winners from 1970 to 2001 were younger than 33 when they won their award.

7. APPLICATION Following the 1998 Academy Awards ceremony, Best Actress nominee Fernanda Montenegro (age 70) said Gwyneth Paltrow (age 26) had won Best Actress for *Shakespeare in Love* because she was younger. This comment caused Pace University student Michael Gilberg and professor Terence Hines to test the theory that younger women and older men are more likely than older women and younger men to receive an Academy Award for Best Actress and Best Actor. Their study was published in the February 2000 issue of *Psychological Reports.*

Assume that you are working with Gilberg and Hines. Use your statistics and graphs from Exercise 6 to confirm or refute the theory that younger women and older men are more likely to win. Prepare a brief report on your conclusions.
Answers will vary. In general, the theory is supported by the statistics and graphs.

8. The 2000 U.S. passenger-car production totals are shown at right.

a. Make a box plot of these data.

b. Make a histogram using a bin width that provides meaningful information about the data.

c. Suppose a different year has a similar distribution but the total number of cars produced is 400 thousand greater than in 2000. Describe how this could affect the shape of your box plot and histogram.

d. What is the percentile rank of Pontiac? 78th percentile

e. What is the percentile rank of Ford? 94th percentile

2000 U.S. Passenger-Car Production

Brand	Number of cars (thousands)
BMW	39
Buick	209
Cadillac	159
Chevrolet	597
Chrysler	80
Dodge	298
Ford	965
Honda	677
Lincoln/Mercury	282
Mazda	107
Mitsubishi	222
Nissan	150
Oldsmobile	235
Plymouth	55
Pontiac	576
Saturn	261
Subaru	108
Toyota	520

(*The World Almanac and Book of Facts 2003*)

TAKE ANOTHER LOOK

1. Which measure of central tendency do you think of when someone says "average"? Without clarification, an "average" could be the mean, the median, or the mode. Find newspaper and magazine articles that state an "average," such as "The average American family has 2.58 children." Read the articles closely and analyze any data that are provided. Can you find enough information to tell which measure of central tendency is being used? Do you find that most articles are or are not specific enough with their mathematics? What conclusions can you make?

2. The calculation of mean that you learned in this chapter—the sum of all data values divided by the number of values—is more precisely called the **arithmetic mean.** Other means include the geometric mean, the harmonic mean, the quadratic mean, the trimean, and the midmean. Research one or more of these means and compare and contrast the calculation to the arithmetic mean.

3. In Lesson 2.3, you learned how to find the median of a data set by looking at a histogram. How would you use the histogram to approximate the mean? The mode?

Exercise 7 As an extension, students could create new box plots and histograms to support or refute the theory. (Graphs might include all data from 1928 to 2002, or they might exclude outliers.) Students could read Gilberg and Hines's study and compare their own statistics to those used in that research.

Take Another Look

1. Students are likely to find that many articles are not specific enough and possibly that most assume the arithmetic mean.

2. Answers should include one or more of these equations for the means:

geometric mean $= \sqrt[n]{x_1 \cdot x_2 \cdot x_3 \cdot \ldots \cdot x_n}$

harmonic mean $= \dfrac{n}{\sum_{i=1}^{n} \frac{1}{x_i}}$

quadratic mean $= \sqrt{\dfrac{\sum_{i=1}^{n} (x_i)^2}{n}}$

trimean $= \dfrac{H_1 + 2M + H_2}{4}$, where M is the median, H_1 is the lower hinge (roughly equivalent to the first quartile but found by including the median as part of the lower half of data values), and H_2 is the upper hinge (roughly equivalent to the third quartile)

midmean $= \dfrac{2 \cdot \sum_{i=n/4}^{3n/4} x_i}{n}$

Answers may also use an example to compare the means. Sample: For the mean monthly temperatures in New York City from the data table on page 92, the arithmetic mean is 53.8, the geometric mean is 51.4, the harmonic mean is 49.0, the quadratic mean is 55.9, the trimean is 54, and the midmean is 60.2. For these data

Take Another Look (continued)
the trimean is closest to the arithmetic mean, and the midmean, which ignores the extremes, differs most from the arithmetic mean. Both the geometric mean and the harmonic mean are below the arithmetic mean. The mean of these six means is 54.1, very close to the arithmetic mean.

3. One strategy for finding the mean begins with picking a representative value for each bin's interval, say the median. An estimate of the mean is calculated by summing the products of the bin heights and the representative values, then dividing by the number of data values.

Because individual data values are not shown in a histogram, students might say that it is impossible to find a mode. A mode can also be defined as the bin interval with the most data values.

See page 879 for answers to Exercises 8a–c.

4. Mean deviation, also called *mean absolute deviation,* is more descriptive but less commonly used than standard deviation.

Sample answer: For the rubber band data on page 88, the mean deviation is 1.14 for Group A and 16.6 for Group B. In both cases the mean deviation is less than the standard deviation. For the group with the larger deviations, the mean deviation and the standard deviation were farther apart than those for the group with the smaller deviations.

ASSESSING

You have several options for written tests, constructive assessment items, and tests constructed with the Test Generator and Worksheet Builder. You might include some student-created items if students write test items as part of their self-assessment.

As a performance assessment, students might demonstrate how to use the graphing calculator or Fathom to calculate statistics and to make graphs of data; in addition to showing all the steps, they should explain what the numbers or graphs represent.

FACILITATING SELF-ASSESSMENT

Students can assemble portfolios for each chapter. You might suggest these items for students' portfolios: Lesson 2.1, Exercise 7; Lesson 2.2, Exercise 13 or 14; Lesson 2.3, Exercise 9.

4. Another measure of spread, the mean deviation, *MD,* uses absolute value to eliminate the effect of the different signs of the individual deviations.

$$MD = \frac{\sum_{i=1}^{n} |x_i - \bar{x}|}{n}$$

Try using mean deviation for some of the exercises in which you calculated standard deviation. How do the values compare? When might standard deviation or mean deviation be the more appropriate measure of spread?

Assessing What You've Learned

BEGIN A PORTFOLIO An artist usually keeps both a notebook and a portfolio. The notebook might contain everything from scratch work to practice sketches to notes about past or future subject matter. The portfolio, in contrast, is reserved for the artist's most significant or best work.

As a student, you probably already keep a notebook that contains everything from your class notes to homework to research for independent projects. You can also start a separate portfolio that collects your most significant work.

Review all the work you've done so far and find your best works of art: the neatest graphs, the most thorough calculations for various statistics, the most complete analysis of a data set, or the most comprehensive project. Add each piece to your portfolio with a paragraph or two that addresses these questions:

- What is the piece an example of?
- Does this piece represent your best work? Why else did you choose it?
- What mathematics did you learn or apply in this piece?
- How would you improve the piece if you redid or revised it?

WRITE TEST ITEMS Writing your own problems is an excellent way to assess and review what you've learned. If you were writing a test for this chapter, what would it include? Start by having a group discussion to identify the key ideas of the chapter. Then divide the lessons among group members, and have each group member write at least one problem for each lesson assigned to him or her. Try to create a mix of problems, from simple one-step exercises that require you to recall facts and formulas, to complex multistep problems that require more thinking. Because you'll be working with data and statistics, you'll need to carefully consider which statistics and graphs are appropriate for the data.

Share your problems with your group members and try out one another's problems. Then discus the problems in your group:

- Were the problems representative of the content of the chapter?
- Were any problems too hard or too easy?
- Were the statistics appropriate for the data?

CHAPTER

3

Linear Models and Systems

Overview

This chapter looks at lines first as mathematical objects that can model two-variable data sets and second as graphical representations of systems of linear equations. In **Lesson 3.1,** students investigate the relationship among a recursive formula generating an arithmetic sequence, its explicit formula, and the corresponding linear equation with its graph. The lesson foreshadows the definition of domain and range in **Lesson 3.2,** where additional real-world situations are explored. In **Lesson 3.3,** students look for lines of fit for two-variable data and make predictions. In **Lesson 3.4,** students see and apply a standard line of fit, the median-median line. Students learn to evaluate quality of fit through residuals and the root mean square error in **Lesson 3.5.** A Fathom **exploration** deepens their understanding of residual plots and least squares.

The focus switches to systems of linear equations and their graphical representation in **Lesson 3.6.** In **Lesson 3.7,** students consider the substitution and elimination methods for solving a system of equations and explore the graphical representations of the equivalent equations obtained through the addition and multiplication properties of equality.

The Mathematics

Linear Models and Residuals

Recursive formulas, which generate sequences, are useful in developing an understanding of rates of change. A more efficient tool for finding the *n*th value of a sequence, however, is an explicit formula, which gives u_n in terms of n rather than u_{n-1}.

Recursive and explicit formulas define discrete functions, which are evaluated only at integers. (The function values might be non-integers, though.) To model continuous change, we use equations that can be evaluated at any real number. In this book, such equations are usually given in terms of *x*'s and *y*'s rather than *u*'s and *n*'s because calculators usually use those variables, but any variables can be used. This chapter focuses on linear equations; later chapters introduce other kinds of continuous equations.

Like *Discovering Algebra,* this book emphasizes the intercept form of linear equations, $y = a + bx$. This form reflects the dynamic graphical thinking of starting at a value a and increasing by b units for each unit of x moved across. The same form also extends the recursive formulas for discrete data: $u_0 = a$, $u_n = u_{n-1} + b$. Note that the variable b represents the slope here, whereas b represents the y-intercept in the intercept form, $y = mx + b$.

In real life, when we look for patterns in data, those data rarely fit exactly on a line or another nice curve. So we try to find an explicit formula or a continuous equation that *fits* the data as well as possible. In this chapter students first find lines of fit through eyeballing, perhaps picking two points so that the line through these data "looks good." Then they learn a more systematic method, which gives the median-median line. In Lesson 13.7, they'll see a method that gives the least-squares line.

Though some books refer to a *best-fit line* or *line of best fit,* the subjective term *best* is not used here. Instead, students evaluate the merits of each line. One way to evaluate the quality of fit is by residuals: the directed distances vertically from the data points to the line. If the line fits the data perfectly, each residual is 0. A line whose residuals have a sum or mean of 0 does not necessarily fit well, but if the residuals also have a spread close to 0 (measured by their standard deviation or root mean square error), then the line is a good fit.

Residuals can also help adjust a line to one of better fit. If the residuals themselves seem to have a linear trend, the slope of the line of fit can be changed accordingly. After that change, if more residuals are positive than negative (or vice versa), the line of fit can be shifted down or up to even things out. Also, if the residuals form a standard nonlinear shape, a nonlinear model of that shape, as considered in Lesson 13.6, will be better than a linear model.

Systems

A linear equation is called *linear* because its graph is a line. A pair of linear equations (or simultaneous equations) is graphed as a pair of lines. If these intersect, the coordinates of the point of intersection comprise a solution to the system of equations. Chapter 6 considers systems of equations in more detail.

Significant Digits

Students might record all digits displayed on a calculator without thinking about significance. The number of significant digits in a result equals the smallest number of significant digits in any number being used in the calculation. See the guidelines for rounding statistics on page 76A.

Using This Chapter

Lesson 3.2 will take two days to complete unless you ask students to build their rockets out of class. You might skip Lesson 3.5 if the material on residuals is not included in your state standards. However this may be the only new content for some students, and an understanding of residuals will help students evaluate linear models. Residuals will be mentioned again in Chapter 13.

If your students are still weak on basic algebra skills, you can download beginning algebra worksheets from www.keymath.com/DA.

Resources

Discovering Advanced Algebra Resources

Teaching and Worksheet Masters
- Lessons 3.1, 3.3–3.6
- Exploration: Residual Plots and Least Squares

Calculator Notes 1B, 1H, and 3A–3G

Fathom Demonstrations
- Lesson 3.3
- Exploration: Residual Plots and Least Squares

Assessment Resources A and B
- Quiz 1 (Lessons 3.1–3.3)
- Quiz 2 (Lessons 3.4, 3.5)
- Quiz 3 (Lessons 3.6, 3.7)
- Chapter 3 Test
- Chapter 3 Constructive Assessment Options
- Chapters 1–3 Exam

More Practice Your Skills for Chapter 3

Condensed Lessons for Chapter 3

Other Resources

www.keypress.com/DAA

Materials

- tape
- butcher paper
- balloons
- straws
- string
- motion sensors
- graph paper
- stopwatch (or watch with a second hand)
- uncooked spaghetti, *optional*
- springs
- mass holders (such as film canisters)
- small unit masses
- rulers
- airline timetables, *optional*

Pacing Guide

	day 1	day 2	day 3	day 4	day 5	day 6	day 7	day 8	day 9	day 10
standard	3.1	3.2	3.2	3.3	quiz, 3.4	3.4	3.5	3.5	quiz, 3.6	3.7
enriched	3.1	3.2	3.2	3.3, project	quiz, 3.4	3.5	3.5	exploration	quiz, 3.6	3.7
block	3.1, 3.2	3.2	3.3, quiz, 3.4	3.5, quiz	exploration, 3.6	3.7, quiz, review, TAL	assessment, mixed review	exam		

	day 11	day 12	day 13	day 14
standard	quiz, review	assessment	mixed review	exam
enriched	quiz, review, TAL	assessment	mixed review	exam

CHAPTER

3 Linear Models and Systems

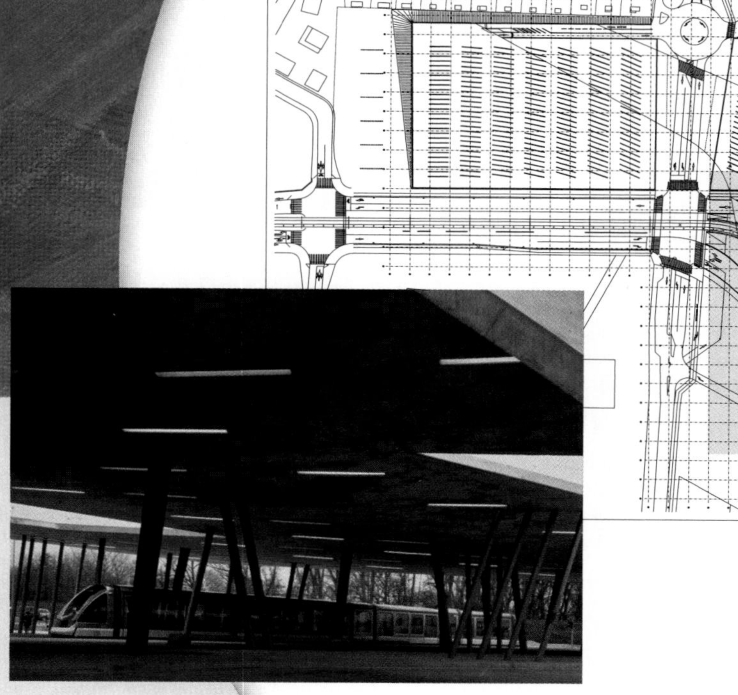

Iraqi-British architect Zaha Hadid (b 1950) designed this commuter train station on the outskirts of Strasbourg, France. She worked with the concept of overlapping fields and lines to represent the interacting patterns of moving cars, trains, bicycles, and pedestrians. The roof of the waiting area in the station is punctured by angled lines that let sunlight shine on the floor, shifting throughout the day. You can see these lines in the photograph, which shows the region of the architectural plan highlighted in blue.

OBJECTIVES

In this chapter you will

- review linear equations in intercept form and point-slope form
- explore connections between arithmetic sequences and linear equations
- find lines of fit for data sets that are approximately linear
- solve systems of linear equations

CHAPTER 3 OBJECTIVES

- Relate recursive formulas for arithmetic sequences to explicit formulas and to linear equations
- Deepen understanding of slope in arithmetic sequences and linear equations
- Find lines of fit for data sets and use them to make predictions through interpolation and extrapolation
- Learn about the median-median line and compare it to other lines of fit
- Evaluate lines of fit using residuals and the root mean square error
- Use the root mean square error to find the error range
- Use systems of linear equations to model problems
- Solve systems of equations by graphing, by tables, by substitution, and by elimination

This station has no right angles, curves, or parallel lines. All of the pillars and walls are slanted to convey a sense of motion. Every source of light also radiates in a straight line: The slits in the roof let in light rays that travel around the station throughout the day; the concealed ceiling lights and the light projectors buried in the floor provide long columns of illumination. These many intersecting lines are representative of the many crossing paths between different modes of transportation in this busy station. Encouraging students to be creative, **[Ask]** "How is a transportation system similar to a system of lines on the coordinate plane?" [The lines of a transportation system each carry a package of information (destination, arrival and departure times, mode of transportation) similar to how a line as a graph of an equation carries information (x- and y-intercepts, slope). As lines intersect in both systems, the information of each intersecting line is the same as that of the others only at that single point. While in a linear system, this point is the solution to the system of equations, in a transportation system, this is the place where a traveler changes lines.]

LESSON

3.1

PLANNING

LESSON OUTLINE

One day:

10 min Examples

15 min Investigation

5 min Sharing

15 min Exercises

MATERIALS

- Growing a Lawn (T) for One Step

TEACHING

In this lesson students see how to write an explicit formula for a discrete function defined recursively.

One Step

Show the Growing a Lawn transparency and pose this problem, adapted from Exercise 10: "A gardener planted a new variety of ornamental grass and kept a record of its height over the first two weeks of growth. What's a recursive formula that will help predict its height after 21 days? What's a quicker way to find that value?" As students work, encourage them to draw graphs, and ask how repeated addition can be represented. During Sharing, introduce the term *explicit formula*.

LESSON 3.1

Linear Equations and Arithmetic Sequences

You can solve many rate problems by using recursion.

Matias wants to call his aunt in Chile on her birthday. He learned that placing the call costs \$2.27 and that each minute he talks costs \$1.37. How much would it cost to talk for 30 minutes?

Valparaiso, Chile

You can calculate the cost of Matias's phone call with the recursive formula

$$u_0 = 2.27$$
$$u_n = u_{n-1} + 1.37 \quad \text{where } n \geq 1$$

To find the cost of a 30-minute phone call, calculate the first 30 terms, as shown in the calculator screen.

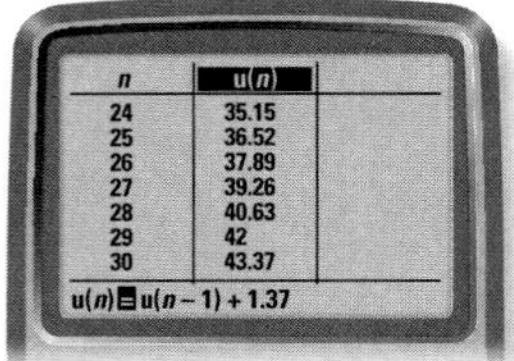

As you learned in algebra, you or Matias can also find the cost of a 30-minute call by using the **linear equation**

$$y = 2.27 + 1.37x$$

where x is the length of the phone call in minutes and y is the cost in dollars. If the phone company always rounds up the length of the call to the nearest whole minute, then the costs become a sequence of discrete points, and you can write the relationship as an explicit formula,

$$u_n = 2.27 + 1.37n$$

where n is the length of the call in whole minutes and u_n is the cost in dollars.

An **explicit formula** gives a direct relationship between two discrete quantities. How does the explicit formula differ from the recursive formula? How would you use each one for calculating the cost of a 15-minute call or an n-minute call?

In this lesson you will write and use explicit formulas for arithmetic sequences. You will also write linear equations for lines through the discrete points of arithmetic sequences.

EXAMPLE A

Consider the recursively defined arithmetic sequence

$$u_0 = 2$$
$$u_n = u_{n-1} + 6 \quad \text{where } n \geq 1$$

a. Find an explicit formula for the sequence.

b. Use the explicit formula to find u_{22}.

c. Find the value of n so that $u_n = 86$.

LESSON OBJECTIVES

- Given a recursive formula, find n for a given u_n
- Graph an arithmetic sequence to locate the u_n-intercept and determine the slope
- Recognize slope as the common difference of an arithmetic sequence
- Use the u_n-intercept and slope to write a linear equation (in x and y)
- Recognize that an arithmetic sequence is always linear

NCTM STANDARDS

CONTENT		PROCESS	
✓	Number	✓	Problem Solving
✓	Algebra	✓	Reasoning
	Geometry	✓	Communication
✓	Measurement	✓	Connections
	Data/Probability	✓	Representation

▶ Solution

a. Look for a pattern in the sequence.

u_0	2
u_1	$8 = 2 + 6 = 2 + 6 \cdot 1$
u_2	$14 = 2 + 6 + 6 = 2 + 6 \cdot 2$
u_3	$20 = 2 + 6 + 6 + 6 = 2 + 6 \cdot 3$

Notice that the common difference (or rate of change) between the terms is 6. You start with 2 and just keep adding 6. That means each term is equivalent to 2 plus 6 times the term number. In general, when you write the formula for a sequence, you use n to represent the number of the term and u_n to represent the term itself.

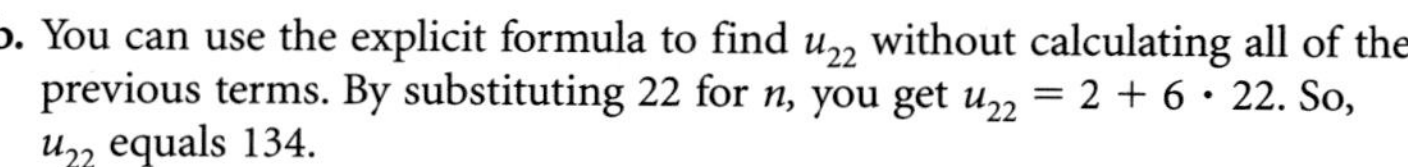

b. You can use the explicit formula to find u_{22} without calculating all of the previous terms. By substituting 22 for n, you get $u_{22} = 2 + 6 \cdot 22$. So, u_{22} equals 134.

c. To find n so that $u_n = 86$, substitute 86 for u_n in the formula $u_n = 2 + 6n$.

$86 = 2 + 6n$	Substitute 86 for u_n.
$14 = n$	Solve for n.

So, 86 is the 14th term.

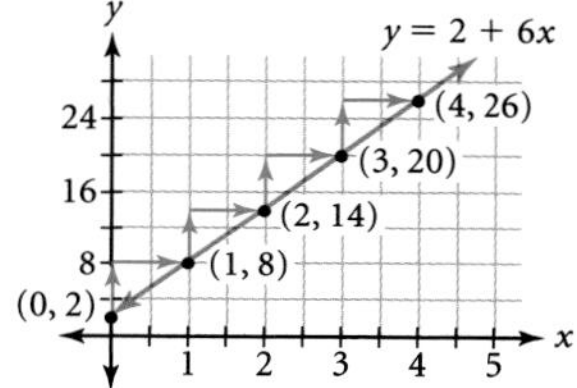

You graphed sequences of points (n, u_n) in Chapter 1. The variable n stands for a term number, so it is a whole number: 0, 1, 2, 3, ... So, using different values for n will produce a set of discrete points. This graph shows the arithmetic sequence from Example A.

When n increases by 1, u_n increases by 6, the common difference. In terms of x and y, the number 6 is the change in the y-value, or function value, that corresponds to a unit change (a change of 1) in the x-value. So the points representing the sequence lie on a line with a slope of 6. In general, the common difference, or rate of change, between consecutive terms of an arithmetic sequence is the **slope** of the line through those points.

The pair (0, 2) names the starting value 2, which is the y-intercept. Using the intercept form of a linear equation, you can now write an equation of the line through the points of the sequence as $y = 2 + 6x$, or $y = 6x + 2$.

In this course you will use x and y to write linear equations. You will use n and u_n to write both recursive formulas and explicit formulas for sequences of discrete points.

In the investigation you will focus on this relationship between the formula for an arithmetic sequence and the equation of the line through the points representing the sequence.

When you download photos from the Internet, sometimes the resolution improves as the percentage of download increases. The relationship between the percentage of download and the resolution could be modeled with a sequence, an explicit formula, or a linear equation.

▶ EXAMPLE A

[Ask] "Why is the common difference the rate of change?" [because the change in n is 1]

The equation in part c can be solved in one of several ways, including undoing, arrow diagrams, or graphing. For a graphical approach, draw a horizontal line at $u_n = 86$ and find the point where the plot meets that line.

Guiding the Investigation

Step 1 **[Alert]** Students might miss the parenthetical note that not all the matches are listed and that the assignment includes creating the missing pieces.

Step 1 1, B, $y = 4 - x$; 2, C, iii;

3, 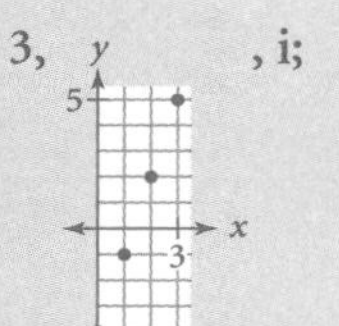 , i;

A, $u_0 = 3$ and $u_n = u_{n-1} + 2$ where $n \geq 1$, $y = 3 + 2x$;

ii, $u_0 = 4$ and $u_n = u_{n-1} + 1$ where $n \geq 1$,

Step 3 **[Language]** *Collinear* means lying on the same line.

Step 3 Yes, the points (n, u_n) of an arithmetic sequence are always collinear because the explicit formula for an arithmetic sequence is a linear equation.

► *EXAMPLE B*

[Alert] Students often have difficulty determining whether to use the first term as u_1 or u_0. **[Ask]** "Why do you think Retta's sequence starts with u_1?" [She has $17 left at the end of Day 1.]

SHARING IDEAS

To the extent possible, choose presenters to show a variety of approaches and ideas. To emphasize the difference between the recursive and explicit formulas, ask if $u_n = u_{n-1} + 5$ is the same as $u_n = n + 5$. The slope of the line through the points on the recursively defined formula is 5, but the slope of the line through the points on the explicitly defined formula is 1. Slope and various forms of linear equations will be recapped in Lesson 3.2.

Investigation
Match Point

Below are three recursive formulas, three graphs, and three linear equations.

1. $u_0 = 4$
$u_n = u_{n-1} - 1$ where $n \geq 1$

2. $u_0 = 2$
$u_n = u_{n-1} + 5$ where $n \geq 1$

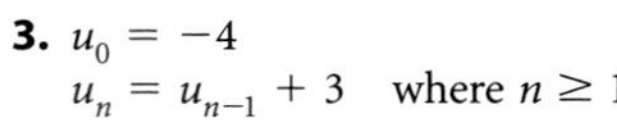

3. $u_0 = -4$
$u_n = u_{n-1} + 3$ where $n \geq 1$

A.

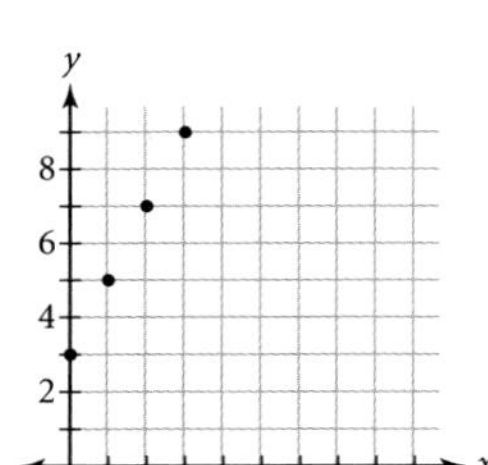

B.

C.

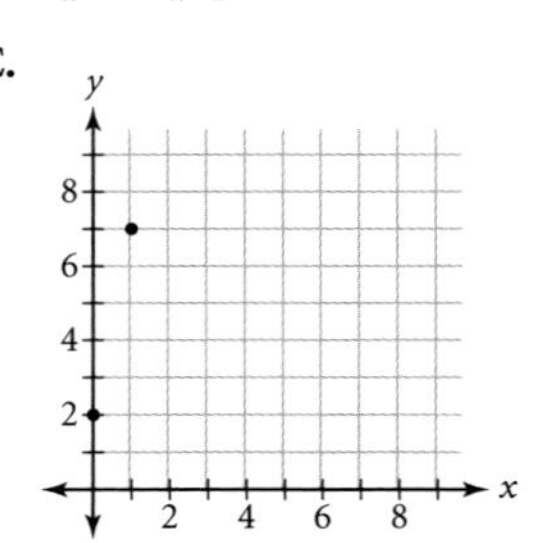

i. $y = -4 + 3x$

ii. $y = 4 + x$

iii. $y = 2 + 5x$

Step 1 Match the recursive formulas, graphs, and linear equations that go together. (Not all of the appropriate matches are listed. If the recursive rule, graph, or equation is missing, you will need to create it.)

Step 2 Write a brief statement relating the starting value and common difference of an arithmetic sequence to the corresponding equation $y = a + bx$.

Step 2 The starting value is a, and the common difference is b.

Step 3 Are points (n, u_n) of an arithmetic sequence always collinear? Write a brief statement supporting your answer.

EXAMPLE B

Retta typically spends $2 a day on lunch. She notices that she has $17 left after today's lunch. She thinks of this sequence to model her daily cash balance.

$u_1 = 17$
$u_n = u_{n-1} - 2$ where $n > 1$

a. Find the explicit formula that represents her daily cash balance and the equation of the line through the points of this sequence.

b. How useful is this formula for predicting how much money Retta will have each day?

► *Solution*

Use the common difference and starting term to write the explicit formula.

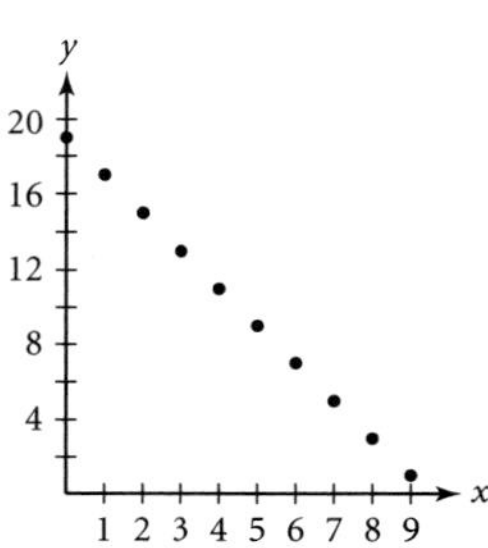

a. Each term is 2 less than the previous term, so the common difference of the arithmetic sequence and the slope of the line are both -2.

The term u_1 is 17, so the previous term, u_0, or the y-intercept, is 19.

[Ask] "What's the difference between discrete and continuous functions?" [There are gaps between the input values of discrete formulas (n) but not between the input values of continuous equations (x), such as linear equations—though there might be gaps in the output values (y).] As students respond, don't stop the thinking by moving on when you hear an answer you like; rather, have the class assess all the responses without prejudice from you. This discussion foreshadows the ideas of domain and range, discussed in the next lesson.

[Ask] "What's a situation in which a continuous linear model would be better than a discrete model?" [One example is distance traveled in terms of time.]

The explicit formula for the arithmetic sequence is $u_n = 19 - 2 \cdot n$, and the equation of the line containing these points is $y = 19 - 2x$.

b. We don't know whether Retta has any other expenses, when she receives her paycheck or allowance, or whether she buys lunch on the weekend. The formula could be valid for eight more days, until she has \$1 left (on u_9), as long as she gets no more money and spends only \$2 per day.

For both sequences and equations, it is important to consider the conditions for which the relationship is valid. For example, a phone company usually rounds up the length of a phone call to determine the charges, so the relationship between the length of the call and the cost of the call is valid only for a call length that is a positive integer. Also, the portion of the line left of the y-axis, where x is negative, is part of the mathematical model but has no relevance for the phone call scenario.

EXERCISES

You will need

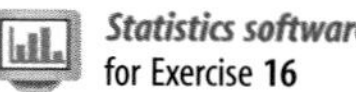

Statistics software for Exercise **16**

Practice Your Skills

1. Consider the sequence

$u_0 = 18$
$u_n = u_{n-1} - 3 \quad \text{where } n \geq 1$

a. Graph the sequence.

b. What is the slope of the line that contains the points? How is that related to the common difference of the sequence? -3; The common difference is the same as the slope.

c. What is the y-intercept of the line that contains these points? How is it related to the sequence? 18; The y-intercept is the u_0-term of the sequence.

d. Write the equation of the line that contains these points. $y = 18 - 3x$

2. Refer to the graph at right.

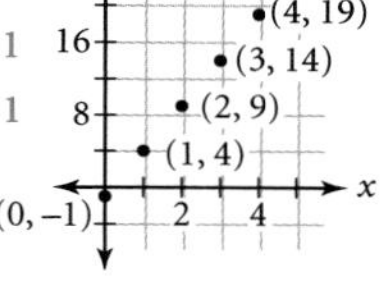

a. Write a recursive formula for the sequence. What is the common difference? What is the value of u_0? $u_0 = -1$ and $u_n = u_{n-1} + 5$ where $n \geq 1$; 5; -1

b. What is the slope of the line through the points? What is the y-intercept? 5; -1

c. Write the equation of the line that contains these points. $y = -1 + 5x$

3. Write the equation of the line that passes through the points of an arithmetic sequence with $u_0 = 7$ and a common difference of 3. $y = 7 + 3x$

4. Write a recursive formula for a sequence whose points lie on the line $y = 6 - 0.5x$.
$u_0 = 6$ and $u_n = u_{n-1} - 0.5$ where $n \geq 1$

5. Find the slope of each line.

a. $y = 2 + 1.7x$ 1.7 **b.** $y = x + 5$ 1 **c.** $y = 12 - 4.5x$ -4.5 **d.** $y = 12$ 0

BUILDING UNDERSTANDING

The exercises let students work with the interplay among recursive formulas, explicit formulas, and linear equations.

As part of the homework assignment you might include instructions for building rockets for the investigation in Lesson 3.2.

ASSIGNING HOMEWORK

Essential	1–4, 6
Performance assessment	7–12
Portfolio	12
Journal	7, 15
Group	9
Review	5, 13–16

MATERIALS

- Calculator Note 1B, *optional*

Helping with the Exercises

Exercises 1–3 It's acceptable for students who are familiar with the intercept form, $y = mx + b$, to use it here. Be sure they use the variable b for the y-intercept instead of for the slope.

Encourage students to use u_n and u_0 for discrete formulas and x and y for linear equations.

1a.

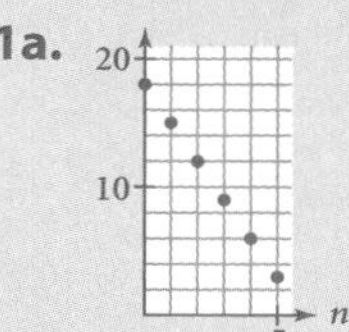

Exercise 4 If students are having difficulty, suggest that they list the first few terms in the sequence.

Exercise 5d Many students will benefit from graphing the line.

Assessing Progress

As students work and present, you can assess their understanding of how recursive formulas can define arithmetic sequences, of multiplication as repeated addition, and of linear equations and their graphs.

Closing the Lesson

The main point of this lesson is that an **explicit formula** $u_n = a + bn$ can model the same situations as a recursive formula $u_0 = a$, $u_n = u_{n-1} + b$. Both models are **discrete,** applying only to whole numbers. The **linear equation** $y = a + bx$ is **continuous,** describing a line that might pass through a given set of discrete points.

Reason and Apply

6. An arithmetic sequence has a starting term, u_0, of 6.3 and a common difference of 2.5.

a. Write an explicit formula for the sequence. $u_n = 6.3 + 2.5n$

b. Use the formula to figure out which term is 78.8. 29th term

7. Suppose you drive through Macon, Georgia, (which is 82 mi from Atlanta) on your way to Savannah, Georgia, at a steady 54 mi/h.

a. What is your distance from Atlanta two hours after you leave Macon? 190 mi

b. Write an equation that represents your distance, y, from Atlanta x hours after leaving Macon. $y = 82 + 54x$

c. Graph the equation.

d. Does this equation model an arithmetic sequence? Why or why not?

Savannah, Georgia

8. APPLICATION Melissa and Roy both sell cars at the same dealership and have to meet the same profit goal each week. Last week, Roy sold only three cars, and he was below his goal by \$2050. Melissa sold seven cars, and she beat her goal by \$1550. Assume that the profit is approximately the same for each car they sell.

a. Use a graph to find a few terms, u_n, of the sequence of sales amounts above or below the goal.

b. What is the real-world meaning of the common difference?

c. Write an explicit formula for this sequence of sales values in relation to the goal. Define variables and write a linear equation.

d. What is the real-world meaning of the horizontal and vertical intercepts?

e. What is the profit goal? How many more cars must Roy sell to be within \$500 of his goal? \$4750; 2 cars

9. The points on this graph represent the first five terms of an arithmetic sequence. The height of each point is its distance from the x-axis, or the value of the y-coordinate of the point.

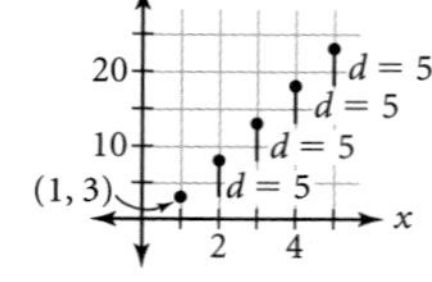

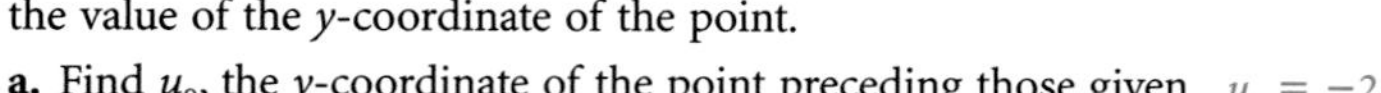

a. Find u_0, the y-coordinate of the point preceding those given. $u_0 = -2$

b. How many common differences (d's) do you need to get from the height of $(0, u_0)$ to the height of $(5, u_5)$? 5

c. How many d's do you need to get from the height of $(0, u_0)$ to the height of $(50, u_{50})$? 50

d. Explain why you can find the height from the x-axis to $(50, u_{50})$ using the equation $u_{50} = u_0 + 50d$. because you need to add 50 d's to the original height of u_0

e. In general, for an arithmetic sequence, the explicit formula is $u_n =$ __?__. $u_n = u_0 + nd$

7c.

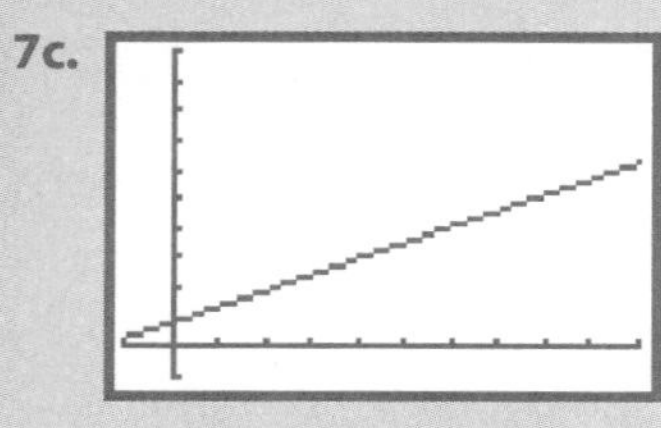

$[-1, 10, 1, -100, 1000, 100]$

Exercise 7d The equation can be evaluated at any value of x, so it can model travel. It can model the arithmetic sequence only if we state that x can take on only whole-number values; the explicit formula would be a less confusing representation. Students might say that it is impossible to travel at a steady rate if the car is starting from a speed of 0; point out that the car is traveling *through* Macon, apparently without slowing from the constant speed of 54 mi/h.

7d. The relationship is linear. So, if only distances on the hour are considered, it is an arithmetic sequence. Otherwise, the relationship is continuous rather than discrete.

Exercise 8 [Alert] Students might miss the idea that the profit goal is a constant number that is the same for the two salespeople. The given deviations, -2050 and 1550, are the 3rd and 7th terms in an arithmetic sequence. In 8d, the horizontal and vertical intercepts are the x- and y-intercepts.

8a.

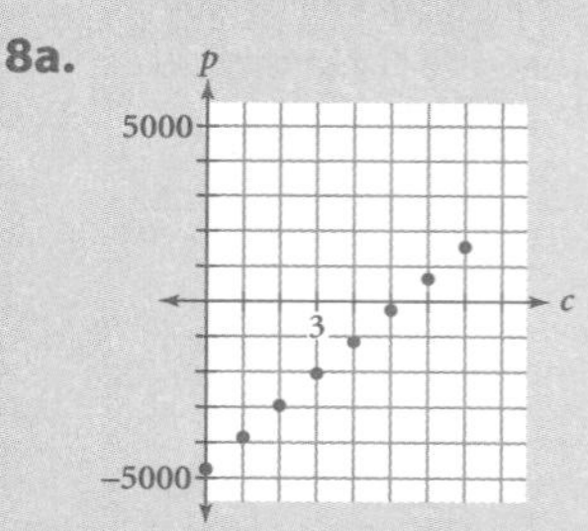

possible terms in the sequence: $-4750, -3850, -2950, -2050, -1150, -250, 650, 1550$

8b. The common difference, \$900, is the profit per car sold.

8c. $u_n = -4750 + 900n$; Let c represent the number of cars sold, and let p represent the value of the sales in relation to the goal: $p = -4750 + 900c$.

8d. The vertical intercept, -4750, represents how far below the goal they are if no cars are sold. The horizontal intercept, 5.28, represents the number of cars that must be sold to break even (6 cars must be sold to surpass the goal).

10. A gardener planted a new variety of ornamental grass and kept a record of its height over the first two weeks of growth.

Time (days)	0	3	7	10	14
Height (cm)	4.2	6.3	9.1	11.2	14

a. How much does the grass grow each day? 0.7 cm

b. Write an explicit formula that gives the height of the grass after n days. $u_n = 4.2 + 0.7n$

c. How long will it take for the grass to be 28 cm tall? 34 days

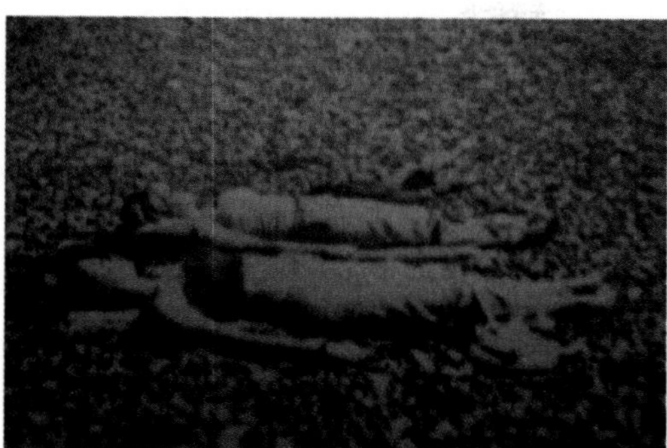

Heather Ackroyd and Dan Harvey print photographs on grass, such as this one, *Sunbathers 2000.* They position a photographic negative over growing grass, and the chlorophyll reacts to give a temporary image in shades of green and yellow. They use genetically modified grass to make their images last longer.

11. An arithmetic sequence of six numbers begins with 7 and ends with 27. Follow 11a–c to find the four missing terms.

a. Name two points on the graph of this sequence: $(\underline{?}, 7)$ and $(\underline{?}, 27)$.

b. Plot the two points you named in 11a and find the slope of the line connecting the points. Regardless of the points chosen in 11a, the slope should be 4.

c. Use the slope to find the missing terms. 7, 11, 15, 19, 23, 27

d. Plot all the points and write the equation of the line that contains them.

12. **APPLICATION** If an object is dropped, it will fall a distance of about 16 feet during the first second. In each second that follows, the object falls about 32 feet farther than in the previous second.

a. Write a recursive formula for the distance fallen each second under free fall. $u_1 = 16$ and $u_n = u_{n-1} + 32$ where $n \geq 2$

b. Find an explicit formula for the distance fallen each second under free fall. $u_n = 32n - 16$

c. How far will the object fall during the 10th second? 304 ft

d. During which second will the object fall 400 feet? 13th second

Science CONNECTION

Leonardo da Vinci (1452–1519) was able to discover the formula for the velocity (directional speed) of a freely falling object by looking at a sequence. He let drops of water fall at equally spaced time intervals between two boards covered with blotting paper. When a spring mechanism was disengaged, the boards clapped together. By measuring the distances between successive blots and noting that these distances increased arithmetically, da Vinci discovered the formula $v = gt$, where v is the velocity of the object, t is the time since it was released, and g is a constant that represents any object's downward acceleration due to the force of gravity.

Exercise 10 [Alert] Students might not realize that the times in the chart are spaced unequally.

11a. Possible answer: (0, 7) and (5, 27). The x-values should have a difference of 5.

11d. $y = 7 + 4x$. The y-intercept will differ if the original points have different x-values.

Exercise 12 You may want to mention that free-fall velocity actually has an upper limit, because of air resistance. Until the object reaches that limit, the speed is constantly changing.

EXTENSIONS

A. Extend Improving Your Reasoning Skills by challenging students to write more than one recursive rule that creates the same slope as rules a–f. Or challenge them to write a generic rule that uses a variable parameter. [For example, rule d could be generalized as any rule in the form $(x_n, y_n) = (x_{n-1} + a, y_{n-1} - 5a)$ where $a \neq 0$.]

B. Pose this problem: "Some cell phone companies now charge their customers in increments of 6 seconds rather than a full minute. Write recursive, explicit, and linear models for a phone call that costs \$0.40 for the first minute and \$0.02 for each additional 6 seconds. Be sure to give real-world meanings for the variables." This extension could be used as an additional example with the introductory phone call problem.

C. To further extend Improving Your Reasoning Skills, students might explore what happens when x_n or y_n is defined with a geometric or shifted geometric rule. Is it possible to generate collinear points when one or both coordinates are geometric or shifted geometric? If so, how can you recognize the slope from the recursive rules? [If $x_n = rx_{n-1} + h$ and $y_n = sy_{n-1} + k$, then the slope $\frac{y_n - y_{n-1}}{x_n - x_{n-1}} = \frac{(s-1)y_{n-1} + k}{(r-1)x_{n-1} + h}$ can be constant in two ways: if $s = r = 1$, in which case both x_n and y_n are arithmetic sequences and the slope is $\frac{k}{h}$; or if $h = k = 0$ and $r = s \neq 1$, in which case both x_n and y_n are geometric sequences with the same common ratio and the slope is $\frac{y_0}{x_0}$. In this latter case, if $x_0 = 0$, then the line is vertical unless y_0 is also 0, in which case the sequence never leaves the origin.]

Exercise 13 **[Alert]** Students might think that they should add \$500 every six months for the option with the starting salary of \$17,900. Help them realize that only half of the \$500, or \$250, should be added every six months.

13. Although the total earnings are different at the end of the odd-numbered six-month periods, the total yearly income is always the same.

14b. No; the long-run value is 750 mL so eventually the level at the end of the day will approach 750 mL. Once the end-of-the-day level passes 700 mL, when 300 mL is added it will overflow.

15b. The median and mean prices indicate the mid-price and average price, respectively. The standard deviation indicates whether there is price variation (and, therefore, it is worth shopping around for a good deal) or all prices are pretty much the same. The median price is the better price to use as a frame of reference. The mean may be low or high if one store is having a sale or is unusually expensive (is an outlier).

Exercise 16 Students can do this exercise on a graphing calculator if they do not have access to dynamic statistics software.

See page 879 for answers to Exercise 16.

Review

1.1 **13.** APPLICATION Suppose a company offers a new employee a starting salary of \$18,150 with annual raises of \$1,000, or a starting salary of \$17,900 with a raise of \$500 every six months. At what point is one choice better than the other? Explain.

1.3 **14.** Suppose that you add 300 mL of water to an evaporating dish at the start of each day, and each day 40% of the water in the dish evaporates.

a. Write and solve an equation that computes the long-run water level in the dish. $x = (1 - 0.4)x + 300$; $x = 750$

b. Will a 1 L dish do the job? Explain why or why not.

2.2 **15.** APPLICATION Five stores in Tulsa, Oklahoma, sell the same model of a graphing calculator for \$89.95, \$93.49, \$109.39, \$93.49, and \$97.69.

a. What are the median price, the mean price, and the standard deviation? \$93.49; \$96.80; \$7.55

b. If these stores are representative of all stores in the Tulsa area, of what importance is it to a consumer to know the median, mean, and standard deviation? Which is probably more helpful, the median or the mean?

2.3 **16.** *Technology* Use statistics software to make a histogram of this data set: 44, 45, 51, 40, 28, 46, 34, 19.

a. Based on the histogram, predict what a box plot of the data will look like.

b. Use the software to create a box plot of the data. Were your predictions accurate?

IMPROVING YOUR REASONING SKILLS

Sequential Slopes

Here's a sequence that generates coordinate points. What is the slope between any two points of this sequence?

$$(x_0, y_0) = (0, 0)$$
$$(x_n, y_n) = (x_{n-1} + 2, y_{n-1} + 3) \quad \text{where } n \geq 1$$

Now match each of these recursive rules to the slope between points.

a. $(x_n, y_n) = (x_{n-1} + 2, y_{n-1} + 2)$

b. $(x_n, y_n) = (x_{n-1} + 1, y_{n-1} + 3)$

c. $(x_n, y_n) = (x_{n-1} + 3, y_{n-1} - 4)$

d. $(x_n, y_n) = (x_{n-1} - 2, y_{n-1} + 10)$

e. $(x_n, y_n) = (x_{n-1} + 1, y_{n-1})$

f. $(x_n, y_n) = (x_{n-1} + 9, y_{n-1} + 3)$

A. 0 **B.** 1 **C.** 3 **D.** −5 **E.** $\frac{1}{3}$ **F.** $\frac{-4}{3}$

In general, how do these recursive rules determine the slope between points?

IMPROVING REASONING SKILLS

Encourage students to plot the first sequence to see that the slope is $\frac{3}{2}$. Students can plot other sequences until they see the pattern that $(x_n, y_n) = (x_{n-1} + h, y_{n-1} + k)$ generates points on a line with slope $\frac{k}{h}$.

Matches: a to B, b to C, c to F, d to D, e to A, and f to E. **[Ask]** "Why can the slope be determined this way?" [It's the amount of rise per unit of run; by formula, $\frac{y_n - y_{n-1}}{x_n - x_{n-1}} = \frac{y_{n-1} + k - y_{n-1}}{x_{n-1} + h - x_{n-1}} = \frac{k}{h}$.]

[Ask] "Does changing the starting term affect the slope?" [No; only the recursive rule affects the slope between points.] "What effect does the starting term have?" [Changing the starting term would change the y-intercept of a line through the points. However, unless the x-value of the starting term is 0, the starting term does not directly translate into the y-intercept.]

Students might review Calculator Note 1B for ways to generate these sequences.

LESSON

3.2

Revisiting Slope

There is more to life than increasing its speed.

MOHANDAS GANDHI

Suppose you are taking a long trip in your car. At 5 P.M., you notice that the odometer reads 45,623 miles. At 9 P.M., you notice that it reads 45,831. You find your average speed during that time period by dividing the difference in distance by the difference in time.

$$\text{Average speed} = \frac{45831 \text{ miles} - 45623 \text{ miles}}{9 \text{ hours} - 5 \text{ hours}} = \frac{208 \text{ miles}}{4 \text{ hours}} = 52 \text{ miles per hour}$$

You can also write the rate 52 miles per hour as the ratio $\frac{52 \text{ miles}}{1 \text{ hour}}$. If you graph the information as points of the form (*time, distance*), the slope of the line connecting the two points is $\frac{52}{1}$, which also tells you the average speed.

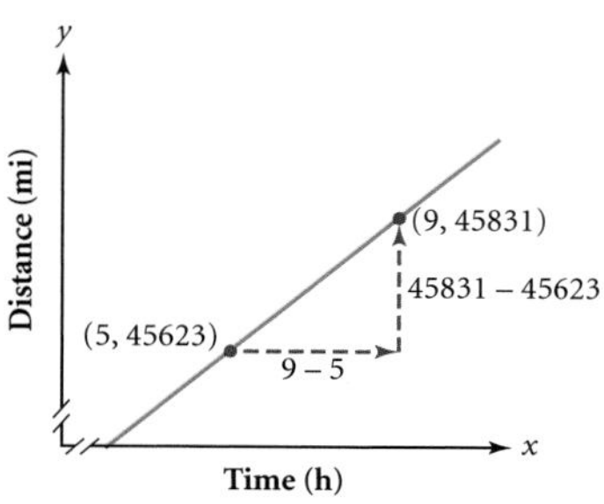

Slope

The formula for the slope between two points, (x_1, y_1) and (x_2, y_2), is

$$slope = \frac{y_2 - y_1}{x_2 - x_1}$$

The slope will be the same for any two points selected on the line. In other words, a line has only one slope. Two points on a line can have the same y-value; in that case, the slope of the line is 0. If they had the same x-value, the denominator would be 0 and the slope would be undefined. So the definition of slope specifies that the points cannot have the same x-value. What kinds of lines have a slope of 0? What kinds of lines have undefined slope?

Slope is another word for the steepness or rate of change of a line. If a linear equation is in **intercept form,** then the slope of the line is the coefficient of x.

Intercept Form of the Equation of a Line

You can write the equation of a line as

$$y = a + bx$$

where a is the y-intercept and b is the slope of the line.

NCTM STANDARDS

CONTENT		PROCESS	
	Number	✓	Problem Solving
✓	Algebra	✓	Reasoning
✓	Geometry	✓	Communication
✓	Measurement	✓	Connections
✓	Data/Probability	✓	Representation

LESSON OBJECTIVES

- Use recursion in application contexts
- Deepen understanding of slope
- Define *domain* and *range*

LESSON

3.2

PLANNING

LESSON OUTLINE

First day:

5 min	Introduction
40 min	Investigation

Second day:

15 min	Sharing
10 min	Example
20 min	Exercises

MATERIALS

- tape
- butcher paper
- balloons
- straws
- string
- motion sensors
- graph paper
- Calculator Note 3C

TEACHING

This lesson reviews linear function concepts from *Discovering Algebra* or other beginning algebra courses. It can take only one day if students have already built the rockets.

One Step

Have students make balloon rockets according to the Procedure Note. Then pose this problem: "What's a linear equation that describes the distance traveled by your rocket after it's launched?" Direct students to use motion sensors. As students work, be sure they use time as the independent variable, and bring up the ideas of slope, y-intercept, and intercept form as needed. During Sharing, remind students of the concepts domain and range.

INTRODUCTION

You might remind students of the formula $d = rt$ and rewrite it as $r = \frac{d}{t}$. Then you can relate the ratio of changes to the rate and the slope.

[Ask] "Is 52 mi/h how fast you were driving most of the time between 5 P.M. and 9 P.M.? [Not necessarily; you might have slowed or stopped and then driven faster than 52 mi/h to compensate.]

[Alert] Students who are more comfortable with the slope-intercept form, $y = mx + b$, than the intercept form, $y = a + bx$, might be confused, especially because b represents the y-intercept in the former and the slope in the latter.

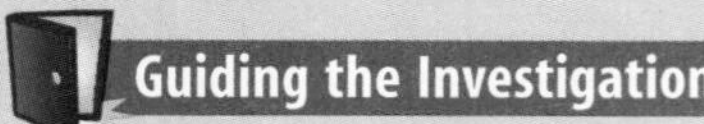

Guiding the Investigation

[Language] *Independent variable, domain,* and *range* are defined in the paragraphs following the investigation.

To set up for this experiment, attach several lengths of string across your classroom just above head height. Thread one or two drinking straws on each string. Be sure the strings are level and taut.

This investigation can be completed in pairs or in groups. If students haven't already built the rockets, give a time limit for the construction. Before distributing materials for the rockets, you might want to require students to show you their design so they don't waste materials. Butcher paper works well as a building material.

Many students will want to turn this investigation into a competition for the fastest rocket. If you would like to have a competition, mention it when you give instructions for building the rockets.

See pages 879–880 for answers to Steps 1–4.

Slope is often represented by the letter m. However, we will use the letter b in linear equations, as in the intercept form $y = a + bx$.

When you are using real-world data, choosing different pairs of points results in choosing lines with slightly different slopes. However, if the data are nearly linear, these slopes should not differ greatly.

Investigation
Balloon Blastoff

You will need
- paper
- tape
- a balloon
- a straw
- string
- a motion sensor

In this investigation you will launch a rocket and use your motion sensor's data to calculate the rocket's speed. Then you will write an equation for the rocket's distance as a function of time. Choose one person to be the monitor and one person to be the launch controller.

Procedure Note

1. Make a rocket of paper and tape. Design your rocket so that it can hold an inflated balloon and be taped to a drinking straw threaded on a string. Color or decorate your rocket if you like.
2. Tape your rocket to the straw on the string.
3. Inflate a balloon but do not tie off the end. The launch controller should insert it into your rocket and hold it closed.

Step 1 The monitor holds the sensor about 2.5 meters in front of the rocket and counts down to blastoff. When the monitor presses the trigger on the sensor and says, "blastoff," the launch controller releases the balloon. [▶ See **Calculator Note 3C.** ◀]

Step 2 Retrieve the data from the sensor to each calculator in the group.

Step 3 Graph the data with time as the independent variable, x. What are the domain and range of your data? Explain.

Step 4 Select four points that you think will give the most accurate slope for the data. Indicate the points you selected on a graph of these data, and explain why you chose them. Use these points in pairs to calculate slopes. This should give six values for the slope.

Step 5 Are all six slope values that you calculated in Step 4 the same? Why or why not? Find the mean, median, and mode of your slopes. With your group, decide what value best represents the slope of your data. Explain why you chose this value.

Step 6 What is the real-world meaning of the slope, and how is this related to the speed of your rocket?

Step 7 Write an equation for the rocket's distance x seconds after it is released, and explain what each part of the equation means.

Step 8 Graph your line and label it "Our rocket." Imagine each of the following scenarios. On the same graph, sketch lines to represent each of the rockets.

Step 5 No, the slopes are not the same; the sample data is approximately linear, but not exactly. $\bar{x} = -3.2687$; *median* $= -3.2670$; no mode. The mean or median would be reasonable choices for the representative slope.

Step 6 The slope is the distance traveled over time. The distance of the balloon rocket from the sensor was decreasing by approximately 3.2687 m/s.

Step 7 $y = 2.5 - 3.2687x$; y represents the distance between the rocket and the motion sensor in meters, and x represents time after launch in seconds; 3.2687 is the speed of the rocket, and 2.5 is the distance at time 0.

Step 1 Students might need to launch their rocket a couple of times before they get good data. See Calculator Note 3C for help in setting up the motion sensor. You might have some groups hold the motion sensor behind their rocket instead of in front and discuss the different outcomes during Sharing; a good distance behind the rocket's starting position is about half a meter. The answers in Steps 3–7 are all calculated from the Step 1 sample data.

Step 8 Encourage students to use a whole sheet of graph paper to display their graph, because they will be adding other lines to it and labeling the lines.

Step 8

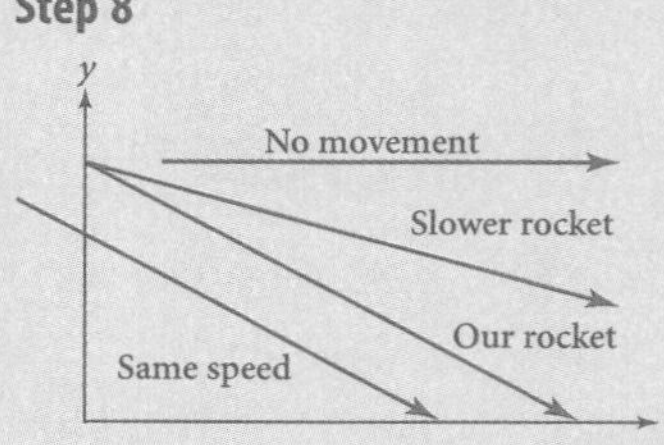

a. A rocket that was released at the same time as yours, but traveled at 75% the speed of your rocket. Label this line "Slower rocket."

b. A rocket that was released two seconds before yours, and traveled at the same speed as yours. Label this line "Same speed."

c. A rocket that was released two seconds after yours, but got caught on the string and did not go anywhere. Label this line "No movement."

Step 9 slower rocket: $y = 2.5 - 2.4515x$; same speed: $y = 9.0 - 3.2687x$; no movement: $y = 2.5$

Step 9 Write the equation for each of the imaginary rockets in Step 8. Label each of the lines on your graph.

In many cases, when you try to model the steepness and trend of the points, you may have some difficulty deciding which points to use. In general, select two points that are far apart to minimize the error. They do not need to be data points. Disregard data points that you think might represent measurement errors.

When you analyze a relationship between two variables, you must decide which variable you will express in terms of the other. When one variable depends on the other variable, it is called the **dependent variable.** The other variable is called the **independent variable.** Time is usually considered an independent variable.

Next, you need to think about the domain and range. The set of possible x-values is called the **domain** and the set of y-values is called the **range.**

EXAMPLE

Daron's car gets 20 miles per gallon of gasoline. He starts out with a full tank, 16.4 gallons. As Daron drives, he watches the gas gauge to see how much gas he has left.

a. Identify the independent and dependent variables.

b. Write a linear equation in intercept form to model this situation.

c. How much gas will be left in Daron's tank after he drives 175 miles?

d. How far can he travel before he has less than 2 gallons remaining?

▶ Solution

The two variables are the distance Daron has driven and the amount of gasoline remaining in his car's tank.

a. The amount of gasoline remaining in the car's tank depends on the number of miles Daron has driven. This means the amount of gasoline is the dependent variable and distance is the independent variable. So use x for the distance (in miles) and y for the amount of gasoline (in gallons).

b. Daron starts out with 16.4 gallons. He drives 20 miles per gallon, which means the amount of gasoline decreases $\frac{1}{20}$, or 0.05, gallon per mile. The equation is $y = 16.4 - 0.05x$.

[Language] *Measurement error* describes a data point that results from a mistake in measuring. Often it doesn't fit the general trend of the data. *Trend* refers to the general pattern of the data. For linear data, we usually look for an evenly increasing or decreasing trend.

▶ EXAMPLE

This example gives further practice with linear equations. **[Ask]** "What are the domain and range for this example?" [The domain is from 0 to 328 mi; the range is from 0 to 16.4 gal.]

SHARING IDEAS

As students present their ideas about slope and linear equations in the investigation, **[Ask]** "How much confidence do you have in your results? Where might errors have occurred?" [Errors might have occurred in making measurements or in estimating the slope.]

[Ask] "Why do the motion sensor and the book consider time to be the independent variable? Doesn't the length of time traveled depend on how far the rocket has gone?" [Time is usually taken as the independent variable because the passage of time is unaffected by other events. The *total* time needed for a task depends on the task, and this time can be a variable over several tasks; for an example see Exercise 10 of this lesson.]

Ask students what they observe in their graphs from Steps 8 and 9 of the investigation. Focus in particular on how the slopes of the lines compare. As students describe slope, watch to be sure they subtract in the same order in both numerator and denominator.

Sharing Ideas (continued)

[Ask] "Does the word *average* in the term *average speed* have the same meaning as the average of a data set?" Encourage discussion, reminding students as needed that the question "Why?" is embedded in many questions, whether or not it's actually asked. Take advantage of the discussion to review measures of central tendency of a data set. The center of a data set could refer to the mean, median, or mode. The average speed can be thought of as the mean of speeds at infinitely many points in time. In some sense, the sum of these infinitely many distances is the total distance, and the sum of the infinitely many instants of time is the total time.

To foreshadow Lesson 3.3, **[Ask]** "How can you tell how well a line fits a data set?" The class need not reach a conclusion about the answer to this question yet.

Assessing Progress

You can assess students' calculator abilities and their understanding of dependent and independent variables, slope, measures of central tendency, linear equations, and distance-rate-time relationships.

Closing the Lesson

Motion at a constant rate can be represented by a straight-line graph whose **slope,** b, gives the rate and whose **y-intercept,** a, gives the location when the clock starts. The linear equation, with **intercept form,** $y = a + bx$, has time as the **independent variable** and distance as the **dependent variable.** Although the equation is defined for all real numbers x, it's a good model for a situation only when the **domain** corresponds to realistic values of x. The **range** is all values of y produced by values of x in that domain.

BUILDING UNDERSTANDING

In the exercises students work with slope and linear equations.

ASSIGNING HOMEWORK

Essential	1–4
Performance assessment	5–12
Portfolio	12
Journal	5, 8
Review	13–17

MATERIALS

- Calculator Note 1H

c. You know the x-value is 175 miles. You can substitute 175 for x and solve for y.

$$y = 16.4 - 0.05 \cdot 175$$
$$= 7.65$$

He will have 7.65 gallons remaining.

d. You know the y-value is 2.0 gallons. You can substitute 2.0 for y and solve for x.

$$2.0 = 16.4 - 0.05x$$
$$-14.4 = -0.05x$$
$$288 = x$$

When he has traveled more than 288 miles, he will have less than 2 gallons in his tank.

EXERCISES

Practice Your Skills

1. Find the slope of the line containing each pair of points.

a. $(3, -4)$ and $(7, 2)$ $\frac{3}{2} = 1.5$ **b.** $(5, 3)$ and $(2, 5)$ $-\frac{2}{3} \approx -0.67$ **c.** $(-0.02, 3.2)$ and $(0.08, -2.3)$ -55

2. Find the slope of each line.

a. $y = 3x - 2$ 3 **b.** $y = 4.2 - 2.8x$ -2.8 **c.** $y = 5(3x - 3) + 2$ 15

d. $y - 2.4x = 5$ 2.4 **e.** $4.7x + 3.2y = 12.9$ $-\frac{47}{32} = -1.46875$ **f.** $\frac{2}{3}y = \frac{2}{3}x + \frac{1}{2}$ 1

3. Solve each equation.

a. Solve $y = 4.7 + 3.2x$ for y if $x = 3$. $y = 14.3$

b. Solve $y = -2.5 + 1.6x$ for x if $y = 8$. $x = 6.5625$

c. Solve $y = a - 0.2x$ for a if $x = 1000$ and $y = -224$. $a = -24$

d. Solve $y = 250 + bx$ for b if $x = 960$ and $y = 10$. $b = -0.25$

4. Find the equations of both lines in each graph.

a.

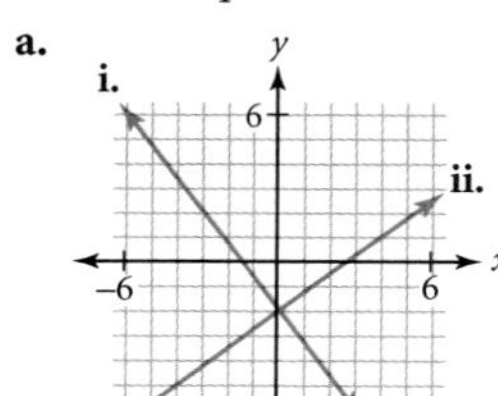

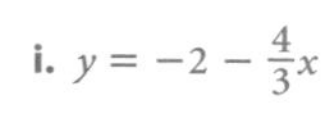

i. $y = -2 - \frac{4}{3}x$

ii. $y = -2 + \frac{3}{4}x$

b.

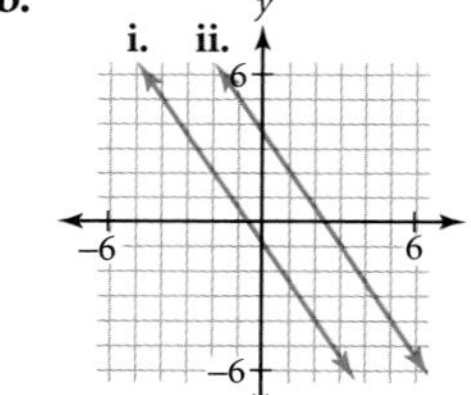

i. $y = -1 - 1.5x$

ii. $y = 3.5 - 1.5x$

5. Consider the equations and graphs of Exercise 4.

a. What do the equations in 4a have in common? What do you notice about their graphs?

b. What do the equations in 4b have in common? What do you notice about their graphs?

Helping with the Exercises

Exercises 1–3 You might suggest that students sketch a graph next to their solutions for each of these exercises.

Exercise 4 *Discovering Algebra* Calculator Note 4E presents a calculator program, LINES, that gives students practice writing the equation of a line based on a graph. You can access this calculator note and the program at www.keymath.com/DA.

5a. The equations have the same constant, -2. The lines share the same y-intercept. The lines are perpendicular, and their slopes are reciprocals with opposite signs.

5b. The equations have the same x-coefficient, -1.5. The lines have the same slope. The lines are parallel.

Reason and Apply

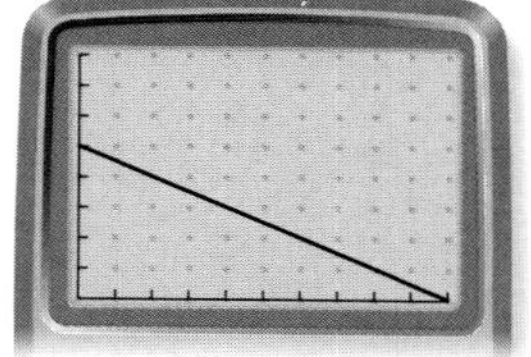
[0, 10, 1, 0, 8, 1]

6. Use this graph to determine the speed of a balloon rocket. The independent variable is time in seconds, and the dependent variable is distance from the sensor in meters. 0.5 m/s toward the motion sensor

7. APPLICATION Layton measures the voltage across different numbers of batteries placed end to end. He records his data in a table.

Number of batteries	1	2	3	4	5	6	7	8
Voltage (volts)	1.43	2.94	4.32	5.88	7.39	8.82	10.27	11.70

a. Let x represent the number of batteries, and let y represent the voltage. Find the slope of a line approximating these data. Be sure to include units with your answer.

b. Which points did you use and why? What is the real-world meaning of this slope?

c. Is this an example of direct variation? Why or why not?

8. This graph shows the relationship between the height of some high-rise buildings and the number of stories in those buildings. A line is drawn to fit the data.

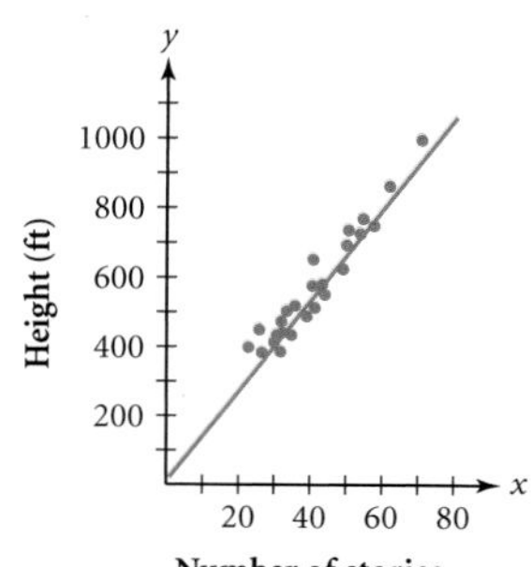

a. Estimate the slope. What is the meaning of the slope?

b. Estimate the y-intercept. What is the meaning of the y-intercept?

c. Explain why some of the points lie above the line and some lie below.

d. According to the graph, what are the domain and range of this relationship? domain: $0 \leq x \leq 80$; range: $20 \leq y \leq 1100$

Engineering CONNECTION

Many earthquake-prone areas in the United States have strict building codes to ensure that high-rise buildings can withstand earthquakes. Some taller buildings have cross-bracing to make them more rigid and lessen the amount of shaking. The extent of damage that an earthquake can cause depends on several factors: strength of the earthquake, type of underlying soil, and building construction. The shaking increases with height, and the period of shaking (in seconds) is approximately equal to 0.1 times the number of stories in the high-rise. For more information on engineering and earthquakes, see the web links at www.keymath.com/DAA .

Steel braces will reduce earthquake damage to this concrete building.

9. This formula models Anita's salary for the last seven years: $u_n = 847n + 17109$. The variable n represents the number of years of experience she has, and u_n represents her salary in dollars.

a. What did she earn in the fifth year? What did she earn in her first year? (Think carefully about what n represents.) \$20,497; \$17,109

b. What is the rate of change of her salary? \$847 per year

c. What is the first year Anita's salary will be more than \$30,000? in her 17th year

Exercise 6 If you skipped the balloon-rocket investigation, you might need to describe it briefly before students work on this exercise.

Exercise 7 [Language] *Voltage* is electric potential, measured in volts. In general, when students describe a real-world meaning, they should use the relevant units. In 7b, the slope's units are volts per battery.

You may need to remind students that a direct variation relationship is a linear relationship that includes the value (0, 0).

7a. Possible answer: Using the 2nd and 7th data points gives a slope of approximately 1.47 volts/battery.

7b. Answers will vary. Students should use points that are not too close together. The slope tells you that the voltage increases by about 1.47 volts for every additional battery.

7c. Yes. There is no voltage produced from zero batteries, so the y-intercept should be 0.

8a. Approximately 13. For each additional story, the building increases by about 13 ft.

8b. Approximately 20. This is the additional height in feet that does not depend on the number of stories; the first floor might be taller than the others or its floor could be higher than ground level.

8c. Some of the buildings have more height (or less height) per story.

MAKING THE CONNECTION

You might ask students what shapes they see in the bracing in the photo and why those shapes are used.

Exercise 9 The answers given assume that Anita started her job with no experience seven years ago. Answers based on different assumptions may also be valid.

10. APPLICATION This table shows how long it took to lay tile for hallways of different lengths.

Length of hallway (ft)	3.5	9.5	17.5	4.0	12.0	8.0
Time (min)	85	175	295	92	212	153

a. What is the independent variable? Why? Make a graph of the data.

b. Find the slope of the line through these data. What is the real-world meaning of this slope? Approximately 15. It takes 15 min to lay tile for each additional ft of hall beyond the first ft.

c. Which points did you use and why?

d. Find the y-intercept of the line. What is the real-world meaning of this value?

11. APPLICATION The manager of a concert hall keeps data on the total number of tickets sold and total sales income, or revenue, for each event. Two different ticket prices are offered.

Total tickets	448	601	297	533	523	493	320
Total revenue ($)	3357.00	4495.50	2011.50	3784.50	3334.50	3604.50	2353.50

a. Find the slope of a line approximating these data. What is the real-world meaning of this slope?

b. Which points did you use and why? Answers will vary. Students should use points that are not too close together.

12. APPLICATION How much does air weigh? The following table gives the weight of a cubic foot of dry air at the same pressure at various temperatures in degrees Fahrenheit.

Temp. (°F)	0	12	32	52	82	112	152	192	212
Weight (lb)	0.0864	0.0842	0.0807	0.0776	0.0733	0.0694	0.0646	0.0609	0.0591

a. Make a scatter plot of the data.

b. What is the approximate slope of the line through the data? Using the 3rd and 7th points, the slope is -0.000134.

c. Describe the real-world meaning of the slope.

Recreation CONNECTION

Hot air rises, cool air sinks. As air is heated up, it becomes less dense and lighter than the cooler air surrounding it. This simple law of nature is the principle behind hot-air ballooning. By heating the air in the balloon envelope, maintaining its temperature, or letting it cool, the balloon's pilot is able to climb higher, fly level, or descend. Joseph and Jacques Montgolfier developed the first hot-air balloon in 1783, inspired by the rising of a shirt that was drying above a fire.

Exercise 10 It's appropriate in this situation to have time as the dependent variable.

10a. The length of the hall is the independent variable. The time the job takes will depend on this length.

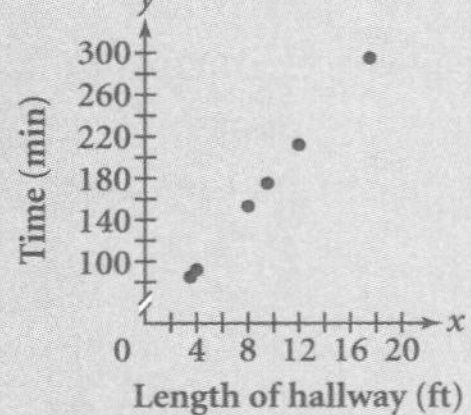

10c. Answers will vary. Students should use points that are not too close together.

10d. Approximately 32. This is the time in minutes it takes to get the tools out before doing the job and put them away after the job is finished or the time it takes to cut tile for the last row.

11a. Possible answer: Using the 2nd and 7th data points, the slope is 7.62. Each additional ticket sold brings in about $7.62 more in revenue. This value is somewhere between the two different ticket prices offered.

Exercise 12 [Language] A *scatter plot* is a graph in which coordinate points (x, y) are plotted. In this case $(temp, weight)$ is plotted. Calculator Note 1H can help students graph a scatter plot on their calculators.

[Ask] "Why does the problem specify dry air? Why does it specify the same pressure?" [At a given temperature, a cubic foot of moist air, or a cubic foot at increased pressure, would give a heavier weight. To study the relationship between temperature and weight, other variables need to be constant.]

12a.

y; 0.10; 0.08; 0.06; 0.04; 0.02; Weight (lb); 0; 50; 100; 150; 200; x; Temperature (°F)

12c. For each degree the temperature increases, the weight of a cubic foot of dry air decreases by 0.000134 lb.

Review

13. Rewrite each expression by eliminating parentheses and then combining like terms.

a. $2 + 3(x - 4)$ $-10 + 3x$ **b.** $(11 - 3x) - 2(4x + 5)$ $1 - 11x$ **c.** $5.1 - 2.7(1 - (2x + 9.7))$ $28.59 + 5.4x$

14. Solve each equation.

a. $12 = 6 + 2(x - 1)$ $x = 4$ **b.** $27 = 12 - 2(x + 2)$ $x = -9.5$

2.1 **15.** Charlotte and Emily measured the pulse rates of everyone in their class in beats per minute and collected this set of data.

{62, 68, 68, 70, 74, 66, 82, 74, 76, 72, 70, 68, 80, 60, 84, 72, 66, 78, 70, 68, 66, 82, 76, 66, 66, 80}

a. What is the mean pulse rate for the class?

b. What is the standard deviation? What does this tell you?

1.4 **16.** Each of these two graphs was generated by a recursive formula in the form $u_0 = a$ and $u_n = (1 + r)u_{n-1} + p$ where $n \geq 1$. Describe the parameters a, r, and p that produce each graph. (There are two answers to 16b.)

a. $a > 0, r = 0, p > 0$

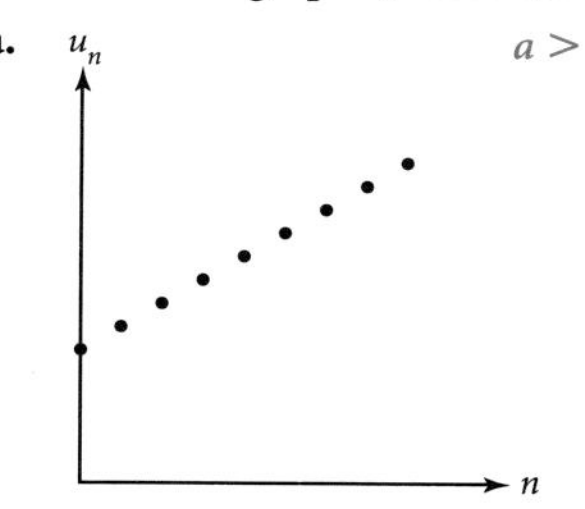

b. $a > 0, r = 0, p = 0$; $a > 0, r = -1, p = a$

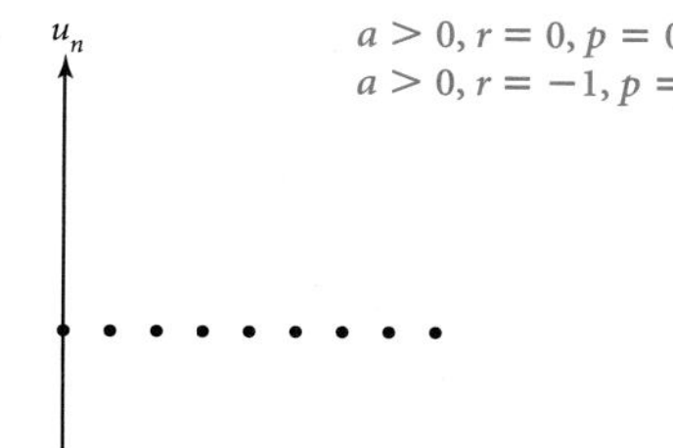

3.1 **17.** Each of these graphs was produced by a linear equation in the form $y = a + bx$. For each case, tell if a and b are greater than zero, equal to zero, or less than zero.

a. $a > 0, b < 0$

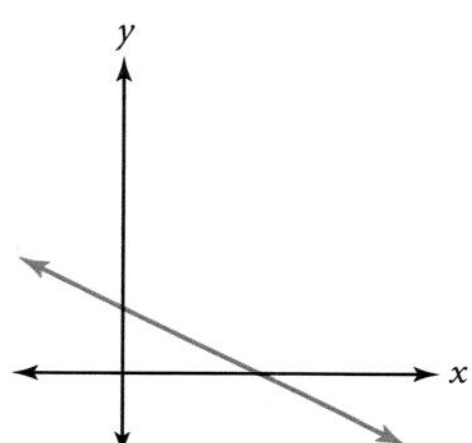

b. $a < 0, b > 0$

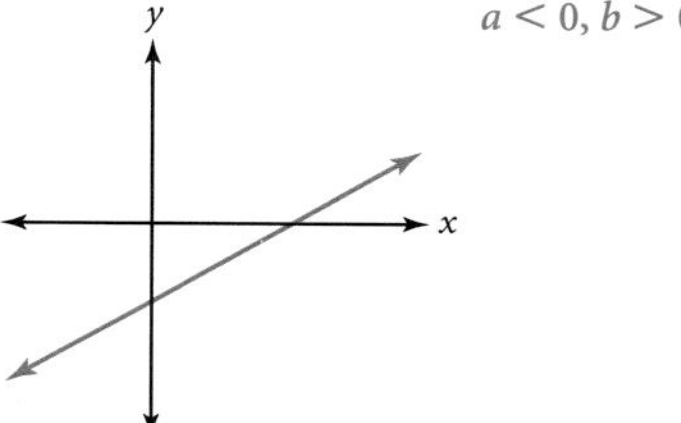

c. $a > 0, b = 0$

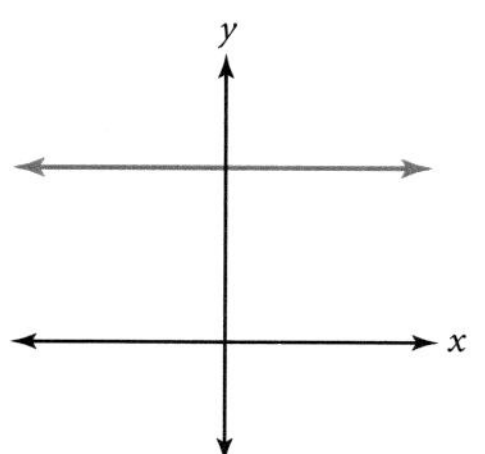

d. $a = 0, b < 0$

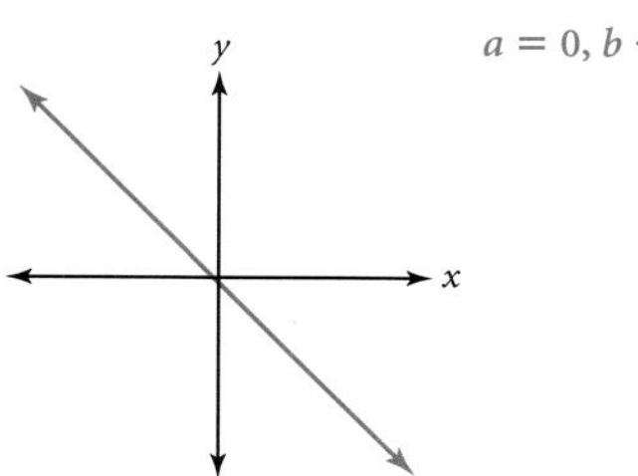

15a. 71.7 beats/min

15b. 6.47 beats/min. The majority of the data falls within 6.47 beats/min of the mean.

Exercise 16 [Language] In this context a *parameter* is a variable that distinguishes special cases of a mathematical expression.

EXTENSION

Have students use a voltage meter, or perhaps a CBL (calculator-based lab), to collect the data referred to in Exercise 7.

LESSON

3.3

PLANNING

LESSON OUTLINE

One day:

10 min Example

20 min Investigation

5 min Sharing

10 min Exercises

MATERIALS

- stopwatch (or watch with a second hand)
- uncooked spaghetti, *optional*
- Exercise 7 (T), *optional*
- Wave Sample Data (W), *optional*
- Fathom demonstration Finding a Line of Fit, *optional*

TEACHING

In this lesson students review the point-slope form of a linear equation while experimenting with lines that fit data sets.

A piece of uncooked spaghetti or the edge of a clear ruler is helpful for seeing lines of fit on paper. Or use the Fathom demonstration Finding a Line of Fit showing the movable line and adjusting it to pass through various data points as the line's equation is displayed.

One Step

Pose this problem: "How can we estimate how long it will take 100 people to do the wave?" Lead the class to design an experiment using different-size groups of students. Agree on a good data set as a class, and then let cooperative groups figure out ways to make the prediction. As students work, you can direct them to use the point-slope form of a linear equation.

LESSON 3.3

Fitting a Line to Data

Odd how the creative power at once brings the whole universe to order.

VIRGINIA WOOLF

All the points of an arithmetic sequence lie on a line. When you collect data and make a graph, sometimes the data will appear to have a linear relationship. However, the points will rarely lie on a single line. They will usually be scattered, and it is up to you to determine a reasonable location for the line that summarizes or gives the trend of the data set. A line that fits the data reasonably well is called a **line of fit.**

There is no single list of rules that will give the best line of fit in every instance, but you can use these guidelines to obtain a reasonably good fit.

Finding a Line of Fit

1. Determine the direction of the points. The longer side of the smallest rectangle that contains most of the points shows the general direction of the line.

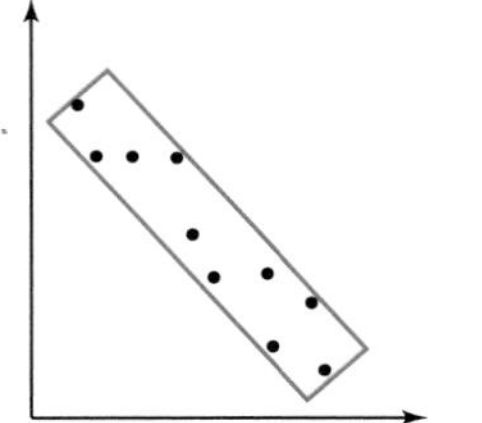

2. The line should divide the points equally. Draw the line so that there are about as many points above the line as below the line. The points above the line should not be concentrated at one end, and neither should the points below the line. The line has nearly the same slope as the longer sides of the rectangle.

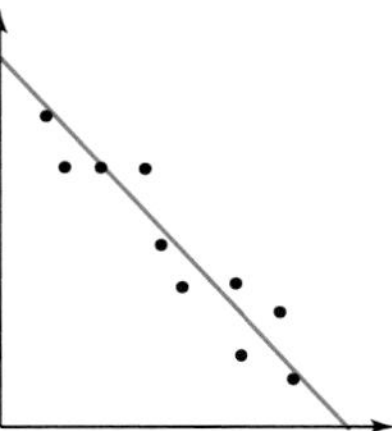

Some computer applications allow you to manually fit a line to data points. You can also graph the data by hand and draw the line of fit.

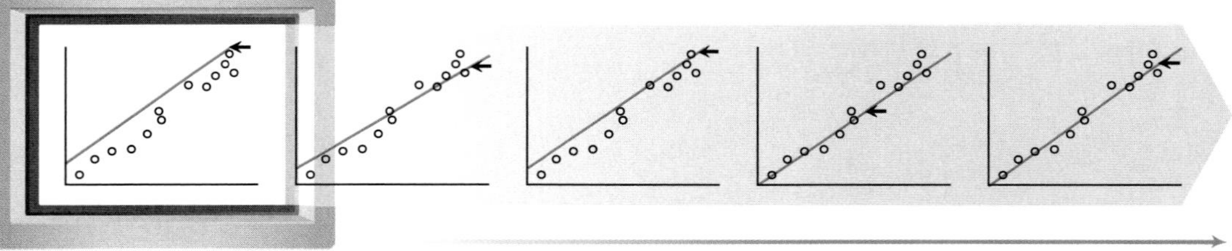

Once you have drawn a line of fit for your data, you can write an equation that expresses the relationship. To indicate that the line is a prediction line, the variable $\hat{y}$ ("y hat") is used in place of y.

LESSON OBJECTIVES

- Find a line of fit for data that are approximately linear
- Use interpolation and extrapolation

NCTM STANDARDS

CONTENT		PROCESS	
	Number	✓	Problem Solving
✓	Algebra	✓	Reasoning
	Geometry	✓	Communication
✓	Measurement	✓	Connections
✓	Data/Probability	✓	Representation

As you learned in algebra, there are several ways to write the equation of a line. You can find the slope and the y-intercept and write the intercept form of the equation. Often, it is easier to choose any two points on the line, use them to calculate the slope, and use the slope and either of the points to write the **point-slope form** of the equation. Either method should give almost exactly the same results. In general, using two points that are farther apart results in a more accurate calculation of the slope.

Point-Slope Form

The formula for the slope is $b = \frac{y_2 - y_1}{x_2 - x_1}$, so you can write the equation of a line with slope b and containing point (x_1, y_1) for any general point (x, y) as $b = \frac{y - y_1}{x - x_1}$ or, equivalently, as

$$y = y_1 + b(x - x_1)$$

This is called the point-slope form for a linear equation.

You can then use this equation to predict points for which data are not available.

EXAMPLE

On a barren lava field on top of the Mauna Loa volcano in Hawaii, scientists have been monitoring the concentration of CO_2 (carbon dioxide) in the atmosphere since 1959. This site is favorable because it is relatively isolated from vegetation and human activities that produce CO_2. The average concentrations for 17 different years, measured in parts per million (ppm), are shown here.

Year	CO_2 (ppm)	Year	CO_2 (ppm)	Year	CO_2 (ppm)
1980	337.84	1987	347.84	1995	359.98
1981	339.06	1988	350.25	1996	362.09
1982	340.57	1989	352.60	1997	363.23
1983	341.20	1990	353.50	1998	365.38
1984	343.52	1993	356.63	1999	368.24
1986	346.11	1994	358.96		

(Carbon Dioxide Information Analysis Center)

a. Find a line of fit to summarize the data.

b. Predict the concentration of CO_2 in the atmosphere in the year 2050.

Science CONNECTION

With a name meaning "long mountain," Mauna Loa has an area of 2035 mi^2, covers half of the island of Hawaii, and is Earth's largest active volcano. This active volcano's last eruption was in 1984. Volcanologists routinely monitor Mauna Loa for signs of eruption and specify hazardous areas of the mountain.

Caldera on Mauna Loa

▶ EXAMPLE

[Context] CO_2 is one of the gases emitted periodically by active volcanoes. These emissions are monitored and taken into account before the data are reported.

The first step mentioned on page 128, drawing the rectangle, is not shown in this solution. You might enter the data into an overhead calculator and project the scatter plot. (If you can project onto a white board, you can draw the rectangle around projected points; if not, you might cut a piece of transparency to the size of the calculator projection screen and then draw on the transparency.) Or you might use the Exercise 7 transparency to show this step.

[Alert] Students might use the last two digits in the year to plot the data and find the slope. If so, they will have to think hard about how to predict the concentration in the year 2050. If they evaluate the CO_2 concentration at 50 instead of 150, say that the result seems low to you and wonder aloud why.

[Ask] "What is the y-intercept? What are the real-world meanings of the slope and the y-intercept?"

MAKING THE CONNECTION

Since 1957, scientists have used measurements from atmospheric observatories on Mauna Loa to study the rising rates of CO_2. These measurements help scientists better understand global warming. Global warming is the gradual increase in Earth's average temperature as a result of the greenhouse effect. In this process, greenhouse gases like CO_2 prevent infrared heat from escaping into space, thus causing temperatures to rise. These gases have increased by 31% since 1750 as a result of the burning of fossil fuels and the destruction of forests that absorb CO_2.

Guiding the Investigation

Step 1 The entire class will need the data points, so it's a good idea to involve everyone in establishing a standard technique. Then choose nine different-size groups from the full class. It's best if students about to do the wave sit in a row (in chairs or bleachers) and practice before collecting data. If time is limited you can use the Wave Sample Data worksheet.

Steps 2, 3 Have students complete these steps in groups.

SHARING IDEAS

As students share results, point out that often more than one line of fit is acceptable, as long as students follow the guidelines and can explain their reasoning. **[Ask]** "What are the units of the slope?" [seconds per person] "Why do we want a line of fit for a data set in the first place?" [Lines of fit help us make predictions.] Use the terms *extrapolation* and *interpolation* for those predictions.

Ask why the book replaces (x_2, y_2) with (x, y) in the slope formula. As students struggle to articulate their ideas, you might ask questions such as this: "Are you saying that x and y satisfy an equation if and only if the point with coordinates (x, y) lies on the graph of that equation?" Help the class see that to find a relationship between the coordinates of all points on the line we let (x, y) represent any point on the line and decide how x and y can be related by an equation.

[Ask] "How does the point-slope form of a linear equation, $y = y_1 + b(x - x_1)$, compare with the intercept form, $y = a + bx$? Does y_1 equal a?" [No. The value y_1 is not the y-intercept; it's the height of the graph when $x - x_1 = 0$, or $x = x_1$.] Dynamically, the point-slope form shows how far the line moves vertically from y_1 as x moves horizontally from x_1. The intercept form shows how far the line moves vertically from a as x moves horizontally from 0. If students have studied transformations of graphs in geometry, you might point out that the point-slope form is a translation of $y = bx$ to make the line pass through the point (x_1, y_1). If students remember that, or the derivation given in the book, they don't need to memorize the new formula. Transformations of graphs are discussed in Chapter 4.

[Ask] "Are point-slope equations the same for different data points?" [They are the same if and only if all the points lie exactly on the same line.] You might want to produce data points that are truly collinear, have students find point-slope equations using various data points, and point out how those equations are equivalent.

If students need more advice about how to find lines of fit, you might use data from the exercises in Lesson 3.2.

▶ ***Solution***

Let x represent the year, and let y represent the concentration of CO_2 in parts per million. A graph of the data shows a linear pattern.

a. You can draw a line that seems to fit the trend of the data.

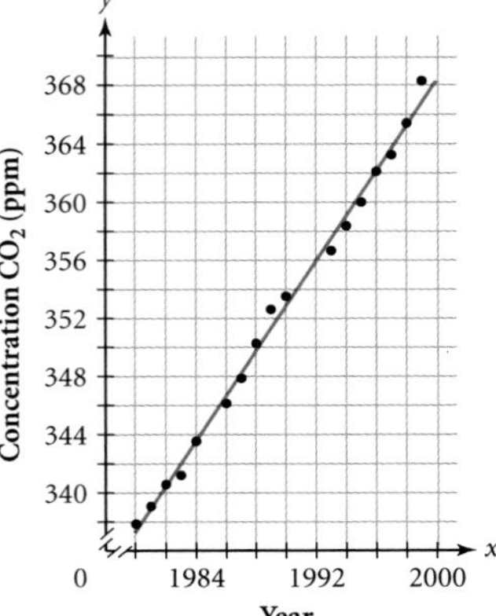

The line shown on the graph is a good fit because many of the points lie on or near the line, the data points above and below the line are roughly equal in number, and they are evenly distributed on both sides along the line. You do not know what the y-intercept should be because you do not know the concentration in the year 0; you have no reason to believe that the line passes through (0, 0).

Next, you need to find the equation for this line of fit. The y-intercept is not easily available, but you can choose two points and use the point-slope form. Note that the points do not need to be data points. You might choose the points (1984, 343.5) and (1994, 359.0). They are far enough apart, and their coordinates are easy to find on the graph.

You can use these points to find the slope.

$$\text{slope} = \frac{359.0 - 343.5}{1994 - 1984} = \frac{15.5}{10} = 1.55$$

This means the concentration of CO_2 in the atmosphere has been increasing at a rate of about 1.55 ppm each year.

Use either of the two points you chose for the slope calculation, and substitute its coordinates for x_1 and y_1 in the point-slope form of a linear equation.

$$\hat{y} = 343.5 + 1.55(x - 1984)$$ Use point (1984, 343.5), substituting 1984 for x_1 and 343.5 for y_1.

b. You can substitute 2050 for x and solve for $\hat{y}$ to predict the CO_2 concentration in the year 2050. The prediction is 445.8 ppm.

$$\hat{y} = 343.5 + 1.55(2050 - 1984)$$
$$= 445.8$$

Environment CONNECTION

Cars and trucks emit carbon dioxide, methane, and nitrous oxide by burning fossil fuels. These gases trap heat from the sun, producing a "greenhouse effect" and causing global warming. Some scientists warn that if accelerated warming continues, higher sea levels will result. To learn how scientists are studying the greenhouse effect, see the web links at www.keymath.com/DAA

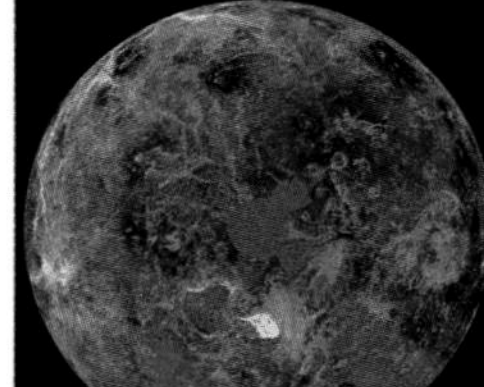

The planet Venus suffers from an extreme greenhouse effect due to constant volcanic activity, which has created a dense atmosphere that is 97% carbon dioxide. As a result, surface temperatures reach 462°C.

Investigation
The Wave

You will need

- a stop watch or watch with second hand

Sometimes at sporting events, people in the audience stand up quickly in succession with their arms upraised and then sit down again. The continuous rolling motion that this creates through the crowd is called "the wave." You and your class will investigate how long it takes different-size groups to do the wave.

Step 1 Using different-size groups, determine the time for each group to complete the wave. Collect at least nine pieces of data of the form (*number of people, time*), and record them in a table.

Step 2 Plot the points, and find the equation of a reasonable line of fit. Write a paragraph about your results. Be sure to answer these questions:

- What is the slope of your line, and what is its real-world meaning?
- What are the x- and y-intercepts of your line, and what are their real-world meanings?
- What is a reasonable domain for this equation? Why?

Step 3 Can you use your line of fit to predict how long it would take to complete the wave if everyone at your school participated? Everyone in a large stadium? Explain why or why not.

Step 3 Sample answer: No, because for a large group of people the wave gains momentum and begins to travel faster. So for a large group of people the data may not be linear.

Keep these data and the equation. You will be using them in a later lesson.

Step 1 sample data:

Number of people	Time (s)
2	2.1
5	4.4
6	5.2
8	5.8
9	4.7
10	6.7
15	7.5
16	10.4
22	11.0

Step 2 for the sample data:

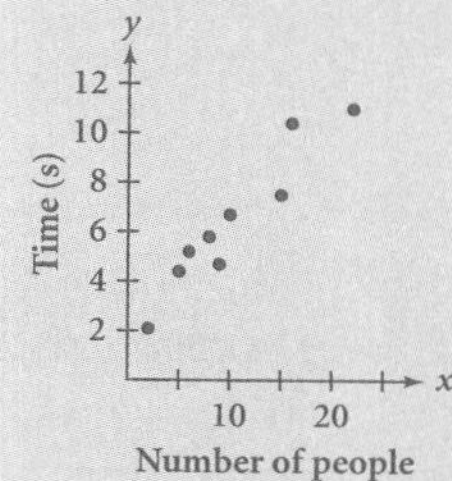

$\hat{y} = 0.45x + 1.9$; The slope indicates that it takes 0.45 s longer per additional person. The x-intercept is approximately -4.2 and does not have real-world meaning in this contest; the y-intercept is 1.9 and indicates the additional time the first person needs to stand and the additional time the last person needs to fully sit down. It might also include reaction time for starting and stopping the stopwatch. The domain could start at 0 people, at 1 person, or at 2 people and increase to the number of students in the entire class.

Finding a value between other values given in a data set is called **interpolation.** Using a model to extend beyond the first or last data points is called **extrapolation.** How would you use the Mauna Loa data in the example to estimate the CO_2 levels in 1960? In 1991? 1960 extrapolate $\hat{y} = 306.3$

1991 interpolate $\hat{y} = 354.35$

EXERCISES

Practice Your Skills

1. Write the equation in point-slope form of each line shown.

a. $y = 1 + \frac{2}{3}(x - 4)$

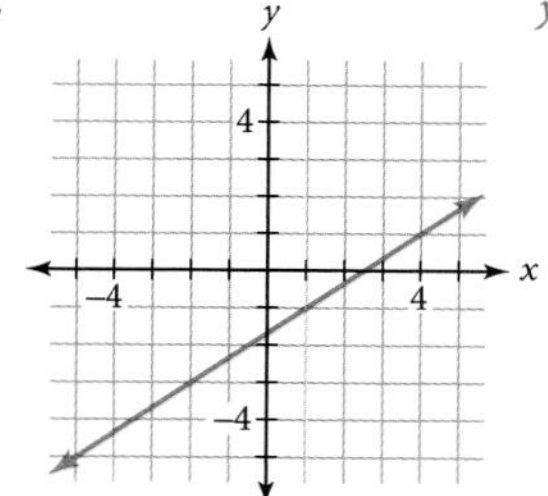

b. $y = 2 - \frac{1}{5}(x - 1)$

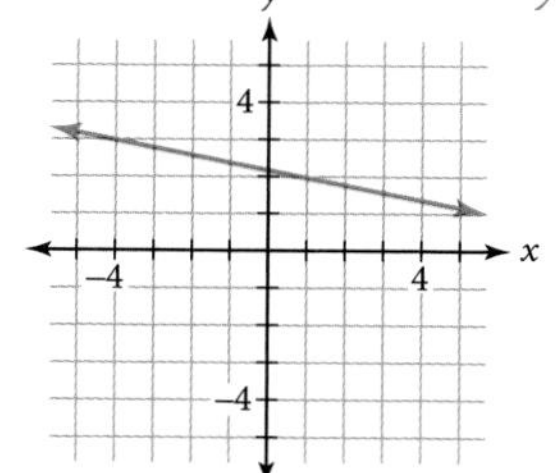

Assessing Progress

In doing the investigation, students will display their ability to organize data and their understanding of slope, y-intercept, and linear equations.

Closing the Lesson

Lines of fit for data sets help you make predictions, through **extrapolation** or **interpolation.** A useful way to get a linear equation when you know the slope but don't know the y-intercept is to use the **point-slope form,** $y = y_1 + b(x - x_1)$.

Ask students to keep their wave data for use in the exercises in Lesson 3.4.

BUILDING UNDERSTANDING

In the exercises students use the point-slope form to find lines of fit and make predictions.

ASSIGNING HOMEWORK

Essential	1–7
Performance assessment	8–10
Journal	4, 5, 8
Group	10
Review	11–14

MATERIALS

- Talkin' Trash (W), *optional*
- Calculator Notes 3A, 3B, *optional*

Helping with the Exercises

Exercise 2 As needed, remind students that parallel lines have the same slope.

Exercises 4, 5 [Alert] Students might not recall that these are equations of horizontal and vertical lines. As needed, stress that the line with the equation $x = -3$ contains all points whose coordinates (x, y) satisfy the equation—that is, all points with -3 as the first coordinate.

4a.

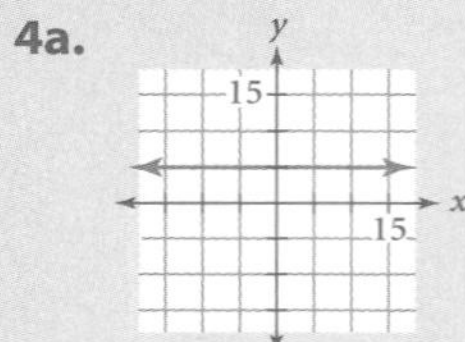

possible answer: (0, 5), (1, 5)

4d. Horizontal lines have no x-intercepts (unless the horizontal line is the x-axis, or $y = 0$); they have a slope of 0; all points have the same y-coordinate.

5a.

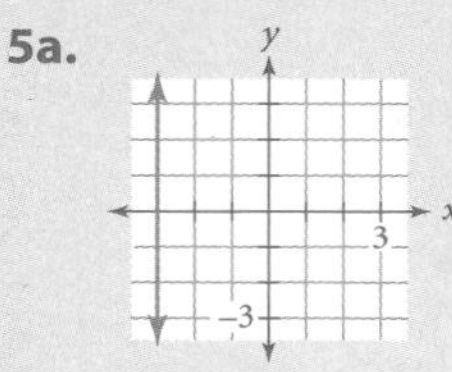

possible answer: $(-3, 0)$, $(-3, 2)$

2. Write the equation in point-slope form of each line described.

a. Slope $\frac{2}{3}$ passing through $(5, -7)$ $y = -7 + \frac{2}{3}(x - 5)$

b. Slope -4 passing through $(1, 6)$ $y = 6 - 4(x - 1)$

c. Parallel to $y = -2 + 3x$ passing through $(-2, 8)$ $y = 8 + 3(x + 2)$

d. Parallel to $y = -4 - \frac{3}{5}(x + 1)$ passing through $(-4, 11)$ $y = 11 - \frac{3}{5}(x + 4)$

3. Solve each equation.

a. Solve $u_n = 23 + 2(n - 7)$ for u_n if $n = 11$. $u_n = 31$

b. Solve $d = -47 - 4(t + 6)$ for t if $d = 95$. $t = -41.5$

c. Solve $y = 56 - 6(x - 10)$ for x if $y = 107$. $x = 1.5$

4. Consider the line $y = 5$.

a. Graph this line and identify two points on it.

b. What is the slope of this line? 0

c. Write the equation of the line that contains the points $(3, -4)$ and $(-2, -4)$. $y = -4$

d. Write three statements about horizontal lines and their equations.

5. Consider the line $x = -3$.

a. Graph it and identify two points on it.

b. What is the slope of this line? undefined

c. Write the equation of the line that contains the points $(3, 5)$ and $(3, 1)$. $x = 3$

d. Write three statements about vertical lines and their equations.

Reason and Apply

6. Of the graphs below, choose the *one* with the line that best satisfies the guidelines on page 128. For each of the other graphs, explain which guidelines the line violates.

a. 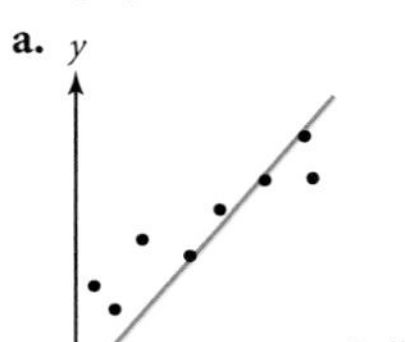

b. 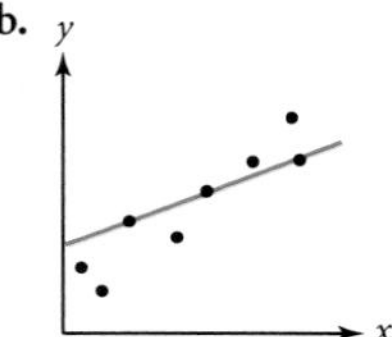

c. 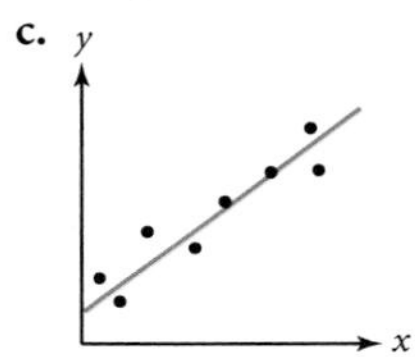

d. 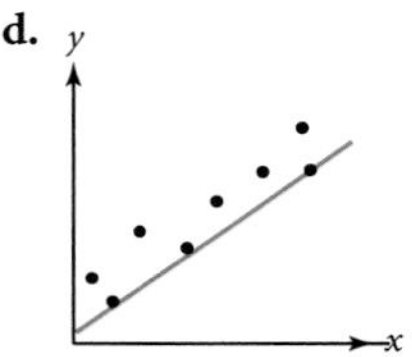

7. For each graph below, lay your ruler along your best estimate of the line of fit. Estimate the y-intercept and the coordinates of one other point on the line. Write an equation in intercept form for the line of fit.

a. 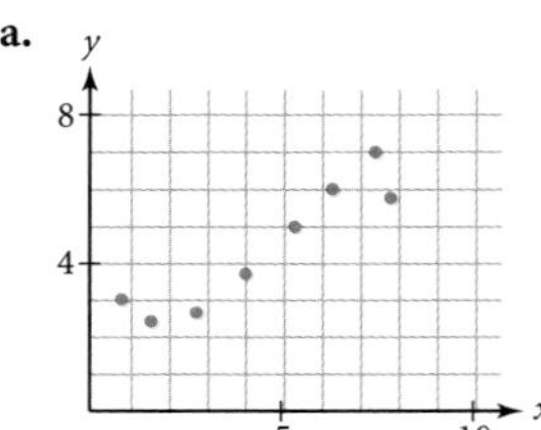

b. 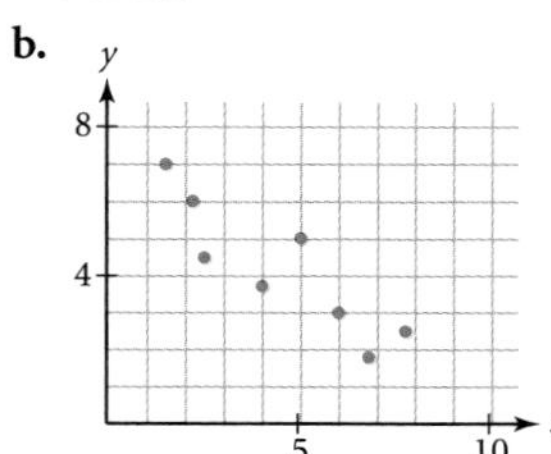

c. 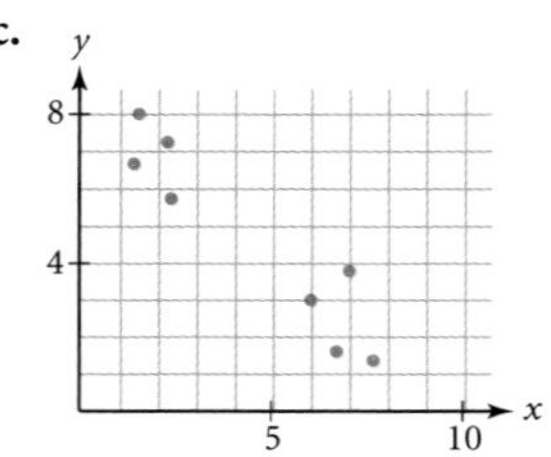

5d. Vertical lines have no y-intercepts (unless the vertical line is the y-axis, or $x = 0$); they have undefined slope; all points have the same x-coordinate.

6. Sample answers:

6a. Most of the points on the left are above the line. Most of the points on the right are below the line.

6b. Most of the points on the left are below the line. Most of the points on the right are above the line.

6c. This is the best.

6d. There are no points below the line.

Exercise 7 You might make worksheets from the Exercise 7 transparency so that students do not write in their books.

7. Possible answers:

7a. The y-intercept is about 1.7; (5, 4.6); $\hat{y} = 1.7 + 0.58x$.

7b. The y-intercept is about 7.5; (5, 3.75); $\hat{y} = 7.5 - 0.75x$.

7c. The y-intercept is about 8.6; (5, 3.9); $\hat{y} = 8.6 - 0.94x$.

8. APPLICATION A photography studio offers several packages to students posing for yearbook photos. Let x represent the number of pictures, and let y represent the price in dollars.

Number of pictures	44	31	24	15
Price ($)	19.00	16.00	13.00	10.00

a. Plot the data, and find an equation of a line of fit. Explain the real-world meaning of the slope of this line.

b. Find the y-intercept of your line of fit. Explain the real-world meaning of the y-intercept. 5.80. There is a set-up cost of $5.80 just for having your picture taken.

c. If the studio offers a 75-print package, what do you think it should charge? $28.30

d. How many prints do you think the studio should include in the package for a $7.99 special? 7 or 8 prints

9. Use height as the independent variable and length of forearm as the dependent variable for the data collected from nine students.

Height (cm)	Forearm (cm)
185.9	48.5
172.0	44.5
155.0	41.0
191.5	50.5
162.0	43.0
164.3	42.5
177.5	47.0
180.0	48.0
179.5	47.5

a. Name a good graphing window for your scatter plot.

b. Write a linear equation that models the data.

c. Write a sentence describing the real-world meaning of the slope of your line.

d. Write a sentence describing the real-world meaning of the y-intercept. Explain why this doesn't make sense and how you might correct it.

e. Use your equation to estimate the height of a student with a 50 cm forearm and to estimate the length of a forearm of a student 158 cm tall. 189.58 cm; 41.79 cm

10. APPLICATION This data set was collected by a college psychology class to determine the effects of sleep deprivation on students' ability to solve problems. Ten participants went 8, 12, 16, 20, or 24 hours without sleep and then completed a set of simple addition problems. The number of addition errors was recorded.

Hours without sleep	8	8	12	12	16	16	20	20	24	24
Number of errors	8	6	6	10	8	14	14	12	16	12

a. Define your variables and create a scatter plot of the data.

b. Write an equation of a line that approximates the data and sketch it on your graph.

c. Based on your model, how many errors would you predict a person to make if she or he hadn't slept in 22 hours? 14 errors

d. In 10c, did you use interpolation or extrapolation? Explain.
interpolation, because you found a value between those given in the table

Exercises 7–10 Equations will vary somewhat depending on which points students choose to be on the lines. Any line that fits the data "by eye" is acceptable if students can explain how they arrived at it.

8a. $\hat{y} = 19 + 0.3(x - 44)$. There is a cost increase of about 30¢ per picture.

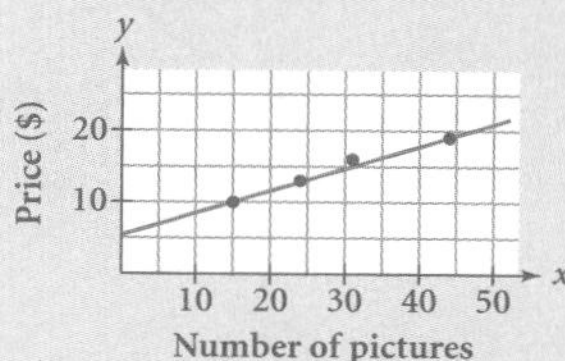

9a. [145, 200, 5, 40, 52, 1]

9b. $\hat{y} = 0.26x + 0.71$

9c. On average, a student's forearm length increases by 0.26 cm for each additional 1 cm of height.

9d. The y-intercept is meaningless because a height of 0 cm should not predict a forearm length of 0.71 cm. The domain should be specified.

Exercise 10 Calculator Note 3A helps students graph equations on top of scatter plots. They can make predictions by using function tables (Calculator Note 3B).

10a. Let x represent the number of hours without sleep, and let y represent the number of errors.

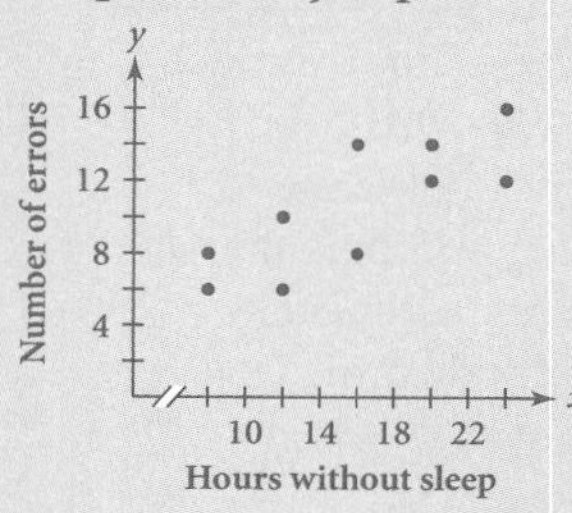

10b.

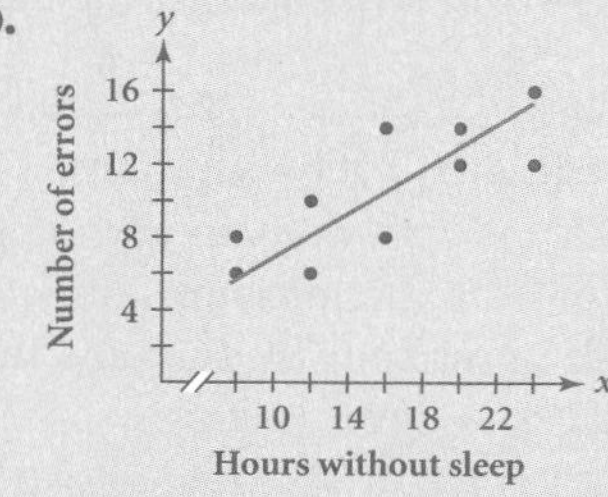

possible answer: $\hat{y} = 3 + 0.5x$

Exercise 11 If students are struggling, you might **[Ask]** "What is the slope of the line between the two points?" $\left[\frac{27}{18} = 1.5\right]$ "What is the zero term of the sequence? [$54 - 3(1.5) = 49.5$] "How can you use those values to find the 35th term?" [Write the explicit formula and substitute 35 for n.]

Exercise 13 As needed, remind students to arrange the data in ascending or descending order before finding the middle number.

14a. $u_0 = 8$ and $u_n = u_{n-1} - 0.5$ where $n \geq 1$

EXTENSIONS

A. Have students find and collect a data set that appears to have a linear relationship and then find the line of fit and extrapolate for unknown data.

B. Extend the project by asking students to research whether their trash predictions apply to other countries. Students might focus on a particular category of trash such as household or industrial.

C. Have students research solutions to the trash problem, such as reducing waste and recycling, and then estimate and predict how much each solution will reduce the amount of waste per year for the entire country.

Review

1.1 **11.** The 3rd term of an arithmetic sequence is 54. The 21st term is 81. Find the 35th term. 102

1.3 **12.** Write the first four terms of this sequence and describe its long-run behavior.

$u_1 = 56$

$u_n = \frac{u_{n-1}}{2} + 4 \quad \text{where } n \geq 2$ 56, 32, 20, 14; the long-run value of the sequence is 8.

2.1 **13.** Given the data set {20, 12, 15, 17, 21, 15, 30, 16, 14}:

a. Find the median. 16

b. Add as few elements as possible to the set in order to make 19.5 the median. Add 19.5 and any three numbers greater than 19.5.

3.2 **14.** You start 8 meters from a marker and walk toward it at the rate of 0.5 m/s.

a. Write a recursive rule that gives your distance from the marker after each second.

b. Write an explicit formula that allows you to find your distance from the marker at any time. $u_n = 8 - 0.5n$

c. Interpret the real-world meaning of a negative value for u_n in 14a or 14b. A negative value means that you have passed the marker.

Project

TALKIN' TRASH

Garbage piles up in New York City during a 1982 sanitation workers strike.

How much trash do you and your family generate each day? How much trash does that amount to for the entire U.S. population daily? Annually? How much land is needed to dump garbage? Research some data on U.S. population and waste production. Find linear models for your data. Use your equations to predict the population and the amount of waste that you might expect in the years 2010 and 2020. Use your graphs and equations to decide if the amount of waste is increasing because of the increase in population or because of other factors.

Your project should include

- Data and sources.
- Linear models for predicting population and waste, an explanation of how you found them, and real-world meanings for each part of your model.
- Domain and range for each model.
- Population and waste predictions for 2010 and 2020, including amount of waste per person per day.
- A complete analysis of your findings, in paragraph form.

Supporting the Project

The Talkin' Trash worksheet has data up to 2000. Students might find data for the current year and check their model. A model for x as years since 1900, and y as trash in millions of tons per year could be $y = -127 + 3.55x$. For population in millions, a linear model might be $y = 34 + 2.4x$.

OUTCOMES

- Report gives data with sources, and equations with domain and range.
- Report's predictions are similar to these: Trash in millions of tons, 263 in 2010 and 299 in 2020, is consistent with the equation for sample data. Predictions for population, in millions, from the U.S. Census Bureau are 300 for 2010 and 325 for 2020 (for the sample linear model, 298 in 2010 and 322 in 2020).
- It is noted that the ratio of waste to population is growing and thus the increase in waste is not completely accounted for by the growth in population.

LESSON

3.4

The growth of understanding follows an ascending spiral rather than a straight line.

JOANNA FIELD

The Median-Median Line

Have you noticed that you and your classmates frequently find different equations to model the same data? Some lines fit data better than others and can be used to make more accurate predictions. In this lesson you will learn a standard method for finding a line of fit that will enable each member of the class to get the same equation for the same set of data.

You can use many different methods to find a statistical line of fit. The **median-median line** is one of the simplest methods. The procedure for finding the median-median line uses three points $(M_1, M_2, \text{and } M_3)$ to represent the entire data set, and the equation that best fits these three points is taken as the line of fit for the entire set of data.

To find the three points that will represent the entire data set, you first order all the data points by their domain value (the x-value) and then divide the data into three equal groups. If the number of points is not divisible by 3, then you split them so that the first and last groups are the same size. For example:

18 data points: split into groups of 6-6-6

19 data points: split into groups of 6-7-6

20 data points: split into groups of 7-6-7

You then order the y-values within each of the groups. The representative point for each group has the coordinates of the median x-value of that group and the median y-value of that group. Because a good line of fit divides the data evenly, the median-median line should pass between M_1, M_2, and M_3, but be closer to M_1 and M_3 because they represent two-thirds of the data. To accomplish this, you can find the y-intercept of the line through M_1 and M_3, and the y-intercept of the line through M_2 that has the same slope. The mean of the three y-intercepts of the lines through M_1, M_2, and M_3 gives you the y-intercept of a line that satisfies these requirements.

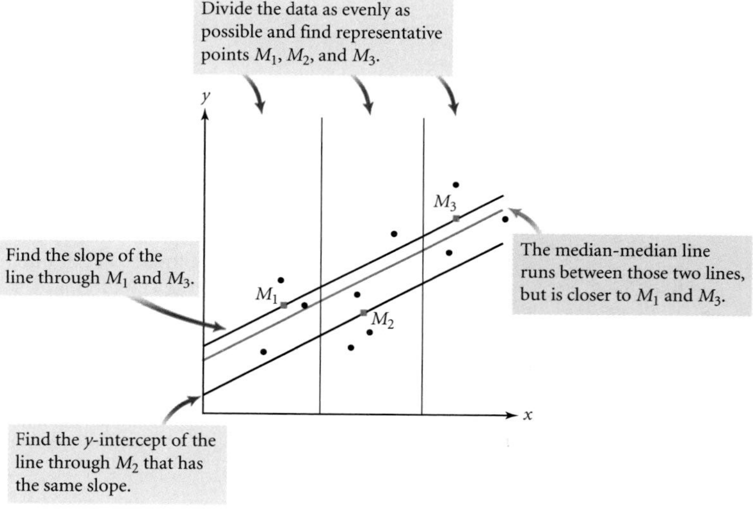

NCTM STANDARDS

CONTENT		PROCESS	
	Number	✓	Problem Solving
✓	Algebra	✓	Reasoning
✓	Geometry	✓	Communication
✓	Measurement	✓	Connections
✓	Data/Probability	✓	Representation

LESSON OBJECTIVES

- Practice writing equations for lines through two points
- Review how to determine the equation of a line parallel to another line
- Introduce the median-median line
- Compare the median-median line to other lines of fit

LESSON

3.4

PLANNING

LESSON OUTLINE

First day:

20 min Example

15 min Investigation

10 min Exercises

Second day:

15 min Investigation

15 min Sharing

15 min Exercises

MATERIALS

- springs
- mass holders
- small unit masses
- rulers
- Median-Median Line (T), *optional*
- Spring Experiment Sample Data (W), *optional*
- Calculator Note 3D

TEACHING

A line of fit that can be found in a standard way is the median-median line.

[Context] The median-median line is similar to the method used by Francis Galton in 1888 to estimate what he was then calling "the index of co-relation." His data were the length of the left forearm and the height of 348 adult males, similar to the data in Lesson 3.3, Exercise 9.

[Ask] "Is the median point of a data set necessarily one of the data points?" [No; it could be the mean of two data points.]

[Alert] Students may be confused by the "three y-intercepts" mentioned in the last sentence. The y-intercept of the line through M_1 and M_3 is used twice.

One Step

Say that the median-median line is a line of fit that is produced by a standard method and direct students to use their calculators or Fathom to find the equation of the median-median line for a very small set of data they invent. Their challenge is to figure out the standard method and write it down clearly enough that another group of students can follow it. As you circulate, encourage groups to change one data point at a time. If there's time, students can apply their method to a larger data set, perhaps to data gathered as in Step 1 of the investigation.

► ***EXAMPLE***

You might use the Median-Median Line transparency as you discuss this example.

[Ask] "Are points M_1, M_2, and M_3 data points?" [In this example point M_1 is an actual data point, but the other two points are not. The x-coordinate of point M_2 is determined by finding the median value of the four x-values 7.8, 8.3, 8.9, and 9.7; their median is the mean of 8.3 and 8.9. To find the median of the four y-values, the values must first be ordered. Their median is the mean of 42 and 50. The coordinates of point M_3 are found by ordering the x-values and y-values individually and then finding the median for each set.]

When the line through points M_1 and M_3 and the parallel line through point M_2 are sketched, you can demonstrate why the median-median line must be closer to the line through points M_1 and M_3.

Don't forget to order the y-values in each group when finding the median y-value. Carefully study the following example to see how this is done.

EXAMPLE

Find the median-median line for these data.

x	y	x	y
4.0	23	8.9	50
5.2	28	9.7	47
5.8	29	10.4	52
6.5	35	11.2	60
7.1	35	11.9	58
7.8	40	12.5	62
8.3	42	13.1	64

► ***Solution***

First, group the data and find M_1, M_2, and M_3.

x	y	(median x, median y)
4.0 5.2 5.8 6.5 7.1	23 28 29 35 35	(5.8, 29)
7.8 8.3 8.9 9.7	40 42 50 47	(8.6, 44.5)
10.4 11.2 11.9 12.5 13.1	52 60 58 62 64	(11.9, 60)

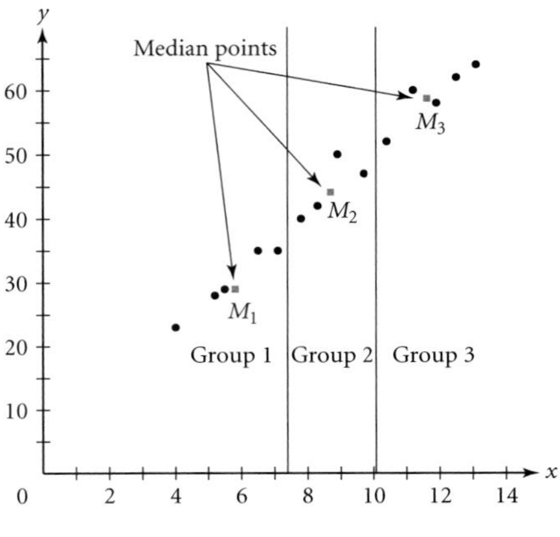

The slope of the median-median line is determined by the slope of the line through M_1 and M_3.

$$\text{slope} = \frac{60 - 29}{11.9 - 5.8} \approx 5.082$$

Next, find the equation of the line containing points $M_1(5.8, 29)$ and $M_3(11.9, 60)$. You have already found that the slope is 5.082. Using M_1, you can write the point-slope form of the equation. Rewrite the equation in intercept form to find the y-intercept.

$y = 29 + 5.082(x - 5.8)$ Write the equation in point-slope form.

$y = 29 + 5.082x - 29.4756$ Distribute the 5.082.

$y = -0.476 + 5.082x$ Add like terms. This is the intercept form. The y-intercept is -0.476.

If you use M_3 instead of M_1, you should get the same equation, because your equation is the line through both M_1 and M_3.

Next, find the equation of the line that is parallel to the line through M_1 and M_3 and passes through the middle representative point, $M_2(8.6, 44.5)$.

$y = 44.5 + 5.082(x - 8.6)$ — Write the equation in point-slope form.

$y = 0.795 + 5.082x$ — Distribute and add like terms to find the intercept form of the equation.

The median-median line is parallel to both of these lines, so it will also have a slope of 5.082. To find the y-intercept of the median-median line, you find the mean of the y-intercepts of the lines through M_1, M_2, and M_3. Note that the y-intercept of the line through M_1 is the same as the y-intercept of the line through M_3.

$\frac{-0.476 + (-0.476) + 0.795}{3} \approx -0.052$ — Find the mean of the y-intercepts.

So, finally, the equation of the median-median line is $\hat{y} = -0.052 + 5.082x$. Note that this line is one-third of the way from the first line to the second line.

Finding a Median-Median Line

1. Order your data by domain value first. Then, divide the data into three sets equal in size. If the number of points does not divide evenly into three groups, make sure that the first and last groups are the same size. Find the median x-value and the median y-value in each group. Call these points M_1, M_2, and M_3.
2. Find the slope of the line through M_1 and M_3. This is the slope of the median-median line.
3. Find the equation of the line through M_1 with the slope you found in Step 2. The equation of the line through M_3 will be the same.
4. Find the equation of the line through M_2 with the slope you found in Step 2.
5. Find the y-intercept of the median-median line by taking the mean of the y-intercepts of the lines through M_1, M_2, and M_3. The y-intercepts of the lines through M_1 and M_3 are the same. Finally, write the equation of the median-median line using this mean y-intercept and the slope from Step 2.

Japanese artist Yoshio Itagaki (b 1967) created *Tourist on the Moon #2* as a commentary on tourists' desire to document their visits to spectacular scenes. He is both amused by and critical of the human appetite for sensation and novelty. This work is a triptych—a piece in three panels.

Example (continued)
[Ask] "Instead of finding the mean of the three y-intercepts, could we find just the mean of the y-coordinates of points M_1, M_2, and M_3?" [Doing so gives only a number, not a point.] "Could that number be the y-coordinate of a point on the line whose x-coordinate is the mean of the x-coordinates of points M_1, M_2, and M_3?" Some experimentation, can confirm that this gives a point on the line, thus providing a shortcut to steps 3, 4, and 5 of Finding a Median-Median Line.

Assessing Progress
Students will demonstrate their understanding of median, point-slope form, and intercept form. You can also assess their skill at rewriting algebraic expressions (using the distributive property) and graphing data.

Guiding the Investigation

If time is short, use the wave data from Lesson 3.3, or use the Spring Experiment Sample Data worksheet.

Step 1 If you can't borrow spring equipment from the science department, use a Slinky Jr. cut in half and place the weights (masses) in film canisters attached to the springs with string. The unit masses can be uniform beans or pennies. The answers to Steps 2–6 use the sample data.

Step 2 Ask students to use a full sheet of graph paper to give them plenty of space to work.

Step 5 The slope of this line is called the *spring constant.* **[Ask]** "Predict the spring length for a very large mass value. Is this length realistic?" [The spring will straighten out as the mass gets large, and thus the length will not follow the linear model.]

SHARING IDEAS

As students present, **[Ask]** "What three y-intercepts are you averaging to get the y-intercept of the median-median line?" [The line between points M_1 and M_3 is used twice, the line through point M_2 once.]

[Ask] "What shape is a spring?" [a helix] "What do you think the ascending spiral is in the quotation that opens the lesson." [It's probably also a helix.]

[Ask] "If there are only two points, is the median-median line the line between those points?" [You could say that the procedure breaks down because there is no middle point to shift the line toward. This is the assumption made by graphing calculators and by Fathom. Or you could say that, because there's no middle point, the line doesn't shift and passes through the two given points.]

See page 880 for answers to Steps 1–4, 5a, 5b, 5e, and 6.

Investigation
Spring Experiment

You will need

- a spring
- a mass holder
- small unit masses
- a ruler

In this investigation you will collect data on how a spring responds to various weights. You will find a median-median line to model this relationship.

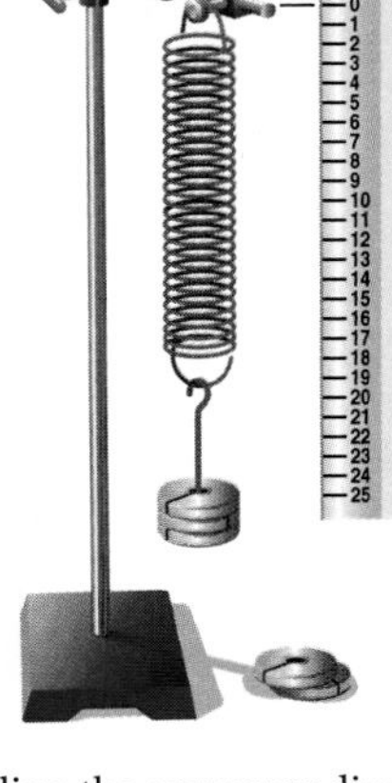

Procedure Note

1. Attach the mass holder to the spring.
2. Hang the spring from a support, and the mass holder from the spring.
3. Measure the length of the spring (in centimeters) from the first coil to the last coil.

Step 1 Place different amounts of mass on the mass holder, recording the corresponding length of the spring each time. Collect about 10 data points of the form (*mass, spring length*).

Step 2 Graph the data on graph paper.

Step 3 Show the steps to calculate the median-median line through the data. Write the equation of this line. Use your calculator to check your work. [▶ See **Calculator Note 3D** to learn how to find the median-median line with your calculator.◀]

Step 4 On your graph, mark the three representative points used in the median-median process. Add the line to this graph.

Step 5 Answer these questions about your data and model.

a. Use your median-median line to interpolate two points for which you did not collect data. What is the real-world meaning of each of these points?

b. Which two points differ the most from the value predicted by your equation? Explain why.

c. What is the real-world meaning of your slope?

d. Find the y-intercept of your median-median line. What is its real-world meaning?

e. What are the domain and range for your data? Why?

f. Compare the median-median line method to the method you used in Lesson 3.3 to find the line of fit. What are the advantages and disadvantages of each? In your opinion, which method produces a better line of fit? Why?

Step 6 Summarize what you learned in this investigation and describe any difficulties you had.

Step 5c The spring's length increases 0.038 cm per gram added.

Step 5d 3.173; The spring's length is 3.173 cm with no mass attached.

Step 5f The median-median method is more standardized and objective, but also more labor-intensive and subject to computation error. Students may validly argue in favor of either method.

There are many ways to find a line of fit for linear data. Estimating the line of fit is adequate in many cases, but different people will estimate different lines of fit and may use their own bias to draw the line higher or lower. A median-median line is a systematic method, accepted by statisticians, that summarizes the overall trend in linear data.

If you don't plan to assign Take Another Look activity 1, you might **[Ask]** "In geometry, didn't we take the means of coordinates of three points?" [The coordinates of the centroid of a triangle are the means of the coordinates of the vertices, so the median-median line passes through the centroid of the triangle with vertices M_1, M_2, and M_3.]

To find the median-median line, we divide the coordinate sets into thirds. **[Ask]** "Why not divide the sets into quarters?" Indeed, this method produces another line of fit, using Q-points, which students encountered in *Discovering Algebra* (Lesson 5.7).

EXERCISES

Practice Your Skills

1. How should you divide the following sets into three groups for the median-median line method?

   a. Set of 51 elements 17, 17, 17 b. Set of 50 elements 17, 16, 17 c. Set of 47 elements 16, 15, 16 d. Set of 38 elements 13, 12, 13

2. Find an equation in point-slope form of the line passing through

   a. (8.1, 15.7) and (17.3, 9.5) b. (3, 47) and (18, 84)

3. Find an equation in point-slope form of the line parallel to $y = -12.2 + 0.75x$ that passes through the point (14.4, 0.9). $y = 0.9 + 0.75(x - 14.4)$

4. Find an equation of the line one-third of the way from $y = -1.8x + 74.1$ to $y = -1.8x + 70.5$. (Hint: The first line came from two points in a median-median procedure, and the other line came from the third point.) $y = 72.9 - 1.8x$

5. Find the equation of the line one-third of the way from the line $y = 2.8 + 4.7x$ to the point (12.8, 64). $y = 3.15 + 4.7x$

Reason and Apply

6. **APPLICATION** Follow these steps to find the equation for the median-median line for the data on life expectancy at birth for males in the United States for different years in the 20th century. Let x represent the year, and let y represent the male life expectancy in years.

   a. How many points are there in each of the three groups? 6, 5, 6

   b. What are the three representative points for these data? Graph these points.

   c. Draw the line through the first and third points. What is the slope of this line? What is the real-world meaning of the slope?

   d. Write the equation of the line through the first and third points. Rewrite this equation in intercept form.

   e. Draw the line parallel to the line in 6d passing through the second point. What is the equation of this line? Rewrite this equation in intercept form.

   f. Find the mean of the y-intercepts and write the equation of the median-median line. Graph this line. Remember to use the intercepts of all three lines.

   g. The year 1978 is missing from the table. Using your model, what would you predict the life expectancy at birth to be for males born in 1978? 69.76 yr

   h. Use your model to predict the life expectancy at birth for males born in 1991. 72.76 yr

   i. Using this model, when would you predict the life expectancy at birth for males in the United States to exceed 80 years? around the year 2022

Year of birth	Male life expectancy (years)
1920	53.6
1925	56.3
1930	58.1
1935	59.4
1940	60.8
1945	62.8
1950	65.6
1955	66.2
1960	66.6
1965	66.8
1970	67.1
1975	68.8
1980	70.0
1985	71.2
1990	71.8
1995	72.5
1998	73.9

(*The World Almanac and Book of Facts 2001*)

6b. (1932.5, 58.75), (1960, 66.6), (1987.5, 71.5)

6c. *Slope* = 0.232; this means that each year the life expectancy for a male increases by 0.232 yr.

6d. $y = 58.75 + 0.232(x - 1932.5)$ or $y = 71.5 + 0.232(x - 1987.5)$; $y = -389.59 + 0.232x$

6e. $y = 66.6 + 0.232(x - 1960)$; $y = -388.12 + 0.232x$

6f. -389.1; $\hat{y} = -389.1 + 0.232x$

6b–f.

Life expectancy (yr): 50, 60, 70, 80
Year of birth: 0, 1920, 1940, 1960, 1980, 2000

Closing the Lesson

Restate that the **median-median line** is a line of fit that can be found in a standard way, and review both the method on page 137 and the shortcut using means of coordinates.

BUILDING UNDERSTANDING

If you take two days for this lesson, you might assign just Exercises 1–6 on the first day.

ASSIGNING HOMEWORK

Essential	1–6
Performance assessment	8–11
Portfolio	9
Journal	10, 11
Group	7, 9
Review	12–16

MATERIALS

- Calculator Notes 3A, 3E, *optional*
- Wave Sample Data (W), *optional*

Helping with the Exercises

2a. $y = 15.7 - 0.6739(x - 8.1)$ or $y = 9.5 - 0.6739(x - 17.3)$

2b. $y = 47 + \frac{37}{15}(x - 3)$ or $y = 84 + \frac{37}{15}(x - 18)$

Exercise 4 The hint is intended to convey the idea that the y-intercept of the first line given should be used twice in finding the mean value.

Exercise 5 Encourage a variety of approaches.

Exercise 6f This exercise refers to three lines; the line through points M_1 and M_3 is counted as two of these, and the parallel line through point M_2 is the third. This equation will be used in Lesson 3.5, Exercise 3. Calculator Note 3A reviews how to graph lines on top of a scatter plot.

Exercise 7 This exercise introduces the idea of residuals. Students might need some discussion of the idea. Residuals are considered in detail in the next lesson. Calculator Note 3E describes how to find residuals on a calculator.

7. Sample answer using the Investigation Spring Experiment: −0.073, 0.047, 0.167, 0.087, 0.207, 0.127, 0.147, −0.033, −0.013, 0.007, −0.073, −0.053, −0.133, −0.113, −0.093, −0.073, 0.147, −0.133, −0.013, 0.107; The model seems to be pretty good because the residuals are small and some are positive and some are negative.

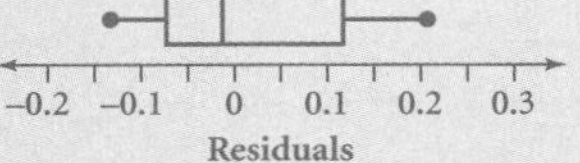

Exercise 8 If students don't have data from the wave investigation, you can use the Wave Sample Data worksheet.

8. Sample answer: $\hat{y} = 0.55x + 1.41$; The median-median line seems to be a better model for fewer people, whereas the line found before seems to be a better model for more people.

Exercise 9 Roger Bannister (UK) was the first person to run a mile in under four minutes.

9b. The world record for the 1-mile run is reduced by 0.389 s every year.

9c. 3:57.014. This prediction is 2.3 s faster than Roger Bannister actually ran.

9d. 4:27.745. This prediction is about 3.2 s slower than Walter Slade actually ran.

9e. This suggests that a world record for the mile in the year 0 would have been about 16.6 minutes. This is doubtful because a fast walker can walk a mile in about 15 minutes. The data are only approximately linear and only over a limited domain.

See pages 880–881 for answers to Exercises 11b–f.

7. Choose an investigation in this chapter. Find the **residual** for each data point (difference between the actual y-value and the model-predicted y-value). Display these residuals with a histogram or box plot. Using the information in your histogram or box plot, describe how good you think your model is. Justify your conclusion.

8. Refer to your data from the Investigation The Wave in Lesson 3.3 and find the equation for the median-median line. Compare this equation with the one you found previously. Which equation do you feel is a better model for the data? Why?

9. APPLICATION Use these data on world records for the 1-mile run to answer the questions below. Times are in minutes and seconds.

World Records for 1-Mile Run

Year	Runner	Time
1915	Norman Taber, U.S.	4:12.6
1923	Paavo Nurmi, Finland	4:10.4
1937	Sydney Wooderson, U.K.	4:06.4
1942	Gunder Haegg, Sweden	4:06.2
1945	Gunder Haegg, Sweden	4:01.4
1958	Herb Elliott, Australia	3:54.5
1967	Jim Ryun, U.S.	3:51.1
1979	Sebastian Coe, U.K.	3:49.0
1985	Steve Cram, U.K.	3:46.31
1993	Noureddine Morceli, Algeria	3:44.39

(*Time Almanac 1999*)

a. Let x represent the year, and let y represent the time in seconds. What is the equation of the median-median line? $\hat{y} = 997.12 - 0.389x$

b. What is the real-world meaning of the slope?

c. Use the equation to interpolate and predict what new record might have been set in 1954. How does this compare with Roger Bannister's actual 1954 record of 3:59.4?

d. Use the equation to extrapolate and predict what new record might have been set in 1875. How does this compare with Walter Slade's 1875 world record of 4:24.5?

e. Describe some problems you might have with the meaning of 997.12 as a y-intercept.

f. Has a new world record been set since 1993? Find more recent information on this subject and compare it with the predictions of your model.
A record of 3:43.13, 3.61 s slower than predicted, was set by Hicham El Guerrouj in 1999.

10. Devise a mean-mean line procedure and use it on the data in Exercise 9. What problems might arise when using this method? Compare the advantages and disadvantages of this method and the median-median line method.

11. The number of deaths caused by automobile accidents, D, per hundred thousand population in the United States is given for various years, t.

t	1924	1925	1926	1927	1928	1929	1930	1931	1932	1933
D	15.5	17.1	18.0	19.6	20.8	23.3	24.5	25.2	21.9	23.3

(W. A. Wilson and J. I. Tracey, *Analytic Geometry,* 3rd ed., Boston: D. C. Heath, 1949, p. 246.)

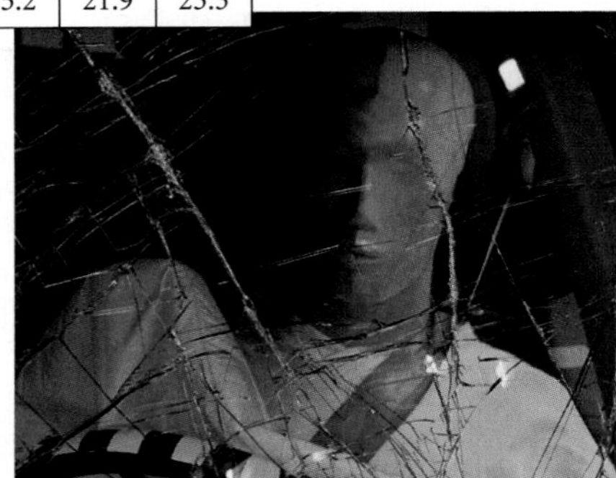

a. Make a scatter plot of the data.

b. Find the three summary points.

c. Write the equation of the median-median line.

d. What does the slope mean?

e. Give a possible explanation for the drop in the number of auto deaths in 1932.

f. Would you use this model to predict the number of deaths from auto accidents in 2000? Explain why or why not.

Exercise 10 This exercise might be quite challenging. Means are more affected by outliers than are medians.

10. Sample answer: $\hat{y} = 1001.816 - 0.383x$. One possibility is to divide the data into three groups and then to use the mean x and mean y from each group and then follow a similar procedure of writing three equations and finding the mean of the y-intercepts.

Exercise 11 Approach this exercise with sensitivity; some students may know someone who was killed in an auto accident.

11a.

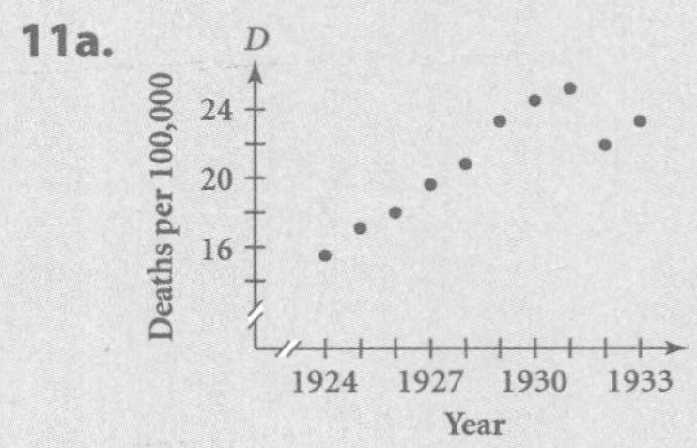

Review

2.1 **12.** Create a data set of 9 values such that the median is 28, the minimum is 11, and there is no upper whisker on a box plot of the data. possible answer: 11, 15, 18, 23, 28, 40, 50, 50, 50

3.1 **13.** What is the equation of the line that passes through a graph of the points of the sequence defined by

$u_1 = 4$

$u_n = u_{n-1} - 3 \quad \text{where } n \geq 2$ $y = 7 - 3x$

2.3 **14.** The histogram at right shows the results of a statewide math test given to eleventh graders. If Ramon scored 35, what is the range of his percentile ranking? between the 40th and 63rd percentile

Number of students (in thousands): 5, 10, 15, 20, 25, 30, 35
Score: 20, 40, 60, 80

2.1 **15.** Earl's science lab group made six measurements of mass and then summarized the results. Someone threw away the measurements. Help the group reconstruct the measurements from these statistics.

- The median and mean are both 3.2 g. 2.3 g, 3.0 g, 3.0 g, 3.4 g, 3.6 g, 3.9 g
- The mode is 3.0 g.
- The *IQR* is 0.6 g.
- The largest deviation is −0.9 g.

2.1 **16.** Travis is riding with his parents on Interstate 15 across Utah. He records the digital speedometer reading in mi/h at 4:00 P.M. and every five minutes for the next hour. His record is

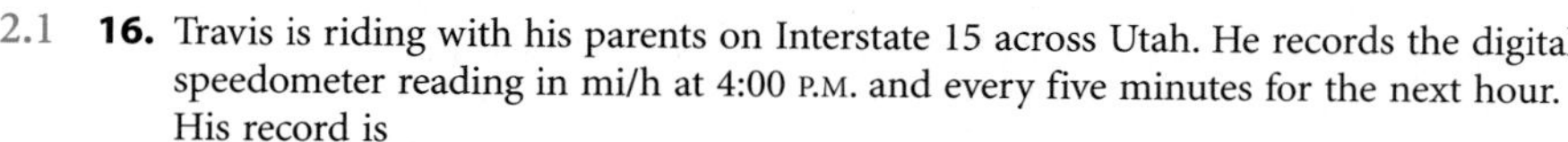

{61.3, 48.7, 62.4, 50.1, 60.3, 64.8, 67.1, 54.0, 60.2, 45.3, 52.3, 67.6, 63.9}

a. What is their mean speed? 58.3 mi/h

b. What is the standard deviation? 7.4 mi/h

c. Interpret the meaning of the standard deviation. Speculate about the traffic conditions.

Project

COUNTING FOREVER

How long would it take you to count to 1 million? Collect data by recording the time it takes you to count to different numbers. Predict the time it would take to count to 1 million, 1 billion, 1 trillion, and to the amount of the federal debt.

Your project should include

- An explanation of the procedure you used to collect these data and the approach you used to solve the problem.
- Your data, graphs, and equations.
- A summary of your predictions.

In 1992, this sign in New York City showed the increasing federal debt.

EXTENSIONS

A. Use Take Another Look activity 1 on page 169.

B. Have students investigate the least-squares regression line (another line of fit on the calculator or Fathom, which will be derived in Lesson 13.7) and compare it to the median-median line.

16c. The standard deviation is rather large, with most of the data within a 14 mi/h range from about 51 mi/h to 65 mi/h. They had to drive a bit slower part of the time, possibly due to trucks, curves, or steep hills.

Supporting the Project

The time required to do repetitive tasks is important for data security. **[Ask]** "Suppose a security code has five digits. Will this be a deterrent, or could a patient intruder break the code?" [Trying a different code each second, it would take 100,000 s, or nearly 28 h, to try them all.]

OUTCOMES

- Data-collection procedures are clearly explained.
- The report includes data, graphs, and equations that are consistent with the procedures.
- The student uses unit conversion to change the answer to reasonable units (not 2,000,000 s, for example).
- The project is extended to include estimates for counting higher, and the report includes the procedures for these higher numbers and compares the additional answers to the answer for 1 million.

LESSON

3.5

PLANNING

LESSON OUTLINE

First day:

15 min Example A

20 min Investigation

10 min Exercises

Second day:

15 min Investigation

10 min Sharing

5 min Example B

15 min Exercises

MATERIALS

- Pizza Supplies (T), *optional*
- Airline Schedules (W) or airline timetables
- Time Zone Map of the United States (W)
- Calculator Note 3E

TEACHING

In this lesson students see how to use residuals and the root mean square error to measure how well a line represents a data set.

One Step

Give students a data set, perhaps one generated as in Step 1 of the investigation. Challenge them to find a measure of how well a line of fit represents the data set. Suggest as needed that they consider how far the line is from each data point. If students want to calculate this distance perpendicular to the line, suggest that they use vertical or horizontal distance for ease of calculation. If any students use horizontal distances, ask one of them to present the ideas during Sharing. At that time, introduce the terms *residual* and *root mean square error* and point out that the book's formula for the root mean square error involves dividing by $(n - 2)$.

LESSON 3.5

Residuals

The median-median line method gives you a process by which anyone will get the same line of fit for a set of data. However, unless your data are perfectly linear, even the median-median line will not be perfect. In some cases you can find a more satisfactory model if you draw a line by hand. Having a line that "looks better" is not a convincing argument that it really is better.

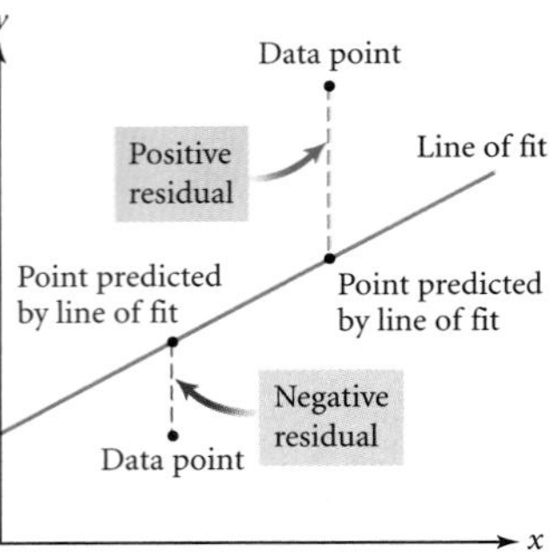

One excellent method to evaluate your line's fit is to look at the **residuals,** or the vertical differences between the points in your data set and the points generated by your line of fit.

residual = y-value of data point − y-value of point on line

Similar to the deviation from the mean that you learned about in Chapter 2, a residual is a signed distance. Here, a positive residual indicates that the point is above the line, and a negative residual indicates that the point is below the line.

A good-fitting line should have about as many points above it as below. This means that the sum of the residuals should be near zero. In other words, if you connect each point to the line with a vertical segment, the sum of the lengths of the segments above the line should be about equal to the sum of those below the line.

EXAMPLE A

The manager of Big K Pizza must order supplies for the month of November. The numbers of pizzas sold in November during the past four years were 512, 603, 642, and 775, respectively. How many pizzas should she plan for this November?

► **Solution**

Let x represent the past four years, 1 through 4, and let y represent the number of pizzas. Graph the data. The median-median method gives the linear model $\hat{y} = 417.3 + 87.7x$.

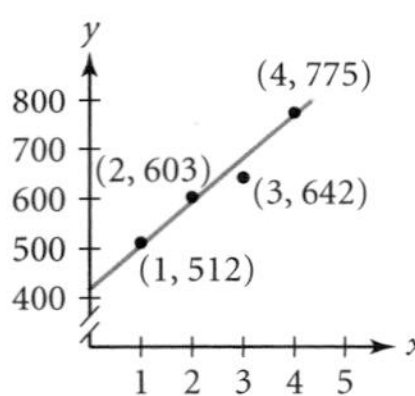

Calculating the residuals is one way to evaluate this model before using it to make a prediction. Evaluate the linear equation when x is 1, 2, 3, and 4. When $x = 1$, for example, $417.3 + 87.7(1) = 505.0$. A table helps organize the information.

► **EXAMPLE A**

Statistics books customarily introduce $\hat{y}$ (pronounced "y hat") to represent a predicted y-value, a y-value on a line of fit given by $\hat{y} = f(x)$. Hence you can define each residual as $y_i - \hat{y}_i$ where $\hat{y}_i = f(x_i)$. The order does matter here, so make sure students find the residual by taking the actual data value minus the predicted value.

LESSON OBJECTIVES

- Define *residual*
- Calculate the residual sum for a small number of data points
- Use residuals to test the fit of a line
- Define *root mean square error*
- Calculate the root mean square error for a small number of data points
- Use the root mean square error to find the error range in the context of a problem

Year (x)	1	2	3	4
Number of pizzas (y)	512	603	642	775
y-value from line $\hat{y} = 417.3 + 87.7x$	505.0	592.7	680.4	768.1
Residual	7	10.3	−38.4	6.9

The sum of the residuals is $7 + 10.3 + (-38.4) + 6.9$, or -14.2 pizzas, which is fairly close to zero in relation to the large number of pizzas purchased. The linear model is therefore a pretty good fit. The sum is negative, which means that all together the points below the line are a little farther away than those above.

If the manager plans for $417.3 + 87.7(5)$, or approximately 856 pizzas, she will be very close to the linear pattern established over the past four years. Because the residuals range from -38.4 to 7, she may want to adjust her prediction higher or lower depending on factors such as whether or not the supplies are perishable or whether or not she can easily order more supplies.

The investigation gives you another opportunity to fit a line to data and to analyze the real-world meaning of the linear model. You'll also calculate residuals and explore their meaning.

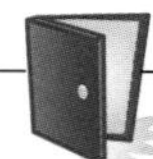

Investigation

Airline Schedules

You will need

- an airline timetable for the continental United States that includes both flight times and distances
- a time zone map for the continental United States

In this investigation you will create a linear model that relates the distance and time of an airline flight. You'll use residuals to judge the fit of your line, and you'll consider factors that may make the fit less than perfect.

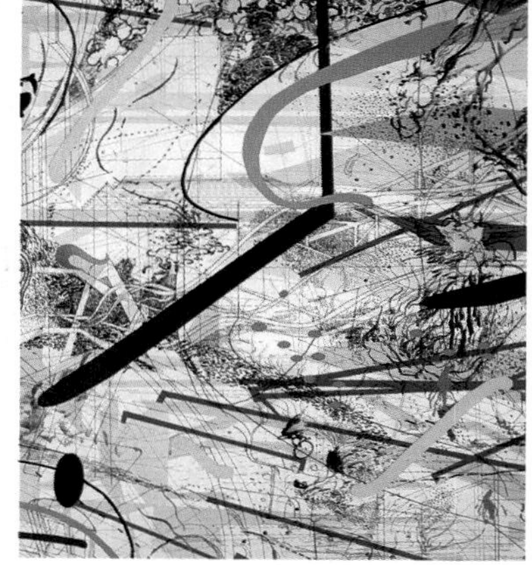

This painting by Julie Mehretu (b 1970), *Retopistics: A Renegade Excavation* (2001), is based on plans of international airports.

Step 1 Decide as a class which major city is going to be the starting point. Then work with your group and record in a table the flight times and distances to at least eight other cities from the chosen starting point. Choose only nonstop flights.

Step 2 Plot your data. Let x represent the flight time, and let y represent the flight distance.

Step 3 Find the median-median line for your data. When you have your linear model, answer these questions.

a. What is the real-world meaning of the slope?

b. What is the meaning of the y-intercept?

c. What is the value of the x-intercept? What is its real-world meaning?

Step 3 $\hat{y} = -235.1 + 7.6x$

Step 3a The slope indicates that the number of miles traveled in 1 minute is approximately 7.6 mi.

Example A (continued)
You might use the Pizza Supplies transparency as you discuss Example A. Plotting the data with the median-median line will help you demonstrate visually what a residual is. As arranged in the book's table, you subtract down the columns.

[Ask] "What is the real-world meaning of the residual -38.4?" [In year 3, the number of pizzas actually sold was 38.4 fewer than predicted by the model.]

By this model, (3, 642) is an outlier because the magnitude of its residual is extreme.

Guiding the Investigation

Step 1 The schedule should contain the times and distances from a large airport hub to other cities. Students can find links to schedules at www.keymath.com. Or use the Airline Schedules worksheets. Encourage students to convert the travel time to minutes if needed.

An alternative approach is to use the same data for all groups but have each group use a different line-fitting method in Step 3. Then in Step 4 students can use the residuals and the residual sums to compare the fit and select the best model.

[Alert] Students might forget about time zones when they calculate the actual flight times. Students might need to limit their attention to cities included on the Time Zone Map of the United States worksheet. The best results are often obtained by using the first flight of the day from the hub to each city.

Step 2 [Alert] If the data do not appear linear even after students verify their calculations, see if a data point is in Arizona or Indiana. Parts of those states do not participate in daylight saving time, so the data might be off by an hour.

See page 881 for answers to Steps 1, 2, and 3b and c.

NCTM STANDARDS

CONTENT		PROCESS	
	Number	✓	Problem Solving
✓	Algebra	✓	Reasoning
	Geometry	✓	Communication
✓	Measurement	✓	Connections
✓	Data/Probability	✓	Representation

Step 2 (continued)
Students might want to consider time as the dependent variable because the length of the flight depends on the distance to the destination city. Allow students to do this, and check that their results are consistent with the way they assign the variables.

Step 3 Students can calculate the median-median line by hand or on a calculator. **[Ask]** "Why aren't all the groups' equations the same?" [Different cities were used. Answers given are for sample data.]

Step 4 You might want to introduce Calculator Note 3E so students can calculate residuals on their calculators.

Step 4b offers an opportunity to discuss outliers. Ask students if they can find a similar flight whose time better fits the model.

Step 4

x	y	$\hat{y}$	$y - \hat{y}$
64	229	251.3	−22.3
189	1092	1201.3	−109.3
288	1979	1953.7	25.3
104	610	555.3	54.7
105	528	562.9	−34.9
248	1671	1649.7	21.3
667	306	274.1	31.9
303	2079	2067.7	11.3

Step 4b The greatest positive residual is 54.7 for Memphis, TN, which means that the actual distance is more miles than predicted. The greatest negative residual is −109.3 for Houston, TX, which means the actual distance is fewer miles than predicted. Geography, prevailing winds, or equipment (type of jet) may be responsible for these extreme residuals.

Step 4c Many factors influence the flight times, including geography, prevailing winds, time of travel, and equipment. If students collect data for flights going both east and west, they will find that flights going west generally take longer.

Assessing Progress

You can assess students' ability to make scatter plots and find median-median lines. You can also check their understanding of y-intercept and slope and their critical thinking skills.

Step 4a The sum is −22, which is small relative to the y-values, so a linear model is a good fit.

Step 4d $\hat{y} = -235.1 + 7.6(147) = 882.1$, or approximately 882 miles for a 147 minute flight; because the sum of the residuals is negative, the estimate might be adjusted to a slightly lower value.

Step 4 Use a table to organize your data and calculate the residuals.

a. What is the sum of the residuals? Does it appear that your linear model is a good fit?

b. Find the greatest positive and negative residuals. What could the magnitude of these residuals indicate?

c. In general, why do you think two flights of the same distance might require different flight times? Are flight times from east to west the same as those from west to east? What other interesting observations can you share?

d. Use your model to predict the distance of a 147-minute flight. Based on the residuals, would you adjust the estimate higher or lower? Explain your reasoning.

The sum of the residuals for your line of fit should be close to 0. However, as shown at right, you could find a poorly fitting line and still get 0 for the sum of the residuals. Due to the residual sizes, you should realize that this model will not make very accurate predictions. A good-fitting line should also follow the direction of the points. This means that the individual residuals should be as close to 0 as possible.

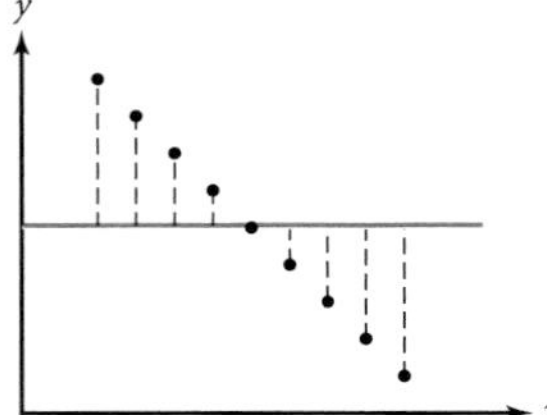

Because the sum of the residuals does not give a complete picture, you need some way to judge how accurate predictions from your model will be. One useful measure of accuracy starts by squaring the residuals to make them all positive. For the pizza data and the linear model in Example A, this gives

Year (x)	1	2	3	4
Number of pizzas (y)	512	603	642	775
Residual	7.0	10.3	−38.4	6.9
(Residual)^2	49	106.09	1474.56	47.61

The sum of the squares is quite large: 1677.26 pizzas^2. Perhaps some kind of average would give a better indication of the error in the predictions from this model. You could divide by 4 since there are four data points. However, this is not necessarily the best thing to do. Consider that it takes a minimum of two points to make any equation of a line. So two of the points can be thought of as defining the line. The other points determine the spread. So you should actually divide by 2 less than the number of data points.

$$\frac{1677.26}{4-2} = 838.63 \text{ pizzas}^2$$

The measure of the error should be measured in numbers of pizzas, rather than pizzas^2, so take the square root of this number.

$$\sqrt{838.63} \approx 29.0 \text{ pizzas}$$

Root Mean Square Error

[Language] This statistic is also known as the *standard error about the line, the standard error of estimate,* and *the root mean square residual.*

[Alert] Students might be surprised that the units are "pizzas^2." The residual is a difference of numbers whose units are pizzas, so the square of each residual (and hence the sum of those squares) has pizzas^2 as its units.

[Alert] Students might be challenged by the discussion of why the denominator is $(n - 2)$, even though it is similar to the earlier explanation of why the denominator in the formula for standard deviation is $(n - 1)$. In fact, as with that formula, different statisticians prefer different explanations.

[Ask] "Why is the name of this statistic so long?" [It describes the formula: square *root* of the *mean* of the *squares* of the *errors* (residuals).] It's called the mean because some statisticians divide by n instead of by $(n - 2)$.

This means that generally this line should predict values for the number of pizzas that are within 29.0 pizzas of the actual data. This value is called the **root mean square error.**

Root Mean Square Error

The root mean square error, s, is a measure of the spread of data points from a model.

$$s = \sqrt{\frac{\sum_{i=1}^{n}(y_i - \hat{y}_i)^2}{n-2}}$$

where y_i represents the y-values of the individual data pairs, $\hat{y}_i$ represents the respective y-values predicted from the model, and n is the number of data pairs.

You should notice that root mean square error is very similar to standard deviation, which you learned about in Chapter 2. Because of their similarities, both are represented by the variable s.

EXAMPLE B

A scientist measures the current in milliamps through a circuit with constant resistance as the voltage in volts is varied. What is the root mean square error for the model $\hat{y} = 0.47x$? What is the real-world meaning of the root mean square error? Predict the current when the voltage is 25.000 volts.

Voltage (x)	5.000	7.500	10.000	12.500	15.000	17.500	20.000
Current (y)	2.354	3.527	4.698	5.871	7.053	8.225	9.403

▶ Solution

A graph of the data and the linear model shows a good fit. To calculate the root mean square error, first calculate the residual for each data point, take the sum of the squares of the residuals, divide by $n - 2$, and take a square root. [▶ See **Calculator Note 3E** for ways to calculate the root mean square error on your calculator. ◀]

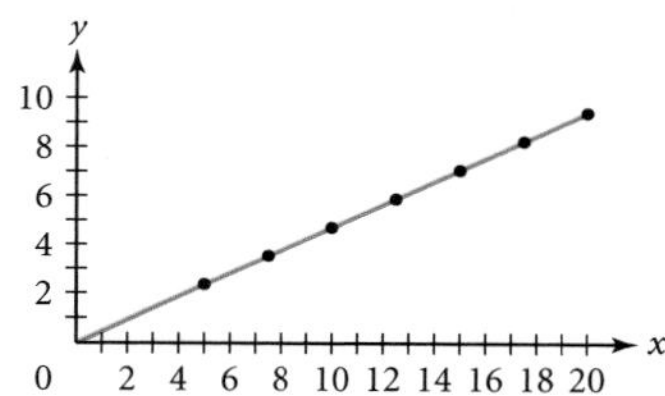

Voltage (x)	5.000	7.500	10.000	12.500	15.000	17.500	20.000
Current (y)	2.354	3.527	4.698	5.871	7.053	8.225	9.403
Prediction from line ($\hat{y}$)	2.350	3.525	4.700	5.875	7.050	8.225	9.400
Residual ($y - \hat{y}$)	0.004	0.002	−0.002	−0.004	0.003	0	0.003
(Residual)^2	1.6×10^{-5}	4.0×10^{-6}	4.0×10^{-6}	1.6×10^{-5}	9×10^{-6}	0	9.0×10^{-6}

▶ EXAMPLE B

When you are demonstrating this calculation, consider working with the units as you complete each step. Seeing the square units might help students understand why the square root is taken at the end.

The principle used in this example is $E = IR$, where E is the voltage, I is the current, and R is the resistance. Usually the principle is stated as $G = \frac{I}{E}$, where G is the conductance, or the reciprocal of the resistance.

SHARING IDEAS

Arrange presentations to include a variety of ideas. Concentrate on Step 4a and b in the investigation. Point out cases in which having a residual sum of 0 does not guarantee a good fit.

The class can also discuss mistakes, intercepts and their real-world meanings, what is actually being timed, what happens if a flight is reversed, prevailing winds, the first flight in the morning versus later flights, local daylight saving time oddities, short flights that may use smaller planes, and so on.

[Ask] "Is it better to calculate distances from the line vertically rather than horizontally?" [Yes, because the line's equation is more likely to be given in $y=$ form than in $x=$ form.] You might draw some similar triangles to show how dividing each residual by the line's slope gives the horizontal distance to the line.

Students might wonder how to adjust a line to find the line that minimizes the root mean square error. The least-squares regression line, which appears in Lesson 13.5, has that property.

Sharing Ideas (continued)

[Ask] "How is the root mean square error like and unlike the standard deviation?" [They're alike in that you calculate a sum of squares. They're different in their denominators and in that there's no constant in the differences that appear in the numerators.] Point out that if the residuals sum to 0, then their mean is 0, in which case each numerator is (*residual* − *mean of residuals*)^2. Thus the root mean square error measures the spread of the residuals.

[Ask] "How can we use the root mean square error?" [Instead of making a prediction that's a single number, we predict a number plus or minus the root mean square error. That is, most values will fall within this distance of the line, just as most data points fall within one standard deviation of the mean.]

$$s = \sqrt{\frac{5.8 \times 10^{-5}}{7-2}} = \sqrt{\frac{5.8 \times 10^{-5}}{5}} = \sqrt{1.16 \times 10^{-5}} \approx 0.0034$$

This means that values predicted by this equation will generally be within 0.0034 milliamp of the actual current.

For a current of 25.000 volts, the model gives 0.47(25.000), or 11.750 milliamps. Considering the root mean square error, the scientist could expect a reading between 11.7466 milliamps and 11.7534 milliamps.

You have seen many ways to find a line of fit for data. Calculating residuals and the root mean square error now gives you tools for evaluating how well your line fits the data.

EXERCISES

Practice Your Skills

1. The median-median line for a set of data is $\hat{y} = 2.4x + 3.6$. Find the residual for each of these data points.

a. (2, 8.2) −0.2 **b.** (4, 12.8) −0.4 **c.** (10, 28.2) 0.6

2. The median-median line for a set of data is $\hat{y} = -1.8x + 94$. This table gives the x-value and the residual for each data point. Determine the y-value for each data point. 82.3, 82.9, 74.5, 56.9

x-value	5	8	12	20
Residual	−2.7	3.3	2.1	−1.1

3. Return to Exercise 6 in Lesson 3.4 about life expectancy for males. Use your median-median line equation to answer these questions.

a. Calculate the residuals.

b. Calculate the root mean square error for the median-median line. 1.22 yr

c. What is the real-world meaning of the root mean square error?

4. Suppose the residuals for a data set are 0.4, −0.3, 0.2, 0.1, −0.2, −0.3, 0.2, 0.1. What is the root mean square error for this set of residuals? approximately 0.28

Reason and Apply

5. APPLICATION This table gives the mean height in centimeters of boys ages 5 to 13 in the United States.

Age	Height (cm)
5	109.2
6	115.7
7	122.0
8	128.1
9	133.7

Age	Height (cm)
10	138.8
11	143.7
12	149.3
13	156.4

(National Center for Health Statistics)

a. Define variables, plot the data, and find the median-median line.

b. Calculate the residuals.

c. What is the root mean square error for the median-median line? 0.83 cm

d. What is the real-world meaning of the root mean square error?

e. If you use the median-median line to predict the mean height of boys age 15, what range of heights should be predicted? between 165.7 cm and 167.3 cm

Closing the Lesson

Residuals of a line representing a data set are the differences between the y-values in the data set and the $\hat{y}$-values on the line right above or below them. For a line of good fit, the sum of these residuals is close to 0, but some lines with this property are not lines of good fit. The **root mean square error** describes the spread of the residuals about their mean and thus measures the quality of fit and can help you decide what numbers to use in making predictions.

BUILDING UNDERSTANDING

In the exercises students evaluate how well lines of fit represent data, using residuals and the root mean square error, and use those lines in making predictions.

ASSIGNING HOMEWORK

Essential	1–4
Performance assessment	5, 7–11
Portfolio	9
Journal	6
Group	11
Review	12–15

Helping with the Exercises

Exercise 3 This exercise uses the data and the median-median line from Lesson 3.4, Exercise 6.

3a. 1920: −2.74; 1925: −1.2; 1930: −0.56; 1935: −0.42; 1940: −0.18; 1945: 0.66; 1950: 2.3; 1955: 1.74; 1960: 0.98; 1965: 0.02; 1970: −0.84; 1975: −0.3; 1980: −0.26; 1985: −0.22; 1990: −0.78; 1995: −1.24; 1998: −0.536

3c. In general, the life expectancy values predicted by the median-median line will be within 1.23 yr of the actual data values.

5a. Let x represent age in years, and let y represent height in cm; $\hat{y} = 82.5 + 5.6x$.

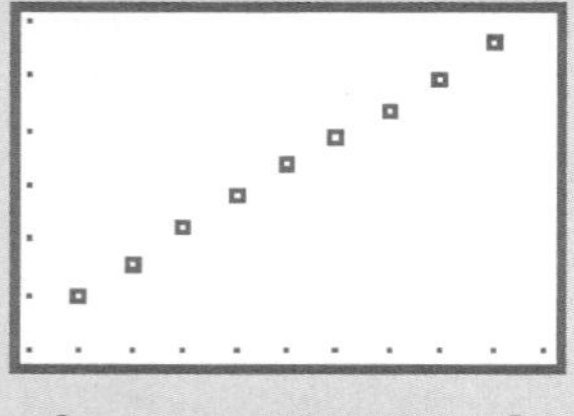

[4, 14, 1, 100, 160, 10]

5b. −1.3, −0.4, 0.3, 0.8, 0.8, 0.3, −0.4, −0.4, 1.1

5d. In general, the mean height of boys ages 5 to 13 will be within 0.83 cm of the values predicted by the median-median line.

Exercise 5e [Ask] "Is this prediction interpolation or extrapolation?" [extrapolation] Discuss whether it is reasonable to use a model based on ages 5 through 13 to extrapolate to age 15.

6. Consider the residuals from Exercise 5b.

a. Make a box plot of these values.

b. Describe the information about the residuals that is shown in the box plot.

7. With a specific line of fit, the data point (6, 47) has a residual of 2.8. The slope of the line of fit is 2.4. What is the equation of the line of fit? $\hat{y} = 29.8 + 2.4x$

8. The following readings were taken from a display outside the First River Bank. The display alternated between °F and °C. However, there was an error within the system that calculated the temperatures.

°F	18	33	37	25	40	46	43	49	55	60	57
°C	−6	2	3	−3	5	8	7	10	12	15	13

a. Plot the data and the median-median line.

b. Calculate the residuals. You will notice that the residuals are generally negative for the lower temperatures and positive for the higher temperatures. How is this represented on the graph of the data and line?

c. Adjust your equation (by adjusting the slope or y-intercept) to improve this distribution of the residuals.

d. Calculate the root mean square error for the median-median line and for the equation you found in 8c. Compare the root mean square errors for the two lines and explain what this tells you.

e. Use your equation from 8c to predict what temperature will be paired with

i. 85°F 27.5°C

ii. 0°C 30°F

9. Alex says, "The formula for the root mean square error is long. Why do you have to square and then take the square root? Isn't that just doing a lot of work for nothing? Can't you just make them all positive, add them up, and divide?" Help Calista show Alex that his method does not give the same value as the root mean square error. Use the residual set −2, 1, −3, 4, −1 in your demonstration. Do you think Alex's method could be used as another measure of accuracy? Explain your reasoning.

10. Leajato experimented by turning the key of a wind-up car different numbers of times and recorded how far it traveled.

Turns	0.5	1	1.5	2	2.5	3	3.5	4
Distance (in.)	33	73	114	152	187	223	256	298

a. Graph the data and find the median-median line.

b. Calculate the root mean square error. 3.65 in.

c. Predict how far the car will go if you turn the key five times. Use the root mean square error to describe the accuracy of your answer.
between 358.5 in. and 376.4 in.

6a.

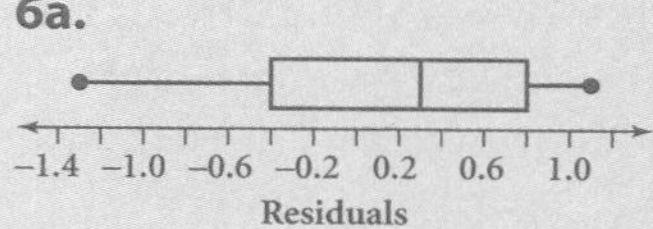

6b. Possible answers: The median residual is positive. The lower half of the residuals have a larger spread than the upper half. Half of the residuals lie between −0.4 and 0.8.

Exercise 7 As needed, suggest that students draw a diagram.

Exercise 8 Students can refer to Calculator Note 3E to see how to have residual calculations adjusted automatically as they change the equation in Y1. In 8c students are expected to use a guess-and-check method by adjusting the y-intercept to shift the line vertically and by adjusting the slope. (This works easily in Fathom.) In 8e the temperatures will be rounded to the nearest degree. **[Ask]** "Is this prediction interpolation or extrapolation?" [extrapolation for part i, interpolation for part ii]

8a. Let x represent temperature in degrees Fahrenheit, and let y represent temperature in degrees Celsius; $\hat{y} = -14.21 + 0.4815x$.

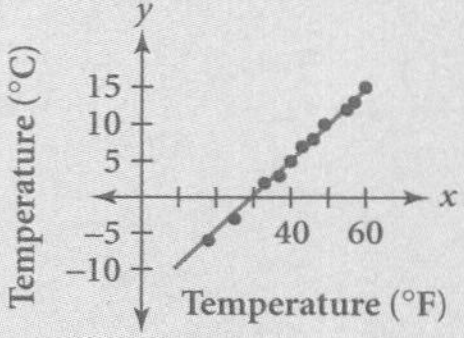

8b. −0.457, 0.3205, −0.606, −0.8275, −0.05, 0.061, 0.5055, 0.6165, −0.2725, 0.32, −0.2355. The points on the left end of the graph are generally below the line whereas those on the right end are generally above the line.

8c. The slope should increase, and the y-intercept should be lowered; possible answer: $\hat{y} = -15 + 0.5x$.

8d. For $\hat{y} = -14.21 + 0.4815x$, $s \approx 0.499$. For $\hat{y} = -15 + 0.5x$, $s \approx 0.441$. The smaller root mean square error for $\hat{y} = -15 + 0.5x$ indicates that this equation is a better fit for the data because it provides more accurate predictions.

Exercise 9 Alex's method is analogous to the mean deviation method of measuring spread, mentioned in Lesson 2.2.

9. Alex's method: $\frac{2+1+3+4+1}{3} = 3.67$; root mean square error method: $\sqrt{\frac{4+1+9+16+1}{3}} \approx 3.21$. Because both methods give values around 3, Alex's method could be used as an alternative measure of accuracy.

Exercise 10 **[Ask]** "Is this prediction interpolation or extrapolation?" [extrapolation]

10a.

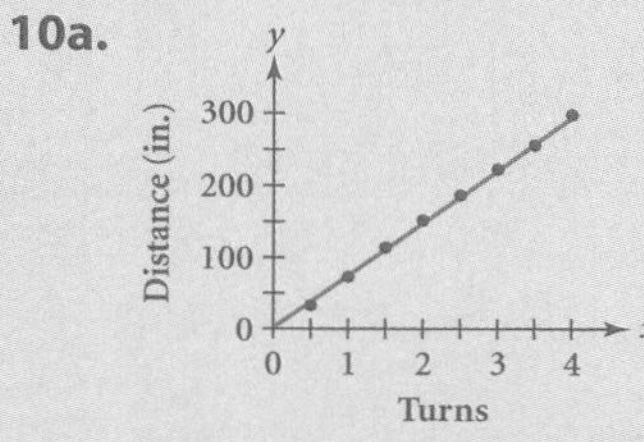

Let x represent turns, and let y represent distance in inches; $\hat{y} = 1.4667 + 73.2x$.

Exercise 11 You might discuss the book's choice of x and y. **[Ask]** "Are these necessarily dependent and independent variables?" **[Context]** You might challenge students to find out who the candidates were in each election listed in the table.

11a.

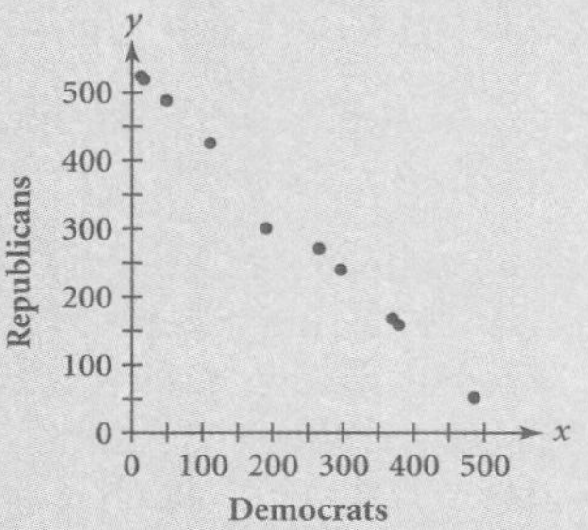

11b. The points are nearly linear because the sum of electoral votes should be 538. The data are not perfectly linear because in a few of the elections, candidates other than the Democrats and Republicans received some electoral votes.

11c.

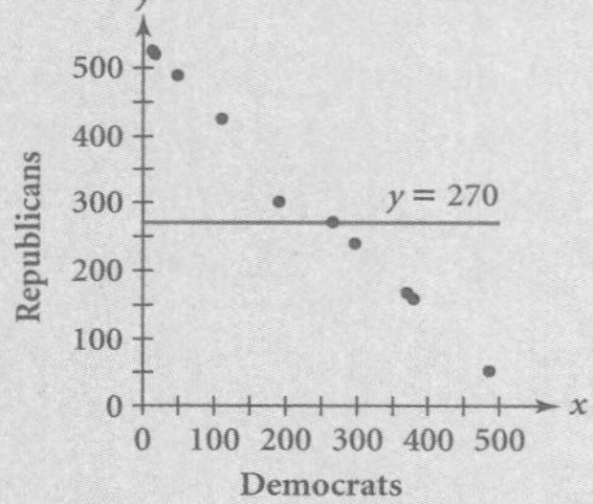

The points above the line are the elections in which the Republican Party's presidential candidate won.

11d. −218, 31, 250, −30, 219, 255, 156, −102, −111, 1
A negative residual means that the Democratic Party's presidential candidate won.

Exercise 13 All valid answers will include this pattern: 28, a, ?, 47, ?, $a + 12$, ?.

Exercise 14 Equations in which the variable appears on both sides cannot be solved easily by undoing or by arrow diagrams unless they are rewritten so the variable appears only once. Students can use balancing, graphing, or guess-and-check.

11. APPLICATION Since 1964, the total number of electors in the electoral college has been 538. In order to declare a winner in a presidential election, a majority, or 270 electoral votes, is needed. The table at right shows the number of electoral votes that the Democratic and Republican parties have received in the presidential elections since 1964.

a. Let x represent the electoral votes for the Democratic Party, and let y represent the votes for the Republican Party. Make a scatter plot of the data.

b. Why are the points nearly linear? What are some factors that make these data not perfectly linear?

c. Sketch the line $y = 270$ on the scatter plot. How are all the points above the line related?

d. Find the residuals for the line $y = 270$. What does a negative residual represent?

e. What does a residual value that is close to 0 represent? a close election

Electoral Votes

Year	Democrats	Republicans
1964	486	52
1968	191	301
1972	17	520
1976	297	240
1980	49	489
1984	13	525
1988	111	426
1992	370	168
1996	379	159
2000	266	271

History CONNECTION

Article II, Section 1, of the U.S. Constitution instituted the electoral college as a means of electing the president. The number of electoral votes allotted to each state corresponds to the number of representatives that each state sends to Congress. The distribution of electoral votes among the states can change every 10 years depending on the results of the U.S. census. The actual process of selecting electors is left for each state to decide.

Election workers in Dade County, Florida, hand check ballots during the 2000 presidential election.

Review

3.3 **12.** Write an equation in point-slope form for each of these lines.

a. The slope is $\frac{3}{5}$ and the line passes through (2, 4.7). $y = 4.7 + 0.6(x - 2)$

b. The line has slope −7 and x-intercept 6. $y = 0 - 7(x - 6)$

c. The line passes through (3, 11) and (−6, −18). $y = 11 + \frac{29}{9}(x - 3)$ or $y = -18 + \frac{29}{9}(x + 6)$

2.1 **13.** Create a set of 7 values with median 47, minimum 28, and interquartile range 12. possible answer: 28, 38, 42, 47, 49, 50, 60

14. Solve.

a. $3 + 5x = 17 - 2x$ $x = 2$

b. $12 + 3(t - 5) = 6t + 1$ $t = -\frac{4}{3}$

1.5 **15.** David deposits $30 into his bank account at the end of each month. The bank pays 7% annual interest compounded monthly.

a. Write a recursive formula to show David's balance at the end of each month.

b. How much of the balance was deposited and how much interest is earned after

i. 1 year **ii.** 10 years **iii.** 25 years **iv.** 50 years

c. What can you conclude about regular saving in a bank with compound interest?

15a. $u_0 = 30$ and $u_n = u_{n-1}\left(1 + \frac{0.07}{12}\right) + 30$ where $n \geq 1$

15b. i. deposited: $360; interest: $11.78

15b. ii. deposited: $3,600; interest: $1,592.54

15b. iii. deposited: $9,000; interest: $15,302.15

15b. iv. deposited: $18,000; interest: $145,442.13

15c. Sample answer: If you earn compound interest, in the long run the interest earned will far exceed the total amount deposited.

EXTENSIONS

A. Challenge students to find a linear model for the data in Example A with a residual sum even closer to 0 than that produced by the median-median line.

B. Extend the investigation by asking students to find and compare the equations if flights are limited to westbound, eastbound, morning, or evening flights.

C. Ask students if they've ever seen a prediction of something "plus or minus x percent" and to speculate as to whether this is the root mean square error.

EXPLORATION

Residual Plots and Least Squares

You have learned a couple of different ways to fit a line to data. You've also used residuals to judge how well a line fits and to give a range for predictions made with that line. In this activity, you will learn two graphical methods to judge how well your line fits the data. You will also use these methods to identify outliers.

Activity

A Good Fit?

Step 1 Start Fathom and open the sample document titled **States–CarsNDrivers.ftm.** When the file opens you will see a collection and a case table. This collection gives you various data about the population, drivers, vehicles, and roadways in each U.S. state and the District of Columbia in the year 1992.

Step 2 Create a new graph. Drag the attribute PopThou (population in thousands) to the x-axis and drag the attribute DriversThou (licensed drivers in thousands) to the y-axis. Your graph will automatically become a scatter plot. Describe the trend in the data and give a possible explanation for the trend.

Step 3 With the graph window selected, choose **Movable Line** from the Graph menu. Drag the movable line until it fits the data well. What is the equation of your estimated line of fit? Based on your line, which states are outliers?

Step 4 Choose **Make Residual Plot** from the Graph menu. What does the residual plot show you? From the residual plot, which states are outliers? Are they the same states you selected in Step 3?

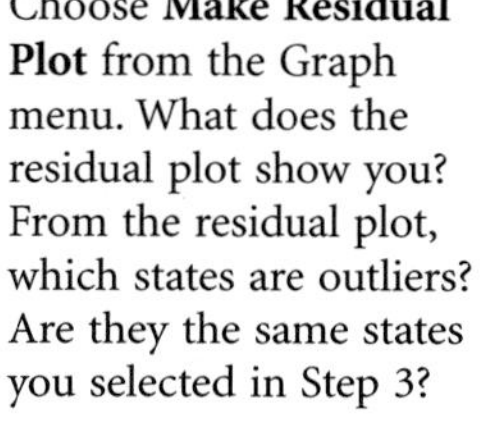

Step 5 Experiment by moving the movable line and observe how the residual plot changes.

Step 2 The data are approximately linear. Sample answer: The percentage of people who drive is approximately the same everywhere, so as population increases, the number of drivers will increase too.

Step 3 Sample answer: $DriversThou = 0.670PopThou - 0.12$; Ohio, Florida, and New York appear to be outliers.

Step 4 The residual plot graphs the independent variable against the residuals of the dependent variable; it shows the vertical distance from the line of fit for each data point. Ohio, Florida, and New York still appear to be outliers.

NCTM STANDARDS

CONTENT	PROCESS
Number	Problem Solving
✓ Algebra	✓ Reasoning
Geometry	✓ Communication
✓ Measurement	✓ Connections
✓ Data/Probability	✓ Representation

LESSON OBJECTIVES

- Use statistics software to make residual plots
- Use statistics software to examine least squares
- Evaluate a line of fit based on residual plots and least squares

EXPLORATION

PLANNING

LESSON OUTLINE

One day:

30 min Activity

15 min Sharing

MATERIALS

- Fathom
- Fathom demonstration A Good Fit?, *optional*

TEACHING

If you have limited resources, you might demonstrate this activity.

Guiding the Activity

Step 1 You might need to give these instructions: Choose **Open** from the File menu. Find the document within the Fathom application folder: **Sample Documents | DataInDepth | States | States–CarsNDrivers.ftm.**

Step 2 You might need to give these instructions: Choose **Graph** from the Insert menu. Drag the corner of the graph window to increase the size of the graph. **[Ask]** "Does it make sense that these data are linear?"

Step 3 After students have a satisfactory line of fit, **[Ask]** "Does your y-intercept make sense?" [Theoretically the y-intercept should be 0.] "What does your slope mean in terms of the problem?" [If the y-intercept is 0, the slope is the portion $\left(\text{about } \frac{2}{3}\right)$ of the population that drives.]

[Alert] Students might consider the point far to the right an outlier; don't correct them yet.

Students can determine the state by double-clicking on a point or by shift-clicking on points and

Step 3 (continued)
seeing what's highlighted in the case table.

Step 4 Now students can see that outliers are points with large or small residuals. **[Ask]** "Why do you think these states are outliers?" [Nearly everyone drives in Ohio and Florida; many people in New York City use public transportation.] California is far to the right because it has a large population, not because it has an unusual percentage of drivers.

A graph of residuals is also possible on a calculator. When median-median lines or least squares lines are calculated, the calculator stores a list called Resid. A graph of (x, Resid) is similar to Fathom's Residual Plot.

Step 8 As needed, help students realize that in order to turn off a line, they choose it again from the Graph menu. They might be confused because the residual plot doesn't change. Actually, the plot is based on the first line for which it is created—probably the movable line. To get a residual plot for another line, students turn it off and then turn it back on when the other line is the latest line created.

Step 8 Answers will vary. If students have found a pretty good line of fit, there may not be much difference between it and its squares and the more formal lines of fit. For the States–CarsNDrivers data, the median-median line and the least squares line are slightly different.

See page 881 for answers to Questions 1 and 2.

Step 6 Each square is drawn by connecting each point to the line of fit with a segment, then constructing a square with this segment as a side.

Step 7 The squares for the outliers are much larger (i.e., have a greater area).

Step 6 Return to your scatter plot and residual plot. With the graph window selected, choose **Show Squares** from the Graph menu. Move the movable line and observe how the squares change. Explain how each square is drawn.

Step 7 Move your line back to a position where it is a good fit. (You might want to turn off the squares while you do this.) Notice the size of the squares for the outliers that you identified in Step 4. How do they compare to the other squares?

Step 8 In addition to the movable line, Fathom will graph a median-median line and a least-squares line. (You'll learn more about the least squares line in Chapter 13.) Try adding a median-median line and a least squares line to your graph, either alone or with your estimate of a line of fit. How do the equations compare? How do the residual plots compare? How do the squares compare?

Questions

1. How can you identify outliers from the squares? How are approaches interrelated? How did you identify outliers from looking at the line of fit? How did you identify outliers from the residual plot? Do you find one approach easier than the other?
2. As you change the slope of your line, what happens to the residual plot? As you change the y-intercept of your line, what happens to the residual plot? Explain how you can use the residual plot to adjust the fit of your line.
3. Graphs A, B, and C are residual plots for different lines of fit for the same data set. How would you adjust each line to be a better fit?

Question 3: The line of fit for Graph A needs to have its slope increased and its y-intercept decreased. The line of fit for Graph B needs to have its y-intercept decreased. The line of fit for Graph C is already a good line of fit and needs no adjustment.

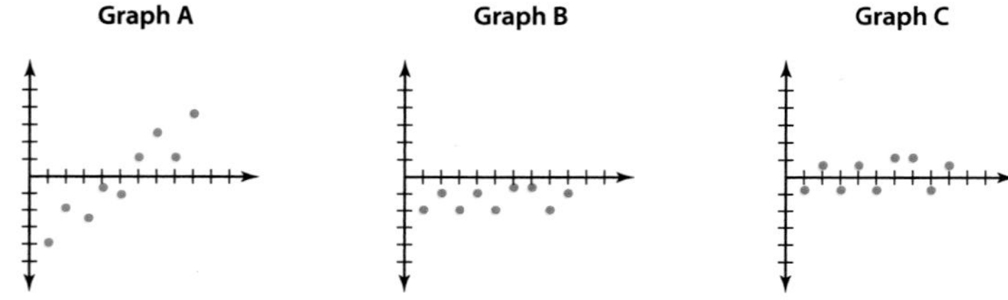

Question 4: A better fitting line will minimize the sum of the areas of the squares. The least squares line is so called because it absolutely minimizes the sum of the areas of the squares.

4. Explain how you can use the squares to adjust your moveable line to a better fit. Based on your explanation, how do you think the least-squares line got its name?
5. When you experimented with all three lines of fit in Step 8, did you get the same equation for all three? Give some reasons why this may or may not have happened. Answers will vary. For this data set at least, the least squares line and the median-median line differ slightly ($DriversThou = 0.655PopThou + 120$ and $DriversThou = 0.678PopThou + 18$, respectively). Outliers, and how each method of finding a line of fit deals with them, is the primary reason that the equations differ. If the data had been perfectly linear, the median-median line and the least squares line would be equivalent.

▶ Helping with the Questions

Questions 1, 2 **[Ask]** "What happens to the residual plot if you move the line dramatically, beyond being a good fit?"

Question 4 If students say "You want to make the squares as small as possible," **[Ask]** "How can you take into account all the squares at once?"

EXTENSION

Have students grab an outlier and drag it even farther away from the other points and then describe what happens to each line of fit. (To return the point to its correct location, choose **Undo** from the Edit menu or select the collection and choose **Revert Collection** from the File menu.) Students will see that the median-median line is quite sensitive to extreme outliers.

LESSON

3.6 Linear Systems

The number of tickets sold for a school activity, like a spaghetti dinner, helps determine the financial success of the event. Income from ticket sales can be less than, equal to, or greater than expenses. The break-even value is the intersection of the expense function and the line $y = x$. This equation models all the situations where the expenses, y, are equal to income, x. In this lesson, you will focus on mathematical situations involving two or more equations or conditions that must be satisfied at the same time. A set of two or more equations that share the same variables and are solved or studied simultaneously is called a **system of equations.**

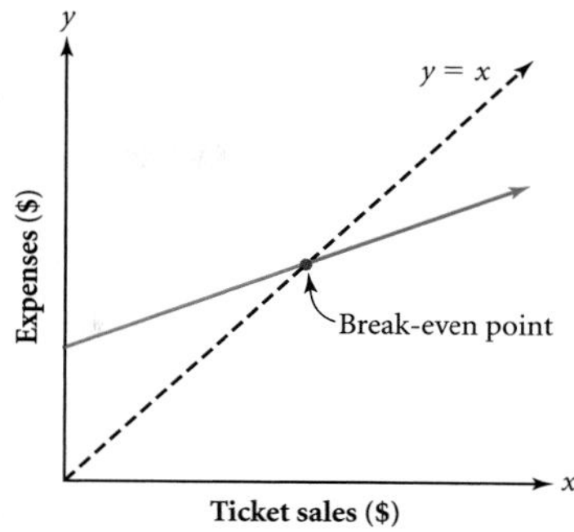

American painter I. Rice Pereira (1907–1971) explored light and space in her works, characterized by intersecting lines in mazelike patterns. This piece is titled *Green Mass* (1950).

EXAMPLE A

Minh and Daniel are starting a business together, and they need to decide between long-distance phone carriers. One company offers the Phrequent Phoner Plan, which costs 20¢ for the first minute of a phone call and 17¢ for each minute after that. A competing company offers the Small Business Plan, which costs 50¢ for the first minute and 11¢ for each additional minute. Which plan should Minh and Daniel choose?

▸ Solution

The plan they choose depends on the nature of their business and the most likely length and frequency of their phone calls. Because the Phrequent Phoner Plan (PPP) costs less for the first minute, it is obviously better for very short calls. However, the Small Business Plan (SBP) probably will be cheaper for longer calls because the cost is less for additional minutes. There is a phone conversation length for which both plans cost the same. To find it, let x represent the call length in minutes, and let y represent the cost in cents.

NCTM STANDARDS

CONTENT		PROCESS	
	Number	✓	Problem Solving
✓	Algebra	✓	Reasoning
✓	Geometry	✓	Communication
✓	Measurement	✓	Connections
	Data/Probability	✓	Representation

LESSON OBJECTIVES

- Examine problems involving two or more conditions that must be satisfied at the same time
- Understand the visual representation of a solution to a system of equations, and solve systems of equations graphically
- Solve systems of equations using the transitive property of equality
- Solve systems of equations using a table

LESSON

3.6

PLANNING

LESSON OUTLINE

One day:

5 min	Example A
20 min	Investigation
5 min	Example B
15 min	Exercises

MATERIALS

- Calculator Notes 3A, 3B, *optional*

TEACHING

This lesson might be review for many. Although students might prefer the algebraic method, it's important that they understand the graphical solution as well.

Referring to the graph that introduces the lesson, **[Ask]** "What part of the graph represents profits?" [green: expenses < income] Help students see that the dotted line represents where expenses equal income. **[Ask]** "What is the independent variable here? Do expenses depend on ticket sales?" [Neither variable depends on the other; either could be used as the independent variable.]

One Step

Show the data from the investigation and pose the problem stated in Step 1: "If the trends continue, when will San Jose have a larger population than Detroit?" Students might recall from a previous course systems of equations and various ways of solving them. If not, they might simply look at the trend in population differences.

▸ EXAMPLE A

[Ask] "Why do the equations include $(x - 1)$ rather than just x?" [The 17 is added on for each minute *after* the first; if $x = 1$, the result should simply be 20.]

Example A (continued)
On a graphing calculator, you can use the zoom function on the graph and the table to help students find the solution. (Calculator Notes 3A and 3B give advice useful to such a demonstration.) Pick a point on one of the lines and **[Ask]** "What is the real-world meaning of this point?"

Some students will recall the substitution or elimination method from *Discovering Algebra.* Use these ideas to make the transition to the next example and to preview the next lesson.

Guiding the Investigation

This investigation can be completed in groups or by individuals and might be assigned as homework. As needed, remind students of Calculator Note 3A.

Most students will choose to solve the system graphically or with substitution, but it is acceptable for them to use elimination or even to consider only the sequence of differences.

Step 1 **[Ask]** "Are the functions linear? Is it appropriate to use a linear model? Why?" Students might use the residuals to justify their answers.

Step 2 Discuss any concerns students might have about these models or about extrapolating for future data.

► ***EXAMPLE B***

[Ask] "What allows us to equate the right sides of these equations?" [the transitive property of equality]

[Ask] "What distance does d represent?" [the distance from Justine's starting point, which is not the same as the distance run by Evan] "Why are the equations combined by setting expressions equal to each other?" [We assume the distances from the starting point are equal, and we want to find the corresponding time.] "Do Justine and Evan run the same distance?" [No; Justine runs 50 ft farther.]

A cost equation that models the Phrequent Phoner Plan is

$$y = 20 + 17(x - 1)$$

A cost equation for the Small Business Plan is

$$y = 50 + 11(x - 1)$$

A graph of these equations shows the Phrequent Phoner Plan cost is below the Small Business Plan cost until the lines intersect. You may be able to estimate the coordinates of this point from the graph.

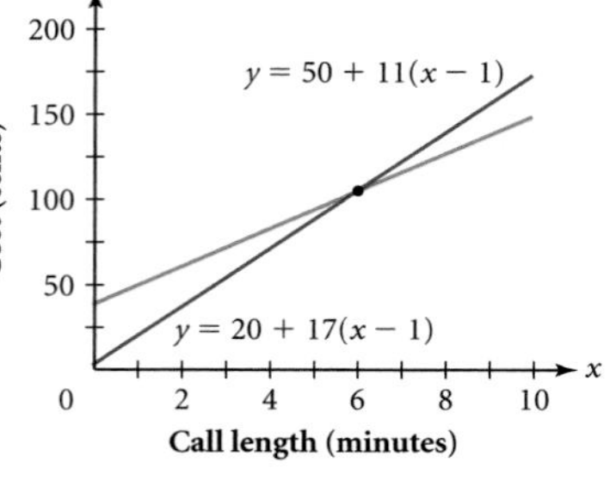

Or you can look in a table to find an answer. The point of intersection at (6, 105) tells you that a six-minute call will cost $1.05 with either plan.

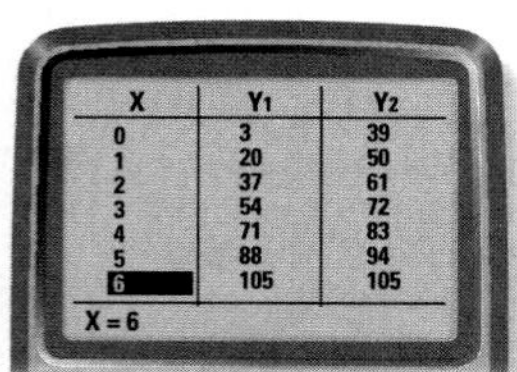

If Minh and Daniel believe their average business call will last less than six minutes, they should choose the Phrequent Phoner Plan. But if they think most of their calls will last more than six minutes, the Small Business Plan is the better option.

You can also use equations to solve for the point of intersection. What equations could you write for Example A?

Investigation
Population Trends

The table below gives the populations of San Jose, California, and Detroit, Michigan.

Populations

Year	1950	1960	1970	1980	1990
San Jose	95,280	204,196	459,913	629,400	782,224
Detroit	1,849,568	1,670,144	1,514,063	1,203,368	1,027,974

(*The World Almanac and Book of Facts 2001*)

Step 1 between 1995 and 1996; about 913,261

Step 1 If the trends continue, when will San Jose be as large as Detroit? What will the two populations be at that time?

Step 2 Students might solve a system of equations with a graph, a table, or algebraically.

Step 2 Show the method you used to make this prediction. Choose a different method to check your answer. Discuss the pros and cons of each method.

[Ask] "Why might this solution have been difficult to arrive at even though it's fairly easy to follow?" This question can help students prepare for encountering similar problems.

SHARING IDEAS

Whenever students demonstrate solving a system of equations, ask how the solution is represented on a graph and, especially, why it is presented that way. Have students reiterate the fact that a point lies on a graph if and only if its coordinates satisfy the equation of the graph.

[Ask] "In the year 2000 the population of San Jose was 894,493 and that of Detroit was 951,270. Is this consistent with your model? How might you change your model?" Encourage thinking about nonlinear models, such as shifted geometric sequences, as well as other linear models.

If no students used an approach that considers only differences, present this approach yourself and ask whether it's legitimate.

In algebra, you studied different methods for finding the exact coordinates of an intersection point by solving systems of equations. One method is illustrated in the next example.

EXAMPLE B

Justine and her little brother Evan are running a race. Because Evan is younger, Justine gives him a 50-foot head start. Evan runs at 12.5 feet per second and Justine runs at 14.3 feet per second. How far will they be from Justine's starting line before Justine passes Evan? What distance should Justine mark for a close race?

▸ Solution

You can compare the time and distance that each person runs. Because distance, d, depends on time, t, you can write these equations:

$d = rt$	Distance equals the rate, or speed, times time.
$d = 14.3t$	Justine's distance equation.
$d = 50 + 12.5t$	Evan's distance equation.

Graphing these two equations shows that Justine eventually catches up to Evan and passes him, if the race is long enough. At that moment, they are at the same distance from the start, at the same time. You can estimate this point from the graph or scroll down until you find the answer in the table. You can also solve the system of equations.

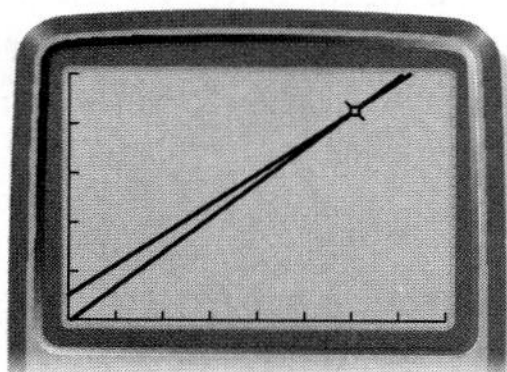

[0, 40, 5, 0, 500, 100]

Because both equations represent distances and you want to know when those distances are equal, you can set the equations equal to each other and solve for the time, t, when the distances are equal.

$14.3t = 50 + 12.5t$	The right side of Justine's equation equals the right side of Evan's equation, because they are equal to the same distance, d.
$1.8t = 50$	Subtract $12.5t$ from both sides.
$t = \frac{50}{1.8} \approx 27.8$	Divide both sides by 1.8.

So, Justine passes Evan after 27.8 seconds. Now you can substitute this value back into either equation to find their distances from the starting line when Justine passes Evan.

$$d = 14.3t = 14.3 \cdot \frac{50}{1.8} \approx 397.2$$

If Justine marks a 400 ft distance, she will win, but it will be a close race.

The method of solving a system demonstrated in Example B uses one form of **substitution.** In this case you substituted one expression for distance in place of the distance, d, in the other equation, resulting in an equation with only one variable, t. When you have the two equations written in intercept form, substitution is a straightforward method for finding an exact solution. The solution to a system of equations with two variables is a pair of values that satisfies both equations. Sometimes a system will have many solutions or no solution.

Sharing Ideas (continued)

Refer students back to Example A. Ask whether the data are discrete, in which case an explicit formula would be better than a linear equation. Students might think the data are discrete because the y-values can be only integers. Remind them that discreteness depends on the domain (x-values) and that telephone charges can be calculated for nonwhole numbers of minutes. Exercise 9 examines this problem again, using the greatest integer function.

While discussing Example B, remind students that previous two-person motion problems (for example, Lesson 1.1, Exercise 9) could be solved by considering "closing speed" and ask whether that's the case here. Bring out the idea that Justine, running 1.8 ft/s faster than Evan, can close the 50 ft gap in $\frac{50}{1.8}$ s, or about 27.8 s.

Point out that in Example B the distances were set equal. Ask whether there are cases in which the *times* would be equal. As a class, create and solve a problem that reflects this situation.

If time allows, you can preview Chapter 6. **[Ask]** "In Example B, what if Evan ran 14.3 feet per second?" As students realize that he would be running at the same rate as Justine and therefore would always be ahead, ask whether the calculations would reflect the constant distance between them. In the calculations, t would disappear and leave the equation $0 = 50$. This is actually a contradiction to the assumption that the system has a solution—an assumption made by working with both equations together. Equations that make up a system with no solution are called *inconsistent.*

[Ask] "When would a system have no solutions? When would it have many solutions?" [graphs of the equations are parallel; the same line]

Assessing Progress

You can assess students' understanding of lines of fit and of how equations and their graphs relate. You can also assess students' ability to solve linear equations and to think critically and creatively.

Closing the Lesson

Restate the main ideas of this lesson: **Systems** of two equations in two variables can be solved **graphically** by tracing. If both equations are in intercept form, then they can also be solved algebraically by equating the right sides.

To motivate the next lesson, you might ask students to solve the system

$$\begin{cases} y = 15 + 8x \\ -10x - 5y = -30 \end{cases}$$

Ask whether there's an easier way to solve the system than changing the second equation into intercept form, but postpone answering this question until Lesson 3.7.

BUILDING UNDERSTANDING

In the exercises students practice setting up and solving systems of two linear equations.

ASSIGNING HOMEWORK

Essential	1, 4, 5
Performance assessment	2, 6–8, 10, 11
Portfolio	7
Journal	6, 8
Group	7, 9
Review	3, 12–14

MATERIALS

- Equations of Parallel and Perpendicular Lines (W), *optional*
- Calculator Note 3F

Helping with the Exercises

Exercise 2 Students might find it helpful to plot the point and sketch two lines through that point. They would then find the equations of each of those lines. This exercise has numerous solutions. Have students compare their answers and come up with even more equations.

2. sample answer:
$$\begin{cases} y = 7.5 + 4(x - 2) \\ y = 7.5 + 1.7(x - 2) \end{cases}$$

Exercise 3 You might want to make available the Equations of Parallel and Perpendicular Lines worksheet.

Exercise 5 Make sure your students verify their answers using a graph or a table. It is important that they practice these methods of solving systems also.

6b. When more than 120 g is placed on the springs, spring 2 will be more than 10 cm longer than spring 1.

EXERCISES

Practice Your Skills

1. Use a table to find the point of intersection for each pair of linear equations.

a. $\begin{cases} y = 3x - 17 \\ y = -2x - 8 \end{cases}$ (1.8, −11.6)

b. $\begin{cases} y = 28 - 3(x - 5) \\ y = 6 + 7x \end{cases}$ (3.7, 31.9)

2. Write a system of equations that has (2, 7.5) as its solution.

3. Write the equation of the line perpendicular to $y = 4 - 2.5x$ and passing through the point (1, 5). $y = 5 + 0.4(x - 1)$

4. Solve each equation.

a. $4 - 2.5(x - 6) = 3 + 7x$ $x = \frac{32}{19} \approx 1.684$

b. $11.5 + 4.1t = 6 + 3.2(t - 4)$ $t = -\frac{61}{3} \approx -20.33$

5. Use substitution to find the point (x, y) where each pair of lines intersect. Use a graph or table to verify your answer.

a. $\begin{cases} y = -2 + 3(x - 7) \\ y = 10 - 5x \end{cases}$ (4.125, −10.625)

b. $\begin{cases} y = 0.23x + 9 \\ y = 4 - 1.35x \end{cases}$ (−3.16, 8.27)

c. $\begin{cases} y = -1.5x + 7 \\ 2y = -3x + 14 \end{cases}$ They intersect at every point; they are the same line.

Reason and Apply

6. The equations $s_1 = 18 + 0.4m$ and $s_2 = 11.2 + 0.54m$ give the lengths of two different springs in centimeters, s_1 and s_2, as mass amounts in grams, m, are separately added to each.

a. When are the springs the same length? When you place 48.6 g on each spring, they will be the same length, 37.4 cm.

b. When is one spring at least 10 cm longer than the other?

c. Write a statement comparing the two springs.

7. APPLICATION This graph shows the Kangaroo Company's production costs and revenue for its pogo sticks. Use the graph to estimate the answers to the questions below.

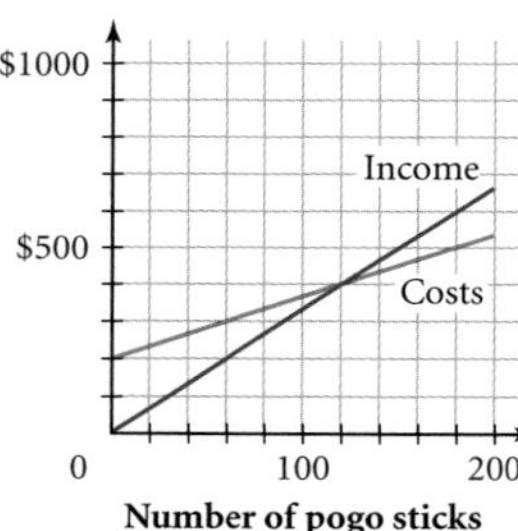

a. If 25 pogo sticks are sold, will the company earn a profit? Describe how you can use the graph to answer this question.

b. If the company sells 200 pogo sticks, will it earn a profit? If so, approximately how much? Yes. The profit is approximately $120.

c. How many pogo sticks must the company sell to break even? How do you know? About 120 pogo sticks. Look for the point where the cost and income lines intersect.

8. APPLICATION Winning times for men and women in the 1500 m Olympic speed skating event are given below, in minutes and seconds.

1500 m Olympic Speed Skating

Year	1964	1968	1972	1976	1980	1984	1988	1992	1994	1998
Men	2:10.3	2:03.4	2:02.96	1:59.38	1:55.44	1:58.36	1:52.06	1:54.81	1:51.29	1:47.87
Women	2:22.6	2:22.4	2:20.85	2:16.58	2:10.95	2:03.42	2:00.68	2:05.87	2:02.19	1:57.58

(*The World Almanac and Book of Facts 2001*)

6c. Answers will vary but should include comments about spring 1 (s_1) being longer than spring 2 (s_2) in its unstretched condition and the fact that spring 2 stretches more for each added gram of mass than spring 1.

Exercise 7 [Language] A pogo stick is a long stick with handles at the top and, near the bottom, footrests attached to a powerful spring.

7a. No. At $x = 25$, the cost line is above the income line.

Exercise 8 You might need to clarify that 2:10.3 means 2 minutes 10.3 seconds.

a. Analyze the data and predict when the winning times for men and women will be the same if the current trends continue.

b. How reasonable do you think your prediction is? Explain your reasoning.

c. Predict the winning times for the 2002 Winter Olympics. How close are your predictions to the actual results?

d. Is it appropriate to use a linear model for these data? Why? No, because the data are only linear over a small domain.

Derek Parra of the United States won the 2002 gold medal for the men's 1500 m speed skating event.

9. **APPLICATION** Suppose the long-distance phone companies in Example A calculate their charges so that a call of exactly 3 min will cost the same as a call of 3.25 min or 3.9 min, and there is no increase in cost until you have been connected for 4 min. Increases are calculated after each additional minute. A function that models this situation is the **greatest integer function,** $y = [x]$, which outputs the greatest integer less than or equal to x. [▶ See **Calculator Note 3F** for instructions on using the greatest integer function on your calculator. ◀]

a. Use the greatest integer function to write cost equations for the two companies in Example A.

b. Graph the two new equations representing the Phrequent Phoner Plan and the Small Business Plan.

c. Now determine when each plan is more desirable. Explain your reasoning.

10. **APPLICATION** At an excavation site, anthropologists use various clues to draw conclusions about people and populations based on skeletal remains. For instance, when a partial skeleton is found, an anthropologist can use the lengths of certain bones to estimate the height of the living person. The humerus bone is the single large bone that extends from the elbow to the shoulder socket. The following formulas, attributed to the work of Mildred Trotter and G. C. Gleser, have been used to estimate a male's height, m, or a female's height, f, when the length, h, of the humerus bone is known: $m = 3.08h + 70.45$ and $f = 3.36h + 58.0$. All measurements are in centimeters.

a. Graph the two lines on the same set of axes.

b. If a humerus bone is found and it measures 42 cm, how tall would the person be according to the model if the bone was determined to come from a male? From a female? male: approximately 199.81 cm; female: approximately 199.12 cm

Science CONNECTION

Physical anthropology is a science that deals with the biological evolution of human beings, the study of human ancestors and non-human primates, and the in-depth analysis of the human skeleton. By studying bones and bone fragments, physical anthropologists have developed methods that can provide a wealth of information on the age, sex, ancestry, height, and diet of a person who lived in ancient times, just by studying his or her skeleton.

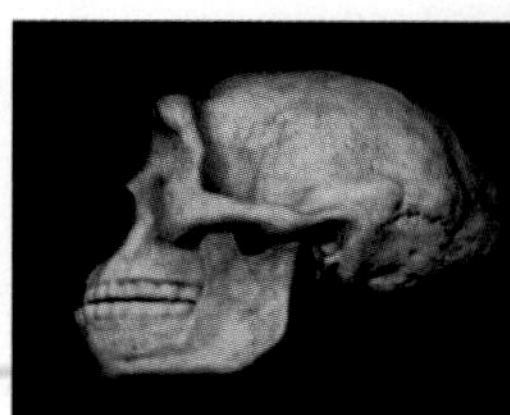
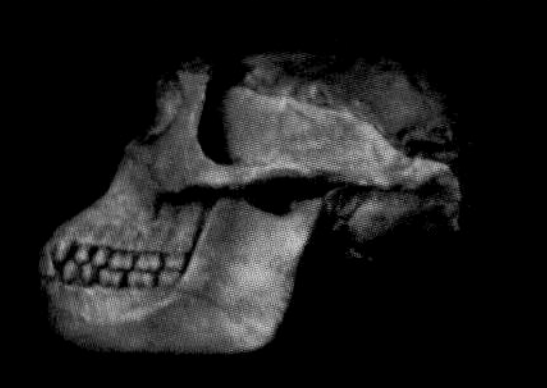
These skulls are from human ancestors—Peking man on the left, and Java man on the right.

8a. Median-median line for men: $\hat{y} = 1040.04 - 0.4658x$; median-median line for women: $\hat{y} = 1670.70 - 0.7773x$. The point of intersection is (2024.6, 97.0). This predicts that the men's and women's times will be about the same in the year 2024 or 2025.

8b. Answers will vary but should include a statement that there is a limit to how fast a person can skate and eventually the winning times will approach a minimal value. It may or may not be as low as the predicted value.

8c. Using the men's model, the predicted time would be 107.51 s, or 1:47.51. Using the women's model, the predicted time would be 114.55 s, or 1:54.55. Actual times for 2002 Olympics are men: 1:43.95; women: 1:54.02.

Exercise 9 The definition given here for the greatest integer function applies only to positive numbers. For negative numbers, the greatest integer function drops the fraction part and subtracts 1 from the whole-number part. For example, −4.6 becomes −5. To obtain good calculator graphs students should change the graph style to dots; see Calculator Note 3A.

9a. Phrequent Phoner Plan: $y = 20 + 17([x] - 1)$; Small Business Plan: $y = 50 + 11([x] - 1)$

9b.

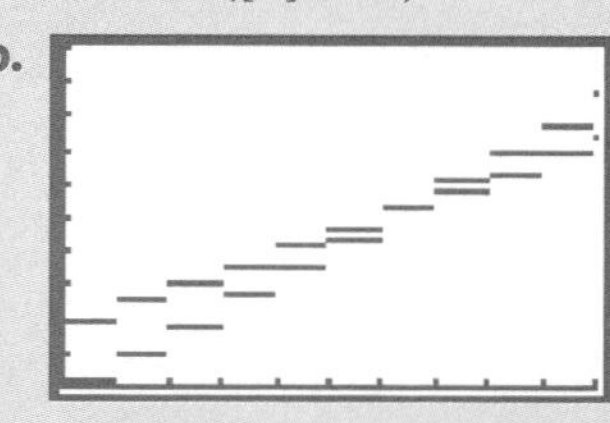
[0, 10, 1, 0, 200, 20]

9c. If the time of the phone call is less than 6 min, PPP is less expensive. For times between 6 and 7 min, the plans charge the same rate. If the time of the phone call is greater than or equal to 7 min, PPP is more expensive than SBP. (You could look at the calculator table to see these results.)

10a. Let x represent the length of the humerus bone in cm, and let y represent the person's height in cm.

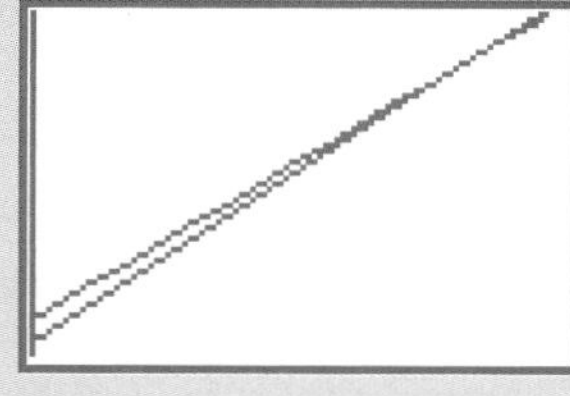
[0, 60, 0, 50, 250, 0]

11a. Let l represent length in centimeters, and let w represent width in centimeters; $2l + 2w = 44$, $l = 2 + 2w$; $w = \frac{20}{3}$ cm, $l = \frac{46}{3}$ cm.

11b. Let l represent length of leg in centimeters, and let b represent length of base in centimeters; $2l + b = 40$, $b = l - 2$; $l = 14$ cm, $b = 12$ cm.

Exercise 11c This is the reading at one time. In general, °F is not equivalent to 3 · °C − 0.4.

The conversion formula is either $C = \frac{5}{9}(F - 32)$ or $F = \frac{9}{5}C + 32$.

11c. Let f represent temperature in degrees Fahrenheit, and let c represent temperature in degrees Celsius; $f = 3c - 0.4$, $f = 1.8c + 32$; $c = 27$°C, $f = 80.6$°F.

Exercise 14 [Alert] Students might try to solve for x. The solution will involve x, though, and will not be just a single number.

EXTENSIONS

A. Ask students to research the recent population growth of San Jose and Detroit. Does it fit the models they made in the investigation?

B. As an extension of Exercise 10, ask students to research other equations used to predict height from bone fragments, either human or animal.

11. Write a system of equations to model each situation, and solve for the values of the appropriate variables.

a. The perimeter of a rectangle is 44 cm. Its length is 2 cm more than twice its width.

b. The perimeter of an isosceles triangle is 40 cm. The base length is 2 cm less than the length of a leg of the triangle.

c. The Fahrenheit reading on a dual thermometer is 0.4 degrees less than three times the Celsius reading. (Hint: Your second equation needs to be a conversion formula between degrees Fahrenheit and degrees Celsius.)

Review

3.3 **12.** Use the model $\hat{y} = 343.5 + 1.55(x - 1984)$ that was found in the example in Lesson 3.3. Recall that x represents the year, and y represents the concentration of CO_2 in parts per million (ppm) at Mauna Loa.

a. Predict the concentration of CO_2 in the year 1984. 343.5 ppm

b. Use the model to predict the concentration of CO_2 in the year 2010. 383.8 ppm

c. According to this model, when will the level of CO_2 be double the preindustrial level of 280 ppm? approximately the year 2124

2.3 **13.** The histogram shows the average annual cost of insuring a motor vehicle in the United States.

a. How many jurisdictions are included in the histogram? 51

b. Mississippi is the median jurisdiction. Mississippi is in what bin? 3rd bin

c. In what percentage of the jurisdictions is the average cost less than \$600? 35%

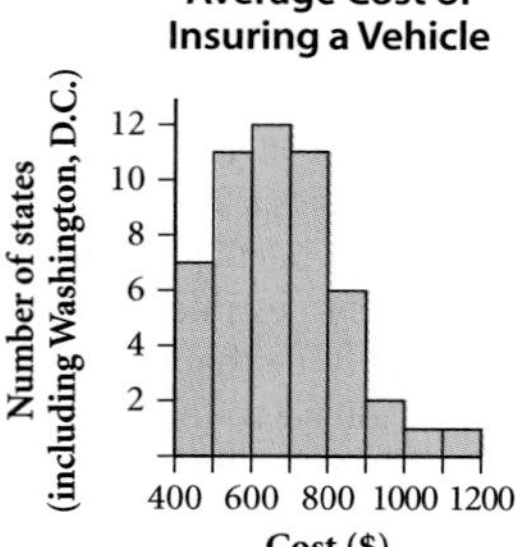

14. Solve these equations for y.

a. $3x - 8y = 12$

b. $5x + 2y = 12$

c. $-3x + 4y = 5$

14a. $y = \frac{3x - 12}{8} = 0.375x - 1.5$

14b. $y = \frac{12 - 5x}{2} = 6 - 2.5x$

14c. $y = \frac{5 + 3x}{4} = 1.25 + 0.75x$

IMPROVING YOUR REASONING SKILLS

Cartoon Watching Causes Small Feet

Lisa did a study for her health class about the effects of cartoon watching on foot size. Based on a graph of her data, she finds that there was an inverse relationship between foot size and hours spent watching cartoons per week. She concludes that "cartoon watching causes small feet." Is this true? Explain any flaws in Lisa's reasoning.

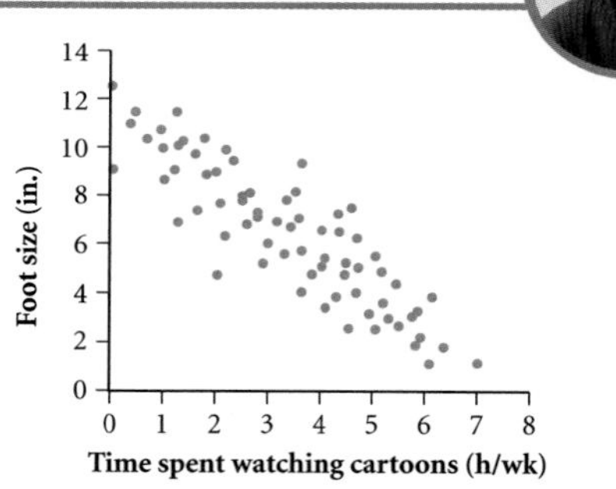

IMPROVING REASONING SKILLS

Children have smaller feet and generally watch more cartoons than adults, but this does not mean that one trait causes the other.

The point of this puzzle is that correlation does not necessarily imply causation.

LESSON 3.7

Substitution and Elimination

A place for everything and everything in its place.

ENGLISH PROVERB

A solution to a system of equations in two variables is a pair of values that satisfies both equations and represents the intersection of their graphs. In Lesson 3.6, you reviewed solving a system of equations using substitution, when both equations are in intercept form. Suppose you want to solve a system and one or both of the equations are not in intercept form. You can rearrange them into intercept form, or you can use a different method.

If one equation is in intercept form, you can still use substitution.

In *Modern Warrior Series, Shirt #1* (1998), northern Cheyenne artist Bently Spang (b 1960) reflects on identity. He presents opposing influences as an equivalence of forms—the modern and the traditional, the spiritual and the mundane, the Cheyenne and the non-Cheyenne—all intersecting in an arrangement of family photographs.

EXAMPLE A Solve this system for x and y.

$$\begin{cases} y = 15 + 8x \\ -10x - 5y = -30 \end{cases}$$

▶ Solution You can solve the second equation for y so that both equations will be in intercept form and substitute the right side of one equation for y in the other equation. Or you can simply substitute the right side of the first equation for y in the second equation.

$-10x - 5y = -30$	Original form of the second equation.
$-10x - 5(15 + 8x) = -30$	Substitute the right side of the first equation for y.
$-10x - 75 - 40x = -30$	Distribute -5.
$-50x = 45$	Add 75 to both sides and combine like terms.
$x = -0.9$	Divide both sides by -50.

Now that you know the value of x, you can substitute it in either equation to find the value of y.

$y = 15 + 8(-0.9)$	Substitute -0.9 for x in the first equation.
$y = 7.8$	Multiply and combine like terms.

Write your solution as an ordered pair. The solution to this system is $(-0.9, 7.8)$.

NCTM STANDARDS

CONTENT		PROCESS	
	Number		Problem Solving
✓	Algebra	✓	Reasoning
	Geometry	✓	Communication
	Measurement	✓	Connections
	Data/Probability	✓	Representation

LESSON OBJECTIVES

- Solve systems of equations by substitution
- Explore how the addition and multiplication properties of equations can be used to solve systems of equations by elimination

LESSON 3.7

PLANNING

LESSON OUTLINE

One day:

10 min	Examples
15 min	Investigation
5 min	Sharing
15 min	Exercises

MATERIALS

- Calculator Note 3G

TEACHING

In this lesson, students encounter the more general substitution method, as well as the elimination method, of solving systems of linear equations. Because the investigation can be a discovery activity, you might want your students to first complete the investigation and then go over the examples. Or you might choose to start with the one-step investigation on page 158.

▶ EXAMPLE A

To motivate the method of substitution, you might actually demonstrate how much more difficult it is to use the method of the previous lesson.

After solving for x, substituting the result into the second equation instead of the first gives the same value for y but requires more rearranging and is less convenient. Let students know that substituting into either equation should result in the same y-value and that this is one way to verify the solution is correct.

The substitution method relies on the substitution property, which says that if $a = b$, then a may be replaced by b in an algebraic expression. Substitution is a powerful mathematical tool that allows you to rewrite expressions and equations in forms that are easier to use and solve. Notice that substituting an expression for y, as you did in Example A, eliminates y from the equation, allowing you to solve a single equation for a single variable, x.

A third method for solving a system of equations is the **elimination** method. The elimination method uses the addition property of equality, which says that if $a = b$, then $a + c = b + c$. In other words, if you add equal quantities to both sides of an equation, the equation is still true. If necessary, you can also use the multiplication property of equality, which says that if $a = b$, then $ac = bc$, or if you multiply both sides of an equation by equal quantities, then the equation is still true.

EXAMPLE B

Solve these systems for x and y.

a. $\begin{cases} 4x + 3y = 14 \\ 3x - 3y = 13 \end{cases}$ **b.** $\begin{cases} -3x + 5y = 6 \\ 2x + y = 6 \end{cases}$

▶ Solution

Because neither of these equations is in intercept form, it is probably easier to solve the systems using the elimination method.

a. You can solve the system without changing either equation to intercept form by adding the two equations.

$$\begin{aligned} 4x + 3y &= 14 && \text{Original equations.} \\ 3x - 3y &= 13 && \text{Add equal quantities to both sides of the equation.} \\ \hline 7x \qquad &= 27 && \text{The variable } y \text{ is eliminated.} \\ x &= \frac{27}{7} && \text{Solve for } x. \\ 4\left(\frac{27}{7}\right) + 3y &= 14 && \text{Substitute } \tfrac{27}{7} \text{ for } x \text{ back into either equation.} \\ y &= -\frac{10}{21} && \text{Solve for } y. \end{aligned}$$

The solution to this system is $\left(\frac{27}{7}, -\frac{10}{21}\right)$. You can substitute the coordinates back into both equations to check that the point is a solution for both.

$$4\left(\frac{27}{7}\right) + 3\left(-\frac{10}{21}\right) = \frac{108}{7} - \frac{30}{21} = \frac{294}{21} = 14$$

$$3\left(\frac{27}{7}\right) - 3\left(-\frac{10}{21}\right) = \frac{81}{7} + \frac{30}{21} = \frac{273}{21} = 13$$

b. Adding the equations as they are written will not eliminate either of the variables. You need to multiply one or both equations by some value so that if you add the equations together, one of the variables will be eliminated.

The easiest choice is to multiply the second equation by -5, and then add it to the first equation.

$$\begin{aligned} -3x + 5y = 6 \quad &\rightarrow \quad -3x + 5y = 6 && \text{Original form of the first equation.} \\ -5(2x + y) = -5(6) \quad &\rightarrow \quad \underline{-10x - 5y = -30} && \text{Multiply both sides of the second equation by } -5. \\ &\qquad -13x \qquad = -24 && \text{Add the equations.} \end{aligned}$$

One Step

Challenge the class to solve this system.

$$\begin{cases} 4x - 3y = -4 \\ x + 3y = 14 \end{cases}$$

Some students will solve both equations for y and use the method of the previous lesson. Others will see that it's easier to solve the second equation for x and substitute. If nobody comes up with the idea of adding the two equations, suggest it to one group. Have all three methods presented during Sharing and compare them. Then have the class work through the system in the investigation, graphing as they go and making observations about the intersection point.

▶ EXAMPLE B

You might ask students for other methods of solving these systems and spend some time as a class discussing the merits of each. For instance, in the system in part b, both expressions equal 6. Students might think of using substitution here. **[Ask]** "Would it be valid to set the left sides of the equations equal to each other?" [yes] "Would it help us solve the system?" [No; we would have one equation with two variables and no way to solve it.]

Guiding the Investigation

This investigation can be completed by hand with graph paper, or with Calculator Note 3G and the accompanying program. Programs are available on the Programs and Data CD or at www.keymath.com/DAA.

You might want students to work with a single partner instead of in larger groups.

Step 1 As needed, review the quickest method for graphing these equations by hand: Find x- and y-intercepts by setting first y and then x equal to 0 to get two points to plot. The calculator program does the graphing for students.

Step 1 The lines appear to intersect at $(-1, 2)$.

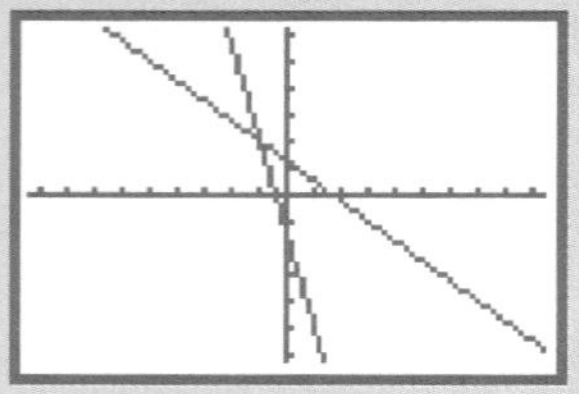

[−9.4, 9.4, 1, −6.2, 6.2, 1]

Step 7 Each pair of students can try a different system and then compare results with other pairs during Sharing.

This eliminates the y-variable and gives $x = \frac{24}{13}$. Substituting this x-value back into either of the original equations gives the y-value. Or you can use the same process to eliminate the x-variable.

$$\begin{array}{rcrl} -3x + 5y = 6 & \rightarrow & -6x + 10y = 12 & \text{Multiply both sides by 2.} \\ 2x + y = 6 & \rightarrow & 6x + 3y = 18 & \text{Multiply both sides by 3.} \\ & & 13y = 30 & \\ & & y = \frac{30}{13} & \end{array}$$

The solution to this system is $\left(\frac{24}{13}, \frac{30}{13}\right)$. You can use your calculator to verify the solution.

It would take a lot of effort to solve this last system using a table on your calculator. If you had used the substitution method to solve the systems in Example B, you would have had to work with fractions to get an accurate answer. To solve these systems, the easiest method to use is the elimination method.

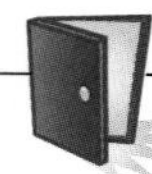

Investigation
It All Adds Up

In this investigation you may discover some interesting things that happen when you multiply both sides of an equation by the same number or add equations. Work with a partner and follow the steps below. [▶ You can also use the program in **Calculator Note 3G** to do this investigation. ◀]

Step 1 Graph each of these equations on the same coordinate axes. Where do the lines appear to intersect?

$$\begin{cases} 7x + 2y = -3 & \text{(Equation 1)} \\ 3x + 4y = 5 & \text{(Equation 2)} \end{cases}$$

Step 2 sample answer: if $M = 5$ and $N = 2$ $\begin{cases} 35x + 10y = -15 \\ 6x + 8y = 10 \end{cases}$

Step 2 One partner needs to select any number, M, and the other partner a different number, N. The first partner multiplies Equation 1 by the number M he or she chose while the other partner multiplies Equation 2 by the number N he or she chose.

Step 3 Add the two new equations to form Equation 3. Graph Equation 3 on the same coordinate axis as the two original lines, and describe the location of this new line in relation to the original lines.

Step 4 $\begin{cases} -21x - 6y = 9 \\ 21x + 28y = 35 \end{cases}$

Step 4 Next, one partner multiplies the original Equation 1 by $M = -3$ while the other partner multiplies the original Equation 2 by $N = 7$.

Step 5 Add the two new equations from Step 4 to form Equation 4. Graph Equation 4 and describe the location of it in relation to the two original lines.

Step 6 The equation eliminates x; because the equation only contains y, it is the equation of a horizontal line and represents the y-coordinate of the intersection.

Step 6 How does Equation 4 differ from the other equations?

Step 7 Repeat this process with different systems of equations, and make a conjecture based on your observations. Summarize your findings.

SHARING IDEAS

As students present, **[Ask]** "How do the lines change as you multiply the entire equation by a number?" [They don't.] Wonder aloud why not. If you start with $7x + 2y = -3$, for example (from the investigation), and multiply by -2 to change the equation to $-14x - 4y = 6$, shouldn't the line swing around somehow to go through 6 instead of -3? Elicit the idea that it's the coordinates of points on the graph that are manipulated to get -3; those same coordinates, if manipulated this new way, will yield 6.

[Ask] "Why does the point of intersection not change as the equations are multiplied by constants and added?" [Multiplying by constants doesn't change the lines, so it doesn't change the point of intersection. And because the coordinates of the intersection point satisfy both equations, they satisfy the sum of those equations, so the intersection point is on that line also.]

[Ask] "Can you predict the graph of the sum line from the graphs of the two lines by adding their x-intercepts and adding their y-intercepts?" [No; this would be equivalent to adding numerators and adding denominators to get the sum of two fractions. If you could, you could never get a horizontal or vertical line as the sum.] The important fact is that the sum line will pass through the point at which the other two lines intersect.

To preview Chapter 6, you might ask what would happen to the solution if the first system in Example B had as its second equation $-4x - 3y = 13$. When the equations are added, the result is $0 = 27$, a contradiction that indicates the equations are inconsistent. **[Ask]** "What if the second equation were $-4x - 3y = -14$?" [The sum

See page 881 for answers to Steps 3, 5, and 7.

Sharing Ideas (continued)

would be $0 = 0$, not a contradiction.] In fact, in this case the two equations are equivalent, representing the same line; there are infinitely many points of intersection (all points on the line). Such equations are said to be *dependent.*

Assessing Progress

As students investigate, you can assess how well they understand graphs of equations, intercepts of lines, and interpretations of intersection points.

Closing the Lesson

In the **substitution method** for solving a system of equations, you get one equation in intercept form, substitute the right side for y in the other equation, and solve for x. In the **elimination method,** you add the two equations to eliminate either x or y, first multiplying one or both equations by a constant if necessary. Using the addition and multiplication properties of equations of the lines in this way does not change the point of intersection of their graphs. The coordinates of this point provide a solution to the system of equations.

BUILDING UNDERSTANDING

If you are doing this lesson in one day, assign only a few exercises, because many of them have several parts.

ASSIGNING HOMEWORK

Essential	1–5
Performance assessment	6–12
Portfolio	8
Journal	2, 3
Group	9
Review	13–18

Helping with the Exercises

Exercises 2, 3 Students might either use their conclusions from the investigation or graph the equations.

Exercises 3, 4 [Alert] Some students will be distracted by trying to see how to predict the graph of the sum from the graphs of the two equations. As needed, focus them on the point of intersection.

The elimination method uses a combination technique to eliminate one of the variables in a system of equations. Solving for the variable that remains gives you the x- or y-coordinate of the point of intersection, if there is a point of intersection.

EXERCISES

Practice Your Skills

1. Solve each equation for the specified variable.

a. $w - r = 11$, for w $w = 11 + r$

b. $2p + 3h = 18$, for h $h = \frac{18 - 2p}{3} = 6 - \frac{2}{3}p$

c. $w - r = 11$, for r $r = w - 11$

d. $2p + 3h = 18$, for p $p = \frac{18 - 3h}{2} = 9 - \frac{3}{2}p$

2. Multiply both sides of each equation by the given value. What is the relationship between the graphs of the new equation and the original equation?

a. $j + 5k = 8$, by -3 $-3j - 15k = -24$; same line

b. $2p + 3h = 18$, by 5 $10p + 15h = 90$; same line

c. $6f - 4g = 22$, by 0.5 $3f - 2g = 11$; same line

d. $\frac{5}{6}a + \frac{3}{4}b = \frac{7}{2}$, by 12 $10a + 9b = 42$; same line

3. Add each pair of equations. What is the relationship between the graphs of the new equation and the original pair?

a. $\begin{cases} 3x - 4y = 7 \\ 2x + 2y = 5 \end{cases}$ $5x - 2y = 12$; passes through the point of intersection of the original pair

b. $\begin{cases} 5x - 7y = 3 \\ -5x + 3y = 5 \end{cases}$ $-4y = 8$; passes through the point of intersection of the original pair and is horizontal

4. Graph each system and find an approximate solution. Then choose a method and find the exact solution. List each solution as an ordered pair.

a. $\begin{cases} y = 3.2x + 44.61 \\ y = -5.1x + 5.60 \end{cases}$ $(-4.7, 29.57)$

b. $\begin{cases} y = \frac{2}{3}x - 3 \\ y = -\frac{5}{6}x + 7 \end{cases}$ $\left(\frac{20}{3}, \frac{13}{9}\right)$

c. $\begin{cases} y = 4.7x + 25.1 \\ 3.1x + 2y = 8.2 \end{cases}$ $(-3.36, 9.308)$

d. $\begin{cases} -6x - 7y = 20 \\ -5x + 4y = -5 \end{cases}$ $\left(-\frac{45}{59}, -\frac{130}{59}\right)$

e. $\begin{cases} 2.1x + 3.6y = 7 \\ -6.3x + y = 8.2 \end{cases}$ $\left(-\frac{1126}{1239}, \frac{146}{59}\right)$

5. Solve each system of equations.

a. $\begin{cases} 5.2x + 3.6y = 7 \\ -5.2x + 2y = 8.2 \end{cases}$ $\left(-\frac{97}{182}, \frac{19}{7}\right) \approx (-0.5330, 2.7143)$

b. $\begin{cases} \frac{1}{4}x - \frac{2}{5}y = 3 \\ \frac{3}{8}x + \frac{2}{5}y = 2 \end{cases}$

c. $\begin{cases} 4x + 9y = 12 \\ 3x - 8y = 10 \end{cases}$

d. $\begin{cases} s = 7 - 3n \\ 7n + 2s = 40 \end{cases}$ $n = 26, s = -71$

e. $\begin{cases} f = 3d + 5 \\ 10d - 4f = 16 \end{cases}$ $d = -18, f = -49$

f. $\begin{cases} \frac{1}{4}x - \frac{4}{5}y = 7 \\ \frac{3}{4}x + \frac{2}{5}y = 2 \end{cases}$ $\left(\frac{44}{7}, -\frac{95}{14}\right) \approx (6.2857, -6.7857)$

g. $\begin{cases} 2x + 3y = 4 \\ 1.2x + 1.8y = 2.6 \end{cases}$ no solution

Exercises 4, 5 Students might choose any method to solve the systems, including using a graph, using a table, substitution, or elimination. **[Ask]** "For each system, is there one method that is better than another? Why is it better?"

5b. $\left(8, -\frac{5}{2}\right) = (8, -2.5)$

5c. $\left(\frac{186}{59}, -\frac{4}{59}\right) \approx (3.1525, -0.0678)$

Reason and Apply

6. Solve each problem.

a. If $4x + y = 6$, then what is $(4x + y - 3)^2$? 9

b. If $4x + 3y = 14$ and $3x - 3y = 13$, what is $7x$? 27

7. The formula to convert between Fahrenheit and Celsius is $C = \frac{5}{9}(F - 32)$. What reading on the Fahrenheit scale is three times the equivalent temperature on the Celsius scale? 80°F

8. APPLICATION Ellen must decide between two cameras. The first camera costs \$47.00 and uses two alkaline AA batteries. The second camera costs \$59.00 and uses one \$4.95 lithium battery. She plans to use the camera frequently enough that she probably would replace the AA batteries six times a year for a total cost of \$11.50 per year. The lithium battery, however, will last an entire year.

a. Let x represent the number of years, and let y represent the cost in dollars. Write an equation to represent the overall expense for each camera.

b. Which camera is less expensive in the short term? In the long term? How long will it take until the overall cost of the less expensive camera is equal to the overall cost of the other camera? the \$47 camera; the \$59 camera; approximately 2 yr

c. Carefully describe three different ways to verify your solution.

9. Write a system of two equations that has a solution of $(-1.4, 3.6)$. possible answer: $\begin{cases} y = 3.6 + 2(x + 1.4) \\ y = 3.6 + 3(x + 1.4) \end{cases}$

10. The two sequences below have one term that is the same. Determine which term this is and find its value. $u_{31} = v_{31} = 21$

$u_1 = 12$ $\quad v_1 = 15$

$u_n = u_{n-1} + 0.3$ where $n \geq 2$ $\quad v_n = v_{n-1} + 0.2$ where $n \geq 2$

11. Formulas play an important part in many fields of mathematics and science. You can create a new formula using substitution to combine formulas.

a. Using the formulas $A = s^2$ and $d = s\sqrt{2}$, write a formula for A in terms of d. $A = \frac{d^2}{2}$

b. Using the formulas $P = IE$ and $E = IR$, write a formula for P in terms of I and R. $P = I^2R$

c. Using the formulas $A = \pi r^2$ and $C = 2\pi r$, write a formula for A in terms of C. $A = \frac{C^2}{4\pi}$

Science CONNECTION

In this simple circuit, a 9-volt battery lights a small light bulb. The power P supplied to the bulb in watts is a product of the voltage E of the battery times the electrical current I in the wire. The electrical current, in turn, can be calculated as the battery voltage E divided by the resistance R of the circuit, which depends on the length and gauge, or diameter, of the wire. It is important to know basic functions and relations when designing a circuit, so that there will be enough power supplied to the components, but not excessive power, which would damage the components.

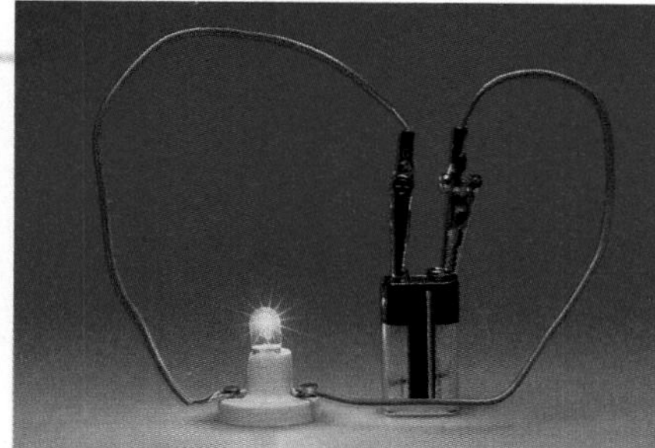

Exercise 6 If students are struggling with 6a, **[Ask]** "How does the squared expression relate to the expression in the equation?" [It is 3 less, so subtract 3 from both sides and then square.] For 6b, **[Ask]** "Does $7x$ appear in the two equations?" [$7x$ appears in the sum; add the equations.]

8a. cost for first camera: $y = 47 + 11.5x$; cost for second camera: $y = 59 + 4.95x$

8c. You could graph each cost function and zoom in for the intersection point; you could use substitution to find the intersection point; or you could look at a table to find the break-even point where the cost for both cameras is the same.

Exercise 9 Another good answer is $x = -1.4$ and $y = 3.6$. Although this seems simple, any students who come up with it are showing understanding that you can praise.

Exercise 10 Students might be disturbed because this exercise connects sequences to systems of equations. As long as the solution involves only integers, it's legitimate.

MAKING THE CONNECTION

Electrical engineers use many tools to control the flow of electricity in an electrical circuit. Resistors, for example, absorb part of an electrical current and convert it into heat, thus reducing the flow of electricity. Transistors, on the other hand, use semiconductor materials such as silicon to amplify and oscillate electrical currents. These devices are combined to create complex circuits that operate advanced electronic equipment like computers, audio devices, and televisions.

Exercise 12 You might ask students how the fulcrum is related to the centroid (center of gravity) of a triangle. In 12b, you might need to describe a seesaw (teeter-totter) as a plank with seats and handles on each end balanced on a fulcrum.

12a. 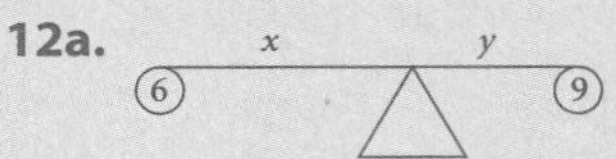

$x + y = 40$ and $6x = 9y$; $y = 16$. The fulcrum should be positioned 16 in. from the 9 lb weight.

12b. 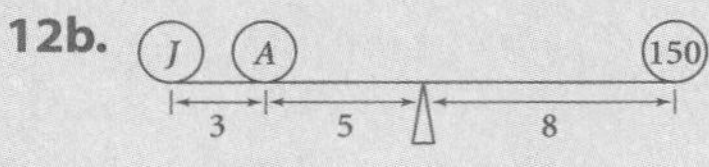

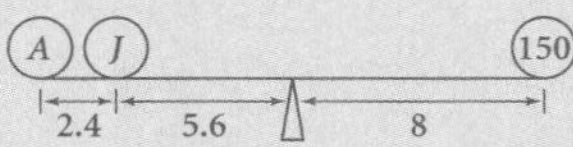

$8J + 5A = 8(150)$ and $8(A) + 5.6(J) = 8(150)$. Solving the system leads to the fact that Justin weighs 100 lb, and Alden weighs 80 lb.

14a. $y = \frac{7 - 3x}{2} = \frac{7}{2} - \frac{3}{2}x = 3.5 - 1.5x$

14b. 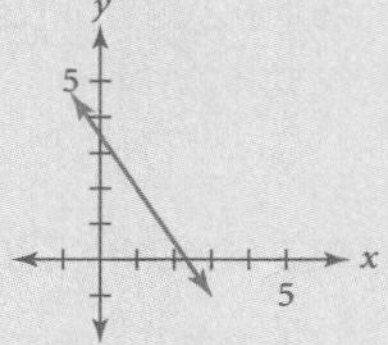

14e. $y = \frac{7}{2} + \frac{2}{3}x$

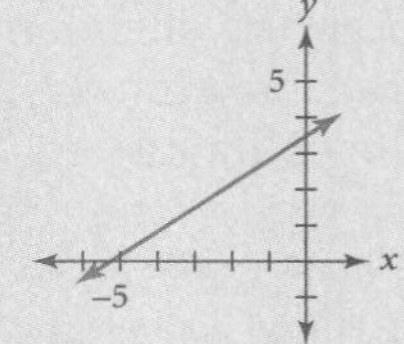

12. APPLICATION A support bar will be in equilibrium (balanced) at the fulcrum, O, if $m_1x + m_2y = m_3z$, where m_1, m_2, and m_3 represent masses and x, y, and z represent the distance of the masses to the fulcrum. Draw a diagram for each question and calculate the answer.

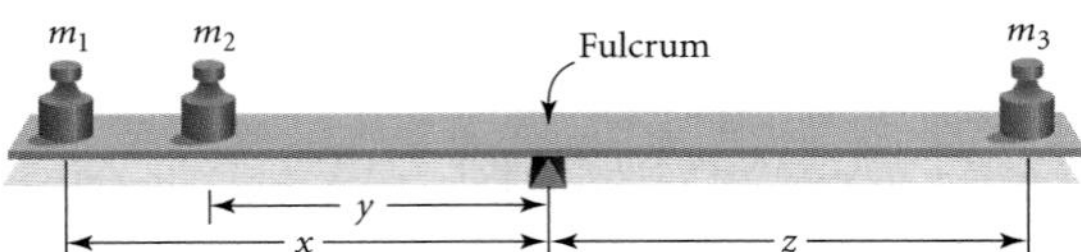

a. A 40 in. bar is in equilibrium when a weight of 6 lb is hung from one end and a weight of 9 lb is hung from the other end. Find the position of the fulcrum.

b. While in the park, Michael and his two sons, Justin and Alden, go on a 16 ft seesaw. Michael, who weighs 150 lb, sits at the edge of one end while Justin and Alden move to the other side and try to balance. The seesaw balances with Justin at the other edge and Alden 3 ft from him. After some additional experimentation the see saw balances once again with Alden at the edge and Justin 5.6 ft from the fulcrum. How much does each boy weigh?

Art CONNECTION

Alexander Calder (1898–1976) was an artistic pioneer who revolutionized the mobile as an art form. After getting a degree in mechanical engineering, he went to art school, supporting himself through school by working as an illustrator. Once out of school, he began creating small three-dimensional sculptures made from wire, wood, and cloth that balanced perfectly, whether or not they were symmetrical. Eventually, he designed sculptures with painted elements that moved mechanically, and then went on to produce pieces that moved with the air. These free-moving, hanging sculptures became known as "mobiles." He also designed "stabiles," essentially mobiles that balance on a fixed support.

Alexander Calder builds a mobile in his studio. At left is one of his stabiles, *Boomerang and Sickle Moon.*

Review

13. Classify each statement as true or false. If the statement is false, change the right side to make it true.

a. $x^2 + 8x + 15 = (x + 3)(x + 5)$ true

b. $x^2 - 16 = (x - 4)(x - 4)$ false; $(x - 4)(x + 4)$

3.2 **14.** Consider the equation $3x + 2y - 7 = 0$

a. Solve the equation for y.

b. Graph this equation.

c. What is the slope? $-\frac{3}{2}$ or -1.5

d. What is the y-intercept? $\frac{7}{2}$ or 3.5

e. Write an equation for a line perpendicular to this one and having the same y-intercept. Graph this equation.

3.4 **15.** **APPLICATION** This table gives the mean price for a gallon of gasoline in the United States from 1950 through 2000.

Year	1950	1960	1970	1980	1990	2000
Price ($)	0.27	0.31	0.36	1.19	1.15	1.56

(*The New York Times Almanac 2002*)

a. Make a scatter plot of the data. Let x represent the year, and y represent the price in dollars.

b. Find the median-median line of the data. $\hat{y} = \frac{213}{8000}x - 51.78$ or $\hat{y} = 0.027x - 51.78$

c. Assuming that the same trend continues, predict the price of gas in 2010. From what you know (or can find out) about current world fossil fuel supplies, is the pattern likely to continue? Explain.

2.1 **16.** **APPLICATION** This table shows the normal monthly precipitation in inches for Pittsburgh, Pennsylvania, and Portland, Oregon.

Month	J	F	M	A	M	J	J	A	S	O	N	D
Pittsburgh	2.5	2.4	3.4	3.1	3.6	3.7	3.8	3.2	3.0	2.4	2.9	2.9
Portland	5.4	3.9	3.6	2.4	2.1	1.5	0.7	1.1	1.8	2.7	5.3	6.1

(*The New York Times Almanac 2002*)

a. Display the data in two box plots on the same axis.

b. Give the five-number summary of each data set.

c. Describe the differences in living conditions with respect to precipitation.

d. Which city generally has more rain annually? Pittsburgh

3.1 **17.** Consider these three sequences.

i. 243, −324, 432, −576, . . . **a.** 768, −1024; **b.** geometric
ii. 22, 26, 31, 37, 44, . . . **a.** 52, 61; **b.** other
iii. 24, 25.75, 27.5, 29.25, 31, . . . **a.** 32.75, 34.5; **b.** arithmetic

a. Find the next two terms in each sequence.

b. Identify each sequence as arithmetic, geometric, or other.

c. If a sequence is arithmetic or geometric, write a recursive routine to generate the sequence.

d. If a sequence is arithmetic, give an explicit formula that generates the sequence. **iii.** $u_n = 1.75n + 22.25$

3.4 **18.** Melina and Angus are designing a fixed speed hot-rod car for a remote-control rally. They need to construct a car that travels at a constant 0.50 m/s. In order to qualify for the rally they must show time trial results with a root mean square error of less than 0.05 m. This table shows their time trial results. Will Melina and Angus qualify or do they need to go back to the drawing board? No, they don't qualify. $s = 0.059$ m

Time (s)	1	2	3	4	5	6	7	8
Distance (m)	0.48	0.95	1.6	2.0	2.52	2.93	3.49	4.05

15a.

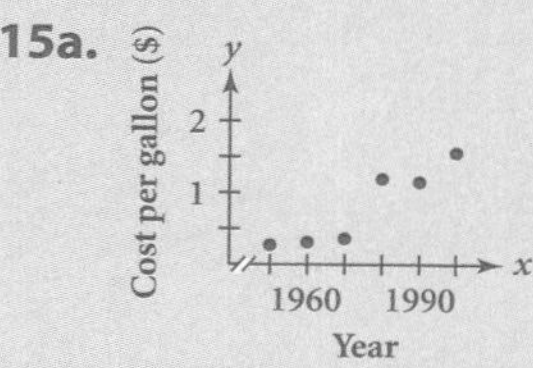

Exercise 15c Students should use the unrounded slope to extrapolate for 2010. If they use 0.027 for the slope, they will get $2.49.

15c. If the same trend continues, the cost of gasoline in 2010 will be $1.74. Answers will vary.

16a.

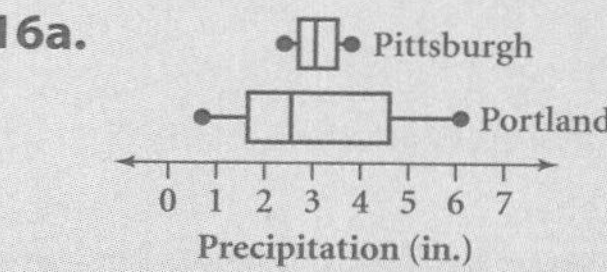

16b. Pittsburgh: 2.4, 2.7, 3.05, 3.5, 3.8; Portland: 0.7, 1.65, 2.55, 4.6, 6.1

16c. Answers will vary. Pittsburgh has rather constant precipitation all year. Portland has a wet and a dry season.

17c. i. $u_1 = 243$ and $u_n = \left(-\frac{4}{3}\right)u_{n-1}$ where $n \geq 2$

17c. iii. $u_1 = 24$ and $u_n = u_{n-1} + 1.75$ where $n \geq 2$

EXTENSIONS

A. Use Take Another Look activity 3 on page 170.

B. If students have studied matrices, have them investigate the reduced-row-echelon method and use it to solve systems of equations by hand and on the calculator.

C. Challenge students to solve a system of three equations with three variables.

CHAPTER REVIEW 3

PLANNING

LESSON OUTLINE

First day:

15 min Reviewing

30 min Exercises

Second day:

35 min Mixed Review

10 min Student self-assessment

REVIEWING

For review, you might refer students back to Lesson 3.5, Example A, in which Big K Pizza has sold 512, 603, 642, and 775 pizzas, respectively, in the past four Novembers. Add the information that Big L Pizza sales for those same four months were 223, 341, 486, and 584 pizzas. Have students predict whether Big L will catch up with Big K. Ask if the best model would be a **recursive formula,** an **explicit formula,** or a **linear equation.** The data given are **discrete,** indicating that a recursive or an explicit formula might be best, but the growth in sales is **continuous,** and we'll want to be able to **interpolate** or **extrapolate** from our model. (Students thinking critically might point out that the model for the whole year probably won't be linear.) As students find **lines of fit** for the data, review the ideas of **intercept form** and **point-slope form;** have students compare the **residuals** and **root mean square errors** of their lines with those of the **median-median line.** Once the class has decided on good linear equations, students can solve the **system** by graphing, **substitution,** or **elimination** to find the point of intersection. Be sure to include some discussion of their solution's reasonableness.

CHAPTER 3 REVIEW

In this chapter you analyzed sets of two-variable data. A plot of two-variable data may be linear, or it may appear nearly linear over a short domain. If it is linear, you can find a **line of fit** to model the data. You can write a **linear equation** for this line and use it to **interpolate** or **extrapolate** points for which data are not available. You can also solve a **system of equations** to find the intersection of two lines, using the methods of **substitution, elimination,** or using a graph or table of values.

To write the equation of a line, you can use its slope and y-intercept to write the equation in **intercept form,** or you can use the coordinates of two points to write the equation in **point-slope form.**

You learned two methods for finding a line of fit for a set of data: estimating by looking at the trend of the data and fitting a line based on certain criteria, and using the more systematic **median-median** method. Regardless of the method you use, you can examine the **residuals** to determine whether your model is a good fit. With a good model, the residuals should be randomly positive and negative, the sum of the residuals should be zero, and each residual should be as small as possible. You also learned about **root mean square error,** a single measure of good fit.

EXERCISES

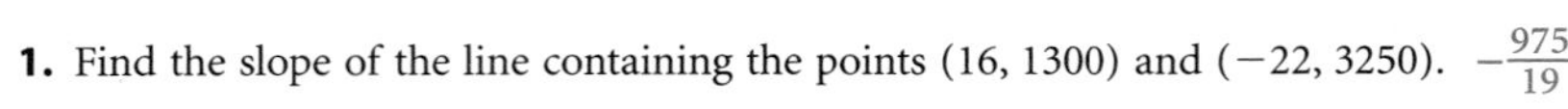

1. Find the slope of the line containing the points (16, 1300) and (−22, 3250). $-\frac{975}{19}$
2. Consider the line $y = -5.02 + 23.45x$.
   a. What is the slope of this line? 23.45
   b. Write an equation for a line that is parallel to this line. possible answer: $y = 23.45x$
   c. Write an equation for a line that is perpendicular to this line. possible answer: $y = -\frac{20}{469}x$
3. Find the point on each line where y is equal to 740.0.
   a. $y = 16.8x + 405$ approximately (19.9, 740.0)
   b. $y = -7.4 + 4.3(x - 3.2)$ approximately (177.0, 740.0)
4. Consider the system of equations

$$\begin{cases} y = 3.2x - 4 \text{ (Equation 1)} \\ y = 3.1x - 3 \text{ (Equation 2)} \end{cases}$$

   a. Substitute the y-value from Equation 1 into Equation 2 to obtain a new equation. Solve the new equation for x. $3.2x - 4 = 3.1x - 3$; $x = 10$
   b. Subtract Equation 2 from Equation 1 and solve for the remaining variable.
   c. Explain why the solutions to 4a and 4b are the same.

ASSIGNING HOMEWORK

You might assign Exercises 1–10 and 18 (perhaps assigning just parts of some of the multi-part exercises) before giving a chapter test. Exercise 18 is the only exercise that explicitly reviews residuals. Use the Mixed Review as preparation for the exam on Chapters 1–3.

Helping with the Exercises

Exercise 2c Students might need to be reminded of how the slopes of perpendicular lines relate.

4b. $0 = 0.1x - 1$; $x = 10$

4c. 4a uses the method of substitution to solve a system of equations, whereas 4b uses elimination.

5. The graphs below show three different lines of fit for the same set of data. For each graph, decide whether the line is a good line of fit or not, and explain why.

a.

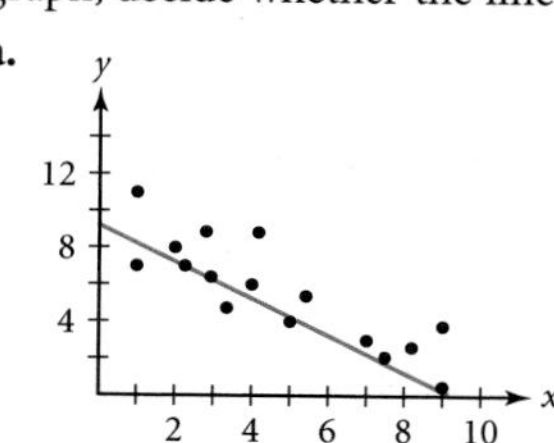

b.

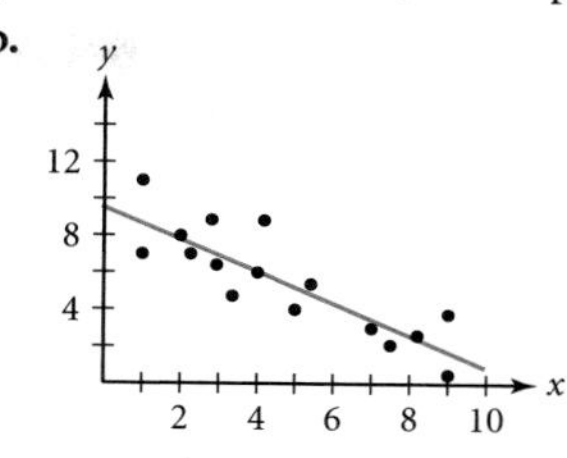

c.

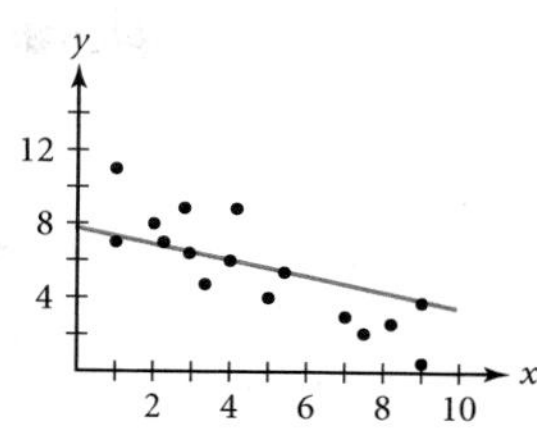

6. Solve each system.

a. $\begin{cases} y = 6.2x + 18.4 \\ y = -2.1x + 7.40 \end{cases}$

b. $\begin{cases} y = \frac{3}{4}x - 1 \\ \frac{7}{10}x + \frac{2}{5}y = 8 \end{cases}$

c. $\begin{cases} 3x + 2y = 4 \\ -3x + 5y = 3 \end{cases}$

7. Find the point (or points) where each pair of lines intersect.

a. $\begin{cases} 5x - 4y = 5 \\ 2x + 10y = 2 \end{cases}$ (1, 0)

b. $\begin{cases} y = \frac{1}{4}(x - 8) + 5 \\ y = 0.25x + 3 \end{cases}$

every point; same line

c. $\begin{cases} \frac{3}{5}x - \frac{2}{5}y = 3 \\ 0.6x - 0.4y = -3 \end{cases}$

No intersection; the lines are parallel.

8. The ratio of the weight of an object on Mercury to its weight on Earth is 0.38.

a. Explain why you can use the equation $m = 0.38e$ to model the weight of an object on Mercury.

b. How much would a 160-pound student weigh on Mercury?

c. The ratios for the Moon and Jupiter are 0.17 and 2.54 respectively. The equations $y_1 = 0.38x$, $y_2 = 1x$, $y_3 = 0.17x$, and $y_4 = 2.54x$ are graphed at right. Match each planet with its graph and equation.

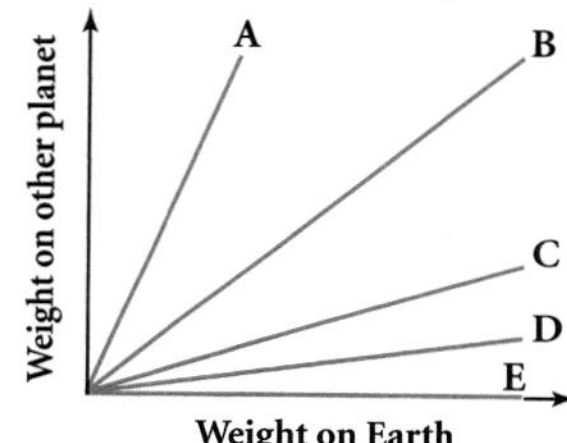

Science CONNECTION

Planning a trip to outer space? This table gives the ratio of an object's weight on each of the planets and the Moon to its weight on Earth.

You can calculate your weight on each of these celestial bodies. Some of these calculations will make you seem like a light-weight, and others will make you seem heavy! But, of course, your body will still be the same. Your *mass* won't change. Your *weight* on other planets depends on your mass, *m*, the planet's mass, *M*, and the distance, *r*, from the center of the planet.

Mercury	0.38
Venus	0.91
Earth	1
Moon	0.17
Mars	0.38
Jupiter	2.54
Saturn	0.93
Uranus	0.80
Neptune	1.19
Pluto	0.06

Exercise 5 As an extension, have students calculate the residuals and compare residual sums and root mean square error.

5a. Poor fit; there are too many points above the line.

5b. Reasonably good fit; the points are well-distributed above and below the line, and not clumped. The line follows the downward trend of the data.

5c. Poor fit; there are an equal number of points above and below the line, but they are clumped to the left and to the right, respectively. The line does not follow the trend of the data.

6a. $\left(-\frac{110}{83}, \frac{4226}{415}\right) \approx$ $(-1.3253, 10.1831)$

6b. $\left(\frac{42}{5}, \frac{53}{10}\right) = (8.4, 5.3)$

6c. $\left(\frac{2}{3}, 1\right) \approx (0.\overline{6}, 1)$

Exercise 8 Slopes can provide a visual or geometric method of ordering fractions. Looking at the steepness of the lines can help in putting the fractions in order.

[Alert] Students might make a ratio of the weights on the Moon and on Jupiter. Reiterate that the ratios are all of the weight on the given planet to the weight on Earth.

8a. The ratio 0.38 represents the slope; that is, for each pound on Earth, you would weigh 0.38 pound on Mercury.

8b. $m = 0.38(160) = 60.8$. The student's weight on Mercury would be about 60.8 lb.

8c. Moon: D, $y_1 = 0.17x$; Mercury: C, $y_2 = 0.38x$; Earth: B, $y_3 = x$; Jupiter: A, $y_4 = 2.54x$

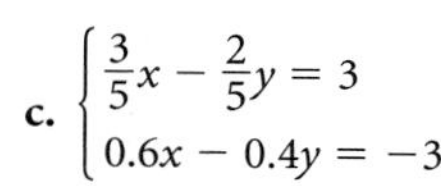

Exercise 9 As needed, remind students to round final answers but to keep and use all the digits as they work through a problem on their calculators.

9a. [Scatter plot: Lean (mm) from 5300 to 5500 vs. Year, 1910, 1960, 2010]

9e. Approximately 5.3 mm; the prediction in 9d is probably accurate within 5.3 mm. In other words, the actual value will probably be between 5469.1 and 5479.7.

Exercise 11 In this context, *linear* means a straight line. Linear equations are called that because their graphs are lines.

Architecture CONNECTION

In 1173 C.E., the Tower of Pisa was built on soft ground and, ever since, has been leaning to one side as it sinks in the soil. This 8-story, 191-foot tower was built with only a 7-foot-deep foundation. The tower was completed in the mid-1300s even though it started to lean after the first 3 stories were completed. The tower's structure consists of a cylindrical body, arches, and columns. Rhombuses and rectangles decorate the surface.

The Tower of Pisa, in Pisa, Italy

9. Read the Architecture Connection. The table lists the amount of lean, measured in millimeters, for thirteen different years.

Tower of Pisa

Year	Lean
1910	5336
1920	5352
1930	5363
1940	5391
1950	5403

Year	Lean
1960	5414
1970	5428
1980	5454
1990	5467

a. Make a scatter plot of the data. Let x represent the year, and let y represent the amount of lean in millimeters.

b. Find a median-median line for the data. $\hat{y} = 2088 + 1.7x$

c. What is the slope of the median-median line? Interpret the slope in the context of the problem. 1.7; for every additional year, the tower leans another 1.7 mm.

d. Find the amount of lean predicted by your equation for 1992 (the year work was started to secure the foundation). 5474.4 mm

e. Find the root mean square error of the median-median line. What does this error tell you about your answer to 8d?

f. What are the domain and range for your linear model? Give an explanation for the numbers you chose. $1173 \leq \text{domain} \leq 1992$ (year built to year retrofit began); $0 \leq \text{range} \leq 5474.4$ mm

10. The 4th term of an arithmetic sequence is 64. The 54th term is -61. Find the 23rd term. $u_{23} = 16.5$

MIXED REVIEW

1.3 **11.** State whether each recursive formula defines a sequence that is arithmetic, geometric, shifted geometric, or none of these. State whether a graph of the sequence would be linear or curved. Then list the first 5 terms of the sequence.

a. $u_1 = 4$ and $u_n = 3u_{n-1}$ where $n \geq 2$
geometric; curved; 4, 12, 36, 108, 324

b. $u_0 = 20$ and $u_n = 2u_{n-1} + 7$ where $n \geq 1$
shifted geometric; curved; 20, 47, 101, 209, 425

1.5 **12. APPLICATION** You receive a $500 gift for high school graduation and deposit it into a savings account on June 15. The account has an annual interest rate of 5.9% compounded annually.

a. Write a recursive formula for this problem. $u_0 = 500$ and $u_n = (1 + 0.059)u_{n-1}$ where $n \geq 1$

b. List the first 3 terms of the sequence. 500, 529.50, 560.74

c. What is the meaning of the value of u_3? the amount in the account after 3 years

d. How much money will you have in your account when you retire, 35 years later? $3718.16

e. If you deposit an additional $100 in your account each year on June 15, how much will you have in savings 35 years after graduation? $14,627.20

1.2 **13. APPLICATION** An Internet web site gives the current world population and projects the population for future years. Its projections for the number of people on Earth on January 1 in the years 2005 through 2009 are given in the table at right.

a. Find a recursive formula to model the population growth. What kind of sequence is this?

b. Predict the population on January 1, 2010. 6,988,249,788 people

c. In what year will the world's population exceed 10 billion?

d. Is this a realistic model that could predict world population in the next millennium? Explain.

Population Projections

Year	World population
2005	6,486,915,022
2006	6,581,251,218
2007	6,676,959,301
2008	6,774,059,223
2009	6,872,843,077

(*www.ibiblio.org*)

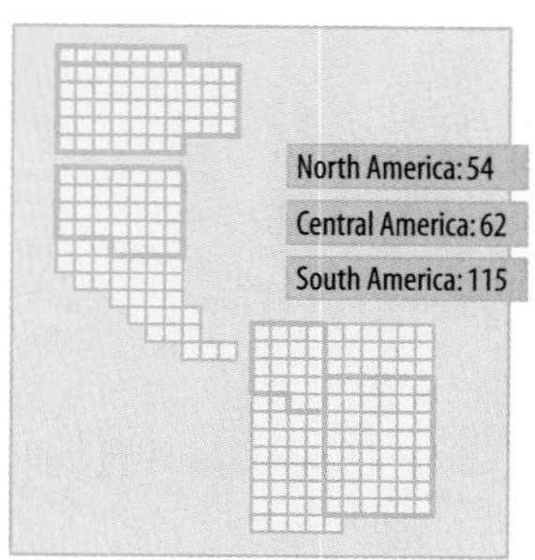

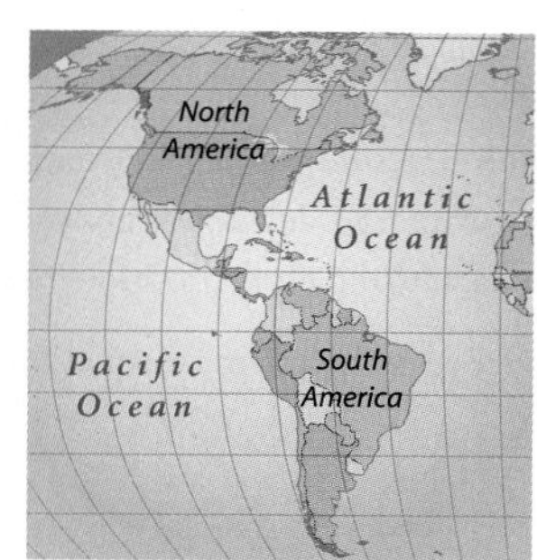

The United Nations estimates that by 2025, the human population will increase by 31 percent. This diagram shows projected growth in the Western Hemisphere. Each square represents an increase of 1 million people. The outlined countries are Canada, the United States, Mexico, Colombia, and Brazil.

1.3 **14. APPLICATION** Jonah must take an antibiotic every 12 hours. Each pill is 25 milligrams, and after every 12 hours, 50% of the drug remains in his body. What is the amount of antibiotic in his body over the first 2 days? What amount will there be in his body in the long run?

2.1 **15.** Create a box-and-whisker plot that has this five-number summary: 5, 7, 12, 13, 17.

a. Are the data skewed left, skewed right, or symmetric? skewed left

b. What is the median of the data? 12

c. What is the *IQR*? 6

d. What percentage of data values are above 12? Above 13? Below 5? 50%; 25%; 0%

Exercises 12, 13 As an extension, ask students to find an explicit formula modeling the situation in each of these exercises.

13a. Possible answer: $u_{2005} = 6486915022$ and $u_n = (1 + 0.015)u_{n-1}$ where $n \geq 2006$. The sequence is geometric.

13c. On January 1, 2035, the population will be just above 10 billion. So the population will first exceed 10 billion late in 2034.

13d. Answers will vary. An increasing geometric sequence has no limit. But the model will not work for the distant future because there is a physical limit to how many people will fit on Earth.

14. $u_0 = 25$ mg, $u_1 = 37.5$ mg, $u_2 = 43.75$ mg, $u_3 = 46.875$ mg, $u_4 = 48.4375$ mg. In the long run, he'll have about 50 mg of the antibiotic in his body.

15.

0 5 10 15 20

16b. Louisiana lies more than 2 standard deviations above the mean.

16c. 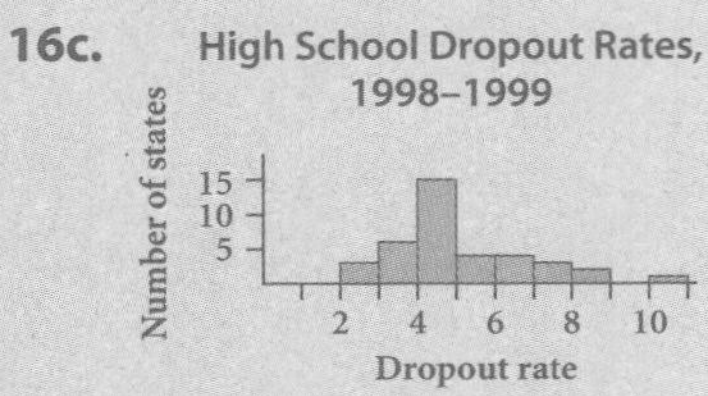

17a. $\left(\frac{110}{71}, -\frac{53}{213}\right) \approx$ (1.5493, −0.2488)

17b. $\left(-\frac{27}{20}, \frac{91}{20}\right) =$ (−1.35, 4.55)

17c. $\left(\frac{46}{13}, \frac{9}{26}\right) \approx$ (3.5385, 0.3462)

Exercise 18 [Ask] "Why is the median age going up?" [Perhaps because more women are working; they need more education; perhaps the age for men is also rising.] As an extension, students might research data on men's median age at first marriage and compare them to the problem data.

18a. 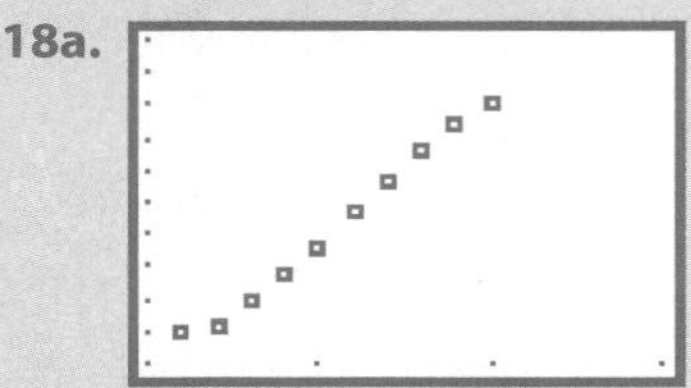

[1970, 2000, 10, 20, 25, 0.5]

The data may be linear.

18d. 48.41 years old. This is probably not realistic.

18e. 0.376, 0.033, −0.01, −0.052, −0.095, −0.038, 0.019, 0.076, 0.033, −0.110; $s = 0.14$. This means that ages predicted by this equation are generally within 0.14 yr of the actual age.

2.3 **16.** The table shows high school dropout rates reported by states and the District of Columbia in 1998–1999. Data are unavailable for some states.

High School Dropout Rates, 1998–1999

State	Rate (%)	State	Rate (%)	State	Rate (%)
Alabama	4.4	Maine	3.3	Oklahoma	5.2
Alaska	5.3	Maryland	4.4	Oregon	6.5
Arizona	8.4	Massachusetts	3.6	Pennsylvania	3.8
Arkansas	6.0	Minnesota	4.5	Rhode Island	4.5
Connecticut	3.3	Mississippi	5.2	South Dakota	4.5
Delaware	4.1	Missouri	4.8	Tennessee	4.6
District of Columbia	8.2	Montana	4.5	Utah	4.7
Georgia	7.4	Nebraska	4.2	Vermont	4.6
Idaho	6.9	Nevada	7.9	Virginia	4.5
Illinois	6.5	New Jersey	3.1	West Virginia	4.9
Iowa	2.5	New Mexico	7.0	Wisconsin	2.6
Kentucky	4.9	North Dakota	2.4	Wyoming	5.2
Louisiana	10.0	Ohio	3.9		

(National Center for Education Statistics)

$\bar{x} = 5.061$, $median = 4.6$, $mode = 4.5$, $s = 1.731$

a. What are the mean, median, mode, and standard deviation of the data?

b. Do any states lie more than 2 standard deviations above or below the mean?

c. Draw a histogram from the data, using an appropriate bin width.

3.7 **17.** Use an appropriate method to solve each system of equations.

a. $\begin{cases} 2.1x - 3y = 4 \\ 5x + 3y = 7 \end{cases}$

b. $\begin{cases} y = \frac{1}{3}x + 5 \\ y = -3x + \frac{1}{2} \end{cases}$

c. $\begin{cases} 3x + 4y = 12 \\ 2x - 6y = 5 \end{cases}$

3.4 **18.** Consider this data on the median age of U.S. women who married for the first time in these years between 1972 and 1990. Approximately 0.08% of Americans get married each year.

a. Create a scatter plot of this data. Do these data seem linear?

b. Find a median-median line for the data. $\hat{y} = -416.533 + 0.2214x$

c. Use your median-median line to predict the median age of women at first marriage in 2000. 26.27 years old

d. Use your median-median line to make a prediction for the year 2100. Does your prediction seem reasonable?

e. Calculate the residuals for each data point, and find the root mean square for your equation. What does this tell you about your model?

Women's Median Age at First Marriage

Year	Age	Year	Age
1972	20.5	1982	22.3
1974	20.6	1984	22.8
1976	21.0	1986	23.3
1978	21.4	1988	23.7
1980	21.8	1990	24.0

(Centers for Disease Control and Prevention, National Center for Health Statistics)

3.1 **19.** Consider the arithmetic sequence 6, 13, 20, 27, 34, ... Let u_1 represent the first term.

a. Write a recursive formula that describes this sequence. $u_1 = 6$ and $u_n = u_{n-1} + 7$ where $n \geq 1$

b. Write an explicit formula for this sequence. $y = 6 + 7x$

c. What is the slope of your equation in 19b? What relationship does this have to the arithmetic sequence?

d. Determine the value of the 32nd term. Is it easier to use your formula from 19a or 19b for this? 230; It's probably easier to use the equation from 19b.

3.1 **20.** For an arithmetic sequence $u_1 = 12$, and $u_{10} = 52.5$.

a. What is the common difference of the sequence? 4.5

b. Find the equation of the line through the points (1, 12) and (10, 52.5). $y = 7.5 + 4.5x$

c. What is the relationship between 20a and 20b? The slope of the line is equal to the common difference of the sequence.

19c. The slope is 7. The slope of the line is the same as the common difference of the sequence.

TAKE ANOTHER LOOK

1. The three representative points shown here are used to find the two parallel lines and, finally, the median-median line for data points that are not shown.

The median-median line is two-thirds of the vertical distance from the top line to the bottom line.

Find the centroid, or balance point, of the triangle formed by the three representative points. Remember, the centroid is the point $(\bar{x}, \bar{y})$. Will the three representative points always form a triangle?

Write an equation of a line that passes through the centroid and has the same slope as the line through (2, 11) and (8, 41). Compare this equation with the median-median equation given by your calculator. Describe your results. Make some conjectures based on your observations.

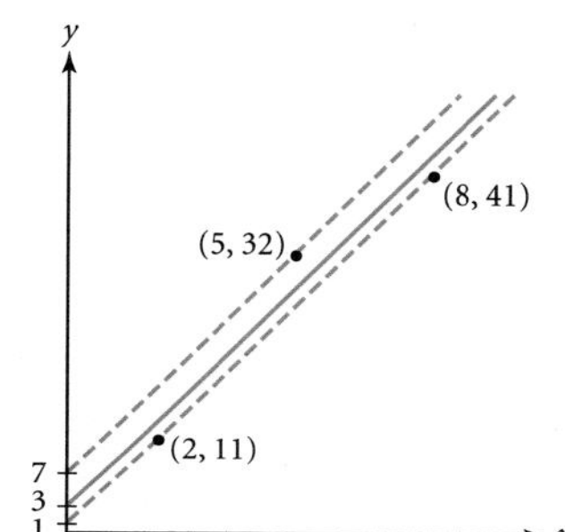

2. The data at right show the average price of a movie ticket for selected years. Find a median-median line for the years 1935–2001. Does your line seem to fit the data well? Which years are not predicted well by your equation? Consider whether or not two or more line segments would fit the data better. Sketch several connected line segments that fit the data. Which model, the single median-median line or the connected segments, do you think is more accurate for predicting the price of a ticket in 2010? Is there another line or curve you might draw that you think would be better? Why do you think these data might not be modeled best by a single linear equation?

Year x	Average ticket price ($) y
1935	0.25
1940	0.28
1948	0.38
1954	0.50
1958	0.69
1963	0.87
1967	1.43
1970	1.56

Year x	Average ticket price ($) y
1974	1.89
1978	2.33
1982	2.93
1986	3.70
1990	4.21
1994	4.10
1998	4.68
2001	5.65

(Motion Picture Association of America)

▶ Take Another Look

1. The *centroid* $(\bar{x}, \bar{y})$ is (5, 28) because $\bar{x} = \frac{5 + 2 + 8}{3} = 5$ and $\bar{y} = \frac{11 + 32 + 41}{3} = 28$. The three representative points will always form a triangle unless all the data points are collinear. The median-median line has the equation $\hat{y} - 28 = 5(x - 5)$, or $\hat{y} = 5x + 3$. This line is the same as the parallel line through the centroid.

2. The median-median line, with the equation $\hat{y} = 0.08326x - 162.02993$, does not fit these data well. A better model might be a piecewise function such as $\hat{y} = 0.01784x - 34.31991$ where $1935 \leq x \leq 1958$ $\hat{y} = 0.11947x - 233.70649$ where $1963 \leq x \leq 1990$, and $\hat{y} = 0.22143x - 437.53048$ where $1994 \leq x \leq 2010$. The third line of the piecewise function would predict the price of a ticket in 2010 better than any single line for all the data.

Perhaps a curve would fit the data better. A quadratic, logistic, or exponential function might be a better model than a linear or even a piecewise linear model. The data are not modeled best by a single linear equation because inflation is not linear.

You might use this activity to introduce the idea of piecewise functions and to discuss the limitations of fitting any mathematical model to a relatively small set of data.

EXTENSION

As an extension of activity 2, pose this problem: "The data for average movie ticket price indicate that prices are rising. However, you know that $0.25 in 1935 is not the same as $0.25 today. If you adjust for inflation, are tickets more or less affordable than they were in 1935?" Students can use Consumer Price Index (CPI) data available at www.keymath.com/DAA.

3. This system is different from systems of linear equations because it has two solutions: $(\sqrt{2}, -2)$ and $(-\sqrt{2}, -2)$.

If students use graphs to check their algebraic results, they might find that they neglected to consider both positive and negative roots.

Solving a quadratic equation by taking the square root of both sides will be formally introduced in Chapter 4, but many students will remember it from beginning algebra.

ASSESSING

The Assessment Resources contain chapter tests and unit exams for this point in the course. You might decide to combine the chapter assessment with a unit exam. Or you might require a presentation or an individual or group performance assessment for the chapter and then give a unit exam. Choose a performance assessment from an exercise you didn't assign that is recommended for that purpose.

FACILITATING SELF-ASSESSMENT

A good sample of student writing in mathematics would be an exercise in which students explain a mathematical concept or relationship. A journal entry in which they also think about their learning can show student understanding and growth. Exercises that require student explanations include Lesson 3.1, Exercises 7 and 15; Lesson 3.2, Exercises 5 and 8; Lesson 3.3, Exercises 4, 5, and 8; Lesson 3.4, Exercises 10 and 11; Lesson 3.5, Exercise 6; Lesson 3.6, Exercises 6 and 8; and Lesson 3.7, Exercises 2 and 3.

3. In this chapter you learned three methods for solving a system of linear equations—graphing, substitution, and elimination. These methods also can be applied to systems of nonlinear equations. Use all three methods to solve this system:

$$\begin{cases} y = x^2 - 4 \\ y = -2x^2 + 2 \end{cases}$$

Did you find the same solution(s) with all three methods? Describe how the process of solving this system was different from solving a system of linear equations. If you were given another system similar to this one, which method of solution would you choose? What special things would you look out for?

Assessing What You've Learned

In Chapters 0, 1, and 2, you were introduced to different ways to assess what you learned. Maybe you have tried all six ways—writing in your journal, giving a presentation, organizing your notebook, doing a performance assessment, keeping a portfolio, or writing test items. By now you should realize that assessment is more than just taking tests and more than your teacher giving you a grade.

In the working world, performance in only a few occupations can be measured with tests. All employees, however, must communicate and demonstrate to their employers, coworkers, clients, patients, or customers that they are skilled in their field. Assessing your own understanding and demonstrating your ability to apply what you've learned gives you practice in this important life skill. It also helps you develop good study habits, and that, in turn, will help you advance in school and give you the best possible opportunities in your life.

WRITE IN YOUR JOURNAL Use one of these prompts to write a paragraph in your journal.

- Find an exercise from this chapter that you could not fully solve. Write out the problem and as much of the solution as possible. Then clearly explain what is keeping you from solving the problem. Be as specific as you can.
- Compare and contrast arithmetic sequences and linear equations. How do you decide which to use?

PERFORMANCE ASSESSMENT Show a classmate, family member, or teacher different ways to find a line of fit for a data set. You may want to go back and use one of the data sets presented in an example or exercise, or you may want to research your own data. Discuss how well the line fits and whether you think a linear model is a good choice for the data.

Good portfolio selections for this chapter include Lesson 3.1, Exercise 12; Lesson 3.2, Exercise 12; Lesson 3.4, Exercise 9; Lesson 3.5, Exercise 9; Lesson 3.6, Exercise 7; and Lesson 3.7, Exercise 8.

CHAPTER

4

Functions, Relations, and Transformations

Overview

This chapter begins with a different look at graphs in **Lesson 4.1. Lesson 4.2** makes the distinction between relations and functions as it introduces function notation. Students look at translations of linear functions in **Lesson 4.3. Lesson 4.4** presents the family of quadratic functions as transformations of the function $y = x^2$ and emphasizes the vertex as key to writing these equations from a graph or graphing the equations. **Lesson 4.5** uses another transformation, reflection, to examine the square root family, with parent function $y = \sqrt{x}$. In the **exploration,** students see a rotation as a composition of two reflections. The absolute-value family is introduced in **Lesson 4.6;** students explore rigid transformations and nonrigid transformations (stretches and shrinks) of the parent function $y = |x|$. **Lesson 4.7** considers transformations of a family of relations, the circle and ellipse family. **Lesson 4.8** looks at compositions of functions.

The Mathematics

Relations and Functions

A technical definition of *function* is a set of ordered pairs in which no two pairs have the same first coordinate. The first elements of the ordered pairs comprise the function's domain; the second elements comprise its range. A function whose domain or range has "gaps" is discrete; otherwise, it's continuous. A function might contain infinitely many ordered pairs, such as one with every real number or every integer as a first coordinate. To illustrate the notions of function and composition and to relate functions to tables and graphs, this book uses functions with a small number of ordered pairs.

The composition of functions f and g is a new function that takes the output from function f as input into function g. For example, if $f(x) = (x - 4)^2$ and $g(x) = 3x$, then the composition $g(f(x))$ is $3f(x)$, or $3(x - 4)^2$. Many applications of compositions break down a complicated function into simpler ones. It's common to start with a function such as $k(x) = 3(x - 4)^2$ and break it down into its smallest components: $f(x) = x - 4$, $g(x) = x^2$, and $h(x) = 3x$. Then $k(x) = h(g(f(x)))$.

Transformations

You can see by looking at graphs that every translation of a nonvertical line can be thought of either as a horizontal translation or as a vertical translation. Algebraically, the vertical translation given by equation $y - h = a + bx$ is the same as the horizontal translation given by $y = a + b\left(x + \frac{h}{b}\right)$. Similarly, for the parent line $y = x$, and for the parent parabola, absolute-value, and square root functions, every vertical stretch can be thought of as a horizontal shrink, and every vertical shrink can be thought of as a horizontal stretch. Students can verify this claim graphically and symbolically. To determine the amount of horizontal and vertical stretch or shrink, you can consider the images of (0, 0) and (1, 1). If the image of (1, 1) is a units to the right of and b units above the image of (0, 0), then there's a horizontal stretch or shrink of a and a vertical stretch or shrink of b. A natural question might be "Is a translation in one direction ever a stretch in the other?" No function in this chapter has this property, but exponential and logarithmic functions, addressed in the next chapter, do.

Compositions of Transformations

Suppose we start with the unit circle, whose equation is $x^2 + y^2 = 1$, and translate its graph 1 unit to the left and 2 units down. Then we stretch it horizontally by a factor of 3. What's the equation of the result? The translation has the equation $(x + 1)^2 + (y + 2)^2 = 1$. But how do we represent the stretch? In particular, do we divide 3 into x or into $x + 1$? We might want to divide x by 3, because we're representing a horizontal stretch, but we're stretching only the translated figure, not the entire plane. So the equation is $\left(\frac{x+1}{3}\right)^2 + (y+2)^2 = 1$.

Similarly, if you're tracking what happens to the point (0, 1) under these transformations, you translate it first to (−1, 1) and then to (−1, −1). Does the horizontal stretch then take it to (−3, −1)? A horizontal stretch of the plane would do so, but a horizontal stretch of the circle leaves its top point (−1, −1) alone. For this reason, when tracking points it's good to think about stretches and shrinks before translations: The horizontal stretch leaves at the top of the circle at point (0, 1); it's then translated to (−1, 1) and finally to (−1, −1).

Using This Chapter

Lessons 4.4 and 4.5 can be covered in one day. If students do not have a good understanding of transformations, you can use the *Discovering Geometry* Practice Your Skills worksheets for Lessons 7.1–7.3, available at www.keymath.com/DG. The investigation in Lesson 4.8 is optional.

The review exercises in each lesson can be very involved; assign only one or two for each lesson.

Resources

Discovering Advanced Algebra Resources

Teaching and Worksheet Masters
Lessons 4.1–4.8, Chapter Review

Calculator Notes 2D, 4A–4H

Sketchpad Demonstrations
Lessons 4.3–4.7

Fathom Demonstration
Lesson 4.6

Assessment Resources A and B
Quiz 1 (Lessons 4.1, 4.2)
Quiz 2 (Lessons 4.3–4.5)
Quiz 3 (Lessons 4.6–4.8)
Chapter 4 Test
Chapter 4 Constructive Assessment Options

More Practice Your Skills for Chapter 4

Condensed Lessons for Chapter 4

Other Resources

A Visual Approach to Functions by Frances Van Dyke.

Functional Melodies by Scott Beall.

Connecting Mathematics with Science: Experiments for Precalculus by Irina Lyublinskaya.

For complete references to these and other resources see www.keypress.com/DAA.

Materials

- graph paper
- motion sensors
- string
- small weights
- stopwatches
- small mirrors
- tape measures or metersticks
- geometry software, *optional*

Pacing Guide

	day 1	day 2	day 3	day 4	day 5	day 6	day 7	day 8	day 9	day 10
standard	4.1	4.2	quiz, 4.3	4.4	4.5	quiz, 4.6	4.6	4.7	4.8	4.8
enriched	4.1	4.2, project	quiz, 4.3	4.4, 4.5	quiz, exploration	4.6	4.7	4.8	4.8, project	quiz, review
block	4.1, 4.2	quiz, 4.3, 4.4	4.5, 4.6	quiz, 4.6, 4.7	4.8	quiz, review	TAL, assessment			

	day 11	day 12
standard	quiz, review	assessment
enriched	TAL, assessment	

CHAPTER

4

Functions, Relations, and Transformations

American artist Benjamin Edwards (b 1970) used a digital camera to collect images of commercial buildings for this painting, *Convergence.* He then projected all the images in succession on a 97-by-146-inch canvas, and filled in bits of each one. The result is that numerous buildings are transformed into one busy impression—much like the impression of seeing many things quickly out of the corner of your eye when driving through a city.

OBJECTIVES

In this chapter you will

- interpret graphs of functions and relations
- review function notation
- learn about the linear, quadratic, square root, absolute-value, and semicircle families of functions
- apply transformations—translations, reflections, stretches, and shrinks—to the graphs of functions and relations
- transform functions to model real-world data

CHAPTER 4 OBJECTIVES

- Describe a graph as discrete or continuous and identify the independent and dependent variables, the intercepts, and the rates of change
- Draw a qualitative graph from a context scenario and create a context scenario given a qualitative graph
- Define *function, domain,* and *range,* and use function notation
- Distinguish conceptually and graphically between functions and relations
- Study linear, quadratic, absolute-value, and square root functions
- See how translations, reflections, stretches, and compressions of the graphs of these functions and of the unit circle affect their equations
- Explore compositions of transformations graphically and numerically in real-world contexts

There are about 250 sites featured in the painting. Edwards aims to capture a look at suburban sprawl; he intends for the painting to be overwhelming and difficult to look at. **[Ask]** "What do you think is the artist's opinion of suburban sprawl?" [Sample answer: It is too busy. Developers try to put too many strip malls and superstores into a small, peaceful space, and it ends up being overwhelming.]

[Ask] "This chapter is partly about transformations. How does this painting represent a transformation?" [It consists of real images that have been transformed into something different and almost unrecognizable. The artist has translated hundreds of images into one place.] "What images do you recognize?" [building in the upper-right corner, chunks of brick, white fence on the left] "What do you think other parts of the painting represent?" [Sample answers: The section at the bottom represents a parking lot, with the lines representing the chaos of traffic. The black splotches represent bushes. The white dot at the top and just right of center represents the sun.]

LESSON
4.1

PLANNING

LESSON OUTLINE

One day:

10 min Example

15 min Investigation

5 min Sharing

15 min Exercises

MATERIALS

- graph paper, *optional*
- More Graph Stories (T), *optional*

TEACHING

This lesson reviews many aspects of representing real-world situations with graphs.

INTRODUCTION

Before students look at the book, you may want to present the haircut scenario and have a discussion about which variable would be independent. Many students will claim that the number of haircuts is the independent variable, especially if you mention it first, as the book does. **[Ask]** "If you owned a hair salon, how would you determine the cost of a haircut?" Indeed, the number of customers per week may be one of several variables that help determine the price. After students look at the graph in the book, **[Ask]** "Why isn't the y-intercept bigger? Is this a linear relationship?" [It might not be; no matter what the price, it seems that someone is still willing to pay it.]

LESSON
4.1 Interpreting Graphs

A picture can be worth a thousand words, if you can interpret the picture. In this lesson you will investigate the relationship between real-world situations and graphs that represent them.

Wigs (portfolio) (1994), by American artist Lorna Simpson (b 1960), uses photos of African-American hairstyles through the decades, with minimal text, to critique deeper issues of race, gender, and assimilation.

Lorna Simpson, *Wigs (portfolio)*, 1994, waterless lithograph on felt, 72 x 162″ overall installed. Collection Walker Art Center, Minneapolis/T. B. Walker Acquisition Fund, 1995

What is the real-world meaning of the graph at right, which shows the relationship between the number of customers getting haircuts each week and the price charged for each haircut?

y

Number of customers each week

Price of a haircut ($)

x

The number of customers depends on the price of the haircut. So the price in dollars is the independent variable and the number of customers is the dependent variable. As the price increases, the number of haircuts decreases linearly. As you would expect, fewer people are willing to pay a high price; a lower price attracts more customers. The slope indicates the number of haircuts lost for each dollar increase. The x-intercept represents the haircut price that is too high for anyone. The y-intercept indicates the number of haircuts when they are free.

EXAMPLE

Students at Central High School are complaining that the soda pop machine is frequently empty. Several student council members decide to study this problem. They record the number of cans in the soda machine at various times during a typical school day and make a graph.

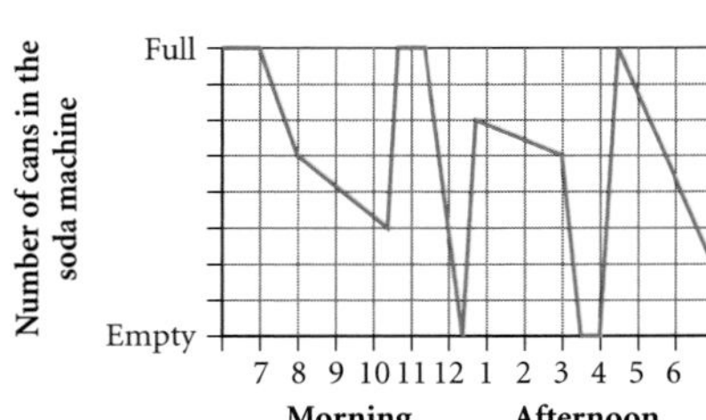

a. Based on the graph, at what times is soda consumed most rapidly?

b. When is the machine refilled? How can you tell?

▶ *EXAMPLE*

[Ask] "Does the graph indicate any other information about the school?" [Apparently students arrive at school at 7 in the morning; classes begin at 8; lunch begins at 11:30; classes let out at 3:00.] If you have time and your own school has vending machines, suggest that students sketch a graph representing their estimate of the stock in one of these machines.

[Ask] "How would you describe the slopes of the lines representing refills?" [The slopes are very large.]

LESSON OBJECTIVES

- Identify independent and dependent variables
- Interpret features of a qualitative graph, including rates of change and x- and y-intercepts
- Decide whether a graph (or a function) is discrete or continuous given a description of the variables
- Draw a qualitative graph from a context scenario and create a context scenario given a qualitative graph
- Distinguish between linear change and nonlinear change

c. When is the machine empty? How can you tell?

d. What do you think the student council will recommend to solve the problem?

► *Solution*

Each horizontal segment indicates a time interval when soda does not sell. Negative slopes represent when soda is consumed, and positive slopes show when the soda machine is refilled.

a. The most rapid consumption is pictured by the steep, negative slopes from 11:30 to 12:30, and from 3:00 to 3:30.

b. The machine is completely refilled overnight, again at 10:30 A.M., and again just after school lets out. The machine is also refilled at 12:30, but only to 75% capacity.

c. The machine is empty from 3:30 to 4:00 P.M., and briefly at about 12:30.

d. The student council might recommend refilling the machine once more at about 2:00 or 3:00 P.M. in order to solve the problem of it frequently being empty. Refilling the machine completely at 12:30 may also solve the problem.

Health CONNECTION

Many school districts and several states have banned vending machines and the sale of soda pop and junk foods in their schools. Proponents say that schools have a responsibility to promote good health. The U.S. Department of Agriculture already bans the sale of foods with little nutritional value, such as soda, gum, and popsicles, in school cafeterias, but candy bars and potato chips don't fall under the ban because they contain some nutrients.

These recycled aluminum cans are waiting to be melted and made into new cans. Although 65% of the United States' aluminum is currently recycled, one million tons are still thrown away each year.

Although the student council members in the example are interested in solving a problem related to soda consumption, they could also use the graph to answer many other questions about Central High School: When do students arrive at school? What time do classes begin? When is lunch? When do classes let out for the day?

Both the graph of haircut customers and the graph in the example are shown as continuous graphs. In reality, the quantity of soda in the machine can take on only discrete values, because the number of cans must be a whole number. The graph might more accurately be drawn with a series of short horizontal segments, as shown at right. The price of a haircut and the number of haircuts can also take on only discrete values. This graph might be more accurately drawn with separate points. However, in both cases, a continuous "graph sketch" makes it easier to see the trends and patterns.

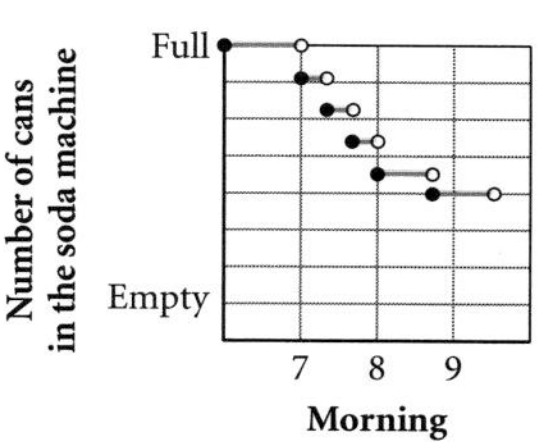

One Step

Go directly to the investigation, without introduction. During Sharing, lead the class in making a table showing relationships between real-world situations and graphs. (See Closing the Lesson.) As needed, go to the example to see whether its solution is consistent with the table.

NCTM STANDARDS

CONTENT		PROCESS	
	Number	✔	Problem Solving
✔	Algebra	✔	Reasoning
✔	Geometry	✔	Communication
	Measurement	✔	Connections
	Data/Probability	✔	Representation

Guiding the Investigation

This creative activity may help deepen students' understanding of slopes as representing rates of change. It also is an additional attraction to mathematics for students who like to write or be creative. If time is limited, have half the class work on Part 1 and the other half on Part 2. You could also have students complete this investigation as an individual activity and display their work in the classroom.

To add to the variety, you might use the More Graph Stories transparency and ask groups to work on different graphs.

SHARING IDEAS

As students share their stories and graphs, ask what units are appropriate for each variable. Suggest that students help communicate their ideas by superimposing a grid on the graph or by labeling points to reference in their story.

Ask students to identify the dependent and independent variables in each case. Encourage discussion; often the distinction isn't clear. Welcome challenges to your own ideas, but try to articulate your intuition. In this context, you can also review domain and range.

[Ask] "Do all stories give continuous graphs?" Some of the stories might describe discrete situations; help students see that in those cases continuous graphs are inappropriate.

Assessing Progress

As students work and present, you can check their understanding of real-world connections to increasing or decreasing curves and of discrete and continuous phenomena. You can also see how well they read and write and how well they work with two variables.

See pages 881–882 for answers to Parts 1 and 2.

Investigation
Graph a Story

Every graph tells a story. Make a graph to go with the story in Part 1. Then invent your own story to go with the graph in Part 2.

Part 1

Sketch a graph that reflects all the information given in this story.

"It was a dark and stormy night. Before the torrents of rain came, the bucket was empty. The rain subsided at daybreak. The bucket remained untouched through the morning until Old Dog Trey arrived as thirsty as a dog. The sun shone brightly through the afternoon. Then Billy, the kid next door, arrived. He noticed two plugs in the side of the bucket. One of them was about a quarter of the way up, and the second one was near the bottom. As fast as you could blink an eye, he pulled out the plugs and ran away."

PEANUTS reprinted by permission of United Feature Syndicate, Inc.

Part 2

This graph tells a story. It could be a story about a lake, a bathtub, or whatever you imagine. Spend some time with your group discussing the information contained in the graph. Write a story that conveys all of this information, including when and how the rates of change increase or decrease.

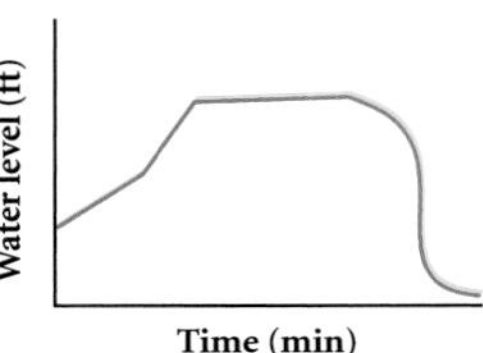

Science **CONNECTION**

Contour maps are a way to graphically represent altitude. Each line marks all of the points that are the same height in feet (or meters) above sea level. Using the distance between two contour lines, you can calculate the rate of change in altitude. These maps are used by hikers, forest fire fighters, and scientists.

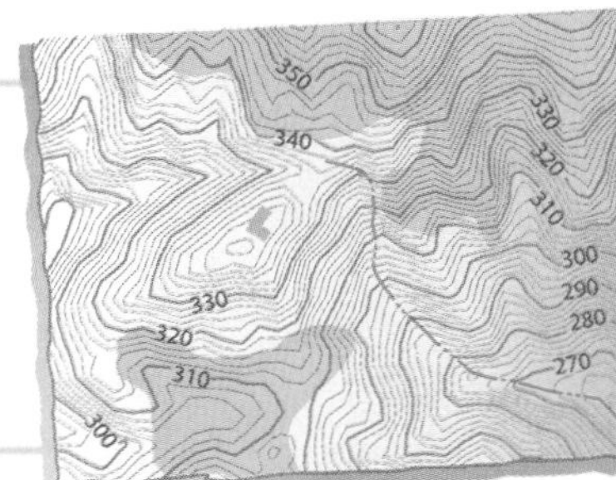

Closing the Lesson

The main point of this lesson is that graphs can represent many aspects of real-world situations.

Real-world	Graph
growing/shrinking/unchanging	increasing/decreasing/horizontal
discrete/continuous	separated points/connected points
linear/nonlinear	straight line/curve
independent/dependent variable	horizontal/vertical axis

As you interpret data and graphs that show a relationship between two variables, you must always decide which is the independent variable and which is the dependent variable. You should also consider whether the variables are discrete or continuous.

EXERCISES

Practice Your Skills

1. Sketch a graph to match each description.

a. increasing throughout, first slowly and then at a faster rate

b. decreasing slowly, then more and more rapidly, then suddenly becoming constant

c. alternately increasing and decreasing without any sudden changes in rate

2. For each graph, write a description like those in Exercise 1.

a.

b.

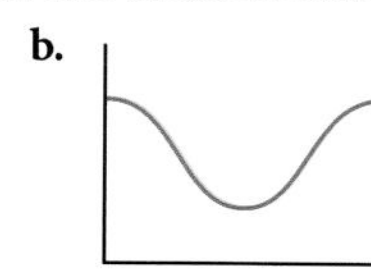

c.

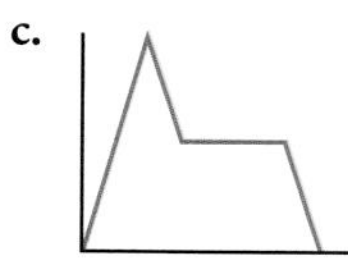

3. Match a description to each graph.

a.

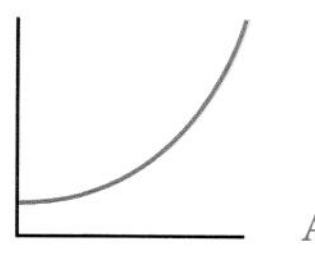

A

b.

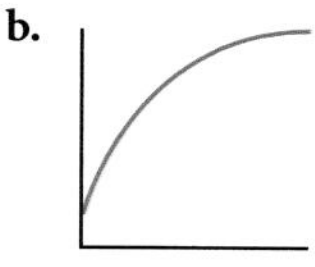

C

c.

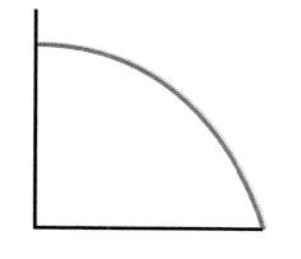

D

d.

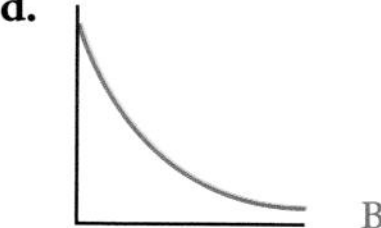

B

A. increasing more and more rapidly
B. decreasing more and more slowly
C. increasing more and more slowly
D. decreasing more and more rapidly

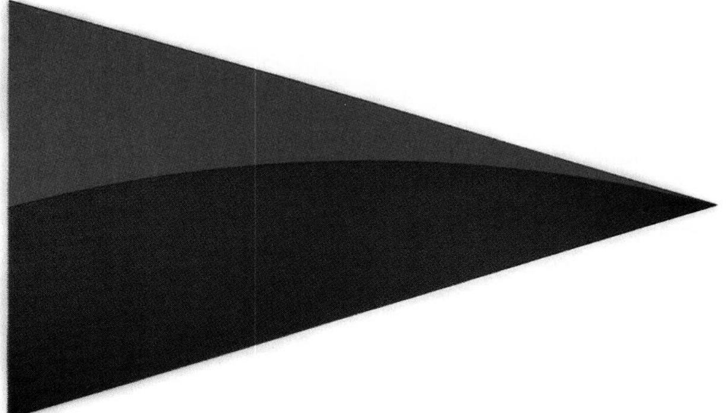

American minimalist painter and sculptor Ellsworth Kelly (b 1923) based many of his works on the shapes of shadows and spaces between objects.

Ellsworth Kelly *Blue Green Curve,* 1972, oil on canvas, 87-3/4 x 144-1/4 in. The Museum of Contemporary Art, Los Angeles, The Barry Lowen Collection

BUILDING UNDERSTANDING

Most of the exercises have more than one correct answer. If you haven't already been stressing that students' work should include responses to the question "Why?" even when this question is not actually stated, now is a good time to do so.

ASSIGNING HOMEWORK

Essential	1–4
Performance assessment	5–9
Portfolio	8
Journal	9
Group	7
Review	10–13

Helping with the Exercises

For each graph, ask students to label each axis with a quantity (such as *time* or *distance*); they need not indicate numerical units. The important factors are which variable is independent, the shape of the graph, and whether the graph is continuous or discrete.

Exercise 1 Similar activities can be found in the book *A Visual Approach to Functions.*

1a.

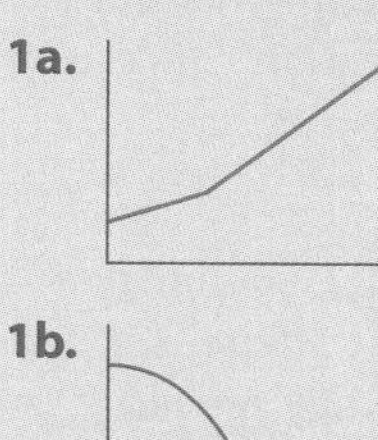

1b.

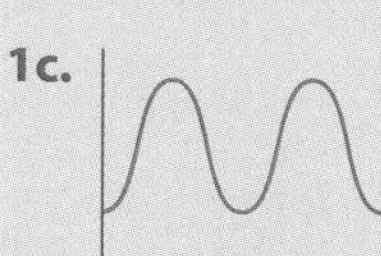

1c.

2a. decreasing at a steady rate; suddenly becoming constant; then suddenly increasing at the same rate it was decreasing at

2b. first decreasing, then increasing back to the same level, without any sudden changes in rate

2c. rapidly increasing from zero; suddenly changing to rapidly decreasing until half the value is reached; constant, then suddenly rapidly decreasing at a constant rate until reaching zero

Exercise 3 **[Ask]** "Graphs a and b are increasing. In which graphs is the rate of growth increasing?" [a and d] The rate itself is given by the slope; the rate is increasing if the slope is getting more positive or less negative. So even when the slope is negative, it can be increasing, as in 3d, from "more negative" to "less negative."

4a. Possible answer: The curve might describe the relationship between the amount of time the ball is in the air and how far away from the ground it is.

4c. possible answer: domain: $0 \leq t \leq 10$ s; range: $0 \leq h \leq 200$ ft

5. Sample answer: Zeke, the fish, swam slowly, then more rapidly to the bottom of his bowl and stayed there for a while. When Zeke's owner sprinkled fish food into the water, Zeke swam toward the surface to eat. The y-intercept is the fish's depth at the start of the story. The x-intercept represents the time the fish reached the surface of the bowl.

Exercise 6 In each part, students need to decide which variable depends on which. In 6b, distance depends on speed; in 6e, the independent variable is time. Although all of these situations are continuous, it's good for students to ask whether the phenomenon is continuous or discrete.

In 6e **[ESL]** A *Ferris wheel* is an amusement-park ride with pairs of seats on a large, slow-moving vertical wheel.

Exercise 7 **[Alert]** In 7b, students may want to take inflation into account. The question concerns the amount of money, not its value.

[Language] In 7d, a *holding pattern* is a circular pattern that planes fly when they are near their destination but must wait to land.

Reason and Apply

4. Harold's concentration often wanders from the game of golf to the mathematics involved in his game. His scorecard frequently contains mathematical doodles and graphs.

a. What is a real-world meaning for this graph found on one of his recent scorecards?

b. What units might he be using? possible answer: seconds and feet

c. Describe a realistic domain and range for this graph.

d. Does this graph show how far the ball traveled? Explain. No, the horizontal distance traveled is not measured.

5. Make up a story to go with the graph at right. Be sure to interpret the x- and y-intercepts.

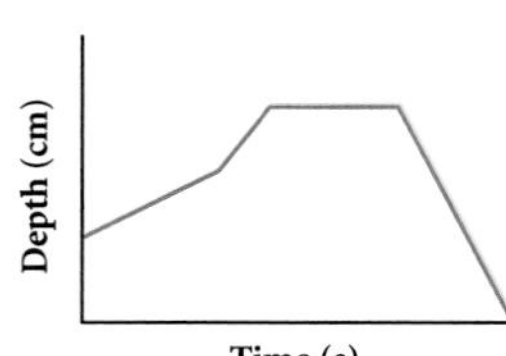

6. Sketch what you think is a reasonable graph for each relationship described. In each situation, identify the variables and label your axes appropriately.

a. the height of a basketball during the last 10 seconds of a game

b. the distance it takes to brake a car to a full stop, compared to the car's speed when the brakes are first applied

c. the temperature of an iced drink as it sits on a table for a long period of time

d. the speed of a falling acorn after a squirrel drops it from the top of an oak tree

e. your height above the ground as you ride a Ferris wheel

7. Sketch what you think is a reasonable graph for each relationship described. In each situation, identify the variables and label your axes appropriately. In each situation, will the graph be continuous or will it be a collection of discrete points or pieces? Explain why.

a. the amount of money you have in a savings account that is compounded annually, over a period of several years, assuming no additional deposits are made

b. the same amount of money that you started with in 7a, hidden under your mattress over the same period of several years

c. an adult's shoe size compared to the adult's foot length

d. your distance from Detroit during a flight from Detroit to Newark if your plane is forced to circle the airport in a holding pattern when you approach Newark

e. the daily maximum temperature of a town, for a month

7a. Time in years is the independent variable; the amount of money in dollars is the dependent variable. The graph will be a series of discontinuous segments.

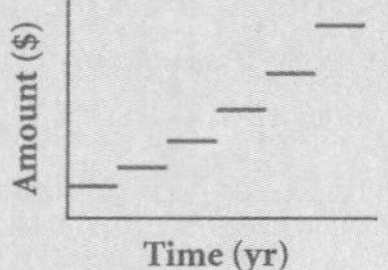

7b. Time in years is the independent variable; the amount of money in dollars is the dependent variable. The graph will be a continuous horizontal segment because the amount never changes.

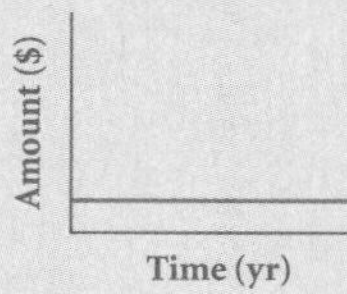

See page 882 for answers to Exercises 6a–e and 7c–e.

8. Describe a relationship of your own and draw a graph to go with it.

9. Car A and Car B are at the starting line of a race. At the green light, they both accelerate to 60 mi/h in 1 min. The graph at right represents their velocities in relation to time.

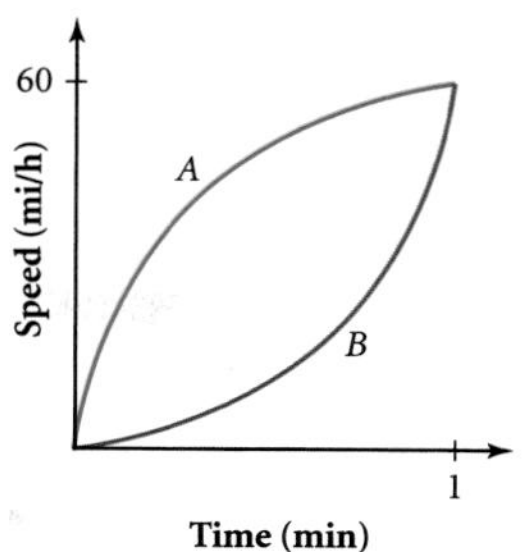

a. Describe the rate of change for each car.

b. After 1 minute, which car will be in the lead? Explain your reasoning. Car A will be in the lead because it is always going faster than Car B, which means it has covered more distance.

Review

3.1 **10.** Write an equation for the line that fits each situation.

a. The length of a rope is 1.70 m, and it decreases by 0.12 m for every knot that is tied in it.

b. When you join a CD club, you get the first 8 CDs for $7.00. After that, your bill increases by $9.50 for each additional CD you purchase.

3.6 **11.** APPLICATION Albert starts a business reproducing high-quality copies of pictures. It costs $155 to prepare the picture and then $15 to make each print. Albert plans to sell each print for $27.

a. Write a cost equation and graph it.

b. Write an income equation and graph it on the same set of axes.

c. How many pictures does Albert need to sell before he makes a profit? 13 pictures

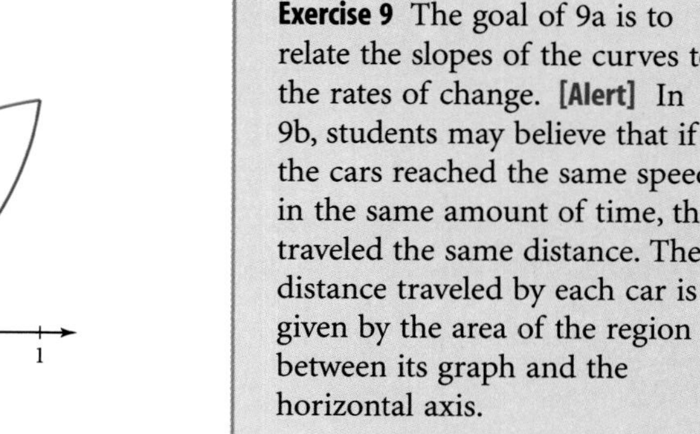

American photographer Gordon Parks (b 1912) holds a large, framed print of one of his photographs.

1.5 **12.** APPLICATION Suppose you have a $200,000 home loan with an annual interest rate of 6.5%, compounded monthly.

a. If you pay $1200 per month, what balance remains after 20 years? $142,784.22

b. If you pay $1400 per month, what balance remains after 20 years? $44,700.04

c. If you pay $1500 per month, what balance remains after 20 years?

d. Make an observation about the answers to 12a–c.

3.7 **13.** Follow these steps to solve this system of three equations in three variables.

$$\begin{cases} 2x + 3y - 4z = -9 & \text{(Equation 1)} \\ x + 2y + 4z = 0 & \text{(Equation 2)} \\ 2x - 3y + 2z = 15 & \text{(Equation 3)} \end{cases}$$

a. Use the elimination method with Equation 1 and Equation 2 to eliminate z. The result will be an equation in two variables, x and y. $3x + 5y = -9$

b. Use the elimination method with Equation 1 and Equation 3 to eliminate z. $6x - 3y = 21$

c. Use your equations from 13a and b to solve for both x and y. $x = 2, y = -3$

d. Substitute the values from 13c into one of the original equations and solve for z. What is the solution to the system? $x = 2, y = -3, z = 1$

Exercise 9 The goal of 9a is to relate the slopes of the curves to the rates of change. **[Alert]** In 9b, students may believe that if the cars reached the same speed in the same amount of time, they traveled the same distance. The distance traveled by each car is given by the area of the region between its graph and the horizontal axis.

9a. Car A speeds up quickly at first and then less quickly until it reaches 60 mi/h. Car B speeds up slowly at first and then quickly until it reaches 60 mi/h.

Exercises 10, 11 Students may note that these are discrete situations. The question is asking for lines that represent the general trends.

10a. Let l represent the length of the rope in meters and let k represent the number of knots; $l = 1.70 - 0.12k$.

Exercise 10b **[Alert]** Students may be confused about how the equation applies to fewer than 8 CDs. The domain of the function includes only values greater than or equal to 8, although the equation is satisfied by points whose x-coordinates are less than 8.

10b. Let b represent the bill in dollars and let c represent the number of CDs purchased; $b = 7.00 + 9.50(c - 8)$ where $c \geq 8$.

11a. Let x represent the number of pictures and let y represent the amount of money (either cost or income) in dollars; $y = 155 + 15x$.

11b. $y = 27x$

Cost: $y = 155 + 15x$
Income: $y = 27x$
Amount of money ($): 80, 160, 240, 320, 400
Number of pictures: 2, 4, 6, 8, 10, 12, 14, 16

12c. $0 (You actually pay off the loan after 19 years 9 months.)

12d. By making an extra $300 payment per month for 20 years, or $72,000, you save hundreds of thousands of dollars in the long run.

Exercise 13 This exercise not only reviews systems of equations but also previews solving systems with matrices in Chapter 6. Because students have not yet had to solve a system of three equations, this exercise is directive. The choice of using elimination with Equations 1 and 2 and then with Equations 1 and 3 to eliminate z is not the only solution method. You might ask students whether they can think of other approaches. [They can use any two pairs of equations first to eliminate any one variable.] **[Ask]** "Why do you need to start by eliminating one variable?" [so you have two equations in two variables that can be solved by either substitution or elimination]

See page 882 for answer to Exercise 8.

LESSON

4.2

PLANNING

LESSON OUTLINE

One day:

10 min Example

15 min Investigation

10 min Sharing

10 min Exercises

MATERIALS

- Calculator Note 4A

TEACHING

This lesson on function notation, evaluating functions, and the vertical line test may be review for many students.

One Step

Pose this problem: "Make a table and a graph of the ages and heights of at least 20 students in this class. Is height a function of age—that is, for every age is there just one height? Is age a function of height?" Encourage students to be creative in measuring ages and heights so that one might be a function of the other. During Sharing, bring out the ideas of the vertical line test and stress that not being one-to-one doesn't mean that a relation isn't a function.

Be sensitive to students who might be self-conscious about their height. A measurement is not needed from every student.

LESSON 4.2

Function Notation

She had not understood mathematics until he had explained to her that it was the symbolic language of relationships. "And relationships," he had told her, "contained the essential meaning of life."

PEARL S. BUCK
THE GODDESS ABIDES, 1972

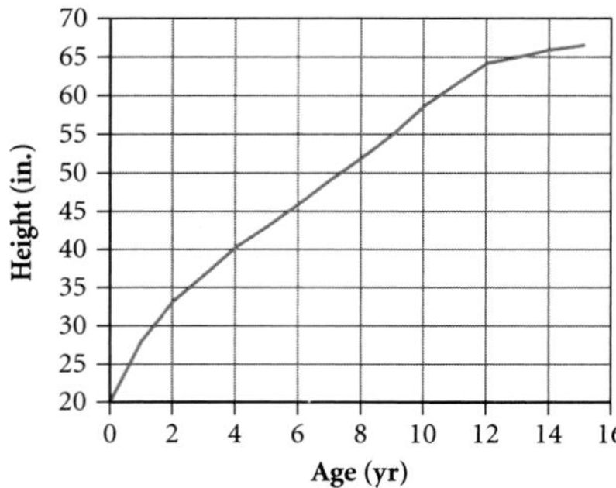

Rachel's parents keep track of her height as she gets older. They plot these values on a graph and connect the points with a smooth curve. For every age you choose on the x-axis, there is only one height that pairs with it on the y-axis. That is, Rachel is only one height at any specific time during her life.

A **relation** is any relationship between two variables. A **function** is a relationship between two variables such that for every value of the independent variable, there is at most one value of the dependent variable. A function is a special type of relation. If x is your independent variable, a function pairs at most one y with each x. You can say that Rachel's height is a function of her age.

You may remember the vertical line test from previous mathematics classes. It helps you determine whether or not a graph represents a function. If no vertical line crosses the graph more than once, then the relation is a function. Take a minute to think about how you could apply this technique to the graph of Rachel's height and the graph in the next example.

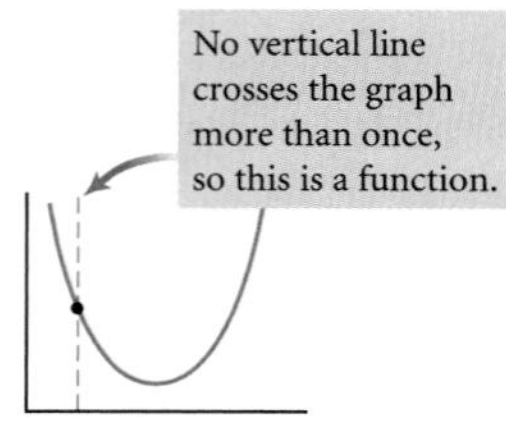

Function

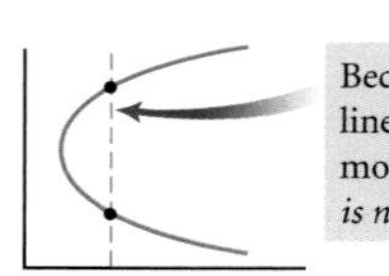

Not a function

Function notation emphasizes the dependent relationship between the variables that are used in a function. The notation $y = f(x)$ indicates that values of the dependent variable, y, are explicitly defined in terms of the independent variable, x, by the function f. You read $y = f(x)$ as "y equals f of x."

Graphs of functions and relations can be continuous, such as the graph of Rachel's height, or they can be made up of discrete points, such as a graph of the maximum temperatures for each day of a month. Although real-world data often have an identifiable pattern, a function does not necessarily need to have a rule that connects the two variables.

Technology CONNECTION

A computer's desktop represents a function. Each icon, when clicked on, opens only one file, folder, or application.

INTRODUCTION

[Ask] "Does the definition of *function* require that there be only one value of x for each value of y?" [No; the graph need not pass a horizontal line test.] You might introduce the term *one-to-one* to describe a function that has not only one y-value for every x-value but also one x-value for every y-value.

The domain of a function might be bounded, or it might be made up of discrete values. A function might not be expressible as a rule, either mathematically or verbally.

LESSON OBJECTIVES

- Define *function* as "a relation with at most one y-value for any x-value"
- Review function notation
- Review the vertical line test for functions
- Distinguish between functions and relations
- Define the domain and range of a function

This handwritten music manuscript by Norwegian composer Edvard Grieg (1843–1907) shows an example of functional relationships. Each of the four simultaneous voices for which this hymn is written can sing only one note at a time, so for each voice the pitch is a function of time.

EXAMPLE

Function f is defined by the equation $f(x) = \frac{2x+5}{x-3}$. Function g is defined by the graph at right.

Find these values.

a. $f(8)$

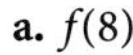

b. $f(-7)$

c. $g(1)$

d. $g(-2)$

▸ *Solution*

When a function is defined by an equation, you simply replace each x with the x-value and evaluate.

a. $f(x) = \dfrac{2x+5}{x-3}$

$$f(8) = \frac{2 \cdot 8 + 5}{8 - 3} = \frac{21}{5} = 4.2$$

b. $f(-7) = \dfrac{2 \cdot (-7) + 5}{-7 - 3} = \dfrac{-9}{-10} = 0.9$

You can check your work with your calculator. [▸ See **Calculator Note 4A** to learn about evaluating functions. ◂]

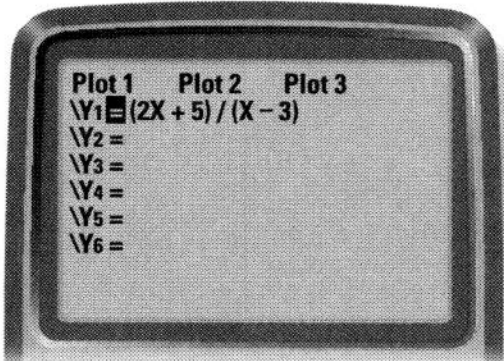

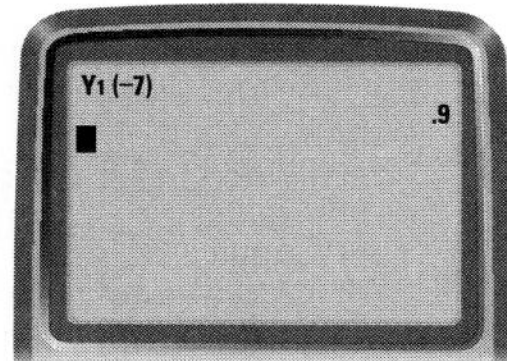

c. The notation $y = g(x)$ tells you that the values of y are explicitly defined, in terms of x, by the graph of the function g. To find $g(1)$, locate the value of y when x is 1. The point $(1, 3)$ on the graph means that $g(1) = 3$.

d. The point $(-2, 0)$ on the graph means that $g(-2) = 0$.

Introduction (continued)

In Chapters 1 and 3, the sequence notation for the nth term, u_n, can be thought of as a modified function notation. You could replace u_n with $u(n)$, which is the way many calculators display the notation.

[Alert] Students may think that $f(x)$ means f times x and want to divide by x or f to simplify the equation. As needed, point out that $f(x)$ is an expression in itself and cannot be separated into parts.

▸ *EXAMPLE*

Using colors when substituting values of x into the function as shown in the solution to $f(8)$ may help students understand the process of evaluating functions.

[Ask] "What is happening to the graph when $x = 3$?" [Evaluating $f(x)$ at $x = 3$ would require dividing by 0, so the value is undefined.] This observation can lead to a discussion about the domain of $f(x)$ and how the vertical line the calculator may have graphed is misleading. To avoid the vertical line, choose a friendly window such as $-9.4 < x < 9.4$ on the TI-83 Plus.

NCTM STANDARDS

CONTENT		PROCESS	
	Number	✓	Problem Solving
✓	Algebra	✓	Reasoning
	Geometry	✓	Communication
	Measurement	✓	Connections
	Data/Probability	✓	Representation

Guiding the Investigation

This investigation includes several important characteristics of relations and functions. If time is limited, you may want to assign the investigation as homework.

Step 1 If students are having difficulty with parts g–i, suggest that they graph several data points.

SHARING IDEAS

Plan presentations to spur debate. For example, students might disagree about whether or not the relation in part g is a function. (It's probably not if your students' ages are measured in years or perhaps even days, but it probably is a function if their ages are measured in seconds.) Or students may be claiming that some relations are not functions because they aren't one-to-one. Let the class critique the different opinions. Try to avoid passing judgment yourself; rather, encourage students to refer to definitions in the book to support their opinions. Help students realize that several different answers can be correct for the assumptions that are being made as in part i.

Assessing Progress

You can assess students' understanding of dependent and independent variables, as well as their willingness to draw graphs.

Award-winning tap dancers Gregory Hines (b 1946) and Savion Glover (b 1973) perform at the 2001 New York City Tap Festival.

At far right is Labanotation, a way of graphically representing dance. A single symbol shows you the direction, level, length of time, and part of the body performing a movement. This is a type of function notation because each part of the body can perform only one motion at any given time. For more information on dance notation, see the links at www.keymath.com/DAA .

In the investigation you will practice identifying functions and using function notation. As you do so, notice how you can identify functions in different forms.

Investigation
To Be or Not to Be (a Function)

Below are nine representations of relations.

a.

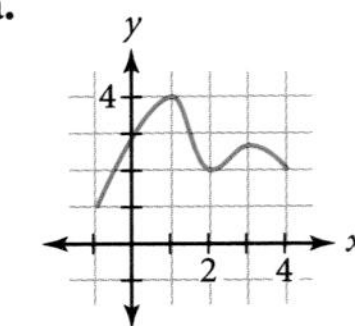

b.

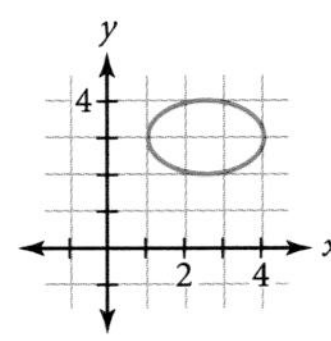

c.

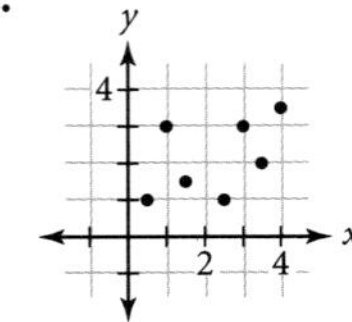

d.

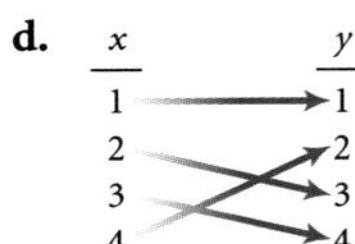

e.

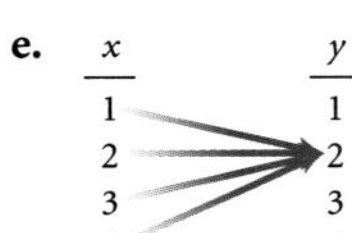

f.

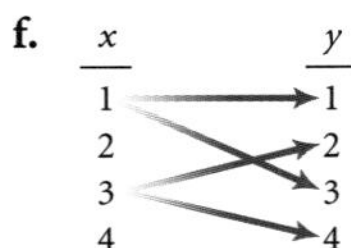

g. independent variable: the age of each student in your class
dependent variable: the height of each student

h. independent variable: an automobile in the state of Kentucky
dependent variable: that automobile's license plate number

i. independent variable: the day of the year
dependent variable: the time of sunset

Step 1a function

Step 1b Not a function; several x-values are paired with two y-values each.

Step 1c function

Step 1d function

Step 1e function

Step 1f Not a function; two x-values are paired with more than one y-value.

Step 1g Not a function; two students may be the same age but different heights.

Step 1h Function; theoretically every automobile has a unique license plate number.

Step 1i Function, if you consider only the days in one year at one location (at one location, the sun can set at only one time for each day); not a function, if you consider the day of any year (the sun could set at different times on March 1, 2002, and March 1, 2003); not a function, if you consider different locations (consider two neighboring towns separated by a time line; the sun will appear to set one hour earlier or later depending on whose clock you use).

Step 1 | Identify each relation that is also a function. For each relation that is not a function, explain why not.

Step 2 | For each function in parts a–f, find the y-value when $x = 2$, and find the x-value(s) when $y = 3$. Write each answer in function notation using the letter of the subpart as the function name, for example, $y = d(x)$ for part d.

When you use function notation to refer to a function, you can use any letter you like. For example, you might use $y = h(x)$ if the function represents height, or $y = p(x)$ if the function represents population. Often in describing real-world situations, you use a letter that makes sense. However, to avoid confusion, you should avoid using the dependent variable as the function name, as in $y = y(x)$. Choose freely but choose wisely.

When looking at real-world data, it is often hard to decide whether or not there is a functional relationship. For example, if you measure the height of every student in your class and the weight of his or her backpack, you may collect a data set in which each student height is paired with only one backpack weight. But does that mean no two students of the same height could have backpacks of equal weight? Does it mean you shouldn't try to model the situation with a function?
No, two students of the same height could have the same backpack weight. You might want to model the data with a function anyway, if a line of fit approximately models the relationship.

EXERCISES

Practice Your Skills

1. Which of these graphs represent functions? Why or why not?

a.

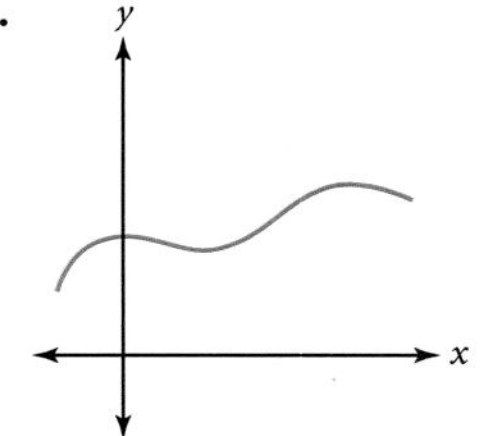

b.

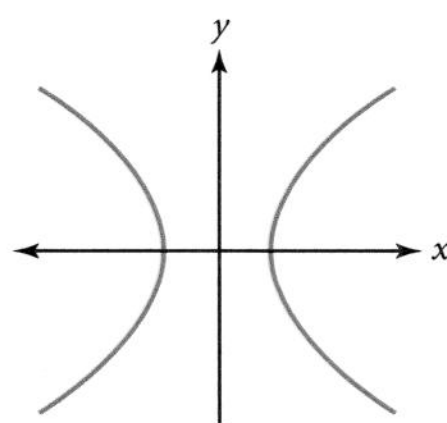

c.

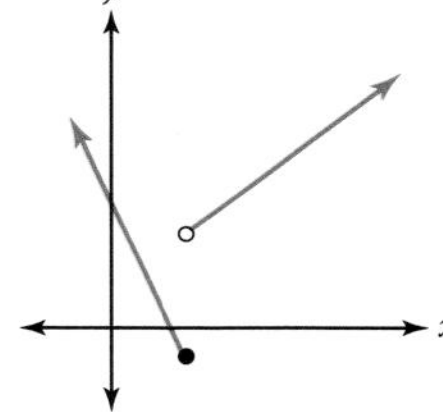

2. Use the functions $f(x) = 3x - 4$ and $g(x) = x^2 + 2$ to find these values.

a. $f(7)$ 17 **b.** $g(5)$ 27 **c.** $f(-5)$ -19 **d.** $g(-3)$ 11 **e.** x when $f(x) = 7$ $\frac{11}{3}$

3. Miguel works at an appliance store. He gets paid \$5.25 an hour and works 8 hours a day. In addition, he earns a 3% commission on all items he sells. Let x represent the total dollar value of the appliances that Miguel sells, and let the function m represent Miguel's daily earnings as a function of x. Which function describes how much Miguel earns in a day? B

A. $m(x) = 5.25 + 0.03x$ **B.** $m(x) = 42 + 0.03x$

C. $m(x) = 5.25 + 3x$ **D.** $m(x) = 42 + 3x$

Step 2a $a(2) = 2$, $a(0) = 3$ or $a(1.5) = 3$

Step 2c $c(2)$ is undefined, $c(1) = 3$ or $c(3) = 3$

Step 2d $d(2) = 3$

Step 2e $e(2) = 2$, no x-value results in $y = 3$

Closing the Lesson

Reiterate the important points of this lesson: A **relation** is a relationship between two variables; a **function** is a relation in which every value of the independent variable corresponds to one and only one value of the dependent variable. If the reverse is also the case, the function is **one-to-one.** Equivalently, graphs of functions pass the **vertical line test.** The **notation** $f(x) = x^2$ means that the function f squares every number x; function values can be found by substitution, such as $f(-3) = (-3)^2 = 9$ or $f(t) = t^2$.

BUILDING UNDERSTANDING

Remind students to explain why for each exercise even if they're not asked to.

ASSIGNING HOMEWORK

Essential	1–5
Performance assessment	7–13
Portfolio	9
Journal	10
Group	9
Review	6, 14–18

MATERIALS

- Exercise 4 (W), *optional*

Helping with the Exercises

Exercise 1 You might ask students to draw graphs of other nonfunctions. Vertical lines and horizontal parabolas can be included in the extensive variety. In 1c, the dots at the ends of the segments on the graph indicate that the value of the function at that x-value is the negative y-value (corresponding to the filled-in dot) rather than the positive y-value (corresponding to the open dot).

1a. Function; each x-value has only one y-value.

1b. Not a function; there are x-values that are paired with two y-values.

1c. Function; each x-value has only one y-value.

Exercise 2d [Alert] As usual, watch for use of the standard order of operations in squaring the negative number.

Exercise 4 You might want to hand out the Exercise 4 worksheet to prevent students from writing in their books.

Exercise 5 Students could logically argue for opposite choices of the independent variable. For example, in 5d, how far you drive might depend on the amount of gas. Most important is students' understanding of the process of choosing an independent variable.

5a. The price of the calculator is the independent variable; function.

5b. The time the money has been in the bank is the independent variable; function.

5c. The amount of time since your last haircut is the independent variable; function.

6a. Let x represent the price of the calculator in dollars and let y represent the sales tax in dollars.

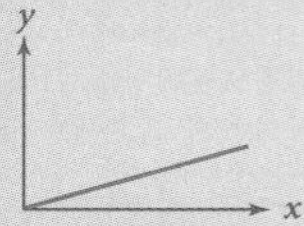

6b. Let x represent the time in months and let y represent the account balance in dollars.

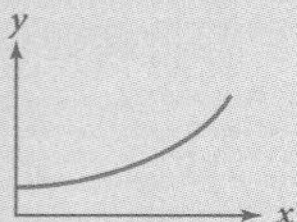

6c. Let x represent the time in days and let y represent the length of your hair.

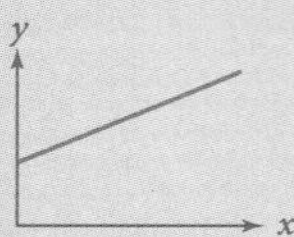

6d. Let x represent the distance you have driven in miles and let y represent the amount of gasoline in your tank in gallons.

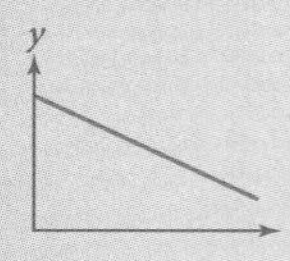

4. Use the graph at right to find each value. Each answer will be an integer from 1 to 26. Relate each answer to a letter of the alphabet (1 = A, 2 = B, and so on), and fill in the name of a famous mathematician.

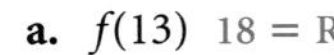

a. $f(13)$ 18 = R

b. $f(25) + f(26)$ 5 = E

c. $2f(22)$ 14 = N

d. $\dfrac{f(3) + 11}{\sqrt{f(3+1)}}$ 5 = E

e. $\dfrac{f(1+4)}{f(1)+4} - \dfrac{1}{4}\left(\dfrac{4}{f(1)}\right)$ 4 = D

f. x when $f(x+1) = 26$ 5 = E

g. $\sqrt[3]{f(21)} + f(14)$ 19 = S

h. x when $2f(x+3) = 52$ 3 = C

i. x when $f(2x) = 4$ 1 = A

j. $f(f(2) + f(3))$ 18 = R

k. $f(9) - f(25)$ 20 = T

l. $f(f(5) - f(1))$ 5 = E

m. $f(4 \cdot 6) + f(4 \cdot 4)$ 19 = S

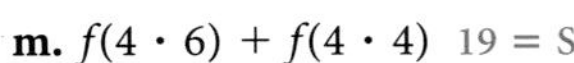

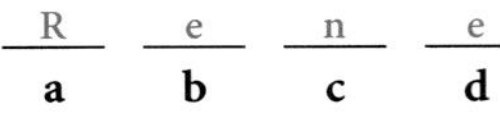
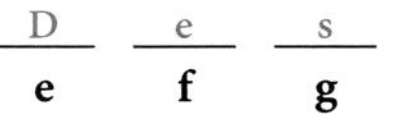
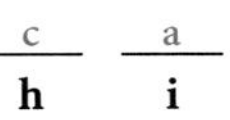
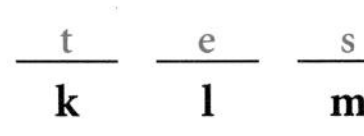

R	e	n	e	D	e	s	c	a	r	t	e	s
a	**b**	**c**	**d**	**e**	**f**	**g**	**h**	**i**	**j**	**k**	**l**	**m**

5. Identify the independent variable for each relation. Is the relation a function?

a. the price of a graphing calculator and the sales tax you pay

b. the amount of money in your savings account and the time it has been in the account

c. the amount your hair has grown since the time of your last haircut

d. the amount of gasoline in your car's fuel tank and how far you have driven since your last fill-up The distance you have driven since your last fill-up is the independent variable; function.

Reason and Apply

6. Sketch a reasonable graph for each relation described in Exercise 5. In each situation, identify the variables and label your axes appropriately.

7. Suppose $f(x) = 25 - 0.6x$.

a. Draw a graph of this function.

b. What is $f(7)$? 20.8

c. Identify the point $(7, f(7))$ by marking it on your graph.

d. Find the value of x when $f(x) = 27.4$. Mark this point on your graph. -4

8. Identify the domain and range of the function of f in the graph at right. domain: $-6 \le x \le 5$; range: $-2 \le y \le 4$

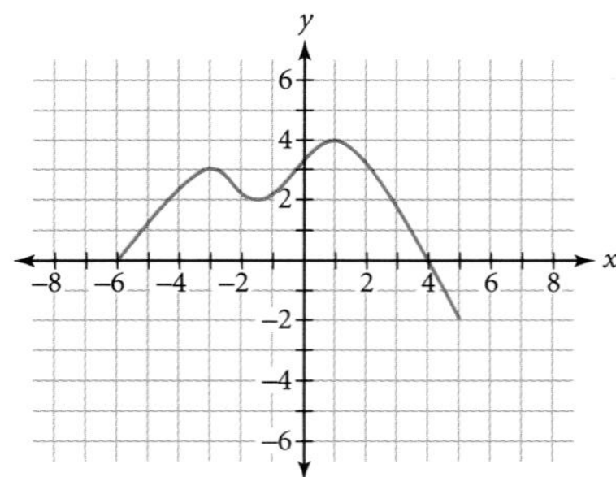

7a, c, d.

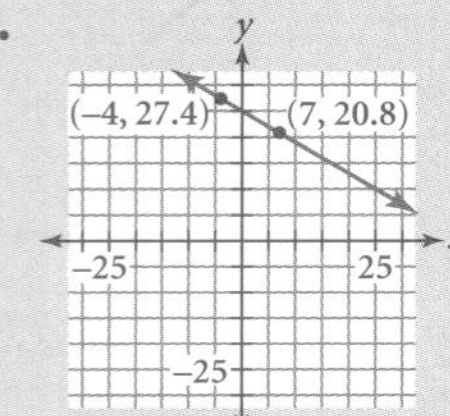

Exercise 7 **[Ask]** "What is a real-world situation that could be represented by this function?" In 7d, students may need to extend their graphs to show the point where x is negative.

Exercise 8 Students may wonder how the graph continues beyond what is drawn. Point out that when a question asks about the domain of a function and only the graph is given, students can assume that the entire graph is showing.

9. Sketch a graph for each function.

a. $y = f(x)$ has domain all real numbers and range $f(x) \leq 0$.

b. $y = g(x)$ has domain $x > 0$ and range all real numbers.

c. $y = h(x)$ has domain all real numbers and range $h(x) = 3$.

10. Consider the function $f(x) = 3(x + 1)^2 - 4$.

a. Find $f(5)$. 104

b. Find $f(n)$. $f(n) = 3(n + 1)^2 - 4$

c. Find $f(x + 2)$. $f(x + 2) = 3(x + 3)^2 - 4$

d. Use your calculator to graph $y = f(x)$ and $y = f(x + 2)$ on the same axes. How do the graphs compare?

11. Kendall walks toward and away from a motion sensor. Is the graph of his motion a function? Why or why not?

12. **APPLICATION** The length of a pendulum in inches, L, is a function of its period, or the length of time it takes to swing back and forth, in seconds, t. The function is defined by the formula $L = 9.73t^2$.

a. Find the length of a pendulum if its period is 4 s. 155.68 in.

b. The Foucault pendulum at the Panthéon in Paris has a 62-pound iron ball suspended on a 220-foot wire. What is its period? approximately 16.5 s

Astronomer Jean Bernard Leon Foucault (1819–1868) displayed this pendulum for the first time in 1851. The floor underneath the swinging pendulum was covered in sand, and a pin attached to the ball traced out the pendulum's path. While the ball swung back and forth in nine straight lines, it changed direction relative to the floor, proving that the Earth was rotating underneath it.

13. The number of diagonals of a polygon, d, is a function of the number of sides of the polygon, n, and is given by the formula $d = \frac{n(n-3)}{2}$.

a. Find the number of diagonals in a dodecagon (a 12-sided polygon). 54 diagonals

b. How many sides would a polygon have if it contained 170 diagonals? 20 sides

Language CONNECTION

You probably have noticed that some words, like biannual, triplex, and quadrant, have prefixes that indicate a number. Knowing the meaning of a prefix can help you determine the meaning of a word. The word "polygon" comes from the Greek *poly-* (many) and *-gon* (angle). Many mathematical words use the following Greek prefixes.

1 mono	6 hexa	
2 di	7 hepta	
3 tri	8 octa	
4 tetra	9 ennea	
5 penta	10 deca	20 icosa

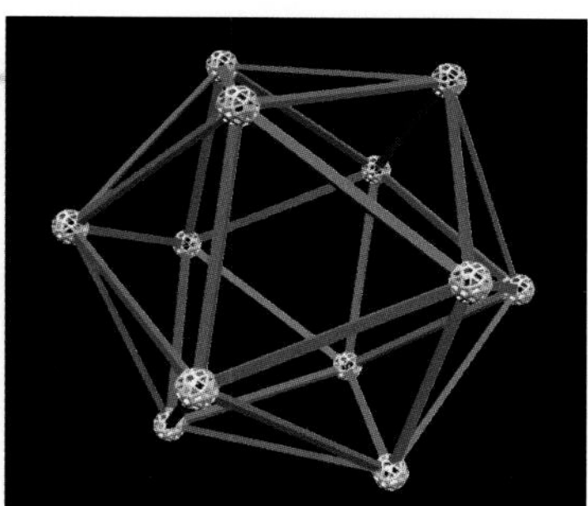

A polyhedron is a three-dimensional shape with many sides. Can you guess what the name of this shape is, using the prefixes given?

Exercise 9 Domains and ranges that are expressed as equations or inequalities can also be expressed in words. For example, the range in 9a is all negative numbers, and for 9c the range is the number 3.

9a. possible answer:

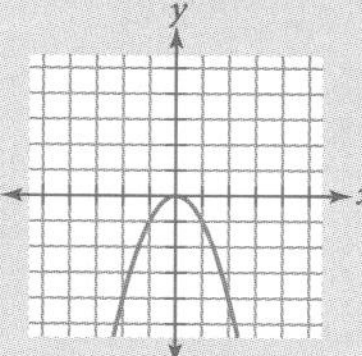

9b. possible answer:

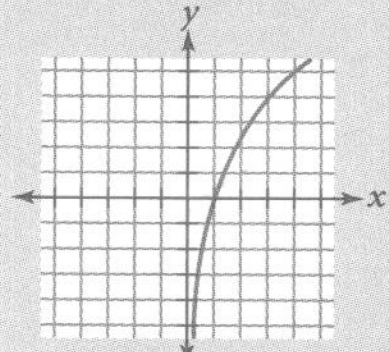

9c.

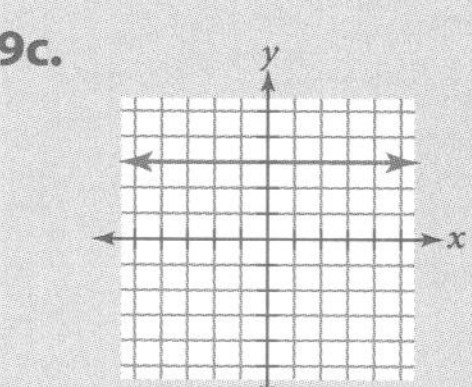

Exercise 10 [Alert] Students might be confused by 10b and 10c. They need only replace x with the letter or expression. Expanding or simplifying is unnecessary. In 10d they can graph on a calculator without squaring $(x + 2)$.

10d.

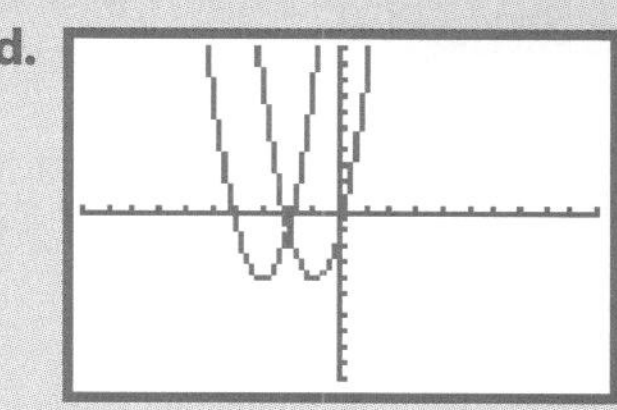

$[-10, 10, 1, -10, 10, 1]$

The graphs are the same shape. The graph of $f(x + 2)$ is shifted 2 units to the left of the graph of $f(x)$.

Exercise 11 If students have not used a motion sensor, you may want to give them a brief explanation.

11. Let x represent the time since Kendall started moving and y represent his distance from the motion sensor. The graph is a function; Kendall can be at only one position at each moment in time, so there is only one y-value for each x-value.

Exercise 12 Students might think that the period is a function of the length rather than the other way around. Either way is legitimate, because the function is one-to-one if the domain is limited to nonnegative values of t. In 12b, the weight of the ball is unneeded information.

Exercise 13b Students may use guess-and-check or a graph if they don't remember other ways to solve quadratic equations.

MAKING THE CONNECTION

A few polygons have names other than those that would be formed using the Greek roots. A three-sided polygon is called a *trigon* or a *triangle,* a four-sided polygon is called a *tetragon* or a *quadrilateral,* and a nine-sided polygon is called an *enneagon* or a *nonagon.*

Exercise 14 [Alert] This exercise might be difficult for students to visualize. You may want to have an interesting bottle and a measuring cup available for students to investigate on their own.

14a.

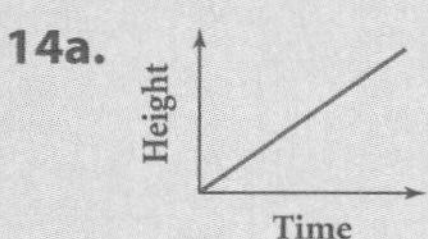

14b.

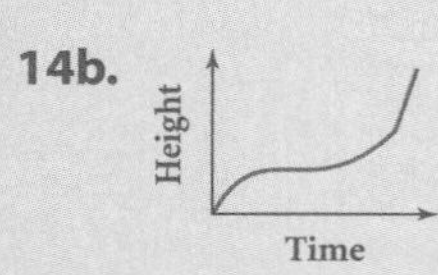

14c.

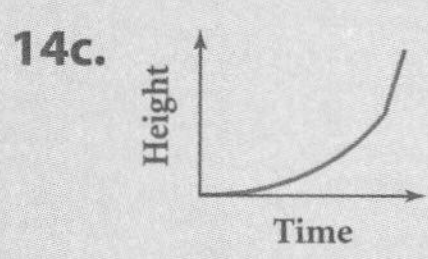

15. Sample answer: Eight students fall into each quartile. Assuming that the mean of each quartile is the midpoint of the quartile, the total will be $8(3.075 + 4.500 + 5.875 + 9.150)$, or $180.80.

17a. possible answer:

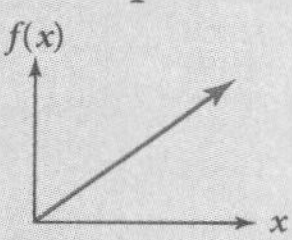

17b. possible answer:

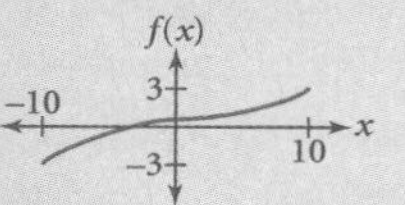

17c. possible answer:

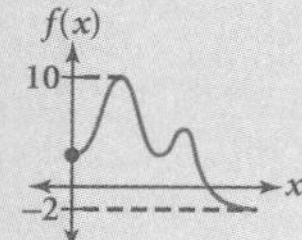

Review

4.1 **14.** Create graphs picturing the water height as each bottle is filled with water at a constant rate.

a.

b.

c.

2.1 **15.** APPLICATION The five-number summary of this box plot is $2.10, $4.05, $4.95, $6.80, $11.50. The plot summarizes the amounts of money earned in a recycling fund drive by 32 members of the Oakley High School environmental club. Estimate the total amount of money raised. Explain your reasoning.

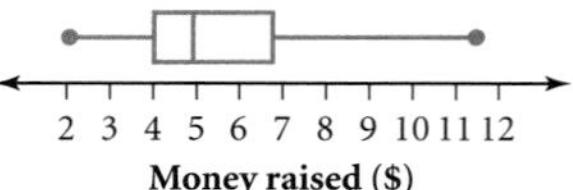

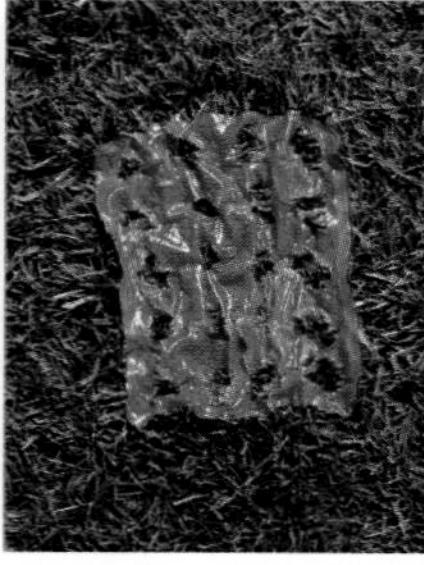

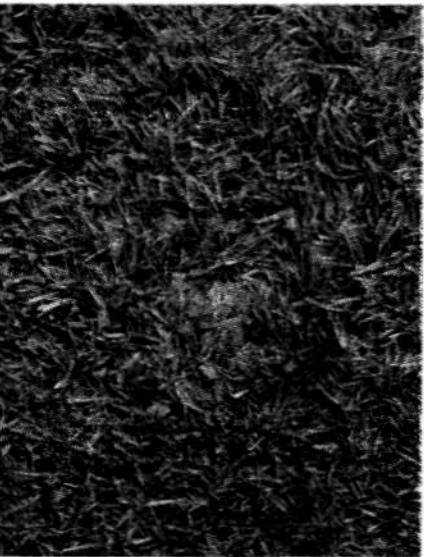

These photos show the breakdown of a newly developed plastic during a one-hour period. Created by Australian scientists, the plastic is made of cornstarch and disintegrates rapidly when exposed to water. This technology could help eliminate the 24 million tons of plastic that end up in American landfills every year.

3.6 **16.** Given the graph at right, find the intersection of lines ℓ_1 and ℓ_2. (7, 25.5)

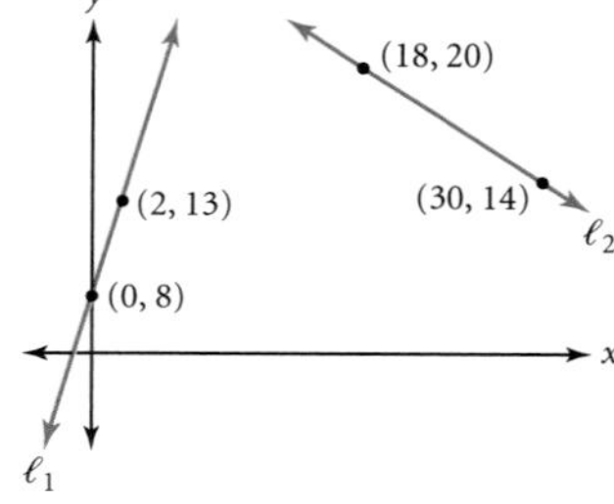

4.1 **17.** Sketch a graph for a function that has the following characteristics.

a. domain: $x \geq 0$
range: $f(x) \geq 0$
linear and increasing

b. domain: $-10 \leq x \leq 10$
range: $-3 < f(x) \leq 3$
nonlinear and increasing

c. domain: $x \geq 0$
range: $-2 < f(x) \leq 10$
increasing, then decreasing, then increasing, and then decreasing

0.1 **18.** You can use rectangle diagrams to represent algebraic expressions. For instance, this diagram demonstrates the equation $(x + 5)(2x + 1) = 2x^2 + 11x + 5$. Fill in the missing values on the edges or in the interior of each rectangle diagram.

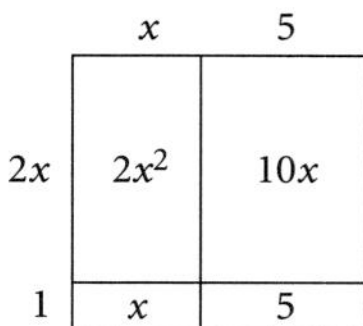

a.

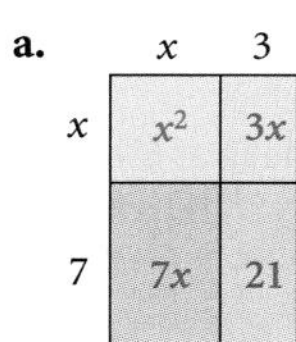

b.

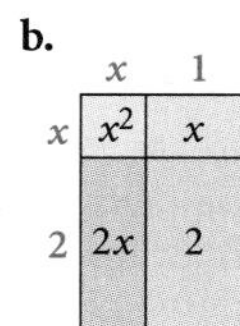

c.

	$2x$	10
x	$2x^2$	$10x$
10	$20x$	100

Exercise 18 An equally valid answer for 18c is $(x + 5)(2x + 20)$.

Project

STEP FUNCTIONS

The graph at right is an example of a **step function.** The open circles mean that those points are not included in the graph. For example, the value of $f(3)$ is 5, not 2. The places where the graph "jumps" are called **discontinuities.**

In Lesson 3.6, Exercise 9, you were introduced to an often-used step function—the **greatest integer function,** $f(x) = [x]$. Two related functions are the ceiling function, $f(x) = \lceil x \rceil$, and the floor function, $f(x) = \lfloor x \rfloor$.

Do further research on the greatest integer function, the ceiling function, and the floor function. Prepare a report or class presentation on the functions. Your project should include

- A graph of each function.
- A written or verbal description of how each function operates, including any relationships among the three functions. Be sure to explain how you would evaluate each function for different values of x.
- Examples of how each function might be applied in a real-world situation.

As you do your research, you might learn about other step functions that you'd like to include in your project.

Step Functions
A step function is a *discontinuous function.* The ceiling function, also known as the *rounding-up function,* is defined as the least integer greater than or equal to x. The floor function, also known as the *rounding-down function,* is defined as the greatest integer less than or equal to x. The floor function is another name for the greatest integer function. The ceiling and floor functions are discrete, because their ranges consist of separated numbers.

Supporting the Project

Student Web research could start at links from www.keymath.com and include some interesting calculus sites, which might cause students to ask some interesting questions.

OUTCOMES

- Graphs show the ceiling and floor (greatest integer) functions. The greatest integer function might have its own graph.
- Descriptions are given for each function and for how to evaluate each function for different values of x, including negative values.
- Examples of real-world applications include things such as phone, parking, and postage rates for the ceiling function.
- Other examples of step functions are given, such as the Heaviside step function.
- The report includes further research on discontinuities.

LESSON

4.3

PLANNING

LESSON OUTLINE

One day:

20 min Investigation

5 min Sharing

5 min Example

15 min Exercises

MATERIALS

- motion sensors
- graph paper
- Coordinate Axes (T), *optional*
- Sketchpad demonstration Lines, *optional*
- Calculator Note 4B

TEACHING

In this lesson students see how equations of lines change as the lines are translated.

One Step

Pose this problem: "What's an equation of the line that results from translating every point on the line $y = 2x$ right 3 units and up 5 units?" Encourage a variety of approaches.

During Sharing, introduce the term *translation* and encourage the class to look for patterns. Elicit the idea that all vertical translations of a line are horizontal translations, and vice versa; investigate together the question of how to determine what translation takes a line to itself.

INTRODUCTION

If necessary, remind students that a is the y-intercept, b is the slope, and (x_1, y_1) is a point on the line.

LESSON 4.3

Lines in Motion

In Chapter 3, you worked with two forms of linear equations:

Intercept form	$y = a + bx$
Point-slope form	$y = y_1 + b(x - x_1)$

In this lesson you will see how these forms are related to each other graphically.

With the exception of vertical lines, lines are functions. That means you could write the forms above as $f(x) = a + bx$ and $f(x) = f(x_1) + b(x - x_1)$. Linear functions are some of the simplest functions.

The investigation will help you see the effect that moving the graph of a line has on its equation. Moving a graph horizontally or vertically is called a **translation.** The discoveries you make about translations of lines will also apply to the graphs of other functions.

Free Basin (2002), shown here at the Wexner Center for the Arts in Columbus, Ohio, is a functional sculpture designed by Simparch, an artists' collaborative in Chicago, Illinois. As former skateboarders, the makers of *Free Basin* wanted to create a piece formed like a kidney-shaped swimming pool, to pay tribute to the empty swimming pools that first inspired skateboarding on curved surfaces. The underside of the basin shows beams that lie on lines that are translations of each other.

Investigation
Movin' Around

You will need
- two motion sensors

In this investigation you will explore what happens to the equation of a linear function when you translate the graph of the line. You'll then use your discoveries to interpret data.

Graph the lines in each step and look for patterns.

Step 1 On graph paper, graph the line $y = 2x$ and then draw a line parallel to it, but 3 units higher. What is the equation of this new line?

Step 2 On the same set of axes, draw a line parallel to the line $y = 2x$, but shifted down 4 units. What is the equation of this line?

Step 3 On a new set of axes, graph the line $y = \frac{1}{2}x$. Mark the point where the line passes through the origin. Plot another point right 3 units and up 4 units from the origin, and draw a line through this point parallel to the original line. Write at least two equations of the new line.

Guiding the Investigation

If you do not have motion sensors, completing Steps 1–5 is sufficient. If you have a few motion sensors, half the class can collect data for Steps 6–9 while the other half works on Steps 1–5. You might do Steps 6 and 7 as a demonstration. The data can be transferred to one calculator in each group.

Steps 1–3 As needed, remind students of how to find equations of lines given two points and how to find equations of lines parallel to another line.

Step 1

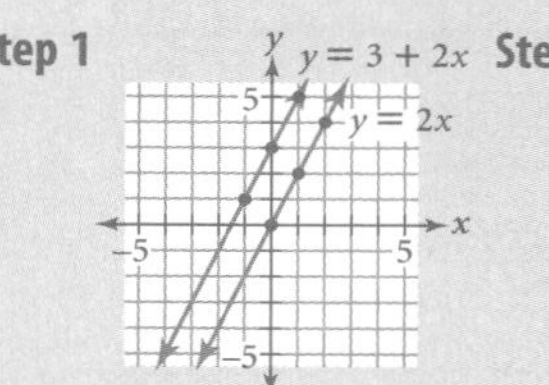

Step 2

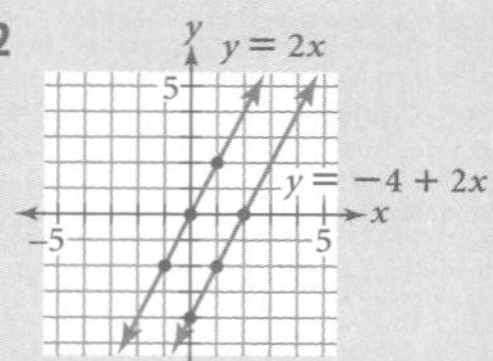

Step 3

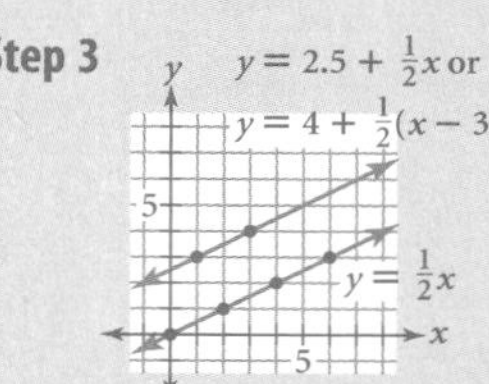

Step 4 What happens if you move every point on $f(x) = \frac{1}{2}x$ to a new point up 1 unit and right 2 units? Write an equation in point-slope form for this new line. Then distribute and combine like terms to write the equation in intercept form. What do you notice?

Step 5 In general, what effect does translating a line have on its equation?

Your group will now use motion sensors to create a function and a translated copy of that function. [▶ See **Calculator Note 4B** for instructions on how to collect and retrieve data from two motion sensors. ◀]

Step 6 Arrange your group as in the photo to collect data.

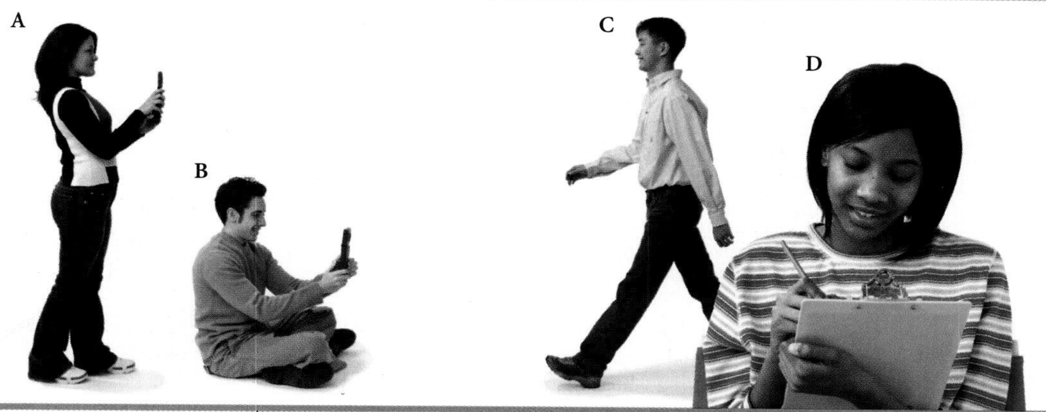

Step 7 Person D coordinates the collection of data like this:

At 0 seconds:	C begins to walk slowly toward the motion sensors, and A begins to collect data.
About 2 seconds:	B begins to collect data.
About 5 seconds:	C begins to walk backward.
About 10 seconds:	A's sensor stops.
About 12 seconds:	B's sensor stops and C stops walking.

Step 8 After collecting the data, follow Calculator Note 4B to retrieve the data to two calculators and then transmit four lists of data to each group member's calculator. Be sure to keep track of which data each list contains.

Step 9 Graph both sets of data on the same screen. Record a sketch of what you see and answer these questions:

a. How are the two graphs related to each other?

b. If A's graph is $y = f(x)$, what equation describes B's graph? Describe how you determined this equation.

c. In general, if the graph of $y = f(x)$ is translated horizontally h units and vertically k units, what is the equation of this translated function?

Step 4 This movement creates the same line; $y = 1 + \frac{1}{2}(x - 2)$; $y = \frac{1}{2}x$; this equation is the same as your original line.

Step 5 The amount you translate to the right or left is subtracted from or added to x, and the amount you translate up or down is added to or subtracted from the function expression.

Steps 7, 8 You might want to demonstrate the setup in front of the class before students try this on their own.

While coordinating the collection of the data, person D may want to count off the seconds out loud so that all group members know when to start their assigned jobs.

Step 9 Encourage students to use a correct scale in their sketches. If a computer and printer are available with TI-Graph Link or TI-Connect, students can print a copy of their computer graph screen to attach to their investigation write-up.

Step 9

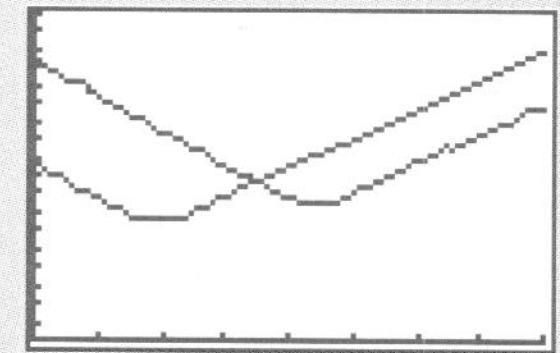

[0, 8, 1, 0, 13, 1]

Step 9a B's graph should be translated left about 2 units and down about 1 unit.

Step 9b $y = f(x + 2) - 1$, because B is delayed by 2 s and sits about 1 ft closer to C.

Step 9c $y = f(x - h) + k$

Assessing Progress
In the investigation, you can observe students' facility with graphing parallel lines, finding equations of lines in point-slope form, and using motion sensors.

NCTM STANDARDS

CONTENT		PROCESS	
	Number		Problem Solving
✓	Algebra	✓	Reasoning
	Geometry	✓	Communication
✓	Measurement	✓	Connections
✓	Data/Probability	✓	Representation

LESSON OBJECTIVES

- Review linear equations
- Describe translations of a line in terms of horizontal and vertical shifts
- Write the equation of a translated line using h and k
- Understand point-slope form as a translation of the line with its equation written in intercept form
- Apply translations to functions

► *EXAMPLE*

If students have been working mechanically so far, this example will push them to deeper understanding. You might draw the line on the Coordinate Axes transparency from Chapter 0 and show the movement.

SHARING IDEAS

As students present ideas about Step 3, be sure at least one group comes up with $y = 4 + \frac{1}{2}(x - 3)$. Elicit the idea that this translation is the same as moving every point on the graph of $f(x) = \frac{1}{2}x$ up 4 units and to the right 3 units.

For Step 9c, **[Ask]** "What is the real-world meaning of the translated graph?" [The data collection began and ended 2 seconds later.]

Ask students to clarify confusion about the vertical height of the graph as representative of the walker's horizontal distance from the motion detector. The difference in the heights of the graphs represents the horizontal distance between motion detectors. **[Ask]** "What does the horizontal axis on the graph represent?" [time]

[Ask] "If you expand or simplify $f(x)$, how does the translation of the graph of $f(x)$ change?" [Equivalent expressions give the same translation. The form that shows the translation is usually the most helpful.] As you lead the discussion, model the use of the terms *map, mapped,* and *mapping.*

As the class focuses on the definition of *translation,* repeat that if h is positive then the translation is to the right and if h is negative then the translation is to the left. Similarly, if k is positive then the translation is up, and if k is negative then the translation is down. **[Ask]** "How can you remember this?" Students will articulate different ways. One approach is to think of what values of x and y give 0 on the left and $f(0)$ on the right. The origin has shifted to the point (h, k). Another approach is to realize that the equation $y = f(x - h) + k$ is equivalent to $y - k = f(x - h)$, so both movement upward and movement to the right involve positive h and k. One way to think of translations is as $(x - h)$ and $(y - k)$ replacing x and y. Replacing x with $(x - h)$ translates the graph h units horizontally, and replacing y with $(y - k)$ translates the graph k units vertically.

By the commutative property, the equation $y = f(x - h) + k$ is equivalent to $y = k + f(x - h)$. **[Ask]** "What are the advantages of writing the equation each way?" [Putting h before k puts the coordinates in standard order; using k first mimics the intercept form of a linear equation.]

The example shows that for a line, one translation that is horizontal and vertical is also a simple vertical translation. **[Ask]** "Is every translation of a straight line equivalent to a vertical translation?" [It is not for vertical lines. A horizontal translation by h units of the graph of $y = a + bx$ gives $y = a + b(x - h)$, which is equivalent to $y = (a - bh) + bx$, a vertical translation by the constant $a - bh$.] Students may be skeptical about

If you know the effects of translations, you can write an equation that translates any function on a graph. No matter what the shape of a function $y = f(x)$ is, the graph of $y = f(x - 3) + 2$ will look just the same as $y = f(x)$, but it will be translated up 2 units and right 3 units. Understanding this relationship will enable you to graph functions and write equations for graphs more easily.

Translation of a Function

A **translation** moves a graph horizontally, or vertically, or both.

Given the graph of $y = f(x)$, the graph of

$$y = f(x - h) + k$$

is a translation horizontally h units and vertically k units.

Pulitzer Prize–winning books *The Color Purple,* written in 1982 by Alice Walker (b 1944), and *The Grapes of Wrath,* written in 1939 by John Steinbeck (1902–1968), are shown here in Spanish translations.

Language CONNECTION

The word "translation" can refer to the act of converting between two languages. Similar to its usage in mathematics, *translation* of foreign languages is an attempt to keep meanings parallel. Direct substitution of words often destroys the nuances and subtleties of meaning of the original text. The subtleties involved in the art and craft of translation have inspired the formation of Translation Studies programs in universities throughout the world.

In a translation, every point (x_1, y_1) is mapped to a new point, $(x_1 + h, y_1 + k)$. This new point is called the **image** of the original point. If you have difficulty remembering which way to move a function, think about the point-slope form of the equation of a line. In $y = y_1 + b(x - x_1)$, the point at (0, 0) is translated to the new point at (x_1, y_1). In fact, every point is translated horizontally x_1 units and vertically y_1 units.

Panamanian cuna (mola with geometric design on red background)

EXAMPLE Describe how the graph of $f(x) = 4 + 2(x - 3)$ is a translation of the graph of $f(x) = 2x$.

► Solution

The graph of $f(x) = 4 + 2(x - 3)$ passes through the point (3, 4). Consider this point to be the translated image of (0, 0) on $f(x) = 2x$. It is translated right 3 units and up 4 units from its original location, so the graph of $f(x) = 4 + 2(x - 3)$ is simply the graph of $f(x) = 2x$ translated right 3 units and up 4 units.

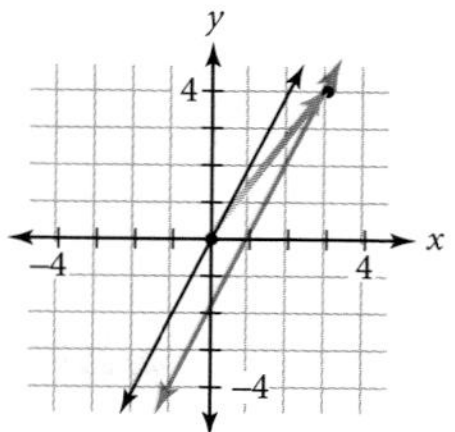

Note that you can distribute and combine like terms in $f(x) = 4 + 2(x - 3)$ to get $f(x) = -2 + 2x$. The fact that these two equations are equivalent means that translating the graph of $f(x) = 2x$ right 3 units and up 4 units is equivalent to translating the line down 2 units. In the graph in the example, this appears to be true.

If you imagine translating a line in a plane, there are some translations that will give you the same line you started with. For example, if you start with the line $y = 3 + x$ and translate every point up 1 unit and right 1 unit, you will map the line onto itself. If you translate every point on the line down 3 units and left 3 units, you also map the line onto itself.

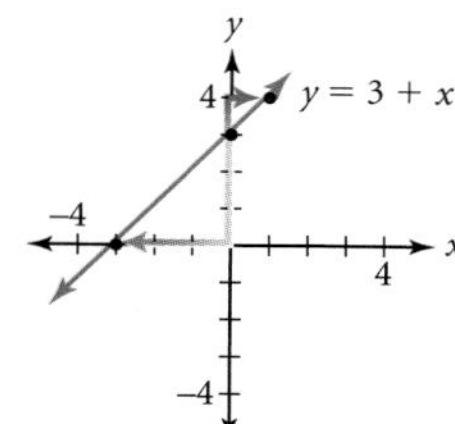

There are infinitely many translations that map a line onto itself. Similarly, there are infinitely many translations that map a line onto another parallel line, m_1. To map the line $y = 3 + x$ onto the line m_1 shown below it, you could translate every point down 2 units and right 1 unit, or you could translate every point down 3 units.

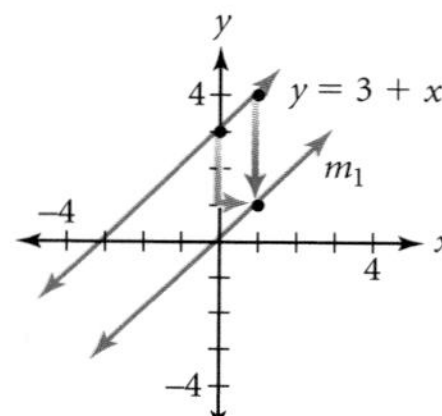

In the next few lessons, you will see how to translate and otherwise transform other functions.

EXERCISES

Practice Your Skills

1. The graph of the line $y = \frac{2}{3}x$ is translated right 5 units and down 3 units. What is the equation of the new line? $y = -3 + \frac{2}{3}(x - 5)$

2. How does the graph of $y = f(x - 3)$ compare with the graph of $y = f(x)$? translated right 3 units

3. If $f(x) = -2x$, find
   a. $f(x + 3)$ $-2(x + 3)$ or $-2x - 6$
   b. $-3 + f(x - 2)$ $-3 + (-2)(x - 2)$ or $-2x + 1$
   c. $5 + f(x + 1)$ $5 + (-2)(x + 1)$ or $-2x + 3$

Sharing Ideas (continued)

horizontal lines. If $b = 0$, then the resulting line is still $y = a$, a vertical translation by 0.

The book states that you can translate the graph of $y = 3 + x$ either down 2 and right 1 or down 3 with the same effect. To encourage critical thinking, express skepticism and ask students whether they agree with the book. Then **[Ask]** "Are there other translations that have the same result? Is there a pattern?" [The sum of the vertical and horizontal translations must be −3 to translate the graph of this equation to $y = x$.] **[Ask]** "Which translations will map a line onto itself?" [If the slope is $\frac{a}{b}$, then a translation to the right by any multiple of a and up by the same multiple of b will do so.]

[Ask] "Are there other figures for which the sets of horizontal and vertical transformations are the same?" [To have $f(x + a) = f(x) + b$, the slope $\frac{f(x + a) - f(x)}{a}$ must be equal to the constant $\frac{b}{a}$ for every value of x. If b is not 0, this requires a straight line. If the amount of the vertical translation is 0, then $f(x + a) = f(x)$ for all values of x; functions satisfying this equation are called *periodic.* Trigonometric functions are good examples of periodic functions.]

BUILDING UNDERSTANDING

Remind students to explain why for each exercise even if they're not asked to.

Closing the Lesson

Restate the main points of this lesson: When a line is **translated** h units horizontally and k units vertically, the equation of the resulting line can be found by replacing y with $y - k$ and x with $x - h$. (Constant h is positive for an upward translation, negative for a downward translation; k is positive for a translation to the right, negative for a translation to the left.) For straight lines, every vertical translation is a horizontal translation, and vice versa.

MATERIALS

- Exercise 6 (T), *optional*

ASSIGNING HOMEWORK

Essential	1–5
Performance assessment	6–10
Portfolio	9
Journal	10
Group	8, 10
Review	11–14

▶ Helping with the Exercises

Exercise 4 [Ask] "Find another equation. Show that the two equations are algebraically equivalent."

4a. $y = -4.4 - 1.1485(x - 1.4)$ or $y = 3.18 - 1.1485(x + 5.2)$

4b. $y = -2.4 - 1.1485(x - 1.4)$ or $y = 5.18 - 1.1485(x + 5.2)$

5a. $y = -3 + 4.7x$

5b. $y = -2.8(x - 2)$

5c. $y = 4 - (x + 1.5)$ or $y = 2.5 - x$

Exercise 6 [Ask] "Didn't we decide that every horizontal translation is a vertical translation?" [That property holds only for lines.] You might use the Exercise 6 transparency as you discuss this exercise.

Exercise 7 [Alert] Students may miss the point that the ropes have the same thickness because they're cut from the same source. **[Ask]** "Why does the rope have to be the same thickness in order to find this equation?" [The equations have the same slope.] "What are the meanings of 102 and 6.3?" [the original length of the rope and the amount it's shortened by each knot]

4. Consider the line that passes through the points $(-5.2, 3.18)$ and $(1.4, -4.4)$, as shown.

a. Find an equation of the line.

b. Write an equation of the parallel line that is 2 units above this line.

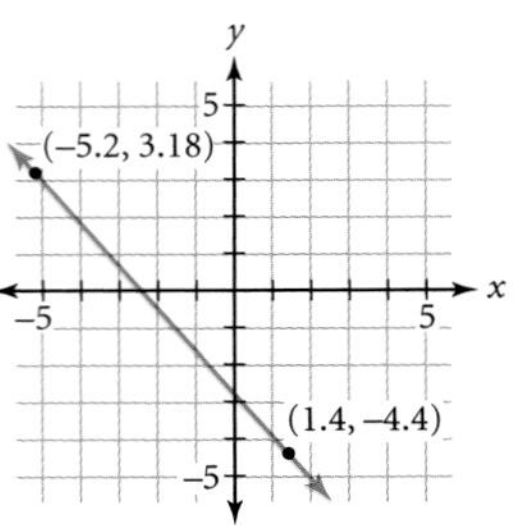

5. Write an equation of each line.

a. the line $y = 4.7x$ translated down 3 units

b. the line $y = -2.8x$ translated right 2 units

c. the line $y = -x$ translated up 4 units and left 1.5 units

▶ Reason and Apply

6. The graph of $y = f(x)$ is shown at right. Write an equation for each of the graphs below.

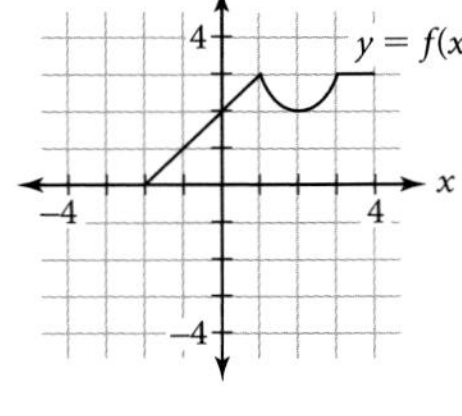

a.

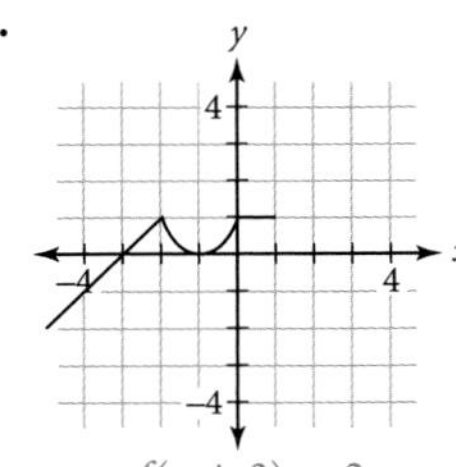

$y = f(x + 3) - 2$

b.

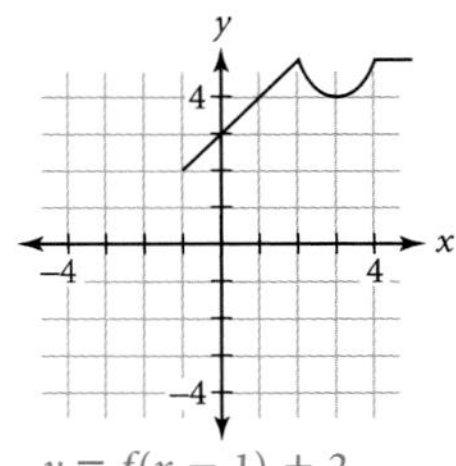

$y = f(x - 1) + 2$

c.

$y = f(x + 2) - 5$

d.

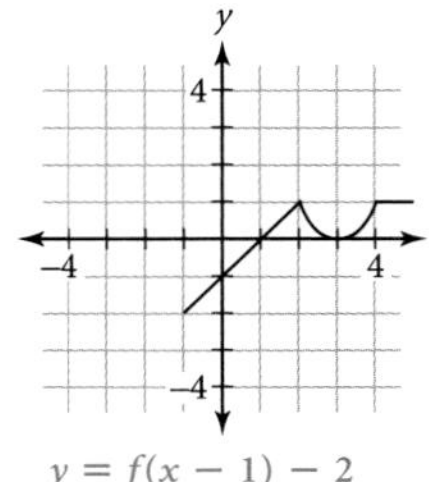

$y = f(x - 1) - 2$

7. Jeannette and Keegan collect data about the length of a rope as knots are tied in it. The equation that fits their data is $y = 102 - 6.3x$, where x represents the number of knots and y represents the length of the rope in centimeters. Mitch had a piece of rope cut from the same source. Unfortunately he lost his data and can remember only that his rope was 47 cm long after he tied 3 knots. What equation describes Mitch's rope? $y = 47 - 6.3(x - 3)$

8. Rachel, Pete, and Brian perform Part 2 of the investigation in this lesson. Rachel walks while Pete and Brian hold the motion sensors. They create the unusual graph at right. The horizontal axis has a mark every 1 s, and the vertical axis has a mark every 1 m.

a. The lower curve is made from the data collected by Pete's motion sensor. Where was Brian standing and when did he start his motion sensor to create the upper curve?

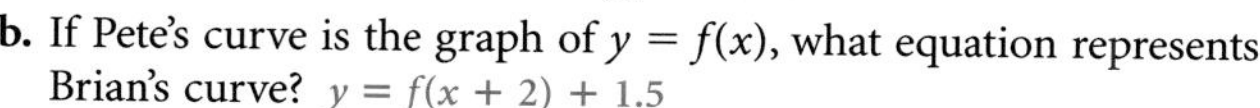

b. If Pete's curve is the graph of $y = f(x)$, what equation represents Brian's curve? $y = f(x + 2) + 1.5$

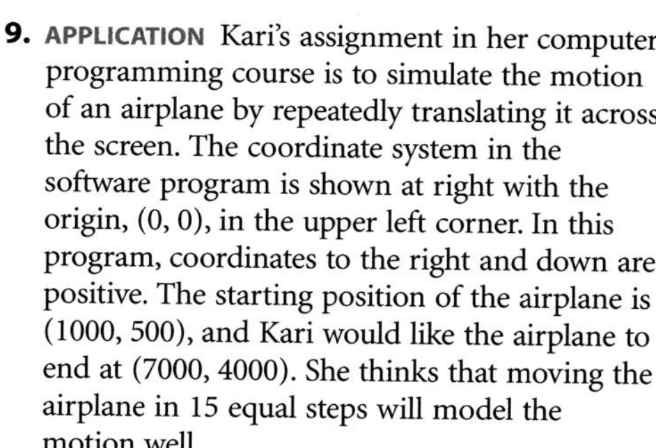

9. APPLICATION Kari's assignment in her computer programming course is to simulate the motion of an airplane by repeatedly translating it across the screen. The coordinate system in the software program is shown at right with the origin, (0, 0), in the upper left corner. In this program, coordinates to the right and down are positive. The starting position of the airplane is (1000, 500), and Kari would like the airplane to end at (7000, 4000). She thinks that moving the airplane in 15 equal steps will model the motion well.

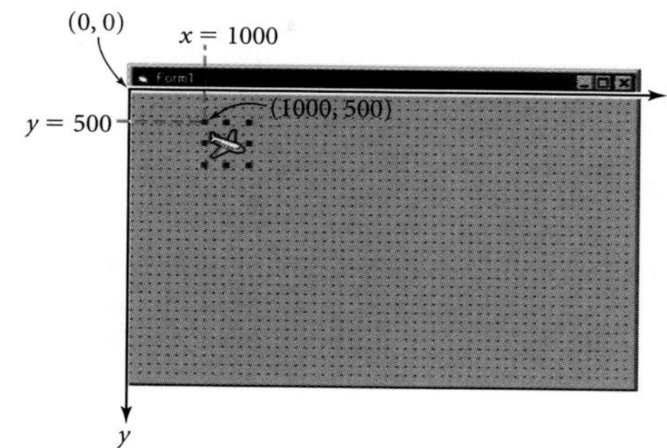

a. What should be the airplane's first position after (1000, 500)? $(1400, 733.\overline{3})$

b. If the airplane's position at any time is given by (x, y), what is the next position in terms of x and y? $(x + 400, y + 233.\overline{3})$

c. If the plane moves down 175 units and right 300 units in each step, how many steps will it take to reach the final position of (7000, 4000)? 20 steps

Art CONNECTION

Animation simulates movement. An old-fashioned way to animate is to make a book of closely related pictures and flip the pages. Flipbook technique is used in cartooning—a feature-length film might have more than 65,000 images. Today, this tedious hand drawing has been largely replaced by computer-generated special effects.

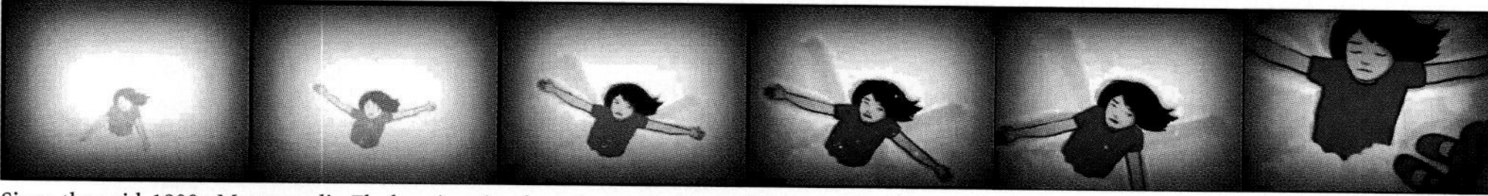

Since the mid-1990s Macromedia Flash animation has given websites striking visual effects.

10. ***Mini-Investigation*** Linear equations can also be written in standard form.

Standard form $\quad ax + by = c$

a. Identify the values of a, b, and c for each of these equations in standard form.

i. $4x + 3y = 12$ **ii.** $-x + y = 5$
iii. $7x - y = 1$ **iv.** $-2x + 4y = -2$
v. $2y = 10$ **vi.** $3x = -6$

10a. i. $a = 4, b = 3, c = 12$
10a. ii. $a = -1, b = 1, c = 5$
10a. iii. $a = 7, b = -1, c = 1$
10a. iv. $a = -2, b = 4, c = -2$
10a. v. $a = 0, b = 2, c = 10$
10a. vi. $a = 3, b = 0, c = -6$

Exercise 8 If students didn't do the last steps of the investigation, you may need to describe them.

8a. Brian stood about 1.5 m behind Pete, and he started his motion sensor 2 s later than Pete started his.

Exercise 9 This is a recursive procedure, because each step depends on the previous one.

Exercise 10 This mini-investigation will take more time than the other exercises, so you might want to assign it to groups. Unlike the coefficients in intercept form or point-slope form, a, b, and c have no direct interpretation as intercepts or slope. One advantage of standard form is that equations for vertical lines, such as part vi of 10a, can be written. Because b is 0, both the y-intercept and the slope are undefined. You could, however, evaluate $-\frac{c}{a}$ to find that the x-intercept is 2.

Another advantage of the standard form is that it's equally easy to find both intercepts.

The equation in part v of 10a is a horizontal line. Because there is no x-term, the slope is $-\frac{a}{b}$ or $-\frac{0}{2} = 0$.

Because the standard form is not in Y= form and the coefficient of y is not necessarily 1, when students just replace y with $(y - k)$ the constant k is multiplied by the original coefficient of y. For example, if you translate the graph of an equation by k units vertically, you replace y with $(y - k)$: $ax + b(y - k) = c$. The original coefficient must be multiplied by the coefficient b. In like manner, when you translate horizontally, h will be multiplied by the coefficient a.

It is worth pointing out that when you expand the standard form of the equation for the translated line, the constant is the only coefficient that changes. The x- and y-coefficients remain the same as in the equation of the original line.

10b. $y = \frac{c}{b} - \frac{a}{b}x$;
y-intercept: $\frac{c}{b}$; slope: $-\frac{a}{b}$

10c. i. y-intercept: 4; slope: $-\frac{4}{3}$

10c. ii. y-intercept: 5; slope: 1

10c. iii. y-intercept: -1; slope: 7

10c. iv. y-intercept: $-\frac{1}{2}$; slope: $\frac{1}{2}$

10c. v. y-intercept: 5; slope: 0

10c. vi. y-intercept: none; slope: undefined

10d. i. $4x + 3y = 20$

10d. ii. $4x + 3y = -8$

10d. iii. $4x + 3y = 24$

10d. iv. $4x + 3y = 9$

10d. v. $4x + 3y = 7$

10d. vi. $4x + 3y = 10$

10e. $ax + by = c + ah + bk$

11a. 12,500; The original value of the equipment is $12,500.

11b. 10; After 10 years the equipment has no value.

11c. -1250; Every year the value of the equipment decreases by $1250.

Exercise 11d The equation can be in standard form.

Exercise 12b The given answer is equivalent to $y = \frac{x + 325}{5}$. The answer equation can be thought of as dividing the sum of the four games (325) by 5 to get 65, the amount each of the four games will contribute to the mean for 5 games, then adding $\frac{1}{5}x$, the amount the fifth score will add to the mean.

Exercise 13 Encourage variety in solution methods.

EXTENSIONS

A. Have students program their calculators to accomplish Kari's task in Exercise 9.

B. Use Take Another Look activity 1 on page 235.

b. Solve the standard form, $ax + by = c$, for y. The result should be an equivalent equation in intercept form. What is the y-intercept? What is the slope?

c. Use what you've learned from 10b to find the y-intercept and slope of each of the equations in 10a.

d. The graph of $4x + 3y = 12$ is translated as described below. Write an equation in standard form for each of the translated graphs.

i. a translation right 2 units
ii. a translation left 5 units
iii. a translation up 4 units
iv. a translation down 1 unit
v. a translation right 1 unit and down 3 units
vi. a translation up 2 units and left 2 units

e. In general, if the graph of $ax + by = c$ is translated horizontally h units and vertically k units, what is the equation of the translated line?

Review

3.1 **11.** **APPLICATION** The Internal Revenue Service has approved ten-year linear depreciation as one method for determining the value of business property. This means that the value declines to zero over a ten-year period, and you can claim a tax exemption in the amount of the value lost each year. Suppose a piece of business equipment costs $12,500 and is depreciated over a ten-year period. At right is a sketch of the linear function that represents this depreciation.

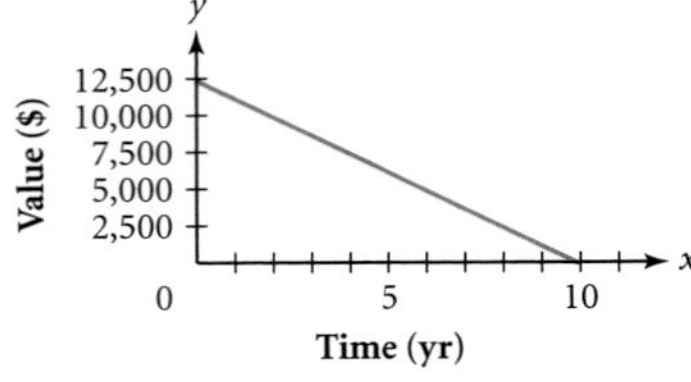

a. What is the y-intercept? Give the real-world meaning of this value.

b. What is the x-intercept? Give the real-world meaning of this value.

c. What is the slope? Give the real-world meaning of the slope.

d. Write an equation that describes the value of the equipment during the ten-year period. $y = 12500 - 1250x$

e. When is the equipment worth $6500? after 4.8 yr

2.1 **12.** Suppose that your basketball team's scores in the first four games of the season were 86 points, 73 points, 76 points, and 90 points.

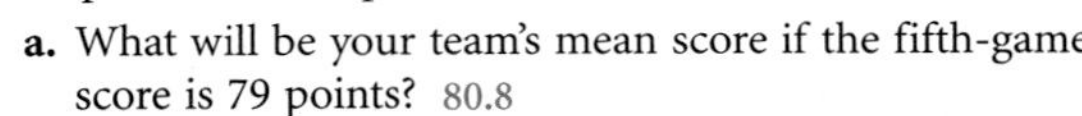

a. What will be your team's mean score if the fifth-game score is 79 points? 80.8

b. Write a function that gives the mean score in terms of the fifth-game score. $y = \frac{1}{5}x + 65$

c. What score will give a five-game average of 84 points? 95 points

13. Solve.

a. $2(x + 4) = 38$ $x = 15$

b. $7 + 0.5(x - 3) = 21$ $x = 31$

c. $-2 + \frac{3}{4}(x + 1) = -17$ $x = -21$

d. $4.7 + 2.8(x - 5.1) = 39.7$ $x = 17.6$

3.4 **14.** The three summary points for a data set are $M_1(3, 11)$, $M_2(5, 5)$, and $M_3(9, 2)$. Find the median-median line. $\hat{y} = \frac{29}{2} - \frac{3}{2}x$

LESSON

4.4 Translations and the Quadratic Family

I see music as the augmentation of a split second of time.

ERIN CLEARY

In the previous lesson, you looked at translations of the graphs of linear functions. Translations can occur in other settings as well. For instance, what will this histogram look like if the teacher decides to add five points to each of the scores? each bin will shift right 5 units

What translation will map the black triangle on the left onto its red image on the right? right 5 units and up 1 unit

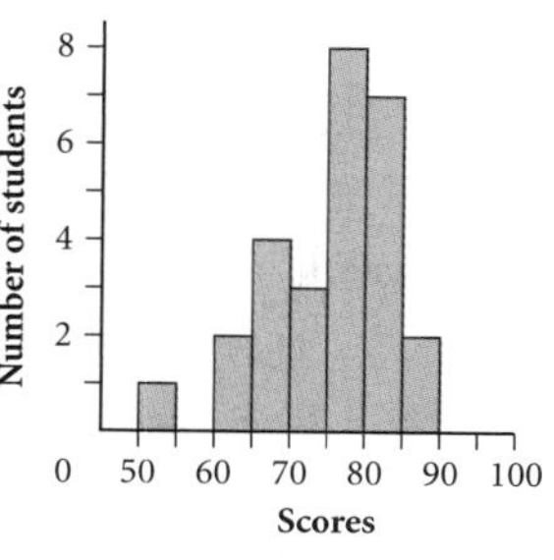

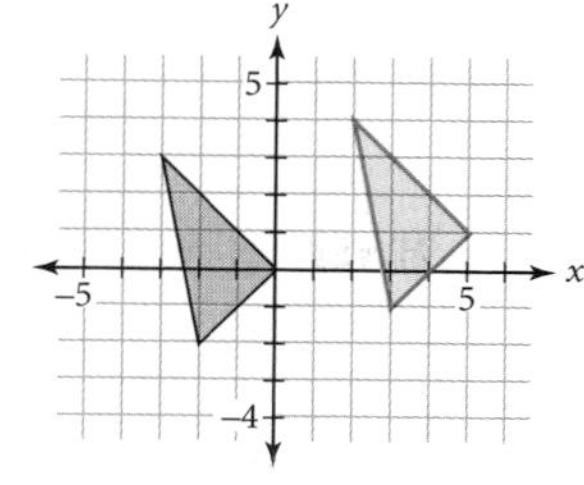

Translations are also a natural feature of the real world, including the world of art. Music can be transposed from one key to another. Melodies are often translated by a certain interval within a composition.

Music CONNECTION

When a song is in a key that is difficult to sing or play, it can be translated, or transposed, into an easier key. To transpose music means to change the pitch of each note without changing the relationships between the notes. Musicians have several techniques for transposing music, and because these techniques are mathematically based, computer programs have been written that can do it as well.

Jazz saxophonist Ornette Coleman (b 1930) grew up with strong interests in mathematics and science. Since the 1950s, he has developed award-winning musical theories, such as "free jazz," which strays from the set standards of harmony and melody.

This suburb of St. Paul, Minnesota, was developed in the 1950s. A close look reveals that some of the houses are translations of each other. A few are reflections of each other.

NCTM STANDARDS

CONTENT		PROCESS	
	Number	✓	Problem Solving
✓	Algebra	✓	Reasoning
✓	Geometry	✓	Communication
	Measurement	✓	Connections
	Data/Probability	✓	Representation

LESSON OBJECTIVES

- Define the parent quadratic function, $y = x^2$
- Determine elements of equations that produce translations of the graphs of parent functions (h and k)
- Introduce the (nonstretched) vertex form of the graph of a parabola, $y = (x - h)^2 + k$
- Define *parabola, vertex of a parabola,* and *line of symmetry*
- Determine the graph from an equation and the equation from a graph

LESSON 4.4

PLANNING

LESSON OUTLINE

One day:

20 min	Investigation
5 min	Sharing
5 min	Example
15 min	Exercises

MATERIALS

- Two Parabolas (T) for One Step
- Calculator Notes 4C, 4D
- Sketchpad demonstration Parabolas, *optional*

TEACHING

This lesson begins a sequence of four lessons that discuss transformations while introducing or reviewing families of relations. Lesson 4.4 extends the discussion of translations to parabolic graphs of quadratic equations. These topics will be explored further in Chapter 7 (Quadratic and Other Polynomial Functions), Chapter 8 (Parametric Equations and Trigonometry), and Chapter 9 (Conic Sections and Rational Functions). Much of the lesson may be review for students who have used *Discovering Geometry* or *Discovering Algebra.*

MAKING THE CONNECTION

The book *Functional Melodies* includes activities that explore transformations in music.

One Step

Show the Two Parabolas transparency and ask students to experiment on their calculators until they find an equation that produces the parabola drawn with the thicker line. As needed, ask groups whether the methods of translating straight lines in Lesson 4.3 apply to parabolas.

One Step (continued)
During Sharing, formalize the method into a conjecture and ask students to test the conjecture on other examples, such as those from the investigation and the example.

INTRODUCTION

[Language] Parabola is pronounced "pə-'ra-bə-lə."

[Language] The word *quadratic* comes from the Latin root *quadrare,* meaning "to square." Generally the prefix *quad* is used in words like *quadrilateral* to mean four; its use as two in *quadratic* stems from the fact that squared terms were represented as square (four-sided) shapes, as in rectangle diagrams.

Ask whether students recall from earlier courses what a dilation is. **[Language]** A *dilation* is a stretch or shrink by the same scale factor in all directions. The term is not used elsewhere in the chapter, but it is mentioned here as a connection to geometry. Stretches and shrinks are in just one direction.

Have students graph the equation $y = x^2$ on their calculators. Make a table of x- and y-values to explore the symmetry of points on either side of the vertex. **[Ask]** "Where would you place a line of symmetry? What is the equation of that line?"

MAKING THE CONNECTION

As the connection on page 390 mentions, a freely hanging cable forms a catenary, not a parabola. When a bridge is hung from cables with its weight evenly distributed, the cables take on a shape close to a parabola.

The equation for a catenary curve is

$$y = \frac{a}{2}\left(e^{x/a} + e^{-x/a}\right)$$

In mathematics, a change in the size or position of a figure or graph is called a **transformation.** Translations are one type of transformation. You may recall other types of transformations, such as reflections, dilations, stretches, shrinks, and rotations, from other mathematics classes.

In this lesson you will experiment with translations of the graph of the function $y = x^2$. The special shape of this graph is called a **parabola.** Parabolas always have a **line of symmetry** that passes through the **vertex.**

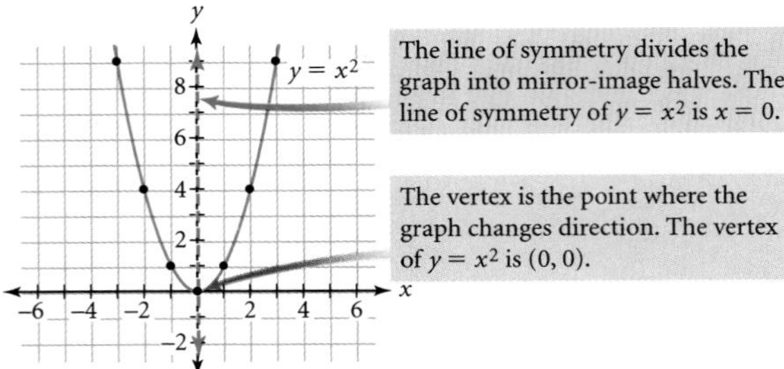

The function $y = x^2$ is a building-block function, or **parent function.** By transforming the graph of a parent function, you can create infinitely many new functions, or a **family of functions.** The function $y = x^2$ and all functions created from transformations of its graph are called **quadratic functions,** because the highest power of x is x-squared.

Quadratic functions are very useful, as you will discover throughout this book. You can use functions in the quadratic family to model the height of a projectile as a function of time, or the area of a square as a function of the length of its side.

The focus of this lesson is on writing the quadratic equation of a parabola after a translation and graphing a parabola given its equation. You will see that locating the vertex is fundamental to your success with understanding parabolas.

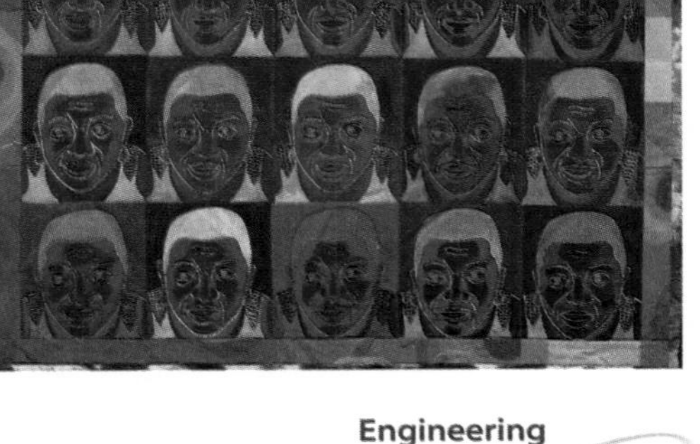

Bessie's Blues, by American artist Faith Ringgold (b 1930), shows 25 stenciled images of blues artist Bessie Smith. Was the stencil translated or reflected to make each image? How can you tell?

Bessie's Blues, by Faith Ringgold ©1997, acrylic on canvas, 76″ × 79.″ Photo courtesy of the artist.

Engineering CONNECTION

Several types of bridge designs involve the use of curves modeled by nonlinear functions. Each main cable of a suspension bridge approximates a parabola. To learn more about the design and construction of bridges, see the links at www.keymath.com/DAA .

The five-mile long Mackinac Bridge in Michigan was built in 1957.

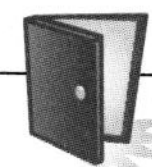

Investigation
Make My Graph

Procedure Note

For this investigation, use a "friendly" calculator window with a factor of 2. [▶ See **Calculator Note 4C** to learn about friendly windows. ◀] Enter the parent function $y = x^2$ into Y1. Enter the equation for the transformation in Y2, and graph both Y1 and Y2 to check your work.

Step 1 Each graph below shows the graph of the parent function $y = x^2$ in black. Find a quadratic equation that produces the congruent, red parabola. Apply what you learned about translations of the graphs of linear equations in Lesson 4.3.

a.

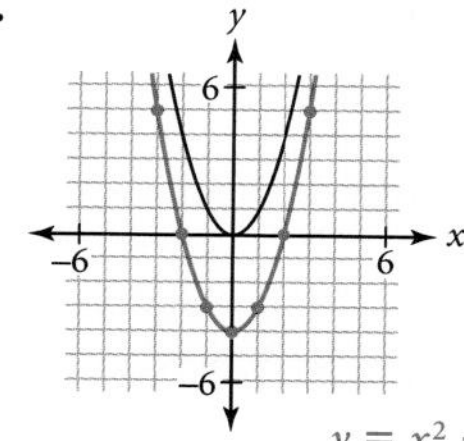

$y = x^2 - 4$

b.

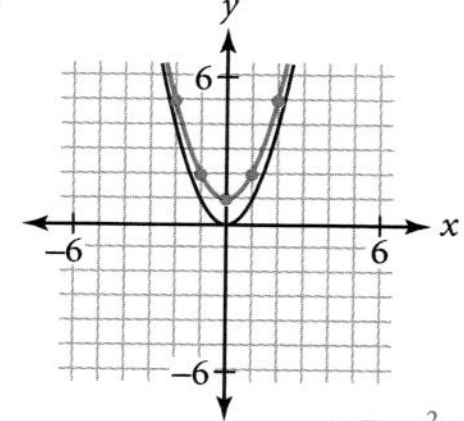

$y = x^2 + 1$

c.

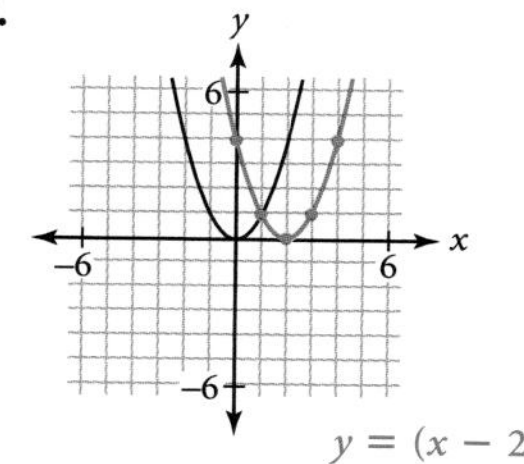

$y = (x - 2)^2$

d.

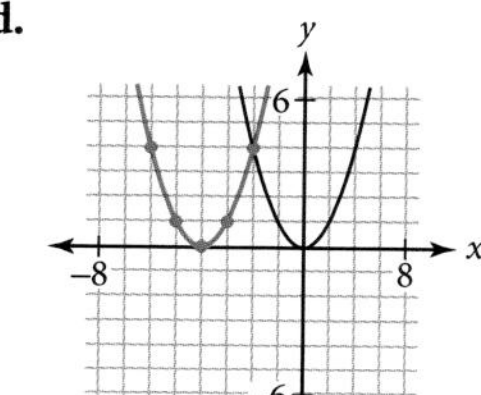

$y = (x + 4)^2$

e.

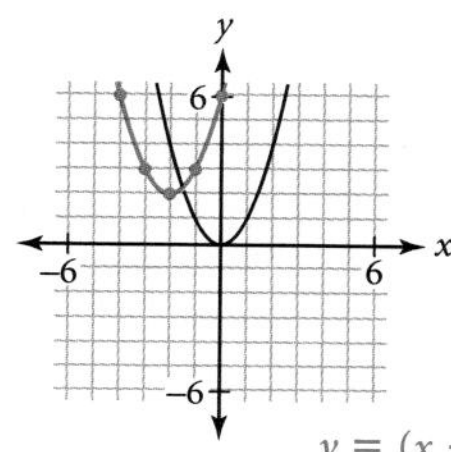

$y = (x + 2)^2 + 2$

f.

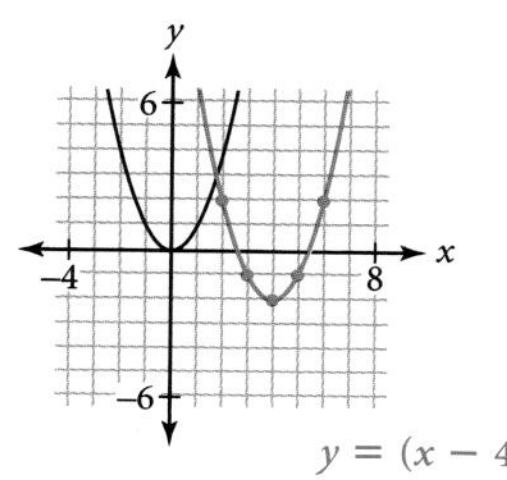

$y = (x - 4)^2 - 2$

Step 2 Write a few sentences describing any connections you discovered between the graphs of the translated parabolas, the equation for the translated parabola, and the equation of the parent function $y = x^2$.

Step 3 In general, what is the equation of the parabola formed when the graph of $y = x^2$ is translated horizontally h units and vertically k units?

The following example shows one simple application involving parabolas and translations of parabolas. In later chapters you will discover many applications of this important mathematical curve.

Guiding the Investigation

The Sketchpad demonstration Parabolas can be used as an alternative to the investigation or to close the lesson.

Encourage students to store the friendly window in their Zoom menu as illustrated in Calculator Note 4C; they will be using this friendly window frequently throughout the course.

Students can use Y1 in place of x^2 when using the calculator in Step 1, as described in Calculator Note 4D. For example, for graph e, students could enter something like $Y_2 = (x + 2)^2 + 2$ or $Y_2 = Y_1(x + 2) + 2$. The latter version is the calculator's equivalent of $y = f(x + 2) + 2$, where $f(x) = x^2$. The notation used for the TI-89, TI-92, and Voyage 200, $Y_1(x)$, is closer to function notation.

It is good to give students time to "play" with translations on their calculators. When students work privately, they tend to be more willing to try equations that might be incorrect and more confident in sharing satisfactory results with the class. You may want to extend the investigation to a class game of Make My Graph, in which you make a graph and students experiment on their calculators to find the equation that will make that graph.

Step 2 Answers will vary. For a translation right, you subtract from x; for a translation left, you add to x; for a translation up, you add to the entire function (or subtract from y); for a translation down, you subtract from the entire function (or add to y). Students may also notice the coordinates of the vertex are equivalent to (*value of horizontal translation, value of vertical translation*).

Step 3 $y = (x - h)^2 + k$ or $y - k = (x - h)^2$

EXAMPLE

This graph shows a portion of a parabola. It represents a diver's position (horizontal and vertical distance) from the edge of a pool as he dives from a 5 ft long board 25 ft above the water.

Vertical distance (ft)
Horizontal distance (ft)

a. Sketch a graph of the diver's position if he dives from a 10 ft long board 10 ft above the water. (Assume that he leaves the board at the same angle and with the same force.)

b. In the scenario described in part a, what is the diver's position when he reaches his maximum height?

▶ Solution

First, make sure that you can interpret the graph. The point (5, 25) represents the moment when the diver leaves the board, which is 5 ft long and 25 ft high. The vertex, (7.5, 30), represents the position where the diver's height is at a maximum, or 30 ft; it is also the point where the diver's motion changes from upward to downward. The x-intercept, approximately (13.6, 0), indicates that the diver hits the water at approximately 13.6 ft from the edge of the pool.

Mark Ruiz placed first in the 2000 U.S. Olympic Diving Team trials with this dive.

a. If the length of the board increases from 5 ft to 10 ft, then the parabola translates right 5 units. If the height of the board decreases from 25 ft to 10 ft, then the parabola translates down 15 units. If you define the original parabola as the graph of $y = f(x)$, then the function for the new graph is $y = f(x - 5) - 15$.

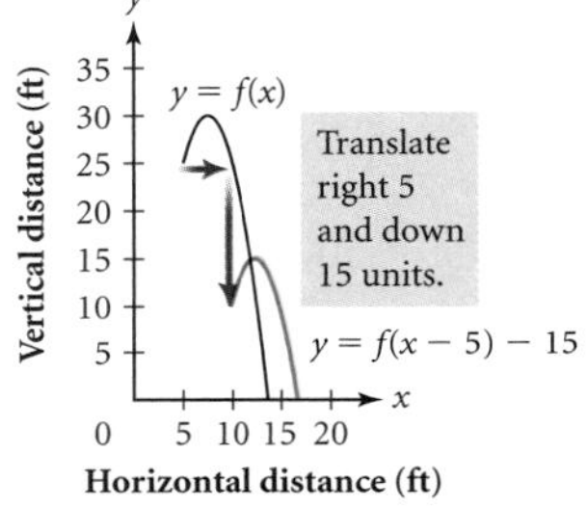

b. As with every point on the graph, the vertex translates right 5 units and down 15 units. The new vertex is $(7.5 + 5, 30 - 15)$, or (12.5, 15). This means that when the diver's horizontal distance from the edge of the pool is 12.5 ft, he reaches his maximum height of 15 ft.

The translations you investigated with linear functions and functions in general work the same way with quadratic functions. If you translate the graph of $y = x^2$ horizontally h units and vertically k units, then the equation of the translated parabola is $y = (x - h)^2 + k$. You may also see this equation written as $y = k + (x - h)^2$ or $y - k = (x - h)^2$. When you translate any equation horizontally, you can think of it as replacing x in the equation with $(x - h)$. Likewise, a vertical translation replaces y with $(y - k)$.

▶ EXAMPLE

Whereas the investigation has students translate the graph of the parent function $y = x^2$, this example asks students to relate two parabolas, neither of which is the parent quadratic function. Students may notice that both graphs actually require a reflection of the graph of $y = x^2$ across a horizontal line. The example does not require students to write a function for either graph.

[Ask] "Why is the translated vertex (h, k)?" [The vertex of the graph of $y = x^2$ is (0, 0), so a translation horizontally h units and vertically k units puts the translated vertex at (h, k).]

SHARING IDEAS

[Language] The book uses the term *congruent* to describe parabolas that are translations of each other. In geometry two polygons are congruent if corresponding sides and corresponding angles are congruent. To induce critical thinking, **[Ask]** "Is the book correct in using the term *congruent*?" Encourage discussion that compares and contrasts parabolas and polygons. Unlike a polygon, a parabola has no angles or sides and is not bounded. But a translation of a polygon is indeed congruent, and in fact figures can be defined to be congruent if one is the image of the other under translations and rotations.

As students present ideas, encourage them to use the form $y = (x - h)^2 + k$. In Chapter 7, students will see that this is the vertex form of a quadratic equation, with vertical scale factor $a = 1$. Also **[Ask]** "What is the line of symmetry of these graphs?" **[Alert]** Students may have difficulty with the equations of vertical lines.

You might point out that some of the graphs don't really look parallel and question whether they're actually translations. *Corresponding* points of translated parabolas are the same distance apart, but, unlike with lines, the *closest* points may not be.

The graphs of all quadratic functions are parabolas. **[Ask]** "Is every parabola the graph of a quadratic function?" [If the line of symmetry of the parabola's graph is vertical, then the parabola is a graph of a function in the family $y = x^2$. If the line of symmetry is horizontal, the parabola has the relation $x = y^2$ as a parent. Here x is a quadratic function of y. Rotations of these graphs through a number of degrees other than a multiple of 90° are parabolas in which neither x nor y is a function of the other, but they still represent quadratic relations.]

[Ask] "In part a of the example, can we tell where the diver hits the water?" [Unlike the maximum height, which is a translation of the vertex, the position when he hits the water is not a translation of the original x-intercept. Instead, it is a translation of the point at which the original function was equivalent to 15, because the second board is 15 ft below the first. The approximate point (11.8, 15) on the original graph translates to the point (16.8, 0)

It is important to notice that the vertex of the translated parabola is (h, k). That's why finding the vertex is fundamental to determining translations of parabolas. In every function you learn, there will be key points to locate. Finding the relationships between these points and the corresponding points in the parent function enables you to write equations more easily.

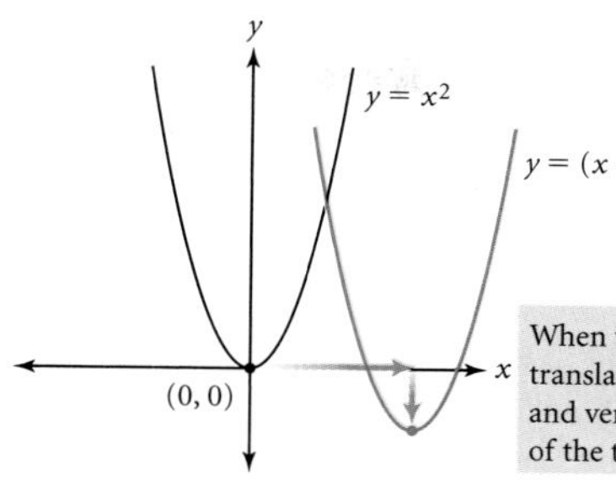

When the graph of $y = x^2$ is translated horizontally h units and vertically k units, the vertex of the translated parabola is (h, k).

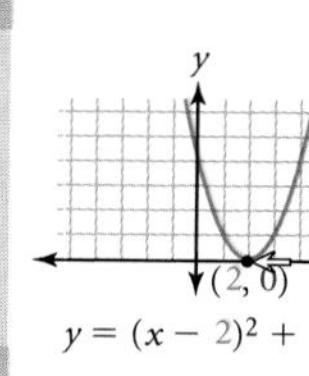

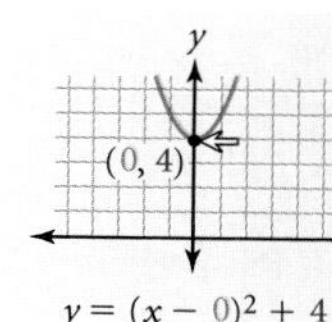

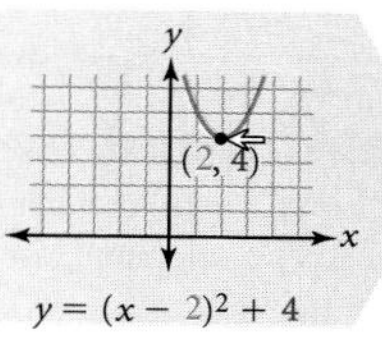

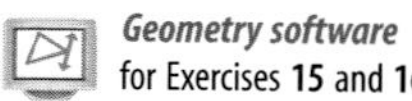

EXERCISES

You will need

Geometry software for Exercises **15** and **16**

Practice Your Skills

1. Write an equation for each parabola. Each parabola is a translation of the graph of the parent function $y = x^2$.

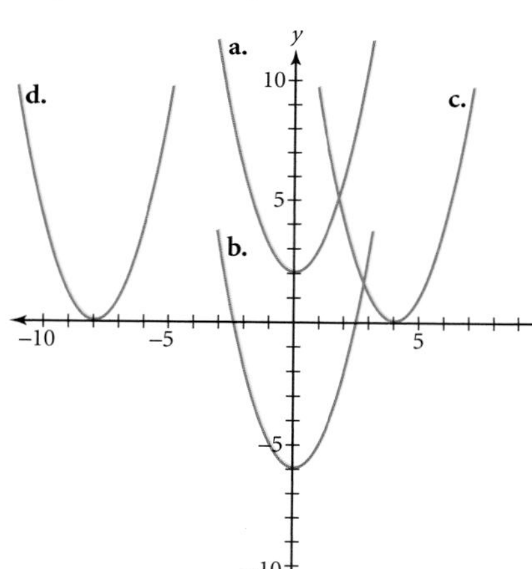

These black sand dunes in the Canary Islands, off the coast of Africa, form parabolic shapes called deflation hollows.

1a. $y = x^2 + 2$

1b. $y = x^2 - 6$

1c. $y = (x - 4)^2$

1d. $y = (x + 8)^2$

Sharing Ideas (continued)

on the new graph. That is, he hits the water approximately 16.8 ft from the edge of the pool.]

You or a student might show the Sketchpad demonstration Transforming Parabolas. Or students can use the first dynamic algebra exploration at www.keymath.com/DAA to explore these transformations.

Assessing Progress

While investigating, students will display their understanding of graphs, of the function $y = x^2$, and of translating straight lines. You can also assess their ability to see patterns.

Closing the Lesson

Reiterate the main point of this lesson: When the graph of the quadratic equation $y = x^2$ is translated to put its vertex at (h, k), the equation becomes $y = (x - h)^2 + k$ or, equivalently, $y - k = (x - h)^2$.

BUILDING UNDERSTANDING

Encourage students to know why for each exercise even if they're not asked to explain why.

ASSIGNING HOMEWORK

Essential	1–4
Performance assessment	6–9, 11
Portfolio	9
Journal	11
Group	8
Review	5, 10, 12–16

MATERIALS

- graph paper
- geometry software
- Exercise 8 (T), *optional*
- Calculator Note 4E, *optional*

Helping with the Exercises

2a. $y = x^2 - 5$

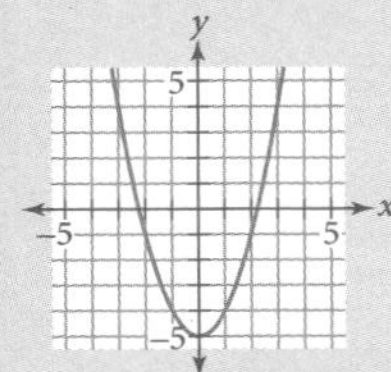

2b. $y = x^2 + 3$

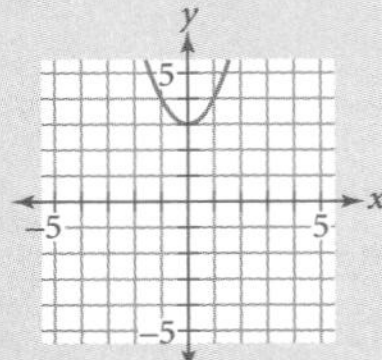

2c. $y = (x - 3)^2$

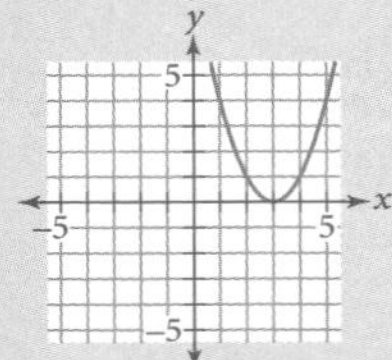

2d. $y = (x + 4)^2$

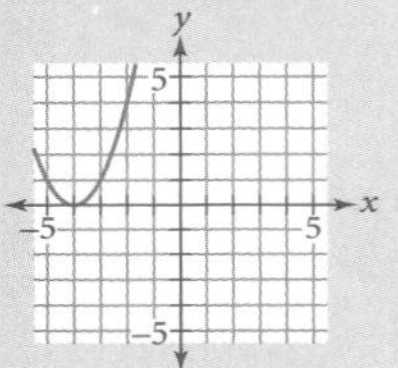

Exercise 3 You might ask students to first solve this problem without graphing and then graph to check their answers.

Exercise 5 You can use this exercise to review solving quadratic equations by isolating x^2 and then taking the square root of both sides. You may want to remind students that nonnegative numbers have two square roots, indicated with the notation $\pm$, and that the radical symbol alone denotes only the positive square root. The intersection of the graphs of $y = x^2$ and $y = 4$ gives the solution $x^2 = 4$.

6a. $y = (x - 2)^2$
6b. $y = (x - 2)^2 - 5$
6c. $y = (x + 6)^2$
6d. $y = (x + 6)^2 + 2$

2. Each parabola described is congruent to the graph of $y = x^2$. Write an equation for each parabola and sketch its graph.

a. The parabola is translated down 5 units.
b. The parabola is translated up 3 units.
c. The parabola is translated right 3 units.
d. The parabola is translated left 4 units.

3. If $f(x) = x^2$, then the graph of each equation below is a parabola. Describe the location of the parabola relative to the graph of $f(x) = x^2$.

a. $y = f(x) - 3$ translated down 3 units
b. $y = f(x) + 4$ translated up 4 units
c. $y = f(x - 2)$ translated right 2 units
d. $y = f(x + 4)$ translated left 4 units

4. Describe what happens to the graph of $y = x^2$ in the following situations.

a. x is replaced with $(x - 3)$. translated right 3 units
b. x is replaced with $(x + 3)$. translated left 3 units
c. y is replaced with $(y - 2)$. translated up 2 units
d. y is replaced with $(y + 2)$. translated down 2 units

5. Solve.

a. $x^2 = 4$
$x = 2$ or $x = -2$

b. $x^2 + 3 = 19$
$x = 4$ or $x = -4$

c. $(x - 2)^2 = 25$
$x = 7$ or $x = -3$

Reason and Apply

6. Write an equation for each parabola at right.

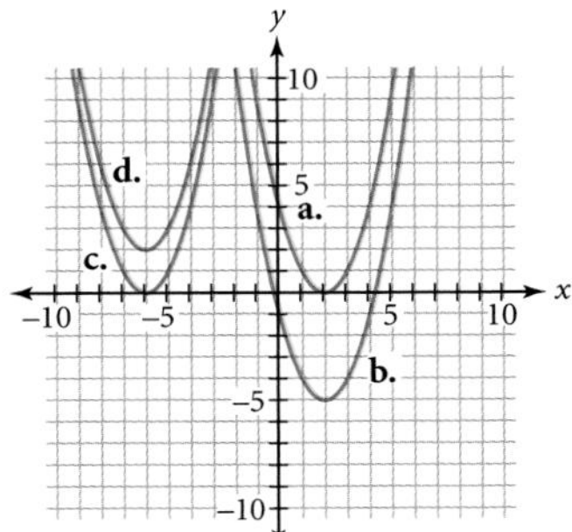

7. The red parabola below is the image of the graph of $y = x^2$ after a translation right 5 units and down 3 units.

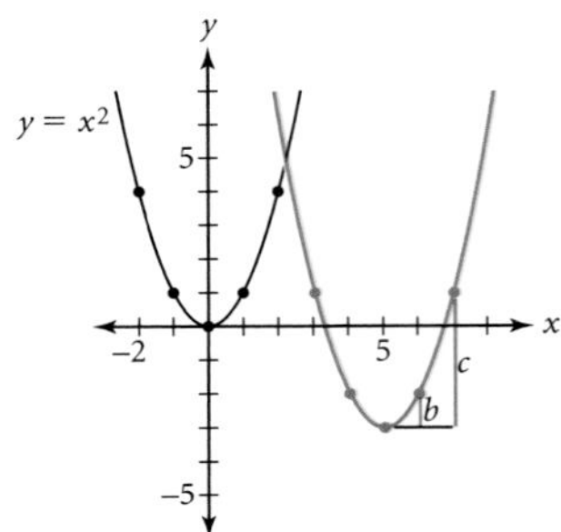

a. Write an equation for the red parabola. $y = (x - 5)^2 - 3$

b. Where is the vertex of the red parabola? $(5, -3)$

c. What are the coordinates of the other four points if they are 1 or 2 horizontal units from the vertex? How are the coordinates of each point on the black parabola related to the coordinates of the corresponding point on the red parabola?

d. What is the length of blue segment b? Of green segment c?

8. Given the graph of $y = f(x)$ at right, draw a graph of each of these related functions.

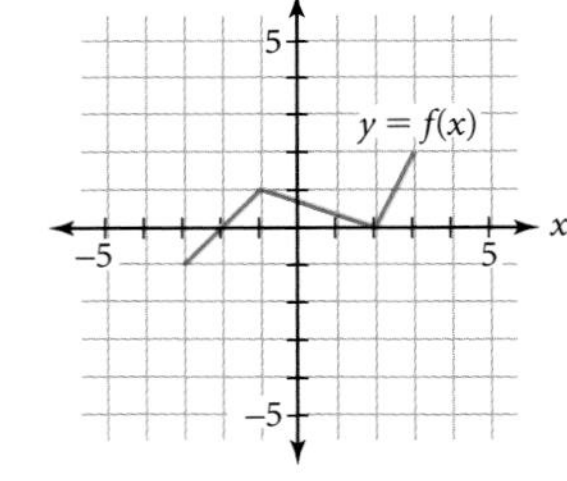

a. $y = f(x + 2)$

b. $y = f(x - 1) - 3$

7c. $(6, -2), (4, -2), (7, 1), (3, 1)$. If (x, y) are the coordinates of any point on the black parabola, then the coordinates of the corresponding point on the red parabola are $(x + 5, y - 3)$.

Exercise 7d This exercise uses the fact that pairs of corresponding points are the same distance apart. **[Ask]** "What is the equation of the line of symmetry?"

7d. Segment b has length 1 unit, and segment c has length 4 units.

Exercise 8 You might use the Exercise 8 transparency as you discuss this problem.

8a.

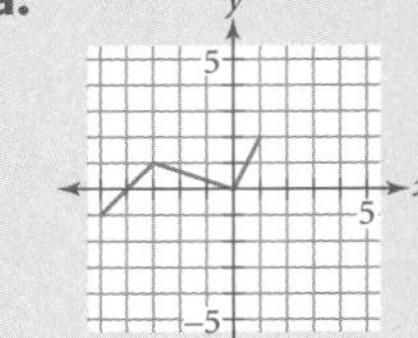

8b.

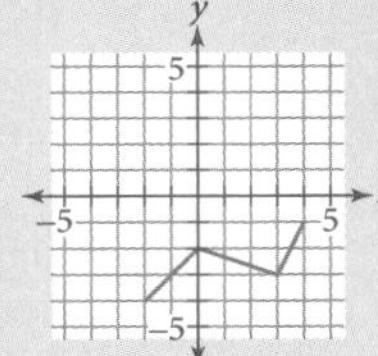

9. **APPLICATION** This table of values compares the number of teams in a pee wee teeball league and the number of games required for each team to play every other team twice (once at home and once away from home).

Number of teams (x)	1	2	3	4	5	6	7	8	9	10
Number of games (y)	0	2	6	12	20	30	42	56	72	90

a. Continue the table out to 10 teams.

b. Plot each point and describe the graph produced.

c. Write an explicit function for this graph. $y = (x - 0.5)^2 - 0.25$

d. Use your function to find how many games are required if there are 30 teams. 870 games

10. Solve.

a. $3 + (x - 5)^2 = 19$ $x = 9$ or $x = 1$

b. $(x + 3)^2 = 49$ $x = 4$ or $x = -10$

c. $5 - (x - 1) = -22$ $x = 28$

d. $-15 + (x + 6)^2 = -7$ $x = -6 \pm \sqrt{8}$

11. This histogram shows the students' scores on a recent quiz in Ms. Noah's class. Sketch what the histogram will look like if Ms. Noah

a. adds five points to everyone's score.

b. subtracts ten points from everyone's score.

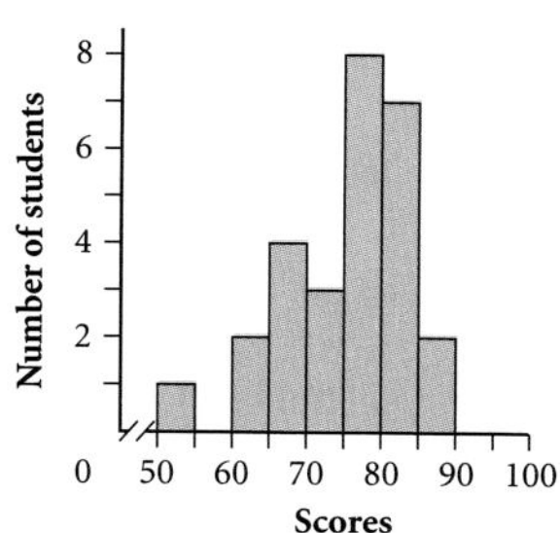

Review

3.1 **12.** Match each recursive formula with the equation of the line that contains the sequence of points, (n, u_n), generated by the formula.

a. $u_0 = -8$
$u_n = u_{(n-1)} + 3$ where $n \geq 1$ B

b. $u_1 = 3$
$u_n = u_{(n-1)} - 8$ where $n \geq 2$ C

A. $y = 3x - 11$

B. $y = 3x - 8$

C. $y = 11 - 8x$

D. $y = -8x + 3$

3.6 **13.** **APPLICATION** You need to rent a car for one day. Mertz Rental charges \$32 per day plus \$0.10 per mile. Saver Rental charges \$24 per day plus \$0.18 per mile. Luxury Rental charges \$51 per day with unlimited mileage.

a. Write a cost equation for each rental agency.

b. Graph the three equations on the same axes.

c. Describe which rental agency is the cheapest alternative under various circumstances.

Exercise 9 Because the number of teams and the number of games must be integers, the graph of this function is a collection of points. Its trend can be seen, and predictions made, by drawing a curve through those points.

Students can use differences to find the explicit formula. Ask whether it makes sense. For each additional team, you will add double the previous number of teams to represent the new team's playing each of the existing teams twice.

9b. The points appear to be part of a parabola.

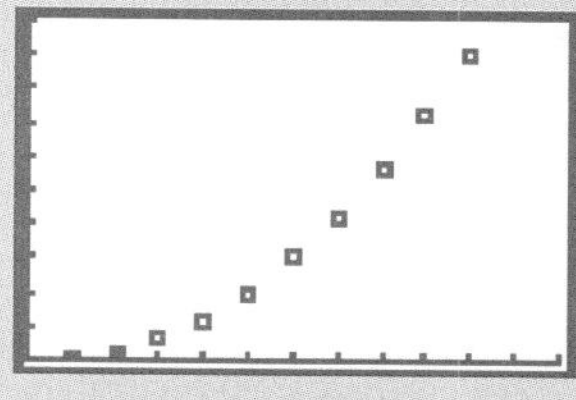

[0, 12, 1, 0, 100, 10]

Exercise 10 As needed, remind students to first isolate the quantity in parentheses. **[Ask]** "What real-world situation might one of these equations represent?"

Exercise 11 To help students connect this exercise with the lesson, you might suggest that students visualize a parabola that follows the trend of the histogram.

11a.

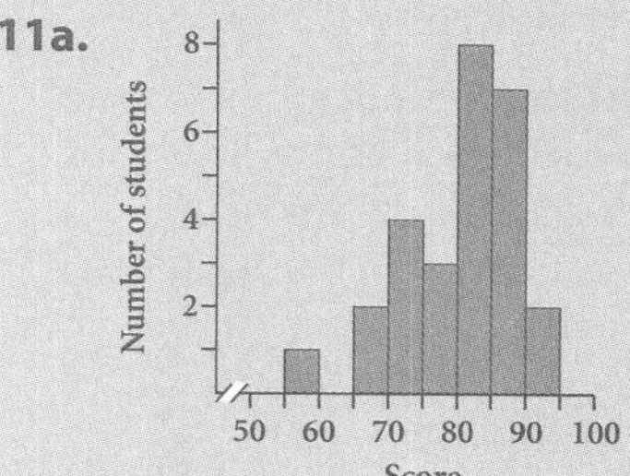

11b.

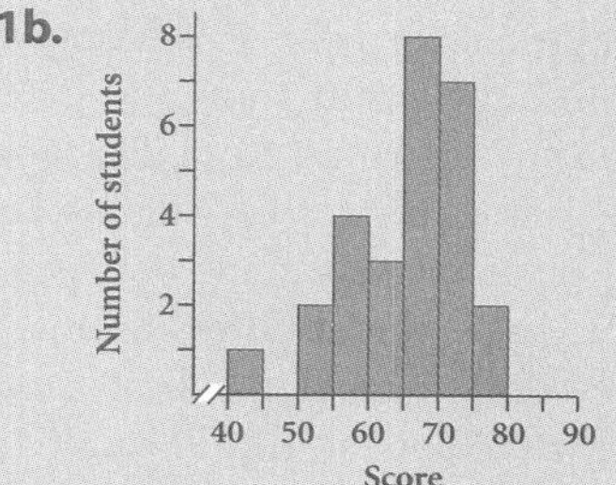

13a. Let m represent the miles driven and let C represent the cost of the one-day rental. Mertz: $C = 32 + 0.1m$; Saver: $C = 24 + 0.18m$; Luxury: $C = 51$.

13b.

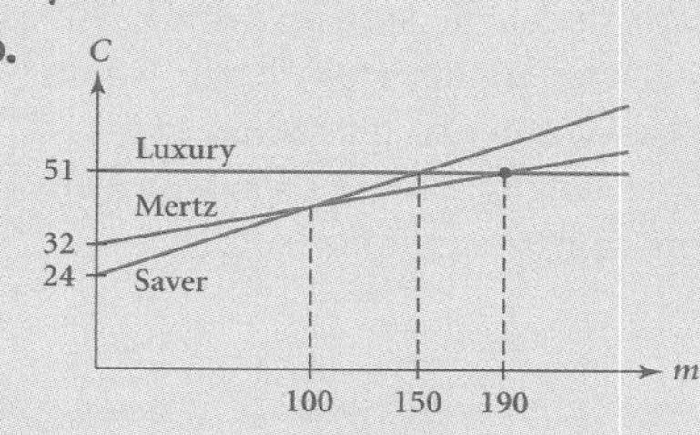

13c. If you plan to drive less than 100 miles, then rent Saver. At exactly 100 miles, Mertz and Saver are the same. If you plan to drive between 100 miles and 190 miles, then rent Mertz. At exactly 190 miles, Mertz and Luxury are the same. If you plan to drive more than 190 miles, then rent Luxury.

Exercise 14 From B to C and from C to E, the graph is actually hyperbolic, but students may not be aware of this subtlety.

14.

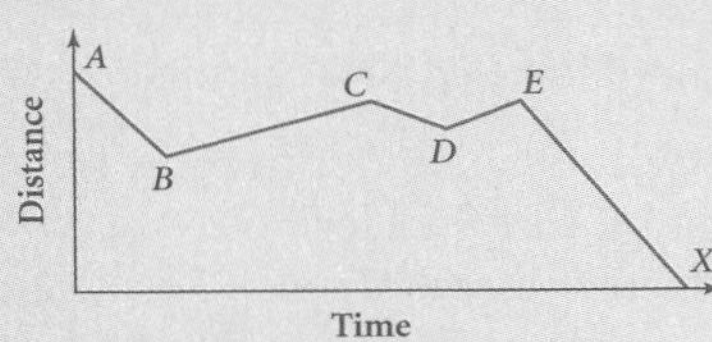

Exercise 15 Rather than manually setting the amount of translation or stretch, students could first create a dynamic sketch with sliders whose lengths represent the common difference or common ratio. Using sliders, students can change the common difference or common ratio and see how the sequence of segments or their endpoints change. You could also challenge students to combine both translations and dilations to create a translated geometric sequence. Students using The Geometer's Sketchpad can either create a custom tool and manually reapply it or use the **Iterate** command.

The word *dilation* is used in the geometry software to indicate a stretch rather than a simultaneous stretch both horizontally and vertically by the same amount. In this case, the "dilation" is equivalent to a vertical stretch only.

Exercise 16 Students can create two sliders, a and b. They can then use those sliders in the equation $y = ax + b$ and vary a and b.

EXTENSION

Ask students to use the program in Calculator Note 4E for practice in using transformations to determine an equation from its graph. The program has varying levels of difficulty that gradually introduce new parent functions and new transformations, similar to the development from Lesson 4.4 to 4.7. Students can use it as they work through these lessons.

4.1 **14.** A car drives at a constant speed along the road pictured at right from point A to point X. Sketch a graph showing the straight line distance between the car and point X as it travels along the road. Mark points A, B, C, D, E, and X on your graph.

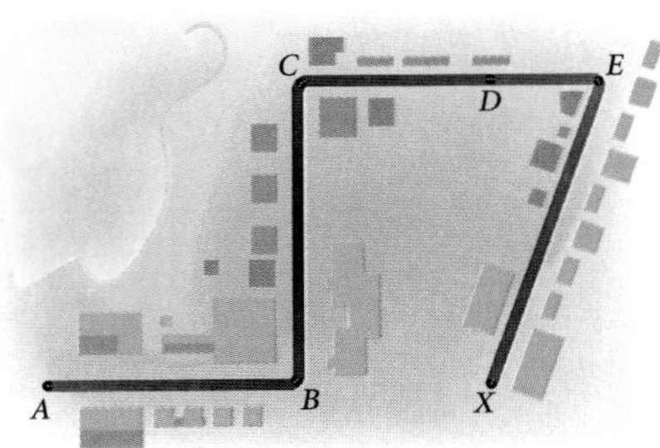

4.3 **15.** ***Technology*** Use geometry software to construct a segment whose length represents the starting term of a sequence. Then use transformations, such as translations and dilations, to create segments whose lengths represent additional terms in the sequence. For example, the segments at right represent the first ten terms of the sequence. Answers will vary.

$a = 2.00$ in.
$b = 1.50$ in.

$$u_1 = 2$$
$$u_n = 0.75 \cdot u_{n-1} \quad \text{where } n \geq 2$$

4.3 **16.** ***Technology*** Use geometry software to investigate the form $y = ax + b$ of a linear function.

a. On the same coordinate plane, graph the lines $y = 0.5x + 4$, $y = x + 4$, $y = 2x + 4$, $y = 5x + 4$, $y = -3x + 4$, and $y = -0.25x + 4$. Describe the graphs of the family of lines $y = ax + 4$ as a takes on different values. The slopes vary, but the y-intercept is always 4.

b. On the same coordinate plane, graph the lines $y = 2x - 7$, $y = 2x - 2$, $y = 2x$, $y = 2x + 3$, and $y = 2x + 8$. Describe the graphs of the family of lines $y = 2x + b$ as b takes on different values. They move up or down, but they all have slope 2.

IMPROVING YOUR REASONING SKILLS

The Dipper

The group of stars known as the Big Dipper, which is part of the constellation Ursa Major, contains stars at various distances from Earth. Imagine translating the Big Dipper to a new position. Would all of the stars need to be moved the same distance? Why or why not?

Now imagine rotating the Big Dipper around the Earth. Do all the stars need to be moved the same distance? Why or why not?

IMPROVING REASONING SKILLS

For the constellation to appear the same from Earth, the stars that are farther away would move a greater distance. If the constellation were translated, all the stars would move the same distance, and it would look different to us. The constellation would look the same to us if it were rotated with Earth as the center of rotation. The stars would move along arcs of great circles on concentric spheres with Earth as the center. The stars farther from Earth would move along arcs with a greater radius and therefore greater length. All the arcs, however, would have the same degree measure.

LESSON

4.5 Reflections and the Square Root Family

Call it a clan, call it a network, call it a tribe, call it a family. Whatever you call it, whoever you are, you need one.

JANE HOWARD

The graph of the **square root function,** $y = \sqrt{x}$, is another parent function that you can use to illustrate transformations. From the graphs below, what are the domain and range of $f(x) = \sqrt{x}$? If you graph $y = \sqrt{x}$ on your calculator, you can trace to show that $\sqrt{3}$ is approximately 1.732. What is the approximate value of $\sqrt{8}$? How would you use the graph to find $\sqrt{31}$? What happens when you try to trace for values of $x < 0$?

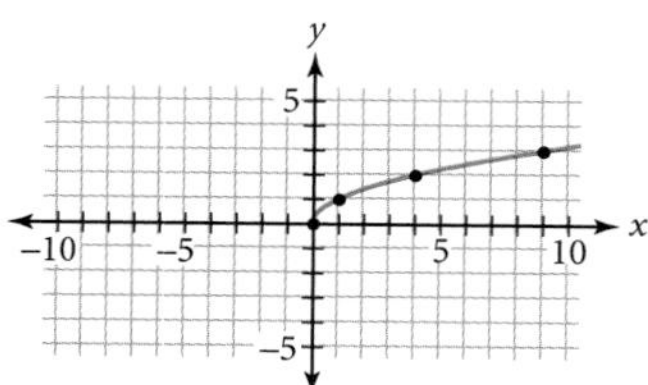

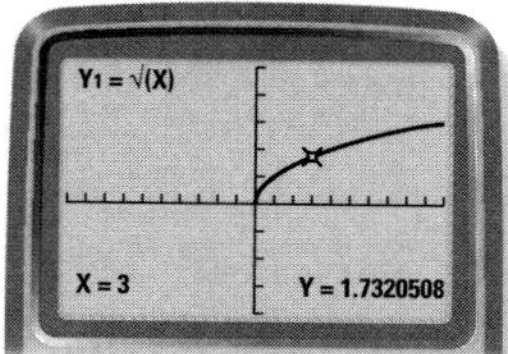

[−9.4, 9.4, 1, −6.2, 6.2, 1]

Investigation
Take a Moment to Reflect

Procedure Note

For this investigation, use a friendly window with a factor of 2.

In this investigation you first will work with linear functions to discover how to create a new transformation—a **reflection.** Then you will apply reflections to quadratic functions and square root functions.

Step 1a $Y_2 = -(0.5x + 2) = -0.5x - 2$. It is reflected across the x-axis.

Step 1b $Y_2 = -(-2x - 4) = 2x + 4$. It is reflected across the x-axis.

Step 1c $Y_2 = -(x^2 + 1) = -x^2 - 1$. It is reflected across the x-axis.

Step 1d $y = -f(x)$ is a reflection of $y = f(x)$ across the x-axis.

Step 2a $Y_2 = 0.5(-x) + 2 = -0.5x + 2$. It is reflected across the y-axis.

Step 2b $Y_2 = -2(-x) - 4 = 2x - 4$. It is reflected across the y-axis.

Step 1 Enter $y = 0.5x + 2$ into Y_1 and graph it on your calculator. Then enter the equation $Y_2 = -Y_1(x)$ and graph it.

a. Write the equation for Y_2 in terms of x. How does the graph of Y_2 compare with the graph of Y_1?

b. Change Y_1 to $y = -2x - 4$ and repeat the instructions in Step 1a.

c. Change Y_1 to $y = x^2 + 1$ and repeat.

d. In general, how are the graphs of $y = f(x)$ and $y = -f(x)$ related?

Step 2 Enter $y = 0.5x + 2$ into Y_1. Enter the equation $Y_2 = Y_1(-x)$ and graph both Y_1 and Y_2.

a. Write the equation for Y_2 in terms of x. How does the graph of Y_2 compare with the graph of Y_1?

b. Change Y_1 to $y = -2x - 4$ and repeat the instructions in Step 2a.

LESSON 4.5

PLANNING

LESSON OUTLINE

One day:

20 min Investigation

5 min Sharing

5 min Example

15 min Exercises

MATERIALS

- Calculator Notes 4C, 4D
- Sketchpad demonstration Square Roots, *optional*

TEACHING

This lesson discusses reflections (across the axes) and the square root function. The one-step investigation appears at the bottom of page 202.

The value of $\sqrt{8}$ is approximately 2.828. To find $\sqrt{31}$, trace until $x = 31$ and $y \approx 5.568$; you can't trace to x-values less than 0 because they aren't in the domain.

Guiding the Investigation

Most students can complete this investigation and be prepared to work on the exercises with little or no help from you. For assistance in setting up a friendly window, see Calculator Note 4C.

Step 1 Calculator Note 4D shows how to use Y_1 in the equation of Y_2. As needed, encourage students to do this instead of entering the first equation with the negative sign distributed, possibly forgetting to negate the second term. If students are neglecting to graph equations, suggest that they reread the instructions carefully.

See page 882 for graphs of Steps 1a–c and 2a and b.

NCTM STANDARDS

CONTENT		PROCESS	
✓	Number		Problem Solving
✓	Algebra	✓	Reasoning
✓	Geometry	✓	Communication
	Measurement	✓	Connections
	Data/Probability	✓	Representation

LESSON OBJECTIVES

- Define *reflection*
- Define the parent square root function, $y = \sqrt{x}$
- Define the square root symbol and function as the positive root
- Compare $f(x)$, $-f(x)$, $f(-x)$, and $-f(-x)$
- Apply the square root function in context
- Apply reflections to functions in general
- Symbolically solve the equation $a + \sqrt{x + b} = c$ for x

Step 2c $Y_2 = (-x)^2 + 1 = x^2 + 1$. It does not change, because the parabola has the y-axis as a line of symmetry, so a reflection across the y-axis maps the graph onto itself.

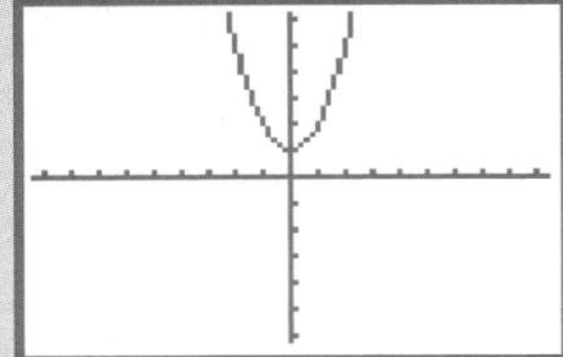

[−9.4, 9.4, 1, −6.2, 6.2, 1]

Step 2d $Y_2 = (-x - 3)^2 + 2$. It is reflected across the y-axis.

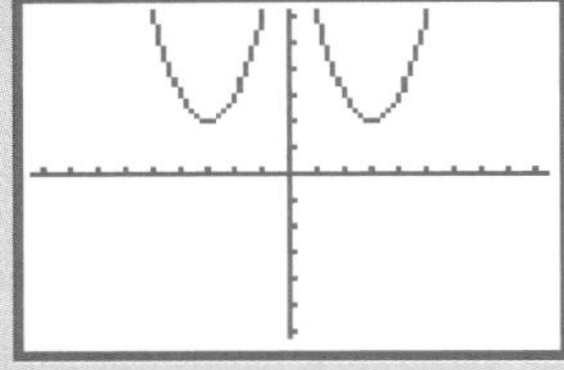

[−9.4, 9.4, 1, −6.2, 6.2, 1]

Step 3 Some graphing calculators will allow you to enter both functions in one equation. For example, on the Texas Instruments calculators, the equation $Y_1 = \{1, -1\}\sqrt{x}$ (note the braces, not brackets or parentheses) represents the two functions $y = \sqrt{x}$ and $y = -\sqrt{x}$.

Step 3a $Y_2 = -Y_1(x)$ will be a reflection across the x-axis; $Y_2 = Y_1(-x)$ will be a reflection across the y-axis.

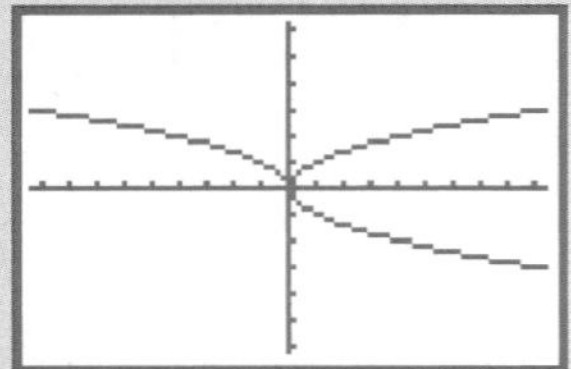

[−9.4, 9.4, 1, −6.2, 6.2, 1]

Step 3b $Y_2 = -Y_1(-x)$ will be a reflection across both axes.

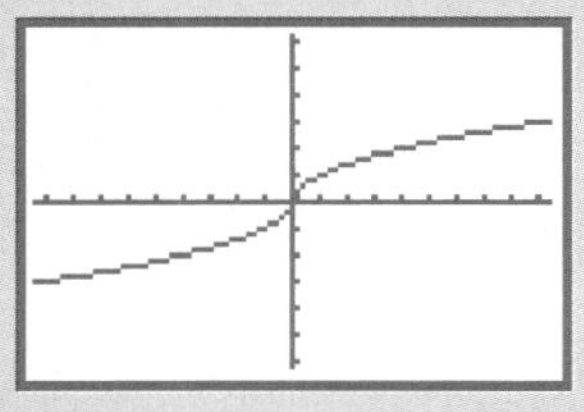

[−9.4, 9.4, 1, −6.2, 6.2, 1]

Step 2e $y = f(-x)$ is a reflection of $y = f(x)$ across the y-axis.

c. Change Y_1 to $y = x^2 + 1$ and repeat. Explain what happens.

d. Change Y_1 to $y = (x - 3)^2 + 2$ and repeat.

e. In general, how are the graphs of $y = f(x)$ and $y = f(-x)$ related?

Step 3 Enter $y = \sqrt{x}$ into Y_1 and graph it on your calculator.

a. Predict what the graphs of $Y_2 = -Y_1(x)$ and $Y_2 = Y_1(-x)$ will look like. Use your calculator to verify your predictions. Write equations for both of these functions in terms of x.

b. Predict what the graph of $Y_2 = -Y_1(-x)$ will look like. Use your calculator to verify your prediction.

c. Do you notice that the graph of the square root function looks like half of a parabola, oriented horizontally? Why isn't it an entire parabola? What function would you graph to complete the bottom half of the parabola?

Reflections over the x- or y-axis are summarized below.

Reflection of a Function

A **reflection** is a transformation that flips a graph across a line, creating a mirror image.

Given the graph of $y = f(x)$,
the graph of $y = f(-x)$ is a reflection across the y-axis, and
the graph of $y = -f(x)$ is a reflection across the x-axis.

Because the graph of the square root function looks like half a parabola, it's easy to see the effects of reflections. The square root family has many real-world applications, such as finding the time it takes a falling object to reach the ground. The next example shows you how you can apply a square root function.

Science CONNECTION

Obsidian, a natural volcanic glass, was a popular material for tools and weapons in prehistoric times because it makes a very sharp edge. In 1960, scientists Irving Friedman and Robert L. Smith discovered that obsidian absorbs moisture at a slow, predictable rate and that measuring the thickness of the layer of moisture with a high-power microscope helps determine its age. Therefore, obsidian hydration dating can be used on obsidian artifacts, just as carbon dating can be used on organic remains. The age of prehistoric artifacts is predicted by a square root function similar to $d = \sqrt{5t}$ where t is time in thousands of years and d is the thickness of the layer of moisture in microns (millionths of a meter).

These flaked obsidian arrowheads—once used for cutting, carving, and hunting—were made by Native Americans near Jackson Lake, Wyoming more than 8500 years ago.

Step 3c An entire horizontal parabola wouldn't be the graph of a function. $y = \sqrt{x}$ has a range of $y \geq 0$. $y = -\sqrt{x}$ would complete the bottom half of the parabola.

One Step

Ask students to graph the equations $y = \sqrt{x}$, $y = -\sqrt{x}$, and $y = \sqrt{-x}$ and to write down as many observations about the graphs as they can. During Sharing, ask about the domains and ranges of these functions and why inserting a negative sign reflects the graph in various ways.

EXAMPLE

Objects fall to the ground because of the influence of gravity. When an object is dropped from an initial height of d meters, the height, h, after t seconds is given by the quadratic function $h = -4.9t^2 + d$. If an object is dropped from a height of 1000 meters, how long does it take for the object to fall to a height of 750 meters? 500 meters? How long will it take the object to hit the ground?

Science CONNECTION

English scientist Isaac Newton (1643–1727) formulated the theory of gravitation in the 1680s, building on the work of earlier scientists. Gravity is the force of attraction that exists between all objects. In general, larger objects pull smaller objects toward them. The force of gravity keeps objects on the surface of a planet, and it keeps objects in orbit around a planet or the Sun.

When an object falls near the surface of Earth, it speeds up, or accelerates. The acceleration caused by gravity is approximately 9.8 m/s^2, or 32 ft/s^2.

This time-lapse photograph by James Sugar shows an apple and feather falling at the same rate in a vacuum chamber. In the early 1600s, Galileo Galilei demonstrated that all objects fall at the same rate regardless of their weight, as long as they are not influenced by air resistance or other factors.

► Solution

The height of an object dropped from a height of 1000 meters is given by the function $h = -4.9t^2 + 1000$. You want to know t for various values of h, so first solve this equation for t.

$$h = -4.9t^2 + 1000$$ Original equation.

$$h - 1000 = -4.9t^2$$ Subtract 1000 from both sides.

$$\frac{h - 1000}{-4.9} = t^2$$ Divide by -4.9.

$$\pm\sqrt{\frac{h - 1000}{-4.9}} = t$$ Take the square root of both sides.

$$t = \sqrt{\frac{h - 1000}{-4.9}}$$ Because it doesn't make sense to have a negative value for time, use only the positive root.

To find when the height is 750 meters, substitute 750 for h.

$$t = \sqrt{\frac{750 - 1000}{-4.9}}$$

$$t \approx 7.143$$

The height of the object is 750 meters after approximately 7 seconds.

Assessing Progress

As students work and present, you can assess their understanding of reflections and their comfort level in working with linear and quadratic equations.

► EXAMPLE

At first glance, the example may not seem to concern reflections. The square root function, used to demonstrate reflections in the investigation, is also used to solve the equation in the example.

The constant –4.9 is measured in m/s^2. In Chapter 7, students will explore this gravitational constant further. (See pages 363 and 377.)

SHARING IDEAS

[Language] Mention that, in the notation $\sqrt{x}$, the symbol $\sqrt{\ }$ is called a *radical* and the variable x is called the *radicand*. Help students become familiar with both terms. For example, $\sqrt{3}$ can be read as "radical three." Students may refer to this as "root 3."
[Ask] "Why does the example use the plus or minus sign in front of the radical? If the radical indicates the square root and there are two of them, isn't the plus or minus sign redundant?" [No; the radical refers only to the positive square root.]

As students present their ideas about Step 3c of the investigation, **[Ask]** "What is the range of the function $f(x) = \sqrt{x}$?" As students look at the graph, they may conjecture that the range omits some positive numbers because the graph appears to approach a limit. Challenging students to find this limit can get them to explore large values of x and to see that they can get as large a value of y as they want. You might ask them what x-value will result in a y-value of 1000. [1000^2, or 1,000,000]

Ask students how they might change a function's equation to reflect its graph across the line $y = x$. You need not answer this question now; it foreshadows the exploration on page 208.

Closing the Lesson

The major points of this lesson are that the graph of $y = -f(x)$ is a **reflection** of the graph of $f(x)$ across the x-axis and that the graph of $y = f(-x)$ is a reflection of the same graph across the y-axis. The lesson also introduces the **square root function,** $f(x) = \sqrt{x}$, whose domain and range are the nonnegative real numbers.

BUILDING UNDERSTANDING

The exercises include practice with all the parent functions and transformations learned to this point.

ASSIGNING HOMEWORK

Essential	1–4
Performance assessment	5–11
Portfolio	11
Journal	7
Group	9
Review	12–16

MATERIALS

- Exercise 4 (T), *optional*

Helping with the Exercises

1a. $y = \sqrt{x} + 3$

1b. $y = \sqrt{x + 5}$

1c. $y = \sqrt{x + 5} + 2$

1d. $y = \sqrt{x - 3} + 1$

1e. $y = \sqrt{x - 1} - 4$

Exercise 2 As needed, suggest that students graph the equations.

3a. $y = -\sqrt{x}$

3b. $y = -\sqrt{x} - 3$

3c. $y = -\sqrt{x + 6} + 5$

3d. $y = \sqrt{-x}$

3e. $y = \sqrt{-(x - 2)} - 3$, or $y = \sqrt{-x + 2} - 3$

A similar substitution shows that the height of the object is 500 meters after approximately 10 seconds.

$$t = \sqrt{\frac{500 - 1000}{-4.9}} \approx 10.102$$

The object hits the ground when its height is 0 meters. That occurs after approximately 14 seconds.

$$t = \sqrt{\frac{0 - 1000}{-4.9}} \approx 14.286$$

From the example, you may notice that square root functions play an important part in solving quadratic functions. Note that you cannot always eliminate the negative root as you did in the example. You'll have to let the context of a problem dictate when to use the positive root, the negative root, or both.

EXERCISES

Practice Your Skills

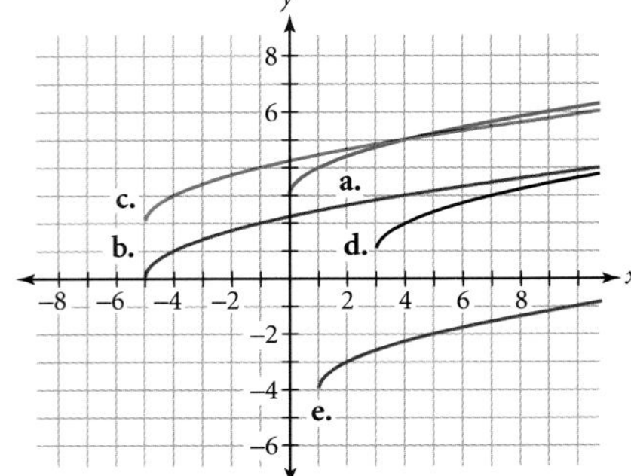

1. Each graph at right is a transformation of the graph of the parent function $y = \sqrt{x}$. Write an equation for each graph.

2. Describe what happens to the graph of $y = \sqrt{x}$ in the following situations.

a. x is replaced with $(x - 3)$. translated right 3 units

b. x is replaced with $(x + 3)$. translated left 3 units

c. y is replaced with $(y - 2)$. translated up 2 units

d. y is replaced with $(y + 2)$. translated down 2 units

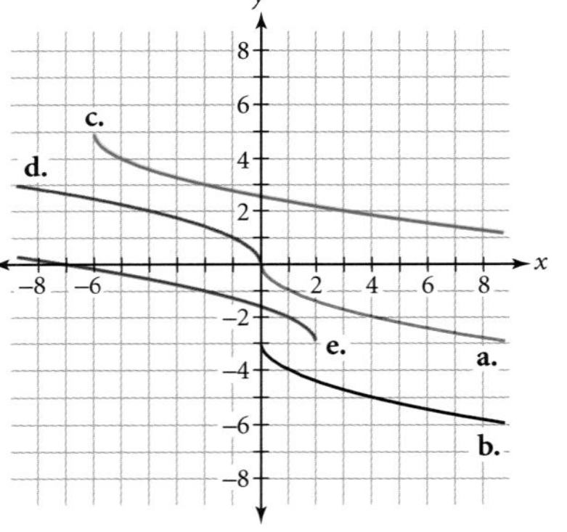

3. Each curve at right is a transformation of the graph of the parent function $y = \sqrt{x}$. Write an equation for each curve.

4. Given the graph of $y = f(x)$ below, draw a graph of each of these related functions.

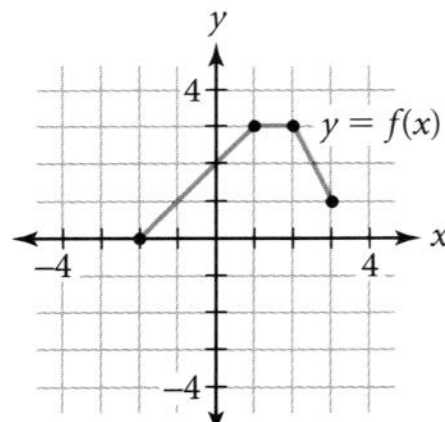

a. $y = f(-x)$ **b.** $y = -f(x)$ **c.** $y = -f(-x)$

Exercise 4 You might use the Exercise 4 transparency as you discuss this exercise.

4a.

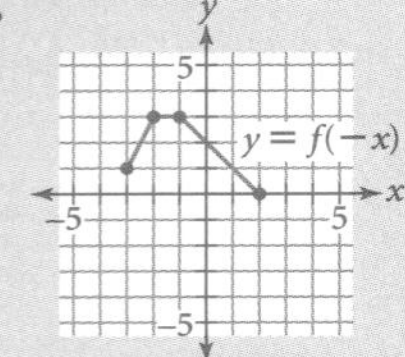

4b.

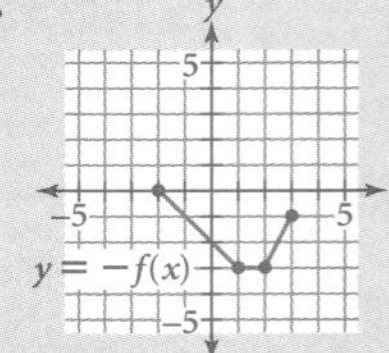

4c.

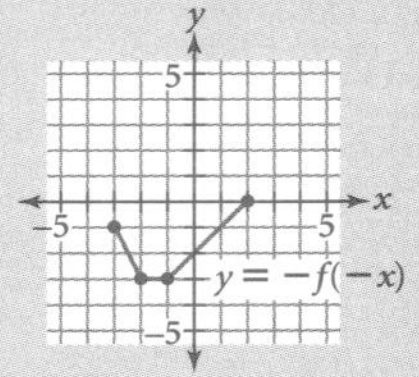

Reason and Apply

5. Consider the parent function $f(x) = \sqrt{x}$.
   a. Name three pairs of integer coordinates that are on the graph of $y = f(x + 4) - 2$. possible answers: $(-4, -2)$, $(-3, -1)$, and $(0, 0)$
   b. Write $y = f(x + 4) - 2$ using a **radical,** or square root symbol, and graph it.
   c. Write $y = -f(x - 2) + 3$ using a radical, and graph it.

6. Consider the parabola at right:
   a. Graph the parabola on your calculator. What two functions did you use?
   b. Combine both functions from 6a using $\pm$ notation to create a single relation. Square both sides of the relation. What is the resulting equation? $y = \pm\sqrt{x}$; $y^2 = x$

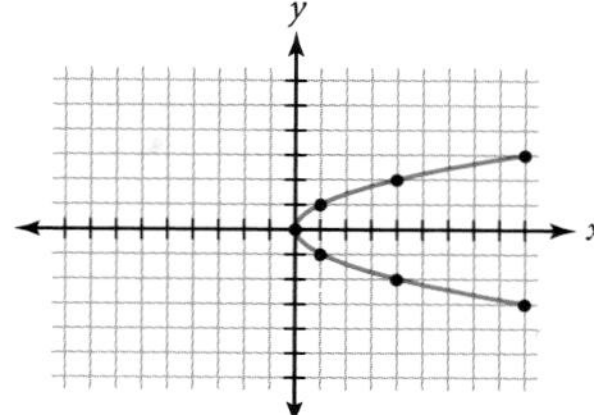

7. Refer to the two parabolas shown.
   a. Explain why neither graph represents a function.
   b. Write a single equation for each parabola using $\pm$ notation.
   c. Square both sides of each equation in 7b. What is the resulting equation of each parabola?

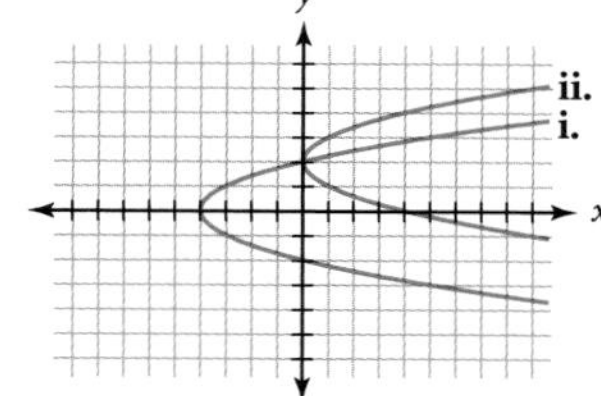

8. As Jake and Arthur travel together from Detroit to Chicago, each makes a graph relating time and distance. Jake, who lives in Detroit and keeps his watch on Detroit time, graphs his distance from Detroit. Arthur, who lives in Chicago and keeps his watch on Chicago time (1 hour earlier than Detroit), graphs his distance from Chicago. They both use the time shown on their watches for their x-axes. The distance between Detroit and Chicago is 250 miles.
   a. Sketch what you think each graph might look like.
   b. If Jake's graph is described by the function $y = f(x)$, what function describes Arthur's graph? $y = -f(x + 1) + 250$
   c. If Arthur's graph is described by the function $y = g(x)$, what function describes Jake's graph? $y = -g(x - 1) + 250$

9. Write the equation of each parabola. Each parabola is a transformation of the graph of the parent function $y = x^2$.

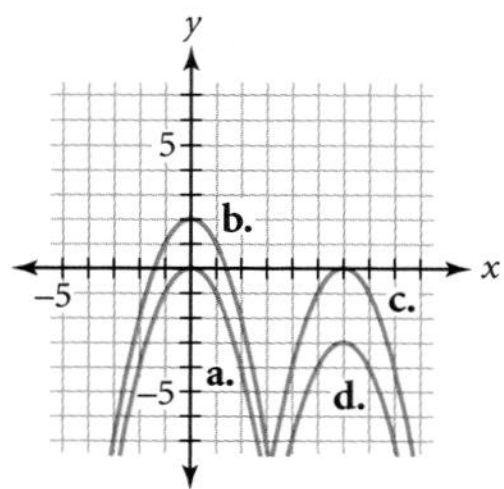

Exercise 5 [Alert] In 5b and 5c, students may enclose the entire right side of the equation under the radical. Suggest that they graph $Y_1 = \sqrt{x}$, $Y_2 = Y_1(x + 4) - 2$, and Y_3 (the equation they wrote) to see whether the graphs of Y_2 and Y_3 agree.

5b. $y = \sqrt{x + 4} - 2$

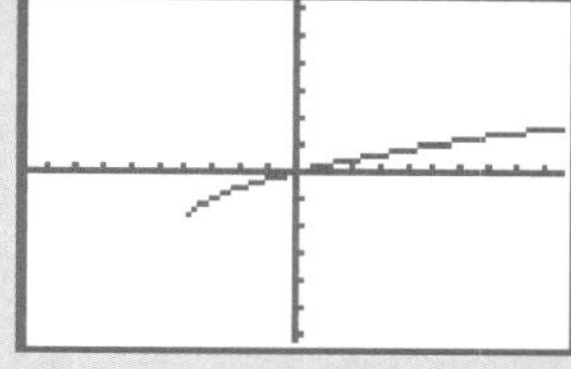

$[-9.4, 9.4, 1, -6.2, 6.2, 1]$

5c. $y = -\sqrt{x - 2} + 3$

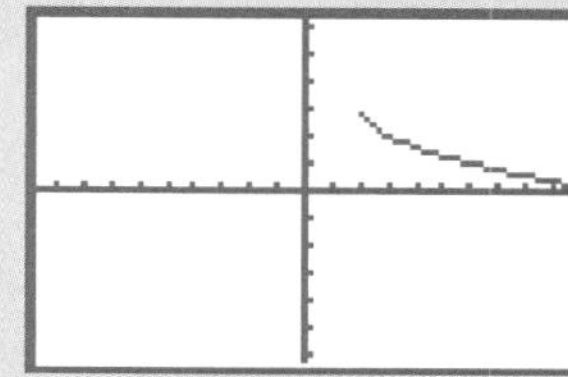

$[-9.4, 9.4, 1, -6.2, 6.2, 1]$

6a. $y = \sqrt{x}$ and $y = -\sqrt{x}$

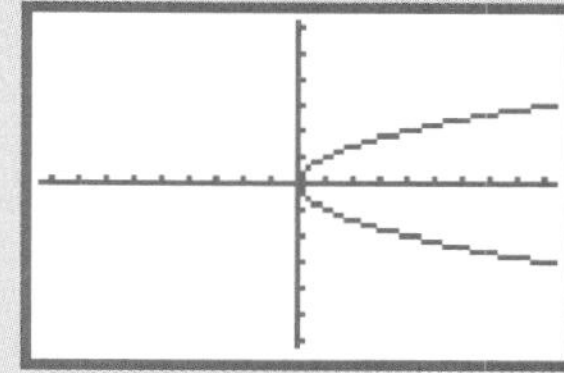

$[-9.4, 9.4, 1, -6.2, 6.2, 1]$

7a. Neither parabola passes the vertical line test.

7b. i. $y = \pm\sqrt{x + 4}$

7b. ii. $y = \pm\sqrt{x} + 2$

7c. i. $y^2 = x + 4$

7c. ii. $(y - 2)^2 = x$

8a. possible answer:

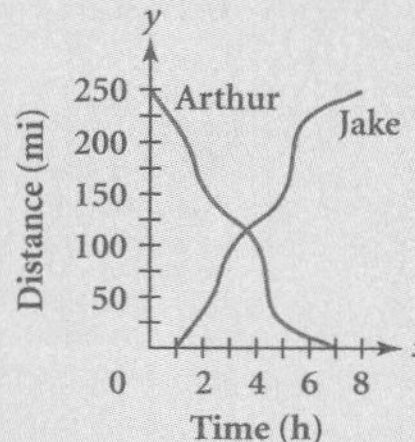

9a. $y = -x^2$

9b. $y = -x^2 + 2$

9c. $y = -(x - 6)^2$

9d. $y = -(x - 6)^2 - 3$

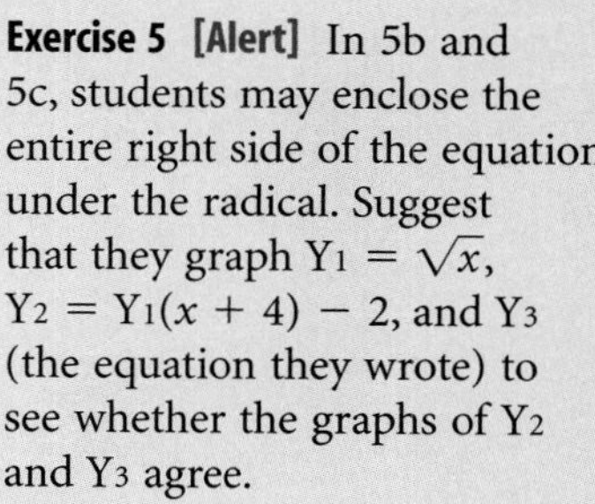

10. Write the equation of a parabola that is congruent to the graph of $y = -(x+3)^2 + 4$, but translated right 5 units and down 2 units. $y + 2 = -((x-5)+3)^2 + 4$ or $y = -(x-2)^2 + 2$

11. APPLICATION Police measure the lengths of skid marks to determine the initial speed of a vehicle before the brakes were applied. Many variables, such as the type of road surface and weather conditions, play an important role in determining the speed. The formula used to determine the initial speed is $S = 5.5\sqrt{D \cdot f}$ where S is the speed in miles per hour, D is the average length of the skid marks in feet, and f is a constant called the "drag factor." At a particular accident scene, assume it is known that the road surface has a drag factor of 0.7.

a. Write an equation that will determine the initial speed on this road as a function of the lengths of skid marks. $S = 5.5\sqrt{0.7D}$

b. Sketch a graph of this function.

c. If the average length of the skid marks is 60 feet, estimate the initial speed of the car when the brakes were applied. approximately 36 mi/h

d. Solve your equation from 11a for D. What can you determine using this equation?

e. Graph your equation from 11d. What shape is it?

f. If you traveled on this road at a speed of 65 miles per hour and suddenly slammed on your brakes, how long would your skid marks be? approximately 199.5 ft

Review

4.1 **12.** Identify each relation that is also a function. For each relation that is not a function, explain why not.

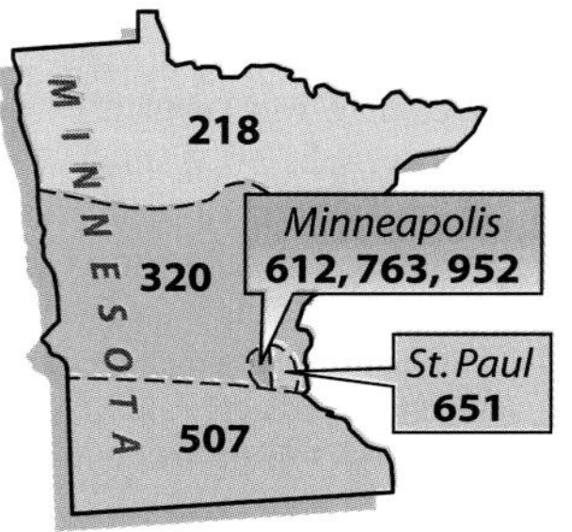

a. independent variable: city
dependent variable: area code

b. independent variable: any pair of whole numbers
dependent variable: their greatest common factor function

c. independent variable: any pair of fractions
dependent variable: their common denominator

d. independent variable: the day of the year
dependent variable: the time of sunrise

13. Solve for x. Solving square root equations often results in **extraneous solutions,** or answers that don't work in the original equation, so be sure to check your work.

a. $3 + \sqrt{x-4} = 20$ $x = 293$

b. $\sqrt{x+7} = -3$ no solution

c. $4 - (x-2)^2 = -21$ $x = 7$ or $x = -3$

d. $5 - \sqrt{-(x+4)} = 2$ $x = -13$

4.4 **14.** Find the equation of the parabola with vertex $(-6, 4)$, a vertical line of symmetry, and containing the point $(-5, 5)$. $y = (x+6)^2 + 4$

Exercise 11a [Alert] Students may not understand that they're being asked simply to substitute 0.7 for f.

11b.

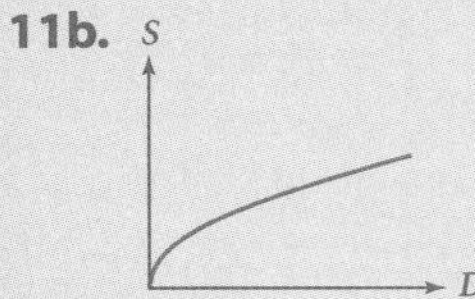

11d. $D = \frac{1}{0.7}\left(\frac{S}{5.5}\right)^2$; the minimum braking distance, when the speed is known.

11e.

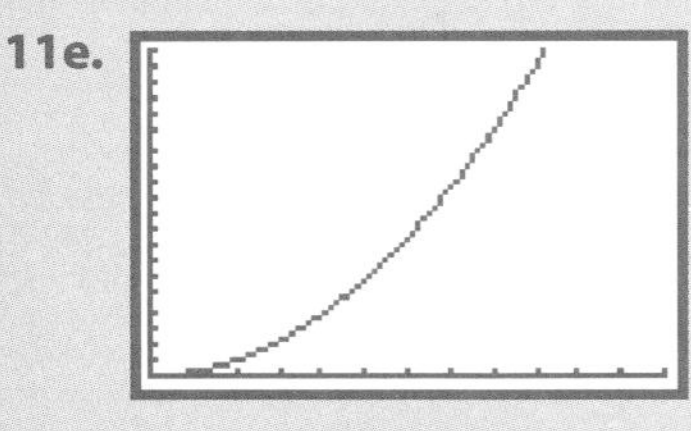

[0, 60, 5, 0, 100, 5]

It is a parabola, but the negative half is not used because the distance cannot be negative.

Exercise 12 Encourage critical thinking to establish in students the tendency to doubt that expressions are functions. **[Alert]** In 12a, students may not know that a city may have more than one area code. See the investigation in Lesson 4.2, Step 1, on page 180, for assumptions that make 12d not a function.

12a. Not a function; some large cities have more than one area code.

12c. Not a function; there are many common denominators for any pair of fractions.

12d. Possible answer: function; the sun rises at only one time on each day of a given year.

Exercise 13 As needed, remind students to isolate the radical first. In 13b, none of the answers work; ask if that means that the equation has no solutions. [The radical refers to the nonnegative square root, so it won't equal -3 for any value of x.]

Exercise 14 The vertex identifies the value of h and k; the other point tells whether or not the parabola is reflected vertically (it is not). As needed, suggest that students graph the given points and use the line of symmetry to find an additional point.

4.3 **15.** The graph of the line ℓ_1 is shown at right.

a. Write the equation of the line ℓ_1. $y = \frac{1}{2}x + 5$

b. The line ℓ_2 is the image of the line ℓ_1 translated right 8 units. Sketch the line ℓ_2 and write its equation in a way that shows the horizontal translation.

c. The line ℓ_2 also can be thought of as the image of the line ℓ_1 after a vertical translation. Write the equation of the line ℓ_2 in a way that shows the vertical translation.

d. Show that the equations in 15b and 15c are equivalent. Both equations are equivalent to $y = \frac{1}{2}x + 1$.

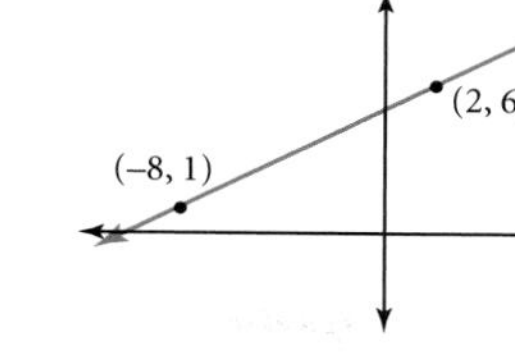

2.2 **16.** Consider this data set:

{37, 40, 36, 37, 37, 49, 39, 47, 40, 38, 35, 46, 43, 40, 47, 49, 70, 65, 50, 73}

a. Give the five-number summary. 35, 37.5, 41.5, 49, 73

b. Display the data in a box plot.

c. Find the interquartile range. 11.5

d. Identify any outliers, based on the interquartile range. 70 and 73

IMPROVING YOUR GEOMETRY SKILLS

Lines in Motion Revisited

Imagine that the graph of any line, $y = a + bx$, is translated 2 units in a direction perpendicular to it. What horizontal and vertical translations would be equivalent to this translation? What are the values of h and k? What is the linear equation of the image? You may want to use your calculator or geometry software to experiment with some specific linear equations before you try to generalize for h and k.

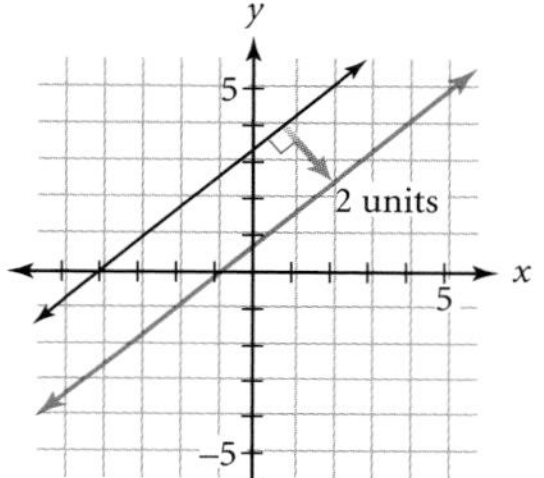

15b. $y = \frac{1}{2}(x - 8) + 5$

15c. $y = \left(\frac{1}{2}x + 5\right) - 4$ or

$y + 4 = \frac{1}{2}x + 5$

16b.

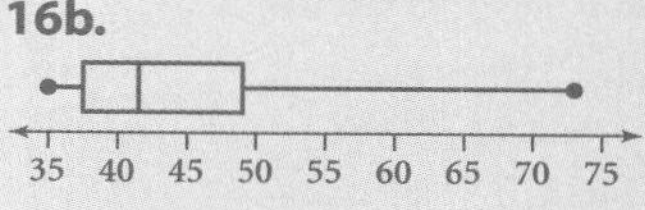

Lines in Motion Revisited

Because any translation of a line is equivalent to a horizontal translation, you might try to find the horizontal shift in terms of the slope, b. If you draw a perpendicular of length 2 to the two lines and then draw from one endpoint of the perpendicular to the other parallel line a horizontal segment (of length h) and a vertical segment (of length k), then $\frac{k}{h}$ is the slope, b, so $k = bh$.

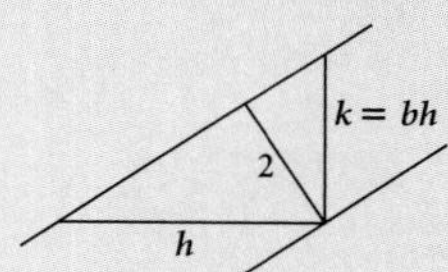

You have constructed a right triangle whose legs have lengths h and $k = bh$ and whose other altitude has length 2. The area of that triangle can be written two ways: $\frac{1}{2}h(bh)$ or, using the Pythagorean Theorem, $\frac{1}{2} \cdot 2\sqrt{b^2h^2 + h^2} = \pm h\sqrt{b^2 + 1}$. Setting these area expressions equal, we get $h = \pm\frac{2}{b}\sqrt{b^2 + 1}$. The two values of h correspond to the two directions in which the line could have been translated. The equations of the new lines are

$$y = a + b\left(x \mp \tfrac{2}{b}\sqrt{b^2 + 1}\right) = \left(a \mp 2\sqrt{b^2 + 1}\right) + bx$$

IMPROVING GEOMETRY SKILLS

The slope of the line is b.

$h = \pm\frac{2}{b}\sqrt{b^2 + 1}$; $k = \pm 2\sqrt{b^2 + 1}$

The equations are $y = a - 2\sqrt{b^2 + 1} + bx$ and $y = a + 2\sqrt{b^2 + 1} + bx$.

There are several ways to derive the result algebraically. See the side column.

EXTENSIONS

A. Use Take Another Look activity 2 on page 235.

B. To extend the investigation, play a game of Make My Graph with graphs you create. (See the investigation in Lesson 4.4.) Include not only reflections but also translations of the graphs of square root functions. Add parabolas and linear equations, including reflections.

EXPLORATION

PLANNING

LESSON OUTLINE

One day:

30 min Activity

15 min Sharing

MATERIALS

- The Geometer's Sketchpad

TEACHING

This will be a review for students who studied rotations as compositions of reflections in *Discovering Geometry.* The dynamic algebra exploration at www.keymath.com/DAA can help students visualize the transformations.

Guiding the Activity

Step 3 To check the results of transformations, students can select corresponding vertices of the original and the rotated images and choose **Coordinates** from the Measure menu. Challenge students to find one set of transformations that involves only rotations.

Helping with the Questions

Question 1 The coordinates of the 90° rotations are reversed (x and y are interchanged), and one of them is negated (depending on the direction of the rotation); the coordinates of the 180° rotation are in the same order but both are negated.

Question 2 [Ask] "What reflection negates the x-coordinate?" [reflection across the y-axis] "What reflection exchanges coordinates?" [reflection across the line $y = x$]

See page 883 for answer to Question 2.

E X P L O R A T I O N

Rotation as a Composition of Transformations

You have learned rules that reflect and translate figures and functions on the coordinate plane. Is it possible to rotate figures on a coordinate plane using a rule? You will explore that question in this activity.

Activity

Revolution

Step 1 Draw a figure using geometry software. Your figure should be nonsymmetric so that you can see the effects of various transformations.

Step 2 Rotate your figure three times: once by 90° counterclockwise, once by 90° clockwise, and once by 180° about the origin. Change your original figure to a different color.

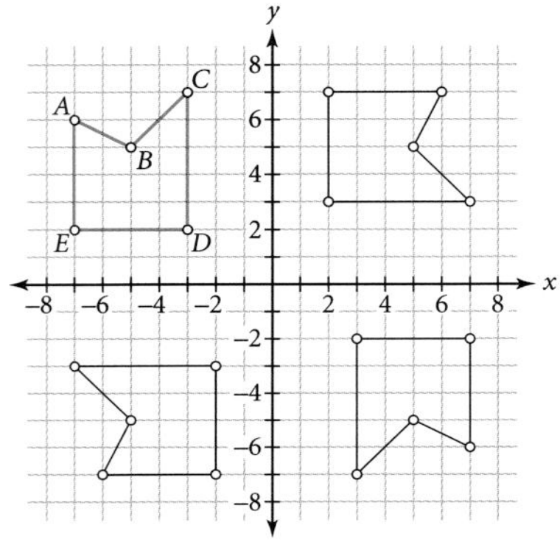

Step 3 Transform your original figure onto each of the three images using only reflections and translations. (You may use other lines of reflection besides the axes.) Keep track of the transformations you use. Find at least two different sets of transformations that map the figure onto each of the three images.

Questions

1. Describe the effects of each rotation on the coordinates of the figure. Give a rule that describes the transformation of the x-coordinates and the y-coordinates for each of the three rotations. Do the rules change if your original figure is in a different quadrant?
2. Choose one of the combinations of transformations you found in Step 3. For each transformation you performed, explain the effect on the x- and y-coordinates. Show how the combination of these transformations confirms the rule you found by answering Question 1.

LESSON OBJECTIVES

- Explore compositions of transformations
- Understand rotation as a composition of two reflections

NCTM STANDARDS

CONTENT		PROCESS	
	Number		Problem Solving
✓	Algebra	✓	Reasoning
✓	Geometry	✓	Communication
	Measurement		Connections
	Data/Probability	✓	Representation

LESSON

4.6

Stretches and Shrinks and the Absolute-Value Family

A mind that is stretched by a new experience can never go back to its old dimensions.

OLIVER WENDELL HOLMES

Hao and Dayita ride the subway to school each day. They live on the same east-west subway route. Hao lives 7.4 miles west of the school, and Dayita lives 5.2 miles east of the school. This information is shown on the number line below.

West — H (Hao) −7.4 mi — S (School) 0 — D (Dayita) 5.2 mi — East

The distance between two points is always positive. However, if you calculate Hao's distance from school, or HS, by subtracting his starting position from his ending position, you get a negative value:

$$-7.4 - 0 = -7.4$$

In order to make the distance positive, you use the absolute-value function, which makes any input positive or zero. For example, the absolute value of -3 is 3, or $|-3| = 3$. For Hao's distance from school, you use the absolute-value function to calculate

$$HS = |-7.4 - 0| = |-7.4| = 7.4$$

What is the distance from D to H? What is the distance from H to D? 12.6; 12.6

In this lesson you will explore transformations of the graph of the parent function $y = |x|$. [► See **Calculator Note 4F** to learn how to graph the absolute-value function. ◄] You will write and use equations of the form $y = a\left|\frac{x-h}{b}\right| + k$. What you have learned about translating and reflecting other graphs will apply to these functions as well. You will also learn about transformations that **stretch** and **shrink** a graph.

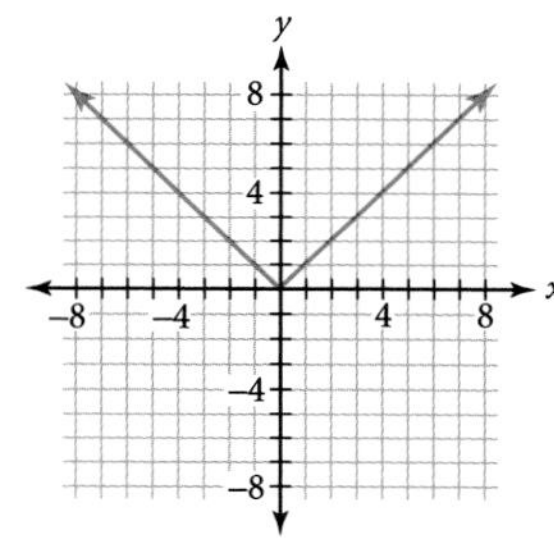

Many computer and television screens have controls that allow you to change the scale of the horizontal or vertical dimension. Doing so stretches or shrinks the images on the screen.

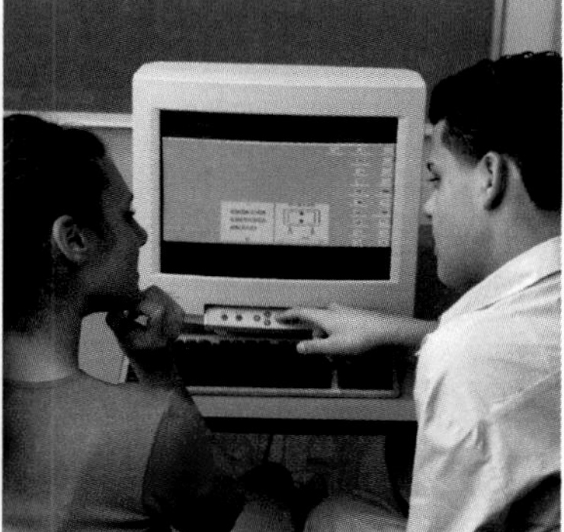

NCTM STANDARDS

CONTENT	PROCESS
✓ Number	✓ Problem Solving
✓ Algebra	✓ Reasoning
✓ Geometry	✓ Communication
✓ Measurement	✓ Connections
✓ Data/Probability	✓ Representation

LESSON OBJECTIVES

- Define absolute value and its notation, and use it to model distance
- Define the parent absolute-value function, $y = |x|$, and the absolute-value family, $y = a|x - h| + k$
- Calculate horizontal and vertical stretch or shrink factors from points on the image of a graph
- Apply horizontal and vertical stretches and shrinks to functions in general

LESSON

4.6

PLANNING

LESSON OUTLINE

First day:

30 min Examples

15 min Exercises

Second day:

25 min Investigation

5 min Sharing

15 min Exercises

MATERIALS

- string
- small weights
- stopwatches
- metersticks or tape measures
- graph paper, *optional*
- Find My Equation (W) for One Step
- Sketchpad demonstration Absolute Value, *optional*
- Calculator Note 4F

TEACHING

This is the third lesson in the sequence discussing transformations. Here the book focuses on stretches and shrinks, with examples primarily from absolute-value and square root functions. Much of the lesson may be review for students who have used *Discovering Algebra.* Begin with the one-step investigation described on page 210, or go over the introduction and examples before starting the investigation.

INTRODUCTION

The absolute-value function models distance. Distances between homes:

$DH = |5.2 - (-7.4)| = |12.6| = 12.6$ and

$HD = |-7.4 - 5.2| = |-12.6| = 12.6$

[Context] The French mathematician Augustin-Louis Cauchy ['kō-shē] (1789–1857) first described the absolute-value function in the 1820s. The German mathematician Karl Weierstrass (1815–1897) introduced the absolute-value symbol used today in 1841.

One Step
Hand out the Find My Equation worksheet (or display the graphs on an overhead calculator) and ask students to find at least two equations for each mystery graph. As needed, remind them of the meaning of the absolute-value function. As groups finish their work, ask them to create (on graph paper) mystery graphs involving reflections and stretches of the graph of the square root function and to exchange them with each other as challenges. During Sharing, formalize the rules for stretches and shrinks and review the rules for translations and reflections. The equations for the graphs on the worksheet:
a. $y = \frac{1}{2}|x|$
b. $y = 2|x|$
c. $y = \frac{1}{4}(x - 1)^2$
d. $y = 3(x - 1)^2$
e. $y = 2f(x - 2)$
f. $y = \frac{1}{2}f(x - 1)$

▶ EXAMPLE A

[Language] Some books refer to shrinks as *compressions.* Students may recall from geometry that a stretch (or) shrink in both directions by the same factor is called a *dilation.* Two figures can be defined as *similar* if one is a dilation of the other.

The vertical stretch in part a can also be thought of as a horizontal shrink, because $y = 2|x|$ is the same as $y = |2x|$. Similarly, the horizontal stretch in part b is a vertical shrink, and the combination in part c is equivalent to either a vertical shrink $\left(y = \frac{2}{3}|x|\right)$ or a horizontal stretch $\left(y = \left|\frac{2}{3}x\right|\right)$.

EXAMPLE A

Graph the function $y = |x|$ with each of these functions. How does the graph of each function compare to the original graph?

a. $y = 2|x|$

b. $y = \left|\frac{x}{3}\right|$

c. $y = 2\left|\frac{x}{3}\right|$

▶ Solution

In the graph of each function, the vertex remains at the origin. Notice, however, how the points (1, 1) and (−2, 2) on the parent function are mapped to a new location.

a. Every point on the graph of $y = 2|x|$ has a y-coordinate that is 2 times the y-coordinate of the corresponding point on the parent function. You say the graph of $y = 2|x|$ is a vertical stretch of the graph of $y = |x|$ by a factor of 2.

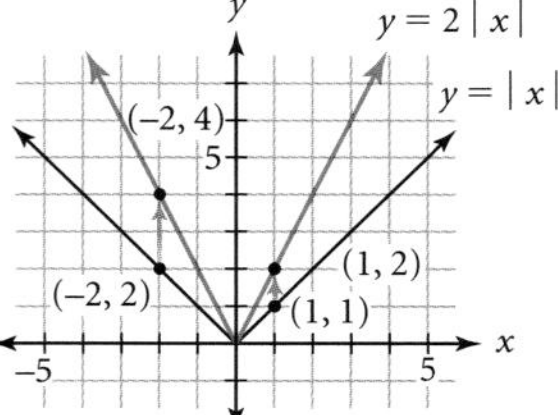

b. Replacing x with $\frac{x}{3}$ multiplies the x-coordinates by a factor of 3. The graph of $y = \left|\frac{x}{3}\right|$ is a horizontal stretch of the graph of $y = |x|$ by a factor of 3.

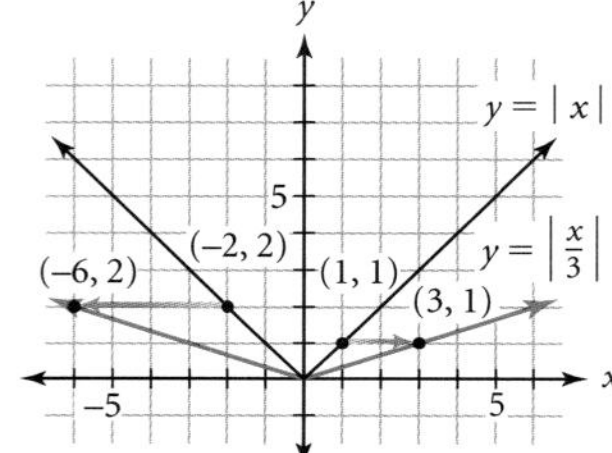

c. The combination of multiplying the parent function by 2 and dividing x by 3 results in a vertical stretch by a factor of 2 *and* a horizontal stretch by a factor of 3.

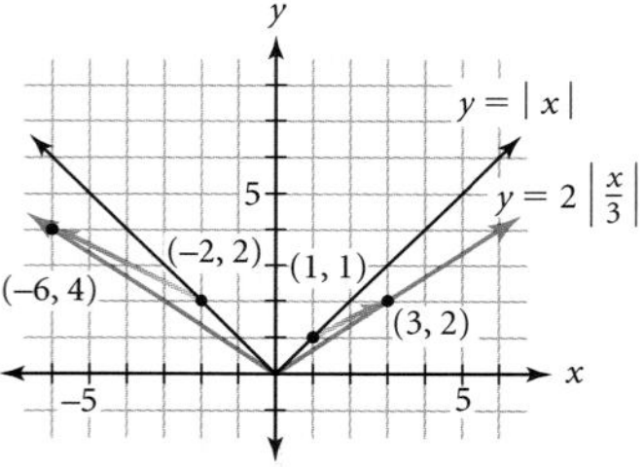

Translations and reflections are **rigid transformations**—they produce an image that is congruent to the original figure. Stretches and shrinks are **nonrigid transformations**—the image is not congruent to the original figure (unless you use a factor of 1 or -1). If you stretch or shrink a figure by the same **scale factor** both vertically and horizontally, then the image and the original figure will be similar, at least. If you stretch or shrink by different vertical and horizontal scale factors, then the image and the original figure will not be similar.

Robert Lazzarini, *payphone, 2002,* Mixed media, 108 x 84 x 48 in. (274.3 x 213.4 x 121.9 cm). As installed in 2002 Biennial Exhibition, Whitney Museum of Art, New York (March 7–May 26, 2002)

Using what you know about translations, reflections, and stretches, you can fit functions to data by locating only a few key points. For quadratic, square root, and absolute-value functions, first locate the vertex of the graph. Then use any other point to find the factors by which to stretch or shrink the image.

EXAMPLE B

These data are from one bounce of a ball. Find an equation that fits the data over this domain.

Time (s) x	Height (m) y
0.54	0.05
0.58	0.18
0.62	0.29
0.66	0.39
0.70	0.46
0.74	0.52
0.78	0.57
0.82	0.59
0.86	0.60

Time (s) x	Height (m) y
0.90	0.59
0.94	0.57
0.98	0.52
1.02	0.46
1.06	0.39
1.10	0.29
1.14	0.18
1.18	0.05

► Solution

Graph the data on your calculator. The graph appears to be a parabola. However, the parent function $y = x^2$ has been reflected, translated, and possibly stretched or shrunken. Start by determining the translation. The vertex has been translated from (0, 0) to (0.86, 0.60). This is enough information for you to write the equation in the form $y = (x - h)^2 + k$, or $y = (x - 0.86)^2 + 0.60$. If you think of replacing x with $(x - 0.86)$ and replacing y with $(y - 0.60)$, you could also write the equivalent equation, $y - 0.6 = (x - 0.86)^2$.

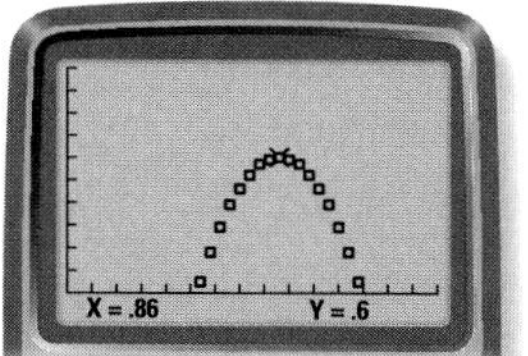

► EXAMPLE B

This example illustrates a composition of translations, stretches, and reflections of the quadratic family of equations in a real-world context. Students might appreciate seeing a more gradual solution. Graph the translation, $Y_1 = (x - 0.86)^2 + 0.6$. Graph the reflection across the vertical line $y = 0.6$, $Y_2 = -(x - 0.86)^2 + 0.6$. Pick a data point, such as (1.14, 0.18). Because this point is $1.14 - 0.86$ or 0.28 unit to the right of the vertex, if the graph were simply a translation of the graph of $y = -x^2$ then the y-coordinate would be 0.28^2 or 0.078 unit lower than the vertex. But 0.18 is 0.42 unit lower than the vertex, so the graph is stretched by a factor of $\frac{0.42}{0.28^2}$, or approximately 5.36. Indeed, a graph of $Y_3 = -5.36(x - 0.86)^2 + 0.6$ passes very close to all data points, and the equation is equivalent to the solution given in the book.

Discovering Algebra Calculator Note 9D presents a calculator program, PARAB, that gives the graph of a parabola and challenges students to write its equation. The program allows students to compare their equation to the original by looking at either a graph or a table of values. Students can use the program to practice problems similar to Example B. You can access this calculator note and the program at www.keymath.com/DA.

Guiding the Investigation

Give students a string at least 2 m long. Encourage students to use a variety of string lengths, including several very short lengths and at least one very long length. If they don't cut their string, they can collect more data later.

Students may wonder whether the measure of the arc of the swing or the amount of weight will affect the period. (Encourage students to test these parameters if there is time. As long as the horizontal displacement of the weight is small compared to the length of the pendulum, the angle measure does not affect the period.)

Theoretically, the period of a pendulum swinging without resistance is given by $2\pi\sqrt{\frac{L}{g}}$, where L is the length and g is the gravitational constant. If students measure in centimeters, g is about 980 cm/s^2, so they'll get about $0.2\sqrt{L}$. If they measure in inches, g is about 384 in./s^2, so they'll get about $0.32\sqrt{L}$.

SHARING IDEAS

To the extent possible, choose students for sharing who obtained different results, especially if they measured in different units. Then have the class look for explanations for the differences.

In discussing Example B, **[Ask]** "How can the book assume that the data point (1.14, 0.18) is the image of (1, 1)? What if some other point on the new curve is the image of (1, 1)? For example, what if we assume that data point (0.54, 0.05) is the image of (1, 1)?" [This data point is $0.54 - 0.86$ or -0.32 from the vertex horizontally and $0.05 - 0.60$ or -0.55 from the vertex vertically, so the new equation is $\frac{y-0.6}{-0.55} = \left(\frac{x-0.86}{-0.32}\right)^2$. This equation is equivalent to $y = -5.37(x - 0.86)^2 + 0.6$, very close to the equation in the example, which can be rewritten as $y = -5.36(x - 0.86)^2 + 0.6$.]

The graph of $y = (x - 0.86)^2 + 0.60$ does not fit the data. The function still needs to be reflected and, as you can see from the graph, shrunken. Both of these transformations can be accomplished together.

Select one other data point to determine the scale factors, a and b. You can use any point, but you will get a better fit if you choose one that is not too close to the vertex. For example, you can choose the data point (1.14, 0.18).

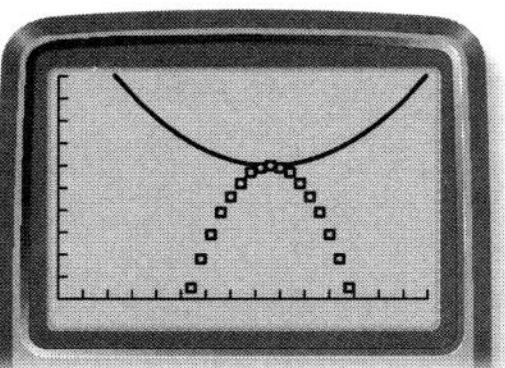

Assume this data point is the image of the point (1, 1) in the parent parabola $y = x^2$. In the graph of $y = x^2$, (1, 1) is 1 unit away from the vertex (0, 0) both horizontally and vertically. The data point we chose in this graph is $1.14 - 0.86$, or 0.28, unit away from the x-coordinate of the vertex, and $0.18 - 0.60$, or -0.42, unit away from the y-coordinate of the vertex. So, the horizontal scale factor is 0.28, and the vertical scale factor is -0.42. The negative vertical scale factor also produces a reflection across the x-axis.

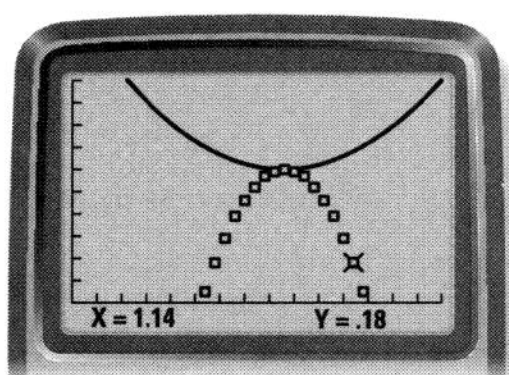

Combine these scale factors with the translations to get the final equation

$$\frac{y-0.6}{-0.42} = \left(\frac{x-0.86}{0.28}\right)^2 \quad \text{or} \quad y = -0.42\left(\frac{x-0.86}{0.28}\right)^2 + 0.6$$

This model, shown at right, fits the data nicely.

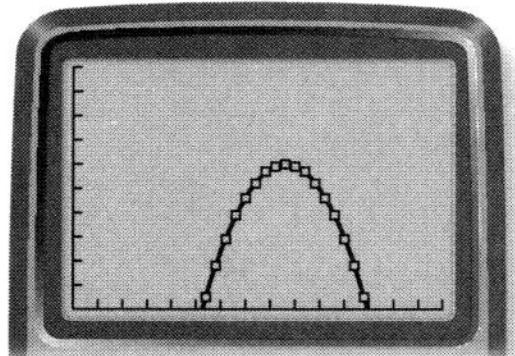

The same procedure works with the other functions you have studied so far. As you continue to add new functions to your mathematical knowledge, you will find that what you have learned about function transformations continues to apply.

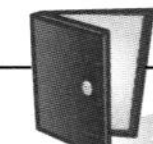

Investigation
The Pendulum

You will need

- string
- a small weight
- a stopwatch or a watch with a second hand

Italian mathematician and astronomer Galileo Galilei (1564–1642) made many contributions to our understanding of gravity, the physics of falling objects, and the orbits of the planets. One of his famous experiments involved the periodic motion of a pendulum. In this investigation you will carry out the same experiment and find a function to model the data.

This fresco, painted in 1841, shows Galileo at age 17, contemplating the motion of a swinging lamp in the Cathedral of Pisa. A swinging lamp is an example of a pendulum.

Students might see that the equations are close because $\frac{-0.42}{0.28^2} \approx \frac{-0.55}{(-0.32)^2}$. In general for a parabola, $\frac{b}{c^2}$ is constant (where b and c are the vertical and horizontal stretch factors, respectively).

[Ask] "Is this similar to having a constant slope? What about stretches of lines?" A vertical stretch of the line $y = x$ by a factor of b gives the line $\frac{y}{b} = x$, or $y = bx$. That is, the vertical stretch factor is the slope. The equation $y = bx$ is equivalent to $y = \frac{x}{\frac{1}{b}}$, so a vertical stretch by a factor of b is equivalent to a horizontal stretch by a factor of $\frac{1}{b}$. Wonder aloud whether lines not through the origin also can be thought of as transformations of the parent line, $y = x$. A vertical translation of the same line by an amount a gives the familiar equation $y = a + bx$, so every nonvertical line is a stretch followed by a translation of the parent line, $y = x$.

Step 1 Follow the Procedure Note to find the period of your pendulum. Repeat the experiment for several different string lengths and complete a table of values. Use a variety of short, medium, and long string lengths.

Step 2 Graph the data using *length* as the independent variable. What is the shape of the graph? What do you suppose is the parent function?

Step 3 The vertex is at the origin, (0, 0). Why do you suppose it is there?

Step 4 Divide up your data points and have each person in your group find the horizontal or vertical stretch or shrink from the parent function. Apply these transformations to find an equation to fit the data.

Step 5 Compare the collection of equations from your group. Which points are the best to use to fit the curve? Why do these points work better than others?

10°

Procedure Note

1. Tie a weight at one end of a length of string to make a pendulum. Firmly hold the other end of the string, or tie it to something, so that the weight hangs freely.
2. Measure the length of the pendulum, from the center of the weight to the point where the string is held.
3. Pull the weight to one side and release it so that it swings back and forth in a short arc, about 10° to 20°. Time ten complete swings (forward and back is one swing).
4. The **period** of your pendulum is the time for one complete swing (forward and back). Find the period by dividing by 10.

In the exercises you will use techniques you discovered in this lesson. Remember that replacing y with $\frac{y}{a}$ stretches a graph by a factor of a vertically. Replacing x with $\frac{x}{b}$ stretches a graph by a factor of b horizontally. When graphing a function, you should do stretches and shrinks before translations to avoid moving the vertex.

Stretch or Shrink of a Function

A **stretch** or a **shrink** is a transformation that expands or compresses a graph either horizontally or vertically.

Given the graph of $y = f(x)$, the graph of

$$\frac{y}{a} = f(x) \quad \text{or} \quad y = af(x)$$

is a vertical stretch or shrink by a factor of a. When $a > 1$, it is a stretch; when $0 < a < 1$, it is a shrink. When $a < 0$, a reflection across the x-axis also occurs.

Given the graph of $y = f(x)$, the graph of

$$y = f\left(\frac{x}{b}\right) \quad \text{or} \quad y = f\left(\frac{1}{b} \cdot x\right)$$

is a horizontal stretch or shrink by a factor of b. When $b > 1$, it is a stretch; when $0 < b < 1$, it is a shrink. When $b < 0$, a reflection across the y-axis also occurs.

Step 1 sample data:

Length (cm) x	Period (s) y
100	2.0
85	1.9
75	1.8
30	1.4
15	0.9
5	0.6
43	1.4
60	1.6
89	2.0
140	2.4
180	2.6
195	2.9

Step 2

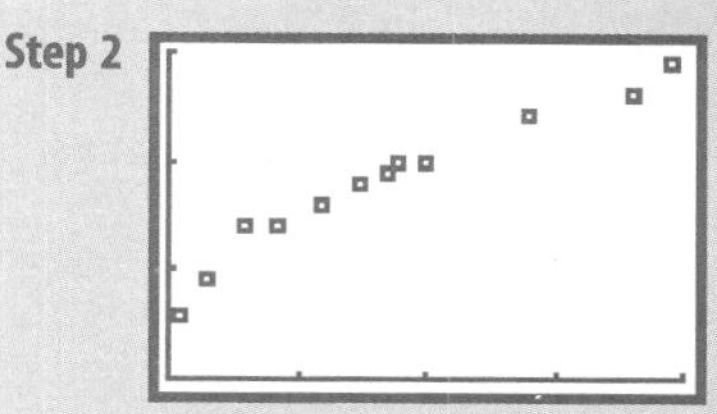

[0, 200, 50, 0, 3, 1]

The parent function is the square root function, $y = \sqrt{x}$.

Step 3 The vertex is at the origin because a pendulum of length 0 cm would have no period.

Step 4 The equation should be in the form $\frac{y}{b} = \sqrt{\frac{x}{a}}$ or $y = b\sqrt{\frac{x}{a}}$. For the sample data, the function $y = 0.2\sqrt{x}$ is a good fit.

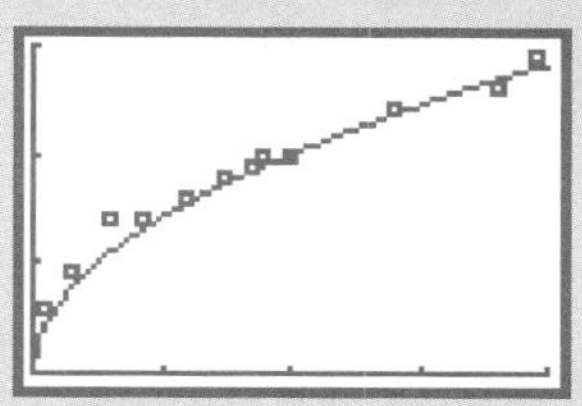

[0, 200, 50, 0, 3, 1]

Step 5 Points farther from the vertex work best. These points represent the longer lengths. They are best for fitting a parabola because they are likely to have less measurement error. A parabola that fits the first few points well would be quite far from the points further from the vertex.

Assessing Progress

You can assess students' familiarity with the absolute-value and square root functions and their ability to see patterns.

Closing the Lesson

Summarize the main ideas of this lesson: **Stretches** and **shrinks** are **nonrigid transformations** that expand or compress graphs horizontally or vertically. In an equation or a function expression, dividing x by a positive number a produces an equation of a horizontal stretch by a factor of a (a shrink if $a < 1$), and dividing y by a positive number b results in an equation of a vertical stretch by a factor of b (a shrink if $b < 1$). If a or b is negative, the graph is reflected across an axis as well as stretched or shrunk.

BUILDING UNDERSTANDING

If you take two days for this lesson, consider assigning the essential exercises and a review exercise the first day and the other exercises the second day.

ASSIGNING HOMEWORK

Essential	1–3, 10
Performance assessment	4–9, 11, 12
Portfolio	9
Journal	4, 8
Group	7, 9
Review	13, 14

MATERIALS

- Fathom demonstration Science Fair, *optional*

EXERCISES

Practice Your Skills

1. Each graph is a transformation of the graph of one of the parent functions you've studied. Write an equation for each graph.

1a. $y = |x| + 2$

1b. $y = |x| - 5$

1d. $y = |x - 3|$

1e. $y = |x| - 1$

1f. $y = |x - 4| + 1$

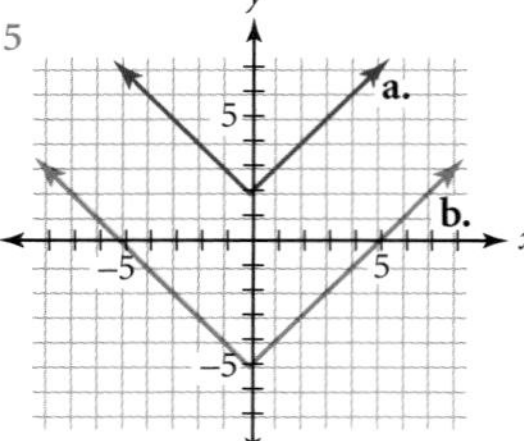

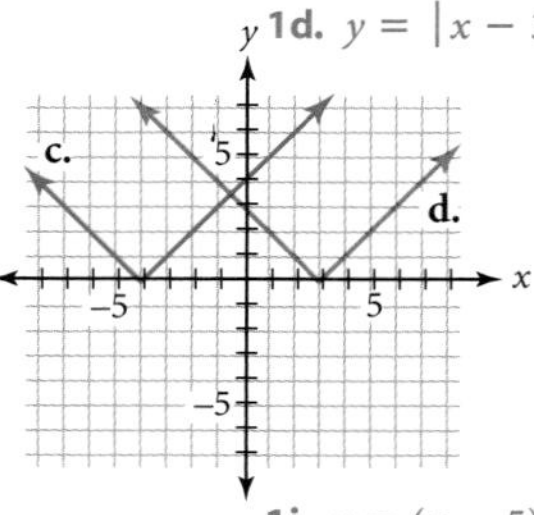

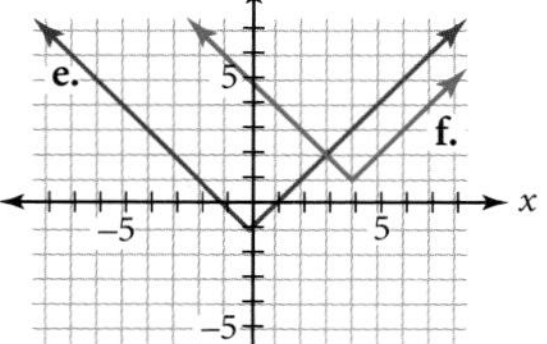

1g. $y = |x + 5| - 3$

1h. $y = 3|x - 6|$

1j. $y = (x - 5)^2$

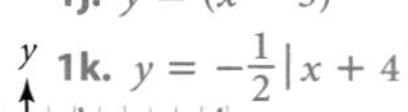

1m. $y = -(x + 3)^2 + 5$

1n. $y = \pm\sqrt{x - 4} + 4$

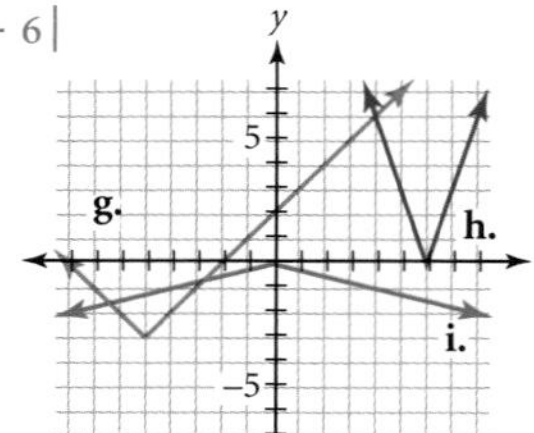

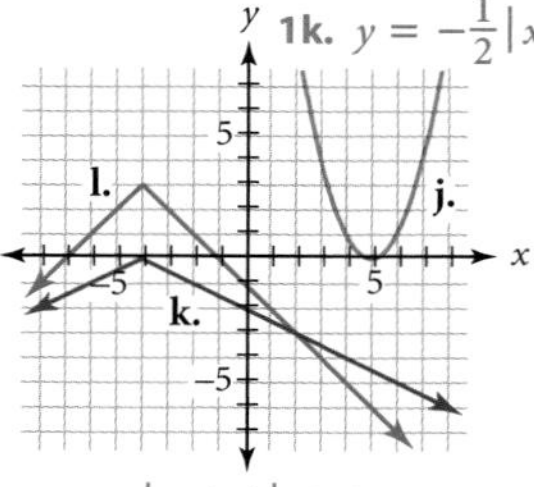

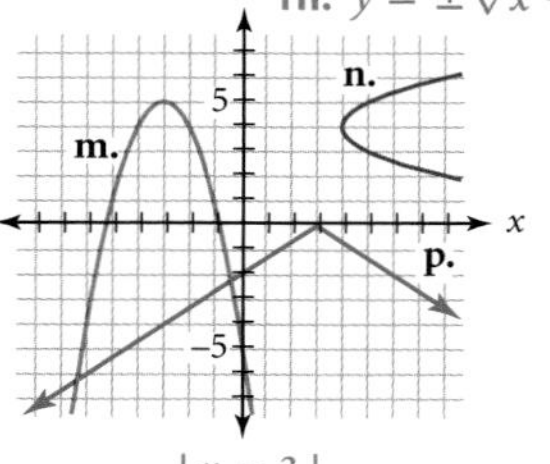

1i. $y = -\left|\frac{x}{4}\right|$

1l. $y = -|x + 4| + 3$

1p. $y = -2\left|\frac{x - 3}{3}\right|$

2. Describe what happens to the graph of $y = f(x)$ in these situations.

a. x is replaced with $\frac{x}{3}$.

b. x is replaced with $-x$.

c. x is replaced with $3x$.

d. y is replaced with $\frac{y}{2}$.

e. y is replaced with $-y$.

f. y is replaced with $2y$.

3. Solve each equation for y.

a. $y + 3 = 2(x - 5)^2$

$y = 2(x - 5)^2 - 3$

b. $\frac{y + 5}{2} = \left|\frac{x + 1}{3}\right|$

$y = 2\left|\frac{x + 1}{3}\right| - 5$

c. $\frac{y + 7}{-2} = \sqrt{\frac{x - 6}{-3}}$

$y = -2\sqrt{\frac{x - 6}{-3}} - 7$

Reason and Apply

4. Choose a few different values for a. What can you conclude about $y = a|x|$ and $y = |ax|$? Are they the same function?

5. The graph at right shows how to solve the equation $|x - 4| = 3$ graphically. The equations $y = |x - 4|$ and $y = 3$ are graphed on the same coordinate axes.

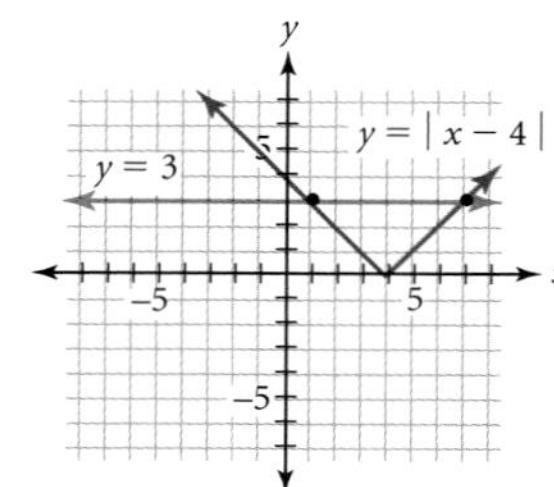

a. What is the x-coordinate of each point of intersection? What x-values are solutions of the equation $|x - 4| = 3$?

b. Solve the equation $|x + 3| = 5$ graphically.

Helping with the Exercises

Exercise 2 Students need not graph these to describe the transformations.

2a. horizontal stretch by a factor of 3

2b. reflection across the y-axis

2c. horizontal shrink by a factor of $\frac{1}{3}$

2d. vertical stretch by a factor of 2

2e. reflection across the x-axis

2f. vertical shrink by a factor of $\frac{1}{2}$

Exercise 3b Students might state the answer as two separate equations, $y = \frac{-2x - 17}{3}$ and $y = \frac{2x - 13}{3}$.

Exercise 4 As needed, point out that these are vertical stretches and horizontal shrinks by the same factor (if $a > 1$). **[Ask]** "Are there other functions for which a vertical stretch by a factor yields the same graph as a horizontal shrink by the same factor?" Students can experiment with the parent parabola ($\frac{y}{a} = x^2$ is not the same as $y = (ax)^2$), the parent square root function ($\frac{y}{a} = \sqrt{x}$ is not equivalent to $y = \sqrt{ax}$), and the parent line ($\frac{y}{a} = x$ is the same as $y = ax$).

4. For $a > 0$, the graphs of $y = a|x|$ and $y = |ax|$ are equivalent. For $a < 0$, the graph of $y = a|x|$ is a reflection of $y = |ax|$ across the x-axis.

Exercise 5a **[Ask]** "Why are there two solutions?" One explanation refers to the graph; another cites the arithmetic; a third gives the two numbers that are 3 units to either side of 4 on the number line.

5a. 1 and 7; $x = 1$ and $x = 7$

5b. $x = -8$ and $x = 2$

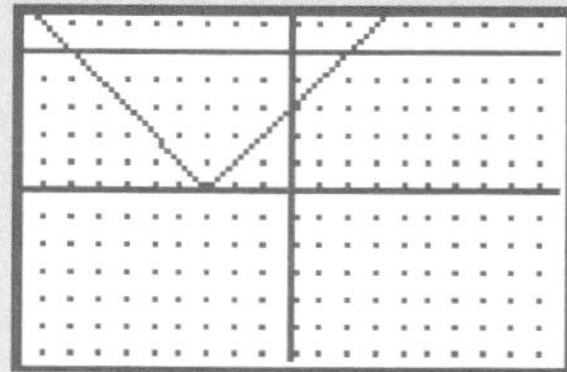

$[-9.4, 9.4, 1, -6.2, 6.2, 1]$

6. APPLICATION You can use a single radio receiver to find the distance to a transmitter by measuring the strength of the signal. Suppose these approximate distances are measured with a receiver while you drive along a straight road. Find a model that fits the data. Where do you think the transmitter might be located?

Miles traveled	0	4	8	12	16	20	24	28	32	36
Distance from transmitter (miles)	18.4	14.4	10.5	6.6	2.5	1.8	6.0	9.9	13.8	17.6

$\hat{y} = |x - 18.4|$; The transmitter is located on the road approximately 18.4 mi from where you started.

7. Assume that the parabola $y = x^2$ is translated so that its vertex is $(5, -4)$.

a. If the parabola is stretched vertically by a factor of 2, what are the coordinates of the point on the parabola 1 unit to the right of the vertex? $(6, -2)$

b. If the parabola is stretched horizontally instead, by a factor of 3, what are the coordinates of the points on the parabola 1 unit above the vertex? $(2, -3)$ and $(8, -3)$

c. If the parabola is stretched vertically by a factor of 2 *and* horizontally by a factor of 3, name two points on the new parabola that are symmetric with respect to the vertex. $(2, -2)$ and $(8, -2)$

8. Given the parent function $y = x^2$, describe the transformations represented by the function $\frac{y-2}{3} = \left(\frac{x+7}{4}\right)^2$. Sketch a graph of the transformed parabola.

9. A parabola has vertex $(4.7, 5)$ and passes through the point $(2.8, 9)$.

a. What is the equation of the axis of symmetry for this parabola? possible answers: $x = 4.7$ or $y = 5$

b. What is the equation of this parabola?

c. Is this the only parabola passing through this vertex and point? Explain. Sketch a graph to support your answer.

10. Sketch a graph of each of these equations.

a. $\frac{y-2}{3} = (x-1)^2$ b. $\left(\frac{y+1}{2}\right)^2 = \frac{x-2}{3}$ c. $\frac{y-2}{2} = \left|\frac{x+1}{3}\right|$

11. Given the graph of $y = f(x)$, draw graphs of these related functions.

a. $\frac{y}{-2} = f(x)$ b. $y = f\left(\frac{x-3}{2}\right)$

c. $\frac{y+1}{\frac{1}{2}} = f(x+1)$

12. APPLICATION A chemistry class gathered these data on the conductivity of a base solution as acid is added to it. Graph the data and use transformations to find a model to fit the data.

Acid volume (mL) x	Conductivity (μS/cm³) y
0	4152.95
1	3140.97
2	2100.34
3	1126.55
4	162.299

Acid volume (mL) x	Conductivity (μS/cm³) y
5	1212.47
6	2358.11
7	3417.83
8	4429.81

Exercise 6 [Alert] Students may say that the transmitter is 1.8 miles off the road 20 miles from the starting point. As needed, encourage them to graph the data in order to find the parent function and to write an equation for the transformation.

8. The parabola is stretched vertically by a factor of 3, stretched horizontally by a factor of 4, and translated left 7 units and up 2 units.

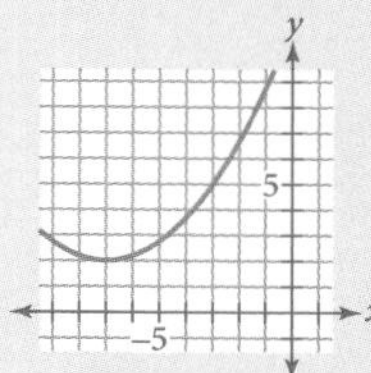

Exercise 9 If students are having difficulty, suggest that they follow the procedure from Example B. For 9c, there are infinitely many parabolas that satisfy the two conditions, but equations for the two whose lines of symmetry are parallel to one of the axes are easiest to find.

9b. possible answers:

$y = 4\left(\frac{x-4.7}{1.9}\right)^2 + 5$ or

$\left(\frac{y-5}{4}\right)^2 = \frac{x-4.7}{-1.9}$

9c. There are at least two parabolas. One is oriented horizontally, and another is oriented vertically.

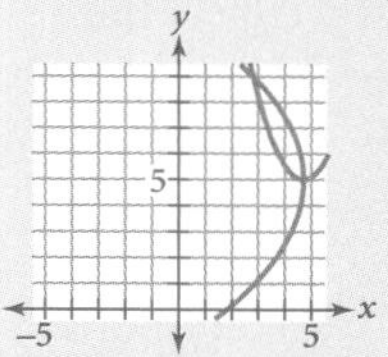

Exercise 12 [Language] μS is the abbreviation for microsiemens. A siemens is equal to one ampere per volt (amp/V). **[Context]** The conductivity of the solution is directly related to the concentration of ions, independent of their charge. As the acid is added, the concentration of ions decreases as water molecules are formed until the solution is neutral and then increases as the solution becomes more acidic. (These data are from *Connecting Mathematics with Science: Experiments for Precalculus.*)

12.

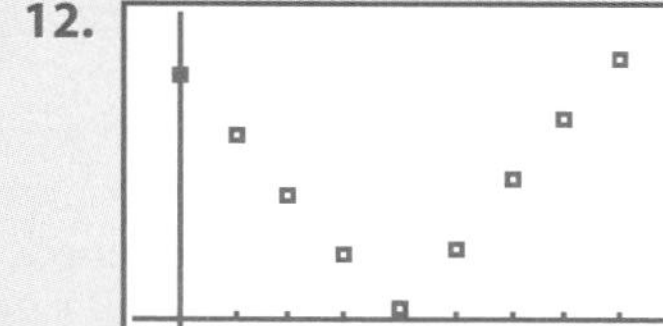

$[-1, 9, 1, -500, 4500, 5000]$

possible equation: $y = 1050|x - 4| + 162$

See page 883 for answers to Exercises 10 and 11.

Exercise 13 If students don't recall how the mean and standard deviation are affected by translations, they might experiment with these data in Fathom. Or use the Science Fair demonstration.

13c. By adding 6 points to each rating, the mean increases by 6, but the standard deviation remains the same.

Exercise 14 Students might do research to compare their predictions for later years with the actual percentages.

14d. Sample answers: A linear model cannot work to predict results for years in the distant future because the percentage cannot increase beyond 100%. There always will be some households without computers, so the long-run percentage will be less than 100%.

EXTENSIONS

A. Use Take Another Look activity 1 or 3 on pages 235 and 236.

B. Have students take a picture of an object whose shape resembles a parabola or the graph of an absolute-value function using a digital camera and then import it into The Geometer's Sketchpad, overlay a coordinate grid, and use transformations to plot a function that models the data.

C. Students might collect their own ball-bounce data and repeat Example B.

See page 883 for answer to Exercise 14a.

Review

2.2 **13.** A panel of judges rate 20 science fair exhibits as shown. The judges decide that the top rating should be 100, so they add 6 points to each rating.

a. What are the mean and the standard deviation of the ratings before adding 6 points? $\bar{x} = 83.75, s = 7.45$

b. What are the mean and the standard deviation of the ratings after adding 6 points? $\bar{x} = 89.75, s = 7.45$

c. What do you notice about the change in the mean? In the standard deviation?

Exhibit number	Rating	Exhibit number	Rating
1	79	11	85
2	81	12	88
3	94	13	86
4	92	14	83
5	68	15	89
6	79	16	90
7	71	17	92
8	83	18	77
9	89	19	84
10	92	20	73

3.4 **14.** APPLICATION This table shows the percentage of households with computers in the United States in various years.

Year	1995	1996	1997	1998	1999	2000
Households (%)	31.7	35.5	39.2	42.6	48.2	53.0

(*The New York Times Almanac 2002*)

a. Make a scatter plot of these data.

b. Find the median-median line. $y = 4.25x - 8447.675$

c. Use the median-median line to predict the percentage of households with computers in 2002. 60.8%

d. Is a linear model a good model for this situation? Explain your reasoning.

In 1946, inventors J. Presper Eckert and J. W. Mauchly created the first general-purpose electronic calculator, named ENIAC (Electronic Numerical Integrator and Computer). The calculator filled a large room and required a team of engineers and maintenance technicians to operate it.

IMPROVING YOUR VISUAL THINKING SKILLS

Miniature Golf

Shannon and Lori are playing miniature golf. The third hole is in a 22-by-14-foot walled rectangular playing area with a large rock in the center. Each player's ball comes to rest as shown. The rock makes a direct shot into the hole impossible.

At what point on the south wall should Shannon aim in order to have the ball bounce off and head directly for the hole? Recall from geometry that the angle of incidence is equal to the angle of reflection. Lori cannot aim at the south wall. Where should she aim?

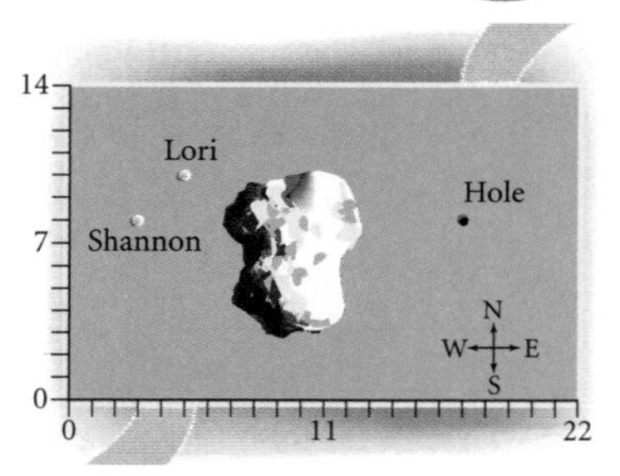

IMPROVING VISUAL THINKING SKILLS

The minimal path from one point to another by way of a line L that doesn't separate the points is along two lines, each of which contains one of the points and the reflection of the other point across line L. The path of the ball will be along a minimal path. Students might copy or make a scale drawing of the rectangle and then use construction to determine the path. They might use guess-and-check to approximate the path, or they might use the coordinate system. Shannon's ball should hit the south wall at (10, 0). Lori should aim at the point (9.8, 14) on the north wall.

[Ask] "What are the coordinates of the hole, of Shannon's ball, and of Lori's ball?" [(17, 8), (3, 8), and (5, 10), respectively] "What absolute-value functions model the paths that Shannon's and Lori's balls travel?" travel?" $\left[y = \frac{8}{7}|x - 10| \text{ and } y = -\frac{5}{6}|x - 9.8| + 14\right]$

LESSON

4.7

Transformations and the Circle Family

Many times the best way, in fact the only way, to learn is through mistakes. A fear of making mistakes can bring individuals to a standstill, to a dead center.

GEORGE BROWN

You have explored several functions and relations and transformed them in a plane. You know that a horizontal translation occurs when x is replaced with $(x - h)$ and that a vertical translation occurs when y is replaced with $(y - k)$. You have reflected graphs across the y-axis by replacing x with $-x$ and across the x-axis by replacing y with $-y$. You have also stretched and shrunk a function vertically by replacing y with $\frac{y}{a}$, and horizontally by replacing x with $\frac{x}{b}$.

This photo shows circular housing developments in Denmark.

In this lesson you will stretch and shrink the graph of a relation that is not a function and discover how to create the equation for a new shape.

You will start by investigating the circle. A **unit circle** has a radius of 1 unit. Suppose P is any point on a unit circle with center at the origin. Draw the slope triangle between the origin and point P.

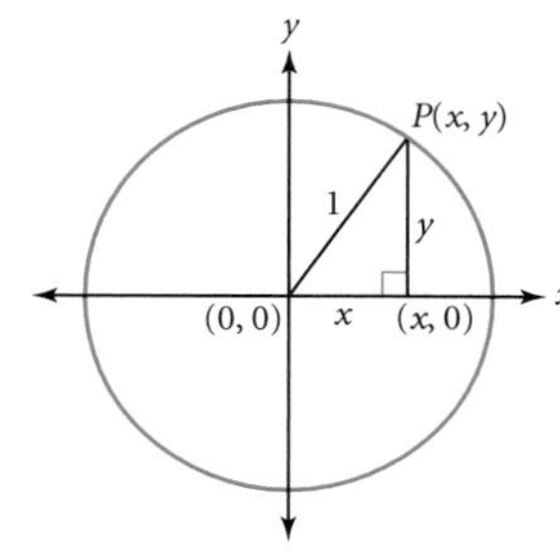

You can derive the equation of a circle from this diagram by using the Pythagorean Theorem. The legs of the right triangle have lengths x and y and the length of the hypotenuse is 1 unit, so its equation is $x^2 + y^2 = 1$. This is true for all points P on the unit circle.

Equation of a Unit Circle

The equation of a **unit circle** with center (0, 0) is

$$x^2 + y^2 = 1$$

What are the domain and the range of this circle? If a value, such as 0.5, is substituted for x, what are the output values of y? Is this the graph of a function? Why or why not? $-1 \leq x \leq 1$ and $-1 \leq y \leq 1$; $y = \pm\frac{\sqrt{3}}{2} \approx \pm 0.866$; no; there are 2 y-values for most x-values.

In order to draw the graph of a circle on your calculator, you need to solve the equation $x^2 + y^2 = 1$ for y. When you do this, you get two equations, $y = +\sqrt{1 - x^2}$ and $y = -\sqrt{1 - x^2}$. Each of these is a function. You have to graph both of them to get the complete circle.

You can transform a circle to get an **ellipse.** An ellipse is a stretched or shrunken circle.

NCTM STANDARDS

CONTENT		PROCESS	
	Number		Problem Solving
✓	Algebra	✓	Reasoning
✓	Geometry	✓	Communication
	Measurement	✓	Connections
	Data/Probability	✓	Representation

LESSON OBJECTIVES

- Define *unit circle* and derive the equation $x^2 + y^2 = 1$
- Express a circle equation as two semicircle functions
- Define *ellipse* as "a vertical and/or horizontal dilation of a circle"
- Transform a circle to get an ellipse
- Apply transformations to relations and to a new function expressed in terms of $f(x)$
- Summarize transformations—translations, reflections, rotations, and stretches and shrinks

LESSON

4.7

PLANNING

LESSON OUTLINE

One day:

10 min Example A

15 min Investigation

10 min Sharing

5 min Example B

5 min Exercises

MATERIALS

- graph paper, *optional*
- When Is a Circle Not a Circle? (W)
- Calculator Note 4C
- Sketchpad demonstration Circles and Ellipses, *optional*

TEACHING

This lesson extends the notions of translation and stretching to circles. You may want to spend two days on this lesson. Start with the one-step investigation on page 218 or discuss Example A before starting the investigation.

INTRODUCTION

Stress the logic involved in concluding that the equation $x^2 + y^2 = 1$ is satisfied by the coordinates of *any* point on the circle because point P was chosen arbitrarily. Students can graph both equations $y = \pm\sqrt{1 - x^2}$ at once by entering Y= {1, −1} $\sqrt{1 - x^2}$ into their calculators.

If students are using the standard window, **[Ask]** "Why doesn't the graph look like a circle?" Encourage students to use a square, friendly window (Calculator Note 4C). **[Alert]** Students might be confused if the left and right parts of a circle don't show in a particular calculator graph because the curves are too steep.

One Step

Hand out the When Is a Circle Not a Circle? worksheet. Ask students to pick one ellipse on the worksheet and find its equation, assuming that the axes are oriented so that the ellipse's center is at the origin and the stretch is horizontal or vertical. Ask students to graph the equation on their calculators. As students work, be prepared to refer them back to Lesson 4.6 to see how stretches affect the graphs of the equations of other figures. Remind them as needed how to graph half a unit circle on a calculator.

▶ EXAMPLE A

When students enter into their calculators complicated equations like the one in this solution, it is easy for them to make mistakes with placement and number of parentheses. To help them, suggest that students first write the equations on paper the way they will be entered. There are two important reasons for tediously solving the equation for y: Students often need practice with symbolic manipulation, and they need to check their solution by graphing.

[Ask] "Are these parabolas?" [The graph of each equation might look something like a parabola, and each function contains the square of an expression. But that square is within a square root, so each curve is half an ellipse.] Another friendly window on the TI-83 Plus is $[-1.7, 7.7, 1, -2.1, 4.1, 1]$, a shifted version of the 9.4-by-6.2 window.

EXAMPLE A

What is the equation of this ellipse?

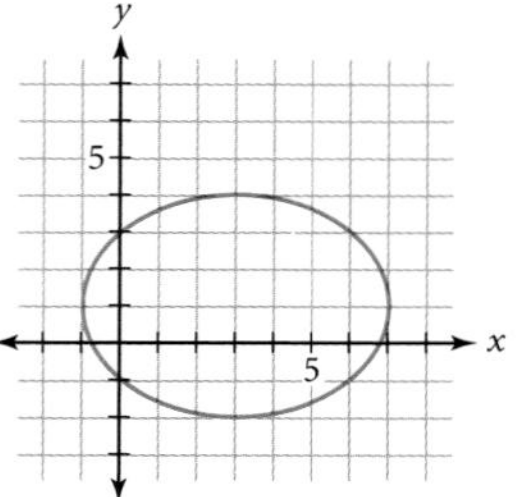

▶ Solution

The original unit circle has been translated and stretched both horizontally and vertically. The new center is at (3, 1). In a unit circle, every radius measures 1 unit. In this ellipse, a horizontal segment from the center to the ellipse measures 4 units, so the horizontal scale factor is 4. Likewise, a vertical segment from the center to the ellipse measures 3 units, so the vertical scale factor is 3. So the equation changes like this:

$$x^2 + y^2 = 1$$ Original unit circle.

$$\left(\frac{x}{4}\right)^2 + y^2 = 1$$ Stretch horizontally by a factor of 4. (Replace x with $\frac{x}{4}$.)

$$\left(\frac{x}{4}\right)^2 + \left(\frac{y}{3}\right)^2 = 1$$ Stretch vertically by a factor of 3. (Replace y with $\frac{y}{3}$.)

$$\left(\frac{x-3}{4}\right)^2 + \left(\frac{y-1}{3}\right)^2 = 1$$ Translate to new center at (3, 1). (Replace x with $x - 3$, and replace y with $y - 1$.)

To enter this equation into your calculator to check your answer, you need to solve for y.

$$\left(\frac{y-1}{3}\right)^2 = 1 - \left(\frac{x-3}{4}\right)^2$$ Subtract $\left(\frac{x-3}{4}\right)^2$ from both sides.

$$\frac{y-1}{3} = \pm\sqrt{1 - \left(\frac{x-3}{4}\right)^2}$$ Take the square root of both sides.

$$y = 1 \pm 3\sqrt{1 - \left(\frac{x-3}{4}\right)^2}$$ Multiply both sides by 3, then add 1.

It takes two equations to graph this on your calculator. By graphing both of these equations, you can draw the complete ellipse and verify your answer.

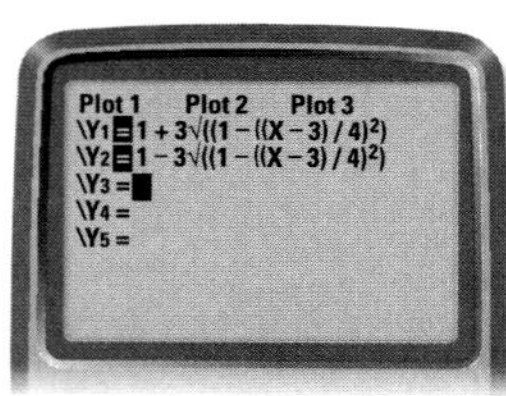

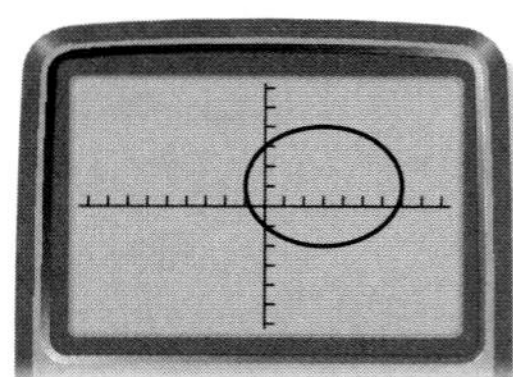

$[-9.4, 9.4, 1, -6.2, 6.2, 1]$

Investigation
When Is a Circle Not a Circle?

You will need

- the worksheet When Is a Circle Not a Circle?

If you look at a circle, like the top rim of a cup, from an angle, you don't see a circle; you see an ellipse. Choose one of the ellipses from the worksheet. Use your ruler carefully to place axes on the ellipse, and scale your axes in centimeters. Be sure to place the axes so that the longest dimension is parallel to one of the axes. Find the equation to model your ellipse. Graph your equation on your calculator and verify that it creates an ellipse with the same dimensions as on the worksheet.

The tops of these circular oil storage tanks look elliptical when viewed at an angle.

Equations for transformations of relations such as circles and ellipses are sometimes easier to work with in the general form before you solve them for y, but you need to solve for y to enter the equations into your calculator. If you start with a function such as the top half of the unit circle, $f(x) = \sqrt{1-x^2}$, you can transform it in the same way you transformed any other function, but it may be a little messier to deal with.

EXAMPLE B If $f(x) = \sqrt{1-x^2}$, find $g(x) = 2f(3(x-2)) + 1$. Sketch a graph of this new function.

▶ ***Solution*** In $g(x) = 2f(3(x-2)) + 1$, note that $f(x)$ is the parent function, x has been replaced with $3(x-2)$, and $f(3(x-2))$ is then multiplied by 2 and 1 is added. You can rewrite the function g as

$$g(x) = 2\sqrt{1-(3(x-2))^2} + 1 \quad \text{or} \quad g(x) = 2\sqrt{1-\left(\frac{x-2}{\frac{1}{3}}\right)^2} + 1$$

This indicates that the graph of $y = f(x)$, a semicircle, has been shrunken horizontally by a factor of $\frac{1}{3}$, stretched vertically by a factor of 2, then translated right 2 units and up 1 unit. The transformed semicircle is graphed at right. What are the coordinates of the right endpoint of the graph? Describe how the original semicircle's right endpoint of $(1, 0)$ was mapped to this new location. $\left(2\frac{1}{3}, 1\right)$; Multiply the x-coordinate by $\frac{1}{3}$ and add 2. Multiply the y-coordinate by 2 and add 1.

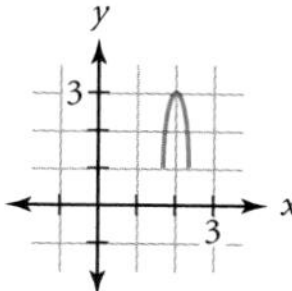

Guiding the Investigation

Students can improve their measurements if they copy the ellipse from the worksheet to graph paper.

As needed, **[Ask]** "How does the ellipse compare to the circle from which it's transformed?" [The diameter of the circle is the shortest distance across the ellipse. The centers are the same.]

[Alert] Students may forget to consider both square roots.

▶ ***EXAMPLE B***

[Alert] The graph on a calculator may seem to have translated the right and left endpoints of the semicircle up 2 units instead of 1 unit. This is because the curve is so steep near those endpoints that it doesn't show. Changing the window to something like [0, 2.4, 1, 0, 3.1, 1] cuts off part of the semicircle but shows more of its transformed image.

The coordinates of the right endpoint of the transformed semicircle are now $\left(2\frac{1}{3}, 1\right)$. To describe how the original endpoint was mapped to the new location, track the images of $(0, 1)$ and $(1, 0)$ under the various transformations, considering stretches and shrinks first (because only the circle, not the entire plane, is being stretched and shrunk).

Start with:	$(0, 1)$	$(1, 0)$
Shrink horizontally by a factor of 3:	$(0, 1)$	$\left(\frac{1}{3}, 0\right)$
Stretch vertically by a factor of 2:	$(0, 2)$	$\left(\frac{1}{3}, 0\right)$
Translate right 2 units:	$(2, 2)$	$\left(2\frac{1}{3}, 0\right)$
Translate up 1 unit:	$(2, 3)$	$\left(2\frac{1}{3}, 1\right)$

SHARING IDEAS

As students present, ask whether they were surprised to find that the images of the circular tanks were not circles. Our brains are very accustomed to receiving elliptical images and interpreting them as circles. Ask whether surprise is a legitimate part of mathematics. Because mathematical calculations and reasoning are used to check intuition, we are surprised when our intuition isn't verified. We then recheck our reasoning and sometimes change our intuition.

[Ask] "What are intercepts of the ellipse given by the equation $\frac{x^2}{a} + \frac{y^2}{b} = 1$?" $\left[\pm\sqrt{a}, \pm\sqrt{b}\right]$ To avoid square roots, we often write the equation as $\frac{x^2}{a^2} + \frac{y^2}{b^2} = 1$ so that intercepts are at $\pm a$ and $\pm b$.

[Ask] "Why does the function $y = f(3x - 6)$ shrink the graph horizontally by a factor of 3 and translate it 6 units to the right whereas $f(3(x-2))$ shrinks it horizontally by 3 and translates it 2 units to the right? Aren't the two functions the same?" [They are the same; in the first case, 6 is subtracted from $3x$, not from x.]

Sharing Ideas (continued)
[Ask] "If you view a circle from more and more of an angle, does the shape remain an ellipse?" [It eventually becomes a line segment.]

Assessing Progress
You can check how well students understand how equations are affected by stretching their graphs in the directions of the axes.

Closing the Lesson

Note the main point of this lesson: Stretching the graph of the unit circle in one direction or stretching it in both directions by different factors gives an **ellipse.** The equation of an ellipse is $\frac{x^2}{a^2} + \frac{y^2}{b^2} = 1$. You might also summarize the relationships between transformed graphs and equations given on this page.

BUILDING UNDERSTANDING

The exercises focus on the semicircle function but also include all the transformations and parent functions introduced in the chapter. The review exercises are quite lengthy; choose carefully which ones to assign.

ASSIGNING HOMEWORK

Essential	1–5
Performance assessment	6–9
Portfolio	9
Group	9
Review	10–15

MATERIALS

- Calculator Notes 2D, 4H, *optional*

Helping with the Exercises

Exercise 1 As needed, encourage students to verify their ideas by graphing on their calculators. A friendly window with a factor of 2 works well.

You have now learned to translate, reflect, stretch, and shrink functions and relations. These transformations are the same for all equations.

Transformations of Functions and Relations

Translations

The graph of $y = k + f(x - h)$ translates the graph of $y = f(x)$ h units horizontally and k units vertically.

or

Replacing x with $(x - h)$ translates the graph h units horizontally.
Replacing y with $(y - k)$ translates the graph k units vertically.

Reflections

The graph of $y = f(-x)$ is a reflection of the graph of $y = f(x)$ across the y-axis. The graph of $y = -f(x)$ is a reflection of the graph of $y = f(x)$ across the x-axis.

or

Replacing x with $-x$ reflects the graph across the y-axis. Replacing y with $-y$ reflects the graph across the x-axis.

Stretches and Shrinks

The graph of $y = af\left(\frac{x}{b}\right)$ is a stretch or shrink of the graph of $y = f(x)$ by a vertical scale factor of a and by a horizontal scale factor of b.

or

Replacing x with $\frac{x}{b}$ stretches or shrinks the graph by a horizontal scale factor of b. Replacing y with $\frac{y}{a}$ stretches or shrinks the graph by a vertical scale factor of a.

EXERCISES

Practice Your Skills

1. Each equation represents a single transformation. Copy and complete this table.

Equation	Transformation (translation, reflection, stretch, shrink)	Direction	Amount or scale factor
$y + 3 = x^2$	Translation	Down	3
$-y = \|x\|$	Reflection	Across x-axis	N/A
$y = \sqrt{\frac{x}{4}}$	Stretch	Horizontal	4
$\frac{y}{0.4} = x^2$	Shrink	Vertical	0.4
$y = \|x - 2\|$	Translation	Right	2
$y = \sqrt{-x}$	Reflection	Across y-axis	N/A

2. The equation $y = \sqrt{1 - x^2}$ is the equation of the top half of the unit circle with center (0, 0) shown on the left. What is the equation of the top half of an ellipse shown on the right? $y = 2\sqrt{1 - x^2}$

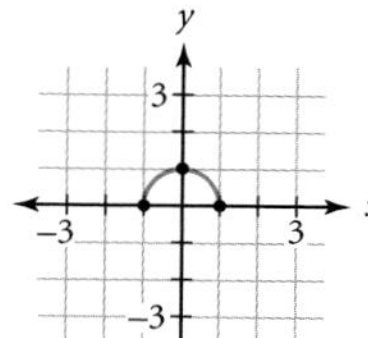
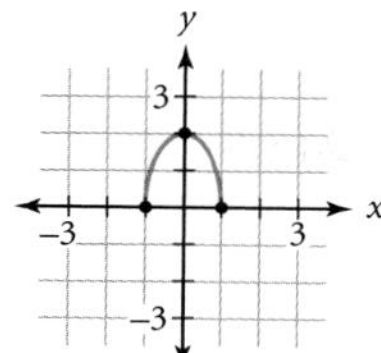

3. Use $f(x) = \sqrt{1 - x^2}$ to graph each of the transformations below.

a. $g(x) = -f(x)$ **b.** $h(x) = -2f(x)$ **c.** $j(x) = -3 + 2f(x)$

4. Each curve is a transformation of the graph of $y = \sqrt{1 - x^2}$. Write an equation for each curve.

a.
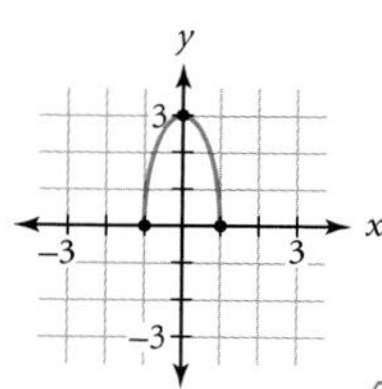
$y = 3\sqrt{1 - x^2}$

b.
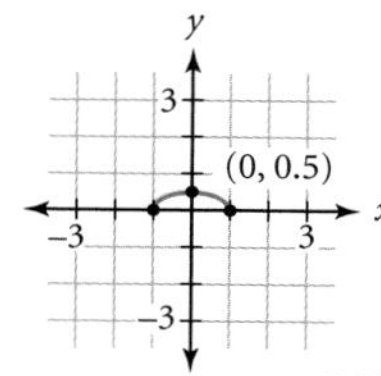

$y = 0.5\sqrt{1 - x^2}$

c.
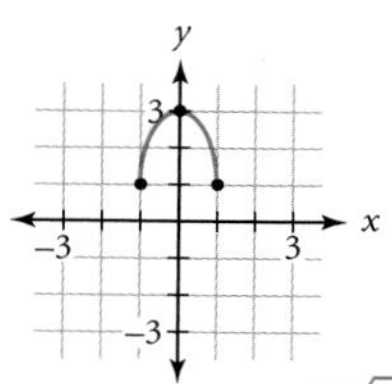
$y = 2\sqrt{1 - x^2} + 1$

d.
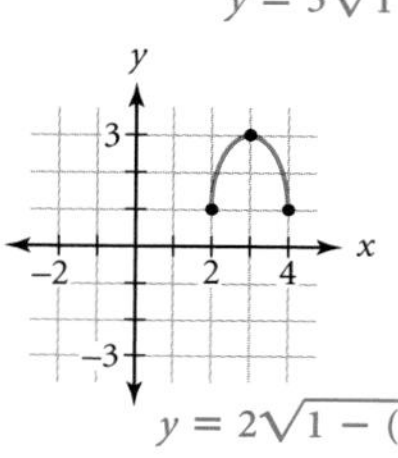
$y = 2\sqrt{1 - (x - 3)^2} + 1$

e.
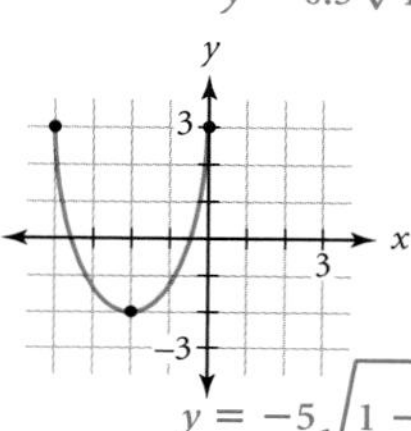
$y = -5\sqrt{1 - \left(\frac{x + 2}{2}\right)^2} + 3$

f.
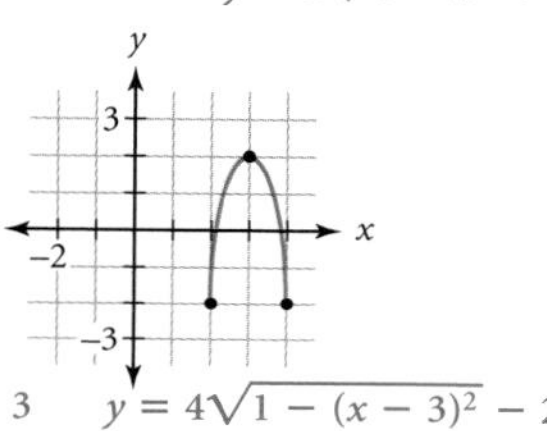
$y = 4\sqrt{1 - (x - 3)^2} - 2$

5. Write an equation and draw a graph for each transformation of the unit circle. Use the form $y = \pm\sqrt{1 - x^2}$.

a. Replace y with $(y - 2)$. **b.** Replace x with $(x + 3)$.

c. Replace y with $\frac{y}{2}$. **d.** Replace x with $\frac{x}{2}$.

Reason and Apply

6. To create the ellipse at right, the x-coordinate of each point on a unit circle has been multiplied by a factor of 3.

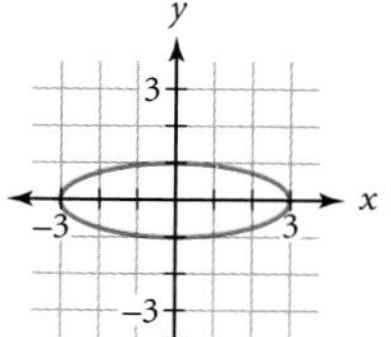

a. Write the equation of this ellipse.

b. What expression did you substitute for x in the parent equation? $\frac{x}{3}$

c. If $y = f(x)$ is the function for the top half of a unit circle, then what is the function for the top half of this ellipse, $y = g(x)$, in terms of f?

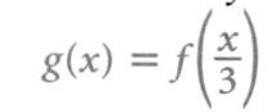
$g(x) = f\left(\frac{x}{3}\right)$

Exercise 3 If students graph the transformations on paper, suggest that they use two or four squares for each unit.

3a.
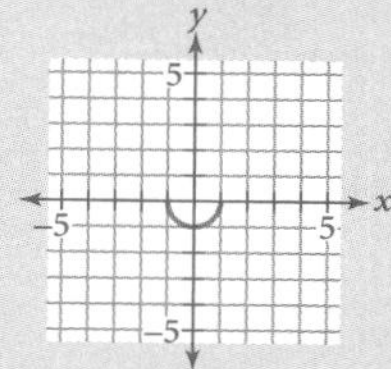

3b.
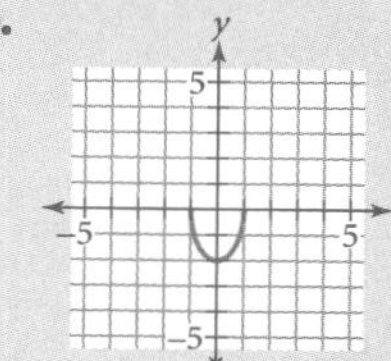

3c.
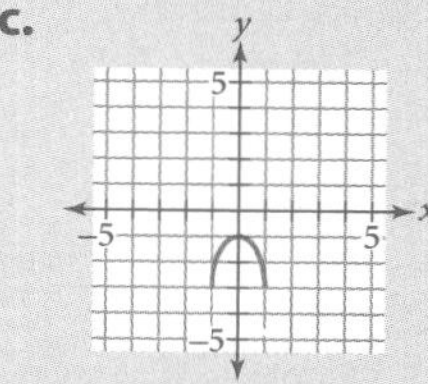

5a. $y = \pm\sqrt{1 - x^2} + 2$ or $x^2 + (y - 2)^2 = 1$

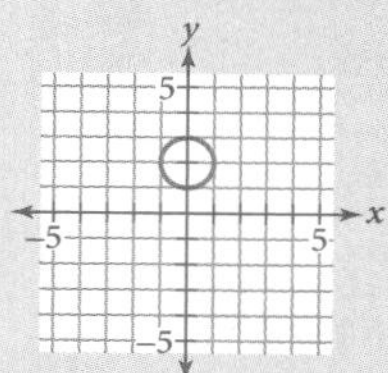

5b. $y = \pm\sqrt{1 - (x + 3)^2}$ or $(x + 3)^2 + y^2 = 1$

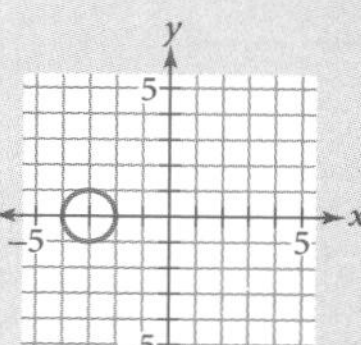

5c. $y = \pm 2\sqrt{1 - x^2}$ or $x^2 + \left(\frac{y}{2}\right)^2 = 1$

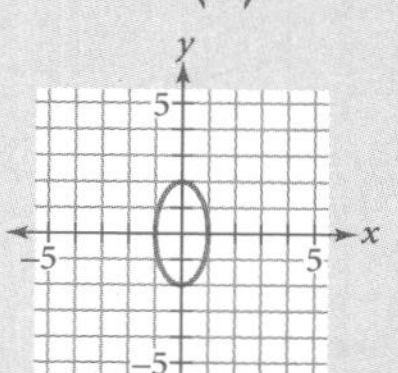

5d. $y = \pm\sqrt{1 - \left(\frac{x}{2}\right)^2}$ or $\frac{x^2}{4} + y^2 = 1$

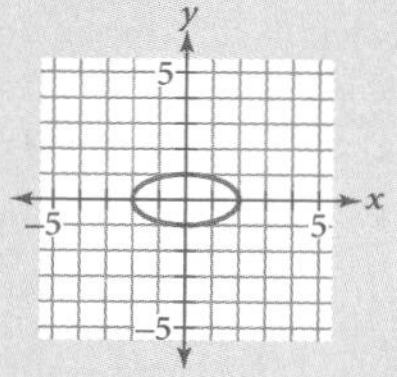

6a. $\left(\frac{x}{3}\right)^2 + y^2 = 1$

7. Given the unit circle at right, write the equation that generates each transformation. Use the form $x^2 + y^2 = 1$.

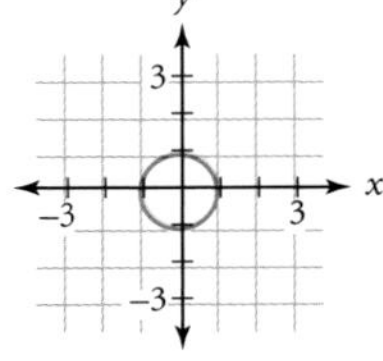

a. Each y-value is half the original y-value. $x^2 + (2y)^2 = 1$

b. Each x-value is half the original x-value. $(2x)^2 + y^2 = 1$

c. Each y-value is half the original y-value, and each x-value is twice the original x-value. $\left(\frac{x}{2}\right)^2 + (2y)^2 = 1$

8. Consider the ellipse at right.

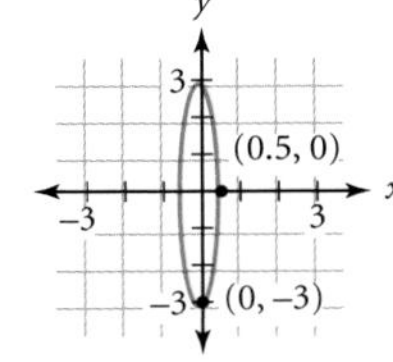

a. Write two functions that you could use to graph this ellipse.

b. Use ± to write one equation that combines the two equations in 8a.

c. Write another equation for the ellipse by squaring both sides of the equation in 8b. $y^2 = 9\left(1 - \left(\frac{x}{0.5}\right)^2\right)$ or $\frac{y^2}{9} + \frac{x^2}{0.25} = 1$

9. ***Mini-Investigation*** Follow these steps to explore a relationship between linear, quadratic, square root, absolute-value, and semicircle functions. Use friendly windows of an appropriate size.

a. Graph these equations simultaneously on your calculator. The first four functions intersect in the same two points. What are the coordinates of these points?

$y = x \qquad y = x^2 \qquad y = \sqrt{x} \qquad y = |x| \qquad y = \sqrt{1 - x^2}$

b. Imagine using the intersection points that you found in 9a to draw a rectangle that just encloses the quarter-circle that is on the right half of the fifth function. How do the coordinates of the points relate to the dimensions of the rectangle?

c. Solve these equations for y and graph them simultaneously on your calculator. Where do the first four functions intersect?

$\frac{y}{2} = \frac{x}{4} \qquad \frac{y}{2} = \left(\frac{x}{4}\right)^2 \qquad \frac{y}{2} = \sqrt{\frac{x}{4}} \qquad \frac{y}{2} = \left|\frac{x}{4}\right| \qquad \frac{y}{2} = \sqrt{1 - \left(\frac{x}{4}\right)^2}$

d. Imagine using the intersection points that you found in 9c to draw a rectangle that just encloses the right half of the fifth function. How do the coordinates of the points relate to the dimensions of the rectangle?

e. Solve these equations for y and graph them simultaneously on your calculator. Where do the first four functions intersect?

i. $\frac{y-3}{2} = \frac{x-1}{4}$ **ii.** $\frac{y-3}{2} = \left(\frac{x-1}{4}\right)^2$ **iii.** $\frac{y-3}{2} = \sqrt{\frac{x-1}{4}}$

iv. $\frac{y-3}{2} = \left|\frac{x-1}{4}\right|$ **v.** $\frac{y-3}{2} = \sqrt{1 - \left(\frac{x-1}{4}\right)^2}$

f. What are the dimensions of a rectangle that encloses the right half of the fifth function? How do these dimensions relate to the coordinates of the two points in 9e?

g. In each set of functions, one of the points of intersection located the center of the transformed semicircle. How did the other points relate to the shape of the semicircle?

Exercise 7 Equivalent forms of the answers include $x^2 + \left(\frac{y}{\frac{1}{2}}\right)^2 = 1$ for 7a, $\left(\frac{x}{\frac{1}{2}}\right)^2 + y^2 = 1$ for 7b, and $\left(\frac{x}{2}\right)^2 + \left(\frac{y}{\frac{1}{2}}\right)^2 = 1$ for 7c.

8a. $y = 3\sqrt{1 - \left(\frac{x}{0.5}\right)^2}$ and $y = -3\sqrt{1 - \left(\frac{x}{0.5}\right)^2}$

8b. $y = \pm 3\sqrt{1 - \left(\frac{x}{0.5}\right)^2}$

Exercise 9 This exercise may take a lot of time. Students might benefit from sketching their solutions on graph paper before graphing them on their calculators. The instructions say to imagine drawing a rectangle, but if students want to draw it on their calculators you can refer them to Calculator Note 4H. A window of [−1.175, 1.175, 1, −0.3875, 1.625, 1] puts the point (1, 1) at a pixel.

9a.

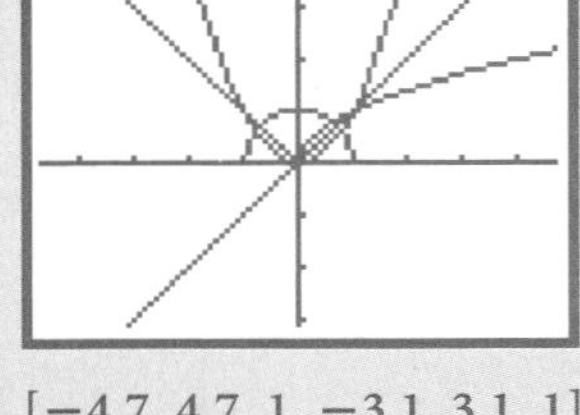

[−4.7, 4.7, 1, −3.1, 3.1, 1]

(0, 0) and (1, 1)

9b. The rectangle has width 1 and height 1. The width is the difference in x-coordinates, and the height is the difference in y-coordinates.

9c.

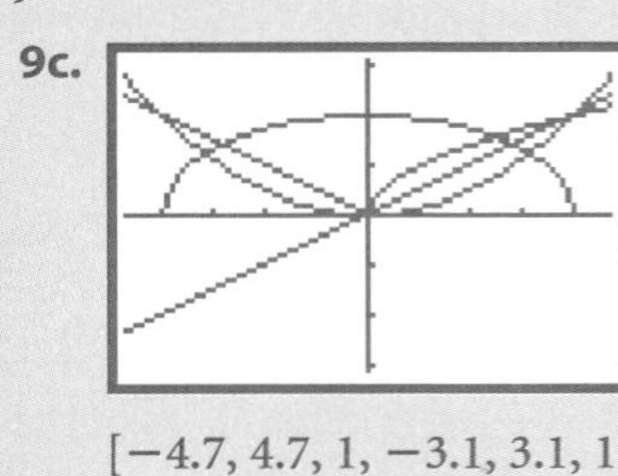

[−4.7, 4.7, 1, −3.1, 3.1, 1]

(0, 0) and (4, 2)

9d. The rectangle has width 4 and height 2. The width is the difference in x-coordinates, and the height is the difference in y-coordinates.

9e.

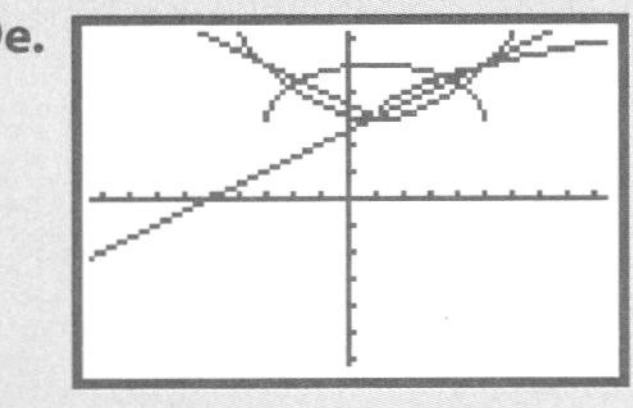

[−9.4, 9.4, 1, −6.2, 6.2, 1]

(1, 3) and (5, 5)

9f. The rectangle has width 4 and height 2. The difference in x-coordinates is 4, and the difference in y-coordinates is 2.

9g. The x-coordinate is the location of the right endpoint, and the y-coordinate is the location of the top of the transformed semicircle.

Science

CONNECTION

Satellites are used to aid in navigation, communication, research, and military reconnaissance. The job the satellite is meant to do will determine the type of orbit it is placed in.

A satellite in geosynchronous orbit moves in an east-west direction and always stays directly over the same spot on Earth, so its orbital path is circular. The satellite and Earth move together, so both orbits take 24 hours. Because we always know where the satellite is, satellite dish antennae on Earth can be aimed in the right direction.

Another useful orbit is a north-south elliptical orbit that takes 12 hours to circle the planet. Satellites in these elliptical orbits cover areas of Earth that are not covered by geosynchronous satellites, and are therefore more useful for research and reconnaissance.

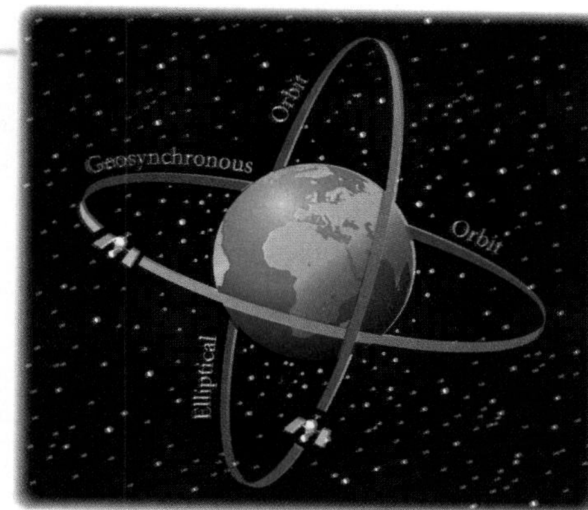

Satellites in a geosynchronus orbit follow a circular path above the equator. Another common orbit is an elliptical orbit in the north-south direction. For more information, see the links at www.keymath.com/DAA .

Review

2.2 **10.** Refer to Exercise 13 in Lesson 4.6. The original data is shown at right. Instead of adding the same number to each score, one of the judges suggests that perhaps they should *multiply* the original scores by a factor that makes the highest score equal 100. They decide to try this method.

Exhibit number	Rating	Exhibit number	Rating
1	79	11	85
2	81	12	88
3	94	13	86
4	92	14	83
5	68	15	89
6	79	16	90
7	71	17	92
8	83	18	77
9	89	19	84
10	92	20	73

a. By what factor should they multiply the highest score, 94, to get 100? $\frac{100}{94}$

b. What are the mean and the standard deviation of the original ratings? Of the altered ratings?

c. Let x represent the exhibit number, and let y represent the rating. Plot the original and altered ratings on the same graph. Describe what happened to the ratings visually. How does this explain what happened to the mean and the standard deviation?

d. Which method do you think the judges should use? Explain your reasoning.

1.1 **11.** Find the next three terms in this sequence: 16, 40, 100, 250, . . . 625, 1562.5, 3906.25

12. Solve. Give answers to the nearest 0.01.

a. $\sqrt{1-(a-3)^2}=0.5$ $a \approx 2.13$ or 3.87

b. $-4\sqrt{1-(b+2)^2}=-1$ $b \approx -2.97$ or -1.03

c. $\sqrt{1-\left(\frac{c-2}{3}\right)^2}=0.8$ $c = 0.2$ or 3.8

d. $3+5\sqrt{1-\left(\frac{d+1}{2}\right)^2}=8$ $d=-1$

Exercise 10 Students might use Fathom or a spreadsheet for this exercise.

10b. Original ratings (from Exercise 13 in Lesson 4.6): $\bar{x}=83.75$, $s=7.45$. New ratings: $\bar{x}=89.10$, $s=7.92$.

10c.

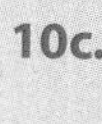

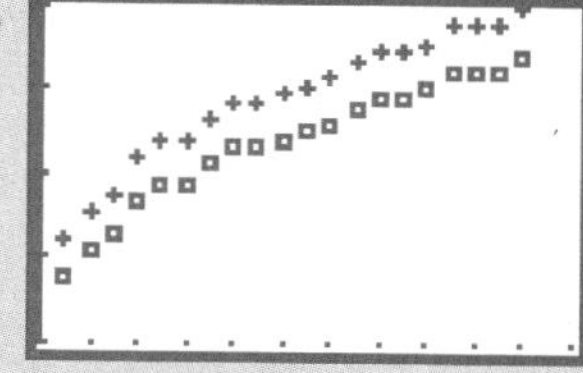

[0, 22, 1, 60, 100, 10]

The scores have been stretched by a factor of $\frac{100}{94}$. All scores increased, so the mean increased. The high scores differ from the original by more than the lower ones, so the scores are more spread out and the standard deviation is increased.

10d. Sample answer: The judge should add 6 points because it does not change the standard deviation. Everyone gets the same amount added instead of those with higher scores getting more.

13a.

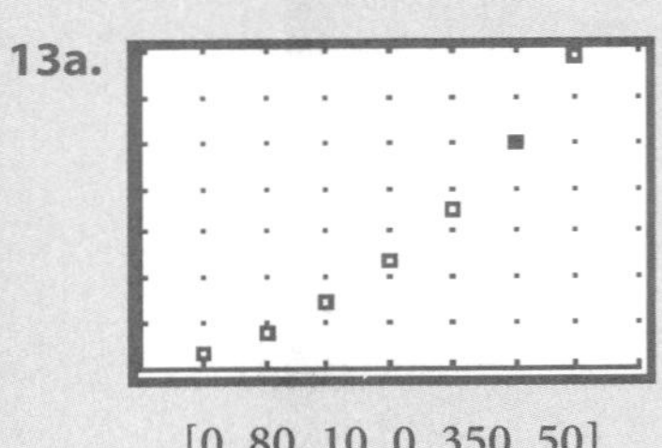

[0, 80, 10, 0, 350, 50]

13b. Sample answer:
$\hat{y} = 0.07(x - 3)^2 + 21$.

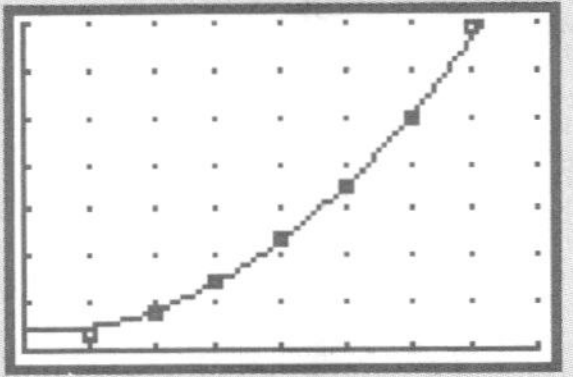

[0, 80, 10, 0, 350, 50]

13c. For the sample answer: residuals: $-5.43, 0.77, 0.97, -0.83, -2.63, -0.43, 7.77$; $s = 4.45$

Exercise 14 To make a histogram for data in which frequencies are in a separate list, students can consult Calculator Note 2D. **[Alert]** Students might not notice that the table skips a couple of intervals in numbers of passengers. **[Alert]** In 14c, students might add up the right-hand column and divide by something. Or they might add up the means of the intervals in the left-hand column and divide. Help them understand that the number in the right-hand column tells how many airports have a number in the corresponding cell of the left-hand column. The estimate is the sum of the products of the interval means and the number of airports in that interval divided by the total number of airports.

15a. $y = -3x - 1$

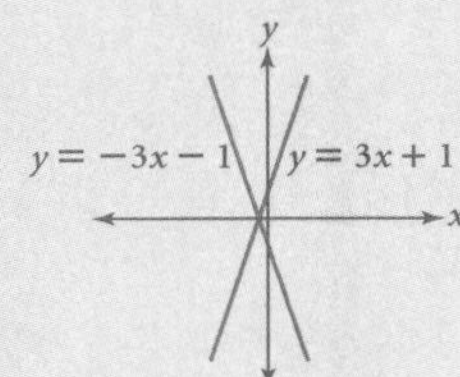

See page 883 for answers to Exercises 15b and c.

4.5 **13.** This table shows the distances needed to stop a car on dry pavement in a minimum length of time for various speeds. Reaction time is assumed to be 0.75 s.

Speed (mi/h) x	10	20	30	40	50	60	70
Stopping distance (ft) y	19	42	73	116	173	248	343

a. Construct a scatter plot of these data.

b. Find the equation of a parabola that fits the points and graph it.

c. Find the residuals for this equation and the root mean square error.

d. Predict the stopping distance for 56.5 mi/h. approximately 221 ft

e. How close should your prediction in 13d be to the *actual* stopping distance? 13d should be correct ±4.45 ft.

4.3 **14.** This table shows passenger activity in the world's 30 busiest airports in 2000.

a. Display the data in a histogram.

b. Estimate the total number of passengers who used the 30 airports. Explain any assumptions you make.

c. Estimate the mean usage among the 30 airports in 2000. Mark the mean on your histogram. 41,333,333 passengers

d. Sketch a box plot above your histogram. Estimate the five-number summary values. Explain any assumptions you make. Five-number summary: 27.5, 32.5, 37.5, 47.5, 82.5; assume that all data occurs at midpoints of bins.

Number of passengers (in millions)	Number of airports
$25 \le p < 30$	5
$30 \le p < 35$	8
$35 \le p < 40$	8
$40 \le p < 45$	1
$45 \le p < 50$	2
$55 \le p < 60$	1
$60 \le p < 65$	2
$65 \le p < 70$	1
$70 \le p < 75$	1
$80 \le p < 85$	1

(*The New York Times Almanac 2002*)

2.3 **15.** Consider the linear function $y = 3x + 1$.

a. Write the equation of the image of the graph of $y = 3x + 1$ after a reflection across the x-axis. Graph both lines on the same axes.

b. Write the equation of the image of the graph of $y = 3x + 1$ after a reflection across the y-axis. Graph both lines on the same axes.

c. Write the equation of the image of the graph of $y = 3x + 1$ after a reflection across the x-axis and then across the y-axis. Graph both lines on the same axes.

d. How does the image in 14c compare to the original line? The two lines are parallel.

IMPROVING YOUR VISUAL THINKING SKILLS

4-in-1

Copy this trapezoid. Divide it into four congruent polygons.

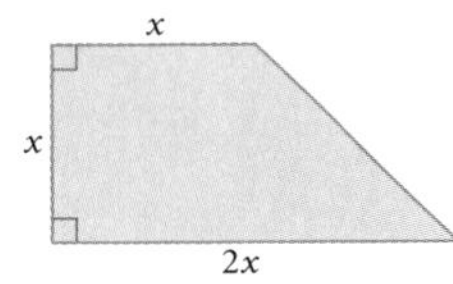

14a, c, d.

Mean

Number of airports

Number of passengers (in millions)

14b. 1,240,000,000 passengers, assuming that all data occur at midpoints of bins.

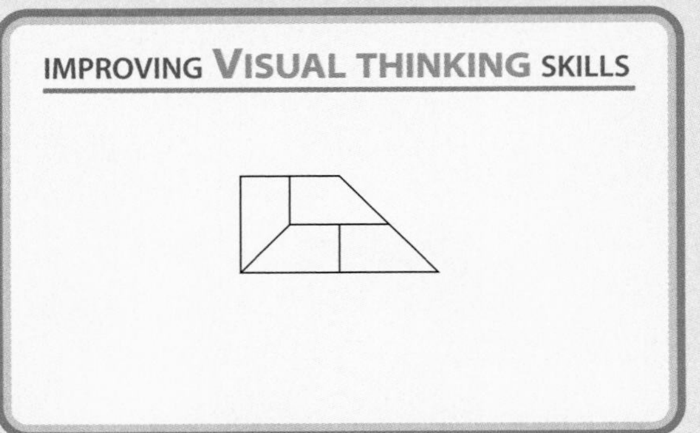

LESSON

4.8 Compositions of Functions

Sometimes you'll need two or more functions in order to answer a question or analyze a problem. Suppose an offshore oil well is leaking. Graph A shows the radius, r, of the spreading oil slick, growing as a function of time, t, so $r = f(t)$. Graph B shows the area, a, of the circular oil slick as a function of its radius, r, so $a = g(r)$. Time is measured in hours, the radius is measured in kilometers, and the area is measured in square kilometers.

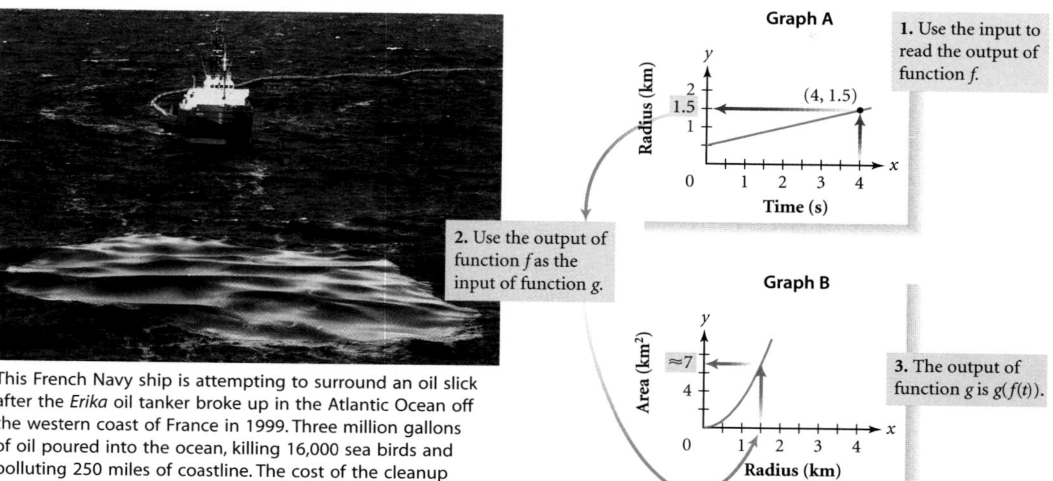

This French Navy ship is attempting to surround an oil slick after the *Erika* oil tanker broke up in the Atlantic Ocean off the western coast of France in 1999. Three million gallons of oil poured into the ocean, killing 16,000 sea birds and polluting 250 miles of coastline. The cost of the cleanup efforts exceeded $160 million.

If you want to find the area of the oil slick after 4 hours, you use function f on Graph A to find that when t equals 4, r equals 1.5. Next, using function g on Graph B, you find that when r equals 1.5, a is approximately 7. So after 4 h, the radius of the oil slick is 1.5 km and its area is 7 km^2.

You used the graphs of two different functions, f and g, to find that after 4 h, the oil slick has area 7 km^2. You actually used the output from one function, f, as the input in the other function, g. This is an example of a **composition of functions** to form a new functional relationship between area and time, that is, $a = g(f(t))$. The symbol $g(f(t))$, read "g of f of t," is a composition of the two functions f and g. The composition $g(f(t))$ gives the final outcome when an x-value is substituted into the "inner" function, f, and its output value, $f(t)$, is then substituted as the input into the "outer" function, g.

EXAMPLE A

Consider these functions:

$$f(x) = \frac{3}{4}x - 3 \quad \text{and} \quad g(x) = |x|$$

What will the graph of $y = g(f(x))$ look like?

▶ Solution

Function f is the inner function, and function g is the outer function. Use equations and tables to identify the output of f and use it as the input of g.

NCTM STANDARDS

CONTENT		PROCESS	
	Number	✓	Problem Solving
✓	Algebra		Reasoning
✓	Geometry	✓	Communication
✓	Measurement	✓	Connections
✓	Data/Probability	✓	Representation

LESSON OBJECTIVES

- Define composition of functions and learn the notation
- See transformations of two or three steps as the composition of functions
- Apply composition to real-world contexts
- Distinguish composition from the product of functions
- Understand composition both graphically and numerically

LESSON 4.8

PLANNING

LESSON OUTLINE

First day:
10 min Example A
30 min Investigation
5 min Exercises

Second day:
10 min Investigation
10 min Sharing
10 min Example B
15 min Exercises

MATERIALS

- small mirrors
- tape measures or metersticks
- Quick Compositions? (T), *optional*
- Calculator Notes 4D, 4H

TEACHING

If the investigation is completed entirely in groups, the lesson may take two days. If it is completed as a class demonstration, one day will be sufficient. You will find the one-step investigation on page 226.

[Alert] Students may still not understand why the output of a function can be read off the vertical axis as in Graphs A and B on this page. The height of a point on the graph, given by the second coordinate, corresponds to a length on the y-axis.

▶ EXAMPLE A

After students have seen the solution in the book, you might encourage them to graph the functions $f(x)$ and $g(f(x))$ on their calculators. Refer students to Calculator Note 4D.

One Step

Hand out materials and pose this problem: "Attach the tape measure (or metersticks) up the wall from the floor to a height of from 1.5 to 2 meters. Then place the mirror on the floor about 0.5 meter from the bottom of the tape measure. As you walk toward the wall, you can see in the mirror various numbers on the tape measure. What's that height as a function of time?" As students work, encourage them to break up the process into simpler steps; suggest that they first find the height as a function of their own distance from the wall and then find their distance from the wall as a function of time. During Sharing, formalize the way they combined the functions as a composition.

Guiding the Investigation

If time is limited, you may want to complete Steps 1 through 4 as a class demonstration.

Steps 1–3 Make sure the student who is looking into the mirror maintains the same upright posture throughout the data collection.

Find several $f(x)$ output values.

x	$f(x)$
-2	-4.5
0	-3
2	-1.5
4	0
6	1.5
8	3

Use the $f(x)$ output values as the input of $g(x)$.

$f(x)$	$g(f(x))$
-4.5	4.5
-3	3
-1.5	1.5
0	0
1.5	1.5
3	3

Match the input of the inner function, f, with the output of the outer function, g, and plot the graph.

x	$g(f(x))$
-2	4.5
0	3
2	1.5
4	0
6	1.5
8	3

The solution is the composition graph at right. All the function values of f, whether positive or negative, give positive output values under the rule of g, the absolute-value function. So, the part of the graph of function f showing negative output values is reflected across the x-axis in this composition.

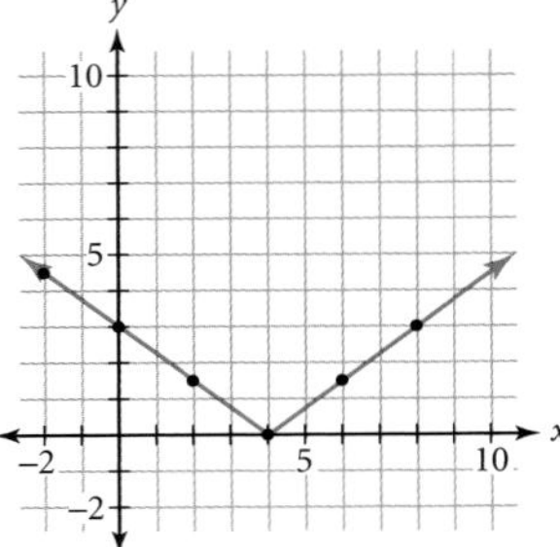

You can use what you know about transformations to get the specific equation for $y = g(f(x))$ in Example A. Use the parent function $y = |x|$, translate the vertex right 4 units, and then stretch horizontally by a factor of 4 and vertically by a factor of 3. This gives the equation $y = 3\left|\frac{x-4}{4}\right|$. You can algebraically manipulate this equation to get $y = \left|\frac{3}{4}x - 3\right|$, which appears to be the equation of f substituted for the input of g. You can always create equations of composed functions by substituting one equation into another.

Investigation
Looking Up

You will need

- a small mirror
- one or more tape measures or metersticks

First, you'll establish a relationship between your distance from a mirror and what you can see in it.

Procedure Note

1. Place the mirror flat on the floor 0.5 m from a wall.
2. Use tape to attach tape measures or metersticks up the wall to a height of 1.5 to 2 m.

Step 1 Set up the experiment as in the Procedure Note. Stand a short distance from the mirror, and look down into it. Move slightly left or right until you can see the tape measure on the wall reflected in the mirror.

Step 2 Have a group member slide his or her finger up the wall to help locate the highest height mark that is reflected in the mirror. Record the height in centimeters, h, and the distance from your toe to the center of the mirror in centimeters, d.

Step 3 Change your distance from the mirror and repeat Step 2. Make sure you keep your head in the same position. Collect several pairs of data in the form (d, h). Include some distances from the mirror that are short and some that are long.

Step 4 Find a function that fits your data by transforming the parent function $h = \frac{1}{d}$. Call this function f.

Now you'll combine your work from Steps 1–4 with the scenario of a timed walk toward and away from the mirror.

Step 5 Suppose this table gives your position at 1-second intervals:

Time (s) t	0	1	2	3	4	5	6	7
Distance to mirror (cm) d	163	112	74	47	33	31	40	62

Use one of the families of functions from this chapter to fit these data. Call this function g. It should give the distance from the mirror for seconds 0 to 7.

Step 6 Use your two functions to answer these questions:

a. How high up the wall can you see when you are 47 cm from the mirror? 157 cm

b. Where are you at 1.3 seconds? 99 cm from mirror

c. How high up the wall can you see at 3.4 seconds? 185 cm

Step 7 Change each expression into words relating to the context of this investigation and find an answer. Show the steps you needed to evaluate each expression.

a. $f(60)$ how high up the wall you can see when you are 60 cm from the mirror; 123 cm

b. $g(5.1)$ your distance from the mirror at 5.1 s; 31 cm

c. $f(g(2.8))$ how high you can see up the wall at 2.8 s; 143 cm

Step 8 Find a single function, $H(t)$, that does the work of $f(g(t))$. Show that $H(2.8)$ gives the same answer as Step 7c above. for sample data: $H(t) = \dfrac{7400}{(6.02t^2 - 56.57t + 162.83)}$

Don't confuse a composition of functions with the product of functions. Composing functions requires you to replace the independent variable in one function with the output value of the other function. This means that it is generally not commutative. That is, $f(g(x)) \neq g(f(x))$, except for certain functions.

Step 3 sample data: (50, 148), (70, 106), (100, 73.5), (130, 57), (160, 45)

Step 4 Students may not be confident that their equation is correct. Ask them to check it against all their data before they continue on to Step 5.

Step 4 $h = f(d) = \dfrac{7400}{d}$

Step 5 You might suggest that students first graph the data and then use transformations to find the equation. Their equations of the parabola may vary from group to group.

Step 5 possible answer: $d = g(t) = 6.02t^2 - 56.57t + 162.83$

Step 6 Answers will vary. These answers are based on the sample data from Step 3.

▶ EXAMPLE B

This example shows that a composition might consist of a function combined with itself. Use the words *balance, principle, payment,* and *interest.* You might want to point out the connection to recursion from Chapter 1.

SHARING IDEAS

To the extent possible, have students present a variety of equations from Step 8 of the investigation. Keep asking why the results differ. Data-collection procedures and differences in assumptions about translations and stretches will account for some differences. Errors in calculation and in students' understanding of composition will account for others.

[Ask] "Is the composition of two functions the same as their product—the result of multiplying them together?" Students might graph on their calculators the product of the functions from the investigation or from Example A $\left(f(x) \cdot g(x) = \frac{3x|x|}{4} - 3|x|\right)$ and see that it's different from the corresponding composition. They might evaluate the product at a few points to verify the difference, or they might look at calculator table values.

Show the Quick Compositions? transparency. Say that someone proposed it as a quick way of evaluating the composition of a function $f(x)$ with itself, and have the students try to understand and critique that idea. Elicit the notion that on the line $y = x$ the two coordinates are equal, so the output from the function can turn into input. Calculate the results of applying the function a few more times. Take Another Look activity 5 on page 236 asks students to make graphs of compositions of linear functions on their calculators. Calculator Note 4H will help them.

You can compose a function with itself. The next example shows you how.

EXAMPLE B Suppose the function $A(x) = \left(1 + \frac{0.07}{12}\right)x - 250$ gives the balance of a loan with an annual interest rate of 7%, compounded monthly, in the month after a \$250 payment. In the equation, x represents the current balance and $A(x)$ represents the next balance. Translate these expressions into words and find their values.

a. $A(15000)$

b. $A(A(20000))$

c. $A(A(A(18000)))$

d. $A(A(x))$

▶ Solution Each expression builds from the inside out.

a. $A(15000)$ asks, "What is the loan balance after one monthly payment if the starting balance is \$15,000?" Substituting 15000 for x in the given equation, you get $A(15000) = \left(1 + \frac{0.07}{12}\right)15000 - 250 = 14837.50$, or \$14,837.50.

b. $A(A(20000))$ asks, "What is the loan balance after two monthly payments if the starting balance is \$20,000?" Substitute 20000 for x in the given equation. You get 19866.67 and use it as input in the given equation. That is, $A(A(20000)) = A(19866.67) = 19732.56$, or \$19,732.56.

c. $A(A(A(18000)))$ asks, "What is the loan balance after three monthly payments if the starting balance is \$18,000?" Working from the inner expression outward, you get $A(A(A(18000)) = A(A(17855)) = A(17709.15) = 17562.46$, or \$17,562.46.

d. $A(A(x))$ asks, "What is the loan balance after two monthly payments if the starting balance is x?"

$A(A(x)) = A\left(\left(1 + \frac{0.07}{12}\right)x - 250\right)$ — Use the given function to substitute $\left(1 + \frac{0.07}{12}\right)x - 250$ for $A(x)$.

$= \left(1 + \frac{0.07}{12}\right)\left[\left(1 + \frac{0.07}{12}\right)x - 250\right] - 250$ — Use the output, $\left[\left(1 + \frac{0.07}{12}\right)x - 250\right]$ in place of the input, x.

$= 1.005833(1.005833x - 250) - 250$ — Convert the fractions to decimal approximations.

$= 1.0117x - 251.458 - 250$ — Apply the distributive property.

$= 1.0117x - 501.458$ — Subtract.

EXERCISES

Practice Your Skills

1. Given the functions $f(x) = 3 + \sqrt{x + 5}$ and $g(x) = 2 + (x - 1)^2$, find these values.

a. $f(4)$ 6 **b.** $f(g(4))$ 7 **c.** $g(-1)$ 6 **d.** $g(f(-1))$ 18

Assessing Progress

As students work on the investigation, especially Step 5, you can assess their understanding of translations and stretches. You can also see how well students interpret data and evaluate functions.

Closing the Lesson

The main point of this lesson is that the **composition** of two functions $f(x)$ and $g(x)$ is a new function $g(f(x))$ that takes the output of $f(x)$ as input to $g(x)$.

2. The functions f and g are defined by these sets of input and output values.

$g = \{(1, 2), (-2, 4), (5, 5), (6, -2)\}$

$f = \{(0, -2), (4, 1), (3, 5), (5, 0)\}$

a. Find $g(f(4))$. 2 b. Find $f(g(-2))$. 1 c. Find $f(g(f(3)))$. 0

3. **APPLICATION** Graph A shows a swimmer's speed as a function of time. Graph B shows the swimmer's oxygen consumption as a function of her speed. Time is measured in seconds, speed in meters per second, and oxygen consumption in liters per minute. Use the graphs to estimate the values.

Graph A

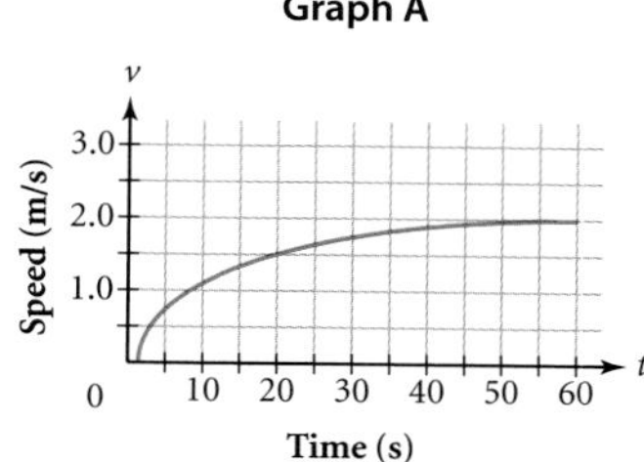

Graph B

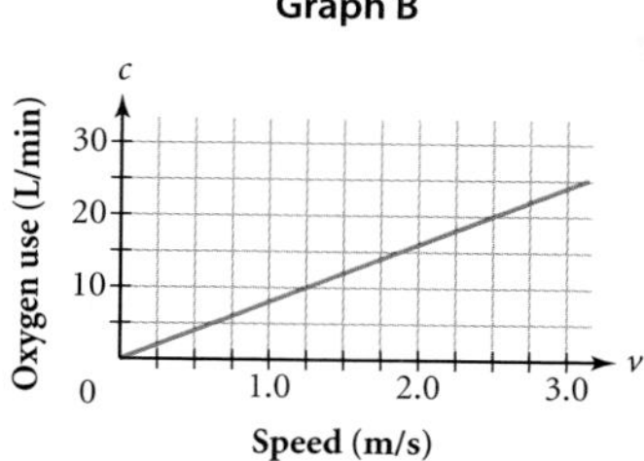

a. the swimmer's speed after 20 s of swimming approximately 1.5 m/s

b. the swimmer's oxygen consumption at a swimming speed of 1.5 m/s approximately 12 L/min

c. the swimmer's oxygen consumption after 40 s of swimming approximately 15 L/min

4. Identify each equation as a composition of functions, a product of functions, or neither. If it is a composition or a product, then identify the two functions that combine to create the equation.

a. $y = 5\sqrt{3 + 2x}$

b. $y = 3 + \left(|x + 5| - 3\right)^2$

c. $y = (x - 5)^2(2 - \sqrt{x})$ product: $f(x) \cdot g(x)$ where $f(x) = (x - 5)^2$ and $g(x) = 2 - \sqrt{x}$

Reason and Apply

5. Consider the graph at right.

a. Write an equation for this graph. $y = |(x - 3)^2 - 1|$

b. Write two functions, f and g, such that the figure is the graph of $y = f(g(x))$. $f(x) = |x|$ and $g(x) = (x - 3)^2 - 1$

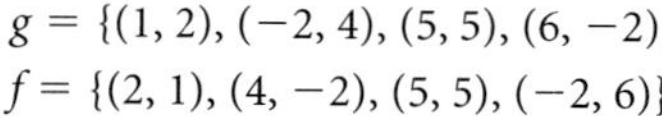

6. The functions f and g are defined by these sets of input and output values.

$g = \{(1, 2), (-2, 4), (5, 5), (6, -2)\}$

$f = \{(2, 1), (4, -2), (5, 5), (-2, 6)\}$

a. Find $g(f(2))$. 2

b. Find $f(g(6))$. 6

c. Select any number from the domain of either g or f, and find $f(g(x))$ or $g(f(x))$, respectively. Describe what is happening. The composition of f and g will always give back the original number because f and g "undo" the effects of each other.

BUILDING UNDERSTANDING

The exercises engage students in working with compositions of functions.

ASSIGNING HOMEWORK

Essential	1–4
Performance assessment	5–12
Portfolio	9
Journal	6, 11
Group	7, 14
Review	13–16

MATERIALS

- Calculator Note 4G, *optional*

Helping with the Exercises

Exercise 2 As needed, remind students that relations, including functions, can be thought of as sets of ordered pairs. In this case, $g(1) = 2$ and $f(4) = 1$. You may need to help students realize that they should evaluate the inner function first and work out from there.

Exercise 4 Different answers are possible. For example, the function in 4b can also be considered as $g(f(x))$ for $g(x) = 3 + x$ and $f(x) = \left(|x + 5| - 3\right)^2$.

4a. product: $f(x) \cdot g(x)$ where $f(x) = 5$ and $g(x) = \sqrt{3 + 2x}$; or composition: $f(g(x))$ where $f(x) = 5\sqrt{x}$ and $g(x) = 3 + 2x$

4b. composition: $g(f(x))$ where $f(x) = |x + 5|$ and $g(x) = 3 + (x - 3)^2$

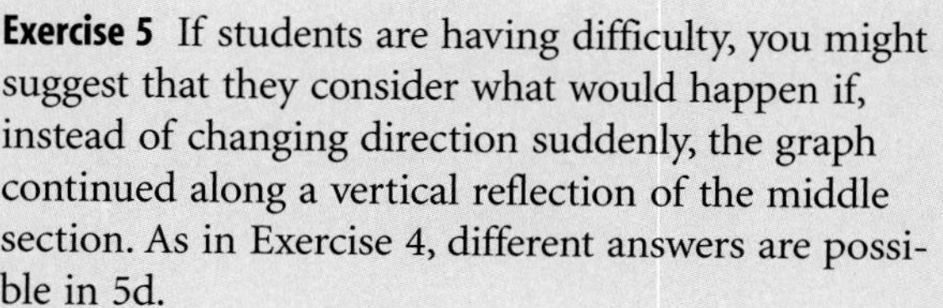

Exercise 5 If students are having difficulty, you might suggest that they consider what would happen if, instead of changing direction suddenly, the graph continued along a vertical reflection of the middle section. As in Exercise 4, different answers are possible in 5d.

Exercise 6c If students do not include a reason in their answer, **[Ask]** "Why?" [The pairs in function g are the reverse of the pairs in function f.]

Exercise 7 Suggest that students first create a table of values.

7a.

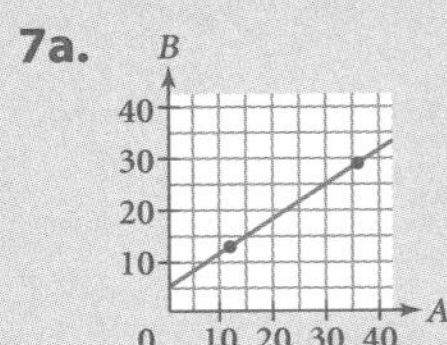

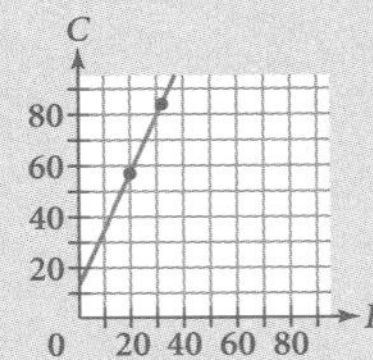

7c. $B = \frac{2}{3}(A - 12) + 13$

7d. $C = \frac{9}{4}(B - 20) + 57$

7e. $C = \frac{9}{4}\left(\frac{2}{3}A + 5\right) + 12 = 1.5A + 23.25$

Exercise 8c Students may be confused by this product—not composition—of a function with itself.

8a.

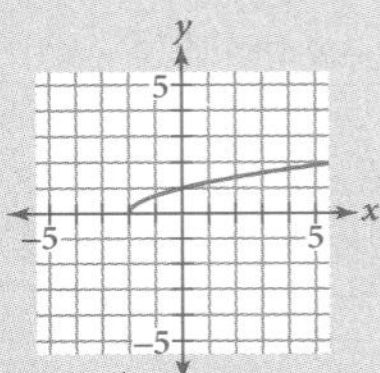

8b.

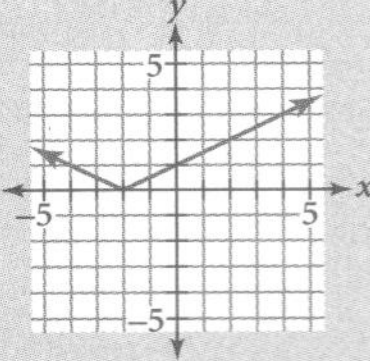

8c.

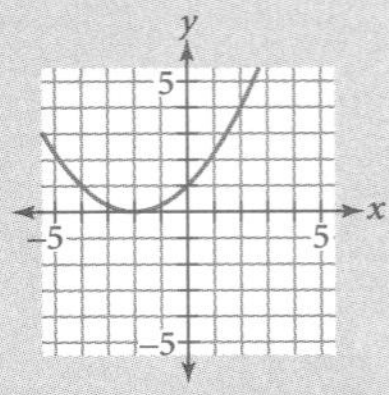

Exercise 9e If students do not include a reason in their answer, **[Ask]** "Why?"

7. A, B, and C are gauges with different linear measurement scales. When A measures 12, B measures 13, and when A measures 36, B measures 29. When B measures 20, C measures 57, and when B measures 32, C measures 84.

a. Sketch separate graphs for readings of B as a function of A and readings of C as a function of B. Label the axes.

b. If A reads 12, what does C read? approximately 41

c. Write a function with the reading of B as the dependent variable and the reading of A as the independent variable.

d. Write a function with the reading of C as the dependent variable and the reading of B as the independent variable.

e. Write a function with the reading of C as the dependent variable and the reading of A as the independent variable.

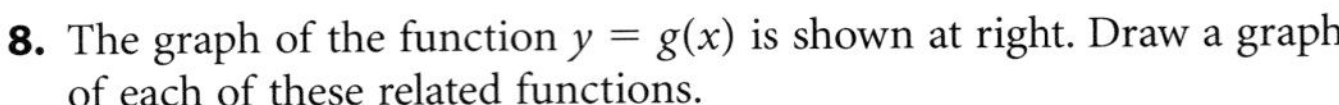

8. The graph of the function $y = g(x)$ is shown at right. Draw a graph of each of these related functions.

a. $y = \sqrt{g(x)}$

b. $y = |g(x)|$

c. $y = (g(x))^2$

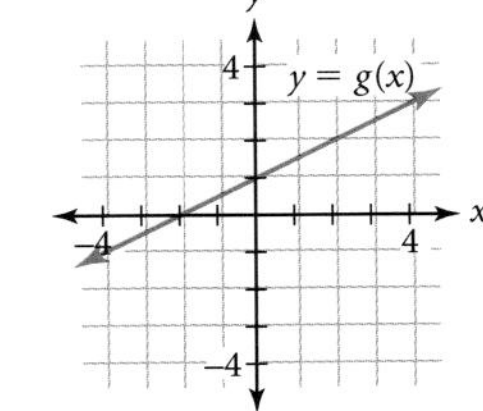

9. The two lines pictured at right are $f(x) = 2x - 1$ and $g(x) = \frac{1}{2}x + \frac{1}{2}$. Solve each problem both graphically and numerically.

a. Find $g(f(2))$. 2

b. Find $f(g(-1))$. −1

c. Pick your own x-value in the domain of f, and find $g(f(x))$.

d. Pick your own x-value in the domain of g, and find $f(g(x))$.

e. Carefully describe what is happening in these compositions.

10. Given the functions $f(x) = -x^2 + 2x + 3$ and $g(x) = (x - 2)^2$, find these values.

a. $f(g(3))$ 4

b. $f(g(2))$ 3

c. $g(f(0.5))$ 3.0625

d. $g(f(1))$ 4

e. $f(g(x))$. Simplify to remove all parentheses. $-x^4 + 8x^3 - 22x^2 + 24x - 5$

f. $g(f(x))$. Simplify to remove all parentheses. $x^4 - 4x^3 + 2x^2 + 4x + 1$

[► See **Calculator Note 4D** to learn how to use your calculator to check the answers to 10e and 10f. ◄]

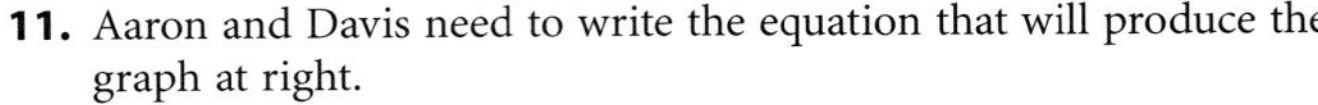

11. Aaron and Davis need to write the equation that will produce the graph at right.

Aaron: "This is impossible! How are we supposed to know if the parent function is a parabola or a semicircle? If we don't know the parent function, there is no way to write the equation."

Davis: "Don't panic yet. I am sure we can determine its parent function if we study the graph carefully."

Do you agree with Davis? Explain completely and, if possible, write the equation of the graph.

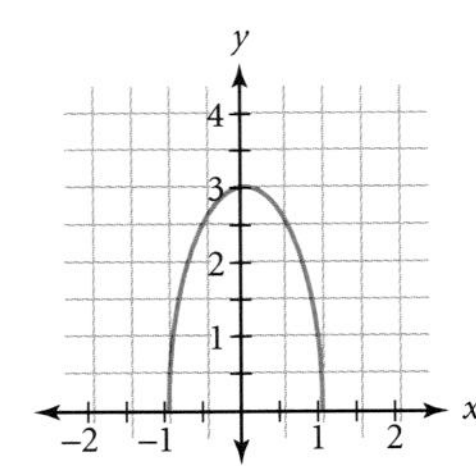

9c. $g(f(x)) = g(2x - 1) = \frac{1}{2}(2x - 1) + \frac{1}{2} = x$ for all x

9d. $f(g(x)) = f\left(\frac{1}{2}x + \frac{1}{2}\right) = 2\left(\frac{1}{2}x + \frac{1}{2}\right) - 1 = x$ for all x

9e. The two functions "undo" the effects of each other and thus give back the original value.

11. If the parent function is $y = x^2$, then the equation is $y = -3x^2 + 3$. If the parent function is $y = \sqrt{1 - x^2}$, then the equation is $y = 3\sqrt{1 - x^2}$. It appears that when $x = 0.5$, $y \approx 2.6$. Substituting 0.5 for x in each equation gives the following results:

$3 - (0.5)^2 + 3 = 2.25$

$3\sqrt{1 - 0.5^2} \approx 2.598$

Thus, the stretched semicircle is the better fit.

12. APPLICATION Jen and Priya decide to go out to the Hamburger Shack for lunch. They each have a 50-cent coupon from the Sunday newspaper for the Super-Duper-Deluxe \$5.49 Value Meal. In addition, if they show their I.D. cards, they'll also get a 10% discount. Jen's server rang up the order as Value Meal, coupon, and then I.D. discount. Priya's server rang it up as Value Meal, I.D. discount, and then coupon.

a. How much did each girl pay? Jen: \$4.49; Priya: \$4.44

b. Write a function, $C(x)$, that will deduct 50 cents from a price, x. $C(x) = x - 0.50$

c. Write a function, $D(x)$, that will take 10% off a price, x. $D(x) = 0.90x$

d. Find $C(D(x))$. $C(D(x)) = 0.90x - 0.50$

e. Which server used $C(D(x))$ to calculate the price of the meal? Priya's server

f. Is there a price for the Value Meal that would result in both girls paying the same price? If so, what is it? There is no price because $0.90x - 0.50 = 0.90(x - 0.50)$ has no solution.

Review

13. Solve.

a. $\sqrt{|x - 4|} = 3$ $x = -5$ or $x = 13$

b. $(3 - \sqrt{x + 2})^2 = 4$ $x = -1$ or $x = 23$

c. $|3 - \sqrt{x}| = 5$ $x = 64$

d. $3 + 5\sqrt{1 + 2x^2} = 13$ $x = \pm\sqrt{1.5} \approx \pm 1.22$

3.4 **14.** APPLICATION Bonnie and Mike are working on a physics project. They need to determine the ohm rating of a resistor. The ohm rating is found by measuring the potential difference in volts and dividing it by the electric current, measured in amperes (amps). In their project they set up the circuit at right. They vary the voltage and observe the corresponding readings of electrical current measured on the ammeter.

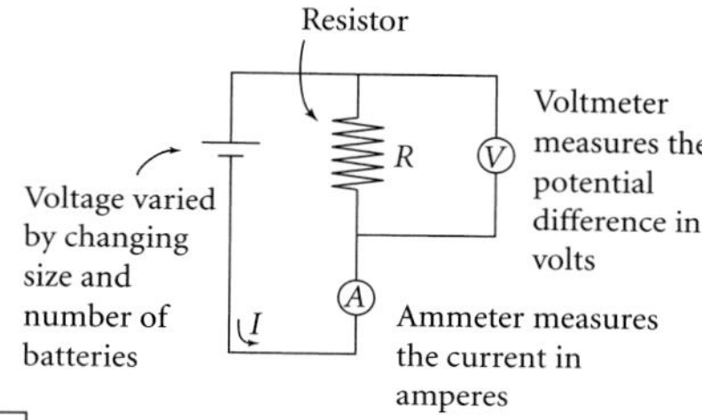

Potential difference (volts)	12	10	6	4	3	1
Current (amps)	2.8	2.1	1.4	1.0	0.6	0.2

a. Identify the independent and dependent variables.

b. Display the data on a graph.

c. Find the median-median line. $\hat{y} = 0.2278x - 0.0167$

d. Bonnie and Mike reason that because 0 volts obviously yields 0 amps the line they really want is the median-median line translated to go through (0, 0). What is the equation of the line through the origin that is parallel to the median-median line? $\hat{y} = 0.2278x$

e. How is the ohm rating Bonnie and Mike are trying to determine related to the line in 14d? The ohm rating is the reciprocal of the slope of this line.

f. What is their best guess of the ohm rating to the nearest tenth of an ohm? 4.4 ohms

Exercise 12 As an extension, **[Ask]** "What would happen if the Sunday coupon were for a 5% discount instead of 50 cents off?" Another extension might involve a store that has items on 50% off clearance, followed by an additional 20% discount for a holiday sale and an additional 15% off if you use the store's credit card. **[Ask]** "Is the total discount 85%?" [No; the cost is $0.85(0.8(0.5p)) = 0.34p$, or a discount of 66%.]

Exercise 13 Although students may previously have solved equations like these with graphing, encourage them to solve the equations symbolically here. **[Ask]** "How do you deal with the two values located within the absolute-value symbol?" [Write two equations.]

Exercise 14 Students may be intimidated by this problem if they don't understand electricity very well. Assure them that they can solve it if they understand the mathematics. Praise success at overcoming the psychological barrier.

14a. The independent variable, x, is potential difference (in volts). The dependent variable, y, is current (in amperes).

14b.

y
3
2
1
Current (amps)
0 3 6 9 12 x
Potential difference (volts)

15a. $\left(\frac{x}{3}\right)^2 + \left(\frac{y}{3}\right)^2 = 1$ or

$x^2 + y^2 = 9$

15b.

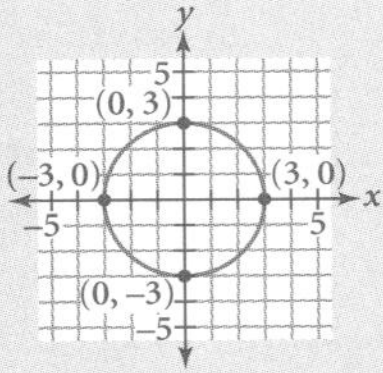

EXTENSION

Use Take Another Look activities 4 and 5 on page 236.

Boolean Graphs Program

Students might wonder why the program divides by Boolean expressions rather than multiplying. The program takes advantage of the fact that no points are plotted when an expression is undefined, such as when it includes dividing by 0. If the expression included multiplication by 0, points that make the expression false would be plotted as $y = 0$ and result in a tail being drawn from the current point on the graph to the x-axis.

4.7 **15.** Begin with the equation of the unit circle, $x^2 + y^2 = 1$.

a. Apply a horizontal stretch by a factor of 3 and a vertical stretch by a factor of 3, and write the equation that results.

b. Sketch the graph. Label the intercepts.

4.4 **16.** Imagine translating the graph of $f(x) = x^2$ left 3 units and up 5 units, and call the image $g(x)$.

a. Give the equation for $g(x)$. $g(x) = (x + 3)^2 + 5$

b. What is the vertex of the graph of $y = g(x)$? $(-3, 5)$

c. Give the coordinates of the image point on the parabola that is 2 units to the right of the vertex. $(-1, 9)$

Project

BOOLEAN GRAPHS

In his book *An Investigation into the Laws of Thought* (1854), the English mathematician George Boole (1815–1864) approached logic in a system that reduced it to simple algebra. In his system, later called Boolean algebra or symbolic logic, expressions are combined using "and" (multiplication), "or" (addition), and "not" (negative), and then interpreted as "true" (1) or "false" (0). Today, **Boolean algebra** plays a fundamental role in the design, construction, and programming of computers. You can learn more about Boolean algebra with the Internet links at www.keymath.com/DAA

An example of a Boolean expression is $x \leq 5$. In this case, if x is 10, the expression is false and assigned a value of 0. If x is 3, then the expression is true and it is assigned a value of 1. You can use Boolean expressions to limit the domain of a function when graphing on your calculator. For example, the graph of $Y_1 = (x + 4)/(x \leq 5)$ does not exist for values of x greater than 5, because your calculator would be dividing by 0. [▸ See **Calculator Note 4G** to learn more about graphing functions with Boolean expressions. ◂]

You can use your calculator to draw this car by entering the following short program.

```
PROGRAM:CAR
ClrDraw
DrawF  1/(X≥1)/(X≤9)
DrawF  (1.2√(X-1)+1)/(X≤3.5)
DrawF  (1.2√(-(X-9))+1)/(X≥6.5)
DrawF  (-0.5(X-5)²+4)/(X≥3.5)/(X≤6.5)
DrawF  -√(1-(X-2.5)²)+1
DrawF  -√(1-(X-7.5)²)+1
DrawF  (abs(X-5.5)+2)/(X≥5.2)/(X≤5.8)
```

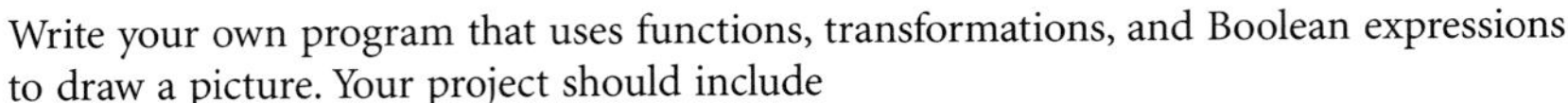

Write your own program that uses functions, transformations, and Boolean expressions to draw a picture. Your project should include

▸ A screen capture or sketch of your drawing.

▸ The functions you used to create your drawing.

Supporting the Project

Encourage students to experiment with the car program until they understand what each part of the program does.

OUTCOMES

▸ The screen capture shows a drawing using a few functions, transformations, and Boolean expressions.

▸ The program uses the list of functions.

• The student produces a complex drawing using one each of the functions learned in this chapter.

• The report includes further research on Boolean algebra and its use in computer programming.

CHAPTER 4 REVIEW

This chapter introduced the concept of a **function** and reviewed **function notation.** You saw real-world situations represented by rules, sets, functions, graphs, and most importantly, equations. You learned to distinguish between functions and other **relations** by using either the definition of a function—at most one y-value per x-value—or the vertical line test.

This chapter also introduced several **transformations,** including **translations, reflections,** and vertical and horizontal **stretches** and **shrinks.** You learned how to transform the graphs of **parent functions** to investigate several families of functions—linear, quadratic, square root, absolute value, and semicircle. For example, if you stretch the graph of the parent function $y = x^2$ by a factor of 3 vertically and by a factor of 2 horizontally, and translate it right 1 unit and up 4 units, then you get the graph of the function $y = 3\left(\frac{x-1}{2}\right)^2 + 4$.

Finally, you looked at the **composition** of functions. Many times, solving a problem involves two or more related functions. You can find the value of a composition of functions by using algebraic or numeric methods or by graphing.

EXERCISES

1. Sketch a graph that shows the relationship between the time in seconds after you start microwaving a bag of popcorn and the number of pops per second. Describe in words what your graph shows.

2. Use these three functions to find each value:

$f(x) = -2x + 7$
$g(x) = x^2 - 2$
$h(x) = (x + 1)^2$

a. $f(4)$ -1 **b.** $g(-3)$ 7 **c.** $h(x + 2) - 3$ $(x + 3)^2 - 3$
d. $f(g(3))$ -7 **e.** $g(h(-2))$ -1 **f.** $h(f(-1))$ 100
g. $f(g(a))$ $-2a^2 + 11$ **h.** $g(f(a))$ $4a^2 - 28a + 47$ **i.** $h(f(a))$ $4a^2 - 32a + 64$

3. The graph of $y = f(x)$ is shown at right. Sketch the graph of each of these functions:

a. $y = f(x) - 3$
b. $y = f(x - 3)$
c. $y = 3f(x)$
d. $y = f(-x)$

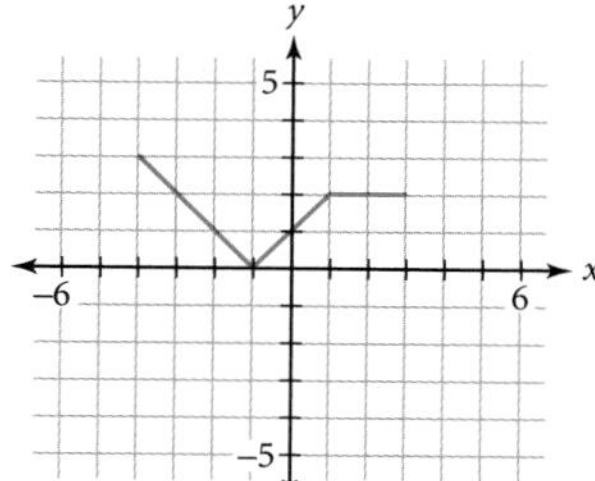

Reviewing (continued)

[Ask] "Is there any figure for which a stretch in one direction is equivalent to a translation in the perpendicular direction?" You need not answer this question; let students play with various graphs to help them better understand exponential and logarithmic graphs in Chapter 5.

ASSIGNING HOMEWORK

If you are using one day to review this chapter, limit the number of exercises you assign. Several of the exercises have many parts.

Helping with the Exercises

Exercise 2 As needed, remind students that $f(g(a))$ is not necessarily the same as $g(f(a))$ and that the result of evaluating these functions at a will not be a number.

Exercise 3 You might pass out copies of the Exercises 3 and 5 worksheet and let students graph and label the answers on the worksheet.

CHAPTER REVIEW 4

PLANNING

LESSON OUTLINE

One day:

15 min Reviewing
20 min Exercises
10 min Student self-assessment

MATERIALS

- Exercises 3 and 5 (W), *optional*
- Calculator Note 4H, *optional*

REVIEWING

To review, present this problem: "For what relations is a vertical transformation equivalent to a horizontal transformation?" Remind students of relations, functions, and graphs. Consider graphs of the parent functions $y = x$, $y = x^2$, $y = \sqrt{x}$, and $y = |x|$ and of the parent relation $x^2 + y^2 = 1$, the unit circle. Take advantage of teachable moments to remind students that $(x + h)^2$ is not the same as $x^2 + h^2$, $\sqrt{x + h}$ is not equivalent to $\sqrt{x} + \sqrt{h}$, and $|x + h|$ is not the same as $|x| + |h|$, so the only function we've seen for which a vertical translation is a horizontal translation is the linear function. Review the laws of exponents and absolute values as students find for each of the above functions that a vertical stretch/shrink is equivalent to a horizontal shrink/stretch. The unit circle can be thought of as a pair of functions, $y = \pm\sqrt{1 - x^2}$; for neither graph of these two functions is any vertical transformation equivalent to a horizontal transformation. Ask what the result of a stretch or a shrink is, to review ellipses.

See page 883 for answers to Exercises 1 and 3.

Exercise 4b [Ask] "Is the left side the same transformation as $-y + 1$?" [A reflection followed by a translation to the left 1 unit is the same as a translation to the right followed by a reflection.]

4a. Translate left 2 units and down 3 units.

4b. Horizontally stretch by a factor of 2, and then reflect across the x-axis.

4c. Horizontally shrink by a factor of $\frac{1}{2}$, vertically stretch by a factor of 2, translate right 1 unit and up 3 units.

Exercise 5 If students have the Exercises 3 and 5 worksheet, they might graph answers in different colors on the worksheet and include a key indicating the corresponding equations.

5a.

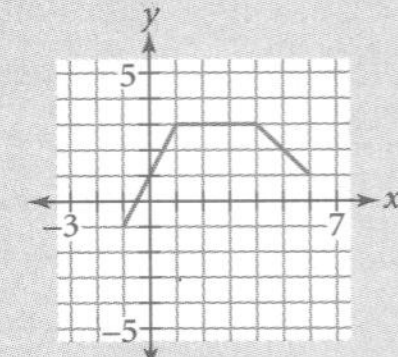

5b.

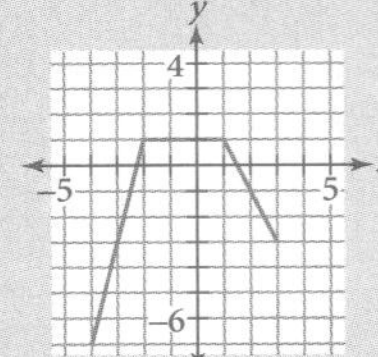

5c.

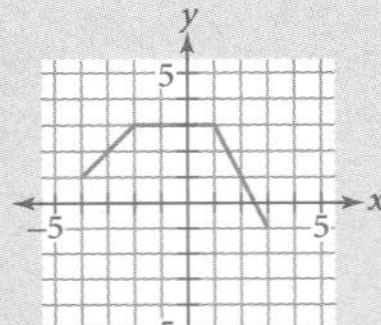

5d.

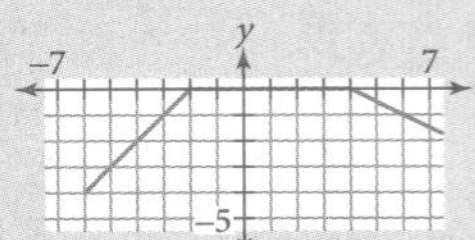

5e.

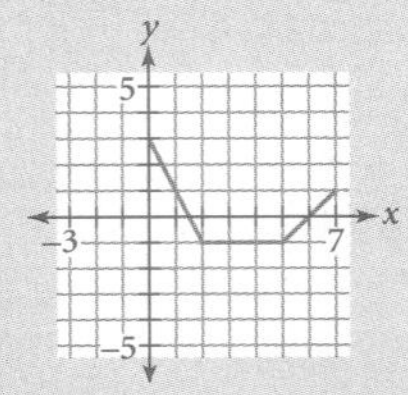

4. Assume you know the graph of $y = f(x)$. Describe the transformations, in order, that would give you the graph of these functions:

a. $y = f(x + 2) - 3$ **b.** $\frac{y-1}{-1} = f\left(\frac{x}{2}\right) + 1$ **c.** $y = 2f\left(\frac{x-1}{0.5}\right) + 3$

5. The graph of $y = f(x)$ is shown at right. Use what you know about transformations to sketch these related functions:

a. $y - 1 = f(x - 2)$ **b.** $\frac{y+3}{2} = f(x + 1)$

c. $y = f(-x) + 1$ **d.** $y + 2 = f\left(\frac{x}{2}\right)$

e. $y = -f(x - 3) + 1$ **f.** $\frac{y+2}{-2} = f\left(\frac{x-1}{1.5}\right)$

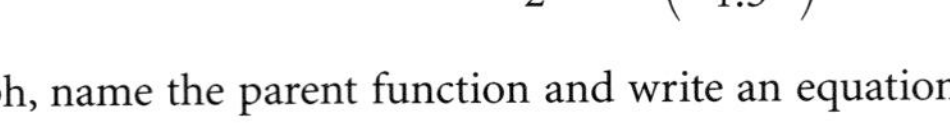

6. For each graph, name the parent function and write an equation of the graph.

a.

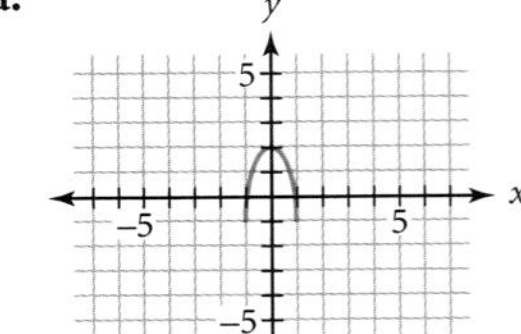

b.

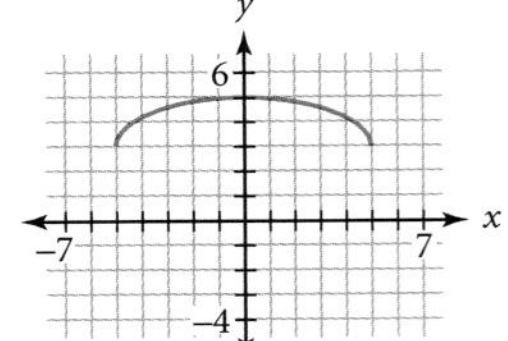

c.

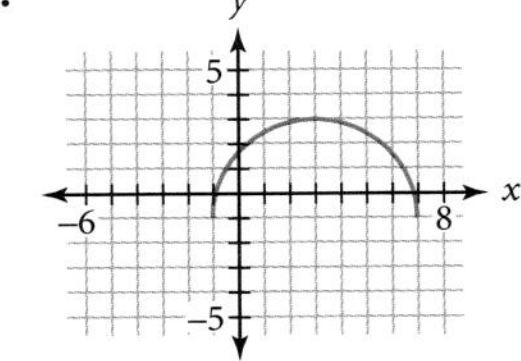

d.

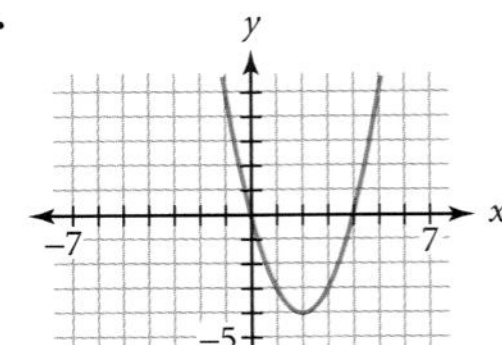

e.

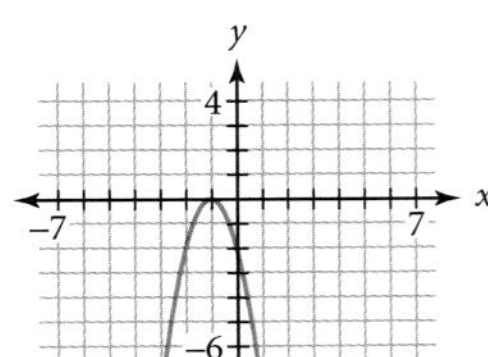

f.

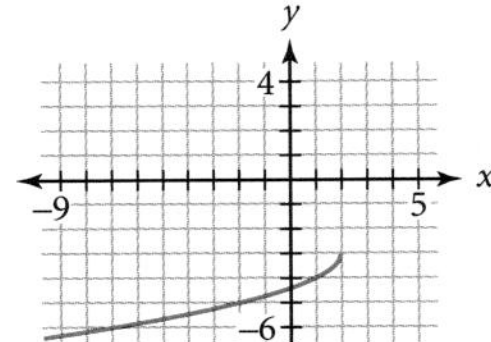

g.

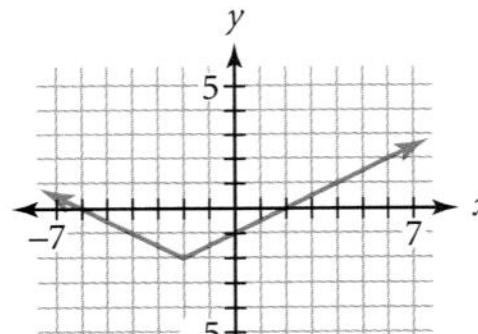

h.

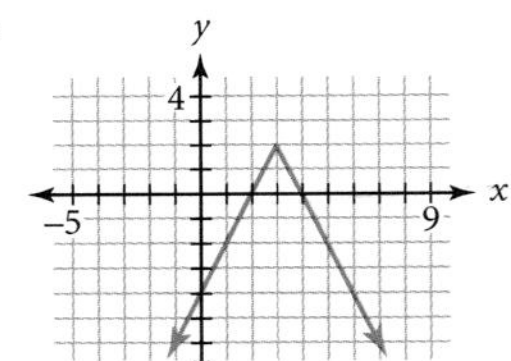

7. Solve for y.

a. $2x - 3y = 6$ $y = \frac{2}{3}x - 2$ **b.** $(y + 1)^2 - 3 = x$ $y = \pm\sqrt{x+3} - 1$ **c.** $\sqrt{1 - y^2} + 2 = x$ $y = \pm\sqrt{-(x-2)^2 + 1}$

8. Solve for x.

a. $4\sqrt{x - 2} = 10$ $x = 8.25$ **b.** $\left(\frac{x}{-3}\right)^2 = 5$ $x = \pm\sqrt{45} \approx \pm 6.7$ **c.** $\left|\frac{x-3}{2}\right| = 4$ $x = 11$ or $x = -5$ **d.** $3\sqrt{1 + \left(\frac{x}{5}\right)^2} = 2$ no solution

5f.

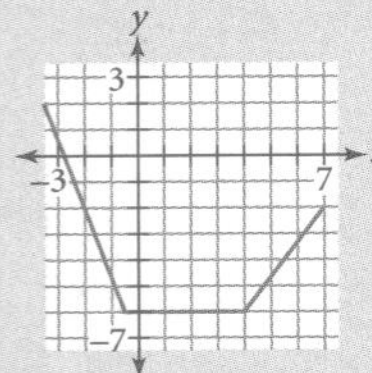

6a. $y = \sqrt{1 - x^2}$; $y = 3\sqrt{1 - x^2} - 1$

6b. $y = \sqrt{1 - x^2}$; $y = 2\sqrt{1 - \left(\frac{x}{5}\right)^2} + 3$

6c. $y = \sqrt{1 - x^2}$; $y = 4\sqrt{1 - \left(\frac{x-3}{4}\right)^2} - 1$

6d. $y = x^2$; $y = (x - 2)^2 - 4$

6e. $y = x^2$; $y = -2(x + 1)^2$

6f. $y = \sqrt{x}$; $y = -\sqrt{-(x - 2)} - 3$

6g. $y = |x|$; $y = 0.5|x + 2| - 2$

6h. $y = |x|$; $y = -2|x - 3| + 2$

9. The Acme Bus Company has a daily ridership of 18,000 passengers and charges \$1.00 per ride. The company wants to raise the fare yet keep its revenue as large as possible. (The revenue is found by multiplying the number of passengers by the fare charged.) From previous fare increases, the company estimates that for each increase of \$0.10 it will lose 1000 riders.

a. Complete this table.

Fare (\$) x	1.00	1.10	1.20	1.30	1.40	1.50	1.60	1.70	1.80
Number of passengers	18000	17000	16000	15000	14000	13000	12000	11000	10000
Revenue (\$) y	18000	18700	19200	19500	19600	19500	19200	18700	18000

b. Make a graph of the the revenue versus fare charged. You should recognize the graph as a parabola.

c. What are the coordinates of the vertex of the parabola? Explain the meaning of each coordinate of the vertex.

d. Find a quadratic function that models these data. Use your model to find $\hat{y} = -10000(x - 1.4)^2 + 19600$

i. the revenue if the fare is \$2.00. \$16,000

ii. the fare(s) that make no revenue (\$0). \$0 or \$2.80

TAKE ANOTHER LOOK

1. Some functions can be described as even or odd. An **even function** has the y-axis as a line of symmetry. If the function f is an even function, then $f(-x) = f(x)$ for all values of x in the domain. Which parent functions that you've seen are even functions? Now graph $y = x^3$, $y = \frac{1}{x}$, and $y = \sqrt[3]{x}$, all of which are **odd functions.** Describe the symmetry displayed by these odd functions. How would you define an odd function in terms of $f(x)$? Can you give an example of a function that is neither even nor odd?

This painting by Laura Domela is titled *sense* (2002, oil on birch panel). The design on the left is similar to an even function, while the one on the right is similar to an odd function.

2. A line of reflection does not have to be the x- or y-axis. Draw the graph of a function and then draw its image when reflected across several different horizontal or vertical lines. Write the equation of each image. Try this with several different functions. In general, if the graph of $y = f(x)$ is reflected across the vertical line $x = a$, what is the equation of the image? If the graph of $y = f(x)$ is reflected across the horizontal line $y = b$, what is the equation of the image?

9b.

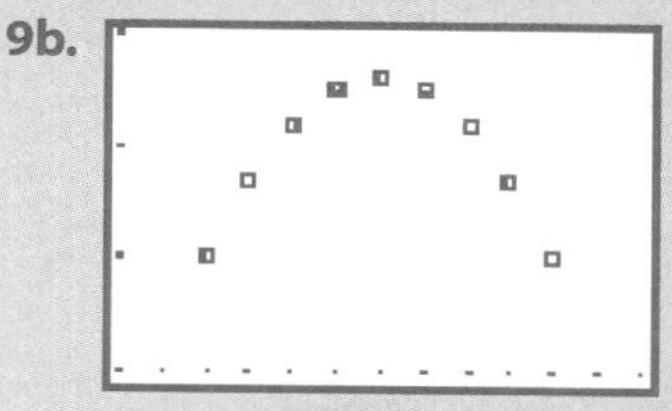

[0.8, 2, 0.1, 17000, 20000, 1000]

9c. (1.40, 19600). By charging \$1.40 per ride, the company achieves the maximum revenue, \$19,600.

Exercise 9d [Ask] "Why, in real life, would neither of these fares result in revenue?" [For \$0, you would be charging no fare, so you would take in no revenue. For \$2.80, the fare is so expensive that no passengers would take the bus.]

Take Another Look

1. The parent functions $y = x^2$ and $y = |x|$ are even functions. An odd function is said to have symmetry with respect to the origin. Students might also describe it as 2-fold rotational symmetry (through 180°). If the function f is an odd function, then $-f(-x) = f(x)$ for all values of x in the domain. The linear function $y = a + bx$ is an example of a function that is neither even nor odd when $a \neq 0$ and $b \neq 0$.

2. Reflecting the graph across the vertical line $x = a$ is equivalent to translating the graph horizontally by the amount a (to move the line $x = a$ to the y-axis), reflecting it across the y-axis, and then translating it back. This composition of transformations yields the equation $y = f(-(x - a) + a) = f(-x + 2a)$. By a similar composition, a reflection across the horizontal line $y = b$ is given by the equation $y = -(f(x) - b) + b = -f(x) + 2b$.

3. The semicircle function, $y = \sqrt{1 - x^2}$, and the circle relation, $x^2 + y^2 = 1$, are two examples for which a vertical stretch or shrink is not equivalent to any horizontal stretch or shrink.

4. The graphs of the compositions of any two linear equations will be parallel. The linear equations resulting from the compositions will have the same slope, or x-coefficient.

Algebraic proof:

Let $f(x) = ax + b$ and $g(x) = cx + d$.

$f(g(x)) = a(cx + d) + b = acx + ad + b$

$g(f(x)) = c(ax + b) + d = acx + cb + d$

5. Refer students to Calculator Note 4H.

Compositions are essentially a series of input-output functions. Drawing a vertical line up to the graph of $g(x)$ gives the value of $g(x)$. Drawing a horizontal line to the graph of $y = x$ makes that y-value into an x-value. Drawing a vertical line to the graph of $f(x)$ evaluates $f(x)$ for that output value, and the horizontal line to the y-axis reveals the answer.

ASSESSING

As a good resource for study, refer students to the table on page 220, Lesson 4.7, which includes a summary of all the transformations included in this chapter.

By the end of this chapter, students might be comfortable finding equations and graphing them without using their calculators. You might consider not using calculators on part of the chapter assessment.

3. For the graph of the parent function $y = x^2$, you can think of any vertical stretch or shrink as an equivalent horizontal shrink or stretch. For example, the equations $y = 4x^2$ and $y = (2x)^2$ are equivalent, even though one represents a vertical stretch by a factor of 4 and the other represents a horizontal shrink by a factor of $\frac{1}{2}$. For the graph of any function or relation, is it possible to think of any vertical stretch or shrink as an equivalent horizontal shrink or stretch? If so, explain your reasoning. If not, give examples of functions and relations for which it is not possible.

4. Enter two linear functions into Y_1 and Y_2 on your calculator. Enter the compositions of the functions as $Y_3 = Y_1(Y_2(x))$ and $Y_4 = Y_2(Y_1(x))$. Graph Y_3 and Y_4 and look for any relationships between them. (It will help if you turn off the graphs of Y_1 and Y_2.) Make a conjecture about how the compositions of any two linear functions are related. Change the linear functions in Y_1 and Y_2 to test your conjecture. Can you algebraically prove your conjecture?

5. One way to visualize a composition of functions is to use a web graph. Here's how you evaluate $f(g(x))$ for any value of x, using a web graph:

Choose an x-value. Draw a vertical line from the x-axis to the function $g(x)$. Then draw a horizontal line from that point to the line $y = x$. Next, draw a vertical line from this point so that it intersects $f(x)$. Draw a horizontal line from the intersection point to the y-axis. The y-value at this point of intersection gives the value of $f(g(x))$.

Choose two functions $f(x)$ and $g(x)$. Use web graphs to find $f(g(x))$ for several values of x. Why does this method work?

Assessing What You've Learned

ORGANIZE YOUR NOTEBOOK Organize your notes on each type of parent function and each type of transformation you have learned about. Review how each transformation affects the graph of a function or relation and how the equation of the function or relation changes. You might want to create a large chart with rows for each type of transformation and columns for each type of parent function; don't forget to include a column for the general function, $y = f(x)$.

UPDATE YOUR PORTFOLIO Choose one piece of work that illustrates each transformation you have studied in this chapter. Try to select pieces that illustrate different parent functions. Add these to your portfolio. Describe each piece in a cover sheet, giving the objective, the result, and what you might have done differently.

WRITE TEST ITEMS Two important skills from this chapter are the ability to use transformations to write and graph equations. Write at least two test items that assess these skills. If you work with a group, identify other key ideas from this chapter and work together to write an entire test.

FACILITATING SELF-ASSESSMENT

You might use some student-written items on the chapter assessment. Ask students to specify whether calculators will be allowed in solving the item they write.

Good portfolio items for this chapter include Lesson 4.1, Exercise 8; Lessons 4.2–4.4, Exercise 9; Lesson 4.5, Exercise 11; and Lessons 4.6–4.8, Exercise 9.

CHAPTER

5

Exponential, Power, and Logarithmic Functions

Overview

Exponential functions are introduced in **Lesson 5.1** to model growth and decay. In **Lesson 5.2,** students review properties of exponents as they become familiar with the power function $y = ax^n$ and are introduced to rational exponents. In **Lesson 5.3,** rational exponents $\left(x^{1/n}\right)$ are related to root notation $\left(\sqrt[n]{x}\right)$. Students then use the point-ratio form, $y = y_1 b^{x-x_1}$, to find an exponential equation through two points. Real-world applications are presented in **Lesson 5.4. Lesson 5.5** introduces inverses of functions and applications of inverses. Students learn to solve logarithmic functions in **Lesson 5.6,** and they also see why the inverse of an exponential function is a logarithmic function. Students increase their understanding of logarithms in **Lesson 5.7,** where they learn to work with logarithms of any base by changing to a common base; they also learn how a slide rule works. In **Lesson 5.8,** students use logarithms as a tool to solve problems with the variable in the exponent. The **exploration** on the transcendental number e introduces students to the natural logarithm function.

The Mathematics

Exponents and Exponential Functions

Exponents, or powers, represent repeated multiplication. Exponent properties such as $b^m b^n = b^{m+n}$ and $\frac{b^m}{b^n} = b^{m-n}$ can be understood for positive integer exponents through multiplication and division. We define other rational exponents in a way that extends the same properties to them. For example, because it is known that $\sqrt[3]{b}$ is the number whose cube is b, $b^{1/3}$ is defined to be $\sqrt[3]{b}$ so that $\left(b^{1/3}\right)^3$ equals b.

But we have to be careful with rational exponents. If we use them carelessly, we can get statements like

$$1 = 1^{1/2} = \left((-1)^6\right)^{1/2} = (-1)^{6/2} = (-1)^3 = -1$$

implying that $1 = -1$. The student book applies rational exponents only to positive numbers, so that $(-1)^{6/2}$ is meaningless. This restriction is relaxed when the base is a variable, as it is for power functions; $y = x^{1/3}$ can be evaluated and graphed even when x is less than 0.

The book also makes the assumption that when a rational exponent is applied to a positive base, the result is positive. Because of this assumption, using rational exponents to solve equations may not produce all solutions. For example, the equation $x^2 = 4$ has two solutions, ± 2. However, if we raise both sides of the equation to the power of $\frac{1}{2}$, we get $x = 4^{1/2}$, which must be positive.

Exponential functions of the form $y = ab^x$ are characterized by the fact that any two pairs of x-values the same distance apart correspond to pairs of y-values with the same ratio, in contrast to linear functions, for which any two pairs of x-values the same distance apart correspond to pairs of y-values with the same difference. One consequence of this property of exponential functions is that every vertical stretch of the graph of an exponential function is the same as some horizontal translation. Another consequence is that the amount of increase in x required to double or halve the value of y is always the same, no matter what the starting value of y. For decreasing exponential functions, this time is called the *half-life;* for increasing exponential functions, it's called the *doubling time.*

Logarithms and Logarithmic Functions

The constant-ratio characteristic of exponential functions also implies that the product of any two values of $y = b^x$ is the image of the sum of the related x-values. That is, $b^{x_1}b^{x_2}$ equals $b^{x_1+x_2}$. This fact is behind the notion of logarithms. The logarithm to base b of a number x is the exponent put on b to get x. Before the days of electronic calculators, logarithms were used to calculate products and roots of very large or very small numbers. These methods underlie the design of slide rules.

The student book includes two modern uses of logarithms. It gives several ways of solving equations for exponents, and it considers transformations. A vertical logarithmic transformation of the plane is like a vertical stretch and shrink, but by uneven amounts so that the graph of an exponential function becomes a straight line. Algebraically, the exponential equation $y = ab^x$ becomes the equation $\log y = \log a + x \log b$; that this equation is linear is seen by rewriting it as $z = c + dx$. This linearizing technique is especially useful when you are trying to find exponential functions that fit real-world data.

Inverse Functions

If points (x, y) are related by the exponential function $y = b^x$, then points (y, x) are related by the logarithmic function $x = \log_b y$. That is, the exponential and logarithmic functions are inverses of each other. In general, functions $f(x)$ and $g(x)$ are inverses if the ordered pairs of one are the ordered pairs of the other but in reverse order; that is, the x's and y's are interchanged. Equivalently, $f(g(x)) = g(f(x)) = x$.

Using This Chapter

To save time, you might combine Lessons 5.1 and 5.2 for students familiar with the topics. Lesson 5.7 can be shortened, but you should at least review the properties of logarithms before you go to the exercises. Most of Lesson 5.8 is not essential, but teach solving equations by taking the logarithm of each side, perhaps with Lesson 5.7.

Resources

Discovering Advanced Algebra Resources

Teaching and Worksheet Masters
Lessons 5.1, 5.2, 5.4, 5.5, 5.7, 5.8

Calculator Notes 1L, 1M, 3B, 3D, 4C, 4D, 5A–5E

Sketchpad Demonstrations
Lessons 5.2, 5.3, 5.5, 5.6

Fathom Demonstration
Lesson 5.8

Assessment Resources A and B
Quiz 1 (Lessons 5.1–5.3)
Quiz 2 (Lessons 5.4, 5.5)
Quiz 3 (Lessons 5.6–5.8)
Chapter 5 Test
Chapter 5 Constructive Assessment Options

More Practice Your Skills for Chapter 5

Condensed Lessons for Chapter 5

Other Resources

Powers of Ten film by Charles and Ray Eames.

Powers of Ten: A Book About the Relative Size of Things in the Universe and the Effect of Adding Another Zero by Philip and Phylis Morrison.

Historical Topics for the Mathematics Classroom from NCTM.

For complete references to these and other resources see www.keypress.com/DAA.

Materials

- dice (1 die per person)
- patty paper, *optional*
- rulers (2 per group)
- temperature probes
- cup of hot water

Pacing Guide

	day 1	day 2	day 3	day 4	day 5	day 6	day 7	day 8	day 9	day 10
standard	5.1	5.2	5.3	quiz, 5.4	5.5	quiz, 5.6	5.6	5.7	5.8	5.8
enriched	5.1, project	5.2	5.3, project	quiz, 5.4	5.5	quiz, 5.6	5.7	5.8	5.8, project	quiz, exploration
block	5.1, 5.2	5.3, quiz, 5.4	5.5, quiz, 5.6	5.6, 5.7	5.8, quiz	exploration, review	TAL, assessment			

	day 11	day 12	day 13
standard	quiz, review	review	assessment
enriched	review, project	review, TAL	assessment

CHAPTER

5

Exponential, Power, and Logarithmic Functions

Art can take on living forms. To create *Tree Mountain,* conceptualized by artist Agnes Denes, 11,000 people planted 11,000 trees on a human-made mountain in Finland, on a former gravel pit. The trees were planted in a mathematical pattern similar to a golden spiral, imitating the arrangement of seeds on a sunflower.

All living things grow and eventually decay. Both growth and decay can be modeled using exponential functions.

Tree Mountain–A Living Time Capsule–11,000 People, 11,000 Trees, 400 Years 1992–1996, Ylöjärvi, Finland, (420 x 270 x 28 meters) © Agnes Denes.

OBJECTIVES

In this chapter you will

- write explicit equations for geometric sequences
- use exponential functions to model real-world growth and decay scenarios
- review the properties of exponents and the meaning of rational exponents
- learn how to find the inverse of a function
- apply logarithms, the inverses of exponential functions

One example of decay in nature is land erosion. Some studies have found that there is a 500-fold difference between erosion rates on forested land and those on cultivated land. Roots and forest litter help keep soil from washing away. Even on land with vegetation, an estimated 200 pounds of soil per acre is swept away each year.

[Ask] "What kind of equation would you write for the decay of an eroding mountain? What kind of equation would you write for the growth of a tree?" [Both equations are approximately logistic.]

"Do you think that this mountain will still be here in 400 years? Do you think the trees will?"

To review Lesson 4.7, you might refer students to the inset model of the mountain and **[Ask]** "Viewed from the top, what shape do you think a cross section of the mountain is?" Students might think that it is a circle that looks elliptical because of the angle. In fact, it actually is an ellipse. The dimensions of the mountain are 420 meters by 270 meters. Ask how you might know whether an image represents an actual ellipse or a circle viewed from an angle.

CHAPTER 5 OBJECTIVES

- Review properties of integer exponents and extend them to rational exponents
- Write explicit equations for geometric sequences
- Generalize explicit equations for geometric sequences to exponential functions for modeling continuous real-world growth and decay
- Distinguish a power function from an exponential function and solve power equations
- Define the inverse relation of a function and study graphs and compositions of inverses
- Find and apply inverse functions in real-world situations
- Define common logarithms and logarithms with other bases and use them to calculate and solve equations in several ways
- Develop properties of logarithms
- Establish that the inverse of an exponential function is a logarithmic function
- Use logarithms to straighten data for help in finding an algebraic model
- Observe the natural logarithm function and learn about its base, *e*

LESSON 5.1

PLANNING

LESSON OUTLINE

One day:

15 min Investigation

10 min Sharing

10 min Example

10 min Exercises

MATERIALS

- dice (1 die per person)
- Radioactive Decay Sample Data (T), *optional*
- Calculator Notes 1L, 1M

TEACHING

In Chapter 1, students modeled situations involving growth. Arithmetic sequences model discrete growth in which the *difference* of consecutive terms is constant; the linear equations of Chapter 3 extended the corresponding recursive formulas to the continuous case. Geometric sequences model discrete growth in which the *ratio* of consecutive terms is constant; the exponential functions of this chapter extend geometric sequences to the continuous case. If you want to start with the one-step investigation, see page 239.

Guiding the Investigation

In place of dice, students might use calculators set to find random integers from 1 to 6 or use another number to investigate a different decay rate. (See Calculator Note 1L.)

Step 1 [Alert] Make sure the recorder labels the initial number of people in the class as stage 0.

See pages 883–884 for answers to Steps 1, 2, and 6.

LESSON 5.1

Exponential Functions

Life shrinks or expands in proportion to one's courage.

ANAÏS NIN

In Chapter 1, you used sequences and recursive rules to model geometric growth or decay of money, populations, and other quantities. Recursive formulas generate only discrete values, such as the amount of money after one year or two years, or the population in a certain year. Usually growth and decay happen continuously. In this lesson you will focus on finding explicit formulas for these patterns, which will allow you to model situations involving continuous growth and decay, or to find discrete points without using recursion.

Science CONNECTION

Certain atoms are unstable—their nuclei can split apart, emitting radiation and resulting in a more stable atom. This process is called radioactive decay. The time it takes for half the atoms in a radioactive sample to decay is called **half-life,** and the half-life is specific to the element. For instance, the half-life of carbon-14 is 5730 years, whereas the half-life of uranium-238 is 4.5 billion years.

Submerged for two years in a storage tank in La Hague, France, this radioactive waste glows blue. The blue light is known as the "Cherenkov glow."

Investigation
Radioactive Decay

You will need

- one die per person

This investigation is a simulation of radioactive decay. Each person will need a standard six-sided die. [▶ See **Calculator Note 1L** to simulate this with your calculator instead. ◀] Each standing person represents a radioactive atom in a sample. The people who sit down at each stage represent the atoms that underwent radioactive decay.

Procedure Note

1. All members of the class should stand up, except for the recorder. The recorder counts and records the number standing at each stage.
2. Each standing person rolls a die, and anyone who gets a 1 sits down.
3. Wait for the recorder to count and record the number of people standing.
4. Repeat Steps 2 and 3 until fewer than three students are standing.

Step 1 Follow the Procedure Note to collect data in the form (*stage, number standing*).

Step 2 Graph your data and write a recursive formula that models it.

Step 3 Write an expression to calculate the 8th term using only u_0 and the ratio.

Step 3 $u_8 = 30 \cdot 0.8186^8$

Step 4 Write an expression that calculates the *n*th term using only u_0 and the ratio.

Step 4 $u_n = 30 \cdot 0.8186^n$

Step 5 What was the half-life of this sample?

Step 5 The half-life of the sample is between 3 and 4 because half the sample remains when there are 15 people standing.

Step 6 Write a paragraph explaining how this investigation simulates the life of a radioactive sample.

If you have fewer than 15 students, run the procedure several times and analyze the totals, or use the Radioactive Decay Sample Data transparency.

Step 2 As needed, refer students back to Chapter 1 to review recursive formulas representing geometric sequences.

Step 5 [Language] *Half-life* is defined in the Science Connection. In this context, it refers to the number of stages.

LESSON OBJECTIVES

- Write explicit equations for geometric sequences
- Define *exponential function* and recognize $y = ab^x$ as the parent function
- See real-world growth and decay situations, and recognize that the exponential function models growth when *b* is greater than 1 and models decay when *b* is less than 1
- Learn about half-life and doubling time
- Evaluate an exponential function using either the explicit equations or graphical methods

In Chapter 3, you learned how to find an equation of the line that passes through points of an arithmetic sequence. In this lesson you will find an equation of the curve that passes through points of a geometric sequence.

You probably recognized the geometric decay model in the investigation. As you learned in Chapter 1, geometric decay is nonlinear. At each step the previous term is multiplied by a common ratio. So, the nth term contains the common ratio multiplied n times. You use exponents to represent a number that appears as a factor n times, so you use exponential functions to model geometric growth. An **exponential function** is a continuous function with a variable in the exponent, and it is used to model growth or decay.

EXAMPLE

Most automobiles depreciate as they get older. Suppose an automobile that originally costs $14,000 depreciates by one-fifth of its value every year.

a. What is the value of this automobile after two years?

b. When is this automobile worth half of its initial value?

▶ Solution

a. The recursive formula gives automobile values only after one year, two years, and so on.

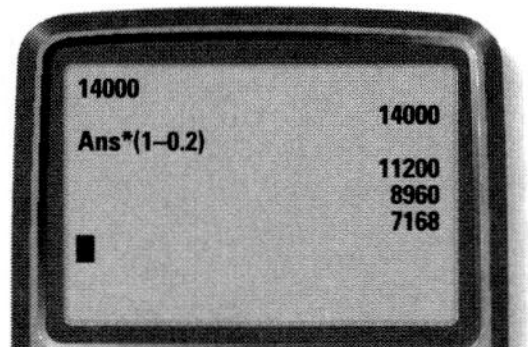

The value decreases by $\frac{1}{5}$, or 0.2, each year, so to find the next term you continue to multiply by another $(1 - 0.2)$. You can use this fact to write an explicit formula.

$14000 \cdot (1 - 0.2)$	Value after 1 year.
$14000 \cdot (1 - 0.2) \cdot (1 - 0.2) = 14000(1 - 0.2)^2$	Value after 2 years.
$14000 \cdot (1 - 0.2) \cdot (1 - 0.2) \cdot (1 - 0.2) = 14000(1 - 0.2)^3$	Value after 3 years.
$14000 \cdot (1 - 0.2)^n$	Value after n years.

So, the explicit formula for automobile value is $u_n = 14000(1 - 0.2)^n$. The equation of the continuous function through the points of this sequence is

$$y = 14000(1 - 0.2)^x$$

You can use the continuous function to find the value of the car at any point. To find the value after $2\frac{1}{2}$ years, substitute 2.5 for x.

$$y = 14000(1 - 0.2)^{2.5} \approx \$8014.07$$

It makes sense that the automobile's value after $2\frac{1}{2}$ years should be between the values for u_2 and u_3, $8960 and $7168. Because this is not a linear function, finding the value halfway between 8960 and 7168 does not give an accurate value for the value of the car after $2\frac{1}{2}$ years.

b. To find when the automobile is worth half of its initial value, substitute 7000 for y and find x.

$y = 14000(1 - 0.2)^x$	Original equation.
$7000 = 14000(1 - 0.2)^x$	Substitute 7000 for y.
$0.5 = (1 - 0.2)^x$	Divide both sides by 14000.
$0.5 = (0.8)^x$	Combine like terms.

One Step

Follow the Procedure Note of the investigation. Ask students to find recursive formulas and function expressions that describe the data. As needed, remind students that repeated multiplication is represented by exponents. During Sharing, ask what other kinds of growth might be modeled by exponential functions; include depreciation.

▶ EXAMPLE

[Language] *Depreciate* means "to lose value." **[Alert]** Students might think that the automobile loses one-fifth of its original $14,000 value each year. The loss during each year is one-fifth of the value at the beginning of that year.

[Alert] In the solution to part a, students may have difficulty with the last paragraph. A graph might help.

In part b, let students guess and check. You might see who can come up with the closest solution before they look in their books. Or students might find the intersection of $y = 7000$ and $y = 1400(1 - 0.2)^x$.

SHARING IDEAS

As students share their results from Step 4, ask them to write the same equation using x and y, representing a continuous function.

Point out that the same function describes processes as different as automobile depreciation and radioactive decay. Both of these examples are decreasing functions. **[Ask]** "Can an exponential function model positive growth?" Chapter 1 has examples of increasing geometric sequences. **[Ask]** "How are increasing exponential functions different from decreasing exponential functions?" [The base b, or common ratio, is greater than 1 for increasing functions and between 0 and 1 for decreasing functions.] "Is b ever negative?" [The exponential function is not defined for negative b.] **[Alert]** The idea of half-life can

Sharing Ideas (continued)

be difficult for students. Although they may believe that this car loses half its initial value in about 3 years 39 days, they may not realize that its value at any time shrinks to about half that value over the next 3 years 39 days.

[Ask] "What might be the equivalent of half-life for increasing functions?" [doubling time] You might pose a problem about various amounts of money invested at an annual rate of 4.5%, compounded monthly. Is the doubling time the same for each

NCTM STANDARDS

CONTENT		PROCESS	
	Number	✓	Problem Solving
✓	Algebra	✓	Reasoning
	Geometry	✓	Communication
✓	Measurement	✓	Connections
✓	Data/Probability	✓	Representation

Sharing Ideas (continued)
initial amount? (This is a good question for students to talk or write about. They might consult Calculator Note 1M.) **[Ask]** "Is the doubling time the same for different interest rates?" [no] "Is it the same if the investment is compounded weekly or yearly?" [no] "If the initial investment takes about 185.2 months to double, how long will it take to double again?" [another 185.2 months]

Assessing Progress
As students work and present, you can assess their ability to follow directions carefully, plot discrete data, model data with a recursive formula, represent repeated multiplication with exponents, and generalize a pattern to express the nth term.

Closing the Lesson

Exponential functions, of the form $y = ab^x$, describe in a continuous way growth that was described discretely by geometric sequences (sequences that have a constant ratio between consecutive terms). If b is greater than 1, the function's values are increasing, as in investments; if b is between 0 and 1, the values are decreasing. Increasing exponential functions have a constant **doubling time,** and decreasing exponential functions have a constant **half-life.**

BUILDING UNDERSTANDING

The exercises help students relate geometric sequences to exponential functions.

ASSIGNING HOMEWORK

Essential	1–4
Performance assessment	5–11
Portfolio	7, 9
Journal	5
Group	11
Review	2, 12–16

You don't yet know how to solve for x when x is an exponent, but you can experiment with different exponents to find one that produces a value close to 0.5. The value of $(0.8)^{3.106}$ is very close to 0.5. This means that the value of the car is about \$7000, or half of its original value, after 3.106 years (about 3 years 39 days). This is the half-life of the value of the automobile, or the amount of time needed for the value to decrease to half of the original amount.

Exponential Function

The general form of an exponential function is

$$y = ab^x$$

where the coefficient a is the y-intercept and the base b is the growth rate.

Exponential growth and decay are both modeled with the general form $y = ab^x$. Growth is modeled by a base that is greater than 1, and decay is modeled by a base that is less than 1. In general, a larger base models faster growth, and a base closer to 0 models faster decay.

All exponential growth curves have a **doubling time,** just as decay has a half-life. This time depends only on the ratio. For example, if the ratio is constant, it takes just as long to double \$1,000 to \$2,000 as it takes to double \$5,000 to \$10,000.

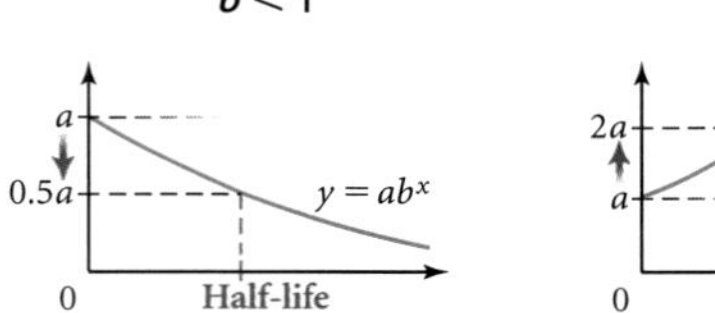

EXERCISES

You will need

Geometry software for Exercise 15

Practice Your Skills

1. Evaluate each function at the given value.

a. $f(x) = 4.753(0.9421)^x$, $x = 5$ $f(5) \approx 3.52738$

b. $g(h) = 238(1.37)^h$, $h = 14$ $g(14) \approx 19{,}528.32$

c. $h(t) = 47.3(0.835)^t + 22.3$, $t = 24$ $h(24) \approx 22.9242$

d. $j(x) = 225(1.0825)^{x-3}$, $x = 37$ $j(37) \approx 3332.20$

2. Record three terms of the sequence, and then write an explicit function for the sequence.

a. $u_0 = 16$
$u_n = 0.75u_{n-1}$ where $n \geq 1$
16, 12, 9; $y = 16(0.75)^x$

b. $u_0 = 24$
$u_n = 1.5u_{n-1}$ where $n \geq 1$
24, 36, 54; $y = 24(1.5)^x$

3. Evaluate each function at $x = 0$, $x = 1$, and $x = 2$, and then write a recursive formula for the pattern.

a. $f(x) = 125(0.6)^x$

b. $f(x) = 3(2)^x$

4. Calculate the ratio of the second term to the first term, and express the answer as a decimal value. State the percent increase or decrease.

a. 48, 36 **b.** 54, 72 **c.** 50, 47 **d.** 47, 50

MATERIALS

- Calculator Notes 4D, 5A, *optional*

Helping with the Exercises

Exercise 1 Students may need help entering exponents on calculators. Refer them to Calculator Note 5A.

Exercise 3 **[Ask]** "What is the effect of a zero exponent?" [The factor always equals 1.]

Exercise 4 For each part, **[Ask]** "Would this be a decay or a growth model?" Point out that 4c and 4d have the same numbers in reverse. **[Ask]** "Why are the percentages different?" [because 6% of 50 is not the same as 6% of 47] Suggest that students write the ratio as (1 + *some value*) or (1 − *some value*).

Reason and Apply

5. In 1991, the population of the People's Republic of China was 1.151 billion, with a growth rate of 1.5% annually.

a. Write a recursive formula that models this growth. Let u_0 represent the population in 1991. $u_0 = 1.151$ and $u_n = (1 + 0.015)u_{n-1}$ where $n \geq 1$

b. Complete a table recording the population for the years 1991 to 2000.

c. Define the variables and write an exponential equation that models this growth. Choose two data points from the table and show that your equation works.

d. The actual population of China in 2001 was 1.273 billion. How does this compare with the value predicted by your equation? What does this tell you?

Cultural CONNECTION

In 2001, the population of China was 1.273 billion. In large cities like Beijing and Shanghai, more than half of the people use bicycles as transportation. What would happen if half a billion Chinese bicyclists switched to cars? What if half of the drivers in U.S. cities switched to bicycles?

6. Jack planted a mysterious bean just outside his kitchen window. It immediately sprouted 2.56 cm above the ground. Jack kept a careful log of the plant's growth. He measured the height of the plant each day at 8:00 A.M. and recorded these data.

Day	0	1	2	3	4
Height (cm)	2.56	6.4	16	40	100

a. Define variables and write an exponential equation for this pattern. If the pattern were to continue, what would be the heights on the fifth and sixth days?

Kudzu, shown here in Oxford, Mississippi, is a fast-growing weed that was brought from Japan and once promoted for its erosion control. Today kudzu covers more than 7 million U.S. acres and spreads across about 120,000 more each year.

b. Jack's younger brother measured the plant at 8:00 P.M. on the evening of the third day and found it to be about 63.25 cm tall. Show how to find this value mathematically. (You may need to experiment with your calculator.) $y = 2.56(2.5)^{3.5} \approx 63.25$

c. Find the height of the sprout at 12:00 noon on the sixth day. 728 cm

d. Find the doubling time for this plant. 0.76 day, or 18 hours

e. Experiment with the equation to find the day and time (to the nearest hour) when the plant reaches a height of 1 km. 11 days 13 hours, or 9 P.M. on day 11

7. *Mini-Investigation* For 7a–d, graph the equations on your calculator.

a. $y = 1.5^x$ b. $y = 2^x$ c. $y = 3^x$ d. $y = 4^x$

e. How do the graphs compare? What points (if any) do they have in common?

f. Predict what the graph of $y = 6^x$ will look like. Verify your prediction by using your calculator.

Exercise 7 For this exercise and others that require graphing and comparing several equations, students will benefit from having the calculator set to Sequential mode rather than Simultaneous mode. You may also want to recommend that students use the "turtle" setting to slow down the graphing. Move the cursor to the symbol to the left of Y1 = and press ENTER until it appears as ◊.

```
Plot1 Plot2 Plot3
Y1=1.5^X
Y2=2^X
Y3=3^X
Y4=4^X
Y5=
Y6=
Y7=
```

3a. $f(0) = 125, f(1) = 75, f(2) = 45; u_0 = 125$ and $u_n = 0.6u_{n-1}$ where $n \geq 1$

3b. $f(0) = 3, f(1) = 6, f(2) = 12; u_0 = 3$ and $u_n = 2u_{n-1}$ where $n \geq 1$

4a. 0.75; 25% decrease

4b. $1.\overline{3}$; $33.\overline{3}$% increase

4c. 0.94; 6% decrease

4d. 1.0638; 6.38% increase

Exercise 5 If students are having difficulty going from recursive to exponential form, suggest that they write the explicit formula first.

5b.

Year	Population (in billions)
1991	1.151
1992	1.168
1993	1.186
1994	1.204
1995	1.222
1996	1.240
1997	1.259
1998	1.277
1999	1.297
2000	1.316

5c. Let x represent the number of years since 1991, and let y represent the population in billions. $y = 1.151(1 + 0.015)^x$

5d. $y = 1.151(1 + 0.015)^{10} \approx 1.336$; the equation gives a population that is greater than the actual population. Sample answer: the growth rate of China's population has slowed since 1991.

Exercise 6 In this exercise, the data have decimal values that appear in the exponent. Students can solve the equation in 6e by either guess-and-check or graphing. They will see logarithms in Lesson 5.6. As needed, remind students that 1 km = 1000 m = 100000 cm.

6a. Let x represent the number of the day and let y represent the height in cm. $y = 2.56(2.5)^x$. For the fifth day, $y = 2.56(2.5)^5 = 250$ cm; for the sixth day, $y = 2.56(2.5)^6 = 625$ cm.

See page 884 for answers to Exercise 7.

Exercises 8, 10 Students use transformations from Chapter 4 to find these growth equations. **[Alert]** Students may be skeptical of the translations in 8b and 8c because the graphs don't look "parallel." As needed, remind them that translations of parabolas aren't equidistant either. Actually, horizontal translations of graphs of exponential functions are also vertical stretches, because $b^{x+h} = b^x b^h$.

9a–d.

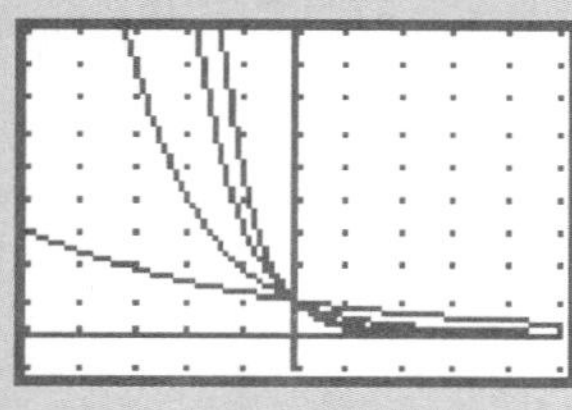

[−5, 5, 1, −1, 9, 1]

9e. As the base increases, the graph flattens out. The curves all intersect the y-axis at (0, 1).

9f. The graph of $y = 0.1^x$ should be the steepest of all of these. It will contain the points (0, 1) and (−1, 10).

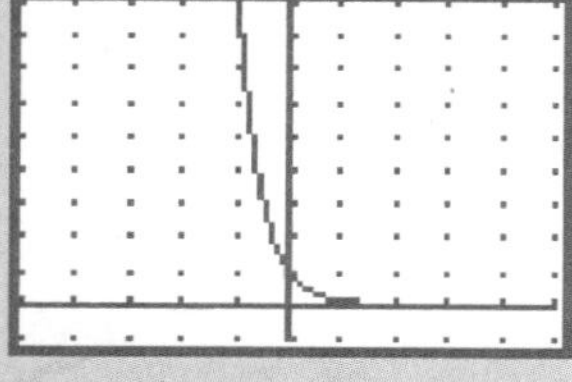

[−5, 5, 1, −1, 9, 1]

8. Each of the red curves is a transformation of the graph of $y = 2^x$, shown in black. Write an equation for each red curve.

a. $y = 2^{x-3}$

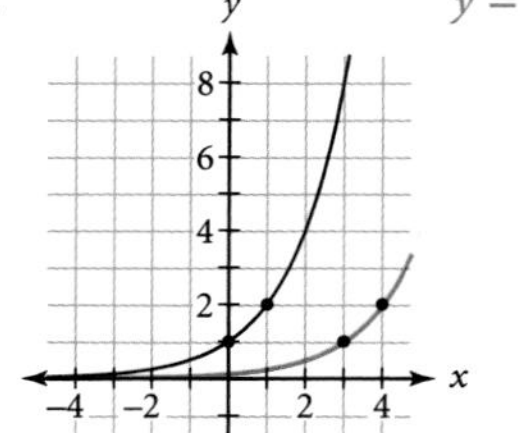

b. $y - 2 = 2^x$ or $y = 2^x + 2$

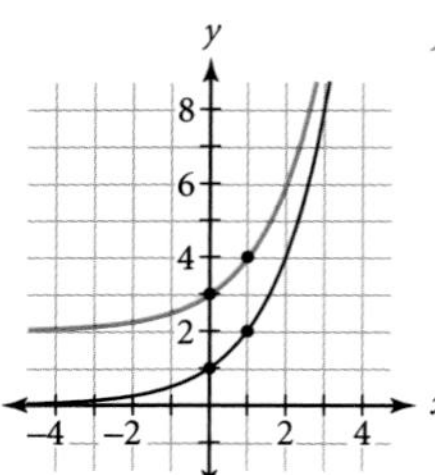

c. $\frac{y}{3} = 2^x$ or $y = 3 \cdot 2^x$

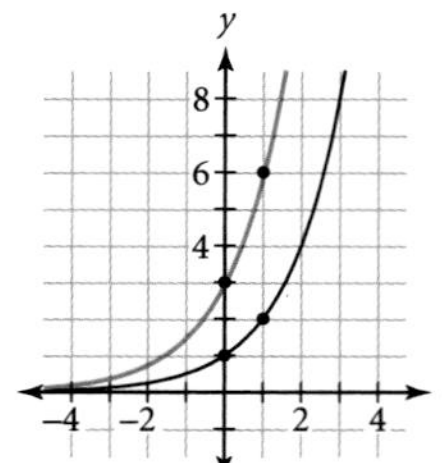

d. $y = 2^{x/3}$

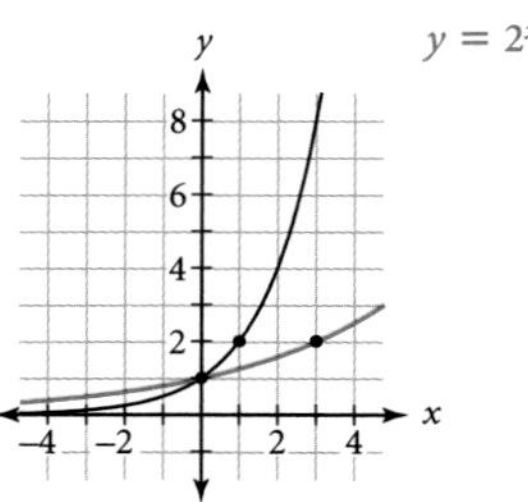

9. ***Mini-Investigation*** For 9a–d, graph the equations on your calculator.

a. $y = 0.2^x$

b. $y = 0.3^x$

c. $y = 0.5^x$

d. $y = 0.8^x$

e. How do the graphs compare? What points (if any) do they have in common?

f. Predict what the graph of $y = 0.1^x$ will look like. Verify your prediction by using your calculator.

10. Each of the red curves is a transformation of the graph of $y = 0.5^x$, shown in black. Write an equation for each red curve.

a. $y - 5 = 0.5^x$ or $y = 5 + 0.5^x$

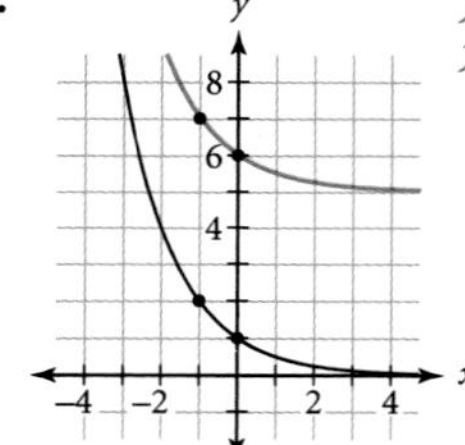

b. $-(y - 5) = 0.5^x$ or $y = -0.5^x + 5$

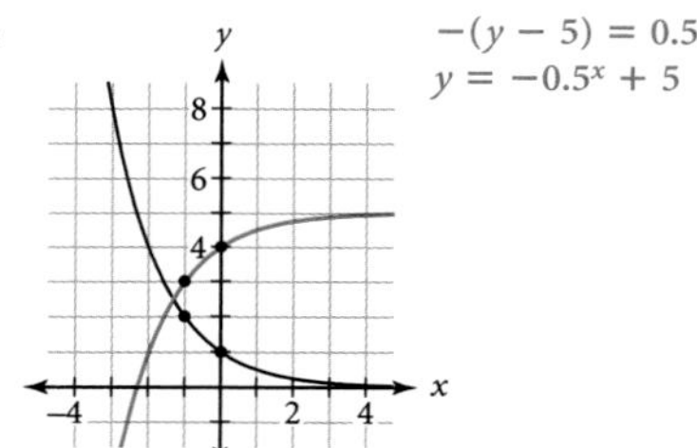

c. $\frac{y-5}{-3} = 0.5^x$ or $y = -3 \cdot 0.5^x + 5$

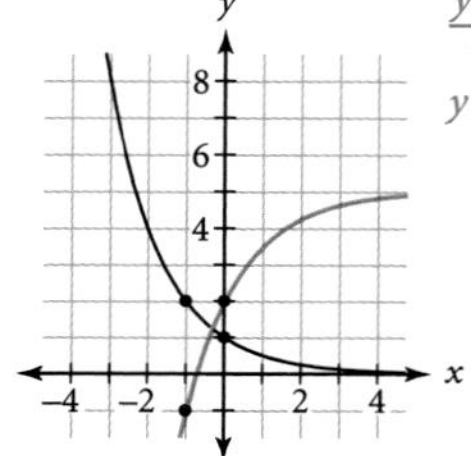

d. $\frac{y-5}{-3} = 0.5^{x/2}$ or $y = -3 \cdot 0.5^{x/2} + 5$

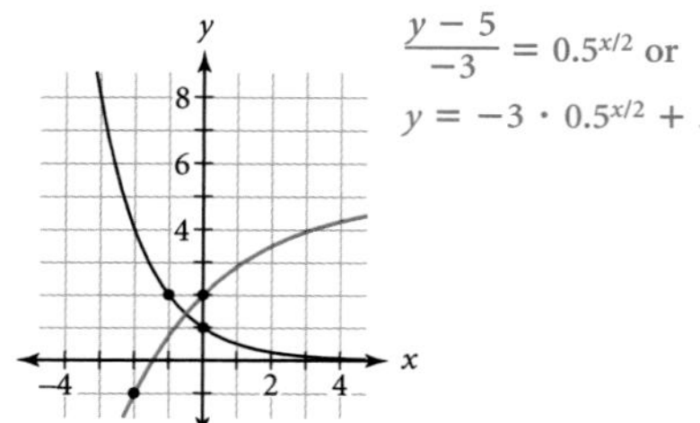

11. The general form of an exponential equation, $y = ab^x$, is convenient when you know the y-intercept. Start with $f(0) = 30$ and $f(1) = 27$.

a. Find the common ratio. $\frac{27}{30} = 0.9$

b. Write the function $f(x)$ that passes through the two data points. $f(x) = 30(0.9)^x$

c. Graph $f(x)$ and $g(x) = f(x - 4)$ on the same axes.

d. What is the value of $g(4)$? $g(4) = 30$

e. Write an equation for $g(x)$ that does not use its y-intercept.

f. Explain in your own words why $y = y_1 \cdot b^{x-x_1}$ might be called the point-ratio form. Sample answer: You can use the x- and y-values of any point on the curve and the common ratio to write the equation.

This painting, *Inspiration Point* (2000), by contemporary American artist Nina Bovasso, implies an explosion of exponential growth.

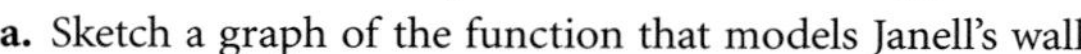

Review

3.3 **12.** The graph shows a line and the graph of $y = f(x)$.

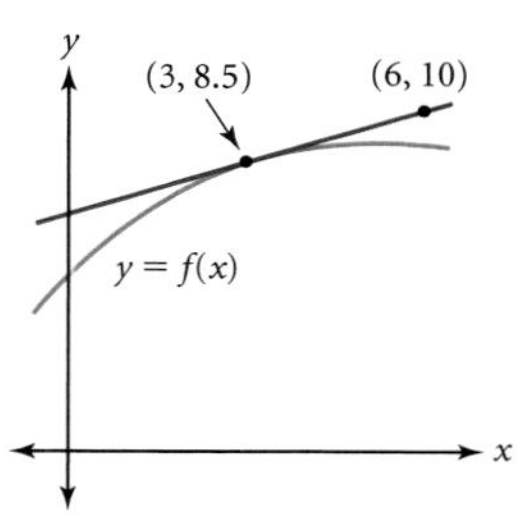

a. Complete the missing values to make a true statement.

$f(\underline{?}) = \underline{?}$. $f(3) = 8.5$

b. Find the equation of the pictured line.

$y = 8.5 + 0.5(x - 3)$, $y = 10 + 0.5(x - 6)$, or $y = 7 + 0.5x$

4.6 **13.** Janell starts 10 m from a motion sensor and walks at 2 m/s toward the sensor. When she is 3 m from the sensor, she instantly turns around and walks at the same speed back to the starting point.

a. Sketch a graph of the function that models Janell's walk.

b. Give the domain and range of the function. domain: $0 \le x \le 7$; range: $3 \le y \le 10$

c. Write an equation of the function. $y = 2|x - 3.5| + 3$

4.8 **14.** ***Mini-Investigation*** Make up two linear functions, f and g. Enter $Y_1 = f(x)$ and $Y_2 = g(x)$. Enter $f(g(x))$ in Y_3 as $Y_1(Y_2)$ and $g(f(x))$ in Y_4 as $Y_2(Y_1)$.

a. Display the graphs of $f(g(x))$ and $g(f(x))$. Describe the relationship between them.

b. Change $f(x)$ or $g(x)$ or both, and again graph $f(g(x))$ and $g(f(x))$. Does the relationship you found in 14a still seem to be true?

c. Explain the relationship algebraically.

15. ***Technology*** Use geometry software to construct a circle. Label it circle M and measure its area.

a. Construct another circle with twice the area of circle M and label it circle L.

b. Construct another circle with half the area of circle M and label it circle S.

c. Describe the method you used to determine the size of each circle.

d. Calculate the ratio of the diameters of circle L to circle M, circle M to circle S, and circle L to circle S. Explain why these ratios make sense.

15c. possible answer: duplicated the circle, measured the areas, dragged radii until areas were in the correct proportion

15d. $\sqrt{2}:1$; $\sqrt{2}:1$; 2:1. The ratios of the areas must be the square of the ratios of diameters; therefore, if the ratio of areas is 2:1, the ratio of diameters will be $\sqrt{2}:1$, and if the ratio of the areas is 4:1, the ratio of diameters will be 2:1.

Exercise 11 This exercise foreshadows the discussion of point-ratio form in Lesson 5.3.

11c.

y; 30; $y = g(x)$; $y = f(x)$; 5; 10; x

11e. possible answer: $g(x) = 30(0.9)^{x-4}$

Exercise 13 If students have not used motion sensors, you may want to summarize their capabilities.

You might use this scenario for an activity or a demonstration.

13a. Let x represent time in seconds, and let y represent distance in meters.

y; 10; (0, 10); (7, 10); 5; (3.5, 3); 5; x

Exercise 14 You might want to remind students of Calculator Note 4D so that they don't need to enter the compositions each time. Students can use computer software to print out graphs of their functions.

14a, b. The graphs of $f(g(x))$ and $g(f(x))$ are parallel lines or the same line.

14c. Let $f(x) = ax + b$ and $g(x) = cx + d$. Then $f(g(x)) = a(cx + d) + b = acx + (ad + b)$ and $g(f(x)) = c(ax + b) + d = cax + (cb + d)$. The slopes of $f(g(x))$ and $g(f(x))$ are the same ($ac = ca$), so the lines are parallel. If the y-intercepts, $ad + b$ and $cb + d$, are also the same, the lines are identical.

Exercise 16 Diagrams for 16a may or may not have dotted lines. Students might say correctly that the first step in 16b could be $x(x - 4) + 6(x - 4)$.

16a.

	x	6
x	x^2	$6x$
-4	$-4x$	-24

16d. A rectangle diagram also uses the distributive property. Each term in the first binomial is multiplied by each term in the second binomial.

EXTENSIONS

A. Have students find real-world examples of growth and decay situations. They might collect data and use transformations to find exponential models.

B. As a follow-up to Exercise 5, suggest that students research population growth in other nations to see whether China's growth rate is comparatively large or small. They might also research China's growth policies.

0.1 **16.** You can use different techniques to find the product of two binomials, such as $(x - 4)(x + 6)$.

a. Use a rectangle diagram to find the product.

b. You can use the distributive property to rewrite the expression $(x - 4)(x + 6)$ as $x(x + 6) - 4(x + 6)$. Use the distributive property again to find all the terms. Combine like terms. $x^2 + 2x - 24$

c. Compare your answers to 16a and 16b. Are they the same? yes

d. Compare the methods in 16a and 16b. How are they alike?

Project

THE COST OF LIVING

You have probably heard someone say something like, "I remember when a hamburger cost five cents!" Did you know that the cost of living tends to increase exponentially? Talk to a relative or an acquaintance to see whether he or she remembers the cost of a specific item in a certain year. The item could be a meal, a movie ticket, a house in your neighborhood, or anything else the person recalls.

Research the current cost of that same item. How much has it increased? Use your two data points to write an exponential equation for the cost of the item.

When can you expect the cost of the item to be double what it is now?

Research the cost of the item in a different year. How close is this third data point to the value predicted by your model?

In 1944 about 10,000 fans formed a line stretching several blocks outside of Manhattan's Paramount Theater to see Frank Sinatra. About 100 police officers were called out to maintain order. Although the cost of seeing a live concert has changed since 1944, the enthusiasm of fans has not.

Your project should include

- Your data and sources.
- Your equation and why you chose that model.
- The doubling time for the cost of your item.
- An analysis of how well your model predicted the third data point.
- An analysis of how accurate you think your model is.

Supporting the Project

As an extension, suggest that students find data giving the cost of a particular item at several times over a long interval and to model those data.

OUTCOMES

- The report contains clear data, sources, an equation, and an explanation.
- The student uses a model that increases exponentially, not linearly.
- Analysis of the model in light of additional data contains suggested reasons when the model does not fit.
- The project includes three or more additional data points to check the model.
- Once new data have been analyzed, the student revises the model to get a better fit.

LESSON

5.2

Properties of Exponents and Power Functions

Frequently, you will need to rewrite a mathematical expression in a different form to make the expression easier to understand or an equation easier to solve. Recall that in an exponential expression, such as 4^3, the number 4 is called the **base** and the number 3 is called the **exponent.** You say that 4 is **raised to the power** of 3. If the exponent is a positive integer, you can write the expression in **expanded form,** for example, $4^3 = 4 \cdot 4 \cdot 4$. Because 4^3 equals 64, you say that 64 is a power of 4.

Investigation

Properties of Exponents

Use expanded form to review and generalize the properties of exponents.

Step 1 Write each product in expanded form, and then rewrite it in exponential form.

a. $2^3 \cdot 2^4$ **b.** $x^5 \cdot x^{12}$ **c.** $10^2 \cdot 10^5$

Step 2 Generalize your results from Step 1. $a^m \cdot a^n = \underline{\ ?\ }$ a^{m+n}

Step 3 Write the numerator and denominator of each quotient in expanded form. Reduce by eliminating common factors, and then rewrite the factors that remain in exponential form.

a. $\frac{4^5}{4^2}$ **b.** $\frac{x^8}{x^6}$ **c.** $\frac{(0.94)^{15}}{(0.94)^5}$

Step 4 Generalize your results from Step 3. $\frac{a^m}{a^n} = \underline{\ ?\ }$ a^{m-n}

Step 5 Write each quotient in expanded form, reduce, and rewrite in exponential form.

a. $\frac{2^3}{2^4}$ **b.** $\frac{4^5}{4^7}$ **c.** $\frac{x^3}{x^8}$

Step 6 Rewrite each quotient in Step 5 using the property you discovered in Step 4.

Step 7 Generalize your results from Steps 5 and 6. $\frac{1}{a^n} = \underline{\ ?\ }$ a^{-n}

Step 6a $2^{3-4} = 2^{-1}$
Step 6b $4^{5-7} = 4^{-2}$
Step 6c $x^{3-8} = x^{-5}$

Step 8 Write several expressions in the form $(a^n)^m$. Expand each, and then rewrite the expression in exponential form. Generalize your results.

Step 9 Write several expressions in the form $(a \cdot b)^n$. Don't multiply a times b. Expand each, and rewrite the expression in exponential form. Generalize your results.

Step 10 Show that $a^0 = 1$, using the properties you have discovered. Write at least two exponential expressions to support your explanation.

NCTM STANDARDS

CONTENT		PROCESS	
✓	Number		Problem Solving
✓	Algebra	✓	Reasoning
	Geometry	✓	Communication
	Measurement		Connections
	Data/Probability	✓	Representation

LESSON OBJECTIVES

- Introduce algebraic proof
- Review the properties of exponents, specifically, rewriting powers with the same base
- Introduce the parent power function, $y = ax^b$, and distinguish it from the exponential function, $y = ab^x$
- Find some solutions to power equations using the properties of exponents
- Introduce rational exponents as a means of solving equations

LESSON

5.2

PLANNING

LESSON OUTLINE

One day:

10 min	Investigation
5 min	Sharing
15 min	Examples
15 min	Exercises

MATERIALS

- Properties of Exponents (W), *optional*
- Calculator Note 5A
- Sketchpad demonstration Power Functions, *optional*

TEACHING

If you decide to use the less-directed one-step investigation, you will find it on page 246.

Guiding the Investigation

If students use the Properties of Exponents worksheet rather than the book, they won't be tempted to look up the properties.

Step 1 [Alert] Remind students who need help that writing in expanded form means writing out all numbers or variables and the multiplication signs between them.

Steps 3, 5 [Alert] After dividing out all common factors in the denominator or numerator, students might replace them with 0 rather than 1, because "none remain."

Step 5 [Alert] Students might be surprised to see negative exponents.

Step 9 You might have some groups explore $\left(\frac{a}{b}\right)^n$ instead of $(a \cdot b)^n$.

See page 884 for answers to Steps 1, 3, 5, and 8–10.

Here's a summary of the properties of exponents. You discovered some of these in the investigation. Try to write an example of each property.

For $a > 0$, $b > 0$, and all values of m and n, these properties are true:

Product Property of Exponents

$$a^m \cdot a^n = a^{m+n}$$

Quotient Property of Exponents

$$\frac{a^m}{a^n} = a^{m-n}$$

Definition of Negative Exponents

$$a^{-n} = \frac{1}{a^n} \quad \text{or} \quad \left(\frac{a}{b}\right)^{-n} = \left(\frac{b}{a}\right)^n$$

Zero Exponents

$$a^0 = 1$$

Power of a Power Property

$$(a^m)^n = a^{mn}$$

Power of a Product Property

$$(ab)^m = a^m b^m$$

Power of a Quotient Property

$$\left(\frac{a}{b}\right)^n = \frac{a^n}{b^n}$$

Power Property of Equality

If $a = b$, then $a^n = b^n$.

Common Base Property of Equality

If $a^n = a^m$, then $n = m$.

In Lesson 5.1, you learned to solve equations that have a variable in the exponent by using a calculator to try various values for x. The properties of exponents allow you to solve these types of equations algebraically. One special case is when you can rewrite both sides of the equation with a common base. This strategy is fundamental to solving some of the equations you'll see later in this chapter.

EXAMPLE A

Solve.

a. $8^x = 4$

b. $27^x = \frac{1}{81}$

c. $\left(\frac{49}{9}\right)^x = \left(\frac{3}{7}\right)^{3/2}$

▶ Solution

If you use the power of a power property to convert each side of the equation to a common base, then you can solve without a calculator.

One Step

Ask each group to solve the equation $4^x = \left(\frac{2^4 \cdot 2^5}{(2 \cdot 2^3)^2}\right)^6$ in as many ways as it can. Encourage creative thinking and attention to exponents as representing repeated multiplication. As groups finish, ask them to repeat the problem with a numerator of $2^2 \cdot 2^3$ on the right side of the equation. During Sharing, help the class reach consensus about properties of exponents and about finding exponents by rewriting the same base to different powers.

▶ *EXAMPLE A*

Ask students to check the answers on their calculators. They can do so by calculating each side on the home screen, by graphing each side and finding the point of intersection of the graphs, or by guess-and-check.

This may be the first time students have seen a fractional exponent. When they check their answers on the calculator, help them see why they must put the fraction in parentheses.

SHARING IDEAS

As students present their work, ask why "canceling" is legal. [You are dividing out common factors.] As you describe solutions, use the phrase *dividing out common factors* rather than the word *cancel.*

Ask whether terms can be divided out as well. Help students see that division cannot be used in the expression $\frac{x+x+x}{x+x}$ to produce x.

Students presenting their ideas from Step 7 of the investigation will probably say that $\frac{1}{a^n} = a^{-n}$. Ask what that says about $\left(\frac{3}{4}\right)^n$. $\left[\frac{3}{4} \text{ is } \frac{1}{\frac{4}{3}}, \text{ so } \left(\frac{3}{4}\right)^n = \left(\frac{4}{3}\right)^{-n}.\right]$ To generalize the result, $\left(\frac{a}{b}\right)^{-n} = \left(\frac{b}{a}\right)^n$.

[Ask] "Why might the book restrict the exponent properties to positive bases?" [The restriction avoids undefined expressions such as 0^0 and dividing by 0. It also avoids taking even roots of negative numbers, but students may not know yet that fractional exponents represent roots.]

Ask whether any of the exponent properties can be derived from other properties. [The power of a quotient property can be derived from the power of a product property and the definition of negative exponents.]

Students may find it helpful to remember the properties of exponents as "one operation simpler." For example, to multiply, you add exponents; to raise an exponent by an exponent, you multiply. Stress having the rules make sense over students' memorizing them.

You might use the Sketchpad demonstration Power Functions to help student visualize the effect of changing the value of n.

[Ask] "How are power functions of the form $y = ax^n$ different from exponential functions of the form $y = ab^x$?" [In a power function, the

a. $8^x = 4$ — Original equation.

$(2^3)^x = 2^2$ — $8 = 2^3$ and $4 = 2^2$.

$2^{3x} = 2^2$ — Use the power of a power property to rewrite $(2^3)^x$ as 2^{3x}.

$3x = 2$ — Use the common base property of equality.

$x = \frac{2}{3}$ — Divide.

b. $27^x = \frac{1}{81}$ — Original equation.

$(3^3)^x = \frac{1}{3^4}$ — $27 = 3^3$ and $81 = 3^4$.

$3^{3x} = 3^{-4}$ — Use the power of a power property and the definition of negative exponents.

$3x = -4$ — Use the common base property of equality.

$x = -\frac{4}{3}$ — Divide.

c. $\left(\frac{49}{9}\right)^x = \left(\frac{3}{7}\right)^{3/2}$ — Original equation.

$\left(\frac{7^2}{3^2}\right)^x = \left(\frac{3}{7}\right)^{3/2}$ — $49 = 7^2$ and $9 = 3^2$.

$\left(\left(\frac{7}{3}\right)^2\right)^x = \left(\left(\frac{7}{3}\right)^{-1}\right)^{3/2}$ — Use the power of a quotient property and the definition of negative exponents.

$\left(\frac{7}{3}\right)^{2x} = \left(\frac{7}{3}\right)^{-3/2}$ — Use the power of a power property.

$2x = -\frac{3}{2}$ — Use the common base property of equality.

$x = -\frac{3}{4}$ — Divide.

Remember, it's always a good idea to check your answer with a calculator. [► See **Calculator Note 5A** to find out how to calculate roots and powers. ◄]

An exponential function in the general form $y = ab^x$ has a variable as the exponent. A **power function,** in contrast, has a variable as the base.

Power Function

The general form of a power function is

$$y = ax^n$$

where a and n are constants.

You use different methods to solve power equations than to solve exponential equations. You must learn to recognize the difference between the two.

EXAMPLE B

Solve.

a. $x^4 = 3000$

b. $6x^{2.5} = 90$

Sharing Ideas (continued)

independent variable is in the base rather than the exponent.] The letters a, b, and n represent constants for any particular function. **[Ask]** "For exponential functions, the scale factor a is the y-intercept. Is that also true for power functions?" [For the parent power function, when $x = 0$, $y = 0$; the y-intercept is the origin.] "Are power functions and exponential functions inverses of each other?" [As needed, let students look up the definition of function inverse and apply it to see that these functions are not inverses of each other.] "What kinds of functions *are* inverses of these functions?" [You need not answer this; students will discover rational powers and logarithmic functions in later lessons.]

[Ask] "Is -7.40 also a solution to the equation in Example B, part a?" [It is.] "Why wasn't this solution found?" [Because the properties of exponents are defined for positive bases only, using these properties produces only the positive solution to the equation.] You might have students graph the curve $y = x^4$ and the line $y = 3000$ and find their intersections.

Both examples contain fractional exponents, which students may not have seen before **[Ask]** "What might a fractional exponent mean?" The use of fractional exponents in this lesson foreshadows their introduction in Lesson 5.3.

► *EXAMPLE B*

As in Example A, students can use calculators to check the answers. You might ask them to check the exact answers rather than the rounded decimal values. **[Ask]** "What property of exponents is being used?" [the power of a power property]

Assessing Progress
You can assess students' understanding of how to represent repeated multiplication with exponents and their ability to see patterns.

Closing the Lesson

Reiterate the main components of this lesson: a review of exponent properties (refer to the summary on page 246); the introduction of power functions; and instruction on how to use exponent properties to solve equations, although they won't always give all the solutions.

BUILDING UNDERSTANDING

Students continue to explore the point-ratio form of exponential functions.

ASSIGNING HOMEWORK

Essential	1–5
Performance assessment	6–12, 14
Portfolio	8
Journal	7, 11
Group	9, 13
Review	15–17

Helping with the Exercises

Exercise 1 Students should use calculators only to check their solutions. **[Alert]** Students may be confused about how to treat the negative signs in 1b, 1c, and 1d. In 1b, they can consider -36 to be the required fraction.

3a. False. Valid reasons include: You must have the same base for the product property of exponents; $243 \cdot 16 \neq 35831808$.

3b. False. You must raise to the power before multiplying.

3c. False. Valid reasons include: You must raise to the power before dividing; only one factor of 4 can be divided out; or it should be 4^{x-1}.

► ***Solution***

To solve a power equation, use the power of a power property and choose an exponent that will undo the exponent on x.

a. $x^4 = 3000$ — Original equation.

$(x^4)^{1/4} = 3000^{1/4}$ — Use the power of a power property. Raising both sides to the power of $\frac{1}{4}$ "undoes" the power of 4 on x.

$x \approx 7.40$ — Use your calculator to approximate the value of $3000^{1/4}$.

b. $6x^{2.5} = 90$ — Original equation.

$x^{2.5} = 15$ — Divide both sides by 6.

$(x^{2.5})^{1/2.5} = 15^{1/2.5}$ — Use the power of a power property and choose the exponent $\frac{1}{2.5}$.

$x \approx 2.95$ — Approximate the value of $15^{1/2.5}$.

Solving equations symbolically is often no more than "undoing" the order of operations. So to solve $6x^{2.5} = 90$ you divide by 6 and then raise the result to the power of $\frac{1}{2.5}$.

The properties of exponents are defined only for positive bases. So, using these properties gives only one solution to each equation. In part a above, is $x \approx -7.40$ also a solution? Yes, because a negative number raised to an even power is positive.

EXERCISES

Practice Your Skills

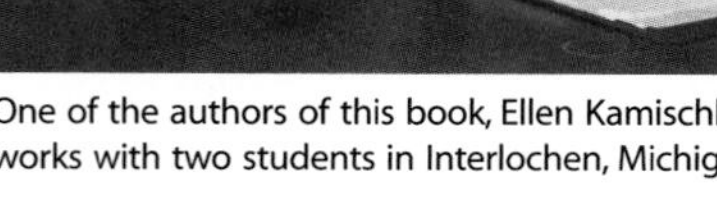
One of the authors of this book, Ellen Kamischke, works with two students in Interlochen, Michigan.

1. Rewrite each expression as a fraction without exponents. Verify that your answer is equivalent to the original expression by evaluating each on your calculator.
   a. 5^{-3} $\frac{1}{125}$
   b. -6^2 -36
   c. -3^{-4} $-\frac{1}{81}$
   d. $(-12)^{-2}$ $\frac{1}{144}$
   e. $\left(\frac{3}{4}\right)^{-2}$ $\frac{16}{9}$
   f. $\left(\frac{2}{7}\right)^{-1}$ $\frac{7}{2}$

2. Rewrite each expression in the form a^n.
   a. $a^8 \cdot a^{-3}$ a^5
   b. $\frac{b^6}{b^2}$ b^4
   c. $(c^4)^5$ c^{20}
   d. $\frac{d^0}{e^{-3}}$ e^3

3. State whether each equation is true or false. If it is false, explain why.
   a. $3^5 \cdot 4^2 = 12^7$
   b. $100(1.06)^x = (106)^x$
   c. $\frac{4^x}{4} = 1^x$
   d. $\frac{6.6 \cdot 10^{12}}{8.8 \cdot 10^{-4}} = 7.5 \cdot 10^{15}$ true

4. Solve.
   a. $3^x = \frac{1}{9}$ $x = -2$
   b. $\left(\frac{5}{3}\right)^x = \frac{27}{125}$ $x = -3$
   c. $\left(\frac{1}{3}\right)^x = 243$ $x = -5$
   d. $5 \cdot 3^x = 5$ $x = 0$

5. Solve each equation. If answers are not exact, approximate to two decimal places.
   a. $x^7 = 4000$ $x \approx 3.27$
   b. $x^{0.5} = 28$ $x = 784$
   c. $x^{-3} = 247$ $x \approx 0.16$
   d. $5x^{1/4} + 6 = 10.2$ $x \approx 0.50$
   e. $3x^{-2} = 2x^4$ $x \approx 1.07$
   f. $-3x^{1/2} + (4x)^{1/2} = -1$ $x = 1$

Exercise 4 This exercise requires using the common base property of equality.

Exercise 5f As needed, suggest that students treat $x^{1/2}$ as a variable with which they can combine like terms.

Reason and Apply

6. Rewrite each expression in the form ax^n.

a. $x^6 \cdot x^6$ x^{12}

b. $4x^6 \cdot 2x^6$ $8x^{12}$

c. $(-5x^3) \cdot (-2x^4)$ $10x^7$

d. $\frac{72x^7}{6x^2}$ $12x^5$

e. $\left(\frac{6x^5}{3x}\right)^3$ $8x^{12}$

f. $\left(\frac{20x^7}{4x}\right)^{-2}$ $\frac{1}{25}x^{-12}$

7. ***Mini-Investigation*** You've seen that the power of a product property allows you to rewrite $(a \cdot b)^n$ as $a^n \cdot b^n$. Is there a power of a sum property that allows you to rewrite $(a + b)^n$ as $a^n + b^n$? Write some numerical expressions in the form $(a + b)^n$ and evaluate them. Are your answers equivalent to $a^n + b^n$ always, sometimes, or never? Write a short paragraph that summarizes your findings.

8. Consider this sequence:

$7^2, 7^{2.25}, 7^{2.5}, 7^{2.75}, 7^3$

a. Use your calculator to evaluate each term in the sequence. If answers are not exact, approximate to four decimal places. 49, 79.7023, 129.6418, 210.8723, 343

b. Find the differences between the consecutive terms of the sequence. What do these differences tell you?

c. Find the ratios of the consecutive terms in 8a. What do these values tell you?

d. What observation can you make about these decimal powers?

9. ***Mini-Investigation*** For 9a–d, graph the equations on your calculator.

a. $y = x^2$

b. $y = x^3$

c. $y = x^4$

d. $y = x^5$

e. How do the graphs compare? How do they contrast? What points (if any) do they have in common?

f. Predict what the graph of $y = x^6$ will look like. Verify your prediction by using your calculator.

g. Predict what the graph of $y = x^7$ will look like. Verify your prediction by using your calculator.

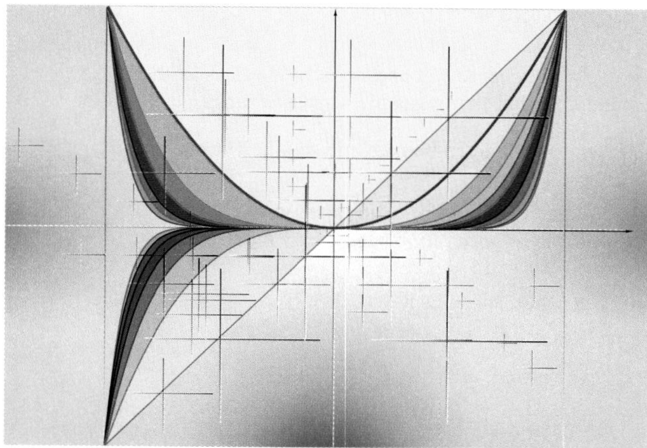

Exercise 6 As needed, remind students to multiply the constants and the variables separately.

Exercise 7 [Alert] Students may be confused by the multiplication dot; it doesn't appear in the list of exponent properties. Use the label *binomial* for expressions such as $a + b$; students may recall from beginning algebra that multiplying binomials requires using the distributive property. If students recall multiplying binomials, have them show algebraically that $(a + b)^2$ is equal not to $a^2 + b^2$ but rather to $a^2 + 2ab + b^2$. In general, students can see that for $a = b = 1$, $a^n + b^n = 2$, which does not equal $(a + b)^n$ for n greater than 1.

7. Sample answer: $(a + b)^n$ is not necessarily equivalent to $a^n + b^n$. For example, $(2 + 3)^2 = 25$ but $2^2 + 3^2 = 13$. However, they are equivalent when $n = 1$, or when $a + b = 0$ and n is odd.

8b. 30.7023; 49.9395; 81.2305; 132.1277. The sequence is not arithmetic because there is not a common difference.

8c. 1.627; 1.627; 1.627; 1.627. The ratio of consecutive terms is always the same, so the difference is growing exponentially.

8d. Possible answers: Non-integer powers may produce non-integer values. If the exponents form an arithmetic sequence, the decimal powers form a geometric sequence.

9a–d.

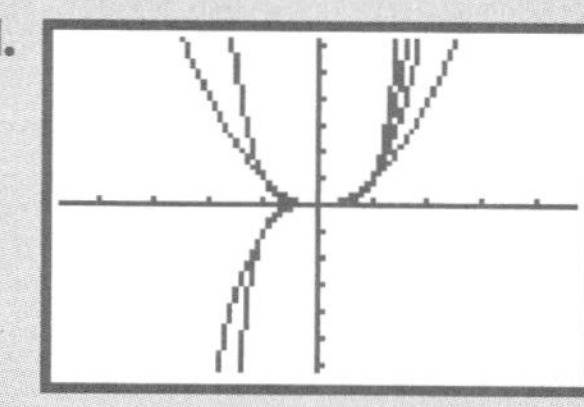

[−4.7, 4.7, 1, −6.2, 6.2, 1]

9e. Sample answer: As the exponents increase, the graphs get narrower horizontally. The even-power functions are U-shaped and always in the first and second quadrants, whereas the odd-power functions have only the right half of the U, with the left half pointed down in the third quadrant. They all pass through (0, 0) and (1, 1).

9f. Sample answer: The graph of $y = x^6$ will be U-shaped, will be narrower than $y = x^4$, and will pass through (0, 0), (1, 1), (−1, 1), (2, 64), and (−2, 64).

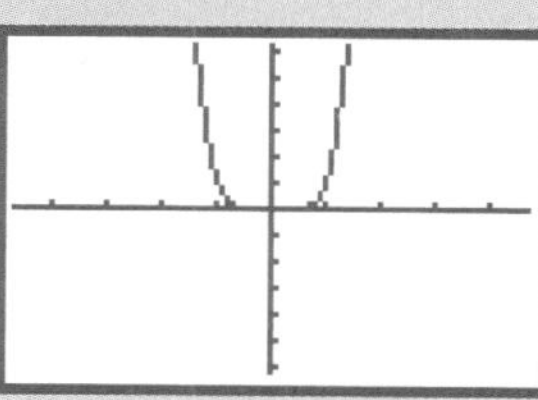

[−4.7, 4.7, 1, −6.2, 6.2, 1]

See page 884 for answer to Exercise 9g.

Exercise 10 This exercise uses transformations from Chapter 4. As needed, remind students that translations of the graphs of functions need not appear parallel.

10. Each of the red curves is a transformation of the graph of $y = x^3$, shown in black. Write an equation for each red curve.

a.

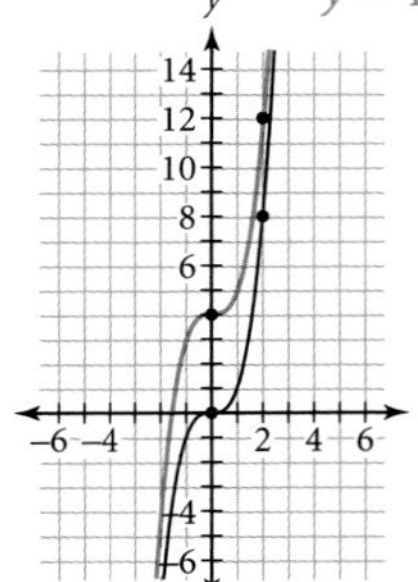

b.

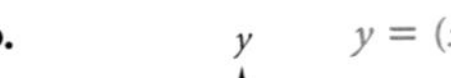

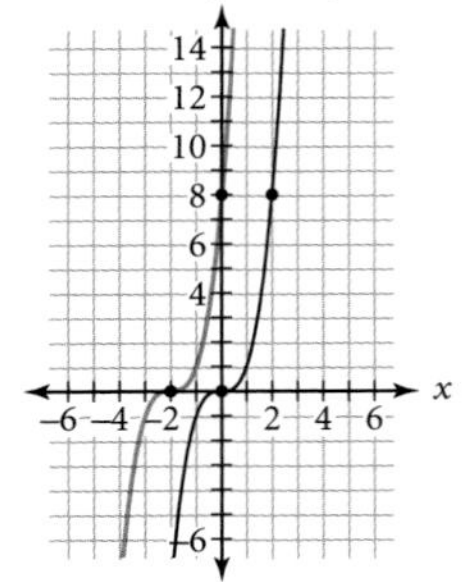

c. $4y = x^3$ or $y = \frac{1}{4}x^3$

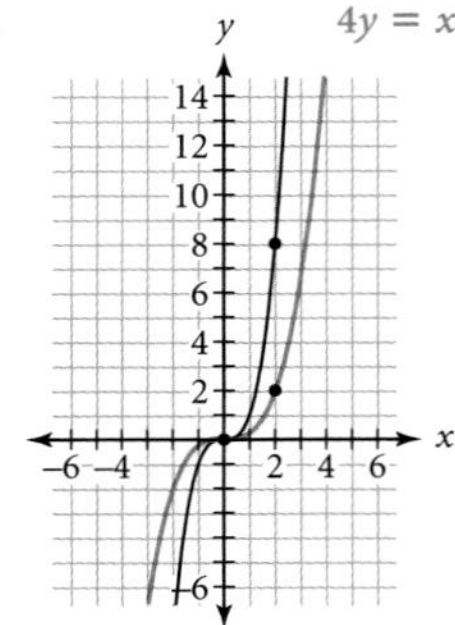

d.

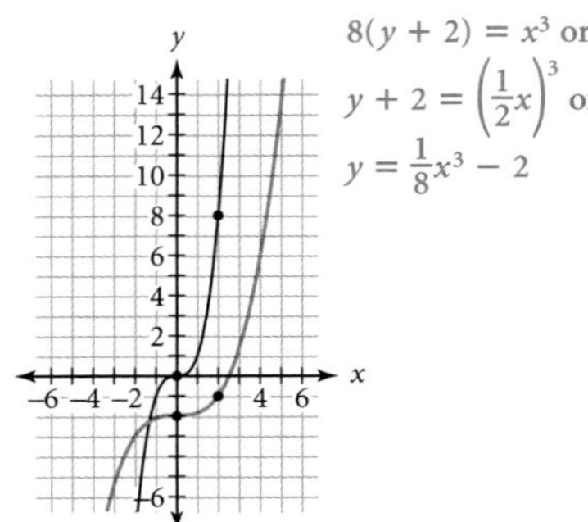

Exercise 11 Because $ab^n = \frac{a}{\frac{1}{b}}b^{n-1}$, the graph of every exponential function is a vertical stretch and a translation to the right of itself.

11a. $47(0.9)(0.9)^{x-1} = 47(0.9)^1(0.9)^{x-1} = 47(0.9)^x$ by the product property of exponents; $42.3(0.9)^{x-1}$.

11c. The coefficients are equal to the values of Y1 corresponding to the number subtracted from x in the exponent. If (x_1, y_1) is on the curve, then any equation $y = y_1 \cdot b^{(x-x_1)}$ is an exponential equation for the curve.

11. Consider the exponential equation $y = 47(0.9)^x$. Several points satisfying the equation are shown in the calculator table. Notice that when $x = 0$, $y = 47$.

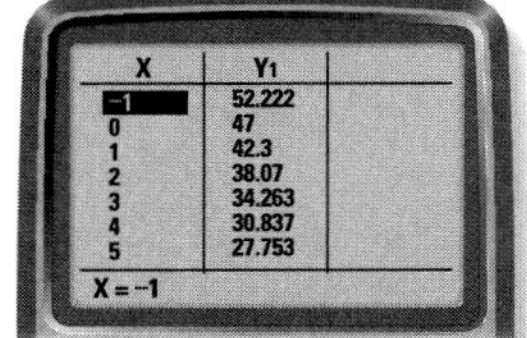

a. The expression $47(0.9)^x$ could be rewritten as $47(0.9)(0.9)^{x-1}$. Explain why this is true. Rewrite $47(0.9)(0.9)^{x-1}$ in the form $a \cdot b^{x-1}$.

b. The expression $47(0.9)^x$ could also be rewritten as $47(0.9)(0.9)(0.9)^{x-2}$. Rewrite $47(0.9)(0.9)(0.9)^{x-2}$ in the form $a \cdot b^{x-2}$. $38.07(0.9)^{x-2}$

c. Look for a connection between your answers to 11a and b, and the values in the table. State a conjecture or general equation that generalizes your findings.

Exercise 12 [Alert] In 12b, students might neglect to distribute the subtraction in $(x - 3) - (x - 6)$. As an alternative solution, students might write $ar^3 = 30$ and $ar^6 = 5.2$, divide the equations to get $r^3 = \frac{5.2}{30}$, and then solve for r.

12. A ball rebounds to a height of 30.0 cm on the third bounce and to a height of 5.2 cm on the sixth bounce.

a. Write two different yet equivalent equations in point-ratio form, $y = y_1 \cdot b^{x-x_1}$, using r for the ratio. Let x represent the bounce number, and let y represent the rebound height in centimeters. $y = 30.0r^{x-3}$; $y = 5.2r^{x-6}$

b. Set the two equations equal to each other. Solve for r. $30.0r^{x-3} = 5.2r^{x-6}$; $r \approx 0.5576$

c. What height was the ball dropped from? 173 cm

13. Solve.

a. $(x - 3)^3 = 64$ $x = 7$

b. $256^x = \frac{1}{16}$ $x = -\frac{1}{2}$

c. $\frac{(x + 5)^3}{(x + 5)} = x^2 + 25$ $x = 0$

14. **APPLICATION** A radioactive sample was created in 1980. In 2002, a technician measures the radioactivity at 42.0 rads. One year later, the radioactivity is 39.8 rads.

a. Find the ratio of radioactivity between 2002 and 2003. Approximate your answer to four decimal places. 0.9476

b. Let x represent the year, and let y represent the radioactivity in rads. Write an equation in point-ratio form, $y = y_1 \cdot b^{x-x_1}$, using the point $(x_1, y_1) = (2002, 42)$.

c. Write an equation in point-ratio form using the point (2003, 39.8). $y = 39.8(0.9476)^{x-2003}$

d. Calculate the radioactivity in 1980 using both equations.

e. Calculate the radioactivity in 2010 using both equations.

f. Use the properties of exponents to show that the equations in 14b and c are equivalent.

Review

15. Name the x-value that makes each equation true.

a. $37000000 = 3.7 \cdot 10^x$ $x = 7$

b. $0.000801 = 8.01 \cdot 10^x$ $x = -4$

c. $47500 = 4.75 \cdot 10^x$ $x = 4$

d. $0.0461 = x \cdot 10^{-2}$ $x = 4.61$

4.4 **16.** Solve this equation for y. Then carefully graph it on your paper.

$$\frac{y+3}{2} = (x+4)^2$$

3.4 **17.** Paul collects these time-distance data for a remote-controlled car.

Time (s)	5	8	8	10	15	18	22	24	31	32
Distance (m)	0.8	1.7	1.6	1.9	3.3	3.4	4.1	4.6	6.4	6.2

a. Define variables and make a scatter plot of these data.

b. Use the median-median line to estimate the car's speed. (*Note:* Don't do more work than necessary.)

IMPROVING YOUR REASONING SKILLS

Breakfast Is Served

Mr. Higgins told his wife, the mathematics professor, that he would make her breakfast. She handed him this message:

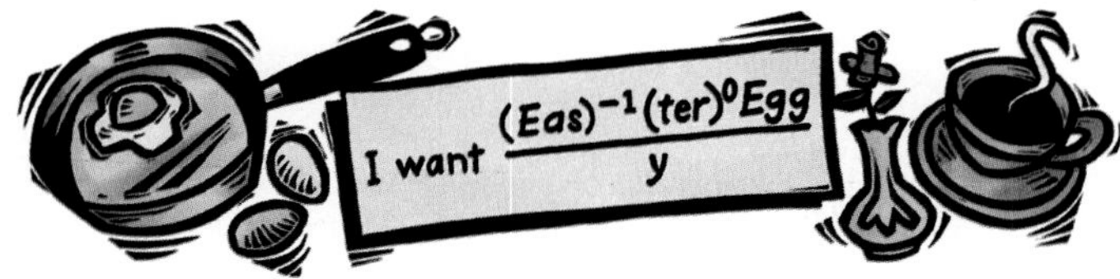

What should Mr. Higgins fix his wife for breakfast?

Exercise 14 This exercise is a preview of Lesson 5.3. The point-ratio form, introduced in Lesson 5.1, Exercise 11, will be developed further in the next lesson.

14b. $y = 42(0.9476)^{x-2002}$

14d. $42(0.9476)^{1980-2002} \approx 137.2$; $39.8(0.9476)^{1980-2003} \approx 137.2$; both equations give 137.2 rads.

14e. $42(0.9476)^{2010-2002} \approx 27.3$; $39.8(0.9476)^{2010-2003} \approx 27.3$; both equations give 27.3 rads.

14f. $y = 42(0.9476)^{x-2002} = 42(0.9476)(0.9476)^{x-2002-1} = 39.8(0.9476)^{x-2003}$

16. $y = 2(x+4)^2 - 3$

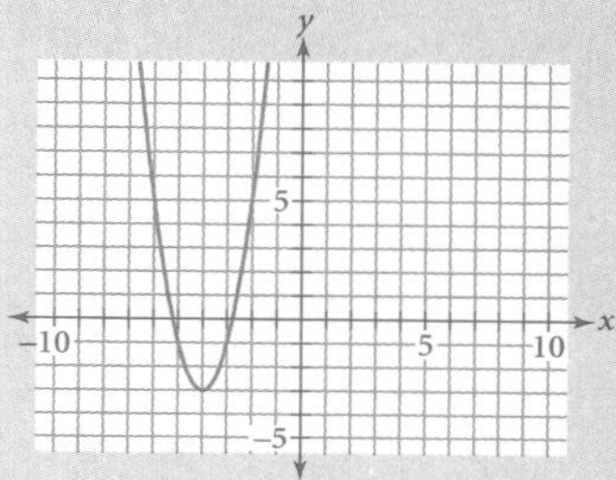

17a. Let x represent time in seconds, and let y represent distance in meters.

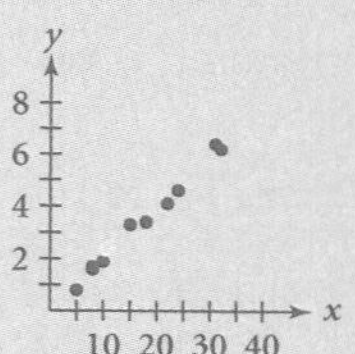

17b. All you need is the slope of the median-median line, which is determined by $M_1(8, 1.6)$ and $M_3(31, 6.2)$. The slope is 0.2. The speed is approximately 0.2 m/s.

EXTENSIONS

A. Have students graph $y = x^{-1}$, $y = x^{-2}$, $y = x^{-3}$, and so on and generalize the shapes of these graphs. [The even-power functions are in the first and second quadrants and go through (1, 1) and (−1, 1). The odd-power functions are in the first and third quadrants and go through (1, 1) and (−1, −1). The two parts of each function get closer and closer to both

IMPROVING REASONING SKILLS

$\frac{(Eas)^{-1}(ter)^0Egg}{y} = \frac{1Egg}{Easy}$, or "one egg over easy"

[ESL] Students new to English may be unfamiliar with the expression for this way of frying an egg.

Extensions (continued)

axes; the smaller the absolute value of the exponent, the faster it moves to the axes.]

B. Use Take Another Look activity 1 on page 297.

LESSON

5.3

PLANNING

LESSON OUTLINE

One day:

15 min	Investigation
5 min	Sharing
15 min	Examples
10 min	Exercises

MATERIALS

- Calculator Notes 3B, 4C, 5A, *optional*
- Sketchpad demonstration Rational Exponents, *optional*

TEACHING

This lesson focuses on rational exponents and their use in solving equations. For help in entering rational exponents and roots into calculators, students can consult Calculator Note 5A.

The one-step investigation is on page 253.

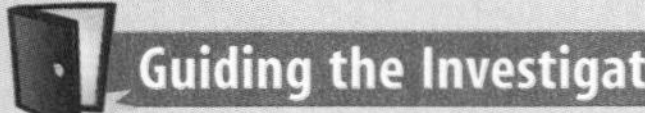

Guiding the Investigation

Step 1 Students can consult Calculator Note 3B if they've forgotten how to make function tables.

Step 2 As needed, remind students that Calculator Note 4C concerns friendly windows and that entering the fractional exponent on a calculator requires using parentheses.

Step 5 If students have difficulty making conjectures from the decimal values of x, you might suggest that they make a table by hand with x-values expressed as fractions.

Step 5 Each entry is the square root of 25, which is 5, raised to the numerator. $49^{3/2}$ would be the square root of 49 raised to the power of 3, or $7^3 = 343$.

LESSON 5.3

Rational Exponents and Roots

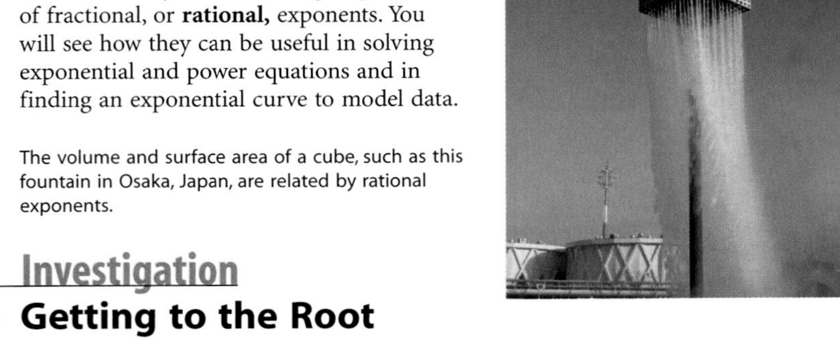

In this lesson you will investigate properties of fractional, or **rational,** exponents. You will see how they can be useful in solving exponential and power equations and in finding an exponential curve to model data.

The volume and surface area of a cube, such as this fountain in Osaka, Japan, are related by rational exponents.

Investigation
Getting to the Root

In this investigation you'll explore the relationship between x and $x^{1/2}$ and learn how to find the values of some expressions with rational exponents.

Step 1 Use your calculator to create a table for $y = x^{1/2}$ at integer values of x. When is $x^{1/2}$ a positive integer? Describe the relationship between x and $x^{1/2}$.

Step 2 Graph $Y_1 = x^{1/2}$ in a friendly window with a factor of 2. This graph should look familiar to you. Make a conjecture about what other function is equivalent to $y = x^{1/2}$, enter your guess in Y_2, and verify that the equations give the same y-value at each x-value.

Step 3 State what you have discovered about raising a number to a power of $\frac{1}{2}$. Include an example with your statement.

Step 3 Raising a number to the $\frac{1}{2}$ power is equivalent to taking the square root of the number. For example, $\sqrt{4} = 2$ and $4^{1/2} = 2$.

Step 4 Clear the previous functions, and make a table for $y = 25^x$ with x incrementing by $\frac{1}{2}$.

Step 5 Study your table and explain any relationships you see. How could you find the value of $49^{3/2}$ without your calculator? Check your answer using the calculator.

Step 6 How could you find the value of $27^{2/3}$ without a calculator? Verify your response, and then test your strategy on $8^{5/3}$. Check your answer.

Step 6 $27^{2/3}$ is the cube root of 27, raised to the power of 2. $3^2 = 9$. $8^{5/3} = \left(\sqrt[3]{8}\right)^5 = 2^5 = 32$.

Step 7 Describe what it means to raise a number to a rational exponent, and generalize a procedure for simplifying $a^{m/n}$.

Step 7 $a^{m/n} = \left(\sqrt[n]{a}\right)^m$; take the nth root of a, then raise it to the mth power.

Rational exponents with a numerator of 1 indicate roots. For example, $x^{1/5}$ is the same as $\sqrt[5]{x}$, or the "fifth root of x," and $x^{1/n}$ is the same as $\sqrt[n]{x}$, or the "nth root of x." Recall that the fifth root of x is the number that, raised to the power of 5, gives you x. For rational exponents with numerators other than 1, such as $9^{3/2}$, the numerator is interpreted as the power to which to raise the root. That is, $9^{3/2}$ is the same as $\left(9^{1/2}\right)^3$, or $\left(\sqrt{9}\right)^3$.

Step 1

X	Y1
3	1.7321
4	2
5	2.2361
6	2.4495
7	2.6458
8	2.8284
9	3

Y1■X^(1/2)

$x^{1/2}$ is a positive integer for values of x that are perfect squares (1, 4, 9, 25, . . .). $x^{1/2}$ is the square root of x.

Step 2

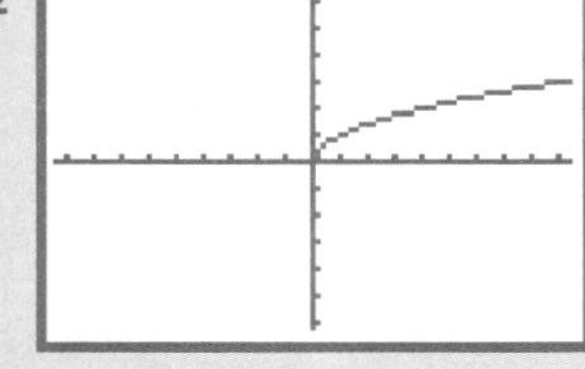

$y = \sqrt{x}$ is equivalent to $y = x^{1/2}$.

Step 4

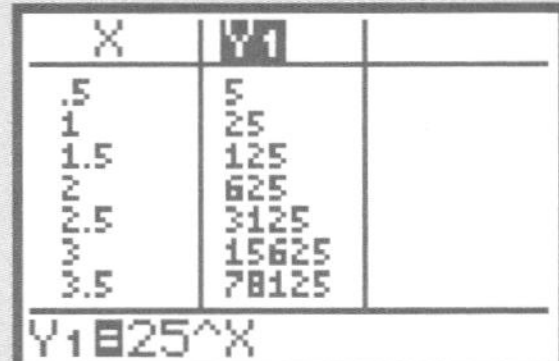

Definition of Rational Exponents

The power of a power property shows that $a^{m/n} = \left(a^{1/n}\right)^m$ and $a^{m/n} = \left(a^m\right)^{1/n}$, so

$$a^{m/n} = \left(\sqrt[n]{a}\right)^m \text{ or } \sqrt[n]{a^m} \quad \text{for } a > 0$$

Properties of rational exponents are useful in solving equations with exponents.

EXAMPLE A

Rewrite with rational exponents, and solve.

a. $\sqrt[4]{a} = 14$

b. $\sqrt[9]{b^5} = 26$

c. $\left(\sqrt[3]{c}\right)^8 = 47$

▸ Solution

Rewrite each expression with a rational exponent, then use properties of exponents to solve.

a.

$\sqrt[4]{a} = 14$	Original equation.
$a^{1/4} = 14$	Rewrite $\sqrt[4]{a}$ as $a^{1/4}$.
$\left(a^{1/4}\right)^4 = 14^4$	Raise both sides to the power of 4.
$a = 38416$	Evaluate 14^4.

b.

$\sqrt[9]{b^5} = 26$	Original equation.
$b^{5/9} = 26$	Rewrite as $\sqrt[9]{b^5}$ as $b^{5/9}$.
$\left(b^{5/9}\right)^{9/5} = 26^{9/5}$	Raise both sides to the power of $\frac{9}{5}$.
$b \approx 352.33$	Approximate the value of $26^{9/5}$.

c.

$\left(\sqrt[3]{c}\right)^8 = 47$	Original equation.
$c^{8/3} = 47$	Rewrite $\left(\sqrt[3]{c}\right)^8$ as $c^{8/3}$.
$\left(c^{8/3}\right)^{3/8} = 47^{3/8}$	Raise both sides to the power of $\frac{3}{8}$.
$c \approx 4.237$	Approximate the value of $47^{3/8}$.

Recall that properties of exponents give only one solution to an equation, because they are only defined for positive bases. Will negative values of a, b, or c work in any of the equations in Example A? A negative value will work for c.

In the previous lesson, you learned that functions in the general form $y = ax^n$ are power functions. A rational function, such as $y = \sqrt[9]{x^5}$, is considered to be a power function because it can be rewritten as $y = x^{5/9}$. All the transformations you discovered for parabolas and square root curves also apply to any function that can be written in the general form $y = ax^n$.

Recall that the equation of a line can be written using the point-slope form if you know a point on the line and the slope between points. Similarly, the equation for an exponential curve can be written if you know a point on the curve and the common ratio between points that are 1 horizontal unit apart. The **point-ratio form** of an exponential curve is $y = y_1 \cdot b^{x-x_1}$ where (x_1, y_1) is a point on the line and b is the ratio between points.

One Step
Pose this problem, adapted from Example B: "Casey hit the bell in the school clock tower. Her pressure reader, held nearby, measured the sound intensity at 40 lb/in.^{2} when 4 seconds had elapsed and at 4.7 lb/in.^{2} after 7 seconds had elapsed. She remembers from her science class that sound decays exponentially. How loud was the bell when it was struck?" Students might solve the problem in a variety of ways; plan to have several approaches presented during Sharing.

[Ask] "What does it mean to raise a number to the power of 4.7?" Use students' ideas about that question to lead into definitions of rational exponents.

Rational Exponents
The Sketchpad demonstration Rational Exponents can be used as you discuss the definition.

▸ EXAMPLE A
This example shows how fractional exponents can be used to solve equations. Lesson 5.2, Example B, included similar cases. In part a, **[Ask]** "Why not raise both sides to the 4th power without using fractional exponents?" Sometimes students can save time if they think about the rational exponent. For example, to solve the equation $\sqrt[10]{x^{20}} = 169$, raising both sides to the 10th power leads to a large number, but rewriting the equation as $x^{20/10} = 169$ helps students see that the equation is simply $x^2 = 169$.

Point-Ratio Form
Students were introduced to this form of an exponential curve in Lesson 5.1, Exercise 11, and Lesson 5.2, Exercises 12 and 14.

NCTM STANDARDS

CONTENT		PROCESS	
✓	Number	✓	Problem Solving
✓	Algebra	✓	Reasoning
	Geometry	✓	Communication
✓	Measurement	✓	Connections
✓	Data/Probability	✓	Representation

LESSON OBJECTIVES

- Discover that $x^{1/2}$ is equivalent to $\sqrt{x}$
- Define rational exponents as equivalent to roots or roots raised to powers
- Introduce the root notation $\sqrt[n]{x}$
- Formally define the point-ratio form of an exponential function, $y = y_1 b^{x-x_1}$
- Use the point-ratio form to find an exponential equation through two points

► *EXAMPLE B*

In this example, students see how a real-world situation can give rise to an equation that can be solved with rational exponents. **[Ask]** "Why is time the independent variable?" [The sound intensity diminishes with time.]

[Ask] "Why can we set the two equations equal to each other?" [We're trying to find a value of b that makes both equations true.] "Why do we get b^3 instead of b^{-11}?" [In the exponent, the negative sign in front of the term $(x - 7)$ requires that we add 7.]

SHARING IDEAS

As students present their ideas, **[Ask]** "Why do you need to use parentheses around fractional exponents on a calculator?" This discussion can lead to a nice review of the standard order of operations.

You might also ask whether the expressions 3^5 and 2^{-4} have rational exponents, to review the fact that rational numbers include all integers as well as fractions.

[Ask] "When evaluating $a^{m/n}$, does it matter whether you take a^m first and then take the nth root, or take the nth root first and then raise it to the mth power?" [The results are equivalent; usually it's easier to raise a smaller number to a power, so it's advisable to take the root first.]

[Ask] "Why does point-ratio form work?" As needed, refer students to Lesson 5.2, Exercise 11, for some insights. **[Ask]** "Can any point on the graph serve as a starting point?" [Yes; one property of an exponential graph is that if you stretch it vertically and shift it horizontally to move one "starting point" to another, you get the same graph back. This feature relies on the product property of exponents, in that the function $f(x) = b^{x-h}$ is equivalent to $f(x) = ab^x$, where $a = b^{-h}$.

Point-Ratio Form

If an exponential curve passes through the point (x_1, y_1) and the function values have ratio b, the point-ratio form of the equation is

$$y = y_1 \cdot b^{x-x_1}$$

You have seen that if $x = 0$, then $y = a$ in the general exponential equation $y = a \cdot b^x$. This means that a is the initial value of the function at time 0 (the y-intercept) and b is the growth or decay ratio. This is consistent with the point-ratio form because when you substitute the point $(0, a)$ into the equation, you get $y = a \cdot b^{x-0}$, or $y = a \cdot b^x$.

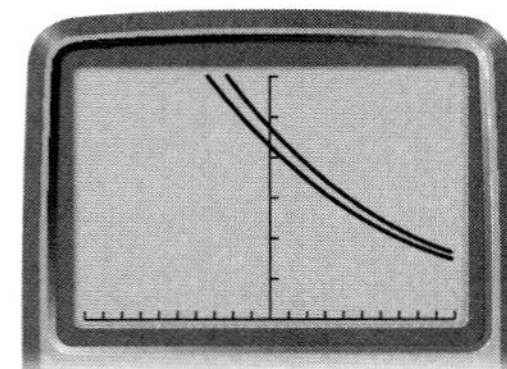

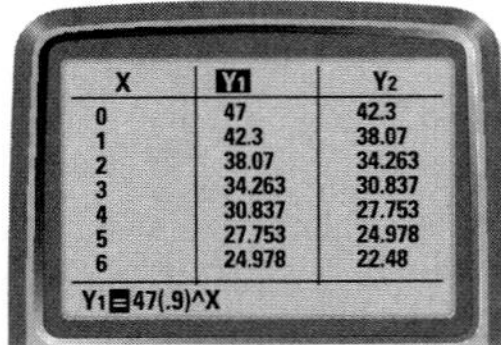

X	Y1	Y2
0	47	42.3
1	42.3	38.07
2	38.07	34.263
3	34.263	30.837
4	30.837	27.753
5	27.753	24.978
6	24.978	22.48

Y1=47(.9)^X

The table and graph above show the exponential functions $Y_1 = f(x) = 47(0.9)^x$ and $Y_2 = g(x) = 42.3(0.9)^x$. Both the table and graph indicate that if the graph of function g is translated right 1 unit, it becomes the same as the graph of the function f. So $f(x) = g(x - 1)$, or $f(x) = 42.3(0.9)^{(x-1)} = 47(0.9)^x$. This shows that using the point (1, 42.3) in the point-ratio form gives you an equation equivalent to $y = a \cdot b^x$.

Try substituting another point, (x_1, y_1), along with the ratio $b = 0.9$ into the point-ratio form to convince yourself that any point (x_1, y_1) on the curve can be used to write an equation, $y = y_1 \cdot b^{x-x_1}$, that is equivalent to $y = a \cdot b^x$. You may want to use your graphing calculator or algebraic techniques.

EXAMPLE B

Casey hit the bell in the school clock tower. Her pressure reader, held nearby, measured the sound intensity, or loudness, at 40 lb/in.^{2} after 4 s had elapsed and at 4.7 lb/in.^{2} after 7 s had elapsed. She remembers from her science class that sound decays exponentially.

a. Name two points that the exponential curve must pass through.

b. Find an exponential equation that models these data.

c. How loud was the bell when it was struck (at 0 s)?

The bell tower at Oglethorpe University in Atlanta, Georgia.

Display this string of equations:

$$1 = 1^{1/2} = \left((-1)^6\right)^{1/2} = (-1)^{6/2} = (-1)^3 = -1$$

Ask whether it shows that $1 = -1$, and let students critique it and each other's critiques. Contradictions like this are one reason why rational exponents are defined only for positive bases.

[Ask] "Why do we not get some solutions to equations we solve using rational exponents?" [Rational exponents give only the positive root. As with $\sqrt{4}$, the value of $4^{1/2}$ is the positive square root of 4.]

"Why?" [For $y = x^a$ to be a function, it must have only one output value for each input value. Therefore, exponential expressions such as $x^{1/2}$ must have only one value.]

To help prepare students for Exercise 7, remind them of power functions from Lesson 5.2. **[Ask]** "What's the domain of $f(x) = x^{2.8}$?" This is an example of a question with no single correct answer. Because $2.8 = \frac{14}{5}$ is a rational exponent, it might make sense to say that the function is defined only for positive values of x. Some calculators, however, will graph

▶ **Solution**

a. Time is the independent variable, x, and loudness is the dependent variable, y, so the two points are (4, 40) and (7, 4.7).

b. Start by substituting the coordinates of each of the two points into the point-ratio form, $y = y_1 \cdot b^{x-x_1}$.

$$y = 40b^{x-4} \quad \text{and} \quad y = 4.7b^{x-7}$$

Note that you don't yet know what b is. If you were given y-values for two consecutive integer points, you could divide to find the ratio. In this case, however, there are 3 horizontal units between the two points you are given, so you'll need to solve for b.

$40b^{x-4} = 4.7b^{x-7}$	Use substitution to combine the two equations.
$b^{x-4} = \dfrac{4.7b^{x-7}}{40}$	Divide both sides by 40.
$\dfrac{b^{x-4}}{b^{x-7}} = \dfrac{4.7}{40}$	Divide both sides by b^{x-7}.
$b^{(x-4)-(x-7)} = 0.1175$	Use the quotient property of exponents.
$b^3 = 0.1175$	Combine like terms in the exponent.
$(b^3)^{1/3} = (0.1175)^{1/3}$	Raise both sides to the power $\frac{1}{3}$.
$b \approx 0.4898$	Approximate the value of $0.1175^{1/3}$.
$y = 40(0.4898)^{x-4}$	Substitute 0.4898 for b in either of the two original equations.

The exponential equation that passes through the points (4, 40) and (7, 4.7) is $y = 40(0.4898)^{x-4}$.

c. To find the loudness at 0 s, substitute $x = 0$.

$$y = 40(0.4898)^{0-4} \approx 695$$

The sound was approximately 695 lb/in.² when the bell was struck.

In Example B, part b, note that the base of 0.4898 was an approximation for b found by dividing 4.7 by 40, then raising that quotient to the power $\frac{1}{3}$. You could use $\left(\frac{4.7}{40}\right)^{1/3}$ as an exact value of b in the exponential equation.

$$y = 40\left(\left(\frac{4.7}{40}\right)^{1/3}\right)^{x-4}$$

Using the power of a power property, you can rewrite this as

$$y = 40\left(\frac{4.7}{40}\right)^{(x-4)/3}$$

This equation indicates that the curve passes through the point (4, 40) and that it has a ratio of $\frac{4.7}{40}$ spread over 3 units (from $x = 4$ to $x = 7$) rather than over 1 unit. Dividing the exponent by 3 stretches the graph horizontally by 3 units. Using this method, you can write an equation for an exponential curve in only one step.

Science CONNECTION

Sound is usually measured in bels, named after American inventor and educator Alexander Graham Bell (1847–1922). A decibel (dB) is one-tenth of a bel. The decibel scale measures loudness in terms of what an average human can hear. On the decibel scale, 0 dB is inaudible and 130 dB is the threshold of pain. However, sound can also be measured in terms of the pressure that the sound waves exert on a drum. In the metric system, pressure is measured in Pascals (Pa), a unit of force per square meter.

In Denver, Colorado, on October 1, 2000, a judge for Guinness World Records holds a device that measured the world record volume of fans roaring in a stadium—127.8 dB.

Sharing Ideas (continued)

this function for negative values of x, taking the 5th root of x and then raising it to the 14th power. (Other calculators consider the function equivalent to $f(x) = e^{2.8\ln(x)}$, which is not defined for negative values of x, as students will see in the exploration on page 293.)

Direct students' attention to Example B, part b. **[Ask]** "What if you used the other equation in the last step?" [The resulting equation is $y = 4.7(0.4898)^{x-7}$.] "Why do you get a different answer?" [The fact that the equations are equivalent can be seen by sequentially graphing them on the calculator, using the turtle display for the second one. The vertical stretch by a factor of $\frac{4.7}{40}$ is canceled by the horizontal translation to the right by 3 units.] "Are there other ways of solving this problem?" A possibility uses the fact that, because the common ratio is $\frac{4.7}{40}$ over 3 seconds, it would be $\sqrt[3]{\frac{4.7}{40}}$, or approximately 0.4898, over each second. (Decay is exponential, so we take the cube root rather than dividing by 3.)

An alternative approach is to use a system of two equations: $40 = ab^4$ and $4.7 = ab^7$. Divide to eliminate a: $b^3 = \frac{4.7}{40}$. Solve for b, and then substitute its value for b in either equation to find the value of a.

The function can also be found through transformations. Begin with the equation $y = \left(\frac{4.7}{40}\right)^x$. The graph is shifted horizontally by 4, so the exponent becomes $(x - 4)$. The resulting graph goes through point (4, 1); to have it pass through point (4, 40), you must stretch it vertically by 40, giving $y = 40\left(\frac{4.7}{40}\right)^{x-4}$. But the ratio $\frac{4.7}{40}$ is over 3 seconds, so the graph must be stretched horizontally by a factor of 3; the equation requires dividing $(x - 4)$ by 3. The equation $y = 40\left(\frac{4.7}{40}\right)^{(x-4)/3}$ is equivalent to $y = 40\left(\left(\frac{4.7}{40}\right)^{1/3}\right)^{x-4}$, or approximately $40(0.4898)^{x-4}$.

Assessing Progress

You can assess students' facility with exponents and calculator tables and their understanding of roots.

Closing the Lesson

A fractional exponent $\frac{m}{n}$ on positive base a indicates the result of raising the nth root of a to the mth power, which is equivalent to taking the nth root of the mth power on a. Rational numbers include integers as well as fractions. The point-ratio form of an exponential equation, $y = y_1 \cdot b^{x-x_1}$, is analogous to the point-slope form of a linear equation.

EXERCISES

Practice Your Skills

1. Match all expressions that are equivalent. a—e—j; b—d—g; c—i; f—h

a. $\sqrt[5]{x^2}$ **b.** $x^{2.5}$ **c.** $\sqrt[3]{x}$ **d.** $x^{5/2}$ **e.** $x^{0.4}$

f. $\left(\frac{1}{x}\right)^{-3}$ **g.** $(\sqrt{x})^5$ **h.** x^3 **i.** $x^{1/3}$ **j.** $x^{2/5}$

2. Identify each function as a power function, an exponential function, or neither of these. (It may be translated, stretched, or reflected.) Give a brief reason for your choice.

a. $f(x) = 17x^5$ **b.** $f(t) = t^3 + 5$ **c.** $g(v) = 200(1.03)^v$ **d.** $h(x) = 2x - 7$

e. $g(y) = 3\sqrt{y-2}$ **f.** $f(t) = t^2 + 4t + 3$ **g.** $h(t) = \frac{12}{3^t}$ **h.** $g(w) = \frac{28}{w-5}$

i. $f(y) = \frac{8}{y^4} + 1$ **j.** $g(x) = \frac{x^3+2}{1-x}$ **k.** $h(w) = \sqrt[5]{4w^3}$ **l.** $p(x) = 5(0.8)^{(x-4)/2}$

3. Rewrite each expression in the form b^n in which n is a rational exponent.

a. $\sqrt[6]{a}$ $a^{1/6}$ **b.** $\sqrt[10]{b^8}$ $b^{4/5}$, $b^{8/10}$, or $b^{0.8}$ **c.** $\frac{1}{\sqrt{c}}$ $c^{-1/2}$ or $c^{-0.5}$ **d.** $(\sqrt[5]{d})^7$ $d^{7/5}$ or $d^{1.4}$

4. Solve each equation and show or explain your step(s).

a. $\sqrt[6]{a} = 4.2$ **b.** $\sqrt[10]{b^8} = 14.3$ **c.** $\frac{1}{\sqrt{c}} = 0.55$ **d.** $(\sqrt[5]{d})^7 = 23$

See page 257.

Reason and Apply

5. APPLICATION Dan placed three colored gels over the main spotlight in the theater so that the intensity of the light on stage was 900 watts per square centimeter (W/cm^2). After he added two more gels, making a total of five over the spotlight, the intensity on stage dropped to 600 W/cm^2. What will be the intensity of the light on stage with six gels over the spotlight if you know that the intensity of light decays exponentially with the thickness of material covering it? 490 W/cm^2

6. *Mini-Investigation* For 6a–d, graph the equations on your calculator. See page 257 for 6a–f.

a. $y = x^{1/2}$ **b.** $y = x^{1/3}$

c. $y = x^{1/4}$ **d.** $y = x^{1/5}$

e. How do the graphs compare? What points (if any) do they have in common?

f. Predict what the graph of $y = x^{1/7}$ will look like. Verify your prediction by using your calculator.

g. What is the domain of each function? Can you explain why?

Colorful stage lights surround Freddie Mercury (1946–1991) of the band Queen in 1978.

BUILDING UNDERSTANDING

You may want to supplement these exercises with others in which students evaluate by hand numbers raised to fractional exponents.

ASSIGNING HOMEWORK

Essential	1–4
Performance assessment	5–13
Portfolio	6, 7
Journal	8
Group	6, 7, 12
Review	14–17

Helping with the Exercises

Exercise 1 As needed, wonder aloud whether it would be good to rewrite each part using rational exponents. **[Alert]** Many students confuse fractions in the base with fractional exponents, rewriting 1f as $x^{1/3}$.

Exercise 2 **[Alert]** Though x is raised to the 1st power in 2d, students might identify the equation as linear and answer "neither." Students may also have difficulty seeing that the function in 2f is a horizontal and vertical translation of the parent quadratic function.

2a. Power; the base is a variable.

2b. Power; the base is a variable.

2c. Exponential; the exponent is a variable.

2d. Power; x is equivalent to x^1.

2e. Power; a square root is equivalent to the power $\frac{1}{2}$.

2f. Power; $t^2 + 4t + 3$ is equivalent to $(t+2)^2 - 1$.

2g. Exponential; $\frac{12}{3^t}$ is equivalent to $12(3)^{-t}$.

2h. Power; $\frac{28}{w-5}$ is equivalent to $28(w-5)^{-1}$.

2i. Power; $\frac{8}{y^4}$ is equivalent to $8y^{-4}$.

2j. Neither; the independent variable appears twice raised to different powers.

2k. Power; the fifth root of a cube is equivalent to the exponent $\frac{3}{5}$.

2l. Exponential; the exponent contains a variable.

Exercise 3 **[Alert]** The variable b in the stipulated form is not the same as the variables in bases in the various parts.

Exercise 4 Students may rewrite 4c with a negative rational exponent or first multiply both sides of the equation by $\sqrt{c}$. Encourage variety, and discuss different approaches if you have time.

4a. $a^{1/6} = 4.2$; raise both sides to the power 6: $a = 4.2^6 = 5489.031744$.

4b. $b^{4/5} = 14.3$; raise both sides to the power $\frac{5}{4}$: $b = 14.3^{5/4} \approx 27.808$.

4c. $c^{-1/2} = 0.55$; raise both sides to the power -2: $c = 0.55^{-2} \approx 3.306$.

4d. $d^{7/5} = 23$; raise both sides to the power $\frac{5}{7}$: $d = 23^{5/7} \approx 9.390$.

Exercise 6g See Sharing for reasons why some of these domains might be considered in different ways.

257

7. ***Mini-Investigation*** For 7a–d, graph the equations on your calculator.

a. $y = x^{1/4}$ b. $y = x^{2/4}$

c. $y = x^{3/4}$ d. $y = x^{4/4}$

e. How do the graphs compare? What points (if any) do they have in common?

f. Predict what the graph of $y = x^{5/4}$ will look like. Verify your prediction by using your calculator.

8. Compare your observations of the power functions in Exercises 6 and 7 to your previous work with exponential functions and power functions with positive integer exponents. How do the shapes of the curves compare? How do they contrast?

9. Identify each graph as an exponential function, a power function, or neither of these.

a. 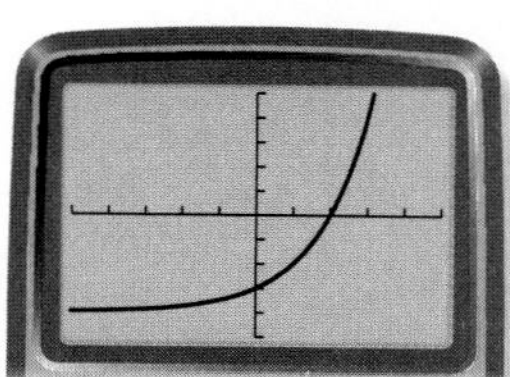 exponential

b. 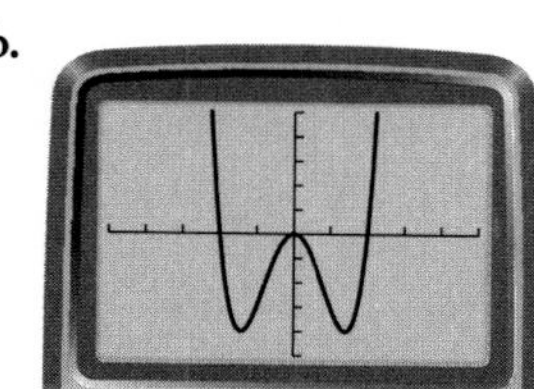 neither

c. 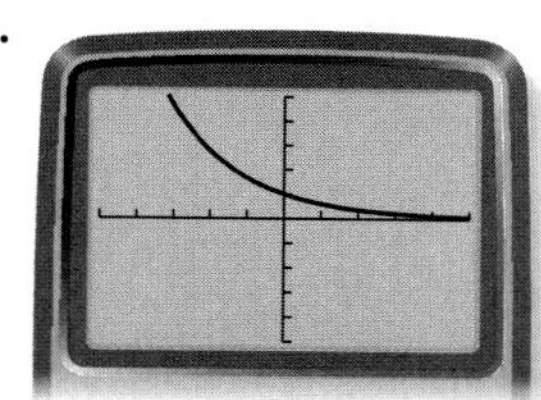 exponential

d. 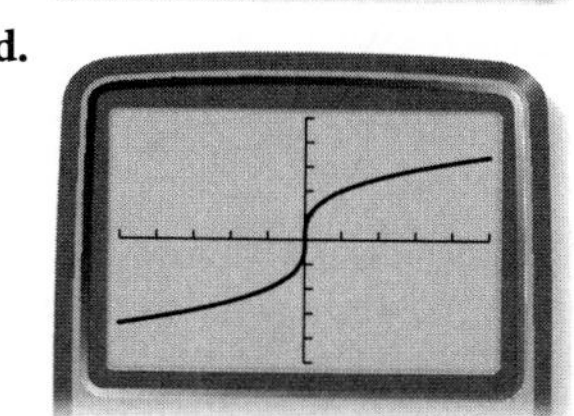 power

10. Each of the red curves is a transformation of the graph of the power function $y = x^{3/4}$, shown in black. Write an equation for each red curve.

a. 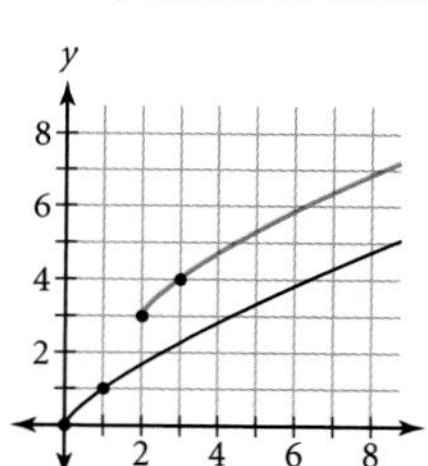 $y = 3 + (x - 2)^{3/4}$

b. 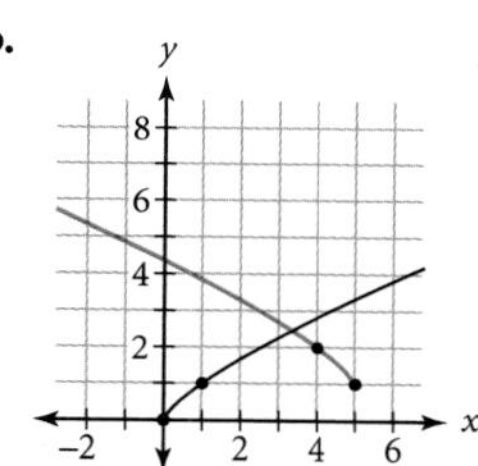 $y = 1 + (-(x - 5))^{3/4}$

c. 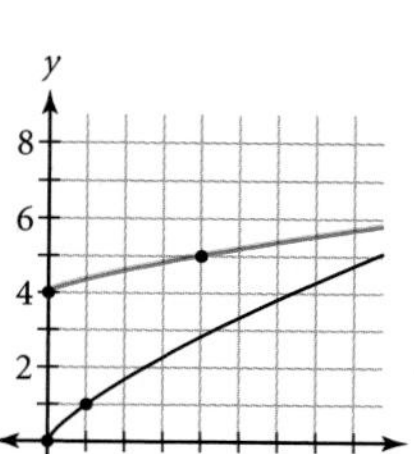 $y = 4 + \left(\frac{x}{4}\right)^{3/4}$

d. 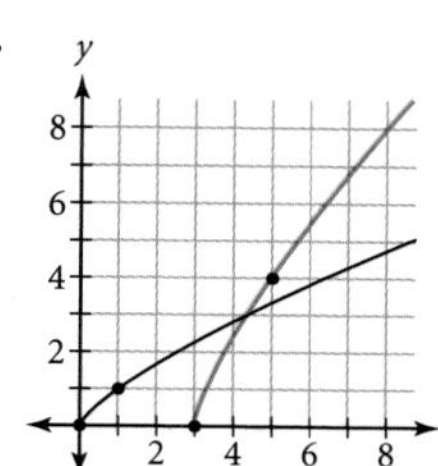 $\frac{y}{4} = \left(\frac{x-3}{2}\right)^{3/4}$ or $y = 4\left(\frac{x-3}{2}\right)^{3/4}$

6a–d. 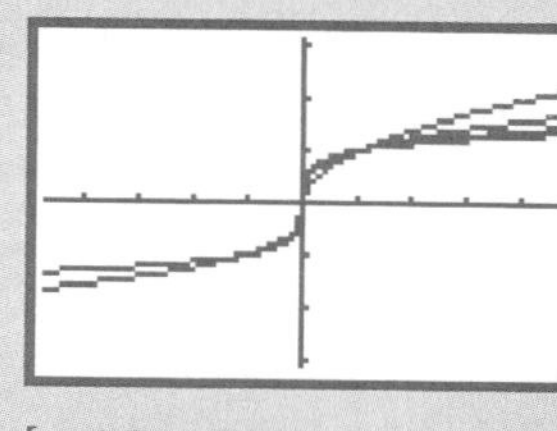

$[-4.7, 4.7, 1, -3.1, 3.1, 1]$

6e. Each curve is less steep than the prior one. The graphs of $y = x^{1/2}$ and $y = x^{1/4}$ are only in the first quadrant, whereas the graphs of $y = x^{1/3}$ and $y = x^{1/5}$ are in the first and third quadrants. All of the functions go through (0, 0) and (1, 1). The graphs of $y = x^{1/3}$ and $y = x^{1/5}$ both go through $(-1, -1)$.

6f. $y = x^{1/7}$ will be less steep than the others graphed and will be in the first and third quadrants.

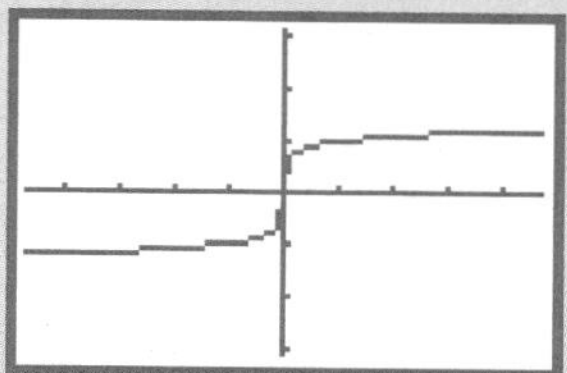

$[-4.7, 4.7, 1, -3.1, 3.1, 1]$

6g. The domains of $y = x^{1/2}$ and $y = x^{1/4}$ are $x \geq 0$ because you can't take a square root or fourth root of a negative number. The domains of $y = x^{1/3}$ and $x^{1/5}$ are all real numbers.

7a–d. 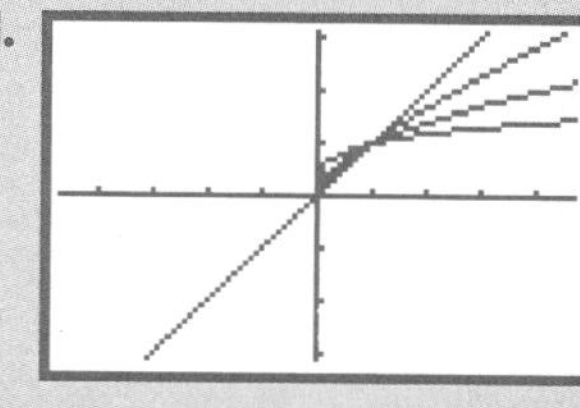

$[-4.7, 4.7, 1, -3.1, 3.1, 1]$

7e. Each graph is steeper and less curved than the previous one. All of the functions go through (0, 0) and (1, 1).

7f. $y = x^{5/4}$ should be steeper and curve upward.

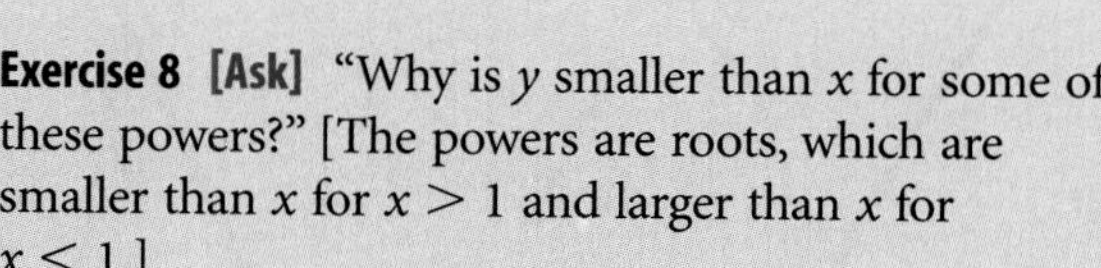

$[-4.7, 4.7, 1, -3.1, 3.1, 1]$

Exercise 8 [Ask] "Why is y smaller than x for some of these powers?" [The powers are roots, which are smaller than x for $x > 1$ and larger than x for $x < 1$.]

8. Sample answer: Power functions with rational exponents can have limited domain. When the exponent is between 0 and 1, the curve increases slowly with a shape similar to $y = \sqrt{x}$. Exponential curves always have a steadily increasing or decreasing slope, unlike power functions.

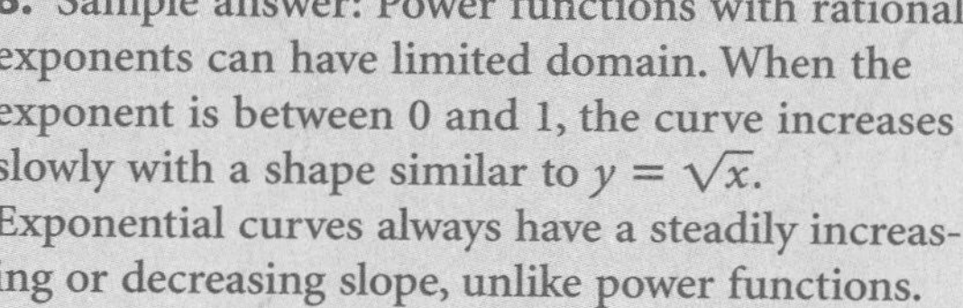

Exercise 11 Students might use undoing or raising to a power after isolating the variable. Encourage them to use rational exponents as well.

11a. $x = \left(\frac{13}{9}\right)^5 \approx 6.29$

11b. $x = 180^{1/4} \approx 3.66$

11c. $x = \left(\frac{\sqrt{35}}{4}\right)^{3/2} \approx 1.80$

Exercise 12 [Alert] This exercise requires care in reading. Students might also benefit from writing the equation that models the situation. **[Ask]** "What are the dependent and independent variables?" [For the equation $radius = time^{2/3}$, *radius* is dependent, and *time* is independent. The equation for 12b is $time = radius^{3/2}$.]

The planets in the photo montage are not to scale.

Exercise 13a This exercise calls for an algebraic proof. The argument should start with what's given ($P = kV^{-1}$) and conclude with $PV = k$. This is an example of inverse variation, which students may remember from *Discovering Algebra.*

13a. $P = kV^{-1}$; $P = \frac{k}{V}$; $PV = k$

MAKING THE CONNECTION

Scuba diving is not just a recreational activity. Professional divers help build and maintain offshore oil rigs, underwater pipelines, and dams. Marine biologists scuba dive to observe undersea plants and animals. Diving is also important for nautical archaeologists, who study past civilizations by exploring shipwrecks and sunken cities.

258

11. Solve. Approximate answers to the nearest hundredth.

a. $9\sqrt[5]{x} + 4 = 17$

b. $\sqrt{5x^4} = 30$

c. $4\sqrt[3]{x^2} = \sqrt{35}$

12. APPLICATION German astronomer Johannes Kepler (1571–1630) discovered in 1619 that the mean orbital radius of a planet, measured in astronomical units (AU), is equal to the time of one complete orbit around the sun, measured in years, raised to a power of $\frac{2}{3}$.

a. Venus has an orbital time of 0.615. What is its radius? 0.723 AU

b. Saturn has a radius of 9.542 AU. How long is its orbital time? 29.475 yr

c. Complete this table.

Planet	Mercury	Venus	Earth	Mars
Orbital radius (AU)	0.387	0.7232	1.00	1.523
Orbital time (yr)	0.2408	0.615	1.00	1.8795

Planet	Jupiter	Saturn	Uranus	Neptune
Orbital radius (AU)	5.201	9.542	19.181	30.086
Orbital time (yr)	11.861	29.475	84.008	165.02

Clockwise from top left, this montage of separate planetary photos includes Mercury, Venus, Earth (and Moon), Mars, Jupiter, Saturn, Uranus, and Neptune.

13. APPLICATION Discovered by Irish chemist Robert Boyle (1627–1691) in 1662, Boyle's law gives the relationship between pressure and volume of gas if temperature and amount remain constant. If the volume in liters, V, of a container is increased, the pressure in millimeters of mercury (mm Hg), P, decreases. If the volume of a container is decreased, the pressure increases. One way to write this rule mathematically is $P = kV^{-1}$, where k is a constant.

a. Show that this formula is equivalent to $PV = k$.

b. If a gas occupies 12.3 L at a pressure of 40.0 mm Hg, find the constant, k. $k = (40)(12.3) = 492$

c. What is the volume of the gas in 13b when the pressure is increased to 60.0 mm Hg? 8.2 L

d. If the volume of the gas in 13b is 15 L, what would the pressure be? 32.8 mm Hg

Science CONNECTION

Scuba divers are trained in the effects of Boyle's law. As divers ascend, water pressure decreases, and so the air in the lungs expands. It is relatively safe to make an emergency ascent from a depth of 60 ft, but you must exhale as you do so. If you were to hold your breath while ascending, the expanding oxygen in your lungs would cause your air sacs to rupture and your lungs to bleed.

A scuba diver swims below a coral reef in the Red Sea.

Review

5.2 **14.** Use properties of exponents to find an equivalent expression in the form ax^n.

a. $(3x^3)^3$ $27x^9$

b. $(2x^3)(2x^2)^3$ $16x^9$

c. $\dfrac{6x^4}{30x^5}$ $0.2x^{-1}$

d. $(4x^2)(3x^2)^3$ $108x^8$

e. $\dfrac{-72x^5y^5}{-4x^3y}$ (Find an equivalent expression in the form ax^ny^m.) $18x^2y^4$

4.5 **15.** For graphs a–h, write the equation of each graph as a transformation of $y = x^2$ or $y = \sqrt{x}$.

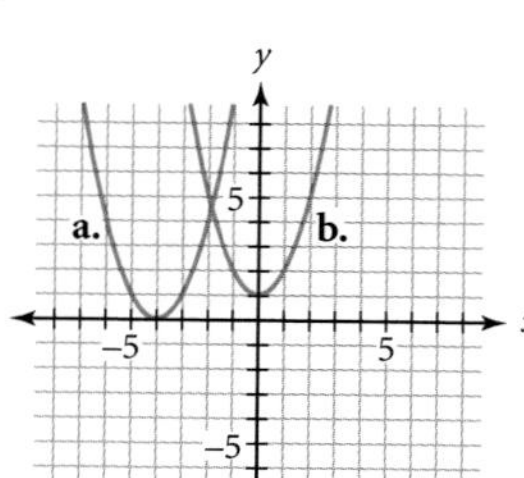

a. $y = (x + 4)^2$
b. $y = x^2 + 1$

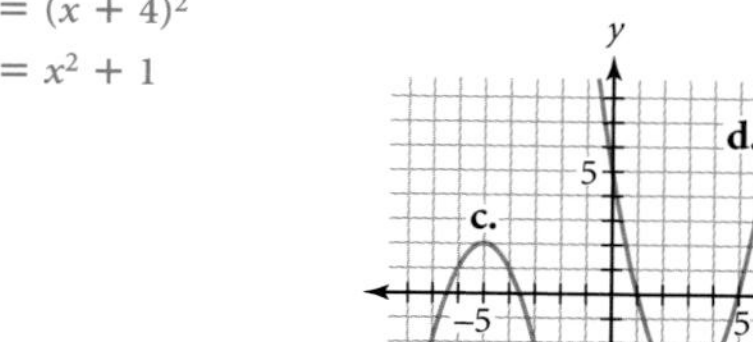

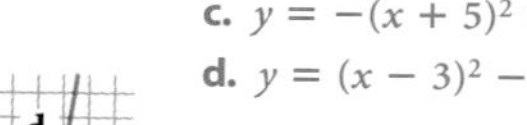

c. $y = -(x + 5)^2 + 2$
d. $y = (x - 3)^2 - 4$

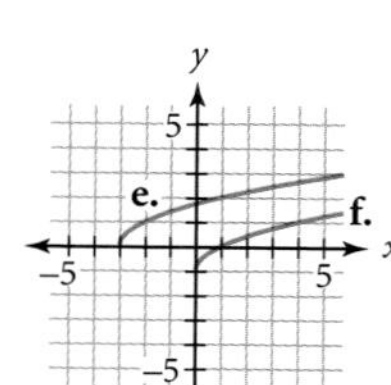

e. $y = \sqrt{x + 3}$
f. $y = \sqrt{x} - 1$

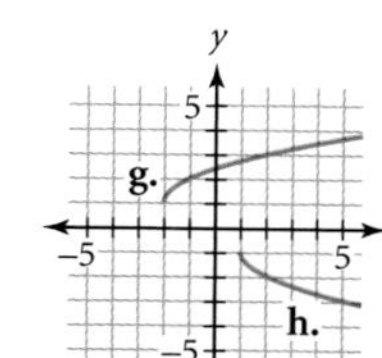

g. $y = \sqrt{x + 2} + 1$
h. $y = -\sqrt{x - 1} - 1$

2.3 **16.** In order to qualify for the state dart championships, you must be in at least the 98th percentile of all registered dart players in the state. There are about 42,000 registered dart players. How many qualify for the championships? about 840

5.1 **17.** The town of Hamlin has a growing rat population. Eight summers ago, there were 20 rat sightings, and the numbers have been increasing by about 20% each year.

a. Give a recursive formula that models the increasing rat population. Use the number of rats in the first year as u_1.

b. About how many rat sightings do you predict for this year? $u_9 \approx 86$; about 86 rats

c. Define variables and write an equation that models the continuous growth of the rat population.

German artist Katharina Fritsch (b 1956) designed *Rattenkönig* (*Rat-King*), giant rat sculptures with tails knotted together, based on true accounts of this rare rat pack phenomenon.

17a. $u_1 = 20$ and $u_n = 1.2u_{n-1}$ where $n \geq 2$

17c. Let x represent the year number, and let y represent the number of rats. $y = 20(1.2)^{x-1}$

EXTENSIONS

A. Use the Sketchpad demonstration Rational Exponents, based on the mini-investigations of Exercises 6 and 7.

B. Use Take Another Look activity 2 on page 298.

Project

POWERS OF 10

How much longer does it take 1 billion seconds to go by than 1 million seconds? How much taller are you than an ant? Are there more grains of sand on a beach than stars in the sky? You've studied how quantities change exponentially, but just how different are 10^9 and 10^{10}?

In this project you'll identify and compare objects whose *orders of magnitude* in size or number are various powers of 10. When scientists describe a quantity as having a certain order of magnitude, they look only at the power of 10, not the decimal multiplier, when the quantity is expressed in *scientific notation.* For example, 9.2×10^3 is on the order of 10^3 even though it is very close to 10^4.

Decide what you're going to measure: length, area, volume, speed, or any other quantity. Then try to find at least one object with a measurement on the order of each power of 10. Your objects can be related in some way, but they don't have to be. For instance, what is the area of your kitchen? Your house? The state you live in? The land surface of Earth? You'll probably find some powers of 10 more easily than others.

Your project should include

- ▶ A list of the object or objects you found for each power of 10, and a source or calculation for each measurement. Try to include at least 15 powers of 10.
- ▶ An explanation of any powers of 10 you couldn't find, and the largest and smallest values you found, if there are any. Don't forget negative powers.
- ▶ A visual aid or written explanation showing the different scales of your objects. If your objects are related, include an explanation of how they're related.

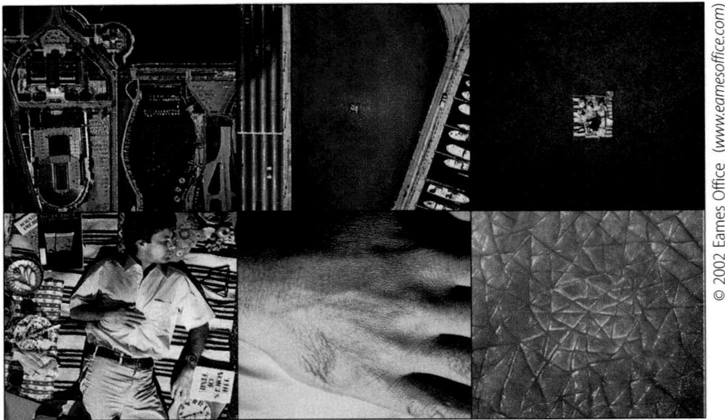

The film *Powers of Ten* (1977), by American designers Charles Eames (1907–1978) and Ray Eames (1912–1988), explores the vastness of the universe using the powers of 10. The film begins with a 1-meter-square image of a man in a Chicago park, which represents 10^0. Then the camera moves 10 times farther away each ten seconds until it reaches the edge of the universe, representing 10^{25}. Then the camera zooms in so that the view is ultimately an atom inside the man, representing 10^{-18}. These stills from the film show images representing 10^3 to 10^{-2}.

Supporting the Project

To motivate this project, you might show the 9-minute film *Powers of Ten.* The images from the film are also in the *Powers of Ten* flipbook. You might also have the book *Powers of Ten: A Book About the Relative Size of Things in the Universe and the Effect of Adding Another Zero* by Philip and Phylis Morrison available for students to read.

OUTCOMES

- ▶ The report includes a clear list of objects for at least 15 powers of 10, with sources for measurements.
- ▶ The explanation includes ideas about largest or smallest possible powers of 10, and any powers students could not find examples for.
- Research encompasses a large range of objects (30 or more).
- Student visits www.keymath.com/DAA and finds out more about the Eames's film.

LESSON

5.4 Applications of Exponential and Power Equations

You have seen that many equations can be solved by undoing the order of operations. In Lesson 5.2, you applied this strategy to some simple power equations. The strategy also applies for more complex power equations that arise in real-world problems.

EXAMPLE A

Rita wants to invest \$500 in a savings account so that its doubling time will be 8 years. What annual percentage rate is necessary for this to happen? (Assume the interest on the account is compounded annually.)

▶ ***Solution***

If the doubling time is 8 yr, the initial deposit of \$500 will double to \$1000. The interest rate, r, is unknown. Write an equation and solve for r.

$1000 = 500(1 + r)^8$	Original equation.
$2 = (1 + r)^8$	Undo the multiplication by 500 by dividing both sides by 500.
$2^{1/8} = \left((1 + r)^8\right)^{1/8}$	Undo the power of 8 by raising both sides to the power of $\frac{1}{8}$.
$2^{1/8} = 1 + r$	Use the properties of exponents.
$2^{1/8} - 1 = r$	Undo the addition of 1 by subtracting 1 from both sides.
$0.0905 \approx r$	Use a calculator to evaluate $2^{1/8} - 1$.

Rita will need to find an account with an annual percentage rate of approximately 9.05%.

You have also seen how you can use the point-ratio form of an exponential equation in real-world applications. The next example shows you a more complex point-ratio application.

EXAMPLE B

A motion sensor is used to measure the distance between it and a swinging pendulum. A table is made to record the greatest distance for every tenth swing. At rest, the pendulum hangs 1.25 m from the motion sensor. Find an equation that models the data in the table on page 262.

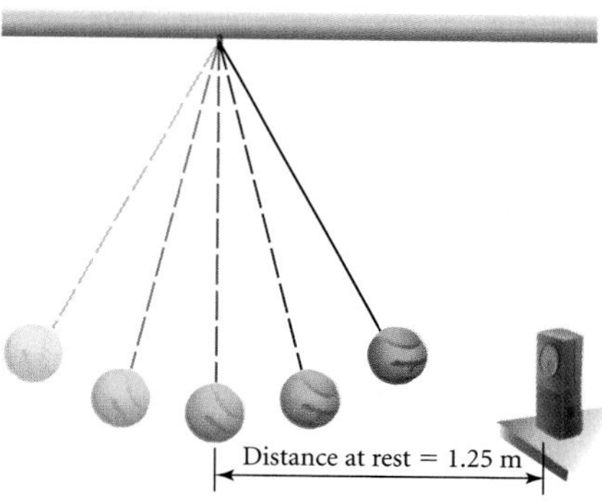

NCTM STANDARDS

CONTENT		PROCESS	
	Number	✔	Problem Solving
✔	Algebra		Reasoning
	Geometry	✔	Communication
	Measurement	✔	Connections
✔	Data/Probability		Representation

LESSON OBJECTIVES

- Find solutions to real-world applications of rational-exponential, exponential, and power functions

LESSON 5.4

PLANNING

LESSON OUTLINE

One day:

15 min Examples

10 min Sharing

20 min Exercises

MATERIALS

- Pendulum Data (T) for One Step

TEACHING

This lesson on exponential and power equations applied to real-world situations is short so that you can focus on the applications in the exercises. If you use the one-step investigation on page 262, begin with it.

▶ ***EXAMPLE A***

This example shows an application of a power equation.

▶ ***EXAMPLE B***

[ESL] A *pendulum* is a heavy object hanging from a fixed point so it can swing freely.

In this example students see an application of exponential decay in which the observational data don't give an exact value for the base b. To help students see exponential decay in context, you might pose some new problems before looking at how to solve those given. For example, "What if we modeled this decay with a linear function?"

Before you have students look at the solution, you might ask them to find a model for these data on their own. Using the point-ratio method, they can come up with a similar b-value (about 0.987), but the equation will not fit the data well. By analyzing this discrepancy, students can see that

Example B (continued)

these data tend toward 1.25, whereas the parent exponential function tends toward 0.

To find the values of b in the table, substitute the x- and y-values into the equation for b. You need to do this only six times, because you can't evaluate b for $x = 10$.

[Ask] "Why do we not evaluate b for the point (10, 1.97)?" [because $\frac{1}{x-10}$ would be undefined]

One Step

Describe the situation of Example B: "A motion sensor is used to measure the distance between it and a pendulum on every tenth swing. At rest, the pendulum hangs 1.25 meters from the motion sensor." If you have time and resources, let students collect data; otherwise, display the Pendulum Data transparency. Ask students to find a model for the data. Encourage them to critique their own models, noting especially whether they predict that the distances will approach 0. As needed, suggest that students sketch a graph of the situation over a long period of time. Encourage a variety of approaches to solving the problem with the dependent variable $(y - 1.25)$.

SHARING IDEAS

[Ask] "Why is the solution method of Example B different from the method used earlier with point-ratio form?" [Previously, the ratio of consecutive terms was constant; observed data aren't quite so nice. In addition, the long-run value is 1.25 rather than 0.]

[Ask] "Does it matter which two points you use in the Example B solution?" [No; the resulting values of b are quite close to each other.]

Ask for other ways of finding this equation. Students might substitute two data points into the equation $y - 1.25 = ab^x$ or the equation $y - 1.25 = (y_1 - 1.25) \cdot b^{x-x_1}$ and work with the two equations. The resulting graph will go through both of these data points but may not come very close to other points.

Students might wonder whether there's an analogue for the median-median line in modeling data with exponential functions. They will see a linearization method in Lesson 5.8. If they ask about the ExpReg function on their calculator, say that it will find a curve of fit, but the curve will model an equation of the form $y = ab^x$ and thus will approach 0. You still need to work with $(y - 1.25)$ to get a good fit. Another strategy is to subtract 1.25 from the y-coordinates of the data values, fit a curve $y = ab^x$ to these values, and then add 1.25 to the model to fit the original data.

If students ask "What's the right equation?" or "What's the best function?" you have an opportunity to mention that applying mathematics is an art and is subject to value judgments and disagreement among those who practice it.

[Ask] "Is it important that the values of b show no pattern?" [If they showed a pattern, an exponential function might be a poor choice for a model.]

Swing number x	0	10	20	30	40	50	60
Greatest distance (m) y	2.35	1.97	1.70	1.53	1.42	1.36	1.32

▶ ***Solution***

Plot these data. The graph shows a curved shape, so the data are not linear. As the pendulum slows, the greatest distance approaches a long-run value of 1.25 m. The pattern appears to be a shifted decreasing geometric sequence, so an exponential decay equation will provide the best model.

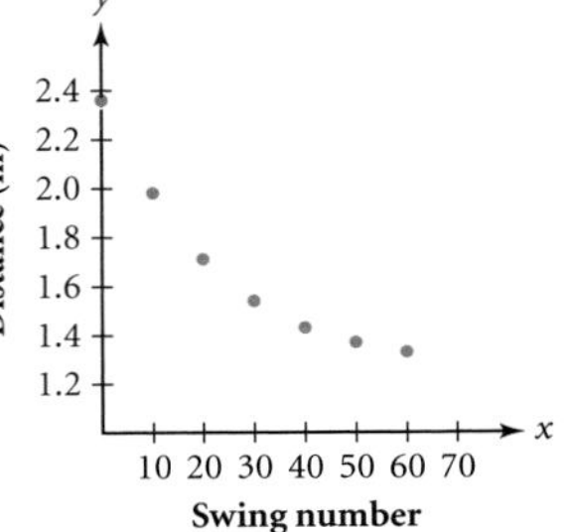

An exponential decay function in point-ratio form, $y = y_1 \cdot b^{x-x_1}$, will approach a long-run value of 0. Because these data approach a long-run value of 1.25, the exponential function must be translated up 1.25 units. To do so, replace y with $y - 1.25$. The coefficient, y_1, is also a y-value, so you must also replace y_1 with $y_1 - 1.25$ in order to account for the translation.

The point-ratio equation is now $y - 1.25 = (y_1 - 1.25) \cdot b^{x-x_1}$. You still need to determine the value of b, so substitute the coordinates of any point, say (10, 1.97), and solve for b.

$$y - 1.25 = (y_1 - 1.25) \cdot b^{x-x_1}$$ Original equation.

$$y - 1.25 = (1.97 - 1.25) \cdot b^{x-10}$$ Substitute (10, 1.97) for (x_1, y_1).

$$y - 1.25 = 0.72 \cdot b^{x-10}$$ Subtract within the parentheses.

$$\frac{y - 1.25}{0.72} = b^{x-10}$$ Divide both sides by 0.72.

$$\left(\frac{y - 1.25}{0.72}\right)^{1/(x-10)} = b$$ Raise both sides to a power of $\frac{1}{x-10}$ to solve for b.

You now have b in terms of x and y. Evaluating b for all the other data points gives these values:

Swing number x	0	20	30	40	50	60
Greatest distance (m) y	2.35	1.70	1.53	1.42	1.36	1.32
b	0.9585	0.9541	0.9539	0.9530	0.9541	0.9545

The values for b are not equal, but they are close and show no pattern. Because four out of six are close to 0.9541, it is a good choice for b, so a model for these data is $y = 1.25 + 0.72(0.9541)^{x-10}$.

In the last example, you really hoped to see the same value for b appear six times, but when working with real measurements, the best you will usually get are close values and a small variation without a pattern.

EXERCISES

Practice Your Skills

1. Solve.
   a. $x^5 = 50$ $x = 50^{1/5} \approx 2.187$
   b. $\sqrt[3]{x} = 3.1$ $x = 29.791$
   c. $x^2 = -121$ no real solution
2. Solve.
   a. $x^{1/4} - 2 = 3$ $x = 625$
   b. $4x^7 - 6 = -2$ $x = 1$
   c. $3(x^{2/3} + 5) = 207$ $x = 512$
   d. $1450 = 800\left(1 + \frac{x}{12}\right)^{7.8}$ $x = 12(-1 + 1.8125^{1/7.8}) \approx 0.951$
   e. $14.2 = 222.1 \cdot x^{3.5}$ $x = \left(\frac{14.2}{222.1}\right)^{1/3.5} \approx 0.456$
3. Rewrite each expression in the form ax^n.
   a. $(27x^6)^{2/3}$ $9x^4$
   b. $(16x^8)^{3/4}$ $8x^6$
   c. $(36x^{-12})^{3/2}$ $216x^{-18}$

Reason and Apply

4. **APPLICATION** A sheet of translucent glass 1 mm thick is designed to reduce the intensity of light. If six sheets are placed together, then the outgoing light intensity is 50% of the incoming light intensity. What is the reduction rate of one sheet in this exponential relation? 10.9%
5. Natalie performs a decay simulation using small colored candies with a letter printed on one side. She starts with 200 candies and pours them onto a plate. She removes all the candies with the letter facing up, counts the remaining candies, and then repeats the experiment using the remaining candies. Here are her data for each stage:

Stage number x	0	1	2	3	4	5	6
Candies remaining y	200	105	57	31	18	14	12

After stage 6, she checked the remaining candies and found that seven did not have a letter on either side.

a. Natalie uses the point-ratio equation, $y = y_1 \cdot b^{x-x_1}$, to model her data. What must she do to the equation to account for the seven unmarked candies? Write the equation.

b. Natalie uses the second data point, (1, 105), as (x_1, y_1). Write her equation with this point and then solve for b in terms of x and y.

c. Make a table that shows the values Natalie gets for b when substituting the other coordinates into the equation from 5b.

d. How should Natalie choose a value for b? What is her model for the data? Graph the equation with the data, and verify that the model fits reasonably well.

BUILDING UNDERSTANDING

In the exercises, students solve equations and work with applications of exponential and power functions.

ASSIGNING HOMEWORK

Essential	4–6
Performance assessment	7–10
Portfolio	6
Group	7
Review	1–3, 11–13

Helping with the Exercises

Exercises 1, 2 Accept decimal approximations as well as exact answers. In 1c, be prepared for imaginary numbers from students who know about them.

Exercise 2 Students may solve these equations by undoing rather than by balancing. Students can do this in one step on their calculators, but ask them to write at least this much (illustrated for 2d): $x = \left(\left(\frac{1450}{800}\right)^{1/7.8} - 1\right) \cdot 12 =$ 0.95072.

Exercise 4 [Alert] Students might believe that the reduction rate of each sheet is $(0.5)^{1/6} = 0.8909$. Help them see that they've found the common ratio, $1 - r$, and they are asked to find r.

5a. She must replace y with $y - 7$ and y_1 with $y_1 - 7$; $y - 7 = (y_1 - 7) \cdot b^{x-x_1}$.

5b. $y - 7 = (105 - 7)b^{x-1}$; $\left(\frac{y-7}{98}\right)^{1/(x-1)} = b$

5c.

x	0	2	3	4	5	6
y	200	57	31	18	14	12
b	0.508	0.510	0.495	0.482	0.517	0.552

5d. Possible answer: The mean of the b-values is 0.511. $y = 7 + 98(0.511)^{x-1}$.

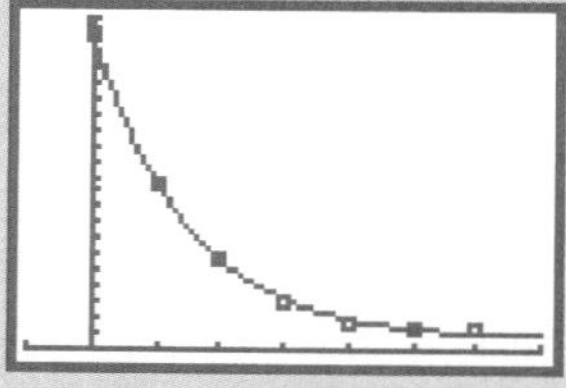

[−1, 7, 1, 0, 210, 10]

Assessing Progress

To the extent that you have students discuss their own ideas, you can assess their understanding of exponential functions and the point-ratio form of an equation.

Closing the Lesson

Applying power and exponential functions to real-world data can be somewhat messier than working with the abstract functions.

Exercise 6 [ESL] An *orbit* is the path of an object around a much larger object. **[Language]** *Orbital time* is the time it takes for an object to make one complete revolution around the object it is circling. Here the orbital time is measured in Earth days.

The moons listed in the table are 11 of the moons that have regular orbits.

Students can use guess-and-check to find their model. Working in groups may expedite this process.

[Context] Earth's own moon is 384,401 km from Earth, and its orbital time is 27.322 d.

6a. 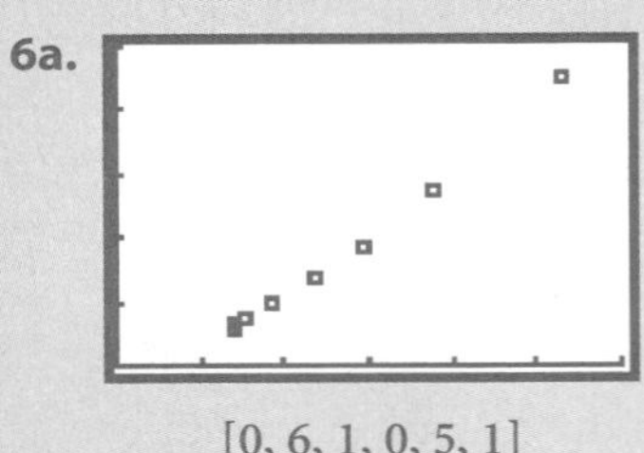

[0, 6, 1, 0, 5, 1]

6b. Sample answer: $\hat{y} = 0.37x^{1.5}$, where x is measured in units of 100,000 km. The graph of the data and the equation appear to be a good fit.

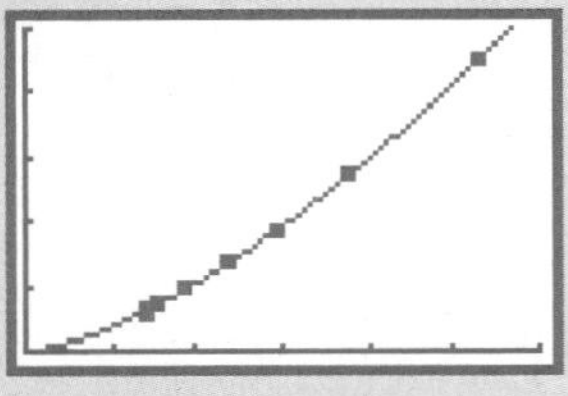

[0, 6, 1, 0, 5, 1]

6c. approximately 1,229,200 km

Exercise 8 [Language] A *botanist* is a scientist who studies plants. The species name of this tree, *altissima,* means "very tall."

6. APPLICATION There is a power relationship between the radius of an orbit, x, and the time of one orbit, y, for the moons of Saturn. (The table at right lists 11 of Saturn's 30 moons.)

a. Make a scatter plot of these data.

b. Experiment with different values of a and b in the power equation $y = ax^b$ to find a good fit for the data. Work with a and b one at a time, first adjusting one and then the other until you have a good fit. Write a statement describing how well $y = ax^b$ fits the data.

c. Use your model to find the orbital radius of Titan, which has an orbit time of 15.945 days.

d. Find the orbital time for Phoebe, which has an orbit radius of 12,952,000 km. 545.390 d

Moons of Saturn

Moon	Radius (100,000 km)	Orbital time (d)
Atlas	1.3767	0.602
Prometheus	1.3935	0.613
Pandora	1.4170	0.629
Epimetheus	1.5142	0.694
Janus	1.5147	0.695
Mimas	1.8552	0.942
Enceladus	2.3802	1.370
Tethys	2.9466	1.888
Dione	3.7740	2.737
Helene	3.7740	2.737
Rhea	5.2704	4.518

(*www.solarsystem.nasa.gov*)

Science CONNECTION

In the year 2000, 12 new moons that orbit Saturn were discovered. Of the 18 previously known moons, 17 were in a regular orbit—orbiting in the same direction as the rotation of Saturn, and approximately around its equator. The 12 new moons were in irregular orbits, making them more difficult to find. Scientists theorize that these moons may have originally been 3 or 4 moons in regular orbit that collided with each other or with asteroids.

These images of Saturn's system are a compilation of photos taken by the *Voyager I* spacecraft in 1980.

7. APPLICATION The relationship between the weight in tons, W, and the length in feet, L, of a sperm whale is given by the formula $W = 0.000137L^{3.18}$.

a. An average sperm whale is 62 ft long. What is its weight? 68.63 tons

b. How long would a sperm whale be if it weighed 75 tons? 63.75 ft

8. APPLICATION In order to estimate the height of an *Ailanthus altissima* tree, botanists have developed the formula $h = \frac{5}{3}d^{0.8}$, where h is the height in meters and d is the diameter in centimeters.

a. If the height of an *Ailanthus altissima* tree is 18 m, find the diameter. 19.58 cm

b. If the circumference of an *Ailanthus altissima* tree is 87 cm, estimate its height. 23.75 m

Science CONNECTION

Allometry is the study of size relationships between different features of an organism as a consequence of growth. Such relationships might involve weight versus length, height of tree versus diameter, or amount of fat versus body mass. Many characteristics vary greatly among different species, but within a species there may be a fairly consistent relationship or growth pattern. The study of these relationships produces mathematical models that scientists use to estimate one measurement of an organism based on another.

9. **APPLICATION** Fat reserves in birds are related to body mass by the formula $F = 0.033 \cdot M^{1.5}$, where F represents the mass in grams of the fat reserves and M represents the total body mass in grams.

a. How many grams of fat reserves would you expect in a 15 g warbler?

b. What percent of this warbler's body mass is fat?

10. According to the consumer price index in July 2002, the average cost of a gallon of whole milk was $2.74. If the July 2002 rate of inflation continued, it would cost $3.41 in the year 2024. What was the rate of inflation in July 2002?

Review

5.1 **11.** **APPLICATION** A sample of radioactive material has been decaying for 5 years. Three years ago, there were 6.0 g of material left. Now 5.2 g are left.

a. What is the rate of decay?

b. How much radioactive material was initially in the sample?

c. Find an equation to model the decay.

d. How much radioactive material will be left after 50 years (45 years from now)?

e. What is the half-life of this radioactive material?

2.2 **12.** In his geography class, Juan makes a conjecture that more people live in cities that are warm (above 50°F) in the winter than live in cities that are cold (below 32°F). In order to test his conjecture, he collects the mean temperatures for January of the 25 largest U.S. cities. These cities contained about 12% of the U.S. population in 2000.

a. Construct a box plot of these data.

b. List the five-number summary.

c. What are the range and the interquartile range for these data?

d. Do the data support Juan's conjecture? Explain your reasoning.

31.8°, 56.0°, 21.4°, 51.4°, 31.2°, 52.3°, 56.8°, 44.0°, 50.4°, 23.4°, 26.0°, 48.5°, 53.2°, 27.1°, 49.1°, 32.7°, 39.6°, 18.7°, 29.6°, 35.2°, 37.1°, 44.2°, 39.1°, 29.5°, 40.5°

(*Time Almanac 2002*)

3.7 **13.** You have solved many systems of two equations with two variables. Use the same techniques to solve this system of three equations with three variables.

$$\begin{cases} 2x + y + 4z = 4 \\ x + y + z = \frac{1}{4} \\ -3x - 7y + 2z = 5 \end{cases}$$

$x = -4.5, y = 2, z = 2.75$

IMPROVING YOUR REASONING SKILLS

Cryptic Clue

Lieutenant Bolombo found this cryptic message containing a clue about where the stolen money was hidden: $\sqrt[\frac{1}{2}]{\text{cin}}$ nati.

Where should the lieutenant look?

IMPROVING REASONING SKILLS

Taking the half root is the same as squaring.

$$\sqrt[\frac{1}{2}]{cin}\ nati = (cin)^2 nati = cin\ cin\ nati$$

He should look in Cincinnati, Ohio.

Challenge students to make up their own Lieutenant Bolombo cryptic clues and ask classmates to solve them.

9a. 1.9 g

9b. 12.8%

10. 1%

11a. 0.0466, or 4.66% per year

11b. 6.6 g

11c. $y = 6.6(1 - 0.0466)^x = 6.6(0.9534)^x$

11d. 0.6 g

11e. 14.5 yr

12a.

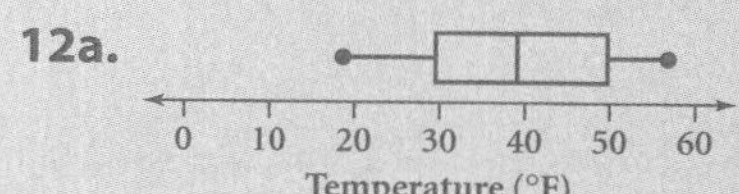

12b. 18.7, 29.55, 39.1, 49.75, 56.8

12c. *range* = 38.1; *IQR* = 20.2

12d. Sample answer: Because $Q_3 = 49.75$, less than 25% of the cities have mean January temperatures above 50°F. Because $Q_1 = 29.55$, more than 25% of the cities have mean January temperatures below 32°F. The data do not seem to support Juan's conjecture.

EXTENSIONS

A. Use the motion sensor to collect actual data for Example B.

B. Create an activity and collect data for an exercise similar to Exercise 5.

LESSON

5.5

PLANNING

LESSON OUTLINE

One day:

20 min Investigation

5 min Sharing

10 min Examples

10 min Exercises

MATERIALS

- patty paper, *optional*
- Gloria and Keith (T) for One Step
- Graphing the Inverse (T), *optional*
- Evaluating Compositions (T), *optional*
- Calculator Notes 5B, 5D
- Sketchpad demonstration The Inverse of a Line, *optional*

TEACHING

This lesson introduces students to inverse relations and their graphs. You'll find the one-step investigation on page 267.

Guiding the Investigation

Part 1 Advise students to complete Steps 1–4 on one function at a time. If you are short on time, use only functions i, iii, iv, and v. Group members might divide up the work, but have them work together on the first function so they all understand the process.

Step 2 Objects drawn (as opposed to graphed) on the calculator can't be traced. A friendly window can help in estimating coordinates.

LESSON 5.5

Building Inverses of Functions

Success is more a function of consistent common sense than it is of genius.

AN WANG

Gloria and Keith are sharing their graphs for the same set of data.

"I know my graph is right!" exclaims Gloria. "I've checked and rechecked it. Yours must be wrong, Keith."

Keith disagrees. "I've entered these data into my calculator too, and I made sure I entered the correct numbers."

The graphs are pictured below. Can you explain what is happening?

The independent and dependent variables are reversed.

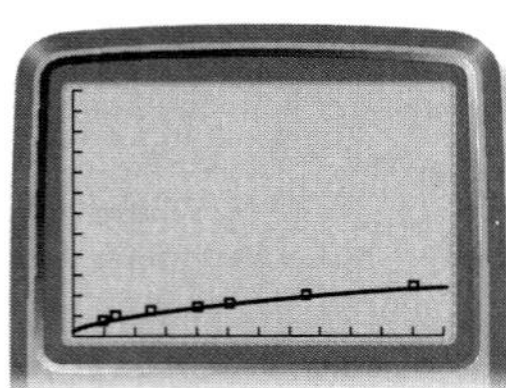

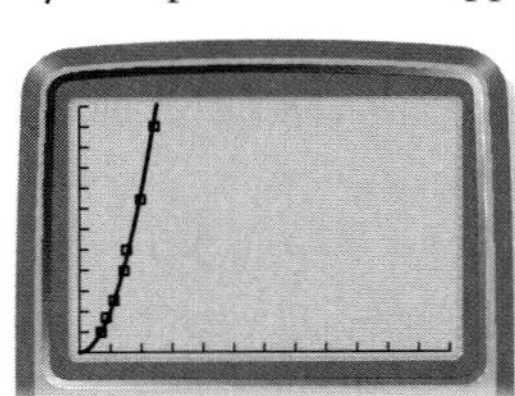

This lesson is about the **inverse** of a function—where the independent variable is exchanged with the dependent variable. Look again at Gloria's and Keith's graphs. If they labeled the axes, they might see that the only difference is their choice of independent variables. In some real-world situations, it makes sense for either of two related variables to be used as the independent variable. In the investigation you will find some equations for some inverses, and then discover how they relate to the original function.

Investigation
The Inverse

Consider the following functions.

i. $f(x) = 6 + 3x$ **ii.** $f(x) = \sqrt{x+4} - 3$

iii. $f(x) = (x-2)^2 - 5$ **iv.** $f(x) = 2 + \sqrt{x+5}$

v. $f(x) = \frac{1}{3}(x-6)$ **vi.** $f(x) = \sqrt[3]{5x}$

Part 1

For each of the functions above, follow Steps 1–4.

Step 1 Using your calculator, graph the function and then draw its inverse [▶ See **Calculator Note 5B** to find out how to draw the inverse of a function. ◀]. Sketch both on your paper.

Step 2 Approximate the coordinates of at least three points on the inverse.

Step 3 Find a function (or functions) to fit the inverse. Check your response by adding this graph to your calculator to see if it matches the inverse.

Step 4 Record the equations of your function and its inverse in a table on your paper.

Step 2

i. $(0,-2), (3,-1), (6,0)$

ii. $(-3,-4), (-1,0), (0,5)$

iii. $(-5,2), (-4,3), (-4,1)$

See page 885 for answers to Step 1.

iv. $(2,-5), (4,-1), (5,4)$

v. $(-2,0), (-1,3), (0,6)$

vi. $(0,0), (2,1.6), (-2,-1.6)$

Step 3 As needed, encourage students to use transformations of parent functions. For function iii, students will need two functions to describe the inverse.

Step 3

i. $y = \frac{1}{3}(x-6)$

ii. $y = (x+3)^2 - 4, x \geq -3$

iii. $y = \pm\sqrt{x+5} + 2$

iv. $y = (x-2)^2 - 5, x \geq 2$

v. $y = 3x + 6$

vi. $y = \frac{1}{5}x^3$

Part 2

Step 5 Study the sketches you made of functions and their inverses. What observations can you make about the graphs of a function and its inverse?

Step 6 Look at the graphs and equations of the pair i and v and of the pair iii and iv. What observations can you make about these pairs?

Step 7 After studying the equations you wrote for the functions and their inverses, describe how you could find the equation of an inverse of a function without looking at its graph. Switch x and y and solve for y.

EXAMPLE A

A 589 mi flight from Washington, D.C., to Chicago took 118 min. A flight of 1452 mi from Washington, D.C., to Denver took 222 min. Model this relationship both as (*time, distance*) data and as (*distance, time*) data. If a flight from Washington, D.C., to Seattle takes 323 min, what is the distance traveled? If the distance between Washington, D.C., and Miami is 910 mi, how long will it take to fly from one of these two cities to the other?

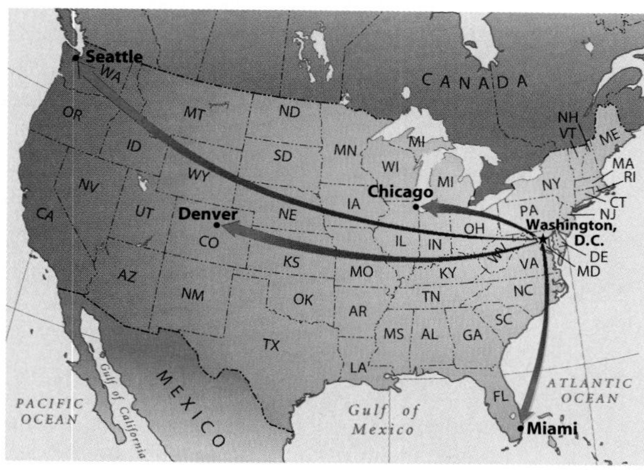

▶ Solution

If you know the time traveled and want to find the distance, then time is the independent variable, and the points known are (118, 589) and (222, 1452). The slope is $\frac{1452-589}{222-118}$, or approximately 8.3 mi/min. Using the first point to write an equation in point-slope form, you get $d = 589 + \frac{863}{104}(t - 118)$.

To find the distance between Washington, D.C., and Seattle, substitute 323 for *time:*

$$d = 589 + \frac{863}{104}(323 - 118) \approx 2290.106$$

The distance is approximately 2290 mi.

If you know distance and want to find time, then distance is the independent variable. The two points then are (589, 118) and (1452, 222). This makes the slope $\frac{222-118}{1452-589}$, or approximately 0.12 min/mi. Using the first point again, the equation for time is $t = 118 + \frac{104}{863}(d - 589)$.

Step 5 You might have patty paper available. Students can copy their graphs and axes onto the paper to test their conjectures.

Step 5 The graph of the inverse of a function is the reflection of the graph of that function over the line $y = x$.

Step 6 i and v are inverses, and iii and iv are partial inverses (the domain of iii is all x, but the range of iv is $y \geq 2$).

Step 7 Encourage students to make and study tables of these functions to get the idea that the x- and y-values are interchanged.

▶ EXAMPLE A

This example illustrates the use of inverse functions in the many cases in which either variable can be considered to depend on the other.

Students should assume this is a linear relationship, but not the simple relationship $d = rt$ passing through the origin. The added constant could be due to various factors.

[Ask] "What if the book hadn't used the first point to find the equation for d?" [Using the second point would have yielded the equivalent equation $d = 1452 + \frac{863}{104}(t - 222)$.]

One Step

Read the introduction to the lesson: "Gloria and Keith are sharing their graphs for the same set of data. 'I know my graph is right!' exclaims Gloria. 'I've checked and rechecked it. Yours must be wrong, Keith.' Keith disagrees. 'I've entered these data into my calculator, and I made sure I entered the correct numbers.'" Show the Gloria and Keith transparency and ask students why the graphs are different. Encourage creative thinking, but bring out the idea that the independent and dependent variables are switched. During Sharing, elicit the notion of an inverse relation and how the graph of the inverse of a function relates to the graph of the function.

NCTM STANDARDS

CONTENT		PROCESS	
	Number	✓	Problem Solving
✓	Algebra	✓	Reasoning
	Geometry	✓	Communication
✓	Measurement	✓	Connections
	Data/Probability	✓	Representation

LESSON OBJECTIVES

- Define the inverse relation of a function and recognize that the inverse may not be a function or may be a function over a restricted domain
- Given several points in a function, find inverse points
- See relation-inverse symmetry across the line $y = x$
- Find the composition of functions with their inverses
- Apply inverses in real-world situations such as time-distance and temperature-pressure

▶ EXAMPLE B

This example shows how to find the inverse of a function and gives you a chance to review composition of functions.

You might relate inverses of functions to additive and multiplicative inverses and what happens when you add or multiply a number and its inverse.

SHARING IDEAS

Students might use the Graphing the Inverse transparency as they present their ideas. As they talk about inverses, especially for function iii in the investigation, **[Ask]** "Under what conditions is the inverse relation of a function also a function?" If students read aloud what the book says, ask what it means to them.

If students are having difficulty seeing how the graphs of a function and its inverse are reflections of each other across the line $y = x$, you might demonstrate using wax paper on an overhead projector. Or students can graph a function on paper, darken the graph with a pencil, fold the paper along the line $y = x$, and rub the reflection to create the graph of the inverse. The Sketchpad demonstration The Inverse of a Line shows an example.

Students might not want to take the time to find an inverse if the inverse isn't going to be a function. **[Ask]** "Is there a way to tell whether or not a function is one-to-one without actually graphing or trying to find an expression for the inverse?" Students may speculate that expressions for one-to-one functions have no even exponents on x. Suggest that they graph some functions such as $y = x^3 + x$ or $y = 2^x$ to check their conjectures. Or point out that the constant in the equation $y = x + 4$ is the same as $4x^0$, and 0 is an even power. Focus on what happens to the graph as it's reflected across the line $y = x$. Arrive at the idea that a one-to-one function will pass the horizontal line test as well as the vertical line test.

[Ask] "If the inverse is not a function, is it useless? Could part of it be a function?" [If the domain of the original function is restricted to an interval over which the function is one-to-one, its inverse will be a function.]

[Ask] "Is $f^{-1}(x)$ the same as $\frac{1}{f(x)}$?" [No, the first is the inverse, and the second is the reciprocal.] Model good mathematical thinking by asking "Is there any function $f(x)$ whose inverse equals its reciprocal?" Exploring this question can lead to a review of the difference between the composition and the product of two functions.

Remind or introduce students to the method called quick compositions using the Lesson 4.8 Quick Compositions? transparency or Calculator Note 5D. This method seems to relate compositions to the line $y = x$. **[Ask]** "Does the method relate to inverse functions, which are also related to compositions and to the line $y = x$?" The method can be extended to

---

To find the time of a flight from Washington, D.C., to Miami, substitute 910 for *distance:*

$$t = 118 + \frac{104}{863}(910 - 589) \approx 156.684$$

The flight will take approximately 157 min.

You can also use the first equation for *distance* and solve for t to get the second equation, for *time.*

$d = 589 + \frac{863}{104}(t - 118)$	First equation.
$d - 589 = \frac{863}{104}(t - 118)$	Subtract 589 from both sides.
$\frac{104}{863}(d - 589) = (t - 118)$	Multiply both sides by $\frac{104}{863}$.
$118 + \frac{104}{863}(d - 589) = t$	Add 118 to both sides.

These two equations are inverses of each other. That is, the independent and dependent variables have been switched. Graph the two equations on your calculator. What do you notice? They are reflections across the line $y = x$.

In the investigation you may have noticed that the inverse of a function is not necessarily a function. Recall from Chapter 4 that any set of points is called a relation. A relation may or may not be a function.

Inverse of a Relation

You get the **inverse** of a relation by exchanging the x- and y-coordinates of all points or exchanging the x- and y-variables in an equation.

When an equation and its inverse are *both* functions, it is called a **one-to-one function.** How can you tell if a function is one-to-one? It has no more than one value of y for each value of x, and no more than one value of x for each value of y. The inverse of a one-to-one function $f(x)$ is written as $f^{-1}(x)$. Note that this notation is similar to the notation for an exponent of -1, but $f^{-1}(x)$ refers to the inverse function, not an exponent.

EXAMPLE B

Find the composition of this function with its inverse.

$$f(x) = 4 - 3x$$

▶ Solution

The first step is to find the inverse. Exchange the independent and dependent variables. Then, solve for the new dependent variable.

$x = 4 - 3y$	Exchange x and y.
$x - 4 = -3y$	Subtract 4 from both sides.
$\frac{x-4}{-3} = y$	Divide by -3.
$f^{-1}(x) = \frac{x-4}{-3}$	Write in function notation.

The next step is to form the composition of the two functions.

$$f(f^{-1}(x)) = 4 - 3\left(\frac{x-4}{-3}\right)$$ Substitute $f^{-1}(x)$ for x in $f(x)$.

Let's see what happens when you distribute and remove some parentheses.

$$f(f^{-1}(x)) = 4 + (x - 4)$$
$$f(f^{-1}(x)) = x$$

What if you had found $f^{-1}(f(x))$ instead of $f(f^{-1}(x))$?

$$f^{-1}(f(x)) = \frac{(4 - 3x) - 4}{-3}$$ Substitute $f(x)$ for x in $f^{-1}(x)$.

$$f^{-1}(f(x)) = \frac{-3x}{-3}$$ Combine like terms in the numerator.

$$f^{-1}(f(x)) = x$$ Divide.

When you take the composition of a function and its inverse, you get x. How does the graph of $y = x$ relate to the graphs of a function and its inverse? Look carefully at the graphs below to see the relationship between a function and its inverse.

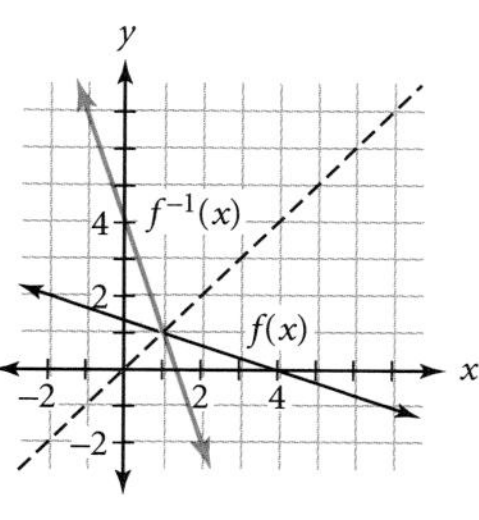

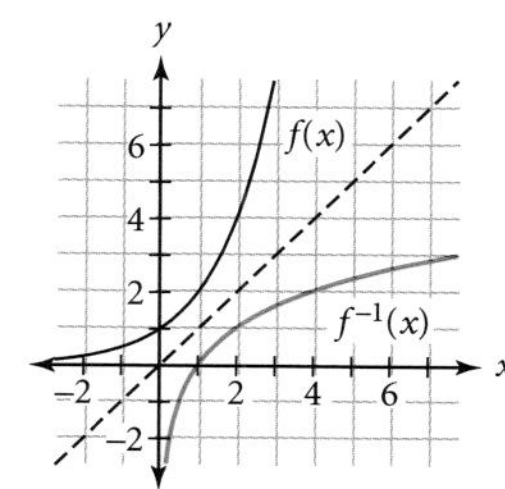

A function and its inverse are reflections across the line $y = x$.

A turntable DJ, like DJ Spooky shown here, applies special effects and mixing techniques to alter an original source of music. If you consider the original record to be one function and the effects or a second record to be another function, the music that the DJ creates is a composition of functions.

Exercises

Practice Your Skills

1. A function $f(x)$ contains the points $(-2, -3)$, $(0, -1)$, $(2, 2)$, and $(4, 6)$. Give the points known to be in the inverse of $f(x)$. $(-3, -2), (-1, 0), (2, 2), (6, 4)$

2. Given $g(t) = 5 + 2t$, find each value.
   a. $g(2)$ 9
   b. $g^{-1}(9)$ 2
   c. $g^{-1}(20)$ $\frac{15}{2}$ or 7.5

Sharing Ideas (continued)
evaluating the composition of any two functions (not just a function and itself) at a point, so it can be applied to a function and its inverse. You can show the Evaluating Compositions transparency.

Assessing Progress
As students investigate and present, you can assess their familiarity with linear, quadratic, and square root functions; their ability to follow new calculator instructions; and their skill at seeing visual patterns.

Closing the Lesson

The main points of this lesson are that a function has an **inverse** relation, consisting of points (x, y) whose coordinates are those of the function but interchanged. If the function is **one-to-one,** then its inverse is also a function; the composition of the function with its inverse is the function $y = x$; and the graphs of a function and its inverse are reflections of each other across the line $y = x$.

BUILDING UNDERSTANDING

Students deepen their understanding of inverse functions and of how their symbolic and graphical representations relate to those of the original functions.

ASSIGNING HOMEWORK

Essential	1–4
Performance assessment	5–13
Portfolio	10
Journal	6
Group	6, 7
Review	14–18

Helping with the Exercises

Exercise 2 [Ask] "How are 2a and 2b related?" [$g(2) = 9$ implies $g^{-1}(9) = 2$.]

3. Which graph below represents the inverse of the relation shown in the graph at right? Explain how you know.

a.

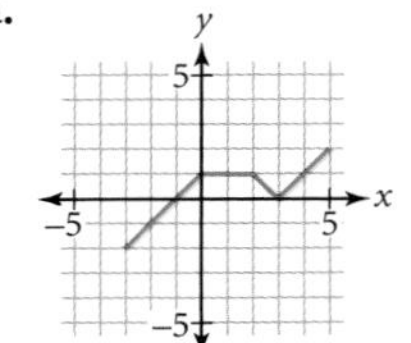

b.

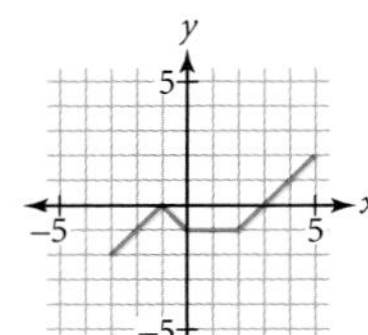

c.

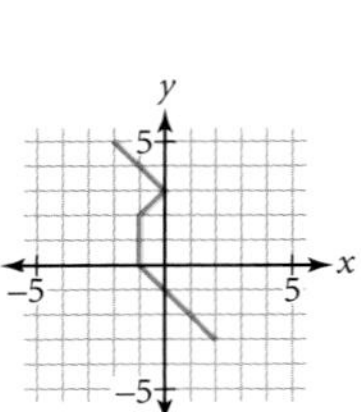

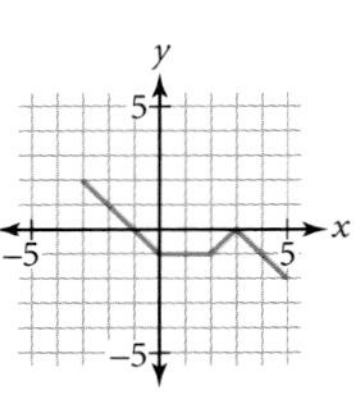

Graph c is the inverse because the x- and y-coordinates have been switched from the original graph so that the graphs are symmetric across line $y = x$.

4. Match each function with its inverse.

a. $y = 6 - 2x$ **b.** $y = 2 - \frac{6}{x}$ **c.** $y = -6(x - 2)$ **d.** $y = \frac{-6}{x - 2}$

e. $y = \frac{-1}{2}(x - 6)$ **f.** $y = \frac{2}{x - 6}$ **g.** $y = 2 - \frac{1}{6}x$ **h.** $y = 6 + \frac{2}{x}$

a and e are inverses; b and d are inverses; c and g are inverses; f and h are inverses.

Reason and Apply

5. Given the functions $f(x) = -4 + 0.5(x - 3)^2$ and $g(x) = 3 + \sqrt{2(x + 4)}$:

a. Find $f(7)$ and $g(4)$. $f(7) = 4$; $g(4) = 7$

b. What does this imply? They might be inverse functions.

c. Find $f(1)$ and $g(-2)$. $f(1) = -2$; $g(-2) = 5$

d. What does this imply? They are *not* inverse functions, at least not over their entire domains and ranges.

e. Over what domain are f and g inverse functions?
$f(x)$ for $x \geq 3$ and $g(x)$ for $x \geq -4$ are inverse functions.

6. Given $f(x) = 4 + (x - 2)^{3/5}$:

a. Solve for x when $f(x) = 12$.

b. Find $f^{-1}(x)$ symbolically.

c. How are solving for x and finding an inverse alike? How are they different?

7. Consider the function $f(x) = 4 + (x - 2)^{3/5}$ given in Exercise 6.

a. Graph $y = f(x)$ and use your calculator to draw its inverse.

b. Graph the inverse function you found in Exercise 6b. How does it compare to the inverse drawn by your calculator?

c. How can you determine whether your answer to Exercise 6b is correct?

8. Write each function using $f(x)$ notation, then find its inverse. If the inverse is a function, write it using $f^{-1}(x)$ notation.

a. $y = 2x - 3$ **b.** $3x + 2y = 4$ **c.** $x^2 + 2y = 3$

9. For each function in 9a and b, find the value of the expressions in i to iv.

a. $f(x) = 6.34x - 140$ **b.** $f(x) = 1.8x + 32$

i. $f^{-1}(x)$
ii. $f(f^{-1}(15.75))$
iii. $f^{-1}(f(15.75))$
iv. $f(f^{-1}(x))$ and $f^{-1}(f(x))$

Note that the equation in 9b will convert temperatures in °C to temperatures in °F. You will use either this function or its inverse in Exercise 10.

Exercise 4 Students can use either symbolic or graphical methods. As needed, help them see that a function is the inverse of its inverse; for example, a and e are inverses of each other.

Exercise 5e Encourage students to graph the functions to determine the entire domain rather than just look at the two points in 5a and 5c.

6a. $4 + (x - 2)^{3/5} = 12$
$(x - 2)^{3/5} = 8$
$x - 2 = 8^{5/3} = 32$
$x = 34$

6b. $4 + (y - 2)^{3/5} = x$
$(y - 2)^{3/5} = x - 4$
$y - 2 = (x - 4)^{5/3}$
$f^{-1}(x) = 2 + (x - 4)^{5/3}$

6c. Sample answer: The steps are the same, but you don't have to do the numerical calculations when you find an inverse.

7a.

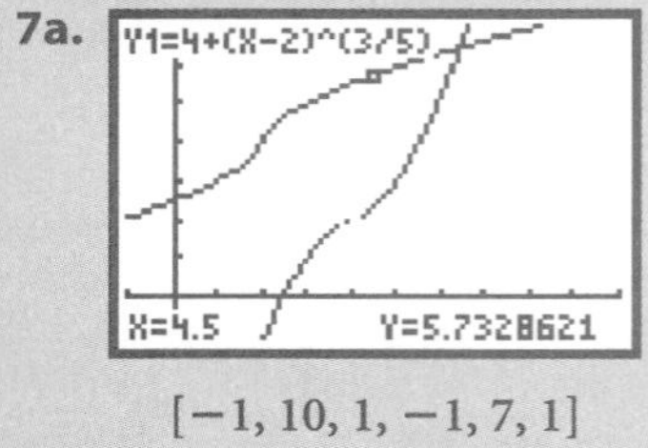

$[-1, 10, 1, -1, 7, 1]$

7b. The inverse function from 6b should be the same as the function drawn by the calculator.

7c. Find the composition of $f^{-1}(f(x))$. If it equals x, you have the correct inverse.

Exercise 8 You might **[Ask]** "How do you know the inverse is a function?" Students may cite the horizontal line test or a table.

8a. $f(x) = 2x - 3$;
$f^{-1}(x) = \frac{x + 3}{2}$, or
$f^{-1}(x) = \frac{1}{2}x + \frac{3}{2}$

8b. $f(x) = \frac{-3x + 4}{2}$;
$f^{-1}(x) = \frac{-2x + 4}{3}$, or
$f^{-1}(x) = -\frac{2}{3}x + \frac{4}{3}$

8c. $f(x) = \frac{-x^2 + 3}{2}$;
$y = \pm\sqrt{-2x + 3}$ (not a function)

Exercise 9 One intent of this exercise is for students to realize that thinking can save them work in ii and iii.

9a. i. $f^{-1}(x) = \frac{x + 140}{6.34}$

9a. ii. $f(f^{-1}(15.75)) = 15.75$

9a. iii. $f^{-1}(f(15.75)) = 15.75$

9a. iv. $f(f^{-1}(x)) = f^{-1}(f(x)) = x$

9b. i. $f^{-1}(x) = \frac{x - 32}{1.8}$

9b. ii. $f(f^{-1}(15.75)) = 15.75$

9b. iii. $f^{-1}(f(15.75)) = 15.75$

9b. iv. $f(f^{-1}(x)) = f^{-1}(f(x)) = x$

271

10. The data in the table describe the relationship between altitude and air temperature.

Feet	Meters	°F	°C
1,000	300	56	13
5,000	1,500	41	5
10,000	3,000	23	−5
15,000	4,500	5	−15
20,000	6,000	−15	−26
30,000	9,000	−47	−44
36,087	10,826	−69	−56

A caribou stands in front of Mt. McKinley in Denali National Park, Alaska. Mt. McKinley reaches an altitude of 6194 m above sea level.

a. Write a best-fit equation for $f(x)$ that describes the relationship (*altitude in meters, temperature in °C*). Use at least three decimal places in your answer.

b. Use your results from 10a to write the equation for $f^{-1}(x)$.

c. Write a best-fit equation for $g(x)$, describing (*altitude in feet, temperature in °F*).

d. Use your results from 10c to write an equation for $g^{-1}(x)$.

e. What would the temperature in °F be at the summit of Mount McKinley, which is 6194 m high?

f. Write a composition of functions that would also provide the answer for 10e. (You will use $f(x)$ or its inverse, $f^{-1}(x)$, from Exercise 9b.)

11. **APPLICATION** On Celsius's original scale, freezing corresponded to 100° and boiling corresponded to 0°.

a. Write a formula that converts a temperature given by today's Celsius scale into the scale that Celsius invented. $y = 100 - C$

b. Explain how you would convert a temperature given in degrees Fahrenheit into a temperature on the original scale that Celsius invented.

History CONNECTION

Anders Celsius (1701–1744) was a Swedish astronomer. He created a thermometric scale using the freezing and boiling temperatures of water as reference points, on which freezing corresponded to 100° and boiling to 0°. His colleagues at the Uppsala Observatory reversed his scale five years later, giving us the current version. Thermometers with this scale were known as "Swedish thermometers" until the 1800s when people began referring to them as "Celsius thermometers."

12. Here is a paper your friend turned in for a recent quiz in her mathematics class:

If it is a four-point quiz, what is your friend's score? For each incorrect answer, provide the correct answer and explain it so that next time your friend will get it right!

QUIZ

1. Rewrite x^{-1}. Answer: $\frac{1}{x}$

2. What does $f^{-1}(x)$ mean? Answer: $\frac{1}{f(x)}$

3. Rewrite $9^{-1/5}$. Answer: $\frac{1}{9^5}$

4. What number is 0^0 equal to? Answer: 0

12. Your friend's score is 1. Sample answers are given for explanations of incorrect answers.

Problem 1 is correct. Problem 2 is incorrect. The notation $f^{-1}(x)$ indicates the inverse function related to $f(x)$, not the exponent −1. Problem 3 is incorrect. The expression $9^{-1/5}$ can be rewritten as $\frac{1}{9^{1/5}}$. Problem 4 is incorrect. The expression 0^0 is not defined.

10a. The equation of the median-median line is $f(x) = -0.006546x + 14.75$.

10b. $f^{-1}(x) = \frac{x - 14.75}{-0.006546}$, or $f^{-1}(x) = -152.76x + 2253.28$

10c. The equation of the median-median line is $g(x) = -0.003545x + 58.814$.

10d. $g^{-1}(x) = \frac{x - 58.814}{-0.003545}$, or $g^{-1}(x) = -282.1x + 16591$

10e. Use the function in 10a to find the temperature in °C first. $f(6194) = -0.006546(6194) + 14.75 = -25.8$°C. Then use the function from 9b to change the °C to °F: $y = -14.44$ °F.

10f. Let $f(x) = -0.006546x + 14.75$ be the function that relates (*altitude in meters, temperature in °C*) and $h(x) = 1.8x + 32$ be the function that relates (°C, °F). Then, $h(f(x))$ with an input of altitude in meters will give an output in °F, $y = 1.8(-0.006546x + 14.75) + 32$, or $y = -0.01178x + 58.55$.

Exercise 11 As needed in 11a, **[Ask]** "What is the independent variable? The dependent variable?" [independent: today's scale, *C*; dependent: original scale, *y*] Students may find it helpful to graph a few points to show that the function is linear. They can then use two of these points to find the point-slope form of the equation. For 11b, students find the composition of the function with one of the functions in Exercise 9.

11b. Solve $F = 1.8C + 32$ for *C* and substitute it into $y = 100 - C$ to get $y = \frac{F - 212}{-1.8} = \frac{212 - F}{1.8}$.

Exercise 12 The expression 0^0 is generally taken as undefined, because 0 to "any power" is 0 but "any base" to the power of 0 is 1. Some students will enjoy exploring values of x^x for very small positive values of *x*.

Exercise 13 As needed, help students see that "and" means "plus." **[Alert]** In 13a, students may not realize that the independent variable is the number of thousands of gallons, not the number of gallons. Students may get different answers to 13f and 13g depending on what assumptions they make about the number of days in a month.

13a. $c(x) = 7.18 + 3.98x$, where c is the cost and x is the number of thousand gallons.

13c. $g(x) = \frac{x - 7.18}{3.98}$, where g is the number of thousands of gallons and x is the cost.

13e. $g(c(x)) = g(7.18 + 3.98x) = \dfrac{7.18 + 3.98x - 7.18}{3.98} = \dfrac{3.98x}{3.98} = x$

$c(g(x)) = c\left(\dfrac{x - 7.18}{3.98}\right) = 7.18 + 3.98\left(\dfrac{x - 7.18}{3.98}\right) =$

$7.18 + x - 7.18 = x$

13g. Answers will vary, but volume should equal $231 \cdot 1500$, or $346{,}500 \text{ in.}^3$ or approximately 200 ft^3.

14. possible answers: $\sqrt[3]{125^2}$, $(\sqrt[3]{125})^2$, 5^2, $\sqrt[3]{15625}$, 25

Exercise 16 To help motivate the next lesson, on logarithms, **[Ask]** "What if you can't rewrite the two sides to the same base?"

Exercise 17 There are infinitely many such parabolas; students can easily find at least the one with a horizontal axis and the one with a vertical axis.

13. In looking over his water utility bills for the past year, Mr. Aviles saw that he was charged a basic monthly fee of \$7.18, and \$3.98 per thousand gallons (gal) used.

a. Write the monthly cost function in terms of the number of thousands of gallons used.

b. What is his monthly bill if he uses 8000 gal of water? \$39.02

c. Write a function for the number of thousands of gallons used in terms of the cost.

d. If his monthly bill is \$54.94, how many gallons of water did he use? 12,000 gal

e. Show that the functions from 13a and c are inverses.

f. Mr. Aviles decides to fix his leaky faucets. He calculates that he is wasting 50 gal/d. About how much money will he save on his monthly bill? about \$13

g. A gallon is 231 cubic inches. Find the dimensions of a rectangular container that will hold the contents of the water Mr. Aviles saves in a month.

Environmental CONNECTION

Although about two-thirds of the world is covered with water, only 1% of the Earth's water is available for drinking water. Many freshwater sources are becoming increasingly polluted or are being affected by changing weather patterns. Increasing population and consumption and the building of dams and reservoirs are damaging ecosystems around the world. Conservation of water is critical.

Leaks account for nearly 12% of the average household's annual water consumption. About one in five toilets leaks at any given time, and that can waste more than 50 gallons each day. Dripping sinks add up fast too. A faucet that leaks one drop per second can waste 30 gallons each day.

Review

5.3 **14.** Rewrite the expression $125^{2/3}$ in as many different ways as you can.

5.3 **15.** Find an exponential function that contains the points (2, 12.6) and (5, 42.525). $f(x) = 12.6(1.5)^{x-2}$ or $f(x) = 42.525(1.5)^{x-5}$

5.2 **16.** Solve by rewriting with the same base.

a. $4^x = 8^3$ $x = \frac{9}{2}$ or 4.5 **b.** $3^{4x+1} = 9^x$ $x = -\frac{1}{2}$ or -0.5 **c.** $2^{x-3} = \left(\frac{1}{4}\right)^x$ $x = 1$

4.4 **17.** Give the equations of two different parabolas with vertex (3, 2) passing through the point (4, 5). $y = 3(x-3)^2 + 2$ and $x = \frac{1}{9}(y-2)^2 + 3$

3.7 **18.** Solve this system of equations.

$$\begin{cases} -x + 3y - z = 4 \\ 2z = x + y \\ 2.2y + 2.2z = 2.2 \end{cases}$$

$x = -1, y = 1, z = 0$

EXTENSIONS

A. To extend Exercise 12, have students make up their own quiz and student solutions. They could trade these quizzes and have their partners correct them.

B. Extend the Environmental Connection by asking students to check with the local utility to find out how local usage is calculated. Some water companies charge by actual usage, whereas others round use to the nearest 1000 gallons. Some meters measure in gallons, others in cubic inches or cubic feet.

LESSON

5.6

Logarithmic Functions

If all art aspires to the condition of music, all the sciences aspire to the condition of mathematics.

GEORGE SANTAYANA

You can model many phenomena with exponential functions. You have already used several methods to solve for x when it is contained in an exponent. You've learned that in special, rare occasions, it is possible to solve by finding a common base. For example, finding the value of x that makes each of these equations true is straightforward because of your experience with the properties of exponents.

$10^x = 1000 \qquad 3^x = 81 \qquad 4^x = \frac{1}{16}$

Solving the equation $10^x = 47$ isn't as straightforward because you may not know how to write 47 as a power of 10. You can, however, solve this equation by graphing $y = 10^x$ and $y = 47$ and finding the intersection—the solution to the system and the solution to $10^x = 47$. Take a minute to verify that $10^{1.672} \approx 47$ is true.

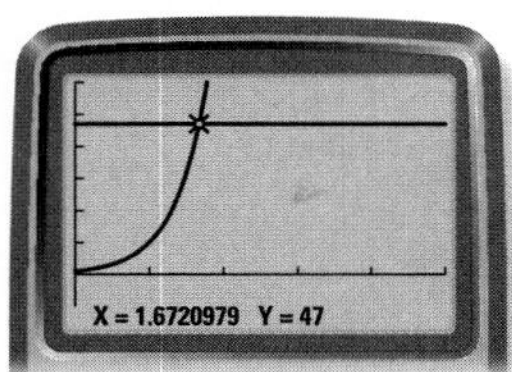

In the investigation you will discover an algebraic strategy to solve for x in an exponential equation. You'll use a new function called a **logarithm,** abbreviated log. Locate the log key on your calculator before going on.

Investigation
Exponents and Logarithms

In this investigation you'll explore the connection between exponents with a base of 10, and logarithms.

Step 1 Enter the equation $Y_1 = 10^x$ into your calculator. Make a table of values for Y_1.

Step 2 Enter the equation $Y_2 = \log(10^x)$ and compare the table values for Y_1 and Y_2. What observations can you make? Try starting your table at different values (including negative values) and using different decimal increment values.

Step 3 Based on your observations in Step 2, what are the values of the following expressions? Use the table to verify your answers.

a. $\log(10^{2.5})$ 2.5 **b.** $\log(10^{-3.2})$ -3.2 **c.** $\log(10^0)$ 0 **d.** $\log(10^x)$ x

Step 4 Complete the following statements.

a. If $100 = 10^2$, then $\log 100 =$ _?_. 2

b. If $400 \approx 10^{2.6021}$, then $\log$ _?_ $\approx$ _?_. 400; 2.6021

c. If _?_ $\approx 10^?$, then $\log 500 \approx$ _?_. 500; 2.6990; 2.6990

d. If $y = 10^x$, then $\log$ _?_ $=$ _?_. y; x

NCTM STANDARDS

CONTENT		PROCESS	
✓	Number	✓	Problem Solving
✓	Algebra	✓	Reasoning
	Geometry	✓	Communication
	Measurement	✓	Connections
	Data/Probability	✓	Representation

LESSON OBJECTIVES

- Review solving equations for exponents
- Define logarithm with base b and common logarithm with base 10
- Discover, using a calculator, that $\log(10^x) = x$
- Solve logarithmic equations with base 10 and with bases other than 10
- Establish that the inverse of an exponential function is a logarithmic function

LESSON

5.6

PLANNING

LESSON OUTLINE

One day:

15 min Investigation

15 min Examples

10 min Sharing

5 min Exercises

MATERIALS

- Calculator Notes 1M, 3B, 5C, *optional*
- Sketchpad demonstration Exponential and Logarithmic Functions, *optional*

TEACHING

This lesson includes both common logarithms (base 10) and logarithms with general bases. If your school's standards require study of natural logarithms, you can extend the Exploration The Number e on page 293.

Students may find the concept of logarithms difficult, so if you have time spend two days on this lesson. The first day might include the investigation; Example A; Exercises 1, 2, and 4; and some review exercises.

This lesson and the next ask students to solve equations for exponents by rewriting both sides with a common base. Not until Lesson 5.8 does the book introduce the idea of "taking the logarithm of both sides" of an equation. You can omit that part of Lesson 5.8 if you teach the technique earlier, but be careful not to do so at the expense of students' understanding logarithms as exponents. For a less structured investigation, begin with the one-step investigation on page 274.

See page 885 for answers to Steps 1 and 2.

Guiding the Investigation

Step 1 Review Calculator Note 3B for instructions on using function tables.

Step 2 Students should use a decimal value for ΔTbl.

Step 4 This step focuses on seeing (common) logarithms as powers of 10.

Step 5 **[Alert]** Students may not have grasped the idea that they can find the power of 10 by taking the log. For example, in part a they might not rewrite 300 as $10^{2.4771}$ to check. After students have finished the investigation, you might present part of Calculator Note 5C. The note is not mentioned in the student book because it usurps the discovery of the investigation and contains antilogs, which are not needed yet.

Step 6

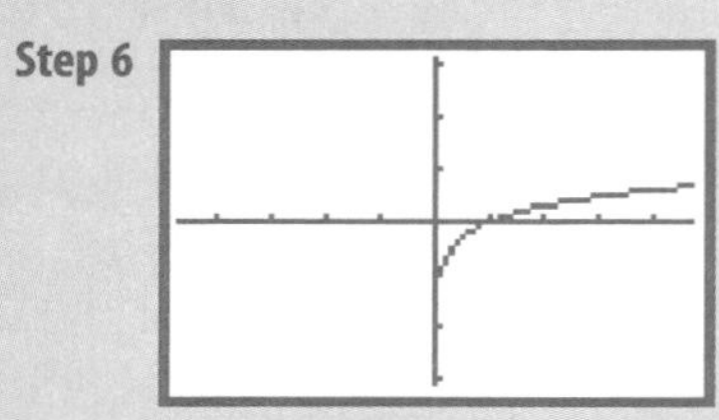

[−4.7, 4.7, 1, −3.1, 3.1, 1]

Yes, $y = \log x$ is a function. Domain: $x > 0$; range: all reals.

Step 7

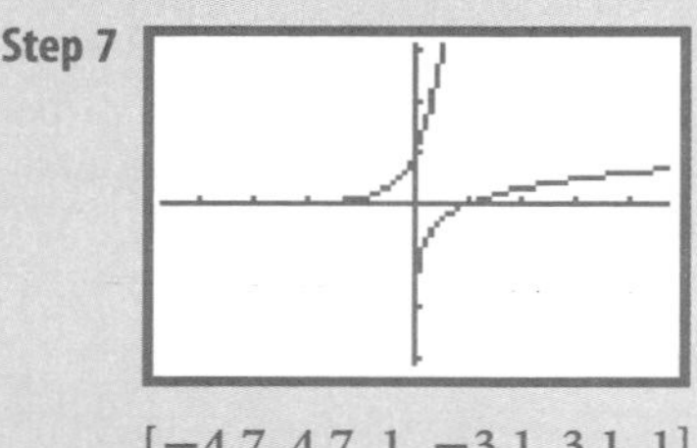

[−4.7, 4.7, 1, −3.1, 3.1, 1]

$y = 10^x$ and $y = \log x$ are inverses.

Step 5a $\log 300 = x$; $x \approx 2.4771$; $10^{2.4771} \approx 300$

Step 5b $\log 47 = x$; $x \approx 1.6721$; $10^{1.6721} \approx 47$

Step 5c $\log 0.01 = x$; $x = -2$; $10^{-2} = 0.01$

Step 5d $\log y = x$

Step 8 $f^{-1}(x) = \log x$; $f(f^{-1}(x)) = x$; $f^{-1}(f(x)) = x$

Step 5 Use logarithms to solve each equation for x. Check your answers.

a. $300 = 10^x$ **b.** $47 = 10^x$ **c.** $0.01 = 10^x$ **d.** $y = 10^x$

Step 6 Use a friendly window with a factor of 1 to investigate the graph of $y = \log x$. Is $y = \log x$ a function? What are the domain and range of $y = \log x$?

Step 7 Graph $y = 10^x$ and draw its inverse on the same set of axes. Now graph $y = \log x$. What observations can you make?

Step 8 If $f(x) = 10^x$, then what is $f^{-1}(x)$? What is $f(f^{-1}(x))$?

The expression $\log x$ is another way of expressing x as an exponent on the base 10. Ten is the common base for logarithms, so $\log x$ is called a **common logarithm** and is shorthand for writing $\log_{10} x$. You read this as "the logarithm base 10 of x." $\operatorname{Log} x$ is the exponent you put on 10 to get x.

The spiral shape of this computer-generated shell was created by a logarithmic function.

EXAMPLE A Solve $4 \cdot 10^x = 4650$.

► **Solution**

$4 \cdot 10^x = 4650$	Original equation.
$10^x = 1162.5$	Divide both sides by 4.
$x = \log_{10} 1162.5$	The logarithm base 10 of 1162.5 is the exponent you place on 10 to get 1162.5.
$x \approx 3.0654$	Use the log key on your calculator to evaluate.

The general **logarithmic function** is an exponent-producing function. The logarithm base b of x is the exponent you put on b to get x.

Definition of Logarithm

For $a > 0$ and $b > 0$, $\log_b a = x$ is equivalent to $a = b^x$.

The general logarithmic function is dependent on the base of the exponential expression. The next example demonstrates how to use logarithms to solve exponential equations when the base is not 10.

EXAMPLE B Solve $4^x = 128$.

► **EXAMPLE A**

The symbol $\log_{10}$ is the same as the symbol log used in the investigation. The answer, $x \approx 3.0654$, is given to five significant figures because that is the number of decimal places you need so that when you substitute back in for x the solution will check.

One Step

Pose the first part of Exercise 7: "Assume the United States national debt can be estimated with the model $y = 0.051517(1.1306727)^x$, where x represents the number of years since 1900 and y represents the debt in billions of dollars. According to the model, when did the debt pass \$1 trillion?" Ask students how to represent 1 trillion. Students from some countries may think of 1 trillion as 1 billion billion, but in the United States it's defined as 1000 billion. Students can solve the equation $1000 = 0.051517(1.1306727)^x$ by graphing or guess-and-check.

During Sharing, point out that a way of writing the equation in words is "x is the exponent put on 1.1306727 to get 19411" (which is $\frac{100}{0.051517}$), and say that a shorthand for those words is $x = \log_{1.1306727} 19411$. Ask students to read Example B and then calculate the value of x.

▶ Solution

You know that $4^3 = 64$ and $4^4 = 256$, so if $4^x = 128$, x must be between 3 and 4. You can rewrite the equation as $x = \log_4 128$ by the definition of a logarithm. But the calculator doesn't have a built-in logarithm base 4 function. Have we hit a dead end?

One way to solve this equation is to rewrite each side of the equation $4^x = 128$ as a power with a base of 10.

$4^x = 128$	Original equation.
$\left(10^{0.6021}\right)^x \approx 128$	$\text{Log}\,4 \approx 0.6021$, so $4 \approx 10^{0.6021}$.
$\left(10^{0.6021}\right)^x \approx 10^{2.1072}$	$\text{Log}\,128 \approx 2.10721$, so $128 \approx 10^{2.1072}$.
$0.6021x \approx 2.1072$	Use the power of a power property of exponents and the common base property of equality.
$x \approx \dfrac{2.1072}{0.6021} \approx 3.500$	Divide both sides by 0.6021.

Recall that $x = \log_4 128$ and that 2.1072 was an approximation for $\log 128$ and 0.6021 was an approximation for $\log 4$. The numerator and denominator of the last step above suggest a more direct way to solve $x = \log_4 128$.

Use log 128 instead of 2.1072.

$$x = \log_4 128 = \frac{\log 128}{\log 4} = 3.5$$

Use log 4 instead of 0.6021.

The relationship above is called the logarithm change-of-base property. It enables you to solve problems involving logarithms with bases other than 10.

Logarithm Change-of-Base Property

$$\log_b a = \frac{\log a}{\log b} \text{ where } a > 0 \text{ and } b > 0$$

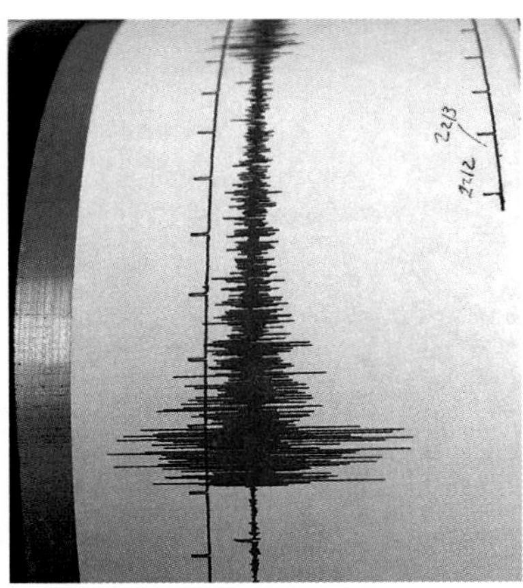

This relationship works because you can write any number using the inverse functions of logarithms and exponents. Doing a composition of functions that are inverses of each other produces an output value that is the same as the input. By definition, the equation $10^x = 4$ is equivalent to $x = \log 4$. Substitution from the second equation into the first equation gives you $10^{\log 4} = 4$. More generally, $10^{\log x} = x$, which means $y = 10^x$ and $y = \log x$ are inverses. This relationship allows you to rewrite any logarithmic expression with base 10. You could also choose to rewrite a logarithmic expression with any other base, so $\log_b a = \frac{\log_c a}{\log_c b}$.

Developed in 1935 by American scientist Charles F. Richter (1900–1985), the Richter scale measures the magnitude of an earthquake by taking the logarithm of the amplitude of waves recorded by a seismograph, shown at left. Because it is a logarithmic scale, each whole number increase in magnitude represents an increase in amplitude by a power of 10.

▶ EXAMPLE B

The emphasis of this example is on writing both sides of an equation as a power of 10, that is, as a common logarithm. Students may notice that both sides of the equation can also be written as 2 to a power: $2^{2x} = 2^7$. Setting the exponents equal leads to a value of x of exactly 3.5. Stress that the goal is to have the same base on both sides so that the exponents can be set equal.

You might want to rework Example B for the general equation $\log_b a = x$:

$$b^x = a$$
$$\left(10^{\log b}\right)^x = \left(10^{\log a}\right)$$
$$x \log b = \log a$$
$$x = \frac{\log a}{\log b}$$
$$\therefore \log_b a = \frac{\log a}{\log b}$$

SHARING IDEAS

As students work and present, ask them to try to put into words what *logarithm* means. Don't let them merely say "exponent"; press for what distinguishes logarithms from other exponents. One way of describing it is to say that the logarithm with base b of x is the exponent put on b to get x. To help students make sense of the idea, ask what $10^{\log x}$ is and what $\log 10^x$ is. That is, what is 10 to the exponent you put on 10 to get x? What is the exponent you put on 10 to get 10 to the exponent x? Give students time to see that the answer to both of these questions is x.

The Sketchpad demonstration Exponential and Logarithmic Functions can help relate this lesson to what students learned in Lesson 5.1.

[Ask] "Why does the book keep specifying that the number you're taking the logarithm of has to be positive?" [Any positive base raised to any power (even a negative power) yields a positive number.]

Sharing Ideas (continued)

Tell students that bankers and accountants sometimes approximate by using the "rule of 72": The number of years it takes an investment to double is about 72 divided by the percent interest rate. For example, an investment at 4% will double in about $\frac{72}{4} = 18$ years. **[Ask]** "How exact is the rule of 72 approximation for the doubling time of a 4% investment?" [The calculator's Finance solver (see Calculator Note 1M) gives 17.67.] From the equation $(1 + r)^n = 2$, students see that $n = \log_{1+r} 2 = \frac{\log 2}{\log(1 + r)}$. For values of r less than 20%, the fraction on the right is indeed close to $\frac{72}{100r}$.

Assessing Progress

You can assess students' ability to make tables and graphs on a calculator and to see patterns, as well as their understanding of rational exponents.

▶ ***EXAMPLE C***

The answer is 6 years, not 5.7613 years, because interest is compounded annually.

Closing the Lesson

The **logarithm** of a number with base b is the exponent put on b to get that number. As exponents, logarithms can be used to solve equations in which the unknown appears as a power. The value of $\log_b a$ can be found as $\frac{\log a}{\log b}$, where log means the **common logarithm,** with base 10. The function $y = \log_b x$ is the inverse of the function $y = b^x$.

BUILDING UNDERSTANDING

The exercises give students their first practice with logarithms.

ASSIGNING HOMEWORK

Essential	1–4
Performance assessment	5–9
Group	8
Review	10–15

▶ Helping with the Exercises

Exercise 2 Students can solve each equation in this exercise by thinking about exponents (for example, $\log_5 625 = \log_5 5^4 = 4$), but they might also use the logarithm change-of-base property.

2a. $x = 3$ **2b.** $x = 4$

2c. $x = \frac{1}{2}$ **2d.** $x = \frac{1}{3}$

2e. $x = -2$ **2f.** $x = 0$

Exercise 3 This exercise (except for 3a) requires the logarithm change-of-base property.

3a. $x = \log_{10} 0.001$; $x = -3$

3b. $x = \log_5 100$; $x \approx 2.8614$

3c. $x = \log_{35} 8$; $x \approx 0.5849$

3f. $x = \log_{17} 0.5$; $x \approx -0.2447$

EXAMPLE C An initial deposit of \$500 is invested at 8.5% interest, compounded annually. How long will it take until the balance grows to \$800?

▶ ***Solution*** Let x represent the number of years the investment is held. Use the general formula for exponential growth, $y = a(1 + r)^x$.

$500(1 + 0.085)^x = 800$	Growth formula for compounding interest.
$(1.085)^x = 1.6$	Divide both sides by 500.
$x = \log_{1.085} 1.6$	Use the definition of logarithm.
$x = \frac{\log 1.6}{\log 1.085}$	Use the logarithm change-of-base property.
$x \approx 5.7613$	Evaluate.

It will take 6 years for the balance to grow to at least \$800.

EXERCISES

▶ Practice Your Skills

1. Rewrite each logarithmic equation in exponential form using the definition of a logarithm.

a. $\log 1000 = x$ $10^x = 1000$ **b.** $\log_5 625 = x$ $5^x = 625$ **c.** $\log_7 \sqrt{7} = x$ $7^x = \sqrt{7}$

d. $\log_8 2 = x$ $8^x = 2$ **e.** $\log_5 \frac{1}{25} = x$ $5^x = \frac{1}{25}$ **f.** $\log_6 1 = x$ $6^x = 1$

2. Solve each equation in Exercise 1 for x.

3. Rewrite each exponential equation in logarithmic form using the definition of a logarithm. Then solve for x. (Give your answers rounded to four decimal places.)

a. $10^x = 0.001$ **b.** $5^x = 100$ **c.** $35^x = 8$

d. $0.4^x = 5$ **e.** $0.8^x = 0.03$ **f.** $17^x = 0.5$

$x = \log_{0.4} 5$; $x \approx -1.7565$ $x = \log_{0.8} 0.03$; $x \approx 15.7144$

4. Graph each equation. Write a sentence explaining how the graph compares to the graph of either $y = 10^x$ or $y = \log x$. See page 277 for 4b–f.

a. $y = \log(x + 2)$ **b.** $y = 3\log x$ **c.** $y = -\log x - 2$

d. $y = 10^{x+2}$ **e.** $y = 3(10^x)$ **f.** $y = -(10^x) - 2$

▶ Reason and Apply

5. Classify each statement as true or false. If false, change the second part to make it true.

a. If $6^x = 12$, then $x = \log_{12} 6$. false; $x = \log_6 12$ **b.** If $\log_2 5 = x$, then $5^x = 2$. false; $2^x = 5$

c. If $2 \cdot 3^x = 11$, then $x = \frac{\log 11}{2\log 3}$. false; $x = \frac{\log 5.5}{\log 3}$ **d.** If $x = \frac{\log 7}{\log 3}$, then $x = \log_7 3$. false; $x = \log_3 7$

6. The function $g(x) = 23(0.94)^x$ gives the temperature in degrees Celsius of a bowl of water x minutes after a large quantity of ice is added. After how many minutes will the water reach 5°C? approximately 25 min

Exercise 4 Comparisons of graphs should include discussion of transformations.

4a. This is a translation of $y = \log x$ left 2 units.

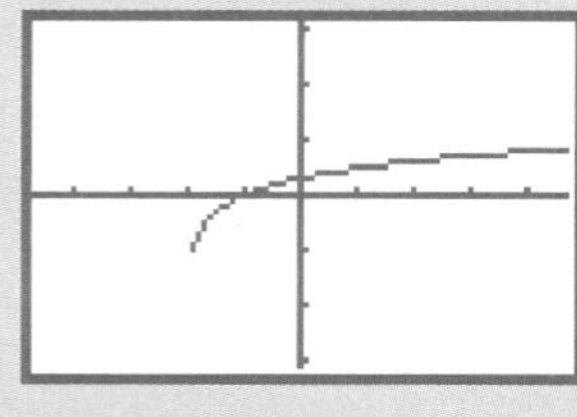

$[-4.7, 4.7, 1, -3.1, 3.1, 1]$

Exercise 5 Students who have not made sense of the logarithm notation will keep looking up how to change between exponential and logarithmic equations. Help them work with words: The logarithm is the *exponent* you put on something to get something else.

7. Assume the United States's national debt can be estimated with the model $y = 0.051517(1.1306727)^x$, where x represents the number of years since 1900 and y represents the debt in billions of dollars.

   a. According to the model, when did the debt pass $1 trillion ($1000 billion)? 1980

   b. According to the model, what is the annual growth rate of the national debt? 13%

   c. What is the doubling time for this growth model? 5.6 yr

8. **APPLICATION** Carbon-14 is an isotope of carbon that is formed when radiation from the sun strikes ordinary carbon dioxide in the atmosphere. Trees, which get their carbon dioxide from the air, contain small amounts of carbon-14. Once a tree is cut down, no more carbon-14 is formed, and the amount that is present begins to decay slowly. The half-life of the carbon-14 isotope is 5730 yr.

   a. Find an equation that models the percentage of carbon-14 in a sample of wood. (Consider that at time zero there is 100% and that at time 5730 yr there is 50%.) $y = 100(0.999879)^x$

   b. A piece of wood contains 48.37% of its original carbon-14. According to this information, approximately how long ago did the tree that it came from die? What assumptions are you making, and why is this answer approximate?

Fossilized wood can be found in Petrified Forest National Park. Some of the fossils are over 200 million years old.

9. **APPLICATION** Crystal looks at an old radio dial and notices that the numbers are not evenly spaced. She hypothesizes that there is an exponential relationship involved. She tunes the radio to 88.7 FM. After six "clicks" of the tuning knob, she is listening to 92.9 FM.

   a. Write an exponential model in point-ratio form. Let x represent the number of clicks past 88.7 FM, and let y represent the station number. $y = 88.7(1.0077)^x$

   b. Use the equation you have found to determine how many clicks Crystal should turn to get from 88.7 FM to 106.3 FM. 23 or 24 clicks

Review

5.3 **10.** Solve.

   a. $(x - 2)^{2/3} = 49$ $x = 345$

   b. $3x^{2.4} - 5 = 16$ $x = 7^{1/2.4} \approx 2.25$

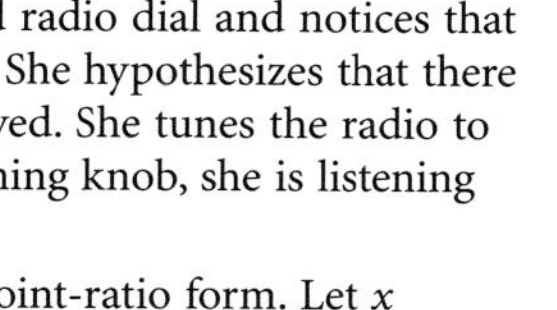

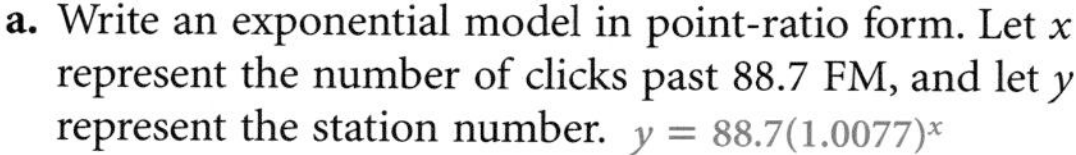

3.5 **11.** **APPLICATION** The number of railroad passengers has been increasing in the United States. The table shows railroad ridership from 1988 to 2000.

   a. Plot the data and find the median-median line.

   b. Calculate the residuals.

   c. What is the root mean square error for this model? Explain what it means in this context.

   d. If the trend continues, what is a good estimate of the ridership in 2010? 126.8 million riders

Year x	Passengers (millions) y
1988	36.9
1989	38.8
1990	40.2
1991	40.1
1992	41.6
1993	55.0
1994	60.7

Year x	Passengers (millions) y
1995	62.9
1996	65.6
1997	68.7
1998	75.1
1999	79.8
2000	84.1

(*Time Almanac 2002*)

Exercise 8 [Language] *Isotopes* of an element are atoms with differing numbers of neutrons. *Radiation,* in this context, is visible light and other forms of energy from the sun.

8b. 6002 yr ago. The technique is approximate and assumes that the carbon-14 concentration in the atmosphere has not changed over the last 6000 years.

11a.

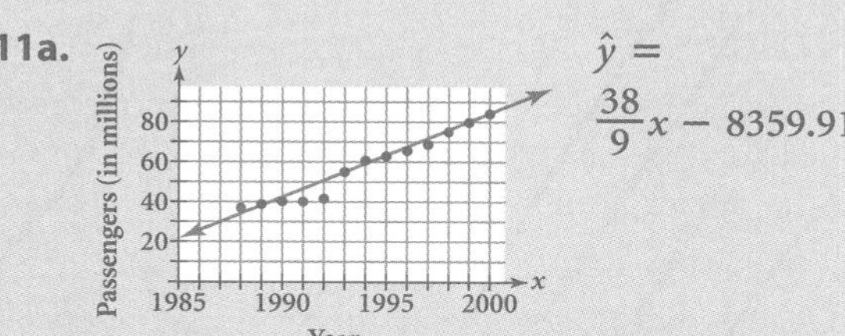

$\hat{y} = \frac{38}{9}x - 8359.91$

11b. 3.03, 0.71, −2.11, −6.43, −9.16, 0.02, 1.50, −0.52, −2.05, −3.17, −0.99, −0.51, −0.43

11c. 3.78 million riders. Most data are within 3.78 million of the predicted number.

4b. This is a vertical stretch of $y = \log x$ by a factor of 3.

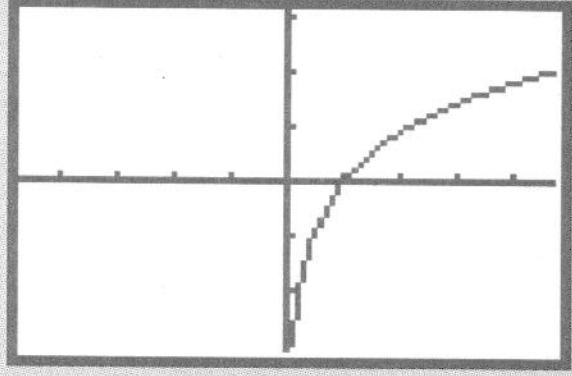

[−4.7, 4.7, 1, −3.1, 3.1, 1]

4c. This is a reflection of $y = \log x$ across the x-axis and a translation down 2 units.

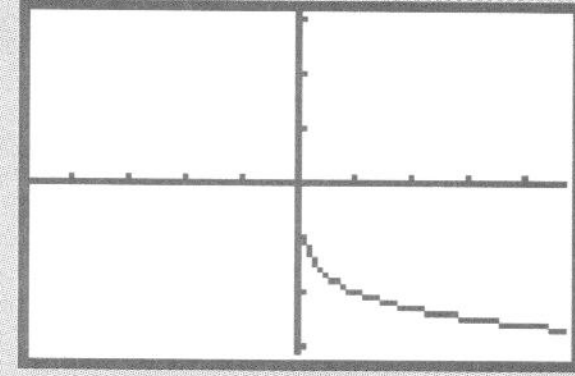

[−4.7, 4.7, 1, −3.1, 3.1, 1]

4d. This is a translation of $y = 10^x$ left 2 units.

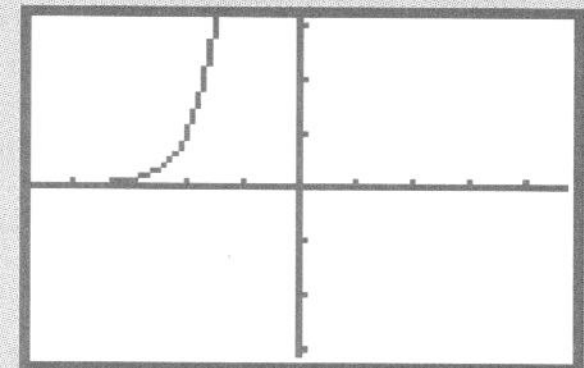

[−4.7, 4.7, 1, −3.1, 3.1, 1]

4e. This is a vertical stretch of $y = 10^x$ by a factor of 3.

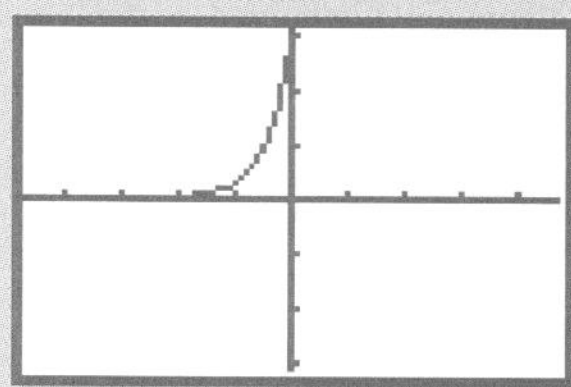

[−4.7, 4.7, 1, −3.1, 3.1, 1]

4f. This is a reflection of $y = 10^x$ across the x-axis and a translation down 2 units.

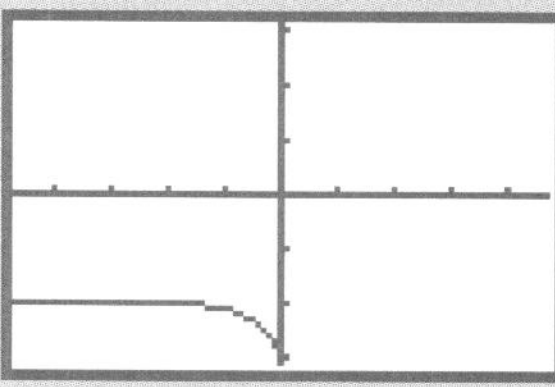

[−4.7, 4.7, 1, −3.1, 3.1, 1]

5.1 **12. APPLICATION** The C notes on a piano $(C_1–C_8)$ are one octave apart. Their relative frequencies double from one C note to the next.

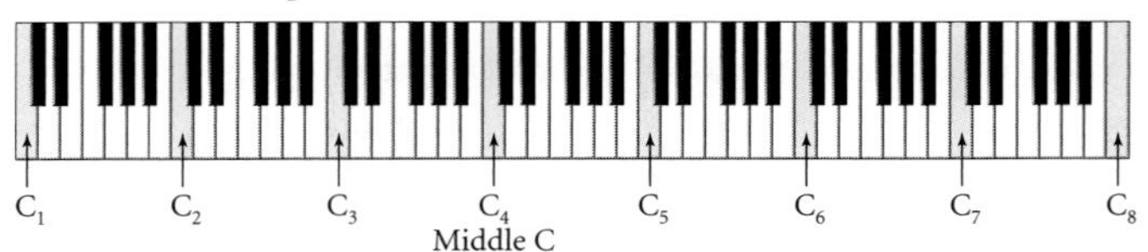

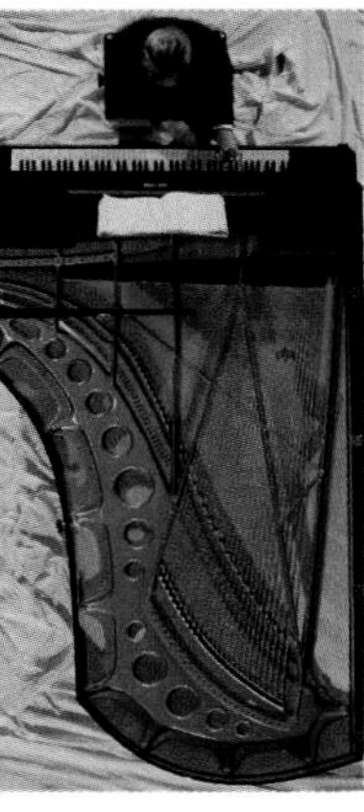

a. If the frequency of middle C (or C_4) is 261.6 cycles per second, and the frequency of C_5 is 523.2 cycles per second, find the frequencies of the other C notes.

b. Even though the frequencies of the C notes form a discrete function, you can model it using a continuous explicit function. Write a function model for these notes.

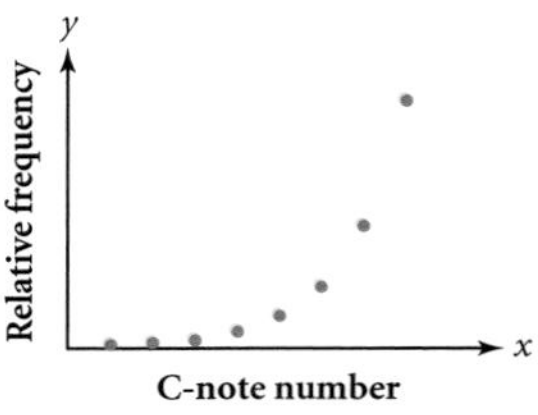

4.6 **13.** In each case below, use the graph and equation of the parent function to write an equation of the transformed image.

a.

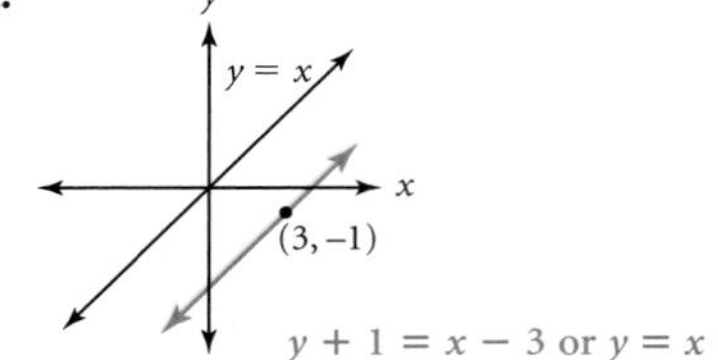

b.

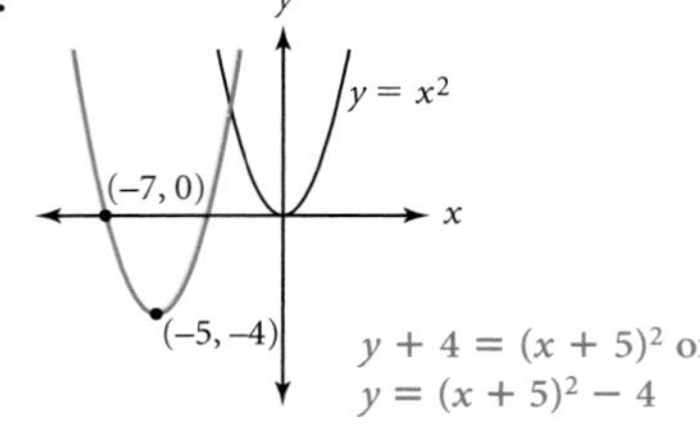

c.

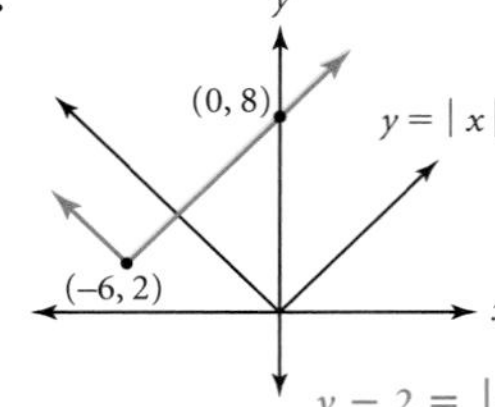

d.

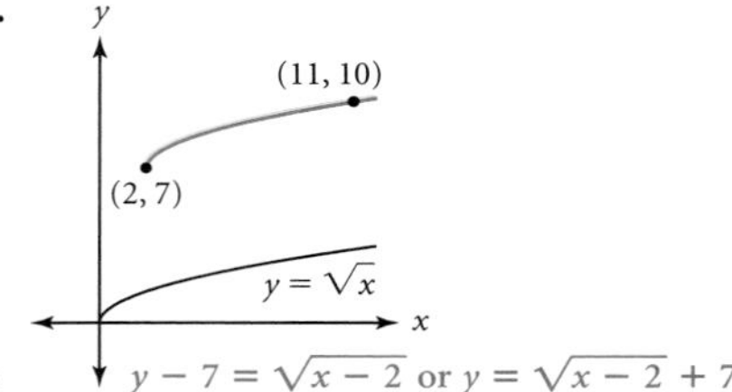

3.7 **14.** A rectangle has a perimeter of 155 inches. Its length is 7 inches more than twice its width.

a. Write a system of equations using the information given.

b. Solve the system and find the rectangle's dimensions.

4.3 **15.** ℓ_1: $2x - 3y = 9$ $\quad$ ℓ_2: $2x - 3y = -1$

a. Graph ℓ_1 and ℓ_2. What is the relationship between these two lines?

b. Give the coordinates of one point, A, on ℓ_1, and two points, P and Q, on ℓ_2.

c. Describe the transformation that maps ℓ_1 onto ℓ_2 and A onto P. Write the equation of the image of ℓ_1 showing the transformation.

d. Describe the transformation that maps ℓ_1 onto ℓ_2 and A onto Q. Write the equation of the image of ℓ_1 showing the transformation.

e. Algebraically show that the equations in 15c and d are equivalent to ℓ_2.

Exercise 12 [Language] A musical note sounds when air molecules vibrate. A motion of the molecules back and forth and back to their starting point is called a *cycle.* The number of cycles in a unit of time is called the *frequency* of the vibration and determines what we hear as the pitch of the note. Notes an *octave* apart sound very similar but are at different pitches.

12a. $C_1 = 32.7$, $C_2 = 65.4$, $C_3 = 130.8$, $C_6 = 1046.4$, $C_7 = 2092.8$, $C_8 = 4185.6$

12b. $y = 16.35(2)^x$ where x represents C-note number and y represents frequency in cycles per second.

14a. $2l + 2w = 155$
$l = 2w + 7$

14b. $l = 54$, $w = 23.5$; length: 54 in., width: 23.5 in.

15a.

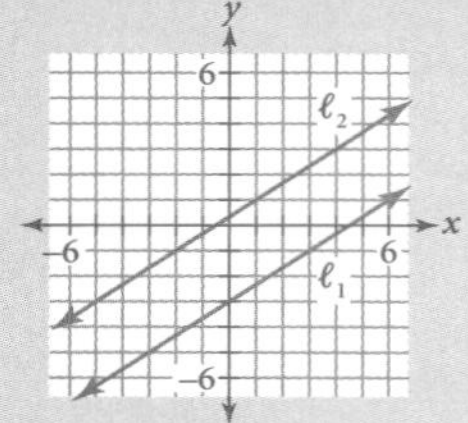

They are parallel.

15b. Possible answer: $A(0, -3)$; $P(1, 1)$; $Q(4, 3)$

15c. Possible answer: Translate 1 unit right and 4 units up.
$2(x - 1) - 3(y - 4) = 9$.

15d. Possible answer: Translate 4 units right and 6 units up.
$2(x - 4) - 3(y - 6) = 9$.

15e.
$2(x - 1) - 3(y - 4) = 9 \rightarrow$
$2x - 2 - 3y + 12 = 9 \rightarrow$
$2x - 3y = -1$, which is ℓ_2.
$2(x - 4) - 3(y - 6) = 9 \rightarrow$
$2x - 8 - 3y + 18 = 9 \rightarrow$
$2x - 3y = -1$, which is also ℓ_2.

EXTENSIONS

A. Extend Exercise 7 by asking students to research the actual amount of national debt and compare it to the model.

B. Extend Exercise 11 by asking students to research train ridership and answer questions such as these: Why is ridership increasing? Is population growth responsible? Has ridership increased in certain geographic areas and not in others?

LESSON

5.7

Properties of Logarithms

Each problem that I solved became a rule which served afterwards to solve other problems.

RENÉ DESCARTES

Before machines and electronics were adapted to do multiplication, division, and raising a number to a power, scientists spent long hours doing computations by hand. Early in the 17th century, Scottish mathematician John Napier (1550–1617) discovered a method that greatly reduced the time and difficulty of these calculations, using a table of numbers that he named logarithms. As you learned in Lesson 5.6, a common logarithm is an exponent—the power of 10 that equals a number—and you already know how to use the multiplication, division, and power properties of exponents. In the next example you will discover some shortcuts and simplifications.

After inventing logarithms, John Napier designed a device for calculating with logarithms in 1617. Later called "Napier's bones," the device used multiplication tables carved on strips of wood or bone. The calculator at left has an entire set of Napier's bones carved on each spindle. You can learn more about Napier's bones and early calculating devices at www.keymath.com/DAA .

EXAMPLE

Convert numbers to logarithms to do these problems.

a. Multiply 183.47 by 19.628 without using the multiplication key on your calculator.

b. Divide 183.47 by 19.628 without using the division key on your calculator.

c. Evaluate $4.70^{2.8}$ without the exponentiation key on your calculator. (You may use the 10ˣ key.)

▶ Solution

You can do parts a and b by hand. Or, you can convert to logarithms and use alternative functions.

a. $\log 183.47 \approx 2.263565$, so $10^{2.263565} \approx 183.47$.
$\log 19.628 \approx 1.292876$, so $10^{1.292876} \approx 19.628$.

$$183.47 \cdot 19.628 \approx 10^{2.263565} \cdot 10^{1.292876} = 10^{2.263565+1.292876} \approx 10^{3.556441} \approx 3601.148$$

b. $\dfrac{183.47}{19.628} \approx \dfrac{10^{2.263565}}{10^{1.292876}} = 10^{2.263565-1.292876} = 10^{0.970689} \approx 9.34736$

c. $\log 4.70 \approx 0.6721$, so $10^{0.6721} \approx 4.70$.

$$4.70^{2.8} \approx \left(10^{0.6721}\right)^{2.8} = 10^{0.6721 \cdot 2.8} \approx 10^{1.8819} \approx 76.2$$

People did these calculations with a table of base-10 logarithms before there were calculators. For example, they looked up log 183.47 and log 19.628 in a table and added those together. Then they worked backward in their table to find the **antilog,** or antilogarithm, of that sum.

NCTM STANDARDS

CONTENT	PROCESS
✓ Number	✓ Problem Solving
✓ Algebra	✓ Reasoning
Geometry	✓ Communication
✓ Measurement	✓ Connections
Data/Probability	✓ Representation

LESSON OBJECTIVES

- Use the properties of exponents to multiply, divide, and exponentiate with logarithms
- Learn to change bases so that all logarithms can be calculated using common logarithms
- See how a slide rule works
- Formally define the properties of logarithms

LESSON

5.7

PLANNING

LESSON OUTLINE

One day:

10 min Example

20 min Investigation

5 min Sharing

10 min Exercises

MATERIALS

- rulers
- Slide Rule (W)
- Calculator Note 5C, *optional*

TEACHING

In this lesson students see how logarithms can be used to do calculations. Napier's method was not actually based on exponents, but rather on the correspondence between arithmetic and geometric scales. See *Historical Topics for the Mathematics Classroom.*

One Step

Ask students to calculate $\left(\frac{10 \cdot 1000}{100}\right)^4$ and its common logarithm and then to calculate the logarithm of each number and see whether the logarithm of the full expression can be found from the logarithms of its parts. As needed, suggest that students investigate simpler problems. They can test their conjectures on numbers that aren't powers of 10. Ask groups to write up rules for the logarithm of a product, a quotient, and a power.

During Sharing reach consensus on statements of these rules and check their applications to rational exponents, such as roots.

▶ EXAMPLE

The example demonstrates how logarithms, as base-10 exponents, can be used to multiply, divide, and exponentiate. If you ask students to solve the problems before the class discusses the solution, help them realize that you are not asking them to perform paper-and-pencil manipulations.

[Ask] "What button on your calculator would you use to find an antilog?" [10^x] Calculator Note 5C shows an example.

Guiding the Investigation

As an alternative to this investigation, you might have your students complete Exercises 2, 3, and 4 to discover the three main properties of logarithms. Be sure to define *antilog* first.

Hand out the Slide Rule worksheet. Most slide rules can approximate numbers to at most three significant digits. They can be more accurate for answers just over 1 than for answers that start with 8 or 9.

Step 1 **[Language]** A decimal ruler is one on which units are divided into tenths.

	0	1	2	3	4
4.0	.6021	.6031	.6042	.6053	.6064
4.1	.6128	.6138	.6149	.6160	.6170
4.2	.6232	.6243	.6253	.6263	.6274
4.3	.6335	.6345	.6355	.6365	.6375
4.4	.6435	.6444	.6454	.6464	.6474
4.5	.6532	.6542	.6551	.6561	.6571
4.6	.6628	.6637	.6646	.6656	.6665
4.7	.6721	.6730	.6739	.6749	.6758
4.8	.6812	.6821	.6830	.6839	.6848
4.9	.6902	.6911	.6920	.6928	.6937

$\log 4.70 \approx 0.6721$

	0	1	2	3	4
7.0	.8451	.8457	.8463	.8470	.8476
7.1	.8513	.8519	.8525	.8531	.8537
7.2	.8573	.8579	.8585	.8591	.8597
7.3	.8633	.8639	.8645	.8651	.8657
7.4	.8692	.8698	.8704	.8710	.8716
7.5	.8751	.8756	.8762	.8768	.8774
7.6	.8808	.8814	.8820	.8825	.8831
7.7	.8865	.8871	.8876	.8882	.8887
7.8	.8921	.8927	.8932	.8938	.8943
7.9	.8976	.8982	.8987	.8993	.8998

$$\operatorname{antilog} 0.8819 \approx 7.62$$
$$\operatorname{antilog} 1 = 10$$
$$\operatorname{antilog} 1.8819 \approx 7.62 \cdot 10 \approx 76.2$$

Can you see why "10 to the power" came to be called the antilog? The antilog of 3 is the same as 10^3, which equals 1000. Later, slide rules were invented to shorten this process, although logarithm tables were still used for more precise calculations. Because a logarithm is an exponent, it must have properties similar to the properties of exponents. The following investigation uses a simple slide rule to explore these properties.

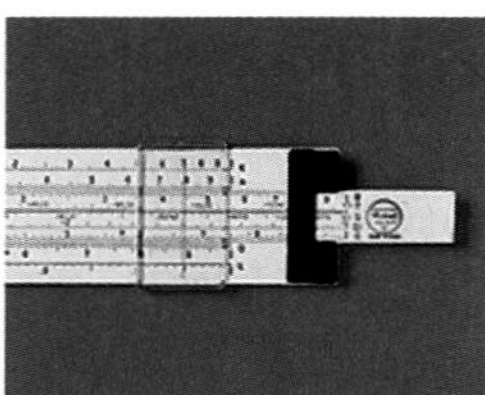

Technology CONNECTION

A few years after Napier's discovery, English mathematician William Oughtred (1574–1660) realized that sliding two logarithmic scales next to each other makes calculations easier, and he invented the slide rule. Over the next three centuries, many people made improvements to the slide rule, making it an indispensable tool for engineers and scientists, until computers and calculators became widely available in the 1970s. For more on the history of computational machines, see the links at www.keymath.com/DAA .

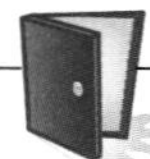

Investigation
Slide Rule

You will need

- a slide-rule worksheet
- two ordinary rulers

Work with a partner. Your slide rule is two rulers marked and scaled in unequal increments. Notice that each part of the slide rule begins with 1 (not 0).

Step 1 $x = 0.3$, $y = 0.7$, $z = 0.9$, $w = 1.0$

Step 1 One part of the slide rule is shown at right, next to a decimal ruler. Use the decimal ruler to measure each of the lengths *w*, *x*, *y*, and *z*, accurate to the nearest tenth of a unit.

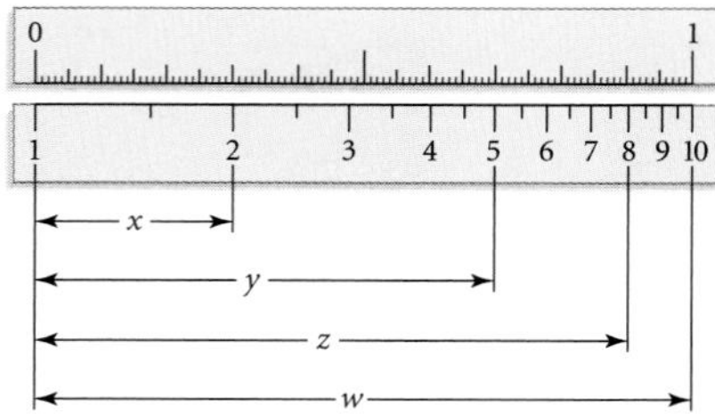

Step 2 | Use the lengths from Step 1 to calculate these ratios and express them as decimals.

a. $\frac{x}{w}$ $\frac{0.3}{1.0} = 0.3$ **b.** $\frac{y}{w}$ $\frac{0.7}{1.0} = 0.7$ **c.** $\frac{y}{x}$ $\frac{0.7}{0.3} \approx 2.3$ **d.** $\frac{z}{x}$ $\frac{0.9}{0.3} = 3.0$

Step 3 | Use the decimal scale and your calculations from Step 2 to find these logarithms.

a. $\log_{10} 2$ **b.** $\log_{10} 5$ **c.** $\log_2 5$ **d.** $\log_2 8$

Step 4 | Describe mathematically how the numbers are placed on the slide rule. Explain clearly enough so that a person reading your description could make an accurate slide rule.

Step 5 | You can use two *ordinary* rulers to find the sum for an addition problem, like $4 + 3 = 7$, by sliding one of the rulers along the other ruler as shown in the diagram below.

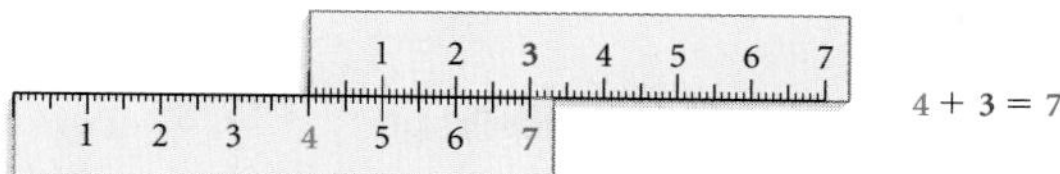

What happens when you use the slide rule to "add" 2 and 3 in the same way? (Instead of aligning the 0 of the ruler, you will have to match the 1 over the first number.) Write a conjecture and explain why this happens. Choose other pairs of numbers to test your conjecture.

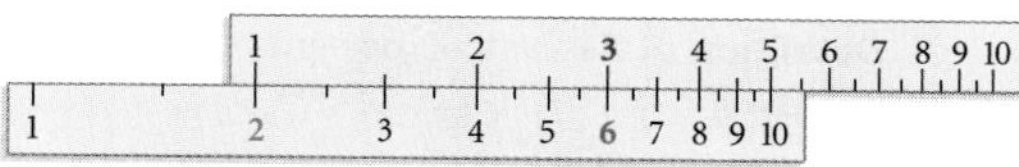

Step 6 | Explain, or sketch a picture, showing how to use the slide rule to do these calculations.

a. $3 \cdot 3$ **b.** $5 \cdot 7$ **c.** $2.5 \cdot 3.5$ **d.** $25 \cdot 35$

Step 7 | Write a sentence explaining how the slide rule uses the properties of logarithms to find the value of $2.5 \cdot 3.5$.

Step 8 | Using ordinary rulers, you can subtract 7 from 3 and get -4. What happens when you use the slide rule to "subtract" 2 from 8 in the same way?

Step 9 | Explain, or sketch a picture, showing how to use the slide rule to find these quotients.

a. $\frac{10}{2}$ **b.** $\frac{2.5}{3.5}$ **c.** $\frac{5}{7}$ **d.** $\frac{18}{5}$

Step 10 | Write a sentence explaining how the slide rule uses the properties of logarithms to find the value of $\frac{2.5}{3.5}$.

Step 7 Sample answer: The logarithm of the product of two numbers is the sum of the logarithms of the two numbers, so you add the logarithmic lengths on a slide rule to multiply the numbers those lengths represent.

Step 8 Sample answer: You get 4, which is $8 \div 2$.

Step 10 Sample answer: The logarithm of the quotient of two numbers is the difference of the logarithms of the two numbers, so you subtract the logarithmic lengths on a slide rule to divide the numbers those lengths represent.

In this chapter you have learned the properties of exponents and logarithms, summarized on the next page. You can use these properties to solve equations involving exponents. Remember to look carefully at the order of operations and then work step by step to undo each operation.

Step 2 Students can round their answers to the nearest tenth.

Step 3 Students can use the change-of-base property to rewrite the logarithms in 3c and 3d.

Step 3a $\log_{10} 2 = \frac{\log 2}{\log 10} = \frac{x}{w} = 0.3$, or $\log_{10} 2 = x = 0.3$

Step 3b $\log_{10} 5 = \frac{\log 5}{\log 10} = \frac{y}{w} = 0.7$, or $\log_{10} 5 = y = 0.7$

Step 3c $\log_2 5 = \frac{\log 5}{\log 2} = \frac{y}{x} \approx 2.3$

Step 3d $\log_2 8 = \frac{\log 8}{\log 2} = \frac{z}{x} = 3.0$

Step 5 You might have students experiment with a few addition and subtraction problems to make sure they understand the process with ordinary rulers. As needed, remind students that the slide rule could extend farther to the left and to the right. On a logarithmic scale, 10 is halfway between 1 and 100.

Step 6 For 6a and 6b, remind students to line up the first number with the 1 on the right, not the 1 on the left. Encourage them to decide on decimal placement in answers in a way that makes sense and then to check, perhaps with scientific notation.

Step 9 **[Alert]** Students may be confused because the denominator goes on the top ruler.

SHARING IDEAS

When formalizing the properties of logarithms, encourage students to make up their own name for each property to make it easier to remember.

[Ask] "What's the domain of the function $y = \log x$"? [positive real numbers] "Why?" [When you raise 10 to any power, even a negative one, you get a positive number.]

See page 885 for answers to Steps 4, 5, 6, and 9.

Sharing Ideas (continued)

[Ask] "Is it possible to model multiplication using ordinary rulers? Can you model 2 times 4? How?" [yes; by adding 2 four times using four rulers] "What about 3.5 times 4.7?" [Decimals are more difficult. You could multiply 3.5 by 47, then divide by 10. Forty-seven is a lot of rulers, which is why logarithms were used.]

Ask whether the properties of logarithms can be used to find roots of numbers. Investigate together how to find the 51st root of 6542 using the power property. Mention that this is the process a calculator uses to make the calculation.

Assessing Progress

You can assess students' understanding of logarithms as exponents.

Closing the Lesson

The three main properties of logarithms are that the log of a product is the sum of the logs, the log of a quotient is the difference of the logs, and the log of a number to a power is the power times the log of the number. These properties made logarithms valuable for multiplication, division, and exponentiation before the days of electronic calculators.

BUILDING UNDERSTANDING

Students work with and apply the properties of logarithms.

ASSIGNING HOMEWORK

Essential	1, 5
Performance assessment	7–10, 13
Portfolio	6
Journal	10
Group	2–4
Review	7, 11–15

Helping with the Exercises

Exercises 2–4 These exercises can be completed as a discovery investigation for the three main properties of logarithms. If you begin the lesson with these exercises rather than with the investigation, remember to define *antilog* first.

Properties of Exponents and Logarithms

Definition of Logarithm

If $x = a^m$, then $\log_a x = m$.

Product Property

$a^m \cdot a^n = a^{m+n}$ or $\log_a xy = \log_a x + \log_a y$

Quotient Property

$\frac{a^m}{a^n} = a^{m-n}$ or $\log_a \frac{x}{y} = \log_a x - \log_a y$

Power Property

$\log_a x^n = n \log_a x$

Power of a Power Property

$(a^m)^n = a^{mn}$

Power of a Product Property

$(ab)^m = a^m b^m$

Power of a Quotient Property

$\left(\frac{a}{b}\right)^n = \frac{a^n}{b^n}$

Change-of-Base Property

$\log_a x = \frac{\log_b x}{\log_b a}$

Definition of Rational Exponents

$a^{m/n} = (\sqrt[n]{a})^m$ or $\sqrt[n]{a^m}$

Definition of Negative Exponents

$a^{-n} = \frac{1}{a^n}$ or $\left(\frac{a}{b}\right)^{-n} = \left(\frac{b}{a}\right)^n$

EXERCISES

Practice Your Skills

1. Change the form of each expression below using properties of logarithms or exponents, without looking back in the book. Name each property or definition you use.

a. g^{h+k} **b.** $\log s + \log t$ **c.** $\frac{f^w}{f^v}$ **d.** $\log \frac{h}{k}$ **e.** $(j^s)^t$

f. $\log b^g$ **g.** $\sqrt[n]{k^m}$ **h.** $\frac{\log_s t}{\log_s u}$ **i.** $w^t w^s$ **j.** p^{-h}

In Exercises 2–4, find the missing values. Then answer the questions to learn about some properties of logarithms.

2. ***Mini-Investigation*** Find the values of 2a–f.

a. $a = \log 18$ $a \approx 1.255$ **b.** $b = \log 71$ $b \approx 1.851$ **c.** $c = a + b$ $c \approx 3.106$

d. $d = \text{antilog}\, c$ $d = 1278$ **e.** $e = 18 \cdot 71$ $e = 1278$ **f.** $f = \log(18 \cdot 71)$ $f \approx 3.106$

1a. $g^h \cdot g^k$; product property of exponents

1b. $\log st$; product property of logarithms

1c. f^{w-v}; quotient property of exponents

1d. $\log h - \log k$; quotient property of logarithms

1e. j^{st}; power property of exponents

1f. $g \log b$; power property of logarithms

1g. $k^{m/n}$; definition of rational exponents

1h. $\log_u t$; change-of-base property

1i. w^{t+s}; product property of exponents

1j. $\frac{1}{p^h}$; definition of negative exponents

g. Describe any patterns you see. $d = e$ and $c = f$

h. Complete the statement "$\log a + \log b = \underline{?}$." $\log ab$

i. The property you discovered is the product property of logarithms. Explain why this property works. (*Hint:* Name another mathematical situation in which you add when multiplying.)

3. ***Mini-Investigation*** Find the values of 3a–f.

a. $a = \log 58$ $a \approx 1.763$ b. $b = \log 22$ $b \approx 1.3424$ c. $c = a - b$ $c \approx 0.4210$

d. $d = \text{antilog}\, c$ $d \approx 2.6364$ e. $e = \frac{58}{22}$ $e \approx 2.6364$ f. $f = \log\left(\frac{58}{22}\right)$ $f \approx 0.4210$

g. Describe any patterns you see. $c = f$ and $d = e$

h. Complete the statement "$\log a - \log b = \underline{?}$." $\log \frac{a}{b}$

i. The property you discovered is the quotient property of logarithms. Explain why this property works. (*Hint:* Name another mathematical situation in which you subtract when dividing.)

4. ***Mini-Investigation*** Find the values of 4a–d.

a. $a = \log 13$ $a \approx 1.1139$ b. $b = 3.6a$ $b \approx 4.0102$ c. $c = \text{antilog}\, b$ $c \approx 10237.55$ d. $d = 13^{3.6}$ $d \approx 10237.55$

e. Compare the values you found. Describe any relationship you see. $d = c$

f. Complete the statement "$\log a^b = \underline{?}$." $b \log a$

g. This property is called the power property of logarithms. How would you write $\log \sqrt{a}$ in terms of $\log a$? $\log \sqrt{a} = \log a^{0.5} = 0.5 \log a$

5. Determine whether each equation is true or false. If false, rewrite one side of the equation to make it true. Check your answer on your calculator.

a. $\log 3 + \log 7 = \log 21$ true b. $\log 5 + \log 3 = \log 8$ c. $\log 16 = 4 \log 2$ true

d. $\log 5 - \log 2 = \log 2.5$ true e. $\log 9 - \log 3 = \log 6$ f. $\log \sqrt{7} = \log \frac{7}{2}$

g. $\log 35 = 5 \log 7$ h. $\log \frac{1}{4} = -\log 4$ true i. $\frac{\log 3}{\log 4} = \log \frac{3}{4}$

j. $\log 64 = 1.5 \log 16$ true

Reason and Apply

6. **APPLICATION** The half-life of carbon-14, which is used in dating archaeological finds, is 5730 yr.

a. Assume that 100% of the carbon-14 is present at time 0 yr, or $x = 0$. Write the equation that expresses the percentage of carbon-14 remaining as a function of time. (This should be the same equation you found in Lesson 5.6, Exercise 8a.)

b. Suppose some bone fragments have 25% of their carbon-14 remaining. What is the approximate age of the bones? 11,460 yr

c. In the movie *Raiders of the Lost Ark* (1981), a piece of the Ark of the Covenant found by Indiana Jones contained 62.45% of its carbon-14. What year would this indicate that the ark was constructed in?

d. Coal is formed from trees that lived about 100 million years ago. Could carbon-14 dating be used to determine the age of a lump of coal? Explain your answer.

2i. The logarithm gives the exponent using a certain base. When numbers with the same base are multiplied, the exponents are added. Or, adding the logarithms of two numbers, then finding the antilog of the sum, gives their product.

3i. When numbers with the same base are divided, the exponents are subtracted.

5b. false; possible answer: $\log 5 + \log 3 = \log 15$

5e. false; possible answer: $\log 9 - \log 3 = \log 3$

5f. false; possible answer: $\log \sqrt{7} = \frac{1}{2} \log 7$

5g. false; possible answer: $\log 35 = \log 5 + \log 7$

5i. false; possible answer: $\log 3 - \log 4 = \log \frac{3}{4}$

Exercise 6b [ESL] A *fragment* is a piece broken off an object.

Students need not have seen the movie to answer 6c; they need only assume that the movie is correct.

6a. $y = 100(0.999879)^x$

6c. $x \approx 3890.706$; about $1981 - 3891 = 1910$ B.C.E.

6d. $y = 100(0.999879)^x$; $y = 100(0.999879)^{100000000}$; $y = 0$. There is virtually nothing left to measure, so you could not use carbon-14 for dating coal. Or, you would need very sensitive instruments to detect the radioactivity.

Exercise 7 [Language] In music, the symbol # means "sharp," a note a halftone higher than the same note without the sharp. As needed, remind students that a geometric sequence is made continuous by an exponential function. Students might use the point-ratio method to find the function, or they might realize that the doubling takes place over 12 steps, and so the common ratio must be $\sqrt[12]{2}$.

7a. Let x represent the note's number of steps above middle C, and let y represent the note's frequency in hertz. $y = 261.6(2^{x/12})$ because the starting value is 261.6 and there are 12 intermediate frequencies to get to the last C note, which has double that frequency.

MAKING THE CONNECTION

The "mathematically simple intervals" referred to in the music connection are the result of frequency ratios which are simple fractions. One mathematically simple scale is often called the *Pythagorean scale.*

Exercise 8 Encourage students to use the properties of logarithms and exponents in solving these equations. If you have taught the idea of "taking the logarithm of both sides," they can use that technique as well.

9b.

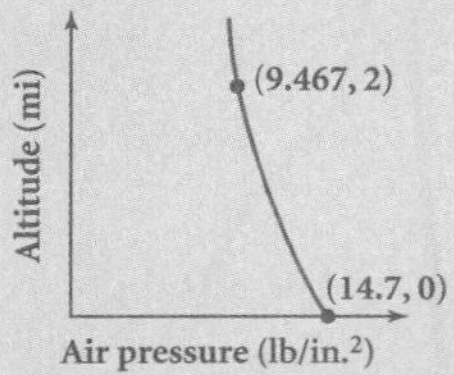

284

7. APPLICATION This table lists the consecutive notes from middle C to the next C note. This scale is called a chromatic scale and it increases in 12 steps, called half-tones. The frequencies measured in cycles per second, or hertz (Hz), associated with the consecutive notes form a geometric sequence, in which the frequency of the last C note is double the frequency of the first C note.

a. Find a function that will generate the frequencies.

b. Fill in the missing table values.

	Note	Frequency (Hz)
Do	C_4	261.6
	C#	277.2
Re	D	293.6
	D#	311.1
Mi	E	329.6
Fa	F	349.2
	F#	370.0
Sol	G	392.0
	G#	415.3
La	A	440.0
	A#	466.1
Ti	B	493.8
Do	C_5	523.2

Music CONNECTION

If an instrument is tuned to the mathematically simple intervals that make one key sound in tune, it will sound out of tune in a different key. With some adjustments, it will be a well-tempered scale—a scale that is in tune for any key. However, not all music is based on an 8- or 12-note scale. Indian musical compositions are based on a *raga,* a structure of 5 or more notes. There are 72 *melas,* or parent scales, on which all ragas are based.

Anoushka Shankar plays the sitar in the tradition of classical Indian music.

8. Use the properties of logarithms and exponents to solve these equations.

a. $5.1^x = 247$ $x \approx 3.3816$

b. $17 + 1.25^x = 30$ $x \approx 11.495$

c. $27(0.93^x) = 12$ $x \approx 11.174$

d. $23 + 45(1.024^x) = 147$ $x \approx 42.739$

9. APPLICATION The altitude of an airplane is calculated by measuring atmospheric pressure on the surface of the airplane. This pressure is exponentially related to the plane's height above Earth's surface. At ground level, the pressure is 14.7 pounds per square inch (abbreviated lb/in.², or psi). At an altitude of 2 mi, the pressure is reduced to 9.46 lb/in.².

a. Write an exponential equation for altitude in miles as a function of air pressure. $y = 14.7(0.8022078)^x$

b. Sketch the graph of air pressure as a function of altitude. Sketch the graph of altitude as a function of air pressure. Graph your equation from 9a and its inverse to check your sketches.

c. What is the pressure at an altitude of 12,000 ft? (1 mi = 5280 ft) $y = 8.91$ lb/in.²

d. What is the altitude of an airplane if the atmospheric pressure is 3.65 lb/in.²? $x = 6.32$ mi

Science CONNECTION

Air pressure is the weight of the atmosphere pushing down on objects within the atmosphere, including Earth itself. Air pressure decreases with increasing altitude because there is less air above you as you ascend. A barometer is an instrument that measures air pressure, usually in millibars or inches of mercury, both of which can be converted to lb/in.², which is the weight of air pressing down on each square inch of surface.

10. APPLICATION Carbon-11 decays at a rate of 3.5% per minute. Assume that 100% is present at time 0 min.

a. What percentage remains after 1 min? 96.5%

b. Write the equation that expresses the percentage of carbon-11 remaining as a function of time. $y = 100(0.965)^x$, with x in minutes

c. What is the half-life of carbon-11? 19.456 min

d. Explain why carbon-11 is not used for dating archaeological finds.
In one day the carbon-11 is virtually gone, so you could never date an archaeological find.

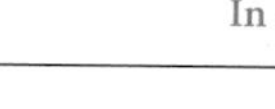

Review

5.5 **11.** Draw the graph of a function whose inverse is not a function. Carefully describe what must be true about the graph of a function if its inverse is not a function.

5.1 **12.** Find an equation to fit each set of data.

a. $y = 5 + 3x$

x	y
1	8
4	17
6	23
7	26

b. $y = 2(3^x)$

x	y
0	2
3	54
4	162
6	1458

5.6 **13.** Describe how each function has been transformed from the parent function $y = 2^x$ or $y = \log x$. Then graph the function.

a. $y = -4 + 3(2)^{x-1}$

b. $y = 2 - \log\left(\frac{x}{3}\right)$

Chapter 2 **14.** Answer true or false. If the statement is false, explain why or give a counterexample.

a. A grade of 86% is always better than being in the 86th percentile.

b. A mean is always greater than a median.

c. If the range of a set of data is 28, then the difference between the maximum and the mean must be 14.

d. The mean for a box plot that is skewed left is to the left of the median. true

4.8 **15.** A driver charges \$14 per hour plus \$20 for chauffeuring if a client books directly with her. If a client books her through an agency, the agency charges 115% of what the driver charges plus \$25.

a. Write a function to model the cost of hiring the driver directly. Identify the domain and range.

b. Write a function to model what the agency charges. Identify the domain and range.

c. Give a single function that you can use to calculate the cost of using an agency to hire the driver for h hours.
$a = 1.15(14h + 20) + 25$, or $a = 16.1h + 48$

EXTENSIONS

A. Use Take Another Look activity 3 on page 298.

B. Research how tables of logarithms were created.

C. Students may be able to bring unusual slide rules from home for sharing. Circular slide rules were quite common, cylindrical slide rules less so.

11. Graphs will vary. If a horizontal line intersects the graph in more than one point, its inverse is not a function.

13a. The graph has been vertically stretched by a factor of 3, then translated to the right 1 unit and down 4 units.

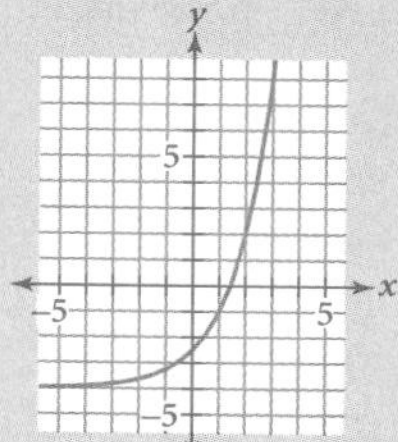

13b. The graph has been horizontally stretched by a factor of 3, reflected across the x-axis, and translated up 2 units.

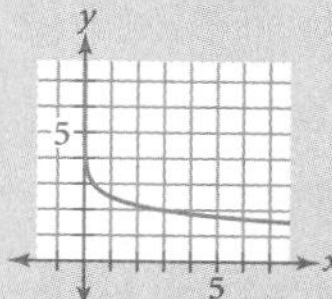

14a. False. If everyone got a grade of 86% or better, one would have to have gotten a much higher grade to be in the 86th percentile.

14b. False. Consider the data set {5, 6, 9, 10, 11}. The mean is 8.2; the median is 9.

14c. False. Consider the data set {0, 2, 28}. The range is 28; the difference between the mean, 10, and the maximum, 28, is 18.

15a. Let h represent the length of time in hours, and let c represent the driver's cost in dollars. $c = 14h + 20$. The domain is the set of possible values of the number of hours, $h > 0$. The range is the set of possible values of the cost paid to the driver, $c > 20$.

15b. Let c represent the driver's cost in dollars, and let a represent the agency's charge in dollars. $a = 1.15c + 25$. The domain is the money paid to the driver if she had been booked directly, c. $c > 20$. The range is the amount charged by the agency, a. $a > 48$.

LESSON

5.8

PLANNING

LESSON OUTLINE

First day:

30 min Examples

15 min Exercises

Second day:

25 min Investigation

5 min Sharing

15 min Exercises

MATERIALS

- cup of hot water
- temperature probes
- Freezer Data (T) for One Step
- Cooling Sample Data (W), *optional*
- Calculator Notes 3D, 5E
- Fathom demonstration Curve Straightening, *optional*

TEACHING

This lesson concerns solving exponential equations by taking the logarithm of both sides and by curve straightening (linearizing).

If you shorten the lesson to one day by omitting one of the two ideas, you can do either Example B, the investigation, and Exercises 7–10 (linearization) or Example A and Exercises 1–4 (taking the logarithm of both sides).

► EXAMPLE A

You might first demonstrate the technique of taking the logarithm of both sides on a simpler equation such as $5 = 2^x$.

[Ask] "Why is the answer 35 and not 35.18 or 36?" [The question asked about the swing number.]

One Step

Show the Freezer Data transparency and pose this problem: "If you put a cup of hot water into the freezer and record the temperature every minute, you might get data like these. The graph indicates that the decay is exponential, but the ratios between consecutive terms vary. Can you make the graph of $y = ab^x$ linear by taking the logarithm of both sides and then using a line of fit to find values of a and b?" As needed, help students see that $\log a$ and $\log b$ are the unknown constants for the line of fit. They can apply any techniques they want to finding a line of fit. During Sharing, point out to students that they took the logarithm of both sides of an equation and **[Ask]** "What if the exponential decay approaches some value other than 0?" [The function is a translation of the parent function.]

LESSON

5.8

Applications of Logarithms

Drowning problems in an ocean of information is not the same as solving them.

RAY E. BROWN

In this lesson you will explore applications of the techniques and properties you discovered in the previous lesson. You can use logarithms to rewrite and solve problems involving exponential and power functions that relate to the natural world as well as to life decisions. You will be better able to interpret information about investing money, borrowing money, disposing of nuclear and other toxic waste, interpreting chemical reaction rates, and managing natural resources if you have a good understanding of these functions and problem-solving techniques.

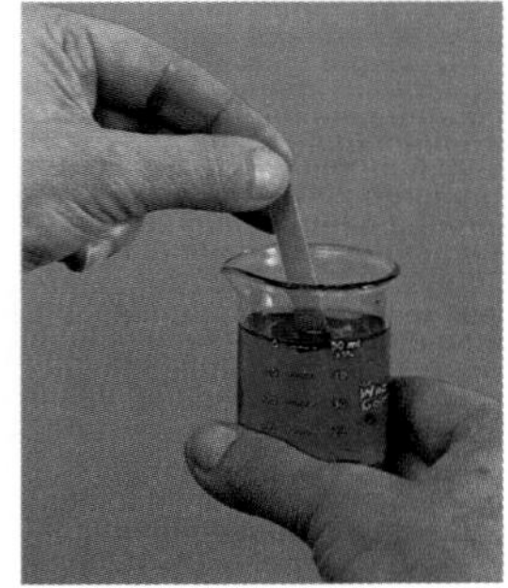

The pH scale is a logarithmic scale. A pH of 7 is neutral. A pH reading below 7 indicates an acid, and each whole-number decrease increases acidity by a power of 10. A pH above 7 indicates an alkaline, or base, and each whole-number increase increases alkalinity by a power of 10.

EXAMPLE A

Recall the pendulum example from Lesson 5.4. The equation $y = 1.25 + 0.72(0.954)^{x-10}$ gave the greatest distance from a motion sensor for each swing of the pendulum based on the number of the swing. Use this equation to find the swing number when the greatest distance was closest to 1.47 m. Explain each step.

► Solution

$y = 1.25 + 0.72(0.954)^{x-10}$	Original equation.
$1.25 + 0.72(0.954)^{x-10} = 1.47$	Substitute 1.47 for y.
$0.72(0.954)^{x-10} = 0.22$	Subtract 1.25 from both sides.
$(0.954)^{x-10} = \frac{0.22}{0.72} \approx 0.3056$	Divide both sides by 0.72.
$\log\left((0.954)^{x-10}\right) \approx \log(0.3056)$	Take the logarithm of both sides.
$(x - 10) \cdot \log(0.954) \approx \log(0.3056)$	Use the power property of logarithms.
$-0.02045(x - 10) \approx -0.51485$	Evaluate the logarithms.
$x - 10 \approx \frac{-0.51485}{-0.02045} \approx 25.18$	Divide both sides by -0.02045.
$x \approx 35.18$	Add 10 to both sides.

On the 35th swing, the pendulum will be closest to 1.47 m from the motion sensor.

As you can do with other operations on equations, you can take the logarithm of both sides, as long as the value of each side is known to be positive. Recall that the domain of $y = \log x$ is $x > 0$, so you cannot find the logarithm of a negative number or zero. In Example A, you knew that both sides were equal to the positive number 0.3056 before you took the logarithm of each side.

It is sometimes difficult to determine whether a relationship is logarithmic, exponential, or neither. You can use a technique called **curve straightening** to help you decide. After completing steps to straighten a curve, all you have to decide is whether or not the new graph is linear.

EXAMPLE B

Eva convinced the mill workers near her home to treat their wastewater before returning it to the lake. She then began to sample the lake water for toxin levels (measured in parts per million, or ppm) once every five weeks. Here are the data she collected.

Week	0	5	10	15	20	25	30
Toxin level (ppm)	349.0	130.2	75.4	58.1	54.2	52.7	52.1

Eva hoped that the level would be much closer to zero after this much time. Does she have evidence that the toxin is still getting into the lake? Find an equation that models these data that she can present to the mill to prove her conclusion.

Two scientists measure toxin levels at a lake clean-up project.

▶ Solution

The scatter plot of the data shows exponential decay. So the model she must fit this data to is $y = k + ab^x$, where k is the toxin level the lake is dropping toward. If k is 0, then the lake will eventually be clean. If not, some toxins are still being released into the lake. If k is 0, then the general equation becomes $y = ab^x$. Take the logarithm of both sides of this equation.

$\log y = \log(ab^x)$	Take the logarithm of both sides.
$\log y = \log a + \log b^x$	Use the product property of logarithms.
$\log y = \log a + x \log b$	Use the power property of logarithms.
$\log y = c + dx$	Because $\log a$ and $\log b$ are numbers, replace them with the letters c and d for simplicity.

In this equation, c and d are the y-intercept and slope of a line, respectively. So, the graph of the logarithm of the toxin level over time should be linear. Let w represent the week and T represent the toxin level.

▶ EXAMPLE B

As students explore curve straightening, they will benefit from consulting the graphs repeatedly. With real-world data, the straightened graph will not be perfectly linear, but it will have a linear trend and a line of fit can be found.

In the equation $\log y = \log(ab^x)$, x is not an exponent on the entire inside expression, but only on b. That is, we don't have $x \log(ab)$. Rather, a is a factor as is b^x, so $\log y = \log a + \log b^x = \log a + x \log b$.

Lesson 5.4, Example B, introduced students to exponential functions that do not approach 0.

If the amount of a vertical translation of an exponential or logarithmic curve is not obvious, students can test different values by trying to make the root mean square error of the linearized data as small as possible. You might ask various students to try different values for the shift, calculating the root mean square error for that value. The class will see that the value 52 minimizes this error.

Assessing Progress

You can assess students' understanding of exponential decay and lines of fit. You can also check their ability to follow directions and solve equations.

NCTM STANDARDS

CONTENT	PROCESS
✓ Number	✓ Problem Solving
✓ Algebra	Reasoning
Geometry	✓ Communication
✓ Measurement	✓ Connections
Data/Probability	✓ Representation

LESSON OBJECTIVES

- Take the logarithm of both sides of an exponential equation to solve it
- Use logarithms to straighten a curve so that an algebraic model of the data can be found

Guiding the Investigation

Step 2 Students may have extra time while data are being collected. You may want to assign exercises or review Example A during this time. If you don't have temperature probes you can use the Cooling Sample Data worksheet.

Step 3 The temperature of the water should approach room temperature. You may want to use an accurate thermometer or an additional temperature probe to measure the room temperature so you have an idea what L should equal.

Step 3 Answers for sample data:

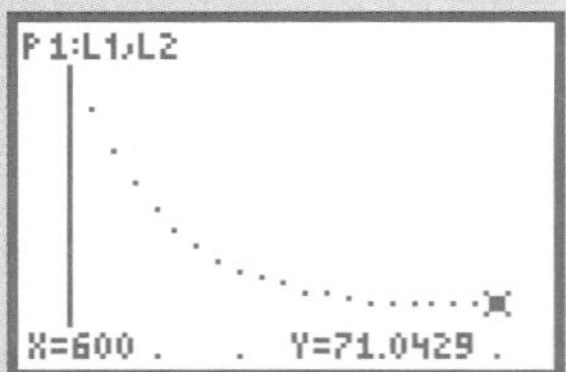

[−60, 660, 120, 67, 93, 50]

The temperature limit for the sample data appears to be 71°.

Step 4 When plotting the data, make sure students use y-values equal to $\log(p - L)$, not $\log p - L$. The data will probably not be perfectly linear. If there are data points for which $(temp - unit)$ equals 0, then the calculator will give an error message. Have students delete those points from their tables and try again. If more than one point with the same temperature appears at the end of the list, students may also delete those points when they graph.

Step 5 Students may use any method for finding a line of fit.

SHARING IDEAS

[Ask] "Can the equation of Example A be solved by undoing?" Work through it together, one step at a time, to get $x = \log_{0.954}\left(\frac{1.47 - 1.25}{0.72}\right) + 10$. Point out the fact that the expression can't be written from left to right because you first write $\frac{1.47 - 1.25}{0.72}$ and then insert log on the left to avoid the potential for errors in placing +10. Explain reasons for using methods such as taking the logarithm of both sides.

[Ask] "What kind of equation do you get when you take the logarithm of both sides of an exponential equation?" [linear] **[Alert]** Students may not think of expressions like log 0.954 and log 0.3056 as numbers, constant coefficients in a linear equation. This realization helps lay the groundwork for curve straightening.

After performing curve straightening, students may ask "How do we know we found the right line?" or "What's the best exponential equation for the data?" Point out that mathematical modeling is an art and that the value of a model is tested by the reasonableness of the predictions it makes.

You might use the Fathom demonstration Curve Straightening to summarize the ideas of the investigation.

The graph of $(w, \log T)$ shown is not linear. This tells Eva that if the relationship is exponential decay, k is not 0. From the table, it appears that the toxin level may be leveling off at 52 ppm. Subtract 52 from each toxin-level measurement to test again whether $(w, \log T)$ will be linear.

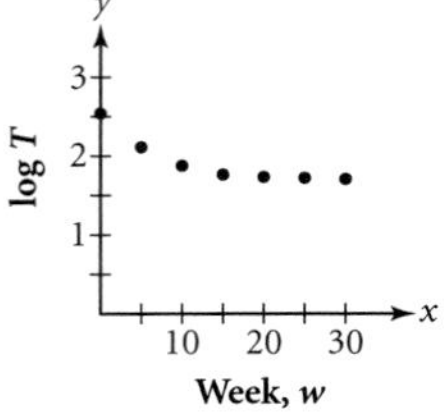

w	0	5	10	15	20	25	30
$T - 52$	297	78.2	23.4	6.1	2.2	0.7	0.1
$\log(T - 52)$	2.47	1.89	1.37	0.79	0.34	−0.15	−1.0

The graph of $(w, \log(T - 52))$ does appear linear, so she can be sure that the relationship is one of exponential decay with a vertical translation of approximately 52. She now knows that the general form of this relationship is $y = 52 + ab^x$.

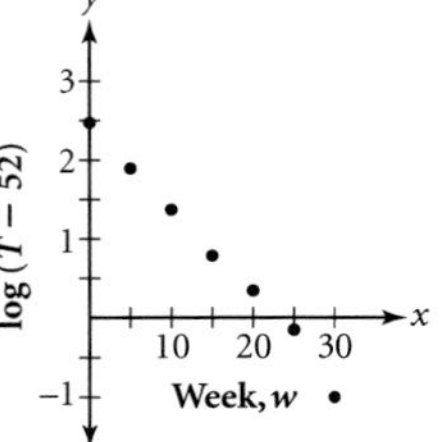

You could now use the same process as in Lesson 5.4 to solve for a and b, but the work you've done so far allows you to use an alternate method. Start by finding the median-median line for the linear data $(w, \log(T - 52))$.

[► See **Calculator Note 3D** to review how to find a median-median line on your calculator. ◄]

$y = -0.110x + 2.453$	Find the median-median line.
$\log(T - 52) = -0.110w + 2.453$	Substitute $\log(T - 52)$ for y and w for x.
$T - 52 = 10^{-0.110w+2.453}$	Use the definition of logarithm.
$T = 10^{-0.110w+2.453} + 52$	Add 52 to both sides.

This is not yet in the form $y = k + ab^x$, so continue to simplify.

$T = 10^{-0.110w} \cdot 10^{2.453} + 52$	Use the product property of exponents.
$T = 10^{-0.110w} \cdot 283.79 + 52$	Evaluate $10^{2.453}$.
$T = \left(10^{-0.110}\right)^w \cdot 283.79 + 52$	Use the power property of exponents.
$T = (0.776)^w \cdot 283.79 + 52$	Evaluate $10^{-0.110}$.
$T = 52 + 283.79(0.776)^w$	Reorder in the form $y = k + ab^x$.

The equation that models the amount of toxin, T, in the lake after w weeks is $T = 52 + 283.79(0.776)^w$.

If you graph this equation with the original data, you see that it fits quite well.

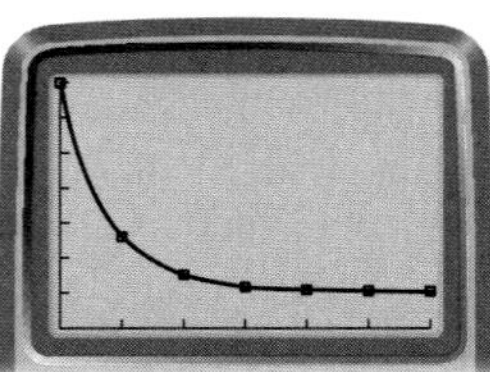

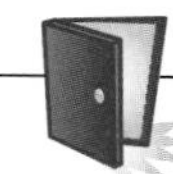

Investigation
Cooling

You will need

- a cup of hot water (optional)
- a temperature probe
- a data collection device
- a second temperature probe (optional)

In this investigation you will find a relationship between temperature of a cooling object and time.

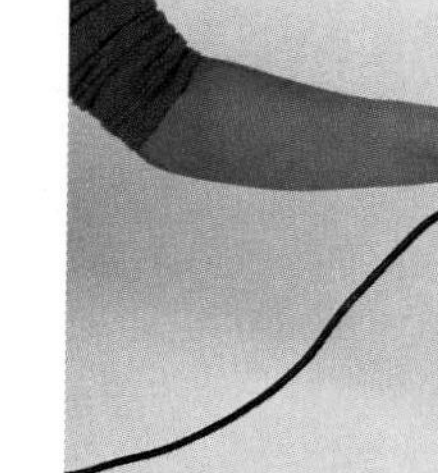

Step 1 Connect a temperature probe to a data collector and set it up to collect 60 data points over 10 minutes, or 1 data point every 10 seconds. Heat the end of the probe by placing it in hot water or holding it tightly in the palm of your hand. When it is hot, set the probe on a table so that the tip is not touching anything and begin data collection. [► See **Calculator Note 5E.** ◄]

Step 2 Let t be the time in seconds, and let p be the temperature of the probe. While you are collecting the data, draw a sketch of what you expect the graph of (t, p) data to look like as the temperature probe cools. Label the axes and mark the scale on your graph. Did everyone in your group draw the same graph? Discuss any differences of opinion.

Step 3 Plot the data in the form (t, p) on an appropriately scaled graph. Your graph should appear to be an exponential function. Study the graph and the data, and guess the temperature limit L. You could also use a second temperature probe to measure the room temperature, L.

Step 4 Subtract this limit from your temperatures and find the logarithm of this new list. Plot data in the form $(t, \log(p - L))$. If the data are not linear, then try a different limit.

Step 5 Find the equation that models the data in Step 4, and use this to find an equation that models the (t, p) data in Step 3. Give real-world meaning to the values in the final equation.

EXERCISES

Practice Your Skills

1. Prove that these statements of equality are true. Take the logarithm of both sides, then use the properties of logarithms to re-express each side until you have two identical expressions.

a. $10^{n+p} = (10^n)(10^p)$ **b.** $\frac{10^d}{10^e} = 10^{d-e}$

2. Solve each equation. Check your answers by substituting your answer for x.

a. $800 = 10^x$ 2.90309 **b.** $2048 = 2^x$ 11 **c.** $16 = 0.5^x$ −4

d. $478 = 18.5(10^x)$ 1.4123 **e.** $155 = 24.0(1.89^x)$ 2.9303 **f.** $0.0047 = 19.1(0.21^x)$ 5.3246

3. Suppose you invest $3000 at 6.75% annual interest compounded monthly. How long will it take to triple your money? $t = \frac{\log 3}{\log 1.005625} \approx 195.9$; about 195.9 mo or about 16 yr 4 mo

Closing the Lesson

Instead of solving an exponential equation by rewriting both sides to have the same base, you can take the logarithm of both sides (if they're positive).

Taking the logarithm of both sides of the general equation $y = ab^x$ and applying the power property gives the linear equation $\log y = \log a + (\log b)x$. Line-of-fit techniques can be applied to find values of $\log a$ and $\log b$. The **curve-straightening,** or **linearizing,** approach can be extended to get a shifted exponential equation of the form $y - k = ab^x$.

BUILDING UNDERSTANDING

The exercises provide practice in solving exponential equations and in curve straightening.

ASSIGNING HOMEWORK

Essential	2–4
Performance assessment	1, 5–10
Portfolio	8, 9
Journal	4
Group	7
Review	11–14

Helping with the Exercises

If you will be assessing curve straightening, you may want to save an exercise or two for your review unit, because the Chapter Review contains no exercises of this type.

Exercise 1 [Alert] Students should use only the properties of logarithms. This is a proof only of the claim that if the logarithm properties are true then the exponent properties are true. Earlier, the logarithm properties were derived from the exponent properties, so this argument would show that the properties are logically equivalent.

Exercise 2 In 2c, students may see that they have powers of 2 on both sides and write $2^4 = 2^{-x}$, from which they see that $x = -4$.

As needed in 2d–f, remind students to isolate the exponent by dividing before taking logarithms.

Besides substituting, students can check each answer by graphing both sides of the equation and finding the x-coordinate of the point of intersection.

See page 886 for answers to Steps 4 and 5 and Exercise 1.

290

Reason and Apply

4. APPLICATION The length of time that milk (and many other perishable substances) will stay fresh depends on the storage temperature. Suppose that milk will stay fresh for 146 hours in a refrigerator at 4°C. Milk that is left out in the kitchen at 22°C will keep for only 42 hours. Because bacteria grow exponentially, you can assume that freshness decays exponentially.

a. Write an equation that expresses the number of hours, h, that milk will keep in terms of the temperature, T. $h = 146(0.9331226)^{T-4}$

b. Use your equation to predict how long milk will keep at 30°C and at 16°C.

c. If a container of milk soured after 147 hours, what was the temperature at which it was stored?

d. Graph the relationship between hours and temperature, using your equation from 4a and the five data points you have found.

e. What is a realistic domain for this relationship? Why?

Science CONNECTION

In 1860, French chemist Louis Pasteur (1822–1895) developed a method of killing bacteria in fluids. Today the process, called pasteurization, is routinely used on milk. It involves heating raw milk not quite to its boiling point, which would affect its taste and nutritional value, but to 63°C (145°F) for 30 min or 72°C (161°F) for 15 s. This kills most, but not all, harmful bacteria. Refrigerating milk slows the growth of the remaining bacteria, but eventually the milk will spoil, when there are too many bacteria for it to be healthful. The bacteria in milk change the lactose to lactic acid, which smells and tastes bad to humans.

Louis Pasteur

5. The equation $f(x) = \frac{12000}{1 + 499(1.09)^{-x}}$ gives the total sales x days after the release of a new video game. Find each value and give a real-world meaning.

a. $f(20)$ **b.** $f(80)$

c. x when $f(x) = 6000$ **d.** Show the steps to solve 5c symbolically.

e. Graph the equation in a window large enough for you to see the overall behavior of the curve. Use your graph to describe how the number of games sold each day changes. Does this model seem reasonable?

6. APPLICATION The loudness of sound, D, measured in decibels (dB) is given by the formula

$$D = 10\log\left(\frac{I}{10^{-16}}\right)$$

where I is the intensity measured in watts per square centimeter (W/cm^2) and 10^{-16} W/cm² is the approximate intensity of the least sound audible to the human ear.

a. Find the loudness of a 10^{-13} W/cm² whisper in decibels.

b. Find the loudness of a normal conversation at $3.16 \cdot 10^{-10}$ W/cm².

c. Find the intensity of the sound (in W/cm^2) experienced by the orchestra members seated in front of the brass section, measured at 107 dB.

d. How many times more intensity does a sound of 47 dB have than a sound of 42 dB?

4b. about 24.1 h at 30°C; about 63.6 h at 16°C

4c. $147 = 146(0.9331226)^{T-4}$; $1.00685 = 0.9331226^{T-4}$; $T - 4 = \frac{\log 1.00685}{\log 0.9331225}$; $T \approx -0.0986 + 4 \approx 3.9°\text{C}$

4d.

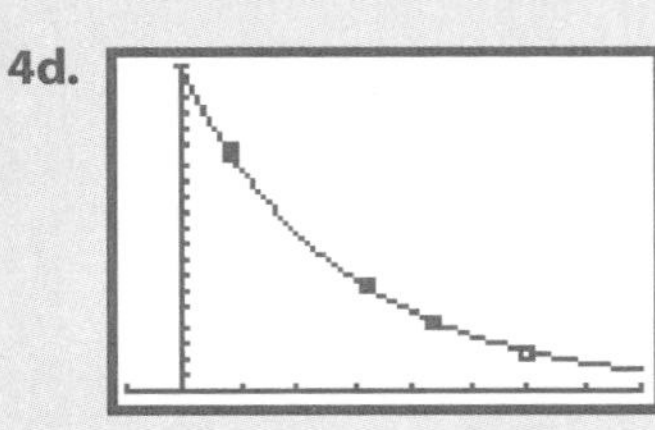

[−5, 40, 5, 0, 200, 10]

4e. A realistic domain is 0° to 100°C; these are the freezing and boiling points of water.

Exercise 5 You might **[Ask]** "What are the independent and dependent variables?" [*days since release; total sales*] This graph is a logistic equation, as in the exploration in Chapter 1.

5a. $f(20) \approx 133.28$; After 20 days 133 games have been sold.

5b. $f(80) \approx 7969.17$; After 80 days 7969 games have been sold.

5c. $x = 72.09$; After 72 days 6000 games have been sold.

5d.

$\frac{12000}{1 + 499(1.09)^{-x}} = 6000$;
$2 = 1 + 499(1.09)^{-x}$;
$1 = 499(1.09)^{-x}$;
$0.002 = (1.09)^{-x}$;
$\log(0.002) = \log(1.09)^{-x}$;
$\log 0.002 = -x\log 1.09$;
$x = -\frac{\log 0.002}{\log 1.09} \approx 72.1$

5e.

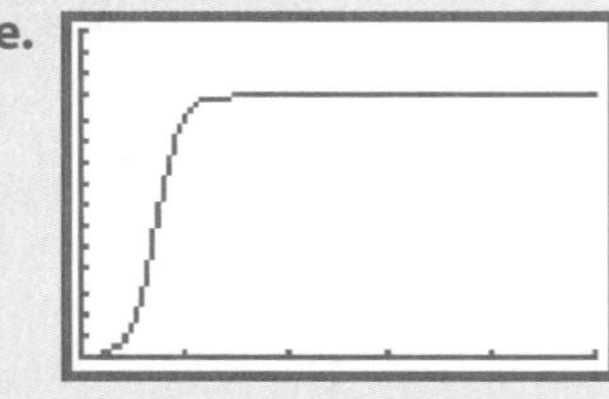

[0, 500, 100, 0, 15000, 1000]

Sample answer: The number of games sold starts out increasing slowly, then speeds up, and then slow down as everyone who wants the game has purchased one.

6a. $D = 10\log\frac{10^{-13}}{10^{-16}} = 30$ dB

6b. $D = 10\log\frac{3.16 \cdot 10^{-10}}{10^{-16}} = 65$ dB

6c. $I = 10^{10.7} \cdot 10^{-16} = 10^{-5.3} \approx 5.01 \times 10^{-6}$ W/cm²

6d. about 3.16 times as loud

7. **APPLICATION** The table gives the loudness of spoken words, measured at the source, and the maximum distance at which another person can recognize the speech. Find an equation that expresses the maximum distance as a function of loudness.

Loudness (dB)	Distance (m)
0.5	0.1
3.2	16.0
5.3	20.4
16.8	30.5
35.8	37.0
84.2	44.5
120.0	47.6
170.0	50.6

a. Plot the data on your calculator and make a rough sketch on your paper.

b. Experiment to find the relationship between x and y by plotting different combinations of x, y, $\log x$, and $\log y$ until you have found the graph that best linearizes the data. Sketch this graph on your paper and label the axes with x, y, $\log x$, or $\log y$, as appropriate.

c. Find the equation of a line that fits the plot you chose in 7b. Remember that your axes did not represent x and y, so substitute $(\log x)$ or $(\log y)$ into your equation as appropriate. $y = 6 + 20x$; $\hat{y} = 6 + 20 \log x$

d. Graph this new equation with the original data. Does it seem to be a good model?

8. A container of juice is left in a room at a temperature of 74°F. After 8 minutes, the temperature is recorded at regular intervals.

Time (min)	8	10	12	14	16	18	20	22	24	26	28	30
Temp. (°F)	35	40	45	49	52	55	57	60	61	63	64	66

a. Plot the data using an appropriate window. Make a rough sketch of this graph.

b. Find an exponential model for temperature as a function of time. (*Hint:* This curve is both reflected and translated.)

9. **APPLICATION** In clear weather, the distance you can see from a window on a plane depends on your height above Earth, as shown in the table at right.

a. Graph various combinations of x, y, $\log x$, and $\log y$ until you find a combination that linearizes the data.

b. Use your results from 9a to find a best-fit equation for data in the form (*height, view*) using the data in this table.

Height (m)	Viewing distance (km)
305	62
610	88
914	108
1,524	139
3,048	197
4,572	241
6,096	278
7,620	311
9,144	340
10,668	368
12,192	393

10. Quinn starts treating her pool for the season with a shock treatment of 4 gal of chlorine. Every 24 h, 15% of the chlorine evaporates. The next morning, she adds 1 qt $\left(\frac{1}{4}\text{ gal}\right)$ of chlorine to the pool, and she continues to do so each morning.

a. How much chlorine is there in the pool after one day (after she adds the first daily quart of chlorine)? After two days? Write a recursive formula for this pattern.

b. Use the formula from 10a to make a table of values and sketch a graph of 20 terms. Find an explicit model that fits the data.

10b.

0	1	2	3	4	5	6
16	14.6	13.41	12.40	11.54	10.81	10.19

7	8	9	10	11	12	13
09.66	9.21	8.83	8.50	8.23	7.99	7.80

14	15	16	17	18	19	20
7.63	7.48	7.36	7.26	7.17	7.09	7.03

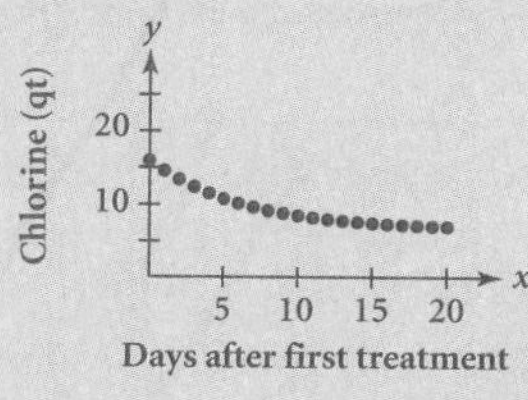

$y = 6.67 + 9.33(0.85)^x$

Exercise 7 This exercise introduces the idea that the logarithms of x-values as well as y-values might be used to straighten curves. You may want to jigsaw the assignment among groups, with each group considering $(x, \log y)$, $(\log x, y)$, or $(\log x, \log y)$. These data approach 0; therefore, the k constant for a shift is not needed as it is in Example B.

7a.

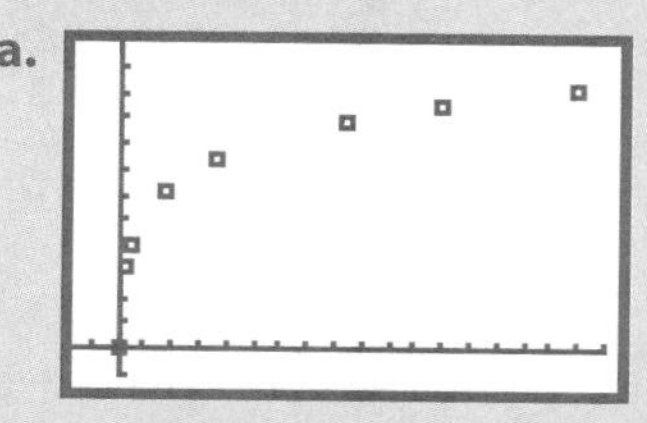

[−16, 180, 10, −5, 60, 5]

7b. $(\log x, y)$ is a linear graph.

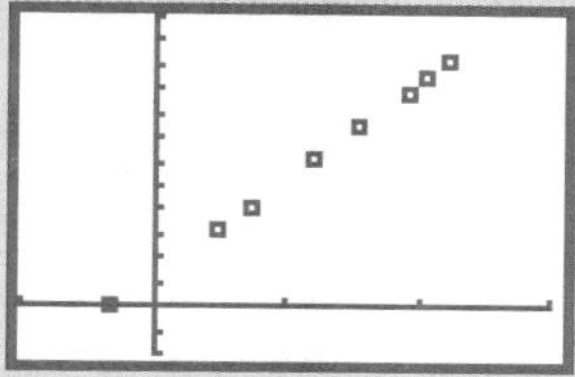

[−1, 3, 1, −10, 60, 5]

7d.

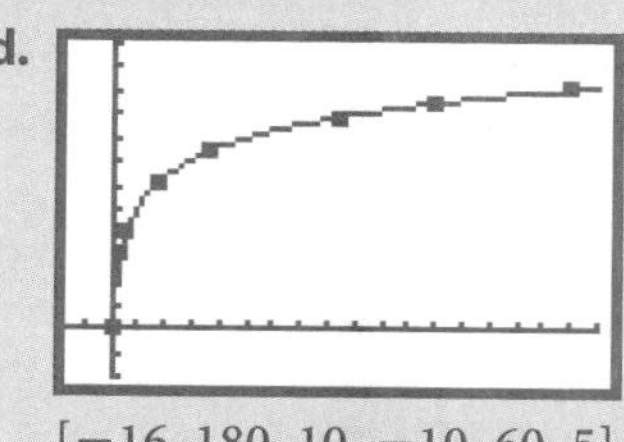

[−16, 180, 10, −10, 60, 5]

Sample answer: Yes; the graph shows that the equation is a good model for the data.

Exercise 8 This exercise is challenging. **[Ask]** "Does the curve approach a limit?" [yes; room temperature]

Exercise 10 This exercise connects recursive shifted geometric sequences and exponential functions.

10a. 14.6 qt after 1 day; 13.41 qt after 2 days; $u_0 = 16$, $u_n = u_{n-1}(1 - 0.15) + 1, n \geq 1$

See pages 886–887 for answers to Exercises 8 and 9.

11a. $y = 18(\sqrt{2})^{x-4}$,
$y = 144(\sqrt{2})^{x-10}$, or
$y = 4.5(\sqrt{2})^{x}$

11b. $y = \dfrac{\log x - \log 18}{\log\sqrt{2}} + 4$,

$y = \dfrac{\log x - \log 144}{\log\sqrt{2}} + 10$, or

$y = \dfrac{\log x - \log 4.5}{\log\sqrt{2}}$

12a. cost: $y = 1.75x + 19000$;
income: $y = 1.92x$

12b.

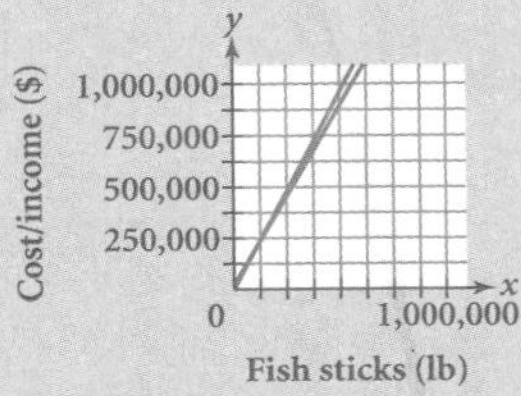

13.

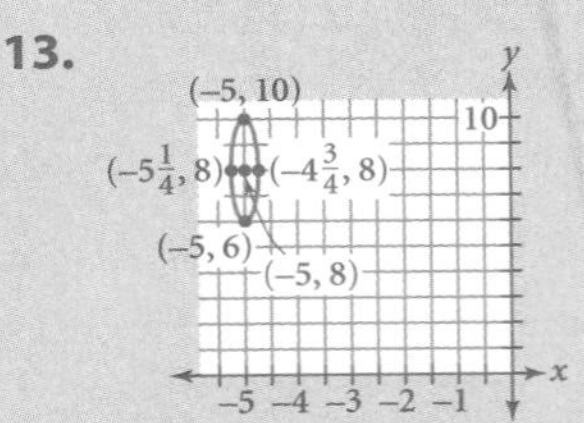

Exercise 14 The method of raising each side to a fractional power produces all real solutions only in 14a (for which there is only one). Because powers are defined only for positive bases, this approach does not find the solutions deriving from negative fourth and sixth roots in 14b and 14c.

Additional Project Outcomes

- The equation for a line fitting these data, such as $\frac{men}{women} = -0.013year + 27.37$, is discussed—the ratio decreases by 1.3% each year.
- Exponential and linear models are compared.

Review

5.6 **11.** Find these functions.

a. Find an exponential function that passes through the points (4, 18) and (10, 144).

b. Find a logarithmic function that passes through the points (18, 4) and (144, 10).

3.6 **12.** The Highland Fish Company is starting a new line of frozen fish sticks. It will cost \$19,000 to set up the production line and \$1.75 per pound to buy and process the fish. Highland Fish will sell the final product at a wholesale cost of \$1.92 per pound.

a. Write a cost function and an income function for HFC's new venture.

b. Graph both functions on the same axes over the domain $0 \le x \le 1{,}000{,}000$.

c. How many pounds of fish sticks will HFC have to produce before it starts making a profit on the new venture? 111,765 lb

d. How much profit can HFC expect to make on the first 500,000 pounds of fish? \$66,000

4.7 **13.** Sketch the graph of $(4(x + 5))^2 + \left(\frac{y - 8}{2}\right)^2 = 1$. Give coordinates of a few points that define the shape.

5.3 **14.** Solve each equation. Round to the nearest hundredth.

a. $x^5 = 3418$
$x = 3418^{1/5} \approx 5.09$

b. $(x - 5.1)^4 = 256$
$x = 256^{1/4} + 5.1 = 9.1$
or $x = 1.1$

c. $7.3x^6 + 14.4 = 69.4$
$x = \pm\left(\frac{55}{7.3}\right)^{1/6} \approx 1.40$

Project

INCOME BY GENDER

The median annual incomes of year-round full-time workers in the United States, ages 25 and above, are listed in this table. Examine different relationships, such as data in the form (*time, men*), (*time, women*), (*women, men*), (*time, men − women*), (*time, men/women*), and so on. Find best-fit models for those relationships that seem meaningful. Write an article in which you interpret some of your models and make predictions about the future. Research some recent data to see if your predictions are accurate so far.

Year	Men	Women
1970	\$9,521	\$5,616
1972	\$11,148	\$6,331
1974	\$12,786	\$7,370
1976	\$14,732	\$8,728
1978	\$16,882	\$10,121
1980	\$20,297	\$12,156
1982	\$22,857	\$14,477
1984	\$25,497	\$16,169
1986	\$27,335	\$17,675

(1990 Statistical Abstract of the United States)

Your project should include

- Your article, including relevant graphs, models, and predictions.
- More recent data (remember to cite your source).
- An analysis of how well the recent data fit your predictions.

"Women constitute half the world's population, perform nearly two-thirds of its work hours, receive one-tenth of the world's income, and own less than one-hundredth of the world's property." (United Nations report, 1980)

Supporting the Project

The data are fairly linear through these 16 years, but someone could argue that they fit a nonlinear model, such as an exponential model. Residuals, however, indicate that the exponential model is a poorer fit than a linear model. The outcomes listed show results assuming a linear model.

OUTCOMES

- The report shows lines of fit such as $men = 1196year - 2347351$ and $women = 795year - 1562000$.
- The student notes that salaries are increasing each year for men by \$1196 but for women by only \$795. This difference is reflected by the line of fit with equation $(men - women) = 376year - 736595$.
- The report concludes that the ratio of men's salaries to women's salaries is decreasing over time. Men's salaries increased by 187% in the 16 years, while women's salaries increased by 215%.
- Recent data are included and analyzed with the student's model.

EXPLORATION

The Number *e*

You've done problems exploring the amount of interest earned in a savings account when interest is compounded yearly, monthly, or daily. But what if interest is compounded continuously? This means that at every instant, your interest is redeposited in your account and the new interest is calculated on it. This type of continuous growth is related to a number, ***e***. This number has a value of approximately 2.71, and like π, it is a **transcendental number**—a number that has infinitely many nonrepeating digits. The logarithm function with base *e*, $\log_e x$, is also written as $\ln x$, and is called the **natural logarithm** function.

Activity

Continuous Growth

The Swiss mathematician Jacob Bernoulli (1654–1705) explored the following problem in 1683. Suppose you put $1 into an account that earns 100% interest per year. If the interest is compounded only once, at the end of the year you will have earned $1 in interest and your balance will be $2. What if interest is compounded more frequently? Follow the steps below to analyze this situation.

Step 1 If interest is compounded 10 times annually, how much money will be in your account at the end of one year? Remember that if 100% interest is compounded ten times, you earn 10% each time. Check your answer with another group to be sure you did this correctly.

Step 2 Predict what will happen if your money earns interest compounded continuously.

Step 3 What will be the balance of your account at the end of one year if interest is compounded 100 times? 1,000 times? 10,000 times? 1,000,000 times? How do your answers compare to your prediction in Step 2?

Step 4 Write an equation that would tell you the balance if the interest were compounded x times annually, and graph it on your calculator. Does this equation seem to be approaching one particular long-run value, or limit? If so, what is it? If not, what happens in the long run?

Step 5 Look for e on your calculator, and find its value to six decimal places. What is the relationship between this number and your answer to Step 4?

Step 6 When interest is compounded continuously, the formula $y = P\left(1 + \frac{r}{n}\right)^{nt}$ becomes $y = Pe^{rt}$, where P is the principal (the initial value of your investment), e is the natural exponential base, r is the interest rate, and t is the amount of time the investment is left in the account. Use this formula to calculate the value of $1 deposited in an account earning 100% annual interest for one year. Calculate the value if it is left in the same account for ten years.

Step 1
$\left(1 + \frac{1}{10}\right)^{10\cdot 1} = \$2.59$

Step 3
$\left(1 + \frac{1}{100}\right)^{100\cdot 1} = \$2.70$
$\left(1 + \frac{1}{1000}\right)^{1000\cdot 1} = \$2.72$
$\left(1 + \frac{1}{10000}\right)^{10000\cdot 1} = \$2.72$
$\left(1 + \frac{1}{1000000}\right)^{1000000\cdot 1} = \$2.72$

Step 5
$e = 2.718282...$

Step 6
$1(e^{1\cdot 1}) = \$2.71828$;
$1(e^{1\cdot 10}) = \$22{,}026.47$

EXPLORATION

PLANNING

LESSON OUTLINE

One day:

5 min	Introduction
20 min	Activity
10 min	Sharing
10 min	Questions

MATERIALS

- none

TEACHING

In this exploration students encounter *e*, the base of the natural logarithm, in conjunction with compound interest.

Guiding the Activity

Step 1 Students may find their solution either recursively or explicitly.

Step 2 This is only a guess. It might be that the investment would grow infinitely large. Students will check their prediction in Step 3.

Step 4 $(1 + 1/n)^{n\cdot 1}$; approaches a long-run value of 2.71828 . . .

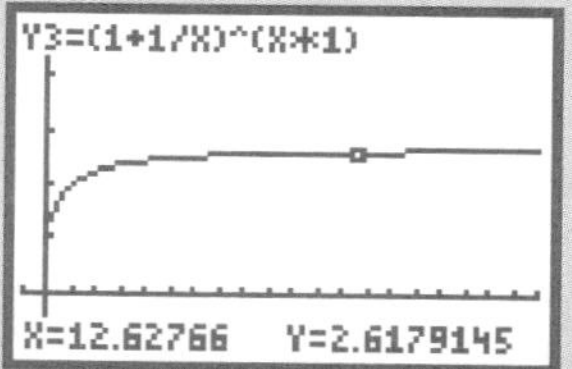

[−1, 20, 1, −1, 5, 1]

Step 5 If a calculator only has a button for e^x, **[Ask]** "What value of x would give the value of e?" [1]

Assessing Progress
You can check students' understanding of compound interest and their ability to see patterns.

NCTM STANDARDS

CONTENT		PROCESS	
✓	Number		Problem Solving
✓	Algebra	✓	Reasoning
	Geometry	✓	Communication
✓	Measurement	✓	Connections
✓	Data/Probability	✓	Representation

LESSON OBJECTIVES

- Understand that *e* is a transcendental number
- Observe the natural logarithm function

SHARING IDEAS

[Ask] "Why does the formula $y = P\left(1 + \frac{r}{n}\right)^{nt}$ become $y = Pe^{rt}$ as n gets larger, that is, with more compounding periods per year?" [The book has shown that $\left(1 + \frac{1}{k}\right)^k$ gets closer and closer to e as k gets larger and larger. Because $\left(1 + \frac{r}{n}\right)^{nt} = \left(1 + \frac{1}{\frac{n}{r}}\right)^{\frac{n}{r}rt}$, this quantity approaches e^{rt} as n $\left(\text{and hence } \frac{n}{r}\right)$ gets larger.]

Closing the Lesson

As interest is compounded more and more frequently, to the point of being compounded continuously, the number e arises naturally. Logarithms to the base e occur so frequently that they are called **natural logarithms;** they are abbreviated **ln** and have their own calculator key.

▶ Helping with the Questions

Question 1 You might encourage students to choose examples in which the growth is obviously continuous. In Lesson 5.1, Exercise 5, the function $y = 1.151e^{0.015t}$ will give the population t years after 1991. The population in 2001 would be $1.151e^{0.015(10)} \approx 1.337$ billion, slightly larger than the 1.336 billion estimated discretely by the function $y = 1.151(1.015)^t$.

EXTENSION

If you have the calculator-based equipment you might include an activity involving light intensity.

Questions

1. Using the new equation, answers will probably be slightly more accurate than before.

2a. $0.80 = 1e^{-k(50)}$. Taking the logarithm of both sides and solving for k, you get $k = 0.0045$.

2b. $0.01 = 1e^{-0.0045t}$. Taking the logarithm of both sides and solving for t, you get $t = 1023.37$ cm, or approximately 10.23 m (or 1031.89 cm $\approx$ 10.32 m if the unrounded value of k is used).

1. The formula $y = Pe^{rt}$ is often an accurate model for growth or decay problems, because things usually grow or decay continuously, not at specific time intervals. For example, a bacteria population may double every four hours, but it is increasing throughout those four hours, not suddenly doubling in value when exactly four hours have passed. Return to any problem involving growth or decay from this chapter, and use this new formula to solve the problem. How does your answer compare with your initial answer?

2. The intensity, I, of a beam of light after passing through t cm of liquid is given by $I = Ae^{-kt}$, where A is the intensity of the light when it enters the liquid, e is the natural exponential base, and k is a constant for a particular liquid. On a field trip, a marine biology class took light readings at Deep Lake. At a depth of 50 cm, the light intensity was 80% of the light intensity at the surface.

a. Find the value of k for Deep Lake.

b. If the light intensity is measured as 1% of the intensity at the surface, at what depth was the reading taken?

Science CONNECTION

Phytoplankton is a generic name for a great variety of microorganisms, including algae, that live in lakes and oceans and provide the lowest step of the food chain in some ecosystems. Phytoplankton require light for photosynthesis. In water, light intensity decreases with depth. As a result, the phytoplankton production rate, which is determined by the local light intensity, decreases with depth. Light levels determine the maximum depth at which these organisms can grow. Limnologists, scientists who study inland waters, estimate this depth to be the point at which the amount of light available is reduced to 0.5–1% of the amount of light available at the lake surface.

Algae grow in abundance on this pond that holds waste water for the nearby milkhouse. At right is a microscopic image of fresh water phytoplankton.

Project

ALL ABOUT *e*

Mathematicians have been exploring e and calculating more digits of the decimal approximation of e since the 1600s. There are a number of procedures that can be used to calculate digits of e. Do some research at the library or on the Internet, and find at least two. Write a report explaining the formulas you find and how they are used to calculate e. Include any interesting historical facts you find on e as well.

Supporting the Project

Students might interview calculus students at their school to find out more about the natural logarithm, *e*.

OUTCOMES

- ▶ The report includes at least two of the many formulas and relationships that involve e: $e^{i\pi} = -1$

$$\lim_{n\to\infty}\left(1 + \frac{1}{n}\right)^n = e \qquad \int_1^e \frac{1}{x}dx = 1$$

$$e \approx \frac{1}{0!} + \frac{1}{1!} + \frac{1}{2!} + \cdots + \frac{1}{(n-1)!} + \frac{1}{n!}$$

- ▶ Historical facts are included.
- The report includes an explanation that the area under the curve $y = \frac{1}{x}$ from $x = 1$ to $x = e$ is exactly 1.
- A connection is made to calculus, where $f(x) = e^x$ is the only function whose integral and derivative are both itself.

CHAPTER 5 REVIEW

295

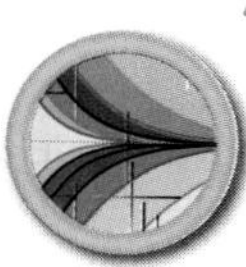

Exponential functions provide explicit and continuous equations to model geometric sequences. They can be used to model the growth of populations, the decay of radioactive substances, and other phenomena. The general form of an exponential function is $y = ab^x$, where a is the initial amount and b is the base that represents the rate of growth or decay. Because the exponent can take on all real number values, including negative numbers and fractions, it is important that you understand the meaning of these exponents. You also used the **point-ratio form** of this equation, $y = y_1 \cdot b_1^{x-x_1}$.

Until you read this chapter, you had no way to solve an exponential equation, other than guess-and-check. Once you defined the **inverse** of the exponential function—the **logarithmic function**—you were able to solve exponential functions symbolically. The inverse of a function is the relation you get when all values of the independent variable are exchanged with the values of the dependent variable. The graphs of a function and its inverse are reflected across the line $y = x$. The definition of the logarithmic function is that $\log_b y = x$ means that $y = b^x$. You learned that the properties of logarithms parallel those of exponents: the logarithm of a product is the sum of the logarithms, the logarithm of a quotient is the difference of the logarithms, and the logarithm of a number raised to a power is the product of the logarithm and that number. By looking at the logarithms of the x-value, or the y-value, or both values in a set of data, you can determine what type of equation will best model the data by finding which of these creates the most linear graph.

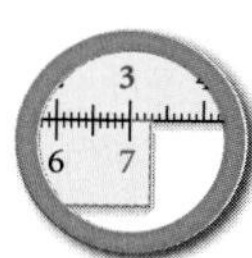

EXERCISES

1. Evaluate each expression without using a calculator. Then check your work with a calculator.
   a. 4^{-2} $\frac{1}{16}$ b. $(-3)^{-1}$ $-\frac{1}{3}$ c. $\left(\frac{1}{5}\right)^{-3}$ 125 d. $49^{1/2}$ 7 e. $64^{-1/3}$ $\frac{1}{4}$
   f. $\left(\frac{9}{16}\right)^{3/2}$ $\frac{27}{64}$ g. -7^0 -1 h. $(3)(2)^2$ 12 i. $\left(0.6^{-2}\right)^{-1/2}$ 0.6

2. Rewrite each expression in another form.
   a. $\log x + \log y$ $\log xy$ b. $\log\frac{z}{v}$ $\log z - \log v$ c. $(7x^{2.1})(0.3x^{4.7})$ $2.1x^{6.8}$
   d. $\log w^k$ $k\log w$ e. $\sqrt[5]{x}$ $x^{1/5}$ f. $\log_5 t$ $\frac{\log t}{\log 5}$

3. Use the properties of exponents and logarithms to solve each equation. Confirm your answers by substituting them for x.
   a. $4.7^x = 28$ b. $4.7^{x^2} = 2209$ c. $\log_x 2.9 = 1.25$ d. $\log_{3.1} x = 47$
   e. $7x^{2.4} = 101$ f. $9000 = 500(1.065)^x$ g. $\log x = 3.771$ h. $\sqrt[5]{x^3} = 47$

Helping with the Exercises

Exercise 3 As students substitute to check their results, be sure they don't assume that they have found a solution and then manipulate the equation to arrive at an identity.

3a. $x = \frac{\log 28}{\log 4.7} \approx 2.153$

3b. $x = \pm\sqrt{\frac{\log 2209}{\log 4.7}} \approx \pm 2.231$

3c. $x = 2.9^{1/1.25} = 2.9^{0.8} \approx 2.344$

3d. $x = 3.1^{47} \approx 1.242 \times 10^{23}$

3e. $x = \left(\frac{101}{7}\right)^{1/2.4} \approx 3.041$

3f. $x = \frac{\log 18}{\log 1.065} \approx 45.897$

3g. $x = 10^{3.771} \approx 5902$

3h. $x = 47^{5/3} \approx 612$

CHAPTER REVIEW 5

PLANNING

LESSON OUTLINE

First day:
15 min Reviewing
20 min Exercises
10 min Student self-assessment

Second day:
30 min Student presentations
15 min Exercises

REVIEWING

Revisit the problem of Lesson 5.8, Example B. Ask students to look at a graph of the data and decide whether the best model is an exponential function or a power function. You might have them find a shifted geometric sequence to fit the data and to find an exponential function in a variety of ways. As you do the latter, review properties of exponents. Then ask what the half-life is; set up an equation representing the time at which half of the toxin that will disappear actually does disappear, and solve the equation in a variety of ways, reviewing properties of logarithms as you go.

ASSIGNING HOMEWORK

You might ask groups to do parts a and b or half the parts of each exercise and assign the remainder of each problem as homework.

If you will be assessing curve straightening, you may want to assign a curve-straightening problem from Lesson 5.8 for review.

Exercise 4 You may want to have students describe each step in their solutions. If students need help with 4d, you might **[Ask]** "Is $f^{-1}(f(x))$ something special? How does it relate to $f(f^{-1}(x))$?" [Both equal x.]

4a. $x = 0.5(2432^{1/8} - 1) \approx 0.825$

4b. $x = 114^{1/2.7} \approx 5.779$

4c. $x = \dfrac{\log\left(\frac{734}{11.2}\right)}{\log 1.56} \approx 9.406$

4e. $x = \left(\frac{147}{12.1}\right)^{1/2.3} - 1 \approx 1.962$

4f. $x = 5.75^2 + 3 \approx 36.063$

Exercise 5 Students may use the point-ratio form to find the solution.

5. $x = \dfrac{16\log\left(\frac{8}{45}\right)}{\log 0.5} \approx 39.9$; about 39.9 h

Exercise 6 You might also ask students to graph the equation and its inverse.

7. $y = 5\left(\frac{32}{5}\right)^{(x-1)/6}$

8.

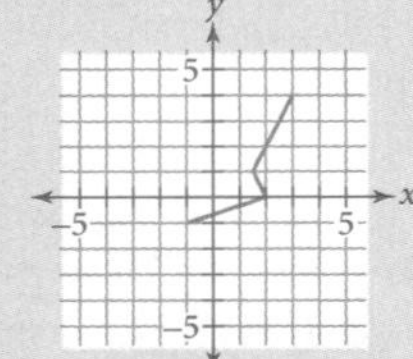

9a.

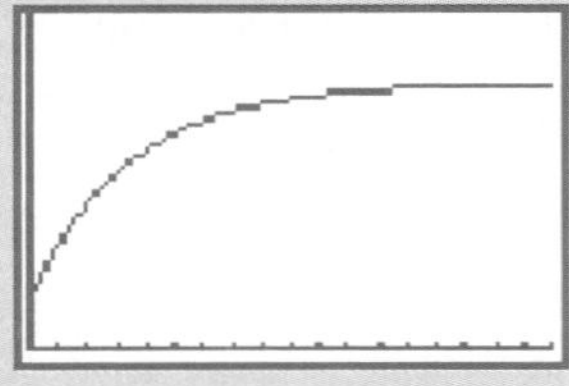

[0, 18, 1, 0, 125, 0]

Exercise 9e [Alert] Students might use the equation $y = 0.75$ instead of $y = 75$.

4. Solve for x. Round your answers to the nearest thousandth.

a. $\sqrt[8]{2432} = 2x + 1$ b. $4x^{2.7} = 456$ c. $734 = 11.2(1.56)^x$

d. $f(f^{-1}(x)) = 20.2$ $x = 20.2$ e. $147 = 12.1(1 + x)^{2.3}$ f. $2\sqrt{x - 3} + 4.5 = 16$

5. Once a certain medicine is in the bloodstream, its half-life is 16 h. How long (to the nearest 0.1 h) will it be before an initial 45 cm^3 of the medicine has been reduced to 8 cm^3?

6. Given $f(x) = (4x - 2)^{1/3} - 1$, find:

a. $f(2.5)$ 1 b. $f^{-1}(x)$ $\frac{(x+1)^3 + 2}{4}$ c. $f^{-1}(-1)$ $\frac{1}{2}$ d. $f(f^{-1}(12))$ 12

7. Find the equation of an exponential curve through the points (1, 5) and (7, 32).

8. Draw the inverse of $f(x)$, shown at right.

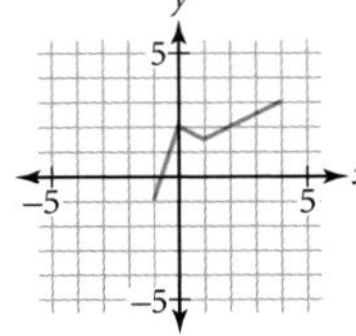

9. Your head gets larger as you grow. Most of the growth comes in the first few years of life, and there is very little additional growth after you reach adolescence. The estimated percentage of adult size for your head is given by the formula $y = 100 - 80(0.75)^x$, where x is your age in years and y is the percentage of the average adult size.

a. Graph this function.

b. What are the reasonable domain and range of this function? domain: $0 \leq x \leq 120$; range: $20 \leq y \leq 100$

c. Describe the transformations of the graph of $y = (0.75)^x$ that produce the graph in 9a. Vertically stretch by a factor of 80; reflect across the x-axis; vertically shift by 100.

d. A 2-year-old child's head is what percentage of the adult size? 55% of the average adult size

e. About how old would a person be if his or her head circumference is 75% that of an average adult? about 4 years old

10. A new incentive plan for the Talk Alot long-distance phone company varies the cost of a call according to the formula $cost = a + b\log t$, where t represents time in minutes. When calling long distance, the cost for the first minute is \$0.50. The cost for 15 min is \$3.44.

a. Find the a-value in the equation.

b. Find the b-value in the equation.

c. What is the x-intercept of the graph of the equation? What is the real-world meaning of the x-intercept?

d. Use your equation to predict the cost of a 30-minute call. \$4.19

e. If you decide you can afford only to make a \$2 call, how long can you talk? about 4 min

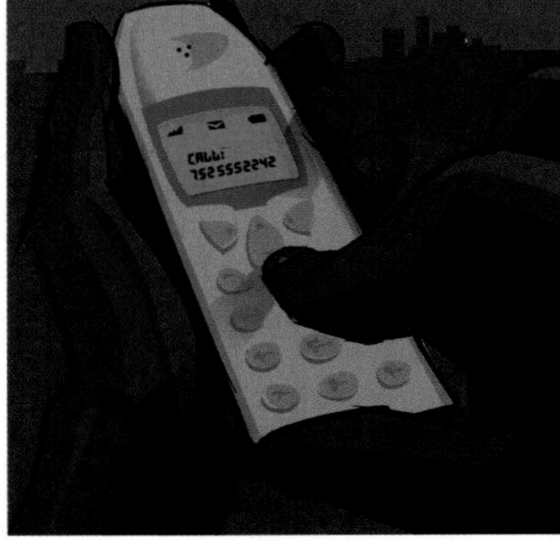

10a. $a = 0.50$

10b. $b = \dfrac{2.94}{\log 15} \approx 2.4998$

10c. $\log x = \frac{-0.50}{2.4998} \approx -0.2$; $x \approx 10^{-0.2} \approx 0.63$. The real-world meaning of the x-intercept is that the first 0.63 of a minute of calling is free.

11. APPLICATION A "learning curve" describes the rate at which a task can be learned. Suppose the equation

$$t = -144\log\left(1 - \frac{N}{90}\right)$$

predicts the time t (in number of short daily sessions) it will take to achieve a goal of typing N words per minute (wpm).

a. Using this equation, how long should it take someone to learn to type 40 wpm? approximately 37 sessions

b. If the typical person had 47 lessons, then what speed would you expect him or her to have achieved? approximately 48 wpm

c. Interpret the shape of the graph as it relates to learning time. What domain is realistic for this problem?

11c. Sample answer: It takes much longer to improve your typing speed as you reach higher levels. 60 wpm is a good typing speed, and very few people type more than 90 wpm, so $0 \le x \le 90$ is a reasonable domain.

12. APPLICATION All humans start as a single cell. This cell splits into two cells, then each of those two cells splits into two cells, and so on.

a. Write a recursive formula for cell division starting with a single cell. $u_0 = 1$; $u_n = (u_{n-1}) \cdot 2, n \ge 1$

b. Write an explicit formula for cell division. $y = 2^x$

c. Sketch a graph to model the formulas in 12a and b.

d. Describe some of the features of the graph.

e. After how many divisions were there more than 1 million cells? after 20 cell divisions

f. If there are about 1 billion cells after 30 divisions, after how many divisions were there about 500 million cells? after 29 divisions

12c.

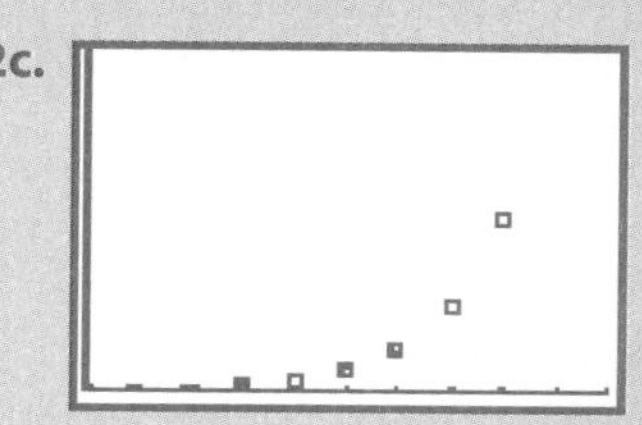

[0, 10, 1, 0, 500, 0]

12d. Answers will vary but can include curving upward, increasing, increasing at an increasing rate, discrete.

Science

Embryology is the branch of biology that deals with the formation, early growth, and development of living organisms. In humans, the growth of an embryo takes about 9 months. During this time a single cell will grow into many different cell types with different shapes and functions in the body.

A similar process occurs in the embryo of any animal. Historically, chicken embryos were among the first embryos studied. A chicken embryo develops and hatches in 20–21 days. Cutting a window in the eggshell allows direct observation for the study of embryonic growth.

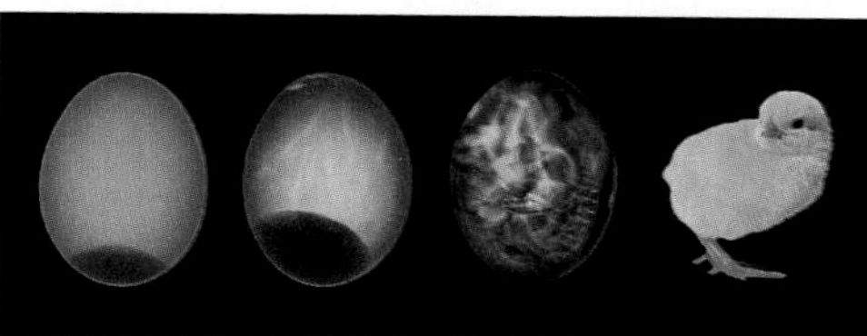

These X-rays show the 21-day growth of a chicken embryo to a newborn chick.

TAKE ANOTHER LOOK

1. Is $(x^{1/m})^n$ always equivalent to $(x^n)^{1/m}$? Try graphing $Y_1 = (x^{1/m})^n$ and $Y_2 = (x^n)^{1/m}$ for various integer values of m and n. Make sure you try positive and negative values for m and n, as well as different combinations of odd and even numbers. Check to see if the expressions are equal by inspecting the graphs and looking at table values for positive and negative values of x. Make observations about when output values are different and when output values do not exist. Make conjectures about the reasons for the occurrence of different values or no values.

Take Another Look

1. When m is even, you are taking an even root. You can take the even root only of a nonnegative number; therefore, the domain of $y = (x^{1/m})^n$ is $x \ge 0$ for all values of n. In the expression $(x^n)^{1/m}$, if n is even, then x^n is positive for all values of x; you can take an even or an odd root, so the domain is all values of x, no matter what the value of m. When m and n are both odd, the domain of both equations will be all real numbers, and all y-values will be the same.

2. For substitution, students will probably first solve for a: $a = \frac{40}{b^4}$ and $a = \frac{4.7}{b^7}$; $\frac{40}{b^4} = \frac{4.7}{b^7}$; $\frac{40}{4.7} = \frac{b^4}{b^7}$; $8.51 = b^{-3}$; $(8.51)^{-1/3} = \left(b^{-3}\right)^{-1/3}$; $0.49 = b$; $a = \frac{40}{0.49^4}$; $a = 693.87$; $y = 693.87(0.49)^x$ ($a = 695.04$, $y = 695.04(0.49)^x$ if the unrounded value of b is used). Students might also solve the system by elimination, dividing the second equation by the first to get $\frac{4.7}{40} = b^3$; $b = \sqrt[3]{\frac{4.7}{40}} \approx 0.4898$.

3. Suggest that students extend their slide rule to each side and label those numbers appropriately. Remind them that one slide-rule length to the right represents 100 and one slide-rule length to the left represents 0.1. There is no 0 on a slide rule.

The shortcut works because lining up the 5 with the 10 is the same as dividing 5 by 10. (The answer 0.5 would be apparent if the top scale extended farther to the left.) The number above 7 is then the product of 0.5 and 7. Multiplying by 10 gives the correct product. The process also works if you line up 7 with 10, which gives 0.7, and look up the number above 5, which then gives 0.7 times 5.

ASSESSING

You might test the chapter in two separate phases. Allow students to use their notebooks or chapter summaries on a test of applications and then turn in that assessment and take a short test on solving equations using the properties.

You might also want to do the individual assessment in two parts: one part without a calculator, including items such as Exercises 1, 2, and 6, and the other part with a calculator.

2. You have learned to use the point-ratio form to find an exponential curve that fits two data points. You could also use the general exponential equation $y = ab^x$ and your knowledge of solving systems of equations to find an appropriate exponential curve. For example, you can use the general form to write two equations for the exponential curve through (4, 40) and (7, 4.7):

$$40 = ab^4$$
$$4.7 = ab^7$$

Which constant will be easier to solve for in each equation, a or b? Solve each equation for the constant you have chosen. Use substitution and the properties you have learned in this chapter to solve this system of equations. Substitute the values you find for a and b into the general exponential form to write a general equation for this function.

Find a problem in this chapter that you did using the point-ratio form, and solve it again using this new method. Did you find this method easier or more difficult to use than the point-ratio form? Are there situations in which one method might be preferable to the other?

3. As you become more familiar with a slide rule, you might discover other shortcuts. For example, here is another way to multiply 5×7:

Line up the 5 on the top scale with 10 on the bottom scale, then find the number on the top scale that is directly above 7. The answer you find is 3.5, which you then have to multiply by 10 to find the correct answer, which is 35.

Why does the shortcut work? Does it also work if you line up 7 with 10 and read off the number above 5?

Assessing What You've Learned

GIVE A PRESENTATION Give a presentation about how to fit an exponential curve to data or one of the Take Another Look activities. Prepare a poster or visual aid to explain your topic. Work with a group, or give a presentation on your own.

ORGANIZE YOUR NOTEBOOK Review your notebook to be sure it's complete and well organized. Make sure your notes include all of the properties of exponents and logarithms, including the meanings of negative and fractional exponents. Write a one-page chapter summary based on your notes.

FACILITATING SELF-ASSESSMENT

Presentations given on topics in this chapter could include Fathom or Sketchpad demonstrations of an exponential function and its inverse. You might split up the topics covered in this chapter. Each group could do a presentation on a different topic for review. The groups could also be responsible for writing review questions about their topic.

As students organize their notebooks, their chapter summaries could be very important in reviewing for a test. You might ask students to hand in their chapter summaries at test time and count it as part of a written test.

CHAPTER

6

Matrices and Linear Systems

Overview

In **Lesson 6.1,** students are introduced to transition diagrams, matrices, and vocabulary related to matrices, and they learn the value of matrices as a way to organize information. Students begin to operate on matrices in **Lesson 6.2,** and they use matrices for transformations of geometric shapes. Students solve systems of equations in **Lesson 6.3** by representing them as augmented matrices. In **Lesson 6.4,** the identity matrix is defined, and the inverse of a matrix—if it exists—is used to solve a system. After reviewing inequalities in **Lesson 6.5,** students use matrices to represent systems of inequalities and constraints in a real-world situation and to solve those systems. In **Lesson 6.6,** students apply linear programming to situations with two variables, analyze feasible regions, and find the optimum value.

The Mathematics

This chapter extends the ideas of Chapter 6 of *Discovering Algebra,* although it makes no assumptions about students' familiarity with matrices.

Matrices for Solving Systems of Linear Equations

Matrices are often used to represent geometric transformations that leave the origin fixed. Multiplication by the matrix $[A] = \begin{bmatrix} a & b \\ c & d \end{bmatrix}$ transforms point $[X] = \begin{bmatrix} x \\ y \end{bmatrix}$ to point $[B] = \begin{bmatrix} ax + by \\ cx + dy \end{bmatrix}$. So a solution to the matrix equation $[A][X] = [B]$ is the point $[X]$ that is transformed to give point $[B]$.

The method of row reduction for solving a matrix equation (and thus the system of equations it represents) changes matrices $[A]$ and $[B]$ so that the unknown point $[X]$ is always being transformed to point $[B]$ by transformation $[A]$. Eventually, the transformation $[A]$ becomes the identity transformation that makes $[B]$ become $[X]$, thus solving the system.

In particular, we can imagine a rectangle with two edges along the axes and with opposite corners at the origin and at unknown point $[X]$. The image of this rectangle under the transformation $[A]$ is a parallelogram with opposite corners at the origin and at point $[B]$.

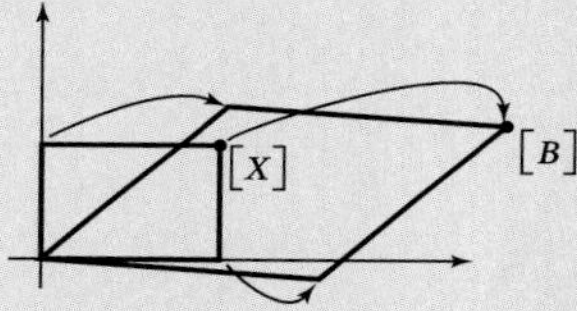

Row multiplications that prepare for adding two rows together stretch or shrink the parallelogram to get one vertex onto the line $y = -x$. (Point $[B]$ moves accordingly.) This ensures that, when the rows are added, the parallelogram is straightened so that one edge is on an axis. Repeating the process with the other variable changes the parallelogram into a rectangle with two edges on the axes. Dividing rows to get coefficients of 1 stretches or shrinks this rectangle into the original rectangle, moving point $[B]$ to coincide with point $[X]$.

Alternately, the combined sequence of changes constitutes the inverse of transformation $[A]$. If you find $[A]^{-1}$ and apply it to $[B]$, the result will be $[X]$.

If transformation $[A]$ squashes the plane to a line or a point, then its action can't be undone, meaning it has no inverse. If that line or point includes $[B]$, then the corresponding system of equations has infinitely many solutions, meaning it is dependent; otherwise the system is inconsistent.

Linear Programming

A common application of solving systems of linear equations is linear programming. The book takes a graphical approach, using two variables. A topic of ongoing research is finding increasingly efficient ways to solve linear programming problems that involve many variables, perhaps hundreds.

In linear programming, a system of linear inequalities represents the constraints of a real-world situation. Graphically, the points satisfying all of the constraints are represented by a region of the plane, perhaps an unbounded region. A linear function of the two variables is maximized or minimized at a vertex or along an edge of that region.

One way to understand why extreme values are at vertices is to realize that the function being optimized is a linear function of two variables. You can think of its graph as a plane lying above the feasible region. Because it's a plane, the graph will be highest and lowest at a vertex or along an edge of the region, if the region is bounded as pictured. If the region is unbounded, the plane may not have a highest or a lowest point over the region.

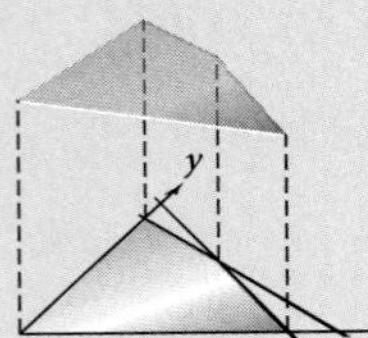

Using This Chapter

Lesson 6.4 is the most important lesson. You might combine Lessons 6.1 and 6.2 by skipping their investigations. Lesson 6.3 is optional. Lessons 6.5 and 6.6 are optional unless your state standards require linear programming, but include at least the graphing of an inequality in two variables.

Resources

Discovering Advanced Algebra Resources

Teaching and Worksheet Masters
Lessons 6.1, 6.2, 6.4–6.6

Calculator Notes 1B, 1G, 1H, 1L, 5A, 6A–G, 6G/App

Sketchpad Demonstration
Lesson 6.6

Assessment Resources A and B
Quiz 1 (Lessons 6.1, 6.2)
Quiz 2 (Lessons 6.3, 6.4)
Quiz 3 (Lessons 6.5, 6.6)
Chapter 6 Test
Chapter 6 Constructive Assessment Options
Chapters 4–6 Exam

More Practice Your Skills for Chapter 6

Condensed Lessons for Chapter 6

Other Resources

An Introduction to the History of Mathematics by Howard Eves.

For complete references to this and other resources see www.keypress.com/DAA.

Materials

- graph paper

Pacing Guide

	day 1	day 2	day 3	day 4	day 5	day 6	day 7	day 8	day 9	day 10
standard	6.1	6.2	quiz, 6.3	6.3	6.4	quiz, 6.5	6.5, 6.6	6.6	quiz, review	review
enriched	6.1	6.2	quiz, 6.3	6.3	6.4	quiz, 6.5	6.6	project	quiz, review	review, TAL
block	6.1, 6.2	quiz, 6.3	6.4, 6.5	quiz, 6.6, project	quiz, review	TAL, assessment	review, exam			

	day 11	day 12	day 13
standard	assessment	review	exam
enriched	assessment	review	exam

CHAPTER

6 Matrices and Linear Systems

American installation artist Amy Stacey Curtis (b 1970) created this sculpture. The rectangular arrangement of egg cartons is used to organize an even larger arrangement of photocopied images. The egg cartons and their compartments divide the piece into rows and columns, while the small images—some darker or lighter than others—help certain elements of the piece to stand out more prominently.

Fragile and detail from *Fragile* by Amy Stacey Curtis
Egg cartons, acrylic, dye, thread, beads, photocopies

OBJECTIVES

In this chapter you will

- use matrices to organize information
- add, subtract, and multiply matrices
- solve systems of linear equations with matrices
- graph two-variable inequalities on a coordinate plane and solve systems of inequalities
- write and graph inequalities that represent conditions that must be met simultaneously

This 11.25-by-6.25-foot sculpture was part of a large installation called *Retrospective.* In her installations, Curtis strives "toward an aesthetic and collective balance of chaos, order, and repetition." **[Ask]** "What aspects of *Fragile* represent order, repetition, and chaos?" [The egg cartons are ordered in rows and columns. There is repetition in the pattern made by the cartons and also in the images inside each compartment. Seen as a whole, the shading of the piece is chaotic, with no pattern as to which cartons are darker or lighter.]

You may want to turn back to this page after students have seen the definition of *matrix* on page 300. Then **[Ask]** "How is this sculpture similar to a matrix?" [The entire piece is divided into rows and columns like a matrix. Each egg carton might represent an entry in the matrix, with each compartment of the carton representing a digit of the entry. Or each compartment itself might represent a numerical entry of the matrix.]

You might also **[Ask]** "Why do you think this sculpture is titled *Fragile*?"

CHAPTER 6 OBJECTIVES

- Use matrices to represent transition diagrams, polygons, and transformations
- Apply matrix operations to solve problems with probabilities and transformations
- Solve systems of equations by matrix row reduction and by inverse matrices
- Write and graph systems of inequalities to describe given real-world constraints
- Learn how to do linear programming—optimizing a function over a feasible region representing real-world situations—with two variables

LESSON

6.1

Matrix Representations

All dimensions are critical dimensions, otherwise why are they there?

RUSS ZANDBERGEN

On Saturday, Karina surveyed visitors to Snow Mountain with weekend passes and found that 75% of skiers planned to ski again the next day and 25% planned to snowboard. Of the snowboarders, 95% planned to snowboard the next day and 5% planned to ski. In order to display the information, she made this diagram.

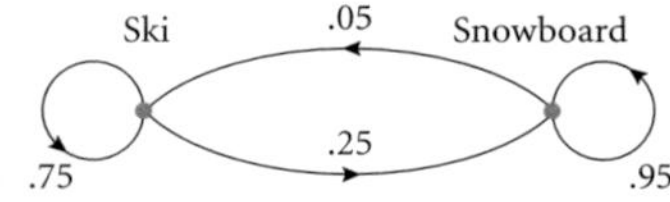

The arrows and labels show the patterns of the visitors' next-day activities. For instance, the circular arrow labeled .75 indicates that 75% of the visitors skiing one day plan to ski again the next day. The arrow labeled .25 indicates that 25% of the visitors who ski one day plan to snowboard the next day.

Diagrams like these are called **transition diagrams** because they show how something changes from one time to the next. The same information is sometimes represented in a **transition matrix.** A **matrix** is a rectangular arrangement of numbers. For the Snow Mountain information, the transition matrix looks like this:

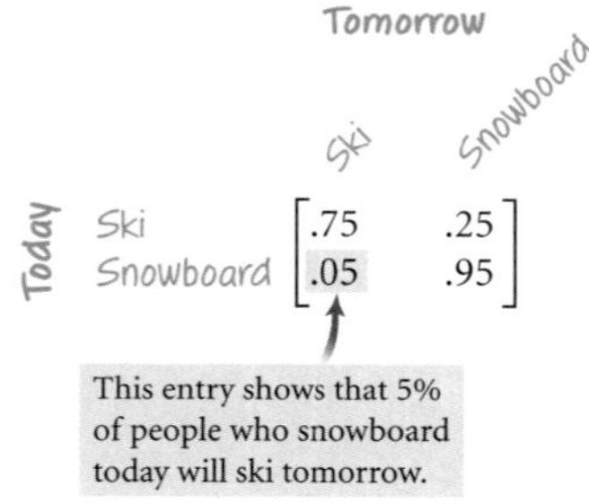

In the investigation you will create a transition diagram and matrix for another situation. You will also use the information to determine how the numbers of people in two different categories change over a period of time.

LESSON

6.1

PLANNING

LESSON OUTLINE

One day:

20 min Investigation

10 min Examples

10 min Sharing

5 min Exercises

MATERIALS

- Cold Desserts (T) for One Step
- Calculator Notes 1B, 6A, *optional*

TEACHING

[Language] In 1850, English mathematician James Joseph Sylvester (1814–1897) invented the term *matrix* to denote "an oblong arrangement of terms consisting, suppose, of *m* lines and *n* columns." Sylvester didn't use matrices, although another British mathematician, his friend Arthur Cayley (1821–1895), did in 1855 and 1858 papers. In English the word *matrix* means "that which gives form to something." In mathematics, a matrix gives form to data.

This lesson introduces transition diagrams and transition matrices and serves as a prelude to matrix multiplication.

One Step

Pose the problem of the investigation: "The school cafeteria offers a choice of ice cream or frozen yogurt for dessert once a week. During the first week of school, 220 students choose ice cream, whereas only 20 choose frozen yogurt. Each week, 10% of the frozen-yogurt eaters switch to ice cream and 5% of the ice-cream eaters switch to frozen yogurt. In the long run, how many students will eat ice cream and how many will eat frozen yogurt?" Display the Cold Desserts transparency to remind students of the numbers.

As students share their work, attach the terms *matrix, transition diagram,* and *transition matrix* to their figures, and collaborate with the class in writing a description of their process. Suggest that the class look at Example A to see how matrices can represent geometric figures.

LESSON OBJECTIVES

- Create transition diagrams and transition matrices
- Relate transition diagrams to matrices
- Understand matrices as a way to organize information
- Learn vocabulary associated with matrices: *dimension, row, column, entry*
- Find subsequent totals from the given initial value and percentages

Investigation
Chilly Choices

The school cafeteria offers a choice of ice cream or frozen yogurt for dessert once a week. During the first week of school, 220 students choose ice cream but only 20 choose frozen yogurt. During each of the following weeks, 10% of the frozen-yogurt eaters switch to ice cream and 5% of the ice-cream eaters switch to frozen yogurt.

Step 1 Complete a transition diagram that displays this information.

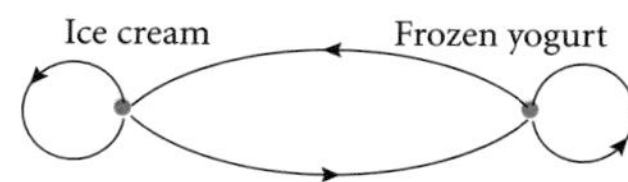

Step 2 Complete a transition matrix that represents this information. The rows should indicate the present condition, and the columns should indicate the next condition after the transition.

		Next week: Ice cream	Next week: Yogurt
This week	Ice cream	?	?
	Yogurt	?	?

Step 3 In the second week, how many students choose ice cream and how many students choose frozen yogurt?

Step 4 How many will choose each option in the third week?

Step 5 Write a recursive routine to take any week's values and give the next week's values.

Step 6 What do you think will happen to the long-run values of the number of students who choose ice cream and the number who choose frozen yogurt?

Guiding the Investigation

Step 1

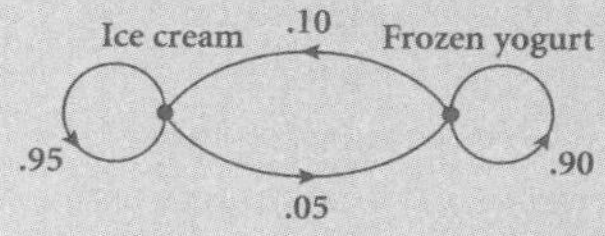

Step 2 $\begin{bmatrix} .95 & .05 \\ .10 & .90 \end{bmatrix}$

Step 3 [Alert] Students may count only those who switch, neglecting those who don't switch.

Step 3 Let i represent ice-cream eaters, and let f represent frozen-yogurt eaters.
$i = 220(.95) + 20(.10) = 211$
$f = 220(.05) + 20(.90) = 29$

Step 4
$i = 211(.95) + 29(.10) \approx 203$
$f = 211(.05) + 29(.90) \approx 37$

Step 5 If students are entering the routine into calculators, they may need reminding of how to generate two recursive sequences at a time. If they are using a TI-83 or TI-83 Plus, refer them to Calculator Note 1B.

Step 5 $i_1 = 220$ and $f_1 = 20$
$i_n = i_{n-1}(.95) + f_{n-1}(.10)$ where $n \geq 2$
$f_n = i_{n-1}(.05) + f_{n-1}(.90)$ where $n \geq 2$

Step 6 Students may recall long-run values (limits) from Chapter 1. Questions like this will be explored further in Lesson 6.2.

Step 6 Ice-cream eaters will approach 160, and frozen-yogurt eaters will approach 80.

NCTM STANDARDS

	CONTENT		PROCESS
	Number	✓	Problem Solving
✓	Algebra	✓	Reasoning
✓	Geometry	✓	Communication
	Measurement	✓	Connections
✓	Data/Probability	✓	Representation

▶ EXAMPLE A

The coordinates could also be arranged in columns of a 4 × 2 matrix. **[Ask]** "What about matrix dimensions for figures of dimension higher than two? Could you use a matrix to represent a three-dimensional figure?" [The matrix will have three rows.] "Can matrices be used to organize other types of information?"

▶ EXAMPLE B

This example begins to lay the groundwork for matrix multiplication in Lesson 6.2. If students are having difficulty deciding on the percentages for a matrix, suggest a transition diagram.

SHARING IDEAS

As students present, you might work toward a formal statement of how to use a starting matrix and a transition matrix to get a result matrix, motivating the definition of matrix multiplication in the next lesson.

[Ask] "Why do some references to matrices use uppercase letters whereas others use lowercase letters?" [An uppercase letter in brackets indicates the name of a matrix. The name of an entry is the same letter but lowercase, with the row and column of the entry as subscripts.]

[Ask] "Is it always true that the sum of the entries in the rows of a transition matrix is 1?" [yes] "Why?" [The rows represent the probabilities that each choice will be picked; the probabilities must sum to 1.]

[Ask] "Are the entries of a matrix specified in a different order from that of coordinates of points on a plane?" [To locate entry a_{mn}, you go down to the mth row and across to the nth column, whereas to locate a point with rectangular coordinates (m, n) in the plane, you go across m units from the origin and then up n units.] To add to the confusion, coordinates of points (pixels) on a calculator or computer screen are often assigned as though each point were an entry in a matrix with the top row and left column numbered 0, that is, (0, 0) is the top left point. To locate the point with coordinates (m, n), you go down m units and across n units. Students may have programmed calculator or computer graphics using this scheme.

Ask whether it's possible to have a matrix of any dimensions. [Single numbers might be thought of as 1 × 1 matrices. Calculator lists resemble 1 × n matrices or n × 1 matrices, though the calculator treats them differently; such matrices are sometimes called *vectors* (see Lesson 8.4). Nonpositive integers and non-integers aren't dimensions of standard matrices.]

[Ask] "Don't we always put zeros in front of decimal places for decimals less than 0? Why are they omitted here?" It is customary to have no leading zeros with probabilities, because their maximum value is 1. Here the figures represent probabilities, although they are presented as parts of a whole.

You can use matrices to organize many kinds of information. For example, the matrix below can be used to represent the number of math, science, and history textbooks sold this week at the main and branch campus bookstores. The rows represent math, science, and history, from top to bottom, and the columns represent the main and branch bookstores, from left to right.

The **dimensions** of the matrix give the numbers of rows and columns, in this case, 3 × 2 (read "three by two"). Each number in the matrix is called an **entry,** or element, and is identified as a_{ij} where i and j are the row number and column number, respectively. In matrix $[A]$ at right, $a_{21} = 65$ because 65 is the entry in row 2, column 1.

$$[A] = \begin{bmatrix} 83 & 33 \\ 65 & 20 \\ 98 & 50 \end{bmatrix}$$

This entry is the number of history books sold at the main book store.

Example A shows how to use matrices to represent coordinates of geometric figures.

EXAMPLE A Represent quadrilateral $ABCD$ as a matrix, $[M]$.

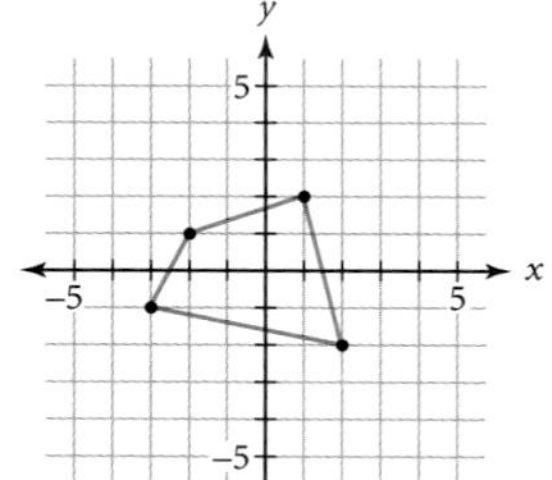

▶ Solution

You can use a matrix to organize the coordinates of the consecutive vertices of a geometric figure. Because each vertex has 2 coordinates and there are 4 vertices, use a 2 × 4 matrix with each column containing the x- and y-coordinates of a vertex. Row 1 contains consecutive x-coordinates and row 2 contains the corresponding y-coordinates.

$$[M] = \begin{bmatrix} 1 & -2 & -3 & 2 \\ 2 & 1 & -1 & -2 \end{bmatrix}$$

Example B shows how a transition matrix can be used to organize data and predictions. In Lesson 6.2, you'll learn how to do computations with matrices.

EXAMPLE B In Karina's survey from the beginning of this lesson, she interviewed 260 skiers and 40 snowboarders. How many people will do each activity the next day if her transition predictions are correct?

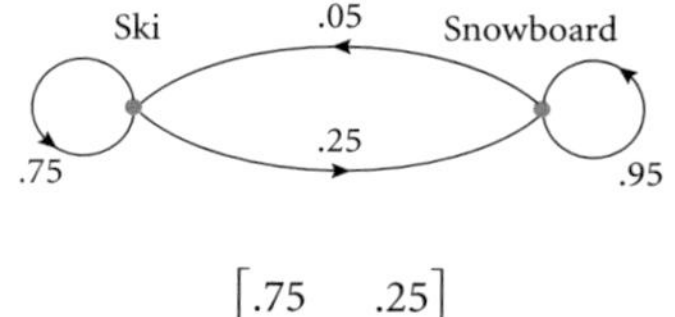

$$\begin{bmatrix} .75 & .25 \\ .05 & .95 \end{bmatrix}$$

▶ Solution

The next day, 75% of the 260 skiers will ski again and 5% of the 40 snowboarders will switch to skiing.

Skiers: $260(.75) + 40(.05) = 197$

So, 197 people will ski the next day.

The next day, 25% of the 260 skiers will switch to snowboarding and 95% of the 40 snowboarders will snowboard again.

Snowboarders: $260(.25) + 40(.95) = 103$

So, 103 people will snowboard the next day.

You can organize the information for the first day and second day as matrices in the form [*number of skiers*   *number of snowboarders*].

[260   40]

[197   103]

You can use transition diagrams and transition matrices to show changes in a closed system. (A closed system is one in which items may change, but nothing is added or removed.) The diagram, though very informative for simple problems, is difficult to use when you have 5 or more starting conditions, as this would create 25 or more arrows, or paths. The transition matrix is just as easy to read for any number of starting conditions as it is for two. It grows in size, but each entry shows what percentage changes from one condition to another.

EXERCISES

Practice Your Skills

1. Russell collected data similar to Karina's at Powder Hill Resort. He found that 86% of the skiers planned to ski the next day and 92% of the snowboarders planned to snowboard the next day.

a. Draw a transition diagram for Russell's information.

b. Write a transition matrix for the same information. Remember that rows indicate the present condition and columns indicate the next condition. List skiers first and snowboarders second. $\begin{bmatrix} .86 & .14 \\ .08 & .92 \end{bmatrix}$

2. Complete this transition diagram:

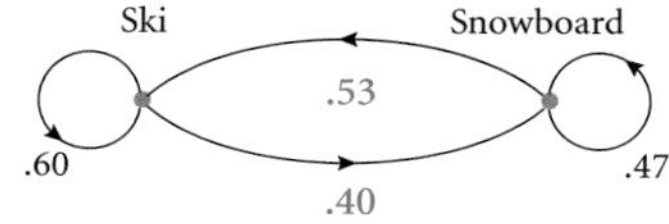

3. Write a transition matrix for the diagram in Exercise 2. Order your information as in Exercise 1b. $\begin{bmatrix} .60 & .40 \\ .53 & .47 \end{bmatrix}$

4. Matrix $[M]$ represents the vertices of $\triangle ABC$.

$$[M] = \begin{bmatrix} -3 & 1 & 2 \\ 2 & 3 & -2 \end{bmatrix}$$

a. Name the coordinates of the vertices and draw the triangle.

b. What matrix represents the image of $\triangle ABC$ after a translation down 4 units?

c. What matrix represents the image of $\triangle ABC$ after a translation right 4 units?

Closing the Lesson

A **matrix** is a rectangular array of numbers. The plural of *matrix* is *matrices;* the singular of *matrices* is not *matrice,* but *matrix.* The **dimensions** of a matrix are the number of the rows and of the columns. Each number is an **entry** of the matrix. A **transition matrix** or a **transition diagram** shows the probabilities associated with changing categories while going from one stage of a process to the next.

4a. $A(-3, 2)$, $B(1, 3)$, and $C(2, -2)$

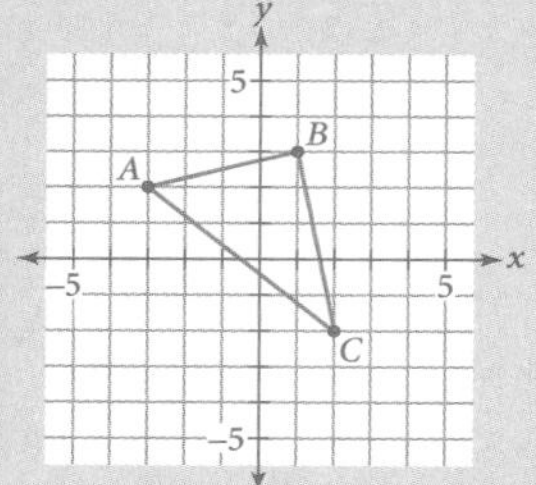

Assessing Progress

You can assess students' ability to find percentages of numbers, to write recursive routines, and to see long-run patterns.

BUILDING UNDERSTANDING

You might have students begin entering matrices into a calculator. See Calculator Note 6A.

ASSIGNING HOMEWORK

Essential	1–4
Performance assessment	5–11
Portfolio	10
Journal	8
Group	9, 11
Review	12–16

MATERIALS

- graph paper
- Calculator Notes 1G, 1H, 5A, *optional*

Helping with the Exercises

Exercise 1 As needed, remind students that their completed transition diagram will have four percentages.

1a.

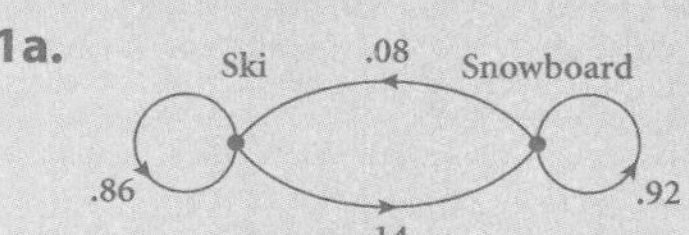

Exercise 4 [Language] *Vertices* is the plural of *vertex.* Graph paper will help students complete 4a. **[Alert]** Students may think that they need to subtract from the *x*-coordinate to move to the right, as they did for equations. If students are ready to generalize, you might **[Ask]** "What matrix represents the image after a translation left *a* units and up *b* units?"

4b. $\begin{bmatrix} -3 & 1 & 2 \\ -2 & -1 & -6 \end{bmatrix}$

4c. $\begin{bmatrix} 1 & 5 & 6 \\ 2 & 3 & -2 \end{bmatrix}$

Exercise 5 If students are having difficulty making sense of the matrix, **[Ask]** "How many left-handed batters participated?" [9]

5. During a recent softball tournament, information about which side players bat from was recorded in a matrix. Row 1 represents girls and row 2 represents boys. Column 1 represents left-handed batters, column 2 represents right-handed batters, and column 3 represents those who can bat with either hand.

$$[A] = \begin{bmatrix} 5 & 13 & 2 \\ 4 & 18 & 3 \end{bmatrix}$$

   a. How many girls and how many boys participated in the tournament? 20 girls and 25 boys
   b. How many boys batted right-handed? 18 boys
   c. What is the meaning of the value of a_{12}? 13 girls batted right-handed.

Reason and Apply

Exercise 6 You may want to compare this exercise to Lesson 1.5, Exercise 12, in which sequences were used for a similar problem.

[Context] N_2O_2 is dinitrogendioxide.

[Context] The disease sickle cell anemia is a chronic hereditary blood disease that changes the red blood cells and causes weakness, joint pain, and blood clots.

6. A mixture of 40 mL of NO and 200 mL of N_2O_2 is heated. During each second at this new temperature, 10% of the NO changes to N_2O_2 and 5% of the N_2O_2 changes to NO.
   a. Draw a transition diagram that displays this information.
   b. Write a transition matrix that represents the same information. List NO first and N_2O_2 second.
   c. If the total amount remains at 240 mL and the transition percentages stay the same, what are the amounts in milliliters of NO and N_2O_2 after 1 s? After 2 s? Write your answers as matrices in the form $[\text{NO} \quad N_2O_2]$.

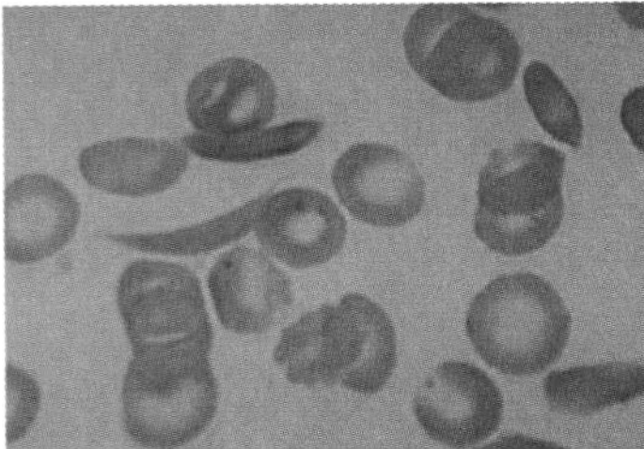

This photo shows red blood cells, some deformed by sickle cell anemia. Researchers have found that nitric oxide (NO) counteracts the effects of sickle cell anemia.

6a. NO .05 N_2O_2 .90 .95 .10

6b. $\begin{bmatrix} .90 & .10 \\ .05 & .95 \end{bmatrix}$

6c. [46 194]; [51.1 188.9]

Exercise 7 [ESL] *Urban dwellers* are people who live in the city. People who do not live in a city are *rural dwellers.*

7. In many countries, more people move into the cities than out of the cities. Suppose that in a certain country, 10% of the rural population moves to the city each year and 1% of the urban population moves out of the city each year.
   a. Draw a transition diagram that displays this information.
   b. Write a transition matrix that represents this same information. List urban dwellers first and rural dwellers second.
   c. If 16 million of the country's 25 million people live in the city initially, what are the urban and rural populations in millions after 1 yr? After 2 yr? Write your answers as matrices in the form [*urban* *rural*].

7a. Rural .01 Urban .90 .99 .10

7b. $\begin{bmatrix} .99 & .01 \\ .10 & .90 \end{bmatrix}$

7c. [16.74 8.26]; [17.3986 7.6014]

Exercise 8 This exercise is a prelude to matrix addition.

8. Recall the matrix $[A]$ on page 302 that represents the number of math, science, and history textbooks sold at the main and branch campus bookstores this week.

$$[A] = \begin{bmatrix} 83 & 33 \\ 65 & 20 \\ 98 & 50 \end{bmatrix}$$

   a. Explain the meaning of the value of a_{32}.
   b. Explain the meaning of the value of a_{21}.
   c. Matrix $[B]$ represents last week's sales. Compare this week's sales of math books with last week's sales.

$$[B] = \begin{bmatrix} 80 & 25 \\ 65 & 15 \\ 105 & 55 \end{bmatrix}$$

   d. Write a matrix that represents the total sales during last week and this week.

8a. There were 50 history books sold at the branch bookstore.

8b. There were 65 science books sold at the main bookstore.

8c. This week there were 3 more math books sold at the main bookstore and 8 more math books sold at the branch bookstore.

8d. $\begin{bmatrix} 163 & 58 \\ 130 & 35 \\ 203 & 105 \end{bmatrix}$

9. The three largest categories of motor vehicles are sedan, SUV, and minivan. Suppose that of the buyers in a particular community who now own a minivan, 18% will change to an SUV and 20% will change to a sedan. Of the buyers who now own a sedan, 35% will change to a minivan and 20% will change to an SUV, and of those who now own an SUV, 12% will buy a minivan and 32% will buy a sedan.

a. Draw a transition diagram that displays these changes.

b. Write a transition matrix that represents this scenario. List the rows and columns in the order minivan, sedan, SUV.

c. What is the sum of the entries in row 1? Row 2? Row 3? Why does this sum make sense? The sum of each row is 1; percentages should sum to 100%.

10. Lisa Crawford is getting into the moving-truck rental business in three nearby counties. She has the funds to buy about 100 trucks. Her studies show that 20% of the trucks rented in Bay County go to Sage County, and 15% go to Thyme County. The rest start and end in Bay County. From Sage County, 25% of rentals go to Bay and 55% stay in Sage, whereas the rest move to Thyme County. From Thyme County, 40% of rentals end in Bay and 30% in Sage.

a. Draw a transition diagram that displays this information.

b. Write a transition matrix that represents this scenario. List your rows and columns in the order Bay, Sage, Thyme.

c. What is the sum of the entries in row 1? Row 2? Row 3? Why does this sum make sense? The sum of each row is 1; percentages should add to 100%.

d. If Lisa starts with 45 trucks in Bay County, 30 trucks in Sage County, and 25 trucks in Thyme County, and all trucks are rented one Saturday, how many trucks will she expect to be in each county the next morning?

11. **APPLICATION** Fly-Right Airways operates routes out of five cities as shown in the route map below. Each segment connecting two cities represents a round-trip flight between them. Matrix $[M]$ displays the information from the map in matrix form with the cities, A, B, C, D, and E, listed in order in the rows and columns. The rows represent starting conditions (departure cities), and the columns represent next conditions (arrival cities). This matrix is called an adjacency matrix. For instance, the value of the entry in row 1, column 5 shows that there are two round-trip flights between City A and City E.

$$[M] = \begin{bmatrix} 0 & 1 & 0 & 1 & 2 \\ 1 & 0 & 1 & 0 & 1 \\ 0 & 1 & 0 & 0 & 0 \\ 1 & 0 & 0 & 0 & 0 \\ 2 & 1 & 0 & 0 & 0 \end{bmatrix}$$

a. What are the dimensions of this matrix? 5×5

b. What is the value of m_{32}? What does this entry represent?

c. Which city has the most flights? Explain how you can tell using the route map and using the matrix.

d. Matrix $[N]$ below represents Americana Airways's routes connecting four cities, J, K, L, and M. Sketch a possible route map.

$$[N] = \begin{bmatrix} 0 & 1 & 2 & 1 \\ 1 & 0 & 2 & 0 \\ 2 & 2 & 0 & 1 \\ 1 & 0 & 1 & 0 \end{bmatrix}$$

9a.

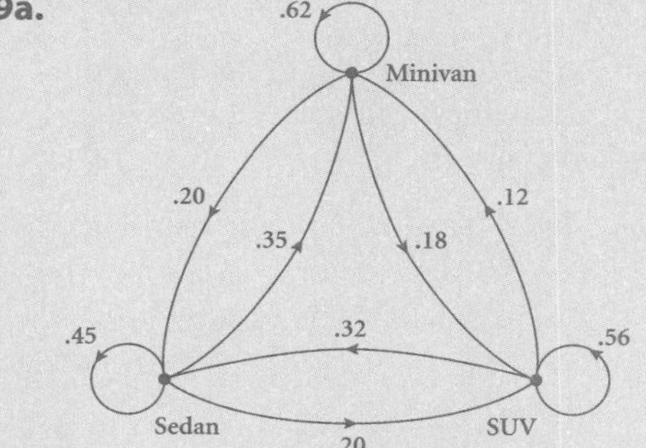

10a.

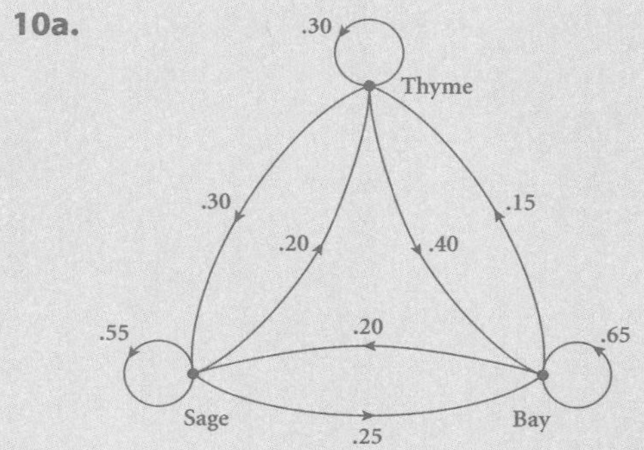

Exercise 9 [ESL] *Sedan, SUV* (sport-utility vehicle), and *minivan* all describe types of cars.

9b. $\begin{bmatrix} .62 & .20 & .18 \\ .35 & .45 & .20 \\ .12 & .32 & .56 \end{bmatrix}$

Exercise 10 For this exercise students should consider all rentals as one day.

10b. $\begin{bmatrix} .65 & .20 & .15 \\ .25 & .55 & .20 \\ .40 & .30 & .30 \end{bmatrix}$

10d. 47 trucks in Bay County, 33 trucks in Sage County, and 20 trucks in Thyme County

Exercise 11 Diagrams like this are known as *vertex-edge graphs,* or just *graphs,* although they appear quite different from graphs of equations. You might use phrases like "from City A to City B" where *from* refers to the rows and *to* refers to the columns. **[Ask]** "In this adjacency matrix, will some entries always be zero even if the flight schedule changes?" [The diagonal from the upper left corner to the lower right corner will always be zeros because this is where the column and row represent the same city.]

11b. $m_{32} = 1$; there is one round-trip flight between City C and City B.

11c. City A has the most flights. From the graph, more paths have A as an endpoint than any other city. From the matrix, the sum of row 1 (or column 1) is greater than the sum of any other row (or column).

11d.

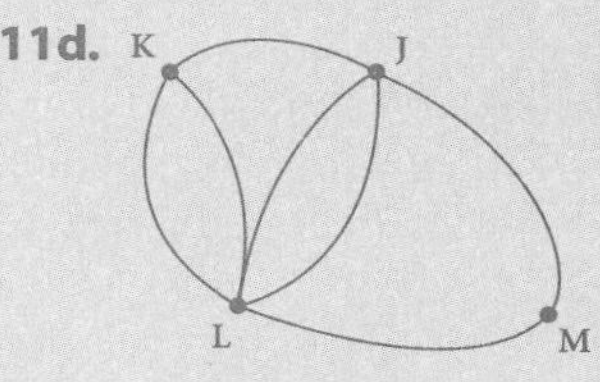

Exercise 14 If students are graphing by hand, they might find it easier to use the original equation and find the intercepts.

14. $y = 4 - \frac{2}{3}x$

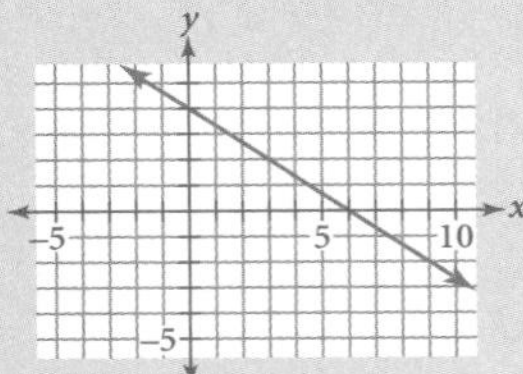

Exercise 15 If students are using calculators to make scatter plots and model the data, you might refer them to Calculator Notes 1G, 1H, and 5A on entering data, scatter plots, and entering exponential equations, respectively.

15a. Let x represent the year, and let y represent the number of subscribers.

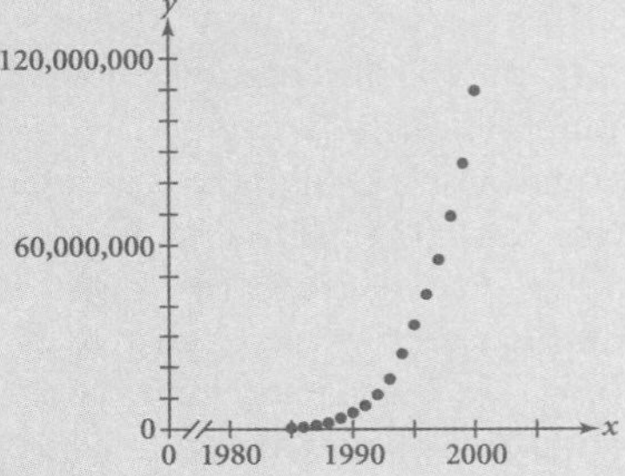

15b. Using the point-ratio method with (1987, 1231000) and (1998, 69209000), $\hat{y} = 1231000(1.44)^{x-1987}$.

15c. About 420,782,749 subscribers. This is not a realistic prediction because it far exceeds the 2003 population of the United States. (The population was about 288 million in 2002.) It is unlikely that there will ever be more than one cellular phone for every person in the country. The number of cell phones cannot possibly continue to increase at a rate of 44% a year. Because the number of cell phones will level off rather than continue to increase exponentially, an exponential model is not appropriate.

Mathematics CONNECTION

Graph theory is a branch of mathematics that deals with connections between items. In Exercise 11, a paragraph description of the flight routes could have been made, but a vertex-edge graph of the routes allows you to show the material quickly and clearly. You could also use a graph to diagram a natural gas pipeline, the chemical structure of a molecule, a family tree, or a computer network. The data in a graph can be represented, manipulated mathematically, and further investigated using matrices.

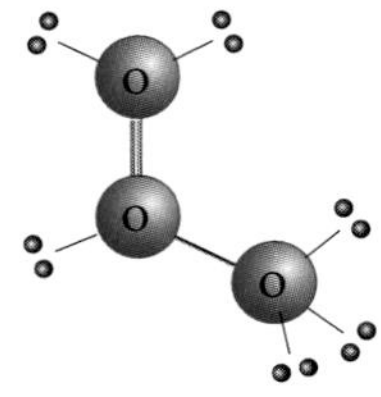

Ozone (O_3)

Review

3.7 **12.** Solve this system using either substitution or elimination.

$$\begin{cases} 5x - 4y = 25 \\ x + y = 3 \end{cases} \quad \left(\frac{37}{9}, -\frac{10}{9}\right)$$

3.1 **13.** Each slice of pepperoni pizza has approximately 7.4 slices of pepperoni on it, and each slice of supreme pizza has approximately 4.7 slices of pepperoni on it. Write an equation that shows that p slices of pepperoni pizza and s slices of supreme pizza would have a total of 100 slices of pepperoni. $7.4p + 4.7s = 100$

3.2 **14.** Solve the equation $2x + 3y = 12$ for y and then graph it.

5.3 **15.** APPLICATION The table at right shows the number of cellular telephone subscribers in the United States from 1985 to 2000.

a. Create a scatter plot of the data.

b. Find an exponential function to model the data.

c. Use your model to predict the number of subscribers in 2003. Do you think this is a realistic prediction? Why or why not? Do you think an exponential model is appropriate? Why or why not?

Cellular Phone Subscribers

Year	Number of Subscribers	Year	Number of Subscribers
1985	340,000	1993	16,009,000
1986	682,000	1994	24,134,000
1987	1,231,000	1995	33,786,000
1988	2,069,000	1996	44,043,000
1989	3,509,000	1997	55,312,000
1990	5,283,000	1998	69,209,000
1991	7,557,000	1999	86,047,000
1992	11,033,000	2000	109,478,000

(The World Almanac and Book of Facts 2002)

5.6 **16.** APPLICATION The equation $y = 20\log\left(\frac{x}{0.00002}\right)$ measures the intensity of a sound as a function of the pressure it creates on the eardrum. The intensity, y, is measured in decibels (dB), and the pressure, x, is measured in Pascals (Pa).

a. What is the intensity of the sound of a humming refrigerator, if it causes 0.00356 Pa of pressure on the eardrum? 45 dB

b. A noise that causes 20 Pa of pressure on the eardrum brings severe pain to most people. What is the intensity of this noise? 120 dB

c. Write the inverse function that measures pressure on the eardrum as a function of intensity of a sound.

d. How much pressure on the eardrum is caused by a 90 dB sound? 0.63246 Pa

16c. $y = (0.00002)(10)^{x/20}$, where x represents the intensity in decibels and y represents the pressure in Pascals

EXTENSION

Ask students to consult the flight schedule for an airline, choose six cities, and create a route map and an adjacency matrix.

LESSON

6.2

Matrix Operations

It is not once nor twice but times without number that the same ideas make their appearance in the world.

ARISTOTLE

A matrix is a compact way of organizing data, similar to a table. Representing data in a matrix instead of a table allows you to perform operations such as addition and multiplication with your data. In this lesson you will see how this is useful.

Consider this problem from Lesson 6.1. Matrix $[A]$ represents math, science, and history textbooks sold this week at the main and branch campus bookstores. Matrix $[B]$ contains the same information for last week. What are the total sales, by category and location, for both weeks?

$$[A] = \begin{bmatrix} 83 & 33 \\ 65 & 20 \\ 98 & 50 \end{bmatrix} \qquad [B] = \begin{bmatrix} 80 & 25 \\ 65 & 15 \\ 105 & 55 \end{bmatrix}$$

To solve this problem, you add matrices $[A]$ and $[B]$.

$$83 + 80 = 163$$

$$\begin{bmatrix} 83 & 33 \\ 65 & 20 \\ 98 & 50 \end{bmatrix} + \begin{bmatrix} 80 & 25 \\ 65 & 15 \\ 105 & 55 \end{bmatrix} = \begin{bmatrix} 163 & 58 \\ 130 & 35 \\ 203 & 105 \end{bmatrix}$$

If 83 math books were sold at the main bookstore this week, and 80 math books were sold at the main bookstore last week, a total of 163 math books were sold at the main bookstore for both weeks.

To add two matrices, you simply add corresponding entries. So in order to add (or subtract) two matrices they both must have the same dimensions. The corresponding rows and columns should also have similar interpretations if the results are to make sense. [► See **Calculator Note 6A** to learn how to enter matrices into your calculator. **Calculator Note 6B** shows how to perform operations with matrices. ◄]

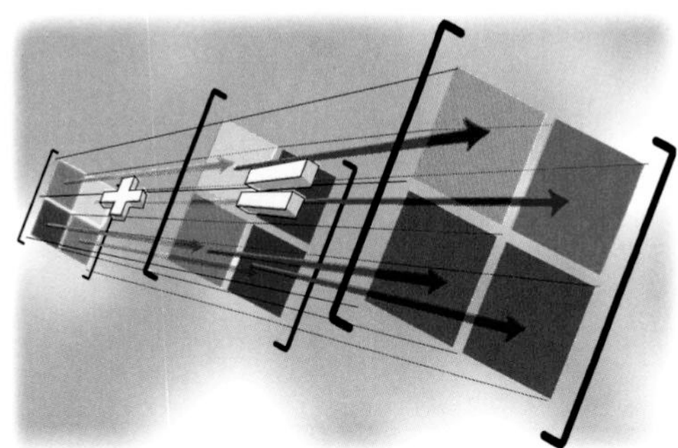

When you add matrices, you add corresponding entries. This illustration uses the addition of color to show how the addition carries through to the matrix representing the sum.

In Lesson 6.1, you used a matrix to organize the coordinates of the vertices of a triangle. You can use matrix operations to transform a figure such as a triangle just as you transformed the graph of a function.

LESSON

6.2

PLANNING

LESSON OUTLINE

One day:

10 min	Examples A, B
15 min	Investigation
10 min	Sharing
5 min	Example C
5 min	Exercises

MATERIALS

- Car Data (T) for One Step
- Find Your Place (T), *optional*
- Calculator Notes 1L, 6A–6C

TEACHING

In this lesson students learn about matrix addition and scalar multiplication and formalize a definition of matrix multiplication.

One Step

Show the Car Data transparency. Pose this problem: "A local rental-car agency has three locations, A, B, and C. Today there are 24, 18, and 11 cars at these locations, but the agency is expecting a shipment of new cars tomorrow. Each location will receive twice as many cars as it already has. Moreover, an additional 31, 23, and 15 cars will be shipped to the three locations, respectively. Experience says that the probabilities that cars will be returned to the various locations follow the transitions given on the transparency. Is there a long-term trend in how many cars will be at each location?" [The long-term trend predicts that after about 30 days there will be a constant 65, 96, and 67 cars at A, B, and C, respectively.] During Sharing, bring out the ideas of matrix addition and scalar multiplication from students' presentations, formalize a definition of matrix

NCTM STANDARDS

CONTENT		PROCESS	
✓	Number	✓	Problem Solving
✓	Algebra	✓	Reasoning
✓	Geometry	✓	Communication
	Measurement	✓	Connections
✓	Data/Probability	✓	Representation

LESSON OBJECTIVES

- Learn these matrix operations: addition, scalar multiplication, and multiplication
- Analyze matrix dimensions to determine whether they can be added or multiplied
- Use matrices as a tool for describing transformations of geometric shapes
- Understand dilations as shrinks or stretches by the same factor both horizontally and vertically

One Step (continued)
multiplication, and refer students to Example A for a geometric application.

▶ ***EXAMPLE A***

[Language] A *scalar* is a real number, a one-dimensional quantity.

This example illustrates how matrix addition and scalar multiplication can represent translations and dilations of a geometric figure.

EXAMPLE A

This matrix represents a triangle.

$$\begin{bmatrix} -3 & 1 & 2 \\ 2 & 3 & -2 \end{bmatrix}$$

a. Graph the triangle and its image after a translation left 3 units. Write a matrix equation to represent the transformation.

b. Describe the transformation represented by this matrix expression:

$$\begin{bmatrix} -3 & 1 & 2 \\ 2 & 3 & -2 \end{bmatrix} + \begin{bmatrix} -4 & -4 & -4 \\ -3 & -3 & -3 \end{bmatrix}$$

c. Describe the transformation represented by this matrix expression:

$$2 \cdot \begin{bmatrix} -3 & 1 & 2 \\ 2 & 3 & -2 \end{bmatrix}$$

▶ ***Solution***

The original matrix represents a triangle with vertices $(-3, 2)$, $(1, 3)$, and $(2, -2)$.

a. After a translation left 3 units, the x-coordinates of the image are reduced by 3. There is no change to the y-coordinates. You can represent this transformation as a subtraction of two matrices.

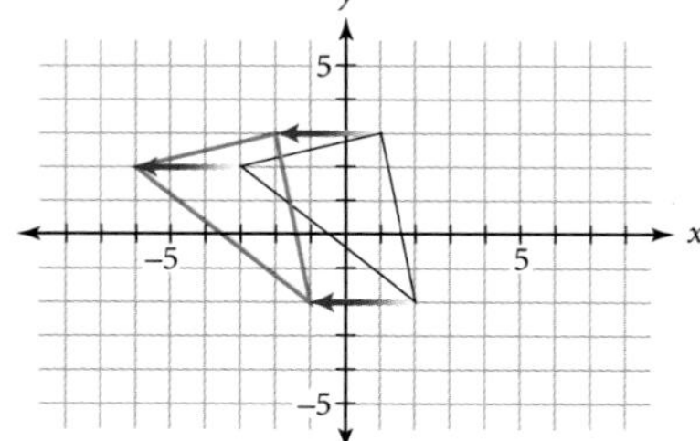

$$\begin{bmatrix} -3 & 1 & 2 \\ 2 & 3 & -2 \end{bmatrix} - \begin{bmatrix} 3 & 3 & 3 \\ 0 & 0 & 0 \end{bmatrix} = \begin{bmatrix} -6 & -2 & -1 \\ 2 & 3 & -2 \end{bmatrix}$$

b. $\begin{bmatrix} -3 & 1 & 2 \\ 2 & 3 & -2 \end{bmatrix} + \begin{bmatrix} -4 & -4 & -4 \\ -3 & -3 & -3 \end{bmatrix} = \begin{bmatrix} -7 & -3 & -2 \\ -1 & 0 & -5 \end{bmatrix}$

This matrix addition represents a translation left 4 units and down 3 units.

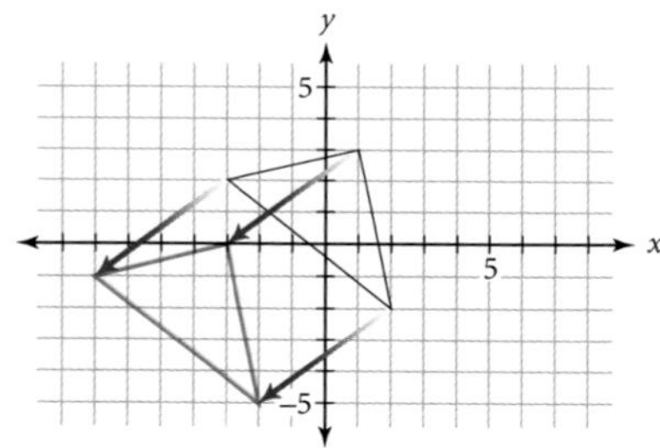

c. $2 \cdot \begin{bmatrix} -3 & 1 & 2 \\ 2 & 3 & -2 \end{bmatrix} = \begin{bmatrix} -3 & 1 & 2 \\ 2 & 3 & -2 \end{bmatrix} + \begin{bmatrix} -3 & 1 & 2 \\ 2 & 3 & -2 \end{bmatrix} = \begin{bmatrix} -6 & 2 & 4 \\ 4 & 6 & -4 \end{bmatrix}$

or

$$2 \cdot \begin{bmatrix} -3 & 1 & 2 \\ 2 & 3 & -2 \end{bmatrix} = \begin{bmatrix} 2 \cdot (-3) & 2 \cdot 1 & 2 \cdot 2 \\ 2 \cdot 2 & 2 \cdot 3 & 2 \cdot (-2) \end{bmatrix} = \begin{bmatrix} -6 & 2 & 4 \\ 4 & 6 & -4 \end{bmatrix}$$

Multiplying a matrix by a number is called **scalar multiplication.** Each entry in the matrix is simply multiplied by the **scalar,** which is 2 in this case.

The resulting matrix represents stretches, both horizontally and vertically, by the scale factor 2. A transformation that stretches or shrinks both horizontally and vertically by the same scale factor is called a **dilation.**

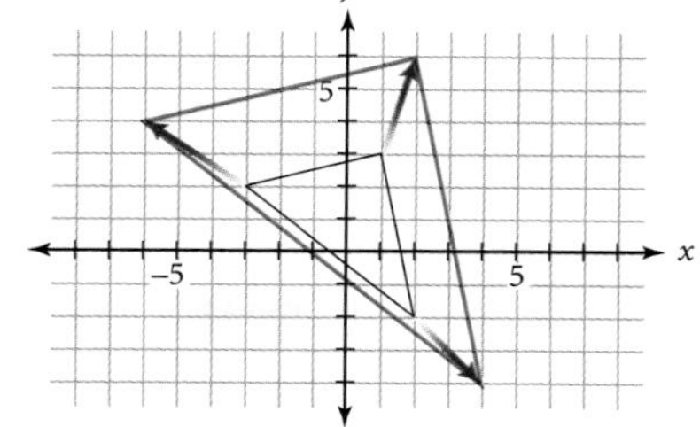

[► See **Calculator Note 6C** to learn how to use your calculator to graph polygons with matrices. ◄]

Addition and scalar multiplication operate on one entry at a time. The multiplication of two matrices is more involved and uses several entries to find one entry of the answer matrix. Recall this problem from the investigation in Lesson 6.1.

EXAMPLE B

The school cafeteria offers a choice of ice cream or frozen yogurt for dessert once a week. During the first week of school, 220 students choose ice cream and 20 choose frozen yogurt. During each of the following weeks, 10% of the frozen-yogurt eaters switch to ice cream and 5% of the ice-cream eaters switch to frozen yogurt. How many students will choose each dessert in the second week? In the third week?

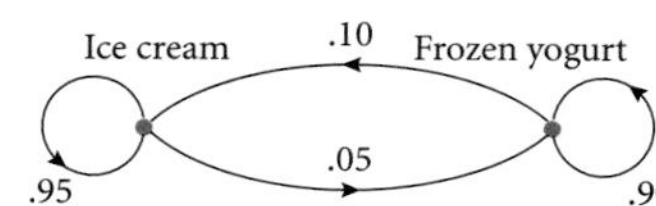

► Solution

You can use this matrix equation to find the answer for the second week:

$$[220 \quad 20]\begin{bmatrix} .95 & .05 \\ .10 & .90 \end{bmatrix} = [\textit{ice cream} \quad \textit{frozen yogurt}]$$

The initial matrix, $[A] = [220 \quad 20]$, represents the original numbers of ice-cream eaters and frozen-yogurt eaters.

In the transition matrix $[B] = \begin{bmatrix} .95 & .05 \\ .10 & .90 \end{bmatrix}$, the top row represents the transitions in the current number of ice-cream eaters, and the bottom row represents the transitions in the current number of frozen-yogurt eaters.

You can define matrix multiplication by looking at how you calculate the numbers for the second week. The second week's number of ice-cream eaters will be $220(.95) + 20(.10)$, or 211 students, because 95% of the 220 original ice-cream eaters don't switch and 10% of the 20 original frozen-yogurt eaters switch to ice cream. In effect, you multiply the two entries in row 1 of $[A]$ by the two entries in column 1 of $[B]$ and add the products. The result, 211, is entry c_{11} in the answer matrix, $[C]$.

Initial matrix		**Transition matrix**		**Answer matrix**
$[A]$	$\cdot$	$[B]$	$=$	$[C]$
$[220 \quad 20]$		$\begin{bmatrix} .95 & .05 \\ .10 & .90 \end{bmatrix}$	$=$	$[211 \quad \textit{frozen yogurt}]$

► EXAMPLE B

This example formalizes matrix multiplication. It shows how to do the multiplication by hand, building on an example from Lesson 6.1. Kinesthetic learners may appreciate seeing how to keep track of the sums of products with their fingers, moving their left hand from left to right on the left matrix one entry at a time while moving their right hand from top to bottom on the right matrix one entry at a time. Even if your curriculum does not explicitly call for manual calculation of matrix products, it's good to spend some time on it so that when students encounter sums of products they will think of multiplying matrices.

When interpreting answers, round off to whole numbers of students. However, if the numbers will be used in a further calculation, do not round off until the end so that the final answer will be as accurate as possible.

[Ask] "Can you calculate the numbers for subsequent weeks recursively on your calculator home screen?" [If the initial matrix is $[A]$ and the transition matrix is $[B]$, then the recursive routine for the fourth week can be $[A]$ (ENTER) * $[B]$ (ENTER) (ENTER) (ENTER). Subsequent weeks can be found by continuing to press (ENTER).] The solution for the fourth week can also be found as $[220 \quad 20]\begin{bmatrix} .95 & .05 \\ .10 & .90 \end{bmatrix}^3$.

Guiding the Investigation

The main objective of the investigation is for students to understand how transition situations work and how the numbers at the various vertices change.

The investigation involves three locations, a good number for about 30 students. For a larger or smaller class size, you might use a four- or two-vertex option. The Find Your Place transparency has information for the two-, three-, and four-vertex models. Push all the furniture into the center of the room and designate a corner of the room for each city. You might want to label each area and have the directions for the next step posted at that area.

Assign students randomly to the cities; you might use the first letter of students' first or last names.

It takes about 10–15 minutes to collect the data.

Step 1 Review how to generate a random number, and make sure students understand the Find Your Place information from the book or the transparency. As needed, **[Ask]** "What would you do if you were in City B and got .984 on the calculator?" [stay in City B] "Where will a person in City C who has generated .252 move?" [to City A]

For dramatic results you might start with one distribution back from the final outcome—that is, with more students in Cities A and C. In the long run, it doesn't matter how many students start out in each location.

Record the initial conditions in a table. Then have each student generate a random number and think about where he or she will go. On a signal have everyone move (or stay) according to the number generated. Add the new numbers to the table. For the first move, you may want to move students from one city at a time to make sure students understand the process.

Likewise, the second week's number of frozen-yogurt eaters will be $220(.05) + 20(.90)$, or 29 students, because 5% of the ice-cream eaters switch to frozen yogurt and 90% of the frozen-yogurt eaters don't switch. The number of frozen-yogurt eaters in the second week is the sum of the products of the entries in row 1 of $[A]$ and column 2 of $[B]$. The answer, 29, is entry c_{12} in the answer matrix, $[C]$.

$$\begin{bmatrix} 220 & 20 \end{bmatrix} \begin{bmatrix} .95 & .05 \\ .10 & .90 \end{bmatrix} = \begin{bmatrix} 211 & 29 \end{bmatrix}$$

To get the numbers for the third week, multiply the result of your previous calculations by the transition matrix again.

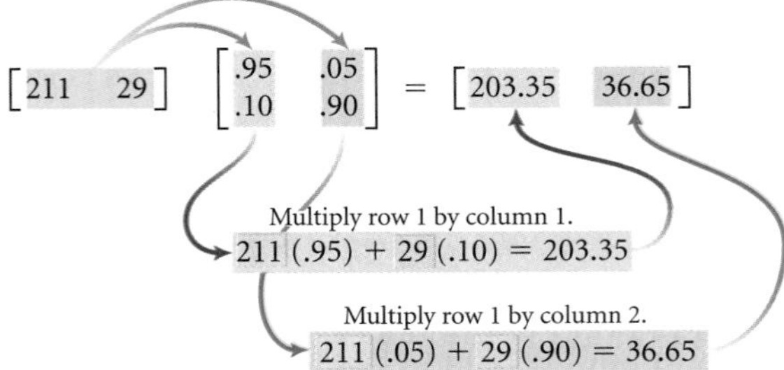

Approximately 203 students will choose ice cream and 37 will choose frozen yogurt in the next week.

You can continue multiplying to find the numbers in the fourth week, the fifth week, and so on. [▶ Revisit **Calculator Note 6B** to learn how to multiply matrices on your calculator. ◀]

In the investigation you will model a real-world situation with matrices. You'll also practice multiplying matrices.

Investigation
Find Your Place

In this investigation you will simulate the weekly movement of rental cars between cities and analyze the results.

Each person represents a rental car starting at City A, City B, or City C.

The procedure says to repeat several times; ten is a good number of rounds. If the numbers haven't stabilized into long-run values and you have time, you might try a few more rounds.

Step 1 Simulation results will vary. The answers for Steps 2–5 give theoretical results for the three-vertex model.

Step 1 In a table, record the number of cars that start in each city. Follow the Procedure Note to simulate the movement of cars.

> **Procedure Note**
>
> **Rental Car Simulation**
>
> 1. Use your calculator to generate a random number, x, between 0 and 1. [▶ See **Calculator Note 1L** to learn how to generate random numbers. ◀] Determine your location for next week as follows:
>   a. If you are at City A, move to City B if $x \leq .2$, move to City C if $.2 < x \leq .7$, or stay at City A if $x > .7$.
>   b. If you are at City B, move to City A if $x \leq .5$, or stay at City B if $x > .5$.
>   c. If you are at City C, move to City B if $x \leq .1$, move to City A if $.1 < x \leq .3$, or stay at City C if $x > .3$.
> 2. Record the number of cars in each city in your table. Repeat the simulation up to 10 times. Each time, record the number of cars in each city.

Step 2 Work with your group to make a transition diagram and a transition matrix that represent the rules of the simulation.

Step 3 Write an initial condition matrix for the starting quantities at each city. Then, show how to multiply the initial condition matrix and the transition matrix for the first transition. How do these theoretical results for week 1 compare with the experimental data from your simulation?

Step 4 Use your calculator to find the theoretical number of cars in each city for the next four weeks. Find the theoretical long-run values of the number of cars in each city.

Step 5 Compare these results with the experimental values in your table. If they are not similar, explain why.

Just as only some matrices can be added (those with the same dimensions), only some matrices can be multiplied. Example C and Exercise 3 will help you explore the kinds of matrices that can be multiplied.

American artist Robert Silvers (b 1968) combined thousands of worldwide money images in a matrix-like arrangement to create this piece titled *Washington*.

Step 2

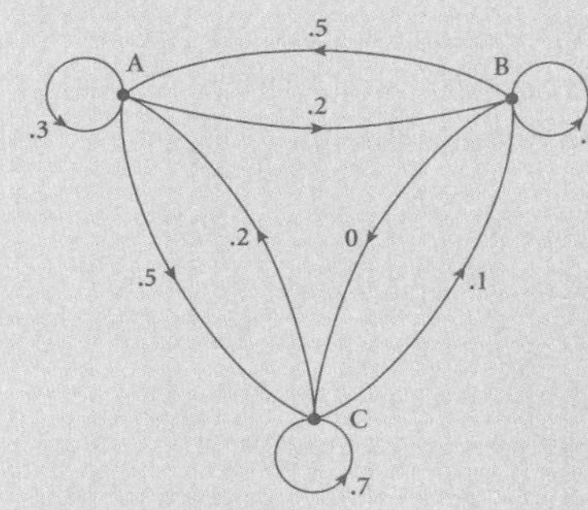

$$\begin{bmatrix} .3 & .2 & .5 \\ .5 & .5 & 0 \\ .2 & .1 & .7 \end{bmatrix}$$

Steps 3–5 [Language] In this context, *theoretical* describes the result based on the mathematical model, and *experimental* describes the numbers from the simulation.

Step 3 Sample data: $[15 \quad 10 \quad 5]$.

$$[15 \quad 10 \quad 5]\begin{bmatrix} .3 & .2 & .5 \\ .5 & .5 & 0 \\ .2 & .1 & .7 \end{bmatrix} =$$

$[10.5 \quad 8.5 \quad 11]$; answers will vary.

Step 4 This is recursion. Although entering a small matrix into a calculator may take longer than doing the matrix operations by hand, this step is intended to help students learn to use calculators for matrices. Also, finding long-run values is much easier with home-screen recursion on a calculator. **[Ask]** "What will happen to the theoretical long-run values if you start with different numbers in each city?" [The long-run values will be the same.] **[Alert]** Student answers may contain fractions. As needed remind them that cars must be whole numbers.

Step 4 week 2: $[9.6 \quad 7.45 \quad 12.95]$
week 3: $[9.195 \quad 6.94 \quad 13.865]$
week 4: $[9.0015 \quad 6.6955 \quad 14.303]$
week 5: $[8.9088 \quad 6.57835 \quad 14.51285]$
long-run value: $[9 \quad 6 \quad 15]$

As a percentage of the entire class, the results are about [30% 20% 50%].

Step 5 Answers will vary. The theoretical results may not be very close to the experimental results because the number of students is relatively small, the number of iterations is small, and randomness is involved.

EXAMPLE C Consider this product.

$$\begin{bmatrix} -1 & 0 \\ 0 & 1 \end{bmatrix}\begin{bmatrix} -3 & 1 & 2 \\ 2 & 3 & -2 \end{bmatrix}$$

a. Determine the dimensions of the answer to this product.

b. Describe how to calculate entries in the answer.

▶ Solution

a. To multiply two matrices, you multiply each entry in a row of the first matrix by each entry in a column of the second matrix.

You can multiply a 2 × 2 matrix by a 2 × 3 matrix because the inside dimensions are the same—the 2 row entries match up with the 2 column entries.

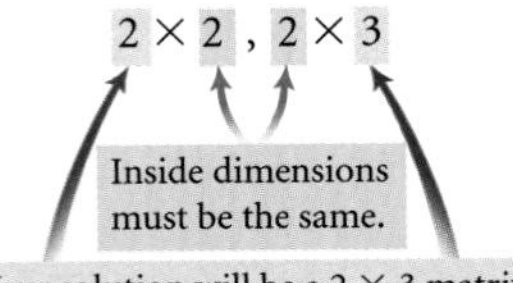

The outside dimensions tell you the dimensions of your answer.

The answer to this product has dimensions 2 × 3.

$$\begin{bmatrix} -1 & 0 \\ 0 & 1 \end{bmatrix}\begin{bmatrix} -3 & 1 & 2 \\ 2 & 3 & -2 \end{bmatrix} = \begin{bmatrix} c_{11} & c_{12} & c_{13} \\ c_{21} & c_{22} & c_{23} \end{bmatrix}$$

b. To find the values of entries in the first row of your solution matrix, you add the products of the entries in the first row of the first matrix and the entries in the columns of the second matrix.

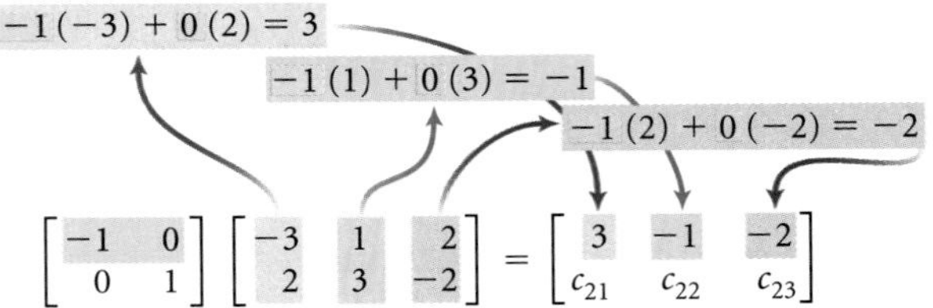

To find the values of entries in the second row of your solution matrix, you add the products of the entries in the second row of the first matrix and the entries in the columns of the second matrix.

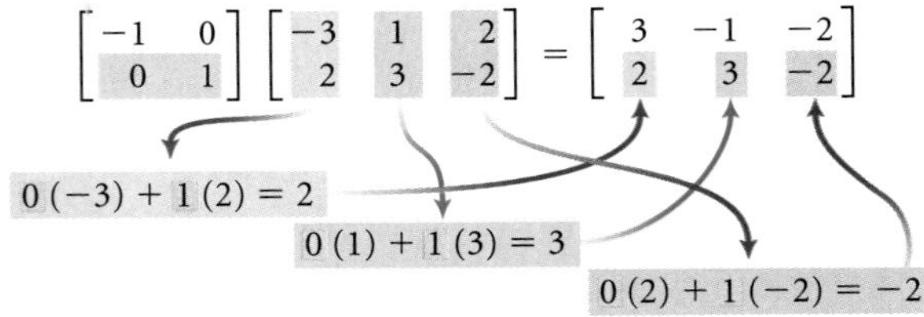

The product is

$$\begin{bmatrix} 3 & -1 & -2 \\ 2 & 3 & -2 \end{bmatrix}$$

▶ EXAMPLE C

You may want students to practice multiplying these matrices together by hand before they use a calculator.

SHARING IDEAS

As students present, wonder aloud whether the same long-run values really come up no matter what the starting configuration. Some students will find this surprising and will argue against it. Encourage discussion by not stopping or declaring a statement right when a student says something you agree with. Focus on the way the discussion is unfolding rather than on the answers students are coming up with.

[Ask] "Can you shrink an object in only the x direction using matrices?" [Multiplying on the right by the matrix $\begin{bmatrix} k & 0 \\ 0 & 1 \end{bmatrix}$ accomplishes a horizontal stretch or shrink.]

[Ask] "Are these matrix operations just like operations on numbers?" Bring out the notion that addition and scalar multiplication are commutative and can be "undone" but that matrix multiplication is not commutative. Wonder aloud whether matrices have "reciprocals" and whether multiplication is distributive over addition. Leave these questions unanswered until later.

Ask whether students know how calculators generate random numbers. Suggest that everyone enter the same number into a calculator as a "seed." On Texas Instrument calculators (see Calculator Note 1L), you can enter a seed such as 0.3 by entering 0.3 (STO→) *rand*. Then have everyone enter *rand* (ENTER) (ENTER) (ENTER) . . . and compare results. They will all be the same. Calculators don't really generate random numbers but rather follow a fixed pattern. They're said to generate *pseudorandom* numbers. However, because the seed is replaced by the latest random number generated, at any time different calculators will probably be generating different numbers.

The following definitions review the matrix operations you've learned in this lesson.

Matrix Operations

Matrix Addition

To add matrices, you add corresponding entries.

$$\begin{bmatrix} 2 & 3 \\ -1 & 0 \end{bmatrix} + \begin{bmatrix} -1 & 2 \\ 1 & 4 \end{bmatrix} = \begin{bmatrix} 1 & 5 \\ 0 & 4 \end{bmatrix}$$

$-1 + 1 = 0$

You can add only matrices that have the same dimension.

Scalar Multiplication

To multiply a scalar by a matrix, you multiply the scalar by each value in a matrix.

$$3 \cdot \begin{bmatrix} 2 & -1 \\ 1 & 3 \\ 0 & -2 \end{bmatrix} = \begin{bmatrix} 6 & -3 \\ 3 & 9 \\ 0 & -6 \end{bmatrix}$$

$3(-2) = -6$

Matrix Multiplication

To multiply two matrices, $[A]$ and $[B]$, you multiply each entry in a row of matrix $[A]$ by corresponding entries in a column of matrix $[B]$.

$$\begin{bmatrix} 0 & -1 \\ 2 & 1 \end{bmatrix} \begin{bmatrix} 3 & -2 & 4 \\ 0 & -3 & 5 \end{bmatrix} = \begin{bmatrix} 0 & 3 & -5 \\ 6 & -7 & 13 \end{bmatrix}$$

$2(-2) + 1(-3) = -7$

Entry c_{ij} in the answer matrix, $[C]$, represents the sum of the products of each entry in row i of the first matrix and the entry in the corresponding position in column j of the second matrix. The number of entries in a row of matrix $[A]$ must equal the number of entries in a column of matrix $[B]$. That is, the inside dimensions must be equal. The answer matrix will have the same number of rows as matrix $[A]$ and the same number of columns as matrix $[B]$, or the outside dimensions.

EXERCISES

Practice Your Skills

1. Look back at the calculations in Example B. Calculate how many students will choose each dessert in the fourth week by multiplying these matrices:

$$[203.35 \quad 36.65]\begin{bmatrix} .95 & .05 \\ .10 & .90 \end{bmatrix} = [\textit{ice cream} \quad \textit{frozen yogurt}]$$

1. [196.85 43.15]; 197 students will choose ice cream, 43 will choose frozen yogurt.

Assessing Progress

You can check students' understanding of transition diagrams and transition matrices. You can also assess their ability to find random numbers and to check numbers against inequalities.

Closing the Lesson

Two matrices of the same dimensions can be **added** or **subtracted** by adding or subtracting corresponding entries. The **scalar product** of a number by a matrix is the matrix whose entries are the number times the entries of the original matrix. In **matrix multiplication,** to get the entry a_{ij} of the result you take the sum of products of corresponding entries of row i of the first matrix and column j of the second matrix. Unlike matrix addition and scalar multiplication, matrix multiplication is not commutative.

BUILDING UNDERSTANDING

The exercises give students practice with operations on matrices in both abstract and applied settings.

ASSIGNING HOMEWORK

Essential	1–4
Performance assessment	5–10, 12, 13
Portfolio	13, 14
Journal	5, 10
Group	11–13
Review	14–17

Helping with the Exercises

2a. $x = 7, y = 54$

2b. $c_{11} = 0.815, c_{12} = 0.185, c_{21} = 0.0925, c_{22} = 0.9075$

2c. $a = 15.6, b = -10.8, c = 10.7, d = 42.2$

2d. $m_{11} = 180, m_{12} = -230, m_{21} = 54, m_{22} = 322$

2e. $a = -5, b = 57, c = 44.5, d = 78$

[ESL] A *quadriplegic* is a person affected with paralysis of both arms and both legs.

5a.

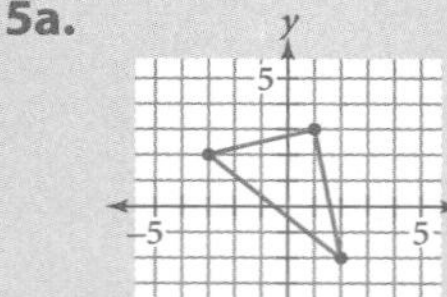

5c.

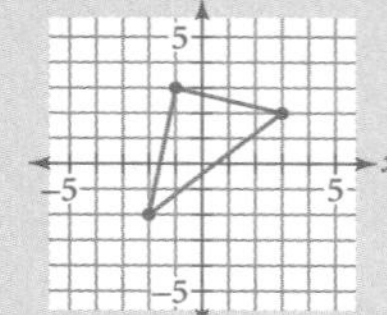

2. Find the missing values.

a. $[13 \quad 23] + [-6 \quad 31] = [x \quad y]$

b. $\begin{bmatrix} .90 & .10 \\ .05 & .95 \end{bmatrix}\begin{bmatrix} .90 & .10 \\ .05 & .95 \end{bmatrix} = \begin{bmatrix} c_{11} & c_{12} \\ c_{21} & c_{22} \end{bmatrix}$

c. $\begin{bmatrix} 18 & -23 \\ 5.4 & 32.2 \end{bmatrix} + \begin{bmatrix} -2.4 & 12.2 \\ 5.3 & 10 \end{bmatrix} = \begin{bmatrix} a & b \\ c & d \end{bmatrix}$

d. $10 \cdot \begin{bmatrix} 18 & -23 \\ 5.4 & 32.2 \end{bmatrix} = \begin{bmatrix} m_{11} & m_{12} \\ m_{21} & m_{22} \end{bmatrix}$

e. $\begin{bmatrix} 7 & -4 \\ 18 & 28 \end{bmatrix} + 5 \cdot \begin{bmatrix} -2.4 & 12.2 \\ 5.3 & 10 \end{bmatrix} = \begin{bmatrix} a & b \\ c & d \end{bmatrix}$

American painter Chuck Close (b 1940) creates photo realistic portraits by painting a matrix-like grid of rectangular cells. Close is a quadriplegic and paints with a mouth brush. This portrait is from 1992.

Janet by Chuck Close, oil on canvas, 102 x 84 in.

3. Perform matrix arithmetic in 3a–f. If a particular operation is impossible, explain why.

a. $\begin{bmatrix} 1 & 2 \\ 3 & -2 \\ 0 & 1 \end{bmatrix}\begin{bmatrix} -3 & -1 & 2 \\ 5 & 2 & -1 \end{bmatrix}$ $\begin{bmatrix} 7 & 3 & 0 \\ -19 & -7 & 8 \\ 5 & 2 & -1 \end{bmatrix}$

b. $\begin{bmatrix} 1 & -2 \\ 6 & 3 \end{bmatrix} + \begin{bmatrix} -3 & 7 \\ 2 & 4 \end{bmatrix}$ $\begin{bmatrix} -2 & 5 \\ 8 & 7 \end{bmatrix}$

c. $[5 \quad -2 \quad 7]\begin{bmatrix} -2 & 3 \\ -1 & 0 \\ 3 & 2 \end{bmatrix}$ $[13 \quad 29]$

d. $\begin{bmatrix} 3 & -8 & 10 & 2 \\ -1 & 2 & 3 & 4 \end{bmatrix}\begin{bmatrix} 2 & -5 & 3 & 12 \\ 8 & -4 & 0 & 2 \end{bmatrix}$
not possible because the inside dimensions do not match

e. $\begin{bmatrix} 3 & 6 \\ -4 & 1 \end{bmatrix} - \begin{bmatrix} -1 & 7 \\ -8 & 3 \end{bmatrix}$ $\begin{bmatrix} 4 & -1 \\ 4 & -2 \end{bmatrix}$

f. $\begin{bmatrix} 4 & 11 \\ 7 & 3 \\ 4 & 2 \end{bmatrix} + \begin{bmatrix} 3 & -2 & 7 \\ 5 & 0 & 2 \end{bmatrix}$
not possible because the dimensions aren't the same

4. Find matrix $[B]$ such that

$$\begin{bmatrix} 8 & -5 & 4.5 \\ -6 & 9.5 & 5 \end{bmatrix} - [B] = \begin{bmatrix} 5 & -1 & 2 \\ -4 & 3.5 & 1 \end{bmatrix} \quad \begin{bmatrix} 3 & -4 & 2.5 \\ -2 & 6 & 4 \end{bmatrix}$$

Reason and Apply

5. This matrix represents a triangle:

$$\begin{bmatrix} -3 & 1 & 2 \\ 2 & 3 & -2 \end{bmatrix}$$

a. Graph the triangle.

b. Find the result of this matrix multiplication:

$$\begin{bmatrix} -1 & 0 \\ 0 & 1 \end{bmatrix}\begin{bmatrix} -3 & 1 & 2 \\ 2 & 3 & -2 \end{bmatrix} \quad \begin{bmatrix} 3 & -1 & -2 \\ 2 & 3 & -2 \end{bmatrix}$$

c. Graph the image represented by the matrix in 5b.

d. Describe the transformation. The original triangle is reflected across the y-axis.

7a.

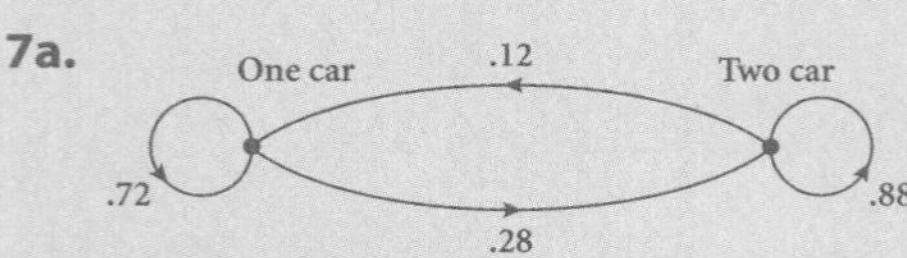

7d. $[4800 \quad 4200]\begin{bmatrix} .72 & .28 \\ .12 & .88 \end{bmatrix} = [3960 \quad 5040]$

8a. $[A][B] = \begin{bmatrix} 6 & 2 \\ -3 & -6 \end{bmatrix}$; $[B][A] = \begin{bmatrix} 2 & 13 \\ 2 & -2 \end{bmatrix}$.

They are not the same.

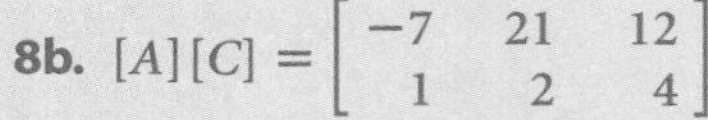

8b. $[A][C] = \begin{bmatrix} -7 & 21 & 12 \\ 1 & 2 & 4 \end{bmatrix}$; you cannot multiply $[C][A]$. In order for both $[A][C]$ and $[C][A]$ to exist, both would have to be square matrices.

8c. $[A][D] = \begin{bmatrix} 2 & 3 \\ -1 & 1 \end{bmatrix}$; $[D][A] = \begin{bmatrix} 2 & 3 \\ -1 & 1 \end{bmatrix}$.

They are the same and equal to $[A]$. Multiplying by $[D]$ does not change $[A]$.

6. Find matrix $[A]$ and matrix $[C]$ such that the triangle represented by

$$[T] = \begin{bmatrix} -3 & 1 & 2 \\ 2 & 3 & -2 \end{bmatrix}$$

matrix $[T]$ is reflected across the x-axis.

$$\begin{bmatrix} a_{11} & a_{12} \\ a_{21} & a_{22} \end{bmatrix}\begin{bmatrix} -3 & 1 & 2 \\ 2 & 3 & -2 \end{bmatrix} = \begin{bmatrix} c_{11} & c_{12} & c_{13} \\ c_{21} & c_{22} & c_{23} \end{bmatrix}$$

$[A] = \begin{bmatrix} 1 & 0 \\ 0 & -1 \end{bmatrix}$; $[C] = \begin{bmatrix} -3 & 1 & 2 \\ -2 & -3 & 2 \end{bmatrix}$

7. Of two-car families in a small city, 88% remain two-car families in the following year and 12% become one-car families in the following year. Of one-car families, 72% remain one-car families and 28% become two-car families. Suppose these trends continue for a few years. At present, 4800 families have one car and 4200 have two cars.

a. Draw a transition diagram that displays this information.

b. What matrix represents the present situation? Let a_{11} represent one-car families that remain one-car families.

c. Write a transition matrix that represents the same information as your transition diagram.

d. Write a matrix equation to find the numbers of one-car and two-car families one year from now.

e. Find the numbers of one-car and two-car families two years from now. [3456 5544]

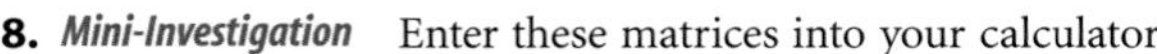

8. ***Mini-Investigation*** Enter these matrices into your calculator.

$$[A] = \begin{bmatrix} 2 & 3 \\ -1 & 1 \end{bmatrix} \quad [B] = \begin{bmatrix} 3 & 4 \\ 0 & -2 \end{bmatrix} \quad [C] = \begin{bmatrix} -2 & 3 & 0 \\ -1 & 5 & 4 \end{bmatrix} \quad [D] = \begin{bmatrix} 1 & 0 \\ 0 & 1 \end{bmatrix}$$

See page 314 for 8a–c.

a. Find $[A][B]$ and $[B][A]$. Are they the same?

b. Find $[A][C]$ and $[C][A]$. Are they the same? What do you notice?

c. Find $[A][D]$ and $[D][A]$. Are they the same? What do you notice?

d. Is matrix multiplication commutative? That is, does order matter?

9. Find the missing values.

a. $\begin{bmatrix} 2 & a \\ b & -1 \end{bmatrix}\begin{bmatrix} 5 \\ 3 \end{bmatrix} = \begin{bmatrix} 19 \\ 17 \end{bmatrix}$ $a = 3, b = 4$

b. $\begin{bmatrix} a & -2 \\ 3 & 1 \end{bmatrix}\begin{bmatrix} -3 \\ b \end{bmatrix} = \begin{bmatrix} -29 \\ -5 \end{bmatrix}$ $a = 7, b = 4$

10. Recall the ice cream and frozen yogurt problem from Example B. Enter these matrices into your calculator, and use them to find the long-run values for the number of students who choose ice cream and the number of those who choose frozen yogurt. Explain why your answer makes sense.

$$[A] = [220 \quad 20] \qquad [B] = \begin{bmatrix} .95 & .05 \\ .10 & .90 \end{bmatrix}$$

11. A spider is in a building with three rooms. The spider moves from room to room by choosing a door at random. If the spider starts in room 1 initially, what is the probability that it will be in room 1 again after four room changes? What happens to the probabilities in the long run?

Exercise 6 This exercise relies on Exercise 5. As needed, encourage students to plot the final image, describe the transformation, and then find matrix $[A]$.

Exercise 7 You might **[Ask]** "Are there long-run values for one- and two-car families?" [Long-run values appear to be 2700 and 6300.]

7b. [4800 4200]

7c. $\begin{bmatrix} .72 & .28 \\ .12 & .88 \end{bmatrix}$

Answers to 7a and 7d are on page 314.

Exercise 8d You may need to remind students of the meaning of *commutative.* For an operation to be commutative, the order in which it is applied to any two elements doesn't matter. A good mathematical question here is "Under what conditions on matrices $[A]$ and $[B]$ does $[A][B]$ equal $[B][A]$"?

8d. No, matrix multiplication is generally not commutative. Order does matter.

Exercise 9 This exercise requires students to multiply matrices by hand.

Exercise 10 These matrices come from Example B. Students can look back at the example to find the meaning of the entries in matrices $[A]$ and $[B]$.

10. [160 80]. An equilibrium is reached because 10% of 80 students is the same as 5% of 160 students.

Exercise 11 This is a challenging problem. Though this is the first mention of probability in the student book, most students will be familiar enough with the ideas that they won't need a review. But they may have trouble understanding what matrices to use. Suggest that students start with a transition diagram, write a matrix, and raise it to the power of 4.

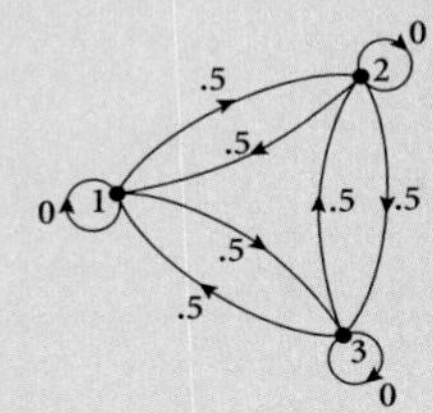

By raising the matrix to a higher power, such as 30 or 40, students will see the long-run value.

11. The probability that the spider is in room 1 after four room changes is .375. The long-run probabilities for rooms 1, 2, and 3 are $[.\overline{3} \quad .\overline{3} \quad .\overline{3}]$.

Exercise 12 Students may find this exercise easier if they've worked on Exercise 10 first.

12a. $\begin{bmatrix} .5 & .45 & .05 \\ .25 & .5 & .25 \\ .3 & .3 & .4 \end{bmatrix}$

12. APPLICATION A researcher studies the birth weights of women and their daughters. The weights were split into three categories: low (below 6 lb), average (between 6 and 8 lb), and high (above 8 lb). This transition diagram shows how birth weights changed from mother to daughter.

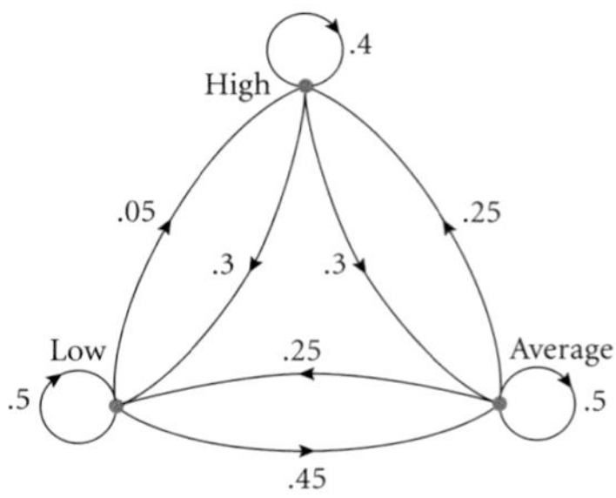

a. Write a transition matrix that represents the same information as the diagram. Put the rows and columns in the order low, average, high.

b. Assume the changes in birth weights can be applied to any generation. If, in the initial generation of women, 25% had birth weights in the low category, 60% in the average category, and 15% in the high category, what were the percentages after one generation? After two generations? After three generations? In the long run? See below.

MAKING THE CONNECTION

[Ask] "How many products can a manufacturer have?" [100,000] "How many manufacturers can be in the system?" [1,000,000] "Does this seem reasonable? Does the bar code on your math book follow the pattern?" Students might be interested to know that it is possible to decipher the numerical code by "reading" the bars. Students can find out about this through links at www.keymath.com.

Consumer CONNECTION

You can find a Universal Product Code, or UPC, symbol on almost every mass-produced product. The symbol consists of vertical lines with a sequence of 12 numbers below them. The lines are readable to a scanning device as numbers. The first six digits represent the manufacturer and the next five represent the specific product. The last digit is a check digit so that when the item is scanned, the computer can verify the correctness of the number before searching its database to get the price. In order to verify the code, each digit in an odd position is multiplied by 3. These products are then added with the digits in the even positions (including the check digit). The check digit is chosen so that this sum is divisible by 10.

13. APPLICATION Read the Consumer Connection about Universal Product Codes and answer these questions.

a. Write a 12×1 matrix that can be multiplied on the left by a UPC to find the sum of each digit in an even position and 3 times each digit in an odd position.

b. Use the matrix from 13a to check the following four UPCs. Which one(s) are valid?

$$\begin{bmatrix} 0 & 3 & 6 & 2 & 0 & 0 & 0 & 0 & 4 & 0 & 0 & 5 \\ 0 & 7 & 6 & 1 & 0 & 7 & 0 & 2 & 2 & 3 & 3 & 6 \\ 0 & 7 & 4 & 2 & 2 & 0 & 0 & 0 & 2 & 9 & 1 & 8 \\ 0 & 8 & 5 & 3 & 9 & 1 & 7 & 8 & 6 & 2 & 2 & 1 \end{bmatrix}$$

c. For the invalid UPC(s), what should the check digit have been so that it is a valid code?

13a. $\begin{bmatrix} 3 \\ 1 \\ 3 \\ 1 \\ 3 \\ 1 \\ 3 \\ 1 \\ 3 \\ 1 \\ 3 \\ 1 \end{bmatrix}$

13b. The first and last UPCs are valid.

13c. For the second code, the check digit should be 7. For the third code, the check digit should be 5.

12b. after one generation:
[32% 45.75% 22.25%];
after two generations:
[34.1125% 43.95% 21.9375%];
after three generations:
[34.625% 43.906875% 21.468125%];
in the long run:
[34.74903475% 44.01544402% 21.23552124%]

Review

3.7 **14.** ***Mini-Investigation*** A system of equations that has at least one solution is called **consistent.** A system of equations that has no solutions is called **inconsistent.** A system with infinitely many solutions is called **dependent.** A system of equations that has exactly one solution is called **independent.** Follow the steps in 14a–g to make some discoveries about inconsistent and dependent systems.

a. Graph each of the following systems of linear equations. Use your graphs to identify each system as consistent, inconsistent, dependent, and/or independent.

i. $\begin{cases} y = 0.7x + 8 \\ y = 1.1x - 7 \end{cases}$ **ii.** $\begin{cases} y = \frac{3}{4}x - 4 \\ y = 0.75x + 3 \end{cases}$ **iii.** $\begin{cases} 4x + 6y = 9 \\ 1.2x + 1.8y = 4.7 \end{cases}$

iv. $\begin{cases} \frac{3}{4}x - \frac{1}{2}y = 4 \\ 0.75x + 0.5y = 3 \end{cases}$ **v.** $\begin{cases} y = 1.2x + 3 \\ y = 1.2x - 1 \end{cases}$ **vi.** $\begin{cases} y = \frac{1}{4}(2x - 1) \\ y = 0.5x - 0.25 \end{cases}$

vii. $\begin{cases} 4x + 6y = 9 \\ 1.2x + 1.8y = 2.7 \end{cases}$ **viii.** $\begin{cases} \frac{3}{5}x - \frac{2}{5}y = 3 \\ 0.6x + 0.4y = 3 \end{cases}$ **ix.** $\begin{cases} x + y = 1 \\ 2x + 2y = 2 \end{cases}$

b. Describe the graphs of the equations of the inconsistent systems.

c. Try to solve each inconsistent system by substitution or by elimination. Show your steps. Describe the outcome of your attempts.

d. How can you recognize an inconsistent linear system without graphing it?

e. Describe the graphs of equations of consistent and dependent systems.

f. Try to solve each consistent and dependent system by substitution or by elimination. Show your steps. Describe the outcome of your attempt.

g. How can you recognize a consistent and dependent linear system without graphing it?

3.3 **15.** For each segment shown in the figure at right, write an equation in point-slope form for the line that contains the segment. Check your equations by graphing them on your calculator.

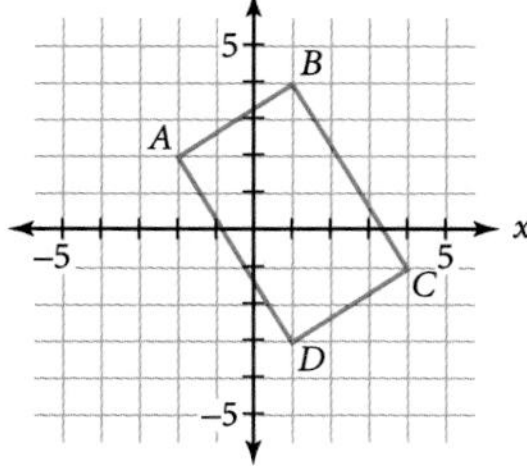

5.7 **16.** If $\log_p x = a$ and $\log_p y = b$, find

a. $\log_p xy$ $a + b$ **b.** $\log_p x^3$ $3a$ **c.** $\log_p \frac{y^2}{x}$ $2b - a$

d. $\log_{p^2} y$ $\frac{1}{2}b$ **e.** $\log_p \sqrt{x}$ $\frac{1}{2}a$ **f.** $\log_m xy$ $\frac{a + b}{\log_p m}$

3.7 **17.** Solve this system of equations for *x*, *y*, and *z*.

$\begin{cases} x + 2y + z = 0 \\ 3x - 4y + 5z = -11 \\ -2x - 8y - 3z = 1 \end{cases}$ $x = 2, y = \frac{1}{2}, z = -3$

Exercise 14 This exercise introduces important terminology: *consistent, inconsistent, dependent,* and *independent* systems of equations. You might want to discuss these terms with your class.

14b. The graphs of inconsistent linear systems are parallel lines.

14c. When you try to solve an inconsistent system, you reach a false statement, such as $-4 = 3$.

14d. You can recognize an inconsistent linear system without graphing it because the equations have the same slope but different intercepts.

14e. The graphs of consistent and dependent linear systems are the same line.

14f. When you try to solve a consistent and dependent system, you get a true but useless statement, such as $0 = 0$.

14g. The lines in a consistent and dependent linear system have the same slope and the same intercept, or the equations are multiples of each other.

15. $\overline{CD}$: $y = -3 + \frac{2}{3}(x - 1)$ or $y = -1 + \frac{2}{3}(x - 4)$; $\overline{AB}$: $y = 2 + \frac{2}{3}(x + 2)$ or $y = 4 + \frac{2}{3}(x - 1)$; $\overline{AD}$: $y = 2 - \frac{5}{3}(x + 2)$ or $y = -3 - \frac{5}{3}(x - 1)$; $\overline{BC}$: $y = 4 - \frac{5}{3}(x - 1)$ or $y = -1 - \frac{5}{3}(x - 4)$

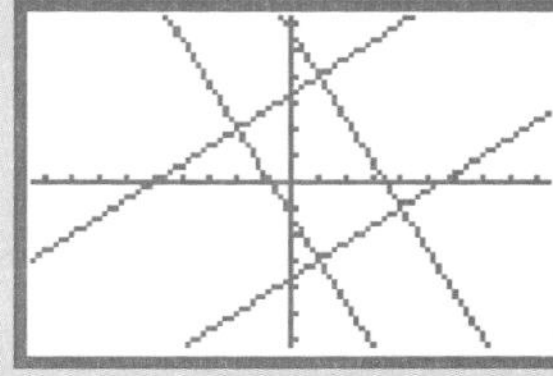

[−9.4, 9.4, 1, −6.2, 6.2, 1]

Exercise 16 To "find" means to write the expression in terms of *a* and/or *b*, except in 16f, where "find" means to write it in terms of *m*, *p*, *a*, and *b*. **[Alert]** Students may have difficulty with 16d and 16f. The solution to 16f can also be written as $(a + b)\log_m p$.

Exercise 17 This task is meant to be difficult so students will appreciate the ease of using matrices to solve systems of equations in Lesson 6.3. Urge students to be systematic, eliminating one variable entirely to get two equations with two unknowns.

EXTENSIONS

A. Ask students to write their own transition-matrix problem.

B. Ask students to explore whether matrix multiplication is distributive over matrix addition.

See page 887 for answer to Exercise 14a.

LESSON

6.3

PLANNING

LESSON OUTLINE

First day:

15 min Example A

20 min Investigation

10 min Exercises

Second day:

10 min Investigation

10 min Example B

10 min Sharing

15 min Exercises

MATERIALS

- Calculator Notes 6D, 6E

TEACHING

Though the inverse-matrix method presented in Lesson 6.4 is quicker using calculators, the row-reduction method in this lesson is similar to the method for solving systems of equations and may be more intuitive. This method is also known as *Gauss-Jordan elimination* or *Gaussian elimination.* You might skip this lesson; students will not use the information later in the book.

One Step

Pose this problem: "Jenny earns \$15.40 per hour, but she earns time and a half for working past 8:00 P.M. Last week she worked 35 hours and earned \$600.60. How many hours past 8:00 P.M. did she work?" Have the class set up a system of equations. Show how to represent the system with an augmented matrix. Then ask students to solve the system, changing the matrix to represent the changing system of equations. Ask what rules might be applied in order to solve the system using only the matrix.

LESSON 6.3

Row Reduction Method

Rather than denying problems, focus inventively, intentionally on what solutions might look or feel like . . .

MARSHA SINETAR

In Chapter 3, you learned how to solve systems of equations using elimination. You added equations, sometimes first multiplying both sides by a convenient factor, to reduce the system to an equation in one variable. In this lesson you will learn how to use matrices to simplify this elimination method for solving systems of equations, especially when you have more than two variables.

Any system of equations in standard form can be written as a matrix equation. For example

$$\begin{cases} 2x + y = 5 \\ 5x + 3y = 13 \end{cases}$$ The original system.

$$\begin{bmatrix} 2x + y \\ 5x + 3y \end{bmatrix} = \begin{bmatrix} 5 \\ 13 \end{bmatrix}$$ Rewrite with matrices.

$$\begin{bmatrix} 2 & 1 \\ 5 & 3 \end{bmatrix}\begin{bmatrix} x \\ y \end{bmatrix} = \begin{bmatrix} 5 \\ 13 \end{bmatrix}$$ The product $\begin{bmatrix} 2 & 1 \\ 5 & 3 \end{bmatrix}\begin{bmatrix} x \\ y \end{bmatrix}$ is equivalent to $\begin{bmatrix} 2x + y \\ 5x + 3y \end{bmatrix}$.

You can also write the system as an **augmented matrix,** which is a single matrix that contains a column for the coefficients of each variable and a final column for the constant terms.

$$\begin{cases} 2x + y = 5 \\ 5x + 3y = 13 \end{cases} \rightarrow \left[\begin{array}{cc|c} 2 & 1 & 5 \\ 5 & 3 & 13 \end{array}\right]$$

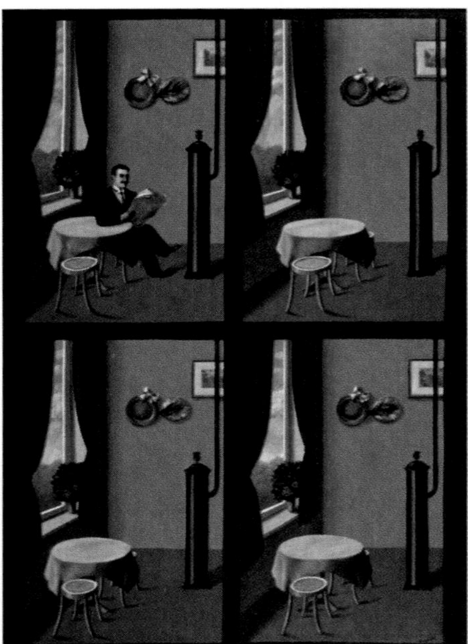

In this piece by Belgian painter René Magritte (1898–1967), a man appears in one frame, but he is "eliminated" from the others.

Man with a Newspaper (1928) by René Magritte, oil on canvas

You can use the augmented matrix to carry out a process similar to elimination.

The **row reduction method** transforms an augmented matrix into a solution matrix. Instead of combining equations and multiples of equations until you are left with an equation in one variable, you add multiples of rows to other rows until you obtain the solution matrix. A solution matrix contains the solution to the system in the last column. The rest of the matrix consists of 1's along the main diagonal and 0's above and below it.

This augmented matrix represents the system

$$\begin{cases} 1x + 0y = a \\ 0x + 1y = b \end{cases}, \text{ or } x = a \text{ and } y = b.$$

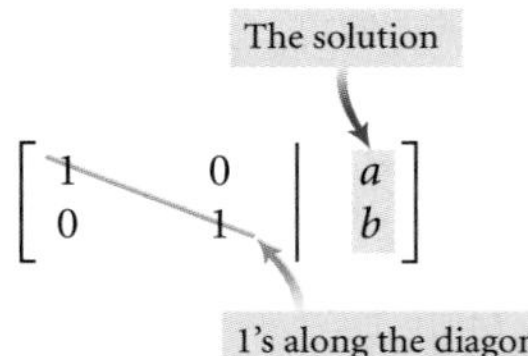

This matrix is in **reduced row-echelon form** because each row is reduced to a 1 and a solution, and the rest of the matrix entries are 0's. The 1's are in echelon, or step, form. The ordered pair (a, b) is the solution to the system.

If groups ask how to keep the matrix the same size after an equation is eliminated, suggest that they just leave in a row representing either of the original equations. During Sharing, have the class formalize the rules, and introduce the terms *row reduction* and *reduced row-echelon form.* Have the class explore how to do row reduction on a calculator and apply their skills to a system such as the one in Example B.

Introduction

[Language] *Augment* means "increase," and an *echelon* is a ladder or a formation resembling stairs.

[Alert] Some students will not realize that in the equation $2x + y = 5$ the coefficient of y is 1. Underlying the matrix equation is the idea that matrices are equal if all of their corresponding entries are equal.

An augmented matrix represents a system of equations, so the same rules apply to row operations in a matrix as to equations in a system of equations.

Row Operations in a Matrix

- You can multiply (or divide) all numbers in a row by a nonzero number.
- You can add all numbers in a row to corresponding numbers in another row.
- You can add a multiple of the numbers in one row to the corresponding numbers in another row.
- You can exchange two rows.

EXAMPLE A

Solve this system of equations.

$$\begin{cases} 2x + y = 5 \\ 5x + 3y = 13 \end{cases}$$

▶ Solution

You can solve the system using matrices or equations. Let's compare the row reduction method using matrices with the elimination method using equations.

Because the equations are in standard form, you can copy the coefficients and constants from each equation into corresponding rows of the augmented matrix.

$$\begin{cases} 2x + y = 5 \\ 5x + 3y = 13 \end{cases} \rightarrow \left[\begin{array}{cc|c} 2 & 1 & 5 \\ 5 & 3 & 13 \end{array}\right]$$

Let's call this augmented matrix $[M]$. Using only the elementary row operations, you can transform this matrix into the solution matrix. You need both m_{21} and m_{12} to be 0, and you need both m_{11} and m_{22} to be 1.

Add −2.5 times row 1 to row 2 to get 0 for m_{21}.

$$\left[\begin{array}{cc|c} 2 & 1 & 5 \\ 0 & 0.5 & 0.5 \end{array}\right]$$

Multiply equation 1 by −2.5 and add to row 2 to eliminate x.

$$\begin{array}{rl} -5x - 2.5y &= -12.5 \\ 5x + 3y &= 13 \\ \hline 0.5y &= 0.5 \end{array}$$

Multiply row 2 by 2 to change m_{22} to 1.

$$\left[\begin{array}{cc|c} 2 & 1 & 5 \\ 0 & 1 & 1 \end{array}\right]$$

Multiply the equation by 2 to find y.

$$y = 1$$

Add −1 times row 2 to row 1 to get 0 for m_{12}.

$$\left[\begin{array}{cc|c} 2 & 0 & 4 \\ 0 & 1 & 1 \end{array}\right]$$

Multiply −1 by this new equation, and add the result to the first equation to eliminate y.

$$\begin{array}{rl} 2x + y &= 5 \\ -y &= -1 \\ \hline 2x &= 4 \end{array}$$

Multiply row 1 by 0.5.

$$\left[\begin{array}{cc|c} 1 & 0 & 2 \\ 0 & 1 & 1 \end{array}\right]$$

Multiply the equation by 0.5 to find x.

$$x = 2$$

The last column of the solution matrix indicates that the solution to the system is (2, 1).

Introduction (continued)

You might point out that the vertical line in the augmented matrix is not really part of the matrix but is only a visual aid.

The matrix $\left[\begin{array}{ccc|c} 1 & 3 & -2 & -8 \\ 0 & 1 & 9 & 26 \\ 0 & 0 & 1 & 3 \end{array}\right]$ is in row-echelon form. If it represents the variable coefficients in a system of equations, then the third variable can be read from the last row; the second variable can be found from the second row after the third is known; and the first can be found from the first row using the other two values.

You might want to demonstrate how the solution matrix is equivalent to a solution set.

$$\left[\begin{array}{cc|c} 1 & 0 & a \\ 0 & 1 & b \end{array}\right] \rightarrow$$

$$\begin{bmatrix} 1 & 0 \\ 0 & 1 \end{bmatrix}\begin{bmatrix} x \\ y \end{bmatrix} = \begin{bmatrix} a \\ b \end{bmatrix} \rightarrow \begin{array}{l} x = a \\ y = b \end{array}$$

Point out how each of the four rules for matrix operations corresponds to a rule for systems of equations. For example, exchanging two rows of a matrix is the same as switching two equations whose order of appearance makes no difference.

▶ EXAMPLE A

There are other ways to produce the solution matrix. **[Ask]** "What multiple of row 1 would give you −5 in the first position?" $\left[-\frac{5}{2}\right]$

When you solve systems of equations, you "substitute" for y to find x. Point out that multiplying the equation $y = 1$ by −1 and adding the result to the first equation is algebraically equivalent.

LESSON OBJECTIVES

- Represent a system of equations as an augmented matrix
- Interpret reduced row-echelon form
- Understand and use row operations in a matrix
- Use matrix row reduction to solve systems of equations

NCTM STANDARDS

CONTENT		PROCESS	
✓	Number	✓	Problem Solving
✓	Algebra	✓	Reasoning
	Geometry	✓	Communication
	Measurement	✓	Connections
✓	Data/Probability	✓	Representation

Guiding the Investigation

Before you begin the investigation, which extends row reduction to three equations in three unknowns, you may want to try more examples with only two variables. The problem of the investigation is the same problem that students solved using transformations in Lesson 4.4, Exercise 9.

The graphing calculator can perform row operations. If you want your students to use this technology in the investigation, hand out Calculator Note 6D now, otherwise, wait until Example B.

You may want to mention that the graph of a linear equation in three variables is actually a plane. Planes will arise again in Improving Your Visual Thinking Skills on page 326 and in Lesson 6.6.

Step 1

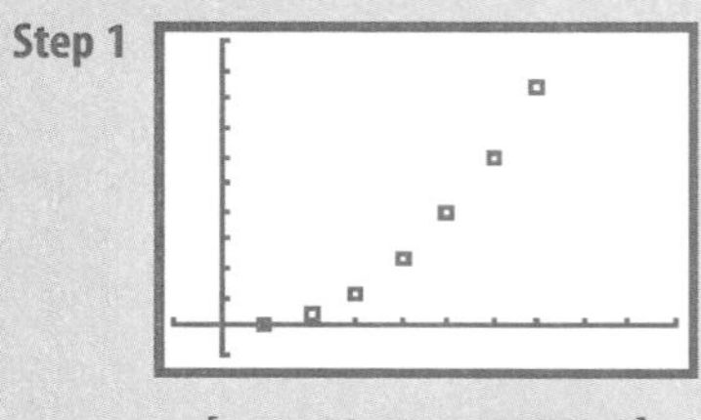

$[-1, 10, 1, -5, 50, 5]$

The data are not linear. The graph curves upward.

Step 2 [Alert] Students may be confused because a, b, and c are being treated as unknowns and x and y have known values—the reverse of their usual roles.

[Ask] "Can you use any three points for the substitution?" [Yes, because the data are exactly modeled by a quadratic equation. In general, you will probably get a better fit for data that are not modeled exactly if you use points that are spread out.]

Step 2 Sample answer using (5, 20), (1, 0), and (7, 42):

$$\begin{cases} 25a + 5b + c = 20 \\ a + b + c = 0 \\ 49a + 7b + c = 42 \end{cases}$$

You can represent row operations symbolically. For example, you can use R_1 and R_2 to represent the two rows of a matrix, as in Example A, and show the steps this way:

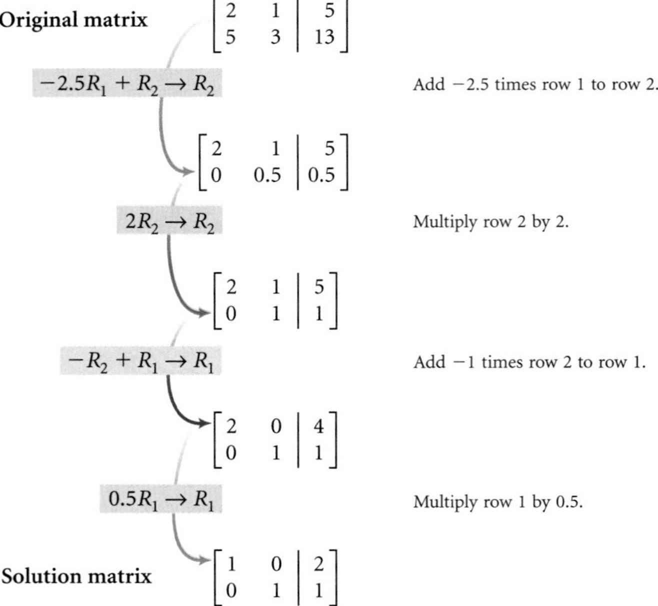

Original matrix $\left[\begin{array}{cc|c} 2 & 1 & 5 \\ 5 & 3 & 13 \end{array}\right]$

$-2.5R_1 + R_2 \rightarrow R_2$ — Add -2.5 times row 1 to row 2.

$\left[\begin{array}{cc|c} 2 & 1 & 5 \\ 0 & 0.5 & 0.5 \end{array}\right]$

$2R_2 \rightarrow R_2$ — Multiply row 2 by 2.

$\left[\begin{array}{cc|c} 2 & 1 & 5 \\ 0 & 1 & 1 \end{array}\right]$

$-R_2 + R_1 \rightarrow R_1$ — Add -1 times row 2 to row 1.

$\left[\begin{array}{cc|c} 2 & 0 & 4 \\ 0 & 1 & 1 \end{array}\right]$

$0.5R_1 \rightarrow R_1$ — Multiply row 1 by 0.5.

Solution matrix $\left[\begin{array}{cc|c} 1 & 0 & 2 \\ 0 & 1 & 1 \end{array}\right]$

Investigation
League Play

The number of games a soccer league must schedule depends on the number of teams playing in that league. This table shows the number of games required for each team in a league to play every other team twice, once at each team's home field. In this investigation you will find a function that describes the number of games for any number of teams.

Number of teams	1	2	3	4	5	6	7
Number of games	0	2	6	12	20	30	42

Step 1 Make a scatter plot of these data. Let x represent the number of teams, and let y represent the number of games. Describe the graph. Is it linear?

Step 2 Based on the shape of the graph, the equation could be quadratic. You can write a quadratic equation in the form $y = ax^2 + bx + c$. You can use each pair of values in the table to write an equation by substituting x and y. Create three equations with the variables a, b, and c by substituting any three pairs of coordinates from the above table. For example, the point (5, 20) creates the equation $a(5)^2 + b(5) + c = 20$, or $25a + 5b + c = 20$.

Step 3 You can now solve for the coefficients a, b, and c. Write a 3×4 augmented matrix for your system of three equations.

Step 4 Find the row operations that will give 0 for m_{13} and m_{23}. Describe the operations and write them symbolically using R_1, R_2, and R_3.

Step 5 Find row operations that give 0's in the other nondiagonal entries of your augmented matrix. Write all the row operations in terms of R_1, R_2, and R_3.

Step 6 Find row operations that give 1's along the main diagonal. Your matrix should now be in the form

$$\left[\begin{array}{ccc|c} 1 & 0 & 0 & k_1 \\ 0 & 1 & 0 & k_2 \\ 0 & 0 & 1 & k_3 \end{array}\right]$$

What does this mean about your equation, $y = ax^2 + bx + c$? Verify that you have the correct values for a, b, and c.

Step 7 Write a summary of the steps you followed to solve this problem. Describe any problems you ran into and any tricks or shortcuts you found.

Equations such as $2x + y = 5$ or $y = 3x + 4$ are called linear equations because their graphs in the coordinate plane are always lines. You may also notice that in linear equations the highest power of x or y is 1 and that x and y are never multiplied together. Equations in three variables such as $2x + y + 3z = 12$, where the highest power is 1, are also called linear equations. In the investigation you used an augmented matrix to solve a system of three linear equations in three variables. Here's another example of solving a larger system with the help of matrices.

Step 3 $\left[\begin{array}{ccc|c} 25 & 5 & 1 & 20 \\ 1 & 1 & 1 & 0 \\ 49 & 7 & 1 & 42 \end{array}\right]$

Step 4 Sample answer:
$-R_3 + R_1 \rightarrow R_1$
$-R_3 + R_2 \rightarrow R_2$

$$\left[\begin{array}{ccc|c} -24 & -2 & 0 & -22 \\ -48 & -6 & 0 & -42 \\ 49 & 7 & 1 & 42 \end{array}\right]$$

Step 5 Students often will find it helpful to use a combination of the row operations listed on page 319. For example, students using points (5, 10), (1, 0), and (7, 42) will find the row operation $49R_2 + 48R_3 \rightarrow R_3$ helpful in avoiding messy fractions.

Step 5 Sample answer:
$-3R_1 + R_2 \rightarrow R_1$
$49R_2 + 48R_3 \rightarrow R_3$
$2R_1 + R_2 \rightarrow R_2$
$7R_2 + R_3 \rightarrow R_3$

$$\left[\begin{array}{ccc|c} 24 & 0 & 0 & 24 \\ 0 & -6 & 0 & 6 \\ 0 & 0 & 48 & 0 \end{array}\right]$$

Step 6 Sample answer:
$\frac{R_1}{24} \rightarrow R_1$

$\frac{R_2}{-6} \rightarrow R_2$

$\frac{R_3}{48} \rightarrow R_3$

$$\left[\begin{array}{ccc|c} 1 & 0 & 0 & 1 \\ 0 & 1 & 0 & -1 \\ 0 & 0 & 1 & 0 \end{array}\right]$$

The equation is $y = x^2 - x$. The values $a = 1$, $b = -1$, and $c = 0$ satisfy the original system.

▸ ***EXAMPLE B***

[Ask] "What information is used to set up the first equation?" [that 50 books were sold, assuming each receipt is for one book] "The second?" [the total amount of sales] "The third?" [that 22 more of one book sold than another]

The solution given is just one of many possible approaches.

This example refers to Calculator Note 6D, which shows how to do the steps of row reduction. Calculator Note 6E, referred to in Exercise 6, shows how to get the calculator to do the reduction with one command. Because your students may discover this command at any time, when you assess their understanding you might ask students to describe the steps of the row-reduction process rather than just to reduce the matrices.

SHARING IDEAS

Take advantage of student presentations to ask why the matrices representing systems of two equations in two variables always have two rows, even after one equation has been eliminated. [To stay the same size, the matrices represent one of the original equations as well as the combined equation.]

Describe how a 2 × 2 matrix represents a transformation.

[Ask] "What is a matrix equation saying about transformations?" [The solution represents a point that is transformed to the point represented by the matrix of constants.] Ask what the row-reduction process does in terms of transformations. Bring out the idea that it changes the transformation and the image until the transformation becomes the identity transformation and the image becomes the unknown point (x_1, y_1):

$$\left[\begin{array}{cc|c} a & b & e \\ c & d & f \end{array}\right] \rightarrow \left[\begin{array}{cc|c} 1 & 0 & x_1 \\ 0 & 1 & y_1 \end{array}\right]$$

EXAMPLE B

The junior class treasurer is totaling the sales and receipts from the last book sale. She has 50 receipts for sales of three different titles of books priced at \$14.00, \$18.50, and \$23.25. She has a total of \$909.00 and knows that 22 more of the \$18.50 books sold than the \$23.25 books. How many of each book were sold?

▸ ***Solution***

The numbers sold of the three different book titles are unknown, so you can assign three variables.

x = the number of \$14.00 books
y = the number of \$18.50 books
z = the number of \$23.25 books

Based on the information in the problem, write a system of three linear equations. The system can also be written as an augmented matrix.

$$\begin{cases} x + y + z = 50 \\ 14x + 18.50y + 23.25z = 909 \\ y - z = 22 \end{cases} \quad \text{or} \quad \left[\begin{array}{ccc|c} 1 & 1 & 1 & 50 \\ 14 & 18.5 & 23.25 & 909 \\ 0 & 1 & -1 & 22 \end{array}\right]$$

Here is one possible sequence of row operations to obtain a solution matrix. Try these row operations to see how they transform the augmented matrix into reduced row-echelon form. [▸ See **Calculator Note 6D** to learn how to do row operations on your calculator. ◂]

$-14R_1 + R_2 \rightarrow R_2$
$-R_3 + R_1 \rightarrow R_1$
$-4.5R_3 + R_2 \rightarrow R_2$
$\frac{R_2}{13.75} \rightarrow R_2$
$R_2 \leftrightarrow R_3$
$R_3 + R_2 \rightarrow R_2$
$-2R_3 + R_1 \rightarrow R_1$

This sequence of row operations gives this reduced row-echelon matrix.

$$\left[\begin{array}{ccc|c} 1 & 0 & 0 & 12 \\ 0 & 1 & 0 & 30 \\ 0 & 0 & 1 & 8 \end{array}\right]$$

This means that 12 of the \$14.00 books, 30 of the \$18.50 books, and 8 of the \$23.25 books were sold.

[Ask] "What does it mean geometrically if a matrix equation has no solution or infinitely many solutions?" [In one sense, the lines represented by the corresponding linear equations are parallel or coincide. From a transformational point of view, the matrix is squashing the plane to a line that either doesn't go through the given point (no solution) or does go through it (infinitely many solutions).

Some systems of equations have no solution, and others have infinitely many solutions. Likewise, not all augmented matrices can be reduced to row-echelon form. An entire row of 0's means that one equation is equivalent to another; therefore, not enough information was given to find a single solution, so there are infinitely many solutions. If, on the other hand, an entire row reduces to 0's, except for a nonzero constant in the last entry, no solution exists because a set of 0 coefficients cannot result in a nonzero constant on the right side of the equation.

EXERCISES

Practice Your Skills

1. Write a system of equations for each augmented matrix.

a. $\left[\begin{array}{cc|c} 2 & 5 & 8 \\ 4 & -1 & 6 \end{array}\right]$ $\begin{cases} 2x + 5y = 8 \\ 4x - y = 6 \end{cases}$

b. $\left[\begin{array}{ccc|c} 1 & -1 & 2 & 3 \\ 1 & 2 & -3 & 1 \\ 2 & 1 & -1 & 2 \end{array}\right]$ $\begin{cases} x - y + 2z = 3 \\ x + 2y - 3z = 1 \\ 2x + y - z = 2 \end{cases}$

2. Write an augmented matrix for each system.

a. $\begin{cases} x + 2y - z = 1 \\ 2x - y + 3z = 2 \\ 2x + y + z = -1 \end{cases}$ $\left[\begin{array}{ccc|c} 1 & 2 & -1 & 1 \\ 2 & -1 & 3 & 2 \\ 2 & 1 & 1 & -1 \end{array}\right]$

b. $\begin{cases} 2x + y - z = 12 \\ 2x + z = 4 \\ 2x - y + 3z = -4 \end{cases}$ $\left[\begin{array}{ccc|c} 2 & 1 & -1 & 12 \\ 2 & 0 & 1 & 4 \\ 2 & -1 & 3 & -4 \end{array}\right]$

3. Perform each row operation on this matrix.

$\left[\begin{array}{ccc|c} 1 & -1 & 2 & 3 \\ 1 & 2 & -3 & 1 \\ 2 & 1 & -1 & 2 \end{array}\right]$

a. $-R_1 + R_2 \rightarrow R_2$ $\left[\begin{array}{ccc|c} 1 & -1 & 2 & 3 \\ 0 & 3 & -5 & -2 \\ 2 & 1 & -1 & 2 \end{array}\right]$

b. $-2R_1 + R_3 \rightarrow R_3$ $\left[\begin{array}{ccc|c} 1 & -1 & 2 & 3 \\ 1 & 2 & -3 & 1 \\ 0 & 3 & -5 & -4 \end{array}\right]$

4. Give the missing row operation or matrix in the table.

	Description	Matrix
a.	The original system. $\begin{cases} 2x + 5y = 8 \\ 4x - y = 6 \end{cases}$	$\left[\begin{array}{cc\|c} 2 & 5 & 8 \\ 4 & -1 & 6 \end{array}\right]$
b.	$-2R_1 + R_2 \rightarrow R_2$	$\left[\begin{array}{cc\|c} 2 & 5 & 8 \\ 0 & -11 & -10 \end{array}\right]$
c.	$\frac{R_2}{-11} \rightarrow R_2$	$\left[\begin{array}{cc\|c} 2 & 5 & 8 \\ 0 & 1 & \frac{10}{11} \end{array}\right]$
d.	$-5R_2 + R_1 \rightarrow R_1$	$\left[\begin{array}{cc\|c} 2 & 0 & \frac{38}{11} \\ 0 & 1 & \frac{10}{11} \end{array}\right]$
e.	$\frac{R_1}{2} \rightarrow R_1$	$\left[\begin{array}{cc\|c} 1 & 0 & \frac{19}{11} \\ 0 & 1 & \frac{10}{11} \end{array}\right]$

Assessing Progress

You can assess students' understanding of the correspondence of an equation to a graph and of the solution to a system of equations, as well as their ability to make a scatter plot.

Closing the Lesson

Row reduction is a way to use matrices to mirror the manipulation of equations in solving a system of equations. You can multiply all coefficients in a row by a nonzero number, add a multiple (perhaps 1) of a row to another row, and rearrange the order of the rows—all toward the goal of having the matrix in **reduced row-echelon form,** with $\begin{bmatrix} 1 & 0 \\ 0 & 1 \end{bmatrix}$ or $\begin{bmatrix} 1 & 0 & 0 \\ 0 & 1 & 0 \\ 0 & 0 & 1 \end{bmatrix}$ as the main part of the augmented matrix.

BUILDING UNDERSTANDING

If you are spending two days on this lesson, assign Exercises 1–4 and some review exercises on the first day. You can assign a selection of the remaining exercises on the second day.

ASSIGNING HOMEWORK

Essential	1–5
Performance assessment	6–10
Portfolio	8, 10
Journal	14
Group	10
Review	11–14

Helping with the Exercises

Exercise 5 If you didn't use Calculator Note 6D for Example B, you might introduce it here.

Exercise 6 The instructions don't say precisely that students need to solve the systems of equations. Indeed, students might be able to solve the problems more easily without solving a system. If you encourage creative thinking, students will see that the situation in 6b is nonsense without their trying to solve any equations. In 6a, if all the animals had two legs there would be 47(2) or 94 legs. Because there are 118 legs, 118 − 94 or 24 legs must belong to the animals that have more than two legs—the goats. With two extra legs each, there must be 12 goats. Therefore there are 47 − 12 or 35 chickens. Ask students what operations on the augmented matrix this reasoning represents. [Start with a matrix equivalent to the one in the answer with rows interchanged: first row minus twice the second row; divide the first row by two; subtract the first row from the second row.]

In 6b, **[Ask]** "What might the neighbor have intended to say?" [47 animals with 118 legs, meaning 12 goats and 35 chickens]

6a. $\begin{cases} x + y = 47 \\ 4x + 2y = 118 \end{cases}$

$\left[\begin{array}{cc|c} 1 & 1 & 47 \\ 4 & 2 & 118 \end{array}\right]$; 12 goats and 35 chickens

6b. $\begin{cases} x + y = 118 \\ 4x + 2y = 47 \end{cases}$

$\left[\begin{array}{cc|c} 1 & 1 & 118 \\ 4 & 2 & 47 \end{array}\right]$; −94.5 goats and 212.5 chickens, which is impossible. She must have made an error in reporting her numbers.

Reason and Apply

5. Rewrite each system of equations as an augmented matrix. If possible, transform the matrix into its reduced row-echelon form using row operations on your calculator.

a. $\begin{cases} x + 2y + 3z = 5 \\ 2x + 3y + 2z = 2 \\ -x - 2y - 4z = -1 \end{cases}$ $\left[\begin{array}{ccc|c} 1 & 0 & 0 & -31 \\ 0 & 1 & 0 & 24 \\ 0 & 0 & 1 & -4 \end{array}\right]$

b. $\begin{cases} -x + 3y - z = 4 \\ 2z = x + y \\ 2.2y + 2.2z = 2.2 \end{cases}$ $\left[\begin{array}{ccc|c} 1 & 0 & 0 & -1 \\ 0 & 1 & 0 & 1 \\ 0 & 0 & 1 & 0 \end{array}\right]$

c. $\begin{cases} 3x - y + z = 7 \\ x - 2y + 5z = 1 \\ 6x - 2y + 2z = 14 \end{cases}$ cannot be reduced to row-echelon form (dependent system)

d. $\begin{cases} 3x - y + z = 5 \\ x - 2y + 5z = 1 \\ 6x - 2y + 2z = 14 \end{cases}$ cannot be reduced to row-echelon form (inconsistent system)

6. A farmer raises only goats and chickens on his farm. All together he has 47 animals, and they have a total of 118 legs.

a. Write a system of equations and an augmented matrix. How many of each animal does he have? [► See **Calculator Note 6E** to learn how to transform a matrix to reduced row-echelon form on your calculator. ◄]

b. The farmer's neighbor also has goats and chickens. She reports having 118 animals with a total of 47 legs. Write a system of equations and an augmented matrix. How many of each animal does she have?

7. The largest angle of a triangle is 4° more than twice the smallest angle. The smallest angle is 24° less than the midsize angle. What are the measures of the three angles? 38°, 62°, 80°

8. APPLICATION The amount of merchandise that is available for sale is called supply. The amount of merchandise that consumers want to buy is called demand. Supply and demand are in equilibrium, or balance, when a price is found that makes supply and demand equal.

Suppose the following data represent supply and demand for a drink manufacturer.

Supply for Mega-Fruit

Price (cents/gal)	Quantity (millions of gal)
80	1304.4
90	2894
100	4483.6
110	6073.2
120	7662.8

Demand for Mega-Fruit

Price (cents/gal)	Quantity (millions of gal)
80	3268.47
90	2724.87
100	2181.27
110	1637.67
120	1094.07

Exercise 7 If students are having difficulty because they don't have a third equation relating the three unknowns, **[Ask]** "Is there anything else you can say about the angles of a triangle?" [The sum of their measures is 180°.]

a. Find linear models for the supply and demand.

b. Find the equilibrium point graphically.

c. Write the supply and demand equations from 8a as a system in an augmented matrix. Use row reduction to verify your answer to 8b.

Economics CONNECTION

Supply and demand are affected by many things. The supply may be affected by the price of the merchandise, the cost of making it, or unexpected events that affect supply, like drought or hurricanes. Demand may be affected by the price, the income level of the consumer, or consumer tastes. An increased price may slow the purchase of the product and thus also increase supply. The stock market illustrates how prices are determined through the interaction of supply and demand in an auction-like environment.

In New York City, January 1996, grocery store shelves emptied as residents stocked up for a severe snowstorm. Unexpected events like this can cause high demand and deplete supply.

9. Find a, b, and c such that the graph of $y = ax^2 + bx + c$ passes through the points $(1, 3)$, $(4, 24)$, and $(-2, 18)$.

10. The yearbook staff sells ads in three sizes. The full-page ads sell for \$200, the half-page ads sell for \$125, and the business-card-size ads sell for \$20. All together they earned \$1715 from 22 ads. There were four times as many business-card-size ads sold as full-page ads. How many of each ad type did they sell?

Review

3.7 **11. APPLICATION** The Life is a Dance troupe has two choices in how it will be paid for its next series of performances. The first option is to receive \$12,500 for the series plus 5% of all ticket sales. The second option is \$6,800 for the series plus 15% of ticket sales. The company will perform three consecutive nights in a hall that seats 2,200 people. All tickets will cost \$12.

Honduran-American dancer Homer Avila performed a solo work titled *Not/Without Words* in February 2002, one year after losing his leg and part of his hip to cancer.

a. How much will the troupe receive under each plan if a total of 3500 tickets are sold for all three performances?

b. Write an equation that gives the amount the troupe will receive under the first plan for any number of tickets sold.

c. Write an equation that gives the amount the troupe will receive under the second plan for any number of tickets sold.

d. How many tickets must the troupe sell for the second plan to be the better choice?

e. Which plan should the troupe choose? Justify your choice.

8a. demand: $\hat{y} = -54.36x + 7617.27$; supply: $\hat{y} = 158.96x - 11412.4$

8b. approximately (89, 2768)

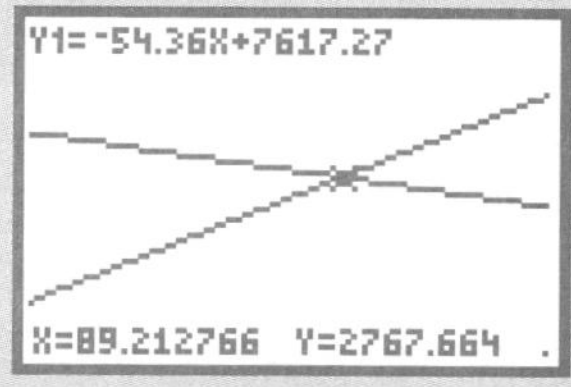

[88, 90, 10, 2500, 3000, 1000]

8c. $\left[\begin{array}{cc|c} 54.36 & 1 & 7617.27 \\ 158.96 & -1 & 11412.4 \end{array}\right]$

$\left[\begin{array}{cc|c} 1 & 0 & 89.2 \\ 0 & 1 & 2768.0 \end{array}\right]$

MAKING THE CONNECTION

Students may be familiar with the terms *buyer's market* and *seller's market.* **[Ask]** "In a buyer's market, do you think supply is high or low? In a seller's market?" [high; low]

9. $y = 2x^2 - 3x + 4$

10. 3 full-page ads, 7 half-page ads, and 12 business-card-size ads

Exercise 11 As needed, suggest that students graph the equations.

11a. first plan: \$14,600; second plan: \$13,100

11b. Let x represent the number of tickets sold, and let y represent the income in dollars; $y = 12500 + 0.6x$.

11c. $y = 6800 + 1.8x$

11d. more than 4750 tickets

11e. The company should choose the first plan if they expect to sell fewer than 4750 tickets and the second if they expect to sell more than 4750 tickets.

Exercise 12 Encourage students to check their solutions by substituting them into the equations.

Exercise 14 [Ask] "How did the multiplication in i and ii change the triangle?" [In i, the triangle is reflected across the line $y = x$. In ii, the triangle is reflected across the line $y = x$ and then reflected across the y-axis.]

14a. $\begin{bmatrix} 2 & 6 & 6 \\ 1 & 1 & 3 \end{bmatrix}$

14b. i. $\begin{bmatrix} 1 & 1 & 3 \\ 2 & 6 & 6 \end{bmatrix}$

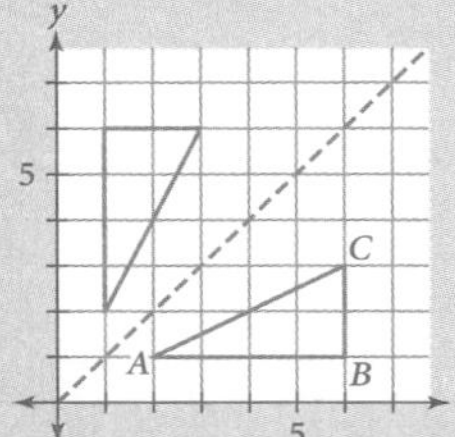

14b. ii. $\begin{bmatrix} -1 & -1 & -3 \\ 2 & 6 & 6 \end{bmatrix}$

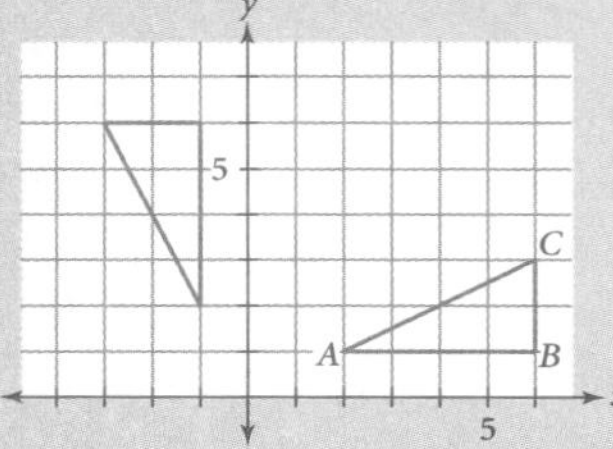

EXTENSIONS

A. Use Take Another Look activity 2 on page 357.

B. Have students make physical models of the intersecting planes from Improving Your Visual Thinking Skills

3.6 **12.** Consider this graph of a system of two linear equations.

a. What is the solution to this system? (4, 2)

b. Write equations for the two lines.
$y_1 = 2 + 2(x - 4)$ or $y_1 = 2(x - 3)$;
$y_2 = 2 - 0.75(x - 4)$ or $y_2 = -1 - 0.75(x - 8)$

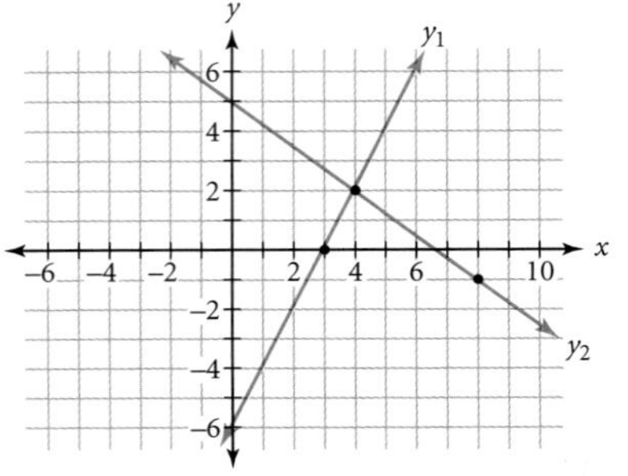

3.3 **13.** For each segment shown in the pentagon at right, write an equation in point-slope form for the line that contains the segment. Check your equations by graphing them on your calculator.
$\overline{AB}$: $y = 6 - \frac{2}{3}(x - 4)$ or $y = 4 + \frac{2}{3}(x - 1)$;
$\overline{BC}$: $y = 4 - \frac{2}{3}(x - 7)$ or $y = 6 - \frac{2}{3}(x - 4)$;
$\overline{CD}$: $y = 1 + 3(x - 6)$ or $y = 4 + 3(x - 7)$;
$\overline{DE}$: $y = 1$; $\overline{AE}$: $y = 4 - 3(x - 1)$ or $y = 1 - 3(x - 2)$

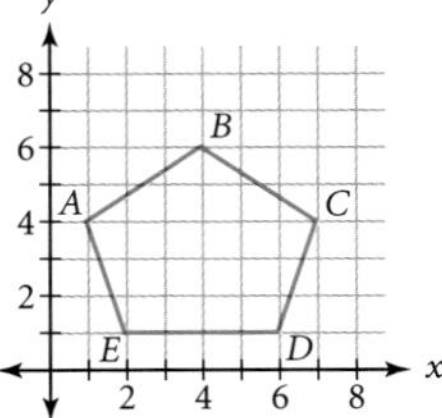

6.2 **14.** Consider the graph of $\triangle ABC$.

a. Represent $\triangle ABC$ with a matrix $[M]$.

b. Find each product and graph the image of the triangle represented by the result.

i. $\begin{bmatrix} 0 & 1 \\ 1 & 0 \end{bmatrix}[M]$

ii. $\begin{bmatrix} 0 & -1 \\ 1 & 0 \end{bmatrix}[M]$

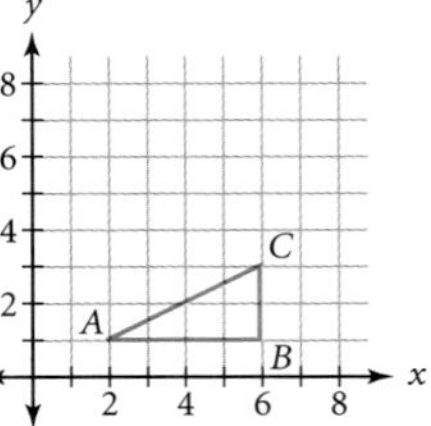

IMPROVING YOUR VISUAL THINKING SKILLS

Intersection of Planes

Graphically, a system of two linear equations in two variables can be represented by two lines. If the lines intersect, the point of intersection is the solution and the system is called consistent and independent. If the lines are parallel, they never intersect, there is no solution, and the system is called inconsistent. If the lines are the same, there are infinitely many solutions, and the system is called consistent and dependent.

An equation such as $3x + 2y + 6z = 12$ is also called a linear equation because the highest power of any variable is 1. But, because there are three variables, the graph of this equation is a plane.

Graphically, a system of three linear equations in three variables can be represented by three planes. Sketch all the possible outcomes for the graphs of three planes. Classify each outcome as consistent, inconsistent, dependent, and/or independent.

IMPROVING VISUAL THINKING SKILLS

There are eight possible outcomes. For one, the three planes are coincident, a dependent case. For two other cases, exactly two of the planes are coincident. If the third plane intersects them in a line, the system is dependent, if the third plane is parallel to them, the system is inconsistent. The other five outcomes are pictured.

consistent and independent

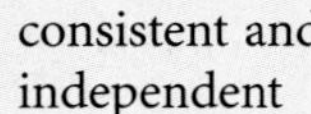

inconsistent

inconsistent

inconsistent

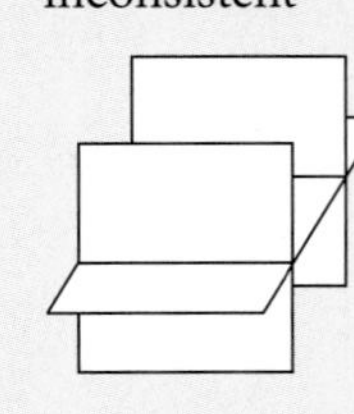

consistent and dependent

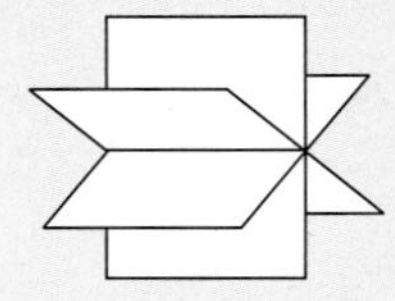

LESSON

6.4

Solving Systems with Inverse Matrices

Things that oppose each other also complement each other.

CHINESE SAYING

Consider the equation $ax = b$. To solve for x, you multiply both sides of the equation by $\frac{1}{a}$, the **multiplicative inverse** of a. The multiplicative inverse of a nonzero number, such as 2.25, is the number that you can multiply by 2.25 to get 1. Also, the number 1 is the **multiplicative identity** because any number multiplied by 1 remains unchanged.

Similarly, to solve a system by using matrices, you can use an **inverse matrix.** If an inverse matrix exists, then when you multiply it by the system matrix you will get the matrix equivalent of 1, which is called the **identity matrix.** Any square matrix multiplied on either side by the identity matrix of the same dimensions remains unchanged, just as any number multiplied by 1 remains unchanged. In Example A, you will first use this multiplicative identity to find a 2 × 2 identity matrix.

EXAMPLE A Find an identity matrix for $\begin{bmatrix} 2 & 1 \\ 4 & 3 \end{bmatrix}$.

▸ Solution You want to find a matrix, $\begin{bmatrix} a & b \\ c & d \end{bmatrix}$, that satisfies the definition of the identity matrix.

$$\begin{bmatrix} 2 & 1 \\ 4 & 3 \end{bmatrix}\begin{bmatrix} a & b \\ c & d \end{bmatrix} = \begin{bmatrix} 2 & 1 \\ 4 & 3 \end{bmatrix}$$ Multiplying by an identity matrix leaves the matrix unchanged.

$$\begin{bmatrix} 2a + c & 2b + d \\ 4a + 3c & 4b + 3d \end{bmatrix} = \begin{bmatrix} 2 & 1 \\ 4 & 3 \end{bmatrix}$$ Multiply the left side.

Because the two matrices are equal, their entries must be equal. Setting corresponding entries equal produces these equations:

$2a + c = 2$ $\quad$ $2b + d = 1$

$4a + 3c = 4$ $\quad$ $4b + 3d = 3$

You can treat these as two systems of equations. Use substitution, elimination, or an augmented matrix to solve each system.

$$\begin{cases} 2a + c = 2 \\ 4a + 3c = 4 \end{cases}$$ A system that can be solved for a and c.

$$-6a - 3c = -6$$ Multiply the first equation by -3.

$$4a + 3c = 4$$

$$-2a = -2$$ Add the equations to eliminate c.

$$a = 1$$ Solve for a.

$$2(1) + c = 2$$ Substitute 1 for a in the first equation to find c.

$$c = 0$$ Solve for c.

This system gives $a = 1$ and $c = 0$. You can use a similar procedure to find that $b = 0$ and $d = 1$.

NCTM STANDARDS

CONTENT		PROCESS	
	Number	✓	Problem Solving
✓	Algebra	✓	Reasoning
✓	Geometry	✓	Communication
	Measurement	✓	Connections
	Data/Probability		Representation

LESSON OBJECTIVES

- Find the inverse of a matrix if it exists
- Use inverse matrices to solve systems of equations
- Understand the characteristics of an identity matrix

LESSON

6.4

PLANNING

LESSON OUTLINE

One day:

5 min	Example A
15 min	Investigation
10 min	Sharing
10 min	Examples B, C
5 min	Exercises

MATERIALS

- At the Movies (T) for One Step
- Calculator Notes 6B, 6F

TEACHING

A matrix equation representing a system of linear equations often can be solved in a way analogous to solving a single linear equation. **[Ask]** "For what type of matrix does an inverse matrix not exist?" [a nonsquare matrix]

▸ EXAMPLE A

As you and your students look at the solution, **[Ask]** "Why have the equations been paired this way?" [Each pair of equations with the same two variables becomes a system.]

If students worked on Lesson 6.3, they can also use row reduction to solve for the variables.

One Step

Show the At the Movies transparency and pose this problem, adapted from Example C: "At the movies, Duane, Marsha, and Parker each purchased snacks. Duane bought two candy bars, a small drink, and two bags of popcorn for a total of $11.85. Marsha spent $9.00 on a candy bar, two small drinks, and a bag of popcorn. Parker spent $12.35 on two small drinks and three bags of popcorn. Use matrices and the

One Step (continued)
x^{-1} key on your calculator to find the price of each item." If anyone asks about sales tax, compliment his or her thinking and tell students to assume that all prices include tax. If students aren't sure what to do with the matrix equation, point out its resemblance to the linear equation $ax = b$ and wonder how they might use the calculator's x^{-1} key to solve that equation. During Sharing, introduce the terms *identity matrix* and *inverse matrix.*

The 2×2 identity matrix is

$$\begin{bmatrix} 1 & 0 \\ 0 & 1 \end{bmatrix}$$

Can you see why multiplying this matrix by any 2×2 matrix results in the same 2×2 matrix?

The identity matrix in Example A is the identity matrix for all 2×2 matrices. Take a minute to multiply $[I][A]$ and $[A][I]$ with any 2×2 matrix. There are corresponding identity matrices for larger square matrices.

Identity Matrix

An **identity matrix,** symbolized by $[I]$, is the square matrix that does not alter the entries of a square matrix $[A]$ under multiplication.

$[A][I] = [A]$ and $[I][A] = [A]$

Matrix $[I]$ must have the same dimensions as matrix $[A]$, and it has entries of 1's along the main diagonal (from top left to bottom right) and 0's in all other entries.

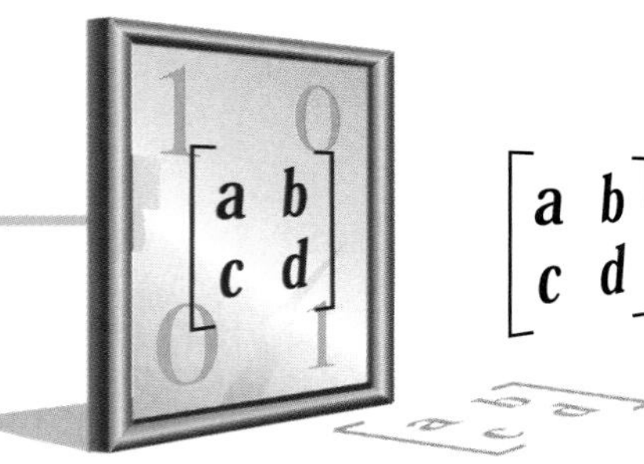

Now that you know the identity matrix for a 2×2 matrix, you can look for a way to find the inverse of a 2×2 matrix.

Inverse Matrix

The **inverse matrix** of $[A]$, symbolized by $[A]^{-1}$, is the matrix that will produce an identity matrix when multiplied by $[A]$.

$[A][A]^{-1} = [I]$ and $[A]^{-1}[A] = [I]$

Investigation
The Inverse Matrix

In this investigation you will learn ways to find the inverse of a 2×2 matrix.

Step 1 Use the definition of an inverse matrix to set up a matrix equation. Use these matrices and the 2×2 identity matrix for $[I]$.

$$[A] = \begin{bmatrix} 2 & 1 \\ 4 & 3 \end{bmatrix} \qquad [A]^{-1} = \begin{bmatrix} a & b \\ c & d \end{bmatrix}$$

Step 2 Use matrix multiplication to find the product of $[A][A]^{-1}$. Set that product equal to matrix $[I]$.

Guiding the Investigation

Step 1 You might have groups use different matrices for $[A]$. If you choose matrices that have determinants ± 1 or ± 2, then during Sharing students may be able to see a pattern for finding inverses of 2×2 matrices. This pattern is the topic of Take Another Look activity 1 on page 357. The determinant of matrix $\begin{bmatrix} a & b \\ c & d \end{bmatrix}$ is $ad - bc$.

Step 1 $\begin{bmatrix} 2 & 1 \\ 4 & 3 \end{bmatrix}\begin{bmatrix} a & b \\ c & d \end{bmatrix} = \begin{bmatrix} 1 & 0 \\ 0 & 1 \end{bmatrix}$

Step 2 $\begin{bmatrix} 2a + c & 2b + d \\ 4a + 3c & 4b + 3d \end{bmatrix} = \begin{bmatrix} 1 & 0 \\ 0 & 1 \end{bmatrix}$

Step 3 Use the matrix equation from Step 2 to write equations that you can solve to find values for a, b, c, and d. Solve the systems to find the values in the inverse matrix.

Step 4 Use your calculator to find $[A]^{-1}$. If this answer does not match your answer to Step 3, check your work for mistakes. [▶ See **Calculator Note 6F** to learn how to find the inverse on your calculator. ◀]

Step 5 Find the products of $[A][A]^{-1}$ and $[A]^{-1}[A]$. Do they both give you $\begin{bmatrix}1 & 0\\0 & 1\end{bmatrix}$? Is matrix multiplication always commutative?

Step 6 Not every square matrix has an inverse. Find the inverse of each of these matrices, if one exists. Make a conjecture about what types of 2×2 square matrices do not have inverses.

a. $\begin{bmatrix}2 & 1\\4 & 2\end{bmatrix}$ **b.** $\begin{bmatrix}50 & -75\\10 & -15\end{bmatrix}$ **c.** $\begin{bmatrix}10.5 & 1\\31.5 & 3\end{bmatrix}$ **d.** $\begin{bmatrix}2 & 1\\2 & 1\end{bmatrix}$

Step 7 Can a nonsquare matrix have an inverse? Why or why not?

You now know how to find the inverse of a square matrix, both by hand and on your calculator. You can use an inverse matrix to solve a system of equations.

Solving a System Using the Inverse Matrix

A system of equations in standard form can be written in matrix form as $[A][X] = [B]$, where $[A]$ is the coefficient matrix, $[X]$ is the variable matrix, and $[B]$ is the constant matrix. Multiplying both sides by the inverse matrix, $[A]^{-1}$, with the inverse on the left, gives the values of variables in matrix $[X]$, which is the solution to the system.

$[A][X] = [B]$	The system in matrix form.
$[A]^{-1}[A][X] = [A]^{-1}[B]$	Left-multiply both sides by the inverse.
$[I][X] = [A]^{-1}[B]$	By the definition of inverse, $[A]^{-1}[A] = [I]$.
$[X] = [A]^{-1}[B]$	By the definition of identity, $[I][X] = [X]$.

EXAMPLE B Solve this system using an inverse matrix.

$$\begin{cases}2x + 3y = 7\\x = 6 - 4y\end{cases}$$

▶ Solution First, rewrite the second equation in standard form.

$$\begin{cases}2x + 3y = 7\\x + 4y = 6\end{cases}$$

The matrix equation for this system is

$$\begin{bmatrix}2 & 3\\1 & 4\end{bmatrix}\begin{bmatrix}x\\y\end{bmatrix} = \begin{bmatrix}7\\6\end{bmatrix}$$

Step 3 $2a + c = 1$, $2b + d = 0$, $4a + 3c = 0$, $4b + 3d = 1$; $a = 1.5$, $b = -0.5$, $c = -2$, $d = 1$; $[A]^{-1} = \begin{bmatrix}1.5 & -0.5\\-2 & 1\end{bmatrix}$

Step 5 [Ask] "What is $[I]^{-1}$? [It is $[I]$.]

Step 5 yes; no

Step 6 [Ask] "Can you tell before calculating that these matrices have no inverses?" [One row is a multiple of the other, perhaps by 1.]

Step 6 None of the matrices has an inverse. A 2×2 square matrix does not have an inverse when one row is a multiple of the other.

Step 7 No. The product of a matrix and its inverse must be a square matrix because an identity matrix is always square and has the dimensions of the matrix and its inverse.

▶ EXAMPLE B

This example illustrates using an inverse matrix to solve a system of two equations. Because the emphasis of this lesson is on solving equations rather than on finding inverses, students find the inverse matrix by calculator, as explained in Calculator Note 6F. As needed, also refer students to Calculator Note 6B. You might ask students to try solving the matrix equation $[A][x] = [B]$ by division. When students try to divide the matrices, they will get an error message leading to discussion that will deepen their understanding of inverse.

[Alert] Students might not yet see how multiplying row 1 of $[A]$ by $[X]$ gives the equation $2x + 3y = 7$ and how multiplying row 2 of $[A]$ by $[X]$ gives the equation $1x + 4y = 6$.

▸ EXAMPLE C

As in Example B, students are expected to find the inverse matrix by calculator, but the calculator may introduce round-off errors. For example,

$$[A]^{-1} = \begin{bmatrix} \frac{4}{9} & \frac{1}{9} & -\frac{1}{3} \\ -\frac{1}{3} & \frac{2}{3} & 0 \\ \frac{2}{9} & \frac{4}{9} & \frac{1}{3} \end{bmatrix}, \text{ but}$$

the calculator will produce something like

$$\begin{bmatrix} .4444 & .1111 & -.3333 \\ -.3333 & .6667 & .0000 \\ .2222 & -.4444 & .3333 \end{bmatrix}$$

unless students use the calculator's MATH ▸Frac command. If the calculator displays 1 E^{-}13, the actual number is probably 0. Likewise, 3.99999999 is probably meant to be 4. If students are entering the inverse matrix by hand, entering fractions will give better results than entering decimal approximations.

[Ask] "What do the rows mean? For example, what does row 2 represent?" [Row 2 represents Marsha's purchases.]

SHARING IDEAS

As students present, ask if it matters whether you multiply each side of the equation on the left or on the right. They may think it doesn't matter, because both $[A]^{-1}[A]$ and $[A][A]^{-1}$ are the identity matrix. But because the right side of the equation is an $n \times 1$ matrix, it can't be multiplied on the right by an $n \times n$ matrix; the multiplication must be on the left. This book uses the term *left-multiply* to describe this action. Wonder aloud whether it matters which side of a 2×2 matrix the identity matrix is multiplied on, and bring out the idea that in this case it doesn't. In general, however, matrix multiplication is not commutative.

Ask whether $[A]^{-1}$ is a base raised to an exponent. [No; $[A]$ is not a number.] The notation comes from the use of the inverse in solving equations, analogous to the inverse of a, or $a^{-1} = \frac{1}{a}$, which is a base with an exponent. On a calculator you use the x^{-1} key to find a matrix inverse. So $[A]^{-1}$ is more like a base with an exponent than, say, a function inverse f^{-1}, which isn't a reciprocal in any sense.

[Ask] "How are the equations $ax = b$ and $[A][X] = [B]$ alike?" [Both show multiplication and a product, and both equations can be solved by multiplying by the inverse of a or $[A]$.] "How are they different?" [You must multiply both sides of the matrix equation on the left by the inverse matrix, but there's no such restriction on number multiplication; you can divide by a in $ax = b$, but you're not dividing by $[A]$ when you multiply by its inverse.]

If your students need additional practice setting up the matrix equation or solving systems using matrices, you might use Lesson 6.3, Exercise 5.

[Ask] "Why can only a square matrix have an inverse?"

In the matrix equation $\begin{bmatrix} 2 & 3 \\ 1 & 4 \end{bmatrix}\begin{bmatrix} x \\ y \end{bmatrix} = \begin{bmatrix} 7 \\ 6 \end{bmatrix}$, the variable matrix, $[X]$, is $\begin{bmatrix} x \\ y \end{bmatrix}$.

The coefficient matrix, $[A]$, is $\begin{bmatrix} 2 & 3 \\ 1 & 4 \end{bmatrix}$, and the constant matrix, $[B]$, is $\begin{bmatrix} 7 \\ 6 \end{bmatrix}$.

Use your calculator to find the inverse of $[A]$.

$$[A]^{-1} = \begin{bmatrix} 0.8 & -0.6 \\ -0.2 & 0.4 \end{bmatrix}$$

Multiply both sides of the equation by this inverse, with the inverse on the left, to find the solution to the system of equations.

$\begin{bmatrix} 2 & 3 \\ 1 & 4 \end{bmatrix}\begin{bmatrix} x \\ y \end{bmatrix} = \begin{bmatrix} 7 \\ 6 \end{bmatrix}$	$[A][X] = [B]$	The system in matrix form.
$\begin{bmatrix} 0.8 & -0.6 \\ -0.2 & 0.4 \end{bmatrix}\begin{bmatrix} 2 & 3 \\ 1 & 4 \end{bmatrix}\begin{bmatrix} x \\ y \end{bmatrix} = \begin{bmatrix} 0.8 & -0.6 \\ -0.2 & 0.4 \end{bmatrix}\begin{bmatrix} 7 \\ 6 \end{bmatrix}$	$[A]^{-1}[A][X] = [A]^{-1}[B]$	Left-multiply both sides by the inverse.
$\begin{bmatrix} 1 & 0 \\ 0 & 1 \end{bmatrix}\begin{bmatrix} x \\ y \end{bmatrix} = \begin{bmatrix} 0.8 & -0.6 \\ -0.2 & 0.4 \end{bmatrix}\begin{bmatrix} 7 \\ 6 \end{bmatrix}$	$[I][X] = [A]^{-1}[B]$	By the definition of inverse, $[A]^{-1}[A] = [I]$.
$\begin{bmatrix} x \\ y \end{bmatrix} = \begin{bmatrix} 0.8 & -0.6 \\ -0.2 & 0.4 \end{bmatrix}\begin{bmatrix} 7 \\ 6 \end{bmatrix}$	$[X] = [A]^{-1}[B]$	By the definition of identity, $[I][X] = [X]$.
$\begin{bmatrix} x \\ y \end{bmatrix} = \begin{bmatrix} 2 \\ 1 \end{bmatrix}$		Multiply the right side.

The solution to the system is (2, 1). Substitute the values into the original equations to check the solution.

$2x + 3y = 7$	$x = 6 - 4y$
$2(2) + 3(1) \stackrel{?}{=} 7$	$2 \stackrel{?}{=} 6 - 4(1)$
$4 + 3 \stackrel{?}{=} 7$	$2 \stackrel{?}{=} 6 - 4$
$7 = 7$	$2 = 2$

The solution checks.

You can also solve larger systems of equations using an inverse matrix. First, decide what quantities are unknown and write equations using the information given in the problem. Then rewrite the system of equations as a matrix equation, and use either row reduction or an inverse matrix to solve the system. Even systems of equations with many unknowns can be solved quickly this way.

EXAMPLE C

On a recent trip to the movies, Duane, Marsha, and Parker each purchased snacks. Duane bought two candy bars, a small drink, and two bags of popcorn for a total of \$11.85. Marsha spent \$9.00 on a candy bar, two small drinks, and a bag of popcorn. Parker spent \$12.35 on two small drinks and three bags of popcorn, but no candy. If all the prices included tax, what was the price of each item?

▶ Solution

The prices of the items are the unknowns. Let c represent the price of a candy bar in dollars, let d represent the price of a small drink in dollars, and let p represent the price of a bag of popcorn in dollars. This system represents the three friends' purchases:

$$\begin{cases} 2c + 1d + 2p = 11.85 \\ 1c + 2d + 1p = 9.00 \\ 0c + 2d + 3p = 12.35 \end{cases}$$

Translate these equations into a matrix equation in the form $[A][X] = [B]$.

$$\begin{bmatrix} 2 & 1 & 2 \\ 1 & 2 & 1 \\ 0 & 2 & 3 \end{bmatrix}\begin{bmatrix} c \\ d \\ p \end{bmatrix} = \begin{bmatrix} 11.85 \\ 9.00 \\ 12.35 \end{bmatrix}$$

The solution to the system is simply the product $[A]^{-1}[B]$.

$$[X] = [A]^{-1}[B] = \begin{bmatrix} 2.15 \\ 2.05 \\ 2.75 \end{bmatrix}$$

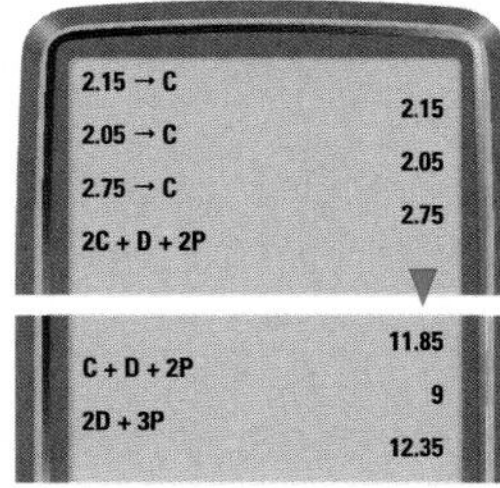

A candy bar costs \$2.15, a small drink costs \$2.05, and a bag of popcorn costs \$2.75.

Substituting these answers into the original system shows that they are correct. You can use your calculator to evaluate the expressions quickly and accurately.

You have probably noticed that in order to solve systems of equations with two variables, you must have two equations. To solve a system of equations with three variables, you must have three equations. In general, you must have as many equations as variables. Otherwise, there will not be enough information to solve the problem. For matrix equations, this means that the coefficient matrix must be square.

If there are more equations than variables, often one equation is equivalent to another equation and therefore just repeats the same information. Or the extra information may contradict the other equations, and thus there is no solution that will satisfy all the equations.

EXERCISES

Practice Your Skills

1. Rewrite each system of equations in matrix form.

a. $\begin{cases} 3x + 4y = 11 \\ 2x - 5y = -8 \end{cases}$ **b.** $\begin{cases} x + 2y + z = 0 \\ 3x - 4y + 5z = -11 \\ -2x - 8y - 3z = 1 \end{cases}$ **c.** $\begin{cases} 5.2x + 3.6y = 7 \\ -5.2x + 2y = 8.2 \end{cases}$ **d.** $\begin{cases} \frac{1}{4}x - \frac{2}{5}y = 3 \\ \frac{3}{8}x + \frac{2}{5}y = 2 \end{cases}$

1a. $\begin{bmatrix} 3 & 4 \\ 2 & -5 \end{bmatrix}\begin{bmatrix} x \\ y \end{bmatrix} = \begin{bmatrix} 11 \\ -8 \end{bmatrix}$

1b. $\begin{bmatrix} 1 & 2 & 1 \\ 3 & -4 & 5 \\ -2 & -8 & -3 \end{bmatrix}\begin{bmatrix} x \\ y \\ z \end{bmatrix} = \begin{bmatrix} 0 \\ -11 \\ 1 \end{bmatrix}$

1c. $\begin{bmatrix} 5.2 & 3.6 \\ -5.2 & 2 \end{bmatrix}\begin{bmatrix} x \\ y \end{bmatrix} = \begin{bmatrix} 7 \\ 8.2 \end{bmatrix}$

1d. $\begin{bmatrix} \frac{1}{4} & -\frac{2}{5} \\ \frac{3}{8} & \frac{2}{5} \end{bmatrix}\begin{bmatrix} x \\ y \end{bmatrix} = \begin{bmatrix} 3 \\ 2 \end{bmatrix}$

Assessing Progress

You can check students' understanding of matrices and matrix multiplication and their skill at solving systems of equations by row reduction.

Closing the Lesson

The matrix equation $[A][X] = [B]$ can be solved by multiplying both sides on the left by the **inverse matrix** of $[A]$. The result is $[I][X] = [A]^{-1}[B]$, where $[I]$ is the **identity matrix.** The product on the left equals matrix $[X]$, so the equation is solved.

BUILDING UNDERSTANDING

Students practice finding inverse matrices and using them to solve matrix equations.

ASSIGNING HOMEWORK

Essential	1–6
Performance assessment	7–14
Portfolio	10
Journal	12
Group	10, 14
Review	15–18

Helping with the Exercises

Exercise 2 Before multiplying, **[Ask]** "What are the dimensions of the resulting matrix?"

2b. $\begin{bmatrix} 7 & -18 & -7 \\ 12 & -27 & 42 \\ 1 & -4 & -21 \end{bmatrix}$

2c. not possible because the inside dimensions do not match

Exercise 3 You might suggest that students check their work by row reduction or by multiplying by inverse matrices.

4b. $\begin{bmatrix} 1 & 0 & 0 \\ 0 & 1 & 0 \\ 0 & 0 & 1 \end{bmatrix}$; yes

Exercise 5 If you think students might spend an unreasonable amount of time on this exercise, you can have them find the inverses with a calculator. Because they'll probably find the work easy, you might ask whether they see any correspondence in 5a between the entries in a matrix and its inverse. Ask whether the pattern applies to 5c in any way. This foreshadows Take Another Look activity 1 on page 357.

5b. $\begin{bmatrix} -\frac{1}{6} & \frac{2}{3} & \frac{1}{9} \\ \frac{1}{2} & -1 & 0 \\ 0 & 0 & \frac{1}{3} \end{bmatrix}$ or $\begin{bmatrix} -0.1\overline{6} & 0.\overline{6} & 0.\overline{1} \\ 0.5 & -1 & 0 \\ 0 & 0 & 0.\overline{3} \end{bmatrix}$

5c. $\begin{bmatrix} \frac{7}{5} & -\frac{3}{5} \\ -2 & 1 \end{bmatrix}$ or $\begin{bmatrix} 1.4 & -0.6 \\ -2 & 1 \end{bmatrix}$

Exercise 7 If students are having difficulty with 7a, ask them what steps they might take to solve the problem. Steps are (1) define the variables; (2) write the equations; (3) write the matrix equation; (4) solve using inverse matrices; (5) explain the solution.

[ESL] The phrase *better off* in 7c refers to saving money.

2. Multiply each pair of matrices. If multiplication is not possible, explain why.

a. $\begin{bmatrix} 5 & 2 \\ 7 & 3 \end{bmatrix}\begin{bmatrix} 1 & -3 \\ 5 & -2 \end{bmatrix}$ $\begin{bmatrix} 15 & -19 \\ 22 & -27 \end{bmatrix}$ b. $\begin{bmatrix} 4 & -1 \\ 3 & 6 \\ 2 & -3 \end{bmatrix}\begin{bmatrix} 2 & -5 & 0 \\ 1 & -2 & 7 \end{bmatrix}$ c. $\begin{bmatrix} 9 & -3 \end{bmatrix}\begin{bmatrix} 4 & -6 \\ 0 & -2 \\ -1 & 3 \end{bmatrix}$

3. Use matrix multiplication to expand each system. Then solve for each variable by using substitution or elimination. See below.

a. $\begin{bmatrix} 1 & 5 \\ 6 & 2 \end{bmatrix}\begin{bmatrix} a & b \\ c & d \end{bmatrix} = \begin{bmatrix} -7 & 33 \\ 14 & -26 \end{bmatrix}$ b. $\begin{bmatrix} 1 & 5 \\ 6 & 2 \end{bmatrix}\begin{bmatrix} a & b \\ c & d \end{bmatrix} = \begin{bmatrix} 1 & 0 \\ 0 & 1 \end{bmatrix}$

4. Multiply each pair of matrices. Are the matrices inverses of each other?

a. $\begin{bmatrix} 5 & 2 \\ 7 & 3 \end{bmatrix}\begin{bmatrix} 3 & -2 \\ -7 & 5 \end{bmatrix}$ $\begin{bmatrix} 1 & 0 \\ 0 & 1 \end{bmatrix}$; yes b. $\begin{bmatrix} 1 & 5 & 4 \\ 6 & 2 & -2 \\ 0 & 3 & 1 \end{bmatrix}\begin{bmatrix} 0.16 & 0.14 & -0.36 \\ -0.12 & 0.02 & 0.52 \\ 0.36 & -0.06 & -0.56 \end{bmatrix}$

5. Find the inverse of each matrix by solving the matrix equation $[A][A]^{-1} = [I]$. Then find the inverse matrix on your calculator to check your answer.

a. $\begin{bmatrix} 4 & 3 \\ 5 & 4 \end{bmatrix}$ $\begin{bmatrix} 4 & -3 \\ -5 & 4 \end{bmatrix}$ b. $\begin{bmatrix} 6 & 4 & -2 \\ 3 & 1 & -1 \\ 0 & 0 & 3 \end{bmatrix}$ c. $\begin{bmatrix} 5 & 3 \\ 10 & 7 \end{bmatrix}$ d. $\begin{bmatrix} 1 & 2 \\ 2 & 4 \end{bmatrix}$ Inverse does not exist.

Reason and Apply

6. Rewrite each system in matrix form and solve by using the inverse matrix. Check your solutions.

a. $\begin{cases} 8x + 3y = 41 \\ 6x + 5y = 39 \end{cases}$ $\begin{bmatrix} 8 & 3 \\ 6 & 5 \end{bmatrix}\begin{bmatrix} x \\ y \end{bmatrix} = \begin{bmatrix} 41 \\ 39 \end{bmatrix}$; $x = 4, y = 3$

b. $\begin{cases} 11x - 5y = -38 \\ 9x + 2y = -25 \end{cases}$ $\begin{bmatrix} 11 & -5 \\ 9 & 2 \end{bmatrix}\begin{bmatrix} x \\ y \end{bmatrix} = \begin{bmatrix} -38 \\ -25 \end{bmatrix}$; $x = -3, y = 1$

c. $\begin{cases} 2x + y - 2z = 1 \\ 6x + 2y - 4z = 3 \\ 4x - y + 3z = 5 \end{cases}$ $\begin{bmatrix} 2 & 1 & -2 \\ 6 & 2 & -4 \\ 4 & -1 & 3 \end{bmatrix}\begin{bmatrix} x \\ y \\ z \end{bmatrix} = \begin{bmatrix} 1 \\ 3 \\ 5 \end{bmatrix}$; $x = 0.5, y = 6, z = 3$

d. 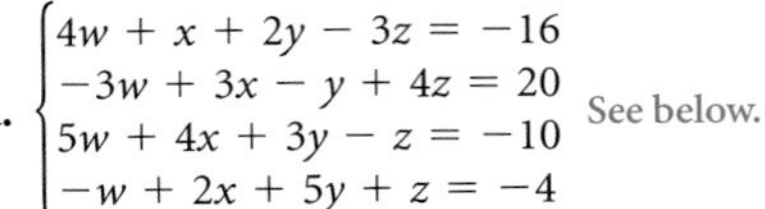
$\begin{cases} 4w + x + 2y - 3z = -16 \\ -3w + 3x - y + 4z = 20 \\ 5w + 4x + 3y - z = -10 \\ -w + 2x + 5y + z = -4 \end{cases}$ See below.

7. At the High Flying Amusement Park there are three kinds of rides: Jolly rides, Adventure rides, and Thrill rides. Admission is free when you buy a book of tickets, which includes ten tickets for each type of ride. Or you can pay \$5.00 for admission and then buy tickets for each of the rides individually. Noah, Rita, and Carey decide to pay the admission price and buy individual tickets. Noah pays \$19.55 for 7 Jolly rides, 3 Adventure rides, and 9 Thrill rides. Rita pays \$13.00 for 9 Jolly rides, 10 Adventure rides, and no Thrill rides. Carey pays \$24.95 for 8 Jolly rides, 7 Adventure rides, and 10 Thrill rides. (The prices above do not include the admission price.)

a. How much does each type of ride cost? Jolly rides cost \$0.50, Adventure rides cost \$0.85, and Thrill rides cost \$1.50.

b. What is the total cost of a 30-ride book of tickets? \$28.50

c. Would Noah, Rita, or Carey have been better off purchasing a ticket book? Carey would have been better off buying a ticket book.

3a. $\begin{bmatrix} 1a + 5c & 1b + 5d \\ 6a + 2c & 6b + 2d \end{bmatrix} = \begin{bmatrix} -7 & 33 \\ 14 & -26 \end{bmatrix}$; $\begin{bmatrix} a & b \\ c & d \end{bmatrix} = \begin{bmatrix} 3 & -7 \\ -2 & 8 \end{bmatrix}$

3b. $\begin{bmatrix} 1a + 5c & 1b + 5d \\ 6a + 2c & 6b + 2d \end{bmatrix} = \begin{bmatrix} 1 & 0 \\ 0 & 1 \end{bmatrix}$; $\begin{bmatrix} a & b \\ c & d \end{bmatrix} = \begin{bmatrix} -\frac{1}{14} & \frac{5}{28} \\ \frac{3}{14} & -\frac{1}{28} \end{bmatrix}$

6d. $\begin{bmatrix} 4 & 1 & 2 & -3 \\ -3 & 3 & -1 & 4 \\ 5 & 4 & 3 & -1 \\ -1 & 2 & 5 & 1 \end{bmatrix}\begin{bmatrix} w \\ x \\ y \\ z \end{bmatrix} = \begin{bmatrix} -16 \\ 20 \\ -10 \\ -4 \end{bmatrix}$; $w = -1, x = 1, y = -2, z = 3$

8. A family invested a portion of \$5000 in an account at 6% annual interest and the rest in an account at 7.5% annual interest. The total interest they earned in the first year was \$340.50. How much did they invest in each account?

8. \$2300 at 6% and \$2700 at 7.5%

9. The midsize angle of a triangle is 30° greater than the smallest angle. The largest angle is 10° more than twice the midsize angle. What are the measures of the three angles?

9. 20°, 50°, 110°

10. Being able to solve a system of equations is definitely not "new" mathematics. Mahāvīra, the best-known Indian mathematician of the 9th century, worked the following problem. See if you can solve it.

The mixed price of 9 citrons and 7 fragrant wood apples is 107; again, the mixed price of 7 citrons and 9 fragrant wood apples is 101. O you arithmetician, tell me quickly the price of a citron and of a wood apple here, having distinctly separated those prices well.

Exercise 10 [Language] A citron is a citrus fruit similar to a lemon with a thick rind. The source of this problem is *An Introduction to the History of Mathematics,* by Howard Eves.

10. The price of a citron is 8; the price of a fragrant wood apple is 5.

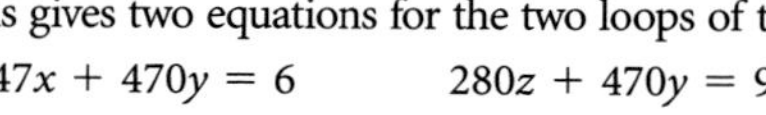

Mahāvīra (ca. 800–870 C.E.) wrote *Ganita Sara Samgraha,* the first Indian text exclusively about mathematics. Writing in his home of Mysore, India, he considered this book to be a collection of insights from other Indian mathematicians, such as Āryabata I, Bhāskara I, and Brahmagupta, who wrote their findings in astronomy texts.

11. APPLICATION The circuit here is made of two batteries (6 volt and 9 volt) and three resistors (47 ohms, 470 ohms, and 280 ohms). The batteries create an electric current in the circuit. Let x, y, and z represent the current in amps flowing through each resistor.

The voltage across each resistor is current times resistance ($V = IR$). This gives two equations for the two loops of the circuit:

$47x + 470y = 6 \qquad 280z + 470y = 9$

The electric current flowing into any point along the circuit must flow out. So, for instance, at junction A, $x + z - y = 0$. Find the current flowing through each resistor.

6 V 9 V y 47 Ω 470 Ω 280 Ω x A z

Exercise 11 [Language] In electrical circuits, *resistors* control the *current,* the flow of electricity. Current is measured in *amperes,* commonly known as *amps.*

11. $x = 0.0016$, $y = 0.0126$, $z = 0.0110$

12. When you use your calculator to find the inverse of the coefficient matrix for this system, you get an error message. What does this mean about the system?

$$\begin{cases} 3.2x + 2.4y = 9.6 \\ 2x + 1.5y = 6 \end{cases}$$

12. An error message means the system is either dependent or inconsistent. In this case, the lines are the same, so the system is dependent.

13. One way to find an inverse of a matrix $\begin{bmatrix} a & b \\ c & d \end{bmatrix}$, if it exists, is to perform row operations on the augmented matrix $\left[\begin{array}{cc|cc} a & b & 1 & 0 \\ c & d & 0 & 1 \end{array}\right]$ to change it to the form $\left[\begin{array}{cc|cc} 1 & 0 & e & f \\ 0 & 1 & g & h \end{array}\right]$. The matrix $\begin{bmatrix} e & f \\ g & h \end{bmatrix}$ is the required inverse. Use this strategy to find the inverse of each matrix.

a. $\begin{bmatrix} 4 & 3 \\ 5 & 4 \end{bmatrix}$

b. $\begin{bmatrix} 6 & 4 & -2 \\ 3 & 1 & -1 \\ 0 & 7 & 3 \end{bmatrix}$

Exercise 13 This exercise refers to the row-reduction method of Lesson 6.3. If you skipped that lesson, don't assign this problem.

13a. $\begin{bmatrix} 4 & -3 \\ -5 & 4 \end{bmatrix}$

13b. $\begin{bmatrix} -0.\overline{5} & 1.\overline{4} & 0.\overline{1} \\ 0.5 & -1 & 0 \\ -1.\overline{6} & 2.\overline{3} & 0.\overline{3} \end{bmatrix}$ or $\begin{bmatrix} -\frac{5}{9} & \frac{13}{9} & \frac{1}{9} \\ \frac{1}{2} & -1 & 0 \\ -\frac{7}{6} & \frac{7}{3} & \frac{1}{3} \end{bmatrix}$

Exercise 14 As needed, encourage students to factor the left side of the equation into $([I] - [A])\,[X]$.

14. $[X] = \begin{bmatrix} 202.9 \\ 228.6 \\ 165.7 \end{bmatrix}$

14. **APPLICATION** An important application in the study of economics is the study of the relationship between industrial production and consumer demand. In creating an economic model, Russian-American economist Wassily Leontief (1906–1999) noted that the total output less the internal consumption equals consumer demand. Mathematically his input-output model looks like $[X] - [A][X] = [D]$, where $[X]$ is the total output matrix, $[A]$ is the input-output matrix, and $[D]$ is the matrix representing consumer demand.

Here is an input-output matrix, $[A]$, for a simple three-sector economy:

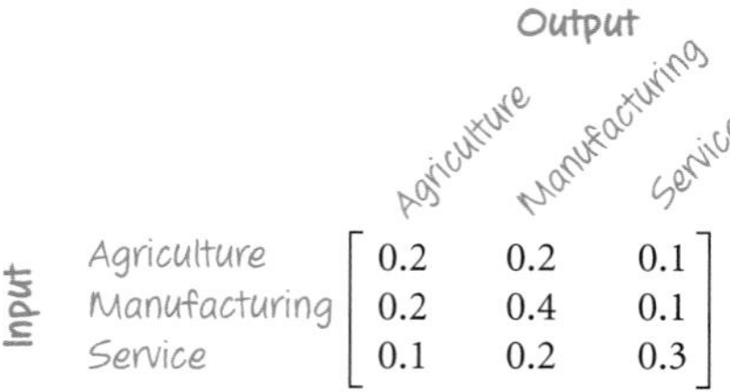

For instance, the first column tells the economist that to produce an output of 1 unit of agricultural products requires the consumption (input) of 0.2 unit of agricultural products, 0.2 unit of manufacturing products, and 0.1 unit of service products.

The demand matrix, $[D]$, represents millions of dollars. Use the equation $[X] - [A][X] = [D]$ to find the output matrix, $[X]$.

$$[D] = \begin{bmatrix} 100 \\ 80 \\ 50 \end{bmatrix}$$

Economics CONNECTION

During World War II, Wassily Leontief's method became a critical part of planning for wartime production in the United States. As a consultant to the U.S. Labor Department, he developed an input-output table for more than 90 economic sectors. During the early 1960s, Leontief and economist Marvin Hoffenberg used input-output analysis to forecast the economic effects of reduction or elimination of militaries. In 1973, Leontief was awarded a Nobel Prize in economics for his contributions to the field.

Wassily Leontief

MAKING THE CONNECTION

Input-output analysis has become essential to economic planning because it allows economists to combine complex relationships to paint a detailed picture of the economy. Leontief's methods are widely used in developing economic policy, predicting economic trends, and preparing government budgets. The United Nations, the World Bank, and more than 30 countries use input-output analysis.

Review

6.2 **15.** For each equation, write a second linear equation that would create a consistent and dependent system.

a. $y = 2x + 4$ **b.** $y = -\frac{1}{3}x - 3$ **c.** $2x + 5y = 10$ **d.** $x - 2y = -6$

Exercises 15, 16 These exercises use the concepts of consistent, inconsistent, and dependent systems introduced in Lesson 6.2, Exercise 14.

15. possible answers:

15a. $2y = 4x + 8$

15b. $3y = -x - 9$

15c. $4x + 10y = 20$

15d. $2x - 4y = -12$

3.6 **16.** For each equation, write a second linear equation that would create an inconsistent system. possible answers:

a. $y = 2x + 4$ — $y = 2x + 6$

b. $y = -\frac{1}{3}x - 3$ — $y = -\frac{1}{3}x + 2$

c. $2x + 5y = 10$ — $2x + 5y = 0$

d. $x - 2y = -6$ — $x - 2y = 6$

6.1 **17.** Four towns, Lenox, Murray, Davis, and Terre, are connected by a series of roads.

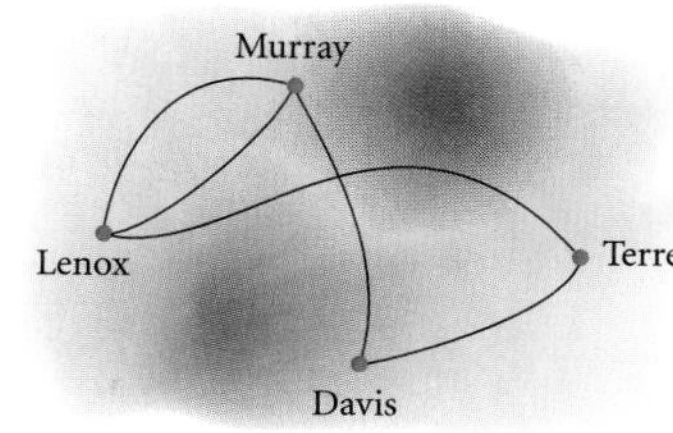

a. Represent the number of direct road connections between the towns in a matrix, $[A]$. List the towns in the order Lenox, Murray, Davis, and Terre.

b. Explain the meaning of the value of a_{22}.

c. Describe the symmetry of your matrix.

d. How many roads are there? What is the sum of the entries in the matrix? Explain the relationship between these two answers.

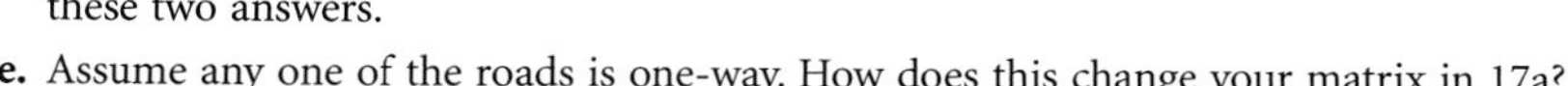

e. Assume any one of the roads is one-way. How does this change your matrix in 17a?

1.1 **18.** The third term of an arithmetic sequence is 28. The seventh term is 80. What is the first term? 2

IMPROVING YOUR REASONING SKILLS

Secret Survey

Eric is doing a survey. He has a deck of cards and two questions written on a sheet of paper. He says, "Pick a card from the deck. Don't show it to me. If it is a red card, answer Question 1. If it is a black card, answer Question 2."

Question 1 (red card): Does your phone number end in an even number?

Question 2 (black card): Do you own a stuffed animal?

You pick a card and look at the paper, and you respond, "Yes." Eric records your answer, shuffles the cards, and goes on to the next person.

At the end of the survey, Eric has gathered 37 yeses and 23 noes. He calculates that 73% responded "yes" to the second question.

Explain how Eric was able to find this result without knowing which question each person was answering.

17a. $[A] = \begin{bmatrix} 0 & 2 & 0 & 1 \\ 2 & 0 & 1 & 0 \\ 0 & 1 & 0 & 1 \\ 1 & 0 & 1 & 0 \end{bmatrix}$

17b. It is 0 because there are zero roads connecting Murray to itself.

17c. The matrix has reflection symmetry across the main diagonal.

17d. 5; 10. The matrix sum is twice the number of roads; each road is counted twice in the matrix because it can be traveled in either direction.

17e. For example, if the road between Davis and Terre is one-way toward Davis, a_{34} changes from 1 to 0. The matrix is no longer symmetric.

EXTENSIONS

A. Use Take Another Look activity 1 on page 357.

B. Have students research other ways to solve systems of linear equations.

Secret Survey

To collect data on sensitive issues, a **randomized response** survey like this might couple the sensitive question with a benign question that has predictable results.

Because the cards in a deck are evenly split (red or black), about half of the 60 people answered each question. About 50% of phone numbers have even last digits, so of the 30 respondents who answered Question 1, roughly 15 answered yes.

IMPROVING REASONING SKILLS

Use the reasoning in the side column. Of the 30 people answering Question 2, approximately 22 of their responses must have been yes and 8 no. Therefore, of those who answered Question 2, about $\frac{22}{30}$, or 73%, answered yes.

Students comfortable with probability might use a probability tree diagram.

There are 37 yes answers, so $P(\text{yes}) = \frac{37}{60}$.

The tree diagram shows $P(\text{yes}) = .25 + .5p$.

$\frac{37}{60} = .25 + .5p \qquad p \approx .73$

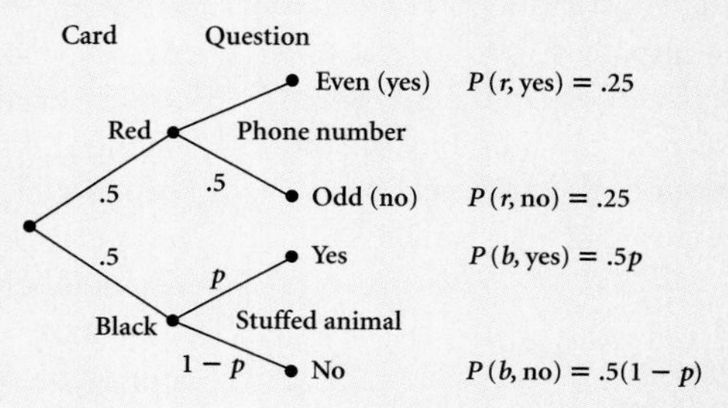

LESSON

6.5

PLANNING

LESSON OUTLINE

One day:

15 min Investigation

10 min Sharing

5 min Example

15 min Exercises

MATERIALS

- graph paper
- Pottery (T) for One Step
- Graphing Inequalities (T), *optional*
- Calculator Notes 6G, 6G/App

TEACHING

This lesson addresses systems of inequalities in two variables as a prelude to linear programming.

One Step
Show the Pottery transparency and pose this problem, part of the investigation of Lesson 6.6: "The Elite Pottery Shoppe makes two kinds of birdbaths: a fancy glazed and a simple unglazed. Each unglazed birdbath requires 0.5 hour on a pottery wheel, and each glazed birdbath requires 1 hour on the wheel. The company's one pottery wheel is available for at most 8 hours per day. Each unglazed birdbath requires 3 hours in a kiln, and each glazed birdbath requires 18 hours in a kiln. The three kilns are available up to 60 hours per day. A standing order requires the company to produce at least 6 unglazed birdbaths per day. What possible numbers of birdbaths of both kinds can the company make each day?"

See page 887 for answer to Step 1.

LESSON 6.5

Systems of Linear Inequalities

Frequently, real-world situations involve a range of possible values. Algebraic statements of these situations are called **inequalities.**

Situation	Inequality
Write an essay between two and five pages in length.	$2 \leq E \leq 5$
Practice more than an hour each day.	$P > 1$
The post office is open from nine o'clock until noon.	$9 \leq H \leq 12$
Do not spend more than \$10 on candy and popcorn.	$c + p \leq 10$
A college fund has \$40,000 to invest in stocks and bonds.	$s + b \leq 40000$

Recall that you can perform operations on inequalities very much like you do on equations. You can add or subtract the same quantity on both sides, multiply by the same number or expression on both sides, and so on. The one exception to remember is that when you multiply or divide by a negative quantity or expression, the inequality symbol reverses.

In this lesson you will learn how to graphically show solutions to inequalities with two variables, such as the last two statements in the table above.

The cost of a college education continues to rise. The good news is that over \$90 billion is available in financial aid. At four-year public colleges, for example, over 60% of students receive some form of financial aid. Financial aid makes college affordable for many students, despite increasing costs.

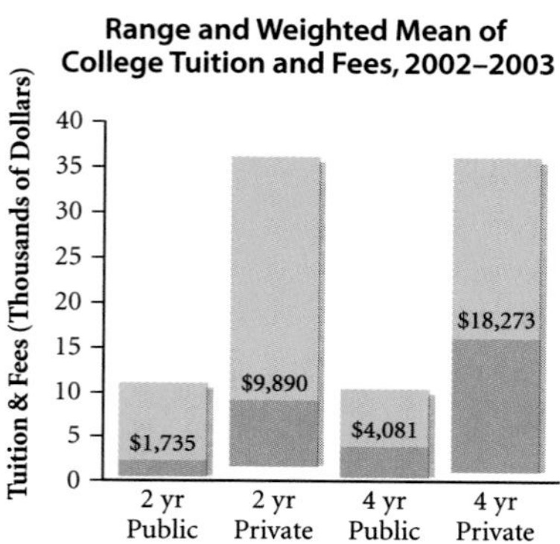

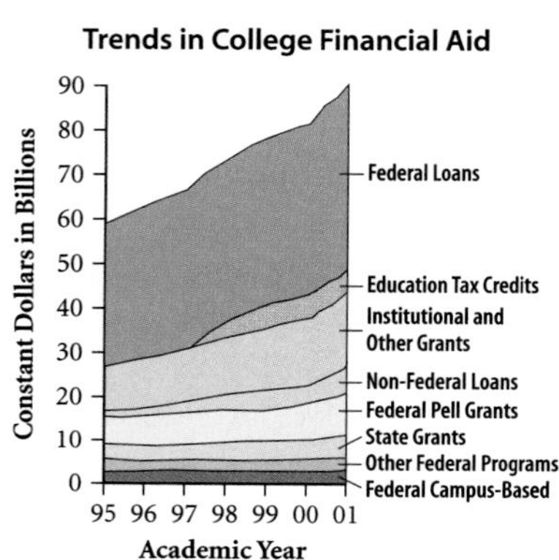

These graphs are based on information provided by The College Board.

Investigation
Paying for College

A total of \$40,000 has been donated to a college scholarship fund. The administrators of the fund are considering how much to invest in stocks and how much to invest in bonds. Stocks usually pay more but are a riskier investment, whereas bonds pay less but are safer.

Step 1 Let x represent the amount in dollars invested in stocks, and let y represent the amount in dollars invested in bonds. Graph the equation $x + y = 40000$.

For motivation, you might mention that students will later investigate how many of each kind to make to maximize profit. Encourage students to assign variables and set up inequalities. If they're having difficulty deciding how to graph the inequalities, ask whether graphing corresponding equations would help. As students find half-planes, ask whether points below the x-axis or to the left of the y-axis make sense, and help students add commonsense constraints. During Sharing, introduce the terms *constraint, feasible region,* and *vertex.*

[Alert] Students might not understand that half-planes extend infinitely in one direction. They are bounded in only one direction; in the other they extend beyond the edges of the drawn graph.

Step 1 Graphs should be drawn on graph paper, not made on calculators. The neater and more accurate the graphs, the easier Step 6 will be. As needed, encourage students to graph using intercepts rather than solving for y.

Step 2 | Name at least five pairs of x- and y-values that satisfy the inequality $x + y < 40000$ and plot them on your graph. In this problem, why can $x + y$ be less than $40,000?

Step 3 | Describe where all possible solutions to the inequality $x + y < 40000$ are located. Shade this region on your graph.

Step 4 Negative values for x or y do not make sense.

Step 4 | Describe some points that fit the condition $x + y \leq 40000$ but do not make sense for the situation.

Assume that each option—stocks or bonds—requires a minimum investment of $5000, and that the fund administrators want to purchase some stocks and some bonds. Based on the advice of their financial advisor, they decide that the amount invested in bonds should be at least twice the amount invested in stocks.

Step 5 | Translate all of the limitations, or **constraints,** into a system of inequalities. A table might help you to organize this information.

Step 6 | Graph all of the inequalities and determine the region of your graph that will satisfy all the constraints. Find each corner, or **vertex,** of this region.

When there are one or two variables in an inequality, you can represent the solution as a set of ordered pairs by shading the region of the coordinate plane that contains those points.

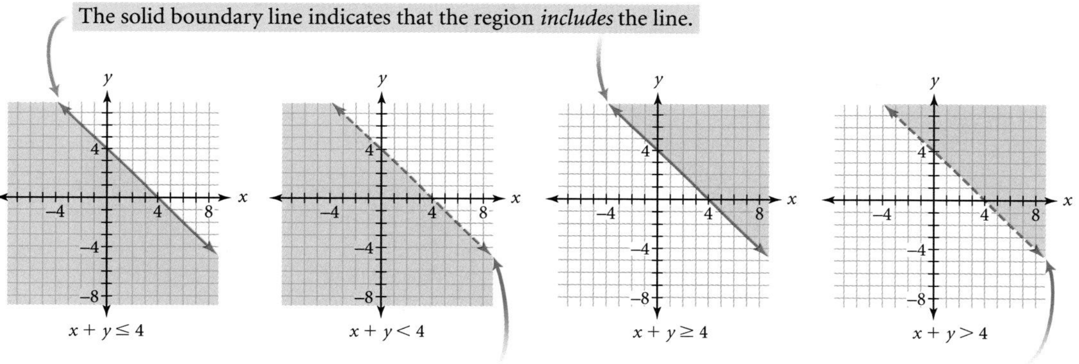

When you have several inequalities that must be satisfied simultaneously, you have a system. The solution to a system of inequalities with two variables will be a set of points rather than a single point. This set of points is called a **feasible region.** The feasible region can be shown graphically as part of a plane, or sometimes it can be described as a geometric shape with its vertices given.

Step 2 This inequality is equivalent to one used in the introduction. Here the variables are called x and y to facilitate graphing. Encourage each group member to pick a different pair. Negative values of x and y fit the model through Step 4. **[Ask]** "Where in your graph does each of these points lie?"

Step 2 Possible answer: (10000, 10000), (5000, 5000), (0, 0), (10000, 29999), (30000, 5000). They don't necessarily have to invest all of the money.

Step 3 Suggest that students make the shading light, because more inequalities will be shaded later in the investigation.

Step 3 They are all below the line $x + y = 40000$.

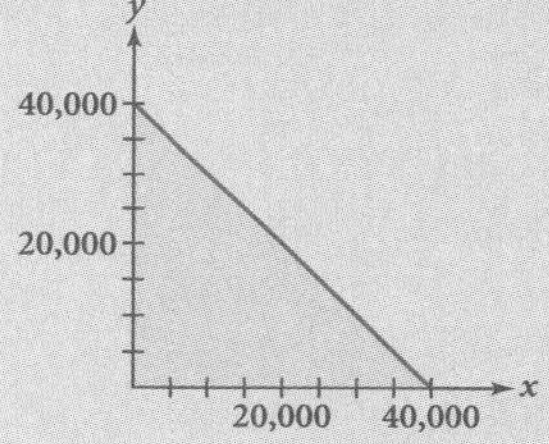

Step 5
$$\begin{cases} x \geq 0 \\ y \geq 0 \\ x \geq 5000 \\ y \geq 5000 \\ y \geq 2x \\ x + y \leq 40000 \end{cases}$$

Step 6 Students will be able to find most of the vertices by examining the graphs, but they can use a method of solving systems of equations if the intersection points aren't clear.

Step 6

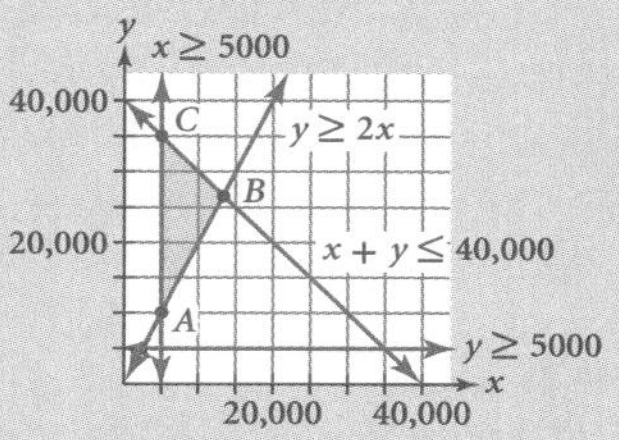

$A(5000, 10000)$, $B(13333.\overline{3}, 26666.\overline{6})$, $C(5000, 35000)$

NCTM STANDARDS

CONTENT		PROCESS	
✓	Number	✓	Problem Solving
✓	Algebra	✓	Reasoning
	Geometry	✓	Communication
✓	Measurement	✓	Connections
	Data/Probability	✓	Representation

LESSON OBJECTIVES

- Review linear inequalities and the solution of an inequality, including multiplying and dividing by a negative number
- Write inequalities to describe given real-world constraints
- Graph systems of inequalities
- Interpret the meaning of the points within a feasible region
- Find the vertices of a feasible region

▶ EXAMPLE

As students graph inequalities on calculators, you might use the Graphing Inequalities transparency, cutting out and overlaying each new graph. As an alternative to Calculator Note 6G for TI-83 Plus calculators, you can use the Inequality Graphing application (available on the *Calculator Programs and Data* CD) that allows special shading so you can see the result of combining inequalities. See Calculator Note 6G/App.

[Ask] "What do x and y represent?" [hours spent on mathematics and on chemistry, respectively] Point out that students should use a solid line when the inequality is inclusive ("greater than or equal to" or "less than or equal to") and a dashed line when the inequality is exclusive ("greater than" or "less than").

When students are finding feasible regions by hand, they often have difficulty seeing the area that is shaded by all constraints. You may want to suggest that students indicate the shaded sides with arrows.

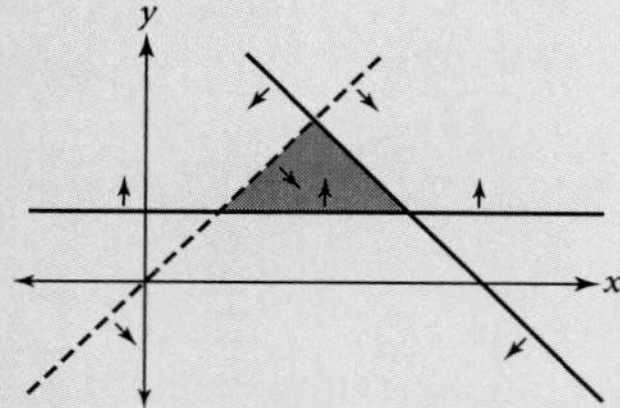

If students find intersection points from a graph, ask how confident they are in the precision of their answers. Help them decide to check by substitution.

[Ask] "Are all points in the region solutions, or only those with integer coordinates?" [The variables represent times, so every point in the feasible region is a solution.]

SHARING IDEAS

[Language] When only one inequality in x and y is graphed, the infinite region is called a *half-plane.*

EXAMPLE

Rachel has 3 hours to work on her homework tonight. She wants to spend more time working on mathematics than on chemistry, and she must spend at least a half hour working on chemistry. State the constraints of this system algebraically with x representing mathematics time in hours and y representing chemistry time in hours. Graph your inequalities, shade the feasible region, and label its vertices.

▶ Solution

Convert each constraint into an algebraic inequality.

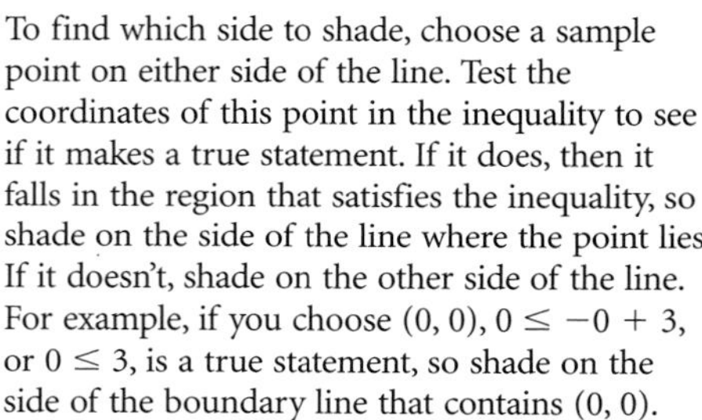

$x + y \leq 3$	Rachel has 3 h to work on homework.
$x > y$	She wants to spend more time working on mathematics than on chemistry.
$y \geq 0.5$	She must spend at least a half hour working on chemistry.

To graph the inequality $x + y \leq 3$, or $y \leq -x + 3$, first graph $y = -x + 3$. Use a solid line because y can be equal to $-x + 3$. This line divides the plane into two regions. One region contains all of the points for which y is less than $-x + 3$, and the other region contains all of the points for which y is greater than $-x + 3$.

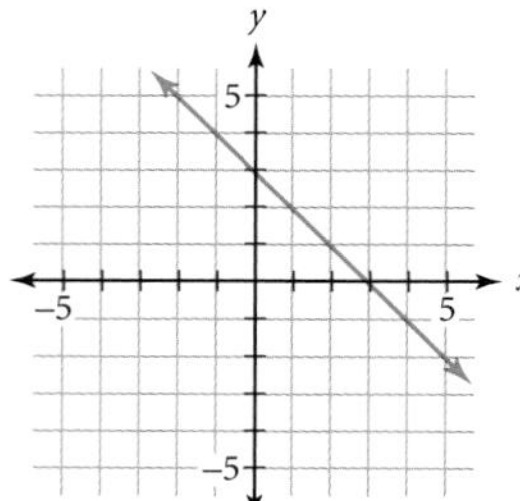

To find which side to shade, choose a sample point on either side of the line. Test the coordinates of this point in the inequality to see if it makes a true statement. If it does, then it falls in the region that satisfies the inequality, so shade on the side of the line where the point lies. If it doesn't, shade on the other side of the line. For example, if you choose (0, 0), $0 \leq -0 + 3$, or $0 \leq 3$, is a true statement, so shade on the side of the boundary line that contains (0, 0).

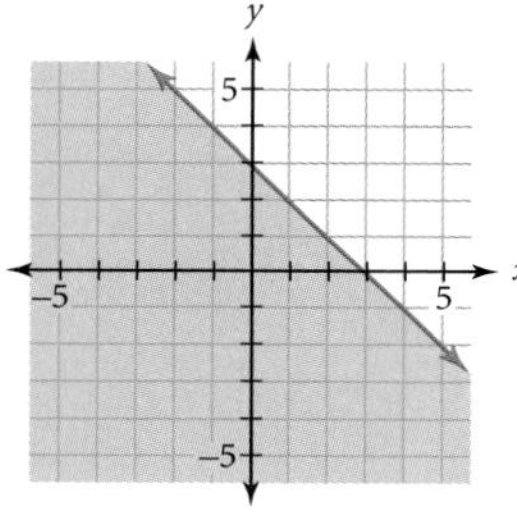

Follow the same steps to graph $x > y$ and $y \geq 0.5$ on the same axes. The graph of $x > y$ will contain a dashed line. [▶ See **Calculator Note 6G** to learn how to graph systems of inequalities using your calculator. ◀]

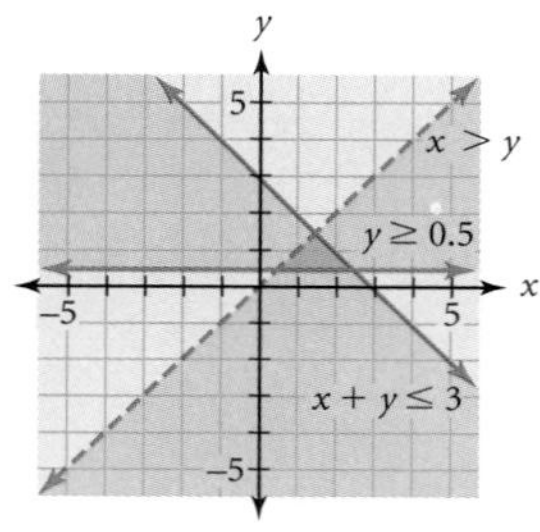

[Ask] "In the example, does it matter whether time spent on mathematics homework is graphed on the x-axis or the y-axis?" [Unlike with earlier equations relating x and y, neither variable can be called dependent or independent, so it doesn't matter.] You might work through the example again with the meanings of the variables interchanged.

Ask students why you need to reverse the direction of an inequality when you multiply by a negative number. If students don't clearly understand this, you can note that the inequality $3 < 5$ is a true statement. Multiplying by -1 gives $-3 < -5$, which is not true. (A picture of a number line might help.) Therefore, the inequality symbol must reverse: $-3 > -5$. Taking the reciprocal of both sides also reverses an inequality symbol. (For example, $\frac{1}{2} > \frac{1}{3}$, but $2 < 3$.)

[Ask] "Why do we look at feasible regions?" [often to find maximum profit or minimum cost] If students worked on the one-step investigation, ask them to save their notes. **[Language]** Remind students that the term *vertex* arises in geometry. Ask

The solution to the system is the set of points in the area that represents the overlap of all the shaded regions—the feasible region. Every point in this region is a possible solution to the system.

To define the area that represents the solutions, name the vertices of the region. You can find the vertices by finding the intersection of each pair of equations using substitution, elimination, or matrices.

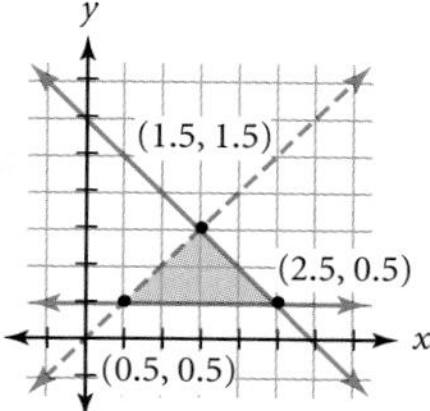

Equations	**Intersections**
$x + y = 3$ and $x = y$	(1.5, 1.5)
$x + y = 3$ and $y = 0.5$	(2.5, 0.5)
$x = y$ and $y = 0.5$	(0.5, 0.5)

The solution to this system is all points in the interior of a triangle with vertices (1.5, 1.5), (2.5, 0.5), and (0.5, 0.5), and the points on the lower and right edges of the triangle. Any point within this region represents a way that Rachel could divide her time. For example, (1.5, 1) means she could spend 1.5 h on mathematics and 1 h on chemistry and still meet all her constraints. Notice, however, that (0.5, 0.5) is not a solution to the system, even though it is a vertex of the feasible region. The point (0.5, 0.5) does not meet the constraint $x > y$.

When you are solving a system of equations based on real-world constraints, it is important to note that sometimes there are constraints that are not specifically stated in the problem. In the example, negative values for x and y would not make sense, because you can't study for a negative number of hours. You could have added the commonsense constraints $x \geq 0$ and $y \geq 0$, although in the example it would not affect the feasible region.

EXERCISES

Practice Your Skills

1. Solve each inequality for y.
   a. $2x - 5y > 10$ $\quad y < \frac{10 - 2x}{-5}$ or $y < -2 + 0.4x$
   b. $4(2 - 3y) + 2x > 14$ $\quad y < \frac{6 - 2x}{-12}$ or $y < -\frac{1}{2} + \frac{1}{6}x$
2. Graph each linear inequality.
   a. $y \leq -2x + 5$
   b. $2y + 2x > 5$
   c. $x > 5$
3. For 3a–d, write the equation of each graph.
   a. $y < 2 - 0.5x$

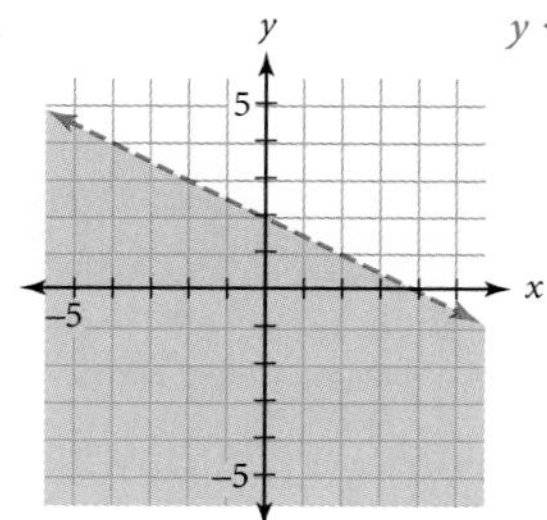

   b. $y \geq 3 + 1.5x$

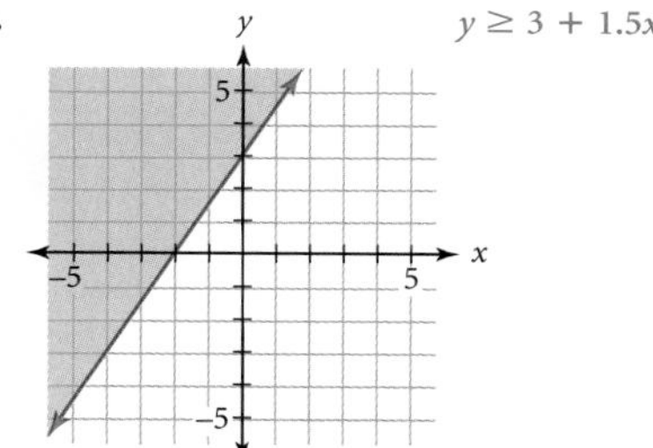

2a.

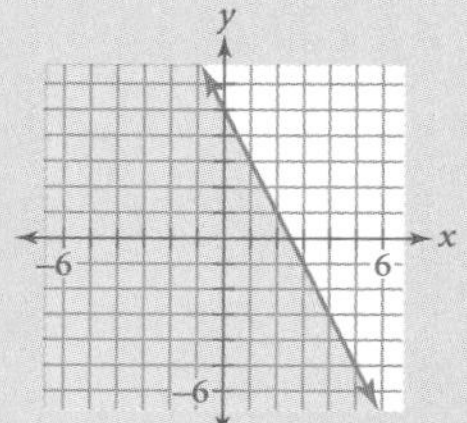

2b.

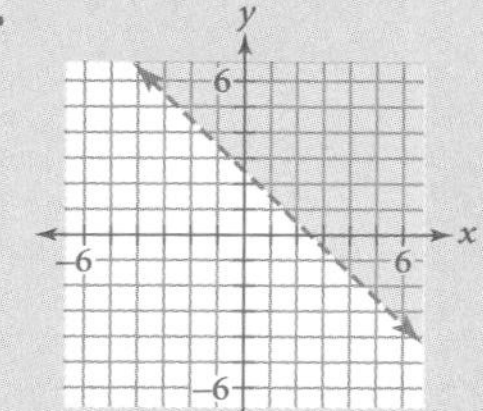

2c.

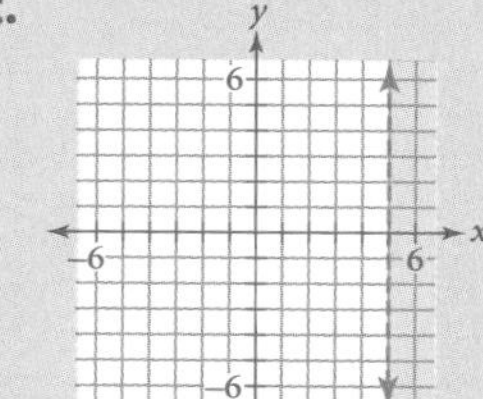

Sharing Ideas (continued)

whether it has the same meaning here. [Each corner here is called a vertex because many feasible regions are polygons.] As needed, remind students that the plural of *vertex* is *vertices* and that the singular of *vertices* is not *vertice*.

[ESL] The *commonsense* constraints are those that are not stated in the problem because they are common knowledge. For example, Rachel can't spend fewer than zero hours on homework.

Assessing Progress

You can assess students' ability to graph equations in standard form and to find intersections of lines from their equations. You can also check their understanding of inequality signs.

Closing the Lesson

A system of inequalities in two variables can be graphed as a planar region called a **feasible region.** Such a system often arises from conditions, or **constraints,** describing a real-life situation. The corners of the feasible region are called **vertices.**

BUILDING UNDERSTANDING

In the exercises students practice graphing inequalities and systems of inequalities in two variables, as well as setting up such systems from constraints present in real-world situations.

ASSIGNING HOMEWORK

Essential	1–3, 5
Performance assessment	4, 6–11
Portfolio	10
Journal	11
Group	9
Review	12–15

MATERIALS

- graph paper

▶ Helping with the Exercises

Exercises 5–8 In each of these exercises, **[Ask]** "Are all the inequalities needed to describe the feasible region?" [In Exercise 5, the inequality $y \geq 0$ is redundant.]

5.

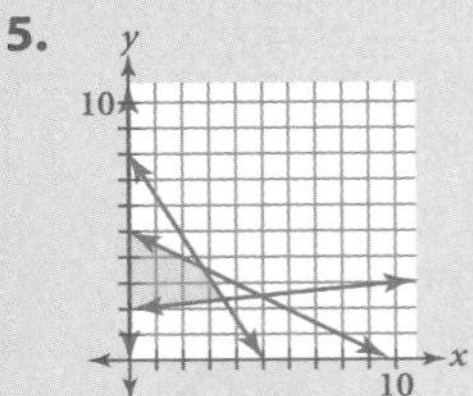

vertices: (0, 2), (0, 5), (2.752, 3.596), (3.529, 2.353)

Exercise 6 The inequalities in this exercise and in Exercise 8 are not all linear, but the process of finding a feasible region remains the same as for linear inequalities.

Students might include the vertex of the parabola, (2, 4), as a vertex, which is legitimate for linear programming.

6.

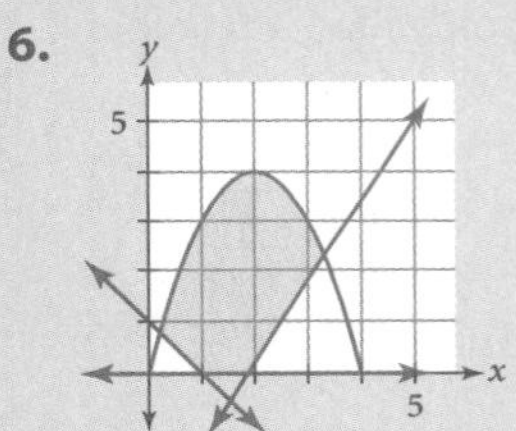

vertices: (1, 0), (1.875, 0), (3.307, 2.291), (0.209, 0.791)

7.

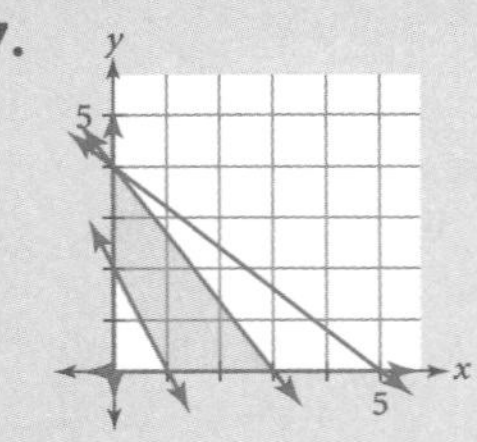

vertices: (0, 4), (3, 0), (1, 0), (0, 2)

8.

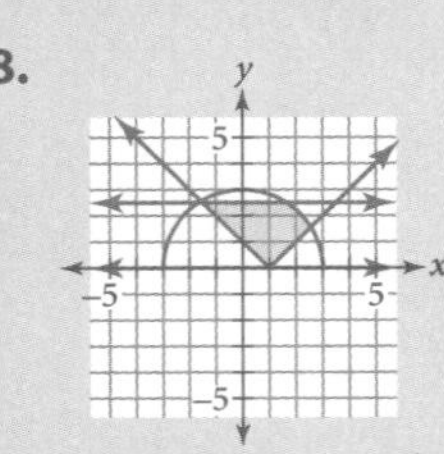

vertices: (1, 0), (2.562, 1.562), (1.658, 2.5), (−1.5, 2.5)

c. $y > 1 - 0.75x$

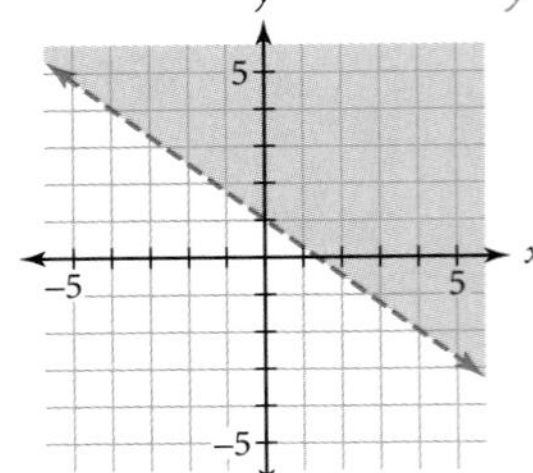

d. $y \leq 1.5 + 0.5x$

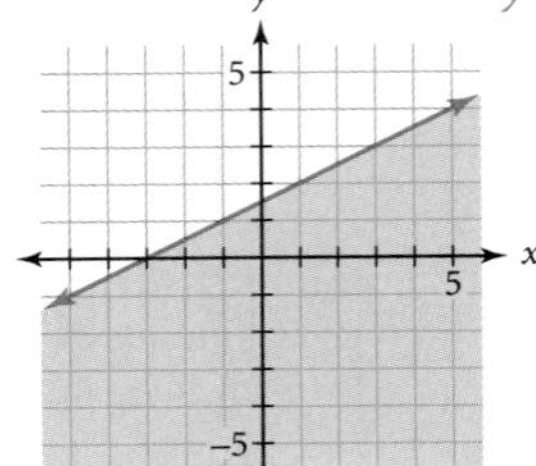

4. The graphs of $y = 2.4x + 2$ and $y = -x^2 - 2x + 6.4$ serve as the boundaries of this feasible region. What two inequalities identify this region?
$y \geq 2.4x + 2$ and $y \leq -x^2 - 2x + 6.4$

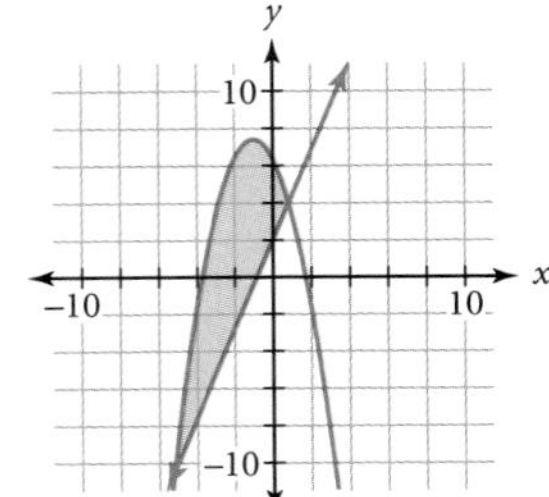

▶ Reason and Apply

For Exercises 5–8, sketch the feasible region of each system of inequalities. Find the coordinates of each vertex.

5. $\begin{cases} y \leq -0.51x + 5 \\ y \leq -1.6x + 8 \\ y \geq 0.1x + 2 \\ y \geq 0 \\ x \geq 0 \end{cases}$

6. $\begin{cases} y \geq 1.6x - 3 \\ y \leq -(x-2)^2 + 4 \\ y \geq 1 - x \\ y \geq 0 \\ x \geq 0 \end{cases}$

7. $\begin{cases} 4x + 3y \leq 12 \\ 1.6x + 2y \leq 8 \\ 2x + y \geq 2 \\ y \geq 0 \\ x \geq 0 \end{cases}$

8. $\begin{cases} y \geq |x - 1| \\ y \leq \sqrt{9 - x^2} \\ y \leq 2.5 \\ y \geq 0 \end{cases}$

This color-stain painting by American artist Morris Louis (1912–1962) shows overlapping regions similar to the graph of a system of inequalities.
Floral (1959) by Morris Louis

9. In the Lux Art Gallery, rectangular paintings must have an area between 200 in.^{2} and 300 in.^{2} and a perimeter between 66 in. and 80 in.

a. Write four inequalities involving length and width that represent these constraints.

b. Graph this system of inequalities to identify the feasible region.

c. Will the gallery accept a painting that measures

i. 12.4 in. by 16.3 in.? no

ii. 16 in. by 17.5 in.? yes

iii. 14.3 in. by 17.5 in.? no

American artist Nina Bovasso (b 1965) carries one of her paintings to an exhibition called Vir Heroicus Snoopicus. Would this piece, titled *Black and White Crowd,* be accepted at the Lux Art Gallery in Exercise 9?

10. APPLICATION As the altitude of a spacecraft increases, an astronaut's weight decreases until a state of weightlessness is achieved. The weight of a 57 kg astronaut, W, at a given altitude in kilometers above Earth's sea level, x, is given by the formula

$$W = 57 \cdot \frac{6400^2}{(6400 + x)^2}$$

a. At what altitudes will the astronaut weigh less than 2 kg?

b. At an altitude of 400 km, how much will the astronaut weigh?

c. Will the astronaut ever be truly weightless? Why or why not?

Science CONNECTION

A typical space shuttle orbits at an altitude of about 400 km. At this height, an astronaut still weighs about 88.8% of her weight on Earth. You have probably seen pictures in which astronauts in orbit on a space shuttle or space station appear to be weightless. This is actually not due to the absence of gravity but, rather, to an effect called microgravity. In orbit, astronauts and their craft are being pulled toward Earth by gravity, but their speed is such that they are in free fall around Earth, rather than toward Earth. Because the astronauts and their spacecraft are falling through space at the same rate, the astronauts appear to be floating inside the craft. This is similar to the fact that a car's driver can appear to be sitting still, although he is actually traveling at a speed of 60 mi/h.

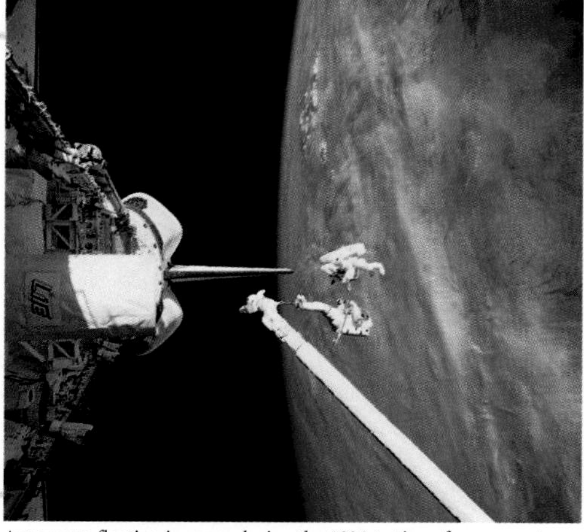

Astronauts floating in space during the 1994 testing of rescue system hardware appear to be weightless. One astronaut floats without being tethered to the spacecraft by using a small control unit.

Exercise 9 [Alert] The two inequalities for area will not be linear. **[Ask]** "Are there any commonsense constraints on the length and width?" [The length and the width must be greater than 0.]

The *Black and White Crowd* piece would not be accepted at the Lux Art Gallery.

9a. Let x represent length in inches, and let y represent width in inches.

$$\begin{cases} xy \geq 200 \\ xy \leq 300 \\ x + y \geq 33 \\ x + y \leq 40 \end{cases}$$

9b.

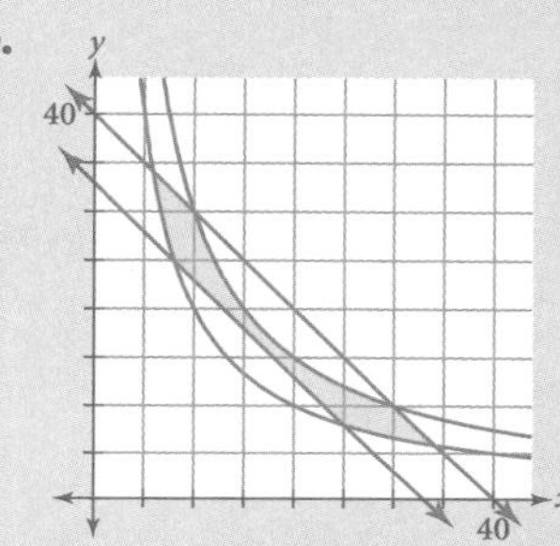

Exercise 10 [Alert] Students may be confused because the unit kg is used for both weight and mass. Weight is a measure of an object's mass under the force of gravity. Although the astronaut's mass is a property of the astronaut and cannot change, the astronaut's weight does change.

10a. $x > 27767$ km

10b. 50.5 kg

10c. In theory no, because as the denominator grows larger, the value of the fraction approaches zero but never gets to zero.

11a. $5x + 2y > 100$

11b. $y < 10$

11c. $x + y \le 40$

11d. common sense: $x \ge 0$, $y \ge 0$

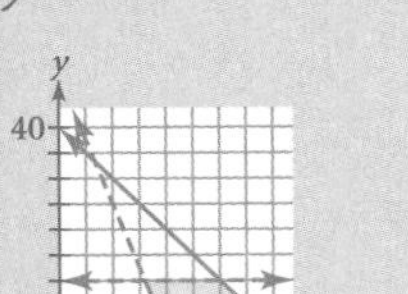

11e. (20, 0), (40, 0), (30, 10), (16, 10)

11. Al just got rid of 40 of his dad's old records. He sold each classical record for \$5 and each jazz record for \$2. The rest of the records could not be sold, so he donated them to a thrift shop. Al knows that he sold fewer than 10 jazz records and that he earned more than \$100.

a. Let x represent the number of classical records sold, and let y represent the number of jazz records sold. Write an inequality expressing that Al earned more than \$100.

b. Write an inequality expressing that he sold fewer than 10 jazz records.

c. Write an inequality expressing that the total number of records sold was no more than 40.

d. Graph the solution to the system of inequalities, including any commonsense constraints.

e. Name all the vertices of the feasible region.

Review

12a. $a = 3, b = 16, c = -12$

12b. $y = 3x^2 + 16x - 12$

12c. Sample answer: Substitute each point into the equation to verify that it lies on the parabola.

6.4 **12.** A parabola with an equation in the form $y = ax^2 + bx + c$ passes through the points $(-2, -32)$, $(1, 7)$, and $(3, 63)$.

a. Set up systems and use matrices to find the values of a, b, and c for this parabola.

b. Write the equation of this parabola.

c. Describe how to verify that your answer is correct.

5.3 **13.** These data were collected from a bouncing-ball experiment. Recall that the height in centimeters, y, is exponentially related to the number of the bounce, x. Find the values of a and b for an exponential model in the form $y = ab^x$. $a = 100, b \approx 0.7$

Bounce number	3	7
Height (cm)	34.3	8.2

Exercise 14 Assign this exercise only if students did Lesson 6.3.

6.3 **14.** Complete the reduction of this augmented matrix to row-echelon form. Give each row operation and find each missing matrix entry. See below.

$$\left[\begin{array}{cc|c} 3 & -1 & 5 \\ -4 & 2 & 1 \end{array}\right] \xrightarrow{?} \left[\begin{array}{cc|c} 1 & ? & ? \\ -4 & 2 & 1 \end{array}\right] \xrightarrow{?} \left[\begin{array}{cc|c} 1 & ? & ? \\ 0 & ? & ? \end{array}\right] \xrightarrow{?} \left[\begin{array}{cc|c} 1 & ? & ? \\ 0 & 1 & ? \end{array}\right] \xrightarrow{?} \left[\begin{array}{cc|c} 1 & 0 & ? \\ 0 & 1 & ? \end{array}\right]$$

15a. 2 or 3 spores

15b. about 1,868,302 spores

15c. $y = \dfrac{\log \frac{x}{2.68}}{\log 3.84}$

15d. after 14 hr 40 min

5.6 **15.** APPLICATION The growth of a population of water fungus is modeled by the function $y = f(x) = 2.68(3.84)^x$ where x represents the number of hours elapsed and y represents the number of fungi spores.

a. How many spores are there initially?

b. How many spores are there after 10 h?

c. Find an inverse function that uses y as the dependent variable and x as the independent variable.

d. Use your answer to 15c to find how long it will take until the number of spores exceeds 1 billion.

EXTENSION

Have students write a real-world application problem that is modeled by a system of inequalities.

14. $\left[\begin{array}{cc|c} 3 & -1 & 5 \\ -4 & 2 & 1 \end{array}\right]$, $\frac{1}{3}R_1 \to R_1$, $\left[\begin{array}{cc|c} 1 & -\frac{1}{3} & \frac{5}{3} \\ -4 & 2 & 1 \end{array}\right]$, $4R_1 + R_2 \to R_2$, $\left[\begin{array}{cc|c} 1 & -\frac{1}{3} & \frac{5}{3} \\ 0 & \frac{2}{3} & \frac{23}{3} \end{array}\right]$,

$\frac{3}{2}R_2 \to R_2$, $\left[\begin{array}{cc|c} 1 & -\frac{1}{3} & \frac{5}{3} \\ 0 & 1 & \frac{23}{2} \end{array}\right]$, $\frac{1}{3}R_2 + R_1 \to R_1$, $\left[\begin{array}{cc|c} 1 & 0 & \frac{11}{2} \\ 0 & 1 & \frac{23}{2} \end{array}\right]$

IMPROVING YOUR REASONING SKILLS

Coding and Decoding

One of the uses of matrices is in the mathematical field of cryptography, the science of enciphering and deciphering encoded messages. Here's one way that a matrix can be used to make a secret code:

Imagine encoding the word "CODE." First you convert each letter to a numerical value, based on its location in the alphabet. For example, C = 3 because it is the third letter in the alphabet. So, CODE = 3, 15, 4, 5. Arrange these numbers in a 2 × 2 matrix: $\begin{bmatrix} 3 & 15 \\ 4 & 5 \end{bmatrix}$. Now multiply by an encoding matrix.

Let's use $[E] = \begin{bmatrix} 1 & -1 \\ -1 & 2 \end{bmatrix}$, so $\begin{bmatrix} 3 & 15 \\ 4 & 5 \end{bmatrix}[E] = \begin{bmatrix} -12 & 27 \\ -1 & 6 \end{bmatrix}$.

Now you have to convert back to letters. Notice that three of these numbers are outside of the numbers 1–26 that represent A–Z. To convert other numbers, simply add or subtract 26 to make them fall within the range of 1 to 26, like this:

$$\begin{bmatrix} -12 & 27 \\ -1 & 6 \end{bmatrix} \to \begin{bmatrix} 14 & 1 \\ 25 & 6 \end{bmatrix} \to \begin{bmatrix} N & A \\ Y & F \end{bmatrix}$$

Now, to *decode* the encoded message "NAYF," you convert back to numbers and multiply by the inverse of the coding matrix, and then you convert each number back into the corresponding letter in the alphabet:

$$\begin{bmatrix} 14 & 1 \\ 25 & 6 \end{bmatrix}[E]^{-1} = \begin{bmatrix} 29 & 15 \\ 56 & 31 \end{bmatrix} = \begin{bmatrix} C & O \\ D & E \end{bmatrix}$$

See if you can decode this Navajo saying. Begin by taking out the spaces and breaking the letters into groups of four letters each.

CC FSLG GTQN YP OPIIY UCB DKIC BYF BEQQ WW URQLPRE.

Language CONNECTION

The Navajo language was used in coding messages by the U.S. Marines in World War II, because it is a complex unwritten language that is unintelligible to anyone without extensive training. Navajo code talkers could encode, transmit, and decode three-line English messages in 20 seconds, whereas machines of the time required 30 minutes to perform the same job. Navajo recruits developed the code, including a dictionary and numerous words for military terms. Learn more about Navajo code talkers by using the links at www.keymath.com/DAA .

Navajo recruits, like these two shown in the Pacific Island of Bougainville in 1943, shared their complex language with U.S. Marines to communicate in code during World War II.

MAKING THE CONNECTION

The Navajo are Native Americans from the southwestern United States, mainly Arizona, Utah, and New Mexico. Their native language is part of the Athapaskan language family, which includes indigenous languages from Alaska to New Mexico. Navajo is one of the most widely spoken Native American languages, with some 100,000 speakers. Like most other indigenous languages, though, the Navajo language is in danger of disappearing. Because Native American children rarely learn their indigenous languages, 149 of the 187 surviving Native American languages are expected to vanish within a generation.

IMPROVING REASONING SKILLS

This coded message uses the same coding matrix $[E]$, so to decode you use the inverse, $\begin{bmatrix} 2 & 1 \\ 1 & 1 \end{bmatrix}$. The message says, "If eyes have no tears the soul can have no rainbow."

[Language] *Enciphering* and *encoding* mean "writing in code." *Deciphering* means "determining what a coded message says." A system of secret writing is also called a *cipher,* a *cryptogram,* or a *cryptograph.*

LESSON 6.6

PLANNING

LESSON OUTLINE

One day:

20 min	Investigation
10 min	Sharing
5 min	Example
10 min	Exercises

MATERIALS

- graph paper
- Pottery (T) for One Step
- Snack Time (T), *optional*
- Sketchpad demonstration Linear Programming, *optional*

TEACHING

Having developed the idea of feasible regions in the previous lesson, students see the rest of the linear programming process for two variables. The Sketchpad demonstration Linear Programming is an excellent series of sketches that demonstrate linear programming.

One Step
Again show the Pottery transparency of Lesson 6.5. Pose this problem: "If the pottery shop's profit on each unglazed birdbath is \$10 and its profit on each glazed birdbath is \$40, how many of each kind should it make every day to maximize profit?"

As needed, suggest that students try out various values in the feasible region they found earlier and look for patterns. After each group finds the profit at a particular point, ask whether any other points yield the same profit. Press groups to describe a method to be used for solving similar problems.

LESSON 6.6

Linear Programming

Love the moment and the energy of that moment will spread beyond all boundaries.
CORITA KENT

Industrial managers often investigate more economical ways of doing business. They must consider physical limitations, standards of quality, customer demand, availability of materials, and manufacturing expenses as restrictions, or constraints, that determine how much of an item they can produce. Then they determine the optimum, or best, amount of goods to produce—usually to minimize production costs or maximize profit. The process of finding a feasible region and determining the point that gives the maximum or minimum value to a specific expression is called **linear programming.**

Polish artist Roman Cieslewicz (1930–1996) formed this 1988 work by gluing strips of paper and fragments of photographs on cardboard.
Les dieux ont soif (1988) by Roman Cieslewicz

Problems that can be modeled with linear programming may involve anywhere from two variables to hundreds of variables. Computerized modeling programs that analyze up to 200 constraints and 400 variables are regularly used to help businesses choose their best plan of action. In this lesson you will look at problems that involve two variables because you are relying on the visual assistance of a two-dimensional graph to help you find the feasible region.

In this investigation you'll explore a linear programming problem and make conjectures about how to find the optimum value in the most efficient way.

Investigation
Maximizing Profit

The Elite Pottery Shoppe makes two kinds of birdbaths: a fancy glazed and a simple unglazed. An unglazed birdbath requires 0.5 h to make using a pottery wheel and 3 h in the kiln. A glazed birdbath takes 1 h on the wheel and 18 h in the kiln. The company's one pottery wheel is available for at most 8 hours per day (h/d). The three kilns can be used a total of at most 60 h/d. The company has a standing order for 6 unglazed birdbaths per day, so it must produce at least that many. The pottery shop's profit on each unglazed birdbath is \$10, and the profit on each glazed birdbath is \$40. How many of each kind of birdbath should the company produce each day in order to maximize profit?

LESSON OBJECTIVES

- Learn about uses of linear programming and optimization
- Apply linear programming to situations with two variables
- Optimize a function over a feasible region

NCTM STANDARDS

CONTENT		PROCESS	
	Number	✓	Problem Solving
✓	Algebra	✓	Reasoning
	Geometry	✓	Communication
	Measurement	✓	Connections
✓	Data/Probability	✓	Representation

Step 1 Organize the information into a table like this one:

	Amount per unglazed birdbath	Amount per glazed birdbath	Constraining value
Wheel hours	0.5	1	≤ 8
Kiln hours	3	18	≤ 60
Profit	\$10	\$40	Maximize

Step 2 Use your table to help you write inequalities that reflect the constraints given, and be sure to include any commonsense constraints. Let x represent the number of unglazed birdbaths, and let y represent the number of glazed birdbaths. Graph the feasible region to show the combinations of unglazed and glazed birdbaths the shop could produce, and label the coordinates of the vertices. (*Note:* Profit is not a constraint; it is what you are trying to maximize.)

Step 3 It will make sense to produce only whole numbers of birdbaths. List the coordinates of all integer points within the feasible region. (There should be 23.) Remember that the feasible region may include points on the boundary lines.

Steps 3 and 4 See below.

Step 4 Write the equation that will determine profit based on the number of unglazed and glazed birdbaths produced. Calculate the profit that the company would earn at each of the feasible points you found in Step 3. You may want to divide this task among the members of your group.

Step 5 What number of each kind of birdbath should the Elite Pottery Shoppe produce to maximize profit? What is the maximum profit possible? Plot this point on your feasible region graph. What do you notice about this point?

Step 5 Maximum profit is \$180 when 14 unglazed birdbaths and 1 glazed birdbath are produced. This point is a vertex of the feasible region.

Step 6 Suppose that you want profit to be exactly \$100. What equation would express this? Carefully graph this line on your feasible region graph.

Step 6 $10x + 40y = 100$

Step 7 Suppose that you want profit to be exactly \$140. What equation would express this? Carefully add this line to your graph.

Step 7 $10x + 40y = 140$

Step 8 Suppose that you want profit to be exactly \$170. What equation would express this? Carefully add this line to your graph.

Step 8 $10x + 40y = 170$

Step 9 How do your results from Steps 6–8 show you that (14, 1) must be the point that maximizes profit? Generalize your observations to describe a method that you can use with other problems to find the optimum value. What would you do if this vertex point did not have integer coordinates? What if you wanted to *minimize* profit?

Linear programming is a very useful real-world application of systems of inequalities. Its value is not limited to business settings, as the following example shows.

Step 3 (6, 0), (7, 0), (8, 0), (9, 0), (10, 0), (11, 0), (12, 0), (13, 0), (14, 0), (15, 0), (16, 0), (6, 1), (7, 1), (8, 1), (9, 1), (10, 1), (11, 1), (12, 1), (13, 1), (14, 1), (6, 2), (7, 2), (8, 2)

Step 4 *profit* $= 10x + 40y$

Point	Profit	Point	Profit	Point	Profit	Point	Profit	Point	Profit	Point	Profit
(6, 0)	\$60	(7, 0)	\$70	(8, 0)	\$80	(9, 0)	\$90	(10, 0)	\$100	(11, 0)	\$110
(12, 0)	\$120	(13, 0)	\$130	(14, 0)	\$140	(15, 0)	\$150	(16, 0)	\$160	(6, 1)	\$100
(7, 1)	\$110	(8, 1)	\$120	(9, 1)	\$130	(10, 1)	\$140	(11, 1)	\$150	(12, 1)	\$160
(13, 1)	\$170	(14, 1)	\$180	(6, 2)	\$140	(7, 2)	\$150	(8, 2)	\$160		

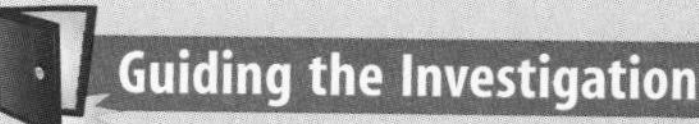

Step 1 [Alert] Students may have difficulty combining information from different sentences to make this table.

Step 2 As needed, remind students that the more careful they are in drawing their graphs, the more accurately they'll be able to identify vertices of the feasible region. Suggest that they draw large graphs on graph paper, taking up about half a page, and that they use rulers. **[Ask]** "Do you need to graph only the first quadrant?" [Commonsense constraints limit the values of x and y to nonnegative numbers.] **[Alert]** Students might forget the constraint $x \geq 6$. Try to let the groups work out their problems before offering assistance.

Steps 3, 4 Students may want to record the points in calculator lists so that they can find the profits easily.

Steps 6–8

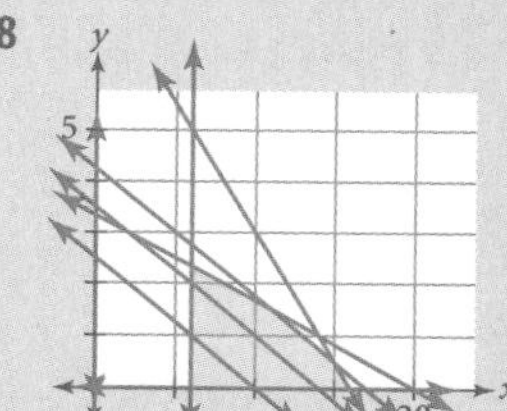

Step 9 As you observe students finishing this step, choose a variety of descriptions to be presented during Sharing.

Step 9 You can graph one profit line and imagine shifting it up until you get the highest profit possible within the feasible region. This should occur at a vertex. If the vertex is not an integer point, you might test the integer points near the optimum vertex. To minimize profit, move the profit line *down* until it leaves the feasible region. This would occur at (0, 0).

See page 887 for answer to Step 2.

EXAMPLE

Marco is planning a snack of graham crackers and blueberry yogurt to provide at his school's track practice. Because he is concerned about health and nutrition, he wants to make sure that the snack contains no more than 700 calories and no more than 20 g of fat. He also wants at least 17 g of protein and at least 30% of the daily recommended value of iron. The nutritional content of each food is listed in the table below. Each serving of yogurt costs $0.30 and each graham cracker costs $0.06. What combination of servings of graham crackers and blueberry yogurt should Marco provide to minimize cost?

	Serving	Calories	Fat	Protein	Iron (percent of daily recommended value)
Graham crackers	1 cracker	60	2 g	2 g	6%
Blueberry yogurt	4.5 oz	130	2 g	5 g	1%

▶ Solution

First organize the constraint information into a table, then write inequalities that reflect the constraints. Be sure to include any commonsense constraints. Let x represent the number of servings of graham crackers, and let y represent the number of servings of yogurt.

	Amount per graham cracker	Amount per serving of yogurt	Limiting value
Calories	60	130	≤ 700
Fat	2 g	2 g	≤ 20 g
Protein	2 g	5 g	≥ 17 g
Iron	6%	1%	$\geq 30\%$
Cost	$0.06	$0.30	Minimize

$$\begin{cases} 60x + 130y \leq 700 & \text{Calories} \\ 2x + 2y \leq 20 & \text{Fat} \\ 2x + 5y \geq 17 & \text{Protein} \\ 6x + 1y \geq 30 & \text{Iron} \\ x \geq 0 & \text{Common sense} \\ y \geq 0 & \text{Common sense} \end{cases}$$

Now graph the feasible region and find the vertices.

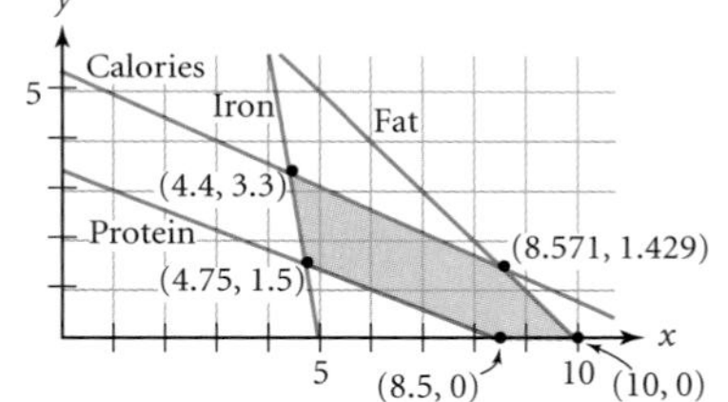

Next, write an equation that will determine the cost of a snack based on the number of servings of graham crackers and yogurt.

$$Cost = 0.06x + 0.30y$$

You could try any possible combination of graham crackers and yogurt that is in the feasible region, but recall that in the investigation it appeared that optimum values will occur at vertices. Calculate the cost at each of the vertices to see which one is a minimum.

▶ *EXAMPLE*

The example applies the linear programming process to finding a minimum value. It uses more constraints than the investigation. You can use the Snack Time transparency as you go over this example.

[Ask] "Is the optimum solution reasonable? What might other constraints of concern be?"

SHARING IDEAS

As students present their ideas about methods, encourage critical analysis by the class. Be open to using students' errors, creative questions, and uncertainty to help deepen understanding. In situations like that in the investigation, presumably naive students can often raise issues that will lead the class to mathematical insights. For example, a student may ask whether the pottery situation would include constraints on demand. Such constraints are not being considered here, but they would be in real life, where computers handle linear programming with many variables.

Ask students whether they feel overwhelmed with the process of linear programming. Sympathize while reminding them that this is a real-world application of graphing inequalities that they might use in their careers.

[Ask] "Why does the maximum or minimum occur at a vertex of the critical region?" Students might explain the situation in terms of lines representing all points with the same profit. These parallel lines shift for higher profits, moving toward a vertex. **[Ask]** "What if those lines are parallel to an edge of the feasible region?" [All feasible points along that edge yield maximum values.] "What if the region is unbounded in that direction?" [There is no maximum.] Students will see examples of such regions in the exercises. **[Ask]** "What if the vertex of the feasible region does not have integer coordinates?" [If all feasible points must have integer coordinates, then the maximum will occur at a nearby point.]

Point out that, though neither x nor y is an independent or dependent variable, the profit function seems dependent on both x and y. Wonder aloud whether that means we have a three-dimensional graph. Graphs of functions such as $p = 10x + 40y$ and $c = 0.06x + 0.30y$ are planes in three-dimensional space. These planes are highest and lowest at vertices or along edges of the feasible region.

The least expensive combination would be 8.5 crackers and no yogurt. However, Marco wants to serve only whole numbers of servings. The points (8, 1) and (9, 0) are the integer points within the feasible region closest to (8.5, 0), so test which point has a lower cost. The point (8, 1) gives a cost of \$0.78 and (9, 0) will cost \$0.54. Therefore Marco should serve 9 graham crackers and no yogurt.

x	y	Cost
4.444	3.333	\$1.27
4.75	1.5	\$0.74
8.571	1.429	\$0.94
10	0	\$0.60
8.5	0	\$0.51

The following box summarizes the steps of solving a linear programming problem. Refer to these steps as you do the exercises.

Solving a Linear Programming Problem

1. Define your variables, and write constraints using the information given in the problem. Don't forget commonsense constraints.
2. Graph the feasible region, and find the coordinates of all vertices.
3. Write the equation of the function you want to optimize, and decide whether you need to maximize or minimize it.
4. Evaluate your optimization function at each of the vertices of your feasible region, and decide which vertex provides the optimum value.
5. If your possible solutions need to be limited to whole number values, and your optimum vertex does not contain integers, test the whole number values within the feasible region that are closest to this vertex.

Exercises

Practice Your Skills

1. Carefully graph this system of inequalities and label the vertices.
$$\begin{cases} x + y \le 10 \\ 5x + 2y \ge 20 \\ -x + 2y \ge 0 \end{cases}$$

2. For the system in Exercise 1, find the vertex that optimizes these expressions:
   a. maximize: $5x + 2y$
   b. minimize: $x + 3y$
   c. maximize: $x + 4y$ (0, 10)
   d. minimize: $5x + y$ (0, 10)
   e. What generalizations can you make about which vertex provides a maximum or minimum value? It is not always obvious which point provides a maximum or minimum value.

3. Graph this system of inequalities, label the vertices of the feasible region, and name the integer coordinates that maximize the function $P = 0.08x + 0.10y$. What is this maximum value of P?
$$\begin{cases} x \ge 5500 \\ y \ge 5000 \\ y \le 3x \\ x + y \le 40000 \end{cases}$$

Assessing Progress
Assess students' ability to read and organize information, represent constraints as inequalities, and graph feasible regions.

Closing the Lesson

The process of **linear programming** involves finding a feasible region that represents the constraints of a situation and then finding at which point(s) of that region a function is maximized or minimized. Any optimum value will occur either at a vertex or along an edge of the feasible region or, if all feasible points have integer coordinates, near the vertex or edge.

BUILDING UNDERSTANDING

The linear programming process is quite lengthy, so be careful how many exercises you assign that require a lot of work.

ASSIGNING HOMEWORK

Essential	1–4
Performance assessment	5–9
Portfolio	7
Journal	2, 7
Group	5, 10
Review	11–15

MATERIALS

- graph paper

1.
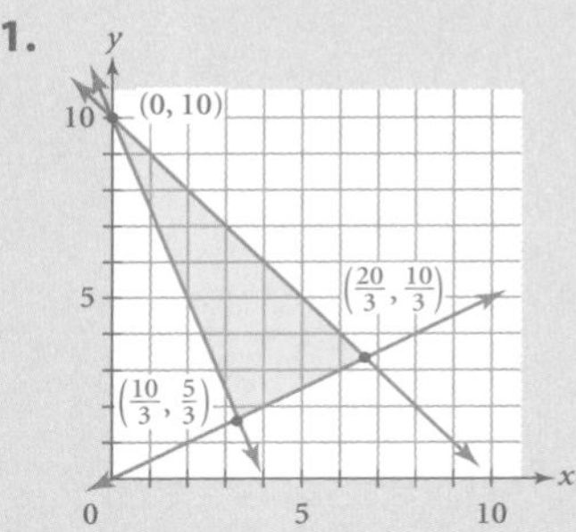

3.
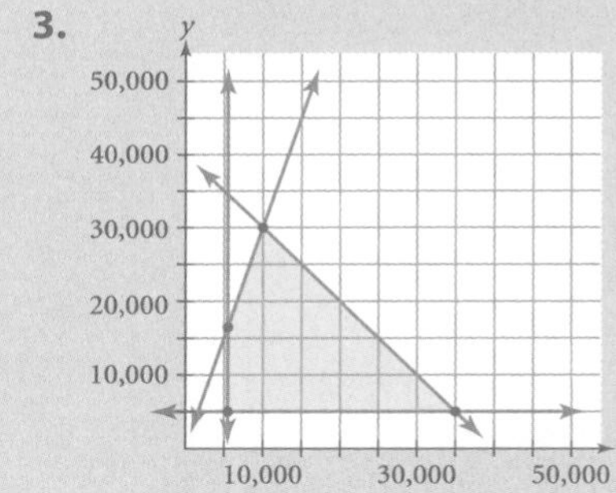

vertices: (5500, 5000), (5500, 16500), (10000, 30000), (35000, 5000); (10000, 30000); maximum: 3800

2a. $\left(\frac{20}{3}, \frac{10}{3}\right)$

2b. $\left(\frac{10}{3}, \frac{5}{3}\right)$

Helping with the Exercises

4a. There are zero or more pairs of each species in the region.

4b. The area required by species X plus the area required by species Y is no more than 180,000 m^2.

4c. The total food requirement of species X plus the total food requirement of species Y is no more than 72,000 kg.

4d.

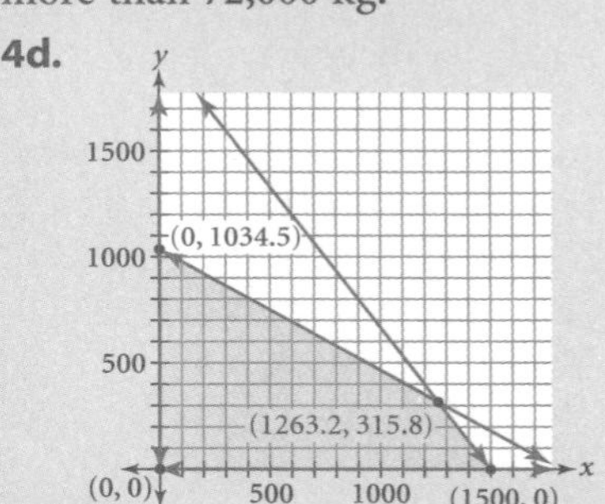

4e. The maximum number of nesting pairs is 1578. Any of the integer points around (1263.2, 315.8), (1261, 317), (1262, 316), (1263, 315), (1264, 314), or (1265, 313), give this total.

Exercise 5 As needed, suggest that students draw each boundary line, find an equation for that line, and then write the appropriate inequality.

6. 12 sled dogs and 12 poodles for a maximum profit of \$3360

7. 5 radio minutes and 10 newspaper ads to reach a maximum of 155,000 people. This assumes that people who listen to the radio are independent of people who read the newspaper, which is probably not realistic, and that the shop buys both. 20 radio minutes and 0 newspaper ads would reach 160,000 people.

Exercise 8 [Alert] Depending on how much you discussed unbounded feasible regions in class, students may be confused by this exercise. The challenge is to find the minimum cost, which does exist even though the cost function has no maximum value over this feasible region.

4. APPLICATION During nesting season, two different bird species inhabit a region with area 180,000 m^2. Dr. Chan estimates that this ecological region can provide 72,000 kg of food during the season. Each nesting pair of species X needs 39.6 kg of food during a specified time period and 120 m^2 of land. Each nesting pair of species Y needs 69.6 kg of food and 90 m^2 of land. Let x represent the number of pairs of species X, and let y represent the number of pairs of species Y.

a. Describe the meaning of the constraints $x \geq 0$ and $y \geq 0$.

b. Describe the meaning of the constraint $120x + 90y \leq 180000$.

c. Describe the meaning of the constraint $39.6x + 69.6y \leq 72000$.

d. Graph the system of inequalities, and identify each vertex of the feasible region.

e. Maximize the total number of nesting pairs, N, by considering the function $N = x + y$.

Reason and Apply

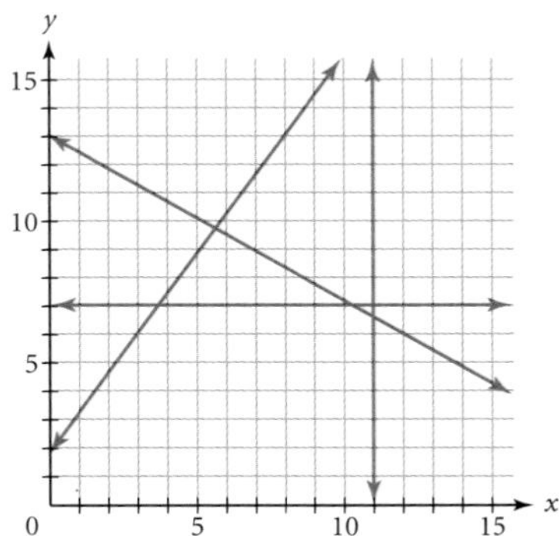

5. Use a combination of the four lines shown on the graph along with the axes to create a system of inequalities whose graph satisfies each description. See below.

a. The feasible region is a triangle.

b. The feasible region is a quadrilateral with one side on the y-axis.

c. The feasible region is a pentagon with sides on both the x-axis and the y-axis.

6. APPLICATION The International Canine Academy raises and trains Siberian sled dogs and dancing French poodles. Breeders can supply the academy with at most 20 poodles and 15 Siberian huskies each year. Each poodle eats 2 lb/d of food and each sled dog eats 6 lb/d. Food supplies are restricted to at most 100 lb/d. A poodle requires 1,000 h/yr of training, whereas a sled dog requires 250 h/yr. The academy cannot provide more than 15,000 h/yr of training time. If each poodle sells for a profit of \$200 and each sled dog sells for a profit of \$80, how many of each kind of dog should the academy raise in order to maximize profits?

7. APPLICATION The Elite Pottery Shoppe budgets a maximum of \$1,000 per month for newspaper and radio advertising. The newspaper charges \$50 per ad and requires at least four ads per month. The radio station charges \$100 per minute and requires a minimum of 5 minutes of advertising per month. It is estimated that each newspaper ad reaches 8,000 people and that each minute of radio advertising reaches 15,000 people. What combination of newspaper and radio advertising should the business use in order to reach the maximum number of people? What assumptions did you make in solving this problem? How realistic do you think they are?

8. APPLICATION A small electric generating plant must decide how much low-sulfur (2%) and high-sulfur (6%) oil to buy. The final mixture must have a sulfur content of no more than 4%. At least 1200 barrels of oil are needed. Low-sulfur oil costs \$18.50 per barrel and high-sulfur oil costs \$14.70 per barrel. How much of each type of oil should the plant use to keep the cost at a minimum? What is the minimum cost?

8. 600 barrels each of low-sulfur and high-sulfur oil for a minimum total cost of \$19,920

5a. possible answer:

$$\begin{cases} y \geq 7 \\ y \leq \frac{7}{5}(x-3)+6 \\ y \leq -\frac{7}{12}x + 13 \end{cases}$$

5b. possible answer:

$$\begin{cases} x \geq 0 \\ y \geq 7 \\ y \geq \frac{7}{5}(x-3)+6 \\ y \leq -\frac{7}{12}x + 13 \end{cases}$$

5c. possible answer:

$$\begin{cases} x \geq 0 \\ y \geq 0 \\ x \leq 11 \\ y \leq \frac{7}{5}(x-3)+6 \\ y \leq 7 \end{cases}$$

9. **APPLICATION** A fair-trade farmers' cooperative in Chiapas, Mexico, is deciding how much coffee and cocoa to recommend to their members to plant. Their 1,000 member families have 7,500 total acres to farm. Because of the geography of the region, 2,450 acres are suitable only for growing coffee and 1,230 acres are suitable only for growing cocoa. A coffee crop produces 30 lb/acre and a crop of cocoa produces 40 lb/acre. The cooperative has the resources to ship a total of 270,000 lb of product to the United States. Fair-trade organizations mandate a minimum price of $1.26 per pound for organic coffee and $0.98 per pound for organic cocoa (note that price is per pound, not per acre). How many acres of each crop should the cooperative recommend planting in order to maximize income?

These coffee beans are growing in the Mexican state of Chiapas.

Consumer CONNECTION

Many small coffee and cocoa farmers receive prices for their crop that are less than the costs of production, causing them to live in poverty and debt. Fair-trade certification has been developed to show consumers which products are produced with the welfare of farming communities in mind. To become fair-trade certified, an importer must meet stringent international criteria: paying a minimum price per pound, providing credit to farmers, and providing technical assistance in farming upgrades. Fair-trade prices allow farmers to make enough money to provide their families with food, education, and health care.

10. **APPLICATION** Teo sells a set of videotapes on an online auction. The postal service he prefers puts these restrictions on the size of a package:

Up to 150 lb
Up to 130 in. in length and girth combined
Up to 108 in. in length

Length is defined as the longest side of a package or object. Girth is the distance all the way around the package or object at its widest point perpendicular to the length. Teo is not concerned with the weight because the videotapes weigh only 15 lb.

a. Write a system of inequalities that represents the constraints on the package size.

b. Graph the feasible region for the dimensions of the package.

c. Teo packages the videotapes in a box whose dimensions are 20 in. by 14 in. by 8 in. Does this box satisfy the restrictions?

Consumer CONNECTION

In the packaging industry, two sets of dimensions are used. Inside dimensions are used to ensure proper fit around a product to prevent damage. Outside dimensions are used in shipping classifications and determining how to stack boxes on pallets. In addition, the type of packaging material and its strength are important concerns. Corrugated cardboard is a particularly strong, yet economical, packaging material.

Exercise 9 The intersection point of lines graphed on the calculator can be found with the intersect command. On the TI-83 Plus this command is in the Calc menu. Calculator notes do not include this command. You might want to show it to your students.

9. 3000 acres of coffee and 4500 acres of cocoa for a maximum total income of $289,800

Exercise 10 If students are having trouble, suggest that they sketch a picture of the package and mark the length and girth.

10a. Let x represent the length in inches, and let y represent the girth in inches.

$$\begin{cases} x + y \leq 130 \\ x \leq 108 \\ x > 0 \\ y > 0 \end{cases}$$

10b.

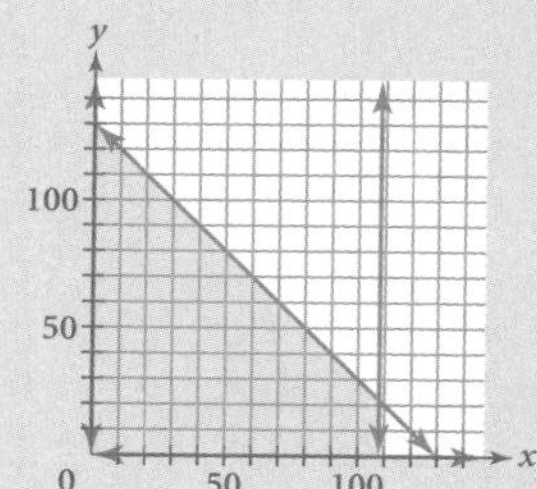

10c. Yes, the box lies in the feasible region.

MAKING THE CONNECTION

[Language] Corrugated cardboard is just regular cardboard that is used for boxes. Corrugated cardboard obtains its extraordinary strength from the use of the arch, a strong structure that is widely used in construction and architecture. Corrugated cardboard is basically a sandwich made of two pieces of paperboard with another piece of paperboard that is molded into wavy curves, or arches, glued between them. This design enables packages made of corrugated cardboard to travel long distances and carry heavy weights without collapsing or tearing. Corrugated cardboard can be made entirely from recycled material and wood scraps, and the old boxes can be recycled many times.

12.

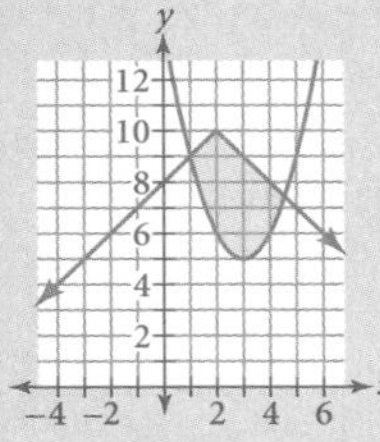

13. $\begin{cases} x \geq 2 \\ y \leq 5 \\ x + y \geq 3 \\ 2x - y \leq 9 \end{cases}$

Exercise 14 This exercise depends on Lesson 6.3, so assign it only if your students completed that lesson.

14a. $\left[\begin{array}{cc|c} 2 & -1 & \frac{1}{2} \\ 5 & -2 & -5 \end{array}\right]$

14b. $\left[\begin{array}{cc|c} 1 & 0 & -6 \\ 0 & 1 & -12.5 \end{array}\right]$; $(-6, -12.5)$

14c. $-12.5 = 2(-6) - 0.5$; $5(-6) - 2(-12.5) + 5 = 0$

EXTENSIONS

A. Use Take Another Look activity 3 on page 357.

B. To extend Exercise 10, ask students to research shipping restrictions on package size and to draw feasibility regions for package sizes with different carriers. Students should find out what types of restrictions there are, whether different companies have different restrictions on size, and whether certain things cannot be mailed because of their size.

Review

6.4 **11.** Solve each of these systems in at least two different ways.

a. $\begin{cases} 8x + 3y = 41 \\ 9x + 2y = 25 \end{cases}$ $x = -\frac{7}{11}, y = \frac{169}{11}$

b. $\begin{cases} 2x + y - 2z = 5 \\ 6x + 2y - 4z = 3 \\ 4x - y + 3z = 5 \end{cases}$ $x = -3.5, y = 74, z = 31$

6.5 **12.** Sketch a graph of the feasible region described by this system of inequalities:

$$\begin{cases} y \geq (x - 3)^2 + 5 \\ y \leq -|x - 2| + 10 \end{cases}$$

6.5 **13.** Give the system of inequalities whose solution set is the polygon at right.

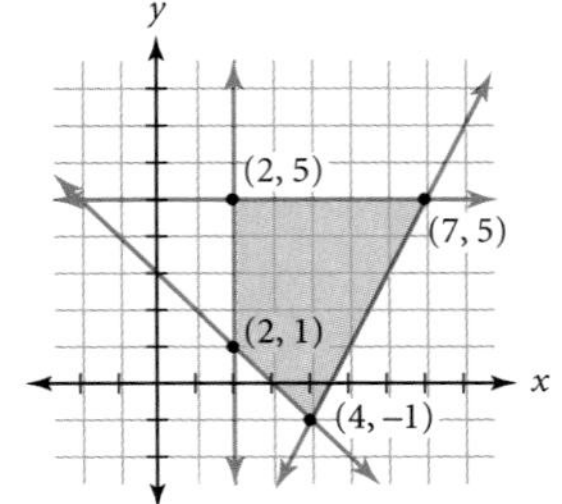

6.3 **14.** Consider this system of equations:

$$\begin{cases} y = 2x - \frac{1}{2} \\ 5x - 2y + 5 = 0 \end{cases}$$

a. Write the augmented matrix for this system.

b. Reduce the augmented matrix to row-echelon form. Write the solution as an ordered pair of coordinates.

c. Check your solution values for x and y by substituting them into the original equations.

4.6 **15.** Find the equation of the parabola at right.

$y = -\left(\frac{x}{2}\right)^2 - \frac{3}{2}$ or $y = -\frac{1}{4}x^2 - \frac{3}{2}$

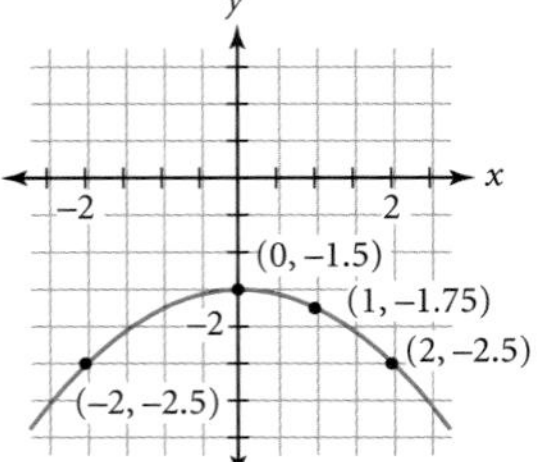

Project

NUTRITIONAL ELEMENTS

Write and solve your own linear programming problem similar to the cracker-and-yogurt snack combination problem in this lesson. Choose two food items from your home or a grocery store, and decide on your constraints and what you wish to minimize or maximize. Record the necessary information. Then write inequalities, and find the feasible region and optimum value for your problem. Your project should include

- Your linear programming problem
- A complete solution, including a graph of the feasible region
- An explanation of your process

Nutrition Facts
Serving Size 1/2 cup (114g)
Servings per container 4

Amount per serving
Calories 90
Calories from Fat 30

	% Daily Value*
Total Fat 3g	5%
Saturated Fat 0g	0%
Cholesterol 0mg	0%
Sodium 300 mg	13%
Total Carbohydrate 13g	4%
Dietary Fiber 3g	12%
Sugars 3g	
Protein 3g	

Vitamin A 80% **Vitamin C** 60%
Calcium 4% **Iron** 4%

*Percent Daily Values are based on a 2,000 calorie diet. Your daily values may be higher or lower depending on your calorie needs.

Supporting the Project

Encourage students to explore problems in which they want to maximize nutrition, perhaps while keeping cost below a certain amount. If students choose criteria that produce no feasible region, they should revise their criteria and include in their write-ups a description of why the criteria were unworkable.

OUTCOMES

- The report includes a clearly written problem statement with at least two constraints in addition to the commonsense constraints.
- A complete solution is given, including a graph of the feasible region and the values that optimize the given function.
- The explanation of the process of writing and solving the problem is clear and complete and explains any difficulties.
- The problem statement includes four or more constraints.
- The student includes further information on linear programming, such as a description of a linear programming problem with more than two variables.

CHAPTER 6 REVIEW

Matrices have a variety of uses. They provide ways to organize data about such things as inventory or the coordinates of vertices of a polygon. A **transition matrix** represents repeated changes that happen to a system. You can use matrix arithmetic to combine data or transform polygons on a coordinate graph, and you can also use **matrix multiplication** to determine quantities at various stages of a transition simulation.

Another important application of matrices is to solve systems of equations. In Chapter 3, you solved systems of linear equations by looking for a point of intersection on a graph or by using substitution or elimination. With two linear equations, the system will be **consistent and independent** (intersecting lines with one solution), or **consistent and dependent** (the same line with infinitely many solutions), or **inconsistent** (parallel lines with no solution). You can use an **inverse matrix** and matrix multiplication to solve a system, or you can use an **augmented matrix** and the **row reduction** method. Matrix methods are generally the simplest way to solve systems that involve more than three equations and three variables.

When a system is made up of inequalities, the solution usually consists of many points that can be represented by a region in the plane. One important use of systems of inequalities is in **linear programming.** In linear programming problems, an equation for a quantity that is to be optimized (maximized or minimized) is evaluated at the vertices of the **feasible region.**

EXERCISES

1. Use these matrices to do the arithmetic problems 1a–f. If a particular operation is impossible, explain why.

$[A] = [1 \quad -2]$ $\quad [B] = \begin{bmatrix} -3 & 7 \\ 6 & 4 \end{bmatrix}$ $\quad [C] = \begin{bmatrix} 1 & 0 \\ 5 & 2 \end{bmatrix}$ $\quad [D] = \begin{bmatrix} -3 & 1 & 2 \\ 2 & 3 & -2 \end{bmatrix}$

a. $[A] + [B]$ **b.** $[B] - [C]$ **c.** $4 \cdot [D]$ **d.** $[C][D]$ **e.** $[D][C]$ **f.** $[A][D]$

2. Find the inverse, if it exists, of each matrix.

a. $\begin{bmatrix} 2 & -3 \\ 1 & -4 \end{bmatrix}$ **b.** $\begin{bmatrix} 5 & 2 & -2 \\ 6 & 1 & 0 \\ -2 & 5 & 3 \end{bmatrix}$ **c.** $\begin{bmatrix} -2 & 3 \\ 8 & -12 \end{bmatrix}$ **d.** $\begin{bmatrix} 5 & 2 & -3 \\ 4 & 3 & -1 \\ 7 & -2 & -1 \end{bmatrix}$

3. Solve each system by using row reduction.

a. $\begin{cases} 8x - 5y = -15 \\ 6x + 4y = 43 \end{cases}$ $x = 2.5, y = 7$

b. $\begin{cases} 5x + 3y - 7z = 3 \\ 10x - 4y + 6z = 5 \\ 15x + y - 8z = -2 \end{cases}$ $x = 1.22, y = 6.9, z = 3.4$

ASSIGNING HOMEWORK

Students might work on the odd Exercises 1–9 in groups and do the even Exercises 2–10 for homework. You might give students the option of completing Exercise 1 or answering the first journal prompt on page 358 and completing Exercises 2a and 3b or answering the second journal prompt. The mixed review can be used before a unit exam.

Helping with the Exercises

Exercise 2 If you would like your students to know how to find inverse matrices without using calculators, ask that they show their work on these problems.

Exercise 3 This exercise reviews row reduction, which was covered in optional Lesson 6.3.

CHAPTER REVIEW 6

PLANNING

LESSON OUTLINE

One day:

15 min Reviewing

25 min Exercises

5 min Student self-assessment

REVIEWING

Remind students of the Investigation Chilly Choices of Lesson 6.1, perhaps displaying the Cold Desserts transparency. Pose this problem to help students review: "Suppose we don't know yet how many of each dessert students ate this week, but we know we can get enough for next week for only 190 students to have ice cream and for only 50 students to have frozen yogurt. If the percentages of switching are as given, what possibilities of choices this week will allow us to be sure we have enough next week? Represent the transitions with a diagram and a matrix, and find the vertex of the feasible region that's not on an axis by two methods: row reduction of an augmented matrix to reduced row-echelon form, and using an inverse matrix."

Encourage students to use the terms *dimensions* of a matrix, *consistent* (and *dependent* and *inconsistent*) system of equations, *identity matrix, inequality,* and *constraint.* Ask how many of each item the school would like to sell if it makes a profit of 30¢ per ice cream and 23¢ per yogurt.

See pages 887–888 for answers to Exercises 1 and 2.

Exercise 5 Students can do this exercise by graphing, by looking for equations with the same slope or y-intercept, or by finding that the coefficient matrix has no inverse and then looking for reasons why.

Exercise 6 You might extend this exercise by asking students to write a real-world exercise that would use each set of constraints.

6a.

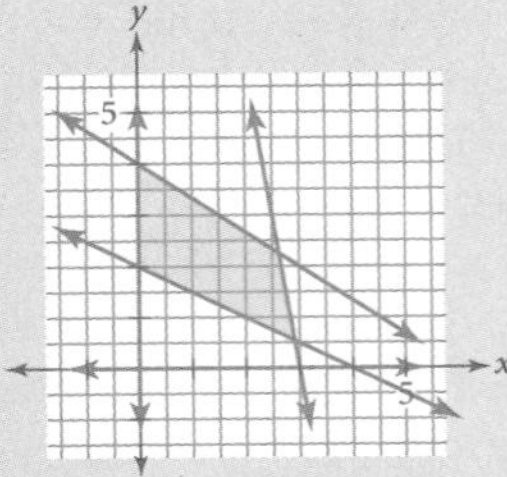

Vertices: (0, 4), (2.625, 2.25), $(2.\overline{90}, 0.\overline{54})$, (0, 2). The maximum occurs at (0, 4): $1.65(0) + 5.2(4) = 20.8$.

6b.

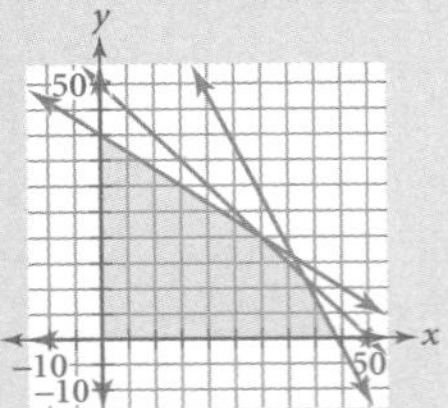

Vertices: (0, 0), (0, 40), (30, 20), (38, 12), (44, 0). The maximum occurs at (30, 20): $6(30) + 7(20) = 320$.

Exercise 7 [Language] The phrase *pay for itself* means "reach the point when the additional cost is equal to the amount of savings."

4. Solve each system by using an inverse matrix.

a. $\begin{cases} 8x - 5y = -15 \\ 6x + 4y = 43 \end{cases}$ $x = 2.5, y = 7$

b. $\begin{cases} 5x + 3y - 7z = 3 \\ 10x - 4y + 6z = 5 \\ 15x + y - 8z = -2 \end{cases}$ $x = 1.22, y = 6.9, z = 3.4$

5. Identify each system as consistent and independent (has one solution), inconsistent (has no solution), or consistent and dependent (has infinitely many solutions).

a. $\begin{cases} y = -1.5x + 7 \\ y = -3x + 14 \end{cases}$ consistent and independent

b. $\begin{cases} y = \frac{1}{4}(x - 8) + 5 \\ y = 0.25x + 3 \end{cases}$ consistent and dependent

c. $\begin{cases} 2x + 3y = 4 \\ 1.2x + 1.8y = 2.6 \end{cases}$ inconsistent

d. $\begin{cases} \frac{3}{5}x - \frac{2}{5}y = 3 \\ 0.6x - 0.4y = -3 \end{cases}$ inconsistent

6. Graph the feasible region of each system of inequalities. Find the coordinates of each vertex. Then identify the point that maximizes the given expression.

a. $\begin{cases} 2x + 3y \leq 12 \\ 6x + y \leq 18 \\ x + 2y \geq 4 \\ x \geq 0 \\ y \geq 0 \end{cases}$

maximize: $1.65x + 5.2y$

b. $\begin{cases} x + y \leq 50 \\ 10x + 5y \leq 440 \\ 40x + 60y \leq 2400 \\ x \geq 0 \\ y \geq 0 \end{cases}$

maximize: $6x + 7y$

American artist Joseph Cornell (1903–1972) assembled sculptures from collections of objects, frequently drugstore items. This piece places medicine bottles in a matrix-like arrangement.

Untitled (Grand Hotel Pharmacy) (1947), Joseph Cornell

7. **APPLICATION** Heather's water heater needs repair. The plumber says it will cost \$300 to fix the unit, which currently costs \$75 per year to operate. Or Heather could buy a new energy-saving water heater for \$500, including installation, and the new heater would save 60% on annual operating costs. How long would it take for the new unit to pay for itself? about 4.4 yr

8. **APPLICATION** A particular color of paint requires a mix of five parts red, six parts yellow, and two parts black. Thomas does not have the pure colors available, but he finds three pre-mixed colors that he can use. The first is two parts red and four parts yellow; the second is one part red and two parts black; the third is three parts red, one part yellow, and one part black.

a. Write an equation that gives the correct portion of red by using the three available pre-mixed colors.

b. Write an equation that gives the correct portion of yellow and another equation that gives the correct portion of black.

c. Solve the systems of equations in 8a and b.

d. Find an integer that you can use as a scalar multiplier for your solutions in 8c to provide integer solution values. 8

e. Explain the real-world meaning to your solutions to 8d.

8a. $2x + 1y + 3z = 5$

8b. $4x + 0y + 1z = 6$ for yellow; $0x + 2y + 1z = 2$ for black

8c. $x = \frac{11}{8}, y = \frac{3}{4}, z = \frac{1}{2}$

8e. 11 parts of pre-mixed color 1, 6 parts of pre-mixed color 2, and 4 parts of pre-mixed color 3 will yield the particular color.

9. Interlochen Arts Academy 9th and 10th graders are housed in three dormitories: Picasso, Hemingway, and Mozart. Mozart is an all-female dorm, Hemingway is an all-male dorm, and Picasso is coed. In September, school started with 80 students in Mozart, 60 in Picasso, and 70 in Hemingway. Students are permitted to move from one dorm to another on the first Sunday of each month. This transition graph shows the movements this past year.

a. Write a transition matrix for this situation. List the dorms in the order Mozart, Picasso, Hemingway.

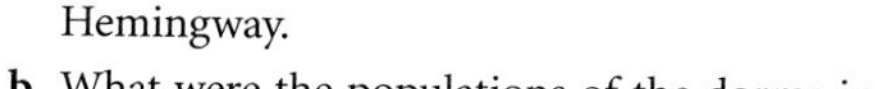

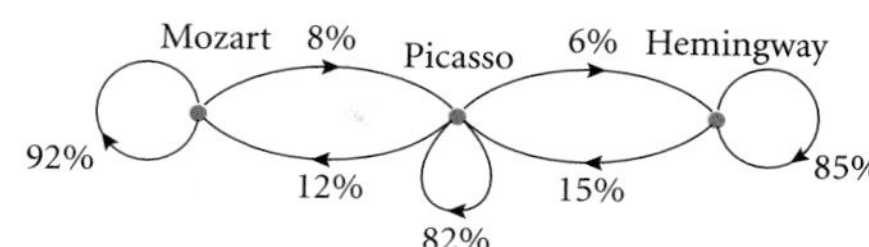

b. What were the populations of the dorms in

i. October?
ii. November?
iii. May?

9a. $\begin{bmatrix} .92 & .08 & 0 \\ .12 & .82 & .06 \\ 0 & .15 & .85 \end{bmatrix}$

9b. i. Mozart: 81; Picasso: 66; Hemingway: 63

9b. ii. Mozart: 82; Picasso: 70; Hemingway: 58

9b. iii. Mozart: 94; Picasso: 76; Hemingway: 40

10. **APPLICATION** Yolanda, Myriam, and Xavier have a small business producing handmade shawls and blankets. They spin the yarn, dye it, and weave it. A shawl requires 1 h of spinning, 1 h of dyeing, and 1 h of weaving. A blanket needs 2 h of spinning, 1 h of dyeing, and 4 h of weaving. They make a \$16 profit per shawl and a \$20 profit per blanket. Xavier does the spinning on his day off, when he can spend at most 8 h spinning. Yolanda dyes the yarn on her day off, when she has at most 6 h. Myriam does all the weaving on Friday and Saturday, when she has at most 14 h available. How many of each item should they make each week to maximize their profit?

10. They should make 4 shawls and 2 blankets to make the maximum profit of \$104.

MIXED REVIEW

1.3 **11.** Graphs 11a–c were produced by a recursive formula in the form

$u_0 = a$

$u_n = u_{n-1}(1 + p) + d \quad \text{where } n \geq 1$

For each case, tell if a, p, and d are greater than zero (positive), equal to zero, or less than zero (negative).

a.

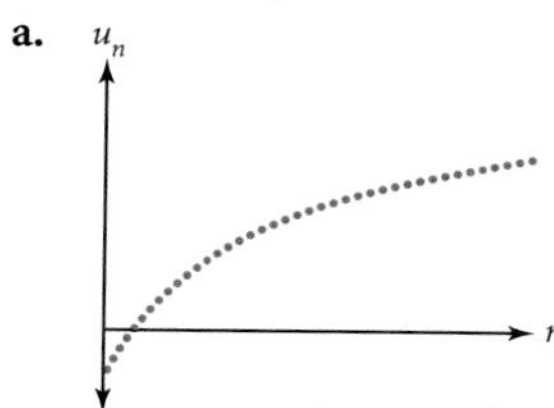

$a < 0; p < 0; d > 0$

b.

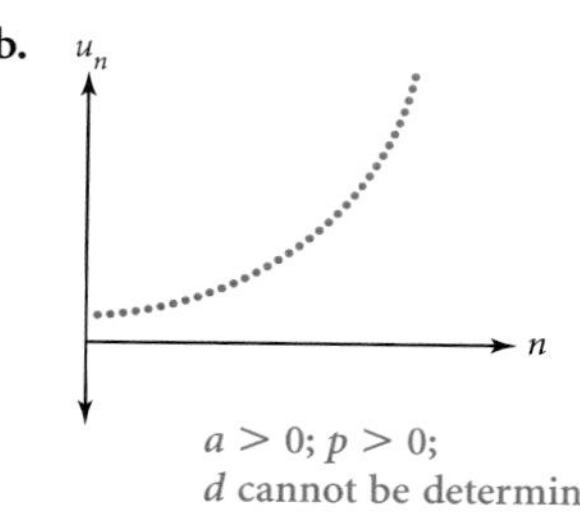

$a > 0; p > 0;$
d cannot be determined

c.

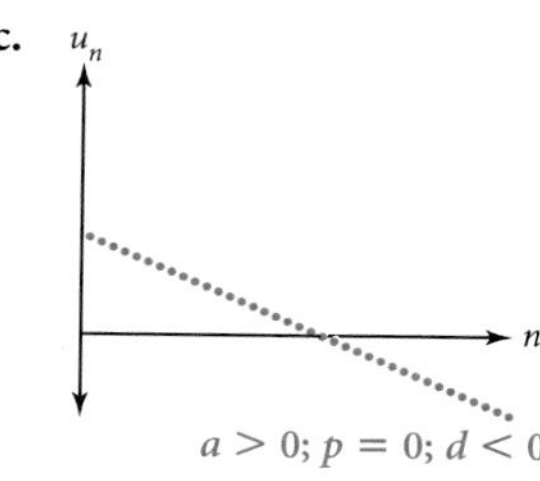

$a > 0; p = 0; d < 0$

4.2 **12.** The graph of $y = f(x)$ is shown at right.

a. Find $f(-3)$. 3

b. Find x such that $f(x) = 1$. -5 or approximately 3.5

c. How can you use the graph to tell whether or not f is a function?

d. What is the domain of f? $-6 \leq x \leq 5$

e. What is the range of f? $-2 \leq y \leq 4$

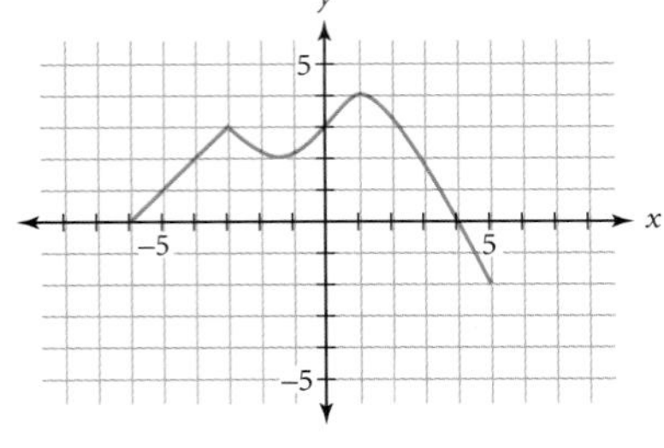

12c. It is a function because no vertical line crosses the graph in more than one place.

6.4 **13.** Last semester, all of Ms. Nolte's students did projects. One-half of the students in her second-period class investigated fractals, one-fourth of the students in that class did research projects, and the remaining students conducted surveys and analyzed their results. In her third-period class, one-third of the students investigated fractals, one-half of the students did research projects, and the remaining students conducted surveys and analyzed their results. In the seventh-period class, one-fourth of the students investigated fractals, one-sixth of the students did research projects, and the remaining students conducted a survey and analyzed their results. Overall, 22 students investigated fractals, 18 students did research projects, and 22 students conducted surveys. How many students are in each of Ms. Nolte's classes?

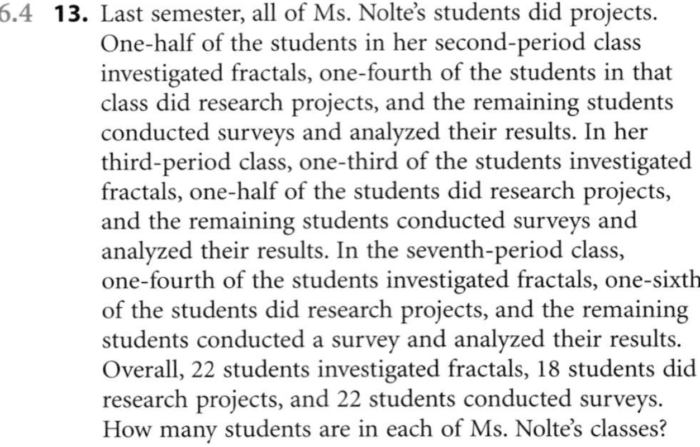

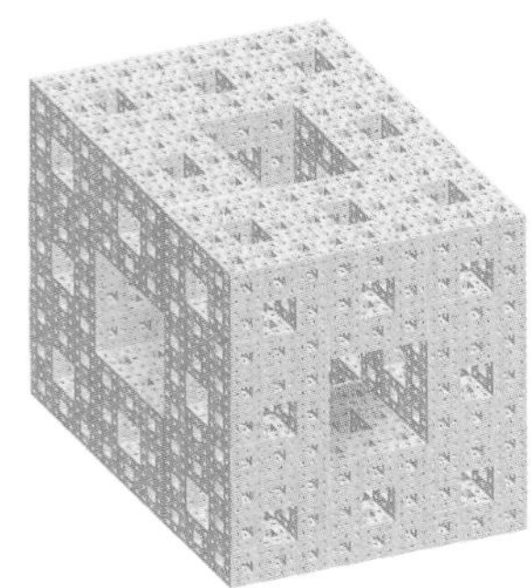

Exercise 13 Students might write a system of equations and solve it by substitution or elimination, or they might create a matrix and find the solution using an inverse matrix or row reduction.

13. 20 students in second period, 18 students in third period, and 24 students in seventh period

3.4 **14.** **APPLICATION** Canada's oil production has increased over the last half century. This table gives the production of oil per day for various years.

Canada's Oil Production

Year	1960	1970	1980	1990	1995	1998	1999
Barrels per day (millions)	0.52	1.26	1.44	1.55	1.80	1.98	1.91

(*The New York Times Almanac 2002*)

a. Define variables and make a scatter plot of the data.

b. Find M_1, M_2, and M_3, and write the equation of the median-median line.

c. Use the median-median line to predict Canada's oil production in 2002. 2.023 million barrels per day

This oil-drilling ship was frozen in six feet of ice on the Beaufort Sea, Northwest Territories, Canada, in 1980.

14a. Let x represent the year, and let y represent the number of barrels per day in millions.

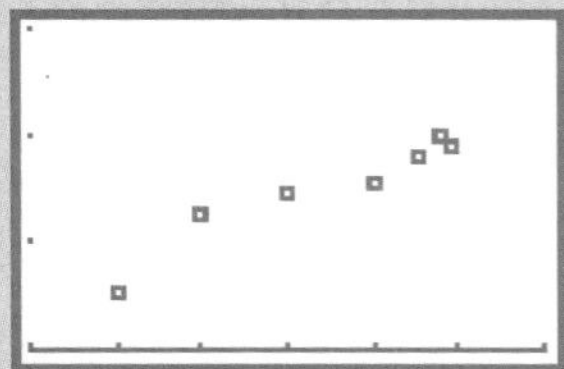

[1950, 2010, 10, 0, 3, 1]

14b. $M_1(1965, 0.89)$, $M_2(1990, 1.55)$, $M_3(1998.5, 1.945)$; $\hat{y} = 0.0315x - 61.04$

5.7 **15.** Solve.

a. $\log 35 + \log 7 = \log x$

b. $\log 500 - \log 25 = \log x$

c. $\log \sqrt{\frac{1}{8}} = x \log 8$

d. $15(9.4)^x = 37000$

e. $\sqrt[3]{(x + 6)} + 18.6 = 21.6$

f. $\log_6 342 = 2x$

15a. $x = 245$

15b. $x = 20$

15c. $x = -\frac{1}{2}$

15d. $x = \dfrac{\log\left(\frac{37000}{15}\right)}{\log 9.4} \approx 3.4858$

15e. $x = 21$

15f. $x = \dfrac{\log 342}{\log 36} \approx 1.6282$

1.2 **16.** **APPLICATION** Suppose the signal strength in a fiber-optic cable diminishes by 15% every 10 mi.

a. What percentage of the original signal strength is left after a stretch of 10 mi? 85%

b. Create a table of the percentage of signal strength remaining in 10 mi intervals, and make a graph of the sequence. See below.

c. If a phone company plans to boost the signal just before it falls to 1%, how far apart should the company place its booster stations? 280 mi

Technology CONNECTION

Fiber-optic technology uses light pulses to transmit information from one transmitter to another down fiber lines made of silica (glass). Fiber-optic strands are used in telephone wires, cable television lines, power systems, and other communications. These strands operate on the principle of total internal reflection, which means that the light pulses cannot escape out of the glass tube and instead bounce information from transmitter to transmitter.

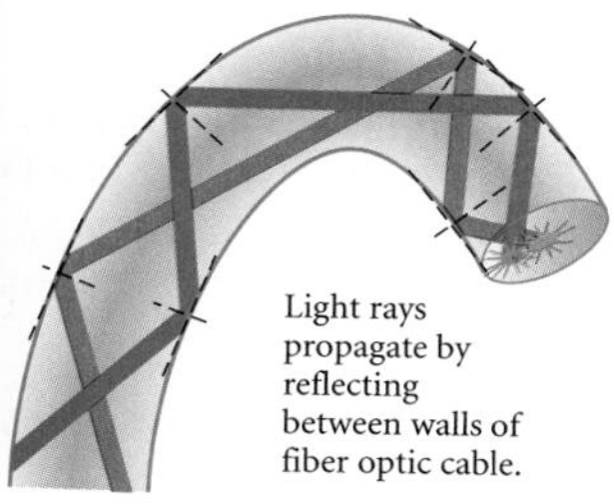

The photo on the left shows strands of fiber-optic cable. The illustration on the right shows how light is reflected along a strand of fiber-optic cable, creating total internal reflection.

5.3 **17.** The graph of an exponential function passes through the points (4, 50) and (6, 25.92).

a. Find the equation of the exponential function.

b. What is the rate of change? Does the equation model growth or decay?

c. What is the y-intercept?

d. What is the long-run value?

2.3 **18.** This data set gives the weights in kilograms of the crew members participating in the 2002 Boat Race between Oxford University and Cambridge University. (*www.cubc.org.uk* and *www.ourcs.org*)

{83, 95, 91, 90, 93, 97.5, 97, 79, 55, 89, 89.5, 94, 89, 100, 90, 92, 96, 54}

a. Make a histogram of these data.

b. Are the data skewed left, skewed right, or symmetric? skewed left

c. Identify any outliers.

d. What is the percentile rank of the crew member who weighs 94 kg? 67th percentile

Photographed on London's Thames River in 1949, this television crew films the Oxford-Cambridge Boat Race, which was the British Broadcasting Corporation's first broadcast with equipment in motion.

16b.

Distance (mi)	0	10	20	30	40	50	60	70	. . .
Percentage of original signal	100	85	72.3	61.4	52.2	44.4	37.7	32.1	. . .

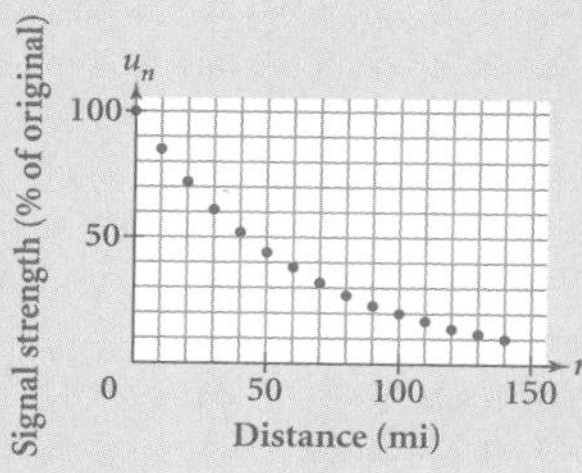

MAKING THE CONNECTION

In communications, fiber-optic cables allow for transmission of more information than a traditional cable of the same size. For example, a copper cable built in 1983 that connected the United States and Great Britain carried 4,200 simultaneous telephone conversations. By contrast, the first transatlantic fiber-optic cable, built by AT&T in 1988, allowed for 37,800 calls between the United States and Europe. Fiber optics have applications far beyond communications. They are used in medical equipment to transmit images, allowing doctors to view inside the human body during laser surgery. They are also used in phototypesetting, computer graphics, and sensor equipment such as thermometers and gyroscopes.

Exercise 17 **[Ask]** "What is the growth or decay rate?" [The difference between 1 and the rate of change is −0.28; the decay rate is 0.28.]

17a. $y = 50(0.72)^{x-4}$ or $y = 25.92(0.72)^{x-6}$

17b. 0.72; decay

17c. approximately 186

17d. 0

Exercise 18 Students might be interested in researching this famous boat race, which has taken place every year since 1829 and is billed as "the world's longest surviving sporting challenge."

18a. sample answer using a bin width of 10:

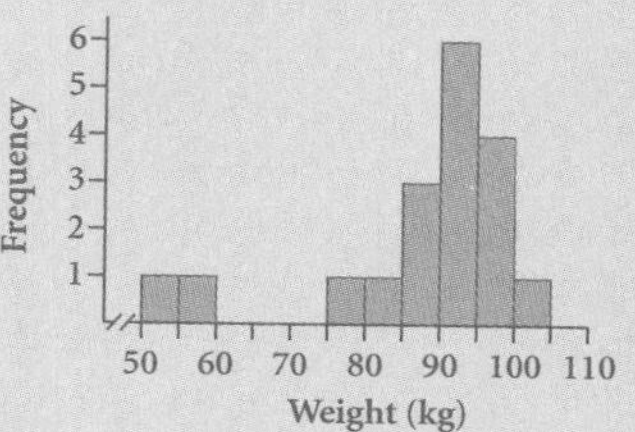

18c. Using the $1.5 \cdot IQR$ method, 54, 55, and 79 are outliers. Using the $2s$ method, only 54 and 55 are outliers.

19a. a translation right 5 units and down 2 units

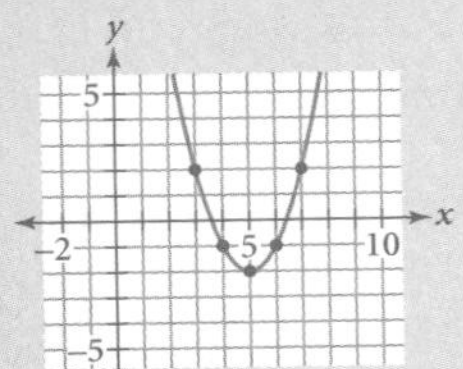

19b. a reflection across the x-axis and a vertical stretch by a factor of 2

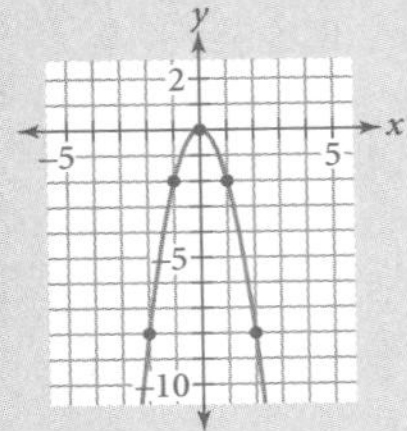

Exercise 19c [Alert] Students may describe this transformation as a reflection only across the x-axis. However, multiplying by the scalar -1 also negates the x-coordinates, so the matrix represents a reflection across the y-axis as well. The symmetry of the graph about the y-axis hides this reflection.

Exercise 20 For 20b and 20c, the linear model may give strange results. For example, using the median-median line model, the mean population in 1955 is approximately 3.49, greater than in 1950. As another example, the median-median line gives the mean population in 1995 as 2.50, which is lower than the actual population even in 1998. This is a good opportunity to talk about the strengths and weaknesses of linear models and of mathematical models in general.

20a. Let x represent the year, and let y represent mean household population. Sample answer using the median-median method: $\hat{y} = -0.0247x + 51.71$.

20b. Sample answer: What was the mean household population in 1965? approximately 3.17

20c. Sample answer: In what year will the mean household population be 2.00? approximately 2013

6.2 **19.** Consider the graph of $y = x^2$. Let matrix $[P]$, which organizes the coordinates of the points shown, represent five points on the parabola.

$$[P] = \begin{bmatrix} -2 & -1 & 0 & 1 & 2 \\ 4 & 1 & 0 & 1 & 4 \end{bmatrix}$$

a. Describe the transformation(s) that would give five corresponding points on the graph of $y = (x - 5)^2 - 2$. Sketch the graph.

b. Describe the transformation(s) that would give five points on the graph of $y = -2x^2$. Sketch the graph.

c. Sketch the image of the portion of the graph of $y = x^2$ represented by the product $-1 \cdot [P]$. Describe the transformation(s). See below.

d. Write a matrix equation that represents the image of five points on the graph of $y = x^2$ after a translation left 2 units and up 3 units. See below.

3.3 **20. APPLICATION** This table gives the mean population per U.S. household for various years from 1890 to 1998.

Mean Household Population

Year	1890	1930	1940	1950	1960	1970	1980	1990	1998
Mean population	4.93	4.11	3.67	3.37	3.35	3.14	2.76	2.63	2.62

(*The New York Times Almanac 2001*)

a. Define variables and find a linear equation that fits these data.

b. Write and solve a problem that you could solve by interpolation with your line of fit.

c. Write and solve a problem that you could solve by extrapolation with your line of fit.

A family poses before their sod house in Nebraska in 1887. Made from strips of earth and plant roots collected with a plow, sod was plastered with clay and ashes in a brick-like pattern. Sod houses were common in the Western U.S. plains because timber was scarce.

19c. $-1 \cdot [P] = \begin{bmatrix} 2 & 1 & 0 & -1 & -2 \\ -4 & -1 & 0 & -1 & -4 \end{bmatrix}$; This is a reflection across the x-axis and a reflection across the y-axis. However, because the graph is symmetric with respect to the y-axis, a reflection over that axis does not change the graph.

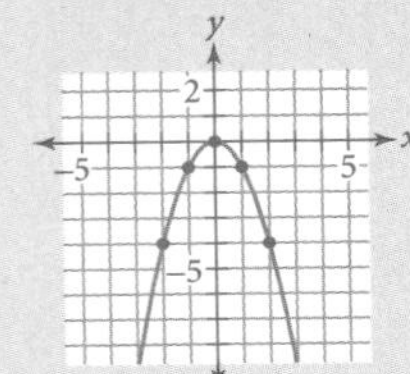

19d. $[P] + \begin{bmatrix} -2 & -2 & -2 & -2 & -2 \\ 3 & 3 & 3 & 3 & 3 \end{bmatrix} = \begin{bmatrix} -4 & -3 & -2 & -1 & 0 \\ 7 & 4 & 3 & 4 & 7 \end{bmatrix}$

TAKE ANOTHER LOOK

1. You have probably noticed that when a matrix has no inverse, one of the rows is a multiple of another row. For a 2 × 2 matrix, this also means that the products of the diagonals are equal, or that the difference of these products is 0.

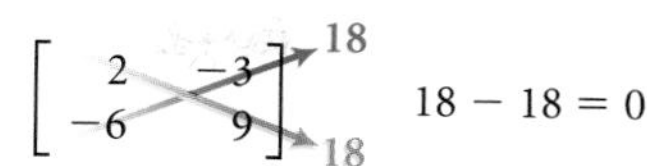

This difference of the diagonals is called the **determinant** of the matrix. For any 2 × 2 matrix $\begin{bmatrix} a & b \\ c & d \end{bmatrix}$, the determinant is $ad - bc$.

Make up some 2 × 2 matrices that have a determinant with value 1. Find the inverses of these matrices. Describe the relationship between the entries of each matrix and its inverse matrix.

Make up some 2 × 2 matrices that have a determinant with value 2. Find the inverses of these matrices. Describe the relationship between the entries of each matrix and its inverse matrix.

Write a conjecture about the inverse of a matrix and how it relates to the determinant. Test your conjecture with several other 2 × 2 matrices. Does your conjecture hold true regardless of the value of the determinant?

2. In Lesson 6.3, Exercise 14, you multiplied $\begin{bmatrix} 0 & -1 \\ 1 & 0 \end{bmatrix}$ by a matrix that represented a triangle. The result was a rotation. Try multiplying this matrix by matrices representing other types of polygons. Does it have the same effect? Find a different rotation matrix—one that will rotate a polygon by a different amount or in a different direction. Show that it works for at least three different polygons. Explain why your matrix works.

3. You have learned how to do linear programming problems, but how would you do *nonlinear* programming? Carefully graph this system of inequalities and label all the vertices. Then find the point within the feasible region that maximizes the value of P in the equation $P = (x + 2)^2 + (y - 2)^2$. Explain your solution method and how you know that your answer is correct.

$$\begin{cases} y \le -|x+2| + 10 \\ 10^{y+2} \ge x + 8 \\ 3x + 8y \le 50 \\ -3y + x^2 \ge 9 \end{cases}$$

4. In Lesson 6.4, Exercise 15, you learned how to find the inverse of a square matrix using an augmented matrix. Use this method to find the inverse of the general 2 × 2 matrix, $\begin{bmatrix} a & b \\ c & d \end{bmatrix}$. Compare your results to your work on Take Another Look 1, where you found the inverse using the determinant. Did you get the same results?

See page 358 (bottom) for answer to Take Another Look 4.

Take Another Look

1. When det = 1,
$$\begin{bmatrix} a & b \\ c & d \end{bmatrix}^{-1} = \begin{bmatrix} d & -b \\ -c & a \end{bmatrix}$$

When det = 2,
$$\begin{bmatrix} a & b \\ c & d \end{bmatrix}^{-1} = \begin{bmatrix} \frac{d}{2} & \frac{-b}{2} \\ \frac{-c}{2} & \frac{a}{2} \end{bmatrix}$$

Conjecture:
$$\begin{bmatrix} a & b \\ c & d \end{bmatrix}^{-1} = \frac{1}{\det}\begin{bmatrix} d & -b \\ -c & a \end{bmatrix}$$

If a matrix is thought of as a transformation, the determinant gives the area of the image of the unit square, thus capturing the amount of stretching or shrinking. Thus, the inverse matrix can be expressed with the determinant being divided.

2. Yes; it is a counterclockwise rotation by 90° of all points and figures in the plane. For other rotations: $\begin{bmatrix} -1 & 0 \\ 0 & -1 \end{bmatrix}$ produces a rotation by 180°, and $\begin{bmatrix} 0 & 1 \\ -1 & 0 \end{bmatrix}$ produces a clockwise rotation by 90°. Students who recall the exploration of Chapter 4 may think of these rotations as compositions of reflections. For example, $\begin{bmatrix} 0 & -1 \\ 1 & 0 \end{bmatrix}$ interchanges x and y (a reflection across the line $y = x$) and then negates the first coordinate (a reflection across the y-axis).

3.

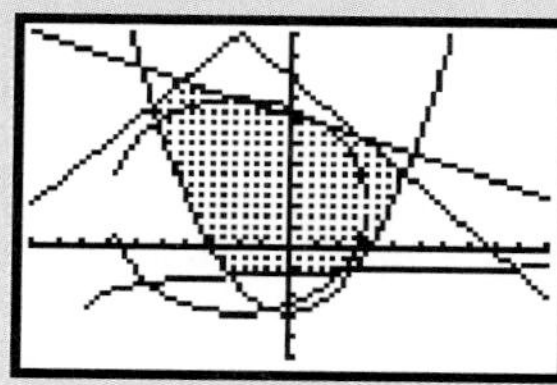

[−10, 10, 1, −5, 10, 1]

Take Another Look 3 (continued)

Vertices: (2.8, 5.2), (4.437, 3.563), (2.461, −0.980), (−5.373, 6.626), (−4.182, 7.818), (−2.295, −1.244)

Students may find answers by graphing the equation for any value of P (the second graph shows the circle with $P = 25$) and imagine increasing the value of P, enlarging the circle, until the last point within the feasible region is hit. This will show that the vertex on the far right p rovides the maximum value. The function to be maximized graphs in three dimensions as a hemisphere.

The maximum value of P occurs at (4.437, 3.563), where $P = 43.878$.

ASSESSING

The Assessment Resources contain a test for this chapter and a unit exam. You might choose to substitute the suggested performance assessment for the chapter test and, after further review, give a unit exam.

Your students may find the calculator command for row reduction at any time. In assessing you might ask students to describe the steps of the row-reduction process rather than just reduce the matrices.

FACILITATING SELF-ASSESSMENT

The question "What kinds of matrices can you multiply?" refers to the dimensions of the matrices. Exercises in which students write about the mathematics include Lesson 6.1, Exercise 8; Lesson 6.2, Exercises 5 and 10; Lesson 6.3, Exercise 14; Lesson 6.4, Exercise 12; Lesson 6.5, Exercise 11; and Lesson 6.6, Exercises 2 and 7.

In addition to a linear programming exercise such as Exercise 7 in Lesson 6.6, students might add to their portfolio exercises such as Lesson 6.1, Exercise 10; Lesson 6.2, Exercises 13 and 14; Lesson 6.3, Exercises 8 and 10; Lesson 6.4, Exercise 10; and Lesson 6.5, Exercise 10.

Assessing What You've Learned

PERFORMANCE ASSESSMENT While a classmate, a friend, a family member, or a teacher observes, show how to solve a system of equations using both an inverse matrix and the row reduction method. Explain all of your steps and why each method works.

WRITE IN YOUR JOURNAL Choose one or more of the following questions to answer in your journal.

- What kinds of matrices can be added to or subtracted from one another? What kinds of matrices can you multiply? Is matrix multiplication commutative? Why or why not? What are the identity matrix and the inverse matrix, and what are they used for?
- You have learned five methods to find a solution to a system of linear equations: graphing, substitution, elimination, matrix row reduction, and multiplication by an inverse matrix. Which method do you prefer? Which one is the most challenging to you? What are the advantages and disadvantages of each method?
- You have now studied half the chapters of this book. What mathematical skills in the previous chapters were most crucial to your success in this chapter? Which concepts are your strengths and weaknesses?

UPDATE YOUR PORTFOLIO Pick a linear programming problem for which you are especially proud of your work, and add it to your portfolio. Describe the steps you followed and how your graph helped you to solve the problem.

4. The matrix $\left[\begin{array}{cc|cc} a & b & 1 & 0 \\ c & d & 0 & 1 \end{array}\right]$ reduces to

$\left[\begin{array}{cc|cc} 1 & 0 & \frac{d}{ad-bc} & \frac{-b}{ad-bc} \\ 0 & 1 & \frac{-c}{ad-bc} & \frac{a}{ad-bc} \end{array}\right]$, which means that

the inverse is $\frac{1}{ad-bc}\begin{bmatrix} d & -b \\ -c & a \end{bmatrix}$.

CHAPTER

7

Quadratic and Other Polynomial Functions

Overview

The chapter opens in **Lesson 7.1** with the definition of *polynomial* and the finite differences method. Students also explore falling objects. The study of quadratic functions in **Lesson 7.2** includes the relationships among the general form, the factored form, and the vertex form. In **Lesson 7.3,** students explore projectile motion and solve problems involving extreme values. Students derive the quadratic formula and use it to solve application problems in **Lesson 7.4.** Complex numbers are introduced in **Lesson 7.5** by including nonreal solutions to polynomial equations. In **Lesson 7.6,** students explore cubic functions and relate the graphs of polynomial functions to the number of zeros. In **Lesson 7.7,** students deepen their understanding of a polynomial function's graph and what it says about degree and extreme values. **Lesson 7.8** shows additional methods for finding zeros of higher-degree polynomial functions with the introduction of the factor theorem, the rational root theorem, and long division.

The Mathematics

Polynomials have the form $a_nx^n + a_{n-1}x^{n-1} + \cdots + a_1x^1 + a_0$, where n is a positive integer (the degree of the polynomial) and the coefficients a_i (i from n to 1) are numbers, usually real numbers. This form, with decreasing powers on x, is the general form of a polynomial.

Polynomials are at the heart of algebra, yet writing a good definition of a polynomial is not easy. How do you describe what x is? The most rigorous definitions use the same trick as is used for a matrix representing a system of linear equations: They ignore x and define a polynomial as a finite sequence of numbers, meaning the coefficients.

So far students' work with polynomials has focused on linear polynomials—those of degree 1. Students have also seen rational, exponential, and logarithmic expressions. Although these expressions are not polynomials, calculators evaluate them by approximating them with polynomials. Sometimes these expressions are considered *polynomials of infinite degree* (more simply, *power series*) for theoretical purposes.

Polynomials as Objects

As objects, polynomials have a lot in common with integers. You can add or subtract them and multiply them. The result of dividing them isn't necessarily a polynomial, just as the quotient of two integers is not necessarily an integer. You can factor polynomials into "smaller" (lower-degree) polynomials that are basic building blocks, similar to prime numbers, but doing this factoring is not always easy. For polynomials with rational coefficients, the rational root theorem helps.

Polynomials as Functions

Polynomials can also be thought of as function expressions. As students have seen with linear polynomials, they can be graphed, and they can be fit to data to make predictions. In this chapter, students learn how to use finite differences to determine the degree of a polynomial of good fit and how to use systems of linear equations to find the coefficients of such a polynomial. In Chapter 13, they'll encounter other ways to fit data with linear functions and one-term polynomial functions of higher degree (power functions).

As functions, polynomials have zeros—input numbers that give the function a value of 0. These zeros are the x-coordinates of the x-intercepts of the function's graph. A polynomial equation is used to find which input numbers the function takes to a given number. The zeros of the polynomial are the roots, or solutions, of the equation setting the polynomial equal to 0. The factor theorem says that the number r is a zero of the polynomial if and only if $(x - r)$ is a factor of the polynomial. Therefore, if you can write the polynomial in factored form as a product of binomials of the form $(x - r)$, then you can find all the roots.

Several lessons of the chapter focus on quadratic functions, functions defined by 2nd-degree polynomials. Their graphs are parabolas. If a 2nd-degree polynomial is written in vertex form (found by completing the square), then the expression not only shows the vertex of the graph of the polynomial function but also indicates how the graph is translated from the parent parabola. Vertex form can also be used for finding the zeros of the quadratic function. If this process is carried out for the general quadratic equation, you derive the quadratic formula. You can use the quadratic formula to solve all quadratic equations in general form.

In general, the graphs of polynomial functions are smooth curves with various turning points at local extreme values (maximums and minimums). If the graph has n local extreme values, the polynomial has degree at least $n + 1$. The graph may or may not have an x-intercept between two local extreme values. If it does, then the intercept marks a real zero of the polynomial. If the graph does not cross the x-axis between extreme values, it indicates a zero that's a nonreal complex number. Complex numbers, of the form $a + bi$, where $i^2 = -1$, consist of the real numbers (when $b = 0$), the imaginary numbers (when $a = 0$), and combinations of both. Complex zeros of polynomial functions with real coefficients come in conjugate pairs of the form $a \pm bi$.

Using This Chapter

Finite differences seen in Lesson 7.1 will be used again in Lesson 11.1. You might skip the investigations in Lessons 7.2 and 7.4; they are extra practice.

Resources

Discovering Advanced Algebra Resources

Teaching and Worksheet Masters
Lessons 7.1, 7.2, 7.5–7.8, Chapter Review

Calculator Notes 6G or 6G/App, 7A–I

Sketchpad Demonstrations
Lessons 7.4, 7.7

FathomDemonstration
Lesson 7.1

Assessment Resources A and B
Quiz 1 (Lessons 7.1–7.3)
Quiz 2 (Lessons 7.4, 7.5)
Quiz 3 (Lessons 7.6–7.8)
Chapter 7 Test
Chapter 7 Constructive Assessment Options

More Practice Your Skills for Chapter 7

Condensed Lessons for Chapter 7

Other Resources

The Mandelbrot and Julia Sets by Robert Devaney.

For complete references to this and other resources, see www.keypress.com/DAA.

Materials

- motion sensors
- small pillows or other soft objects
- empty coffee cans or poster tubes
- long tables
- scissors
- graph paper
- rulers
- cubes, *optional*
- algebra tiles, *optional*
- tape, *optional*
- centimeter grid paper, *optional*

Pacing Guide

	day 1	day 2	day 3	day 4	day 5	day 6	day 7	day 8	day 9	day 10
standard	7.1	7.2	7.3	7.3	quiz, 7.4	7.5	quiz, 7.6	7.7	7.7	7.8
enriched	7.1	7.2	7.3	7.3	quiz, 7.4, project	7.5, project	quiz, 7.6	7.7	7.8	quiz, review
block	7.1, 7.2	7.3	quiz, 7.4, 7.5	quiz, 7.6, 7.7	7.8	quiz, review	TAL, assessment			

	day 11	day 12	day 13	day 14
standard	7.8	quiz, review	review	assessment
enriched	review, TAL	assessment		

CHAPTER

7

Quadratic and Other Polynomial Functions

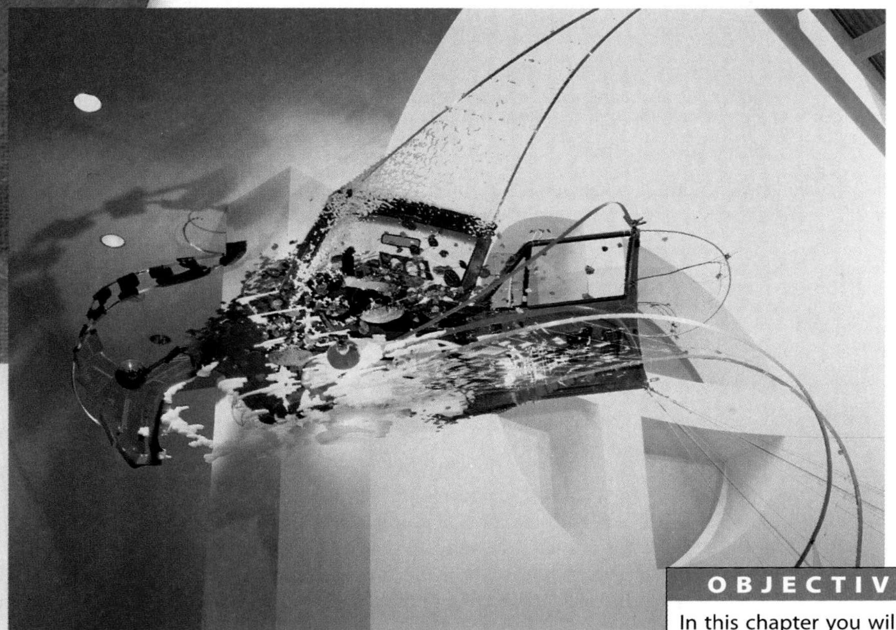

American artist Sarah Sze (b 1969) creates flowing sculptures, such as this one created for an exhibit at the San Francisco Museum of Modern Art. This piece features a fractured sport utility vehicle whose pieces have been replaced with disposable household items, including foam packing peanuts. Some of the curves in this artwork's cascade resemble the graphs of polynomial functions.

Things Fall Apart: 2001, mixed media installation with vehicle; variable dimensions/San Francisco Museum of Modern Art, Accessions Committee Fund purchase © Sarah Sze

OBJECTIVES

In this chapter you will

- find polynomial functions that fit a set of data
- study quadratic functions in general form, vertex form, and factored form
- find roots of a quadratic equation from a graph, by factoring, and by using the quadratic formula
- define complex numbers and operations with them
- identify features of the graph of a polynomial function
- use division and other strategies to find roots of higher-degree polynomials

The sculpture pictured here is a small part of a large installation that cascades through several floors of the atrium of the San Francisco Museum of Modern Art. It was created specifically for the museum.

Sze uses many items found in everyday life in her artwork. **[Ask]** "What items do you recognize in this sculpture?" [parts of a vehicle, desk lamps, Styrofoam popcorn] "With the title of the work in mind, what do you think the artist is trying to convey with this work?" [Sample answer: The sculpture conveys a sense of motion and destruction. Sze seems to be saying that, although we feel secure with these familiar objects, they will fall apart as they are seen to be doing here. She might be trying to make a statement about SUVs.]

[Ask] "Why do you think the artist included the curved shapes that come out of the sculpture?" [Sample answer: They convey a sense of growth, of infinite expansion or falling apart.] "Do you see any representations of mathematical objects?" [curves, lines, spirals, polygons, circles, ellipses]

CHAPTER 7 OBJECTIVES

- Define types and properties of polynomials
- Use finite differences and systems of equations to find a polynomial function that fits a data set
- Understand the correspondence between the zeros of a polynomial, the x-intercepts of its graph, and the roots of an equation
- Find roots of polynomial equations from factored form, using the zero-product property
- Change quadratic polynomials from general form to vertex form by completing the square
- Relate the vertex form of a quadratic equation to its roots, its parent function, its relative extreme points, and the quadratic formula
- Define and use complex and imaginary numbers and conjugate pairs
- Learn relationships among the graphs of polynomial equations, functions, the number and types of roots, the possible degrees of the polynomial, and extreme values and end behavior
- Change polynomials from general form to factored form using graphs, the Rational Root Theorem, long or synthetic division, and the quadratic formula

LESSON 7.1

PLANNING

LESSON OUTLINE

One day:

15 min Example

20 min Investigation

5 min Sharing

5 min Exercises

MATERIALS

- motion sensors
- small pillows or other soft objects
- Free Fall Sample Data (W) for One Step
- Finite Differences (T), *optional*
- Calculator Notes 7A, 7B
- Fathom demonstration Free Fall, *optional*

TEACHING

This lesson uses finite differences to find polynomials that fit data. **[Link]** The finite differences method foreshadows differential calculus.

One Step

Hand out the Free Fall Sample Data worksheet, and ask whether the data are linear. Students will check first differences to see that they are not. Suggest checking differences of differences, and perhaps of those differences and so on, to find the kind of polynomial that fits a set of data. Ask students to experiment with polynomials of their own design, checking first, second, third, and perhaps more differences and looking for patterns that they can apply to the free fall data. As students work, encourage them to focus first on finding which differences are constant. If some groups quickly find a relationship to the highest power in the polynomial, ask whether they can find the coefficient of the highest power of x from the constant difference. During Sharing, introduce the terms *degree* and *finite differences method.*

INTRODUCTION

Students are used to seeing an ellipsis to stand for something left out, but they may not have seen one raised as in the definition of a polynomial. You might say that a raised ellipsis is used when an operation repeats.

LESSON OBJECTIVES

- Define *polynomial, monomial, binomial,* and *trinomial*
- Determine the degree of a polynomial by using finite differences
- Explore falling objects
- Write polynomials in general form
- Use finite differences and systems of equations to find a polynomial function that fits a data set

LESSON 7.1

Polynomial Degree and Finite Differences

Differences challenge assumptions.

ANNE WILSON SCHAEF

In Chapter 1, you studied arithmetic sequences, which have a common difference between consecutive terms. If you graph the points of an arithmetic sequence and draw a line through them, this line has a constant slope. So, if you choose x-values along the line that form an arithmetic sequence, the corresponding y-values will also form an arithmetic sequence.

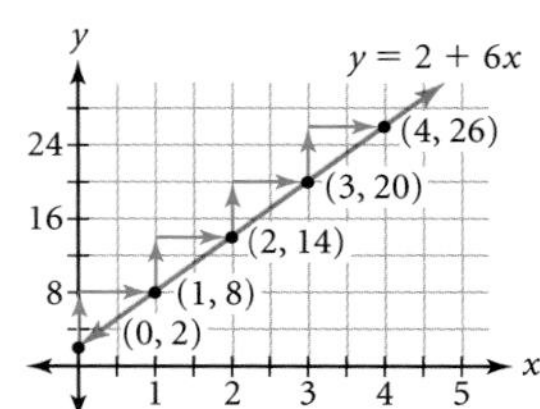

You have also studied several kinds of nonlinear sequences and functions, which do not have a common difference or a constant slope. In this lesson you will discover that even nonlinear sequences sometimes have a special pattern in their differences.

A **polynomial** expression is a sum of **terms** containing the same variable raised to different powers. Each term is a product of numbers and variables. When a polynomial is set equal to a second variable, such as y, you have a **polynomial function.**

Definition of a Polynomial

A **polynomial** in one variable is any expression that can be written in the form

$$a_n x^n + a_{n-1}x^{n-1} + \cdots + a_1 x^1 + a_0$$

where x is a variable, the exponents are nonnegative integers, and the coefficients are real numbers.

The **degree** of a polynomial or polynomial function is the power of the term that has the greatest exponent. Linear functions are 1st-degree polynomial functions because the largest power of x is 1. The polynomial function below has degree 3. If the degrees of the terms of a polynomial decrease from left to right, the polynomial is in **general form.**

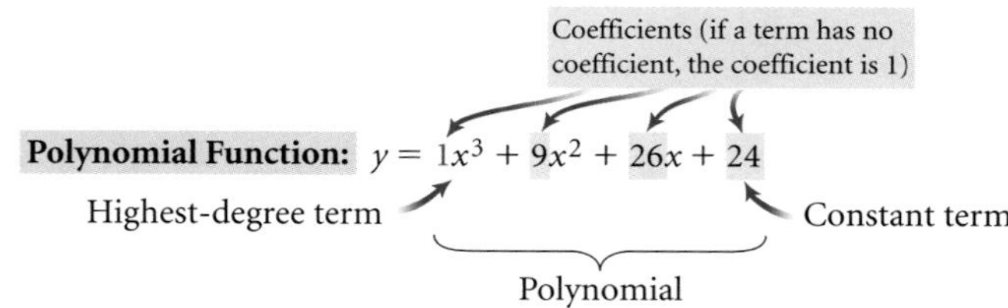

A polynomial that has only one term is called a **monomial.** A polynomial with two terms is a **binomial,** and a polynomial with three terms is a **trinomial.** Polynomials with more than three terms are usually just called "polynomials."

In modeling linear functions, you have already discovered that for x-values that are uniformly spaced, the differences between the corresponding y-values must be the same. With 2nd- and 3rd-degree polynomial functions, the differences between the corresponding y-values are not the same. However, finding the differences between those differences produces an interesting pattern.

1st degree
$y = 3x + 4$

x	y	D_1
2	10	
		3
3	13	
		3
4	16	
		3
5	19	
		3
6	22	
		3
7	25	

2nd degree
$y = 2x^2 - 5x - 7$

x	y	D_1	D_2
3.7	1.88		
		1	
3.8	2.88		0.04
		1.04	
3.9	3.92		0.04
		1.08	
4.0	5.00		0.04
		1.12	
4.1	6.12		0.04
		1.16	
4.2	7.28		

3rd degree
$y = 0.1x^3 - x^2 + 3x - 5$

x	y	D_1	D_2	D_3
−5	−57.5			
		52.5		
0	−5		−50	
		2.5		75
5	−2.5		25	
		27.5		75
10	25		100	
		127.5		75
15	152.5		175	
		302.5		
20	455			

Note that in each case the x-values are spaced equally. You find the first set of differences, D_1, by subtracting each y-value from the one after it. You find the second set of differences, D_2, by finding the differences of consecutive D_1 values in the same way. Notice that for the 2nd-degree polynomial function, the D_2 values are constant, and that for the 3rd-degree polynomial function, the D_3 values are constant. What do you think will happen with a 4th- or 5th-degree polynomial function?

The D_4 and D_5 values, respectively, will be constant.

You can use this method to find the degree of the polynomial function that models a certain set of data. Analyzing differences to find a polynomial's degree is called the **finite differences method.**

Similar types of foods are grouped together at this market in Camden Lock, London, England. Polynomials are often grouped into similar types as well.

EXAMPLE Find a polynomial function that models the relationship between the number of sides and the number of diagonals of a polygon. Use the function to find the number of diagonals of a dodecagon (a 12-sided polygon).

▶ ***Solution*** You need to create a table of values with evenly spaced x-values. Sketch polygons with increasing numbers of sides. Then draw all of their diagonals.

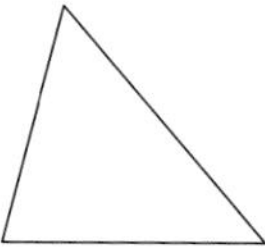 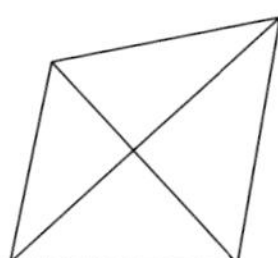 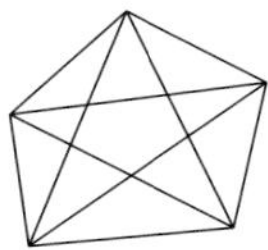 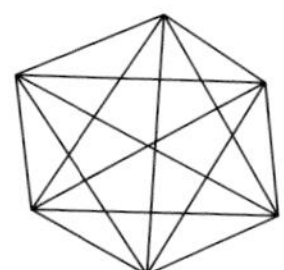

[Ask] "What is the degree of the polynomial x?" [1] "What is the degree of 24?" [0, because $24 = 24x^0$]

[Ask] "What do common differences represent?" [constant slope] "Are there sequences and functions besides quadratics that do not have common differences?" [yes; exponential functions, for example]

You might use the Finite Differences transparency as you discuss the method. The method will be used again in Chapter 11, Series.

▶ ***EXAMPLE***

This example illustrates constant second differences in a quadratic function. You might have students work on the problem alone or in groups and then discuss methods of finding the number of diagonals of a dodecagon.

Students may notice a pattern in the number of diagonals (add 2, add 3, add 4, and so on); this pattern is described by the first differences.

[Ask] "What would happen if you continued to find differences after you had a set of constant differences?" [You would obtain only sets of zeros.]

[Ask] "How did the quadratic equation in one variable become three linear equations in three variables?" Students may be confused about whether a, b, and c are constants or variables. They are constant coefficients of the quadratic polynomial, but they're being treated temporarily as variables because they are unknown.

The system of equations can be solved by several methods. Students can check their results by using a different method.

NCTM STANDARDS

CONTENT	PROCESS
✓ Number	✓ Problem Solving
✓ Algebra	✓ Reasoning
✓ Geometry	✓ Communication
✓ Measurement	✓ Connections
✓ Data/Probability	✓ Representation

[Ask] "Often in mathematics an answer to a problem suggests that there might be a different way to solve the problem. Is that true here?" Students might realize that each of the x vertices is connected by a diagonal to $x - 3$ vertices (not counting itself or the two adjacent vertices) and that the number of diagonals is half the product of $x(x - 3)$ because each diagonal $\overline{AB}$ is the same as the diagonal $\overline{BA}$.

Guiding the Investigation

The pillow does not have to be small; a regular bed pillow will work well. Although pillows work best, you can also use plastic grocery bags filled with crumpled newspaper. Students can drop a ball toward a sensor as long as the sensor is protected, for example, by setting it between two stacks of books. (Or you might use a ball falling *away* from a sensor held 2.5 m above the floor. In this case, subtract each data value from 2.5 m.) You could also replace the investigation with the Fathom demonstration Free Fall.

Step 1 Set the trigger and hear the motion sensor clicking before releasing the pillow. In the main menu of the RANGER program choose Plot Menu and then Plot Tools to select the domain of the data. Refer students to Calculator Note 7A.

Step 3 After students enter the shortened list of time values into list L3, they take the differences of the values in list L2 and enter those differences into list L4.

Students might complete this step by hand, finding the differences in a table and graphing them on graph paper.

Step 4 Encourage students to use words like *increasing, decreasing, horizontal,* and *constant* to describe their graphs.

Step 4 The graph of (L1, L2) appears parabolic and suggests that the correct model may be a quadratic (2nd-degree) polynomial function. The graph of (L3, L4) shows that the first differences are not constant; because they decrease in a linear fashion, the second differences are likely to be constant. The graph of (L5, L6) shows that the second differences are nearly constant, so the correct model should be a 2nd-degree polynomial function.

Let x be the number of sides and y be the number of diagonals. You may notice a pattern in the number of diagonals that will help you extend your table beyond the sketches you make. Calculate the finite differences to determine the degree of the polynomial function. (Remember that your x-values must be spaced equally in order to use finite differences.)

Number of sides x	Number of diagonals y	D_1	D_2
3	0		
		2	
4	2		1
		3	
5	5		1
		4	
6	9		1
		5	
7	14		1
		6	
8	20		

You can stop finding differences when the values of a set of differences are constant. Because the values of D_2 are constant, you can model the data with a 2nd-degree polynomial function like $y = ax^2 + bx + c$.

To find the values of a, b, and c, you need a system of three equations. Choose three of the points from your table, say (4, 2), (6, 9), and (8, 20), and substitute the coordinates into $y = ax^2 + bx + c$ to create a system of three equations in three variables. Can you see how these three equations were created?

$$\begin{cases} 16a + 4b + c = 2 \\ 36a + 6b + c = 9 \\ 64a + 8b + c = 20 \end{cases}$$

Solve the system to find $a = 0.5$, $b = -1.5$, and $c = 0$. Use these values to write the function $y = 0.5x^2 - 1.5x$. This equation gives the number of diagonals of any polygon as a function of the number of sides.

Now substitute 12 for x to find that a dodecagon has 54 diagonals.

$$y = 0.5x^2 - 1.5x$$
$$y = 0.5(12)^2 - 1.5(12)$$
$$y = 54$$

With exact function values, you can expect the differences to be equal when you find the right degree. But with experimental or statistical data, as in the investigation, you may have to settle for differences that are nearly constant and that do not show an increasing or decreasing pattern when graphed.

Science CONNECTION

Italian mathematician, physicist, and astronomer Galileo Galilei (1564–1642) performed experiments with free-falling objects. He discovered that the speed of a falling object at any moment is proportional to the amount of time it has been falling. In other words, the longer an object falls, the faster it falls. To learn more about Galileo's experiments and discoveries, see the links at www.keymath.com/DAA

Step 3

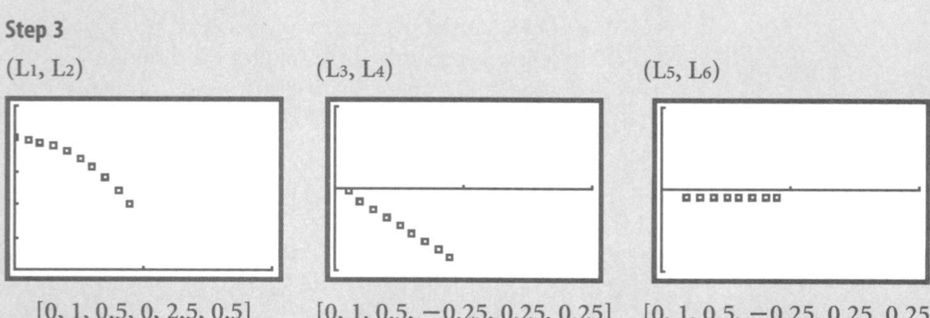

[0, 1, 0.5, 0, 2.5, 0.5]   [0, 1, 0.5, −0.25, 0.25, 0.25]   [0, 1, 0.5, −0.25, 0.25, 0.25]

Investigation
Free Fall

You will need

- a motion sensor
- a small pillow or other soft object

What function models the height of an object falling due to the force of gravity? Use a motion sensor to collect data, and analyze the data to find a function.

Procedure Note

1. Set the sensor to collect distance data approximately every 0.05 s for 2 to 5 s. [▶ See **Calculator Note 7A** to learn how to set up your calculator. ◀]
2. Place the sensor on the floor. Hold a small pillow at a height of about 2 m, directly above the sensor.
3. Start the sensor and drop the pillow.

Step 1 Follow the procedure note to collect data for a falling object. Let x represent time in seconds, and let y represent height in meters. Select about 10 points from the free-fall portion of your data, with x-values forming an arithmetic sequence. Record this information in a table. Round all table values to the nearest 0.001.

Step 2 Use the finite differences method to find the degree of the polynomial function that models your data. Stop when the differences are nearly constant.

Step 3 Enter your time values, x, into list L1 on your calculator. Enter your height values, y, into list L2. For your first differences, enter your time values without the first value into list L3, and enter the first differences, D_1, into list L4. For your second differences, enter the time values without the first two values into list L5, and enter the second differences, D_2, into list L6. Continue this process for any other differences you calculated. Then make scatter plots of (L1, L2), (L3, L4), (L5, L6), and so on. [▶ See **Calculator Note 7B** to learn how to calculate finite differences and how to graph them. ◀]

Step 4 Write a description of each graph from Step 3 and what these graphs tell you about the data.

Step 5 2nd degree; $y = ax^2 + bx + c$

Step 5 Based on your results from using finite differences, what is the degree of the polynomial function that models free fall? Write the general form of this polynomial function.

Step 6 Systems will vary depending on the points chosen; the function should be approximately equivalent to $y = -4.9x^2 + 2$.

Step 6 Follow the example on page 362 to write a system of three equations in three variables for your data. Solve your system to find an equation to model the position of a free-falling object dropped from a height of 2 m.

Step 5 [Ask] If students want to keep finding finite differences because they don't have differences that are exactly the same, refer them to the paragraph preceding the investigation. Ask them to look for a graph of finite differences that is approximately horizontal, not increasing or decreasing.

Step 6 [Ask] "Is it better to pick the three points from the beginning, the end, or the middle of the data? Why?" The paragraph following the investigation addresses this question.

SHARING IDEAS

As students present their ideas, **[Ask]** "Why are the nth differences constant for a polynomial of degree n?" Be careful not to discourage thinking by talking too quickly or saying too much. [Intuitively, the first differences give the rate of change; they are found by dividing through by the independent variable (for example, from meters to meters/sec), so the first differences are given by a polynomial one degree lower than the original. The second differences are the rate of change of the first differences, and so on.] **[Link]** Students will see when they study calculus that finite differences are analogous to derivatives and the first derivative of a polynomial is a polynomial one degree lower.

[Alert] Students may think of functions as being written with the notation $f(x)$. The equation $y = polynomial$ is also a function, because each value of x yields just one y-value.

Ask whether there's a way to find the coefficients of the 2nd-degree polynomial other than by solving a system of equations. For linear functions $f(x)$ with constant difference b, students can find that $f(x) = bx + f(0)$. (This is the intercept form, slightly disguised.)

Sharing Ideas (continued)

If students find a constant second difference a, then the quadratic function will have $\frac{a}{2}$ as a coefficient of the x^2 term. They can then make a table of values for x, $f(x)$, and $f(x) - \frac{a}{2}x^2$ and find the linear expression $bx + c$ for the last column, implying that $f(x) = \frac{a}{2}x^2 + bx + c$. (In general, the coefficient of the highest power x^n equals the constant nth finite difference divided by $n!$.)

Ask whether the finite differences are ever constant for exponential functions. For functions of the form $y = ab^x$, the differences will all be geometric sequences with common ratio b. You might mention that exponential, logarithmic, and trigonometric functions are sometimes expressed as infinite polynomials with coefficients that form a sequence. Calculators and computers might evaluate a nonpolynomial function by approximating it with a polynomial over a small domain and then evaluating that polynomial.

For help in understanding the meaning of the coefficient −4.9, see Free Fall on page 364.

See page 888 for answers to Steps 1 and 2.

Free Fall
You might help students see that the equation in Step 6 shows the distance traveled as the *average speed* times the *time*. The beginning speed is zero; the ending speed is determined by the acceleration due to gravity, 9.8 m/s^2. Thus the speed of an object x s after it is dropped is $9.8x$ m/s. The average speed is $\frac{1}{2}(0 + 9.8x)$, or $4.9x$. The distance fallen is $(4.9x)(x)$, or $4.9x^2$ m. If students measure in feet, their equation will have the coefficient that is half of the acceleration due to gravity, 16.1 ft/s^2.

Assessing Progress
As students work and present, you can assess their ability to collect data systematically, to evaluate polynomials, to follow calculator notes, and to solve systems of three linear equations.

Closing the Lesson

Reiterate the main points of this lesson: If the nth **finite differences** of a polynomial function are constant, then the polynomial has **degree** n. If the nth finite differences of a data set are approximately constant, the data set might be fit by a polynomial of degree n. The actual polynomial can be found by setting up a system of equations whose unknowns are the polynomial's coefficients.

BUILDING UNDERSTANDING

Students practice finding polynomials to fit data sets.

ASSIGNING HOMEWORK

Essential	1–5
Performance assessment	6–9
Portfolio	9
Journal	8
Group	9
Review	10–14

When using experimental data, you must choose your points carefully. When you collect data, as you did in the investigation, your equation will most likely not fit all of the data points exactly due to some errors in measurement and rounding. To minimize the effects of these errors, choose representative points that are not close together, just as you did when fitting a line to data.

History CONNECTION

The method of finite differences was used by the Chinese astronomer Li Shun-Fêng in the 7th century to find a quadratic equation to model the Sun's apparent motion across the sky as a function of time. The Persian astronomer Jamshid Masud al-Kashi, who worked at the Samarkand Observatory in the 15th century, also used the finite differences method when calculating the celestial longitudes of planets.

The finite differences method was further developed in 17th- and 18th-century Europe. Scientists used it to eliminate calculations involving multiplication and division when constructing tables of polynomial values. It was not uncommon for a late-18th-century European scientist to have more than 125 volumes of various kinds of tables. In the 19th century, early automatic calculating machines were programmed to calculate differences and were called difference engines.

English mathematician and inventor Charles Babbage (1792–1871) designed the first difference engine in the early 1820s, and completed his Difference Engine No. 1, shown here, in 1832.

Note that some functions, such as logarithmic and trigonometric functions, cannot be expressed as polynomials. The finite differences method will not produce a set of constant differences for functions other than polynomial functions.

EXERCISES

Practice Your Skills

1. Identify the degree of each polynomial.

a. $x^3 + 9x^2 + 26x + 24$ 3

b. $7x^2 - 5x$ 2

c. $x^7 + 3x^6 - 5x^5 + 24x^4 + 17x^3 - 6x^2 + 2x + 40$ 7

d. $16 - 5x^2 + 9x^5 + 36x^3 + 44x$ 5

2. Determine which of these expressions are polynomials. For each polynomial, state its degree and write it in general form. If it is not a polynomial, explain why not.

a. $-3 + 4x - 3.5x^2 + \frac{5}{9}x^3$

b. $5p^4 + 3.5p - \frac{4}{p^2} + 16$

c. $4\sqrt{x^3} + 12$

d. $x^2\sqrt{15} - x - 4^{-2}$

MATERIALS

- cubes, *optional*
- algebra tiles, *optional*

Helping with the Exercises

Exercise 1d [Alert] This polynomial is not written in general form, so its degree may not be obvious.

2a. polynomial; 3; $\frac{5}{9}x^3 - 3.5x^2 + 4x - 3$

2b. not a polynomial because $\frac{4}{p^2} = 4p^{-2}$ has a negative exponent

2c. not a polynomial because $4\sqrt{x^3} = 4x^{3/2}$ has a non-integer exponent

2d. polynomial; 2; already in general form

3. For each data set, decide whether the last column shows constant values. If it does not, calculate the next set of finite differences.

a.

x	y
2	4.4
3	6.6
4	9.2
5	11.0
6	10.8
7	7.4

b.

x	y	D_1
3.7	−8.449	
3.8	−8.706	−0.257
3.9	−8.956	−0.250
4.0	−9.200	−0.244
4.1	−9.436	−0.236
4.2	−9.662	−0.226

c.

x	y	D_1	D_2
−5	−101		
0	−6	95	
5	−11	−5	−100
10	34	45	50
15	279	245	200
20	874	595	350

4. Find the degree of the polynomial function that models these data. 3

x	0	2	4	6	8	10	12
y	12	−4	−164	−612	−1492	−2948	−5124

Reason and Apply

5. Consider the data at right.

n	1	2	3	4	5	6
s	1	3	6	10	15	21

a. Calculate finite differences to find the degree of the polynomial function that models these data.

b. Describe how the degree of this polynomial function is related to the finite differences you calculated.

c. What is the minimum number of data points required to determine the degree of this polynomial function? Why?

d. Find the polynomial function that models these data and use it to find s when n is 12.

e. The values in the s row are called triangular numbers. Why do you think they are called triangular? (*Hint:* Find some pennies and try to arrange each number of pennies into a triangle.)

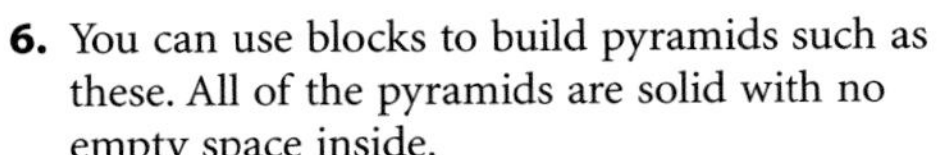

6. You can use blocks to build pyramids such as these. All of the pyramids are solid with no empty space inside.

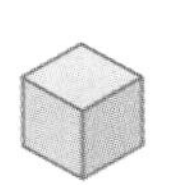

a. Create a table to record the number of layers, x, in each pyramid and the total number of blocks, y, needed to build it. You may need to build or sketch a few more pyramids, or look for patterns in the table.

b. Use finite differences to find a polynomial function that models these data.

c. Find the number of blocks needed to build a pyramid with eight layers. 204 blocks

d. Find the number of layers in a pyramid built with 650 blocks. 12 layers

3a. no; {2.2, 2.6, 1.8, −0.2, −3.4}

3b. no; {0.007, 0.006, 0.008, 0.010}

3c. no; {150, 150, 150}

Exercise 5c [Ask] "In general, how many data points do you need to find a polynomial model of degree n?" [$n + 2$ points]

5a. $D_1 = \{2, 3, 4, 5, 6\}$; $D_2 = \{1, 1, 1, 1\}$; 2nd degree

5b. The polynomial is 2nd degree, and the D_2 values are constant.

5c. 4 points. You have to find the finite differences twice, so you need at least four data points to calculate two D_2 values that can be compared.

5d. $s = 0.5n^2 + 0.5n$; $s = 78$

5e. The pennies can be arranged to form triangles.

Exercise 6a Students need to make enough columns in their table to see a pattern. They might see the pattern with five columns and add another column to see if their pattern holds.

6a.

Layers x	1	2	3	4	5	6
Blocks y	1	5	14	30	55	91

6b. $y = \frac{1}{3}x^3 + \frac{1}{2}x^2 + \frac{1}{6}x$

7a. i. $D_1 = \{15.1, 5.3, -4.5, -14.3, -24.1, -33.9\}$; $D_2 = \{-9.8, -9.8, -9.8, -9.8, -9.8\}$

7a. ii. $D_1 = \{59.1, 49.3, 39.5, 29.7, 19.9, 10.1\}$; $D_2 = \{-9.8, -9.8, -9.8, -9.8, -9.8\}$

7b. i. 2; **ii.** 2

Exercise 7c [Ask] "What are the similarities and differences between the models for the two data sets? Between their graphs?"

7c. i. $h = -4.9t^2 + 20t + 80$; **ii.** $h = -4.9t^2 + 64t + 4$

Exercise 8 As needed in 8b, remind students that because the measurements are inexact, the differences will probably not be exactly constant. At best they can find a horizontal trend in some finite differences. In 8d **[Ask]** "How well does your curve approximate the data? Do you think it is a good model for these data?"

8a. $D_1 = \{0.07, 0.06, 0.04, 0.02, 0.01, 0.01, 0, 0, 0, 0.01, 0.01, 0.02, 0.03, 0.05, 0.07\}$. The graph is approximately parabolic.

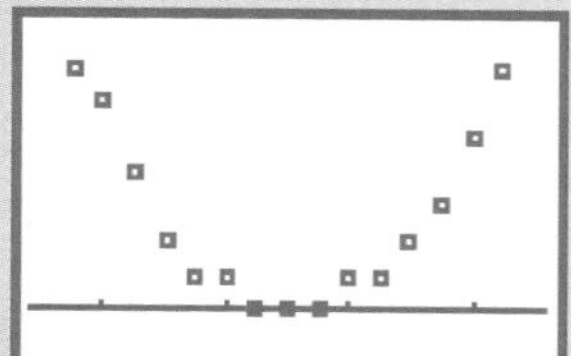

[9.5, 13.5, 1, −0.02, 0.08, 1]

8b. $D_2 = \{-0.01, -0.02, -0.02, -0.01, 0, -0.01, 0, 0, 0.01, 0, 0.01, 0.01, 0.02, 0.02\}$.

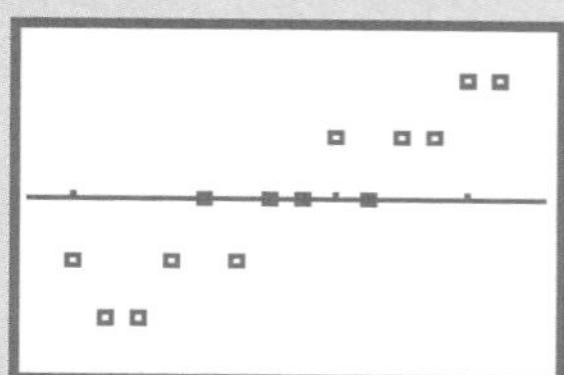

[9.5, 13.5, 1, −0.03, 0.03, 1]

7. The data in these tables represent the heights of two objects at different times during free fall.

i.

Time (s) t	0	1	2	3	4	5	6
Height (m) h	80	95.1	100.4	95.9	81.6	57.5	23.6

ii.

Time (s) t	0	1	2	3	4	5	6
Height (m) h	4	63.1	112.4	151.9	181.6	201.5	211.6

a. Calculate the finite differences for each table.

b. What is the degree of the polynomial function that you would use to model each data set?

c. Write a polynomial function to model each set of data. Check your answer by substituting one of the data points into your function.

8. Andy has measured his height every three months since he was $9\frac{1}{2}$ years old. Below are his measurements in meters.

Age (yr)	Height (m)	Age (yr)	Height (m)
9.5	1.14	11.5	1.35
9.75	1.21	11.75	1.35
10	1.27	12	1.36
10.25	1.31	12.25	1.37
10.5	1.33	12.5	1.39
10.75	1.34	12.75	1.42
11	1.35	13	1.47
11.25	1.35	13.25	1.54

a. Find the first differences for Andy's heights and make a scatter plot of points in the form (age, D_1). Remember to shorten the list of ages to match D_1. Describe the pattern you see.

b. Repeat your process from 8a until the differences are nearly constant and show no pattern.

c. What type of model will fit these data? Why?

d. Define variables and find a model. For what domain values do you think this model is reasonable?

$D_3 = \{-0.01, 0, 0.01, 0.01, -0.01, 0.01, 0, 0.01, -0.01, 0.01, 0, 0.01, 0\}$. There is no pattern to these numbers.

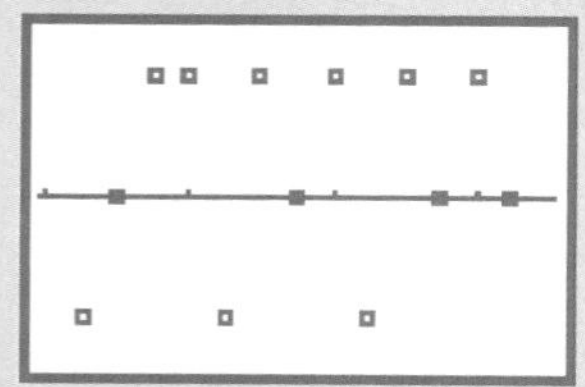

[9.5, 13.5, 1, −0.013, 0.013, 1]

8c. Third-degree polynomial; third differences are nearly constant and show no pattern.

8d. Let x represent Andy's age in years, and let y represent his height in meters. $y = 0.0308x^3 - 1.055x^2 + 12.03x - 44.40$. The model appears to be reasonable for about $8.5 \leq x \leq 14$.

9. APPLICATION In an atom, electrons spin rapidly around a nucleus. An electron can occupy only specific energy levels, and each energy level can hold only a certain number of electrons. This table gives the greatest number of electrons that can theoretically be in any one level (although there are no known atoms that actually have more than 32 electrons in any one level).

Energy level	1	2	3	4	5	6	7
Maximum number of electrons	2	8	18	32	50	72	98

$D_1 = \{6, 10, 14, 18, 22, 26\}$; $D_2 = \{4, 4, 4, 4, 4\}$. The second differences are constant, so a quadratic function expresses the relationship. Let x represent the energy level, and let y represent the maximum number of electrons. $y = 2x^2$.

Is it possible to find a polynomial function that expresses the relationship between the energy level and the maximum number of electrons? If so, find the function. If not, explain why not.

Science
CONNECTION

The electrons in an atom exist in various energy levels. When an electron moves from a lower energy level to a higher energy level, the atom absorbs energy. When an electron moves from a higher to a lower energy level, energy is released (often as light). This is the principle behind neon lights. The electricity running through a tube of neon gas makes the electrons in the neon atoms jump to higher energy levels. When they drop back to their original level, they give off light.

A visitor admires a neon art display at the Yerba Buena Center for the Arts in San Francisco, California.

Review

4.4 **10.** Sketch a graph of each function without using your calculator.

a. $y = (x - 2)^2$ b. $y = x^2 - 4$ c. $y = (x + 4)^2 + 1$

11. Solve.

a. $12x - 17 = 13$ $x = 2.5$ b. $2(x - 1)^2 + 3 = 11$ $x = 3$ or $x = -1$ c. $3(5^x) = 48$ $x = \frac{\log 16}{\log 5} \approx 1.7227$

0.1 **12.** You may recall that a rectangle diagram can represent the product of two binomials. For example, the rectangle at right represents the product $(x + 2)(x + 3)$, which you can write as the trinomial $x^2 + 5x + 6$.

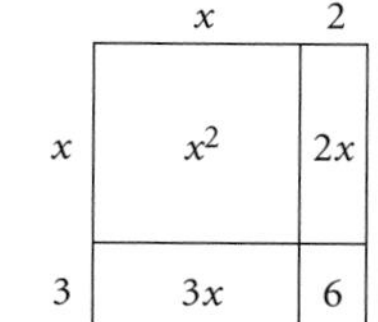

a. Draw a rectangle diagram that represents the product $(2x + 3)(3x + 1)$.

b. Express the area in 12a as a polynomial in general form.

c. Draw a rectangle whose area represents the polynomial $x^2 + 8x + 15$. (*Hint:* You need to break $8x$ into two terms.)

d. Express the area in 12c as a product of two binomials.

6.5 **13.** Write a system of inequalities that describes the feasible region graphed at right.

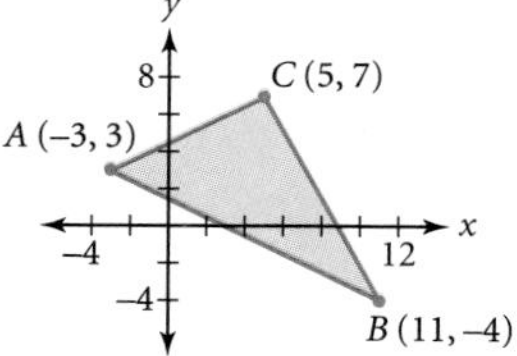

14. Find the product $(x + 3)(x + 4)(x + 2)$. $x^3 + 9x^2 + 26x + 24$

Exercise 10 As needed, ask whether it helps to think about transforming parent functions. Students can use calculators to check their sketches.

10a.

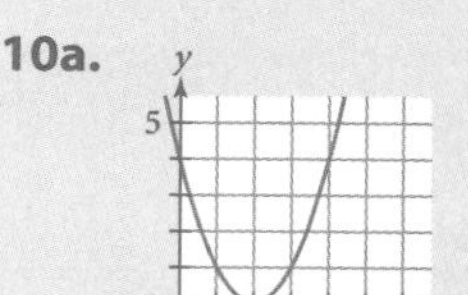

10b.

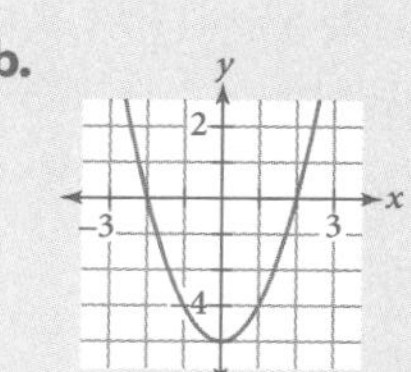

10c.

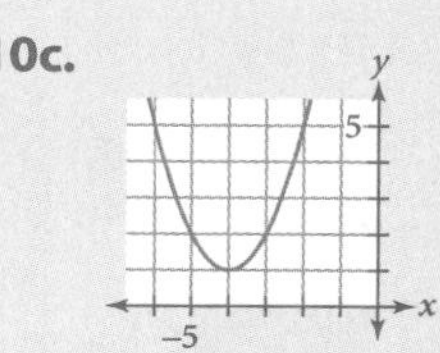

Exercise 12 Algebra tiles or the pieces made from the Algebra Tiles worksheet (Chapter 0) are a good tool for deepening student understanding. You might want to call the process used in 12c "factoring a trinomial into two binomials." This idea will reappear in Lesson 7.2.

12a.

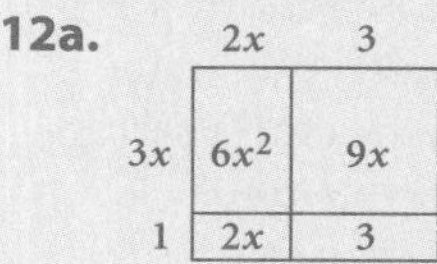

12b. $6x^2 + 11x + 3$

12c.

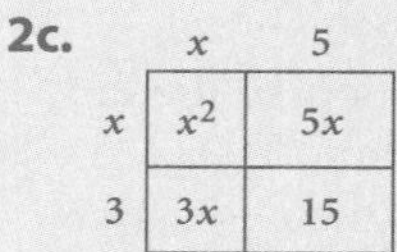

12d. $(x + 3)(x + 5)$

13. $\begin{cases} y \geq -\frac{1}{2}x + \frac{3}{2} \\ y \leq \frac{1}{2}x + \frac{9}{2} \\ y \leq -\frac{11}{6}x + \frac{97}{6} \end{cases}$

EXTENSIONS

A. Extend the investigation by asking students to toss the pillow up in the air and compare the model with the one they found when they dropped the pillow.

B. Use Take Another Look activity 1 on page 421.

C. Students might explore finite differences for the function $y = e^x$ starting with a table of y-values for $x = \{1, 2, 3, 4, 5, \ldots\}$.

Exercise 14 Students can multiply these factors systematically or use blocks or cubes to make a three-dimensional representation. If you have time, encourage students to think about which x's go into each term, to foreshadow Lesson 7.6.

LESSON 7.2

PLANNING

LESSON OUTLINE

One day:

5 min	Example A
10 min	Example B
20 min	Investigation
10 min	Exercises

MATERIALS

- motion sensors
- empty coffee cans or poster tubes
- long tables
- Rolling Along Sample Data (W), *optional*
- Calculator Notes 7B, 7C, 7H

TEACHING

In this lesson students learn about the vertex and factored forms of quadratic equations and how to solve equations written in factored form.

A dynamic algebra exploration at www.keymath.com/DAA can help students explore the equivalent quadratic forms.

One Step

Have students gather data as in the investigation, or use the Rolling Along Sample Data worksheet. Ask them to find an equation for the parabola, which they can do using transformations, and to use a rectangle diagram to rewrite the quadratic equation as a product of binomials. If students have difficulty with breaking up the linear coefficient for this last step, suggest that they consider using the x-intercepts of the graph. During Sharing, introduce the terms *vertex form, factored form,* and *zeros* of a function, and examine how the zeros relate to the factored form.

LESSON 7.2

Equivalent Quadratic Forms

I'm very well acquainted, too,
with matters mathematical.
I understand equations both the
simple and quadratical.

WILLIAM S. GILBERT AND ARTHUR SULLIVAN

In Lesson 7.1, you were introduced to polynomial functions, including 2nd-degree polynomial functions, or **quadratic functions.** The **general form** of a quadratic function is $y = ax^2 + bx + c$. In this lesson you will work with two additional, equivalent forms of quadratic functions.

This fountain near the Centre Pompidou in Paris, France, contains 16 animated surreal sculptures inspired by the music of Russian-American composer Igor Stravinsky (1882–1971). It was designed by artists Jean Tinguely (1925–1991) and Niki de Saint-Phalle (b 1930). The arc formed by spouting water can be described with a quadratic equation.

Recall from Chapter 4 that every quadratic function can be considered as a transformation of the graph of the parent function $y = x^2$. A quadratic function in the form $\frac{y-k}{a} = \left(\frac{x-h}{b}\right)^2$ or $y = a\left(\frac{x-h}{b}\right)^2 + k$ identifies the location of the vertex, (h, k), and the vertical and horizontal scale factors, a and b.

Consider the parabola at right with vertex $(4, -2)$. If you consider the point $(7, 4)$ to be the image of the point $(1, 1)$ on the graph of $y = x^2$, the horizontal scale factor is 3 and the vertical scale factor is 6. So, the quadratic function is $\frac{y+2}{6} = \left(\frac{x-4}{3}\right)^2$ or $y = 6\left(\frac{x-4}{3}\right)^2 - 2$. Choosing a different point as the image of $(1, 1)$ would give an equivalent equation.

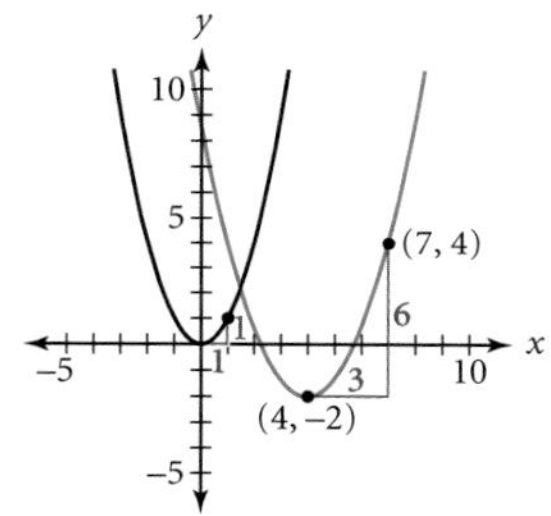

If you move the denominator outside the parentheses, the quadratic function above can also be written as $y = \frac{6}{9}(x-4)^2 - 2$ or $y = \frac{2}{3}(x-4)^2 - 2$. Notice that the horizontal and vertical scale factors are now represented by one vertical scale factor of $\frac{2}{3}$. This coefficient, $\frac{a}{b^2}$, combines the horizontal and vertical scale factors into one vertical scale factor, which you can think of as a single coefficient, say a. This new form, $y = a(x-h)^2 + k$, is called the **vertex form** of a quadratic function because it identifies the vertex, (h, k), and a single vertical scale factor, a. If you know the vertex of a parabola and one other point, then you can write the quadratic function in vertex form.

LESSON OBJECTIVES

- Understand the correspondence between the zeros of a polynomial function and the roots of an equation
- Use the zero-product property to find the roots of equations
- Comprehend the relationships among the general form, the factored form, and the vertex form of a quadratic equation
- Relate the vertex form of a quadratic equation to the parent function $y = x^2$

NCTM STANDARDS

CONTENT		PROCESS	
	Number	✓	Problem Solving
✓	Algebra	✓	Reasoning
✓	Geometry	✓	Communication
✓	Measurement		Connections
✓	Data/Probability	✓	Representation

Now consider these parabolas. The x-intercepts are marked.

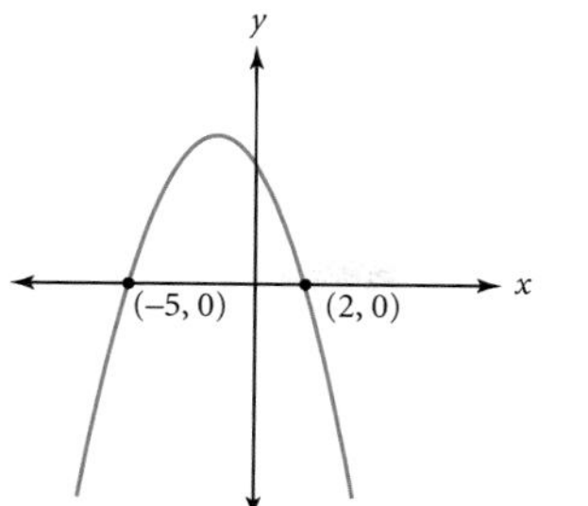

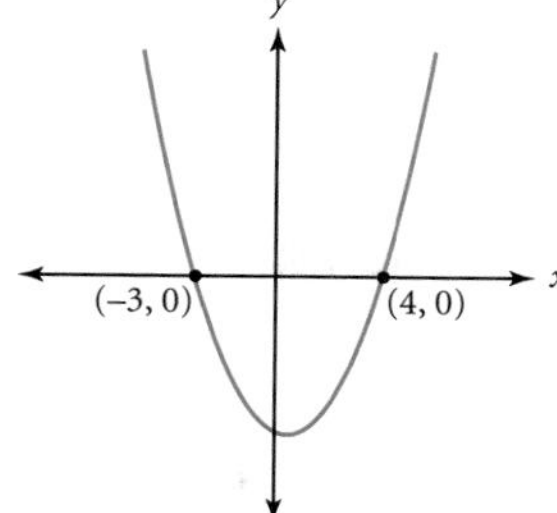

The y-coordinate of any point along the x-axis is 0, so the y-coordinate is 0 at each x-intercept. For this reason, the x-intercepts of the graph of a function are called the **zeros** of the function. You will use this information and the **zero-product property** to find the zeros of a function without graphing.

> **Zero-Product Property**
>
> For all real numbers a and b, if $ab = 0$, then $a = 0$, or $b = 0$, or $a = 0$ and $b = 0$.

To understand the zero-product property, think of numbers whose product is zero. Whatever numbers you think of will have this characteristic: *At least one of the factors must be zero.* Before moving on, think about numbers that satisfy each equation below.

$\underline{?} \cdot 16.2 = 0$ 0

$3(\underline{?} - 4)(\underline{?} - 9) = 0$ 4 or 9

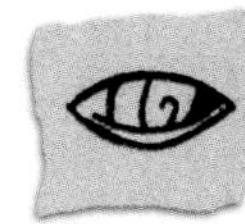

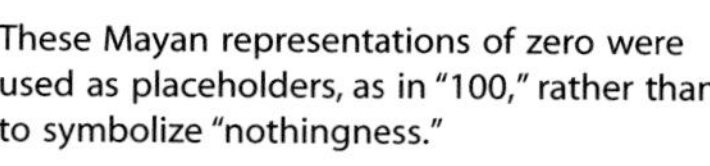
These Mayan representations of zero were used as placeholders, as in "100," rather than to symbolize "nothingness."

EXAMPLE A | Find the zeros of the function $y = -1.4(x - 5.6)(x + 3.1)$.

▶ Solution

The zeros will be the x-values that make y equal 0. First, set the function equal to zero.

$$0 = -1.4(x - 5.6)(x + 3.1)$$

Because the product of three factors equals zero, the zero-product property tells you that at least one of the factors must equal zero.

$-1.4 = 0$	or	$x - 5.6 = 0$	or	$x + 3.1 = 0$
not possible		$x = 5.6$		$x = -3.1$

INTRODUCTION

You may want to review the process of finding scale factors. In the graph of $y = x^2$, the vertex is at (0, 0) and the point (1, 1) is 1 unit right and 1 unit up from the vertex. In the graph of this parabola with vertex (4, −2), the point (7, 4) is 3 units right and 6 units up from the vertex. So the graph is stretched horizontally by a factor of $\frac{3}{1}$ and vertically by a factor of $\frac{6}{1}$.

To help students appreciate the zero-product property, you might ask whether there are two nonzero numbers whose product is 0. They may suggest pairs of opposites or reciprocals. Let them critique one another's ideas until they reach consensus that there are no such pairs—that the only way the product can be 0 is if at least one of the numbers is 0.

Referring to page 368, **[Ask]** "Why did the book choose the point (7, 4) to be the image of the point (1, 1)? Will other points work?" [You can consider point (7, 4) as the image of any nonvertex point on the graph of $y = x^2$.] In fact, because point (7, 4) is 3 units to the right of the vertex, it's more direct to think of (7, 4) as the image of the point (3, 9), which is 3 units to the right of the vertex of the parent parabola. Then there's only a *vertical* scale factor of $\frac{6}{9}$, or $\frac{2}{3}$. The resulting equation is $y + 2 = \frac{2}{3}\left(\frac{x-4}{1}\right)^2$, which is equivalent to the equation in the book.

[Ask] "What's the difference between zeros, roots, solutions, and x-intercepts?" Give students time to discuss the similarities and differences. [They all refer to the same numbers or points. The *graph* has x-intercepts—points where it crosses the x-axis. The *function* has zeros—the x-values the function takes to zero, or the x-coordinates of the x-intercepts. The *equation* $f(x) = 0$ has roots or solutions, which are the zeros of the function $f(x)$.]

▶ EXAMPLE A

You might ask students to graph this equation on graph paper by simply substituting x-values. **[Ask]** "How would you find the vertex of this parabola?" [Evaluate the function at the mean of −3.1 and 5.6.]

[Alert] Students may mistakenly believe that they need to expand the quadratic in order to enter it as a calculator function.

If students use the graphing calculator to check their work, they can trace the graph to approximate the x-intercepts. They may have to zoom in several times to get a reasonably close approximation. In the graphing window shown, the closest students can come is −2.9 and 5.3. You might want to introduce Calculator Note 7H, which shows how to approximate a function's zeros on a graphing calculator.

[Context] The art on page 369 shows Mayan symbols. Mayans (ca. 300 B.C.E.–99 C.E.) discovered and used zero both as a number to represent nothing and to show the value of a number's position, as in 100 to represent in their base-20 system the number 400 base 10.

► EXAMPLE B

To help students review finding the vertex form of a parabola, you might want to have them find equations of transformed parabolas, as in Chapter 4.

For the solution to part a, students might benefit from seeing the extra step $\frac{y+4}{1} = \left(\frac{x-1}{1}\right)^2$.

Assessing Progress
You can check students' ability to calculate finite differences, identify solutions and x-intercepts, write equations for transformed parabolas, and solve systems of linear equations.

So the solutions, or **roots,** of the equation $0 = -1.4(x - 5.6)(x + 3.1)$ are $x = 5.6$ or $x = -3.1$. That means the zeros of the function $y = -1.4(x - 5.6)(x + 3.1)$ are $x = 5.6$ and $x = -3.1$.

Use your graphing calculator to check your work. You should find that the x-intercepts of the graph of $y = -1.4(x - 5.6)(x + 3.1)$ are 5.6 and -3.1.

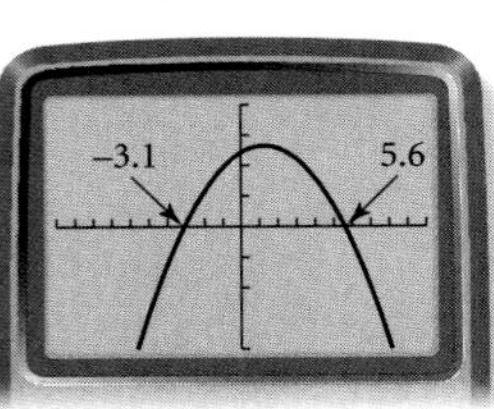

[−10, 10, 1, −40, 40, 10]

If you know the x-intercepts of a parabola, then you can write the quadratic function in **factored form,** $y = a(x - r_1)(x - r_2)$. This form identifies the locations of the x-intercepts, r_1 and r_2, and a vertical scale factor, a.

EXAMPLE B

Consider the parabola at right.

a. Write an equation of the parabola in vertex form.

b. Write an equation of the parabola in factored form.

c. Show that both equations are equivalent by converting them to general form.

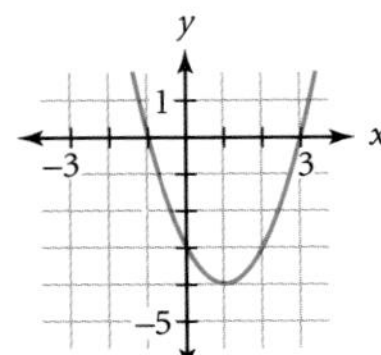

► Solution

The vertex is $(1, -4)$. If you consider the point $(2, -3)$ to be the image of the point $(1, 1)$ on the graph of $y = x^2$, then the vertical and horizontal scale factors are both 1. So, the single vertical scale factor is $a = \frac{1}{1^2} = 1$.

a. The vertex form is

$$y = (x - 1)^2 - 4$$

b. The x-intercepts are -1 and 3. You know the scale factor, a, is 1. So the factored form is

$$y = (x + 1)(x - 3)$$

c. To convert to general form, multiply the binomials and then combine like terms. The use of rectangle diagrams may help you multiply the binomials.

$$y = (x - 1)^2 - 4$$
$$y = (x - 1)(x - 1) - 4$$
$$y = (x^2 - x - x + 1) - 4$$
$$y = x^2 - 2x - 3$$

$$y = (x + 1)(x - 3)$$
$$y = x^2 + x - 3x - 3$$
$$y = x^2 - 2x - 3$$

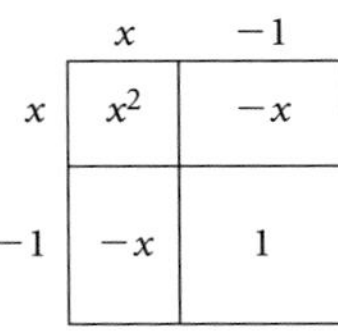

	x	-1
x	x^2	$-x$
-1	$-x$	1

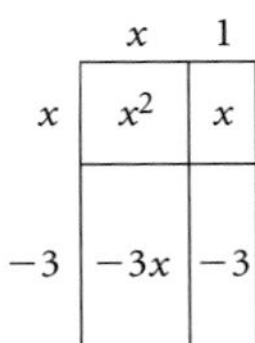

	x	1
x	x^2	x
-3	$-3x$	-3

The vertex form and the factored form are equivalent because they are both equivalent to the same general form.

You now know three different forms of a quadratic function.

Three Forms of a Quadratic Function

General form	$y = ax^2 + bx + c$
Vertex form	$y = a(x - h)^2 + k$
Factored form	$y = a(x - r_1)(x - r_2)$

The investigation will give you practice in using the three forms with real data. You'll find that the form you use guides which features of the data you focus on. Conversely, if you know only a few features of the data, you may need to focus on a particular form of the function.

This painting by Elizabeth Catlett, which depicts people singing songs in different forms, was inspired by a poem titled "For My People" by American writer Margaret Walker Alexander (1915–1998).

Elizabeth Catlett (American, b 1915), *Singing Their Songs* (1992) Lithograph on paper (a.p.#6) 15-3/4 x 13-3/4 in. / National Museum of Women in the Arts, purchased with funds donated in memory of Florence Davis by her family, friends, and the NMWA Women's Committee

Investigation
Rolling Along

You will need

- a motion sensor
- an empty coffee can
- a long table

Procedure Note

Prop up one end of the table slightly. Place the motion sensor at the low end of the table and aim it toward the high end. With tape or chalk, mark a starting line 0.5 m from the sensor on the table.

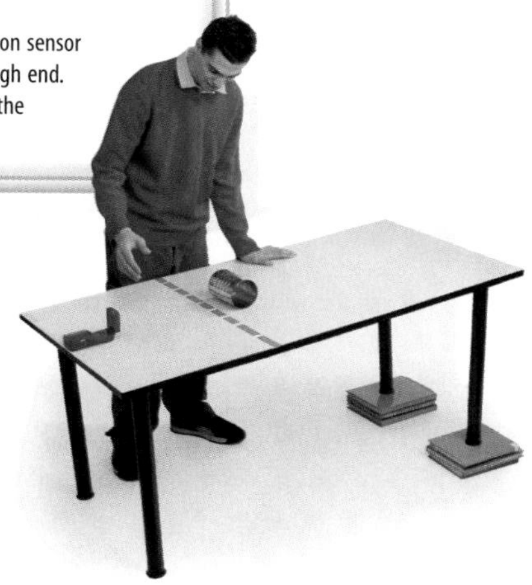

Step 1 Practice rolling the can up the table directly in front of the motion sensor. Start the can behind the starting line. Give the can a gentle push so that it rolls up the table on its own momentum, stops near the end of the table, and then rolls back. Stop the can after it crosses the line and before it hits the motion sensor.

Guiding the Investigation

If you are short on time, you could collect one set of data as a class and share the data by linking to one calculator in each group, or use the Rolling Along Sample Data worksheet.

Step 1 A 12-to-14-inch poster tube can be used in place of a coffee can.

Step 2 If 6 seconds is not long enough, students can adjust the time. The student who is rolling the can should wait until the motion sensor starts clicking before rolling the can.

Step 3 **[Alert]** Students may unnecessarily doubt their results when they see negative values for the first and last numbers.

Step 4 You might have students graph the data on graph paper as well as on calculators. Students can use finite differences either in a table or on their calculator to find the degree of the polynomial. See Calculator Note 7B.

Step 5 Students can trace the calculator graphs to approximate the vertex and an additional point.

Step 7 Students should adjust the values for a and for the intercepts until they have a good fit to their data.

SHARING IDEAS

As students present their ideas about the investigation, **[Ask]** "Is this the same as free fall due to gravity?" [No; the falling is not directly downward, so the equation is different, though it is still quadratic.]

You can address interesting misconceptions if you ask whether a zero of a function is the number 0. [Not usually; it's a number that the function takes to zero, or a solution to the equation $f(x) = 0$.]

You might point out that the factored form uses r_1 and r_2 for the x-intercepts because of how

Sharing Ideas (continued)

the x-intercepts are related to the roots of the equation $f(x) = 0$.

[Ask] "In the factored form, a is a scale factor. What's being scaled?" [a represents the vertical stretch of the parabola given by the function $y = x^2$.] As needed, remind students that any stretch of a parabola is a vertical stretch (similarly, any shift of a line can be thought of as a vertical shift). In this situation, a is the vertical scale factor that captures both horizontal and vertical scale factors, the vertical over the square of the horizontal. You might also refer to Example B, where both scale factors are 1 and $a = \frac{1}{1^2}$.

If you're listing zeros of a function, x-intercepts of its graph, or the roots of the corresponding equation, you use the word *and*. If you're describing the values of x that solve an equation, you use the word *or*, because x can't equal more than one number at the same time. For example, you'd say "The roots are 3 and −4," but "x is 3 or −4."

Sharing Ideas (continued)

[Ask] "If you have an equation of degree higher than 2, what might be its factored form, and how might it relate to zeros, roots, and x-intercepts?" Let students conjecture about answers to this question; it will be addressed in Lesson 7.6.

Closing the Lesson

Review the main points: A 2nd-degree polynomial in **general form** is $ax^2 + bx + c$. Its **vertex form** is $a(x - h)^2 + k$, which shows the vertex of a parabola at point (h, k) and the vertical stretch factor a. The **factored form** of the 2nd-degree polynomial is $a(x - r_1)(x - r_2)$. By the **zero-product property,** the value of the polynomial is 0 only if one of these factors is 0, which is the case only if $x = r_1$ or $x = r_2$. This means that r_1 and r_2 are the **zeros** of the quadratic function, or **roots** of the quadratic equation.

BUILDING UNDERSTANDING

Encourage students to use a friendly window when graphing on their calculators.

ASSIGNING HOMEWORK

Essential	1–5
Performance assessment	6–12
Portfolio	10, 12
Journal	12
Group	8
Review	13–16

MATERIALS

- Calculator Note 6G or 6G/App, *optional*

See pages 888–889 for answers to Steps 2–4 and 8.

Step 2 Set up your calculator to collect data for 6 seconds. [▶ See **Calculator Note 7C.** ◀] When the sensor begins, roll the can up the table.

Step 3 The data collected by the sensor will have the form (*time, distance*). Adjust for the position of the starting line by subtracting 0.5 from each value in the distance list.

Step 4 Let x represent time in seconds, and let y represent distance from the line in meters. Draw a graph of your data. What shape is the graph of the data points? What type of function would model the data? Use finite differences to justify your answer.

Step 5 Mark the vertex and another point on your graph. Approximate the coordinates of these points and use them to write the equation of a quadratic model in vertex form.

Step 5 vertex: (3.2, 4.257); point: (5.2, 0.897); $y = -0.84(x - 3.2)^2 + 4.257$

Step 6 From your data, find the distance of the can at 1, 3, and 5 seconds. Use these three data points to find a quadratic model in general form.

Step 6 (1, 0.546), (3, 4.256), and (5, 1.493); $y = -0.81x^2 + 5.09x - 3.74$

Step 7 Mark the x-intercepts on your graph. Approximate the values of these x-intercepts. Use the zeros and the value of a from Step 5 to find a quadratic model in factored form.

Step 7 (0.9, 0) and (5.5, 0); $y = -0.84(x - 0.9)(x - 5.5)$

Step 8 Verify by graphing that the three equations in Steps 5, 6, and 7 are equivalent, or nearly so. Write a few sentences explaining when you would use each of the three forms to find a quadratic model to fit parabolic data.

You can find a model for data in different ways, depending on the information you have. Conversely, different forms of the same equation give you different kinds of information. Being able to convert one form to another allows you to compare equations written in different forms. In the exercises, you will convert both the vertex form and the factored form to the general form. In later lessons you will learn other conversions.

EXERCISES

Practice Your Skills

For the exercises in this lesson, you may find it helpful to use a window on your calculator that has friendly x-values. A background grid may also be helpful.

1. Identify each quadratic function as being in general form, vertex form, factored form, or none of these forms.

a. $y = -3.2(x + 4.5)^2$ factored form and vertex form **b.** $y = 2.5(x + 1.25)(x - 1.25) + 4$ none of these forms

c. $y = 2x(3 + x)$ factored form **d.** $y = 2x^2 - 4.2x - 10$ general form

2. Each quadratic function below is written in vertex form. What are the coordinates of each vertex? Graph each equation to check your answers.

a. $y = (x - 2)^2 + 3$ (2, 3) **b.** $y = 0.5(x + 4)^2 - 2$ (−4, −2) **c.** $y = 4 - 2(x - 5)^2$ (5, 4)

Helping with the Exercises

Exercise 1b This expression is not in factored form because of the constant term; it is not in vertex form because the binomials do not make a perfect square.

3. Each quadratic function below is written in factored form. What are the zeros of each function? Graph each equation to check your answers.

a. $y = (x + 1)(x - 2)$ −1 and 2 **b.** $y = 0.5(x - 2)(x + 3)$ −3 and 2 **c.** $y = -2(x - 2)(x - 5)$ 2 and 5

4. Convert each function to general form. Graph both forms to check that the equations are equivalent.

a. $y = (x - 2)^2 + 3$ **b.** $y = 0.5(x + 4)^2 - 2$ **c.** $y = 4 - 2(x - 5)^2$

5. Convert each function to general form. Graph both forms to check that the equations are equivalent.

a. $y = (x + 1)(x - 2)$ **b.** $y = 0.5(x - 2)(x + 3)$ **c.** $y = -2(x - 2)(x - 5)$

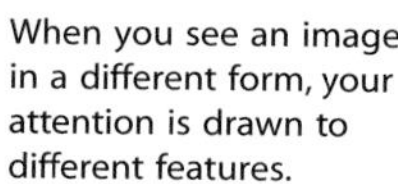

When you see an image in a different form, your attention is drawn to different features.

Exercises 4, 5 Students may want to use rectangle diagrams to expand the binomials.

4a. $y = x^2 - 4x + 7$

4b. $y = 0.5x^2 + 4x + 6$

4c. $y = -2x^2 + 20x - 46$

5a. $y = x^2 - x - 2$

5b. $y = 0.5x^2 + 0.5x - 3$

5c. $y = -2x^2 + 14x - 20$

Reason and Apply

6. As you learned in Chapter 4, the graphs of all quadratic functions have a line of symmetry that contains the vertex and divides the parabola into mirror-image halves. Consider this table of values generated by a quadratic function.

x	y
1.5	−8
2.5	7
3.5	16
4.5	19
5.5	16
6.5	7
7.5	−8

a. What is the line of symmetry for the graph of this quadratic function? $x = 4.5$

b. The vertex of a parabola represents either the **maximum** or **minimum** value of the quadratic function. Name the vertex of this function and determine whether it is a maximum or minimum. (4.5, 19); maximum

c. Use the table of values to write the quadratic function in vertex form. $y = -3(x - 4.5)^2 + 19$

Exercise 6 If students want to draw vertical lines on the calculator graph screen, refer them to Calculator Note 6G or 6G/App.

7. Write each function in general form.

a. $y = 4 - 0.5(x + h)^2$ **b.** $y = a(x - 4)^2$

c. $y = a(x - h)^2 + k$ **d.** $y = -0.5(x + r)(x + 4)$

e. $y = a(x - 4)(x + 2)$ **f.** $y = a(x - r)(x - s)$

7a. $y = -0.5x^2 - hx - 0.5h^2 + 4$

7b. $y = ax^2 - 8ax + 16a$

7c. $y = ax^2 - 2ahx + ah^2 + k$

7d. $y = -0.5x^2 - (0.5r + 2)x - 2r$

7e. $y = ax^2 - 2ax - 8a$

7f. $y = ax^2 - a(r + s)x + ars$

Exercise 8 This exercise teaches an important method for finding the vertical scale factor a without considering stretches or shrinks. This method works for either factored form or vertex form. **[Alert]** Students may be confused because a is a constant in the equation but is being treated as a variable until its numeric value is determined.

8a. $y = a(x + 2.4)(x - 0.8)$

8b. $y = -1.8(x + 2.4)(x - 0.8)$

8c. $x = -0.8, y = 4.608$

8d. $y = -1.8(x + 0.8)^2 + 4.608$

Exercise 9c Although not taught in this lesson, students will probably be able to extend the concepts of zeros and factored form for quadratic functions to a cubic function. **[Alert]** Students may not recognize the shape as that of a cubic function.

Exercise 10 Encourage students to ask whether their function expression makes sense. Dimensional analysis might help.

10b. $D_1 = \{9.5, 8.5, 7.5, 6.5\}$; $D_2 = \{-1, -1, -1\}$

10c. $y = -50x^2 + 300x$

10d. The maximum revenue is \$450 at a selling price of \$3.

8. At right is the graph of the quadratic function that passes through $(-2.4, 0)$, $(0.8, 0)$, and $(1.2, -2.592)$.

a. Use the x-intercepts to write the quadratic function in factored form. For now, leave the vertical scale factor as a.

b. Substitute the coordinates of $(1.2, -2.592)$ into your function from 8a, and solve for a. Write the complete quadratic function in factored form.

c. The line of symmetry for the graph of this quadratic function passes through the vertex and the point on the x-axis halfway between the two x-intercepts. What is the x-coordinate of the vertex? What is the y-coordinate?

d. Write this quadratic function in vertex form.

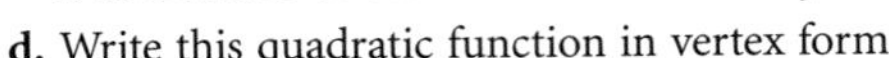

9. Write the factored form for each polynomial function. (*Hint:* Substitute the coordinates of the y-intercept to solve for the scale factor, a.)

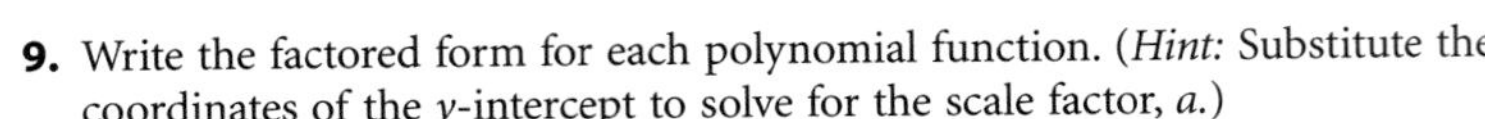

a.

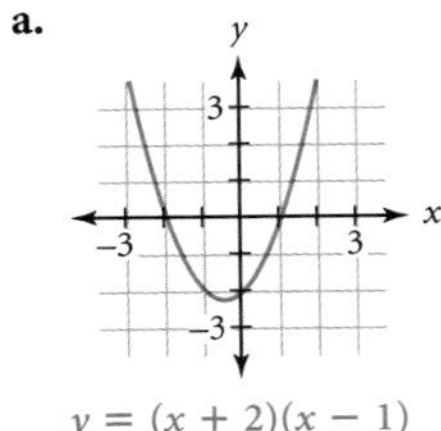

$y = (x + 2)(x - 1)$

b.

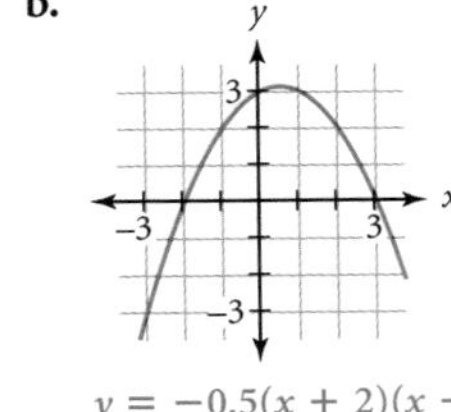

$y = -0.5(x + 2)(x - 3)$

c.

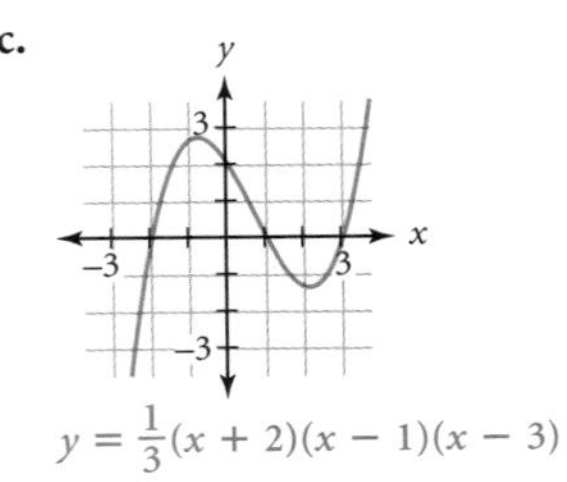

$y = \frac{1}{3}(x + 2)(x - 1)(x - 3)$

10. APPLICATION A local outlet store charges \$2.00 for a pack of four AA batteries. On an average day, 200 packs are sold. A survey indicates that sales will decrease by 5 packs per day for each \$0.10 increase in price.

Selling price (\$)	2.00	2.10	2.20	2.30	2.40
Number sold	200	195	190	185	180
Revenue (\$)	400	409.50	418	425.50	432

a. Complete the table above based on the results of the survey.

b. Calculate the first and second differences for the revenue.

c. Let x represent the selling price in dollars, and let y represent the revenue in dollars. Write a function that describes the relationship between the revenue and the selling price.

d. Graph your function and find the maximum revenue. What selling price provides maximum revenue?

11. APPLICATION Delores has 80 m of fence to surround an area where she is going to plant a vegetable garden. She wants to enclose the largest possible rectangular area.

Width (m)	5	10	15	20	25
Length (m)	35	30	25	20	15
Area (m^2)	175	300	375	400	375

a. Copy and complete this table.

b. Let x represent the width in meters, and let y represent the area in square meters. Write a function that describes the relationship between the area and the width of the garden.

c. Which width provides the largest possible area? What is that area?

d. Which widths result in an area of 0 m^2?
0 m and 40 m

12. APPLICATION Photosynthesis is the process in which plants use energy from the sun, together with CO_2 (carbon dioxide) and water, to make their own food and produce oxygen. Various factors affect the rate of photosynthesis, such as light intensity, light wavelength, CO_2 concentration, and temperature. Below is a graph of how temperature relates to the rate of photosynthesis for a particular plant. (All other factors are assumed to be held constant.)

When chlorophyll fades for the winter, leaves change color. When they appear red or purple, it is because glucose is trapped in the leaves and changes color when exposed to sunlight and cool nights.

a. Describe the general shape of the graph. What does the shape of the graph mean in the context of photosynthesis?

b. Approximate the optimum temperature for photosynthesis in this plant and the corresponding rate of photosynthesis.

c. Temperature has to be kept within a certain range for photosynthesis to occur. If it gets too hot, then the enzymes in chlorophyll are killed and photosynthesis stops. If the temperature is too cold, then the enzymes stop working. At approximately what temperatures is the rate of photosynthesis equal to zero?

d. Write a function in at least two forms that will produce this graph.

Review

13. Use a rectangle diagram to find each product.

0.1 a. $3x(4x - 5)$ b. $(x + 3)(x - 5)$ c. $(x + 7)(x - 7)$ d. $(3x - 1)^2$

Exercise 11 If students have difficulty with 11b, you might wonder aloud whether finite differences would help. In 11c, students may recall from geometry that if the perimeter is held constant, the rectangle with the largest area will be a square.

Students with a dictionary understanding of *length* will object to the table, in which a length is less than a width. They are free to use the words *base* and *height* for the dimensions of the rectangles when they create their own tables.

11b. $y = x(40 - x)$ or $y = -x^2 + 40x$

11c. A width of 20 m (and length of 20 m) maximizes the area at 400 m^2.

Exercise 12 In 12b, **[Language]** *Optimum* means "most favorable." The optimum temperature is the temperature that results in the fastest rate of photosynthesis.

[Alert] In 12d, students may miss the fact that the scale factor is negative.

12a. The graph is parabolic. As the temperature increases, the rate of photosynthesis also increases, until a maximum rate is reached, then the rate decreases.

12b. At approximately 23°C, the rate of photosynthesis is maximized at 100%.

12c. 0°C and 46°C

12d. $y = -0.19x(x - 46)$; $y = -0.19(x - 23)^2 + 100$

13a. $12x^2 - 15x$

	$4x$	-5
$3x$	$12x^2$	$-15x$

13b. $x^2 - 2x - 15$

	x	-5
x	x^2	$-5x$
3	$3x$	-15

13c. $x^2 - 49$

	x	7
x	x^2	$7x$
-7	$-7x$	-49

13d. $9x^2 - 6x + 1$

	$3x$	-1
$3x$	$9x^2$	$-3x$
-1	$-3x$	1

Exercise 14 [Alert] Students may not see how to do this with a direct application of the distributive property. Remind them that, by the commutative property of multiplication, $(x + 1)x = x(x + 1)$.

Exercise 15 Students may be frustrated that they don't know a consistent method for factoring. Factoring, like much of mathematics, is an art. They will have to guess and check.

15a. $(x + 5)(x - 2)$

	x	5
x	x^2	$5x$
-2	$-2x$	-10

15b. $(x + 4)(x + 4)$

	x	4
x	x^2	$4x$
4	$4x$	16

15c. $(x + 5)(x - 5)$

	x	5
x	x^2	$5x$
-5	$-5x$	-25

Exercise 16b As needed, remind students to follow the conventional order of operations, which puts exponentiation before multiplication. Therefore, $-5x^2 = -5$ when $x = -1$.

14. Recall that the distributive property allows you to distribute a factor through parentheses. The factor that is distributed doesn't have to be a monomial. Here's an example with a binomial.

$$(x + 1)(x - 3)$$
$$x(x - 3) + 1(x - 3)$$
$$x^2 - 3x + x - 3$$
$$x^2 - 2x - 3$$

Use the distributive property to find each product in Exercise 13.

a. $12x^2 - 15x$
b. $x^2 - 2x - 15$
c. $x^2 - 49$
d. $9x^2 - 6x + 1$

15. You can also use a rectangle diagram to help you **factor** some trinomials, such as $x^2 - 7x + 12$.

	x	
x	x^2	
		12

To factor $x^2 - 7x + 12$, the constants of the binomials must multiply to 12, and add up to -7.

	x	-3
x	x^2	$-3x$
-4	$-4x$	12

$(x - 3)(x - 4)$
The constants of the binomials need to be -3 and -4.

Use rectangle diagrams to help you factor these trinomials.

a. $x^2 + 3x - 10$ **b.** $x^2 + 8x + 16$ **c.** $x^2 - 25$

4.2 **16.** Use the function $f(x) = 3x^3 - 5x^2 + x - 6$ to find these values.

a. $f(2)$ 0 **b.** $f(-1)$ -15 **c.** $f(0)$ -6 **d.** $f\left(\frac{1}{2}\right)$ $-6\frac{3}{8}$ **e.** $f\left(-\frac{4}{3}\right)$ $-23\frac{1}{3}$

IMPROVING YOUR REASONING SKILLS

Sums and Differences

Use the method of finite differences to find a formula for the sum of the first n terms in the arithmetic sequence 1, 2, 3, 4, ... In other words, find a formula for the sum

$$1 + 2 + 3 + \cdots + u_n$$

Then find a formula for the first n terms of the sequence 1, 3, 5, 7, ... How about 1, 4, 7, 10, . . . ? Look for patterns, and see if you can write a formula that will determine the sum of the first n terms of any arithmetic sequence with a first term of 1, and common difference d.

IMPROVING REASONING SKILLS

Students can see patterns for the first three sequences, leading to sums: $S = \frac{1}{2}n^2 + \frac{1}{2}n$, $S = n^2$, and $S = \frac{3}{2}n^2 - \frac{1}{2}n$. The main goal is to generalize to the formula $S = \frac{d}{2}n^2 + \left(1 - \frac{d}{2}\right)n$. The general formula can be proved, and perhaps derived, by the technique of writing the summation in reverse order and adding.

$$S = 1 + (1 + d) + (1 + 2d) + \cdots + (1 + (n - 1)d)$$
$$S = (1 + (n - 1)d) + (1 + (n - 2)d) + (1 + (n - 3)d) + \cdots + 1$$
$$2S = (2 + (n - 1)d) + (2 + (n - 1)d) + \cdots + (2 + (n - 1)d)$$
$$S = \frac{n(2 + (n - 1)d)}{2}$$

LESSON

7.3

Completing the Square

The graph of $y = -5.33(x - 0.86)^2 + 0.6$ at right models one bounce of a ball, where x is time in seconds and y is height in meters. The maximum height of this ball occurs at the vertex (0.86, 0.6), which means that after 0.86 s the ball reaches its maximum height of 0.6 m. Finding the **maximum** or **minimum** value of a quadratic function is often necessary to answer questions about data. Finding the vertex is straightforward when you are given an equation in vertex form and sometimes when you are using a graph. However, you often have to estimate values on a graph. In this lesson you will learn a procedure called **completing the square** to convert a quadratic equation from general form to vertex form accurately.

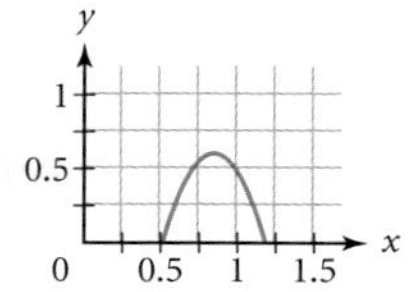

An object that rises and falls under the influence of gravity is called a projectile. You can use quadratic functions to model **projectile motion,** or the height of the object as a function of time.

The height of a projectile depends on three things: the height from which it is thrown, the upward velocity with which it is thrown, and the effect of gravity pulling downward on the object. So, the polynomial function that describes projectile motion has three terms. The leading coefficient of the polynomial is based on the acceleration due to gravity, g. On Earth, g has an approximate numerical value of 9.8 m/s^2 when height is measured in meters and 32 ft/s^2 when height is measured in feet. The leading coefficient of a projectile motion function is always $-\frac{1}{2}g$.

Projectile Motion Function

The height of an object rising or falling under the influence of gravity is modeled by the function

$$y = ax^2 + v_0x + s_0$$

where x represents time in seconds, y represents the object's height from the ground in meters or feet, a is half the downward acceleration due to gravity (on Earth, a is -4.9 m/s^2 or -16 ft/s^2), v_0 is the initial upward velocity of the object in meters per second or feet per second, and s_0 is the initial height of the object in meters or feet.

The water erupting from these geysers in Black Rock Desert, Nevada, follows a path that can be described as projectile motion.

NCTM STANDARDS

CONTENT		PROCESS	
✓	Number	✓	Problem Solving
✓	Algebra	✓	Reasoning
	Geometry	✓	Communication
	Measurement	✓	Connections
	Data/Probability	✓	Representation

LESSON OBJECTIVES

- Explore projectile motion
- Understand completing the square as one way to convert the general form of a quadratic equation to vertex form
- Use formulas to convert the general form of a quadratic equation to vertex form
- Use the vertex form of a quadratic equation to solve problems involving maximums or minimums

LESSON

7.3

PLANNING

LESSON OUTLINE

First day:

15 min	Example A
20 min	Investigation
10 min	Exercises

Second day:

15 min	Sharing
10 min	Example B
10 min	Example C
10 min	Exercises

MATERIALS

- algebra tiles, *optional*

TEACHING

This lesson focuses on finding the vertex of a graph of a quadratic function. You might start with the one-step investigation on page 378.

INTRODUCTION

[Language] The *leading coefficient* of a polynomial is the coefficient of the highest power of x.

In Lesson 7.1, the free-falling pillow was dropped, so its initial velocity was 0 and its height was given by a function such as $y = -4.9x^2 + 2$. You might use dimensional analysis to show that the three terms in the projectile motion function each represent a distance: a is distance divided by the square of time and is multiplied by the square of time; v_0x is rate times time; s_0 is a distance. **[Alert]** Students may be confused about nonzero initial velocity. A thrown object begins with a velocity of 0 and then rapidly accelerates to a fast speed, but the timing doesn't need to start before the object is released; it can begin at the instant the object achieves the speed v_0.

[Link] The projectile motion function is derived using calculus, from the assumption of constant acceleration due to gravity.

One Step

Pose this problem: "A machine launches a baseball straight up from ground level. How high does it go?" After some thought, students will object that they don't have enough information. Add that a stopwatch records that the ball is launched at 0.25 s and hits the ground at 7.75 s. As needed, encourage groups to write the quadratic function in factored form: $y = -16(x - 0.25)(x - 7.75)$ ft or $y = -4.9(x - 0.25)(x - 7.75)$ m. A graph might convince them that the x-coordinate of the vertex of the parabola is at 4.0; push them for an explanation in terms of midpoints and means. Then ask how high the ball would go if, instead of the times, they knew that the machine gave the ball an initial velocity of 120 ft/s beginning 2 ft above the ground. Describe the projectile motion function $y = ax^2 + v_0x + s_0$. Then suggest that students rewrite the general form of the quadratic equation in vertex form, perhaps using rectangle diagrams to help them. During Sharing introduce the term *completing the square,* and formalize the method.

▶ EXAMPLE A

This example shows how to find the vertex of a parabola whose equation is written in factored form. **[Ask]** "How could you verify that the scale factor a in the factored form $y = a(x - r_1)(x - r_2)$ is the same as the leading coefficient in the general form $y = ax^2 + bx + c$?" [Expand $y = -16(x - 0.25)(x - 0.83)$ to get the quadratic function $y = -16x^2 + 17.28x - 3.32$.]

[Alert] Students may not have thought about the fact that the point halfway between two numbers is their mean.

EXAMPLE A A stopwatch records that when Julie jumps in the air, she leaves the ground at 0.25 s and lands at 0.83 s. How high was her jump, in feet?

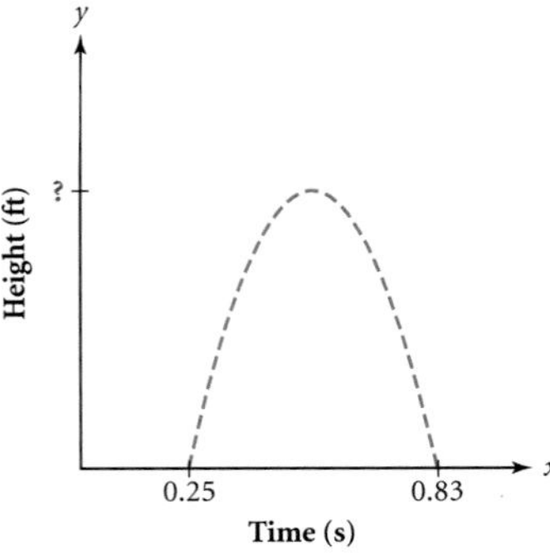

▶ Solution

You don't know the initial velocity, so you can't yet use the projectile motion function. But you do know that height is modeled by a quadratic function and that the leading coefficient must be approximately -16 when using units of feet. Use this information along with 0.25 and 0.83 as the x-intercepts (when Julie's jump height is 0) to write the function

$$y = -16(x - 0.25)(x - 0.83)$$

The vertex of the graph of this equation represents Julie's maximum jump height. The x-coordinate of the vertex will be midway between the two x-intercepts, 0.25 and 0.83. The mean of 0.25 and 0.83 is $\frac{0.25 + 0.83}{2}$, or 0.54.

$y = -16(x - 0.25)(x - 0.83)$	The original function.
$y = -16(0.54 - 0.25)(0.54 - 0.83)$	Substitute the x-coordinate of the vertex.
$y \approx 1.35$	Evaluate.

Julie jumped 1.35 ft, or about 16 in.

Example A showed how to find the vertex of a quadratic function in factored form. If the equation were in general form instead, you might be able to put it in factored form and then follow the same steps, but there's another way. First, note that each rectangle diagram below represents a **perfect square** because both factors are the same.

$$(x + 5)^2 = (x + 5)(x + 5)$$
$$= x^2 + 5x + 5x + 25$$
$$= x^2 + 10x + 25$$

The square of the first term of the binomial. (x^2)

Twice the product of the first and second terms of the binomial. ($10x$)

The square of the second term of the binomial. (25)

	x	5
x	x^2	$5x$
5	$5x$	25

$$(a + b)^2 = (a + b)(a + b)$$
$$= a^2 + ab + ab + b^2$$
$$= a^2 + 2ab + b^2$$

The square of the first term of the binomial. (a^2)

Twice the product of the first and second terms of the binomial. ($2ab$)

The square of the second term of the binomial. (b^2)

	a	b
a	a^2	ab
b	ab	b^2

[Ask] How high was the jump in meters?" [Students can convert directly or recalculate using -4.9 instead of -16 as the leading coefficient to get 0.41 m.]

Perfect Squares

Point out that the rectangle diagrams are more specifically square diagrams for these perfect squares. **[Ask]** "Where do you see symmetry in the square diagrams?" [along a diagonal] You might use algebra tiles or pieces from the Lesson 0.1 worksheet to illustrate these square diagrams.

You might also want to work through a couple of other examples of perfect squares, but omitting the last square. For example, draw the rectangle diagram representing $(x + 6)^2$ with the 36 left out, and ask students to complete the square by determining what is missing.

Notice the pattern. For a perfect square, the first and last terms of the trinomial are squares, and the middle term is twice a product. This knowledge will be useful in the investigation, which helps you convert a quadratic function from general form to vertex form.

Investigation
Complete the Square

You can use rectangle diagrams to help convert from general form to vertex form.

Step 1 Consider the expression $x^2 + 6x$.

	x	3
x	x^2	$3x$
3	$3x$	?

a. What could you add to the expression to make it a perfect square? That is, what must you add to complete this rectangle diagram? 9

b. If you add a number to an expression, then you must also subtract the same amount in order to preserve the value of the original expression. Fill in the blanks to rewrite $x^2 + 6x$ as the difference between a perfect square and a number.

$$x^2 + 6x = x^2 + 6x + \underline{?} - \underline{?} = (x + 3)^2 - \underline{?}$$

c. Use a graph or table to verify that your expression in the form $(x - h)^2 + k$ is equivalent to the original expression, $x^2 + 6x$.

Step 2 Consider the expression $x^2 + 6x - 4$.

	x	3
x	x^2	$3x$
3	$3x$	?

a. Focus on the 2nd- and 1st-degree terms of the expression, $x^2 + 6x$. What must be added to and subtracted from these terms to complete a perfect square yet preserve the value of the expression? 9

b. Rewrite the expression $x^2 + 6x - 4$ in the form $(x - h)^2 + k$. $x^2 + 6x - 4 = x^2 + 6x + 9 - 9 - 4 = (x + 3)^2 - 13$

c. Use a graph or table to verify that your expression is equivalent to the original expression, $x^2 + 6x - 4$.

Step 3 Rewrite each expression in the form $(x - h)^2 + k$. If you use a rectangle diagram, focus on the 2nd- and 1st-degree terms first. Verify that your expression is equivalent to the original expression.

a. $x^2 - 14x + 3$ **b.** $x^2 - bx + 10$

When the 2nd-degree term has a coefficient, you can first factor it out of the 2nd- and 1st-degree terms. For example, $3x^2 + 24x + 5$ can be written $3(x^2 + 8x) + 5$. Completing a diagram for $x^2 + 8x$ can help you rewrite the expression in the form $a(x - h)^2 + k$.

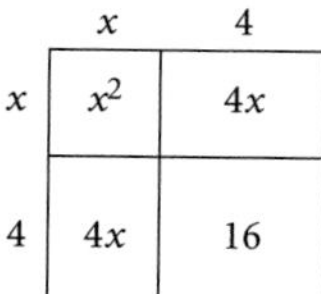

$3x^2 + 24x + 5$	The original expression.
$3(x^2 + 8x) + 5$	Factor the 2nd- and 1st-degree terms.
$3(x^2 + 8x + 16) - 3(16) + 5$	Complete the square. You add $3 \cdot 16$, so you must subtract $3 \cdot 16$.
$3(x + 4)^2 - 43$	An equivalent expression in the form $a(x - h)^2 + k$.

Step 2c

X	Y1	Y2
-1	-9	-9
0	-4	-4
1	3	3
2	12	12
3	23	23
4	36	36
5	51	51

Y2=(X+3)²-13

Step 3a $x^2 - 14x + 3 = (x - 7)^2 - 46$

Step 3b $x^2 - bx + 10 = \left(x - \frac{b}{2}\right)^2 + \left(-\frac{b^2}{4} + 10\right)$

Guiding the Investigation

Step 1b Students may be accustomed to adding to both sides of an equation when completing the square. They can continue to use that approach when they have an equation, but here they have only an expression, so the same value must be added *and* subtracted to maintain its value.

Step 1b $x^2 + 6x = x^2 + 6x + 9 - 9 = (x + 3)^2 - 9$

Step 1c Students need to set each expression equal to y in order to graph or check the tables on a calculator.

Step 1c

X	Y1	Y2
-1	-5	-5
0	0	0
1	7	7
2	16	16
3	27	27
4	40	40
5	55	55

Y2=(X+3)²-9

Step 2b If students are having difficulty, you might wonder aloud whether temporarily ignoring 4 and substituting the result of Step 1 might be useful. After they have rewritten $x^2 + 6x$ in the form $(x - h)^2 + k$, they simply subtract 4 from k to find their new expression.

Step 3b On most calculators students can enter the expression $x^2 + Bx + 10$ (and on some $x^2 + bx + 10$) for graphing. If the variable B (or b) has previously been given a value, then the calculator will graph the function, substituting that value. This may mislead students into thinking that the general function has been graphed. Suggest that they enter the variable B (or b) on the home screen and see what value it has, if any. They can substitute their own value by entering that value, pressing STO→, entering B, and pressing ENTER.

Step 4b Here the comment about Step 3b applies to the coefficient a.

Step 4b $a\left(x + \frac{5}{a}\right)^2 + \left(7 - \frac{25}{a}\right)$

Step 5 [Ask] "Have we seen the form $y = a(x - h)^2 + k$ before?" [It's the vertex form of a quadratic equation.] Completing the square changes the general form to the vertex form. The method will be used in Lesson 7.4 to derive the quadratic formula.

Step 6 $\left(-\frac{b}{2a}, c - \frac{b^2}{4a}\right)$. These are the values of h and k when the expression $ax^2 + bx + c$ is converted into the form $a(x - h)^2 + k$.

▸ ***EXAMPLE B***

This example shows how to convert quadratic functions from general form to vertex form. Part b formalizes the nongeometric approach to completing the square that some students will have noticed during the investigation. Students who have difficulty understanding this method can continue to rely on rectangle diagrams until they see the shortcut for themselves.

Assessing Progress

As students investigate, you can assess their facility with rectangle diagrams, factoring monomials, and applying the distributive property. Also evaluate their ability to see patterns. Be open to the possibility that students who previously haven't shown much skill at seeing patterns might do so here.

Step 4 Rewrite each expression in the form $a(x - h)^2 + k$. Use a graph or table to verify that your expression is equivalent to the original expression.

a. $2x^2 - 6x + 1$ $2(x - 1.5)^2 - 3.5$ **b.** $ax^2 + 10x + 7$

Step 5 Use the strategy from Step 4 to rewrite this expression in the form $a(x - h)^2 + k$:

$ax^2 + bx + c$ $a\left(x + \frac{b}{2a}\right)^2 + \left(c - \frac{b^2}{4a}\right)$

Step 6 If you graph the quadratic function $y = ax^2 + bx + c$, what will be the coordinates of the vertex in terms of a, b, and c? Why?

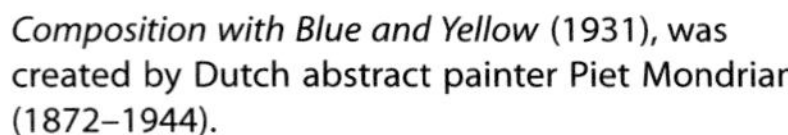

In the investigation you saw how to convert a quadratic expression from the form $ax^2 + bx + c$ to the form $a(x - h)^2 + k$. This process is called **completing the square.** As you saw in Steps 5 and 6, the two forms are related through the relationships $h = -\frac{b}{2a}$ and $k = c - \frac{b^2}{4a}$. You can use these relationships to quickly calculate the coordinates of the vertex of a quadratic function in general form.

Composition with Blue and Yellow (1931), was created by Dutch abstract painter Piet Mondrian (1872–1944).

EXAMPLE B Convert each quadratic function to vertex form. Identify the vertex.

a. $y = x^2 - 18x + 100$ **b.** $y = 3x^2 + 21x - 35$

▸ ***Solution*** To convert to vertex form, you must complete the square.

a. First separate the constant from the first two terms.

$y = \left(x^2 - 18x\right) + 100$ Original equation.

To find what number you must add to complete the square, use a rectangle diagram.

	x	-9
x	x^2	$-9x$
-9	$-9x$	81

$x^2 - 18x + 100 \rightarrow \left(x^2 - 18x + ?\right) + 100 - ? \rightarrow$

$\left(x^2 - 18x + 81\right) + 100 - 81 \rightarrow (x - 9)^2 + 19$

When you add 81 to complete the square, you must also subtract 81 to keep the expression equivalent.

$y = \left(x^2 - 18x + 81\right) + 100 - 81$ Add 81 to complete the square, and subtract 81 to keep the equation equivalent.

$y = (x - 9)^2 + 19$ Factor into a perfect square, and add the constant terms.

The vertex form is $y = (x - 9)^2 + 19$, and the vertex is $(9, 19)$.

b. As an alternative to completing the square for $y = 3x^2 + 21x - 35$, you can use the formulas for h and k. First, identify the coefficients, a, b, and c.

$$y = 3x^2 + 21x - 35$$

$$a = 3 \quad b = 21 \quad c = -35$$

Substitute the values of a, b, and c into the formulas for h and k.

$$h = -\frac{b}{2a} \qquad k = c - \frac{b^2}{4a}$$

$$h = -\frac{21}{2(3)} = -3.5 \qquad k = -35 - \frac{21^2}{4(3)} = -71.75$$

The vertex is $(-3.5, -71.75)$, and the vertex form is $y = 3(x + 3.5)^2 - 71.75$. Remember to include the value of a in the vertex form.

You may find that using the formulas for h and k is often simpler than completing the square. Both methods will allow you to find the vertex of a quadratic equation and write the equation in vertex form. However, the procedure of completing the square will be used again in your work with ellipses and other geometric shapes, so you should become comfortable using it.

EXAMPLE C

Nora hits a softball straight up at a speed of 120 ft/s. If her bat contacts the ball at a height of 3 ft above the ground, how high does the ball travel? When does the ball reach its maximum height?

1999 U.S. Olympic Softball Team player Kim Maher at bat

▶ Solution

Using the projectile motion function, you know that the height of the object at time x is represented by the equation $y = ax^2 + v_0x + s_0$. The initial velocity, v_0, is 120 ft/s, and the initial height, s_0, is 3 ft. Because the distance is measured in feet, the approximate leading coefficient is -16. Thus, the function is $y = -16x^2 + 120x + 3$. To find the maximum height, locate the vertex.

$y = -16x^2 + 120x + 3$	Original equation. Identify the coefficients, $a = -16$, $b = 120$, and $c = 3$.
$h = -\frac{b}{2a} = -\frac{120}{2(-16)} = 3.75$	Use the formula for h to find the x-coordinate of the vertex.
$k = c - \frac{b^2}{4a} = 3 - \frac{120^2}{4(-16)} = 228$	Use the formula for k to find the y-coordinate of the vertex.

The softball reaches a maximum height of 228 ft at 3.75 s.

You now have several strategies for finding the vertex of a quadratic function. You can convert from general form to vertex form by completing the square or by using the formulas for h and k.

Sharing Ideas (continued)

value will be the second term, with 0 being added or subtracted.

Let students know that completing the square to find an optimum value is a method that applies only to quadratics. Other methods are needed for other polynomials. **[Link]** Calculus provides a general method that applies to all polynomials and most other common functions.

If you have time, you might prepare students for Exercise 14 and foreshadow Chapter 9 by reminding them that the equation $x^2 + y^2 = 16$ represents a circle centered at the origin and having radius 4. Then **[Ask]** "What might the equation $x^2 - 6x + y^2 = 16$ represent?" [Completing the square gives $x^2 + 6x + 9 + y^2 = 25$, which is equivalent to $(x - 3)^2 + y^2 = 5^2$, representing a translation and dilation of the unit circle to a circled centered at the point (3, 0) and having radius 5.]

▶ EXAMPLE C

[ESL] "How high" is asking for the greatest height of the ball, not just any height the ball reaches.

[Language] *Velocity* means "speed in a specific direction." The velocity of 120 ft/s in this example is a speed (rate of change of distance in feet for each second) of 120 ft/s in the upward direction. A negative velocity is downward. For example, a negative initial velocity would indicate that something was being thrown down.

Students may point out that a softball normally doesn't travel straight up and down. Even if the motion has a horizontal component, the projectile motion function describes the vertical component.

As an alternative approach to finding k, once students find that the x-coordinate of the vertex is $h = 3.75$, they could substitute that value for x into the equation $y = -16x^2 + 120x + 3$ and get a height of 228 ft.

SHARING IDEAS

As students discuss ideas, ask why they'd ever need to find the coordinates of a parabola's vertex. [Its coordinates give a maximum or minimum value in a real-world situation.]

[Ask] "Is there an alternative to remembering the formulas for h and k?" [The values can always be rederived by completing the square.]

[Ask] "Does it make sense that the expression $a\left(x + \frac{b}{2a}\right)^2 + \left(c - \frac{b^2}{4a}\right)$ has an optimum value at $\left(-\frac{b}{2a}, c - \frac{b^2}{4a}\right)$?" One way to make sense of this is to think of the first term as being added to (or subtracted from) the second. The square of the binomial is never negative, so the sum or difference will be optimized when this square is 0, which is when $x = -\frac{b}{2a}$. The optimum

Closing the Lesson

Reiterate the main points of this lesson: A parabola's vertex is useful for finding extreme values in real-world situations. If you have a quadratic function in factored form, the x-coordinate of the vertex is the mean of the zeros (x-intercepts). If you have a quadratic function in general form, you can **complete the square** to convert it to vertex form, from which you can read off the coordinates of the vertex. You can complete the square by using a rectangle diagram or by adding and subtracting the square of half the x-coefficient.

BUILDING UNDERSTANDING

The exercises provide students with practice in converting to the vertex form and using that form to solve problems.

ASSIGNING HOMEWORK

Essential	2, 3, 5, 6
Performance assessment	7, 9, 11
Portfolio	7, 11
Journal	11
Group	8
Review	1, 4, 8, 10, 12–15

Helping with the Exercises

Exercise 1 Students may need to use rectangle diagrams to see that these are all perfect squares.

1b. $\left(x + \frac{5}{2}\right)^2$

1c. $(2x - 3)^2$ or $4\left(x - \frac{3}{2}\right)^2$

2b. 12.25 or $\frac{49}{4}$

3a. $y = (x + 10)^2 - 6$

3b. $y = (x - 3.5)^2 + 3.75$

EXERCISES

Practice Your Skills

1. Factor each quadratic expression.

a. $x^2 - 10x + 25$ $(x - 5)^2$ **b.** $x^2 + 5x + \frac{25}{4}$

c. $4x^2 - 12x + 9$ **d.** $x^2 - 2xy + y^2$ $(x - y)^2$

2. What value is required to complete the square?

a. $x^2 + 20x + \underline{?}$ 100 **b.** $x^2 - 7x + \underline{?}$

c. $4x^2 - 16x + \underline{?}$ 16 **d.** $-3x^2 - 6x + \underline{?}$ -3

3. Convert each quadratic function to vertex form.

a. $y = x^2 + 20x + 94$ **b.** $y = x^2 - 7x + 16$

c. $y = 6x^2 - 24x + 147$ $y = 6(x - 2)^2 + 123$ **d.** $y = 5x^2 + 8x$ $y = 5(x + 0.8)^2 - 3.2$

4. Rewrite each expression in the form $ax^2 + bx + c$, and then identify the coefficients, a, b, and c.

a. $3x^2 + 2x - 5$ **b.** $14 + 2x^2$

c. $-3 + 4x^2 - 2x + 8x$ **d.** $3x - x^2$

Hungarian modern sculptor Màrton Vàrò (b 1943) titled this piece *15 Cubes* (1998). It is located at the Elektro building in Trondheim, Norway.

Reason and Apply

5. What is the vertex of the graph of the quadratic function $y = -2x^2 - 16x - 20$? $(-4, 12)$

6. Convert the function $y = 7.51x^2 - 47.32x + 129.47$ to vertex form. Use a graph or table to verify that the functions are equivalent. $y = 7.51(x - 3.15)^2 + 54.93$

7. Imagine that an arrow is shot from the bottom of a well. It passes ground level at 1.1 s and lands on the ground at 4.7 s.

a. Define variables and write a quadratic function that describes the height of the arrow, in meters, as a function of time.

b. What was the initial velocity of the arrow in meters per second? 28.42 m/s

c. How deep was the well in meters? 25.333 m

8. APPLICATION Suppose you are enclosing a rectangular area to create a rabbit cage. You have 80 ft of fence and want to build a pen with the largest possible area for your rabbit, so you build the cage using an existing building as one side.

a. Make a table showing the areas for some selected values of x, and write a function that gives the area, y, as a function of the width, x. See page 383.

b. What width maximizes the area? What is the maximum area? 20 ft; 800 ft^2

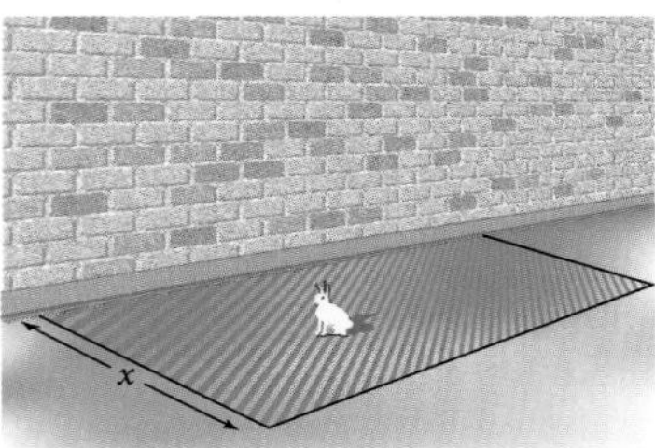

4a. no rewriting necessary; $a = 3, b = 2, c = -5$

4b. $2x^2 + 14$; $a = 2, b = 0, c = 14$

4c. $4x^2 + 6x - 3$; $a = 4, b = 6, c = -3$

4d. $-x^2 + 3x$; $a = -1, b = 3, c = 0$

Exercise 5 Students can use graphing calculators to verify their solution.

Exercise 7 Encourage students to sketch a picture and label important parts. They can assume that the arrow was shot from the very bottom of the well.

7a. Let x represent time in seconds, and let y represent height in meters; $y = -4.9(x - 1.1)(x - 4.7)$ or $y = -4.9x^2 + 28.42x - 25.333$.

9. A rock is thrown upward from the edge of a 50 m cliff overlooking Lake Superior, with an initial velocity of 17.2 m/s. Define variables and write an equation that models the height of the rock.

10. An object is projected upward, and these data are collected.

Time (s) t	1	2	3	4	5	6
Height (m) h	120.1	205.4	280.9	346.6	402.4	448.4

a. Write a function that relates time and height for this object. $y = -4.9t^2 + 100t + 25$

b. What was the initial height? The initial velocity? 25 m; 100 m/s

c. When does the object reach its maximum height? What is the maximum height? 10.2 s; 535 m

11. **APPLICATION** The members of the Young Entrepreneurs Club decide to sell T-shirts in their school colors for Spirit Week. In a marketing survey, the members ask students whether or not they would buy a T-shirt for a specific price. In analyzing the data, club members find that at a price of \$20 they would sell 60 T-shirts. For each \$5 increase in price, they would sell 10 fewer T-shirts.

a. Find a linear function that relates the price in dollars, p, and the number of T-shirts sold, n.

b. Write a function that gives revenue as a function of price. (Use your function in 11a as a substitute for the number of T-shirts sold.)

c. Convert the revenue function to vertex form. What is the real-world meaning of the vertex?

d. If the club members want to receive at least \$1050 in revenue, what price should they charge for the T-shirts?

Business CONNECTION

Entrepreneurs are individuals who take a risk to create a new product or a new business. Some famous American entrepreneurs include Sarah Breedlove ("Madam C. J. Walker") (1867–1919), who was a pioneer in the cosmetics industry for African-Americans; Clarence Birdseye (1886–1956), who made frozen food available; Ray Kroc (1902–1984), who developed a way to provide fast service and created McDonald's; and Jeff Bezos (b 1964), who founded Amazon.com and popularized a way to sell merchandise without the traditional retail stores.

Sarah Breedlove Walker expanded her cosmetics company across the United States, the Caribbean, and Europe.
The Granger Collection, New York City

Around the time of World War II (1939–1945), Clarence Birdseye, shown here dehydrating chopped carrots, created foods that were fast and easy to prepare.

8a. Possible table with x representing the sides adjacent to the building:

x	5	10	15	20	25	30	35
y	350	600	750	800	750	600	350

$y = -2x^2 + 80x$

Exercise 8 Some students will believe that two pens with the same perimeter will have the same area. You might suggest that they sketch several different pens and calculate their areas. In the given answer, x is the length of each side perpendicular to the building. If students let x equal the length of the side parallel to the building, their area function will be $y = x\left(\frac{80 - x}{2}\right)$, or $y = -\frac{1}{2}x^2 + 40x$. A value of $x = 40$ ft gives the same area, 800 ft^2.

[Alert] If students remember from geometry that the largest rectangle with a given perimeter is a square, they may be confused that the result here is not a square. That's because one edge of the rectangle is against a wall. Suggest that they think of combining the rectangle with its reflection across the wall and imagine having twice as much fencing (160 ft) to enclose this larger rectangle. Ignoring the wall, the largest combined rectangle will be a square 40 feet on a side. Half of that square, a 20-by-40 ft rectangle, will be on each side of the wall.

9. Let x represent time in seconds, and let y represent height in meters; $y = -4.9x^2 + 17.2x + 50$.

Exercise 11 **[Language]** *Revenue* is the total amount of income or money they take in from selling the T-shirts.

11a. $n = -2p + 100$

11b. $R(p) = -2p^2 + 100p$

11c. Vertex form: $R(p) = -2(p - 25)^2 + 1250$. The vertex is (25, 1250). This means that the maximum revenue is \$1250 when the price is \$25.

11d. between \$15 and \$35

Review

12. Multiply.

a. $(x - 3)(2x + 4)$ $2x^2 - 2x - 12$

b. $(x^2 + 1)(x + 2)$ $x^3 + 2x^2 + x + 2$

7.2 **13.** Solve $(x - 2)(x + 3)(2x - 1) = 0$. $x = 2, x = -3$, or $x = \frac{1}{2}$

4.7 **14.** Consider a graph of the unit circle, $x^2 + y^2 = 1$. Stretch it vertically by a scale factor of 3, and translate it left 5 units and up 7 units.

a. Write the equation of this new shape. What is it called?

b. Sketch a graph of this shape. Label the center and at least four points.

3.4 **15.** **APPLICATION** This table shows the number of endangered species in the United States for selected years from 1980 to 2000.

Endangered Species

Year	1980	1985	1990	1995	1996	1997	1998	1999	2000
Number of endangered species	224	300	442	756	837	896	924	939	961

(*The New York Times Almanac 2002*)

a. Define variables and create a scatter plot of these data.

b. Find the equation of the median-median line for these data.

c. Use the median-median line to predict the number of endangered species in 2005 and in 2050.

Environmental CONNECTION

Most species become endangered when humans damage their ecosystems through pollution, habitat destruction, and introduction of nonnative species. Over-hunting and over-collecting also threaten animal and plant populations. Growing human and livestock populations have made this a constantly increasing problem—the current global extinction rate is about 20,000 species a year. For information about what is being done to protect endangered species, see the weblinks at www.keymath.com/DAA .

The Karner blue butterfly, native to the Great Lakes region, has become endangered as the availability of its primary food, blue lupine, has become scarce due to development and fire suppression.

The aye-aye is a nocturnal primate native to Madagascar. Their numbers have declined due to habitat destruction, and because they are considered to be a bad omen, they are often killed. There are estimated to be only 100 left.

Exercise 14 This exercise reviews Chapter 4 and previews the conic sections of Chapter 9.

14a. $(x + 5)^2 + \left(\frac{y - 7}{3}\right)^2 = 1$; ellipse

14b.

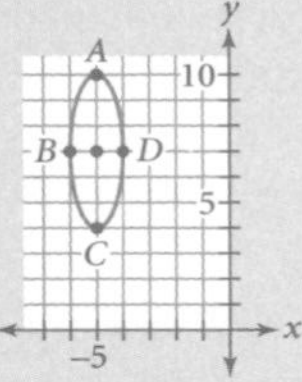

$A(-5, 10)$, $B(-6, 7)$, $C(-5, 4)$, $D(-4, 7)$; center: $(-5, 7)$

Exercise 15c If students round off differently or begin counting years at some number other than 0, they may get slightly different results.

15a. Let x represent the year, and let y represent the number of endangered species.

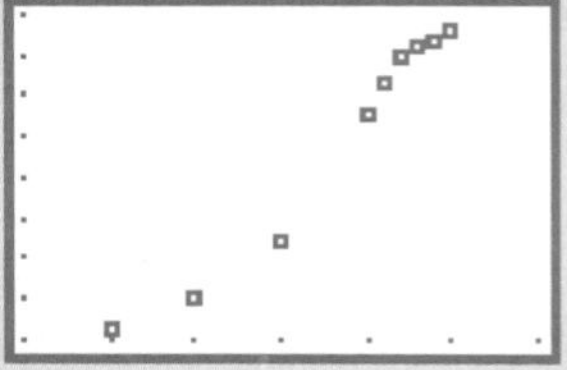

[1975, 2005, 5, 200, 1000, 100]

15b. $\hat{y} = 45.64x - 90289$

15c. Using the equation from 15b, approximately 1219 species in 2005; 3273 species in 2050

MAKING THE CONNECTION

Efforts to protect endangered species occur at local, national, and international levels. In the United States, the Fish and Wildlife Service and the National Marine Fisheries Service enforce environmental policy and maintain a list of the more than 900 endangered and threatened species. Nongovernmental organizations like the Sierra Club and the National Audubon Society work to protect habitats and inform the public of issues affecting endangered species. For a number of species, however, protection requires international efforts. Conservation groups and the United Nations, for example, have made efforts to halt whaling, the killing of dolphins by tuna fishermen, and wildlife trafficking. The International Union for the Conservation of Nature and Natural Resources compiles a list of endangered species worldwide.

LESSON 7.4

The Quadratic Formula

Although you can always use a graph of a quadratic function to approximate the x-intercepts, you are often not able to find exact solutions. This lesson will develop a procedure to find the exact roots of a quadratic equation by first converting the equation to vertex form. Consider again this situation from Example C in the last lesson.

EXAMPLE A

Nora hits a softball straight up at a speed of 120 ft/s. Her bat contacts the ball at a height of 3 ft above the ground. Recall that the equation relating height in meters, y, and time in seconds, x, is $y = -16x^2 + 120x + 3$. How long will it be until the ball hits the ground?

▶ Solution

The height will be zero when the ball hits the ground, so you want to find the solutions to the equation $-16x^2 + 120x + 3 = 0$. You can approximate the x-intercepts by graphing, but as you can see it's difficult to be accurate. Even after you zoom in a few times, you may not be able to find the exact x-intercept.

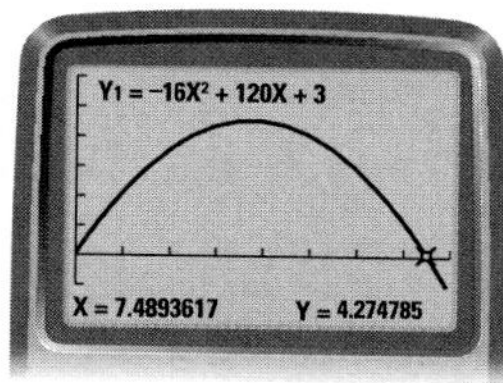

[0, 8, 1, −50, 300, 50]

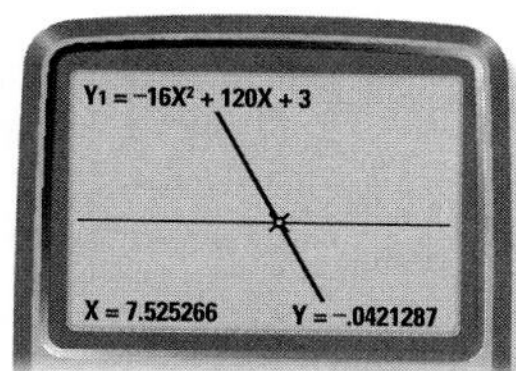

[7.46, 7.58, 1, −2.28, 3.18, 50]

You will not be able to factor this equation using a rectangle diagram, so you can't use the zero-product property. Instead, to solve this equation symbolically, first write the equation in the form $a(x - h)^2 + k = 0$.

$-16x^2 + 120x + 3 = 0$ Original equation.

$h = -\frac{b}{2a} = -\frac{120}{2(-16)} = 3.75$

$k = c - \frac{b^2}{4a} = 3 - \frac{120^2}{4(-16)} = 228$ Find the values of h and k.

$-16(x - 3.75)^2 + 228 = 0$ Use the values of h and k to convert to the form $a(x - h)^2 + k = 0$.

$-16(x - 3.75)^2 = -228$ Subtract 228 from both sides.

$(x - 3.75)^2 = 14.25$ Divide by -16.

$x - 3.75 = \pm\sqrt{14.25}$ Take the square root of both sides.

$x = 3.75 \pm \sqrt{14.25}$ Add 3.75 to both sides.

$x = 3.75 + \sqrt{14.25}$ or $x = 3.75 - \sqrt{14.25}$ Write the two exact solutions to the equation.

$x \approx 7.525$ or $x \approx -0.025$ Approximate the values of x.

The zeros of the function are $x \approx 7.525$ and $x \approx -0.025$. The negative time, -0.025 s, does not make sense in this situation, so the ball hits the ground after approximately 7.525 s.

LESSON 7.4

PLANNING

LESSON OUTLINE

One day:

15 min	Example A
10 min	Investigation
5 min	Example B
10 min	Sharing
5 min	Exercises

MATERIALS

- Calculator Note 7D, *optional*
- Sketchpad demonstration Quadratic Functions, *optional*

TEACHING

This lesson derives the quadratic formula. Students who used *Discovering Algebra* may recall it from Chapter 10 of that book. See page 386 for the one-step investigation.

▶ EXAMPLE A

This example revisits the situation of Lesson 7.3, Example C, but it poses a problem that reviews completing the square and extends it to solving an equation. Resist the temptation to skip this example and go right to the quadratic formula; the example provides a special case for the derivation of that formula.

Encourage students to draw a graph. You might want to complete the square rather than using formulas for h and k.

NCTM STANDARDS

CONTENT		PROCESS	
✓	Number		Problem Solving
✓	Algebra	✓	Reasoning
	Geometry	✓	Communication
	Measurement	✓	Connections
	Data/Probability	✓	Representation

LESSON OBJECTIVES

- Use the vertex form of a quadratic equation to find the equation's roots
- Derive the quadratic formula from the vertex form of a quadratic equation
- Use the quadratic formula to solve application problems

One Step
Remind students of the second part of the one-step problem of Lesson 7.3, in which they knew the initial velocity of a baseball. Ask them when the ball hits the ground. Students can use the vertex form they found, set it equal to 0, and solve for time. Or they can double the x-coordinate of the vertex. In either case, remind them that they had to complete the square or use formulas for h and k to get the vertex form. Challenge them to solve the general equation $ax^2 + bx + c = 0$ by completing the square and to come up with a formula for the solution to any quadratic equation. Don't be satisfied if they already can reel off the quadratic formula; the goal is for them to derive it.

The Quadratic Formula
In applying the quadratic formula to Example A, you might want to simplify to the exact solutions, $x = 3.75 \pm \frac{\sqrt{57}}{2}$.

If students won't be doing the project at the end of this lesson, you might let them use the calculator program found in Calculator Note 7D.

[Alert] Most mistakes made while using a calculator with the quadratic formula can be blamed on not enclosing the radicand within parentheses, not enclosing the entire numerator within parentheses, or not enclosing the denominator within parentheses.

Guiding the Investigation

Step 1 Students are to use the projectile motion function of Lesson 7.3.

Step 3 If groups are completing the square or using formulas for h and k, challenge them to use the quadratic formula.

Step 3 $-16x^2 + 88x - 21 = 0$; $x = 0.25$ or $x = 5.25$. The ball rises to 24 ft on the way up, at 0.25 s, and it falls to 24 ft on the way down, at 5.25 s.

If you follow the same steps with a general quadratic equation, then you can develop the **quadratic formula.** This formula provides solutions to $ax^2 + bx + c = 0$ in terms of a, b, and c.

$ax^2 + bx + c = 0$	Original equation.
$h = \frac{-b}{2a}$ and $k = c - \frac{b^2}{4a}$	Find the values of h and k.
$a\left(x + \frac{b}{2a}\right)^2 + c - \frac{b^2}{4a} = 0$	Rewrite the equation in the form $a(x - h)^2 + k = 0$.
$a\left(x + \frac{b}{2a}\right)^2 = \frac{b^2}{4a} - c$	Subtract c from both sides. Add $\frac{b^2}{4a}$ to both sides.
$a\left(x + \frac{b}{2a}\right)^2 = \frac{b^2}{4a} - \frac{4ac}{4a}$	Rewrite the right side with a common denominator.
$a\left(x + \frac{b}{2a}\right)^2 = \frac{b^2 - 4ac}{4a}$	Add terms with a common denominator.
$\left(x + \frac{b}{2a}\right)^2 = \frac{b^2 - 4ac}{4a^2}$	Divide both sides by a.
$x + \frac{b}{2a} = \pm\sqrt{\frac{b^2 - 4ac}{4a^2}}$	Take the square root of both sides.
$x + \frac{b}{2a} = \pm\frac{\sqrt{b^2 - 4ac}}{2a}$	Use the power of a quotient property to take the square roots of the numerator and denominator.
$x = -\frac{b}{2a} \pm \frac{\sqrt{b^2 - 4ac}}{2a}$	Subtract $\frac{b}{2a}$ from both sides.
$x = \frac{-b \pm \sqrt{b^2 - 4ac}}{2a}$	Add terms with a common denominator.

The Quadratic Formula

Given a quadratic equation written in the form $ax^2 + bx + c = 0$, the solutions are

$$x = \frac{-b \pm \sqrt{b^2 - 4ac}}{2a}$$

To use the quadratic formula on the equation in Example A, $-16x^2 + 120x + 3 = 0$, first identify the coefficients as $a = -16$, $b = 120$, and $c = 3$. The solutions are

$$x = \frac{-120 \pm \sqrt{120^2 - 4(-16)(3)}}{2(-16)}$$

$$x = \frac{-120 + \sqrt{14592}}{-32} \quad \text{or} \quad x = \frac{-120 - \sqrt{14592}}{-32}$$

$$x \approx -0.025 \quad \text{or} \quad x \approx 7.525$$

The quadratic formula gives you a way to find the roots of any equation in the form $ax^2 + bx + c = 0$. The investigation will give you an opportunity to apply the quadratic formula in different situations.

Step 4 A graph of the function can help students answer this question.

Step 4 The vertex is the maximum. The ball reaches the maximum height only once. The ball reaches other heights once on the way up and once on the way down, but the top of the ball's height, the maximum point, can be reached only once.

Step 5 In Step 3, the symmetry of the two solutions about the x-coordinate of the vertex is consistent with the symmetry of the parabola.

Step 6 This step foreshadows the introduction of complex numbers in Lesson 7.5.

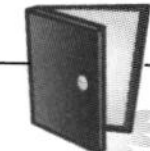

Investigation
How High Can You Go?

Salvador hits a baseball at a height of 3 ft and with an initial upward velocity of 88 feet per second.

Step 1 Let x represent time in seconds after the ball is hit, and let y represent the height of the ball in feet. Write an equation that gives the height as a function of time. $y = -16x^2 + 88x + 3$

Step 2 Write an equation to find the times when the ball is 24 ft above the ground. $24 = -16x^2 + 88x + 3$

Step 3 Rewrite your equation from Step 2 in the form $ax^2 + bx + c = 0$, then use the quadratic formula to solve. What is the real-world meaning of each of your solutions? Why are there two solutions?

Step 4 The vertex of this parabola has a y-coordinate of 124. Explain why the ball will reach a height of 124 ft only once.

Step 5 Write an equation to find the time when the ball reaches a height of 124 ft. Use the quadratic formula to solve the equation. At what point in the solution process does it become obvious that there is only one solution to this equation? $-16x^2 + 88x + 3 = 124$; $x = 2.75$; $\sqrt{b^2 - 4ac} = 0$

Step 6 Write an equation to find the time when the ball reaches a height of 200 ft. What happens when you try to solve this impossible situation with the quadratic formula? $-16x^2 + 88x + 3 = 200$. You get the square root of a negative number, so there are no real solutions.

It's important to note that a quadratic equation must be in the general form $ax^2 + bx + c = 0$ before you use the quadratic formula.

EXAMPLE B Solve $3x^2 = 5x + 8$.

▶ Solution

To use the quadratic formula, first write the equation in the form $ax^2 + bx + c = 0$ and identify the coefficients.

$$3x^2 - 5x - 8 = 0$$

$$a = 3, b = -5, c = -8$$

Substitute a, b, and c into the quadratic formula.

$$x = \frac{-b \pm \sqrt{b^2 - 4ac}}{2a}$$

$$x = \frac{-(-5) \pm \sqrt{(-5)^2 - 4(3)(-8)}}{2(3)}$$

$$x = \frac{5 \pm \sqrt{121}}{6}$$

$$x = \frac{5 \pm 11}{6}$$

$$x = \frac{5 + 11}{6} = \frac{8}{3} \quad \text{or} \quad x = \frac{5 - 11}{6} = -1$$

▶ EXAMPLE B

You might ask students to do the calculations on graphing calculators to give them an opportunity to practice inserting parentheses around the numerator and around the terms under the radical.

In the picture of the calculator screen on page 388, the colons separate instructions.

As the book says, the quadratic formula will solve any quadratic equation, but some solutions will not be real numbers. Students will see nonreal solutions in Lesson 7.5.

SHARING IDEAS

[Language] During student presentations, discourage the use of the term *quadratic equation* to mean *quadratic formula.* The quadratic formula can be used to solve all quadratic equations.

[Ask] "Why are the two solutions in the form of a certain amount added to and subtracted from another number?" [The "other number" is $\frac{-b}{2a}$, the x-coordinate of the parabola's vertex. The symmetry of the parabola ensures that its x-intercepts will be equidistant on either side of this coordinate.]

Ask whether the value of k, the y-value of the vertex, also appears in the quadratic formula. [The number being added to and subtracted from $\frac{-b}{2a}$ is the square root of $-\frac{k}{a}$.]

Remind students that they can gain insight from looking at extreme cases. **[Ask]** "When the value of a, b, or c is 0, what can be said about the equation and what happens to the formula?" [When $a = 0$, the equation is linear, not quadratic, because the quadratic formula requires dividing by a, the result when $a = 0$ is not defined; the formula doesn't apply to linear equations. When $b = 0$, the equation's graph is symmetric about the y-axis; the formula gives two solutions equidistant from 0. When $c = 0$,

Sharing Ideas (continued)
the equation factors to show a root at $x = 0$, and the formula returns 0 as one of the roots.]

[Ask] "What if the number represented by $b^2 - 4ac$ in the square root is 0?" [Both solutions are the same, $\frac{-b}{2a}$. The parabolic graph of the quadratic function touches the x-axis at just one point, a point of tangency at the vertex: $\left(\frac{-b}{2a}, 0\right)$.] You might describe the quantity $b^2 - 4ac$ as the *discriminant.*

[Ask] "What if the number represented by $b^2 - 4ac$ is negative?" [The equation has no real solutions, indicating that its parabolic graph doesn't cross the x-axis.]

You might use the Sketchpad demonstration Quadratic Functions to investigate how various values of a, b, and c affect the graph of a quadratic function.

Assessing Progress
You can check students' familiarity with the general form of a quadratic equation and with the projectile motion function, and their understanding of time and height variables.

Closing the Lesson

Restate the **quadratic formula** and perhaps remind students of how it's derived from completing the square, with or without using the formulas for h and k.

BUILDING UNDERSTANDING

Students practice applying the quadratic formula.

ASSIGNING HOMEWORK

Essential	2–5
Performance assessment	6–12
Portfolio	11
Journal	10
Group	9
Review	1, 13–17

Helping with the Exercises

Exercise 1 As needed, remind students that each of these problems will have two solutions.

2a. $3x^2 - 13x - 10 = 0; a = 3, b = -13, c = -10$

2b. $x^2 - 5x - 13 = 0; a = 1, b = -5, c = -13$

2c. $3x^2 + 5x + 1 = 0; a = 3, b = 5, c = 1$

2d. $3x^2 - 3x - 2 = 0; a = 3, b = -3, c = -2$

2e. $x^2 - 15x + 50 = 0; a = 1, b = -15, c = 50$

Exercise 5c This exercise extends the definition of *factored form* to include non-integer roots.

The solutions are $x = \frac{8}{3}$ or $x = -1$.

To check your work, substitute these values into the original equation. Here's a way to use your calculator to check.

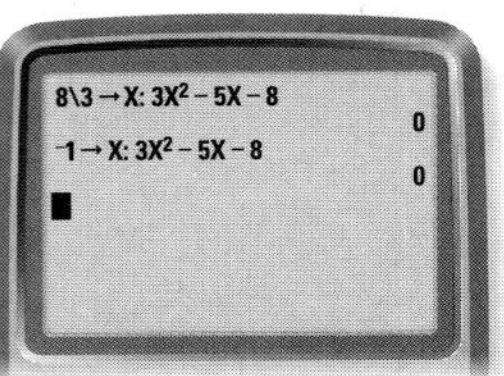

Remember, you can find exact solutions to some quadratic equations by factoring. However, most don't factor easily. The quadratic formula can be used to solve any quadratic equation.

EXERCISES

Practice Your Skills

1. Solve.

a. $(x - 2.3)^2 = 25$ $x = 7.3$ or $x = -2.7$

b. $(x + 4.45)^2 = 12.25$ $x = -0.95$ or $x = -7.95$

c. $\left(x - \frac{3}{4}\right)^2 = \frac{25}{16}$ $x = 2$ or $x = -\frac{1}{2}$

2. Rewrite each equation in general form, $ax^2 + bx + c = 0$. Identify a, b, and c.

a. $3x^2 - 13x = 10$

b. $x^2 - 13 = 5x$

c. $3x^2 + 5x = -1$

d. $3x^2 - 2 - 3x = 0$

e. $14(x - 4) - (x + 2) = (x + 2)(x - 4)$

3. Evaluate each expression using your calculator. Round your answers to the nearest thousandth.

a. $\frac{-30 + \sqrt{30^2 - 4(5)(3)}}{2(5)}$ -0.102

b. $\frac{-30 - \sqrt{30^2 - 4(5)(3)}}{2(5)}$ -5.898

c. $\frac{8 - \sqrt{(-8)^2 - 4(1)(-2)}}{2(1)}$ -0.243

d. $\frac{8 + \sqrt{(-8)^2 - 4(1)(-2)}}{2(1)}$ 8.243

4. Solve by any method.

a. $x^2 - 6x + 5 = 0$ $x = 1$ or $x = 5$

b. $x^2 - 7x - 18 = 0$ $x = -2$ or $x = 9$

c. $5x^2 + 12x + 7 = 0$ $x = -1$ or $x = -1.4$

5. Use the roots of the equations in Exercise 4 to write each of these functions in factored form, $y = a(x - r_1)(x - r_2)$.

a. $y = x^2 - 6x + 5$ $y = (x - 1)(x - 5)$

b. $y = x^2 - 7x - 18$ $y = (x + 2)(x - 9)$

c. $y = 5x^2 + 12x + 7$ $y = 5(x + 1)(x + 1.4)$

Reason and Apply

6. Beth uses the quadratic formula to solve an equation and gets

$$x = \frac{-9 \pm \sqrt{9^2 - 4(1)(10)}}{2(1)}$$

a. Write the quadratic equation Beth started with.

b. Write the simplified forms of the exact answers.

c. What are the x-intercepts of the graph of this quadratic function?

Exercise 6 **[Language]** *Simplified form* means with the arithmetic performed and the radical reduced if possible. (In this exercise, the radical cannot be reduced.)

[Ask] "Without graphing, can you tell whether the parabola's vertex is a maximum or a minimum?" [It's a minimum because a is positive.]

6a. $x^2 + 9x + 10 = 0$

6b. $x = \frac{-9 \pm \sqrt{41}}{2}$

6c. $\frac{-9 + \sqrt{41}}{2}$ and $\frac{-9 - \sqrt{41}}{2}$

7. Write a quadratic function whose graph has these x-intercepts.

a. 3 and -3
$y = a(x - 3)(x + 3)$ for $a \neq 0$

b. 4 and $-\frac{2}{5}$

c. r_1 and r_2
$y = a(x - r_1)(x - r_2)$ for $a \neq 0$

8. Use the quadratic formula to find the zeros of $y = 2x^2 + 2x + 5$. Explain what happens. Graph $y = 2x^2 + 2x + 5$ to confirm your observation. How can you recognize this situation before using the quadratic formula?

9. Write a quadratic function that has no x-intercepts.

10. Show that the mean of the two solutions provided by the quadratic formula is $-\frac{b}{2a}$. Explain what this tells you about a graph.

11. These data give the amount of water in a draining bathtub and the amount of time after the plug was pulled.

Time (min) x	1	1.5	2	2.5
Amount of water (L) y	38.4	30.0	19.6	7.2

a. Write a function that gives the amount of water as a function of time.

b. How much water was in the tub when the plug was pulled? 49.2 L

c. How long did it take the tub to empty? 2.76 min

12. A **golden rectangle** is a rectangle that can be divided into a square and another rectangle that is also a golden rectangle similar to the original. In the figure at right, $ABCD$ is a golden rectangle because it can be divided into square $ABFE$ and golden rectangle $FCDE$. Setting up a proportion of the side lengths of the similar rectangles leads to $\frac{a}{a+b} = \frac{b}{a}$. Let $b = 1$ and solve this equation for a. $\frac{a}{a+1} = \frac{1}{a}$, $a = \frac{1 \pm \sqrt{5}}{2}$

B a F b C
a
A E D

History CONNECTION

Many people and cultures throughout history have felt that the golden rectangle is one of the most visually pleasing geometric shapes. It was used in the architectural designs of the Cathedral of Notre Dame in Paris, as well as in music and famous works of art. It is believed that the early Egyptians used the ratio when building their pyramids, temples, and tombs, and that they knew the value of the **golden ratio** (the ratio of the length of the golden rectangle to the width) to be $\frac{1+\sqrt{5}}{2}$.

The Fibonacci Fountain in Bowie, Maryland, was designed by mathematician Helaman Ferguson using Fibonacci numbers and the golden ratio. It has 14 water spouts arranged horizontally at intervals proportional to Fibonacci numbers.

Review

7.2 **13.** Complete each equation.

a. $x^2 + \underline{?} + 49 = (x + \underline{?})^2$

b. $x^2 - 10x + \underline{?} = (\underline{?})^2$

c. $x^2 + 3x + \underline{?} = (\underline{?})^2$

d. $2x^2 + \underline{?} + 8 = 2(x^2 + \underline{?} + \underline{?}) = \underline{?}(x + \underline{?})^2$

5.5 **14.** Find the inverse of each function. (The inverse does not need to be a function.)

a. $y = (x + 1)^2$
$y = \pm\sqrt{x} - 1$

b. $y = (x + 1)^2 + 4$
$y = \pm\sqrt{x - 4} - 1$

c. $y = x^2 + 2x - 5$
$y = \pm\sqrt{x + 6} - 1$

10. $\frac{1}{2}\left(\frac{-b + \sqrt{b^2 - 4ac}}{2a} + \frac{-b - \sqrt{b^2 - 4ac}}{2a}\right) = \frac{1}{2}\left(\frac{-2b}{2a}\right) = -\frac{b}{2a}$

The x-coordinate of the vertex, $-\frac{b}{2a}$, is midway between the two x-intercepts.

13a. $x^2 + 14x + 49 = (x + 7)^2$

13b. $x^2 - 10x + 25 = (x - 5)^2$

13c. $x^2 + 3x + \frac{9}{4} = \left(x + \frac{3}{2}\right)^2$

13d. $2x^2 + 8x + 8 = 2(x^2 + 4x + 4) = 2(x + 2)^2$

Exercise 7b You might want to ask students to write this equation without a fraction.

7b. $y = a(x - 4)\left(x + \frac{2}{5}\right)$ or $y = a(x - 4)(5x + 2)$ for $a \neq 0$

8. The solution includes the square root of -36, so there are no real solutions. The graph shows no x-intercepts. Before using the quadratic function, evaluate $b^2 - 4ac$. If $b^2 - 4ac < 0$, then there will be no real solutions.

Exercise 9 [Language] You might define $b^2 - 4ac$ as the *discriminant*. This exercise can build on conclusions reached in Exercise 8.

9. The function can be any quadratic function for which $b^2 - 4ac$ is negative. Sample answer: $y = x^2 + x + 1$.

Exercise 11 This exercise requires using finite differences and the quadratic formula. **[Alert]** The plug was pulled at time 0, not time 1.

11a. $y = -4x^2 - 6.8x + 49.2$

Exercise 12 The equation can be solved by the quadratic formula. Only the positive solution, $\frac{1 + \sqrt{5}}{2}$, makes sense as a length. The golden rectangle was a topic of an exploration in Chapter 1.

MAKING THE CONNECTION

Students might be interested to know how the golden ratio and Fibonacci sequence are related. In the Fibonacci sequence (1, 1, 2, 3, 5, 8, . . . , 4181, 6765, 10946, . . .) each term is the sum of the two preceding terms. The ratio of consecutive numbers in the sequence approaches the golden ratio.

$\frac{10946}{6765} \approx 1.618033999$

$\frac{1 + \sqrt{5}}{2} \approx 1.618033989$

Ratios of larger Fibonacci numbers will be even closer to the golden ratio.

Exercise 16 Students may need to sketch a diagram to figure out the equation using the Pythagorean Theorem.

Exercise 17 Although there are 11 support cables labeled, their distance apart is $\frac{1}{12}$ of 160 ft, or $13\frac{1}{3}$ ft. Students may correctly reason that a bridge would have two parabolic cables, one on each side of the road. Their answer of 458.32 ft is correct for the assumption they are making.

17. $a = k = 52.08\overline{3}$ ft; $b = j = 33.\overline{3}$ ft; $c = i = 18.75$ ft; $d = h = 8.\overline{3}$ ft; $e = g = 2.08\overline{3}$ ft; $f = 0$; $229.1\overline{6}$ ft

MAKING THE CONNECTION

Students who completed the Chapter 5 Exploration The Number *e* might be interested to know that the equation for a catenary curve contains the number *e*.

$$y = \frac{a}{2}\left(e^{x/a} + e^{-x/a}\right)$$

The graph of this function is symmetric about the *y*-axis; *a* is the *y*-intercept.

EXTENSION

Have students use geometry software to analyze what happens to the vertex of a parabola when you vary *a* in the equation of the general form but hold *b* and *c* constant. Students then can describe what happens when *b* varies and *a* and *c* are held constant.

7.2 **15.** Convert these quadratic functions to general form.

a. $y = (x - 3)(2x + 5)$ $y = 2x^2 - x - 15$

b. $y = -2(x - 1)^2 + 4$ $y = -2x^2 + 4x + 2$

16. A 20 ft ladder leans against a building. Let *x* represent the distance between the building and the foot of the ladder, and let *y* represent the height the ladder reaches on the building.

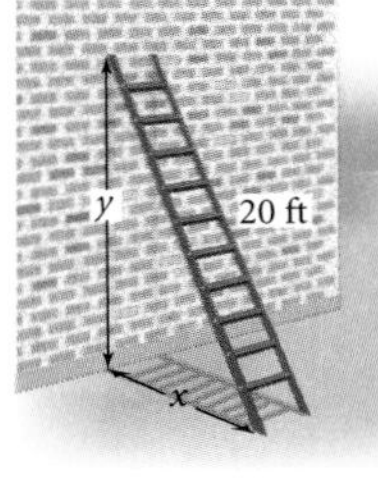

a. Write an equation for *y* in terms of *x*. $y = \sqrt{400 - x^2}$

b. Find the height the ladder reaches on the building if the foot of the ladder is 10 ft from the building. approximately 17.32 ft

c. Find the distance of the foot of the ladder from the building if the ladder must reach 18 ft up the wall. approximately 8.72 ft

17. **APPLICATION** The main cables of a suspension bridge typically hang in the shape of parallel parabolas on both sides of the roadway. The vertical support cables, labeled *a–k*, are equally spaced, and the center of the parabolic cable touches the roadway at *f*. If this bridge has a span of 160 ft between towers, and the towers reach a height of 75 ft above the road, what is the length of each support cable, *a–k*? What is the total length of vertical support cable needed for the portion of the bridge between the two towers?

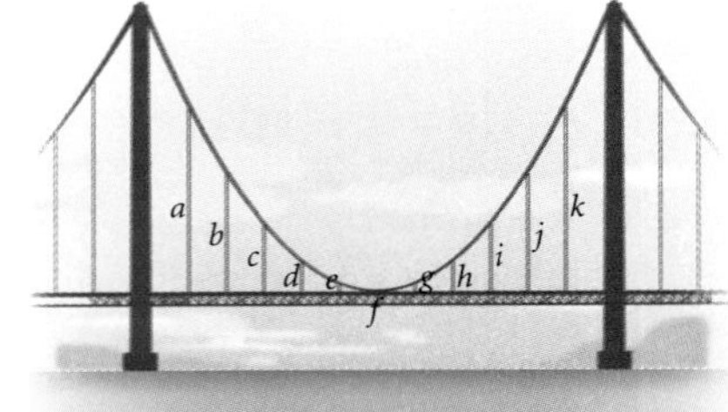

Engineering CONNECTION

The roadway of a suspension bridge is suspended, or hangs, from large steel support cables. By itself, a cable hangs in the shape of a *catenary* curve. However, with the weight of a roadway attached, the curvature changes, and the cable hangs in a parabolic curve. It is important for engineers to ensure that cables are the correct lengths to make a level roadway.

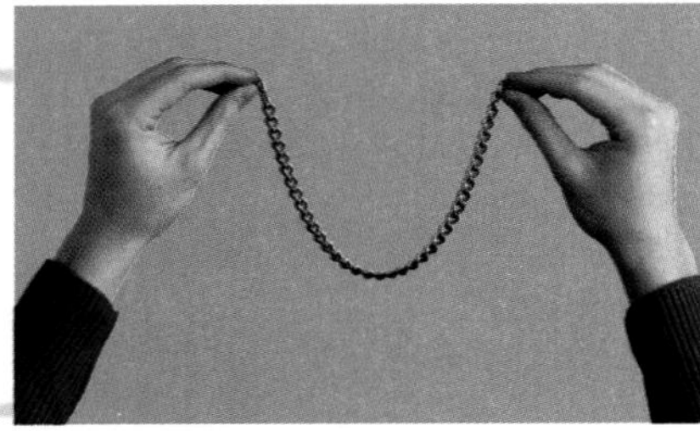

A chain hangs in the shape of a catenary curve.

Project

CALCULATOR PROGRAM FOR THE QUADRATIC FORMULA

Write a calculator program that uses the quadratic formula to solve equations. The program should prompt the user to input values for *a*, *b*, and *c* for a quadratic equation in the form $ax^2 + bx + c = 0$, and it should calculate and display the two solutions. Your program may be quite elaborate or very simple.

Your project should include

- A written record of the steps your program uses.
- An explanation of how the program works.
- The results of solving at least two equations by hand and with your program to verify that your program works.

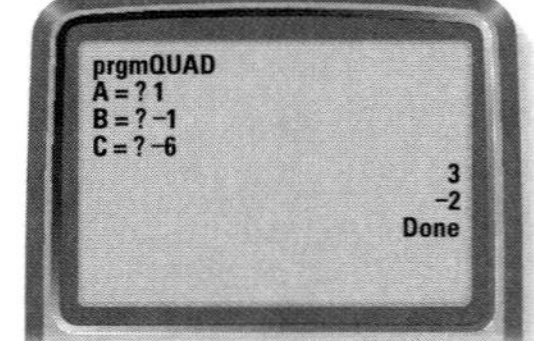

Supporting the Project

If you don't want to challenge students to devise their own programs, you can give them Calculator Note 7D, which contains a sample program.

OUTCOMES

- The report includes a simple program that gives the solutions as decimal approximations.
- Documentation is provided to confirm that the program works.
- The student has created a program that can give solutions as exact values in the form of reduced radical expressions.
- The student has created a program that checks the discriminant to tell the user when the number of roots is 0, 1, or 2.

LESSON

7.5

Complex Numbers

Things don't turn up in the world until somebody turns them up.

JAMES A. GARFIELD

You have explored several ways to solve quadratic equations. You can find the x-intercepts on a graph, you can solve by completing the square, or you can use the quadratic formula. What happens if you try to use the quadratic formula on an equation whose graph has no x-intercepts?

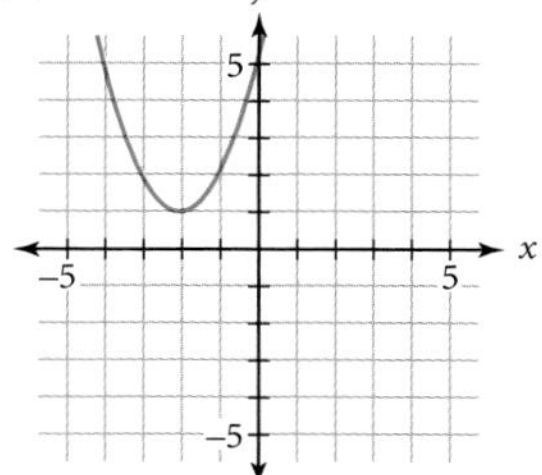

The graph of $y = x^2 + 4x + 5$ at right shows that this function has no x-intercepts. Using the quadratic formula to try to find x-intercepts, you get

$$x = \frac{-4 \pm \sqrt{16 - 4(1)(5)}}{2(1)} = \frac{-4 \pm \sqrt{-4}}{2}$$

How do you take the square root of a negative number? The two numbers $\frac{-4 + \sqrt{-4}}{2}$ and $\frac{-4 - \sqrt{-4}}{2}$ are unlike any of the numbers you have worked with this year—they are nonreal, but they are still numbers. In the development of mathematics, new sets of numbers have been defined in order to solve problems. Mathematicians have defined fractions and not just whole numbers, negative numbers and not just positive numbers, irrational numbers and not just fractions. For the same reasons, we also have square roots of negative numbers, not just square roots of positive numbers. Numbers that include the real numbers as well as the square roots of negative numbers are called **complex numbers.**

History CONNECTION

Since the 1500s, the square root of a negative number has been called an **imaginary number.** In the late 1700s, the Swiss mathematician Leonhard Euler (1707–1783) introduced the symbol i to represent $\sqrt{-1}$. He wrote:

> It is evident that we cannot rank the square root of a negative number amongst possible numbers, and we must therefore say that it is an impossible quantity. . . . But notwithstanding this these numbers present themselves to the mind; they exist in our imagination, and we still have a sufficient idea of them; since we know that by $\sqrt{-4}$ is meant a number which, multiplied by itself, produces -4; for this reason also, nothing prevents us from making use of these imaginary numbers, and employing them in calculation.

Leonhard Euler

Defining imaginary numbers made it possible to solve previously unsolvable problems.

To express the square root of a negative number, we use an **imaginary unit** called ***i***, defined by $i^2 = -1$ or $i = \sqrt{-1}$. You can rewrite $\sqrt{-4}$ as $\sqrt{4} \cdot \sqrt{-1}$, or $2i$. Therefore, you can write the two solutions to the quadratic equation above as the complex numbers $\frac{-4 + 2i}{2}$ and $\frac{-4 - 2i}{2}$, or $-2 + i$ and $-2 - i$. These two solutions are a **conjugate pair.** That is, one is $a + bi$ and the other is $a - bi$. The two numbers in a complex pair are **complex conjugates.** Why will nonreal solutions to the quadratic formula always give answers that are a conjugate pair?

NCTM STANDARDS

CONTENT		PROCESS	
✓	Number		Problem Solving
✓	Algebra	✓	Reasoning
	Geometry	✓	Communication
	Measurement	✓	Connections
	Data/Probability	✓	Representation

LESSON OBJECTIVES

- Define complex numbers as numbers of the form $a + bi$, where $i^2 = -1$
- Identify and find the conjugate of a complex number
- Find nonreal solutions as conjugate pairs
- Explore arithmetic computations with complex numbers
- Introduce a complex plane with a real axis and an imaginary axis

LESSON 7.5

PLANNING

LESSON OUTLINE

One day:

15 min	Example
15 min	Investigation
5 min	Sharing
10 min	Exercises

MATERIALS

- Quadratic List (T) for One Step
- Number System Venn Diagram (T), *optional*
- Calculator Notes 7E, 7F (for project)

TEACHING

This lesson introduces imaginary and complex numbers arising out of quadratic equations.

One Step

Have students change the mode on their calculators from Real to Complex or $a + bi$. Then show the Quadratic List transparency. Ask students to graph each function and then find decimal approximations to its zeros on their calculators. As they begin finding results that involve i, challenge them to figure out what i means. You might say it's a number and ask that they find its properties. During Sharing, introduce the terms *imaginary number, complex number,* and *conjugate pair,* and have the class develop rules for operating on complex numbers, following the rules for binomials.

INTRODUCTION

[Language] An *imaginary number* has only an imaginary component and can be written in the form bi. A *complex number* might have a real part, an imaginary part, or both and can be written

Roots of polynomial equations can be real numbers or nonreal complex numbers, or there may be some of each. If the polynomial has real coefficients, any nonreal roots will come in conjugate pairs such as $2i$ and $-2i$ or $3 + 4i$ and $3 - 4i$.

> **Complex Numbers**
>
> A **complex number** is a number in the form $a + bi$, where a and b are real numbers and $i = \sqrt{-1}$.

For any complex number in the form $a + bi$, a is the real part and b is the imaginary part. The set of complex numbers contains all real numbers and all imaginary numbers. This diagram shows the relationship between these numbers and some other sets you may be familiar with, as well as examples of numbers within each set.

- Complex numbers: $3 + 4i, 2i, \frac{5}{4}, -3 - i\sqrt{2}$
  - Real numbers: $\frac{5}{4}, \sqrt{3}, -15, 2 + \sqrt{7}$
    - Rational numbers: $\frac{5}{4}, -15, \frac{6}{11}, 1.2$
      - Integers: $\ldots, -1, 0, 1, \ldots$
        - Natural numbers: $1, 2, 3, 4, \ldots$
    - Irrational numbers: $\sqrt{3}, 2 + \sqrt{7}, e, \pi$
  - Imaginary numbers: $2i, -i, i\sqrt{2}, \frac{1}{5}i$

EXAMPLE Solve $x^2 + 3 = 0$.

▶ ***Solution*** You can use the quadratic formula, or you can isolate x^2 and take the square root of both sides.

$$x^2 + 3 = 0$$
$$x^2 = -3$$
$$x = \pm\sqrt{-3}$$
$$x = \pm\sqrt{3} \cdot \sqrt{-1}$$
$$x = \pm\sqrt{3} \cdot i$$
$$x = \pm i\sqrt{3}$$

To check the two solutions, substitute them into the original equation.

$x^2 + 3 = 0$	$x^2 + 3 = 0$
$(i\sqrt{3})^2 + 3 \stackrel{?}{=} 0$	$(-i\sqrt{3})^2 + 3 \stackrel{?}{=} 0$
$i^2 \cdot 3 + 3 \stackrel{?}{=} 0$	$i^2 \cdot 3 + 3 \stackrel{?}{=} 0$
$-1 \cdot 3 + 3 \stackrel{?}{=} 0$	$-1 \cdot 3 + 3 \stackrel{?}{=} 0$
$-3 + 3 \stackrel{?}{=} 0$	$-3 + 3 \stackrel{?}{=} 0$
$0 = 0$	$0 = 0$

The two imaginary numbers $\pm i\sqrt{3}$ are solutions to the original equation, but because they are not real, the graph of $y = x^2 + 3$ shows no x-intercepts.

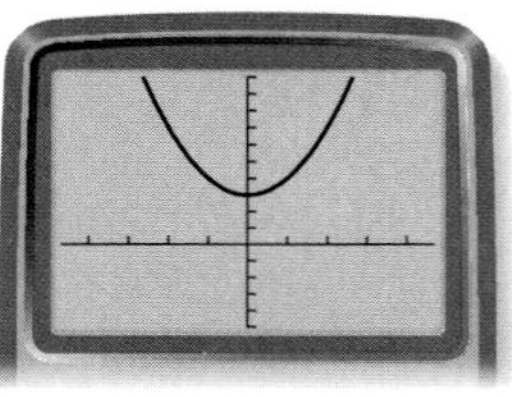

$[-4.7, 4.7, 1, -5, 10, 1]$

Introduction (continued)
in the form $a + bi$. The set of complex numbers therefore contains the disjoint subsets of real numbers (when $b = 0$) and imaginary numbers (when $a = 0$), as well as numbers that are neither. You might want to use the Number System Venn Diagram transparency to review all the subsets of the complex numbers.

[Alert] The word *complex* is often used to mean "nonreal complex." For example, students might say "The equation has two complex roots," meaning nonreal roots. Saying that a number is complex does not rule out the possibility that it is real.

[Context] Complex numbers arose historically through derivation of a formula for solving cubic equations, analogous to the quadratic formula.

▶ ***EXAMPLE***

For practice in using zero coefficients, you might ask students to solve this equation using the quadratic formula.

The rule $\sqrt{ab} = \sqrt{a} \cdot \sqrt{b}$ applies when both a and b are nonnegative or when one is negative and the other is nonnegative.

Numbers such as $\sqrt{-3}$ are usually rewritten as $i\sqrt{3}$ before performing any computations. Avoid writing $\sqrt{3}i$, because it's difficult to tell whether i is or isn't under the radical.

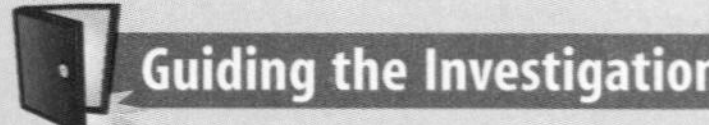

Guiding the Investigation

You might have students first make a conjecture about each computation and then check it on a calculator. Part 4 is the most difficult part of the investigation. See page 394 for ideas on guiding students.

SHARING IDEAS

As students present their ideas, ask whether they find it easier to simplify complex expressions with the calculator or without it. Once they see the patterns, many students won't use the calculator functions again.

Remind students that complex solutions to a quadratic equation form a conjugate pair. **[Ask]** "Are the solutions in the example a conjugate pair?" Students may have difficulty verifying that they are because $a = 0$.

[Ask] "Does the definition $i = \sqrt{-1}$ mean that i is a positive number, since the square root sign indicates positives?" [The square root symbol is being extended to negative radicands, so there's no guarantee that the result is positive; in fact, imaginary numbers are neither positive nor negative, because they can't be represented on the number line. In a complex plane, i is represented by a positive vertical coordinate.]

[Context] Tell students that for hundreds of years mathematicians were uncomfortable with the idea of square roots of negative numbers and that that's why they're called *imaginary*. Ask students whether

Complex numbers are used to model many applications, particularly in science and engineering. To measure the strength of an electromagnetic field, a real number represents the amount of electricity, and an imaginary number represents the amount of magnetism. The state of a component in an electronic circuit is also measured by a complex number, where the voltage is a real number and the current is an imaginary number. The properties of calculations with complex numbers apply to these types of physical states more accurately than calculations with real numbers do. In the investigation you'll explore patterns in arithmetic with complex numbers.

The Heart Revealed: Portrait of Tita Thirifays (1936), by Belgian Surrealist painter Rene Magritte (1898–1967), is a portrait with an imaginary element.

Investigation
Complex Arithmetic

When computing with complex numbers, there are conventional rules similar to those you use when working with real numbers. In this investigation you will discover these rules. You may use your calculator to check your work or to explore other examples. [▶ See **Calculator Note 7E** to learn how to enter complex numbers into your calculator. ◀]

Part 1: Addition and Subtraction

Addition and subtraction of complex numbers is similar to combining like terms. Use your calculator to add these complex numbers. Make a conjecture about how to add complex numbers without a calculator.

Part 1 Conjecture: You add the real parts, and you add the imaginary parts.

a. $(2 - 4i) + (3 + 5i)$ $5 + i$

b. $(7 + 2i) + (-2 + i)$ $5 + 3i$

c. $(2 - 4i) - (3 + 5i)$ $-1 - 9i$

d. $(4 - 4i) - (1 - 3i)$ $3 - i$

Part 2: Multiplication

Use your knowledge of multiplying binomials to multiply these complex numbers. Express your products in the form $a + bi$. Recall that $i^2 = -1$.

a. $(2 - 4i)(3 + 5i)$ $26 - 2i$

b. $(7 + 2i)(-2 + i)$ $-16 + 3i$

c. $(2 - 4i)^2$ $-12 - 16i$

d. $(4 - 4i)(1 - 3i)$ $-8 - 16i$

Part 3: The Complex Conjugates

Recall that every complex number $a + bi$ has a complex conjugate, $a - bi$. Complex conjugates have some special properties and uses.

Sharing Ideas (continued)

they are also uncomfortable with them. Students may be very surprised that these numbers are taken seriously in mathematics and science, especially if they have heard from previous teachers that they "can't take the square root of a negative."

[Ask] "Can you determine the conjugate-pair zeros of a quadratic function from its graph?" [If a parabola opens upward with vertex (a, b) above the x-axis, so that it has no x-intercepts, then its equation has the form $y = k(x - a)^2 + b$, where k is a positive vertical scale factor. Then the zeros of the quadratic function are $a \pm \sqrt{-\frac{b}{k}}$. Because $b > 0$, $\sqrt{-\frac{b}{k}}$ is imaginary, showing the complex conjugate zeros. A similar situation occurs if the parabola is opening downward and has vertex below the x-axis, in which case $b < 0$ and $k < 0$.] As needed, remind students that zeros come in conjugate pairs only if the coefficients of the polynomial are real numbers.

Although complex numbers don't fit into the real number line, they can be represented on a plane, as described at the end of the lesson. If you have time, you can ask students to experiment to find geometric rules for addition and multiplication of points on a complex plane. They may find a rule for addition fairly easily—it's the same as vector addition. The rule for multiplication is more difficult to see: The angle of the product with the real axis is the sum of the angles of the two numbers being multiplied, and the distance of the product from the origin is the product of the distances of these two numbers. Once they've found this result, wonder aloud whether it is consistent with what they know about the product of conjugate pairs.

Assessing Progress

The work in this lesson is especially good for checking students' ability to multiply binomials.

Guiding the Investigation (continued)
Part 4 [Alert] This is the most difficult part of the investigation. For struggling students, wonder aloud how to get a real number from a complex number, perhaps by multiplying. Then question whether you can multiply the denominator of a fraction by something without changing the value of the fraction. Your goal for Part 4a, for example, is to have students multiply the fraction by $\frac{1+i}{1+i}$. The resulting denominator is $1 - i^2 = 2$.

Closing the Lesson

Review the main points: **Imaginary numbers** have the form bi, where b is real and $i^2 = -1$. **Complex numbers** consist of the real numbers, the imaginary numbers, and their sums. Imaginary numbers cannot be represented on a line with real numbers, but they can be pictured on a plane. If a complex number is a solution to a quadratic equation (with real coefficients), then its conjugate is also a solution to that equation.

BUILDING UNDERSTANDING

Students can decide for themselves whether or not to use calculators for these exercises.

ASSIGNING HOMEWORK

Essential	1–5, 9
Performance assessment	6–8, 10, 11
Portfolio	14
Journal	8, 13, 15
Group	12, 14
Review	16, 17

Helping with the Exercises

1a. $8 + 4i$

Exercise 2 Ask students to report their answers in the form $a + bi$.

Part 3 Multiplying or adding a complex number and its conjugate results in a real number.

Each expression below shows either the sum or product of a complex number and its conjugate. Simplify these expressions into the form $a + bi$, and generalize what happens.

a. $(2 - 4i) + (2 + 4i)$ 4 **b.** $(7 + 2i) + (7 - 2i)$ 14

c. $(2 - 4i)(2 + 4i)$ 20 **d.** $(-4 + 4i)(-4 - 4i)$ 32

Part 4: Division

To divide two complex numbers in the form $a + bi$, you need to eliminate the imaginary part of the denominator. First, use your work from Part 3 to decide how to change each denominator into a real number. Once you have a real number in the denominator, divide to get an answer in the form $a + bi$.

a. $\frac{7+2i}{1-i}$ **b.** $\frac{2-5i}{3+4i}$ **c.** $\frac{2-i}{8-6i}$ **d.** $\frac{2-4i}{2+4i}$

Part 4a $2.5 + 4.5i$
Part 4b $-0.56 - 0.92i$
Part 4c $0.22 - 0.04i$
Part 4d $-0.6 - 0.8i$

You cannot graph a complex number, such as $3 + 4i$, on a real number line, but you can graph it on a **complex plane,** where the horizontal axis is the **real axis** and the vertical axis is the **imaginary axis.** In the graph at right, $3 + 4i$ is located at the point with coordinates (3, 4). Any complex number $a + bi$ has (a, b) as its coordinates on a complex plane.

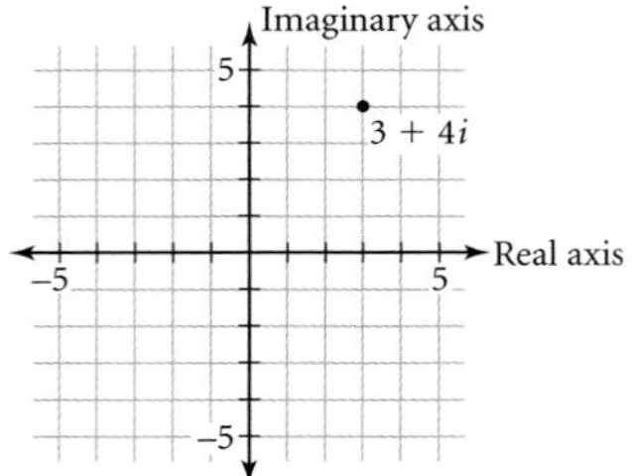

You'll observe some properties of a complex plane in the exercises.

EXERCISES

Practice Your Skills

1. Add or subtract.

a. $(5 - 1i) + (3 + 5i)$ **b.** $(6 + 2i) - (-1 + 2i)$ 7

c. $(2 + 3i) + (2 - 5i)$ $4 - 2i$ **d.** $(2.35 + 2.71i) - (4.91 + 3.32i)$ $-2.56 - 0.61i$

2. Multiply.

a. $(5 - 1i)(3 + 5i)$ $20 + 22i$ **b.** $6(-1 + 2i)$ $-6 + 12i$

c. $3i(2 - 5i)$ $15 + 6i$ **d.** $(2.35 + 2.71i)(4.91 + 3.32i)$ $2.5413 + 21.1081i$

3. Find the conjugate of each complex number.

a. $5 - i$ $5 + i$ **b.** $-1 + 2i$ $-1 - 2i$

c. $2 + 3i$ $2 - 3i$ **d.** $-2.35 - 2.71i$ $-2.35 + 2.71i$

4. Name the complex number associated with each point, A through G, on the complex plane at right.

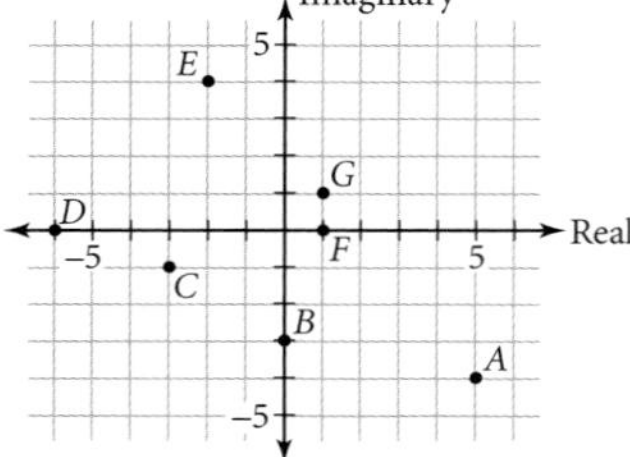

4. A: $5 - 4i$; B: $-3i$; C: $-3 - i$; D: -6; E: $-2 + 4i$; F: 1; G: $1 + i$

5. Draw **Venn diagrams** to show the relationships between these sets of numbers.
   a. real numbers and complex numbers
   b. rational numbers and irrational numbers
   c. imaginary numbers and complex numbers
   d. imaginary numbers and real numbers
   e. complex numbers, real numbers, and imaginary numbers

History CONNECTION

In his book *Symbolic Logic,* English logician John Venn (1834–1923) proposed using diagrams as a method of representing logic relationships. For example, this diagram shows "if it's an eagle, then it's a bird," and "if it's a bird, then it's not a whale." It must also be true, therefore, that "if it's an eagle, then it's not a whale." A Venn diagram of this situation shows this conclusion clearly. Venn diagrams have become a tool for representing many kinds of relationships.

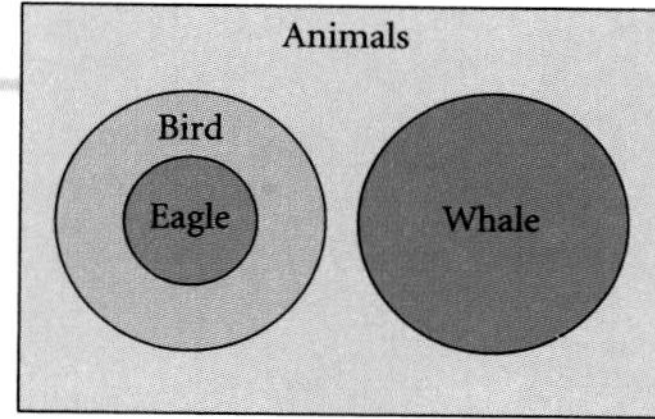

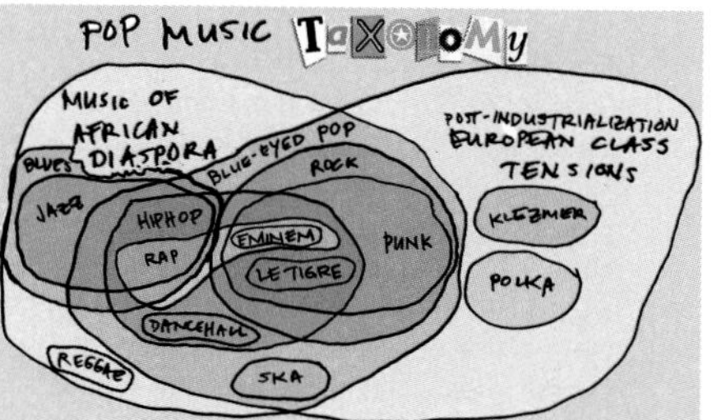

This Venn diagram by Jason Luz shows a taxonomy of music. Do you think speed metal should be included? The Beatles? Madonna? Make your own Venn diagram.

Reason and Apply

6. Rewrite this quadratic equation in general form.
   $(x - (2 + i))(x - (2 - i)) = 0$ $x^2 - 4x + 5 = 0$

7. Use the definitions $i = \sqrt{-1}$ and $i^2 = -1$ to rewrite each power of i as 1, i, -1, or $-i$.
   a. i^3 $-i$
   b. i^4 1
   c. i^5 i
   d. i^{10} -1

8. ***Mini-Investigation*** Plot the numbers i, i^2, i^3, i^4, i^5, i^6, i^7, and i^8 on a complex plane. What pattern do you see? What do you expect the value of i^{17} to be? Verify your conjecture.

9. Rewrite the quotient $\frac{2+3i}{2-i}$ in the form $a + bi$. $0.2 + 1.6i$

10. Solve each equation. Label each solution as real, imaginary, and/or complex.
   a. $x^2 - 4x + 6 = 0$ $2 \pm i\sqrt{2}$; complex
   b. $x^2 + 1 = 0$ $\pm i$; complex and imaginary
   c. $x^2 + x = -1$ $-\frac{1}{2} \pm i\frac{\sqrt{3}}{2}$; complex
   d. $x^2 - 1 = 0$ ± 1; complex and real

11. Write a quadratic function in general form that has the given zeros, and leading coefficient of 1.
   a. $x = -3$ and $x = 5$ $y = x^2 - 2x - 15$
   b. $x = -3.5$ (double root) $y = x^2 + 7x + 12.25$
   c. $x = 5i$ and $x = -5i$ $y = x^2 + 25$
   d. $x = 2 + i$ and $x = 2 - i$ $y = x^2 - 4x + 5$

12. Write a quadratic function in general form that has a zero of $x = 4 + 3i$ and whose graph has y-intercept 50. $y = 2x^2 - 16x + 50$

13. Solve.
   a. $x^2 - 10ix - 9i^2 = 0$
   b. $x^2 - 3ix = 2$ $x = 2i$ or $x = i$
   c. Why don't the solutions to 13a and 13b come in conjugate pairs?
   The coefficients of the quadratic equations are nonreal.

Exercise 11 As needed, ask what form of the quadratic function might be useful if you know the zeros. (You may need to review *zeros.*) Then ask how to get from factored form to general form.

Exercise 12 This exercise might be challenging. You might suggest that students first write the quadratic equation in root form with both roots (the given root and its complex conjugate). Once students have simplified the equation to $y = a(x^2 - 8x + 25)$, they can solve for a using the point (0, 50).

Exercise 13 This exercise assumes that the quadratic formula extends to complex coefficients; it does. **[Ask]** "Can you say anything about graphs of complex functions?" [The graph of a complex function in two variables is four-dimensional. These imaginary parabolas can be thought of as resulting from transformations of the plane.]

13a. $x = (5 + \sqrt{34})i \approx 10.83i$ or $x = (5 - \sqrt{34})i \approx -0.83i$

Exercise 5 You might want to review the properties of Venn diagrams before assigning this exercise.

[Language] *Taxonomy* means "an orderly classification."

5a.

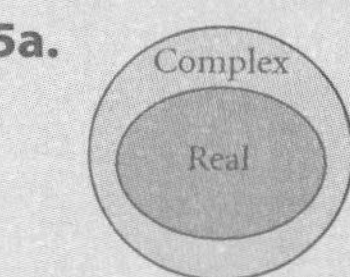

5b.

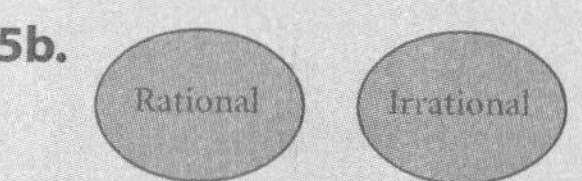

5e.

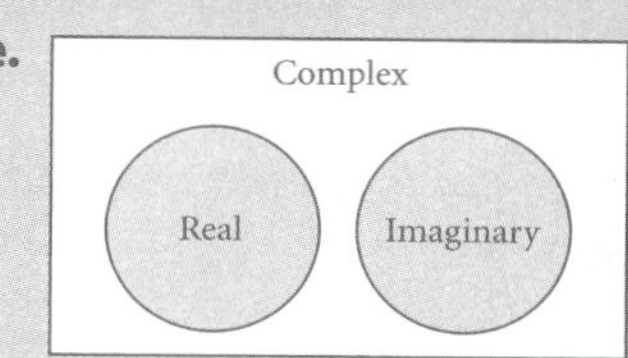

Exercise 7 [Ask] "In general, how can you find another name for i^n?" [You can simplify any power of i, i^n, by dividing n by 4. If the remainder is 1, $i^n = i$; if the remainder is 2, $i^n = -1$; if the remainder is 3, $i^n = -i$; if the remainder is 0, $i^n = 1$.

If students aren't going to work on Exercise 8, you might show the circle of i. To simplify any power of i, you start at i^1 and count around the circle; for example, for i^{10} count ten places: $i, -1, -i, +1, i, -1, -i, +1, i, -1$.

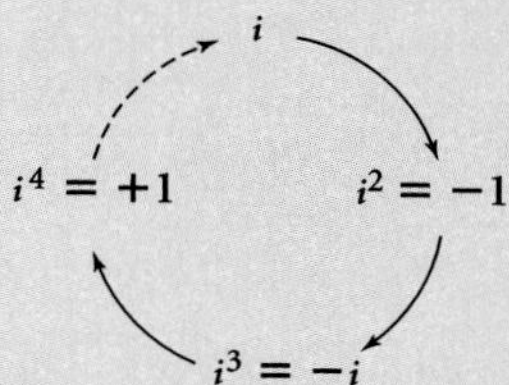

Exercise 8 [Ask] "What would i^0, i^{-1}, and i^{-2} equal?"[1; $\frac{1}{i} \cdot \frac{i}{i} = \frac{i}{-1} = -i$; -1]

Exercise 9 Assign this problem only if students did the investigation.

Exercise 10a An approximate form of this answer is $2 \pm 1.14i$.

See page 889 for answers to Exercises 5c and d and 8.

Exercise 14 [Language] You might tell or remind students that $b^2 - 4ac$ is called the *discriminant*.

Exercise 15 If a calculator is in Complex mode, it can do home-screen recursion with these complex numbers. The mathematical convention is to use z for complex numbers. Each part in this exercise shows an equation that is used in fractal geometry. 15a and 15d are recursive functions that are "tending to fixed points"; 15b is "tending to a 2-cycle"; 15c is "tending to infinity" or "escaping." An escaping long-run value can be said to increase in magnitude, where the magnitude of the complex number is its distance from the origin on the complex plane. (By the Pythagorean Theorem, the magnitude of $z = a + bi$ is $\sqrt{a^2 + b^2}$.)

15a. 0, 0, 0, 0, 0, 0; remains constant at 0

15b. $0, i, -1 + i, -i, -1 + i, -i$; alternates between $-1 + i$ and $-i$

15c. $0, 1 - i, 1 - 3i, -7 - 7i, 1 + 97i, -9407 + 193i$; no recognizable pattern in these six terms

15d. $0, 0.2 + 0.2i, 0.2 + 0.28i, 0.1616 + 0.312i, 0.12877056 + 0.3008384i, 0.1260781142 + 0.2774782585i$; approaches $0.142120634 + 0.2794237653i$

16a. $x = \dfrac{-3 \pm \sqrt{15}}{2}$; $x = -3.44$ or $x = 0.44$

16b.

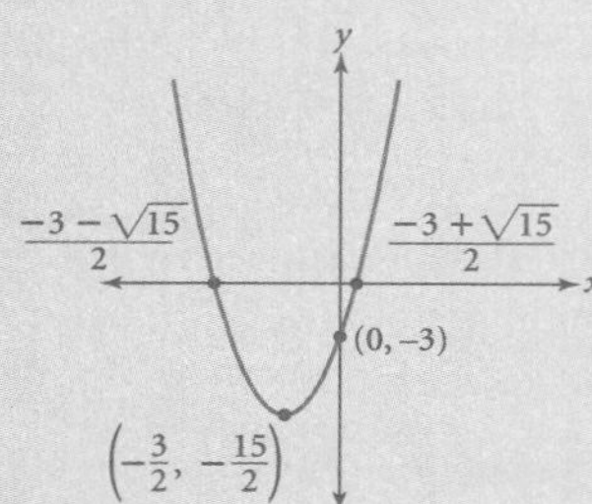

14. The quadratic formula, $x = \frac{-b \pm \sqrt{b^2 - 4ac}}{2a}$, provides solutions to $ax^2 + bx + c = 0$. Make up some rules involving a, b, and c that determine each of these conditions.

a. The solutions are nonreal. $b^2 - 4ac < 0$

b. The solutions are real. $b^2 - 4ac \geq 0$

c. There is only one real solution. $b^2 - 4ac = 0$

15. Use these recursive formulas to find the first six terms $(z_0$ to $z_5)$ of each sequence. Describe what happens in the long run for each sequence.

a. $z_0 = 0$
$z_n = z_{n-1}^{\ 2} + 0$ where $n \geq 1$

b. $z_0 = 0$
$z_n = z_{n-1}^{\ 2} + i$ where $n \geq 1$

c. $z_0 = 0$
$z_n = z_{n-1}^{\ 2} + 1 - i$ where $n \geq 1$

d. $z_0 = 0$
$z_n = z_{n-1}^{\ 2} + 0.2 + 0.2i$ where $n \geq 1$

Mathematics CONNECTION

Fractals can appear quite complicated, yet they are generated by simple rules. Complex numbers c which converge according to the recursive formula $z_0 = 0$ and $z_n = z_{n-1}^{\ 2} + c$, where $n \geq 1$, are members of the Mandelbrot set. In the picture of the Mandelbrot set on the opposite page, these convergent points are plotted as black points in a complex plane. Polish mathematician Benoit Mandelbrot (b 1924) noted that fractals aren't just a mathematical curiosity but, rather, the geometry of nature. Clouds, coastlines, and trees can be described using fractal geometry. Fractals are used in medicine to study the growth of cancer tissue, in art to date early paintings, and in computer programming to compress large sets of data.

American abstract painter Jackson Pollock (1912–1956) created pieces such as *Number 31* (1950) using oil and enamel paints on unprimed canvas. Physicist and abstract artist Richard P. Taylor recently discovered, with the aid of a computer, that Pollock's paintings display the fractal characteristic of self-similarity.

Review

7.4 **16.** Consider the function $y = 2x^2 + 6x - 3$.

a. List the zeros in exact radical form and as approximations to the nearest hundredth.

b. Graph the function and label the exact coordinates of the vertex and points where the graph crosses the x-axis and the y-axis.

6.5 **17.** Consider two positive integers that meet these conditions:

- three times the first added to four times the second is less than 30
- twice the first is less than five more than the second

a. Define variables and write a system of linear inequalities that represents this situation.

b. Graph the feasible region.

c. List all integer pairs that satisfy the conditions listed above.

17a. Let x represent the first integer, and let y represent the second integer.

$$\begin{cases} x > 0 \\ y > 0 \\ 3x + 4y < 30 \\ 2x < y + 5 \end{cases}$$

17b.

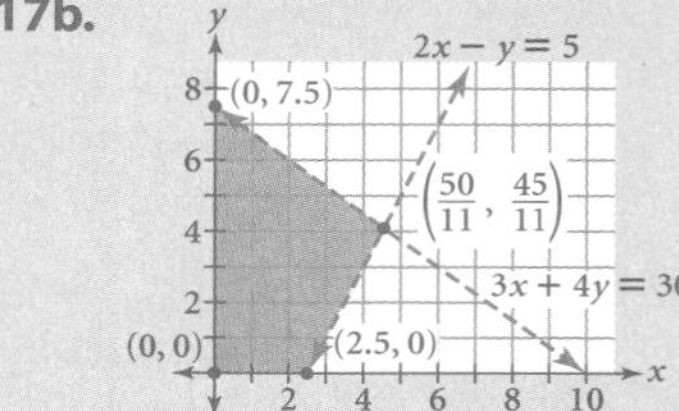

17c. (1, 1), (2, 1), (1, 2), (2, 2), (3, 2), (1, 3), (2, 3), (3, 3), (1, 4), (2, 4), (3, 4), (4, 4), (1, 5), (2, 5), (3, 5), (1, 6)

Project

THE MANDELBROT SET

You have seen geometric **fractals** such as the Sierpiński triangle, and you may have seen other fractals that look much more complicated. The Mandelbrot set is a famous fractal that relies on repeated calculations with complex numbers. To create the Mandelbrot set, you use the recursive formula $z_0 = 0$ and $z_n = z_{n-1}^2 + c$ where $n \geq 1$. Depending on the complex number you choose for the constant, c, one of two things will happen: either the magnitude of the values of z will get increasingly large, or they will not. (The magnitude of a complex number is defined as its distance from the origin of the complex plane, or $\sqrt{a^2 + b^2}$.) You already explored a few values of c in Exercise 15. Try a few more. Which values of c make the magnitude of z get increasingly large? Which values of c make z converge to a single value or alternate between values?

This Mandelbrot set shows how fractal geometry creates order out of what seem like irregular patterns. Points that are not in the Mandelbrot set are colored based on how quickly they diverge. Benoit Mandelbrot (b 1924), left, was the first person to study and name fractal geometry.

Use your calculator to determine what happens if $z_0 = 0$ and $c = 0.25$. What happens if c or z is a complex number, for example, if $z_0 = 0$ and $c = -0.4 + 0.5i$?

The Mandelbrot set is all of the values of c that do not make the magnitude of z get increasingly large. If you plot these points on a complex plane, then you'll get a pattern that looks like this one. Your project is to choose a small region on the boundary of the black area of this graph and create a graph of that smaller region. [▶ **Calculator Note 7F** includes a program that analyzes every point in the window to determine whether it is in the Mandelbrot set. ◀] Look at this graph, select a window, and then run the program. It may take several hours.

Your project should include

- A sketch of your graph.
- A report that describes any similarities between your portion of the Mandelbrot set and the complete graph shown above.
- Any additional research you do on the Mandelbrot set, or fractals in general.

You can learn more about the Mandelbrot set and other fractals by using the links at www.keymath.com/DAA .

EXTENSIONS

A. Use Take Another Look activities 3 and 4 on page 422.

B. If students wrote a program for the Project Calculator Program for the Quadratic Formula in Lesson 7.4, ask them to revise the program to show complex roots.

C. Ask students to find an application of complex numbers in the real world.

D. Refer students interested in the Mandelbrot set to *The Mandelbrot and Julia Sets* by Robert Devaney.

Supporting the Project

The color of a point is determined by how fast the value at that point gets very large (that is, the number of iterations it takes for the value to *escape*). The black points, which don't escape but have a numerical long-term value, are in the Mandelbrot set. Note that running the calculator program may take several hours.

OUTCOMES

- The report includes a sketch of one graph created by the student and notes the window used. The window must be on the boundary between black and white of the original image.
- Similarities between the student's sketch and the original image are described in detail.
- The student "zooms in" more times and notes similarities in successive graphs.
- The report compares the Mandelbrot fractal to other fractals.
- The report includes further research on fractals.

LESSON

7.6

PLANNING

LESSON OUTLINE

One day:

20 min Investigation
10 min Sharing
5 min Example
10 min Exercises

MATERIALS

- scissors
- graph paper or 16-by-20 Grid Paper (W)
- tape, *optional*
- Equations and Parabolas (T), *optional*

TEACHING

This lesson concerns the relationship between the zeros and the factors of cubic functions.

One Step

Challenge groups to find as many different shapes as they can of cubic functions. (You may need to define cubic functions as 3rd-degree polynomial functions.) Geometry software is useful but not necessary. During Sharing, try to distill how the various coefficients affect the shapes, and see how the zeros relate to the x-intercepts.

INTRODUCTION

Take time to make sure students can visualize the expanded cube. **[Ask]** "Which boxes share a face with the cube?" [$2x^2$, $3x^2$, and $4x^2$, the 2nd-degree terms] "Which share an edge with the cube?" [$8x$, $6x$, and $12x$, the linear terms] "Which share only a vertex?" [24, which is 2(3)(4)]

[Alert] Some students will be confused by the changing role of a from constant to unknown variable and back again.

LESSON 7.6

Factoring Polynomials

Ideas are the factors that lift civilization.

JOHN H. VINCENT

Imagine a cube with any side length. Imagine increasing the height by 2 cm, the width by 3 cm, and the length by 4 cm.

Imagine a cube.

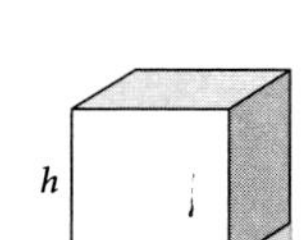

Increase its height 2 cm.

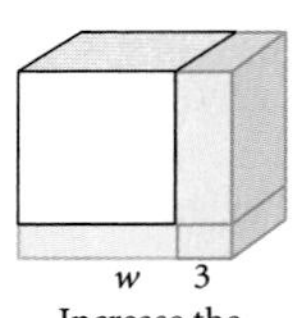

Increase the width 3 cm.

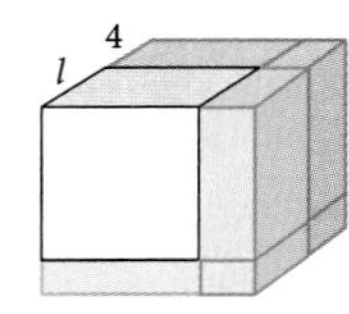

Increase the length 4 cm.

The starting figure is a cube, so you can let x be the length of each its sides. So, $l = w = h = x$. The volume of the starting figure is x^3. To find the volume of the expanded box, you can see it as the sum of the volumes of eight different boxes. You find the volume of each piece by multiplying length by width by height.

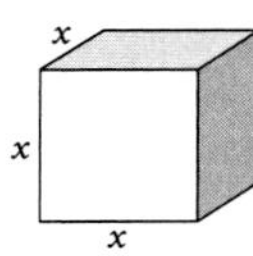

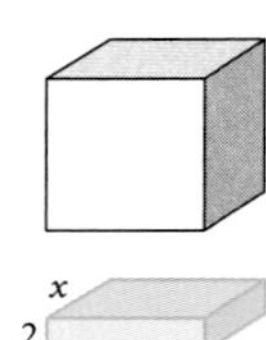

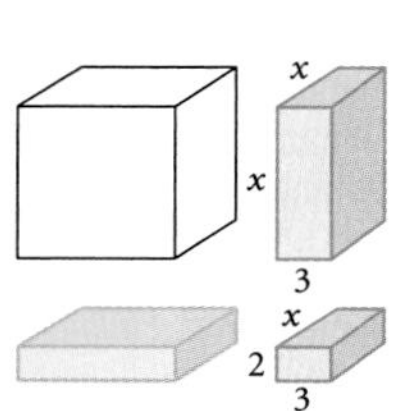

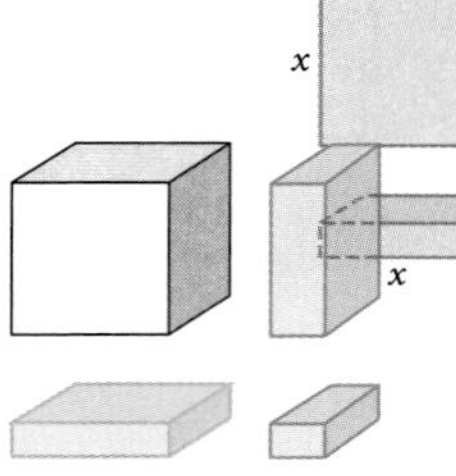

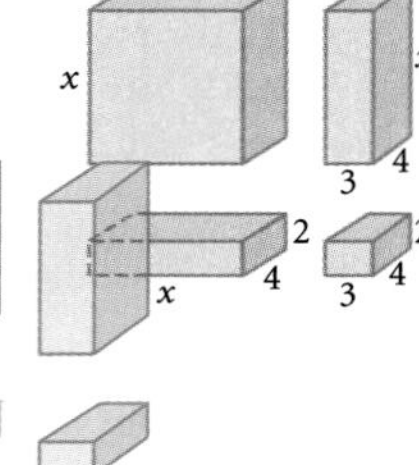

The total expanded volume is this sum:

$$V = x^3 + 2x^2 + 3x^2 + 6x + 4x^2 + 8x + 12x + 24 = x^3 + 9x^2 + 26x + 24$$

You can also think of the expanded volume as the product of the new height, width, and length.

$$V = (x + 2)(x + 3)(x + 4)$$

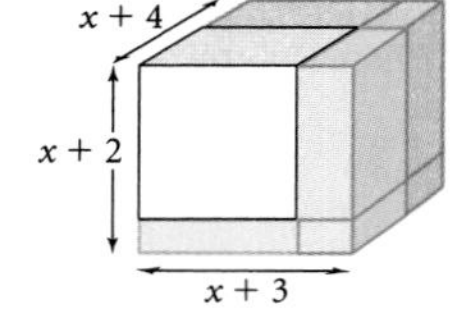

This function in factored form is equivalent to the polynomial function in general form. (Try graphing both functions on your calculator.)

You already know that there is a relationship between the factored form of a quadratic equation, and the roots and x-intercepts of that quadratic equation. In this lesson you will learn how to write higher-degree polynomial equations in factored form when you know the roots of the equation. You'll also discover useful techniques for converting a polynomial in general form to factored form.

LESSON OBJECTIVES

- Explore functions defined by 3rd-degree polynomials (cubic functions)
- Use graphs of polynomial equations to find the roots and write the equation in factored form
- Relate the graphs of polynomial equations to the number and types of roots

NCTM STANDARDS

CONTENT		PROCESS	
	Number	✓	Problem Solving
✓	Algebra	✓	Reasoning
✓	Geometry	✓	Communication
✓	Measurement		Connections
	Data/Probability	✓	Representation

A 3rd-degree polynomial function is called a **cubic function.** Let's examine the features of the graph of a cubic function. The graphs of the two cubic functions below have the same x-intercepts: -2.5, 3.2, and 7.5. So both functions have the factored form $y = a(x + 2.5)(x - 7.5)(x - 3.2)$, but the vertical scale factor, a, is different for each function.

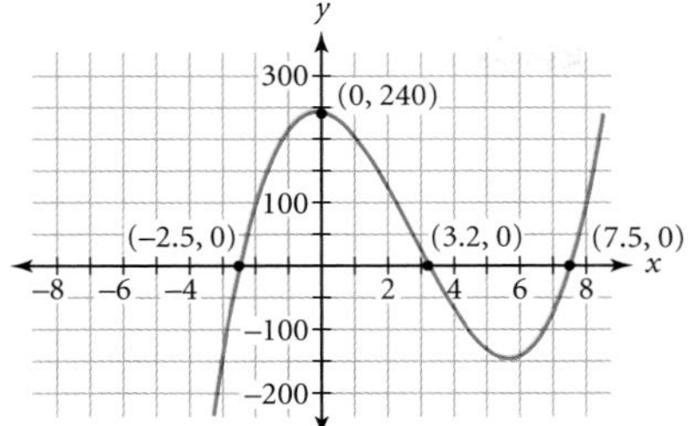

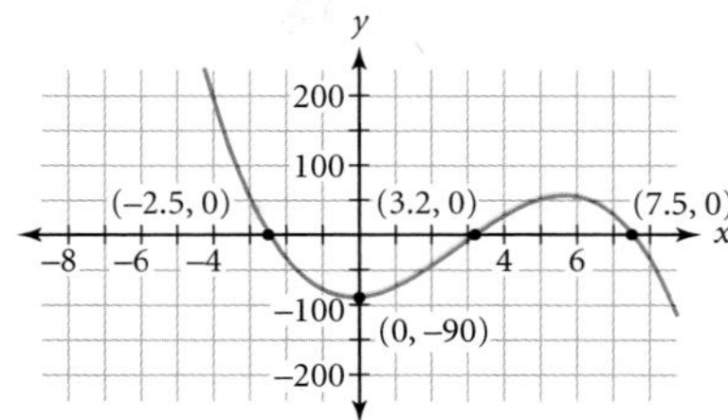

As you know by now, one way to find a is to substitute coordinates of one other point, such as the y-intercept, into the function.

The curve on the left has y-intercept $(0, 240)$. Substituting this point into the equation gives $240 = a(2.5)(-7.5)(-3.2)$. Solving for a, you get $a = 4$. So the equation of the cubic function on the left is

$$y = 4(x + 2.5)(x - 7.5)(x - 3.2)$$

The curve on the right has y-intercept $(0, -90)$. Substituting this point into the equation gives $-90 = a(2.5)(-7.5)(-3.2)$. So $a = -1.5$, and the equation of the cubic function on the right is

$$y = -1.5(x + 2.5)(x - 7.5)(x - 3.2)$$

The factored form of a polynomial function tells you the zeros of the function and the x-intercepts of the graph of the function. Recall that zeros are solutions to the equation $f(x) = 0$. Factoring, if a polynomial can be factored, is one strategy for finding the real solutions of a polynomial equation. You will practice writing a higher-degree polynomial function in factored form in the investigation.

English sculptor Cornelia Parker (b 1956) creates art from damaged objects that have cultural or historical meaning. *Mass (Colder Darker Matter)* (1997) is made of the charred remains of a building struck by lightning—the building has been reduced to its charcoal factors. The sculpture looks flat when viewed from the front, but it is actually constructed in the shape of a cube.

Cornelia Parker *Mass (Colder Darker Matter)* (1997) charcoal, wire, and black string, Collection of Phoenix Art Museum, Gift of Jan and Howard Hendler 2002.1.

[Context] Some astronomers theorize that 90% of the universe is made up of *cold dark matter,* which is matter that neither emits nor reflects light or radio signals. The existence of cold dark matter would explain anomalies in the motion of galaxies. Cold dark matter may consist of dust, planets, intergalactic gas, or black holes, but it can only be detected indirectly. In the title of this sculpture, Parker uses the idea of cold dark matter as a metaphor. Ask students what they think she might mean to convey.

Guiding the Investigation

Step 1 Students can use the 16-by-20 Grid Paper worksheet or any other graph paper. **[Ask]** "What is the domain of x?" [$0 < x < 8$; x need not be an integer.] In Step 7, students will rethink the domain of x.

Step 1 sample data:

x	Volume y
1	252
2	384
3	420
4	384
5	300
6	192

Step 2 If students are struggling, suggest that they sketch the original rectangle with the corners removed and try to match it up with the box.

Step 3

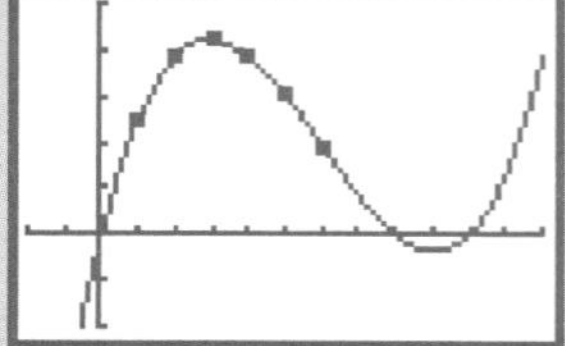

[−2, 12, 1, −200, 500, 100]

The points lie on the graph of the function.

Step 4 If students use the finite differences method, they will find a constant after three iterations.

Step 4 3rd degree. If the factors are multiplied, the highest-degree term is x^3. The shape is that of a cubic function.

Step 5 0, 8, 10; $y = (x - 0)(x - 8)(x - 10)$

Step 6 **[Ask]** "Why doesn't this graph fit your data points?" [The value of the leading coefficient, a, has been left out.]

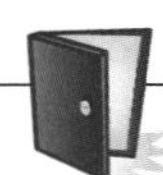

Investigation
The Box Factory

You will need
- graph paper
- scissors

What are the different ways to construct an open-top box from a 16-by-20–unit sheet of material? What is the maximum volume this box can have? What is the minimum volume? Your group will investigate this problem by constructing open-top boxes using several possible integer values for x.

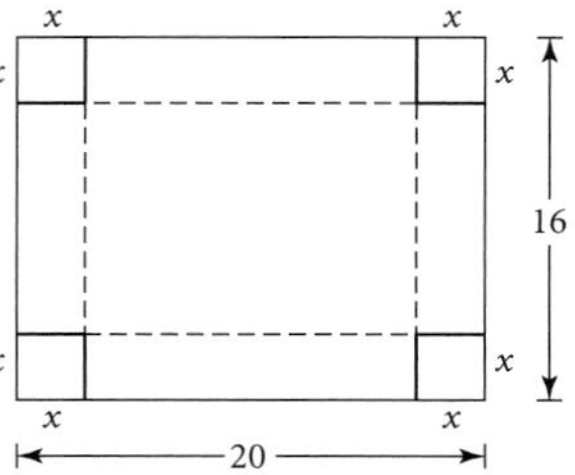

Procedure Note

1. Cut several 16-by-20–unit rectangles out of graph paper.
2. Choose several different values for x.
3. For each value of x, construct a box by cutting squares with side length x from each corner and folding up the sides.

Step 1 Follow the procedure note to construct several different-size boxes from 16-by-20–unit sheets of paper. Record the dimensions of each box and calculate its volume. Make a table to record the x-values and volumes of the boxes.

Step 2 For each box, what are the length, width, and height, in terms of x? Use these expressions to write a function that gives the volume of a box as a function of x.

Step 2 $16 - 2x$, $20 - 2x$, and x; $y = (16 - 2x)(20 - 2x)(x)$

Step 3 Graph your volume function from Step 2. Plot your data points on the same graph. How do the points relate to the function?

Step 4 What is the degree of this function? Give some reasons to support your answer.

Step 5 Locate the x-intercepts of your graph. (There should be three.) Call these three values r_1, r_2, and r_3. Use these values to write the function in the form $y = (x - r_1)(x - r_2)(x - r_3)$.

Step 6 Graph the function from Step 5 with your function from Step 2. What are the similarities and differences between the graphs? How can you alter the function from Step 5 to make both functions equivalent?

Step 7 What happens if you try to make boxes by using the values r_1, r_2, and r_3 as x? What domain of x-values makes sense in this context? What x-value maximizes the volume of the box?

Step 6

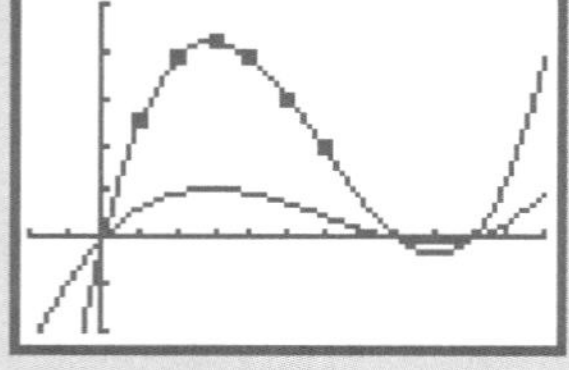

[−2, 12, 1, −200, 500, 100]

They have the same x-intercepts and general shape, but different vertical scale factors. A vertical scale factor of 4 makes them equivalent: $y = 4x(x - 8)(x - 10)$.

Step 7 Students may say there is no maximum; the graph of the function continues upward as x increases. Although the function has no maximum, only the values of x between 0 and 8 model boxes, and over this domain the function does have a maximum.

Step 7 For $x = r_1$, $x = r_2$, or $x = r_3$, the box will be flat. Only a domain of $0 < x < 8$ makes sense in this context. An x-value of about 2.94 maximizes the volume.

The connection between the roots of a polynomial equation and the x-intercepts of a polynomial function helps you factor any polynomial that has real roots.

EXAMPLE

Find the factored form of each function.

a. $y = x^2 - x - 2$

b. $y = 4x^3 + 8x^2 - 36x - 72$

▸ Solution

You can find the x-intercepts of each function by graphing. The x-intercepts tell you the real roots, which help you factor the function.

a. The graph shows that the x-intercepts are -1 and 2. Because the coefficient of the highest-degree term, x^2, is 1, the vertical scale factor is 1. The factored form is $y = (x + 1)(x - 2)$.

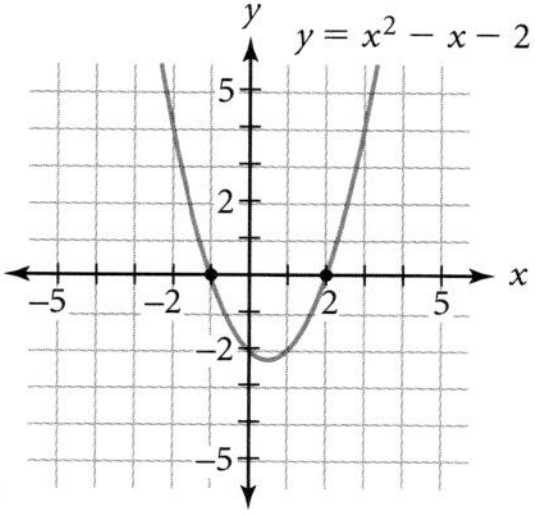

You can verify that the expressions $x^2 - x - 2$ and $(x + 1)(x - 2)$ are equivalent by graphing $y = x^2 - x - 2$ and $y = (x + 1)(x - 2)$. You can also check your work algebraically by finding the product $(x + 1)(x - 2)$. This rectangle diagram confirms that the product is $x^2 - x - 2$.

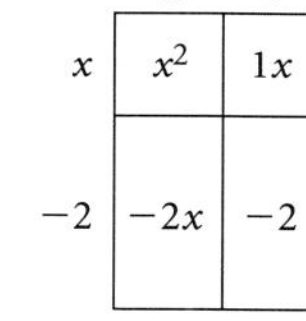

b. The x-intercepts are -3, -2, and 3. So, you can write the function as

$$y = a(x + 3)(x + 2)(x - 3)$$

Because the leading coefficient needs to be 4, the vertical scale factor is also 4.

$$y = 4(x + 3)(x + 2)(x - 3)$$

To check your answer, you can compare graphs or algebraically find the product of the factors.

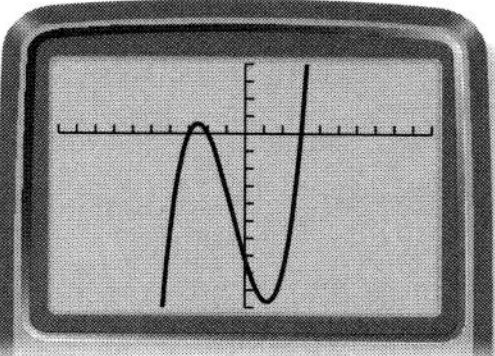

[−10, 10, 1, −100, 40, 10]

In the example, you converted a function from general form to factored form by using a graph and looking for the x-intercepts. This method works especially well when the zeros are integer values. Once you know the zeros of a polynomial function, r_1, r_2, r_3, and so on, you can write the factored form,

$$y = a(x - r_1)(x - r_2)(x - r_3) \cdots$$

You can also write a polynomial function in factored form when the zeros are not integers, or even when they are nonreal.

▸ EXAMPLE

Demonstrate how to use two rectangle diagrams to expand a product of three binomials.

$y = 4(x + 3)(x + 2)(x - 3)$

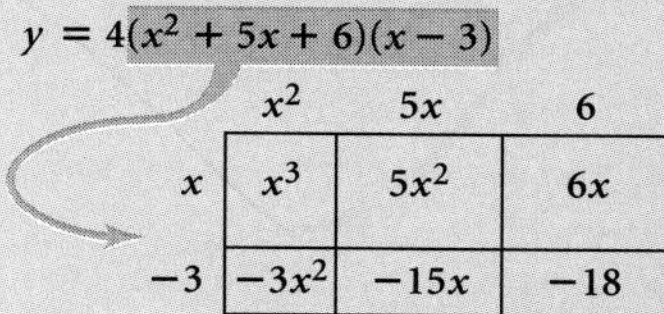

$y = 4(x^2 + 5x + 6)(x - 3)$

	x^2	$5x$	6
x	x^3	$5x^2$	$6x$
-3	$-3x^2$	$-15x$	-18

$y = 4(x^3 + 2x^2 - 9x - 18)$

$y = 4x^3 + 8x^2 - 36x - 72$

[Ask] "In the solution to part b, why does the leading coefficient need to be 4?" [In the original equation, which is in general form, the leading coefficient is 4.]

For students who did not do Lesson 7.5, Exercise 11, you'll need to introduce the term *double root.* **[Language]** When the parabola has exactly one point of intersection with the x-axis, this root of the corresponding quadratic equation is known as a *double root.*

The statements, following the example, about conjugate pairs and factoring do not apply if the polynomial has complex coefficients but instead relate only to polynomials with real-number coefficients.

SHARING IDEAS

As students present their ideas **[Ask]** "Why is x^3 called x cubed?" [It can be represented by a physical cube, just as x^2 can be represented by a square.]

Ask whether the graph of a cubic function is a physical cube. Some students will confuse the physical representation with the graphical one. The graph isn't a cube any more than the graph of the function $y = x^2$ is a physical square.

To preview the next lesson **[Ask]** "What shape is the graph of a 1st-degree function?" [line] "Of a 2nd-degree function?" [parabola] "Of higher-degree functions?"

To preview Lesson 12.7, challenge students to expand $(x - 1)(x - 2)(x - 3)$ by writing first the x^3 term, then the x^2 terms together, then the x terms together, and finally the constant term.

Factoring the Quadratic Functions
As you discuss the three quadratic functions that end the lesson, you might ask students to find the factored form. $\left[y = \left(x - \left(\frac{1}{2} + i\frac{\sqrt{3}}{2}\right)\right)\left(x - \left(\frac{1}{2} - i\frac{\sqrt{3}}{2}\right)\right);\right.$ $y = \left(x - \frac{1+\sqrt{5}}{2}\right)\left(x - \frac{1-\sqrt{5}}{2}\right);$ $\left. y = (x+1)(x-2)\right]$

Assessing Progress
You can assess students' ability to follow directions and visualize in two and three dimensions. You can also check their understanding of the dimensions and volume of a box, the degree of a polynomial, and the idea of stretching graphs.

Closing the Lesson

The main point of this lesson is that for cubic polynomial functions, as for quadratic polynomial functions, $x - r$ is a factor if and only if r is a zero. This property also extends to polynomials of higher degree. If you can find the zeros from a graph, then you can write the polynomial in factored form. You'll need to substitute one point on the graph to find the vertical scale factor. You might show the Equations and Parabolas transparency to summarize the possibilities for roots of quadratic functions.

BUILDING UNDERSTANDING

Students practice working with cubic functions and equations and applying them to real-world situations.

ASSIGNING HOMEWORK

Essential	1–4
Performance assessment	5–9
Portfolio	7
Journal	5
Group	8, 9
Review	10–14

Polynomials with real coefficients can be separated into three types: polynomials that can't be factored with real numbers; polynomials that can be factored with real numbers, but the roots are not "nice" integer or rational values; and polynomials that can be factored and have integer or rational roots. For example, consider these cases of quadratic functions:

$y = x^2 - x + 1$

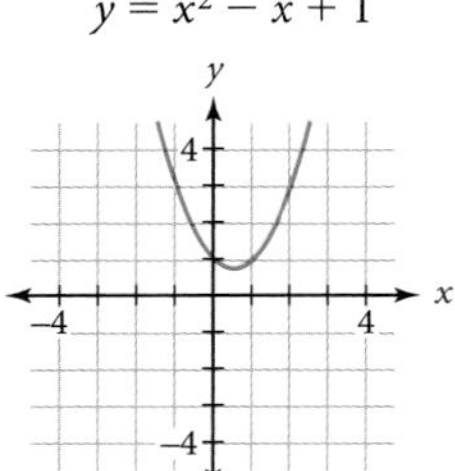

If the graph of a quadratic function does not intercept the x-axis, then you cannot factor the polynomial using real numbers. However, you can use the quadratic formula to find the complex zeros, which will be a conjugate pair.

$y = x^2 - x - 1$

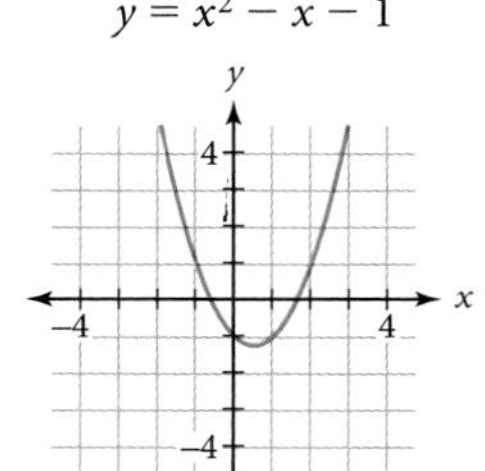

If the graph of a quadratic function intercepts the x-axis, but not at integer or rational values, then you can use the quadratic formula to find the real zeros.

$y = x^2 - x - 2$

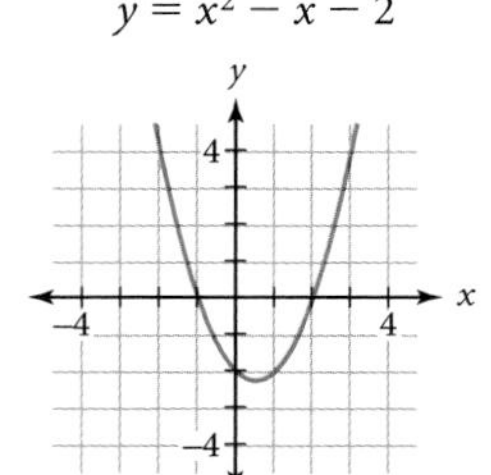

If the graph of a quadratic function intercepts the x-axis at integer or rational values, then you can use the x-intercepts to factor the polynomial. This is often quicker and easier than using the quadratic formula or a rectangle diagram.

What happens when the graph of a quadratic function has exactly one point of intersection with the x-axis? It has one root that occurs twice, so it is a perfect square. It's factored form is $y = a(x - r_1)^2$.

EXERCISES

Practice Your Skills

1. Without graphing, find the x-intercepts and the y-intercept for the graph of each equation. Check each answer by graphing.

a. $y = -0.25(x + 1.5)(x + 6)$
b. $y = 3(x - 4)(x - 4)$
c. $y = -2(x - 3)(x + 2)(x + 5)$
d. $y = 5(x + 3)(x + 3)(x - 3)$

2. Write the factored form of the quadratic function for each graph. Don't forget the vertical scale factor.

a.

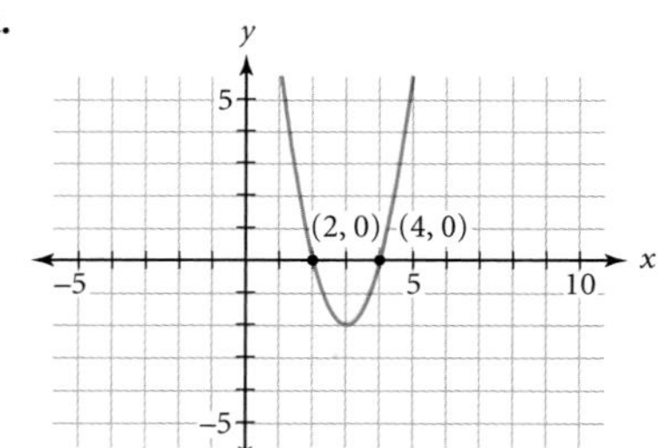

$y = 2(x - 2)(x - 4)$

b.

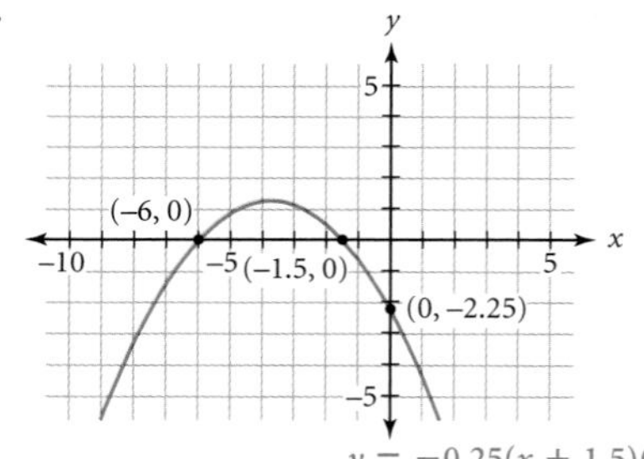

$y = -0.25(x + 1.5)(x + 6)$

Helping with the Exercises

Exercise 1 An x-intercept corresponding to a double root, as in 1b and 1d, should not be listed twice.

1a. x-intercepts: -1.5, -6; y-intercept: -2.25
1b. x-intercept: 4; y-intercept: 48
1c. x-intercepts: 3, -2, -5; y-intercept: 60
1d. x-intercepts: -3, 3; y-intercept: -135

3. Convert each polynomial function to general form.

a. $y = (x - 4)(x - 6)$ $y = x^2 - 10x + 24$

b. $y = (x - 3)(x - 3)$ $y = x^2 - 6x + 9$

c. $y = x(x + 8)(x - 8)$ $y = x^3 - 64x$

d. $y = 3(x + 2)(x - 2)(x + 5)$ $y = 3x^3 + 15x^2 - 12x - 60$

4. Given the function $y = 2.5(x - 7.5)(x + 2.5)(x - 3.2)$,

a. Find the x-intercepts without graphing.

b. Find the y-intercept without graphing. 150

c. Write the function in general form. $y = 2.5x^3 - 20.5x^2 - 6.875x + 150$

d. Graph both the factored form and the general form of the function to check your work.

Reason and Apply

5. Use your work from the investigation to answer these questions.

a. What x-value maximizes the volume for your box? What is the maximum volume possible? approximately 2.94 units; approximately 420 cubic units

b. What x-value or values give a volume of 300 cubic units? 5 and approximately 1.28

c. The portion of the graph with domain $x > 10$ shows positive volume. What does this mean in the context of the problem?

d. Explain the meaning of the parts of the graph showing negative volume. The graph exists, but these x- and y-values make no physical sense for this context.

These boxes, on display during the 2002 Cultural Olympiad in Salt Lake City, Utah, through the organization "Children Beyond Borders," were created by children with disabilities in countries worldwide. The children decorated identical 4-inch square boxes with their own creative visions, often in scenes from their countries and themes of love and unity.

1. The original cardboard box; **2.** © Diana Edna Cruz Yunes, *Corazon Mío, Mi Corazon*/Mexico; **3.** © Manal Deibes, *Are You Hungry?*/Jordan; **4.** © Leslie Hendricks, *Art Is What Makes the World Go 'Round*/USA; **5.** © Earl Hasith Vanabona, *Untitled*/Sri Lanka; **6.** © Renato Pinho, *Ocean*/Portugal. Participating artists of VSA arts (*www.vsarts.org*)

6. Write each polynomial as a product of factors.

a. $4x^2 - 88x + 480$

b. $6x^2 - 7x - 5$

c. $x^3 + 5x^2 - 4x - 20$

d. $2x^3 + 16x^2 + 38x + 24$

e. $a^2 + 2ab + b^2$

f. $x^2 - 64$ $(x - 8)(x + 8)$

g. $x^2 + 64$ $(x + 8i)(x - 8i)$

h. $x^2 - 7$ $(x - \sqrt{7})(x + \sqrt{7})$

i. $x^2 - 3x$ $x(x - 3)$

7. Sketch a graph for each situation if possible.

a. a quadratic function with only one real zero

b. a quadratic function with no real zeros

c. a quadratic function with three real zeros

d. a cubic function with only one real zero

e. a cubic function with two real zeros

f. a cubic function with no real zeros

Exercises 3, 4 To expand these expressions, students can either draw rectangle diagrams or distribute systematically.

4a. 7.5, −2.5, 3.2

4d.

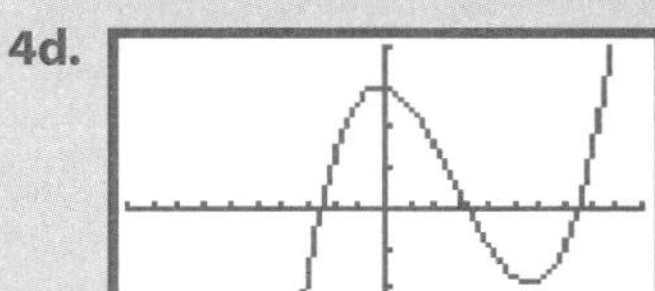

[−10, 10, 1, −200, 200, 50]

Exercise 5 In 5a, students can find the maximum either by examining the graph or by substituting into the function expression the value of x they found in the investigation. For 5c, the function doesn't model volumes of real boxes outside the interval $0 < x < 8$. For $8 < x < 10$, one of the dimensions of the box would be negative, so the product is negative. For $x > 10$, two dimensions are negative, so the product is positive.

5c. The graph exists, but these x- and y-values make no physical sense for this context. If $x \geq 8$, there will be no box left after you take out two 8-unit square corners from the 16-unit width.

6a. $4(x - 12)(x - 10)$

6b. $6\left(x - \frac{5}{3}\right)\left(x + \frac{1}{2}\right)$ or $(3x - 5)(2x + 1)$

6c. $(x + 2)(x - 2)(x + 5)$

6d. $2(x + 1)(x + 3)(x + 4)$

6e. $(a + b)(a + b)$ or $(a + b)^2$

Exercise 7 As needed, remind students to look for x-intercepts in the graphs.

7a. sample answer:

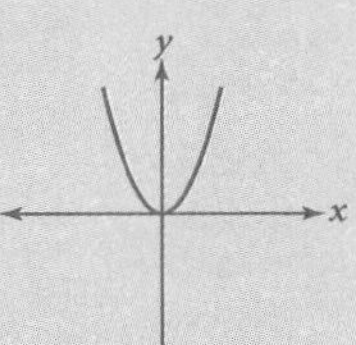

7b. sample answer:

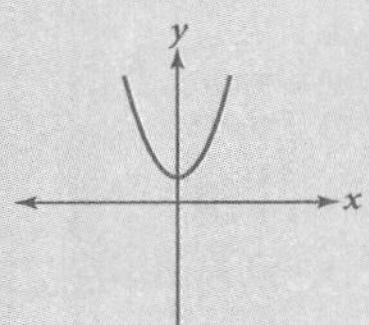

7c. not possible

7d. sample answer:

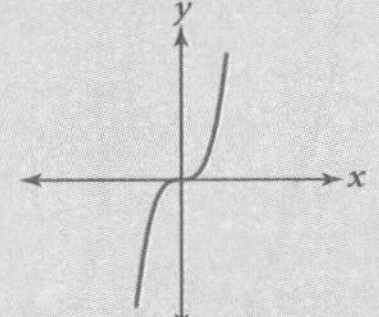

7e. sample answer:

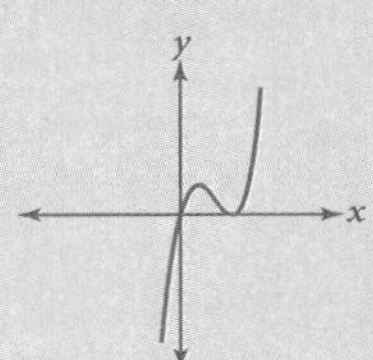

7f. not possible

8a. $y = a(x + 5)(x - 3)(x - 6)$

8b. $y = 2(x + 5)(x - 3)(x - 6)$

8c. $y = 2(x + 5)(x - 3)(x - 6) + 100$

8d. $y = 2(x + 9)(x + 1)(x - 2)$

9a. $(T + t)^2$ or $T^2 + 2Tt + t^2$

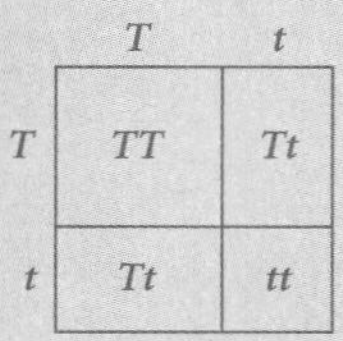

Exercise 9 The rectangle diagram might show the gene inherited from the mother in the rows and the gene from the father in the columns. If the dominant characteristic, T, is inherited from either parent, the child is a taster. Students need to realize that the set of tasters includes both TT and Tt, because T is dominant. Therefore $T^2 + 2Tt = 0.70$. **[Ask]** "What proportion of the population will, if they have children, have only children that are tasters?" [The answer to 9f, about 20%.]

Exercise 10 Instead of stating that the points are collinear, students might answer that any attempt to find a 2nd-degree equation gives an a-value of 0.

Exercise 12 **[Ask]** "Are there other solutions?" [In 12b there are two nonreal roots, in 12d there are two nonreal roots.] You might challenge some students to look for nonreal solutions. For example, in 12d students can factor $x^3 + 64$ into $(x + 4)(x^2 - 4x + 16)$ and then apply the quadratic formula to factor the quadratic factor. Students will learn more about finding nonreal solutions in the next lesson.

12a. $x = \pm\sqrt{50.4} \approx \pm 7.1$

12b. $x = \pm\sqrt{13} \approx \pm 3.6$

12c. $x = 2.4 \pm \sqrt{40.2} \approx 2.4 \pm 6.3$; $x \approx 8.7$ or $x \approx -3.9$

12d. $x = -4$

8. Consider the function in this graph.

a. Write the equation of a polynomial function that has the x-intercepts shown in the graph. Use a for the vertical scale factor.

b. Use the y-intercept to determine the vertical scale factor. Write the function from 8a, replacing a with the value of the vertical scale factor.

c. Imagine that this graph is translated up 100 units. Write the equation of the image.

d. Imagine that this graph is translated left 4 units. Write the equation of the image.

9. **APPLICATION** The way you taste certain flavors is a genetic trait inherited from your parents. For instance, the ability to taste the bitter compound phenyltheocarbamide (PTC) is inherited as a dominant trait in humans. In the United States, approximately 70% of the population can taste PTC, whereas 30% cannot.

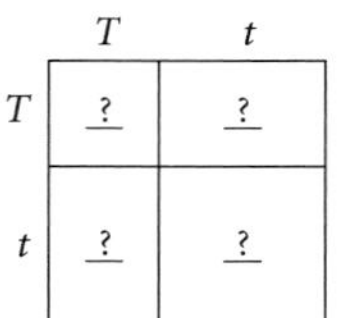

Every person inherits a pair of genes from their parents. Let T represent the gene for tasters (dominant), and let t represent the gene for nontasters (recessive). The presence of at least one T means that a person can taste PTC.

a. Complete the rectangle diagram of possible gene-pair combinations. Using the variables T and t, what algebraic expression does this diagram represent?

b. The sum of all possible gene-pair combinations must equal 1, or 100%, for the entire population. Write an equation to express this relationship. $(T + t)^2 = 1$ or $T^2 + 2Tt + t^2 = 1$

c. Use the fact that 70% of the U.S. population are tasters to write an equation that you can use to solve for t. $0.70 + t^2 = 1$

d. Solve for t, the frequency of the recessive gene in the population. $t \approx 0.548$

e. What is the frequency of the dominant gene in the population? $T \approx 0.452$

f. What percentage of the U.S. population has the gene-pair TT? $TT \approx 0.204$, or about 20% of the population

Review

7.1 **10.** Is it possible to find a quadratic function that contains the points $(-4, -2)$, $(-1, 7)$, and $(2, 16)$? Explain why or why not. No. These points are collinear.

7.2 **11.** Find the quadratic function whose graph has vertex $(-2, 3)$ and contains the point $(4, 12)$. $y = 0.25(x + 2)^2 + 3$

5.3 **12.** Find all real solutions.

a. $x^2 = 50.4$ **b.** $x^4 = 169$ **c.** $(x - 2.4)^2 = 40.2$ **d.** $x^3 = -64$

5.5 **13.** Algebraically find the inverse of each function. Then choose a value of x and check your answer.

a. $f(x) = \frac{2}{3}(x + 5)$ **b.** $g(x) = -6 + (x + 3)^{2/3}$ **c.** $h(x) = 7 - 2^x$

7.1 **14.** Use the finite differences method to find the function that generates this table of values. Explain your reasoning.

x	2.2	2.6	3.0	3.4
$f(x)$	-4.5	-5.5	-6.5	-7.5

Exercise 13 Be open to solutions by undoing as well as by balancing. In a different form, the inverse function of 13c is $h^{-1}(x) = \frac{\log(7 - x)}{\log 2}$. A consistency check might be $h^{-1}(3) = \frac{\log 4}{\log 2} = \frac{\log 2^2}{\log 2} = \frac{2 \log 2}{\log 2} = 2$.

13a. $f^{-1}(x) = \frac{3}{2}x - 5$

sample check: $f(4) = 6$; $f^{-1}(6) = 4$

13b. $g^{-1}(x) = -3 + (x + 6)^{3/2}$

sample check: $g(5) = -2$; $g^{-1}(-2) = 5$

13c. $h^{-1}(x) = \log_2(7 - x)$

sample check: $h(2) = 3$; $h^{-1}(3) = 2$

14. $f(x) = -2.5x + 1$

The differences are all -1, so the function is linear. Find an equation for the line through any two of the points.

LESSON

7.7 Higher-Degree Polynomials

It is good to have an end to journey towards, but it is the journey that matters in the end.

URSULA K. LEGUIN

Polynomials with degree 3 or higher are called higher-degree polynomials. Frequently, 3rd-degree polynomials are associated with volume measures, as you saw in Lesson 7.6. If you create a box by removing small squares of side length x from each corner of a square piece of cardboard that is 30 inches on each side, the volume of the box in cubic inches is modeled by the function $y = x(30 - 2x)^2$, or $y = 4x^3 - 120x^2 + 900x$. The zero-product property tells you that the zeros are $x = 0$ or $x = 15$, the two values of x for which the volume is 0. The x-intercepts on the graph below confirm this.

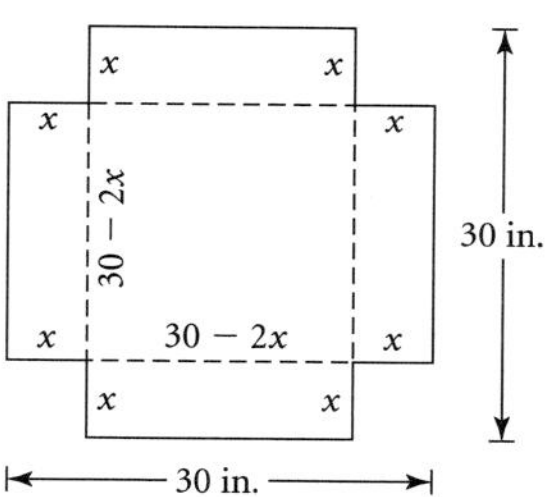

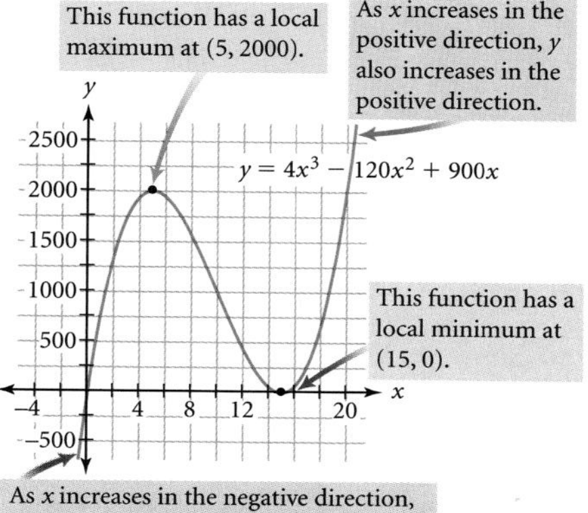

The shape of this graph is typical of the higher-degree polynomial graphs you will work with in this lesson. Note that it has one **local maximum** at (5, 2000) and one **local minimum** at (15, 0). These are the points that are higher or lower than all other points near them. You can also describe the **end behavior**—what happens to $f(x)$ as x takes on larger positive and negative values of x. In the case of this cubic function, as x increases in the positive direction, y also increases in the positive direction. As x increases in the negative direction, y also increases in the negative direction.

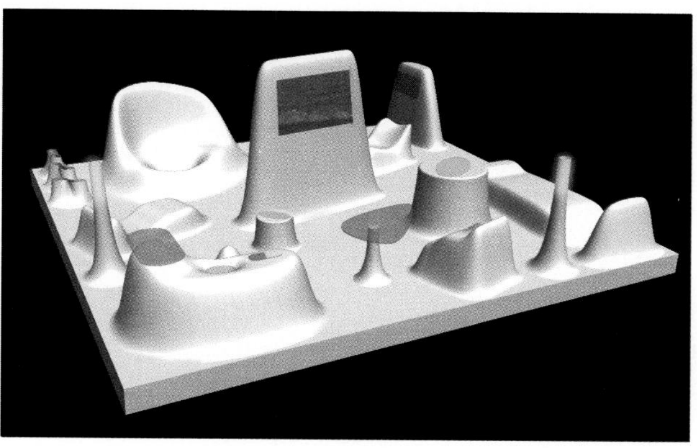

Polynomials with real coefficients have graphs that have a y-intercept, and possibly one or more x-intercepts. You can also describe other features of polynomial graphs, such as local maximums or minimums, and end behavior. Maximums and minimums, collectively, are called **extreme values.**

Egyptian-American artist Karim Rashid (b 1960) is a contemporary designer of fine art, as well as commercial products—from trash cans to sofas. This piece, *Softscape* (2001), is the artist's vision of a futuristic living room with chairs, tables, and a television melding together.

NCTM STANDARDS

CONTENT		PROCESS	
	Number		Problem Solving
✓	Algebra	✓	Reasoning
✓	Geometry	✓	Communication
	Measurement		Connections
	Data/Probability	✓	Representation

LESSON OBJECTIVES

- Investigate extreme values and the end behavior of polynomial functions
- Identify possible degrees of a polynomial function by looking at its graph
- Identify and find the lowest-degree polynomial that has given roots
- Find additional roots when given one complex root
- Relate the graphs of polynomial equations to the number and types of roots

LESSON 7.7

PLANNING

LESSON OUTLINE

First day:

25 min	Investigation
10 min	Sharing
10 min	Exercises

Second day:

10 min	Example A
10 min	Example B
5 min	Sharing
20 min	Exercises

MATERIALS

- rulers
- centimeter grid paper or 1-Centimeter Grid Paper (W)
- Paper Folding (T) for One Step
- Sketchpad demonstration Higher Degree, *optional*

TEACHING

In this lesson, students extend their knowledge of cubic functions. It is not necessary to discuss the opening remarks before doing the investigation.

One Step

Show the Paper Folding transparency or illustrate by folding a piece of paper, and pose this problem from the investigation: "If you fold the top left corner of a sheet of paper to touch the bottom left edge x units from the bottom left corner, what value of x will maximize the area of the triangle formed in the bottom left corner?"

Encourage a variety of approaches. During Sharing, try to make sure a full graph of the cubic function is displayed. Introduce the terminology *local maximum, local minimum,* and *end behavior.* Ask students how to factor the function and what its zeros are.

Guiding the Investigation

If you can't use this investigation in class, you might assign it as a project. It allows for rich discovery. Students often expect a quadratic model for area, so they may be surprised to find that the model is a cubic function. If it is graphed only in Quadrant I, though, it looks quadratic.

Students can use a variety of methods to find the area of the triangle.

- Fold a sheet of grid paper and count the squares
- Measure the triangle's base and height and calculate the area
- Use the Pythagorean Theorem to find a general area function

For the first two approaches, students might find the area function by using finite differences and creating a system of four equations whose four unknowns are the coefficients of a cubic function.

▸ *EXAMPLE A*

[Language] The word *domain* is used here to refer to the part of the domain showing in the window. *End behavior* refers to what happens to graphs as x gets very large or very small.

This example could be solved with a higher-degree polynomial function, but the simplest solution is a cubic function.

If you introduce the concepts of absolute maximum and absolute minimum, point out that neither $(4, -25)$ nor $(-1.5, 225)$ is an absolute extreme value because the end behavior of the graph goes to plus and minus infinity. (The symbols, ∞ and $-\infty$, will be introduced in Lesson 11.2.)

See page 889 for answers to the investigation.

Investigation
The Largest Triangle

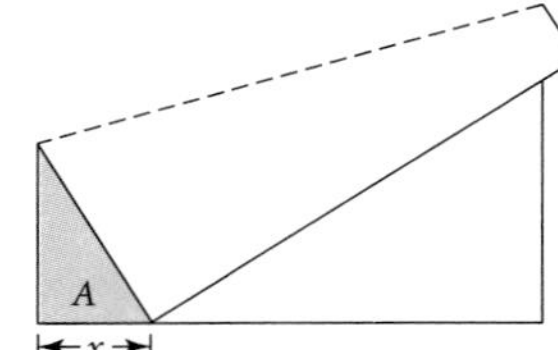

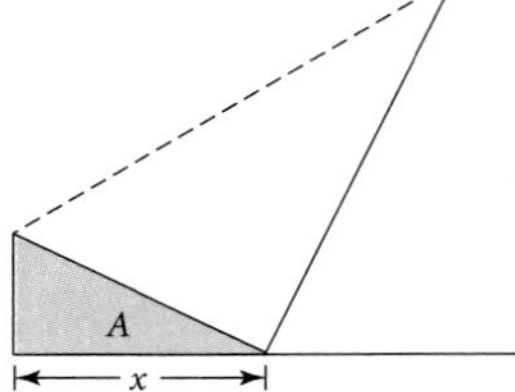

Take a sheet of notebook paper and orient it such that the longest edge is closest to you. Fold the upper left corner so that it touches some point on the bottom edge. Find the area, A, of the triangle formed in the lower left corner of the paper. What distance, x, along the bottom of the paper produces the triangle with the greatest area?

Work with your group to find a solution. You may want to use strategies you've learned in several lessons in this chapter. Write a report that explains your solution and your group's strategy for finding the largest triangle. Include any diagrams, tables, or graphs that you used.

In the remainder of this lesson you will explore the connections between a polynomial equation and its graph, which will allow you to predict when certain features will occur in the graph.

EXAMPLE A Find a polynomial function whose graph has x-intercepts 3, 5, and -4, and y-intercept 180. Describe the features of its graph.

▸ Solution A polynomial function with three x-intercepts has too many x-intercepts to be a quadratic function. It could be a 3rd-, 4th-, 5th-, or higher-degree polynomial function. Consider a 3rd-degree polynomial function, because that is the lowest degree that has three x-intercepts. Use the x-intercepts to write the equation $y = a(x - 3)(x - 5)(x + 4)$ where $a \neq 0$.

Substitute the coordinates of the y-intercept, $(0, 180)$, into this function to find the vertical scale factor.

$$180 = a(0 - 3)(0 - 5)(0 + 4)$$
$$180 = a(60)$$
$$a = 3$$

The polynomial function of the lowest degree through the given intercepts is

$$y = 3(x - 3)(x - 5)(x + 4)$$

Graph this function to confirm your answer and look for features.

[Ask] "Is there a 4th-degree polynomial with the same three roots and an additional real root?" [Yes; multiply the factors by a fourth factor, $(x + a)$.] "Is there a 4th-degree polynomial with the same three roots and an additional imaginary root?" [No; nonreal roots come in conjugate pairs.]

A small window may show features of a graph but might not indicate end behavior. A large viewing screen can show end behavior, but individual features might be hard to see.

This graph shows a local minimum at about $(4, -25)$ because that is the lowest point in its immediate neighborhood of x-values. There is also a local maximum at about $(-1.5, 220)$ because that is the highest point in its immediate neighborhood of x-values. The small domain shown in the graph already suggests the end behavior. As x increases in the positive direction, y also increases in the positive direction. As x increases in the negative direction, y also increases in the negative direction. If you increase the domain of this graph to include more x-values at the right and left extremes of the x-axis, you'll see that the graph does continue this end behavior.

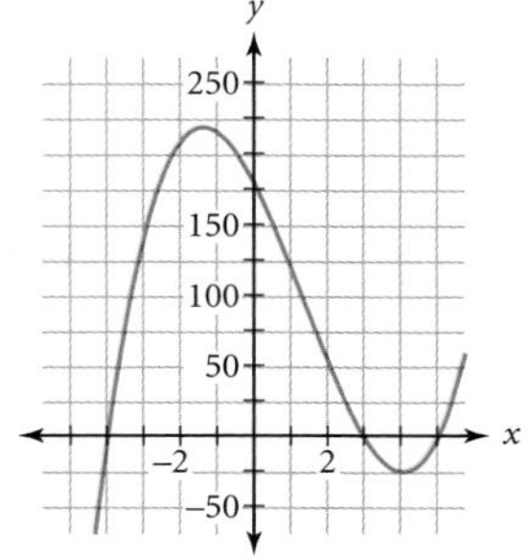

You can identify the degree of many polynomial functions by looking at the shapes of their graphs. Every 3rd-degree polynomial function has essentially one of the shapes shown below. Graph A shows the graph of $y = x^3$. It can be translated, stretched, or reflected. Graph B shows one possible transformation of Graph A. Graphs C and D show the graphs of general cubic functions in the form $y = ax^3 + bx^2 + cx + d$. In Graph C, a is positive, and in Graph D, a is negative.

Graph A

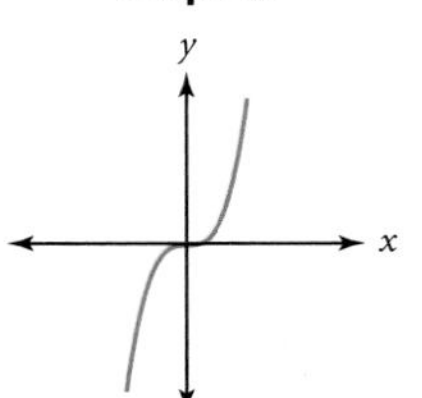

Graph B

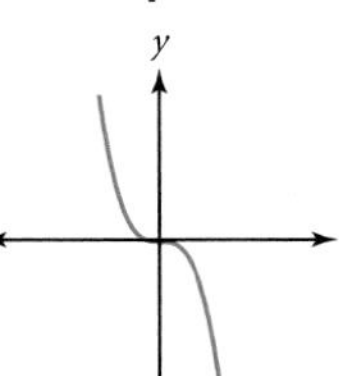

Graph C

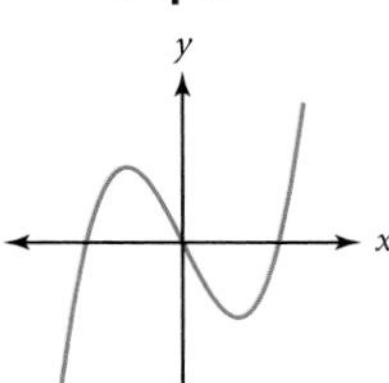

Graph D

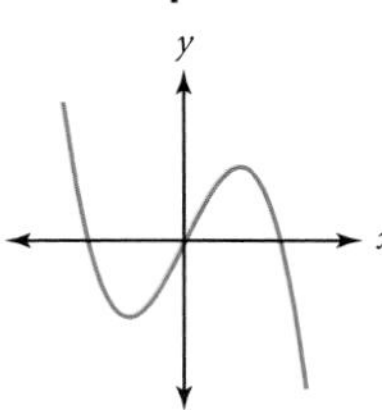

You'll explore the general shapes and characteristics of other higher-degree polynomials in the exercises.

EXAMPLE B

Write a polynomial function with real coefficients and zeros $x = 2$, $x = -5$, and $x = 3 + 4i$.

▶ Solution

For a polynomial function with real coefficients, complex zeros occur in conjugate pairs, so $x = 3 - 4i$ must also be a zero. In factored form the polynomial function of the lowest degree is

$$y = (x - 2)(x + 5)(x - (3 + 4i))(x - (3 - 4i))$$

Multiplying the last two factors to eliminate complex numbers gives $y = (x - 2)(x + 5)(x^2 - 6x + 25)$. Multiplying all factors gives the polynomial function in general form:

$$y = x^4 - 3x^3 - 3x^2 + 135x - 250$$

Graph this function to check your solution. You can't see the complex zeros, but you can see x-intercepts 2 and -5.

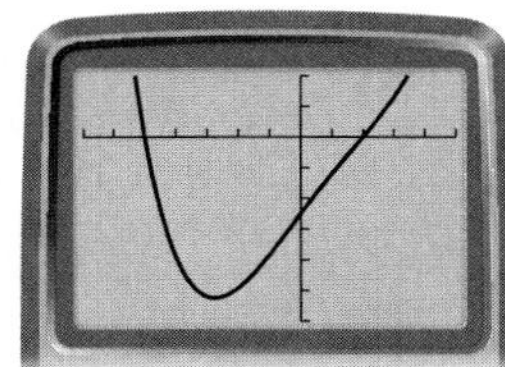

$[-7, 5, 1, -600, 200, 100]$

▶ **EXAMPLE B**

This example asks students to find any polynomial function that satisfies the criteria. The solution given is one possibility. Multiplying this solution by a constant or by any other factor $x - r$ will also give a solution. Indeed, many students will benefit from the practice of multiplying this function by a constant.

SHARING IDEAS

Have students share several of the many different solution strategies for the investigation. Students' answers will depend on the orientation and height of the paper (in whatever units). You can use a general solution to check students' work; you might have them work through it themselves. If the corner is being folded to cut a height b of the paper down to a height y of the triangle, then the Pythagorean Theorem gives the equation $x^2 + y^2 = (b - y)^2$, or $y = \frac{b^2 - x^2}{2b}$. This gives the area function $A = \frac{1}{2}xy = -\frac{1}{4b}x^3 + \frac{b}{4}x$.

Cubic functions have local extreme values but no absolute extreme values, because their end behavior exceeds all bounds. **[Ask]** "Do any functions have absolute extreme values?" [Polynomial functions of even degree, such as quadratic functions, have either an absolute maximum or an absolute minimum but not both.] In Chapter 10, students will see trigonometric functions that have both absolute maximums and absolute minimums.

[Ask] "How could you switch the end behaviors of this cubic function and still have a cubic function?" [Change the sign of the leading coefficient.]

[Ask] "If area functions are usually quadratic, why is this one cubic?" If possible, be persistent in asking "why" to encourage a deeper answer than "because the general function works out that

Sharing Ideas (continued)

way." In fact, in the general area function, the units of each term are quadratic, because b has the same measurement unit as x.

[Ask] "Can you always tell the degree of a polynomial from the shape of its graph?" If students believe so, suggest that they graph the functions $y = x^4$ and $y = x^9$. A polynomial curve with n local extreme values has degree at least $n + 1$ and perhaps much higher.

Ask students to imagine having eight points on a plane. Ask whether there is necessarily a polynomial whose graph will pass through all eight of the points. If no two of the points are on the same vertical line, then you can set up eight equations in eight unknowns and find the eight coefficients of a polynomial of degree 7 that will fit the data perfectly. A simpler polynomial may be a better model for the overall situation, however.

Assessing Progress

You can assess students' concept of area and their ability to find the area of a right triangle and to apply the Pythagorean Theorem. The investigation also gives you an opportunity to see how free students are of dependence on you for guidance in exploring.

Closing the Lesson

As with a quadratic function, the zeros of a cubic function $f(x)$ are the same as the x-intercepts of the function's graph, the roots (solutions) of the equation $f(x) = 0$, and the numbers in the factors of $f(x)$: $a(x - r_1)(x - r_2)(x - r_3)$. You might use the Sketchpad demonstration Higher Degree to show the effects of changing the coefficients of several different polynomials.

BUILDING UNDERSTANDING

Students work primarily with cubic functions, finding local extreme values, zeros, and x-intercepts.

ASSIGNING HOMEWORK

Essential	1–4
Performance assessment	5–13
Portfolio	10, 12
Journal	9
Group	6, 12
Review	14–18

Note that in Example B, the solution was a 4th-degree polynomial function. It had four complex zeros, but the graph had only two x-intercepts, corresponding to the two real zeros. Any polynomial function of degree n always has n complex zeros (including repeated zeros) and at most n x-intercepts. Remember that complex zeros of polynomial functions with real coefficients always come in conjugate pairs.

EXERCISES

Practice Your Skills

For Exercises 1–4, use these four graphs.

a.

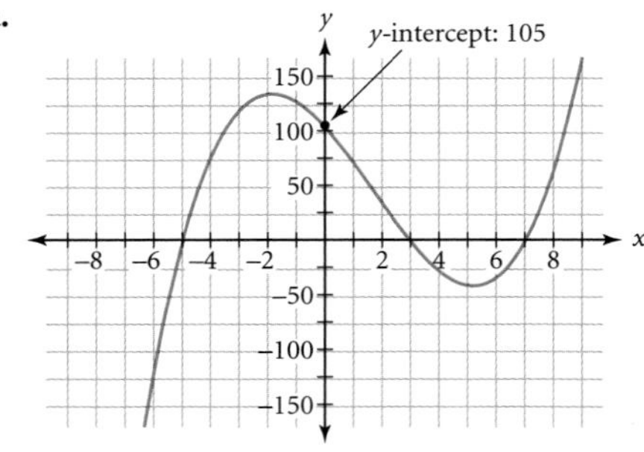

b.

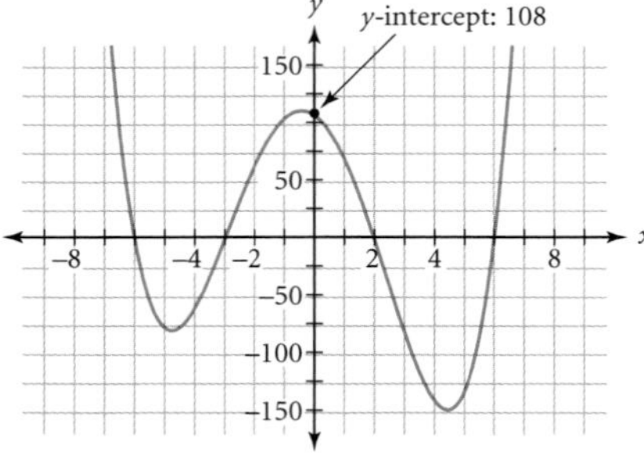

c.

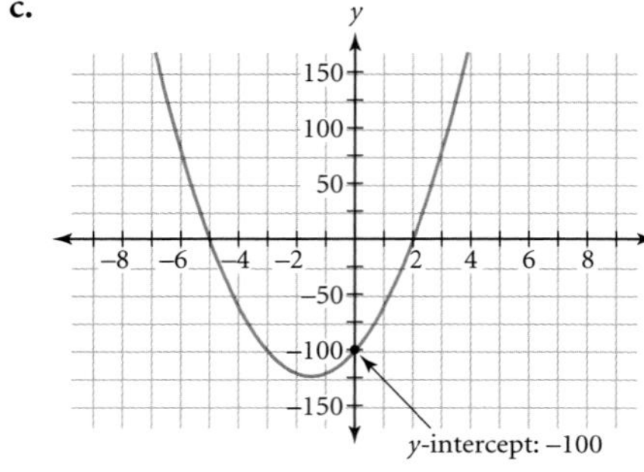

d.

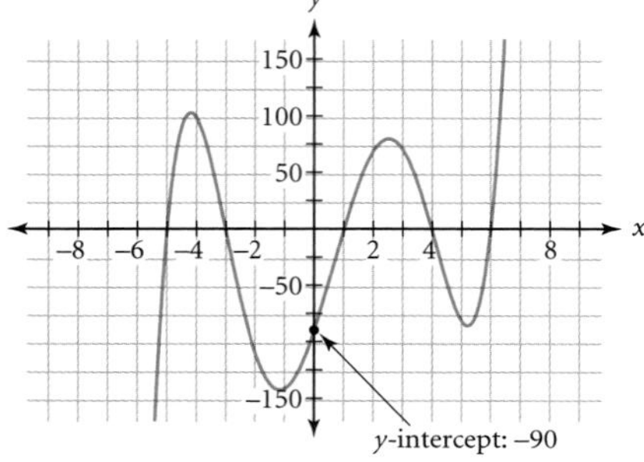

1. Identify the zeros of each function.

2. Give the coordinates of the y-intercept of each graph. **a.** (0, 105); **b.** (0, 108); **c.** (0, −100); **d.** (0, −90)

3. Identify the lowest possible degree of each polynomial function. **a.** 3; **b.** 4; **c.** 2; **d.** 5

4. Write the factored form for each polynomial function. Check your work by graphing on your calculator.

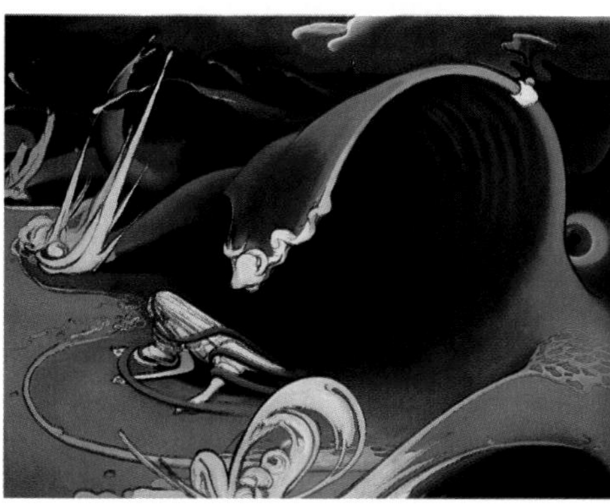

American painter Inka Essenhigh (b 1969) calls her works "cyborg mutations." She draws and paints images, and then sands them and layers them with enamel-based oil paint. This piece, *Green Wave* (2002), contains polynomial-like waves.

1a. $x = -5, x = 3$, and $x = 7$

1b. $x = -6, x = -3, x = 2$, and $x = 6$

1c. $x = -5$ and $x = 2$

1d. $x = -5, x = -3, x = 1, x = 4$, and $x = 6$

4a. $y = (x + 5)(x - 3)(x - 7)$

4b. $y = 0.5(x + 6)(x + 3)(x - 2)(x - 6)$

4c. $y = 10(x + 5)(x - 2)$

4d. $y = 0.25(x + 5)(x + 3)(x - 1)(x - 4)(x - 6)$

Reason and Apply

5. Write polynomial functions with these features.

a. A linear function whose graph has x-intercept 4.

b. A quadratic function whose graph has only one x-intercept, 4. $y = a(x - 4)^2$ where $a \neq 0$

c. A cubic function whose graph has only one x-intercept, 4.

Andrea Champlin's paintings are often called "cyber" or "digital" landscapes. Can you identify curves that look like polynomials in this painting?

Wandee Love (2001), Andrea Champlin, oil on canvas, 70 in. × 46 in. Courtesy of the artist and Clifford-Smith Gallery, Boston; photo courtesy of the artist.

6. The graph of $y = 2(x - 3)(x - 5)(x + 4)^2$ has x-intercepts 3, 5, and -4 because they are the only possible x-values that make $y = 0$. This is a 4th-degree polynomial, but it has only three x-intercepts. The root $x = -4$ is called a **double root** because the factor $(x + 4)$ occurs twice. Make a complete graph—one that displays all of the relevant features, including local extreme values—of each of the functions in parts a–f.

a. $y = 2(x - 3)(x - 5)(x + 4)^2$

b. $y = 2(x - 3)^2(x - 5)(x + 4)$

c. $y = 2(x - 3)(x - 5)^2(x + 4)$

d. $y = 2(x - 3)^2(x - 5)(x + 4)^2$

e. $y = 2(x - 3)(x - 5)(x + 4)^3$

f. $y = 2(x - 3)(x - 5)^2(x + 4)^3$

g. Based on your graphs from 6a–f, describe a connection between the power of a factor and what happens at that x-intercept.

7. The graph at right is a complete graph of a polynomial function.

a. How many x-intercepts are there? 4

b. What is the lowest possible degree of this polynomial function? 5

c. Write the factored form of this function if the graph includes the points (0, 0), (−5, 0), (4, 0), (−1, 0), and (1, 216). $y = -x(x + 5)^2(x + 1)(x - 4)$

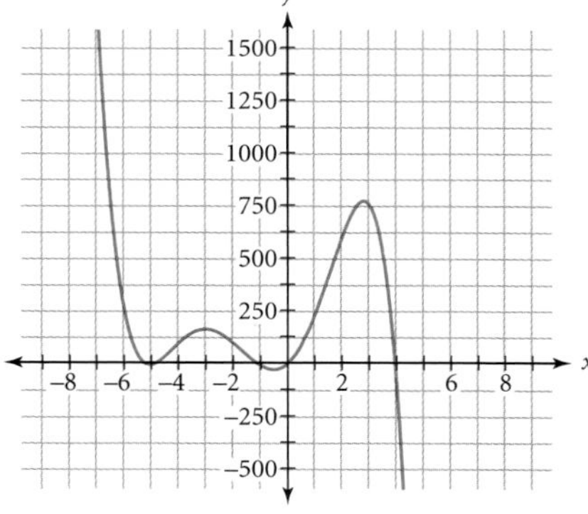

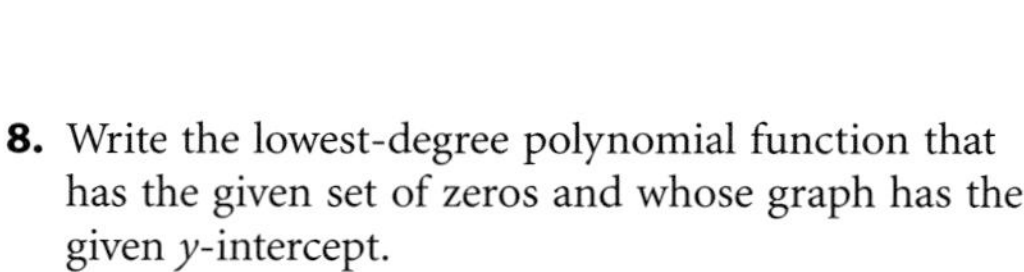

8. Write the lowest-degree polynomial function that has the given set of zeros and whose graph has the given y-intercept.

a. zeros: $x = -4$, $x = 5$, $x = -2$ (double root); y-intercept: -80

b. zeros: $x = -4$, $x = 5$, $x = -2$ (double root); y-intercept: 160

c. zeros: $x = \frac{1}{3}$, $x = -\frac{2}{5}$, $x = 0$; y-intercept: 0

d. zeros: $x = -5i$, $x = -1$ (triple root), $x = 4$; y-intercept: -100

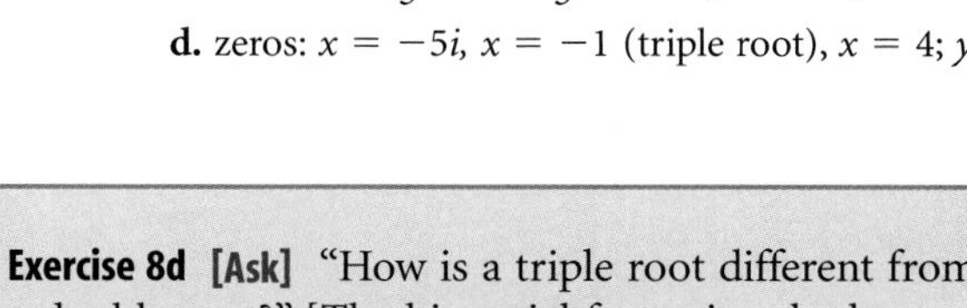

Exercise 8d [Ask] "How is a triple root different from a double root?" [The binomial factor is cubed rather than squared.]

8a. $y = (x + 4)(x - 5)(x + 2)^2$

8b. $y = -2(x + 4)(x - 5)(x + 2)^2$

8c. $y = ax\left(x - \frac{1}{3}\right)\left(x + \frac{2}{5}\right)$ or $y = ax(3x - 1)(5x + 2)$ where $a \neq 0$

8d. $y = (x + 5i)(x - 5i)(x + 1)^3(x - 4)$ or $y = (x^2 + 25)(x + 1)^3(x - 4)$

Helping with the Exercises

Exercise 5 [Ask] "What degree is a linear function?" [first] "What would a polynomial of degree 0 look like?" [a horizontal line] You might consider having students use the same leading coefficient for each part so they can see the pattern. **[Language]** If students use $y = a(x - 4)^3$ in 5c, you might point out that the graph changes between bending upward and bending downward at $x = 4$ and say that such a point is called an *inflection point.*

5a. $y = a(x - 4)$ where $a \neq 0$

5c. $y = a(x - 4)^3$ where $a \neq 0$; or $y = a(x - 4)(x - r_1)(x - r_2)$ where $a \neq 0$, and r_1 and r_2 are complex conjugates

Exercise 6 [Alert] If students are graphing on a calculator, they will need a large window vertically to include the complete graphs. See the solutions to give students guidance on how large the windows should be.

6g. A factor raised to the power of 1 results in an x-intercept that crosses the x-axis. A factor raised to the power of 2 results in an x-intercept that touches, but does not cross, the x-axis. A factor raised to the power of 3 results in an x-intercept that crosses the x-axis in a curved fashion. It appears that if the power of the factor is odd, the graph crosses the x-axis, whereas if the power of the factor is even, it touches but does not cross the x-axis.

Exercise 7 Students can use their results from Exercise 6 to realize that the function has a double root at (−5, 0) because the graph touches but does not cross the x-axis at $x = -5$. If students are having difficulty with 7c, suggest that they use the point (1, 216) just as they used the y-intercept to find the value of a.

See pages 889–890 for answers to Exercise 6a–f.

9. The leading coefficient is equal to the y-intercept divided by the product of the zeros if the degree of the function is even, or the y-intercept divided by -1 times the product of the zeros if the degree of the function is odd.

Exercise 10–13 You might want to use these exercises as a mini-investigation for the second day of the lesson.

10. Graphs will be a basic "W" shape, pointed either up or down. In some cases the "W" shape is less apparent because the local maximums and minimums, and/or points of inflection, are close together or concurrent. Sample graphs:

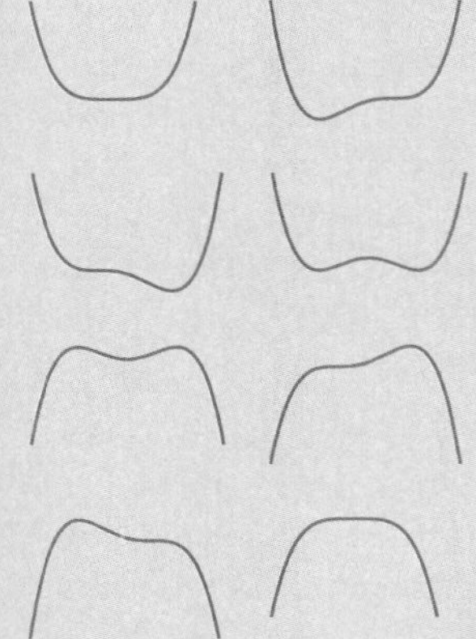

Exercise 11 Students might write each of the multiple roots as a separate factor or use powers to show multiplicity.

11b. i. $x = -5, x = -5,$ $x = -2,$ and $x = 1$

11b. ii. $x = -5, x = -5,$ $x = -2,$ and $x = 1$

11b. iii. $x = -5, x = -5,$ $x = -2, x = 1,$ and $x = 1$

11b. iv. $x = -5, x = -2,$ $x = -2, x = -2,$ and $x = 1$

9. Look back at Exercises 1–4. Find the products of the zeros in Exercise 1. How does the value of the leading coefficient, a, relate to the y-intercept, the product of the zeros, and the degree of the function?

10. A 4th-degree polynomial function has the general form $y = ax^4 + bx^3 + cx^2 + dx + e$ for real values of $a, b, c, d,$ and e, where $a \neq 0$. Graph several 4th-degree polynomial functions by trying different values for each coefficient. Be sure to include positive, negative, and zero values. Make a sketch of each different type of curve you get. Concentrate on the shape of the curve. You do not need to include axes in your sketches. Compare your graphs with the graphs of your classmates, and come up with six or more different shapes that describe all 4th-degree polynomial functions.

11. Each of these is the graph of a polynomial function with leading coefficient $a = 1$ or $a = -1$.

i.

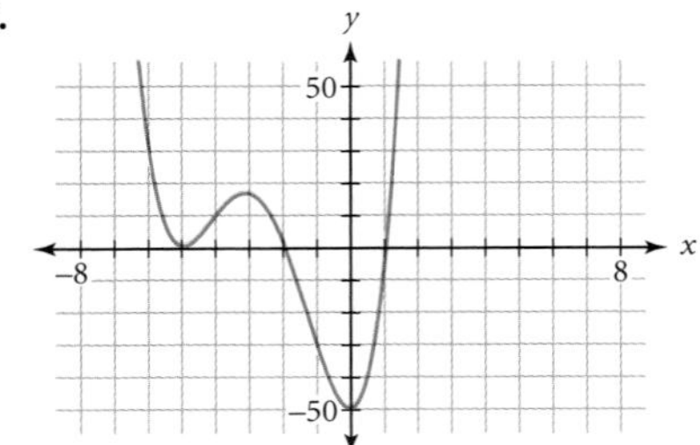

ii.

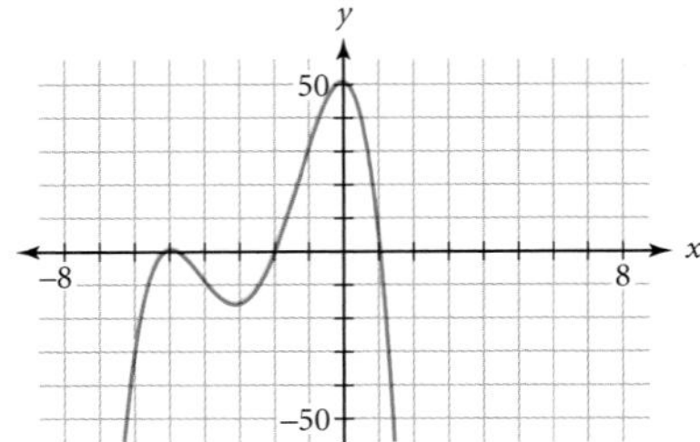

iii.

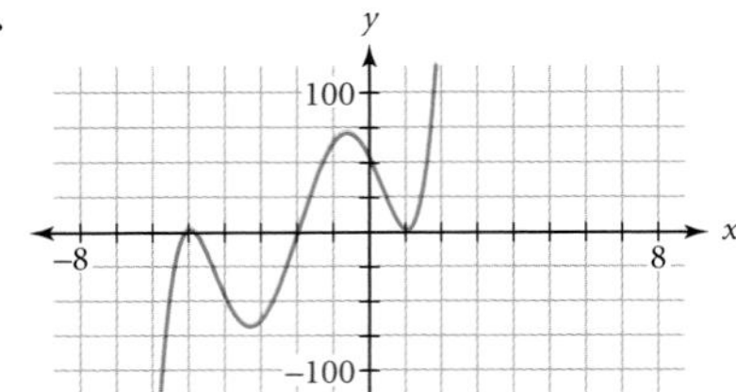

iv.

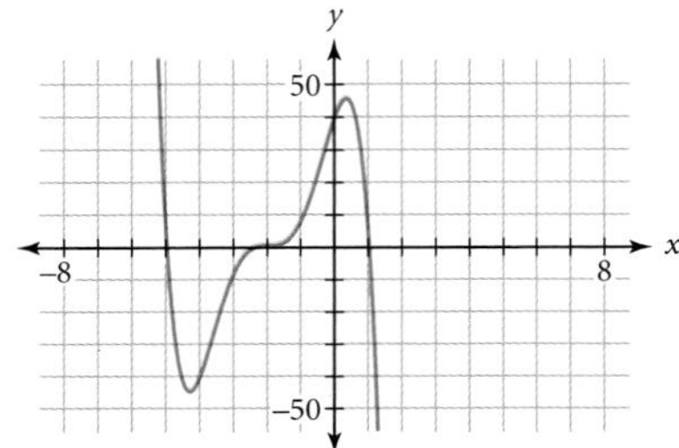

a. Write a function in factored form that will produce each graph.

b. Name the zeros of each polynomial function in 11a. If a factor is raised to the power of n, list the zero n times.

12. Consider the polynomial functions in Exercise 11.

a. What is the degree of each polynomial function?

b. How many extreme values does each graph have?

c. What is the relationship between the degree of the polynomial function and the number of extreme values?

d. Complete these statements:

i. The graph of a polynomial curve of degree n has at most ? x-intercepts. n

ii. A polynomial function of degree n has at most ? real zeros. n

iii. A polynomial function of degree n has ? complex zeros. n

iv. The graph of a polynomial function of degree n has at most ? extreme values. $n - 1$

11a. i. $y = (x + 5)^2(x + 2)(x - 1)$

11a. ii. $y = -(x + 5)^2(x + 2)(x - 1)$

11a. iii. $y = (x + 5)^2(x + 2)(x - 1)^2$

11a. iv. $y = -(x + 5)(x + 2)^3(x - 1)$

12a. i. 4; **ii.** 4; **iii.** 5; **iv.** 5

12b. i. 3; **ii.** 3; **iii.** 4; **iv.** 2

12c. The number of extreme values of a polynomial function of degree n is at most $n - 1$.

13. In the lesson you saw various possible appearances of the graph of a 3rd-degree polynomial function, and in Exercise 10 you explored possible appearances of the graph of a 4th-degree polynomial function. In Exercises 11 and 12, you found a relationship between the degree of a polynomial function and the number of zeros and extreme values. Use all the patterns you have noticed in these problems to sketch one possible graph of

a. A 5th-degree function.

b. A 6th-degree function.

c. A 7th-degree function.

13a. sample answer:

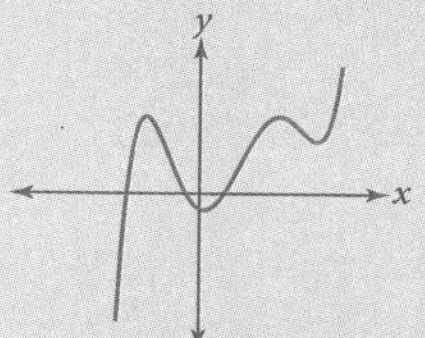

13b. sample answer:

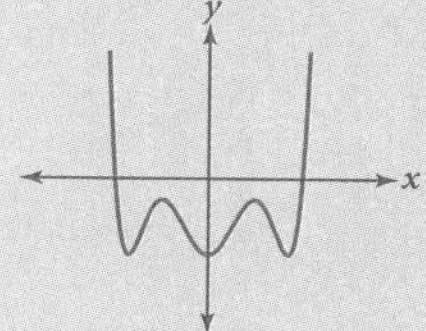

13c. sample answer:

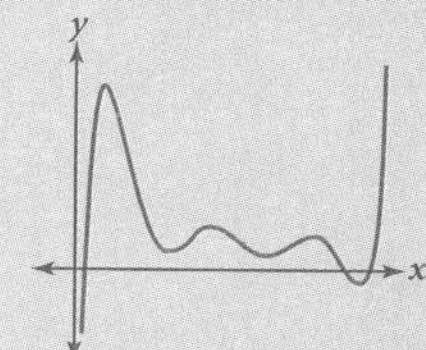

Review

7.4 **14.** Find the roots of these quadratic equations. Express them as fractions.

a. $0 = 3x^2 - 13x - 10$

b. $0 = 6x^2 - 11x + 3$

c. List all the factors of the constant term, c, and the leading coefficient, a, for 14a and b. What do you notice about the relationship between the factors of a and c, and the roots of the functions?

7.4 **15.** If $3 + 5\sqrt{2}$ is a solution of a quadratic equation with rational coefficients, then what other number must also be a solution? Write an equation in general form that has these solutions. $3 - 5\sqrt{2}$; $0 = a(x^2 - 6x - 41)$ where $a \neq 0$

7.5 **16.** Given the function $Q(x) = x^2 + 2x + 10$, find these values.

a. $Q(-3)$ 13 **b.** $Q\left(-\frac{1}{5}\right)$ $\frac{241}{25}$ **c.** $Q(2 - 3\sqrt{2})$ $36 - 18\sqrt{2}$ **d.** $Q(-1 + 3i)$ 0

6.4 **17.** Solve this system using each method specified.

$$\begin{cases} 4x + 9y = 4 \\ 2x = 7 + 3y \end{cases}$$

a. Use an inverse matrix and matrix multiplication.

b. Write an augmented matrix, and reduce it to reduced row-echelon form.

5.4 **18. APPLICATION** According to Froude's Law, the speed at which an aquatic animal can swim is proportional to the square root of its length. (*On Growth and Form,* Sir D'Arcy Thompson, Cambridge University Press, 1961.) If a 75-foot blue whale can swim at a maximum speed of 20 knots, write a function that relates its speed to its length. How fast would a similar 60-foot-long blue whale be able to swim?

$S = \frac{20}{\sqrt{75}}\sqrt{\ell}$; approximately 17.9 knots

A blue whale surfaces for air in the Gulf of St. Lawrence near Les Escoumins, Québéc, Canada. The blue whale is the world's largest mammal.

Exercise 14 This exercise previews the rational root theorem, which students will encounter in Lesson 7.8 As needed, review roots or solutions of equations, zeros of functions, and x-intercepts of graphs.

14a. $x = -\frac{2}{3}$ or $x = 5$

14b. $x = \frac{3}{2}$ or $x = \frac{1}{3}$

14c. For equation 14a, factors of the constant term are ±1, ±2, ±5, ±10; factors of the leading coefficient are ±1, ±3. For equation 14b, the factors of the constant term are ±1, ±3; factors of the leading coefficient are ±1, ±2, ±3, ±6. Each root is the quotient of a factor of the constant term and a factor of the leading coefficient.

Exercise 15 [Ask] "Why is the value $3 - 5\sqrt{2}$ necessarily another root?" [When the roots are multiplied, the last terms must multiply to a rational number, so the other root must be of the form $a - b\sqrt{2}$. The sum of the roots must also be a rational number, so b must be 5, meaning that a must be 3.]

Exercise 17 Assign only the parts of this exercise that review what your class actually covered.

17a. $\begin{bmatrix} 4 & 9 \\ 2 & -3 \end{bmatrix}\begin{bmatrix} x \\ y \end{bmatrix} = \begin{bmatrix} 4 \\ 7 \end{bmatrix}$ $\begin{bmatrix} x \\ y \end{bmatrix} = \begin{bmatrix} \frac{5}{2} \\ -\frac{2}{3} \end{bmatrix}$

17b. $\left[\begin{array}{cc|c} 4 & 9 & 4 \\ 2 & -3 & 7 \end{array}\right] \rightarrow \left[\begin{array}{cc|c} 1 & 0 & \frac{5}{2} \\ 0 & 1 & -\frac{2}{3} \end{array}\right]$

Exercise 18 There are several ways to write an equation. For example, let l represent length in feet and s represent speed in knots; $s = \frac{4}{3}\sqrt{3l}$

EXTENSIONS

A. Use Take Another Look activity 2 on page 421.

B. Challenge students to find a real-world problem that can be modeled by a polynomial of degree higher than 2.

LESSON 7.8

PLANNING

LESSON OUTLINE

First day:

15 min Example A

20 min Example B

10 min Exercises

Second day:

20 min Synthetic division

5 min Sharing

20 min Exercises

MATERIALS

- Polynomial Long Division (T), *optional*
- Synthetic Division (T), *optional*
- Calculator Notes 7G, 7H, *optional*

TEACHING

In this lesson students see ways to find zeros of higher-degree polynomial functions.

One Step

Display the function from Example B,

$y = 3x^3 + 5x^2 - 15x - 25$

and challenge students to try to factor it by finding its zeros exactly. Encourage them to think about how the factors of 3 and 25 might relate to a rational root, perhaps considering analogies to a quadratic function. After they find the rational root, again draw analogies to the quadratic case to encourage dividing by the binomial. Refer students back to long division of whole numbers for this division of polynomials.

During Sharing, formalize students' observations with the terms *Factor Theorem* and *Rational Root Theorem,* and have students develop synthetic division as a shortcut for long division of polynomials.

LESSON 7.8 More About Finding Solutions

It isn't that they can't see the solution. It is that they can't see the problem.

G. K. CHESTERTON

You can find zeros of a quadratic function by factoring or by using the quadratic formula. How can you find the zeros of a higher-degree polynomial? Sometimes a graph will show you zeros in the form of x-intercepts, but only if they are real. And this method is often accurate only if the zeros have integer values. Fortunately, there is a method for finding exact zeros of many higher-degree polynomial functions. It is based on the procedure of long division. You first need to find one or more zeros. Then you divide your polynomial function by the factors associated with those zeros. Repeat this process until you have a polynomial function that you can find the zeros of by factoring or using the quadratic formula. Let's start with an example in which we already know several zeros. Then you'll learn a technique for finding some zeros when they're not so obvious.

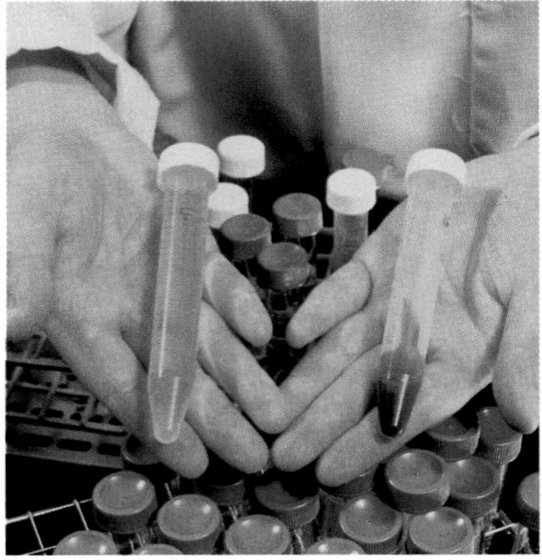

Blood is often separated into two of its factors, plasma and red blood cells.

EXAMPLE A What are the zeros of $P(x) = x^5 - 6x^4 + 20x^3 - 60x^2 + 99x - 54$?

▶ ***Solution*** The graph appears to have x-intercepts at 1, 2, and 3. You can confirm that these values are zeros of the function by substituting them into $P(x)$.

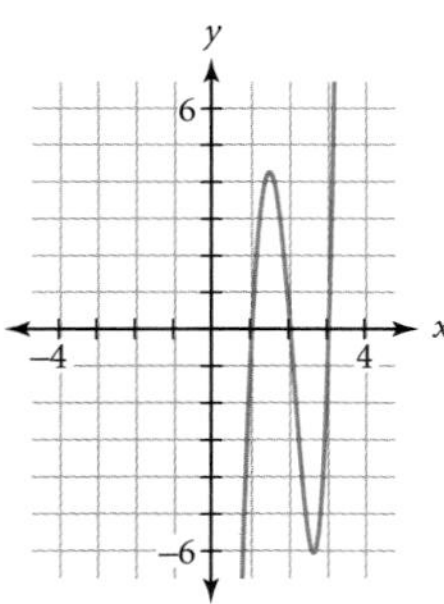

$$P(1) = (1)^5 - 6(1)^4 + 20(1)^3 - 60(1)^2 + 99(1) - 54 = 0$$
$$P(2) = (2)^5 - 6(2)^4 + 20(2)^3 - 60(2)^2 + 99(2) - 54 = 0$$
$$P(3) = (3)^5 - 6(3)^4 + 20(3)^3 - 60(3)^2 + 99(3) - 54 = 0$$

LESSON OBJECTIVES

- Learn to find zeros of higher-degree polynomial functions when only a few of the zeros can be found from its graph
- Use the Rational Root Theorem to identify rational numbers that might be zeros
- Confirm that a number is a zero of a polynomial function by using the Factor Theorem and use long division to factor and find zeros of higher-degree polynomial functions
- Understand and use synthetic division as a shortened form of long division for polynomials

NCTM STANDARDS

	CONTENT		PROCESS
✓	Number		Problem Solving
✓	Algebra		Reasoning
	Geometry		Communication
	Measurement	✓	Connections
	Data/Probability		Representation

For all three values, you get $P(x) = 0$, which shows that $x = 1$, $x = 2$, and $x = 3$ are zeros. This also means that $(x - 1)$, $(x - 2)$, and $(x - 3)$ are factors of $x^5 - 6x^4 + 20x^3 - 60x^2 + 99x - 54$. None of the x-intercepts has the appearance of a repeated root, and you know that a 5th-degree polynomial function has five complex zeros, so this function must have two additional nonreal zeros.

You know that $(x - 1)$, $(x - 2)$, and $(x - 3)$ are all factors of the polynomial, so the product of these three factors, $x^3 - 6x^2 + 11x - 6$, must be a factor also. Your task is to find another factor such that

$$\left(x^3 - 6x^2 + 11x - 6\right)(\textit{factor}) = x^5 - 6x^4 + 20x^3 - 60x^2 + 99x - 54$$

You can find this factor by using long division.

$$\begin{array}{r} x^2 \phantom{{}- 6x^4 + 20x^3 - 60x^2 + 99x - 54} \\ x^3 - 6x^2 + 11x - 6 \overline{\smash{)}\, x^5 - 6x^4 + 20x^3 - 60x^2 + 99x - 54} \\ \underline{x^5 - 6x^4 + 11x^3 - 6x^2 \phantom{{}+ 99x - 54}} \\ 9x^3 - 54x^2 + 99x - 54 \end{array}$$

First, divide x^5 by x^3 to get x^2.

Then, multiply x^2 by the divisor.

Subtract.

$$\begin{array}{r} x^2 + 9 \phantom{{}+ 20x^3 - 60x^2 + 99x - 54} \\ x^3 - 6x^2 + 11x - 6 \overline{\smash{)}\, x^5 - 6x^4 + 20x^3 - 60x^2 + 99x - 54} \\ \underline{x^5 - 6x^4 + 11x^3 - 6x^2 \phantom{{}+ 99x - 54}} \\ 9x^3 - 54x^2 + 99x - 54 \\ \underline{9x^3 - 54x^2 + 99x - 54} \\ 0 \end{array}$$

Now divide $9x^3$ by x^3 to get 9.

Then, multiply 9 by the divisor.

Subtract.

The remainder is zero, so the division is finished, resulting in two factors.

Now you can rewrite the original polynomial as a product of factors:

$$\begin{aligned} x^5 - 6x^4 + 20x^3 - 60x^2 + 99x - 54 &= \left(x^3 - 6x^2 + 11x - 6\right)\left(x^2 + 9\right) \\ &= (x - 1)(x - 2)(x - 3)\left(x^2 + 9\right) \end{aligned}$$

Now that the polynomial is in factored form, you can find the zeros. You knew three of them from the graph. The two additional zeros are contained in the factor $x^2 + 9$. What values of x make $x^2 + 9$ equal zero? If you solve the equation $x^2 + 9 = 0$, you get $x = \pm 3i$.

Therefore, the five zeros are $x = 1$, $x = 2$, $x = 3$, $x = 3i$, and $x = -3i$.

To confirm that a number is a zero, you can use the **Factor Theorem.**

Factor Theorem

$(x - r)$ is a factor of a polynomial function $P(x)$ if and only if $P(r) = 0$.

In the example, you showed that $P(1)$, $P(2)$, and $P(3)$ equal zero. You can check that $P(3i)$ and $P(-3i)$ will also equal zero.

$P(3i) = (3i)^5 - 6(3i)^4 + 20(3i)^3 - 60(3i)^2 + 99(3i) - 54 = 243i^5 - 486i^4 + 540i^3 - 540i^2 + 297i - 54 = 243i - 486 - 540i + 540 + 297i - 54 = 0$

$P(-3i) = (-3i)^5 - 6(-3i)^4 + 20(-3i)^3 - 60(-3i)^2 + 99(-3i) - 54 = -243i^5 - 486i^4 - 540i^3 - 540i^2 - 297i - 54 = -243i - 486 + 540i + 540 - 297i - 54 = 0$

► ***EXAMPLE A***

You might want to use the Polynomial Long Division transparency and do a simple long division problem of numbers $\left(\text{for example, } \frac{134}{2}\right)$ alongside the polynomial long division to show the similarities in each step.

As you talk about representing missing terms for some powers in a polynomial, you can make an analogy to the difference between 10,358 and 1358. The zero is necessary as a placeholder and must be used in both long division and synthetic division.

Polynomial long division is tedious and can be frustrating for students. Additional examples might relieve some of the frustration.

[Language] In a division problem, the *dividend* is the expression being divided, and the *divisor* is the expression that is doing the dividing.

▶ **EXAMPLE B**

Using the rational root theorem can be very time-consuming. Before going over the solution, you may want to brainstorm all the possible rational roots of an equation, or zeros of a function. Consider giving each person in the class a different potential zero to check. A discussion on how to narrow down the zeros by looking at a graph can follow this activity.

You may want to teach your students how to have a calculator estimate the zeros. (See Calculator Note 7H.) If a rational zero is found, students can use that zero to divide the polynomial. Students must be able to recognize repeating decimals as fractions or must have a calculator that will display numbers in Exact mode in order to use this method.

[Language] You might remind students that the *zeros of a polynomial function* are the values that make $f(x)$ equal zero. The solutions to the equation $f(x) = 0$ are also called *roots of the equation.*

Division of polynomials is similar to the long-division process that you may have learned in elementary school. Both the original polynomial and the divisor are written in descending order of the powers of x. If any degree is missing, insert a term with coefficient 0 as a placeholder. For example, you can write the polynomial $x^4 + 3x^2 - 5x + 8$ as

$$x^4 + 0x^3 + 3x^2 - 5x + 8$$

Insert a zero placeholder because the polynomial did not have a 3rd-degree term.

Often you won't be able to find any zeros for certain by looking at a graph. However, there is a pattern to rational numbers that might be zeros.

Rational Root Theorem

If the polynomial equation $P(x) = 0$ has rational roots, they are of the form $\frac{p}{q}$, where p is a factor of the constant term and q is a factor of the leading coefficient.

The Rational Root Theorem helps you narrow down the values that might be zeros of a polynomial function. Notice that this theorem will identify only possible *rational* roots. It won't find roots that are irrational or contain imaginary numbers.

EXAMPLE B

Find the roots of this polynomial equation:

$$3x^3 + 5x^2 - 15x - 25 = 0$$

▶ **Solution**

First, graph the function $y = 3x^2 + 5x^2 - 15x - 25$ to see if there are any identifiable integer x-intercepts.

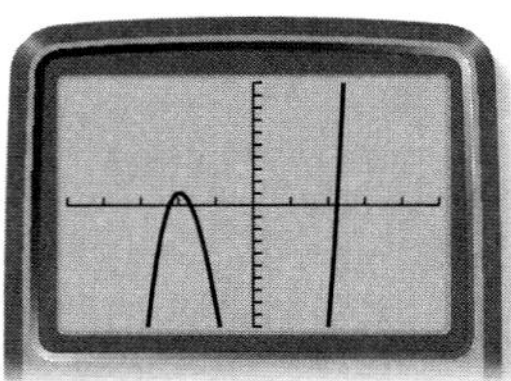

$[-5, 5, 1, -10, 10, 1]$

There are no integer x-intercepts, but the graph shows x-intercepts between -3 and -2, -2 and -1, and 2 and 3. Any rational root of this polynomial will be a factor of -25, the constant term, divided by a factor of 3, the leading coefficient. The factors of -25 are ±1, ±5, and ±25, and the factors of 3 are ±1 and ±3, so the possible rational roots are ±1, ±5, ±25, $\pm\frac{1}{3}$, $\pm\frac{5}{3}$, or $\pm\frac{25}{3}$. The only one of these that looks like a possibility on the graph is $-\frac{5}{3}$. Try substituting $-\frac{5}{3}$ into the original polynomial.

$$3\left(-\frac{5}{3}\right)^3 + 5\left(-\frac{5}{3}\right)^2 - 15\left(-\frac{5}{3}\right) - 25 = 0$$

Because the result is 0, you know that $-\frac{5}{3}$ is a root of the equation. If $-\frac{5}{3}$ is a root of the equation, then $\left(x+\frac{5}{3}\right)$ is a factor. Use long division to divide out this factor.

$$\begin{array}{r} 3x^2 - 15 \\ x+\frac{5}{3}\overline{\smash{)}3x^3 + 5x^2 - 15x - 25} \\ \underline{3x^3 + 5x^2} \\ 0 - 15x - 25 \\ \underline{-15x - 25} \\ 0 \end{array}$$

So $3x^3 + 5x^2 - 15x - 25 = 0$ is equivalent to $\left(x+\frac{5}{3}\right)(3x^2 - 15) = 0$. You already knew $-\frac{5}{3}$ was a root. Now solve $3x^2 - 15 = 0$.

$$3x^2 = 15$$
$$x^2 = 5$$
$$x = \pm\sqrt{5}$$

The three roots are $x = -\frac{5}{3}$, $x = \sqrt{5}$, and $x = -\sqrt{5}$. As decimal approximations, $-\frac{5}{3}$ is about -1.7, $\sqrt{5}$ is about 2.2, and $-\sqrt{5}$ is about -2.2. These values appear to be correct based on the graph.

Now that you know the roots, you could write the equation in factored form as $3\left(x+\frac{5}{3}\right)\left(x-\sqrt{5}\right)\left(x+\sqrt{5}\right) = 0$ or $(3x+5)\left(x-\sqrt{5}\right)\left(x+\sqrt{5}\right) = 0$. You need the coefficient of 3 to make sure you have the correct leading coefficient in general form.

When you divide a polynomial by a linear factor, such as $\left(x+\frac{5}{3}\right)$, you can use a shortcut method called **synthetic division.** Synthetic division is simply an abbreviated form of long division.

Consider this division of a cubic polynomial by a linear factor:

$$\frac{6x^3 + 11x^2 - 17x - 30}{x+2}$$

Here are the procedures using both long division and synthetic division:

Long Division

$$\begin{array}{rr} & 6x^2 - 1x - 15 \\ x+2\overline{\smash{)}} & 6x^3 + 11x^2 - 17x - 30 \\ (-) & \underline{6x^3 + 12x^2} \\ & -1x^2 - 17x \\ (-) & \underline{-1x^2 - 2x} \\ & -15x - 30 \\ (-) & \underline{-15x - 30} \\ & 0 \end{array}$$

Synthetic Division

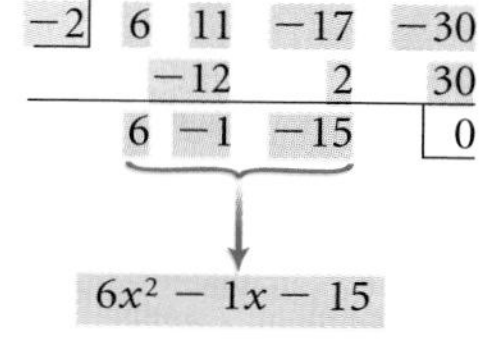

Both methods give a quotient of $6x^2 - 1x - 15$, but synthetic division certainly looks faster. The corresponding numbers in each process are shaded. Notice that synthetic division contains all of the same information, but in a condensed form.

Synthetic Division

Synthetic division simplifies long division much as matrices simplify operations with systems of equations. In both cases it is easier to work just with the coefficients and not have to write variables repeatedly.

As you look at the top of page 416, guide students to follow the arrows. You might use the Synthetic Division transparency. You might give students Calculator Note 7G, which includes a calculator program that performs synthetic division.

SHARING IDEAS

Students may wonder whether formulas such as the quadratic formula exist for solving higher-degree equations. **[Context]** Formulas for solving general cubic and quartic (4th-degree polynomial) equations were found beginning in the 1500s, but no one was able to find a formula for solving all polynomial equations of higher degree in terms of sums, differences, products, quotients, and roots. In the mid-1820s, the young Norwegian mathematician Niels Abel proved that there can be no such formula for equations of any degree higher than 4.

Assessing Progress

From students' responses and questions, you can assess their understanding of the connections among zeros, roots, solutions, and x-intercepts.

Closing the Lesson

According to the **Rational Root Theorem,** any rational zero of a polynomial function will be a ratio of a factor of the constant term to a factor of the leading coefficient. Instead of checking all ratios of this form, you can see which ones appear close to x-intercepts in the graph of the function and test only those ratios. Once you've found one zero, r, the **Factor Theorem** tells you that the binomial $x - r$ is a factor of the polynomial. You can divide it out using long division or synthetic division and then find a zero of the quotient, repeating the process until you get a quotient that's quadratic and can be dealt with using the quadratic formula. This method will find all zeros of a polynomial function that has no more than two nonrational zeros.

BUILDING UNDERSTANDING

The exercises give students practice in factoring and solving polynomial functions and equations by using long division and the Rational Root Theorem.

ASSIGNING HOMEWORK

Essential	1–5
Performance assessment	6–10
Group	6, 10
Review	11–15

MATERIALS

- Calculator Note 7I

Helping with the Exercises

Exercise 2 [ESL] The terms *dividend, divisor,* and *quotient* all refer to parts of a division calculation. For example, in the division problem $8 \div 2 = 4$, the dividend (8) is the number that is being divided, the divisor (2) does the dividing, and the quotient (4) is the result.

Here's how to do synthetic division:

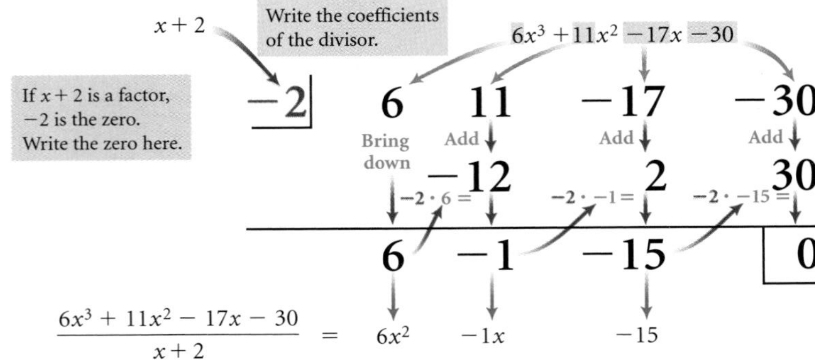

$$\frac{6x^3 + 11x^2 - 17x - 30}{x + 2} = 6x^2 \quad -1x \quad -15$$

The number farthest to the right in the last row of a synthetic division problem is the remainder, which in this case is 0. When the remainder in a division problem is 0, you know that the divisor is a factor. This means -2 is a zero and the polynomial $6x^3 + 11x^2 - 17x - 30$ factors into the product of the divisor and the quotient, or $(x + 2)(6x^2 - 1x - 15)$. You could now use any of the methods you've learned—simple factoring, the quadratic formula, synthetic division, or perhaps graphing—to factor the quotient even further.

EXERCISES

Practice Your Skills

1. Find the missing polynomial in each long-division problem.

a.

$$\begin{array}{r} \boxed{a}\;\; 3x^2 + 7x + 3 \\ x + 5\,\overline{)\,3x^3 + 22x^2 + 38x + 15} \\ \underline{3x^3 + 15x^2 \qquad\qquad\quad} \\ 7x^2 + 38x + 15 \\ \underline{7x^2 + 35x \qquad} \\ 3x + 15 \\ \underline{3x + 15} \\ 0 \end{array}$$

b.

$$\begin{array}{r} 2x^2 + \quad 5x - \quad 3 \\ 3x - 2\,\overline{)\,6x^3 + 11x^2 - 19x + 6} \\ \underline{\boxed{b}\;\; 6x^3 - 4x^2 \qquad\qquad} \\ 15x^2 - 19x + 6 \\ \underline{15x^2 - 10x \qquad} \\ -9x + 6 \\ \underline{-9x + 6} \\ 0 \end{array}$$

2. Use the dividend, divisor, and quotient to rewrite each long-division problem in Exercise 1 as a factored product in the form $P(x) = D(x) \cdot Q(x)$. For example, $x^3 + 2x^2 + 3x - 6 = (x - 1)(x^2 + 3x + 6)$.

3. Find the missing value in each synthetic-division problem.

a.

$$\begin{array}{c|cccc} 4 & 3 & -11 & 7 & -44 \\ & & \boxed{a} & 4 & 44 \\ \hline & 3 & 1 & 11 & \vert\; 0 \end{array}$$

$a = 12$

b.

$$\begin{array}{c|cccc} -3 & 1 & 5 & -1 & -21 \\ & & -3 & -6 & 21 \\ \hline & 1 & \boxed{b} & -7 & \vert\; 0 \end{array}$$

$b = 2$

c.

$$\begin{array}{c|cccc} 1.5 & 4 & -8 & \boxed{c} & -6 \\ & & 6 & -3 & 6 \\ \hline & 4 & -2 & 4 & \vert\; 0 \end{array}$$

$c = 7$

d.

$$\begin{array}{c|cccc} \boxed{d} & 1 & 7 & 11 & -4 \\ & & -4 & -12 & 4 \\ \hline & 1 & 3 & -1 & \vert\; 0 \end{array}$$

$d = -4$

4. Use the dividend, divisor, and quotient to rewrite each synthetic-division problem in Exercise 3 as a factored product in the form $P(x) = D(x) \cdot Q(x)$.

5. Make a list of the possible rational roots of $0 = 2x^3 + 3x^2 - 32x + 15$.

2a. $3x^3 + 22x^2 + 38x + 15 = (x + 5)(3x^2 + 7x + 3)$

2b. $6x^3 + 11x^2 - 19x + 6 = (3x - 2)(2x^2 + 5x - 3)$

4a. $3x^3 - 11x^2 + 7x - 44 = (x - 4)(3x^2 + x + 11)$

4b. $x^3 + 5x^2 - x - 21 = (x + 3)(x^2 + 2x - 7)$

4c. $4x^3 - 8x^2 + 7x - 6 = (x - 1.5)(4x^2 - 2x + 4)$

4d. $x^3 + 7x^2 + 11x - 4 = (x + 4)(x^2 + 3x - 1)$

5. $\pm 15, \pm 5, \pm 3, \pm 1, \pm\frac{15}{2}, \pm\frac{5}{2}, \pm\frac{3}{2}, \pm\frac{1}{2}$

Reason and Apply

6. Division often results in a remainder. In each of these problems, use the polynomial that defines P as the dividend and the polynomial that defines D as the divisor. Write the result of the division in the form $P(x) = D(x) \cdot Q(x) + R$, where R is an integer remainder. For example, $x^3 + 2x^2 + 3x - 4 = (x - 1)(x^2 + 3x + 6) + 2$.

a. $P(x) = 47$, $D(x) = 11$ $47 = 11 \cdot 4 + 3$

b. $P(x) = 6x^4 - 5x^3 + 7x^2 - 12x + 15$, $D(x) = x - 1$ $P(x) = (x - 1)(6x^3 + x^2 + 8x - 4) + 11$

c. $P(x) = x^3 - x^2 - 10x + 16$, $D(x) = x - 2$ $P(x) = (x - 2)(x^2 + x - 8) + 0$

7. Consider the function $P(x) = 2x^3 - x^2 + 18x - 9$.

a. Verify that $3i$ is a zero. $2(3i)^3 - (3i)^2 + 18(3i) - 9 = -54i + 9 + 54i - 9 = 0$

b. Find the remaining zeros of the function P. $x = -3i$ and $x = \frac{1}{2}$

8. Consider the function $y = x^4 + 3x^3 - 11x^2 - 3x + 10$.

a. How many zeros does this function have? 4

b. Name the zeros. $x = 1, x = 2, x = -5$, and $x = -1$

c. Write the polynomial function in factored form. $y = (x + 5)(x + 1)(x - 1)(x - 2)$

9. Use your list of possible rational roots from Exercise 5 to write this function in factored form.

$y = 2x^3 + 3x^2 - 32x + 15$ $y = (x - 3)(x + 5)(2x - 1)$ or $y = 2(x - 3)(x + 5)\left(x - \frac{1}{2}\right)$

10. When you trace the graph of a function on your calculator to find the value of an x-intercept, you often see the y-value jump from positive to negative when you pass over the zero. By using smaller windows, you can find increasingly more accurate approximations for x. This process can be automated by your calculator. The automation uses successive midpoints of each region above and below zero; it is called the **bisection method.** Approximate the x-intercepts for each equation by using the program BISECTN, then use synthetic or long division to find any nonreal zeros. [▶ See **Calculator Note 7I** for the BISECTN program. ◀]

a. $y = x^5 - x^4 - 16x + 16$

b. $y = 2x^3 + 15x^2 + 6x - 6$

c. $y = 0.2(x - 12)^5 - 6(x - 12)^3 - (x - 12)^2 + 1$

d. $y = 2x^4 + 2x^3 - 14x^2 - 9x - 12$

Technology CONNECTION

Many computer programs employ search methods that find a particular data item in a large collection of items. It would be inefficient to search for the item one piece of data at a time, so, instead, a binary search algorithm is used. First, the computer sorts the data items and checks the middle entry. If it is too low, the search algorithm will move halfway up toward the highest entry to check, or if it's too high the algorithm will check halfway toward the lowest entry. Each time, the item list is cut in half (going higher or lower) until the item being searched is reached. In a list of n items, the maximum number of times the list would have to be cut in half before finding the target is $\log_2 n + 1$.

Search

algorithms

Search

Exercise 6 [Alert] If students are having difficulty, you may want to work through the given example with the class. The degree of remainder R must be less than the degree of D, just as the remainder is less than the divisor when we divide numbers.

Exercise 7b [Ask] "Do you know more than one zero of this function?" [The conjugate of $3i$, $-3i$, is also a zero.] "Dividing through by an imaginary number can be difficult; is there an easier method?" [Dividing by $(x - 3i)(x + 3i)$, or $x^2 + 9$, is simpler because its coefficients are real.]

Exercise 9 A graph might help students pick which rational roots are reasonable.

Exercise 10 As needed, impress upon students how difficult these problems would be without calculators.

10a. $x = \pm 2, x = 1$, and $x = \pm 2i$

10b. $x \approx -7.01, x \approx -0.943$, and $x \approx 0.454$

10c. $x \approx 6.605, x \approx 12.501$, $x \approx 17.556$, and $x \approx 11.675 \pm 0.380i$

10d. $x \approx -3.033, x \approx 2.634$, and $x \approx -0.3 \pm 0.812i$

MAKING THE CONNECTION

[Language] An *algorithm* is a step-by-step procedure for finding the solution to a particular problem. *Binary search algorithms* repeatedly eliminate half of a given set of data until the desired term is found, but they require other programs to collect and order that data first. Internet search engines, for example, use computer programs called "spiders" to navigate the Internet and collect sets of words found on websites. Complex indexing programs then rank each term according to various criteria, such as popularity of the website and the number of times the word appeared on the page.

Students can try the binary search algorithm in a number guessing game. Have a student think of a whole number between 1 and 100. When others guess a number, the student will only indicate to guess higher or lower until the number is guessed. Can the number be found in at most seven guesses?

Exercise 13 Challenge students to rephrase each inequality as a statement about the real-world situation.

14a. $y = x^2 - 4x - 12$, $y = (x - 6)(x + 2)$; vertex: $(2, -16)$; y-intercept: -12; x-intercepts: 6, -2

14b. $y = 3x^2 + 6x - 24$, $y = 3(x - 2)(x + 4)$; vertex: $(-1, -27)$; y-intercept: -24; x-intercepts: 2, -4

14c. $y = -\frac{1}{2}x^2 + 5x + 12$, $y = -\frac{1}{2}(x - 12)(x + 2)$; vertex: $\left(5, \frac{49}{2}\right)$; y-intercept: 12; x-intercepts: 12, -2

EXTENSION

Have students find the roots of the functions $y = x^3 - 1$, $y = x^4 - 1$, and $y = x^6 - 1$; graph them on the complex plane; and make a conjecture about the roots of the general function $y = x^n - 1$.

Review

5.5 **11.** **APPLICATION** The relationship between the height and the diameter of a tree is approximately determined by the equation $f(x) = kx^{3/2}$, where x is the height in feet, $f(x)$ is the diameter in inches, and k is a constant that depends on the kind of tree you are measuring.

a. A 221 ft British Columbian pine is about 21 in. in diameter. Find the value of k, and use it to express diameter as a function of height. $f(x) = 0.00639x^{3/2}$

b. Give the inverse function. $f^{-1}(x) \approx (156x)^{2/3}$

c. Find the diameter of a 300 ft British Columbian pine. 33 in.

d. What would be the height of a similar pine that is 15 in. in diameter? about 176 ft

7.1 **12.** Find a polynomial function of lowest possible degree whose graph passes through the points $(-2, -8.2)$, $(-1, 6.8)$, $(0, 5)$, $(1, -1)$, $(2, 1.4)$, and $(3, 24.8)$. $y = 2.1x^3 - 2.1x^2 - 6x + 5$

6.6 **13.** **APPLICATION** Sam and Beth have started a hat business in their basement. They make baseball caps and sun hats. Let b represent the number of baseball caps, and let s represent the number of sun hats. Manufacturing demands and machinery constraints confine the production per day to the feasible region defined by

$$\begin{cases} b \geq 0 \\ s \geq 0 \\ 4s - b \leq 20 \\ 2s + b \leq 22 \\ 7b - 8s \leq 77 \end{cases}$$

They make a profit of \$2 per baseball hat and \$1 per sun hat.

a. Graph the feasible region. Give the coordinate of the vertices.

b. How many of each type of hat should they produce per day for maximum profit? (*Note:* At the end of each day, all partially made hats are recycled at no profit.) What is the maximum daily profit? 15 baseball caps and 3 sun hats; \$33

7.2 **14.** Write each quadratic function in general form and in factored form. Identify the vertex, y-intercept, and x-intercepts of each parabola.

a. $y = (x - 2)^2 - 16$

b. $y = 3(x + 1)^2 - 27$

c. $y = -\frac{1}{2}(x - 5)^2 + \frac{49}{2}$

d. $y = 2(x - 3)^2 + 3$

7.5 **15.** Solve.

a. $6x + x^2 + 5 = -4 + 4(x + 3)$ $x = -3$ or $x = 1$

b. $7 = x(x + 3)$ $x = \frac{-3 \pm \sqrt{37}}{2}$

c. $2x^2 - 3x + 1 = x^2 - x - 4$ $x = 1 \pm 2i$

13a.

s
$2s + b = 22$
$4s - b = 20$
$(8, 7)$
$7b - 8s = 77$
$(0, 5)$
$(15, 3.5)$
b
$(0, 0)$
$(11, 0)$

14d. $y = 2x^2 - 12x + 21$; $y = 2\left(x - \frac{6 + i\sqrt{6}}{2}\right)\left(x - \frac{6 - i\sqrt{6}}{2}\right)$; vertex: $(3, 3)$; y-intercept: 21; x-intercept: none

CHAPTER 7 REVIEW

Polynomials can be used to represent the motion of projectiles, the areas of regions, and the volumes of boxes. When examining a set of data whose x-values form an arithmetic sequence, you can calculate the **finite differences** to find the **degree** of a polynomial that will fit the data. When you know the degree of the polynomial, you can define a system of equations to solve for the coefficients. Polynomial equations can be written in several forms. The form $a_nx^n + a_{n-1}x^{n-1} + \cdots + a_1x^1 + a_0$ is called **general form.** Quadratic equations, which are 2nd-degree polynomial equations, can also be written in **vertex form** or **factored form,** with each factor corresponding to a **root** of the equation. In a quadratic equation, you can find the roots by using the **quadratic formula.**

There are the same number of roots as the degree of the polynomial. In some cases these roots may include **imaginary** or **complex numbers.** If the coefficients of a polynomial are real, then any nonreal roots come in **conjugate pairs.** The degree of a polynomial function determines the shape of its graph. The graphs may have hills and valleys where you will find **local minimums** and **maximums.** By varying the coefficients, you can change the relative sizes of these hills and valleys.

EXERCISES

1. Factor each expression completely.

a. $2x^2 - 10x + 12$ $2(x-2)(x-3)$
b. $2x^2 + 7x + 3$ $(2x+1)(x+3)$ or $2(x+0.5)(x+3)$
c. $x^3 - 10x^2 - 24x$ $x(x-12)(x+2)$

2. Solve each equation by setting it equal to zero and factoring.

a. $x^2 - 8x = 9$ $x = 9$ or $x = -1$
b. $x^4 + 2x^3 = 15x^2$ $x = 0, x = 3,$ or $x = -5$

3. Using three noncollinear points as vertices, how many different triangles can you draw? Given a choice of four points, no three of which are collinear, how many different triangles can you draw? Given a choice of five points? n points? 1; 4; 10; $\frac{1}{6}n^3 - \frac{1}{2}n^2 + \frac{1}{3}n$

4. Tell whether each equation is written in general form, vertex form, or factored form. Write each equation in the other two forms, if possible.

a. $y = 2(x-2)^2 - 16$
b. $y = -3(x-5)(x+1)$
c. $y = x^2 + 3x + 2$
d. $y = (x+1)(x-3)(x+4)$
e. $y = 2x^2 + 5x - 6$
f. $y = -2 - (x+7)^2$

5. Sketch a graph of each function. Label all zeros and the coordinates of all maximum and minimum points. (Each coordinate should be accurate to the nearest hundredth.)

a. $y = 2(x-2)^2 - 16$
b. $y = -3(x-5)(x+1)$
c. $y = x^2 - 3x + 2$
d. $y = (x+1)(x-3)(x+4)$
e. $y = x^3 + 2x^2 - 19x + 20$
f. $y = 2x^5 - 3x^4 - 11x^3 + 14x^2 + 12x - 8$

ASSIGNING HOMEWORK

If you spend two days on the review to allow some students to give presentations to the class, you can assign all the exercises. Groups might work together on some exercises, such as Exercises 4, 5, 10, and 12.

▶ Helping with the Exercises

Exercise 3 Encourage students to sketch several diagrams using different numbers of vertices and drawing and counting the triangles. Students can then use finite differences to find a model.

Exercise 4 You might accept answers for factored form that include only rational or real numbers. For example, 4a could be $y = 2(x^2 - 4x - 4)$ and 4f could be $y = -(x^2 + 14x + 51)$

Exercise 5 For most of these equations, have students graph the function on paper and use calculators to check their work.

CHAPTER REVIEW 7

PLANNING

LESSON OUTLINE

First day:
15 min Reviewing
15 min Exercises
15 min Student self-assessment

Second day:
20 min Student self-assessment
25 min Exercises

MATERIALS

- Review Data (T)

REVIEWING

Show the Review Data transparency, and ask students to find a good function representing these data and the zeros of that function. Remind students of the terms *polynomial, degree,* and *general form;* how to determine the degree of a polynomial using finite differences; how to find the coefficients through a system of equations; and the distinctions among zeros, roots, and x-intercepts. The graph and the Rational Root Theorem can help students find one zero. **[Ask]** "Polynomials of what other degrees might have a graph of this shape?" After finding one zero, review the Factor Theorem and long or synthetic division to find the quadratic factor. Review the factored form and the vertex form of the quadratic function. Review completing the square to convert general form to vertex form and to derive the quadratic formula and find the roots. Review complex numbers and the fact that complex roots come in conjugate pairs if the coefficients are real.

See page 890 for answers to Exercises 4 and 5.

6a. $y = 2(x + 1)(x - 4)$

6b. $y = 2(x + 3)^2 (x - 1)$

6c. $y = -(x + 2)(x - 3)^3$

6d. $y = 0.5(x + 4)(x - 2)(x - 3i)(x + 3i)$

6. Write the equation of each graph in factored form.

a.

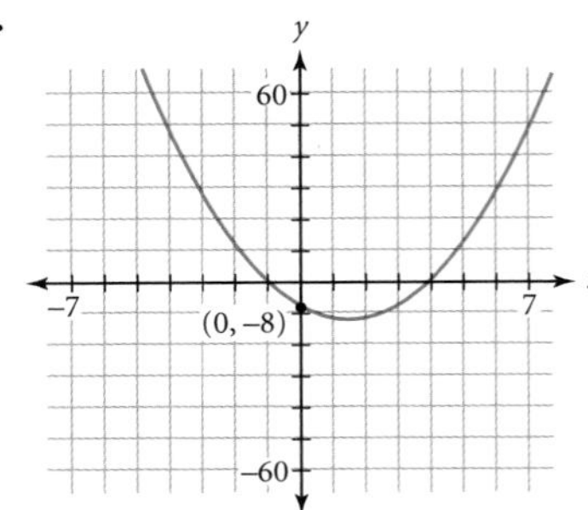

b.

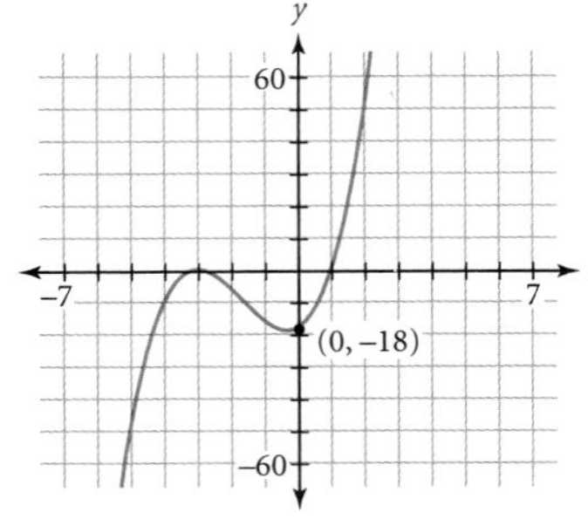

c.

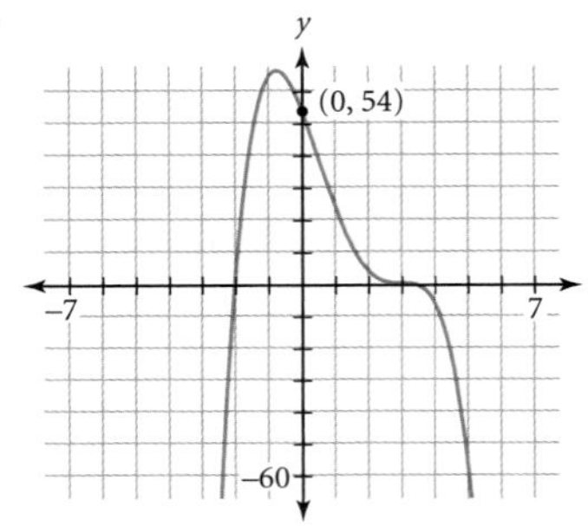

d.

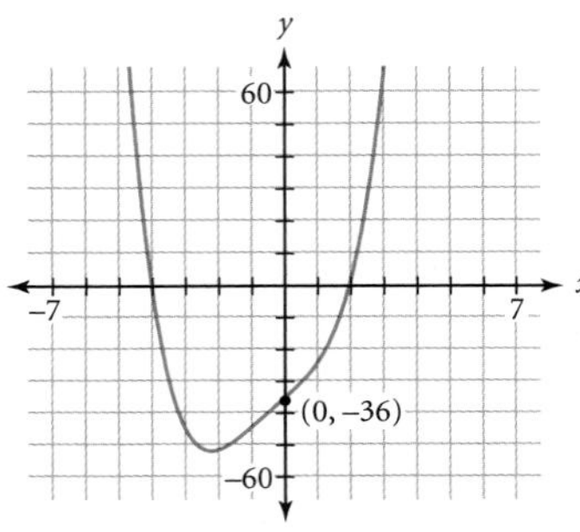

(*Hint:* One of the zeros occurs at $x = 3i$.)

7. 18 in. by 18 in. by 36 in.

7. APPLICATION By postal regulations, the maximum combined girth and length of a rectangular package sent by Priority Mail is 108 in. The length is the longest dimension, and the girth is the perimeter of the cross section. Find the dimensions of the package with maximum volume that can be sent through the mail. (Assume the cross section is always a square with side length x.) Making a table might be helpful.

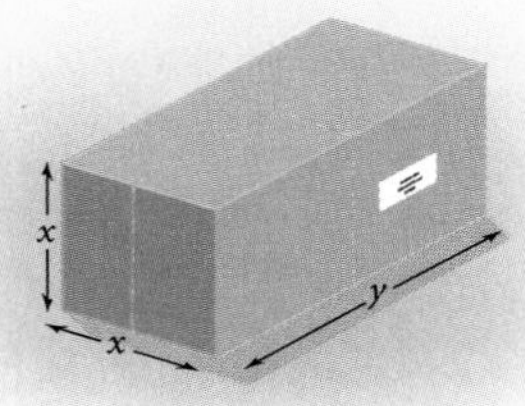

Exercise 8 This exercise uses the projectile motion function from Lesson 7.3.

8. approximately 227 m, or 740 ft

8. An object is dropped from the top of a building into a pool of water at ground level. There is a splash 6.8 s after the object is dropped. How high is the building in meters? In feet?

Exercise 9 Students can use finite differences to find a model, but they probably will need to generate more data first.

9a. $y = 0.5x^2 + 0.5x + 1$

9b. 16 pieces; 56 pieces

9. Consider this puzzle:

a. Write a formula relating the greatest number of pieces of a circle, y, you can obtain from x cuts.

b. Use the formula to find the maximum number of pieces with five cuts and with ten cuts.

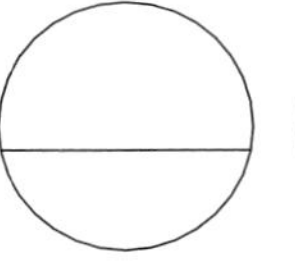

One cut

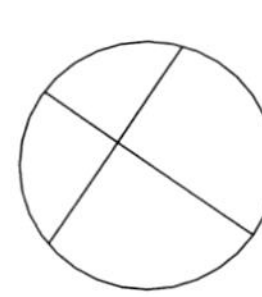

Two cuts

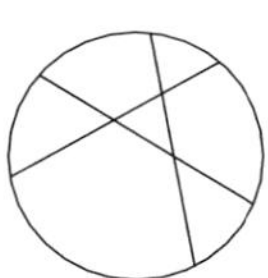

Three cuts

10. This 26-by-21 cm rectangle has been divided into two regions. The width of the unshaded region is x cm, as shown.

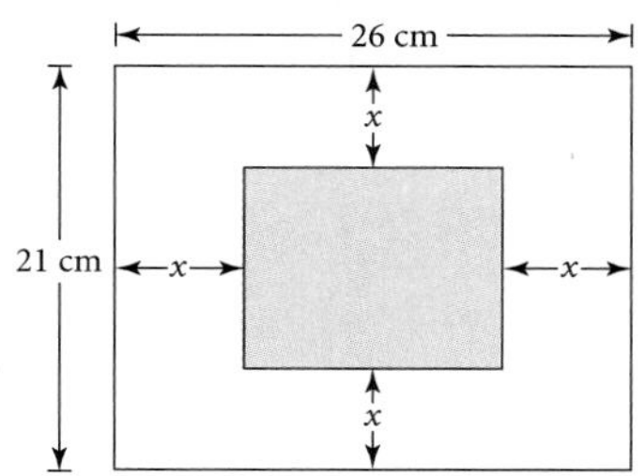

a. Express the area of the shaded part as a function of x, and graph it.

b. Find the domain and range for this function.

c. Find the x-value that makes the two regions (shaded and unshaded) equal in area.

11. Consider the polynomial equation $0 = 3x^4 - 20x^3 + 68x^2 - 92x - 39$.

a. List all possible rational roots.

b. Find the four roots of the equation.

The Grande Arche building at La Defense in Paris, France, is in the form of a hollowed-out cube and functions as an office building, conference center, and exhibition gallery.

12. Write each expression in the form $a + bi$.

a. $(4 - 2i)(-3 + 6i)$ $30i$ **b.** $(-3 + 4i) - (3 + 13i)$ $-6 - 9i$ **c.** $\frac{2 - i}{3 - 4i}$ $0.4 + 0.2i$

13. Divide.

$$\frac{6x^3 + 8x^2 + x - 6}{3x - 2} \quad 2x^2 + 4x + 3$$

TAKE ANOTHER LOOK

1. Use the method of finite differences to find the degree of a polynomial function that fits the data at right. What do you notice? Plot the points. What type of curve do you think might best fit the data?

x	y
0	60
1	42
2	28
3	20
4	14
5	10
6	7

2. How many points do you need to determine a line? How many points do you need to determine a parabola? Cubic curve? Quartic curve? Does the orientation of the curve—horizontal or vertical—matter? How can your conjectures be justified using the method you learned in this chapter for finding the equations of polynomial curves?

10a. $y = (26 - 2x)(21 - 2x)$

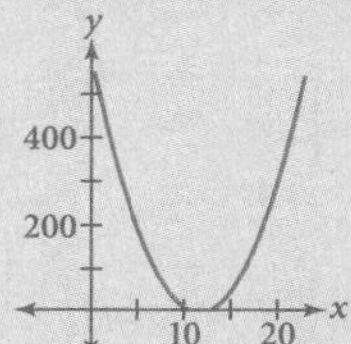

10b. domain: $0 < x < 10.5$; range: $0 < A < 546$

Exercise 10c The area of the unshaded region is $\frac{1}{2}(26)(21)$.

10c. $x \approx 3.395$ cm

11a. $\pm1, \pm3, \pm13, \pm39, \pm\frac{1}{3}, \pm\frac{13}{3}$

Exercise 11b Students might first graph this polynomial to find any integer roots.

11b. $x = -\frac{1}{3}, x = 3, x = 2 + 3i$, and $x = 2 - 3i$

Take Another Look

1. Using the method of finite differences, you never reach a constant difference, so no polynomial function perfectly fits these data. Based on the graph, it appears that an exponential decay curve may fit these data.

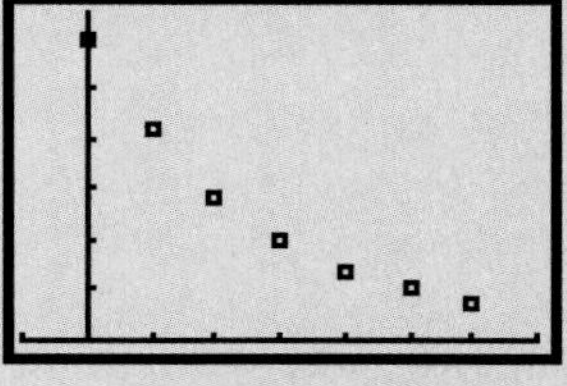

$[-1, 7, 1, 0, 60, 10]$

2. A line is determined by two points. A quadratic curve (parabola) is determined by three points if you know its orientation; if not, you need an additional point to determine the orientation. Continuing the pattern, four points determine a cubic curve, and five points determine a quartic (4th-degree) curve if you know the orientation; if not, you need an additional point. In this chapter students used a system of three equations in three variables to find the coefficients a, b, and c in a quadratic equation. As the degree of the equation increases, the number of coefficients increases, and so does the number of points you need.

3. If you connect the origin and the three points in a particular order, you can construct a parallelogram. The only difference between the parallelograms formed by adding or subtracting is the order in which the points are connected.

4.

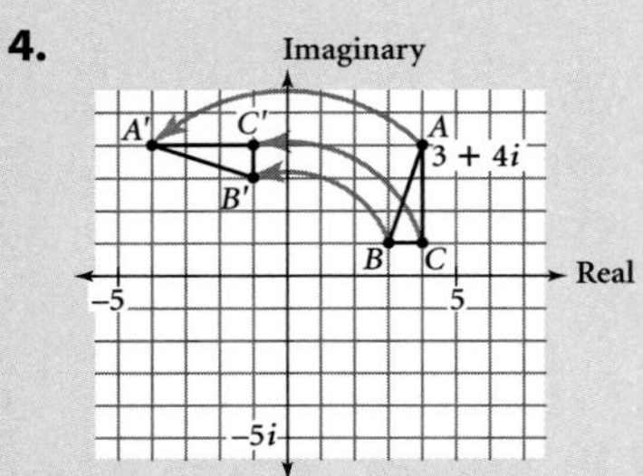

$i \cdot (3 + 4i) = 3i + 4i^2 = -4 + 3i$
$i \cdot (2 + i) = 2i + i^2 = -1 + 2i$
$i \cdot (3 + i) = 3i + i^2 = -1 + 3i$

Plotting the complex numbers associated with the image of $\triangle ABC$ suggests that multiplying by i provides a 90° counterclockwise rotation about the origin.

Multiplying by i^2 rotates the point 180° counterclockwise; multiplying by i^3 rotates it 270° counterclockwise; multiplying by i^n rotates it $n \cdot 90°$ counterclockwise.

In general, multiplying a point by a complex number rotates that point counterclockwise by the angle formed between a segment drawn from the complex number to the origin and the positive x-axis and multiplies the distance of the point from the origin by the distance of the complex number from the origin. For imaginary number i^n, the angle is $n(90°)$ and the distance from the origin is 1.

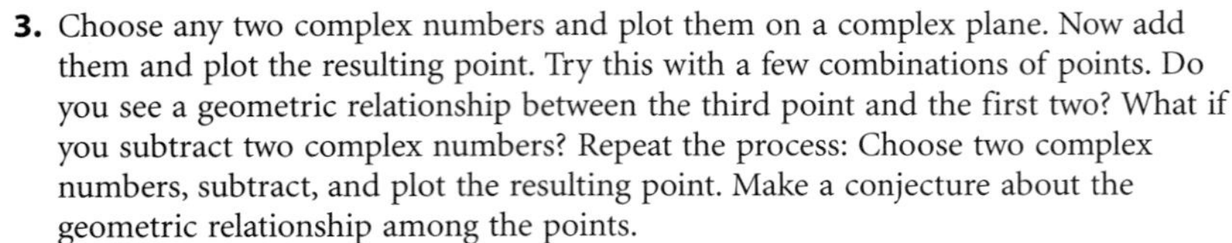

3. Choose any two complex numbers and plot them on a complex plane. Now add them and plot the resulting point. Try this with a few combinations of points. Do you see a geometric relationship between the third point and the first two? What if you subtract two complex numbers? Repeat the process: Choose two complex numbers, subtract, and plot the resulting point. Make a conjecture about the geometric relationship among the points.

4. Multiply each complex number represented by the vertices of $\triangle ABC$ by i. Plot the numbers associated with the results. Make a conjecture about the geometric meaning of $i(a + bi)$. Confirm your conjecture using other points and figures. Explore the geometric meaning of $i^2(a + bi)$. One way to do this is to multiply each complex number associated with the vertices of $\triangle ABC$ by i^2. Plot the points resulting from each multiplication. Make a conjecture for $i^n(a + bi)$. Confirm your conjecture.

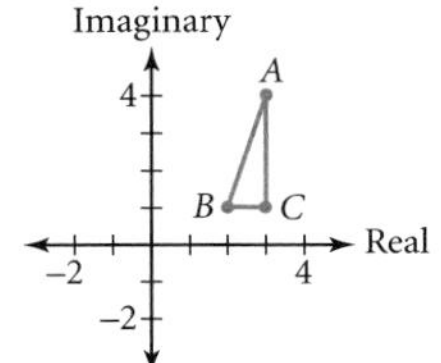

Assessing What You've Learned

WRITE TEST ITEMS In this chapter you learned what complex numbers are, how to do computations with them, and how they relate to polynomial functions. Write at least two test items that assess understanding of complex numbers. Be sure to include complete solutions.

PERFORMANCE ASSESSMENT While a classmate, a friend, a family member, or a teacher observes, show how you would find all zeros of a polynomial equation given in general form, or how you would find an equation in general form given the zeros. Explain the relationship between the zeros and the graph of a function, including what happens when a particular zero occurs multiple times.

GIVE A PRESENTATION Give a presentation on how to do long division or synthetic division. Explain the advantages and the limitations of the method you have chosen, and describe a problem that could be solved using this procedure. If you like, solve the same problem using both methods, and show how they compare.

ASSESSING

Though the primary purpose of asking students to write test questions is for them to review, you might use some of their questions on your chapter test. You might suggest that students write a question for each lesson as you work through the chapter. Add to the student questions by choosing from constructive assessment or other items in the Assessment Resources. During the test you will probably want to limit the use of programs student wrote for Lesson 7.4.

FACILITATING SELF-ASSESSMENT

If you can spend two days on review, you might use some time on the second day for students to present some test items they have written and for the class to work through the problems.

Students might consider these exercises for addition to their portfolios: Lesson 7.1, Exercise 9; Lesson 7.2, Exercises 10 and 12; Lesson 7.3, Exercises 7 and 11; Lesson 7.4, Exercise 11; Lesson 7.5, Exercise 14; Lesson 7.6, Exercise 7; and Lesson 7.7, Exercises 10 and 12.

CHAPTER

8

Parametric Equations and Trigonometry

Overview

Lesson 8.1 introduces parametric equations and guides students in exploring translations of parametric equations. In **Lesson 8.2,** students convert between parametric equations and single equations using only x and y, and they write a relation in x and y as two functions of the parameter. **Lesson 8.3** reviews the trigonometric ratios sine, cosine, and tangent and uses them to model and solve problems about motion. The **exploration** introduces the parametric equations for a circle. In **Lesson 8.4,** students are introduced to vectors and use trigonometry to solve problems associated with setting or determining a course with, against, or across strong currents. In **Lesson 8.5,** students solve problems involving the horizontal and vertical components of projectile motion, including motion that begins at an angle. Students solve problems using the Law of Sines in **Lesson 8.6** and the Law of Cosines in **Lesson 8.7.**

The Mathematics

In this chapter, students use parametric equations and trigonometry to study objects moving under the force of gravity and objects moving under the influence of water and air currents.

Parametric Equations

Parametric functions are used in this chapter to describe horizontal and vertical components of motion that might be influenced by the flow of water or air currents. Many students have difficulty understanding how the variables interact. The projectile motion function from Lesson 7.3, $y = ax^2 + v_0x + s_0$, can be rephrased as the parametric equation $y(t) = -\frac{1}{2}gt^2 + (v_0 \sin A)t + y_0$, which describes the vertical component of motion where the initial velocity is at $\angle A$ with the horizontal. The horizontal component of that same motion is given by the parametric equation $x(t) = (v_0 \cos A)t + x_0$. (In Lesson 7.3, all motion was vertical; thus the measure of $\angle A$ was 90°, which means $\sin A$ was 1 and $\cos A$ was 0.)

Trigonometry

The trigonometry of this chapter is the trigonometry of right triangles. Only the sine, cosine, and tangent ratios are defined, and angles are measured in degrees. Besides applications to motion, students encounter the Law of Sines and the Law of Cosines for finding missing parts of nonright triangles when they know various combinations of side lengths and angle measures. In general, the Law of Cosines is used to determine angle measures and to determine the length of a third side when two side lengths and their included angle measure are known. The Law of Sines is better for determining side lengths than for finding angle measures, because two angles with measures between 0° and 180° can have the same sine. Chapter 10 will extend these ideas to the other trigonometric ratios, to the trigonometry of the unit circle, and to trigonometric functions of angles measured in radians.

Using This Chapter

Lessons 8.3 and 8.4 will each take two days in many classes. The investigation in Lesson 8.2 is optional; you might assign it as a project. The exploration is optional because it addresses a topic not traditionally taught in advanced algebra. However, it provides a good change for students and extends trigonometric function definitions beyond acute angles. If time is limited, Lessons 8.6 and 8.7 can be combined into one day.

Resources

Discovering Advanced Algebra Resources

Teaching and Worksheet Masters
Lessons 8.1–8.3, 8.5, 8.6

Calculator Notes 1H, 4C, 8A–H

Sketchpad Demonstration
Lesson 8.4

Assessment Resources A and B
Quiz 1 (Lessons 8.1, 8.2)
Quiz 2 (Lessons 8.3–8.5)
Quiz 3 (Lessons 8.6, 8.7)
Chapter 8 Test
Chapter 8 Constructive Assessment Options

More Practice Your Skills for Chapter 8

Condensed Lessons for Chapter 8

Other Resources

www.keypress.com/DAA

Materials

- motion sensors
- masking tape
- rulers
- protractors
- metersticks or tape measures
- graph paper, *optional*
- basketball court, *optional*
- basketball, *optional*

Pacing Guide

	day 1	day 2	day 3	day 4	day 5	day 6	day 7	day 8	day 9	day 10
standard	8.1	8.2	quiz, 8.3	8.3	8.4	8.4	8.5	quiz, 8.6	8.7	quiz, review
enriched	8.1	8.2	quiz, 8.3	exploration	8.4	8.4, project	quiz, 8.5, project	8.6	8.7, project	quiz, TAL, review
block	8.1, 8.2	quiz, 8.3	exploration	8.4	project, 8.5	quiz, 8.6, 8.7	quiz, review, project	TAL, assessment		

	day 11
standard	assessment
enriched	assessment

CHAPTER

8 Parametric Equations and Trigonometry

Project Bandaloop is a group of contemporary dancers who combine dance, rock climbing, and rapelling. Their choreography relies upon a blend of aerial, horizontal, and vertical movement. By performing in a variety of venues, ranging from skyscrapers to granite cliffs, the group hopes to stimulate the viewer's awareness of his or her natural and human-made environment.

OBJECTIVES

In this chapter you will

- use a third variable to write parametric equations that separately define x and y
- simulate objects in motion with parametric equations
- convert between parametric equations and equations that use only x and y
- review the trigonometric ratios—sine, cosine, and tangent
- use the trigonometric ratios and their inverses to solve application problems

Sites such as this water tower in Salina, Kansas, give dancers the versatility to move in many directions. This troupe has performed at heights of up to 2500 ft, such as when they danced suspended above Yosemite Valley. Other performance sites include the New York Stock Exchange, the Space Needle in Seattle, and a United Nations conference. For more pictures and information, students can follow a link from www.keymath.com.

[Ask] "What do you see that is mathematical in this photograph?" [circles, sphere, cylinder, lines, angles, distances, time-space relationships, movement horizontally, vertically, and at an angle] "What would you need to know to write equations that model the curve followed by a rope as it swings?" [angle from the point of suspension, length of the rope, shape of the dome, pull of gravity, position of dancer along the rope] "What would you need to know to write equations that model the movement of a dancer?" [the dancer's position on the rope and the rope's movement and speed, the dancer's position in space, the dancer's center of gravity, the gravitational force, the force dancers apply when they rappel]

CHAPTER 8 OBJECTIVES

- Explore translations and other transformations of parametric equations
- Learn to simulate motion on a calculator screen using the appropriate window
- Convert between parametric equations and single equations using only x and y
- Understand parametric equations as a way of writing a relation in x and y as two functions of the parameter, which can be graphed directly
- Define the trigonometric ratios sine, cosine, and tangent
- Use the definitions of trigonometric ratios, inverse trigonometric ratios, the Law of Sines, and the Law of Cosines to find the unknown side lengths and angle measures of a right triangle
- Use trigonometric ratios and parametric equations to model and solve problems about motion
- Use trigonometry and parametric equations to solve problems associated with setting or determining a course for traveling with, against, or across strong currents
- Use trigonometric equations and parametric equations to model projectile motion that begins with an initial velocity at an angle

LESSON

8.1

PLANNING

LESSON OUTLINE

One day:

10 min Example A

15 min Investigation

5 min Sharing

5 min Example B

10 min Exercises

MATERIALS

- Axes for Ships (W) for One Step
- Calculator Notes 8A–D

TEACHING

In this lesson students see how to describe *x*- and *y*-coordinates in terms of a parameter representing time.

One Step

Hand out the Axes for Ships worksheet to each student pair and pose this problem: "Each hour, a ship moves 3 miles southward while traveling 18 miles eastward. Get in pairs facing each other, one of you with two pencils and the other with one pencil. The person with two pencils points both of them at the origin and then moves them along the axes, showing the eastward and southward parts of the ship's motion. Every time the ship has moved the distance traveled per hour, the other person marks a point whose coordinates are pointed to by the two pencils."

The goal is for students to get a kinesthetic understanding of the different components of motion rather than merely achieve facility at drawing these components. Ask students to switch roles. As pairs finish, direct them to do the same kind of drawing for the two tankers in Example A and for the graph in Example B. Then have them set up their calculators to do Example B again. (See Calculator Notes 8A–D.)

▶ EXAMPLE A

[ESL] A *tanker* is a ship that carries oil or other liquid in tanks.

To aid in the discussion of parametric equations, you might want to remind students that distance is calculated by multiplying rate times time ($d = rt$).

LESSON OBJECTIVES

- Use a parameter to write parametric equations that separately define *x* and *y*
- Explore translations and other transformations of parametric equations
- Learn to simulate motion on a calculator screen using the appropriate window
- Graph parametric equations with and without a calculator

LESSON 8.1

Graphing Parametric Equations

Envisioning the end is enough to put the means in motion.

DOROTHEA BRANDE

Sherlock Holmes followed footprints and other clues to track down suspected criminals. As he followed the clues, he knew exactly where the person had been. The path could be drawn on a map, every location described by *x*- and *y*-coordinates. But how could he determine *when* the suspect was at each place? Two variables are often not enough to describe interesting situations fully. You can use **parametric equations** to describe the *x*- and *y*-coordinates of a point separately as functions of a third variable, *t*, called the **parameter.** Parametric equations provide you with more information and better control over what points you plot.

In this example, the variable *t* represents time, and you will write parametric equations to simulate motion on your calculator screen. Observe how *t* controls the *x*- and *y*-values.

EXAMPLE A

Two tankers leave Corpus Christi, Texas, at the same time, traveling toward St. Petersburg, Florida, 900 mi east. Tanker A travels at a constant speed of 18 mi/h, and Tanker B travels at a constant speed of 22 mi/h.

Write parametric equations and use your calculator to simulate the motion involved in this situation.

Environmental CONNECTION

Many oil spills occur when overcrowded seaports and poor weather cause oil tankers to collide in the ocean. Whether tankers are traveling toward land or to an offshore refinery to deliver oil, these conditions threaten the safety of less sturdy, single-hulled ships. Since the passing of the Oil Pollution Act of 1990, which enforced federal safety regulations on the transport of oil, tanker spills have been at an all-time low.

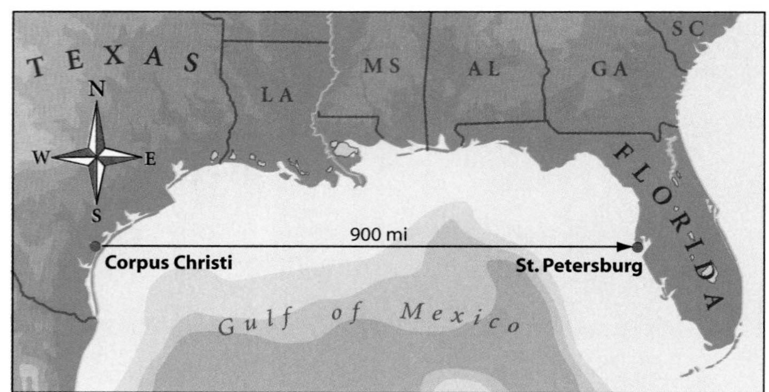

▶ Solution

In order to graph the situation, you must first establish a coordinate system. Locate the origin, (0, 0), at Corpus Christi. Because St. Petersburg is directly east, its coordinates are (900, 0). The *x*-coordinate for each plotted point is the distance of a tanker from Corpus Christi, and the *y*-coordinate for each path will remain constant because the tankers travel directly east.

Set your calculator in Parametric and Simultaneous mode. [▶ See **Calculator Note 8A** to learn about the mode settings for parametric equations. ◀] To determine your equations, think about the motion of the tankers. After 1 h traveling at 18 mi/h, Tanker A will be 18 mi from Corpus Christi. After 2 h, it will be 36 mi away; after 10 h, it will be 180 mi away; and after *t* h, it will be 18*t* mi away. The horizontal distance traveled, then, is determined by $x = 18t$. This equation locates the horizontal position of Tanker A at any given time; the x-value is dependent on the time, or t-value. The tanker does not travel north or south at all, so the y-value must remain constant. If you choose a y-value of 0, the tanker will travel on the x-axis, and you won't be able to see it on the calculator. Instead, indicate this is the first tanker, Tanker A, by setting $y = 1$. The equations $x = 18t$ and $y = 1$ are a pair of parametric equations. You can model the motion of Tanker B with the parametric equations $x = 22t$ and $y = 2$. Why is its horizontal position determined by $22t$? Because its speed, 22 mi/h, multiplied by time, gives the distance traveled.

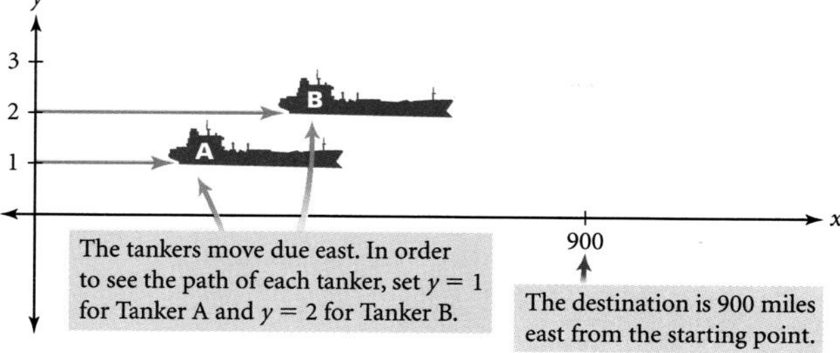

To find a good graphing window, consider the situation. The tankers must travel 900 mi east, so the x-values should be in the domain $0 \le x \le 900$. You chose constant y-values of 1 and 2, so the range $-1 \le y \le 3$ is sufficient. When graphing parametric equations, you must also determine an interval for t. The slower tanker goes 18 miles per hour, so it takes 50 h to go 900 mi; therefore, t-values must range from 0 to 50. Enter these values into your calculator as shown below. Note that you must also enter a t-step. A t-step of 0.1 means that a point is plotted every 0.1 h (or 6 min). Graph the equations on your calculator and observe the motion of the tankers. [► See **Calculator Note 8B** to learn how to enter and graph parametric equations, and to learn more about the window settings. ◄]

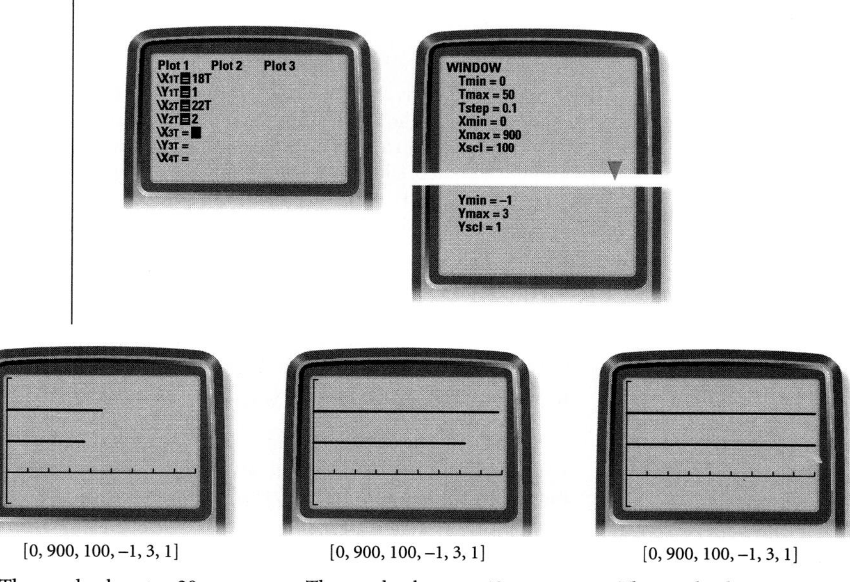

[0, 900, 100, −1, 3, 1]

The graph when $t = 20$.

[0, 900, 100, −1, 3, 1]

The graph when $t = 40$.

[0, 900, 100, −1, 3, 1]

The graph when $t = 50$.

Example A (continued)

Take your time setting the window for this simulation. **[Ask]** "What is the real-world meaning of each variable?" [The horizontal distance between Corpus Christi and St. Petersburg is x; the time of travel is t.]

Have students look at screens in their books to verify they have the correct entries in their calculators. Have all students press GRAPH at the same time.

[Ask] "Why are the lines different even though the ships are following the same paths?" [Different y-values allow you to see the different motions.]

[Ask] "Would the simulation be different if you used a different t-step?" [The size of the t-step controls the speed at which the ships move across the calculator screen.]

For students to see the actual motion again, they must clear the calculator screen. If they change an equation or a window setting, the screen will clear automatically. One quick way to clear the graph is to put the cursor on an = sign in the Y= menu and press ENTER twice.

NCTM STANDARDS

	CONTENT		PROCESS
	Number	✓	Problem Solving
✓	Algebra		Reasoning
	Geometry	✓	Communication
✓	Measurement	✓	Connections
	Data/Probability		Representation

When you model motion using parametric equations, you need to consider the object's direction as well as speed. Directed speed is called **velocity.** Velocity, unlike speed, can be either positive or negative. If you correctly determine whether the velocity is positive or negative, you will be able to see a realistic simulation of the motion on your calculator screen. The table at right shows how to relate the sign of the velocity to the direction of the motion.

Motion	Velocity
Up or north	Positive
Down or south	Negative
Left or west	Negative
Right or east	Positive

Investigation
Simulating Motion

In this investigation you will explore how to use parametric equations and graphs to answer questions about motion.

Step 1 Enter the equations and graphing window from Example A into your calculator. Trace the path of the appropriate tanker, and solve equations to help you answer each question. [▶ See **Calculator Note 8C** to learn about tracing parametric equations. ◀]

a. How long does it take the faster tanker to reach St. Petersburg?

b. Where is the slower tanker when the faster tanker reaches its destination?

c. When, during the trip, is the faster tanker exactly 82 mi in front of the slower tanker?

d. During what part of the trip are the tankers less than 60 mi apart?

Step 2 Create another question involving these two tankers. Write an explanation and answer for your question on a separate sheet of paper. Exchange your question with another group and try to answer each other's questions.

Parametric equations allow you to graph paths when the location of points is dependent on time or some other parameter. A parametric representation lets you see the dynamic nature of the motion, and you can adjust the plotting speed by changing the t-step. The parameter, t, doesn't always represent time; it can be a unitless number. In the next example, you will control which x- and y-values are plotted by limiting the range of t, and you'll explore transformations of parametric functions.

EXAMPLE B Consider the parametric equations $x = t$ and $y = t^2$ for $-1 \leq t \leq 2$.

a. Graph the equations on graph paper and on your calculator.

b. Write equations to translate this parabola right 2 units and down 3 units.

▶ ***Solution*** Use the equations to calculate x- and y-values that correspond to values of t in the range $-1 \leq t \leq 2$. If you use more t-values, you will have a smoother graph.

a. Graph the points as t increases, connecting each point to the previous one, and add arrows to indicate the direction.

Guiding the Investigation

Step 1 Make sure each group answers the questions in two ways: with pencil and paper, and with a calculator. Students might answer the questions in a variety of ways. For example, in Step 1b, they might note that the speed of separation is 4 mi/h, so after 40.9 h the tankers are 163.6 mi apart. The same kind of reasoning leads to the realization in Step 1c that the tankers are 82 mi apart at $\frac{82}{4}$ or 20.5 h, and in Step 1d that they are less than 60 mi apart for the first 15 h. This speed of separation might be graphed as a third pair of parametric equations: $X_{3T} = 22T - 18T$ and $Y_{3T} = 1.5$.

This simulation is continued in Lesson 8.2, Exercise 14.

▶ ***EXAMPLE B***

Before students simulate this situation on their calculators, ask the class to conjecture what the shape will be. If students have no doubt that it will be the graph of $y = x^2$, later ask them about the equations $x = t^2$ and $y = t^3$. In any event, as a class create the table of t-values, substituting several values and plotting each pair of coordinates on the axes. Use arrows to show the direction corresponding to increasing values of t. If t were decreasing in this example, the arrows would point in the opposite direction.

You might want to demonstrate on a calculator the effect of the number of t-values plotted by changing the window to include t-steps of 1, 0.5, and 0.1.

[Ask] "Why do you add to translate a graph horizontally to the right, when we've always subtracted to move to the right?" [You can think of the equation $x = t + 2$ as $(x - 2) = t$ and note that replacing x with $(x - 2)$ is a horizontal translation 2 units to the right.] To see what happens after the shift to a point with horizontal coordinate x, you look to see what happened before the shift to the point with coordinate $x - 2$, a point 2 units to the left. You might use Simultaneous mode on a calculator to dramatize this relationship.

SHARING IDEAS

As students present their ideas, be aware that they often have difficulty thinking of the different components (horizontal and vertical) of motion.

[Ask] "Why would we want to divide motion into vertical and horizontal components?" [so we can describe it with equations and graph it]

Ask what a *parameter* is. You might cite several examples: In parametric equations such as $x = 3t$ and $y = t$, the variable t is a parameter; in the equation $y = ax + b$, the letters a and b designate parameters that determine the slope and y-intercept of the line; in English, students might hear statements such as "We must act within the parameters of school policy." Let students discuss the question, with the goal of writing their own definition of

See pages 890–891 for answers to Step 1.

t	x	y
−1	−1	1
0	0	0
1	1	1
2	2	4

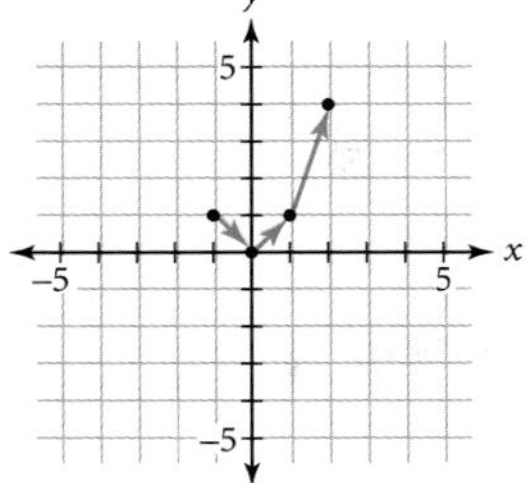

Verify this graph on your calculator.

b. To translate the graph right 2 units, every x-coordinate should be increased by 2. To translate the graph down 3 units, every y-coordinate should be decreased by 3. The equations are

$$x = t + 2$$
$$y = t^2 - 3$$

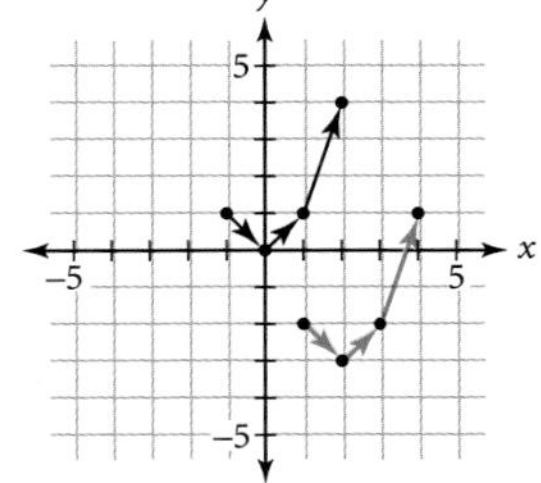

A graph defined parametrically is the set of points (x, y) defined by t. What was the effect of limiting the values of the variable t on the parabola in Example B? What do you think the effect will be if t-values are limited to $-2 \le t \le 1$? You will continue to explore translations and transformations of parametric functions in the exercises. Only a portion of the parabola is graphed. The domain of the parabola will be $-2 \le x \le 1$.

EXERCISES

Practice Your Skills

1. Create a table for each equation with $t = \{-2, -1, 0, 1, 2\}$.

a. $x = 3t - 1$, $y = 2t + 1$ **b.** $x = t + 1$, $y = t^2$ **c.** $x = t^2$, $y = t + 3$ **d.** $x = t - 1$, $y = \sqrt{4 - t^2}$

2. Graph each pair of parametric equations on your calculator. Sketch the result and use arrows to indicate the direction of increasing t-values along the graph. Limit your t-values as indicated, or, if an interval for t isn't listed, then find one that shows all of the graph that fits in a friendly window with a factor of 2.

a. $x = 3t - 1$, $y = 2t + 1$ **b.** $x = t + 1$, $y = t^2$ **c.** $x = t^2$, $y = t + 3$, $-2 \le t \le 1$ **d.** $x = t - 1$, $y = \sqrt{4 - t^2}$, $-2 \le t \le 2$

3. Explore the graphs described in 3a–e, using a friendly window with a factor of 2 and $-10 \le t \le 10$.

a. Graph $x = t$ and $y = t^2$.

b. Graph $x = t + 2$ and $y = t^2$. How does this graph compare with the graph in 3a?

c. Graph $x = t$ and $y = t^2 - 3$. How does this graph compare with the graph in 3a?

Sharing Ideas (continued)

parameter. **[Language]** In general, a *parameter* is a characteristic that determines or controls something.

[Ask] "If a baseball is hit in the usual way (not straight up), what are its parametric equations?" [You might let students research this question. The equations depend on the angle and initial velocity, but (neglecting air resistance) the horizontal equation has the form $x = kt$ and the vertical equation is the same as if the ball were hit directly upward: $y = -4.9t^2 + v_0t + h_0$. Here k is the horizontal component of the initial velocity, and v_0 is the initial velocity's vertical component. Students will analyze these components by trigonometric methods later in this chapter.]

BUILDING UNDERSTANDING

Students practice working with parametric equations and their graphs, including transformations.

ASSIGNING HOMEWORK

Essential	1–4
Performance assessment	5–12
Portfolio	3, 4
Journal	5
Group	6, 8
Review	13–17

MATERIALS

- Calculator Note 4C, *optional*

Assessing Progress

You can assess students' understanding of constant rates of change and their ability to create questions of their own.

Closing the Lesson

Parametric equations express several variables in terms of a single variable (the parameter). Expressing x- and y-coordinates of an object's path in terms of a time parameter t allows a description of the time at which the object is located at various points on the path.

Helping with the Exercises

Exercise 2 You might ask students to graph these on graph paper instead of calculators.

Exercise 3 Students do not need to graph these on graph paper. Friendly windows are described in Calculator Note 4C.

See page 891 for answers to Exercises 1, 2, and 3a–c.

[Alert] The graph in 3c may not look the same shape as the graph in 3a. Students can see that it's a translation by tracing. For 3d, **[Ask]** "What would the equation be if written as a single equation in x and y?" $[y = (x - 5)^2 + 2]$

3d. The graph is translated right 5 units and up 2 units.

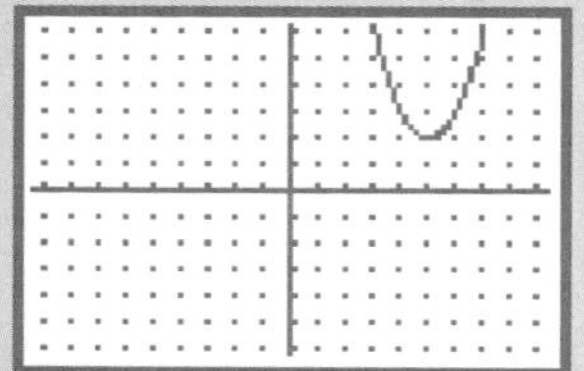

$[-9.4, 9.4, 1, -6.2, 6.2, 1]$

4a.

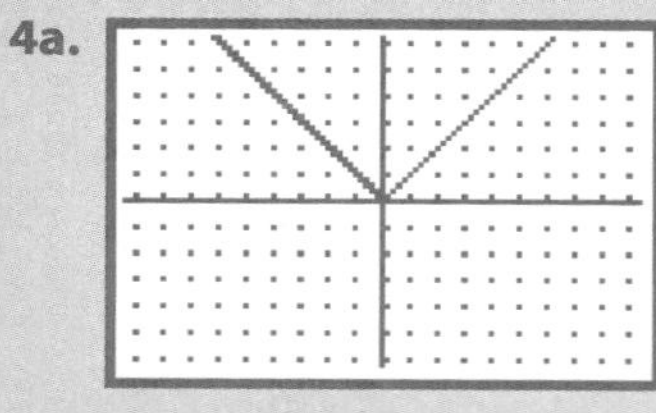

$[-9.4, 9.4, 1, -6.2, 6.2, 1]$

4b.

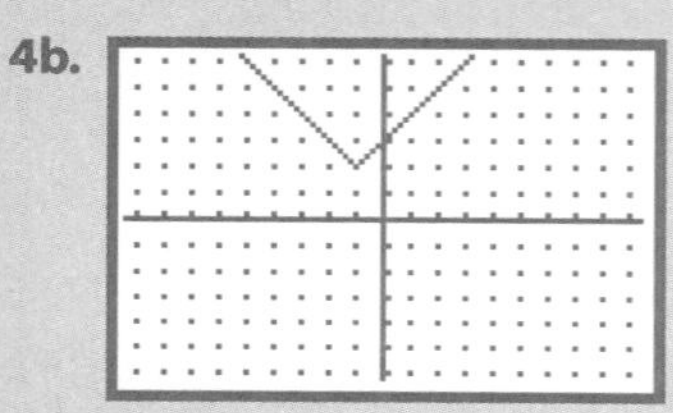

$[-9.4, 9.4, 1, -6.2, 6.2, 1]$

The graph is translated left 1 unit and up 2 units.

4c. $x = t - 4, y = |t| - 3$

$[-9.4, 9.4, 1, -6.2, 6.2, 1]$

4d.

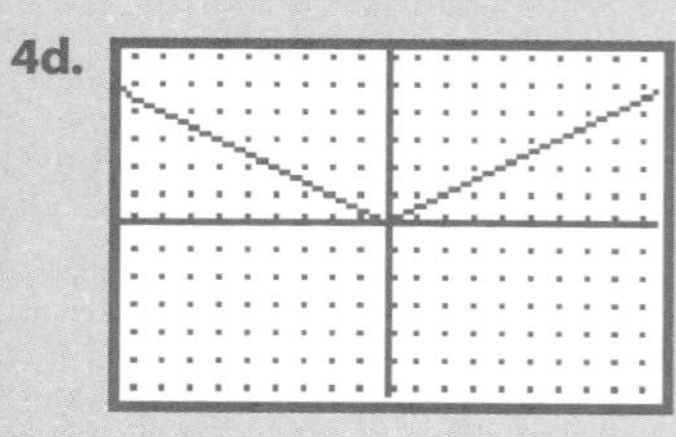

$[-9.4, 9.4, 1, -6.2, 6.2, 1]$

The graph is stretched horizontally by a factor of 2.

See page 891 for answers to Exercises 4f and 5f.

d. Predict how the graph of $x = t + 5$ and $y = t^2 + 2$ compares with the graph in 3a. Verify your answer with a graph.

e. Predict how the graph of $x = t + a$ and $y = t^2 + b$ compares with the graph in 3a. The graph is translated horizontally a units and vertically b units.

4. Explore these graphs, using a friendly window with a factor of 2 and $-10 \leq t \leq 10$.

a. Graph $x = t$ and $y = |t|$.

b. Graph $x = t - 1$ and $y = |t| + 2$. How does this graph compare with the graph in 4a?

c. Write a pair of parametric equations that will translate the graph in 4a left 4 units and down 3 units. Verify your answer with a graph.

d. Graph $x = 2t$ and $y = |t|$. How does this graph compare with the graph in 4a?

e. Graph $x = t$ and $y = 3|t|$. How does this graph compare with the graph in 4a?

f. Describe how the numbers 2, 3, and 4 in the equations $x = t + 2$ and $y = 3|t| - 4$ change the graph in 4a. Verify your answer with a graph.

Reason and Apply

5. The graphs below display a simulation of a team's mascot walking toward the west-end goal on the high school football field. Starting at a point 65 yards (yd) from the goal line and 50 ft from the sideline, she moves toward the goal line and waves at the crowd when she is 35 yd from the goal line. The parameter, t, represents time in seconds.

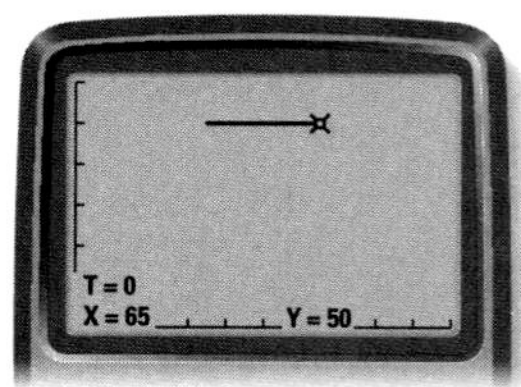

[0, 100, 10, 0, 60, 10]

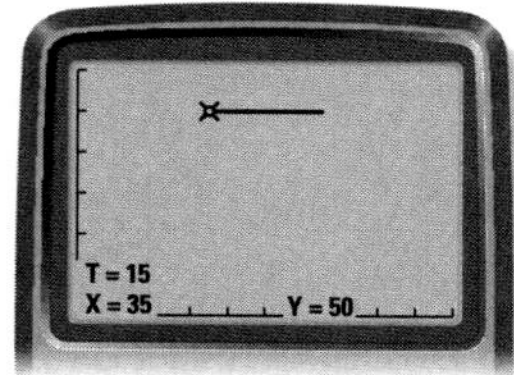

[0, 100, 10, 0, 60, 10]

a. According to the graphs, how much time has elapsed? 15 s

b. How far did she travel? 30 yd

c. What is her average velocity? -2 yd/s

d. Explain the meaning of each number in these parametric equations.

$x = 65 - 2t$
$y = 50$

Sample answer: 65 yd is her starting position relative to the goal line, -2 yd/s is her velocity, and 50 yd is her position relative to the sideline.

e. Using the equations from 5d, simulate the mascot's motion on your calculator screen in an appropriate window.

f. Increase the maximum t-value in your graphing window to determine when the mascot crosses the 10-yard line.

g. Write and solve an equation that will determine when the mascot crosses the 10-yard line. $65 - 2t = 10$; 27.5 s

4e.

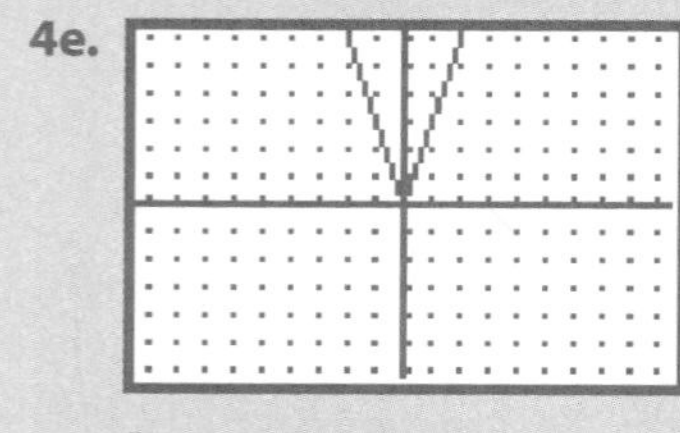

$[-9.4, 9.4, 1, -6.2, 6.2, 1]$

The graph is stretched vertically by a factor of 3.

Exercise 4f **[Ask]** "What would the equation be if written as a single equation in x and y?" $[y = 3|x - 2| - 4]$

Exercise 5 **[ESL]** A *mascot* is a person or animal that represents a certain team.

5e. The graph simulation will produce the graphs pictured in the problem. A good window is $[0, 100, 10, 0, 60, 10]$ with $0 \leq t \leq 15$.

6. Write parametric equations for each graph. (*Hint:* You can create parametric equations from a single equation that uses only x and y by letting $x = t$ and changing y to a function of t by replacing x with t.)

a.

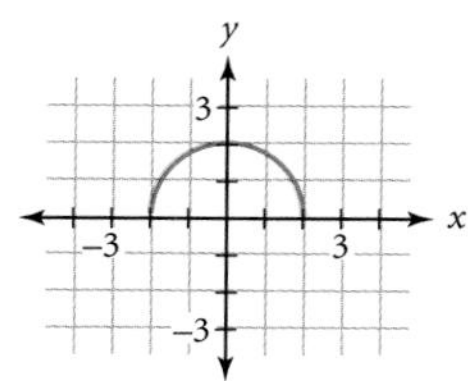

b.

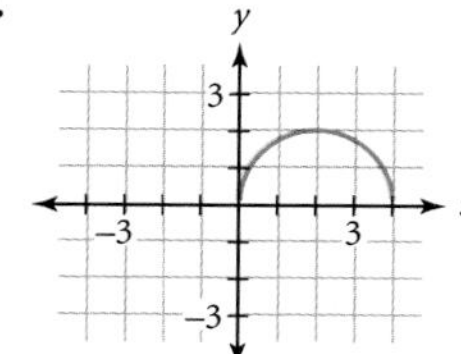

c.

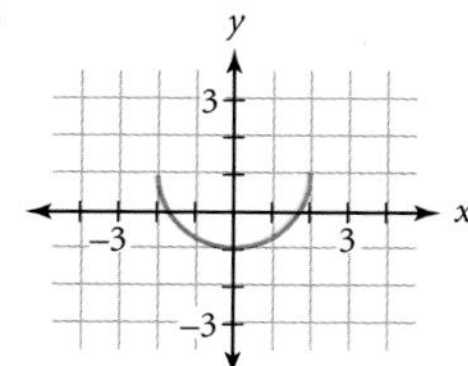

d.

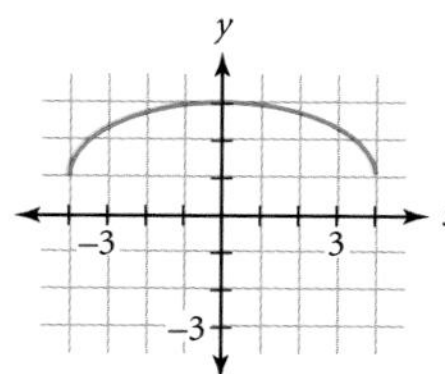

7. The graph of the parametric equations $x = f(t)$ and $y = g(t)$ is pictured at right.

a. Sketch a graph of $x = f(t)$ and $y = -g(t)$ and describe the transformation.

b. Sketch a graph of $x = -f(t)$ and $y = g(t)$ and describe the transformation.

8. The graph of the parametric equations $x = r(t)$ and $y = s(t)$ is pictured at right. Write the parametric equations for each graph below in terms of $r(t)$ and $s(t)$.

a.

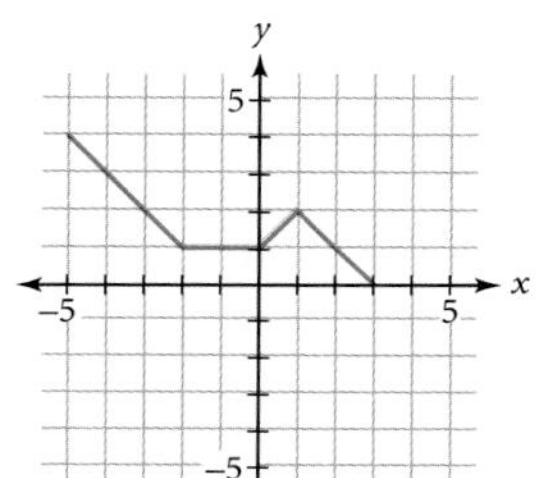

$x = r(t) - 2, y = s(t) + 2$

b.

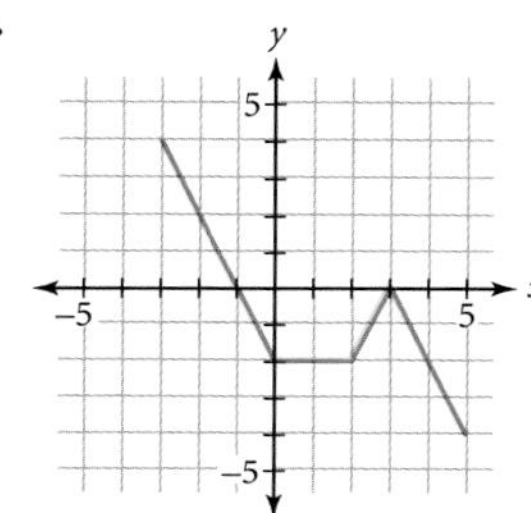

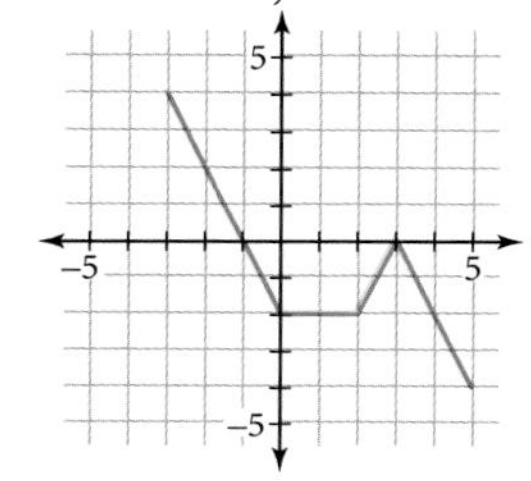

$x = r(t), y = 2s(t)$

c.

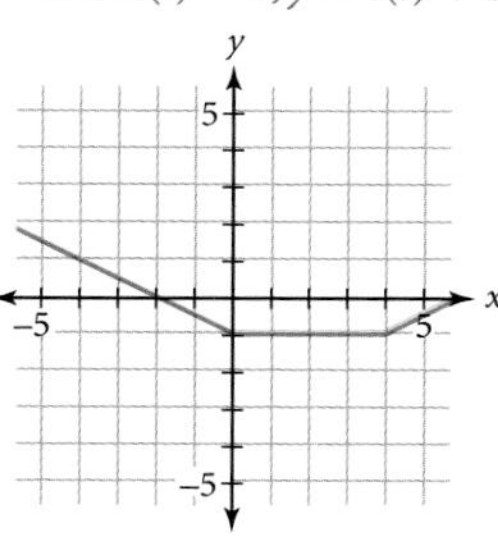

$x = 2r(t), y = s(t)$

d.

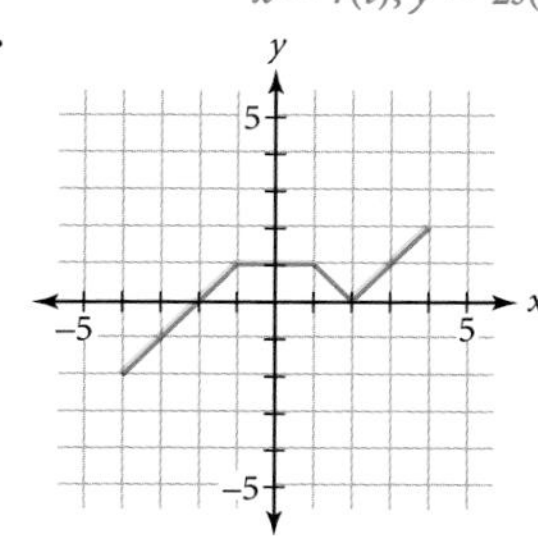

$x = r(t) - 1, y = -s(t)$

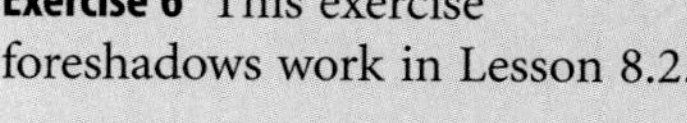

Exercise 6 This exercise foreshadows work in Lesson 8.2.

6a. possible answer:

$x = t, y = 2\sqrt{1 - \left(\frac{t}{2}\right)^2}$

6b. possible answer:

$x = t + 2, y = 2\sqrt{1 - \left(\frac{t}{2}\right)^2}$

6c. possible answer:

$x = t, y = -2\sqrt{1 - \left(\frac{t}{2}\right)^2} + 1$

6d. possible answer:

$x = 2t, y = 2\sqrt{1 - \left(\frac{t}{2}\right)^2} + 1$

7a. The graph is reflected across the x-axis.

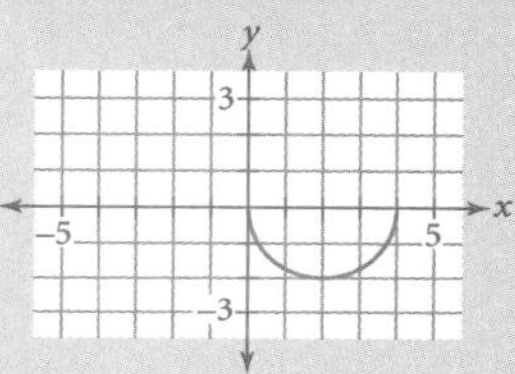

7b. The graph is reflected across the y-axis.

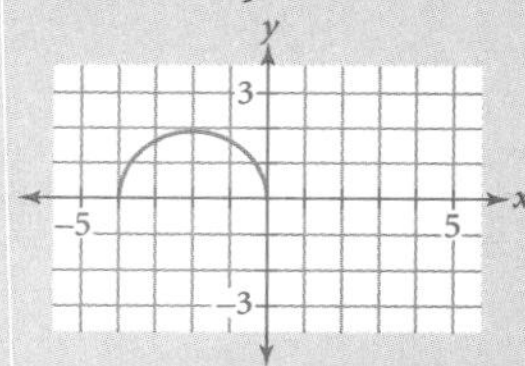

Exercise 9 A t-step of 0.5 is good for simulating the race. You might want to have students solve 9e using paper and pencil in addition to doing the simulation on the calculator. The parameter is useful primarily for simulating the race on a calculator screen.

9a. $x = 0.4t$ and $y = 1$

9b. [0, 50, 5, 0, 3, 1]; $0 \le t \le 125$

9c. $x = 1.8(t - 100), y = 2$

9d. The tortoise will win.

9e. The tortoise takes 125 s and the hare takes approximately 28 s, but because he starts 100 s later, he finishes at 128 s.

Exercise 10a The first pair of parametric equations represents the plane flying from Los Angeles to Honolulu.

10a. The Los Angeles to Honolulu plane flies west at 450 mi/h and leaves 2 h later than the Honolulu to Los Angeles plane. The Honolulu to Los Angeles plane flies east at 525 mi/h and starts 2500 mi west of Los Angeles.

10b. 3.5 h; 675 mi west of Los Angeles

10c. $450(t - 2) = 2500 - 525t$; 3.5 h, 675 mi west of Los Angeles

Exercise 11 [Alert] One line is vertical. You might take advantage of 11d to remind students that a major reason for using parametric equations is to see the times at which a point is located at various places on a path. The paths intersect, but the walkers arrive at that intersection point at different times. A good t-step is 0.2.

9. Each spring a hare challenges a tortoise to a 50 m race. The hare knows that he can run faster than the tortoise, and he boasts that he can still win the race even if he gives the tortoise a 100 s head start. The tortoise crawls at a rate of 0.4 m/s, and the hare's running speed is 1.8 m/s.

a. Write equations to simulate the motion of the tortoise.

b. Determine a graphing window and a range of t-values that will show the tortoise's motion.

c. Write equations to simulate the motion of the hare, who crosses the starting line at $t = 100$.

d. Who wins the race?

e. How long does it take each runner to finish the race?

This illustration of the fable *The Tortoise and the Hare* is a wood engraving by French artist Gustave Doré (1832–1883).

10. Los Angeles, California, and Honolulu, Hawaii, are about 2500 mi apart. One plane flies from Los Angeles to Honolulu, and a second plane flies in the opposite direction.

a. Describe the meaning of each number in the x-equations. (The equations for y simply assign noncolliding flight paths.)

$$x = 450(t - 2), \quad y = 1 \quad \text{and} \quad x = 2500 - 525t, \quad y = 2$$

b. Use tables or a graph to find the approximate time and location of the planes relative to Los Angeles when the planes pass each other.

c. Write and solve an equation to find the time and location of the planes when they pass each other.

Career CONNECTION

Air traffic controllers coordinate airplane takeoffs and landings from airport control towers. They manage air traffic safety, track weather conditions, and communicate with pilots via radio. Sophisticated computer equipment and radar displays allow them to monitor airspace and prevent aircraft collisions. Air traffic control is considered one of the most demanding jobs in the United States. You can learn more about the mathematics required to become an air traffic controller with the Internet links at www.keymath.com/DAA.

An airport control tower

11. These parametric equations simulate two walkers, with x and y measured in meters and t measured in seconds.

$$x = 1.4t, \quad y = 3.1 \quad \text{and} \quad x = 4.7, \quad y = 1.2t$$

a. Graph their motion for $0 \le t \le 5$.

b. Give real-world meanings for the values of 1.4, 3.1, 4.7, and 1.2 in the equations.

c. Where do the two paths intersect? (4.7, 3.1)

d. Do the walkers collide? How do you know this?

11a.

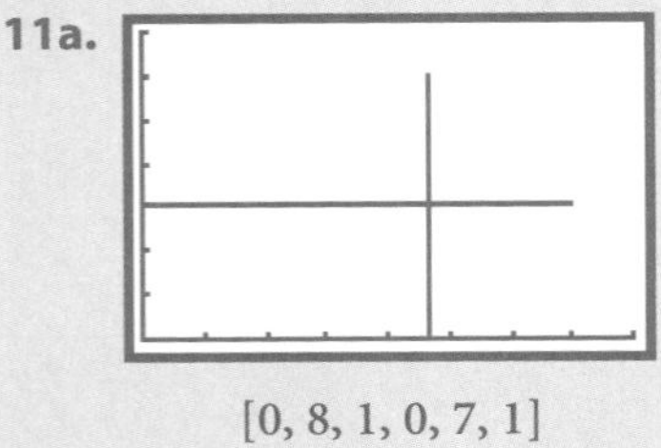

[0, 8, 1, 0, 7, 1]

11b. 1.4 m/s is the velocity of the first walker, 3.1 m is the vertical distance between the walkers when they start, 4.7 m is the horizontal distance between the walkers when they start, and 1.2 m/s is the velocity of the second walker.

11d. No, the first walker arrives at (4.7, 3.1) at 3.357 s, and the second walker arrives there at 2.583 s.

12. APPLICATION An elephant stomps the ground creating sound waves in the air and vibrations (waves) in the ground. Sound waves travel through the air at approximately 0.3 km/s, and a vibration of the Earth's crust travels at approximately 6.1 km/s.

a. Write parametric equations that model both waves for 3 s, and graph them on your calculator in an appropriate window.

b. How far does the wave in the ground travel in 3 s? How long does it take the sound wave in the air to travel that same distance?

c. A researcher's equipment detects the sound wave in the air 10 s after detecting the sound vibration in the ground. How far is the elephant from the researcher?

Science CONNECTION

American biologist and researcher Caitlin O'Connell-Rodwell proposes that elephants communicate with their feet. By stomping on the ground, elephants create seismic waves in the Earth's surface that can travel nearly 32 km—much farther than their communication by audible sound. Other elephants may detect these vibrations with their feet and interpret them as a warning of danger. Some researchers also believe elephants and other animals may detect earthquakes by hearing grinding rock and feeling tremors in the ground. Elephants may also be able to locate water by hearing thunderstorms and feeling the rumble of thunder through the ground.

Caitlin O'Connell-Rodwell listens to sounds that may be long-distance elephant communication.

Review

3.7 **13.** Solve this system.

$$\begin{cases} 3x + 5y = 6 \\ 4y = x - 19 \end{cases}$$

7.8 **14.** Find the exact roots of this equation without using a calculator.

$$0 = x^3 - 4x^2 + 2x + 4$$

7.1 **15.** Consider this sequence.

$-6, -4, 3, 15, 32, \ldots$

a. Find the nth term using finite differences. Assume -6 is u_1.

b. Find u_{20}.

3.3 **16.** Find the equation of the line through $(-3, 10)$ and $(6, -5)$.

6.3 **17.** Find the equation of the parabola that passes through the points $(-2, -20)$, $(2, 0)$, and $(4, -14)$.

12a. possible answer:
air: $x = 0.3t$, $y = 1$
ground: $x = 6.1t$, $y = 2$

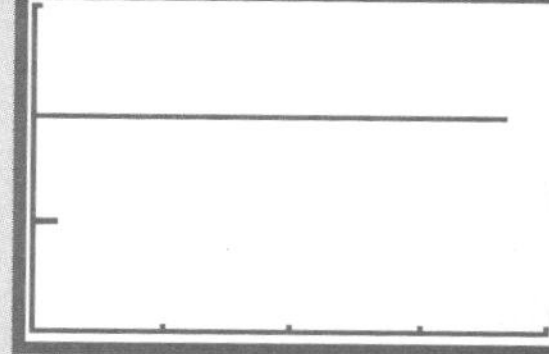

$[0, 20, 5, 0, 3, 1]$
$0 \leq t \leq 3$

12b. 18.3 km; 61 s

12c. 3.2 km

13. $(7, -3)$

14. $2, 1 - \sqrt{3}, 1 + \sqrt{3}$

15a. $2.5n^2 - 5.5n - 3$

15b. 887

16. $y = -\frac{5}{3}x + 5$

Exercise 17 A horizontally oriented parabola will also pass through these points.

17. $y = -2x^2 + 5x - 2$

LESSON

8.2

PLANNING

LESSON OUTLINE

One day:

25 min Investigation

5 min Sharing

10 min Examples

5 min Exercises

MATERIALS

- motion sensors (two per group)
- masking tape
- Parametric Walk Sample Data (T), *optional*
- Calculator Notes 8D, 8E

TEACHING

In this lesson students see how to eliminate a parameter in parametric equations to get a single equation using only x and y.

One Step

Pose this problem: "How would you describe the path followed by an object moving according to the parametric equations $x = t^2 + 2$ and $y = t^6$?" After graphing the equations, students may guess that the path is half a parabola; ask them for evidence. Encourage a variety of approaches. As needed, in some groups plant the idea of finding an equation in terms of x and y.

Guiding the Investigation

You might want to demonstrate the procedure before groups start the investigation. If you are short on time, the class can complete Steps 1 and 2 together or use the Parametric Walk Sample Data transparency.

See page 892 for answer to Step 2.

LESSON 8.2

Converting from Parametric to Nonparametric Equations

An unhurried sense of time is in itself a form of wealth.

BONNIE FRIEDMAN

In the previous lesson you saw parametric equivalents of functions you have studied earlier, like parabolas and absolute-value graphs. You can create these equations and graphs by letting $x = t$ and making y a function of t instead of a function of x. For example, you can graph $y = x^2$ in parametric form using $x = t$ and $y = t^2$. The focus of this lesson is to do the reverse—to start with parametric equations and eliminate the parameter t, to get a single equation using only x and y.

In this investigation you will use parametric equations to model motion by measuring changes in both the x- and y-directions. You will discover the relationship between the graphs of the parametric equations, and the corresponding graph of the relation between x and y.

Investigation
Parametric Walk

You will need

- two motion sensors
- masking tape

This investigation involves four participants: the walker, recorder X, recorder Y, and a director.

Procedure Note

1. The walker starts at one end of the segment and walks slowly for 5 s to reach the other end.
2. Recorder X holds a motion sensor pointed at the walker, set for about 5 s, and moves along the y-axis keeping even with the walker, thus measuring the x-coordinate of the walker's path as a function of time.
3. Simultaneously, recorder Y holds a motion sensor pointed at the walker, set for the same amount of time, and moves along the x-axis keeping even with the walker, measuring the y-coordinate of the walker's path as a function of time.
4. The director starts all three participants at the same moment and counts out the 5 seconds.

Step 1 Mark a quadrant of a coordinate graph on the floor with tape identifying the x- and y-axes and a segment, as in the diagram at right.

Step 2 Perform the activity as described in the procedure note. [▶ See **Calculator Note 8D** for additional instructions on how to set up your motion sensors. ◀]

Step 3 Download the data from recorder X's motion sensor into a calculator, and find a function in the form $x = f(t)$ that fits the data.

Step 4 Download the data from recorder Y's motion sensor into a different calculator, and find a function in the form $y = g(t)$ that fits the data.

There is an alternative investigation that focuses on the information you get with a parametric plot. See Extension B on page 437.

Step 2 A group with only three members can perform the activity without a director. It's best if the segment to be walked is not parallel to either axis. **[Alert]** Students may not realize that the distances from the walker to the axes are the walker's coordinates.

Step 3 For the sample data set: $\hat{x} = 0.17t + 0.91$

Step 4 For the sample data set: $\hat{y} = -0.10t + 2.51$

Step 5 | On a third calculator, transfer the distance values from recorder X's motion sensor into list L1 and the distance values from recorder Y's motion sensor into list L2. Plot these data as ordered pairs (x, y) along with the parametric functions $x = f(t)$ and $y = g(t)$. How do they compare?

Step 6 | Solve $x = f(t)$ for t and substitute this expression for t into $y = g(t)$.

Step 7 | Graph your solution to Step 6 with the (x, y) data. [▶ See **Calculator Note 8E** to learn about drawing functions while still in Parametric mode. ◀]

Step 8 | Based on this investigation, explain what eliminating the parameter does to parametric equations.

During this investigation, two motion sensors captured data that you used to create a parametric model of a walk. You then merged these two graphs into a single graphic representation of the relation between x and y, and you merged the two parametric equations into a single equation using only x and y. You merge a pair of parametric equations into a single equation by eliminating the parameter t.

EXAMPLE A | Graph the curve described by the parametric equations $x = t^2 - 4$ and $y = \frac{t}{2}$. Then eliminate t from the equations and graph the result.

▶ Solution | Make a table of values and plot the points, connecting them as t increases. Verify this graph on your calculator. Notice that the graph shows that y is not a function of x, even though both x and y are functions of t.

t	x	y
−3	5	−1.5
−2	0	−1
−1	−3	−0.5
0	−4	0
1	−3	0.5
2	0	1
3	5	1.5

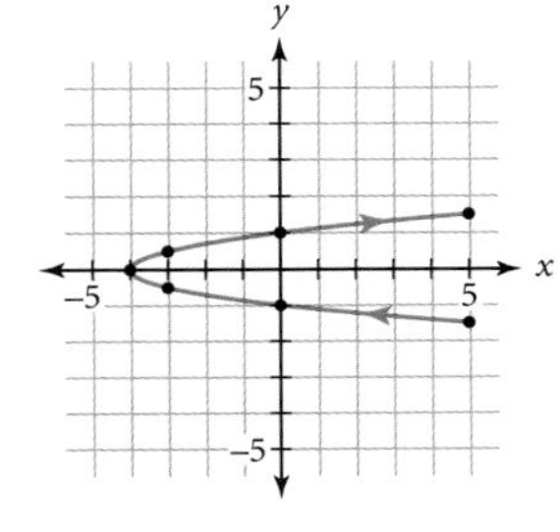

To eliminate the parameter, solve one of the parametric equations for t and substitute into the other parametric equation.

$x = t^2 - 4$ and $y = \frac{t}{2}$ — The parametric equations for x and y.

$t^2 = x + 4$ — Add 4 to both sides in the parametric equation for x.

$t = \pm\sqrt{x+4}$ — Take the square root of both sides to solve for t.

$y = \frac{t}{2} = \frac{\pm\sqrt{x+4}}{2}$ — Substitute $\pm\sqrt{x+4}$ for t in the parametric equation for y to get a single equation using only x and y.

$y = \pm\frac{\sqrt{x+4}}{2}$ — The single equation for y in terms of x.

Step 5 These lists can be entered into an additional calculator or into one of the calculators used in Step 3 or 4.

Step 5

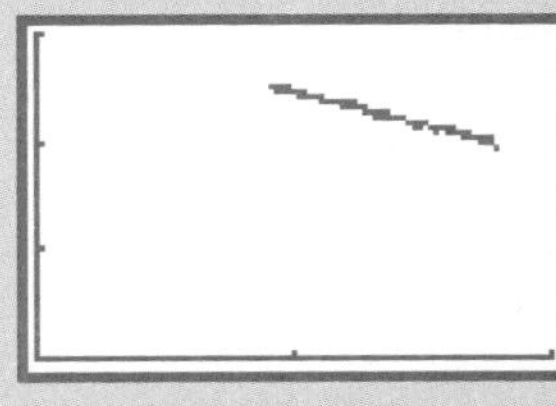

[0, 2, 1, 0, 3, 1]
$0 \le t \le 5$

The graph of $x = f(t)$ and $y = g(t)$ fits the data (x, y).

Step 6
$y = -0.10\left(\frac{x - 0.91}{0.17}\right) + 2.51$

Step 7 When you change to Function mode, the parametric equations will automatically shut off. The data lists will still plot. After eliminating t, you can graph an equation in x and y while in Parametric mode. Use $x = t$ and $y = f(t)$ rather than $y = f(x)$.

Step 7

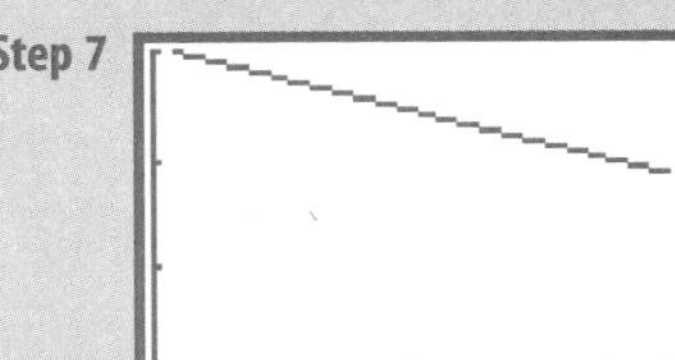

[0, 2, 1, 0, 3, 1]

Step 8 Eliminating the parameter gives the same graph, but you lose the information about location at particular times, and you cannot limit the values of t to show only the segment on the line that was actually walked.

▶ EXAMPLE A

If you discuss this example after the investigation, remember to change the calculators back to Parametric mode.

You might need to remind students that positive numbers have two square roots.

NCTM STANDARDS

CONTENT		PROCESS	
	Number	✓	Problem Solving
✓	Algebra		Reasoning
	Geometry	✓	Communication
✓	Measurement	✓	Connections
✓	Data/Probability	✓	Representation

LESSON OBJECTIVES

- Convert between parametric equations and single equations using only x and y
- Understand parametric equations as a way of writing a relation in x and y as two functions of the parameter, which can be graphed directly
- Given a data set, write the parametric equations and a single equation using only x and y to fit the data

▶ EXAMPLE B

Lead the class in making a diagram of the situation. Note that, instead of using the y-axis to represent north-south motion, this example uses the y-axis for up-and-down motion.

If students are having difficulty seeing the graph, plot points one at a time. You could change the t-step to 0.5 second to add more points to the graph. Alternatively, find y in terms of x: Because $x = 24t$, $t = \frac{1}{24}x$; thus, $y = 15t$ gives $y = \frac{15}{24}x$. A graph of this line passes safely above the power lines at the point (300, 95). Once students understand how the graph is created, you might have them simulate the motion on their calculators. Most calculators include a Draw menu with an instruction for displaying (turning on) a single point with given coordinates, to represent the power lines.

SHARING IDEAS

[Ask] "We lose information about time when we convert to a single equation using only x and y. Do we need that information to find out if Hanna misses the power lines in Example B?" [No; the time when she's over the power lines is irrelevant.]

Point out that the last paragraph of the lesson says that some parametric equations cannot be written as a single equation using only x and y. If students ask, you might mention some examples: the equations $x = t^2, y = t^2$ would give more than one equation in x and y; the equations $x = 5, y = 2$ give a point not an equation.

You could also solve for t in the original parametric equation for y and substitute into the parametric equation for x.

$x = t^2 - 4$ and $y = \frac{t}{2}$	The parametric equations for x and y.
$t = 2y$	Multiply by 2 to solve for t in the parametric equation for y.
$x = (2y)^2 - 4$	Substitute $2y$ for t into the parametric equation for x.
$x = 4y^2 - 4$	Expand.
$x + 4 = 4y^2$	Add 4 to both sides.
$\frac{x+4}{4} = y^2$	Divide both sides by 4.
$y = \pm\sqrt{\frac{x+4}{4}}$	Take the square root of both sides.
$y = \pm\frac{\sqrt{x+4}}{2}$	Take the square root of 4.

Notice that both methods result in the same equation.

You might recognize this as the equation of a horizontally oriented parabola, similar to equations you studied in Chapter 4. Check your result by graphing to show that the graphs of

$$y = \pm\frac{\sqrt{x+4}}{2} \quad \text{and} \quad \begin{aligned} x &= t^2 - 4 \\ y &= \frac{t}{2} \end{aligned}$$

are the same. [▶ Revisit **Calculator Note 8E** to learn how to simultaneously graph parametric equations and equations that use only x and y. ◀]

Although the same graph can often be created with parametric equations, or a single equation using only x and y, parametric equations show your position at particular times and allow you to graph relations that are not functions directly. The next example shows how two independent actions can combine to make a single path.

EXAMPLE B

Hanna's hot-air balloon is ascending at a rate of 15 ft/s. A wind is blowing continuously from west to east at 24 ft/s. Write parametric equations to model this situation, and decide whether or not the hot-air balloon will clear power lines that are 300 ft to the east and 95 ft tall. Find the time it takes for the balloon to reach or pass over the power lines.

Hot-air balloons are made in all sorts of shapes.

Assessing Progress

Through students' work on the investigation, you can assess their understanding of parametric equations and of how to model data with an equation.

Closing the Lesson

Parametric equations for $x = f(t)$ and $y = g(t)$ can be combined by solving one of the equations for t and then substituting for t in the other equation. The result is an equation describing a path but not how time relates to the graph.

▶ Solution Create a table of time, ground distance, and height for a few seconds of flight. Set the origin as the initial launching location of the balloon. Let x represent the ground distance traveled to the east in feet, and let y represent the balloon's height above the ground in feet. The table below shows these values for the first 4 s of flight.

Time (s) t	Ground distance (ft) x	Height (ft) y
0	0	0
1	24	15
2	48	30
3	72	45
4	96	60

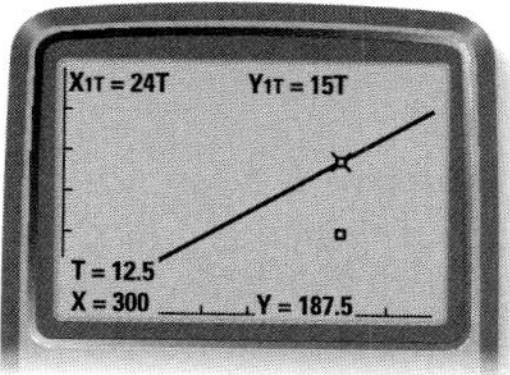

[0, 400, 100, 0, 300, 100]

The parametric equations that model the motion are $x = 24t$ and $y = 15t$. Graph this pair of equations on your calculator. You can picture the power lines by plotting the point (300, 95). When you trace the graph to a time of 1 s, you will see that the balloon is 24 ft to the east, at a height of 15 ft. At 12.5 s, it has traveled 300 ft to the east and has reached a height of 187.5 ft. Hanna's balloon will not touch the power lines.

Being able to model motion with parametric equations is much like the graphing you have done in earlier chapters, but you deal with each of the directions independently. This will often make difficult relations easier to model. Many pairs of parametric equations can be written as a single equation using only x and y. Being able to eliminate the parameter in parametric equations is an important skill because it gives you two different ways to study a relationship.

BUILDING UNDERSTANDING

The exercises provide practice in changing pairs of parametric equations to single equations using only x and y. For curves that are unbounded, such as straight lines, the parameter's domain will be all real numbers, and more than one set of parametric equations will be a solution.

ASSIGNING HOMEWORK

Essential	2–5
Performance assessment	6–12
Portfolio	8
Journal	6
Group	7, 9, 12
Review	1, 13–16

▶ Helping with the Exercises

1a. $t = x - 1$

1b. $t = \frac{x+1}{3}$

1c. $t = \pm\sqrt{x}$

1d. $t = x + 1$

3a. $y = \frac{x+7}{2}$

3b. $y = \pm\sqrt{x} + 1$

3c. $y = \frac{2x-4}{3}$

3d. $y = 2(x + 2)^2$

EXERCISES

▶ Practice Your Skills

1. Solve each equation for t.

a. $x = t + 1$ **b.** $x = 3t - 1$ **c.** $x = t^2$ **d.** $x = t - 1$

2. Write each pair of parametric equations as a single equation using only x and y. Graph this new relation in a friendly graphing window. Verify that the graph of the new equation is the same as the graph of the pair of parametric equations.

a. $x = t + 1$, $y = t^2$ **b.** $x = 3t - 1$, $y = 2t + 1$ **c.** $x = t^2$, $y = t + 3$ **d.** $x = t - 1$, $y = \sqrt{4 - t^2}$

3. Write a single equation (using only x and y) that is equivalent to each pair of parametric equations.

a. $x = 2t - 3$, $y = t + 2$ **b.** $x = t^2$, $y = t + 1$ **c.** $x = \frac{1}{2}t + 1$, $y = \frac{t-2}{3}$ **d.** $x = t - 3$, $y = 2(t - 1)^2$

2a. $y = (x - 1)^2$

[−9.4, 9.4, 1, −6.2, 6.2, 1]

2b. $y = \frac{2}{3}x + \frac{5}{3}$

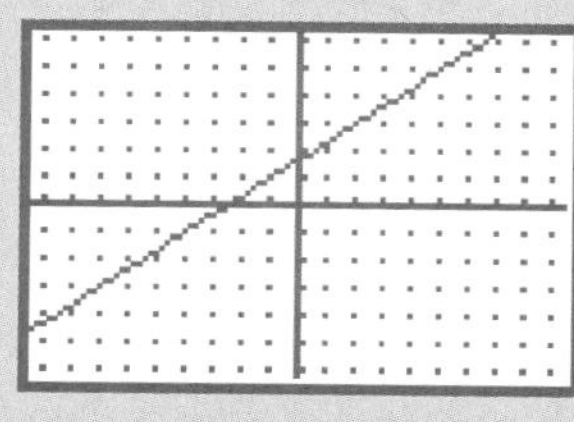

[−9.4, 9.4, 1, −6.2, 6.2, 1]

2c. $y = \pm\sqrt{x} + 3$

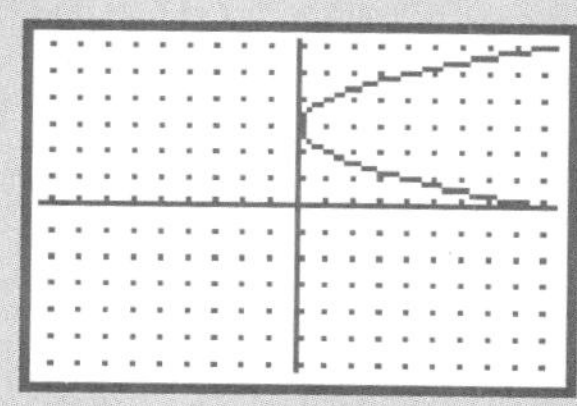

[−9.4, 9.4, 1, −6.2, 6.2, 1]

2d. $y = \sqrt{4 - (x + 1)^2}$

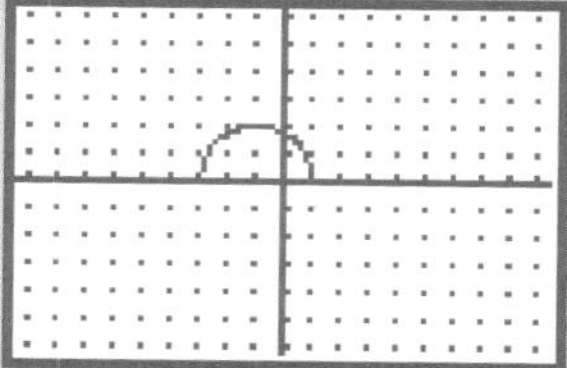

[−9.4, 9.4, 1, −6.2, 6.2, 1]

4c. $y = |x - 5| - 1$

X	Y_1
2	2
3	1
4	0
5	-1
6	0
7	1
8	2

Y_1=abs(X−5)−1

Exercise 5 [Alert] Students may find this exercise difficult because no equations are given. Encourage students to make tables or create function expressions.

5.

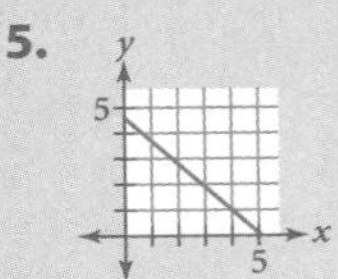

Exercises 6, 9, 10 These exercises show how slope is represented in parametric equations of a straight line. Elicit the fact that if y is increasing j times as fast as t and x is increasing k times as fast as t (so t is increasing $\frac{1}{k}$ times as fast as x), then y is increasing $\frac{j}{k}$ times as fast as x.

6. $x = -\frac{2}{3}t + 4, y = \frac{3}{5}t + 1$; $y = -\frac{9}{10}x + \frac{23}{5}$. The slope of (x, y) is the ratio of the two slopes of (t, y) and (t, x).

Exercise 7 The exact interval is $-\sqrt{6} \leq t \leq \sqrt{6}$, but the interval $-2.5 \leq t \leq 2.5$ is very close because $\sqrt{6} \approx 2.449$. The values $-\sqrt{6}$ and $\sqrt{6}$ can be entered into the calculator for Tmin and Tmax. Every value of t in this interval will give a value of x between -5 and 5.

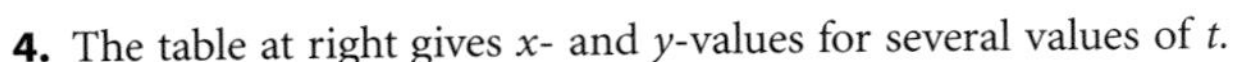

4. The table at right gives x- and y-values for several values of t.

a. Write an equation for x in terms of t. $x = t + 2$

b. Write an equation for y in terms of t. $y = |t - 3| - 1$

c. Eliminate the parameter and combine the equations in 4a and 4b. Verify that this equation fits the values of (x, y).

t	x	y
0	2	2
1	3	1
2	4	0
3	5	−1
4	6	0
5	7	1
6	8	2

5. Use the graphs of $x = f(t)$ and $y = g(t)$ to create a graph of y as a function of x.

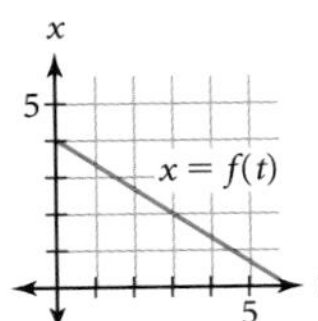

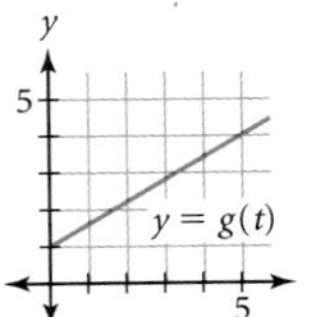

Reason and Apply

6. Write parametric equations for $x = f(t)$ and $y = g(t)$ given in Exercise 5, and an equation for y as a function of x. How do the slopes of these equations compare?

7. Find the smallest interval for t that produces a graph of the parametric equations $x = t + 2$ and $y = t^2$ that just fits in a window with $-5 \leq x \leq 5$ and $-6 \leq y \leq 6$. $-2.5 \leq t \leq 2.5$

8. Consider the parametric equations $x = f(t) = t + 2$ and $y = g(t) = \sqrt{1 - t^2}$.

a. Graph $x = f(t)$ and $y = g(t)$.

b. Graph $x = f(t)$ and $y = -g(t)$ and identify the transformations of the original equations. Eliminate the parameter to write a single equation using only x and y.

c. Graph $x = -f(t)$ and $y = g(t)$ and identify the transformations of the original equations. Eliminate the parameter to write a single equation using only x and y.

d. Graph $x = -f(t)$ and $y = -g(t)$ and identify the transformations of the original equations. Eliminate the parameter to write a single equation using only x and y.

Titled *Tree-Lined Canal* (1971), this image of reflections was photographed in the Netherlands by Brett Weston.

8a.

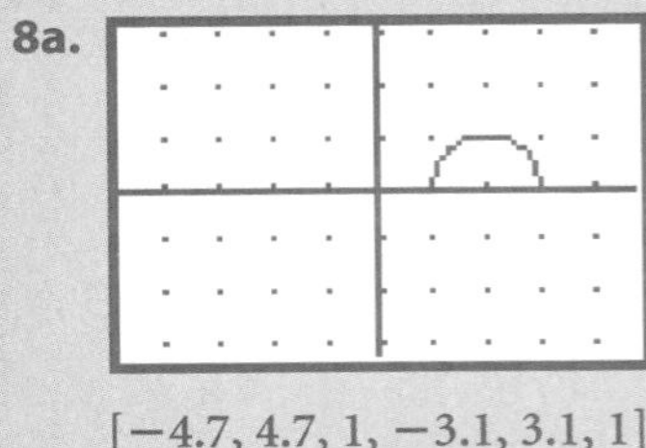

$[-4.7, 4.7, 1, -3.1, 3.1, 1]$

8b.

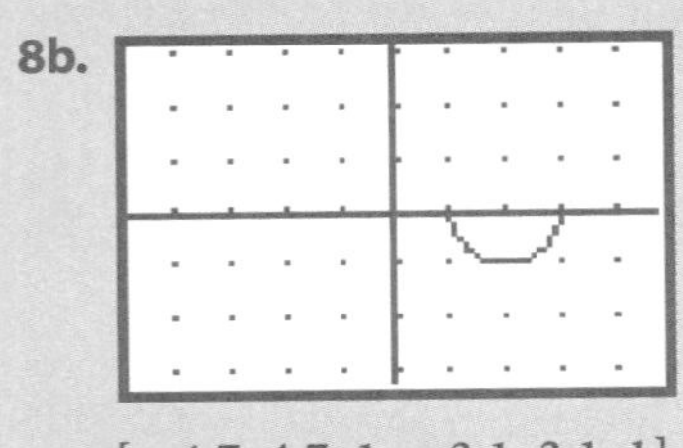

$[-4.7, 4.7, 1, -3.1, 3.1, 1]$

The graph is reflected across the x-axis; $y = -\sqrt{1 - (x - 2)^2}$.

8c.

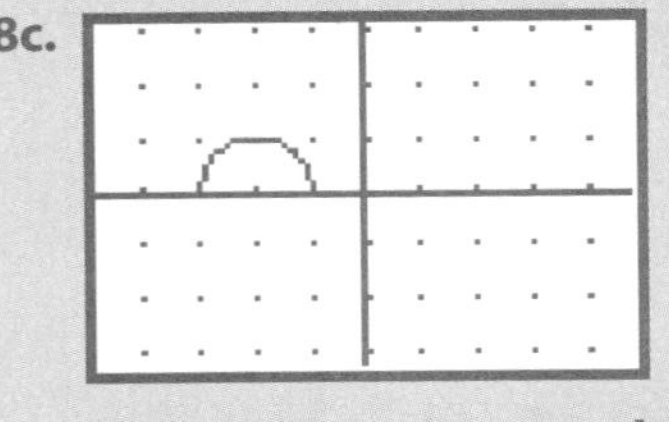

$[-4.7, 4.7, 1, -3.1, 3.1, 1]$

The graph is reflected across the y-axis; $y = \sqrt{1 - (x + 2)^2}$.

8d.

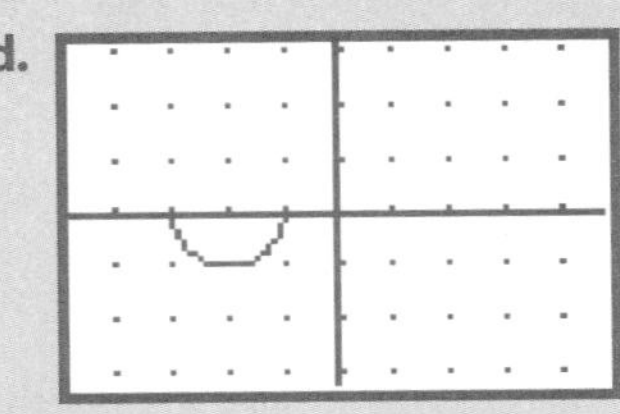

$[-4.7, 4.7, 1, -3.1, 3.1, 1]$

The graph is reflected across the x-axis and reflected across the y-axis; $y = -\sqrt{1 - (x + 2)^2}$.

9. A bug is crawling up a wall with locations given in the table at right. The variables x and y represent horizontal and vertical distances from the lower left corner of the wall, measured in inches, and t represents time measured in seconds.

t	x	y
0	20	5
2	24	7
4	28	9
6	32	11
8	36	13
10	40	15

a. Write parametric equations for x and y, in terms of t, that generate the information given in the table. $x = 20 + 2t$, $y = 5 + t$

b. Graph your parametric equations from 9a with the data points, (x, y). How do they relate?

c. Using only x and y, write the equation of the line that passes through the data points. $y = \frac{1}{2}x - 5$

d. How can the parametric equations be used to find the slope of the line in 9c?

In an area known for its many wood carvers, giant wooden bugs decorate the wall of this house on the Jersey Cove in Québec, Canada.

10. Write parametric equations for two perpendicular lines that intersect at the point (3, 2), with one line having a slope of -0.5. possible answer: $x = 3 + t$, $y = 2 + 2t$; $x = 3 + 2t$, $y = 2 - t$

11. The functions $d_1 = 1.5t$ and $d_2 = 12 - 2.5t$ represent Edna's and Maria's distances in miles from a trailhead, as functions of time in hours.

a. Write parametric equations to simulate Edna's hike north away from the trailhead. Use $x = 1$. $x = 1$, $y = 1.5t$

b. Write parametric equations to simulate Maria's hike south toward the trailhead. Use $x = 1.1$ so that Maria will come close to meeting Edna without actually bumping into her. $x = 1.1$, $y = 12 - 2.5t$

c. Name a graphing window and a range of t-values that show these hikes up to the moment the hikers meet.

d. Use your graph to approximate when and where the two hikers meet.

e. What equation can you write to find when Edna and Maria meet? Solve this equation symbolically to verify your answer to 11d. $1.5t = 12 - 2.5t$; $t = 3$; substitute $t = 3$ into either y-equation to get $y = 4.5$.

9b.

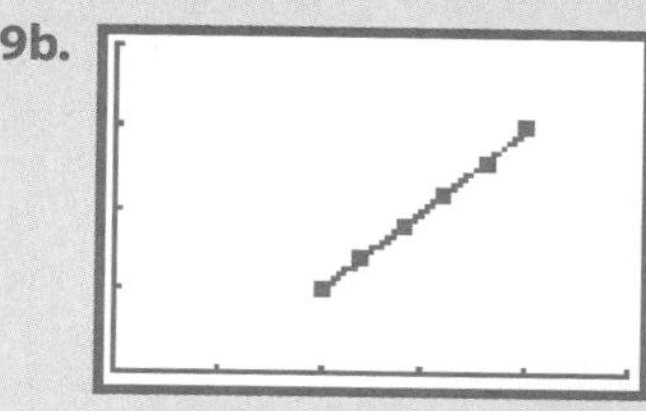

[0, 50, 10, 0, 20, 5]

$0 \le t \le 10$

The points lie on the line.

9d. The slope of the line in 9c is the ratio of the y-slope over the x-slope in the parametric equations.

Exercise 11 The trail is assumed to be directly north-south. The instruction "Use $x = 1$" indicates that Edna is traveling along a vertical line. **[Alert]** Students still may not realize how to write parametric equations to represent a vertical line.

[Ask] "If $x = 1$, how much movement is there in the east-west direction?" [none] Thus all the movement is in the north-south direction, so d_1 will equal y.

11c. possible answer: [0, 2, 1, 0, 12, 1]; $0 \le t \le 3$

11d.

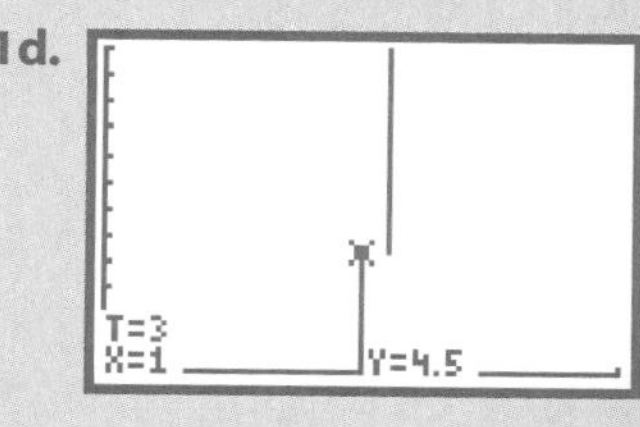

[0, 2, 1, 0, 12, 1]

$0 \le t \le 3$

They meet after hiking 3 h, when both are 4.5 mi north of the trailhead.

EXTENSIONS

A. Use Take Another Look activity 1 on page 486.

B. Use this extension of the Parametric Walk Investigation.

Mark out Quadrant 1 on the floor with tape identifying the x- and y-axes. A walker creates a figure eight or other pattern by walking about in the quadrant. Student X sets a motion sensor for about 10 seconds, and then moves along

Extensions (continued)

the y-axis capturing a graph of the x-coordinate of the walker's path with respect to time. Simultaneously, Student Y, with a motion sensor set for the same amount of time, moves along the x-axis capturing a graph of the y-coordinate of the walker's path with respect to time.

Sketch the two functions $x = f(t)$ and $y = g(t)$, recording values (t, x) and (t, y) from the two different calculators. Sketch a graph of the set of points (x, y), at a few critical values of t, from the two functions on the calculators. Describe what you have created with this graph.

Transfer the list of distances from one calculator to the other and create a calculator graph of the set of points (x, y), effectively eliminating the parameter t. Describe what you have created as you trace this graph.

Exercise 12 [Alert] In 12a, you might need to remind students of the projectile motion function, $y = -4.9x^2 + v_0x + s_0$, and that the egg hits the ground when its height is 0. **[Ask]** "What is the value of the initial velocity v_0?" [Because the egg is dropped, $v_0 = 0$.] "In which direction is this motion?" [Vertical (y-direction) and downward; the horizontal component is 0.] In 12b, the equation for the horizontal component of the motion can have x set to any constant value.

12b. possible answer: $x = 1$, $y = 98 - 4.9t^2$

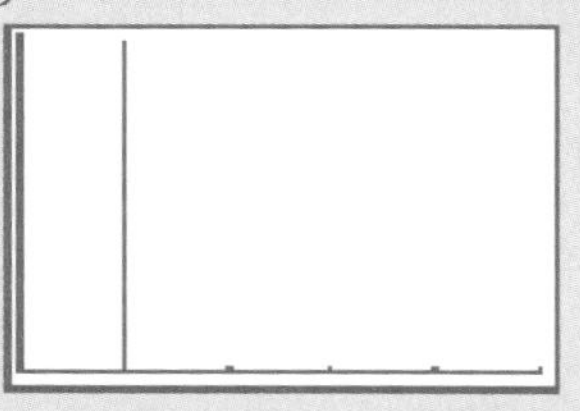

[0, 5, 1, 0, 100, 100]

$0 \leq t \leq 5$

12e. possible answer: $x = 5.32$, $y = 98 - 4.9t^2$; $x = 1.2t$, $y = 1.75$; $0 \leq t \leq 5$

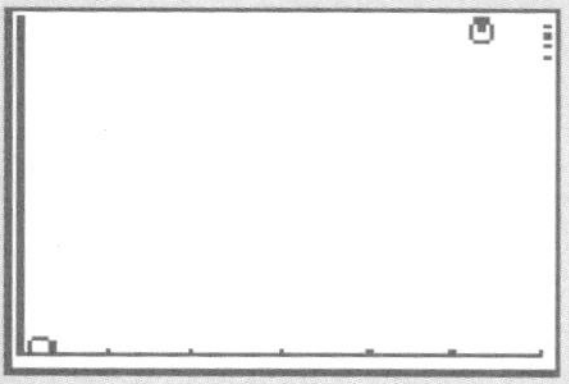

[0, 6, 1, 0, 100, 100]

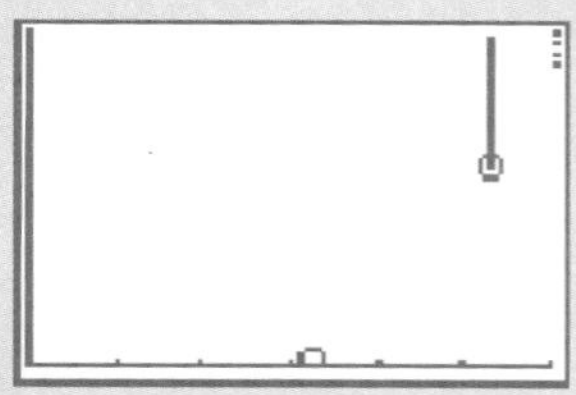

[0, 6, 1, 0, 100, 100]

[0, 6, 1, 0, 100, 100]

See page 892 for answers to Exercises 14d and 16d.

12. An egg is dropped from the roof of a 98 m building.

a. How long will it take the egg to reach the ground? 4.47 s

b. Write and graph parametric equations to model the motion.

c. When will the egg be 1.75 m above the ground? 4.43 s

d. A 1.75 m high trampoline is rolled at a rate of 1.2 m/s toward the egg drop site, starting at the instant when the egg is dropped. How far away should the trampoline start so that when the egg is dropped it makes a direct hit? 5.32 m

e. Simulate both motions with parametric equations.

Review

8.1 **13.** At right are the graphs of

$$x = t \quad\text{and}\quad x = t$$
$$y = t \qquad\quad y = t^2$$

Write parametric equations of the parabola's reflection across the line $y = x$. $x = t^2, y = t$

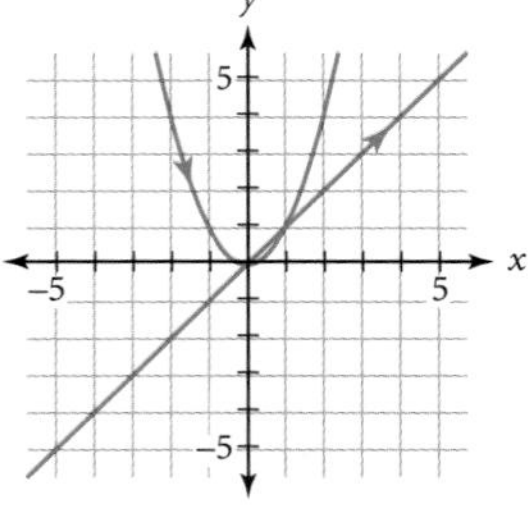

8.1 **14.** Tanker A moves at 18 mi/h and Tanker B moves at 22 mi/h. Both are traveling from Corpus Christi, Texas, to St. Petersburg, Florida, 900 mi directly east. Simulate the tanker movements if Tanker A leaves Corpus Christi at noon and Tanker B leaves at 5 P.M.

a. Write parametric equations to simulate the motions.

b. Name a graphing window and a range of t-values that show this situation.

c. When and where does Tanker B pass Tanker A?

d. Simulate the tanker movements if both tankers leave at noon, but Tanker A leaves from Corpus Christi and Tanker B leaves from St. Petersburg, each heading toward the other. Record your equations and determine the time interval during which they are within 50 mi of each other.

An oil tanker travels in the Gulf of Mexico near Tampa, Florida.

4.3 **15.** What is the equation of the image of $y = \frac{2}{3}x - 2$ after a translation right 5 units and up 3 units?

5.5 **16.** Consider the function $f(x) = 3 + \sqrt[3]{(x-1)^2}$.

a. Find

i. $f(9)$ 7

ii. $f(1)$ 3

iii. $f(0)$ 4

iv. $f(-7)$ 7

b. Find the equation(s) of the inverse of $f(x)$. Is the inverse a function? $y = 1 \pm \sqrt{(x-3)^3}$; not a function

c. Describe how you can use your calculations in 16a to check your inverse in 16b.

d. Use your calculator to graph $f(x)$ and its inverse on the same axes.

Exercise 13 You may want to remind students that reflections across the line $y = x$ are graphs of inverse relations.

Exercise 14a The calculator simulation works perfectly for these equations if your window starts at $x = 0$. If you lower the Xmin to -10, you'll notice that Tanker B actually starts at the same time as Tanker A but starts behind Tanker A. For a good simulation, the window must be set so that x is greater than or equal to 0.

14a. Tanker A: $x = 18t$ and $y = 1$; Tanker B: $x = 22(t - 5)$ and $y = 2$

14b. possible answer: [0, 900, 100, −1, 3, 1]; $0 \leq t \leq 50$

14c. 27.5 h after leaving; 495 mi east of Corpus Christi

15. $y = \left(\frac{2}{3}(x-5) - 2\right) + 3$ or $y = \frac{2}{3}x - \frac{7}{3}$

16c. Substitute each y-value found in 16a for x in the inverse. Check that the output is equivalent to the original x-value.

LESSON

8.3 Right Triangle Trigonometry

Happiness is not a destination.
It is a method of life.
BURTON HILLIS

Panama City is 750 miles from Corpus Christi, Texas, at a bearing of 73°. Model the movement of a tanker as it travels from Corpus Christi to Panama City, Florida.

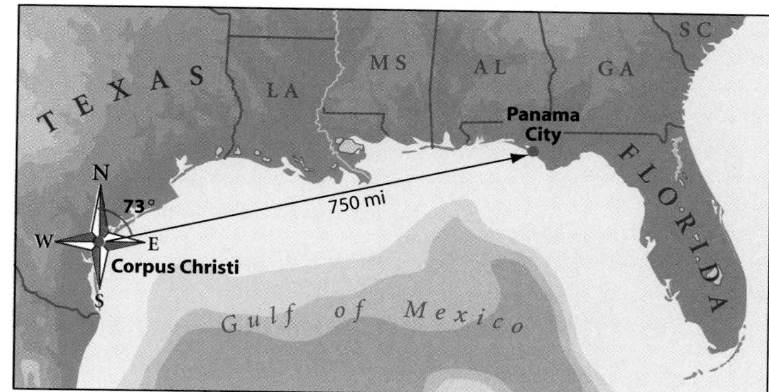

Trigonometry can be used with parametric equations to model motion that is not directly horizontal or vertical, such as the problem above. You can begin by separating any motion in two dimensions into its horizontal and vertical components. A **bearing** of 73° refers to a 73° angle measured clockwise from north, as shown below.

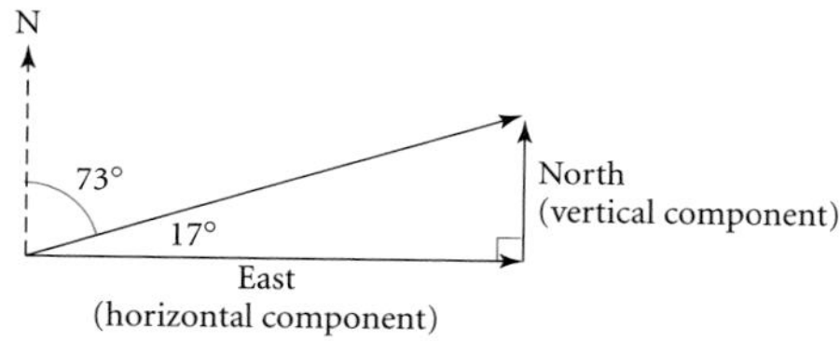

To solve a problem like this one, you will use **trigonometric ratios.**

The word **trigonometry** comes from the Greek words for "triangle" and "measure." Trigonometry relates angle measures to ratios of sides in similar triangles. For example, in the similar right triangles shown below, all corresponding angles are congruent. The ratio of the length of the shorter leg to the length of the longer leg is always 0.75, and the ratios of the lengths of other pairs of corresponding sides are also equal. In right triangles, there are special names for each of these ratios.

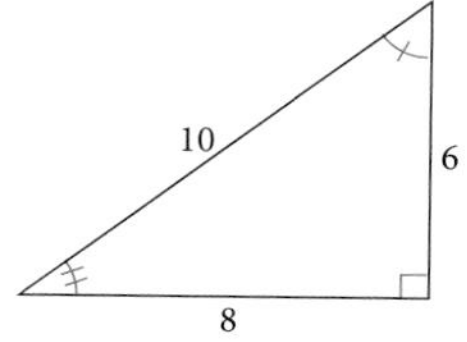

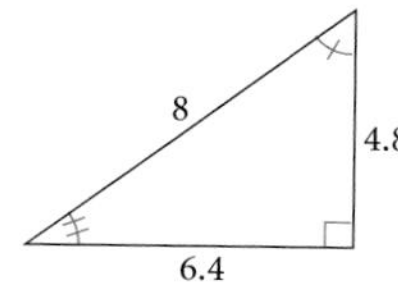

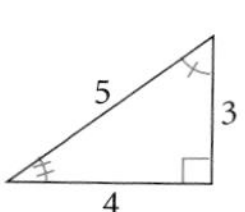

LESSON 8.3

PLANNING

LESSON OUTLINE

First day:
25 min Examples
20 min Exercises

Second day:
20 min Investigation
10 min Sharing
15 min Exercises

MATERIALS

- Trigonometric Ratios (T), *optional*
- Similar Right Triangles (W), *optional*
- Calculator Note 8F

TEACHING

In this lesson students see how to use right triangle trigonometry to describe motion at angles. You might use two days for the lesson—one to practice finding the side lengths and angle measures of right triangles (Examples A and B, Exercises 1–4) and another to do the investigation and additional exercises.

One Step

Pose this problem: "An airplane takes off at an angle of 30° with the ground, traveling at 200 mi/h. The sun is directly overhead. What parametric equations describe the location of the plane's shadow on the ground and the height of the plane during the ascent?" As needed, urge students to draw diagrams. As students express a need to find the ratios of the lengths of sides of a right triangle, remind them of triangle trigonometry (if they've seen it before) or define the basic trigonometric ratios for them and show them how to calculate these ratios on their calculators. You might use the Trigonometric Ratios transparency.

NCTM STANDARDS

CONTENT		PROCESS	
	Number	✓	Problem Solving
✓	Algebra	✓	Reasoning
✓	Geometry	✓	Communication
✓	Measurement	✓	Connections
	Data/Probability	✓	Representation

LESSON OBJECTIVES

- Define the trigonometric ratios sine, cosine, and tangent
- Use trigonometric ratios to find the unknown lengths of the sides of a right triangle
- Use inverse trigonometric ratios to find the unknown angle measures of a right triangle
- Use trigonometric ratios and parametric equations to model and solve problems about motion
- Find bearings corresponding to angles with the x- and y-axes, and find angles corresponding to given bearings

Trigonometric Ratios
[Alert] Students may be confused about the distinctions among the hypotenuse and adjacent and opposite legs.

[Ask] "Is the hypotenuse ever the opposite or adjacent leg?" [Although it may be adjacent to an angle, it's not the side that is called the leg adjacent to the angle.] Help students understand that the *opposite leg* is the side across from the angle and the *adjacent leg* is the nonhypotenuse side that forms one side of the angle.

You might show students how to use a trigonometric table; tables are available on the Internet.

If students do not have a firm understanding of trigonometric ratios, have them complete the Similar Right Triangles worksheet. Then display the Trigonometric Ratios transparency to summarize their findings.

MAKING THE CONNECTION

[Language] Another place you see the Latin word *sinus* in English is in the word *sinus,* which refers to the indentation in our nasal passage where the air we breathe is warmed. **[Context]** As the Sanskrit word indicates, trigonometric ratios originally were associated with chords of a circle rather than with angles. Trigonometry was first developed by the Greeks to aid in the study of astronomy.

Trigonometric Ratios

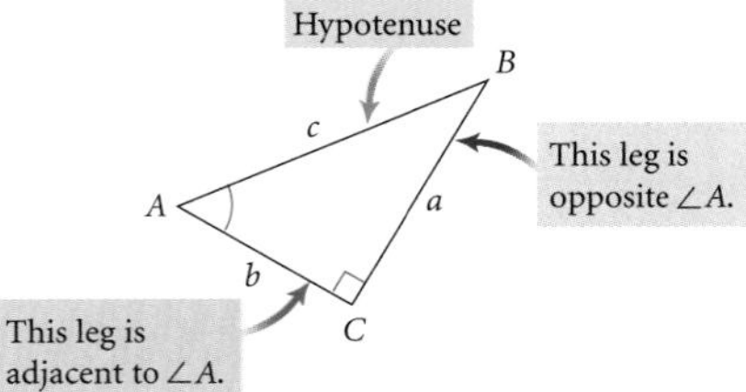

For any acute angle A in a right triangle, the **sine** of $\angle A$ is the ratio of the length of the leg opposite $\angle A$ to the length of the hypotenuse.

$$\sin A = \frac{\text{opposite leg}}{\text{hypotenuse}} = \frac{a}{c}$$

The **cosine** of $\angle A$ is the ratio of the length of the leg adjacent to $\angle A$ to the length of the hypotenuse.

$$\cos A = \frac{\text{adjacent leg}}{\text{hypotenuse}} = \frac{b}{c}$$

The **tangent** of $\angle A$ is the ratio of the length of the opposite leg to the length of the adjacent leg.

$$\tan A = \frac{\text{opposite leg}}{\text{adjacent leg}} = \frac{a}{b}$$

Language CONNECTION

The word *sine* has a curious history. The Sanskrit term for sine was *jya-ardha* ("half-chord"), later abbreviated to *jya.* Islamic scholars, who learned about sine from India, called it *jiba.* In Segovia, around 1140, Robert of Chester read *jiba* as *jaib* when he was translating al-Khwārizmī's book, *Kitāb al-jabr wa'al-muqābalah,* from Arabic into Latin. One meaning of *jaib* is "indentation" or "gulf." So *jiba* was translated into Latin as *sinus,* meaning "fold" or "indentation," and from that we get the word *sine.*

You can use the trigonometric ratios to find unknown side lengths of a right triangle when you know the measure of one acute angle and the length of one of the sides. [► See **Calculator Note 8F** to learn about calculating the trigonometric ratios on your calculator. ◄]

EXAMPLE A Find the unknown length, b.

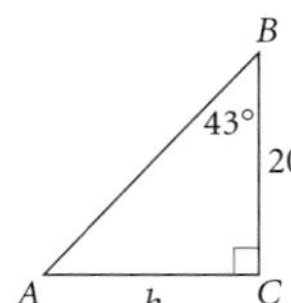

▶ Solution

In this problem, you know the length of one leg, you know the measure of one acute angle, and you want to find the length of the other leg. The tangent ratio relates the lengths of the legs to the measure of the angle. Therefore, you can use the tangent ratio. (It would be more difficult to use sine or cosine because you would need to write an expression for the length of the hypotenuse.)

$\tan 43° = \frac{b}{20}$ Write the tangent ratio and substitute the known values of the angle measure and length of the adjacent leg.

$b = 20 \tan 43°$ Multiply both sides by 20.

$b \approx 18.65$ Find the tangent of 43°, and multiply it by 20.

The length, b, of side $\overline{AC}$ is approximately 18.65 units.

Note that the trigonometric ratios apply to both acute angles in a right triangle. In this triangle, b is the leg adjacent to A and the leg opposite B, whereas a is the leg opposite A and the leg adjacent to B. As always, c is the hypotenuse.

$\sin A = \frac{a}{c}$ $\sin B = \frac{b}{c}$

$\cos A = \frac{b}{c}$ $\cos B = \frac{a}{c}$

$\tan A = \frac{a}{b}$ $\tan B = \frac{b}{a}$

Investigation
Two Ships

In this investigation you will model the motion of two cargo ships traveling from Corpus Christi. Ship A is traveling on a bearing of 73° toward Panama City, 750 mi away. Ship B is traveling on a bearing of 90° toward St. Petersburg, 900 mi away. Both ships are traveling at 23 mi/h.

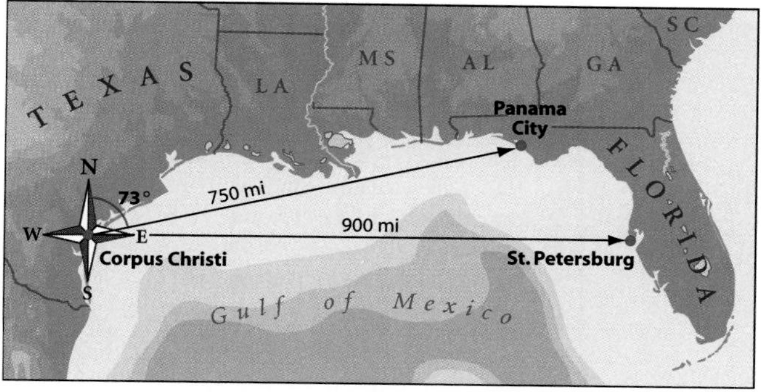

Step 1 $d = 23t$ for both ships

Step 2 Ship A: in 32.6 h; Ship B: in 39.1 h

Step 1 For each ship, write an equation that gives its distance from Corpus Christi as a function of time.

Step 2 Solve each equation from Step 1 to find out when each ship will arrive at its destination.

▶ EXAMPLE A

[Alert] If students get an answer of 45.8, their calculator is in Radian mode. Calculators should be in Degree mode for this chapter. Chapter 10 will introduce Radian mode.

Warn students that rounding trigonometric values too much can lead to inaccurate answers. For example, if students evaluate $20 \tan 43°$ as $20(0.9)$, they will get an answer of 18 instead of 18.65. Students should round trigonometric values in intermediate steps to four decimal places or, even better, simply enter $20 \tan 43°$ into the calculator.

[Ask] "What is the measure of $\angle A$?" [47°] "What is the length of the side opposite $\angle C$?" [about 27 units] To find c, students can use the Pythagorean Theorem or another trigonometric ratio such as $c = \frac{20}{\sin 47°}$.

Guiding the Investigation

You might give students some problems for practice in finding bearings so they get used to this angle measurement.

If you are concerned that this investigation is too advanced for your class, you might want to demonstrate the methods by first working through Exercise 10 as a class.

Step 1 Students should write one equation for each ship in the form $d = rt$, not the parametric equations.

Step 3 Encourage students to draw a triangle for the path of Ship A. Make sure they place the angle that measures 73° appropriately. Students should use the triangle with an angle measure of 17° that shares a side with the x-axis.

Step 3 East: Ship A: 22 mi after 1 h, 44 mi after 2 h; Ship B: 23 mi after 1 h, 46 mi after 2 h. North: Ship A: 6.7 mi after 1 h, 13.4 mi after 2 h; Ship B: 0 mi after 1 and 2 h.

Step 4 **[Alert]** You might derive these equations as a class. For example, to find x (the eastern component), start by writing the trigonometric ratio that uses x, the hypotenuse ($23t$), and the angle. You will use $\cos 17° = \frac{x}{23t}$. You should then solve for x, obtaining $x = 23t\cos 17°$. You can use the same method for the northerly direction, y. Students often have difficulty understanding the term $23t$. **[Ask]** "What is the distance at 1 h? At 2 h? At t h?"

Step 4 Ship A: $x = 22t$, $y = 6.7t$; Ship B: $x = 23t$, $y = 0$. The coefficient in the x-equation for Ship A comes from $23\cos 17°$, and the coefficient for y comes from $23\sin 17°$; Ship A: $x = 23t\cos 17°$, $y = 23t\sin 17°$. The coefficient in the x-equation for Ship B comes from 23 mi/h; no change.

Step 5 Students can use their calculator simulation to find the distances, or they can use trigonometry with the 17°-73°-90° triangle and a hypotenuse of length 750 miles.

Step 6 Answers are the same as those in Step 2, except the solution for $y = 0$ for Ship B, which results in $\frac{0}{0}$ and is undefined.

▶ EXAMPLE B

Calculators should be in Degree mode. Ask all students to draw diagrams; some students are reluctant to sketch pictures.

As with other problems in this chapter, you will often need to choose a coordinate system or point of reference for application problems. Most of the time, it makes sense to locate the initial point of the problem at the origin.

Step 3 How far east of Corpus Christi is each ship after 1 h? After 2 h? How far north is each ship at those times? (*Hint:* You may need to use trigonometry for Ship A.)

Step 4 Write a pair of parametric equations for each ship's location as a function of time. Explain where each number in each equation comes from. Change numbers that are approximations back to exact form (using trigonometric ratios).

Step 5 How far north of Corpus Christi is Panama City? How far east?

Step 5 219.3 mi; 717.2 mi

Step 6 Use the parametric equations you wrote in Step 4 to find out when each ship will arrive at its destination. Explain how your answers relate to your answers from Step 2.

Each trigonometric ratio is a function of an acute angle measure, because each angle measure has a unique ratio associated with it. The inverse of each trigonometric function gives the measure of the angle. For example, $\tan^{-1}\left(\frac{18}{20}\right) \approx 42°$.

EXAMPLE B

Two hikers leave their campsite. One walks east 2.85 km and the other walks south 6.03 km.

a. After the hikers get to their destinations, what is the bearing from the southern hiker to the eastern hiker?

b. How far apart are they?

▶ Solution

Draw a diagram using the information given.

N, W, E, S; C, 2.85 km, E; 6.03 km; S

a. Angle S measures the bearing from the southern hiker to the eastern hiker. This is a right triangle and you know the lengths of both legs, so you can use the tangent ratio.

$$\tan S = \frac{2.85}{6.03}$$

Take the inverse tangent of both sides to find the angle measure. Since you are composing tangent with its inverse, $\tan^{-1}(\tan S)$ is equivalent to S. [▶ Revisit **Calculator Note 8F** to learn about calculating the inverse trigonometric functions. ◀]

$$S = \tan^{-1}\left(\frac{2.85}{6.03}\right) \approx 25°$$

The eastern hiker is at a bearing of about 25° from the southern hiker.

b. You can use the Pythagorean Theorem to find the distance from S to E.

$$6.03^2 + 2.85^2 = (SE)^2$$
$$SE = \sqrt{6.03^2 + 2.85^2}$$
$$SE \approx 6.67$$

The distance between the two hikers is approximately 6.67 km.

SHARING IDEAS

[Ask] "Which tells you more, the distance equation or the corresponding parametric equations?" [The parametric equations tell the ship's coordinates at various times but might make the shape of its path less obvious.]

Ask students what they think $\tan^{-1} x$ means, in their own words. In particular, does it mean $\frac{1}{\tan x}$? Try to delay approving any answer to this question until you know what all students think. This notation for inverse tangent is the same as that used for other inverse functions explored in Lesson 5.5. A good mathematical question is "Does $\frac{1}{\tan x}$ *ever* equal $\tan^{-1} x$?" [No; $\frac{1}{\tan x}$ is a ratio of the lengths of sides of a triangle, but $\tan^{-1} x$ refers to an angle measure, specifically, the measure of the angle whose tangent is x. Even if they had the same numerical value at some point (which they can't), their units would be different.]

[Language] Reading $\tan^{-1} x$ as "the angle whose tangent is x" will help reinforce the meaning of the inverse function notation for trigonometric ratios.

Recreation

CONNECTION

A compass is a useful tool to have if you're hiking, camping, or sailing in an unfamiliar setting. The circular edge of a compass has 360 marks representing degrees of direction. North is 0° or 360°, east is 90°, south is 180°, and west is 270°. Each degree on a compass shows the direction of travel, or bearing. The needle inside a compass always points north. Magnetic poles on the Earth guide the direction of the needle and allow you to navigate along your desired course. Learn how to use a compass with the links at **www.keymath.com/DAA** .

Your calculator will display each trigonometric ratio to many digits, so your final answer could be displayed to several decimal places. However, it is usually appropriate to round your final answer to the nearest degree or 0.1 unit of length, as in the solution to part a in Example B. If the problem gives more precise measurements, you can use that same amount of precision in your answer. In the example, distances were given to the nearest 0.01 km, so the answer in part b was rounded to the nearest 0.01 also.

EXERCISES

You will need

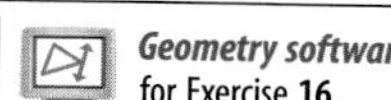
Geometry software for Exercise **16**

Practice Your Skills

1. Write all the trigonometric formulas (including inverses) relating the sides and angles in this triangle. There should be a total of 12.

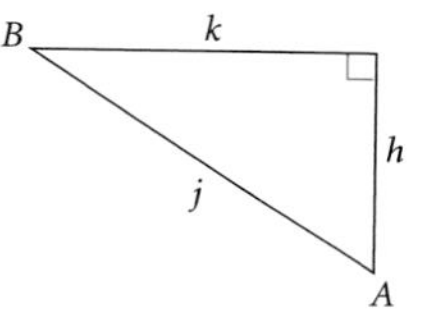

2. Draw a right triangle for each problem. Label the sides and angle, then solve to find the unknown measure.

a. $\sin 20° = \frac{a}{12}$ **b.** $\cos 80° = \frac{25}{b}$ **c.** $\tan 55° = \frac{c+4}{c}$ **d.** $\sin^{-1}\frac{17}{30} = D$

Reason and Apply

3. For each triangle, find the length of the labeled side.

a.

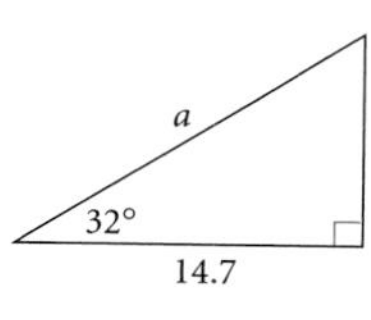

$a \approx 17.3$

b.

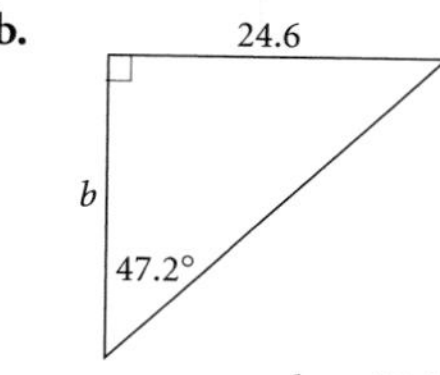

$b \approx 22.8$

c.

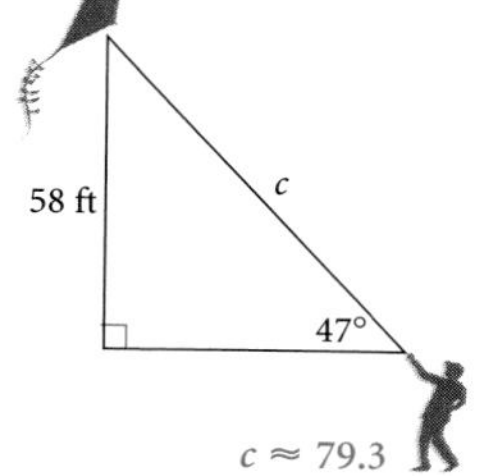

$c \approx 79.3$

2a. 12, 20°, a — $a \approx 4.1$

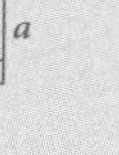

2b. 80°, b, 25 — $b \approx 144.0$

2c.

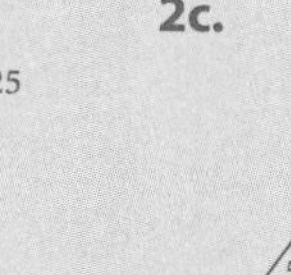

$c \approx 9.3$

2d. 30, 17, D — $D \approx 34.5°$

Assessing Progress

As students investigate and present, you can check their understanding of equations of motion and the separation of the components of motion into parametric equations. You can also observe their ability to solve linear equations and their willingness to draw diagrams.

Closing the Lesson

The main point of this lesson is that distances related to angles, such as a distance traveled at a particular angle, can be described using **trigonometric ratios** of the sides of a right triangle. As needed, redefine the three basic trigonometric ratios: sine as $\frac{\text{opposite leg}}{\text{hypotenuse}}$, cosine as $\frac{\text{adjacent leg}}{\text{hypotenuse}}$, and tangent as $\frac{\text{opposite leg}}{\text{adjacent leg}}$.

BUILDING UNDERSTANDING

Students practice using trigonometric ratios.

ASSIGNING HOMEWORK

Essential	1–4
Performance assessment	5–12
Portfolio	11
Journal	7
Group	9
Review	13–16

1. $\sin A = \frac{k}{j}$; $\sin B = \frac{h}{j}$; $\sin^{-1}\left(\frac{k}{j}\right) = A$; $\sin^{-1}\left(\frac{h}{j}\right) = B$; $\cos B = \frac{k}{j}$; $\cos A = \frac{h}{j}$; $\cos^{-1}\left(\frac{k}{j}\right) = B$; $\cos^{-1}\left(\frac{h}{j}\right) = A$; $\tan A = \frac{k}{h}$; $\tan B = \frac{h}{k}$; $\tan^{-1}\left(\frac{k}{h}\right) = A$; $\tan^{-1}\left(\frac{h}{k}\right) = B$

▶ Helping with the Exercises

5.

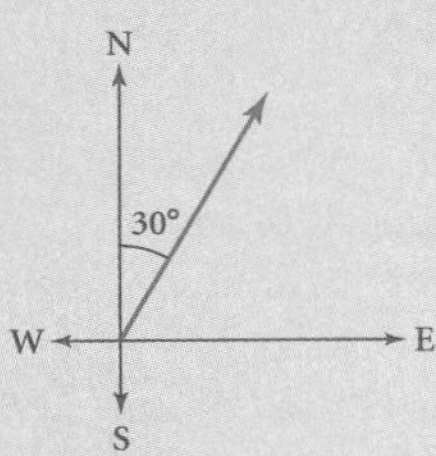

5b.

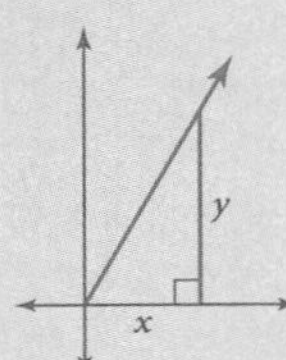

5c. 180 mi east, 311.8 mi north

Exercises 6 and 7 [Alert] Students might be concerned that the angles on the screen are not 39° and 40°. The visible angles are a function of the graphing window. The coordinates of a point on the line must be used to find the angle.

Exercise 6 [Ask] "What is the bearing of this motion?" [51°]

6a.

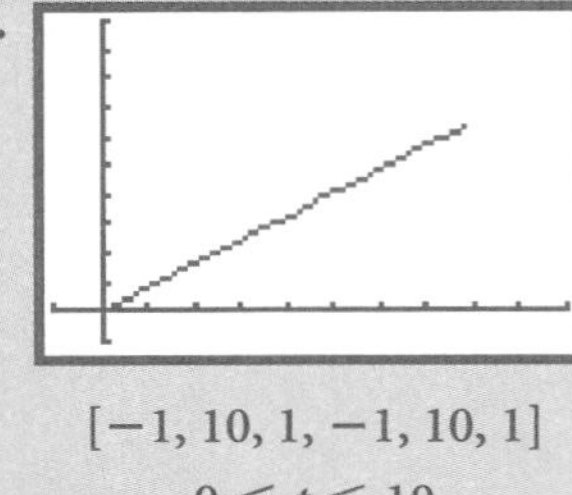

[−1, 10, 1, −1, 10, 1]

$0 \le t \le 10$

6b. The graph is a line segment 10 units long, at an angle of 39° with the horizontal axis. Changing the range of t-values changes the length (starting and ending points) of the segment.

6c. 39°

7a.

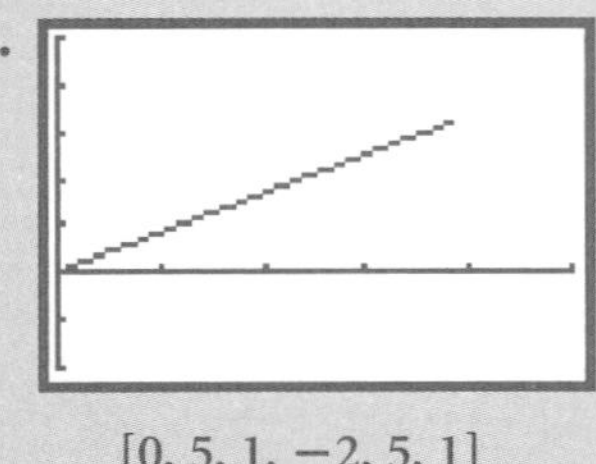

[0, 5, 1, −2, 5, 1]

$0 \le t \le 1$

4. For each triangle, find the measure of the labeled angle.

a. $A \approx 17°$

b. $B \approx 30°$

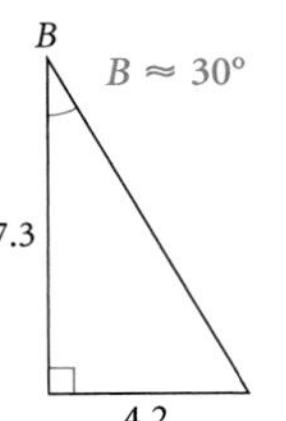

c. $C \approx 11°$

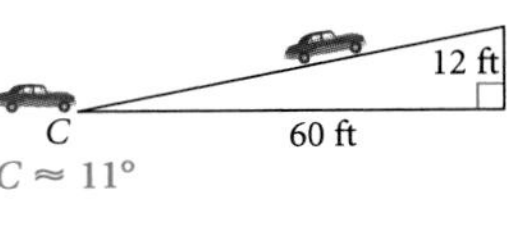

A
36 ft
125 ft
C
60 ft

5. Draw a pair of intersecting horizontal and vertical lines, and label north, east, south, and west. Sketch the path of a plane flying on a bearing of 30°.

a. What is the measure of the angle between the plane's path and the horizontal axis? 60°

b. Choose any point along the plane's path. From this point, draw a segment perpendicular to the horizontal axis to create a right triangle. Label the length of the horizontal leg, x, and the vertical leg, y.

c. The plane flies 180 mi/h for 2 h. How far east and how far north does it travel?

6. Consider the parametric equations

$x = t\cos 39°$

$y = t\sin 39°$

a. Make a graph with window $-1 \le x \le 10$, $-1 \le y \le 10$, and $0 \le t \le 10$.

b. Describe the graph. What happens if you change the minimum and maximum values of t?

c. Find the measure of the angle between this line and the x-axis. (*Hint:* Trace to a point on the line and find the coordinates.)

7. Consider the parametric equations

$x = 5t\cos 40°$

$y = 5t\sin 40°$

a. Make a graph with window $0 \le x \le 5$, $-2 \le y \le 5$, and $0 \le t \le 1$.

b. Describe the graph and the measure of the angle between the graph and the x-axis.

c. What is the relationship between this angle and the parametric equations?

d. What is the effect of the 5 in each equation? Change the 5 to a 1 in the first equation. What happens? What happens when you change 5 to 1 in both equations?

8. Write parametric equations for each graph.

a.

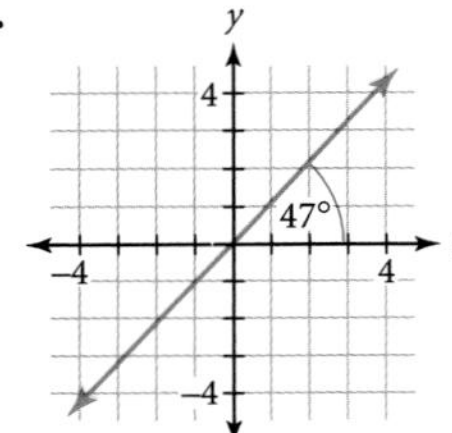

b.

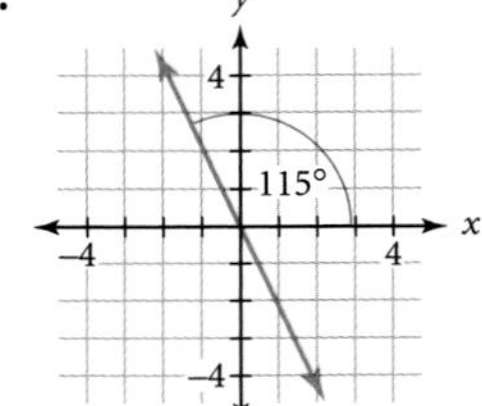

7b. It is a segment 5 units long, at an angle of 40° above the x-axis.

7c. This is the value of the angle in the equations.

7d. It makes the segment 5 units long when $t = 1$; the graph becomes steeper, and the segment becomes shorter; the graph becomes shorter, but the slope is the same as it was originally.

8a. $x = t\cos 47°, y = t\sin 47°$

8b. $x = t\cos 115°, y = t\sin 115°$

9. A plane is flying at 100 mi/h on a bearing of 60°.

a. Draw a diagram of the motion. Draw a segment perpendicular to the x-axis to create a right triangle. Write equations for x and y, in terms of t, to model the motion.

b. What range of t is required to display 500 mi of plane travel? (Assume t represents time in hours.) $0 \le t \le 5$

c. Explain the real-world meaning of the numbers and variables you used in your equations.

10. Tanker A is moving at a speed of 18 mi/h from Corpus Christi, Texas, toward Panama City, Florida. Panama City is 750 mi from Corpus Christi at a bearing of 73°.

a. Make a sketch of the tanker's motion, including coordinate axes.

b. How long does the tanker take to get to Panama City? 41.7 h

c. How far east and how far north is Panama City from Corpus Christi? 717.2 mi east, 219.3 mi north

11. Tanker B is traveling at a speed of 22 mi/h from St. Petersburg, Florida, to New Orleans, Louisiana, on a bearing of 285°. The distance between the two ports is 510 mi.

a. Make a sketch of the tanker's motion, including coordinate axes.

b. How long will it take the tanker to get to New Orleans? 23.2 h

c. How far west and how far north is New Orleans from St. Petersburg?

d. Suppose Tanker A in Exercise 10 leaves at the same time as Tanker B. Describe where the ships' paths intersect. Recall that St. Petersburg is 900 miles east of Corpus Christi. Will the ships collide? Explain your answer.

12. **APPLICATION** Civil engineers generally bank, or angle, a curve on a road so that a car going around the curve at the recommended speed does not skid off the road. Engineers use this formula to calculate the proper banking angle, θ, where v represents the velocity in meters per second, r represents the radius of the curve in meters, and g represents the gravitational constant, 9.8 m/s^2.

$$\tan\theta = \frac{v^2}{rg}$$

a. If the radius of an exit ramp is 60 m and the recommended speed is 40 km/h, at what angle should the curve be banked? 12°

b. A curve on a racetrack is banked at 36°. The radius of the curve is about 1.7 km. What speed is this curve designed for? 396 km/h

Science CONNECTION

When a car rounds a curve, the driver must rely on the friction between the car's tires and the road surface to stay on the road. Unfortunately, this does not always work—especially if the road surface is wet!

In car racing, where cars travel at high speeds, tracks banked steeply allow cars to go faster, especially around the corners. Banking on NASCAR tracks ranges from 36° in the corners to just a slight degree of banking in the straighter portions.

Exercise 12 The Greek letter *theta*, θ, often represents an angle measure. As needed, remind students to convert to meters for the formula and back to kilometers per hour for their answer to 12b.

MAKING THE CONNECTION

NASCAR stands for National Association for Stock Car Auto Racing.

Exercise 9 The diagram will include x, y, an angle that measures 30°, and $100t$ as the hypotenuse. You might want to discuss using arrowheads or vectors to show direction along each component. Students could solve the problem in 9b by using guess-and-check on their calculators or by solving the equation $100t = 500$ for t.

9a.

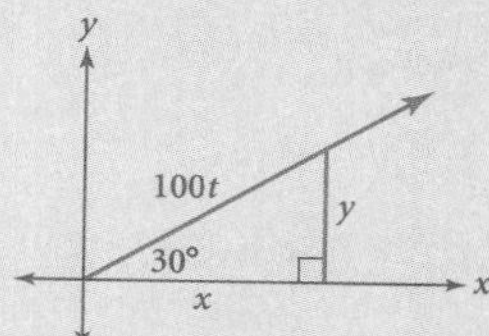

$x = 100t\cos 30°$
$y = 100t\sin 30°$

9c. 100 represents the speed of the plane in miles per hour, t represents time in hours, 30° is the angle the plane is making with the x-axis, x is the horizontal position at any time, and y is the vertical position at any time.

Exercise 10 This exercise is similar to the investigation and could be used as an example prior to the investigation.

10a.

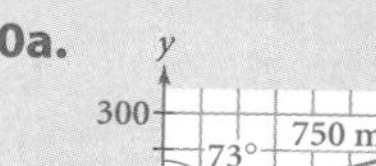

11a.

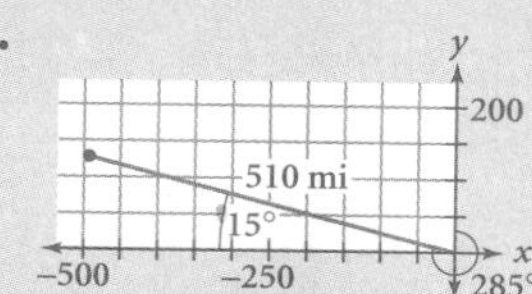

11c. 492.6 mi west, 132.0 mi north

Exercise 11d This exercise uses information from Exercise 10.

11d. The paths cross at approximately 480 mi west and 129 mi north of St. Petersburg. No, the ships do not collide because Tanker A reaches this point after 24.4 h and Tanker B reaches this point after 22.6 h.

$13a.\ y = 5 + \frac{3}{4}(x - 6)$ or $y = \frac{1}{2} + \frac{3}{4}x$

13b. $y = 5 + \frac{3(x-6)}{4}$. They are the same equation.

14a. (3.2, 35)

14b. $x = 3.2 + \sqrt{\frac{35}{4.9}} \approx 0.528$ and $x = 3.2 - \sqrt{\frac{35}{4.9}} \approx 5.873$

14c. $x = 3.2 + \sqrt{\frac{20}{4.9}} \approx 5.220$ and $x = 3.2 - \sqrt{\frac{20}{4.9}} \approx 1.180$

15. $(x - 2.6)^2 + (y + 4.5)^2 = 12.96$

Exercise 16 A line segment is turned into a slider when its length is used to affect another figure or formula. The dynamic exploration Vertex Form and Factored Form of Quadratic Equations at www.keymath.com/DAA is an example of what students can create.

16a. Constructions will vary, but for any graph scale and any setting of a, h, and k, the graph should have vertex (h, k) and scale factor a.

16b. Constructions will vary, but for any graph scale and any setting of a, r_1, and r_2, the graph should have x-intercepts r_1 and r_2 and scale factor a.

EXTENSIONS

A. Use Take Another Look activity 3 on page 486.

B. Give students a map and ask them to pick two cities and write parametric equations for a plane's motion between those cities. Assume that the plane travels at a speed of 180 mi/h.

Review

8.2 **13.** This table gives the position of a walker at several times.

Time (min) t	Horizontal distance (m) x	Vertical distance (m) y
0	6	5
2	14	11
4	22	17
6	30	23
8	38	29
10	46	35

a. Write a single equation for y in terms of x that fits the data points, (x, y), listed in the table.

b. Parametric equations modeling this table are $x = 6 + 4t$ and $y = 5 + 3t$. Eliminate the parameter, t, from these equations and compare your final equation to the answer you found in 13a.

4.4 **14.** Graph the parabola $y = 35 - 4.9(x - 3.2)^2$.

a. What are the coordinates of the vertex?

b. What are the x-intercepts?

c. Where does the parabola intersect the line $y = 15$?

4.7 **15.** Write the equation of the circle with center (2.6, −4.5) and radius 3.6.

7.2 **16.** ***Technology*** With geometry software you can create sliders—changeable line segments whose lengths represent the values of variables. The sliders can then be used to dynamically change the equation and graph of a function.

a. Create a sketch that uses sliders for a, h, and k, and shows how these parameters affect the vertex form of a quadratic equation, $y = a(x - h)^2 + k$.

b. Create another sketch that uses sliders for a, r_1, and r_2, and shows how these parameters affect the factored form of a quadratic equation, $y = a(x - r_1)(x - r_2)$.

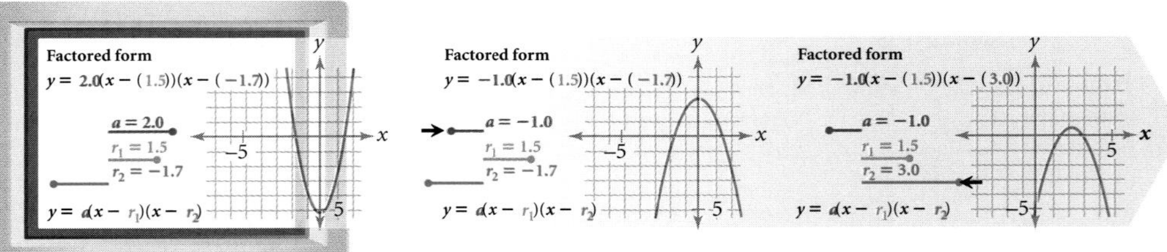

EXPLORATION

Parametric Equations for a Circle

By definition, a **circle** is the set of all the points in a plane at a given **radius** from a given **center** in the plane. To graph a complete circle on your calculator, you have used two separate functions: one for the top half of the circle and one for the bottom half. Graphing a circle is much simpler with parametric equations.

Imagine a circle with radius r and center at the origin. For a right triangle in the first quadrant with central angle measuring t degrees, $\sin t = \frac{y}{r}$ and $\cos t = \frac{x}{r}$. Solving these equations for x and y, you get the parametric equations for a circle:

$x = r\cos t$

$y = r\sin t$

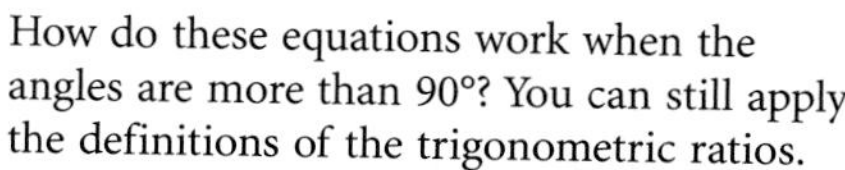

How do these equations work when the angles are more than 90°? You can still apply the definitions of the trigonometric ratios. However, when the angle is greater than 90°, you must use a right triangle situated in another quadrant. In each case, you form the triangle by connecting the point on the circle to the x-axis. For example, if the angle is 150°, you form a triangle where the angle with the x-axis is 30°. To find the values of the trigonometric ratios for 150°, you use the newly formed right triangle. Using a circle allows you to extend the definitions of sine, cosine, and tangent for any real angle value.

$$\sin t = \frac{y}{r} \qquad \sin 150° = \frac{1}{2}$$

$$\cos t = \frac{x}{r} \qquad \cos 150° = -\frac{\sqrt{3}}{2}$$

$$\tan t = \frac{y}{x} \qquad \tan 150° = -\frac{1}{\sqrt{3}}$$

EXPLORATION

PLANNING

LESSON OUTLINE

One day:

5 min	Example
20 min	Activity
10 min	Sharing
10 min	Questions

MATERIALS

- Calculator Note 4C, *optional*

TEACHING

Students have seen curves, such as circles and vertical lines, in which y is not a function of x because the curve doesn't pass the vertical line test. One important use of parametric equations is to describe these curves as functions.

This exploration will help students understand circles as functions of a parameter, laying the groundwork for studying other conic sections in Chapter 9. It also foreshadows Chapter 10, in which students will explore the trigonometry of the unit circle and define sine, cosine, and tangent for all values.

[Alert] Students might be thinking that the parameter t always represents time. Point out that here t represents an angle measure.

NCTM STANDARDS

CONTENT		PROCESS	
	Number		Problem Solving
✓	Algebra	✓	Reasoning
✓	Geometry	✓	Communication
✓	Measurement	✓	Connections
	Data/Probability	✓	Representation

LESSON OBJECTIVES

- Extend the definition of trigonometric functions to angles of any measure
- Use trigonometric ratios to find parametric equations for circles or ellipses
- Use parametric equations to graph geometric figures

► EXAMPLE

[Ask] "What would you do to graph a circle with radius 2? With radius 1? What happens if you use a t-step of 120°? What happens if you use the range $30° \leq t \leq 180°$?"

[Ask] The circle might look squashed if students don't use a friendly window; see Calculator Note 4C.]

EXAMPLE Use parametric equations to graph the circle with radius 3 and center (0, 0).

► Solution The parametric equations for a circle with radius 3 and center (0, 0) are

$$x = 3\cos t$$
$$y = 3\sin t$$

The variable t represents the central angle of the circle. Use the range $0° \leq t \leq 360°$ with a t-step of 1° to graph the complete circle on your calculator.

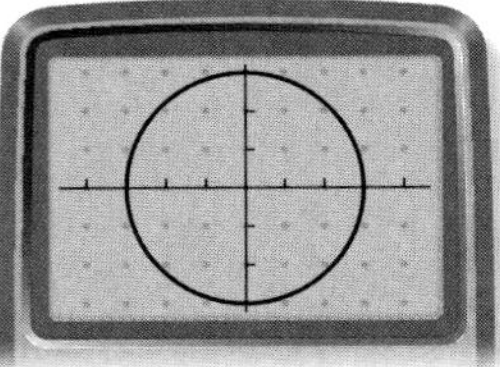

$[-4.7, 4.7, 1, -3.1, 3.1, 1]$

The t-step tells your calculator how often to plot a point. The calculator then connects these points with straight segments. When you make the t-step larger, the points are farther apart on the circle and your calculator's graph stops looking like a circle. This gives you a way to draw some interesting geometric shapes on your calculator.

The Star of Hisham from the Umayyad Dynasty (660–750 C.E.), located in the Khirbat al-Mafjar palace, Israel, uses circles and a star-like shape inscribed within the larger circle.

Guiding the Activity

Calculators need to be in Degree mode for this activity.

Step 1 If students are feeling frustrated instead of having fun, you might have them work in pairs. Alternatively, you might start the activity as a class and then let students work on their own and share different ways of making the same graph.

Activity
Variations on a Circle

In this activity you'll explore what happens to the graph of a circle when you change the parameter t. Work individually on Step 1. Then work with a partner or group for the remainder of the activity.

Step 1 Start with the parametric equations $x = 3\cos t$ and $y = 3\sin t$. Experiment with the parameter t, changing the minimum and maximum values and the t-step. Use these questions to guide your exploration.

a. What effect does changing the range of t have on the graph?

b. What effect does changing the t-step have on the graph?

c. How can you make a triangle? A square? A hexagon? An octagon? Try to find more than one way to draw each figure.

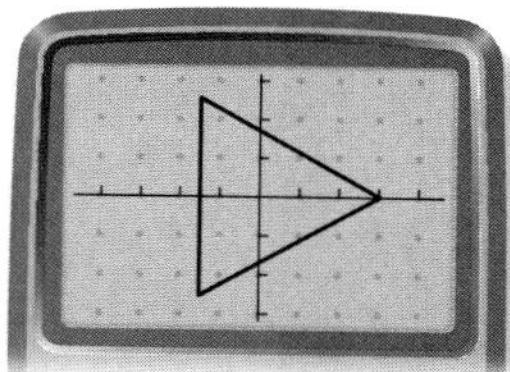

[−4.7, 4.7, 1, −3.1, 3.1, 1]

[−4.7, 4.7, 1, −3.1, 3.1, 1]

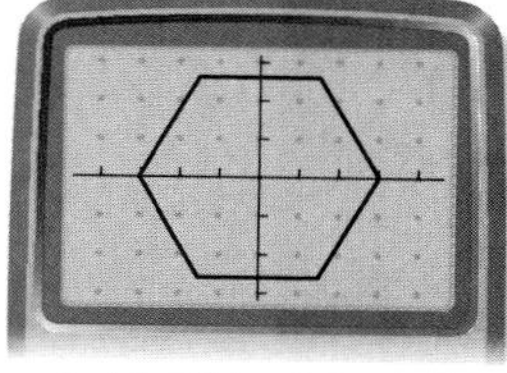

[−4.7, 4.7, 1, −3.1, 3.1, 1]

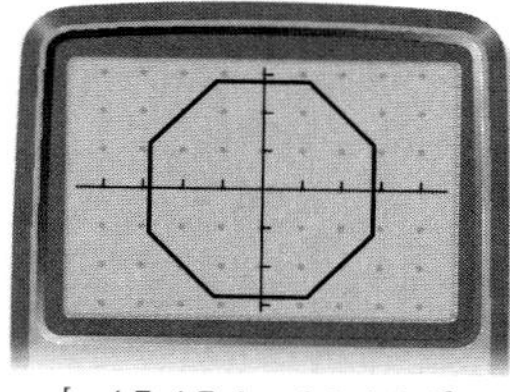

[−4.7, 4.7, 1, −3.1, 3.1, 1]

d. How can you make a square with sides parallel to the axes?

e. How can you rotate a polygon shape about the origin by altering the parametric equations?

Step 2 Share your results from Step 1 with a partner or your group. Work together to write a paragraph summarizing your discoveries.

Step 3 Find a way to translate the circle $x = 3\cos t$ and $y = 3\sin t$ so that it is centered at (5, 2).

Step 4 Reflect the graph from Step 3 across the y-axis, across the x-axis, across the line $y = x$, and across the line $x = -1$. Describe the method you used for each of these reflections.

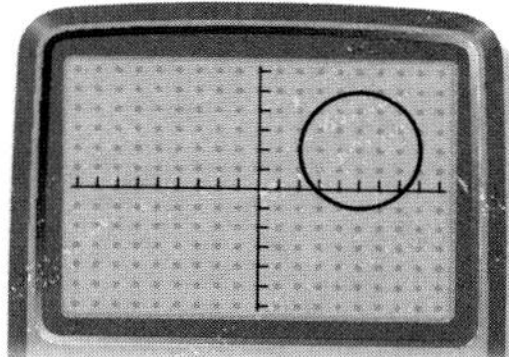

[−9.4, 9.4, 1, −6.2, 6.2, 1]

Step 5 Graph the equations $x = 3\cos t$ and $y = 3\sin t$, using the range $0° \le t \le 3600°$ with t-step 125°. Then try other t-step values that are not factors of 360°, such as 100°, 150°, and 185°. (You may also need to increase the maximum value of t.) Write a paragraph explaining what happens in each case.

Step 5 The paragraph can do more than describe what happens; it can also include reasons why a star is formed.

Step 5 When the value of the t-step is not a factor of 360°, a "star" is created. Sample graph:

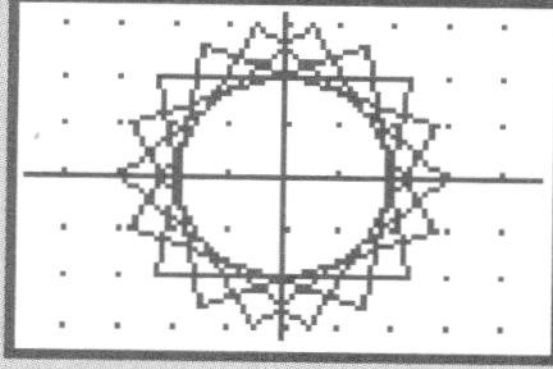

[−4.7, 4.7, 1, −3.1, 3.1, 1]

$0° \le t \le 3600°$, t-step 100°

Step 1a Changing the range of t changes the starting and stopping points around the circle. If the entire range is still equivalent to 360°, the graph appears rotated.

Step 1b Changing the t-step changes how often a point is plotted. For values much larger than 30°, the circle begins to look like a polygon because the individual segments are visible.

Step 1c triangle: $0° \le t \le 360°$, t-step 120°; square: $0° \le t \le 360°$, t-step 90°; hexagon: $0° \le t \le 360°$, t-step 60°; octagon: $22.5° \le t \le 382.5°$, t-step 45°

Step 1d $45° \le t \le 405°$, t-step 90°

Step 1e You can alternatively add a constant angle measure to t or subtract a constant angle measure from t in the parametric equations to create a rotation. For example, $x = 3\cos(t + 45)$, $y = 3\sin(t + 45)$ with $0° \le t \le 360°$ and t-step 90° is equivalent to the square in Step 1d.

Step 3 Add constants to the expressions for x and y to represent the translation right 5 units and up 2 units: $x = 3\cos t + 5$, $y = 3\sin t + 2$ with $0° \le t \le 360°$ and t-step 1°.

Step 4 For each of these reflections, $0° \le t \le 360°$ and t-step is 1°.

Reflect across the y-axis: multiply the expression for x by −1: $x = -(3\cos t + 5)$, $y = 3\sin t + 2$

Reflect across the x-axis: multiply the expression for y by −1: $x = 3\cos t + 5$, $y = -(3\sin t + 2)$

Reflect across the line $y = x$: interchange the expressions for x and y: $x = 3\sin t + 2$, $y = 3\cos t + 5$

Reflect across the line $x = -1$: $x = -(3\cos t + 5) - 2$, $y = 3\sin t + 2$

SHARING IDEAS

Students may ask what the parametric equations of polygons are if they don't have the form $x = r\cos t$, $y = r\sin t$. Generally, because the parameter is continuous, each edge of the polygon has a different set of parametric equations.

Challenge students to see what unusual graphs they can create by combining a parametric equation that has a trigonometric ratio with a parametric equation that doesn't.

▶ Helping with the Questions

Question 1 This question restates the concept discussed in the paragraph before the activity. It is important for students to realize that, although the calculator shows a polygon, the parametric equations represent a circle unless the domain is restricted to discrete values of t. You might make the analogy to string art. Imagine pegs in the shape of a circle. The shape is a circle, but you can wrap string around pegs separated by 90° to make a square.

1. The parametric equations $x = 3\cos t$ and $y = 3\sin t$ are the equations for a circle if the domain of t is continuous. The graph of a polygon, such as a square or hexagon, is the result of changing the t-step and connecting the discrete points with line segments. Mathematically, the continuous curve is always a circle.

MAKING THE CONNECTION

[Language] An opaque gem is one that light will not pass through, such as the white stone in the picture.

Art CONNECTION

By about 2800 B.C.E., gemstone cutting was a widespread practice throughout Egypt and Asia Minor (modern Turkey). Today's gem cutters use the same geometric designs that ancient gem cutters used. In multiples of 8, they carve small symmetric planes on a gem, called facets. Rubies, sapphires, and emeralds are often square or rectangular in shape, whereas other gems are cut into triangular, diamond, or trapezoidal shapes. The oldest gemstone shape, however, is circular or rounded, which is how many opal and opaque gems are still cut today.

Questions

1. In the investigation you used the parametric equations for a circle, $x = 3\cos t$ and $y = 3\sin t$, to graph other geometric shapes on your calculator. Mathematically, do you think it is correct to say that $x = 3\cos t$ and $y = 3\sin t$ are the parametric equations of a square or a hexagon? Explain your reasoning.

2. Find parametric equations for each translated circle.

a. $x = 2\cos t + 2, y = 2\sin t$

b.

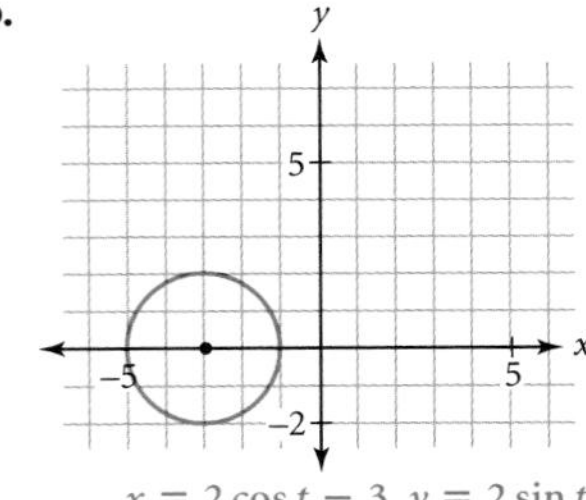

$x = 2\cos t - 3, y = 2\sin t$

c. $x = 2\cos t, y = 2\sin t + 4$

d.

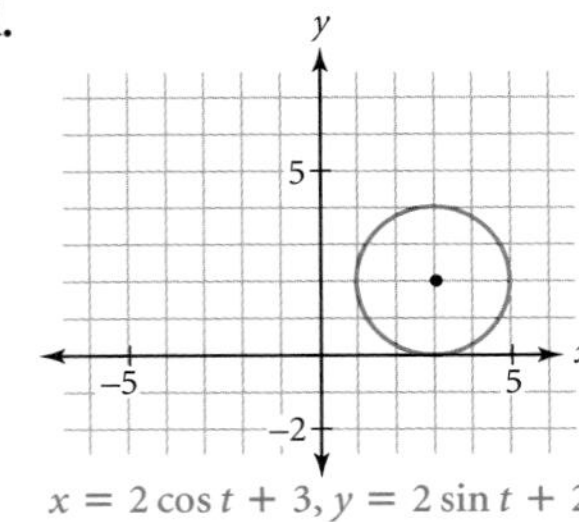

$x = 2\cos t + 3, y = 2\sin t + 2$

3. Use the parametric equations $x = 3\cos t$ and $y = 3\sin t$ to make each of these figures on your calculator. What range of t-values and what t-step are required for each?

a. $0° \le t \le 360°$, t-step 45°

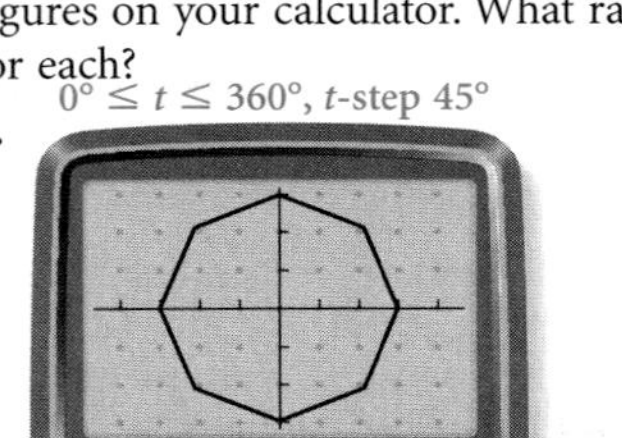

$[-4.7, 4.7, 1, -3.1, 3.1, 1]$

b. $90° \le t \le 450°$, t-step 72°

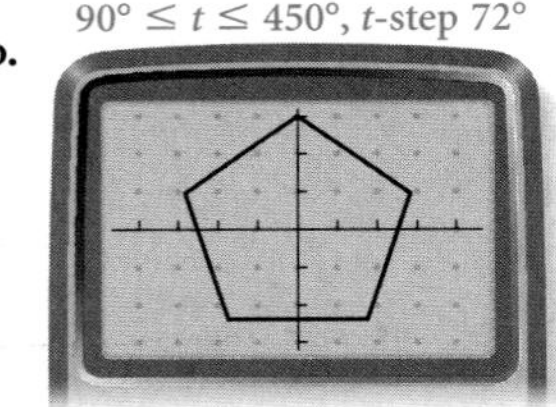

$[-4.7, 4.7, 1, -3.1, 3.1, 1]$

c. $-90° \le t \le 270°$, t-step 120°

$[-4.7, 4.7, 1, -3.1, 3.1, 1]$

d. $0° \le t \le 1080°$, t-step 108°

$[-4.7, 4.7, 1, -3.1, 3.1, 1]$

4. Consider a unit circle (a circle with radius 1) centered at the origin.

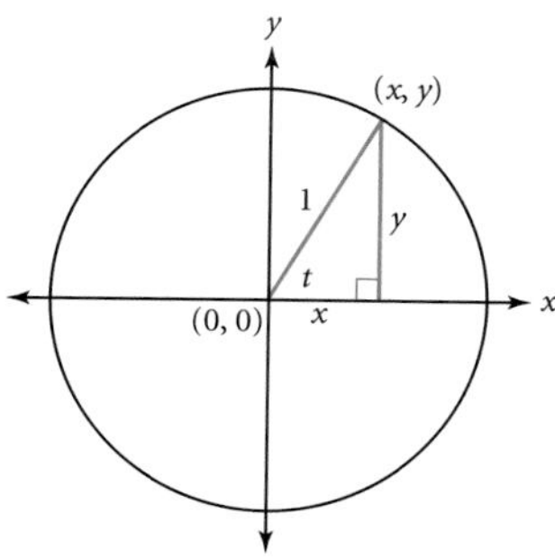

a. What are the parametric equations for the unit circle?

b. From Chapter 4, you know that the Pythagorean Theorem yields the equation of the unit circle, $x^2 + y^2 = 1$. Substitute the parametric equations for x and y to get an equation in terms of sine and cosine.

c. Use your calculator to verify that your equation in 4b is true for $t = 47°$.

5. Experiment to find parametric equations for each ellipse.

a.

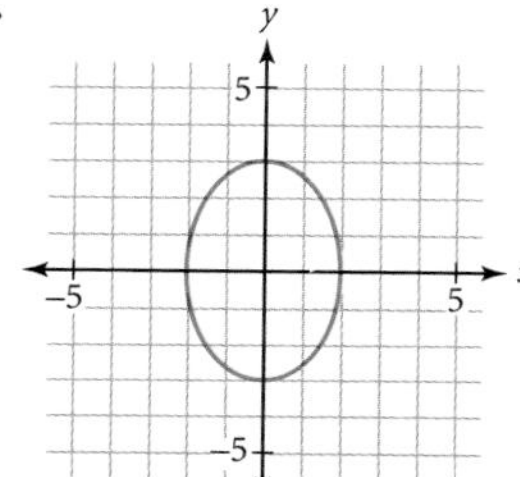

b.

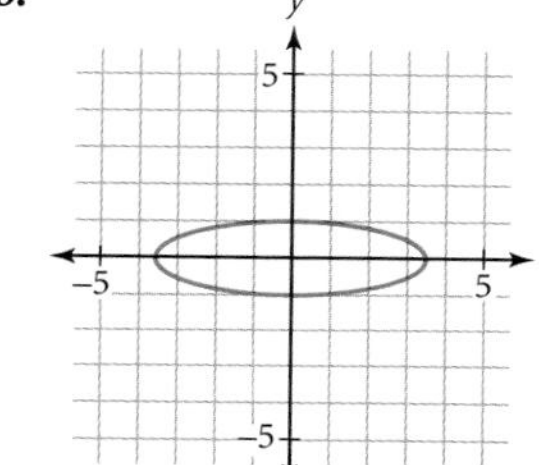

c.

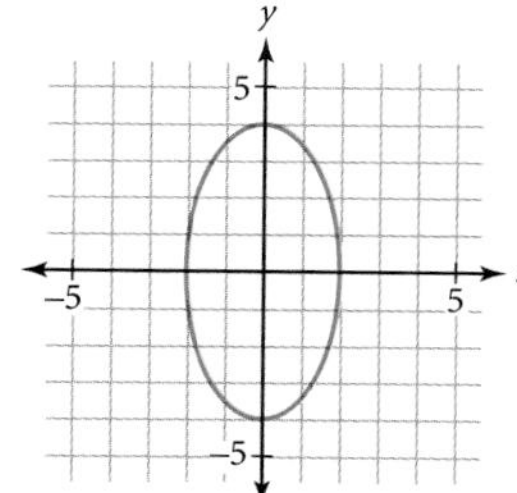

d.

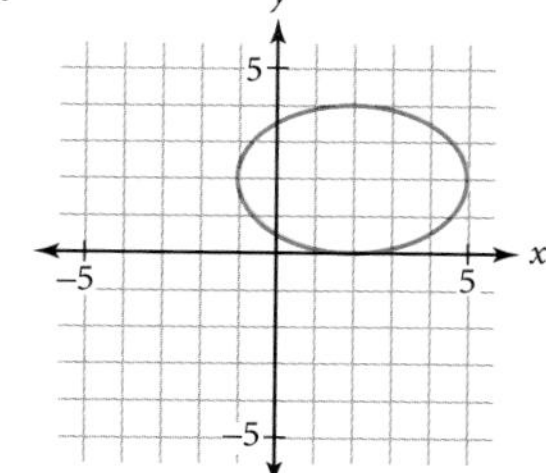

Question 4 In this question students derive the trigonometric identity $\sin^2 t + \cos^2 t = 1$, which they will see formally in Lesson 10.6.

4a. $x = \cos t$, $y = \sin t$

4b. $(\cos t)^2 + (\sin t)^2 = 1$, which is also written as $\sin^2 t + \cos^2 t = 1$

4c. $(\cos 47°)^2 + (\sin 47°)^2 \approx (0.6820)^2 + (0.7314)^2 \approx 0.4651 + 0.5349 = 1$

5a. $x = 2 \cos t$, $y = 3 \sin t$

5b. $x = 3.5 \cos t$, $y = \sin t$

5c. $x = 2 \cos t$, $y = 4 \sin t$

5d. $x = 3 \cos t + 2$, $y = 2 \cos t + 2$

Assessing Progress

You can assess students' understanding of trigonometric ratios, the Pythagorean Theorem, and circles.

Closing the Lesson

The key point of this exploration is that the parametric equations $x = r \cos t$ and $y = r \sin t$ describe a circle, with each point (x, y) a function of a parameter t that represents an angle measure. Translations, reflections, and stretches of the circle can be graphed by making simple adjustments to these parametric equations.

LESSON

8.4

PLANNING

LESSON OUTLINE

First day:

20 min Investigation

5 min Sharing

15 min Example A

5 min Exercises 1–6

Second day:

5 min Sharing

15 min Example B

25 min Exercises

MATERIALS

- graph paper, *optional*

TEACHING

Inverse trigonometric ratios can be combined with parametric equations to help set a course for a boat or plane encountering water or wind currents.

One Step

Pose this problem, adapted from the examples: "A pilot flies a plane due west from Memphis, Tennessee, toward Albuquerque, New Mexico. The cities are 1000 mi apart, and the pilot sets the plane's controls to fly at 250 mi/h. However, a constant wind is blowing at 20 mi/h from the north. If the pilot doesn't compensate for the wind, where will the plane be relative to Albuquerque after flying for 4 h? How should the pilot compensate to make the plane fly straight to Albuquerque?" As students work, urge them to draw pictures and to think carefully about how the plane moves relative to the ground. During Sharing, introduce the terms *ground speed* and *air speed* and describe how pilots' bearings relate to angles measured in other ways.

LESSON 8.4

Using Trigonometry to Set a Course

Not snow, no, nor rain, nor heat, nor night keeps them from accomplishing their appointed courses with all speed.

HERODOTUS

Winds and air currents affect the direction and speed a plane will travel. A pilot flying an airplane has to compensate for these effects. Similarly, as you swim across a river a current can sweep you downstream, so that when you reach the other side you are not directly across from the point where you began. You can use parametric equations to model and simulate motion affected by a combination of forces.

In 1926, Gertrude Ederle (b 1906) of the United States swam across the 21-mile-wide English Channel in 14 h 31 min, breaking the previous male record by more than 2 h and becoming the first female to complete the challenge. Gale-force winds, rough waters, and strong currents made the swim nearly impossible.

This investigation simulates what happens when you try to swim or fly with, against, or across a strong water or air current.

Investigation
Motion in a Current

Asuka, Ben, and Chelsea are playing with remote-controlled boats in a pool. Each boat is moving 4 ft/s in the direction indicated. All the boats start moving at the same time.

Step 1 Create a table like the one below showing the x- and y-positions of the three boats for 3 s.

Time (s)	Boat A		Boat B		Boat C	
t	x	y	x	y	x	y
0	0	10	25	5	5	0
1	4	10	21	5	5	4
2	8	10	17	5	5	8
3	12	10	13	5	5	12

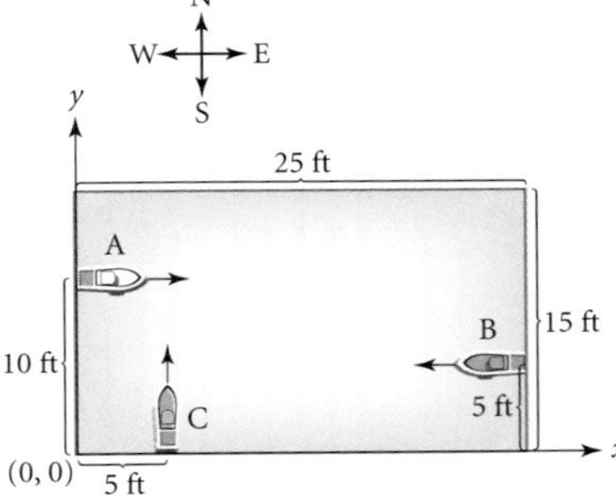

Step 2 Write and graph parametric equations to model the motion of the three boats. Identify the window and range of t-values you use to graph the simulation.

Guiding the Investigation

Step 2 As needed, help students see from the picture that the value of y is constant for Boats A and B and that the value of x is constant for Boat C.

Step 2 Boat A: $x = 4t, y = 10$; Boat B: $x = 25 - 4t, y = 5$; Boat C: $x = 5, y = 4t$

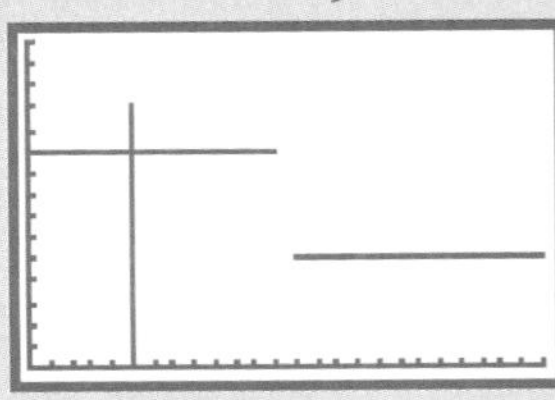

[0, 25, 1, 0, 15, 1]

$0 \le t \le 3$

Step 3 Asuka, Ben, and Chelsea return their boats to the starting positions and repeat the motion, but a gust of wind starts blowing from west to east at a constant rate of 3 ft/s. Create another table of the positions of the boats over 3 s.

Step 4 Write and graph parametric equations to model the motion of the boats in Step 3. Show how to write each of these using the $4t$ from the boat's speed and the $3t$ from the wind's speed. Identify the window and range of t-values you use to graph the simulation.

Step 5 15 ft; 5 ft/s

Step 5 Use the Pythagorean Theorem to determine the distance Boat C travels in 3 s, and its velocity.

Step 6 53° above horizontal

Step 6 At what angle, A, does Boat C travel?

Step 7 $x = 5 + 5t\cos 53°$, $y = 5t\sin 53°$. The graph of this motion should be the same as that in Step 4.

Step 7 Use the velocity and angle you found in Steps 5 and 6 to write parametric equations in the form $x = x_0 + vt\cos A$ and $y = y_0 + vt\sin A$ to represent the motion of Boat C. The constants x_0 and y_0 represent the boats' starting coordinates. Verify that these equations model Boat C's motion accurately.

The investigation showed you how motion can be affected by another factor, such as wind or current. In this example you will explore what happens when a pilot doesn't compensate for the effect of wind.

EXAMPLE A

A pilot heads a plane due west from Memphis, Tennessee, toward Albuquerque, New Mexico. The cities are 1000 mi apart, and the pilot sets the plane's controls to fly at 250 mi/h. However, there is a constant 20 mi/h wind blowing from the north. Where does the plane end up after 4 h?

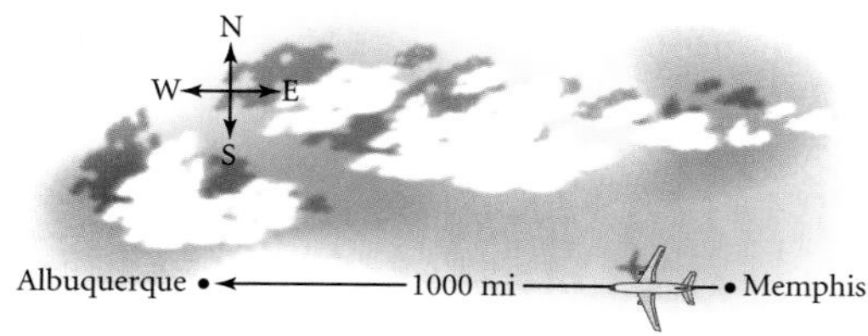

▶ Solution

Set up a coordinate system with Memphis at the origin.

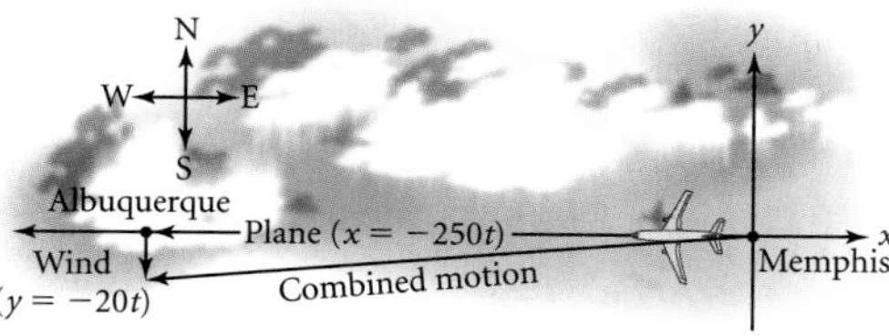

The plane's motion can be described by the equation $x = -250t$. Notice that velocity is negative because the plane is flying west. The effect of the wind on the plane's motion can be described by the equation $y = -20t$. Why is the wind's velocity negative? Because it is blowing south.

Graph $x = -250t$ and $y = -20t$ in an appropriate window with $0 \leq t \leq 4$.

Step 3 As needed, **[Ask]** "How will the wind affect the motion of each boat?" [The wind affects only the horizontal motion. Boat A will move faster, Boat B will move slower, and Boat C will drift eastward.]

Step 4 **[Alert]** Students may have difficulty seeing that the parametric equation for Boat C's x-component will no longer be constant.

Step 4 Boat A: $x = 7t$, $y = 10$; $x = 4t + 3t$; Boat B: $x = 25 - 1t$, $y = 5$; $x = 25 - 4t + 3t$; Boat C: $x = 5 + 3t$, $y = 4t$

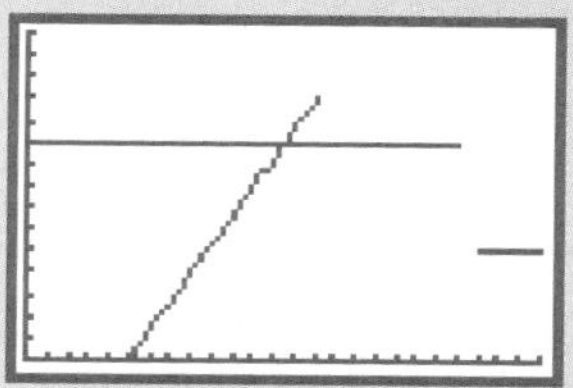

[0, 25, 1, 0, 15, 1]
$0 \leq t \leq 3$

Step 5 Suggest that your students sketch a triangle for this step. **[Alert]** Students might think the boat starts at the origin rather than at the point (5, 0).

Step 7 Students should use only the angle measure, the original x-coordinate of 5, and the diagonal velocity of 5 to write these parametric equations. They do not need to use the wind velocity or the boat's initial velocity. As needed, note that the term vt is the distance (along the hypotenuse) traveled over t seconds.

▶ EXAMPLE A

[ESL] To travel due west means to go exactly west, not at all north or south of west.

Before students look at the solution, have them sketch what they think the resulting motion would be. **[Ask]** "Where do you think the plane will end up with respect to Albuquerque?" [It will be south of Albuquerque.]

See page 892 for answer to Step 3.

LESSON OBJECTIVES

- Review the Pythagorean Theorem
- Learn the meanings of *air speed* and *ground speed*
- Use trigonometry and parametric equations to solve problems associated with setting or determining a course for traveling with, against, or across strong currents
- Understand vectors as directed distances
- See connections among coordinates, trigonometric functions, and vectors

NCTM STANDARDS

CONTENT		PROCESS	
	Number	✓	Problem Solving
✓	Algebra	✓	Reasoning
✓	Geometry	✓	Communication
✓	Measurement	✓	Connections
	Data/Probability	✓	Representation

Example A (continued)
The wind's velocity is negative because it is blowing toward the south.

If students are having difficulty understanding the difference between air speed and ground speed, give them an example about riding in the cockpit of an airplane. Suppose the speedometer reads 120 mi/hr. With a tail wind, the plane will be going faster than that speed relative to the ground.

► ***EXAMPLE B***

Students might legitimately want to start with the second equation in the solution, saying that the north-south component must equal the wind speed, if they realize that the wind's velocity is actually negative and is added to the north-south component to get 0. Most students need to do this first step.

To see the motion on the graph, students can turn off the axes or trace the finished graph.

In discussing this example, ask students how much difference using bearings to various numbers of decimal places makes. For example, does it matter if a pilot uses a bearing of 275° rather than 274.589°? A bearing of 274.589° puts the plane 0.007 mi north of Albuquerque; a bearing of 275° puts it 7 mi north. At least two decimal places are needed to get close enough to the airport for easy adjustment.

After doing this example, you might want to assign groups to solve Exercise 12 as a form of guided practice.

Solving the equation $-1000 = -250t$, or tracing the graph, will show that after 4 h the plane has traveled the necessary 1000 mi west, but it is also 80 mi south of Albuquerque, somewhere over the White Sands Missile Range!

The Pythagorean Theorem indicates that the plane has actually traveled $\sqrt{1000^2 + 80^2}$, or about 1003 mi, in 4 h.

Because speed is the distance traveled per unit of time, you can find the plane's speed by dividing $\frac{1003 \text{ mi}}{4 \text{ h}}$ to get the rate of 250.8 mi/h. This tells you that, while the air speed of the plane was 250 mi/h, the ground speed was 250.8 mi/h. The air speed is the plane's flying velocity, and the ground speed is its rate of motion relative to a fixed point on the ground.

The actual angle of motion in Example A is $\tan^{-1}\left(\frac{80}{1000}\right)$, or about 4.57°. To determine the plane's bearing, look at the compass rose below. The bearing is always between 0° and 360° measured clockwise from north. This plane intended to travel west (270°), but actually traveled south of west. Its bearing was 270° − 4.57°, or 265.43°.

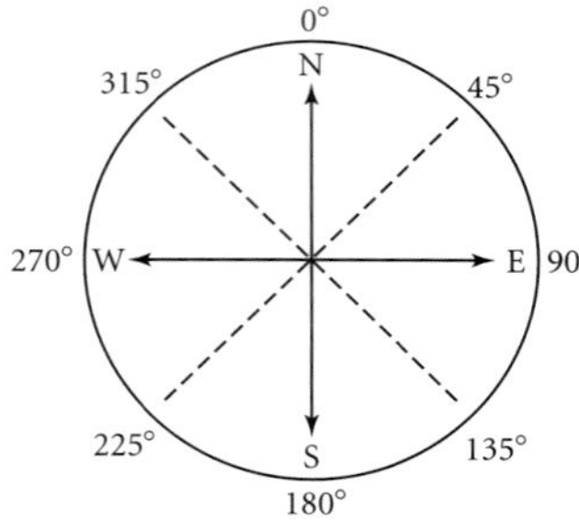

This portable compass and sundial dates from China's Ming Dynasty (1368–1644 C.E.).

EXAMPLE B

What angle and bearing to the nearest hundredth of a degree should the pilot in Example A set so that the plane actually lands in Albuquerque?

► ***Solution***

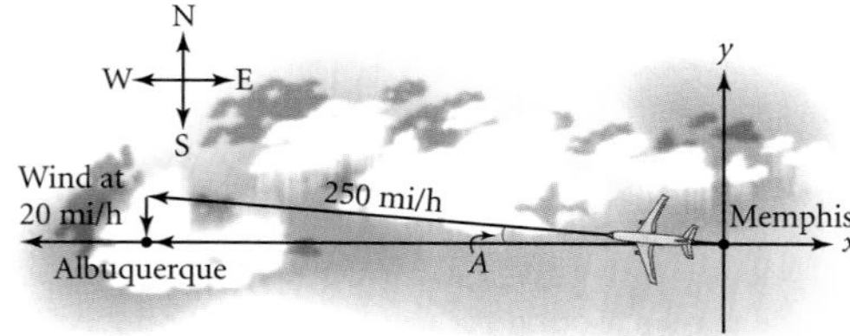

Set up a coordinate system with Memphis at the origin. Because the plane will be blown to the south, it should actually head in a direction slightly to the north.

SHARING IDEAS

As students present ideas about Steps 4 and 7 of the investigation, **[Ask]** "Do these two different sets of equations really model the same motion?" [Yes; the equations in Step 4 are written entirely in terms of the x- and y-components, whereas the equations in Step 7 are written with respect to the diagonal motion.]

Draw two vectors with their tails at the origin, representing two velocities. Ask students how to add them to get the resulting velocity. Elicit the idea that one vector must be moved so its tail is at the tip of the other. With the class, investigate the question of whether it matters which vector is moved.

Sketch the plane's path. The plane flies 250 mi/h, so its distance along this path is $250t$. This distance is broken into two separate components. The east-west component is $x = -250t\cos A$, and the north-south component is $y = 250t\sin A$ where A is the angle toward the north that the pilot must set.

The effect of the wind on the plane's motion can be described by the equation $y = -20t$. The sum of the north-south component of the plane's course and the wind's velocity must be 0 if the pilot hopes to land in Albuquerque.

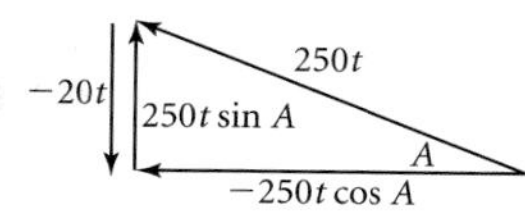

$250t\sin A + (-20t) = 0$	The sum of the north-south velocities of the wind and the plane is 0.
$250t\sin A = 20t$	Add $20t$ to both sides.
$250\sin A = 20$	Divide by t. (Assume $t \neq 0$.)
$\sin A = 0.08$	Divide both sides by 250, and evaluate.
$A = \sin^{-1} 0.08$	Take the inverse sine of both sides.
$A \approx 4.59°$	Evaluate.

The plane must head out at 4.59° north of west. This is equivalent to a bearing of 270° + 4.59°, or 274.59°.

Graph $x = -250t\cos 4.59°$ and $y = 250t\sin 4.59° - 20t$ to verify that the plane moves directly west. As you trace the graph, notice that the value of y increases slightly. By the time the plane has traveled west 996.79 mi, the plane is slightly north of Albuquerque by 0.02 mi. This means that the angle, 4.59°, is not accurate enough to result in motion directly west. Depending upon the sensitivity of the real-world situation, the pilot may need to increase accuracy by using more decimal places.

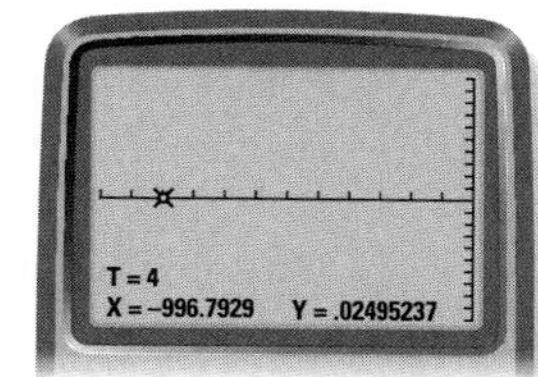

[−1200, 0, 100, −10, 10, 1]

Also notice that that the plane does not reach Albuquerque within 4 h. Because of the effect of the wind, the plane must travel slightly longer to complete the 1000 mi trip.

The directed distances in this lesson are **vectors.** Vectors are used when you are working with quantities that have both a magnitude (size) and a direction, such as the velocity of the wind, the force of gravity, and the forces you feel when you ride a roller coaster. Working with vectors is a common practice in many fields, including physics, geology, and engineering. The exercises will give you an introduction to this valuable tool.

EXERCISES

Practice Your Skills

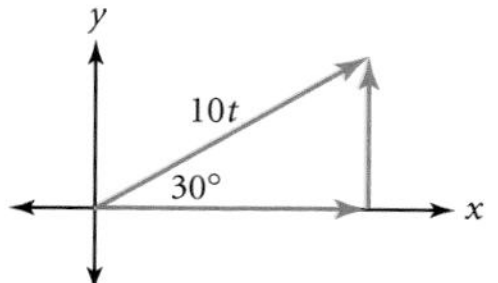

1. An object is moving at a speed of 10 units per second, at an angle of 30° above the x-axis, as shown. What parametric equations describe the horizontal and vertical components of this motion?

Assessing Progress

You can assess students' facility with thinking about horizontal and vertical components of motion, evaluating inverse trigonometric ratios, and applying the Pythagorean Theorem.

Closing the Lesson

When wind or water currents affect the motion of a plane or boat, parametric equations modeling the motion, involving **trigonometric ratios,** can be used to determine the **bearing** that must be set to bring the vehicle to the intended destination.

BUILDING UNDERSTANDING

You might want to solve Exercise 2a as a class before students begin work on the other exercises.

ASSIGNING HOMEWORK

Essential	1–5, 12
Performance assessment	6–11, 13
Portfolio	13
Journal	9
Group	7, 9, 12
Review	14–16

MATERIALS

- Sketchpad demonstration Parametric Motion, *optional*

1. $x = 10t\cos 30°$
$y = 10t\sin 30°$

Helping with the Exercises

Exercise 2 [ESL] "South of east" means farther south than due east on a compass rose. You count the degrees from east in the direction of south.

2a.

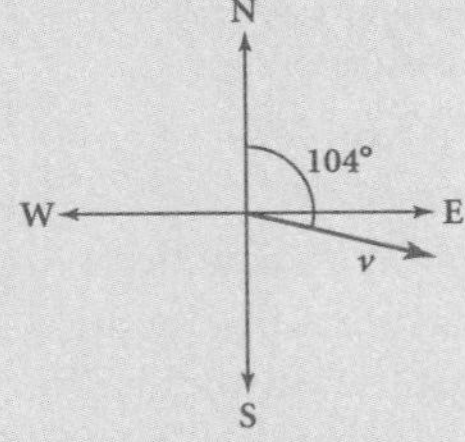

2b.

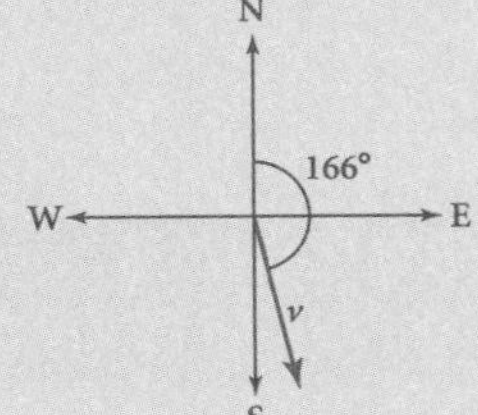

2c.

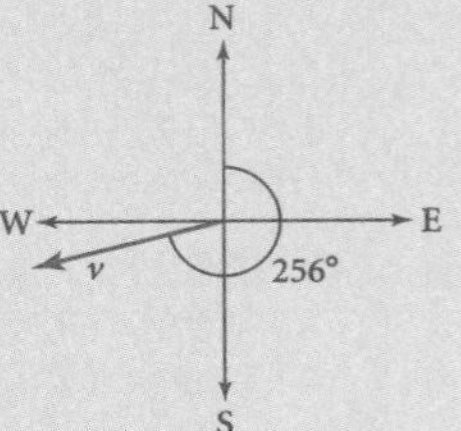

2d.

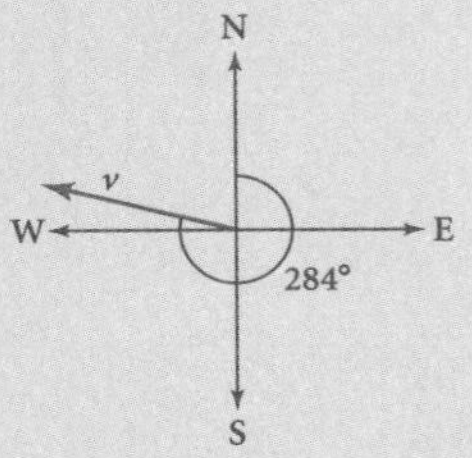

4a. x is positive, y is negative.

4b. x is negative, y is negative.

4c. x is positive, y is positive.

4d. x is negative, y is positive.

Exercise 5 [Ask] "Will the velocity of the river current be negative or positive?" [negative, because it is flowing south] You might also ask how students think this kind of navigation is really done. [by successive approximations]

See page 892 for answers to Exercise 3.

2. Draw a compass rose and vector with magnitude v to find the bearing of each direction.

a. 14° south of east **b.** 14° east of south **c.** 14° south of west **d.** 14° north of west

3. Draw a compass rose and vector with magnitude v for each bearing. Find the angle made with the x-axis.

a. 147° **b.** 204° **c.** 74° **d.** 314°

4. Give the sign of each component vector for the bearings in Exercise 3. For example, for a bearing of 290°, x is negative and y is positive.

Reason and Apply

5. APPLICATION A river is 0.3 km wide and flows south at a rate of 7 km/h. You start your trip on the river's west bank, 0.5 km north of the dock, as shown in the diagram at right.

a. If the dock is at the origin, (0, 0), what are the coordinates of the boat's starting location? $(-0.3, 0.5)$

b. Write an equation for x in terms of t that models the boat's horizontal position if you aim the boat directly east traveling at 4 km/h. $x = -0.3 + 4t$

c. Write an equation for y in terms of t that models the boat's vertical position, as a result of the flow of the river. $y = 0.5 - 7t$

d. Enter the parametric equations from 5b and 5c into your calculator, determine a good viewing window and range of t-values, and make a graph to simulate this situation.

e. Determine when and where the boat meets the river's east bank. Does your boat arrive at the dock? At 0.075 h (4.5 min), the boat lands 0.025 km (25 m) south of the dock.

f. How far have you traveled? 0.605 km

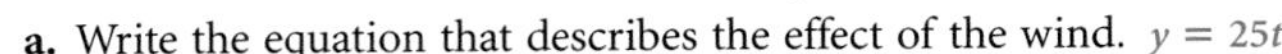

6. APPLICATION A pilot wants to fly from Toledo, Ohio, to Chicago, Illinois, which lies 280 mi directly west. Her plane can fly at 120 mi/h. She ignores the wind and heads directly west. However, there is a 25 mi/h wind blowing from the south.

a. Write the equation that describes the effect of the wind. $y = 25t$

b. Write the equation that describes the plane's contribution to the motion. $x = -120t$

c. Graph these equations.

d. How far off course is the plane after traveling 280 mi west? 58.3 mi north

e. How far has the plane actually traveled? 286 mi

f. What was the plane's ground speed? 122.6 mi/h

7. Fred rows his small boat directly across a river, which is 4 mi wide. There is a 5 mi/h current. When he reaches the opposite shore, Fred finds that he has landed at a point 2 mi downstream.

a. Write the equation that describes the effect of the river current. $y = -5t$

b. If Fred's boat can go s mi/h, what equation describes his contribution to the motion? $x = st$

5d.

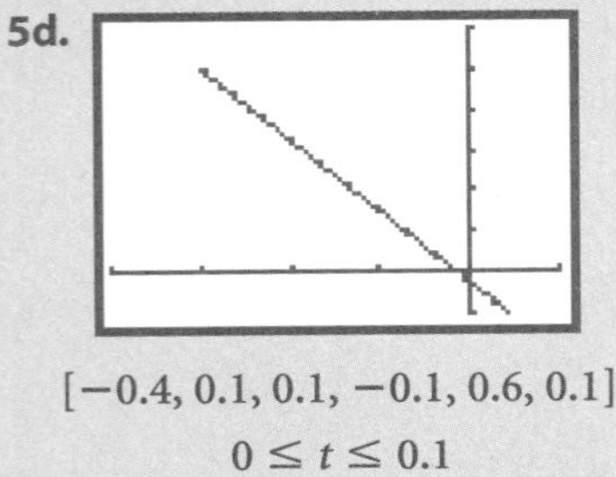

$[-0.4, 0.1, 0.1, -0.1, 0.6, 0.1]$

$0 \le t \le 0.1$

Exercise 6 [Ask] "Where will the plane end up relative to Chicago?" [north] Encourage students to solve 6d with and without their calculators.

6c.

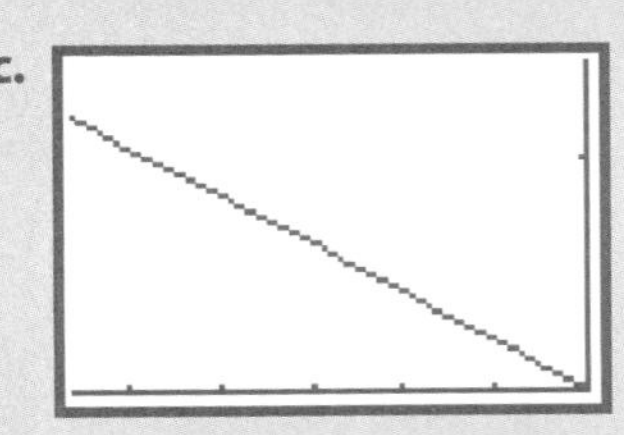

$[-280, 0, 50, 0, 70, 50]$

$0 \le t \le 3$

c. Solve the system of equations from 7a and 7b for s so that he reaches the correct point 2 mi downstream on the opposite shore.

d. How far did Fred actually travel?

e. How long did it take him?

f. What was Fred's actual speed?

g. As the boat travels down the river, what angle does it make with the riverbank?

8. APPLICATION A plane takes off from Orlando, Florida, heading 975 mi due north toward Cleveland, Ohio. The plane flies at 250 mi/h, and there is a 25 mi/h wind blowing from the west.

a. Where is the plane after it has traveled 975 mi north?

b. How far did the plane actually travel?

c. How fast did the plane actually travel?

d. At what angle from the east-west axis did the plane actually fly?

e. What was the bearing?

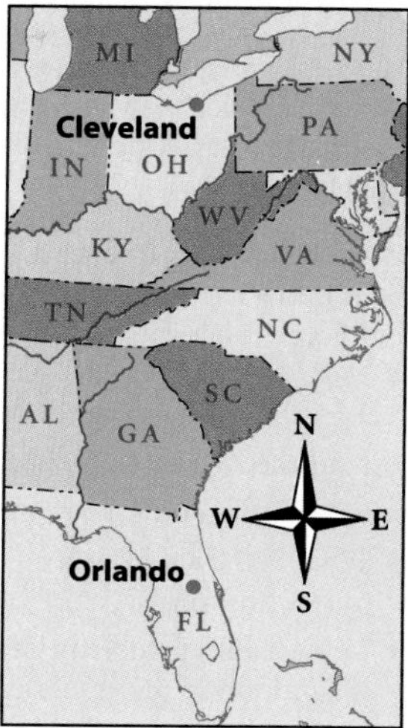

9. APPLICATION A plane is headed from Memphis, Tennessee, to Albuquerque, New Mexico, 1000 mi due west. The plane flies at 250 mi/h, and the pilot encounters a 20 mi/h wind blowing from the northwest. (That means the direction of the wind makes a 45° angle below the x-axis.)

a. Write an equation modeling the southward component of the wind.

b. Write an equation modeling the eastward component of the wind.

c. If the pilot does not compensate for the wind, explain why the final equations for the flight are $x = -250t + 20t\cos 45°$ and $y = -20t\sin 45°$.

d. What graphing window and range of t-values can you use to simulate this flight?

e. Solve the equation $-1000 = -250t + 20t\cos 45°$. What is the real-world meaning of your answer?

f. Use your answer from 9e to find how far south of Albuquerque the plane ended up.

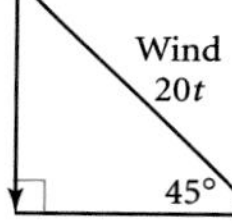

10. APPLICATION For the plane in Exercise 9 to land in Albuquerque, it must head a bit north. Let A represent the measure of the angle north of west.

a. For the plane to fly directly west, the northward component of the plane's motion and the wind's southward component must sum to zero. At what angle must the plane fly to head directly to Albuquerque? Write an equation and solve for A.

b. Using the value of A you found in 10a, write parametric equations to model the plane's flight, and graph them to verify that the plane travels directly west.

c. For what bearing should the pilot set his instruments?

Exercise 7c The boat traveled 2 mi down the river, so the equation $-2 = -5t$ gives the component of motion down the river. The boat traveled 4 mi across the river, so the other equation in the system is $4 = st$.

7c. $s = 10$ mi/h

Exercise 7d Students can use a triangle and the Pythagorean Theorem to answer this question.

7d. 4.47 mi

7e. 0.4 h

7f. 11.18 mi/h

7g. 63.4°

8a. 97.5 mi east of Cleveland

8b. 979.9 mi

8c. 251.3 mi/h

8d. 84.3°

8e. 5.7°

Exercise 9 Urge students who aren't drawing pictures to sketch a compass rose with a vector for the wind.

9a. $y = -20t\sin 45°$

9b. $x = 20t\cos 45°$

9c. Both the plane's motion and the wind contribute to the actual path of the plane, so you add the x-components and add the y-components to form the final equations.

9d. possible answer: $[-1000, 0, 100, -100, 0, 10]$; $0 \le t \le 5$

9e. 4.24. It takes the plane 4.24 h to fly 1000 mi west.

9f. 60 mi

10a. $250t\sin A - 20t\sin 45° = 0$; 3.24°

10c. 273.243°

10b. $x = -250t\cos 3.24° + 20t\cos 45°$, $y = 250t\sin 3.24° - 20t\sin 45°$

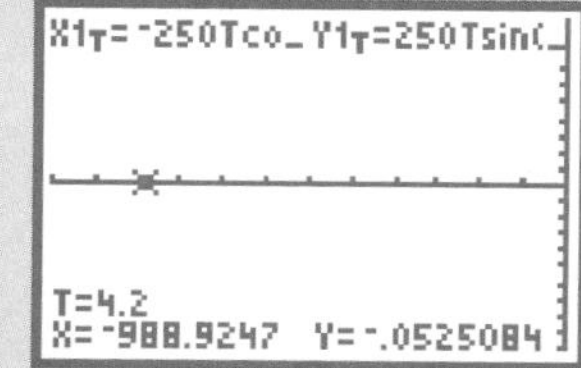

$[-1200, 0, 100, -10, 10, 1]$

$0 \le t \le 5$

11a.

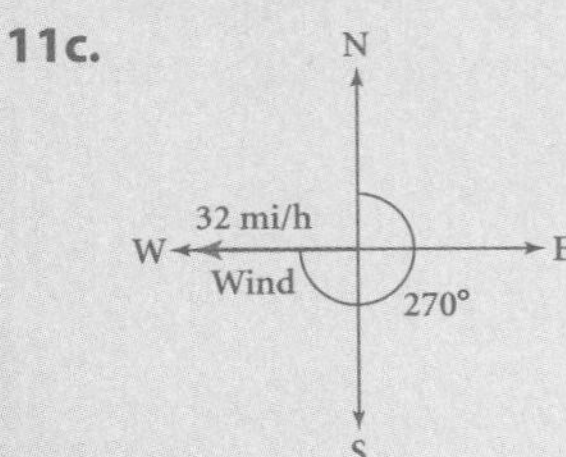

11b. $x = -320t\cos 40°$, $y = 320t\sin 40°$

11c.

N
32 mi/h
W
E
Wind
270°
S

11d. $x = -32t$, $y = 0$

11e. $x = -320t\cos 40° - 32t$, $y = 320t\sin 40°$

11f. 1385.7 mi west and 1028.5 mi north

Exercise 12 You might use the demonstration Parametric Motion as you discuss this exercise.

12. 48.59°

13a. x-component: $50\cos 40° \approx 38.3$; y-component: $50\sin 40° \approx 32.1$

13b. x-component: $90\cos 140° \approx -68.9$; y-component: $90\sin 140° \approx 57.9$

13c. x-component: -30.6; y-component: 90.0

13d. 95.1 N

13e. 109°

13f. 95.1 N at 289°

MAKING THE CONNECTION

Yoga is increasingly becoming a part of the training of professional and Olympic athletes. Biomechanics experts, trainers, and even the coach of the Los Angeles Lakers are turning to yoga to prevent sports injuries and increase athletic performance. Among yoga's benefits for athletes are increased muscle symmetry and flexibility.

11. APPLICATION A plane is flying on a bearing of 310° at a speed of 320 mi/h. The wind is blowing directly from the east at a speed of 32 mi/h.

a. Make a compass rose and vector to indicate the plane's motion.

b. Write equations that model the plane's motion without the wind.

c. Make a compass rose and vector to indicate the wind's motion.

d. Write equations that model the wind's motion.

e. What are the resulting equations that model the motion of the plane with the wind?

f. Where is the plane after 5 h?

12. Angelina wants to travel directly across the Wyde River, which is 2 mi wide in this stretch. Her boat can move at a speed of 4 mi/h. The river current flows south at 3 mi/h. At what angle upstream should she aim the boat so that she ends up going straight across?

13. APPLICATION Two forces are pulling on an object. Force A has magnitude 50 newtons (N) and pulls at an angle of 40°, and Force B has magnitude 90 N and pulls at an angle of 140°, as shown. (Note that the lengths of the vectors show their magnitude.)

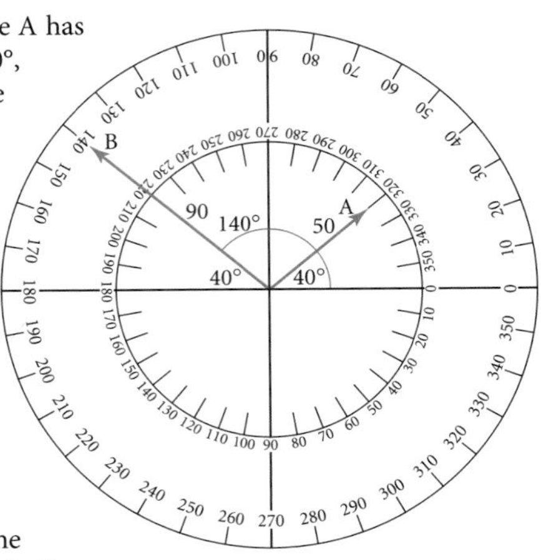

a. Find the x- and y-components of Force A.

b. Find the x- and y-components of Force B.

c. What is the sum of the x- and y-components of the two forces?

d. Using the Pythagorean Theorem, find the magnitude of the resulting force.

e. Find the angle of the resulting force. If your angle is negative, add 180° to get the direction.

f. What additional force will balance Forces A and B and keep the object in equilibrium? (It should be the same magnitude as the sum of Forces A and B, but in the opposite direction.)

Science CONNECTION

Biomechanics provides an understanding of the internal and external forces acting on the human body during movement. Knowing the role muscles play in generating force and controlling movement is necessary to understanding the limitations of human motion. Information gained from biomechanics helps athletes prepare better for their sports, and sporting goods manufacturers produce better equipment. Research in biomechanics also contributes to better treatment and rehabilitation in case of injury. You can learn more about the study and application of biomechanics with the Internet links at www.keymath.com/DAA.

Yoga is a form of exercise that focuses on breathing, stretching, balance, and meditation. In balancing poses, yoga practitioners must carefully balance the forces that act on the body.

Review

8.3 **14.** A rectangle's length is three times the width. Find the angles, to the nearest degree, at which the diagonals intersect.

7.5 **15.** Without graphing, determine whether each quadratic equation has no real roots, one real root, or two real roots. If a root is real, indicate whether it is rational or irrational.

a. $y = 2x^2 - 5x - 3$ two real, rational roots

b. $y = x^2 + 4x - 1$ two real, irrational roots

c. $y = 3x^2 - 3x + 4$ no real roots

d. $y = 9x^2 - 12x + 4$ one real, rational root

6.3 **16.** Consider this system of equations:

$$\begin{cases} 5x - 3y = -1 \\ 2x + 4y = 5 \end{cases}$$

a. Write the augmented matrix for the system of equations.

b. Use row reduction to write the augmented matrix in row-echelon form. Show each step and indicate the operation you use.

c. Give the solution to the system. Check your answer.

Project

VIEWING ANGLE

When classrooms are arranged, one thing that should be considered is how well all students will be able to see the board. Students who sit in seats toward the center of the room have no difficulty. However, students who sit in seats on the sides, along the walls, have a more limited view. Viewing angle, the angle required to see the entire board, is one measure of how well a student can see. Generally, a large viewing angle is better than a small one.

Consider the row of seats in the classroom shown below. Each desk is 3 ft wide. Find the viewing angle for the student sitting in each of these five seats.

Which seat will have the best view of the board?

Plan an arrangement of the seats in your classroom that you believe will provide all students with the best possible viewing angle.

Your project should include

- Calculations of the viewing angles from the five seats in this illustration.
- An answer to "Which seat will have the best view?"
- A plan for the arrangement of seats in your classroom.
- An explanation of why you chose your plan.

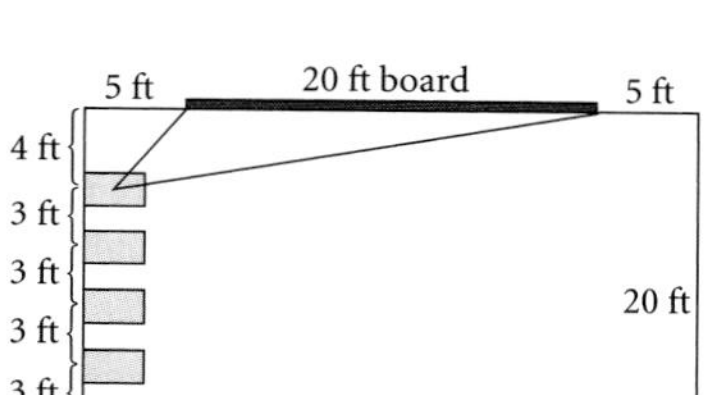

THE GEOMETER'S SKETCHPAD®

Geometry software, such as The Geometer's Sketchpad, will be useful in planning your arrangement of seats. Sketchpad allows you to construct triangles and measure each angle.

Exercise 14 [Alert] Students may have forgotten that the sum of the measures of the angles of a triangle is 180°.

14. 143° and 37°

16a. $\left[\begin{array}{cc|c} 5 & -3 & -1 \\ 2 & 4 & 5 \end{array}\right]$

16c. $\left(\frac{11}{26}, \frac{27}{26}\right)$

Project Answers

Assume that the desks are 3 ft wide and the students' heads are in the middle of the desks. The angles of view can be calculated with these expressions:

First student:
$\tan^{-1}\left(\frac{23.5}{4}\right) - \tan^{-1}\left(\frac{3.5}{4}\right) = 39.2°$

Second student:
$\tan^{-1}\left(\frac{23.5}{7}\right) - \tan^{-1}\left(\frac{3.5}{7}\right) = 46.8°$

Third student:
$\tan^{-1}\left(\frac{23.5}{10}\right) - \tan^{-1}\left(\frac{3.5}{10}\right) = 47.7°$

Fourth student:
$\tan^{-1}\left(\frac{23.5}{13}\right) - \tan^{-1}\left(\frac{3.5}{13}\right) = 46.0°$

Fifth student:
$\tan^{-1}\left(\frac{23.5}{16}\right) - \tan^{-1}\left(\frac{3.5}{16}\right) = 43.3°$

See page 892 for answer to Exercise 16b.

Supporting the Project

Viewing angles are not the only factors that determine how well students can see. Distance is another crucial factor.

OUTCOMES

- The report includes calculations of the viewing angle for each desk.
- The student indicates that the best view is from the third seat.
- The report contains a simple plan for the seats in your classroom and an explanation of why the student chose this arrangement.

• The report includes a detailed plan for arranging the seats in your classroom, with calculations of viewing angles to support the plan.
• The student has done additional research on viewing angles or other factors that influence view.

LESSON

8.5

PLANNING

LESSON OUTLINE

One day:

15 min Examples

15 min Investigation

10 min Sharing

5 min Exercises

MATERIALS

- basketball court, *optional*
- basketball, *optional*
- Parametric Free Throws (T) for One Step
- Calculator Notes 1H, 8G, *optional*

TEACHING

In Lesson 8.4, students saw how parametric equations and trigonometry can model components of motion involving wind and water currents. This lesson extends students' understanding of falling bodies to projectiles, whose motion has a horizontal component.

One Step

Display the Parametric Free Throws transparency and pose this problem: "A basketball player is trying to make a free throw. Set up a calculator to simulate the motion and to help you determine what angles and initial velocities will project the ball through the hoop." As students work, encourage them to adjust the projectile motion function to describe the vertical component of motion parametrically, and help them think about the horizontal component as well. During Sharing, state the parametric projectile motion equations explicitly.

LESSON 8.5

Projectile Motion

It is a mathematical fact that the casting of this pebble from my hand alters the centre of gravity of the universe.

THOMAS CARLYLE

In this lesson you will model motion affected by gravity, building on your earlier work with the quadratic equation $y = at^2 + v_0t + s_0$. Recall that a is based on the acceleration due to gravity, so the equation can also be written as $y = -\frac{1}{2}gt^2 + v_0t + s_0$. This equation models the changing vertical height of an object in free fall. Recall that t represents time, v_0 represents the vertical component of the initial velocity, and s_0 represents the initial height. Some numerical values for the force of gravity, g, are given below. What are the corresponding values of a? The values of a are $-\frac{1}{2}g$.

g	Earth	Moon	Mars	
m/s²	9.8	1.6	3.7	−4.9; −0.8; −1.85
ft/s²	32	5.3	12	−16; −2.65; −6
cm/s²	980	162	370	−490; −81; −185
in./s²	384	64	144	−192; −32; −72

In Lesson 7.3, you dealt with only the vertical component, the height, of objects in projectile motion. In this lesson you'll model the horizontal component as well, using parametric equations.

EXAMPLE A

A ball rolls off the end of a table with a horizontal velocity of 1.5 ft/s. The table is 2.75 ft high.

a. What equation describes the x-direction position of the ball?

b. Write an equation to model the vertical position of the ball.

c. Enter these two equations into your calculator and graph them. Where and when does the ball appear to hit the floor?

d. Solve algebraically to find where and when the ball hits the floor.

▶ Solution

The vertical component of the ball's motion is affected by the force of gravity, whereas the horizontal component is not.

a. The horizontal component of the motion is described by $x = 1.5t$. The total distance traveled is the velocity multiplied by the time elapsed.

b. An equation for the height is $y = -\frac{1}{2} \cdot 32 \cdot t^2 + 0 \cdot t + 2.75$. Here, t is the time measured in seconds, 32 is the acceleration due to gravity in feet per second squared, the coefficient 0 implies that none of the initial velocity is directed upward or downward, and 2.75 is the initial height in feet.

▶ EXAMPLE A

Emphasize that the term v_0 in the projectile motion equation represents vertical velocity only. The horizontal velocity is not considered in the projectile motion equation.

LESSON OBJECTIVES

- Solve problems involving projectile motion that include a horizontal velocity in addition to the effects of gravity and an initial height
- Use trigonometric equations and parametric equations to model motion that begins with an initial velocity at an angle

c. Graph the equations $x = 1.5t$ and $y = -16t^2 + 2.75$ with $0 \leq t \leq 1$ and a t-step of 0.01. The ball hits the floor when $y = 0$. Trace the graph to approximate when this happens. The graph shows that the ball hits the floor approximately 0.41 s after it leaves the edge of the table. At that time it is 0.62 ft from a point directly below the edge of the table.

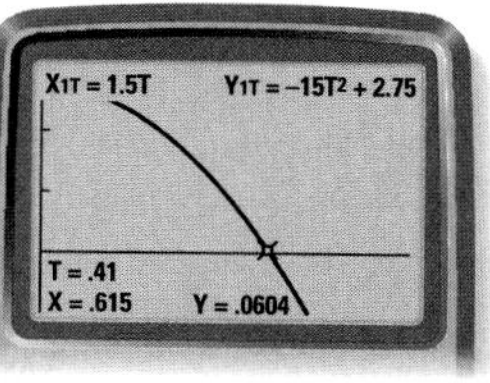

[0, 1, 1, −1, 3, 1]

d. The ball hits the floor at the point where $y = 0$. Solve the equation $0 = -16t^2 + 2.75$.

$0 = -16t^2 + 2.75$	Original equation.
$16t^2 = 2.75$	Add $16t^2$ to both sides.
$t^2 = \frac{2.75}{16}$	Divide both sides by 16.
$t = \pm\sqrt{\frac{2.75}{16}}$	Take the square root of both sides.
$t \approx \pm 0.41$	Evaluate.

Only the positive answer makes sense in this situation, so the ball hits the ground at approximately 0.41 s. To find where this occurs, substitute 0.41 for t into the parametric equation for x.

$x = 1.5t$

$x = 1.5(0.41) \approx 0.62$

The ball hits the ground at a horizontal distance of approximately 0.62 ft from the edge of the table.

In Example A, the initial motion was only in a horizontal direction. In the previous chapter, you explored motion that was only in a vertical direction, like a free-falling object. Using trigonometric functions, you can parametrically model motion that begins at an angle, using techniques similar to those in the previous lesson.

Parametric Equations for Projectile Motion

You can model projectile motion parametrically with these equations, where x is a measure of horizontal position, y is a measure of vertical position, and t is a measure of time.

$$x = v_0 t \cos A + x_0$$

$$y = -\frac{1}{2}gt^2 + v_0 t \sin A + y_0$$

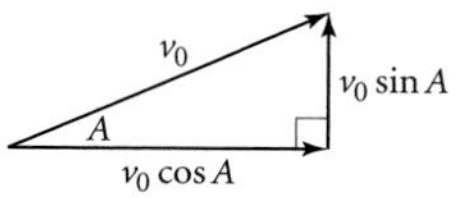

The point (x_0, y_0) is the initial position at time $t = 0$, v_0 is the velocity at time $t = 0$, A is the angle of motion from the horizontal, and g is the acceleration due to gravity.

Example A (continued)
Tracing the graph in part c might help students realize that the floor is at height $y = 0$.

[Ask] "What is the meaning of the interval $0 \leq t \leq 1$ and a t-step of 0.01?" [The time is limited to the first second, and the graph will plot the values every hundredth of a second.]

[Ask] "Do you know other ways to solve the equation in part d?" [yes; by the quadratic formula and by graphing]

Parametric Projectile Motion
[Ask] "How were the velocity components derived?" [If the initial velocity, v_0, is in the direction of the terminal side of $\angle A$, sketch the triangle that represents the hypotenuse, v_0, and the horizontal and vertical components, $x = v_0 \cos A$ and $y = v_0 \sin A$, respectively. Then solve for x and y.] If students remember this derivation, they will not need to memorize the parametric projectile motion equations. **[Alert]** Students might miss that in the equation for y the coefficient of t has been broken up. You might want to rewrite the equation as $y = \left(-\frac{1}{2}g\right)t^2 + \left(v_0 \sin A\right)t + y_0$ and compare it to the free-fall motion equation in the form $y = \left(-\frac{1}{2}g\right)t^2 + \left(v_0\right)t + y_0$.

NCTM STANDARDS

CONTENT		PROCESS	
	Number	✓	Problem Solving
✓	Algebra	✓	Reasoning
✓	Geometry	✓	Communication
✓	Measurement	✓	Connections
	Data/Probability	✓	Representation

▶ ***EXAMPLE B***

[Ask] "What is the real-world meaning of the term 3 in the vertical distance equation?" [the initial vertical height]

Guiding the Investigation

If time is limited, you might work on the investigation as a whole class or assign it as a project. Make every effort to include it, because students find it engaging.

Step 1 Measurements in the game of basketball are given in feet, so it's probably best to use feet as measurements.

Step 3 **[Ask]** "What do the values 18.8 and 12.4 represent?" [The distance from the free throw line to the out-of-bounds line is 18.8 ft; 12.4 ft represents a friendly height above the rim of the basket.] If students aren't sure how to plot points, refer them to Calculator Note 1H.

Step 3 (13, 10) and (14.5, 10)

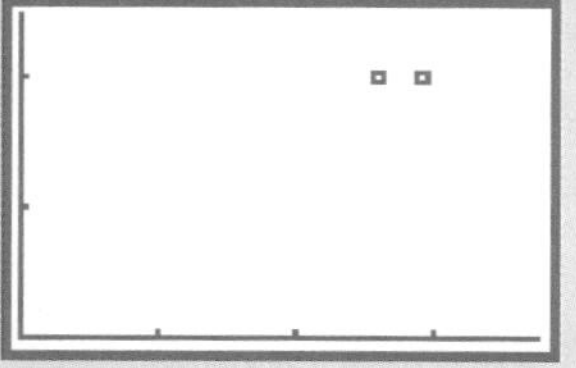

[0, 18.8, 5, 0, 12.4, 5]

Step 4 If time permits, let several students shoot a basketball to collect data. Collecting exact data is not necessary. Students can estimate the values.

Step 6 You might suggest that students start with $y_0 = 5$ and experiment with changing A and v_0. As an extension they can vary y_0. See Calculator Note 8G for ideas about simulating free throws. You might distribute this note after students have begun to demonstrate success with their own parametric equations. Be prepared for some students to want to experiment extensively, cheering when the simulated ball hits its target and arguing over whether the ball will actually go through the hoop at various initial angles.

EXAMPLE B

Carolina hits a baseball so that it travels at an initial speed of 120 ft/s and at an angle of 30° above the ground. If her bat contacts the ball at a height of 3 ft above the ground, how far does the ball travel horizontally before it hits the ground?

▶ ***Solution***

Draw a picture and write equations for the x- and y-components of the motion.

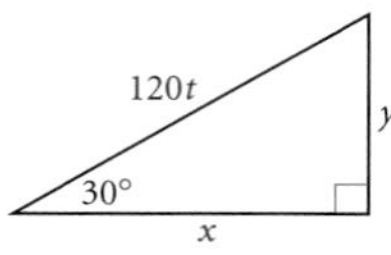

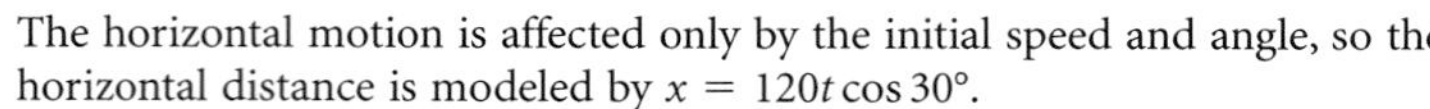

$$\cos 30° = \frac{x}{120t} \qquad \sin 30° = \frac{y}{120t}$$

$$x = 120t\cos 30° \qquad y = 120t\sin 30°$$

The horizontal motion is affected only by the initial speed and angle, so the horizontal distance is modeled by $x = 120t\cos 30°$.

The vertical motion is also affected by the force of gravity pulling the ball down. In this case the equation that models the vertical distance is $y = -16t^2 + 120t\sin 30° + 3$. Compare this equation with the one given in the box on the previous page. Notice how the values from this problem appear in the equation.

To find out when the ball hits the ground, find when the y-value is 0.

$-16t^2 + 120t\sin 30° + 3 = 0$	Original equation.
$-16t^2 + 120t(0.5) + 3 = 0$	Evaluate sin 30°.
$-16t^2 + 60t + 3 = 0$	Multiply.
$t = \dfrac{-60 \pm \sqrt{60^2 - 4(-16)(3)}}{2(-16)}$	Use the quadratic formula. Substitute −16 for *a*, 60 for *b*, and 3 for *c*.
$t \approx -0.049$ or $t \approx 3.799$	Evaluate.

A negative value for t doesn't make sense, so use only the positive answer. The ball reaches the ground about 3.8 seconds after being hit.

To determine how far the ball has traveled, substitute this t-value into the parametric equation for x:

$$x = 120(3.799)\cos 30°$$

$$x \approx 395$$

The ball will travel about 395 ft horizontally.

In the investigation you will simulate a basketball free throw. This is another instance where you must consider motion at an angle.

Step 2

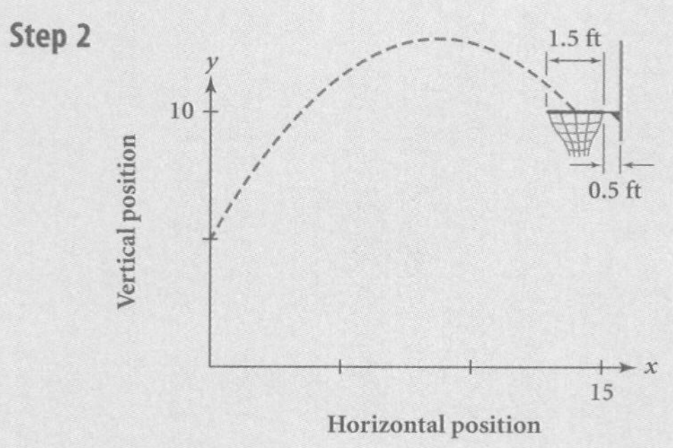

Step 6 possible answer: $x = 25.2t\cos 57°$, $y = -16t^2 + 25.2t\sin 57° + 5$

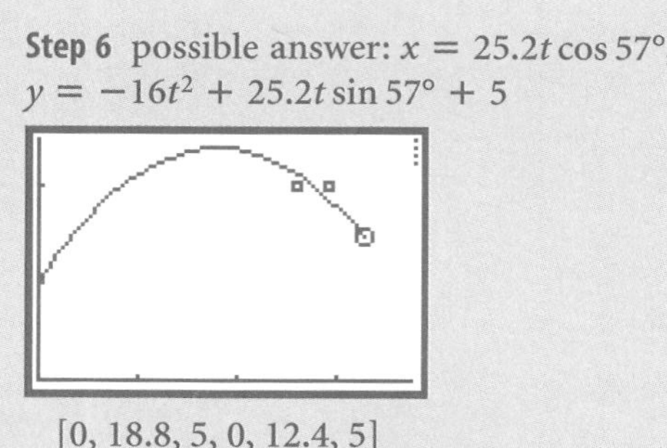

[0, 18.8, 5, 0, 12.4, 5]

Investigation
Basketball Free Throw

(Based on an activity developed by Arne Engebretsen.)

Basketball players decide upon the angle and velocity of the ball necessary to make a basket from various positions on the court. In this investigation you'll explore the relationship between the angle and velocity necessary for a successful free throw shot.

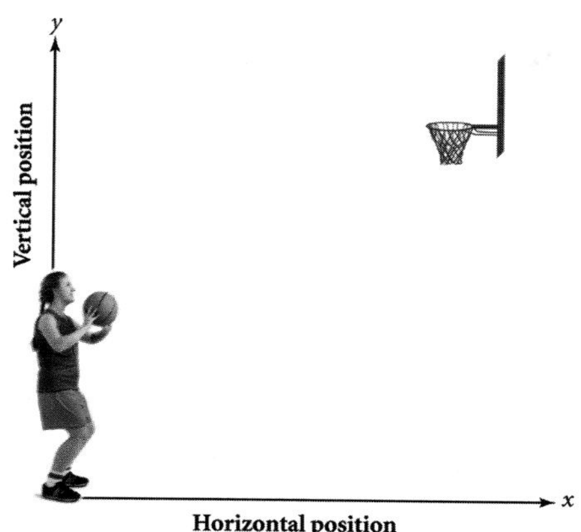

Step 1 The distance from floor to rim of basket is 10 ft; floor distance from free throw line to backboard is 15 ft; diameter of basket is 1.5 ft; length of bracket is 0.5 ft.

Step 4 Answers will vary. y_0 should be between 4 ft and 7 ft, A between 10° and 80°, and v_0 between 5 ft/s and 30 ft/s.

Step 5 Substitute values from Step 4 into the equations given.

Step 7 There are many combinations that will work. If you increase A, you must also increase v_0. If you increase y_0, you must decrease v_0 or A or both.

Step 1 Discuss with your class or get data from your teacher on free throw measurements. You'll need the distance from the floor to the rim of the basket, the horizontal distance from the free throw line to the backboard, the diameter of the basket, and the length of the bracket that fastens the basket to the backboard.

Step 2 Draw a diagram with the measurements from Step 1, and sketch the typical path of a successful free throw. See page 462.

Step 3 Using the free throw line as the origin, (0, 0), what are the coordinates of the front and back rims of the basket? Plot these two data points in a graphing window with $0 \le x \le 18.8$ and $0 \le y \le 12.4$. See page 462.

Step 4 Create some reasonable data for a free throw shooter. Include the height of the ball at release (y_0), the measure of the angle at release (A), and the initial velocity of the ball (v_0).

Step 5 Using your data from Step 4, write parametric equations, $x = v_0 t \cos A$ and $y = -16t^2 + v_0 t \sin A + y_0$, to model a free throw. Use your equations to simulate a free throw on your calculator.

Step 6 Experiment with different values of y_0, A, and v_0 until you can simulate a successful free throw on your graphing calculator. See page 462.

Step 7 Is there only one combination of values that will produce a successful free throw? If so, why? If not, generalize patterns in the relationships between the variables.

Assessing Progress

You can check students' understanding of components of motion and the projectile motion function, as well as their ability to plot and graph on calculators.

Closing the Lesson

The familiar projectile motion function, $y = -\frac{1}{2}gx^2 + v_0 x + s_0$, can be adjusted if the motion has a **horizontal component.** Given an initial velocity of v_0 at an angle A to the horizontal, the **vertical component** of the motion is given by the equation $y = -\frac{1}{2}gt^2 + v_0 t \sin A + y_0$. In this case, the horizontal component is described by the parametric equation $x = v_0 t \cos A$.

SHARING IDEAS

As students present their results, keep asking about the meanings of the variables A, v_0, and y_0 (angle measure, velocity, height) and emphasizing the different components of the motion.

Ask how projectile motion is similar to and different from motion in water and air currents. Both cases involve velocity in two directions; with currents the forces in all directions are usually constant, whereas with projectiles the horizontal force is operative only at the beginning.

The opening paragraph of the lesson refers to free fall. Ask what free fall is. Students may think it's an object falling after being dropped. Actually, the object may have a nonzero initial velocity from being thrown directly upward or downward, but its horizontal velocity is zero.

[Ask] "How did the familiar projectile motion function, $y = -\frac{1}{2}gx^2 + v_0 x + s_0$, become $y = -\frac{1}{2}gt^2 + v_0 t \sin A + y_0$?" [The variable t replaces x; it still represents time. Like s_0, the parameter y_0 represents the initial height. Angle A is the angle with the horizontal; with free fall, $\angle A$ measures 90°, so $\sin A$ is 1.]

Refer back to the examples and **[Ask]** "Do the negative times, as negative solutions to the quadratic equations, have any meaning?" [Yes, the curves found are the same as curves of projectiles that were launched before the clock started and have reached the initial height and initial velocity at time 0.]

[Ask] "How accurate do you think these equations for motion are?" [All of these equations ignore air resistance, which is powerful enough to prevent falling objects from exceeding a terminal velocity.] Air resistance can be studied with the ideas of calculus.

BUILDING UNDERSTANDING

Students practice using parametric equations for projectile motion with a horizontal as well as a vertical component.

ASSIGNING HOMEWORK

Essential	1–4
Performance assessment	5–12
Portfolio	10
Journal	5
Group	6–8
Review	13–16

MATERIALS

- graph paper

Helping with the Exercises

Exercise 1 As needed, refer students to the table of gravity constants on page 460. **[Alert]** Students may have difficulty with 1c, especially if they try graphing. The vertical component of the initial velocity is upward and therefore positive ($50 \sin 30°$), and the horizontal component is leftward and therefore negative ($-50 \cos 30°$). The projectile is moving "up-left" for only a very short time after $t = 0$, until about $t = 0.2$.

1a. the Moon; centimeters and seconds

1b. right 400 cm and up 700 cm

1c. up-left

1d. 50 cm/s

Exercise 2 **[Alert]** Students who can calculate values of x and y for the various values of t might still be unable to describe the position accurately.

2a. right 40 cm and up 60 cm

2b. left 3.3 cm and up 4 cm

2c. left 46.6 cm and down 214 cm

2d. left 133.2 cm and down 1136 cm

EXERCISES

Practice Your Skills

1. A projectile's motion is described by the equations

$$x = -50t \cos 30° + 400$$
$$y = -81t^2 + 50t \sin 30° + 700$$

a. Is this projectile motion occurring on Earth, the Moon, or Mars? What are the units used in the problem? (*Hint:* Look for the value of g.)

b. What is the initial position? Include units in your answer.

c. At time $t = 0$, what direction is the projectile moving? (up, up-right, right, down-right, down, down-left, left, or up-left)

d. What is the initial velocity? Include units.

In dog and disc competitions, the Frisbee is one projectile (although it does face wind resistance) and the dog is another. Each object has a horizontal and vertical component to its motion.

2. Find the position at the time given of a projectile in motion described by the equations

$$x = -50t \cos 30° + 40$$
$$y = -81t^2 + 50t \sin 30° + 60$$

a. 0 seconds
b. 1 second
c. 2 seconds
d. 4 seconds

3. A ball rolls off the edge of a 12 m tall cliff at a velocity of 2 m/s.

a. Write parametric equations to simulate this motion.

b. What equation can you solve to determine when the ball hits the ground?

c. When and where does the ball hit the ground?

d. Describe a graphing window that you can use to model this motion.

4. Consider the scenario in Exercise 3. When and where will the ball hit the ground if the motion occurred

a. On the Moon?

b. On Mars?

Reason and Apply

5. These parametric equations model projectile motion of an object:

$$x = 6t \cos 52°$$
$$y = -4.9t^2 + 6t \sin 52° + 2$$

a. Name a graphing window and a range of t-values that allow you to simulate the motion.

b. Describe a scenario for this projectile motion. Include a description of every variable and number listed in the parametric equations.

3a. $x = 2t, y = -4.9t^2 + 12$

3b. $-4.9t^2 + 12 = 0$

3c. 1.56 s, 3.13 m from the cliff

3d. possible answer: [0, 4, 1, 0, 12, 1]

4a. 3.87 s, 7.75 m from the cliff

4b. 2.55 s, 5.09 m from the cliff

5a. possible answer: [0, 5, 1, 0, 4, 1], $0 \leq t \leq 1.5$

5b. Sample answer: This projectile was launched from 2 m above Earth with a velocity of 6 m/s at an inclination of 52°.

6. A ball rolls off a 3 ft high table and lands at a point 1.8 ft away from the table.

a. How long did it take for the ball to hit the floor? Give your answer to the nearest hundredth of a second.

b. How fast was the ball traveling when it left the table? Give your answer to the nearest hundredth, and include units.

7. **APPLICATION** An archer aims at a target 70 m away with diameter 1.22 m. The bull's-eye is 1.3 m above the ground. She holds her bow level at a height of 1.2 m and shoots an arrow with an initial velocity of 83 m/s.

a. What equations model this motion?

b. Will she hit the target? If not, by how much will she miss it?

c. At what range of angles could the archer hold her bow to hit somewhere on the target?

d. What initial velocity is necessary in order to hit the target if she holds her bow level?

Paola Fantato of Italy won the gold medal in archery in the Women's Individual Sitting Contest at the 2000 Paralympic Games in Sydney, Australia.

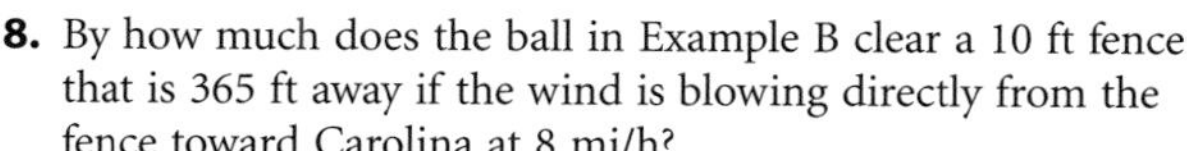

Sports CONNECTION

Archery is one of the oldest sports that is still practiced today. Modern archery became an Olympic event in 1972. Olympic archers aim at a target 1.22 m in diameter, 70 m away—the bull's-eye is just 12.2 cm in diameter. From where the archers stand, the target looks about the same size as the head of a thumbtack held at arm's length. Archery is used as a source of rehabilitation and recreation worldwide.

8. By how much does the ball in Example B clear a 10 ft fence that is 365 ft away if the wind is blowing directly from the fence toward Carolina at 8 mi/h?

9. Gonzo, the human cannonball, is fired out of a cannon 10 ft above the ground at a speed of 40 ft/s. The cannon is tilted at an angle of 60°. His net hangs 5 ft above the ground. Where does his net need to be positioned so that he will land safely?

Pictured here in Berlin, Germany, a spring-loaded cannon propelled the "Human Cannonball" of the 1920s, Paul Leinert.

6a. 0.43 s

6b. 4.16 ft/s

Exercise 7 Students should ignore the influence of wind.

[Ask] "Are there any factors besides gravity that would affect an arrow's motion?" [Arrows have feathers that keep them flying straight and help them stay aloft, but the feathers increase wind resistance.]

7a. $x = 83t\cos 0°$, $y = -4.9t^2 + 83t\sin 0° + 1.2$

7b. No; it will hit the ground 28.93 m before reaching the target.

7c. The angle must be between 2.44° and 3.43°.

7d. at least 217 m/s

8. The ball does not clear the fence.

9. 46 ft from the end of the cannon

Exercise 10 As needed, urge students to draw diagrams for this exercise.

10. The ball will bounce on the fourth step (3 steps down from the top step).

Exercise 11 [Language] The 7-iron and 9-iron are golf clubs. If students are confused about loft, direct them to the related Sports Connection. The loft of a golf club is measured by the angle its face makes with the handle of the golf club. That angle is congruent to the angle the ball makes with the ground when it is hit by the club.

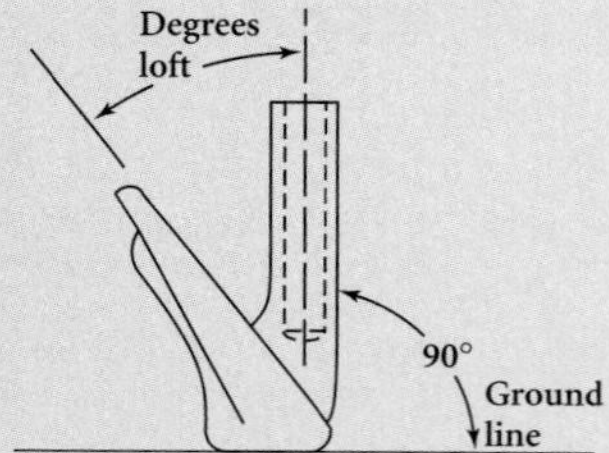

The higher the number of the club, the more loft the club will give the ball.

11a. $x = 122t \cos 38°$, $y = -16t^2 + 122t \sin 38°$

11b. 451 ft

11c. 378 ft

12a.

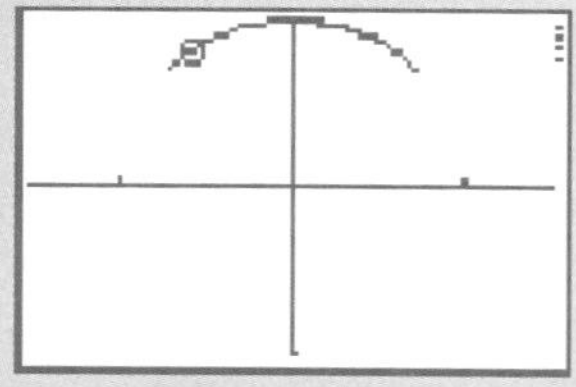

$[-1.5, 1.5, 1, -1, 1, 1]$

$0° \leq t \leq 360°$

The tip starts at (0, 1) and moves back and forth along a circular arc from (0.7, 0.714) to (−0.7, 0.714).

10. A golf ball rolls off the top step of a flight of 14 stairs with a horizontal velocity of 5 ft/s. The stairs are each 8 in. high and 8 in. wide. On which step does the ball first bounce?

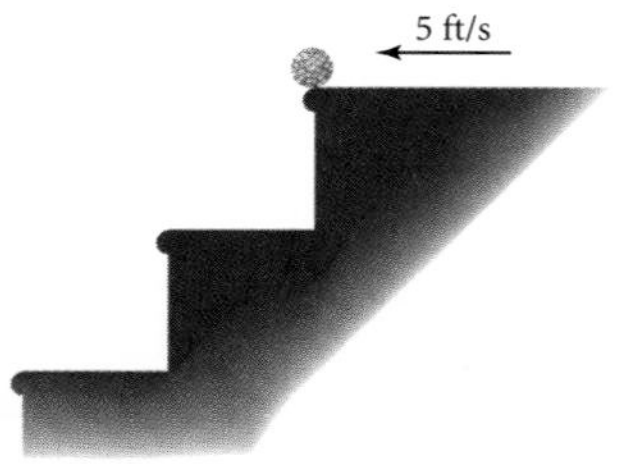

Swedish-born Annika Sorenstam (b 1970) is a member of the Ladies Professional Golf Association.

Sports CONNECTION

Golfers have a range of golf clubs used for hitting distance shots, including "irons" and "woods." Golf clubs have faces with a variety of angles. A club with a lesser angle, such as a No. 1 wood, is referred to as having less "loft"—the loft is the angle at which the ball should leave the ground. A low loft will cause the ball to leave the ground at a low angle and travel for more distance. A club with a high loft, such as a No. 7 wood, will cause a ball to travel higher and a shorter distance.

11. A golfer swings a 7-iron golf club with a loft of 38° and an initial velocity of 122 ft/s on level ground.

a. Write parametric equations to simulate this golf shot.

b. How far away does the ball first hit ground?

c. How far away would the ball land if a golfer chose a 9-iron golf club with a loft of 46° and an initial velocity of 110 ft/s?

12. The tip of a metronome travels on a path modeled by the parametric equations $x = 0.7 \sin t$ and $y = \sqrt{1 - (0.7 \sin t)^2}$.

a. Sketch the graph when $0° \leq t \leq 360°$. Describe the motion.

b. Eliminate the parameter, t, and write a single equation using only x and y. Sketch this graph.

c. Compare the two graphs.

d. Rewrite the parametric equations so that the graph is reflected across the x-axis.

e. Sketch the graph when $0° \leq t \leq 720°$. What does changing 360° to 720° do?

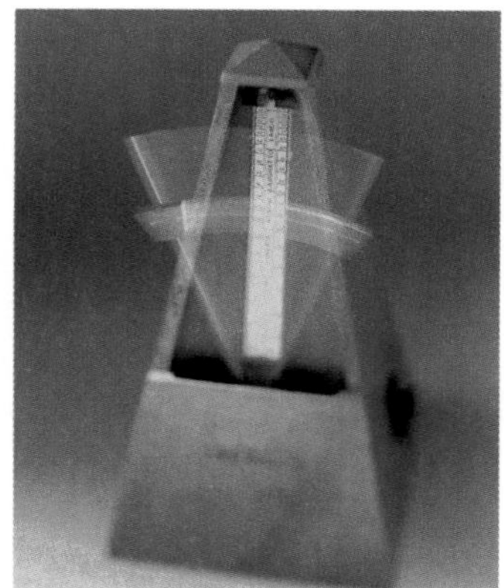

A metronome is an instrument that marks exact time for musicians. It can be set to produce a regular beat at a fast or slow pace.

12b. $y = \sqrt{1 - x^2}$

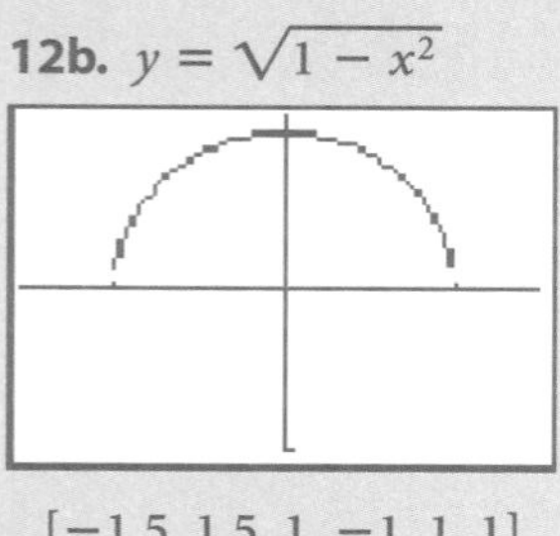

$[-1.5, 1.5, 1, -1, 1, 1]$

12c. The single equation is an entire semicircle, whereas the parametric equation is the part of the circle from $x = -0.7$ to $x = 0.7$.

12d. $x = 0.7 \sin t$ and $y = -\sqrt{1 - (0.7 \sin t)^2}$

12e. The graph appears the same, but the number of back-and-forth movements is increased.

Review

8.4 **13.** Two forces act simultaneously on a ball positioned at (4, 3). The first force imparts a velocity of 2.3 m/s to the east, and the second force imparts a velocity of 3.8 m/s to the north.

2.3 m/s

3.8 m/s

a. Enter parametric equations into your calculator to simulate the resulting movement of the ball. Sketch your graph, and give your equations and graphing window.

b. What is the ball's velocity? Give the magnitude and direction.

8.3 **14.** Find the height, width, area, and distance specified.

a. total height of the tree

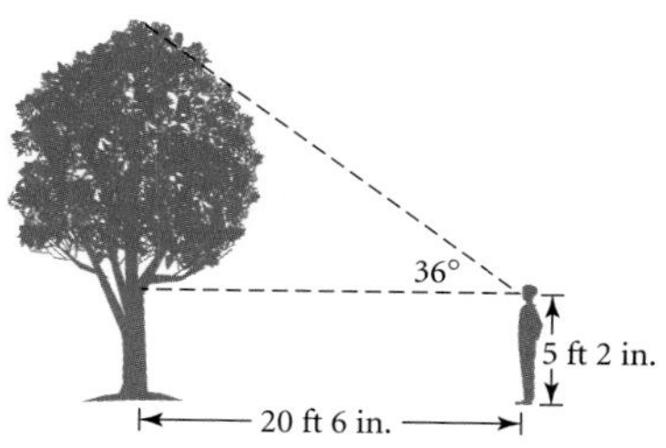

b. width of the lake

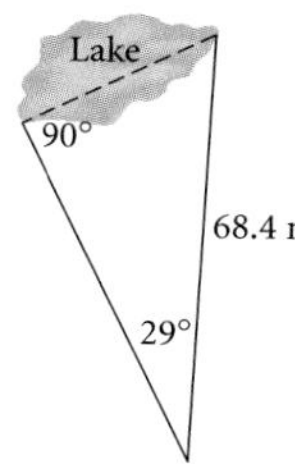

c. area of the triangle

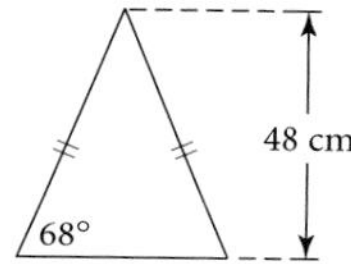

d. distance from the boat to the lighthouse

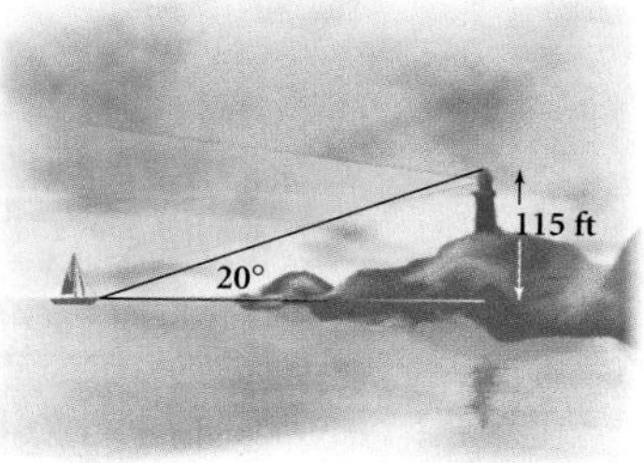

7.7 **15.** Find a polynomial equation of least degree with integer coefficients that has roots -3 and $\left(\frac{1}{2} - \sqrt{3}\right)$.

16. Give parametric equations and a single equation using only x and y for the ellipse at right.

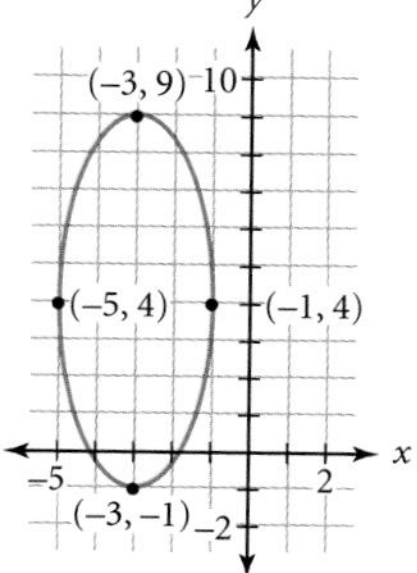

EXTENSIONS

A. Use Take Another Look activity 2 on page 486.

B. Have students model the motion of a paper airplane parametrically. They should use a motion sensor to approximate the initial velocity.

Exercise 13 [Alert] The ball is on the ground; gravity plays no role in this situation.

13a. $x = 2.3t + 4$, $y = 3.8t + 3$

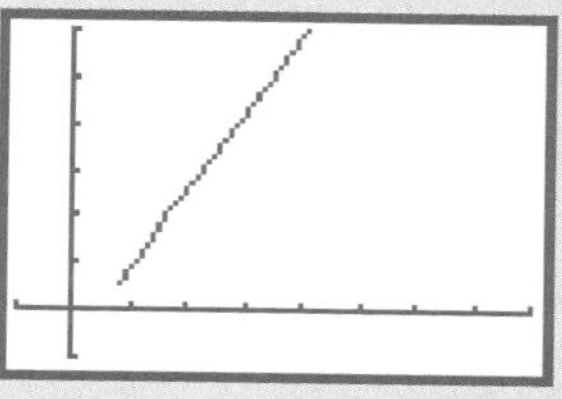

$[-5, 40, 5, -5, 30, 5]$

13b. 4.44 m/s on a bearing of 31°

14a. 20 ft 1 in.

14b. 33 m

14c. 930.9 cm²

14d. 315.96 ft

Exercise 15 This exercise reviews Lesson 7.7, Exercise 15. If students are struggling, ask them what must be another root.

15. $a(4x^3 + 8x^2 - 23x - 33) = 0$, where a is an integer, $a \neq 0$

Exercise 16 This exercise reviews the Exploration Parametric Equations for a Circle. Do not assign it if students did not complete that exploration.

16. $x = 2\cos t - 3$
$y = 5\sin t + 4$;
$\left(\frac{x+3}{2}\right)^2 + \left(\frac{y-4}{5}\right)^2 = 1$

LESSON

8.6

PLANNING

LESSON OUTLINE

One day:

10 min Investigation

5 min Sharing

5 min Examples A, B

10 min Example C

15 min Exercises

MATERIALS

- rulers
- protractors
- Towers (T) for One Step

TEACHING

Students who used *Discovering Geometry* may have encountered the Law of Sines in Chapter 12 of that book.

The introductory problem motivates this lesson and the next and appears in Lesson 8.7, Exercise 5. **[ESL]** *Cruising* means "traveling," usually at constant speed.

The one-step investigation is presented on page 469.

Guiding the Investigation

Students might use geometry software to do the construction and check the conjectured proportions with measurements. Note that students work alone until Step 5.

Step 1 **[Language]** You may need to help students recall that an *acute triangle* has only *acute angles,* with measures less than 90°. An *altitude* of a triangle is a line segment through an angle and perpendicular to the opposite side.

LESSON 8.6

The Law of Sines

Two airplanes pass over Chicago at the same time. Plane A is cruising at 400 mi/h on a bearing of 105°, and Plane B is cruising at 450 mi/h on a bearing of 260°. How far apart will they be after 2 hours?

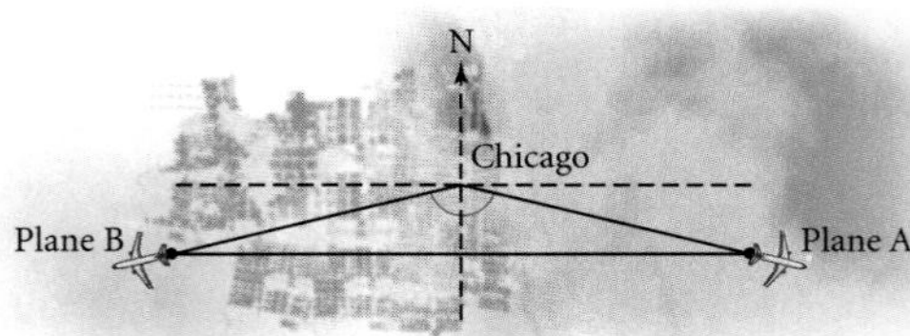

The problem above is a familiar scenario, but the triangle formed by the planes' paths is not a right triangle. In the next two lessons, you will discover useful relationships involving the sides and angles of nonright, or **oblique,** triangles and apply those relationships to situations like the distance problem presented above.

Investigation
Oblique Triangles

You will need

- a ruler
- a protractor

In this investigation you'll explore a special relationship between the sines of the angle measures of an oblique triangle and the lengths of the sides.

Step 1 Have each group member draw a different acute triangle ABC. Label the length of the side opposite $\angle A$ as a, the length of the side opposite $\angle B$ as b, and the length of the side opposite $\angle C$ as c. Draw the altitude from $\angle A$ to $\overline{BC}$. Label the height h.

Step 2 The altitude divides the original triangle into two right triangles, one containing $\angle B$ and the other containing $\angle C$. Use your knowledge of right triangle trigonometry to write an expression involving $\sin B$ and h, and an expression with $\sin C$ and h. Combine the two expressions by eliminating h. Write your new expression as a proportion in the form

$$\frac{\sin B}{?} = \frac{\sin C}{?}$$

Step 2 $\sin B = \frac{h}{c}$; $\sin C = \frac{h}{b}$; $\frac{\sin B}{b} = \frac{\sin C}{c}$

Step 3 Now draw the altitude from $\angle B$ to $\overline{AC}$ and label the height j. Repeat Step 2 using expressions involving j, $\sin C$, and $\sin A$. What proportion do you get when you eliminate j?

Step 4 Compare the proportions that you wrote in Steps 2 and 3. Use the transitive property of equality to combine them into an extended proportion:

$$\frac{?}{?} = \frac{?}{?} = \frac{?}{?}$$

Step 1

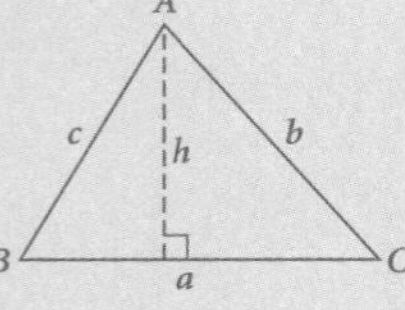

Step 3

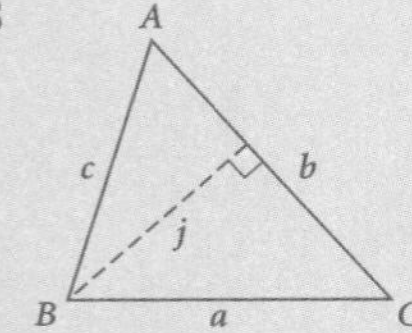

$\sin A = \frac{j}{c}$

$\sin C = \frac{j}{a}$

$\frac{\sin A}{a} = \frac{\sin C}{c}$

Step 4 You may need to review the transitive property of equality: If $a = b$ and $b = c$, then $a = c$. (Quantities equal to the same quantity equal each other.)

Step 4 $\frac{\sin A}{a} = \frac{\sin B}{b} = \frac{\sin C}{c}$

Step 5 | Share your results with the members of your group. Did everyone get the same proportion in Step 4?

Sine, cosine, and tangent are defined for all real angle measures. (See the exploration on page 447 to learn how these definitions are extended beyond right triangles.) Therefore, you can find the sine of obtuse angles as well as acute angles and right angles. Does your work from Steps 1–5 hold true for obtuse triangles as well?

Step 6 Answers will vary, but the proportions should hold for all triangles.

Step 6 | Have each group member draw a different obtuse triangle. Measure the angles and the sides of your triangle. Substitute the measurements and evaluate to verify that the proportion from Step 4 holds true for your obtuse triangles as well.

The relationships that you discovered in the investigation allow you to solve many problems involving oblique triangles.

EXAMPLE A

Towers A, B, and C are located in a national forest. From Tower B, the angle between Towers A and C is 53.3°, and from Tower C the angle between Towers A and B is 46.7°. The distance between Towers A and B is 4084 m. A lake between Towers A and C makes it difficult to measure the distance between them directly. What is the distance between Towers A and C?

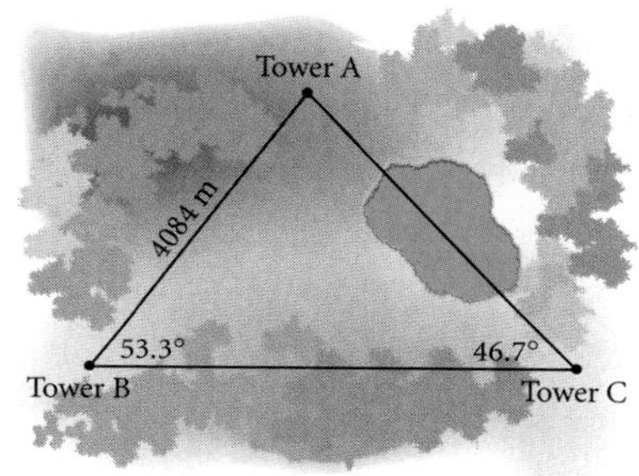

This forest fire observation tower is located in Great Smoky Mountains National Park, Tennessee.

Step 5 Students' results may have the ratios in different orders.

Step 6 [Language] An *obtuse angle* measures more than 90°. An *obtuse triangle* contains an obtuse angle.

To help students understand conceptually why the trigonometric functions can be extended from right triangles to circles, you might review the introduction to the Exploration Parametric Equations for a Circle on page 447.

One Step

Show the Towers transparency and pose this problem, from Example A: "Towers A, B, and C are located in a national forest. You have measured the angles and distances as marked, but a lake between Towers A and C makes it difficult to measure the distance between them directly. What is that distance?" As students work, suggest as needed that they drop a perpendicular to make a right triangle. Also be prepared to ask students how right triangles can be useful, leading to the idea of using trigonometric ratios. During Sharing, formalize students' approaches into the Law of Sines, and point out that the problem could be thought of as asking for a missing part of a triangle.

▸ **EXAMPLE A**

[Ask] "Why do you use the altitude from $\angle A$ to $\overline{BC}$ rather than another altitude?" [You don't want to split up known angles B and C or sides $\overline{AC}$ and $\overline{AB}$.]

LESSON OBJECTIVES

- Understand trigonometric ratios for angle measures greater than 90°
- Solve problems using the Law of Sines to find missing side lengths and angle measures of nonright triangles
- Use the Law of Sines to find two possible solutions to a problem when there is ambiguity

NCTM STANDARDS

CONTENT		PROCESS	
	Number	✓	Problem Solving
✓	Algebra	✓	Reasoning
✓	Geometry	✓	Communication
✓	Measurement	✓	Connections
	Data/Probability	✓	Representation

Example A (continued)

Remind students that sketches should accurately show the placement of the sides and angles. As needed, also remind them that the supplement of an angle forms a linear pair with that angle and that the sum of their measures is 180°.

▶ Solution

First, convince yourself that $\triangle ABC$ is not a right triangle. The sum of the measures of the angles in a triangle is 180°, so $\angle A$ measures 80°.

On your paper, sketch and label a diagram. Include the altitude from $\angle A$ to $\overline{BC}$. As in the investigation, two right triangles are formed. Set up sine ratios for each.

$$\sin 53.3° = \frac{h}{4084} \quad \text{or} \quad h = 4084 \sin 53.3°$$

and

$$\sin 46.7° = \frac{h}{b} \quad \text{or} \quad h = b \sin 46.7°$$

Substituting for h gives $4084 \sin 53.3° = b \sin 46.7°$. Solving for b gives

$$b = \frac{4084 \sin 53.3°}{\sin 46.7°}$$

$$b \approx 4499$$

The distance between Towers A and C is approximately 4499 m.

In Example A, notice that the height, h, was eliminated from the final calculations. You did not need a measurement for h! The equation $4084 \sin 53.3° = b \sin 46.7°$ can also be written as $\frac{\sin 53.3°}{b} = \frac{\sin 46.7°}{4084}$, or $\frac{\sin B}{b} = \frac{\sin C}{c}$, which is the relationship you found in the investigation.

For all three angles of a triangle the ratio of the sine of an angle to the length of the opposite side is constant. This relationship is called the **Law of Sines.**

Law of Sines

For any triangle with angles A, B, and C, and sides of lengths a, b, and c (a is opposite $\angle A$, b is opposite $\angle B$, and c is opposite $\angle C$),

$$\frac{\sin A}{a} = \frac{\sin B}{b} = \frac{\sin C}{c}$$

You use the Law of Sines to find missing parts of triangles when you know the measures of two angles and the length of one side of a triangle.

▶ EXAMPLE B

You can apply the Law of Sines without sketching an altitude.

If you round both sides of the equation $18 \sin 52.5° = a \sin 72.6°$ to two decimal places, you get the equation $14.28 \approx a(0.95)$. Dividing shows that a equals approximately 15.03. On the other hand, if you wait to use the calculator until you have the exact quotient for a, as in the text, you get a value for a of approximately 14.75. You might use this discrepancy to make the point that students should manipulate the expression using exact values as long as possible before they approximate with a calculator.

EXAMPLE B

Find the length of $\overline{BC}$.

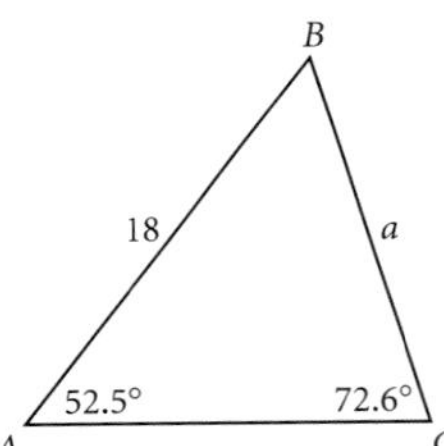

▸ Solution

Use the Law of Sines.

$$\frac{\sin A}{a} = \frac{\sin C}{c}$$ Select the proportion for the given angles and sides.

$$\frac{\sin 52.5°}{a} = \frac{\sin 72.6°}{18}$$ Substitute the angle measures and the known side length.

$$18 \sin 52.5° = a \sin 72.6°$$ Multiply both sides by $18a$ and reduce.

$$\frac{18 \sin 52.5°}{\sin 72.6°} = a$$ Divide both sides by $\sin 72.6°$ and reduce the right side.

$$a \approx 15$$ Evaluate.

The length of $\overline{BC}$ is approximately 15 units.

You may also use the Law of Sines when you know two side lengths and the measure of the angle opposite one of the sides. However, in this case you may find more than one possible solution. This is because two different angles—one acute and one obtuse—may share the same value of sine. Look at this diagram to see how this works.

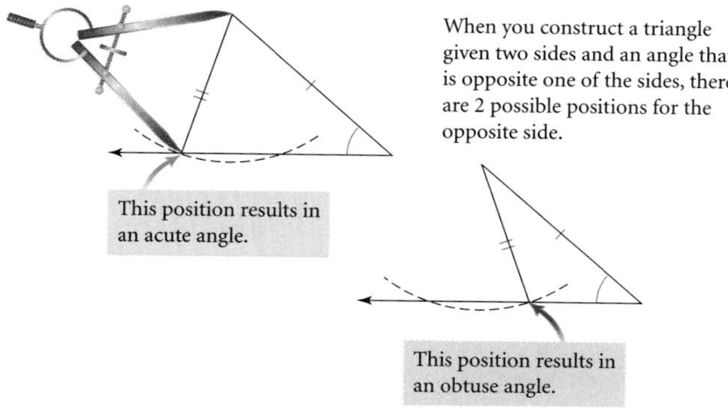

EXAMPLE C

Tara and Yacin find a map that they think will lead to buried treasure. The map instructs them to start at the 47° fork in the river. They need to follow the line along the southern branch for 200 m, then walk to a point on the northern branch that's 170 m away. Where along the northern branch should they dig for the treasure?

▸ Solution

As the map shows, there are two possible locations to dig. Consider the angles formed by the 170 m segment and the line along the northern branch as $\angle A$. Use the Law of Sines to find one possible measure of $\angle A$.

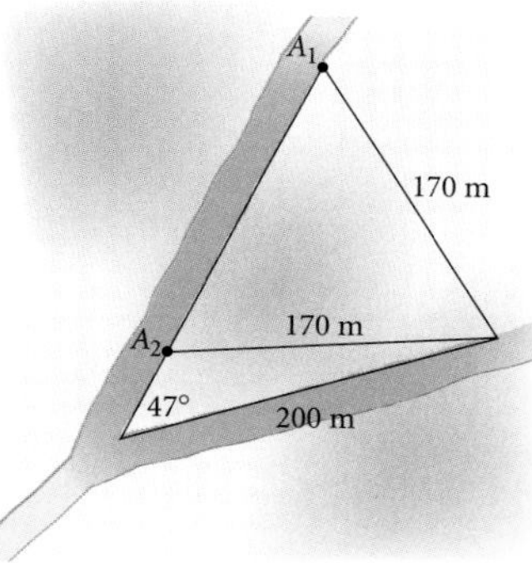

Sharing Ideas (continued)

[Ask] "Is the Law of Sines limited to oblique triangles? What happens in the case of right triangles?" [If $\angle C$ is the right angle, $\sin C = 1$. The equation $\frac{\sin C}{c} = \frac{\sin A}{a}$ is equivalent to $\sin A = \frac{a}{c}$, which is simply the definition of *sine*, so the Law of Sines does apply. However, to find an unknown part of a right triangle, it's probably easier to use the trigonometric ratios than to use the Law of Sines.]

▸ *EXAMPLE C*

[Ask] "Why are there two possible locations for the treasure?" [Students may recall from geometry that SSA does not guarantee congruence, so two possible triangles exist. This ambiguity is reflected in the fact that a given value of $\sin A$ corresponds to two angles A, one acute and one obtuse.]

[Ask] "Are the two possible angles related?" [They are always supplements. Suggest that students test their conjectures using a unit circle.]

[Language] *Ambiguous* means "capable of being understood in two or more ways." Here the value of $\sin A$ yields more than one meaning for the measure of $\angle A$.

SHARING IDEAS

If your students have studied geometry, ask whether they saw anything like the Law of Sines in their geometry course. They may already have studied this relationship. Even if they haven't, they may have seen a theorem stating that larger angles of a triangle are opposite longer sides. This idea might lead students to conjecture that $\frac{A}{a}$ equals $\frac{B}{b}$. This conjecture doesn't agree with reality, but $\frac{\sin A}{a}$ does equal $\frac{\sin B}{b}$. This relation is part of the Law of Sines.

Also if your students have studied geometry, ask them whether the Law of Sines relates to theorems about triangles. A discussion of this question might deepen students' understanding of the triangle congruency theorems as descriptions of what determines a triangle. For example, the measures of two angles and a side opposite one of them (SAA) determine a unique triangle. The Law of Sines can be used to find the other three parts of this triangle. The measures of two sides and an angle opposite one of them (SSA), however, do not determine a unique triangle but rather two triangles. Again, the Law of Sines can help in finding those two triangles (this is the ambiguous case).

Sharing Ideas (continued)

Referring to Example C, **[Ask]** "Can the Law of Sines ever be used to find the measure of an angle of a triangle?" [Because two angles with measures between 0° and 180° have the same sine, the Law of Sines won't determine an angle unambiguously.]

Ask whether the Law of Sines can be restated using cosines. $\left[\text{Yes; } \frac{\cos(90° - A)}{a} = \frac{\cos(90° - B)}{b} = \frac{\cos(90° - C)}{c}\right]$. This is not the Law of Cosines, but it does emphasize that the cosine is the sine of an angle's complement.

Ask how to find unknown parts of nonright triangles if no pair of measures of an angle and its opposite side is known. For example, **[Ask]** "What if the three angle measures are known (AAA)?" [The triangle is not determined, except for similarity.] "What if two angle measures and the length of the included side are known (ASA)?" [The third angle measure can be found from the fact that the sum of the measures of the angles in a triangle is 180°; then the Law of Sines can be used.] "What if three side lengths are known (SSS)?" [The ratios of side lengths and the fact that the angle measures sum to 180° can lead to three equations in three unknowns, but the process can be messy. Also, there will be ambiguity about the angles.] "What if the lengths of two sides and the included angle measure are known (SAS)?" This question motivates the Lesson 8.7.

$\frac{\sin 47°}{170} = \frac{\sin A}{200}$ Set up a proportion using opposite sides and angles.

$\sin A = \frac{200 \sin 47°}{170}$ Solve for sin A.

$A = \sin^{-1}\left(\frac{200 \sin 47°}{170}\right)$ Take the inverse sine of both sides.

$A \approx 59.4°$ Evaluate.

If $\angle A$ is acute, it measures approximately 59.4°. The other possibility for $\angle A$ is the obtuse supplement of 59.4°, or 120.6°. You can verify this with geometry as shown in the diagram below. Use your calculator to check that sin 59.4° is equivalent to sin 120.6° and that both angle measures satisfy the Law of Sines equation $\frac{\sin 47°}{170} = \frac{\sin A}{200}$.

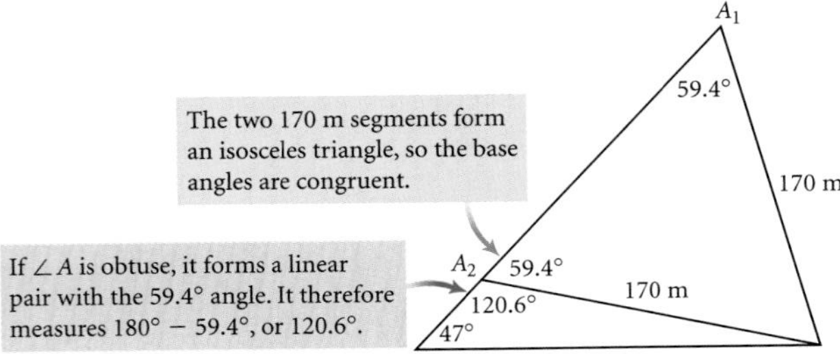

In order to find the distance along the northern branch, you need the measure of the third angle in the triangle. Use the known angle measure, 47°, and the approximations for the measure of $\angle A$.

$180° - (47° + 59.4°) \approx 73.6°$ or $180° - (47° + 120.6°) \approx 12.4°$

Use the Law of Sines to find the distance along the northern branch, x.

$\frac{\sin 73.6°}{x} = \frac{\sin 47°}{170}$ or $\frac{\sin 12.4°}{x} = \frac{\sin 47°}{170}$

$x = \frac{170 \sin 73.6°}{\sin 47°}$ or $x = \frac{170 \sin 12.4°}{\sin 47°}$

$x \approx 223$ or $x \approx 50$

Tara and Yacin should dig two holes along the northern branch, one 50 m and the other 223 m from the fork of the river.

A situation like that in Example C, where more than one possible solution exists, is called an **ambiguous case.** You can't tell which of the possibilities is correct unless there is more information in the problem, such as knowing whether the triangle is acute or obtuse. In general, you should report both solutions in cases like this.

EXERCISES

Practice Your Skills

1. Find the length of side $\overline{AC}$. 9.7 cm

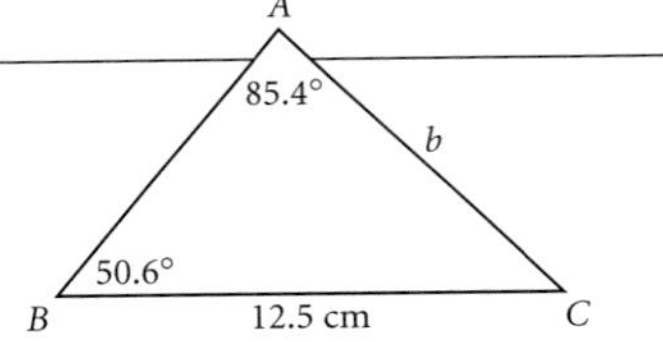

Assessing Progress

You can assess students' knowledge of the definition of *sine* as a ratio of side lengths of a right triangle and their understanding of how the definition extends to obtuse angles.

Closing the Lesson

The **Law of Sines** states that the ratios of the sines of the angles to the lengths of the opposite sides are all equal: $\frac{\sin A}{a} = \frac{\sin B}{b} = \frac{\sin C}{c}$. For acute triangles, this law is useful for finding a missing angle measure or side length of a triangle in which one angle measure and the length of the opposite side are known. If one angle is obtuse, there are two possible angles with one of the sines, so it is an **ambiguous case.**

2. Assume $\triangle PQR$ is an acute triangle. Find the measure of $\angle P$.

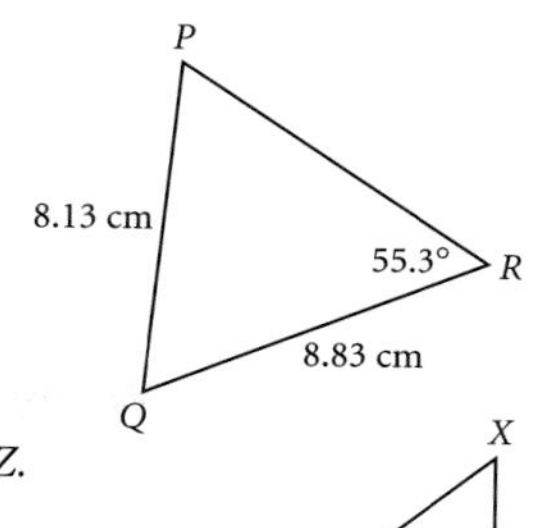

3. In $\triangle XYZ$, at right, $\angle Z$ is obtuse. Find the measures of $\angle X$ and $\angle Z$.

4. Find the length of $\overline{XY}$ in Exercise 3.

Reason and Apply

5. Find all of the unknown angle measures and side lengths.

a.

b.

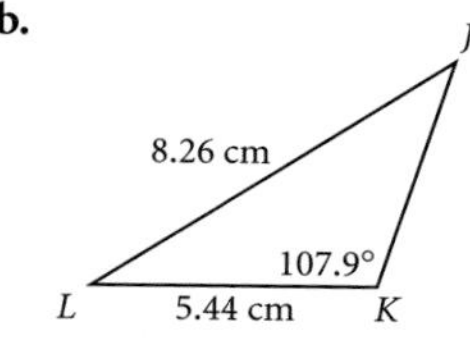

6. The Daredevil Cliffs rise vertically from the beach. The beach slopes gently down to the water at an angle of 3° from the horizontal. Scott lies at the water's edge, 50 ft from the base of the cliff, and determines that his line of vision to the top of the cliff makes a 70° angle with the line to the beach. How high is the cliff? 160.7 ft

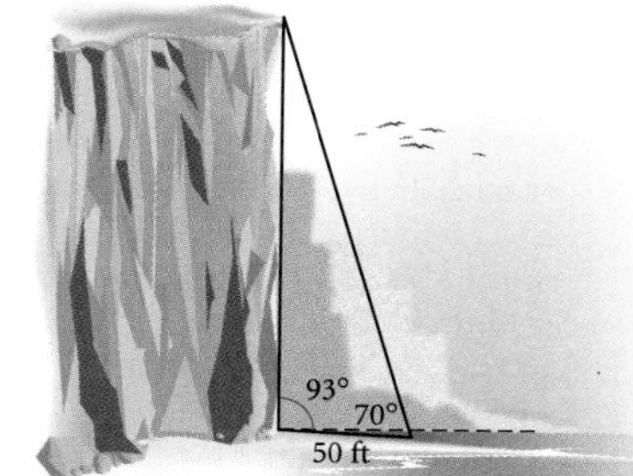

7. In an isosceles triangle, one of the base angles measures 42°. The length of each leg is 8.2 cm.

a. Find the length of the base. 12.19 cm

b. Even though you are given one angle and two sides not including the angle, this is not an ambiguous case. Why not?

8. **APPLICATION** Venus is 67 million mi from the Sun. Earth is 93 million mi from the Sun. Gayle measures the angle between the Sun and Venus as 14°. At that moment in time, how far is Venus from Earth?

Chabot Observatory in Oakland, California

BUILDING UNDERSTANDING

The exercises provide practice in working with the Law of Sines.

ASSIGNING HOMEWORK

Essential	1–5
Performance assessment	6–11
Portfolio	11
Journal	6
Group	9, 10
Review	12–16

Helping with the Exercises

2. 63.2°

3. $X \approx 50.2°$ and $Z \approx 92.8°$

4. 7.8 cm

5a. $B = 25.5°$; $BC \approx 6.4$ cm; $AB \approx 8.35$ cm

5b. $J \approx 38.8°$; $L \approx 33.3°$; $KJ \approx 4.77$ cm

Exercise 7 [Language] In an isosceles triangle, the base angles are the angles of equal measure, and the legs are the sides of equal length.

7b. Because the triangle is isosceles, knowing the measure of one angle allows you to determine the measures of all three angles.

Exercise 8 This is an ambiguous case.

8. approximately 27 million mi or approximately 153 million mi

Exercise 9 If students are having difficulty finding the angle measure of the triangle at the point of the second sighting, you may need to remind them that when two parallel lines are crossed by a transversal the same-side interior angles are supplementary.

9. 2.5 km

MAKING THE CONNECTION

Modern lighthouses use a Fresnel [frā-'nel] lens to emit powerful beams of light. The lens, invented in 1822 by French physicist Augustin Fresnel, is constructed of several prisms that concentrate available light into a single beam. Using this technology, lighthouses can project a beam that is as bright as five thousand 50-watt light bulbs and can be seen 28 miles away.

10. 5.4685 light-years at the first reading and 5.4684 light-years at the second reading

MAKING THE CONNECTION

When astronomers use telescopes to observe distant stars, they are looking back in time. Because the North Star, Polaris, is about 300 light-years away, it takes light from the star 300 years to reach Earth. That means astronomers see it as it was 300 years ago. When we look at the sun, we see it as it was 8 minutes earlier.

9. **APPLICATION** The SS *Minnow* is lost at sea in a deep fog. Moving on a bearing of 107°, the skipper sees a light at a bearing of 60°. The same light reappears through the fog after the skipper has sailed 1.5 km on his initial course. The second sighting of the light is at a bearing of 34°. How far is the boat from the source of the light at the time of the second sighting?

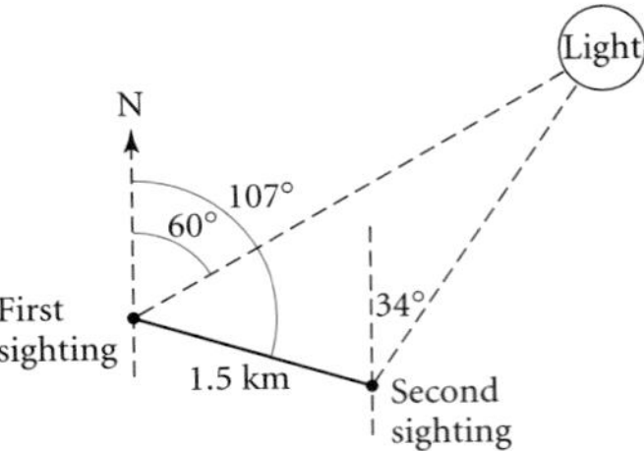

History CONNECTION

Lighthouses project light through darkness or poor weather to help guide ships ashore. The first lighthouses were actually bonfires—one was even mentioned in the *Iliad,* a Greek epic poem by Homer written sometime before 700 B.C.E. Today, most lighthouses hold powerful electric lights that flash automatically. Every lighthouse has a distinct sequence of flashes that allows ship captains to identify the nearby harbor.

10. **APPLICATION** One way to calculate the distance between Earth and a nearby star is to measure the angle between the star and the ecliptic (the plane of Earth's orbit) at 6-month intervals. A star is measured at a 42.13204° angle. Six months later, the angle is 42.13226°. The diameter of Earth's orbit is 3.13×10^{-5} light-years. What is the distance to the star at the time of each reading? Use this diagram to help you solve this problem.

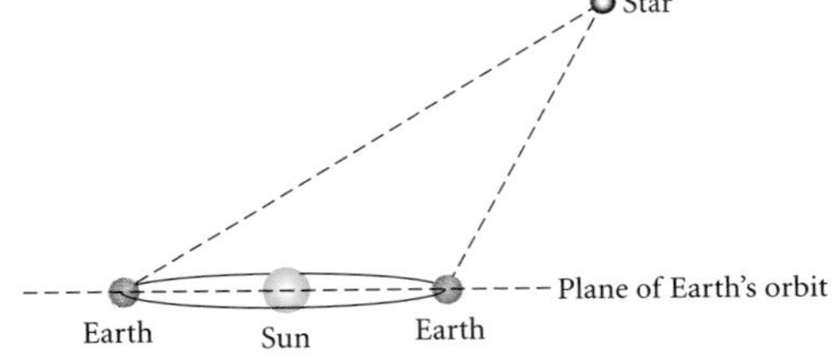

Science CONNECTION

A light-year is the distance that light can travel in one year. Light moves at a velocity of about 300,000 km/s, so one light-year is equal to about 9,461,000,000,000 km. Distances in space are so large that it's difficult to express them with relatively small units such as kilometers. For example, the distance to the next nearest big galaxy is 21×10^{18} km! Another unit of distance used by astronomers to measure distances within our solar system is the astronomical unit (AU). One AU is the average distance between Earth and the Sun, about 150 million km. Pluto averages about 40 AU from the Sun.

11. **APPLICATION** When light travels from one transparent medium into another, the rays bend, or refract. Snell's Law of Refraction states that

$$\frac{\sin\theta_1}{n_2} = \frac{\sin\theta_2}{n_1}$$

where θ_1 is the angle of incidence, θ_2 is the angle of refraction, and n_1 and n_2 are the indexes of refraction for the two mediums, as shown in the diagram.

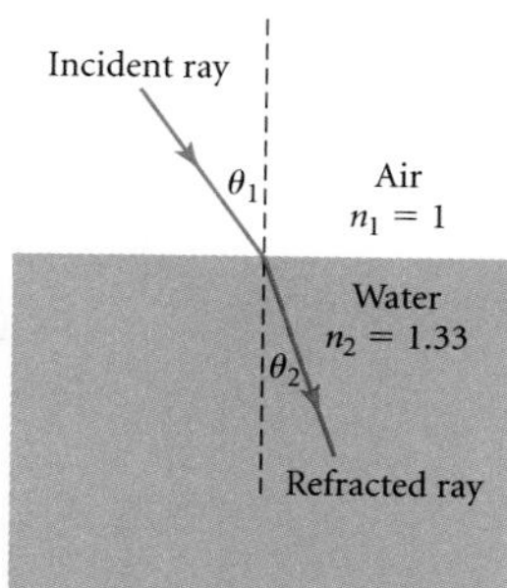

a. Find the angle of refraction in water if the angle of incidence from air is 60°. 41°

b. If the angle of refraction from air to water is 45°, at what angle did the ray enter the water? 70°

c. If the angle of incidence is 0°, what is the angle of refraction? 0°

Review

7.4 **12.** Use the quadratic formula to solve each equation.

a. $2x^2 - 8x + 5 = 0$ $x = \frac{4 \pm \sqrt{6}}{2}$

b. $3x^2 + 4x - 2 = 7$ $x = \frac{-2 \pm \sqrt{31}}{3}$

8.4 **13.** Draw a compass rose and show each vector. Find the x- and y-components of each, and show the angle with the x-axis used to find the components. Indicate the direction of the components with the proper sign.

a. 12 units on a bearing of 168°

b. 16 units on a bearing of 221°

8.4 **14.** Give the magnitude and bearing for each vector.

a. x-component: −9.1 units
y-component: 4.1 units

b. x-component: 16.6 units
y-component: 14.4 units

5.1 **15.** The value of a building depreciates at a rate of 6% per year. When new, the building is worth $36,500.

a. How much is the building worth after 5 years 3 months? $26,376.31

b. To the nearest month, when will the building be worth less than $10,000? 20 years 11 months

16. Find the volume of the greenhouse at right. Round your answer to the nearest cubic foot. 13824 ft³

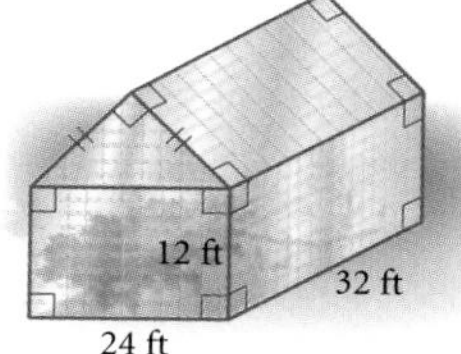

IMPROVING YOUR GEOMETRY SKILLS

A New Area Formula

You are given the lengths of two sides of a triangle, a and b, and the measure of the angle between them, C. How can you find the area of the triangle using only these three measurements?

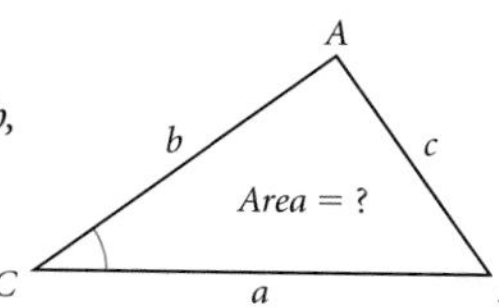

Exercise 11 [ESL] A *transparent medium* is a solid, liquid, or gas that you can see through.

The bending of a light ray as it travels from air to water makes the water look shallower than it actually is.

Snell's Law looks similar to the Law of Sines, except that the constants refer to a *refraction index* rather than to the side lengths of a triangle. **[Context]** Snell's Law is named after Dutch scientist Willebrord Snell (1580–1626).

13a.

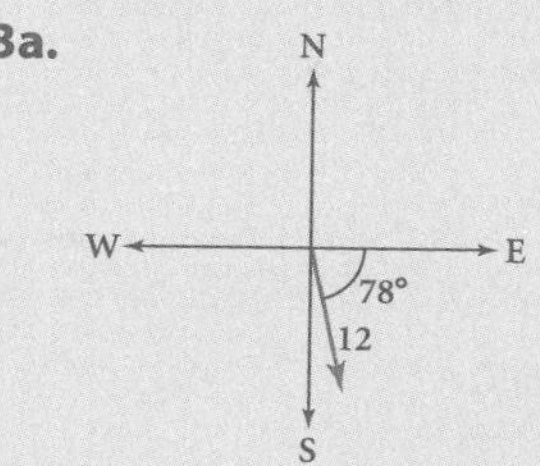

x-component: $12\cos 78° \approx 2.5$;
y-component:
$-12\sin 78° \approx -11.7$

13b.

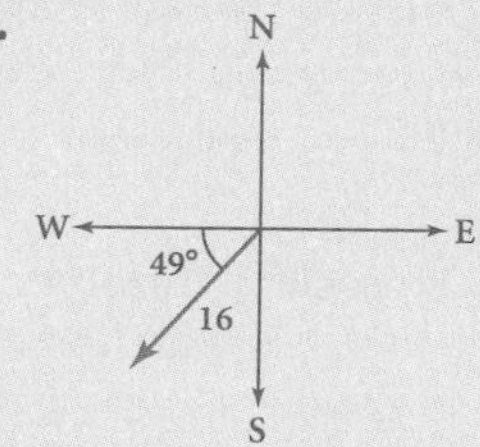

x-component:
$-16\cos 49° \approx -10.5$;
y-component:
$-16\sin 49° \approx -12.1$

14a. 10 units on a bearing of 294°

14b. 22 units on a bearing of 49°

Exercise 16 This exercise reviews geometry skills.

EXTENSION

Have students write their own problems that can be solved using the Law of Sines.

IMPROVING GEOMETRY SKILLS

If you consider a to be the length of the base ($\overline{BC}$), the area is given by $\frac{1}{2}ah$, where h is the height of the triangle to base $\overline{CB}$. Then $\sin C = \frac{h}{b}$, or $b\sin C = h$. Substituting $b\sin C$ for h in the area formula gives the equation $Area = \frac{1}{2}ab\sin C$. The symmetry of this expression shows that $\overline{AC}$ could have been considered the base as well.

Students may remember this formula from *Discovering Geometry,* Chapter 12.

LESSON

8.7

PLANNING

LESSON OUTLINE

One day:

10 min Example A

10 min Investigation

10 min Sharing

5 min Example B

10 min Exercises

MATERIALS

- metersticks or tape measures
- protractors

TEACHING

The Law of Cosines can be used to find missing parts of triangles to which the Law of Sines does not apply.

One Step

Pose this problem, from the investigation: "Position three members of your group so that two people are on opposite sides of a barrier and the third person can see both of them. Find the distance between the first two persons without trying to measure it directly."

As needed, encourage students to find the distances to the third person and the angle with the third person at the vertex. Once they have a triangle, as needed wonder aloud whether the method of dropping a perpendicular, used in the previous lesson, would be helpful here. You might also need to ask how right triangles can be useful, leading to the ideas of both the Pythagorean Theorem and trigonometric ratios.

LESSON

8.7

The Law of Cosines

The Law of Sines enabled you to find the lengths of sides of a triangle or the measures of the angles in certain situations. To use the Law of Sines, you needed to know the measures of two angles and the length of any side, or the lengths of two sides and the measure of the angle opposite one of the sides. What if you know a different combination of sides and angles?

EXAMPLE A

Two hot-air balloons approach a landing field. One is 12 m from the landing point and the other is 17 m from the landing point. The angle between the balloons is 70°. How far apart are the two balloons?

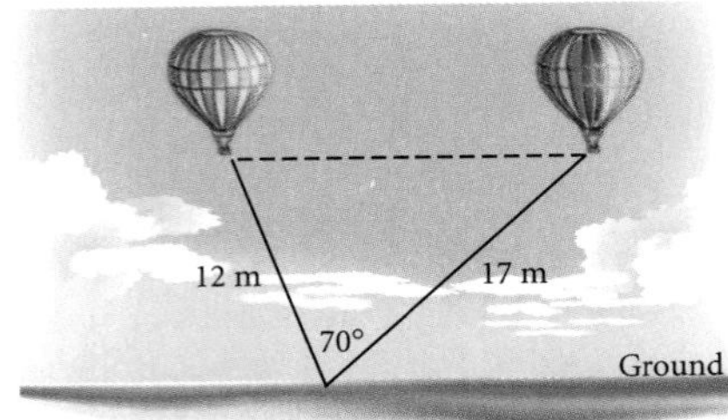

▶ Solution

In this case the Law of Sines does not help. You know only the included angle, or the angle between the two sides. If you try to set up an equation using the Law of Sines, you will always have more than one variable. So you must try something else.

Sketch one altitude to form two right triangles, so that one of the right triangles contains the 70° angle.

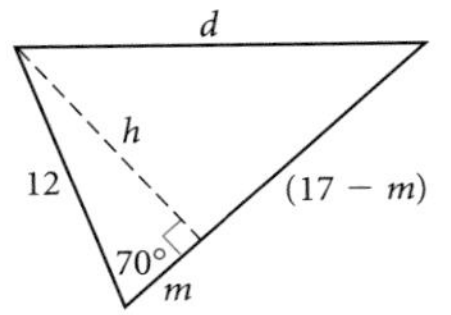

If you use the altitude from the balloon on the left, the 17 m side is split into two parts. Label one part m and the other part $17 - m$. Label the height h, and label the distance between the balloons d. You can now write two equations using the Pythagorean Theorem.

$$m^2 + h^2 = 12^2 \quad \text{and} \quad (17 - m)^2 + h^2 = d^2$$

You can multiply and expand the binomial in the second equation.

$$289 - 34m + m^2 + h^2 = d^2$$

Now you can rearrange the first equation and use substitution to solve the system of equations.

$h^2 = 144 - m^2$ — Solve $m^2 + h^2 = 144$ for h^2.

$289 - 34m + m^2 + (144 - m^2) = d^2$ — Substitute $144 - m^2$ for h^2 into the second equation.

$289 + 144 - 34m = d^2$ — Combine like terms.

LESSON OBJECTIVES

- Use the Law of Cosines to solve problems that can be represented as a triangle with the lengths of two sides and the measure of the included angle known
- See the relationship between the Law of Cosines and the Pythagorean Theorem
- Understand which problems can be solved with the Law of Sines and which can be solved with the Law of Cosines

NCTM STANDARDS

CONTENT		PROCESS	
	Number	✓	Problem Solving
✓	Algebra	✓	Reasoning
✓	Geometry	✓	Communication
✓	Measurement	✓	Connections
✓	Data/Probability	✓	Representation

Use the right triangle that contains the 70° angle to write

$$\cos 70° = \frac{m}{12}$$

Solve this equation for m to get $m = 12 \cos 70°$, and substitute this value for m into the equation for d^2.

$289 + 144 - 34\,(12 \cos 70°) = d^2$ Substitute $12 \cos 70°$ for m.

$\sqrt{289 + 144 - 34(12 \cos 70°)} = d$ Take the square root of both sides. You need only the positive root, because d represents a distance.

$d \approx 17.1$ Evaluate.

The distance between the two balloons is approximately 17.1 m.

You can repeat the procedure that is used in Example A any time you know the lengths of two sides of a triangle and the measure of the included angle, and when you need to find the length of the third side. Notice that you could also write the equation for d^2 as

$$d^2 = 17^2 + 12^2 - 2(17)(12) \cos 70°$$

which looks similar to the Pythagorean Theorem with an extra term that is twice the product of the length of the sides and the cosine of the angle between them. This modified Pythagorean relationship is called the **Law of Cosines.**

Law of Cosines

For any triangle with angles A, B, and C and sides of lengths a, b, and c (a is opposite $\angle A$, b is opposite $\angle B$, and c is opposite $\angle C$),

$$a^2 = b^2 + c^2 - 2bc \cos A$$

$$b^2 = a^2 + c^2 - 2ac \cos B$$

$$c^2 = a^2 + b^2 - 2ab \cos C$$

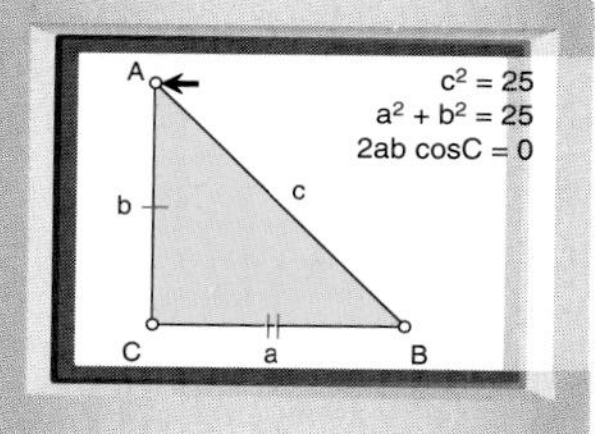

In this right triangle, c^2 is equivalent to $a^2 + b^2$.
$c^2 = a^2 + b^2$

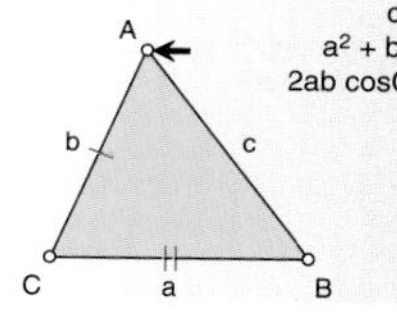

In this acute triangle, c^2 is less than $a^2 + b^2$. The difference is $2ab \cos C$.
$c^2 = a^2 + b^2 - 2ab \cos C$

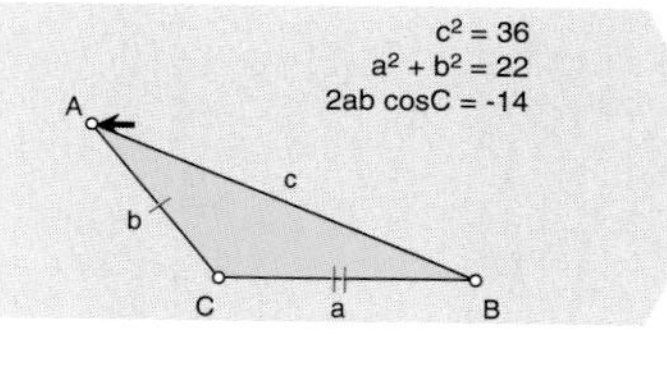

In this obtuse triangle, c^2 is more than $a^2 + b^2$. Again, the difference is $2ab \cos C$.
$c^2 = a^2 + b^2 - 2ab \cos C$

In the investigation you'll apply the Law of Cosines to a real situation.

One Step (continued)

During Sharing, formalize students' approaches into the Law of Cosines, and point out that the problem could be thought of as asking for a missing part of a triangle in the SAS case.

► ***EXAMPLE A***

This example illustrates the derivation of the Law of Cosines.

[Alert] Students may think that the distances from the landing point refer to horizontal distances; rather, they are direct distances from the balloons to the point on the ground.

Point out that the Pythagorean Theorem is applied to the two right triangles constructed—not to the original triangle, which isn't a right triangle.

[Alert] Through the calculations, students may lose track of the goal: to find d. You might emphasize that m is the excess caused by the angle's not being a right angle; if it had measure 90° instead of 70°, m would be 0. You might make these points by following the role of m through a restatement of the calculations, something like this:

$d^2 = h^2 + (17 - m)^2 =$

$12^2 - m^2 + 17^2 - 2(17)m + m^2 =$

$12^2 + 17^2 - 2(17)(12 \cos 70°)$

After working through the example, take a minute to have students write equations using the Law of Sines to verify the solution.

[Ask] "Why drop the perpendicular to the 17-meter side?" [It was one possible choice. If you drop the perpendicular from the other balloon, you will get an equivalent solution.]

Law of Cosines

A dynamic algebra exploration at www.keymath.com/DAA can help students visually validate this law.

Guiding the Investigation

Try to have the students not be directly opposite each other through the wall, so they can't simply measure their distances to the wall and add them. If a wall is not available, use any barrier the students can't measure through, such as a stack of books, a desk, or an audiovisual cart. Students can even imagine a wall, as long as they don't measure directly.

Sample answer:

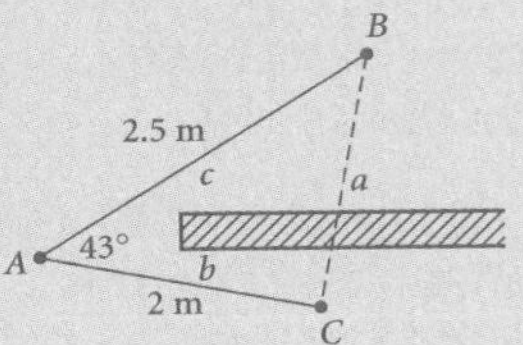

$a^2 = b^2 + c^2 - 2bc\cos A$

$a^2 = 2^2 + 2.5^2 - 2(2)(2.5)\cos 43°$

$a^2 = 4 + 6.25 - 20\cos 43°$

$a = \sqrt{10.25 - 10\cos 43°}$

$a \approx 1.71$

approximately 1.71 m

▶ *EXAMPLE B*

Emphasize the importance of the order of operations in solving for $m\angle A$.

The accuracy of the calculation of the measure of $\angle A$ depends on the accuracy used for the length c. For the sake of clarity, the solution shown uses the rounded value of c. However, this jeopardizes the accuracy of the measure of $\angle A$; the evaluated result is 95.93°. Students could store their unrounded evaluation of c on their calculators and use the variable c in place of 1.42. Alternatively, they could enter the exact expression $\sqrt{3^2 + 2.5^2 - 15\cos 28°}$ in place of 1.42. Either of these approaches will yield a measure for $\angle A$ of 96.03°.

Although using the triangle sum property to find the measure of $\angle B$ is easy, you might mention that $\angle B$ can also be found by using the Law of Cosines again.

Investigation
Around the Corner

You will need

- metersticks or a tape measure
- a protractor

Position three members of your group so that two people are on opposite sides of a wall and the third person can see both of them. Use trigonometry to find the distance between the two persons on opposite sides of the wall. Sketch a diagram of the situation, show the measurements you make, and show your calculations.

You can use the Law of Cosines alone or in combination with other triangle properties.

EXAMPLE B Find the unknown angle measures and side lengths.

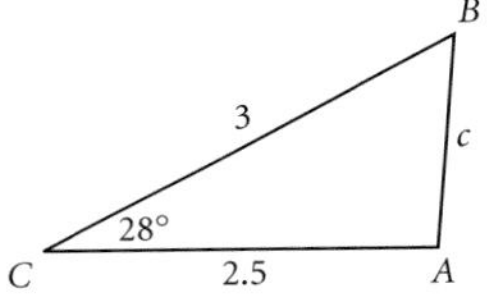

▶ *Solution* First, use the Law of Cosines to find the length of $\overline{AB}$.

$c^2 = a^2 + b^2 - 2ab\cos C$	The Law of Cosines for finding c when a, b, and C are known.
$c^2 = 3^2 + 2.5^2 - 2(3)(2.5)\cos 28°$	Substitute 3 for a, 2.5 for b, and 28° for C.
$c^2 = 9 + 6.25 - 15\cos 28°$	Multiply.
$c = \sqrt{9 + 6.25 - 15\cos 28°}$	Take the positive square root of both sides.
$c \approx 1.42$	Evaluate.

The length of $\overline{AB}$ is approximately 1.42 units.

SHARING IDEAS

After students present their results, **[Ask]** "Can you find the other angle measures as well?" Let students try to use the Law of Sines, and help them see that the results might be ambiguous, because two angles with measures between 0° and 180° have the same sine. **[Ask]** "Is the Law of Cosines any better for finding the measures of these angles?" [Yes; any two angles between 0° and 180° have different cosines, which is why this law was used in the second part of Example B.]

Ask students to restate the Law of Cosines in their own words. If they can easily assign letters to various parts of a triangle, they need only remember one form. The most frequently used is the third form listed, which extends the most common form of the Pythagorean Theorem: If c is the length of the side opposite $\angle C$, then $c^2 = a^2 + b^2 - 2ab\cos C$.

Remind students of various possibilities regarding what can be known about a triangle: AAA, SSS, SAA, ASA, SAS, SSA. **[Ask]** "In which cases is the triangle determined, and how can you find the missing parts?"

Now use the Law of Cosines to find the measure of $\angle A$.

$a^2 = b^2 + c^2 - 2bc\cos A$	The Law of Cosines for finding A when a, b, and c are known.
$3^2 \approx 2.5^2 + 1.42^2 - 2(2.5)(1.42)\cos A$	Substitute values for a, b, and c.
$9 \approx 8.2664 - 7.1\cos A$	Multiply.
$0.7336 \approx -7.1\cos A$	Subtract 8.2664 from both sides.
$\cos A \approx \frac{0.7336}{-7.1}$	Divide by -7.1.
$A \approx \cos^{-1}\left(\frac{0.7336}{-7.1}\right)$	Take the inverse cosine of both sides.
$A \approx 96°$	Evaluate.

Angle A measures approximately 96°.

To find the measure of the last angle, use the fact that the measures of the three angles in any triangle sum to 180°. The measure of $\angle B$ is approximately $180° - 28° - 96°$, or 56°.

During a calculation, it is best to use the entire previous answer for the next calculation. Rounding before the last step can reduce the accuracy of your answer. In Example B, you could find the measure of $\angle A$ with more accuracy by using $\sqrt{9 + 6.25 - 15\cos 28°}$ for c instead of the approximation of 1.42. In all cases, you need to verify that the answers you get make sense in the context of the problem or in a sketch of the triangle.

In deciding whether to use the Law of Sines or the Law of Cosines, consider the triangle parts whose measurements you know and their relationships to each other.

Law of Sines	**Law of Cosines**
Side-Angle-Angle	Side-Angle-Side
Side-Side-Angle (ambiguous case)	Side-Side-Side

EXERCISES

Practice Your Skills

1. Find the length of $\overline{AC}$. approximately 6.1 km

B, 38°, 9.2 km, 5.1 km, A, C, b

2. Find the measure of $\angle T$. approximately 35.33°

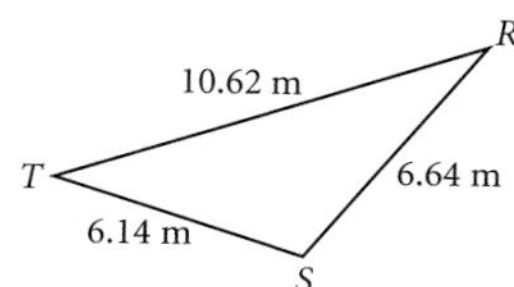

3. Solve for A and b. (Assume b is positive.)

   a. $16 = 25 + 36 - 2(5)(6)\cos A$ $A \approx 41.4°$

   b. $49 = b^2 + 9 - 2(3)(b)\cos 60°$ $b = 8$

Assessing Progress

You can assess students' understanding of the Law of Sines, as well as their willingness to draw diagrams.

Closing the Lesson

The **Law of Cosines** is an extension of the Pythagorean Theorem to nonright triangles: $c^2 = a^2 + b^2 - 2ab\cos C$, where $\angle C$ is opposite the side with length c and where a and b are the other two side lengths of the triangle. The Law of Cosines is used to find missing parts of a triangle in which the measures of all three sides, or two sides and the included angle, are known.

Sharing Ideas (continued)

Let students discuss this question as they try to organize the information they have. Tolerate repetition of questions and ideas as different students make meaning for themselves. The triangle is not determined for AAA (which determines only similarity) and SSA (which is the ambiguous case). When the triangle is determined, missing angle measures are determined by the Law of Cosines and missing side lengths by the Law of Sines. However, if no angle/opposite side pair is known (SAS), the Law of Cosines is used to find a third side. In the ambiguous case of SSA, the Law of Sines is used to determine the two possible side lengths.

BUILDING UNDERSTANDING

Students practice using the Law of Cosines.

ASSIGNING HOMEWORK

Essential	1–4
Performance assessment	5–10
Portfolio	9
Group	7, 9, 10
Review	11–14

Helping with the Exercises

Exercise 3b This exercise shows that the Law of Cosines can lead to an ambiguous case for side length. Technically $b = -5$ is a solution of the equation (as well as $b = 8$), but a negative value of b doesn't make sense as a side length.

4a. $AC \approx 6.4$, $A \approx 78°$, $C \approx 53°$

4b. $D = 72°$, $F = 36°$, $DE \approx 7.7$

4c. $G \approx 114°$, $I \approx 28°$, $H \approx 38°$

Exercise 5 This is the problem that opened Lesson 8.6. You may want to use this exercise to discuss or investigate the fact that the cosine of an acute angle, with measure between 0° and 90°, is positive, whereas the cosine of an obtuse angle, with measure between 90° and 180°, is negative.

5. 1659.8 mi

6. 112.3°

7. From point A, the underground chamber is at a 22° angle from the ground between A and B. From point B, the chamber is at a 120° angle from the ground. If the truck goes 1.5 km farther in the same direction, the chamber will be approximately 2.6 km directly beneath the truck.

MAKING THE CONNECTION

Many environmentalists oppose the use of "thumper trucks" to find underground petroleum deposits. They argue that the seismic waves produced by the 25-ton trucks are harmful to fragile ecosystems. The vehicles, opponents say, damage soils, disrupt sensitive species, and harm the tourism industry in nature areas.

4. Find all of the unknown angle measures and side lengths.

a.

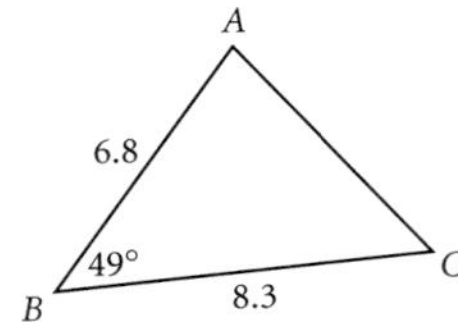

b.

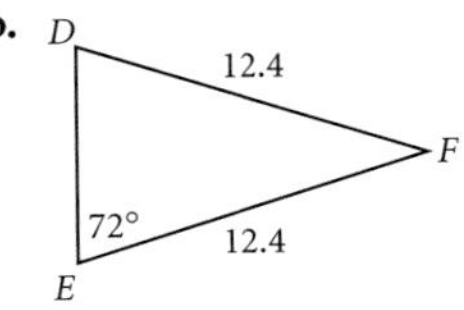

c.

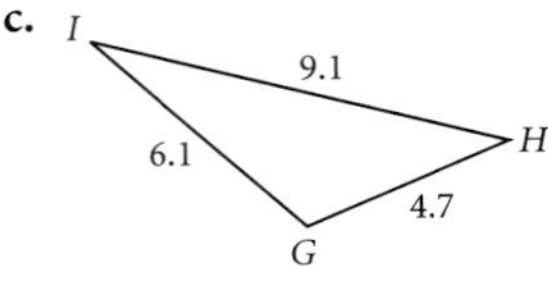

Reason and Apply

5. Two airplanes pass over Chicago, Illinois, at the same time. One is cruising at 400 mi/h on a bearing of 105°, and the other is cruising at 450 mi/h on a bearing of 260°. How far apart will they be after 2 h?

Pilots use the control panels of this passenger aircraft to follow air traffic control commands, to adjust for wind currents, and to avoid the airspace of other planes.

6. Find the measure of $\angle S$.

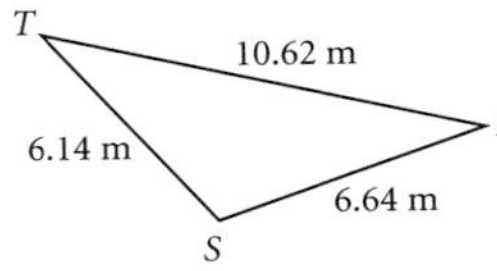

7. APPLICATION Seismic exploration identifies underground phenomena, such as caves, oil pockets, and rock layers, by transmitting sound into the earth and timing the echo of the vibration. From a sounding at point A, a "thumper" truck locates an underground chamber 7 km away. Moving to point B, 5 km from point A, the truck takes a second sounding and finds the chamber is 3 km away from that point. Assume that the underground chamber lies in the same vertical plane as A and B. What more can you say about the location of the underground chamber?

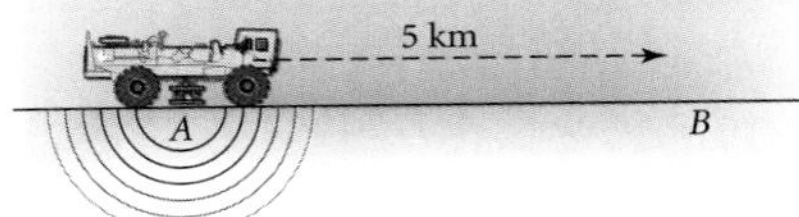

Science CONNECTION

Sources of oil are often found via seismic exploration. At one time, seismologists used explosives to generate shock waves, but now they use "thumper" trucks that send controlled vibrations through the ground. Because seismic exploration may be disruptive to a particular environment, oil explorers sometimes use gravitational or magnetic exploration to determine the composition of rock formations based upon Earth's natural gravity or magnetic fields.

8. A folding chair's legs meet to form a 50° angle. The rear leg is 55 cm long and attaches to the front leg at a point 75 cm from the front leg's foot. How far apart are the legs at the floor?

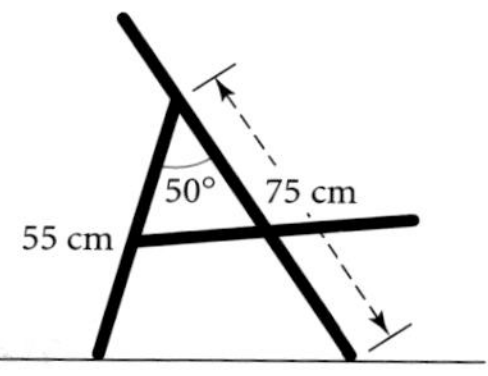

American designer Charles Eames (1907–1978) used mathematics to design this chair, which is suitable for sitting or sprawling.

9. **APPLICATION** The Hear Me Now Phone Company plans to build a cell tower to serve the needs of Pleasant Beach and the beachfront. It decides to locate the cell tower so that Pleasant Beach is 1 mi away at a bearing of 60° from the tower. The range of the signal from the cell tower is 1.75 mi. The beachfront runs north to south. How far south of Pleasant Beach will customers be able to use their cell phones?

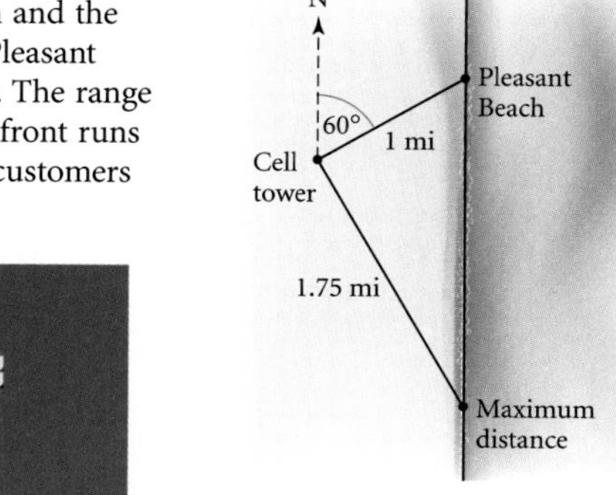

Technology CONNECTION

The placement of cell towers is crucial to providing a variety of cellular services. Mathematical models are used to analyze possible sites. Cell towers are located by individual companies based on their own business plan for the market they serve. For greatest cost efficiency, cellular companies consider the physical design, topography, population density, environmental impact, engineering, and aesthetics of their towers.

This cell phone tower is located in Jonesboro, Georgia.

10. **APPLICATION** Triangulation is used to locate airplanes, boats, or vehicles that transmit radio signals. The distances to the vehicle are found and the directions calculated by measuring the strength of the signal at three fixed receiving locations. Receiver B is 18 km from Receiver A at a bearing of 122°. Receiver C is 26 km from Receiver A at a bearing of 80°. The signal from a source vehicle to Receiver A indicates a distance of 15 km. The distance from the source vehicle to Receiver B is 8 km and to Receiver C is 25 km. What is the bearing from Receiver A to the source vehicle? (*Hint:* You might try making a scale drawing of this situation, and use your compass to get a general idea of the location of the source before starting the calculations.)

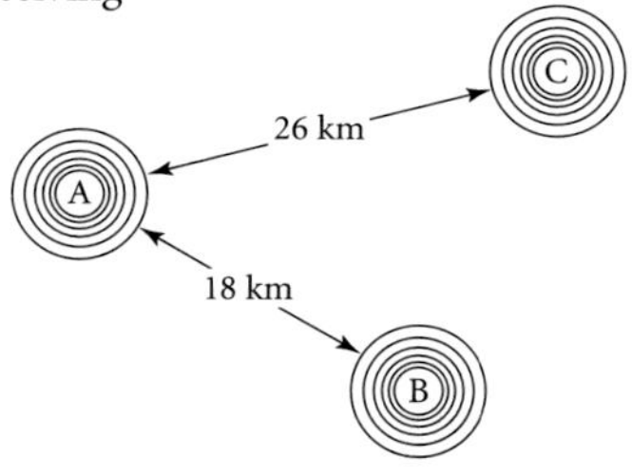

8. approximately 58 cm

Exercise 9 **[Ask]** "Does the solution $x = -1.021$ have any meaning?" [The signal will also reach 1.021 mi north of Pleasant Beach.]

9. 2.02 mi

MAKING THE CONNECTION

About half of Americans now carry cellular phones, a situation that has caused a growing need for cellular phone towers. One problem is that, although everyone wants good service for his or her phone, nobody wants a cellular tower in his or her backyard. Cellular companies have begun camouflaging their towers so they won't be obtrusive in people's communities. About 25% of cellular towers now reside in flagpoles, artificial trees, fake chimneys, water towers, silos, large signs and billboards, or windmills.

Exercise 10 This exercise can be stated only as a range of answers. The measured distances from each receiver do not coincide at a single point. Using Receivers A and B and the source gives a result of approximately 148.08°. Using Receivers A and C gives a result of approximately 149.28°.

10. 148° to 149°

Exercise 11 [Language] A *nautical mile* is a unit of measure based on a minute of arc $\left(\frac{1}{60}\text{ of a degree}\right)$ of a great circle of Earth. The length of a minute of arc varies in different parts of the world because Earth is not a perfect sphere, but the internationally recognized unit that is used officially in the United States is equal to 1852 m, or 6076.115 ft.

12a.

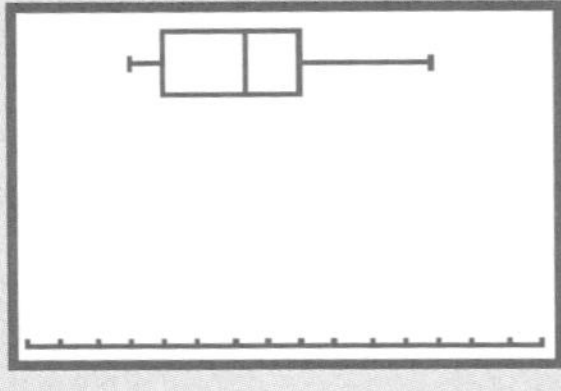

[0.25, 0.4, 0.01, 0, 1, 0]

Exercises 13, 14 These exercises review geometry skills.

EXTENSION

Ask students to use geometry software to model an exercise in this lesson.

Catapult Angles

As students work on the catapult project, encourage thinking about extreme cases, such as "How could any angle measure other than 90° result in a ball that travels zero distance?" As needed, suggest that students consider how far the ball travels horizontally before returning to the initial height. Because $y = y_0$ when $t = \frac{2v}{g}\cos A$, it follows that $x = (v\sin A)t = \frac{2v^2}{g}\sin A\cos A$, so an angle and its complement give the same horizontal distance. Students may find this result counterintuitive.

Review

8.4 **11.** A ship's captain sees a lighthouse at a bearing of 105°. Then the captain sails 8.8 nautical miles on a bearing of 174°. The lighthouse is now at a bearing of 52°. How far is the ship from the lighthouse? 10.3 nautical mi

2.2 **12.** Here are the batting averages of the National League's Most Valuable Players from 1980 to 2000. (*The New York Times Almanac 2002*)

{.286, .316, .281, .302, .314, .353, .290, .287, .290, .291, .301, .319, .311, .336, .368, .319, .326, .366, .308, .319, .334}

a. Make a box plot of these data.

b. Give the five-number summary. .281, .2905, .314, .330, .368

c. Find the range and interquartile range. *range* = .087, *IQR* = .0395

d. Find the mean and standard deviation. $\bar{x} \approx .315$, $s \approx .025$

13. Find the total surface area of the figure at right. Round your answer to the nearest square centimeter. 1751 cm²

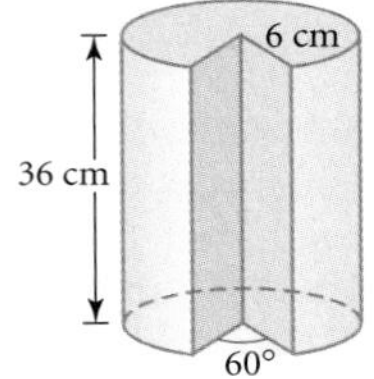

14. Congruent circles *A* and *B* are tangent at point *C*. The radius of each circle is 3 units. Rays *RU* and *ST* are tangent at *U* and *S*, respectively, and intersect at *T*. Find *ST*. $ST = 3\sqrt{2}$ units

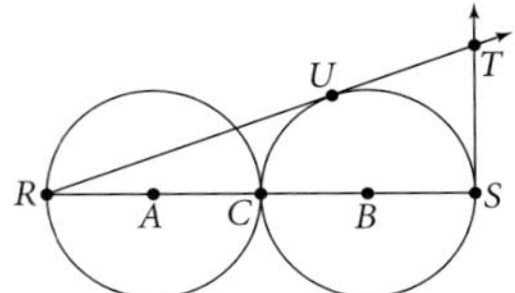

Project

CATAPULT

If you launch a ball at a particular angle and initial velocity, you can determine how far it will travel. Is there another angle at which a ball can be launched, with the same initial velocity, that will cause the ball to travel exactly the same horizontal distance? What angle(s) will cause the ball to travel the farthest distance possible?

Your project should include

- A conjecture about what kinds of angles (if any) will cause a ball to travel equal distances, and evidence to support it.
- Angle(s) that will cause a ball to travel the farthest distance possible.

Supporting the Project

Students can use the same calculator idea they used for simulating free throws in Lesson 8.5. See the information on catapult angles in the side column.

OUTCOMES

- The report states that angles that are complementary will cause a ball to travel the same distance before it returns to the initial height and supports this conjecture with calculator experimentation, graphs and tables, or a proof.
- The report states that an angle measure of 45° will cause a ball to travel the longest horizontal distance possible.
- The report discusses the effects of air resistance on the motion of the ball.

CHAPTER 8 REVIEW

Parametric equations describe the locations of points by using a third variable, t, called a **parameter.** In many cases this third variable represents time. In other cases it can be interpreted as an angle or simply a number. By controlling the range of t-values, you can graph part of a function. To convert from parametric form to regular form, solve either the x- or the y-equation for t. Then substitute this expression into the other equation. The result is an equation involving only x and y.

One common use of parametric equations is to simulate motion. This often involves the use of right triangle **trigonometry.** The **trigonometric ratios**—sine, cosine, and tangent—relate the side lengths of a triangle to the measure of an angle. The **sine** of an angle is the ratio of the opposite leg to the hypotenuse in a right triangle. The **cosine** of an angle is the ratio of the adjacent leg to the hypotenuse, and the **tangent** of an angle is the ratio of the opposite leg to the adjacent leg. You can use these ratios to find missing side lengths and angles in right triangles. You can use the **Law of Sines** and the **Law of Cosines** to find missing side lengths and angles in triangles that do not contain a right angle.

Modeling motion at an angle involves the use of the trigonometric ratios. If an object, such as a plane or a boat, is traveling in a direction that is not directly north, south, east, or west, you must break the motion into east-west and north-south components. The east-west component is $x = vt\cos A$, and the north-south component is $y = vt\sin A$, where A is the angle the object makes with the x-axis and v is the **velocity** of the object. If the motion is directed below the x-axis or to the left of the y-axis, then the velocity is negative in either the horizontal or vertical direction, or both. Sometimes the wind or a current is present and influences the motion. If this is the case, the motion of the wind or current also needs to be broken into its x- and y-components and then added to the equations for the object's motion. Parametric equations can also be used to model projectile motion with the equations $x = v_0t\cos A + x_0$ and $y = -16t^2 + v_0t\sin A + y_0$.

EXERCISES

1. Use the parametric equations $x = -3t + 1$ and $y = \frac{2}{t+1}$ to answer each question.
   a. Find the x- and y-coordinates of the points that correspond to the values of $t = 3$, $t = 0$, and $t = -3$. $t = 3$: $x = -8, y = 0.5$; $t = 0$: $x = 1, y = 2$; $t = -3$: $x = 10, y = -1$
   b. Find the y-value that corresponds to an x-value of -7. $y = \frac{6}{11}$
   c. Find the x-value that corresponds to a y-value of 4. $x = \frac{5}{2}$
   d. Sketch the curve for $-3 \le t \le 3$, showing the direction of movement. Trace the graph and explain what happens when $t = -1$.

CHAPTER REVIEW 8

PLANNING

LESSON OUTLINE

One day:

20 min Reviewing

15 min Exercises

10 min Student self-assessment

MATERIALS

- Calculator Note 8H

REVIEWING

Pose this review problem: "Two boats leave a dock at the same time, aiming for different points on the opposite shore of a lake. One boat's motion is modeled by parametric equations $x_1(t) = -\frac{\sqrt{3}}{2}15t$ and $y_1(t) = \frac{15}{2}t$. The other boat's motion is modeled by equations $x_2(t) = \frac{10}{\sqrt{2}}t$ and $y_2(t) = \frac{10}{\sqrt{2}}t$. (Both sets of equations have units of miles and hours.) After 10 minutes, how far apart are the two boats, and at what bearing is the second boat relative to the first?" In solving this problem, you can revisit bearings, parametric equations for motion, simple trigonometric ratios, and the Law of Sines and the Law of Cosines. [From the equations, the first boat's velocity is 15 mi/h on a bearing of 300°. The second boat's velocity is 10 mi/h on a bearing of 45°. You can eliminate the variable t to find the single equation that models each path. When $t = \frac{1}{6}$ h, the boats are $\frac{5}{2}$ and $\frac{5}{3}$ mi from the dock, respectively. The angle between their paths is $180° - 30° - 45°$, or 105°.

Reviewing (continued)

By the Law of Cosines, their distance apart is $\sqrt{\left(\frac{5}{2}\right)^2 + \left(\frac{5}{3}\right)^2 - 2\left(\frac{5}{2}\right)\left(\frac{5}{3}\right)\cos 105°}$, or about 3.3 mi. The measure of the angle between the segments connecting the first boat with the dock and with the second boat, by the Law of Sines, is about 28.8°, or 1.2° south of due east. Therefore the second boat is at a bearing of about 91.2° with respect to the first.]

ASSIGNING HOMEWORK

Exercises 8, 9, and 10 are good group problems.

Helping with the Exercises

Exercise 1d [Ask] "Why does this happen to the graph at $t = -1$?" [The y-value is undefined at that point because the denominator is zero.]

See page 892 for answer to Exercise 1d.

Exercise 2 Students might be helped by considering the raft's initial location to be at the origin.

3a.

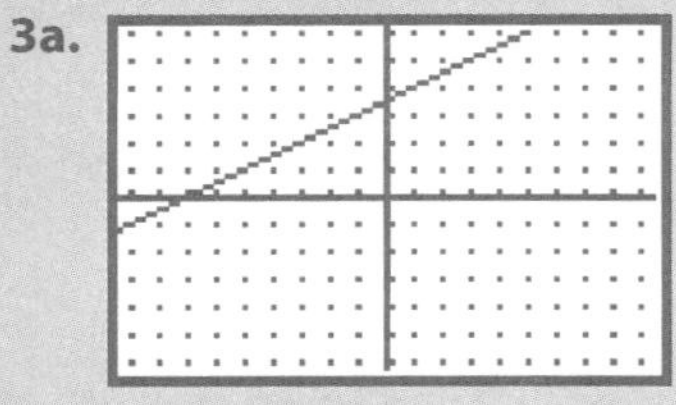

$[-9.4, 9.4, 1, -6.2, 6.2, 1]$

$y = \frac{x+7}{2}$. The graph is the same.

3b.

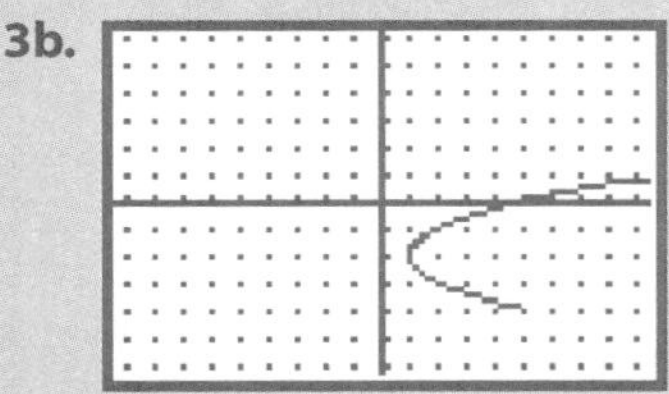

$[-9.4, 9.4, 1, -6.2, 6.2, 1]$

$y = \pm\sqrt{x-1} - 2$. The graph is the same except for the restrictions on t.

3c.

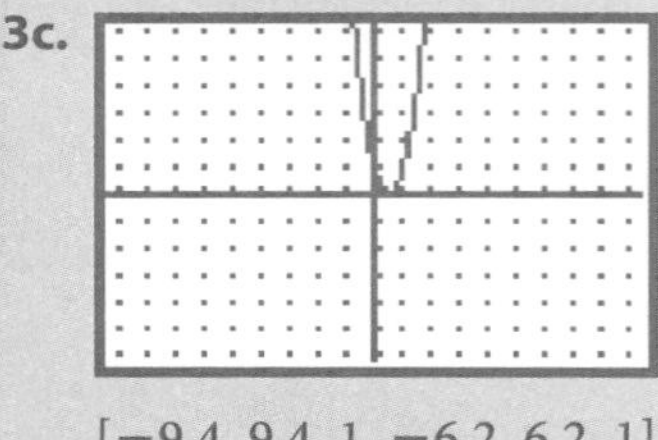

$[-9.4, 9.4, 1, -6.2, 6.2, 1]$

$y = (2x-1)^2$. The graph is the same. The values of t are restricted, but endpoints are not visible within the calculator screen given.

3d.

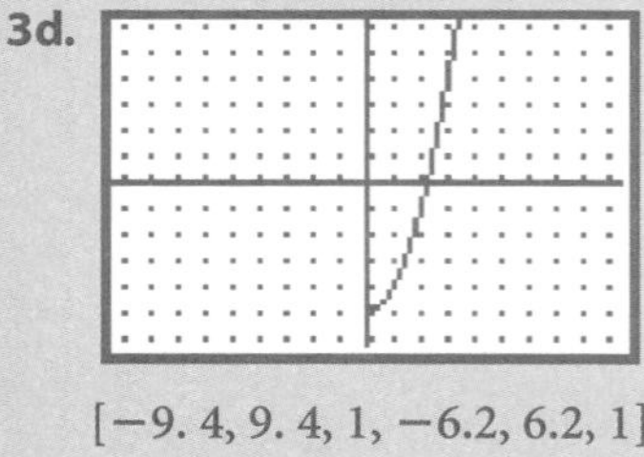

$[-9.4, 9.4, 1, -6.2, 6.2, 1]$

$y = x^2 - 5$. The graph is the same, except the parametric equations will not allow for negative values for x.

2. A raft is being moved by a wind blowing east at 20 m/s and a current flowing south at 30 m/s.

a. What is the raft's position after 8 s relative to its starting position? 160 m east and 240 m south

b. What equations simulate this motion? $x = 20t,\ y = -30t$

3. Graph each pair of parametric equations in a friendly window with factor 2, then eliminate the parameter to get a single equation using only x and y. Graph the resulting equation and describe how it compares with the original graph.

a. $x = 2t - 5$ and $y = t + 1$

b. $x = t^2 + 1$ and $y = t - 2$, $-2 \leq t \leq 6$

c. $x = \dfrac{t+1}{2}$ and $y = t^2$, $-4 \leq t \leq 3$

d. $x = \sqrt{t+2}$ and $y = t - 3$

The Family (1962) by Venezuelan sculptor and painter Marisol Escobar (b 1930) has individual panels that collectively contribute to the whole piece, just as parametric equations combine individual equations to describe one mathematical piece.

4. Write parametric equations that will result in each transformation below for the equations $x = 2t - 5$ and $y = t + 1$.

a. Reflect the curve across the y-axis.

b. Reflect the curve across the x-axis.

c. Translate the curve up 3 units.

d. Translate the curve left 4 units and down 2 units.

5. For each triangle, find the measure of the labeled angle or the length of the labeled side.

a.

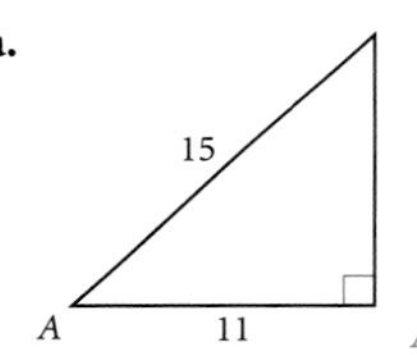

$A \approx 43°$

b.

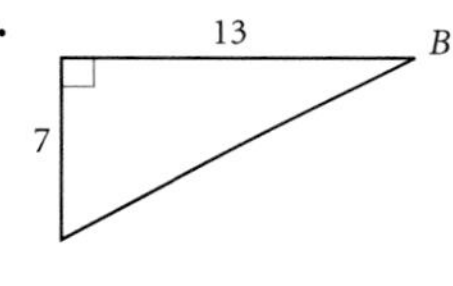

$B \approx 28°$

c.

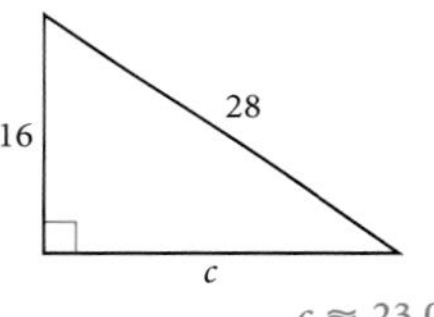

$c \approx 23.0$

d.

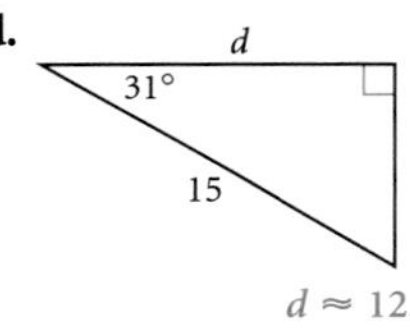

$d \approx 12.9$

e.

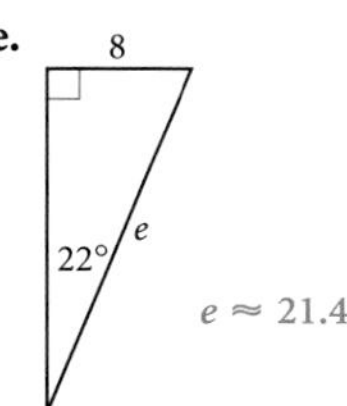

$e \approx 21.4$

f.

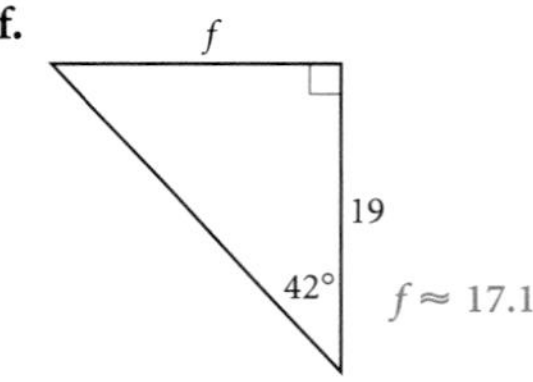

$f \approx 17.1$

6. Sketch a graph of $x = t\cos 28°$ and $y = t\sin 28°$. What is the angle between the graph and the x-axis?

4a. $x = -(2t-5),\ y = t + 1$

4b. $x = 2t - 5,\ y = -(t+1)$

4c. $x = 2t - 5,\ y = t + 4$

4d. $x = 2t - 9,\ y = t - 1$

Exercise 6 If needed, suggest that an appropriate domain for t might be $0 \leq t \leq 6$.

6. 28°

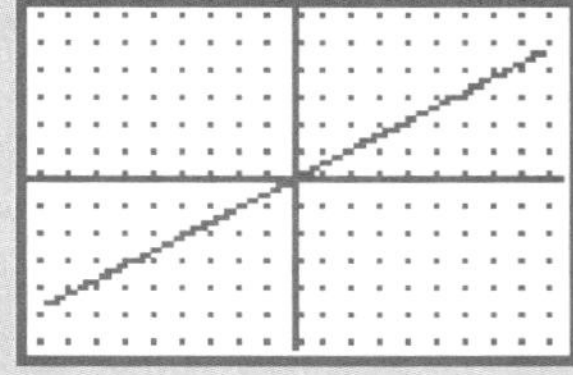

$[-9.4, 9.4, 1, -6.2, 6.2, 1]$

7. A diver runs off a 10 m platform with an initial horizontal velocity of 4 m/s. The edge of the platform is directly above a point 1.5 m from the pool's edge. Simulate her motion on your graphing calculator. How far from the edge of the pool will she hit the water?

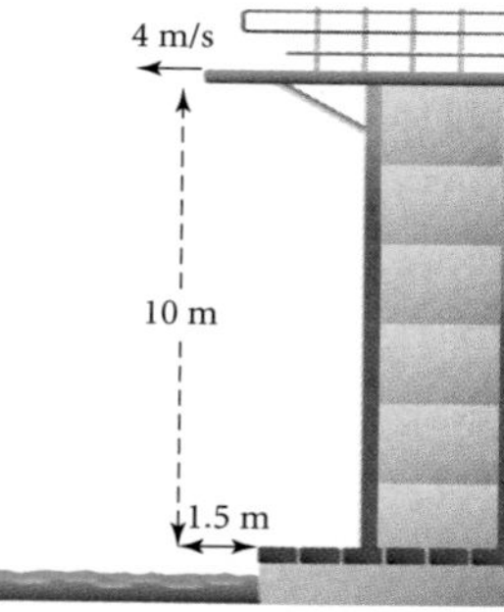

Sports CONNECTION

In competitive diving, a running dive must be at least four steps long. The takeoff phase determines the diver's path through the air. Once in the air, the diver has less than 2 seconds to finish the dive, which should end with the diver's body almost perpendicular to the water's surface.

A diver competes in the women's 10 m platform competition in the 2000 Olympic Games in Sydney, Australia.

8. A duck paddles at a rate of 2.4 ft/s, aiming directly for the opposite bank of a 47 ft wide river. When he lands, he finds himself 28 ft downstream from the point where he started. What is the speed of the current? 1.43 ft/s

9. Aliya sees a coconut 66 ft up in a coconut palm that is 20 ft away from her. She has a slingshot capable of launching a rock at 100 ft/s. If she launches a rock at an angle of 72°, will she hit the coconut? If not, by how much will she miss it? She will miss it by 11.1 ft.

10. APPLICATION A pilot is flying to a destination 700 mi away at a bearing of 105°. The cruising speed of the plane is 500 mi/h, and the wind is blowing between 20 mi/h and 30 mi/h at a bearing of 30°. At what bearing should she aim the plane to compensate for the wind?

11. Use the Law of Sines and the Law of Cosines to find all of the missing side lengths and angle measures.

a.

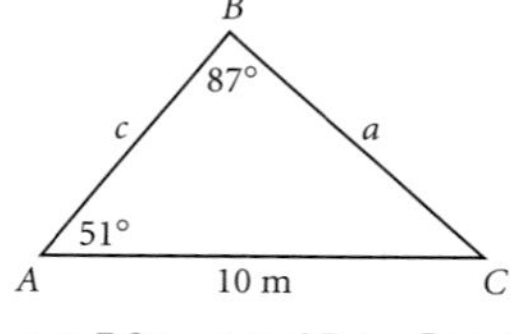

$a \approx 7.8$ m, $c \approx 6.7$ m, $C = 42°$

b.

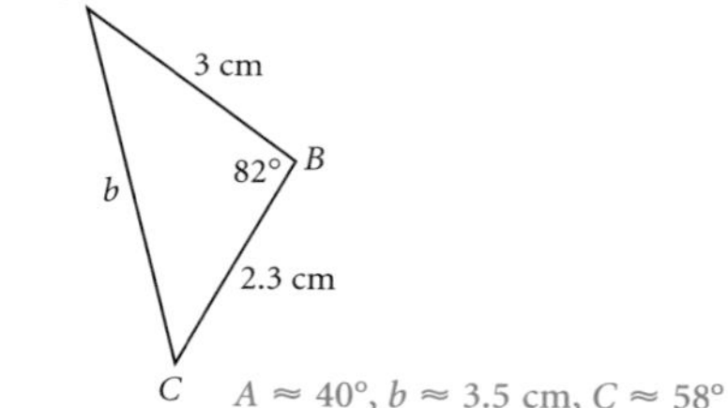

$A \approx 40°$, $b \approx 3.5$ cm, $C \approx 58°$

7. 7.2 m

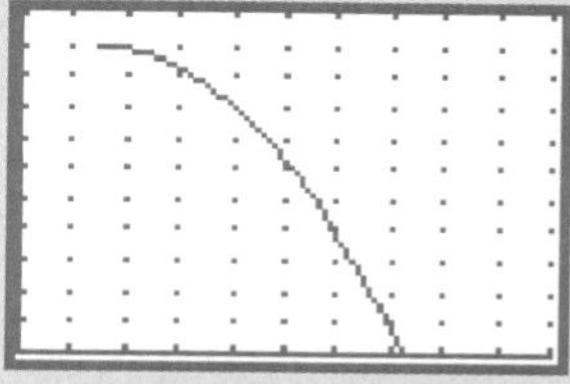

[0, 10, 1, 0, 11, 1]

MAKING THE CONNECTION

Beginning in the 1980s, divers from China have been the dominant force in women's diving competitions. Chinese divers won all but one of the gold medals in Olympic competitions held between 1984 and 1996.

Exercise 9 [ESL] A *slingshot* is a forked stick with a rubber band attached to it that can be pulled back and used to shoot small objects at targets.

10. She should fly on a bearing of 107.77° if the wind averages 25 mi/h.

Take Another Look

1. Along with the sample answers for combinations of constant, linear, and quadratic equations given here, students may include higher-degree polynomial equations, exponential equations, absolute-value equations, or root equations.

If both equations are constant, with $x = c$ and $y = d$, the graph is a single point at (c, d).

If the parametric equation for x is constant and the parametric equation for y is linear, that is, $x = c$ and $y = a + bt$ $(b \neq 0)$, the graph is a vertical line at $x = c$.

If the parametric equation for x is linear and the parametric equation for y is constant, that is, $x = a + bt$ $(b \neq 0)$ and $y = c$, the graph is a horizontal line at $y = c$.

If both equations are linear, that is, $x = a + bt$ and $y = c + dt$ $(bd \neq 0)$, the graph is a line that is neither vertical nor horizontal.

Take Another Look (continued)

If the parametric equation for x is constant and the parametric equation for y is quadratic, that is, $x = d$ and $y = at^2 + bt + c$, the graph is a vertical ray along the line $x = d$, starting at point $\left(d, \frac{-b}{4a} + c\right)$ and heading in the direction of the sign of a.

If the parametric equation for x is quadratic and the parametric equation for y is constant, that is, $x = at^2 + bt + c$ and $y = d$, the graph is a horizontal ray along the line $y = d$, starting at point $\left(\frac{-b}{4a} + c, d\right)$ and heading in the direction of the sign of a.

If the parametric equation for x is linear and the parametric equation for y is quadratic, that is, $x = d + et$ and $y = at^2 + bt + c$, the graph is a vertically oriented parabola.

If the parametric equation for x is quadratic and the parametric equation for y is linear, that is, $x = at^2 + bt + c$ and $y = d + et$, the graph is a horizontally oriented parabola.

If both equations are quadratic, with $x = at^2 + bt + c$ and $y = dt^2 + et + f$, the graph is a parabola that is oriented neither vertically nor horizontally.

Take Another Look (continued)

3. For a supplementary pair, $\angle A$ and $\angle B$, $\sin A = \sin B$, $\cos A = -\cos B$, and $\tan A = -\tan B$.

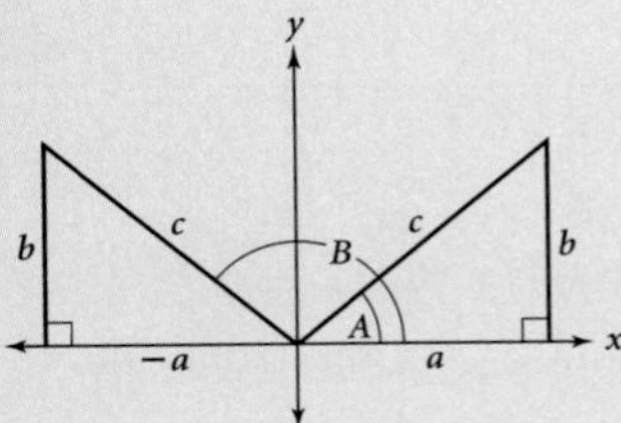

For a complementary pair, $\angle C$ and $\angle D$, $\sin C = \cos D$, $\cos C = \sin D$, and $\tan C = \frac{1}{\tan D}$. (In fact, the word *cosine* means "complement's sine.")

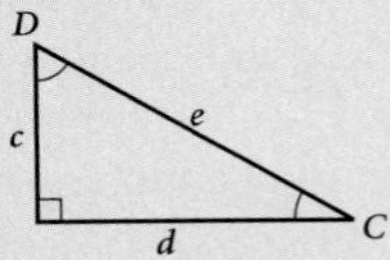

ASSESSING

If students write test questions as part of their self-assessment, you might use some of those items in your assessment. Alternatively, you might ask students to present their problems to their group or to the class during a review session.

FACILITATING SELF-ASSESSMENT

If you know that your students have studied trigonometry in earlier classes, you might use this journal prompt: "You may remember studying trigonometry in previous mathematics classes. How has your understanding of trigonometry changed or improved? Have you developed strategies, either in this class or in previous classes, that help you recall the trigonometric ratios and understand the mathematical concepts?"

Items that ask students to explain the mathematics include Lesson 8.1, Exercise 5; Lesson 8.2, Exercise 6; Lesson 8.3, Exercise 7; Lesson 8.4, Exercise 9; Lesson 8.5, Exercise 5; and Lesson 8.6, Exercise 6.

TAKE ANOTHER LOOK

1. In previous chapters you made connections between equations and their graphs. For example, the graph of an equation in the form $y = a + bx$ is a line, and the graph of an equation in the form $y = ax^2 + bx + c$ is a parabola. Can you make similar connections for parametric equations? What type of graph results if the parametric equation for x is quadratic and the parametric equation for y is linear? If both parametric equations are quadratic? Experiment with different combinations of parametric equations for x and y, and make conjectures about the resulting graphs. See page 485.

2. You can use Boolean expressions to simulate motion that changes at a particular time. (See the project on page 232 for a description of Boolean expressions.) For example, Todd walks 3 mi/h on a bearing of 210° for 2.5 h, then turns and walks due east for 1.75 h. He then returns directly to his starting point. What parametric Boolean equations model this scenario? Include a sketch of your graph, including the window used. [► See **Calculator Note 8H** to see how to graph Boolean expressions. ◄] See below.

3. Select a pair of noncongruent angles that are supplementary (whose measures sum to 180°). Use your calculator to find the sine, cosine, and tangent of each angle measure. What relationships do you notice? Try other supplementary pairs to verify your relationships. Then select a pair of complementary angles (whose measures sum to 90°), and find the sine, cosine, and tangent of each angle measure. What relationships do you notice? Verify these relationships with other complementary pairs. Draw geometric diagrams that prove the relationships you find.

Assessing What You've Learned

WRITE IN YOUR JOURNAL In this chapter you used parametric equations to model several different real-world situations, such as the motion of an airplane traveling on a bearing and the motion of a projectile under the influence of gravity. These two situations are physically different, but you can use parametric equations to model both types of motion. In what ways are the two situations different? Are there any physical similarities between the two situations? How do the resulting parametric equations represent the similarities and differences between the two types of motion?

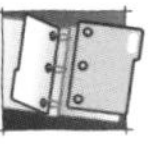

ORGANIZE YOUR NOTEBOOK Make sure your notebook is complete and well organized. Be sure to include all of the definitions and formulas that you have learned in this chapter. You may want to include at least one example of each of the different applications of parametric equations and trigonometry.

WRITE TEST ITEMS Write at least four test items for this chapter. Include items that cover different applications of both parametric equations and trigonometry. You may want to include the use of parametric equations for motion on a bearing and projectile motion, and the use of trigonometry for right triangles and oblique triangles.

2. $x = -3t\cos 60° \ (t \leq 2.5) + (-3.75 + 3(t - 2.5)\cos 0°)\ (t > 2.5)\ (t \leq 4.25) + (1.5 + 3(t - 4.25)\cos 103°)\ (t > 4.25)$

$y = -3t\sin 60° \ (t \leq 2.5) + (-6.495 + 3(t - 2.5)\sin 0°)\ (t > 2.5)(t \leq 4.25) + (-6.495 + 3(t - 4.25)\sin 103°)\ (t > 4.25)$

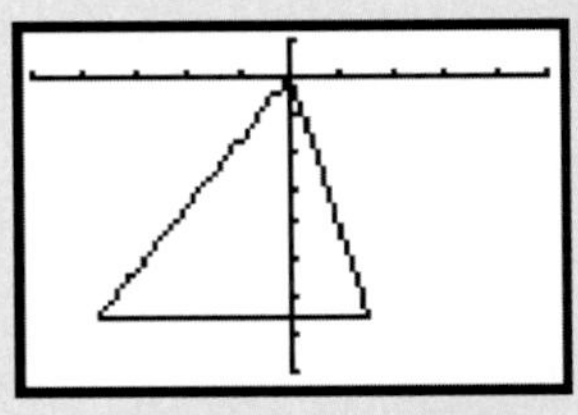

$[-5, 5, 1, -8, 1, 1]$

$0 \leq t \leq 6.47$, t-step 0.05

CHAPTER

9

Conic Sections and Rational Functions

Overview

Students already know many properties of circles, ellipses, and parabolas. This chapter explores these shapes in the context of conic sections. In **Lesson 9.1,** students solve problems involving minimum distances or loci of points. In the next three lessons each of the conic sections is defined as a locus of points. In **Lesson 9.2,** students write equations for circles and ellipses and use them to solve problems. Students learn new vocabulary associated with parabolas in **Lesson 9.3** and see the relationship between the definition and applications. **Lesson 9.4** explores the hyperbola. The first **exploration** asks students to construct the conic sections using geometry software. In **Lesson 9.5,** students explore the general quadratic equation and its relationship to the conic sections. Students rotate conic sections in the second **exploration.** The last three lessons explore rational functions. In **Lesson 9.6,** students explore transformations of the parent function $y = \frac{1}{x}$, a rotated hyperbola. In **Lesson 9.7,** students relate characteristics of the graph of a rational function to the equation. In **Lesson 9.8,** students review factoring as they operate on rational expressions.

The Mathematics

Conic Sections

Conic sections, cuts through a double cone, get their names from Greek words. The word *ellipse* comes from a word meaning "missing," *parabola* from a word meaning "resemblance" or "equivalence," and *hyperbola* from a word meaning "excess." One possible explanation for the terms lies in the equation $y^2 = 2px + kx^2$. If $k < 0$, with k "missing" something, the equation represents an ellipse; if $k = 0$, it represents a parabola; and if $k > 0$, it represents a hyperbola.

If one or two spheres are inscribed in the cone and are tangent to the conic section, each point of tangency is called a *focus.*

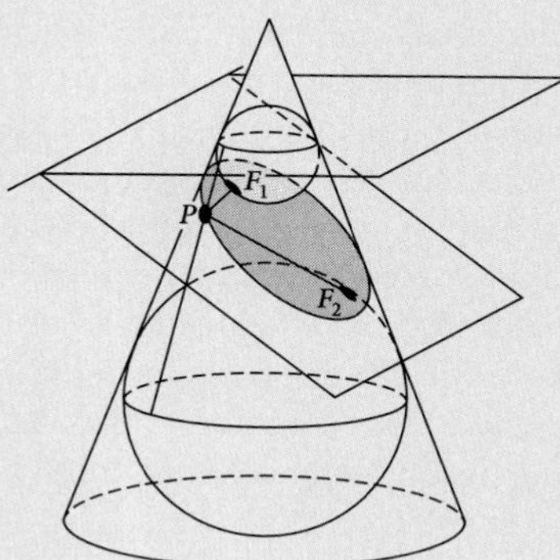

Ellipses and hyperbolas have two foci; parabolas have only one. For any point on an ellipse, the sum of its distances from the two foci is the distance (along the cone) between the circles of tangency and, thus, is constant. For any point on a hyperbola, the difference of its distances from the two foci is this same constant distance. These constants are the basis of the definitions of an ellipse and a hyperbola.

Each inscribed sphere that determines a focus intersects the cone in a circle, which lies in a plane. Each of these planes intersects the plane of the conic section in a line called a *directrix.* One fact not known to the Greeks is that, for any point on a conic section, the ratio of its distance from a focus to its distance from the corresponding directrix depends only on the cone angle and the tilt of the conic section's plane. Therefore this ratio—called the *eccentricity, e,* of the conic section—is constant. For a circle, $e = 0$; for an ellipse, $e < 1$; for a parabola, $e = 1$; and for a hyperbola, $e > 1$. The book defines the parabola in terms of this property: If P is a point on the parabola, then $\frac{\textit{distance from P to focus}}{\textit{distance from P to directrix}} = 1$.

The quadratic equation in two variables, $Ax^2 + Bxy + Cy^2 + Dx + Ey + F = 0$, with nonzero A, B, or C, corresponds to the conic sections. If $B = 0$ but A or C is nonzero, the type of conic section can be determined from the signs of A and C, and the standard form of the equation can be obtained by completing the square. The value of B determines how the axis of the conic section is rotated relative to the horizontal coordinate axis.

Rational Functions

A rational function is a function that can be expressed as a ratio of polynomials, just as a rational number can be expressed as a ratio of integers. If both polynomials are linear and neither is a factor of the other, then the rational function is a transformation of the function $y = \frac{1}{x}$, whose graph is a hyperbola. Division can reveal the nature of that transformation and can also be used to find slant asymptotes. Zeros of only the polynomial in the numerator indicate x-intercepts, zeros of only the polynomial in the denominator indicate vertical asymptotes, and zeros common to both the numerator and the denominator indicate holes or vertical asymptotes in the graph.

Using This Chapter

The exploration in Chapter 8 on the equation of a circle is a prerequisite for the parametric equations of conic sections. Depending on curriculum standards, optional sections include Lesson 9.2, the investigations in Lessons 9.3 and 9.4, the second exploration, and Lesson 9.8.

Resources

Discovering Advanced Algebra Resources

Teaching and Worksheet Masters
Lessons 9.1–9.4, 9.6

Calculator Notes 5D, 9A–C

Sketchpad Demonstrations
Lessons 9.2–9.6
Exploration: Constructing the Conic Sections

Assessment Resources A and B
Quiz 1 (Lessons 9.1, 9.2)
Quiz 2 (Lessons 9.3–9.5)
Quiz 3 (Lessons 9.6–9.8)
Chapter 9 Test
Chapter 9 Constructive Assessment Options
Chapters 7–9 Exam

More Practice Your Skills for Chapter 9

Condensed Lessons for Chapter 9

Other Resources

Exploring Conic Sections with The Geometer's Sketchpad by Daniel Scher.

For complete references to this and other resources see www.keypress.com/DAA.

Materials

- graph paper
- centimeter graph paper
- rulers
- flashlights
- patty paper or tracing paper
- motion sensors
- protractors
- compasses
- dry spaghetti
- small film canisters
- string
- small weights (pennies, beans)
- tape

Pacing Guide

	day 1	day 2	day 3	day 4	day 5	day 6	day 7	day 8	day 9	day 10
standard	9.1	9.2	quiz, 9.3	9.4	9.4	9.5	9.5	quiz, 9.6	9.7	9.8
enriched	9.1	9.2	quiz, 9.3	9.4	9.4	exploration, 9.5	9.5	exploration	quiz, 9.6	9.7, project
block	9.1, 9.2	quiz, 9.3, 9.4	9.4, exploration	9.5, exploration	quiz, 9.6	9.7, project, 9.8	quiz, review, TAL	assessment, review	exam	

	day 11	day 12	day 13	day 14	day 15
standard	quiz, review	assessment	review	exam	
enriched	9.8	quiz, review, TAL	assessment	review	exam

CHAPTER

9 Conic Sections and Rational Functions

Timetable (2000), designed by American architect and sculptor Maya Lin (b 1959), is a rotating circular clock/fountain located at Stanford University in Palo Alto, California. Made of black granite, steel, stone, and water, with the clock rings, motorized discs, and rotating parts submerged, the geometric sculpture gives the time in Pacific standard time, daylight saving time, and Universal time. Maya Lin's message, "Although we tend to think of time as an absolute, it is relative to location," is inscribed on a panel near the fountain.

OBJECTIVES

In this chapter you will

- use the distance formula to find the distance between two points on a plane and to solve distance and rate problems
- learn about conic sections—circles, ellipses, parabolas, and hyperbolas—which are created by intersecting a plane and a cone
- investigate the properties of conic sections
- write the equations of conic sections in different forms
- study rational functions and learn special properties of their graphs
- add, subtract, multiply, and divide rational expressions

CHAPTER 9 OBJECTIVES

- Derive and apply the distance formula
- Introduce conic sections using cones
- Define the circle, ellipse, and hyperbola as loci of points having fixed distance properties relative to a center or to foci
- Define the parabola as a locus of points the same distances from a focus and a directrix
- Derive rectangular and parametric equations of all four conic sections
- Learn to relate the properties, the equation, and the graph of a conic section
- Convert between a general quadratic equation and the standard form of the equation of a conic section
- Apply conic sections and rational functions to solve real-world problems
- Find the graph of a rational function from its equation, and vice versa
- Learn to add, subtract, multiply, and divide rational expressions

Sculptor Maya Lin is best known for designing the Vietnam Veterans Memorial in Washington, D.C. She created *Timetable* primarily to emphasize the need for "unified" time in the age of the Internet. The piece consists of a system of circles with different radii, some of which intersect. One of the circles rotates every minute, one rotates every hour, and one rotates every 12 hours. The whole fountain rotates on an off-center pivot, marking the months as it makes this annual rotation. Unfortunately, the piece does not yet keep correct time. The water, as well as passersby touching it, disturbs its rhythm.

[Ask] "What shape does the fountain appear to be as viewed in this picture?" [ellipse] "What shape would it be if you viewed it from the top?" [circle] "If the pivot of the fountain is off-center, what shape would a single point on the edge of the fountain trace as the circular fountain rotates?" [a circle, because a single point of the fountain is always the same distance from the pivot point] This previews the locus-of-points definition of a circle in Lesson 9.2. **[Ask]** "What shape will a point on one of the smaller turning circles trace as the fountain rotates?"

LESSON

9.1

PLANNING

LESSON OUTLINE

One day:

15 min Investigation

10 min Examples

10 min Sharing

10 min Exercises

MATERIALS

- rulers
- centimeter grid paper or Centimeter Grid Paper (W)
- Bucket Race (T), *optional*
- Oil Rig Rescue (T), *optional*
- Calculator Note 9A, *optional*

TEACHING

In this lesson students see applications of the Pythagorean Theorem, including a derivation of the distance formula for coordinate geometry. If you decide to use the one-step investigation, you will find it on page 489.

Guiding the Investigation

[Ask] "Why not just run 5 meters to the pool, 20 meters along the pool, and then 7 meters up to the finish line?" [This is not the shortest path.]

Step 1 [Language] In a *scale drawing,* all the dimensions are proportional to those in the original situation. On centimeter grid paper, students can use 5 cm, 7 cm, and 20 cm for their scale drawings.

See page 893 for answers to Steps 2–5.

LESSON 9.1

Using the Distance Formula

It is impossible to be a mathematician without being a poet in soul.

SOPHIA KOVALEVSKAYA

Imagine a race in which you carry an empty bucket from the starting line to the edge of a pool, fill the bucket with water, and then carry the bucket to the finish line. Luck, physical fitness, common sense, a calm attitude, and a little mathematics will make a difference in how you perform. Finding the shortest path will help minimize your effort, distance, and time involved. In the investigation you will mathematically analyze this situation.

This illustration of "Jack and Jill" was created by the English illustrator Walter Crane (1845–1915).

Investigation
Bucket Race

You will need

- centimeter graph paper
- a ruler

The starting line of a bucket race is 5 m from one end of a pool, the pool is 20 m long, and the finish line is 7 m from the opposite end of the pool, as shown. In this investigation you will find the shortest path from point A to a point C on the edge of the pool to point B. That is, you will find the value of x, the distance in meters from the end of the pool to point C, such that $AC + CB$ is the shortest path possible.

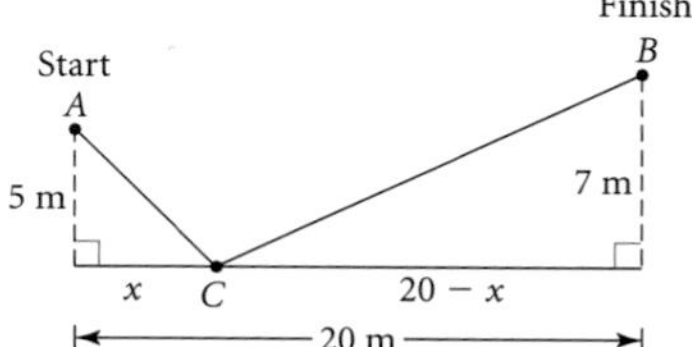

Step 1 Make a scale drawing of the situation on graph paper.

Step 2 Plot several different locations for point C. For each, measure the distance x and find the total length $AC + CB$. Record your data.

Step 3 What is the best location for C such that the length $AC + BC$ is minimized? What is the distance traveled? Is there more than one best location? Describe at least two different methods for finding the best location for C.

Step 4 Make a scale drawing of your solution.

Imagine that the amount of water you empty out at point B is an important factor in winning the race. This means you must move carefully so as not to spill water, and you'll be able to move faster with the empty bucket than you can with the bucket full of water. Assume that you can carry an empty bucket at a rate of 1.2 m/s and that you can carry a full bucket, without spilling, at a rate of 0.4 m/s.

Step 5 Go back to the data collected in Step 2 and find the time needed for each x-value.

Step 2 Distances are measured in centimeters. Students might organize their data in a table with columns for x, AC, CB, and $AC + CB$. Have them leave additional room for another column, which they will use in Step 5.

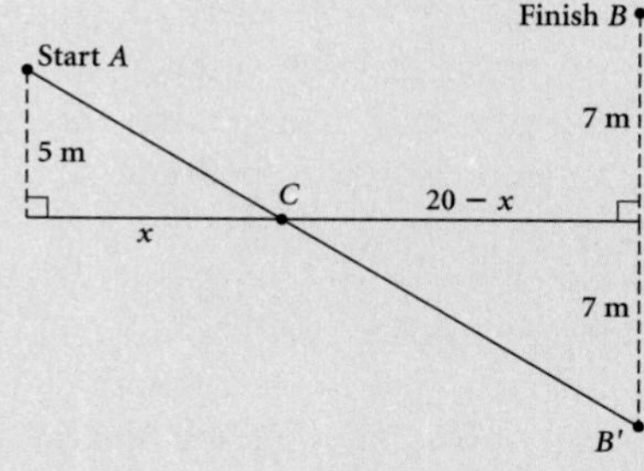

Step 3 Students may have encountered a reflection technique for finding point C in Lesson 4.6, Improving Your Visual Thinking Skills. Have students share ideas so they can learn from one another.

Step 6 Now find the best location for point C so that you minimize the time from point A to the pool edge, then to point B. What is your minimum time? What is the distance traveled? How does this compare to your answer in Step 3? Describe your solution process.

Many of the equations you will study in this chapter are based on finding the distance between two points. Consider the distance, d, between two points with coordinates $(-5, -3)$ and $(9, 6)$. Based on the x- and y-coordinates, the horizontal distance between the points is 14 units and the vertical distance between them is 9 units. The horizontal and vertical components of the distance create a right triangle. By the Pythagorean Theorem, the distance between the two points is $\sqrt{14^2 + 9^2}$, which is $\sqrt{277}$, or approximately 16.64 units. In general, if two points have coordinates (x_1, y_1) and (x_2, y_2), then the Pythagorean Theorem gives

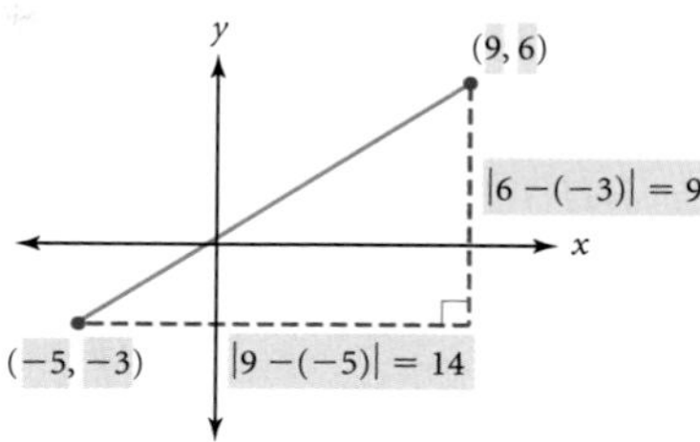

$$(x_2 - x_1)^2 + (y_2 - y_1)^2 = d^2$$

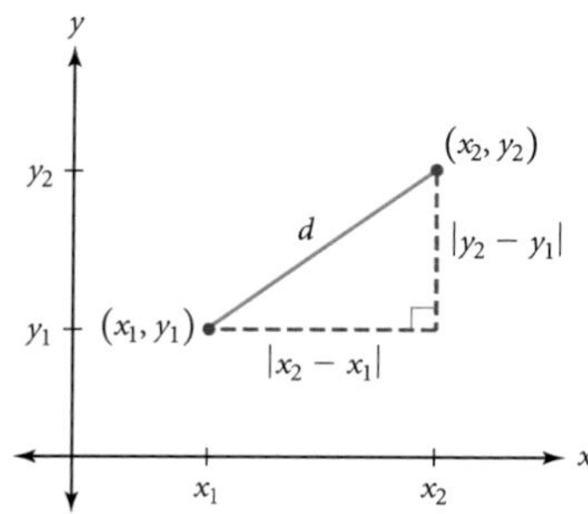

Taking the square root of both sides gives you a formula for distance on a coordinate plane. Because quantities are squared in the formula, two positive numbers are being added, so absolute value signs are no longer necessary.

Distance Formula

The distance, d, between two points on a coordinate plane, $P_1(x_1, y_1)$ and $P_2(x_2, y_2)$, is given by the formula

$$d = \sqrt{(x_2 - x_1)^2 + (y_2 - y_1)^2}$$

In Chapter 4, you used the Pythagorean Theorem to find the equation of a circle centered at the origin. You can also use the distance formula. If (x, y) is any point located on the circumference of a circle, its distance from the center, $(0, 0)$, is $\sqrt{(x - 0)^2 + (y - 0)^2}$. Because the distance from the center of the circle is defined as the radius, r, you get $r = \sqrt{x^2 + y^2}$, or $r^2 = x^2 + y^2$.

Step 6 Students might use tables, or they might have other creative ideas. To help students move away from measuring and toward using the distance formula, you could display a geometric proof of the Pythagorean Theorem.

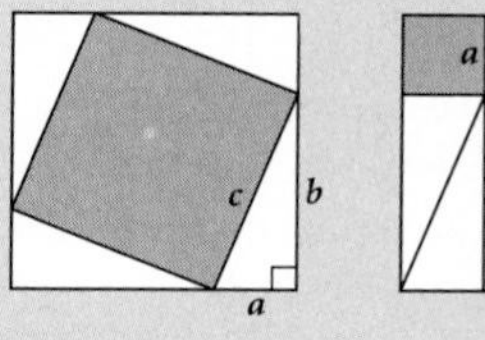

$c^2 = a^2 + b^2$

Step 6 Using the table of data from Step 5, the best location for point C is 18 m from the end of the pool. The minimum time is approximately 33.77 s. Minimizing the equation $y = \frac{\sqrt{x^2 + 5^2}}{1.2} + \frac{\sqrt{(20 - x)^2 + 7^2}}{0.4}$, where y represents the time in seconds, the best location for point C is approximately 17.63 m. The minimum time by this method is approximately 33.75 s. The distance is approximately 25.72 m. This distance is longer, but the second leg, CB, is shorter.

One Step

Pose this problem: "A kicked football travels along a path given by the equation $y = -0.005x^2 + x$. What function of x describes the distance of the ball from the goalposts, located at the point (200, 10)?" If a group remains stuck for some time, suggest that they draw a right triangle. If necessary, mention the Pythagorean Theorem. Encourage testing of ideas with calculator graphs and tables. (Students need not expand binomials to enter functions into their calculators. They might enter $Y_1 = -0.005x^2 + x$ and $Y_2 = \sqrt{(200 - x)^2 + (10 - Y_1)^2}$.) During Sharing, have them generalize their approach to the distance formula.

NCTM STANDARDS

CONTENT		PROCESS	
	Number	✓	Problem Solving
✓	Algebra		Reasoning
✓	Geometry	✓	Communication
✓	Measurement	✓	Connections
✓	Data/Probability	✓	Representation

LESSON OBJECTIVES

- Derive the distance formula from the Pythagorean Theorem
- Apply the distance formula to problems involving a locus of points

► ***EXAMPLE A***

[Language] *Loci* ['lō-sī] is the plural of *locus*. *Locuses* is not generally accepted as a plural form of *locus*. The phrase *locus of points* means "a collection of points." *Equidistant* means "equally distant."

An alternative approach to the calculation can provide a review of factoring a difference of squares:

$$(x-1)^2+(y-3)^2 = (x-5)^2+(y-6)^2$$

$$(x-1)^2-(x-5)^2 = (y-6)^2-(y-3)^2$$

$$(x-1+x-5)(x-1-x+5) = (y-6+y-3)(y-6-y+3)$$

$$(2x-6)(4)=(2y-9)(-3)$$

$$8x-24=-6y+27$$

$$8x+6y=51$$

If you demonstrate this approach, ask students to compare and contrast it with the one in the book. **[Ask]** "What are the strengths of each approach?" [The approach in the book is shorter, but this approach avoids squaring four binomials.]

To induce critical thinking, **[Ask]** "Is the locus of points really the perpendicular bisector?" A discussion of this question can review the midpoint formula, the slope formula, the slope property of perpendicular lines, and the point-slope equation of a line.

► ***EXAMPLE B***

You might use the Oil Rig Rescue transparency as you talk about this example.

Ask why the rescuers don't travel straight from the oil rig to the hospital. [The ambulance travels faster than the boat. If they traveled directly by boat, they'd go a distance of about 99.14 mi, taking 4.3 h. The path found in part b is longer but takes only 3 h.]

The distance formula also enables you to write equations that represent other distance situations. One use is to write an equation that describes a set of points that all meet a certain condition. A set of points that fit a given condition is called a **locus.** For example, the locus of points that are 1 unit from the point (0, 0) is the circle with the equation $x^2 + y^2 = 1$. In this chapter you will explore equations describing a variety of different loci (the plural of locus).

EXAMPLE A

Find the equation of the locus of points that are equidistant from the points (1, 3) and (5, 6).

► ***Solution***

Let d_1 represent the distance between (1, 3) and any point, (x, y), on the locus. By the distance formula,

$$d_1=\sqrt{(x-1)^2+(y-3)^2}$$

Let d_2 represent the distance between (5, 6) and the same point on the locus, so

$$d_2=\sqrt{(x-5)^2+(y-6)^2}$$

The locus of points contains all points whose coordinates satisfy the equation $d_1 = d_2$, or

$$\sqrt{(x-1)^2+(y-3)^2}=\sqrt{(x-5)^2+(y-6)^2}$$

Use algebra to transform this equation into something more familiar.

$\sqrt{(x-1)^2+(y-3)^2}=\sqrt{(x-5)^2+(y-6)^2}$	Original equation.
$(x-1)^2+(y-3)^2=(x-5)^2+(y-6)^2$	Square both sides.
$x^2-2x+1+y^2-6y+9=x^2-10x+25+y^2-12y+36$	Expand the binomials.
$-2x+1-6y+9=-10x+25-12y+36$	Subtract x^2 and y^2 from both sides.
$8x+6y=51$	Rewrite in the form $ax + by = c$ by moving variables to the left side and constants to the right.

The locus is the line with the equation $8x + 6y = 51$, or $y=-\frac{8}{6}x+\frac{51}{6}$. You may recognize this locus as the perpendicular bisector of the segment joining the two points.

Just as the Pythagorean Theorem and the distance formula are useful for finding the equation of a locus of points, they are also helpful for solving real-world problems.

EXAMPLE B

An injured worker must be rushed from an oil rig 15 mi offshore to a hospital in the nearest town 98 mi down the coast from the oil rig.

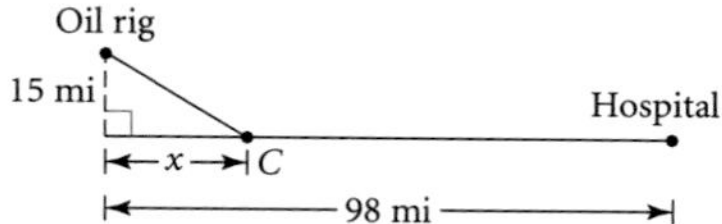

a. Let x represent the distance in miles from the point on the shore closest to the oil rig and another point, C, on the shore.

[Ask] "What's the minimum time to get the injured worker to the hospital?" Students can trace the graph and zoom in on the minimum. Alternatively, you can refer students to Calculator Note 9A to find intersection points and minimum points without tracing.

SHARING IDEAS

Students might use the Bucket Race transparency as they present their ideas. Find out whether students have seen the distance formula before. They may have encountered it in algebra or geometry. They saw an application of the same ideas in Chapter 4 when they applied the Pythagorean Theorem to derive the equation of a circle.

[Ask] "Why does the distance formula subtract the coordinates of P_1 from those of P_2 instead of the other way around?" [The two approaches are equivalent, because the square will be positive either way.] As students discuss this question, be especially careful to watch their faces and body language and respond appropriately.

How far does the injured worker travel, in terms of x, if a boat takes him to C and then an ambulance takes him to the hospital?

b. Assume the boat travels at an average rate of 23 mi/h and the ambulance travels at an average rate of 70 mi/h. What value of x makes the trip 3 h?

► ***Solution***

Use the distance formula, $d = \sqrt{(x_2 - x_1)^2 + (y_2 - y_1)^2}$.

a. The boat must travel $\sqrt{15^2 + x^2}$, and the ambulance must travel $98 - x$. The total distance in miles is $\sqrt{15^2 + x^2} + 98 - x$.

b. Distance equals rate times time, or $d = rt$. Solving for time, $t = \frac{d}{r}$. So the boat's time is $\frac{\sqrt{15^2 + x^2}}{23}$, and the ambulance's time is $\frac{98 - x}{70}$. The total time in hours, y, is represented by

$$y = \frac{\sqrt{15^2 + x^2}}{23} + \frac{98 - x}{70}$$

One way to find the value of x that gives a trip of 3 h is to graph the total time equation and $y = 3$, and trace to approximate the intersection. The graphs intersect when x is approximately 51.6. For the trip to be 3 h, the boat and the ambulance should meet at the point on the shore 51.6 mi from the point closest to the oil rig.

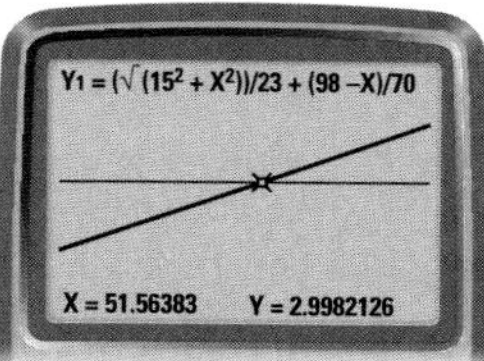

[38, 63, 10, 2.3, 3.6, 1]

History CONNECTION

In 1790, the U.S. Coast Guard was formed to prevent smuggling and maintain customs laws. Combined with the Life Saving Service in 1915, it now oversees rescue missions, environmental protection, navigation, safety during weather hazards, port security, boat safety, and oil tanker transfers. The U.S. Coast Guard has both military and volunteer divisions.

U.S. Coast Guard ship *Acushnet*

EXERCISES

You will need

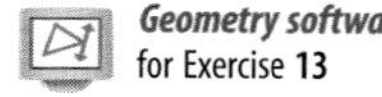

Geometry software for Exercise 13

Practice Your Skills

1. Find the distance between each pair of points.

a. (2, 5) and (8, 13) 10 units

b. (0, 3) and (5, 10) $\sqrt{74}$ units

c. (−4, 6) and (−2, −3) $\sqrt{85}$ units

d. (3, d) and (−6, 3d) $\sqrt{81 + 4d^2}$ units

2. The distance between the points (2, 7) and (5, y) is 5 units. Find the possible value(s) of y. $y = 11$ or $y = 3$

Assessing Progress

Check students' skills at organizing data into tables, measuring, and applying the Pythagorean Theorem.

Closing the Lesson

Restate the main idea of this lesson: The Pythagorean Theorem can be applied in many ways, including deriving the **distance formula,** $d = \sqrt{(x_2 - x_1)^2 + (y_2 - y_1)^2}$.

BUILDING UNDERSTANDING

Students can use geometry software to sketch many of these exercises.

ASSIGNING HOMEWORK

Essential	1–5
Performance assessment	6–13
Portfolio	8, 10
Journal	10
Group	6, 7, 12
Review	14–19

MATERIALS

- graph paper, *optional*

► Helping with the Exercises

If you skipped the first part of Chapter 8 (parametric equations), do not assign Exercise 10d.

Exercise 1d The distance will be in terms of d.

Exercise 2 Students may be tempted to guess and check with integer values of y. Although this approach shows an understanding of the question, encourage use of the distance formula to express other values of y.

Exercises 4, 5 If students have difficulty visualizing these triangles, you might suggest that they sketch a graph for each.

Exercise 5 Students can express the exact perimeter as a sum of radicals $(7\sqrt{2} + 5 + \sqrt{109})$, or they might approximate the perimeter with a decimal.

Exercise 6 You might have students make conjectures from sketches before they find the equation. **[Alert]** Students might believe that this locus will be a straight line if they inappropriately generalize from Example A. You might suggest that they plot a few points that meet the criteria until they see the circular pattern.

Exercise 7 Ask students to make an accurate sketch of this scenario, perhaps using geometry software. Students can more easily see that this is a 30°-60°-90° triangle if the drawing is to scale.

7. $\frac{6-\sqrt{3}}{2} < y < \frac{6+\sqrt{3}}{2}$, or approximately between the points (2.5, 2.134) and (2.5, 3.866)

8a. in miles, $\sqrt{x^2+4}$ through the field and $3 - x$ on the road

8b. in hours, $\frac{\sqrt{x^2+4}}{9}$ through the field and $\frac{3-x}{22}$ on the road

Exercise 8c Students can trace a calculator graph or use the minimum function on a calculator (Calculator Note 9A).

8c. When x is approximately 0.897 mi, Josh gets home in approximately 0.339 h, a little over 20 min.

9a. $y = \sqrt{10^2 + x^2} + \sqrt{(20-x)^2 + 13^2}$

Exercise 9b Encourage students to study the picture, not their equation.

9b. domain: $0 \le x \le 20$; range: $30 < y < 36$

3. The distance between the points $(-1, 5)$ and $(x, -2)$ is 47. Find the possible value(s) of x. $x = -1 \pm \sqrt{2160}$ or $x = -1 \pm 12\sqrt{15}$

4. Which side is longest in the triangle with vertices $A(1, 2)$, $B(3, -1)$, and $C(5, 3)$? $\overline{BC}$

5. Find the perimeter of the triangle with vertices $A(8, -2)$, $B(1, 5)$, and $C(4, -5)$. approximately 25.34 units

Reason and Apply

6. Find the equation of the locus of points that are twice as far from the point (2, 0) as they are from (5, 0). $x^2 - 12x + y^2 = -32$ or $y = \pm\sqrt{-x^2 + 12x - 32}$

7. If you are too close to a radio tower, you will be unable to pick up its signal. Let the center of a town be represented by the origin of a coordinate plane. Suppose a radio tower is located 2 mi east and 3 mi north of the center of town, or at the point (2, 3). A highway runs north-south 2.5 mi east of the center of town, along the line $x = 2.5$. Where on the highway will you be less than 1 mi from the tower and therefore unable to pick up the signal?

8. Josh is riding his mountain bike when he realizes that he needs to get home quickly for dinner. He is 2 mi from the road, and home is 3 mi down that road. He can ride 9 mi/h through the field separating him from the road and can ride 22 mi/h on the road.

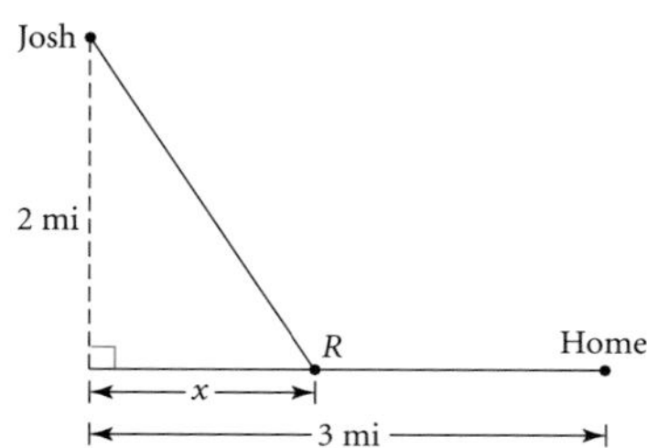

a. If Josh rides through the field to a point R on the road, and then home along the road, how far will he ride through the field? How far on the road? Let x represent the distance in miles between point R and the point on the road that is closest to his current location.

b. How much time will Josh spend riding through the field? How much time on the road?

c. What value of x gets Josh home the fastest? What is the minimum time?

9. A 10 m pole and a 13 m pole are 20 m apart at their bases. A wire connects the top of each pole with a point on the ground between them.

a. Let y represent the total length of the wire. Write an equation that relates x and y.

b. What domain and range make sense in this situation?

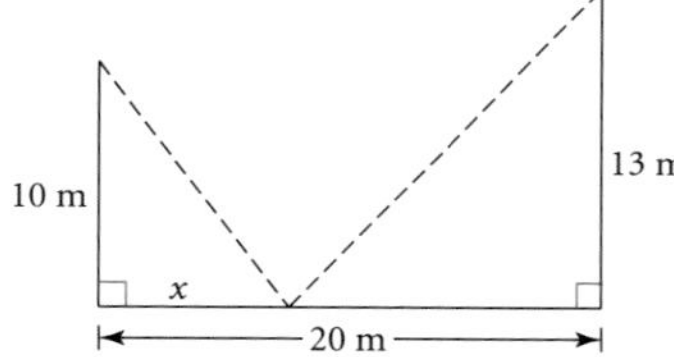

c. Where should the wire be fastened to the ground so that the length of wire is minimized? What is the minimum length?

This cable-stay bridge, the Fred Hartman Bridge, connects Baytown, Texas, and La Porte, Texas. Taut cables stretch from the tops of two towers to support the roadway. For more information on cable-stay bridges, see the links at www.keymath.com/DAA .

10. A 24 ft ladder is placed upright against a wall. Then the top of the ladder slides down the wall while the foot of the ladder is pulled outward along the ground at a steady rate of 2 ft/s.

24 ft

2 ft/s

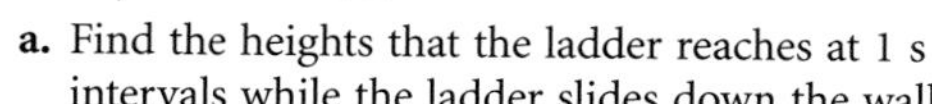

a. Find the heights that the ladder reaches at 1 s intervals while the ladder slides down the wall.

b. How long will it take before the ladder is lying on the ground? 12 s

c. Does the top of the ladder also slide down the wall at a steady rate of 2 ft/s? Explain your reasoning.

d. Write parametric equations that model the distance in feet of the foot of the ladder from the wall, x, and the height in feet that the top of the ladder reaches, y. Let t represent time in seconds.

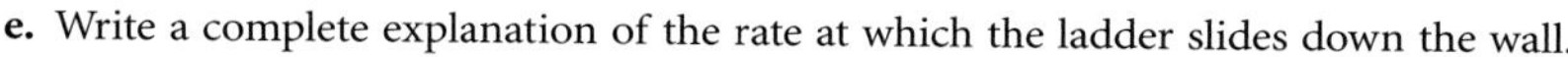

e. Write a complete explanation of the rate at which the ladder slides down the wall.

11. Let d represent the distance between the point $(5, -3)$ and any point, (x, y), on the parabola $y = 0.5x^2 + 1$.

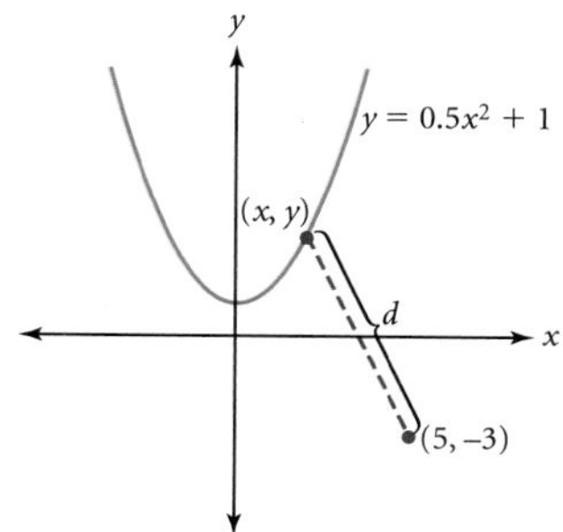

a. Write an equation for d in terms of x.

b. What is the minimum distance? What are the coordinates of the point on the parabola that is closest to the point $(5, -3)$?

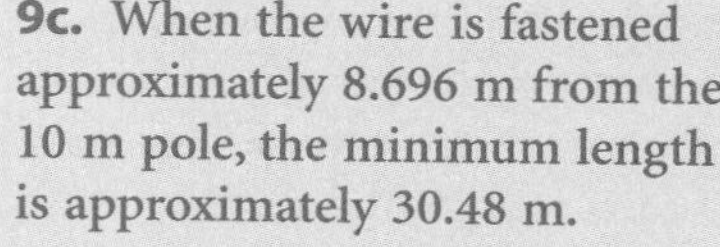

9c. When the wire is fastened approximately 8.696 m from the 10 m pole, the minimum length is approximately 30.48 m.

Exercise 10 Urge students to conjecture before they calculate.

10a.

Time (s)	Height (ft)
0	24
1	23.92
2	23.66
3	23.24
4	22.63
5	21.82
6	20.78
7	19.49
8	17.89
9	15.87
10	13.27
11	9.59
12	0

10c. No, the distance the ladder slides down increases during each second.

10d. $x = 2t$, $y = \sqrt{24^2 - (2t)^2}$

10e. Answers should include a statement that the rate at which the ladder is sliding down the wall increases as the ladder is pulled out.

Exercise 11 To use the distance formula, students will consider the point (x, y) on the curve as $(x, 0.5x^2 + 1)$. You can thus check their understanding that an equation of a curve is a relationship that is satisfied by coordinates of exactly those points on the curve.

11a. $d = \sqrt{(5 - x)^2 + \left(0.5x^2 + 4\right)^2}$

11b. approximately 6.02 units; approximately (0.92, 1.42)

Exercise 12a The solution is the intersection of the perpendicular bisectors of the triangle's sides. Students might recall from geometry that this point is called the *circumcenter.*

12b. The city councils couldn't build the recreation center equidistant from the towns if they are collinear because the perpendicular bisectors of $\overline{AB}$, $\overline{BC}$, and $\overline{AC}$ would have the same slope, making them parallel. There would be no intersection.

MAKING THE CONNECTION

Voronoi diagrams are named for Russian mathematician Georgy Fedoseevuch Voronoy (1868–1908). Though he did not develop the diagrams, he was the first to study them extensively and to apply their properties. As a professor in the Department of Pure Mathematics at Poland's University of Warsaw, Voronoy made important contributions to arithmetic theory of quadratic forms and theories of asymptotic functions.

Exercise 13 The graph given applies to all the subparts. With Sketchpad, 13b requires two steps: First you construct the midpoint of each segment; then you construct a line through the midpoint perpendicular to the segment. 13d explores a geometric property of the circumcenter.

13b. All three perpendicular bisectors intersect at the same point. No, you could find the intersection by constructing only two perpendicular bisectors.

13c. Approximately (6.17, 5.50); this should agree with the answer to 12a.

13d. Regardless of which point is chosen, the circle passes through *A*, *B*, and *C*. Because the radius of the circle is constant, the distance from the recreation center to all three towns is the same.

12. **APPLICATION** The city councils of three neighboring towns—Ashton, Bradburg, and Carlville—decide to pool their resources and build a recreation center. To be fair, they decide to locate the recreation center equidistant from all three towns.

a. When a coordinate plane is placed on a map of the towns, Ashton is at (0, 4), Bradburg is at (3, 0), and Carlville is at (12, 8). At what point on the map should the recreation center be located? approximately (6.17, 5.50)

b. If the three towns were collinear (along a line), could the recreation center be located equidistant from all three towns? Explain your reasoning.

c. What other factors might the three city councils consider while making their decision as to where to locate the recreation center? Answers will vary but could include the population of each town or the arrangement of roads between the towns.

Career CONNECTION

A Voronoi diagram shows regions formed by a set of points such that any point inside one of the regions is closer to that region's site than to any other site. Voronoi diagrams for two and three sites are shown below. Marketing analysts use Voronoi diagrams as well as demographic data, topological features, and traffic patterns to place stores and restaurants strategically.

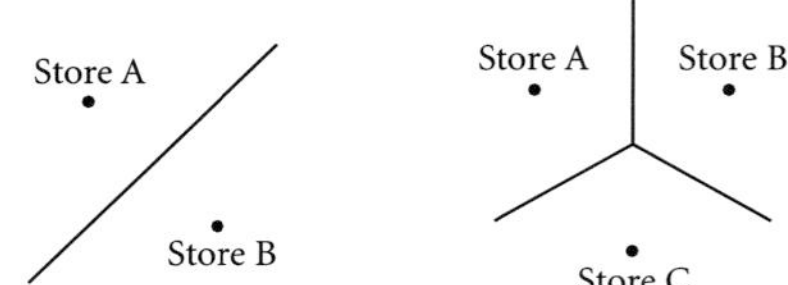

Boundary functions, by Scott Snibbe, is an interactive art piece that divides space into a Voronoi diagram as people move on a section of floor. This piece is a commentary on personal space and the separation of people.

13. ***Technology*** Follow these steps to solve Exercise 12a with geometry software.

a. Open a new sketch. Define a coordinate system and plot three points, *A*, *B*, and *C*, that represent the locations of Ashton, Bradburg, and Carlville.

b. Connect the three points with line segments. Construct the perpendicular bisector of each segment. What happens with the perpendicular bisectors? Did you really need to construct all three bisectors?

c. Locate the intersection of the perpendicular bisectors. Do the coordinates of the intersection agree with your answer to Exercise 12a?

d. Construct a circle using the intersection of the perpendicular bisectors as the center and *A*, or *B*, or *C* as a point on the circle. Describe what happens. How does this confirm that the recreation center is equidistant from all three towns?

Review

7.3 **14.** Complete the square in each equation such that the left side represents a perfect square or a sum of perfect squares.

a. $x^2 + 6x = 5$ **b.** $y^2 - 4y = -1$ **c.** $x^2 + 6x + y^2 - 4y = 4$

13a–d.

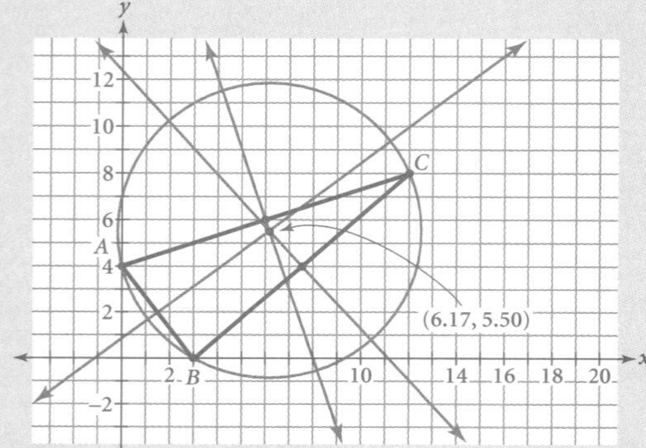

14a. $(x + 3)^2 = 14$

14b. $(y - 2)^2 = 3$

14c. $(x + 3)^2 + (y - 2)^2 = 17$

15. Triangle ABC has vertices $A(8, -2)$, $B(1, 5)$, and $C(4, -5)$.

a. Find the midpoint of each side.

b. Write the equations of the three medians of the triangle. (A median of a triangle is a segment connecting one vertex to the midpoint of the opposite side.)

c. Locate the point where the medians meet.

7.3 16. Give the domain and range of the function $f(x) = x^2 + 6x + 7$. domain: all real numbers; range: $y \geq -2$

8.7 17. A ship leaves port and travels on a bearing of 205° for 2.5 h at 8 knots, and then on a bearing of 150° for 3 h at 10 knots. How far is the ship from its port? (A knot is equivalent to 1 nautical mile per hour.) approximately 44.6 nautical mi

History CONNECTION

Any cross-section of Earth is close to a circle, so it can be divided into 360 degrees. Each degree can be divided into 60 minutes. The length of 1 minute of Earth's surface is called a nautical mile. However, Earth is not a perfect sphere, so the length of a nautical mile could vary depending on where you are on Earth's surface. Since 1959, all countries have agreed to define a nautical mile as 1.852 km. A knot is defined as a speed of 1 nautical mile per hour.

In the 1500s, ships would trail ropes with knots tied every 47 ft 3 in. The crew would measure the number of knots that were pulled into the water as a 28 s hourglass emptied. Counting the number of knots gave them their speed, in nautical miles per hour.

A print of an early view of New York Harbor

18. A sealed 10 cm tall cone resting on its base is filled to half its height with liquid. It is then turned upside down. To what height, to the nearest hundredth of a centimeter, does the liquid reach? 9.56 cm

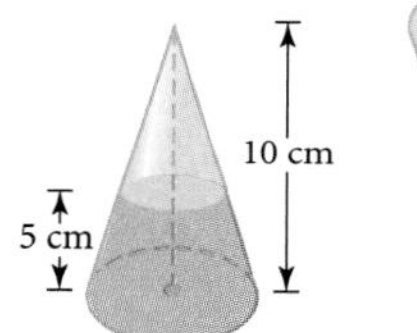

19. Find w and x. $w = 74°$, $x = 50°$

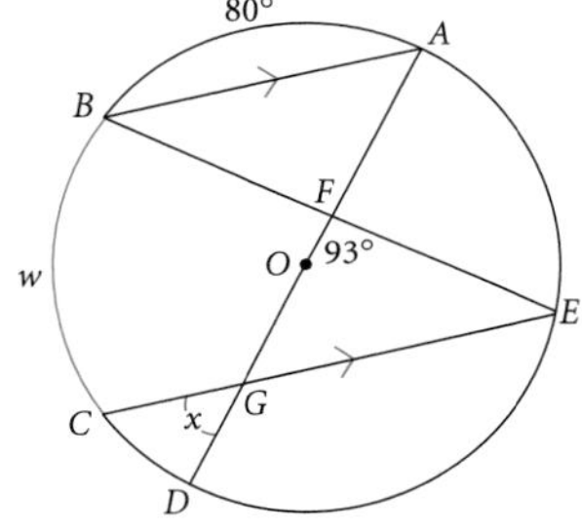

Exercise 15 Students could use geometry software for this exercise. You might want to review from geometry that the intersection of the medians is called the *centroid.*

15a. midpoint of $\overline{AB}$: (4.5, 1.5); midpoint of $\overline{BC}$: (2.5, 0); midpoint of $\overline{AC}$: (6, −3.5)

15b. median from A to $\overline{BC}$: $y = -0.\overline{36}x + 0.\overline{90}$ or $y = -\frac{4}{11}x + \frac{10}{11}$; median from B to $\overline{AC}$: $y = -1.7x + 6.7$; median from C to $\overline{AB}$: $y = 13x - 57$

15c. $(4.\overline{3}, -0.\overline{6})$ or $\left(4\frac{1}{3}, -\frac{2}{3}\right)$

Exercise 17 This exercise requires applying the Law of Cosines.

Exercise 18 This exercise reviews the volume of a cone. Remind students to justify their answers, so they don't just stop with the intuitive answer "half." In fact, they may find the result very counterintuitive. Students might solve the problem in several different ways. If the linear dimensions of a solid are multiplied by k, the volume is multiplied by k^3. The volume of the top (empty) cone inside the original is therefore $\frac{1}{8}$ of the original, so the frustrum below it has $\frac{7}{8}$ of the volume of the original cone. When the cone is turned over, $\frac{7}{8}$ of its volume is taken up by a cone having $\sqrt[3]{\frac{7}{8}}$ or approximately 0.956 of its height.

LESSON

9.2

PLANNING

LESSON OUTLINE

One day:

15 min Examples

15 min Investigation

10 min Sharing

5 min Exercises

MATERIALS

- graph paper
- flashlights
- a relatively dark classroom
- ring stands and clamps, *optional*
- Ellipse in a Cone (W) for One Step
- Definitions of Circle and Ellipse (T), *optional*
- Sketchpad demonstration Definitions of Circle and Ellipse, *optional*

TEACHING

This lesson extends students' understanding of circles and ellipses by relating them to the cone, to parametric equations, to the distance formula, and (for ellipses) to foci. You can skip the parametric equations if you wish. If possible, have one or more cones available for students to handle. **[Language]** A *planar curve* is a curve that can be entirely contained in a plane. You might **[Ask]** "What is the locus of points equidistant from a point in three dimensions?"

One Step

Remind students that they saw in Chapter 4 how to make an ellipse by stretching a unit circle. Hand out the Ellipse in a Cone worksheet and ask students to see what they can figure out about the sum of the distances, $PF_1 + PF_2$. As needed, help students recall from geometry that all tangent segments from one external point to a circle have the same length $(PF_1 = PT_1)$. Eventually students will see that the sum of the distances is the distance between the two spheres' circles of tangency along the edge of the cone. During Sharing, define *focus* and *foci* ['fō-sī], state the constant-sum definition of the ellipse, derive the parametric equations of an ellipse by thinking of it as a stretched circle, and define *eccentricity.*

LESSON OBJECTIVES

- Introduce the conic sections and vocabulary associated with the circle and the ellipse
- Write the equations of a circle and of an ellipse, both centered at point (h, k), in standard and parametric form
- Solve problems involving ellipses (such as orbits) and circles (such as gears)
- Find the equation of an ellipse that models a given set of data

LESSON 9.2

Circles and Ellipses

Before you can be eccentric you must know where the circle is.

ELLEN TERRY

In the next few lessons, you will learn about circles, ellipses, parabolas, and hyperbolas. The orbital paths of the planets around the Sun are not exactly circular. These paths are examples of an important mathematical curve—the ellipse. The curved path of a stream of water from a water fountain, the path of a football kicked into the air, and the pattern of cables hanging between the towers of the Golden Gate Bridge are all examples of parabolas. The design of nuclear cooling towers, transmission gears, and the long-range navigational system known as LORAN all depend on hyperbolas. These curves all belong to a family of planar mathematical curves.

These curves—the circle, the ellipse, the parabola, and the hyperbola—are called **conic sections** because each can be created by slicing a double cone.

Sonia Delaunay's (1885–1979) oil-on-canvas painting, *Rhythm and Colors* (1939), contains many circles.

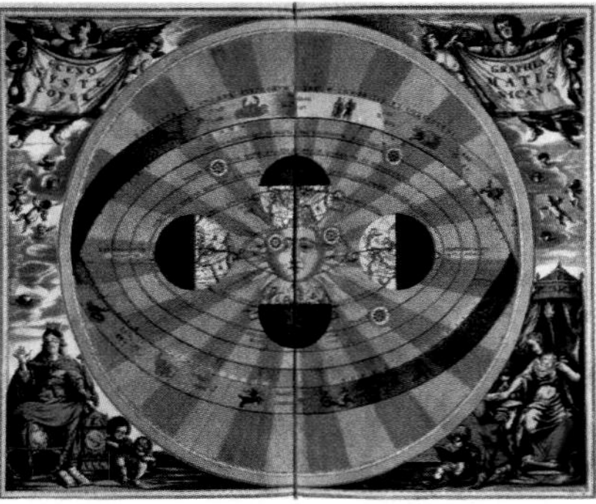

Dutch-German mathematician and cosmographer Andreas Cellarius (ca. 1595–1665) showed elliptical orbits in this celestial atlas titled *Harmonia Macrocosmica* (1660).

The Swann Memorial Fountain at Logan Circle in Philadelphia, Pennsylvania, was designed by American sculptor Alexander Stirling Calder (1898–1976). The jets of water form parabolas.

The McDonnell Planetarium, built in 1963 in St. Louis, Missouri, is a **hyperboloid,** a three-dimensional shape created by revolving a hyperbola.

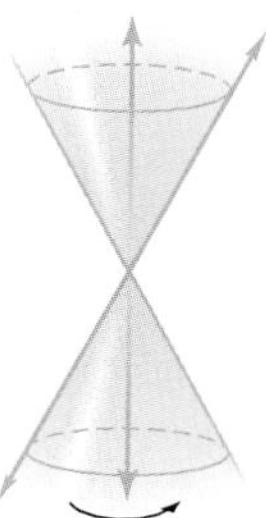

When two lines meet at an acute angle, revolving one of the lines about the other creates a double cone. These cones do not have bases. They continue infinitely, like the original lines.

Slicing these cones with a plane at different angles produces different conic sections.

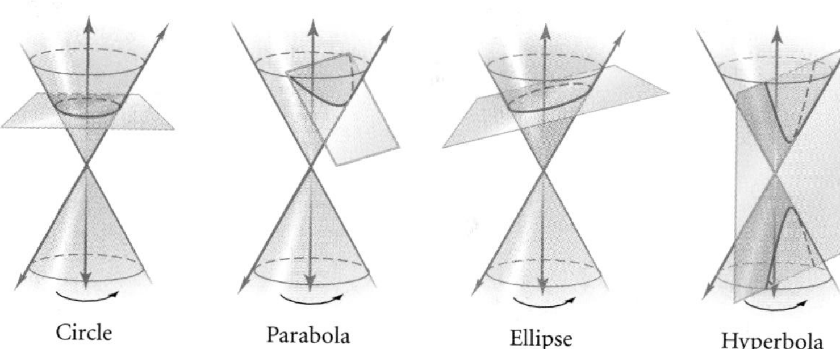

History CONNECTION

Students of mathematics have studied conic sections for more than 2000 years. Greek mathematician Menaechmus (ca. 380–320 B.C.E.) thought of conic sections as coming from different kinds of cones. Parabolas came from right-angled cones, ellipses from acute-angled cones, and hyperbolas from obtuse-angled cones. Apollonius of Perga (ca. 262–190 B.C.E.) later showed how all three kinds of curves could be obtained from the same cone. Known as the "Great Geometer," he wrote the eight-book *Treatise on Conic Sections* and named the ellipse, hyperbola, and parabola.

Conic sections have some interesting properties. Each of the shapes can also be defined as a locus of points. For example, all the points on a circle are the same distance from the center. So, you can describe a circle as a locus of points that are a fixed distance from a fixed point.

Definition of a Circle

A **circle** is a locus of points P in a plane, that are located a constant distance, r, from a fixed point, C. Symbolically, $PC = r$. The fixed point is called the **center** and the constant distance is called the **radius.**

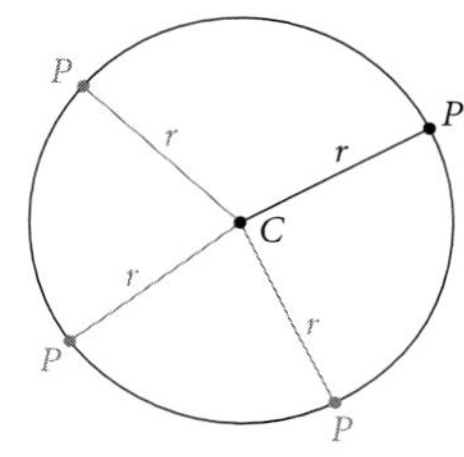

You can use the locus definition to write an equation that describes all the points on a circle.

EXAMPLE A

Write the equation for the locus of points (x, y) that are 4 units from the point $(0, 0)$.

▶ Solution

The locus describes a circle with radius 4 and center $(0, 0)$. The distance from each point of the circle, (x, y), to the center of the circle, $(0, 0)$, is 4. Using the distance formula, you can write

$$\sqrt{(x-0)^2 + (y-0)^2} = 4$$

Squaring both sides gives the equation

$$x^2 + y^2 = 16$$

▶ EXAMPLE A

In Chapter 4, students were given the equation of a unit circle, justified by the Pythagorean Theorem, and found equations of other circles (and ellipses) by doing transformations. This example uses the distance formula to derive the equation of a circle with radius r and center (h, k). If you think this is a big leap for your students, you might want to preface the example with some practice in finding the distance between a given point and the origin or a given point and the point (h, k).

NCTM STANDARDS

CONTENT		PROCESS	
	Number	✓	Problem Solving
✓	Algebra		Reasoning
✓	Geometry	✓	Communication
✓	Measurement	✓	Connections
	Data/Probability	✓	Representation

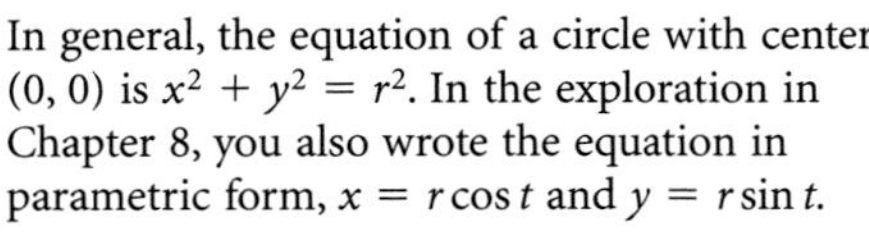

In general, the equation of a circle with center (0, 0) is $x^2 + y^2 = r^2$. In the exploration in Chapter 8, you also wrote the equation in parametric form, $x = r\cos t$ and $y = r\sin t$.

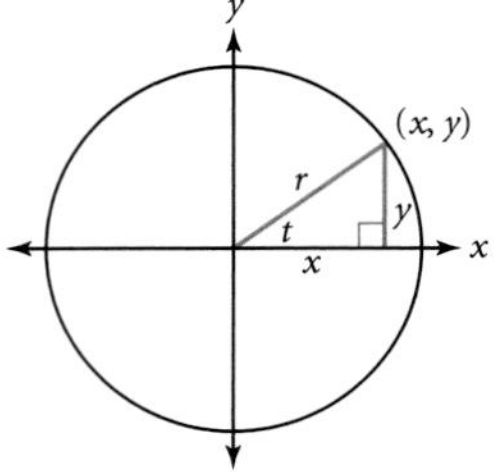

If the circle is translated horizontally and/or vertically, you can modify the equations by replacing x with $(x - h)$ and replacing y with $(y - k)$.

Equation of a Circle

The **standard form** of the equation of a circle with center (h, k) and radius r is

$$(x - h)^2 + (y - k)^2 = r^2$$

or, in parametric form,

$$x = r\cos t + h$$
$$y = r\sin t + k$$

▶ EXAMPLE B

[Language] In Chapter 8, students learned about the trigonometric ratio the tangent. In this example, *tangent* has the geometry definition of "a line that intersects a circle or other curve at only one point." The tangent of an angle is related to a tangent of a circle, as this diagram shows:

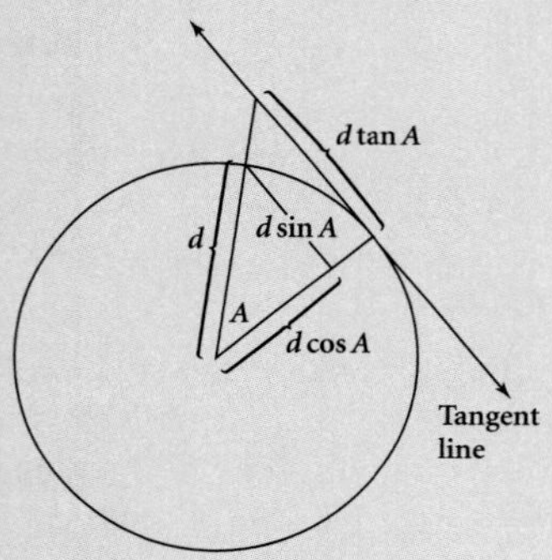

This example demonstrates how to find the equation of a circle in a situation in which the equation of a tangent line is known. Encourage students to plan an approach and try to solve the problem first.

You may want to ask students to find the point of intersection, $(-0.6, -0.2)$, by solving the system

$$\begin{cases} y = -2 - \frac{1}{2}(x - 3) \\ y = 2x + 1 \end{cases}$$

EXAMPLE B A circle has center $(3, -2)$ and is tangent to the line $y = 2x + 1$. Write the equation of the circle.

▶ Solution To write the equation of a circle, you need to know the center and the radius. You know the center, $(3, -2)$, but you need to find the radius.

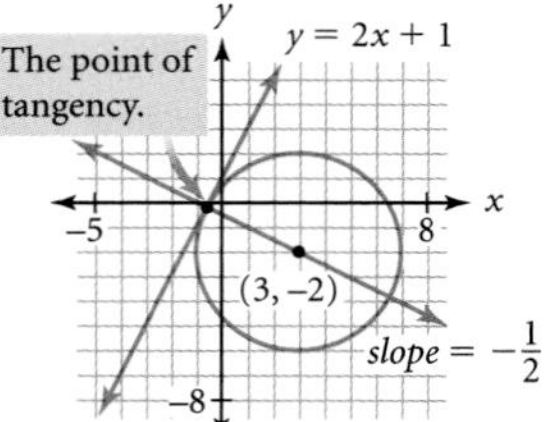

Recall from geometry that a line tangent to a circle intersects the circle at only one point and is perpendicular to a diameter of the circle at the point of tangency. The tangent line has slope 2. A line perpendicular to this line will have slope $-\frac{1}{2}$. So, the line containing this diameter will have slope $-\frac{1}{2}$, and will pass through the center of the circle, $(3, -2)$.

Use this information to write the equation of the line that contains the diameter.

$$y = -2 - \frac{1}{2}(x - 3)$$

Now find the point of intersection of this line with the tangent line by solving the system of equations. The point of intersection is $(-0.6, -0.2)$. You can now find the radius, which is the distance from the point of tangency to the center.

$$\sqrt{(3 + 0.6)^2 + (-2 + 0.2)^2} = \sqrt{16.2} \approx 4.025$$

The radius of the circle is $\sqrt{16.2}$ units. Therefore, the equation of this circle is

$$(x - 3)^2 + (y + 2)^2 = 16.2$$

or, in parametric form,

$$x = \sqrt{16.2}\cos t + 3$$
$$y = \sqrt{16.2}\sin t - 2$$

The equation for the circle, $(x - 3)^2 + (y + 2)^2 = 16.2$, is exact, because $r^2 = \left(\sqrt{16.2}\right)^2 = 16.2$. Students might also write the approximate equation $(x - 3)^2 + (y + 2)^2 = (4.025)^2$. The equations $x = 4.025\cos t + 3$ and $y = 4.025\sin t - 2$ are approximate equations. Students could write them as exact equations using $\sqrt{16.2}$ in place of 4.025.

In Chapter 4, you stretched a circle horizontally and vertically by different amounts to create ellipses. You can think of the equation of an ellipse as the equation of a unit circle that has been translated and stretched.

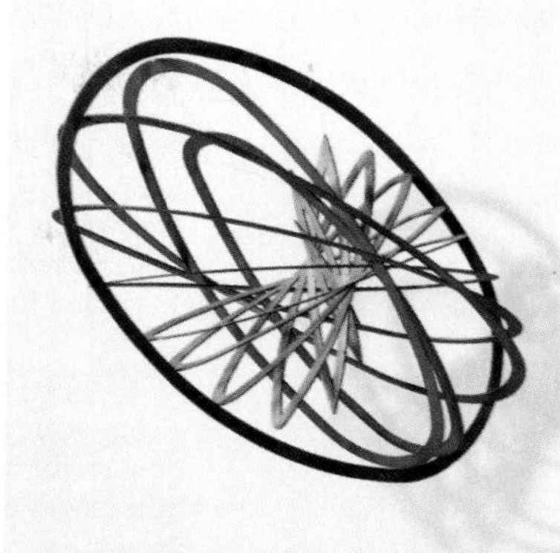

This plywood and wire elliptical sculpture by Russian artist Alexander Rodchenko (1891–1956) is titled *Oval Hanging Construction Number 12* (1920).

Equation of an Ellipse

The standard form of the equation of an ellipse with center (h, k), horizontal scale factor of a, and vertical scale factor of b is

$$\left(\frac{x-h}{a}\right)^2 + \left(\frac{y-k}{b}\right)^2 = 1$$

or, in parametric form,

$$x = a\cos t + h$$
$$y = b\sin t + k$$

An ellipse is like a circle, except that it involves two points called **foci** instead of just one point at the center. You can construct an ellipse by tying a string around two pins and tracing a set of points, as shown.

The sum of the distances, $d_1 + d_2$, is the same for any point on the ellipse.

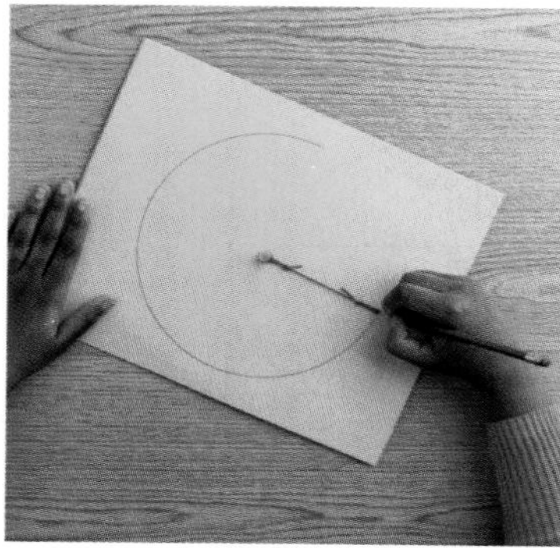

A piece of string attached to one pin helps you draw a circle. This is the same concept as using a compass to construct a circle.

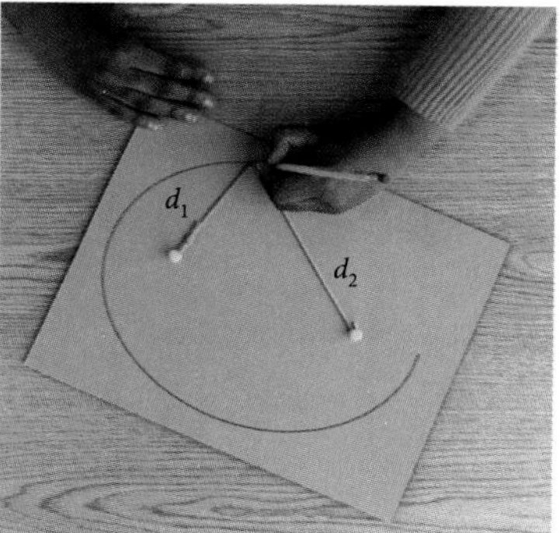

A piece of string attached to two pins helps you draw an ellipse.

Equation and Definition of an Ellipse
[Language] *Foci* are also sometimes called *focal points.* The segments a and b are also called the *semimajor axis* and the *semiminor axis.*

For consistency with Chapter 4, this book will always associate a with the horizontal axis. If the major axis were vertical, its length would be $2b$ and would equal $d_1 + d_2$.

In the definition of an ellipse, F_1P represents the length of the segment with endpoints F_1 and P.

You might use the Sketchpad demonstration Definitions of Circle and Ellipse as you talk about the definition and the equation of an ellipse.

In reference to the art at the top of the page, you might **[Ask]** "Is an oval the same thing as an ellipse?" [*Oval* is a general, nonmathematical term that describes an oblong, rounded, noncircular shape, while *ellipse* has a specific mathematical definition.]

A dynamic sketch at www.keymath.com/DAA helps students visualize the construction of an ellipse.

Definition of an Ellipse

An **ellipse** is a locus of points P in a plane, the sum of whose distances, d_1 and d_2, from two fixed points, F_1 and F_2, is always a constant, d. That is, $d_1 + d_2 = d$, or $F_1P + F_2P = d$. The two fixed points, F_1 and F_2, are called **foci** (the plural of focus).

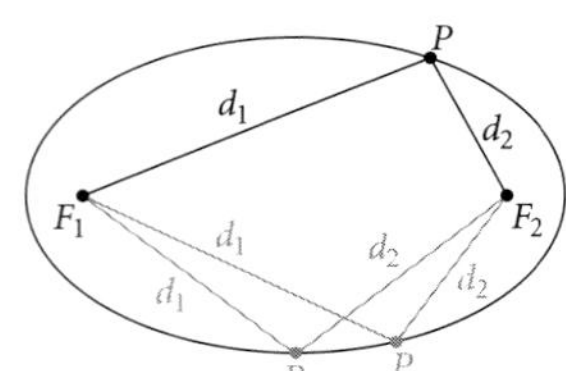

The segment that forms the longer dimension of an ellipse, and contains the foci, is the **major axis.** The shorter dimension is the **minor axis.** Recall from Chapter 4 that the length of half the horizontal axis of an ellipse corresponds to the horizontal scale factor, so the horizontal axis has length $2a$, and half the horizontal axis has length a. Similarly, half the vertical axis has length b. When the major axis is horizontal, the length of the major axis, $2a$, is equal to $d_1 + d_2$, as shown in the diagram below at right. So the sum of the distances between any point on the ellipse and the two foci is $2a$. What would be true if the major axis were vertical? $d_1 + d_2 = 2b$

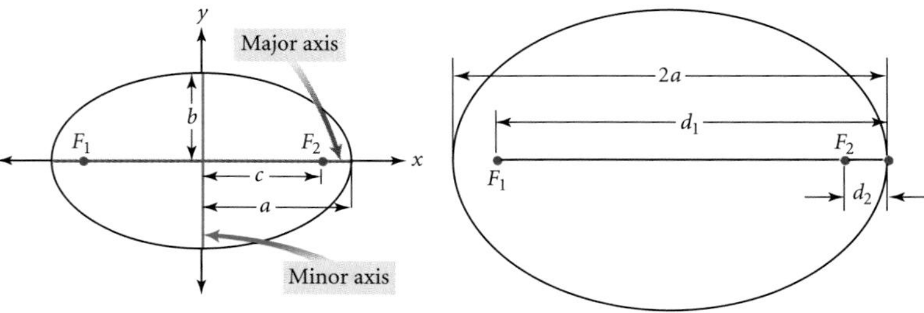

If you connect an endpoint of the minor axis to the foci, you form two congruent right triangles. For a horizontally oriented ellipse, the sum of the lengths of the hypotenuses is the same as the length of the major axis, so each hypotenuse has length a. Half the length of the minor axis is b. To locate the foci of the ellipse, call the distance from the center to each focus c, and write the equation $b^2 + c^2 = a^2$.

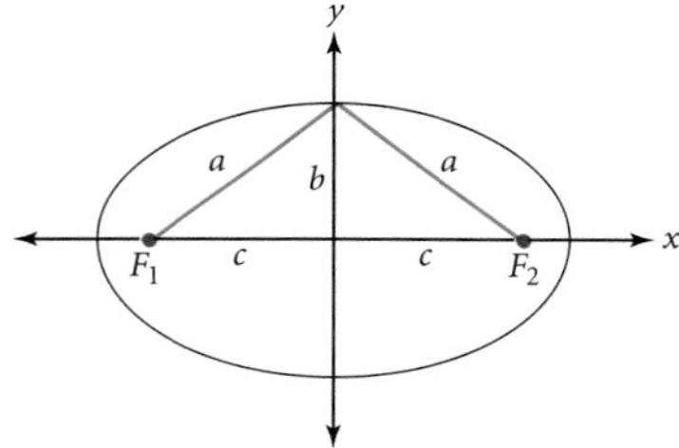

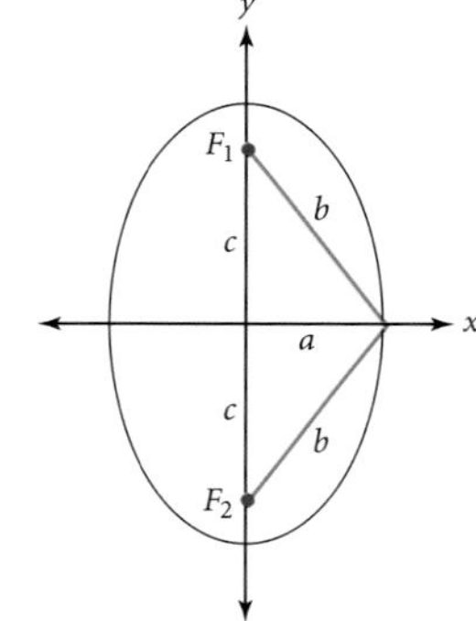

When the major axis is vertical, the hypotenuse of each triangle is equivalent to b, half the length of the major axis, so $a^2 + c^2 = b^2$.

▶ *EXAMPLE C*

This example applies the terms *major axis* and *minor axis* to the idea from Chapter 4 of an ellipse as a stretched circle. **[Alert]** Students may think the length of an axis is the stretch factor rather than twice the stretch factor in that direction.

Provide graph paper for all groups. Students will be pleasantly surprised to find that it is easier to sketch these graphs in function form on graph paper than to graph them on calculators.

Students can use the dynamic graphs at www.keymath.com/DAA to explore translations of functions. The dynamic exploration closely follows the investigation and this example.

EXAMPLE C Graph an ellipse that is centered at the origin, with a vertical major axis of 6 units and a minor axis of 4 units. Where are the foci?

▶ Solution Start with a unit circle, $x^2 + y^2 = 1$. The radius is 1 unit and the diameter is 2 units. You can stretch this circle vertically by a factor of 3 to make it 6 units tall. To make it 4 units wide, you must stretch it horizontally by a factor of 2.

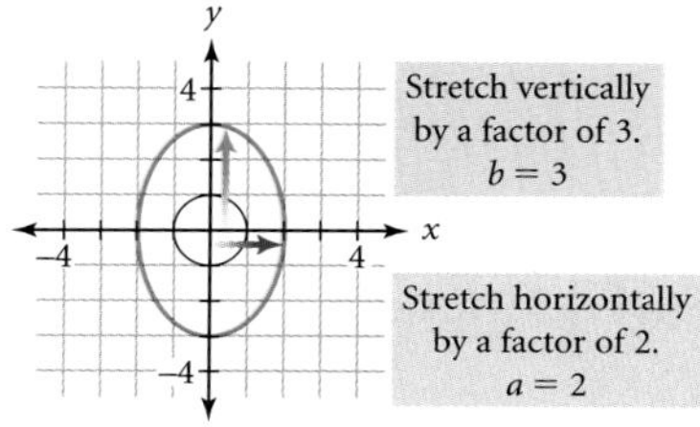

Replace y with $\frac{y}{3}$ and replace x with $\frac{x}{2}$. The equation is

$$\left(\frac{x}{2}\right)^2 + \left(\frac{y}{3}\right)^2 = 1 \quad \text{or} \quad \frac{x^2}{4} + \frac{y^2}{9} = 1$$

To sketch $\left(\frac{x}{2}\right)^2 + \left(\frac{y}{3}\right)^2 = 1$ by hand, plot the center, the endpoints of the major axis that are vertically 3 units from the center, and the endpoints of the minor axis that are horizontally 2 units from the center. Then connect the endpoints with a smooth curve.

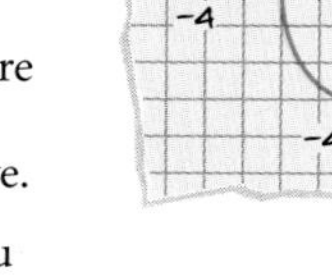

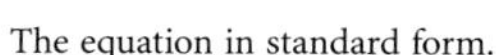

To graph the ellipse on your calculator, you will need to solve for y. It then takes two equations to graph the entire shape.

$$\left(\frac{x}{2}\right)^2 + \left(\frac{y}{3}\right)^2 = 1 \qquad \text{The equation in standard form.}$$

$$\left(\frac{y}{3}\right)^2 = 1 - \left(\frac{x}{2}\right)^2 \qquad \text{Subtract } \left(\tfrac{x}{2}\right)^2 \text{ from both sides.}$$

$$\frac{y}{3} = \pm\sqrt{1 - \left(\frac{x}{2}\right)^2} \qquad \text{Take the square root of both sides.}$$

$$y = \pm 3\sqrt{1 - \left(\frac{x}{2}\right)^2} \qquad \text{Multiply both sides by 3.}$$

Use your calculator to check the graph.

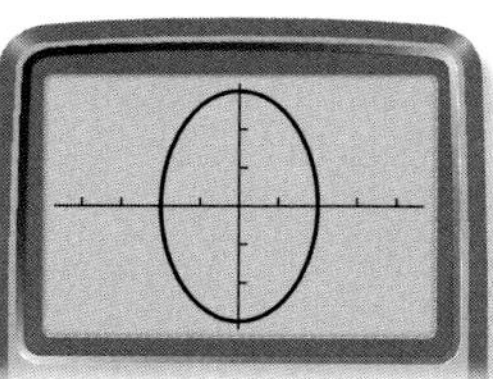

[–4.7, 4.7, 1, –3.1, 3.1, 1]

To locate the foci, recall the relationship $a^2 + c^2 = b^2$ for an ellipse with a vertical major axis:

$$a^2 + c^2 = b^2$$
$$2^2 + c^2 = 3^2$$
$$4 + c^2 = 9$$
$$c^2 = 5$$
$$c = \pm\sqrt{5}$$

Circles and Ellipses

Show the Definitions of Circle and Ellipse transparency and ask whether a circle is a special kind of ellipse. A discussion of this question can motivate students to study the definition of an ellipse. Try to be careful not to cut off discussion by focusing more on content than on students' thinking. If you assume that the foci of an ellipse are distinct, *ellipse* and *circle* are distinct conic sections. Or you can define *ellipse* as a stretched circle, in which case the circle is a special kind of ellipse with stretch factors equal to 1. The legitimacy of different approaches can help students realize that mathematical definitions vary and can even be contradictory. Students may have seen other variances, such as different axiom systems in geometry that lead to non-Euclidean geometries.

Guiding the Investigation

If time is limited, you can skip this investigation or assign it as a project. If your curriculum must include eccentricity, discuss the paragraph following Step 2.

Make the room as dim as possible. Test the flashlights to ensure that the sections are visible.

Step 1 Students can use ring stands and clamps to hold the flashlights steady.

Step 2 After students find that the sums of the distances from a point to the foci are equal for two points, **[Ask]** "Are two points enough to conclude that the distances are always equal?" [Good inductive reasoning is based on more than two instances. The same sum from two points per group member would make a stronger argument.]

SHARING IDEAS

As students present their ideas about Step 4, note that when the eccentricity becomes 1, the ellipse becomes a parabola. The eccentricity of a hyperbola is greater than 1. **[Link]** Students will study eccentricity in precalculus. **[Ask]** "What is the eccentricity of a circle?" [Zero; the distance from the center to the focus is zero.]

Ask about the meaning of the word *section,* as in *conic section.* Students may have heard of cross sections, but they may not realize that a cross section (perpendicular to an axis) is one kind of section.

[Ask] "Why use a double cone?" [It's necessary only for the hyperbola.] One branch of a hyperbola looks somewhat like a parabola, but unlike a parabola, it has asymptotes.

[Ask] "Are there other ways a plane can intersect a double cone?" [The intersection is a point if the plane passes through the point common to the two parts of the double cone; it's a line if the plane is tangent to the double cone; and it's a pair of intersecting lines if the plane passes through the axis of the cones.]

In Chapter 4, students saw ellipses as stretched circles. This lesson defines ellipses using the constant-sum property. Wonder aloud whether the two properties define the same kind of curve. The stretch property leads to the stretched-circle equation $\frac{x^2}{a^2} + \frac{y^2}{b^2} = 1$. Setting c equal to $\sqrt{a^2 - b^2}$ (if $a > b$), challenge students to use the equation to find algebraically the distances from any point (x, y) on the ellipse to the points $(\pm c, 0)$. Those distances are $a \pm \frac{cx}{a}$; their sum is the constant $2a$. Reversing the reasoning shows equivalence.

[Ask] "Is the eccentricity of an ellipse related to eccentric behavior in people?" [Eccentric behavior deviates from the norm, just as ellipses and other conic sections deviate from circles.]

Assessing Progress

You can assess students' understanding of the Pythagorean Theorem, the distance formula, and the idea of ellipses as stretched circles.

So, the foci are $\sqrt{5}$ units above and below the center, $(0, 0)$. The coordinates of the foci are $(0, \sqrt{5})$ and $(0, -\sqrt{5})$, or approximately $(0, 2.24)$ and $(0, -2.24)$.

In the investigation you will find the equation of an ellipse that you create yourself.

Investigation
A Slice of Light

You will need

- graph paper
- a flashlight
- a relatively dark classroom

The beam of a flashlight is close to the shape of a cone. A sheet of paper held in front of the flashlight shows different slices, or sections, of the cone of light.

Work with a partner, then share results with your group.

Procedure Note

1. Shine a flashlight on the graph paper at an angle.
2. Align the major axis of the ellipse formed by the beam with one axis of the paper. You might start by placing four points on the paper to help the person holding the flashlight stay on target.
3. Carefully trace the edge of the beam as your partner holds the light steady.

Step 1 Draw a pair of coordinate axes at the center of your graph paper. Follow the procedure note and trace an ellipse.

Step 2 Write an equation that fits the data as closely as possible. Find the lengths of both the major and minor axes. Use the values in your equation to locate the foci. Finally, verify your equation by selecting any two pairs of points on the ellipse and checking that the sum of the distances to the foci is constant.

Step 2 Answers will vary.

Eccentricity is a measure of how elongated an ellipse is. Eccentricity is defined as the ratio $\frac{c}{a}$, for an ellipse with a horizontal major axis, or $\frac{c}{b}$, for an ellipse with a vertical major axis. If the eccentricity is close to 0, then the ellipse looks almost like a circle. The higher the ratio, the more elongated the ellipse.

Step 3 Use your flashlight to make ellipses with different eccentricities. Trace three different ellipses. Calculate the eccentricity of each one and label it on your paper. What is the range of possible values for the eccentricity of an ellipse?

Step 4 Continue to tilt your flashlight until the eccentricity becomes too large and you no longer have an ellipse. What shape can you trace now?

Step 3 Answers will vary. The range of ratios is between 0 and 1.

Step 4 When the eccentricity becomes too large, the ellipse becomes a parabola and then a single branch of a hyperbola.

Exercises

Practice Your Skills

1. Sketch each circle on your paper, and label the center and the radius. For a–d, rewrite the equation as two functions. Use your calculator to check your work.

a. $x^2 + y^2 = 4$ **b.** $(x - 3)^2 + y^2 = 1$ **c.** $(x + 1)^2 + (y - 2)^2 = 9$

d. $x^2 + (y - 1.5)^2 = 0.25$ **e.** $x = 2\cos t + 1$, $y = 2\sin t + 2$ **f.** $x = 4\cos t - 3$, $y = 4\sin t$

2. Write an equation in standard form for each graph.

a.

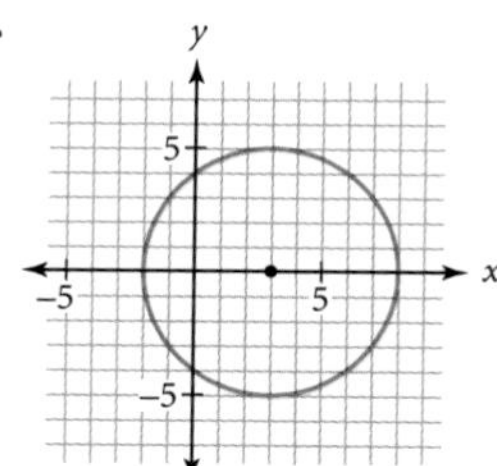

$(x - 3)^2 + y^2 = 25$

b.

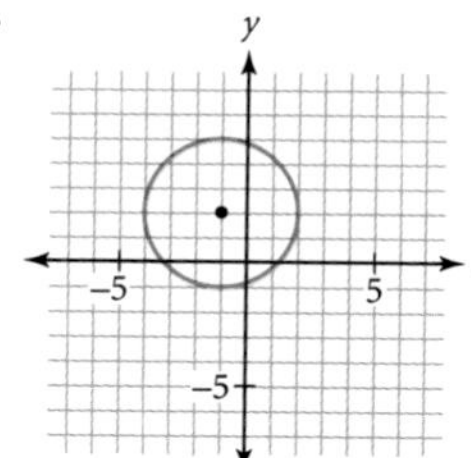

$(x + 1)^2 + (y - 2)^2 = 9$

c.

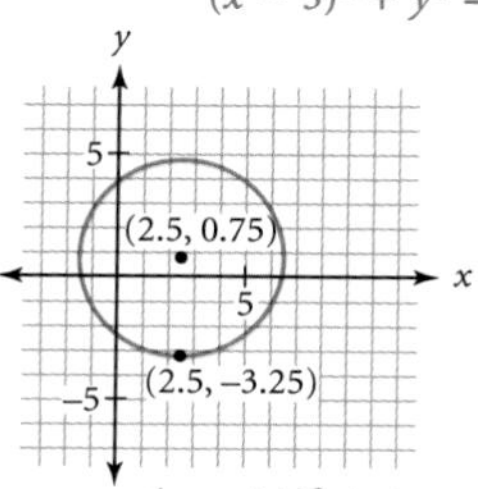

$(x - 2.5)^2 + (y - 0.75)^2 = 16$

d.

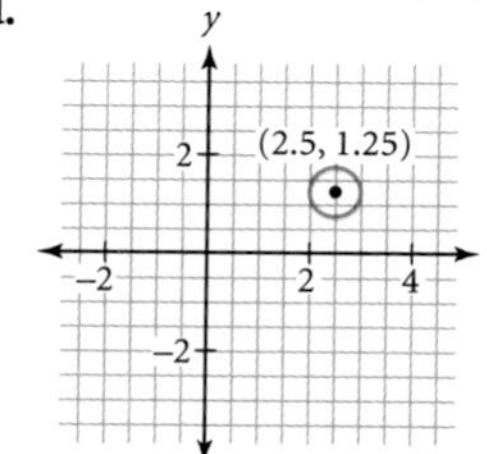

$(x - 2.5)^2 + (y - 1.25)^2 = 0.25$

3. Write parametric equations for each graph in Exercise 2.

4. Sketch a graph of each equation. Label the coordinates of the endpoints of the major and minor axes.

a. $\left(\frac{x}{2}\right)^2 + \left(\frac{y}{4}\right)^2 = 1$

b. $\left(\frac{x-2}{3}\right)^2 + \left(\frac{y+2}{1}\right)^2 = 1$

c. $\left(\frac{x-4}{3}\right)^2 + \left(\frac{y-1}{3}\right)^2 = 1$

d. $y = \pm 2\sqrt{1 - \left(\frac{x+2}{3}\right)^2} - 1$

e. $x = 4\cos t - 1$, $y = 2\sin t + 3$

f. $x = 3\cos t + 3$, $y = 5\sin t$

The Meeting Center (1973), nicknamed "The Egg," at the Governor Nelson A. Rockefeller Empire State Plaza in Albany, New York, contains two interior auditoriums. It appears to be the lower half of an **ellipsoid,** a three-dimensional shape created by revolving an ellipse about one of its axes.

Closing the Lesson

The main point of this lesson is that there are ways of thinking about circles and ellipses that go beyond those presented in Chapter 4. They can be thought of as **conic sections**—intersections of cones with planes. The distance formula leads from the standard definition of a circle as a locus of points (in a plane) equidistant from a fixed point to the equation of a circle. An **ellipse** can be defined as a locus of points (in a plane) having the same sum of distances from two fixed points, called the **foci** of the ellipse. Transforming the equation of a circle leads to the equation of an ellipse.

BUILDING UNDERSTANDING

Students practice working with the distance formula, circles, and ellipses. If your class did not study parametric equations in Chapter 8, skip Exercises 1e, 1f, 3, 4e, 4f, and 5.

ASSIGNING HOMEWORK

Essential	1–7
Performance assessment	8–12
Portfolio	8
Group	8, 11
Review	13–16

MATERIALS

- graph paper

Helping with the Exercises

3a. $x = 5\cos t + 3, y = 5\sin t$

3b. $x = 3\cos t - 1,$ $y = 3\sin t + 2$

3c. $x = 4\cos t + 2.5,$ $y = 4\sin t + 0.75$

3d. $x = 0.5\cos t + 2.5,$ $y = 0.5\sin t + 1.25$

Ellipsoids

[Ask] "Is an egg an ellipsoid?" [An egg is not symmetrical across an axis through the shorter dimension; a true ellipsoid would be.] **[Language]** The largest circular section of an ellipsoid is called the *equator.* Students might be interested in kinds of ellipsoids. A *prolate ellipsoid* is one with a diameter at the equator that is less than the length of the axis of revolution. An *oblate ellipsoid* is one with a diameter at the equator that is greater than the length of the axis of revolution.

See pages 893–894 for answers to Exercises 1 and 4.

5a. $x = 2\cos t,\ y = 2\sin t + 3$

5b. $x = 6\cos t - 1,\ y = 6\sin t + 2$

7a. $(\sqrt{27}, 0), (-\sqrt{27}, 0)$

7b. $(3, \sqrt{21}), (3, -\sqrt{21})$

7c. $(-1 + \sqrt{7}, 2), (-1 - \sqrt{7}, 2)$

7d. $(3 + \sqrt{27}, -1), (3 - \sqrt{27}, -1)$

Exercise 8 If you skipped the investigation, you might want to discuss how to find the equation of an ellipse.

[Context] Although many comets appear to have parabolic orbits, astronomers have determined that these comets really have elliptical orbits of great eccentricity. The comets can have periods of up to 40,000 years. For example, the comet Hyakutake, which could be seen from Earth in 1996, takes 10,000 years to orbit the Sun. The astronomy connection on page 525 gives more information.

8a. $\left(\frac{x-493}{497}\right)^2 + \left(\frac{y}{63}\right)^2 = 1$

8b. 63 AU or −63 AU

8c. 990 AU

8d. (0, 0), which is the Sun, and (986, 0)

5. Write parametric equations for each circle described.

a. radius 2, center (0, 3)

b. radius 6, center (−1, 2)

6. Write an equation in standard form for each graph.

a.

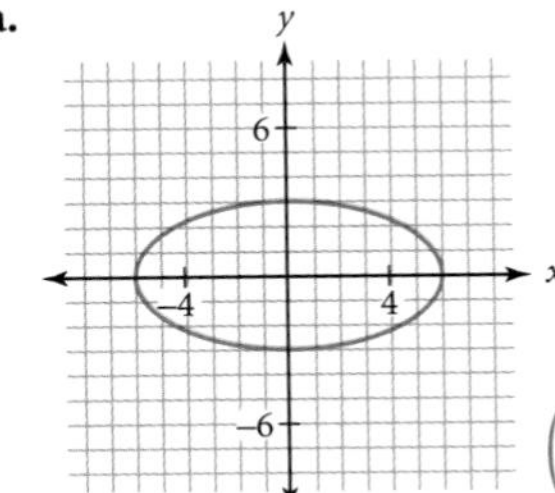

$\left(\frac{x}{6}\right)^2 + \left(\frac{y}{3}\right)^2 = 1$

b.

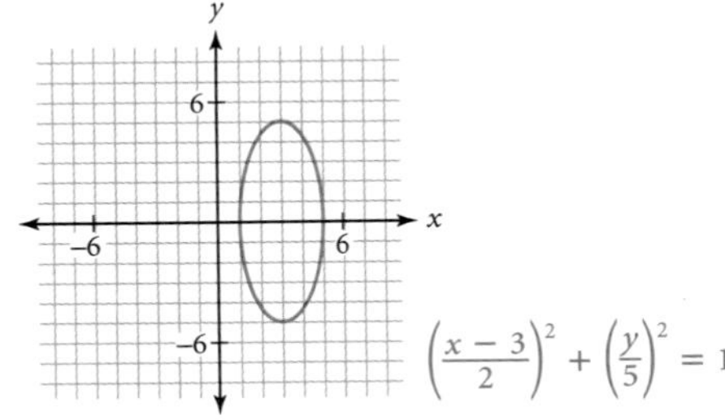

$\left(\frac{x-3}{2}\right)^2 + \left(\frac{y}{5}\right)^2 = 1$

c.

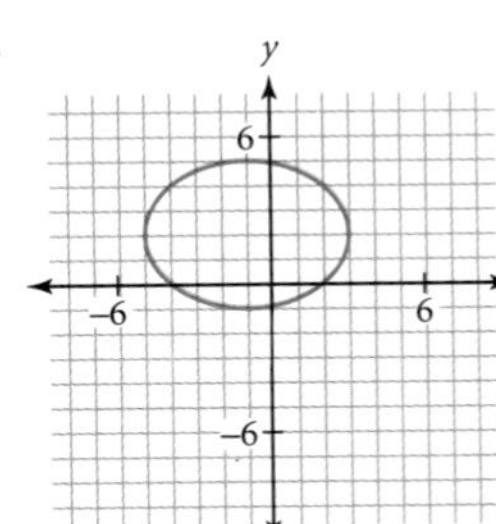

$\left(\frac{x+1}{4}\right)^2 + \left(\frac{y-2}{3}\right)^2 = 1$

d.

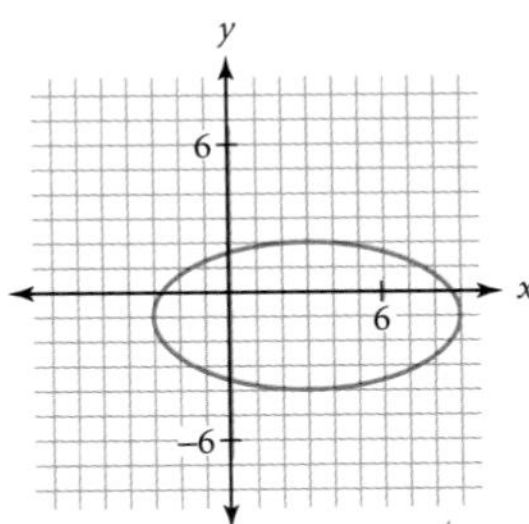

$\left(\frac{x-3}{6}\right)^2 + \left(\frac{y+1}{3}\right)^2 = 1$

7. Find the exact coordinates of the foci for each ellipse in Exercise 6.

Reason and Apply

8. Suppose you placed a grid on the plane of a comet's orbit, with the origin at the sun and the x-axis running through the longer axis of the orbit, as shown in the diagram. The table gives the approximate coordinates of the comet as it orbits the Sun. Both x and y are measured in astronomical units (AU).

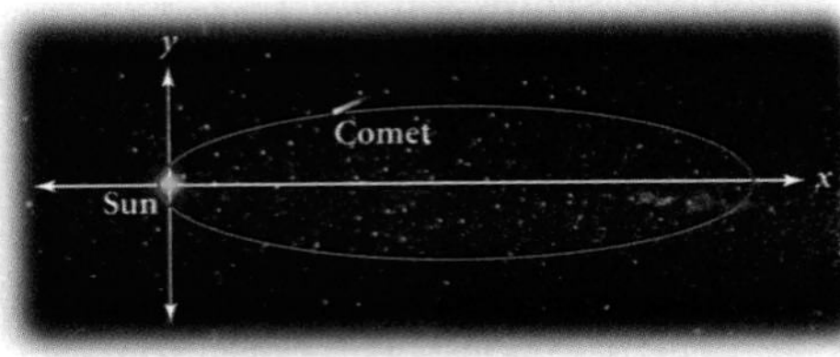

x	−2.1	12.9	62.6	244.5	579.3	778.1	900.1	982.4	923.4	663.0	450.0	141.6
y	5.5	16.3	31.5	54.6	62.0	51.6	36.1	10.9	−31.5	−59.2	−62.8	−44.5

a. Find an equation to fit these data.

b. Find the y-coordinate when the x-coordinate is 493.0 AU.

c. What is the greatest distance of the comet from the Sun?

d. What are the coordinates of the foci?

9. **APPLICATION** The top of a doorway is designed to be half an ellipse. The width of the doorway is 1.6 m, and the height of the half-ellipse is designed to be 62.4 cm. The crew have nails and string available. They want to trace the half-ellipse with a pencil before they cut the plywood to go over the doorway.

   a. How far apart should they place the nails? 1.0 m

   b. How long should the string be? 1.6 m

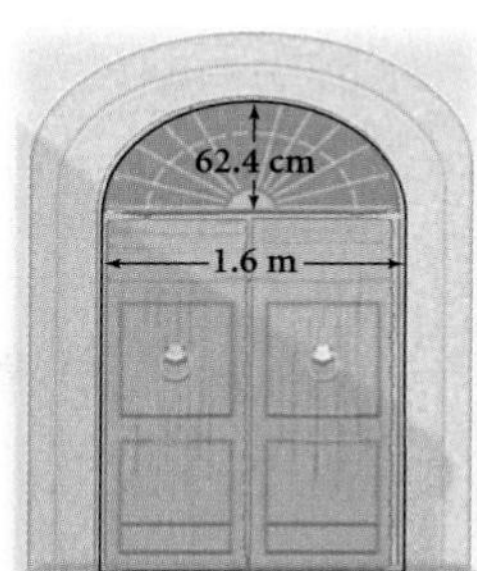

10. Read the connection below about the reflection property of an ellipse. If a room is constructed in the shape of an ellipse, and you stand at one focus and speak softly, a person standing at the other focus will hear you clearly. Such rooms are often called whispering chambers. Consider a whispering chamber that is 12 m long and 6 m wide.

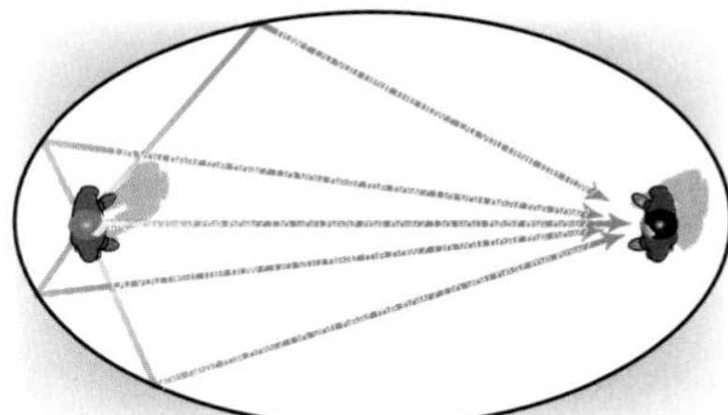

   a. Where should two whisperers stand to talk to each other?

   b. How far does the sound travel from one person to the other, bouncing off the wall in between?

The Whispering Gallery (1937) at Chicago's Museum of Science and Industry is constructed in an ellipsoid shape with two parabolic dishes that reflect the quietest sounds in perfect clarity from one dish's focus to the other's.

Science CONNECTION

A signal from one focus of an ellipse will always bounce off the ellipse in such a way that it will travel to the other focus.

This is called the reflection property of an ellipse.

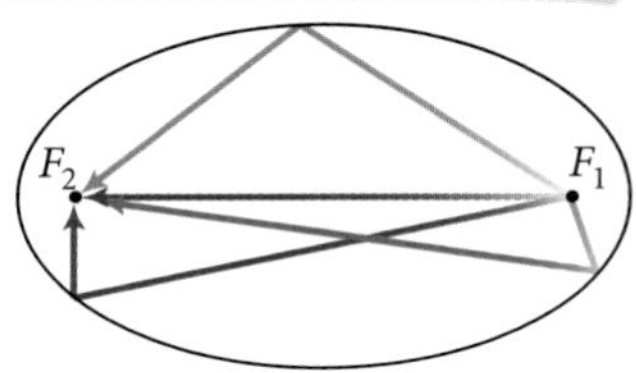

11. **APPLICATION** One possible gear ratio on Matthew's mountain bike is 4 to 1. This means that the front gear has four times as many teeth as the gear on the back wheel. So each revolution of the pedal causes the rear wheel to make four revolutions.

   a. If Matthew is pedaling 60 revolutions per minute (r/min), how many revolutions per minute is the rear tire making?

   b. If the diameter of the rear tire is 26 in., what speed in miles per hour will Matthew attain?

   c. Matt downshifts to a front gear that has 22 teeth and a rear gear that has 30 teeth. If he keeps pedaling 60 r/min, what will his new speed be?

Exercise 10 Ask whether circles and straight lines have similar reflective properties. A signal from the center of a circle bounces back to the center. Students have seen previously that a signal hitting a straight line bounces off so that the angle of incidence equals the angle of reflection. **[Ask]** "How can you use the reflective property of a line to construct a tangent to an ellipse?" [Draw segments from the two foci to the point of tangency, bisect the angle between these segments, and draw the line perpendicular to that bisector at the point of tangency.]

10a. The whisperers should stand at the two foci, approximately 5.2 m from the center of the room, along the major axis.

10b. The distance will be 12 m, the length of the major axis.

11a. 240 r/min

Exercise 11b Students may need reminding that the circumference of a circle is given by $2\pi r$, where r is the radius. **[Alert]** Students may confuse the formula products $2\pi r$ and πr^2, forgetting which is for circumference and which is for area. Suggest that they think about dimensions. The dimensions of $2\pi r$ are the same as the dimensions of r; they measure length. The dimensions of πr^2 are in square units and measure area (which is measured in square units).

11b. 18.6 mi/h

11c. 6.3 mi/h

Exercise 12 As needed, suggest that students set up a coordinate system with the center of the ellipse at the origin, (0, 0), which corresponds to a point in space, not Earth.

12. Let x represent distance in miles measured parallel to the major axis and measured from the intersection of the major and minor axes. Let y represent distance in miles measured parallel to the minor axis and measured from the intersection of the axes.

$$\left(\frac{x}{237177.5}\right)^2 + \left(\frac{y}{236667.3}\right)^2 = 1$$

Exercise 15 Students need to select only three points to find the parabola that models the data. They might use a fourth point to verify their equation.

EXTENSIONS

A. Use Take Another Look activity 1 on page 562.

B. If you did not use the Sketchpad demonstration Definitions of Circle and Ellipse while discussing the lesson, you could have students explore it on their own.

C. Ask students to investigate how builders make ellipses with a carpenter's square.

12. The Moon's greatest distance from Earth is 252,710 mi, and its smallest distance is 221,643 mi. Write an equation that describes the Moon's orbit around Earth. Earth is at one focus of the Moon's elliptical orbit.

Review

4.5 **13.** Write the equation of a parabola congruent to $y = x^2$ that has been reflected across the x-axis and translated left 3 units and up 2 units. $y = -(x + 3)^2 + 2$

14. Solve for y.

$$\frac{y-4}{0.5} = \left(\frac{x+2}{3}\right)^2 \quad y = 0.5\left(\frac{x+2}{3}\right)^2 + 4$$

6.3 **15.** Solve a system of equations and find the quadratic equation, $y = ax^2 + bx + c$, that fits these data points. $y = 2x^2 - 24x + 117$

x	0	1	2	3	4	5
y	117	95	77	63	53	47

9.1 **16.** Find the perimeter of this triangle. about 34.45 units

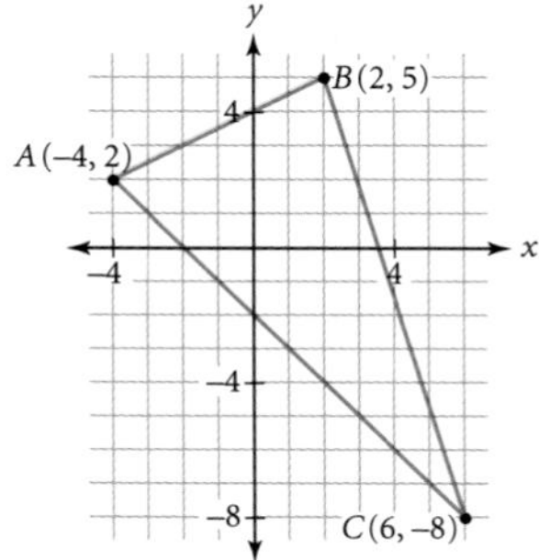

IMPROVING YOUR REASONING SKILLS

Elliptical Pool

You could use the reflection property of an ellipse to design an unusual pool table. On an elliptical pool table, if you start with a ball at one focus and hit it in any direction, it will always rebound off the side and roll toward the other focus. Suppose a pool table is designed in the shape of an ellipse with a pocket at one focus. Describe how you will hit ball 1 to land in the pocket, even though ball 2 is in the way.

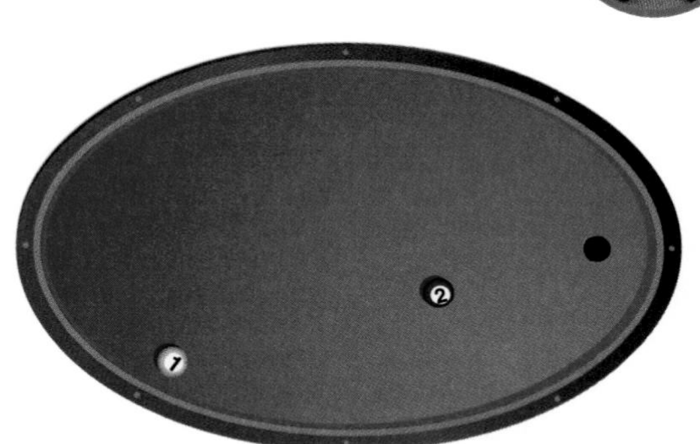

IMPROVING REASONING SKILLS

Hit ball 1 through the focus without the pocket. It will then bounce off the side and go in the pocket at the other focus.

Or hit ball 1 harder directly away from the pocket. It will bounce off the side, go through the other focus, bounce off the side again, and go in the pocket.

LESSON

9.3

Parabolas

There are two ways of spreading light: to be the candle or the mirror that reflects it.

EDITH WHARTON

You have studied parabolas in several different lessons, and you have used parabolic equations to model a variety of situations. In this lesson you will study the parabola from a different perspective. In previous chapters you worked with parabolas as variations on the equation $y = x^2$ or the parametric equations $x = t$ and $y = t^2$. However, there is also a locus definition of a parabola.

Built in 1969, one side of this building in Odeillo, France, is a large parabolic mirror that focuses sunlight on the building's solar-powered furnace.

Technology CONNECTION

A reflecting telescope is a type of optical telescope that uses a curved, mirrored lens to magnify objects. The most powerful reflecting telescope uses a parabolic or hyperbolic mirror and can bring the faintest light rays into clear view. The larger the mirror, the more distant objects a telescope can detect. To avoid the expense and weight of producing one massive lens, today's most sophisticated telescopes have a tile-like combination of hexagonal mirrors that produce the same effect as one concave mirror.

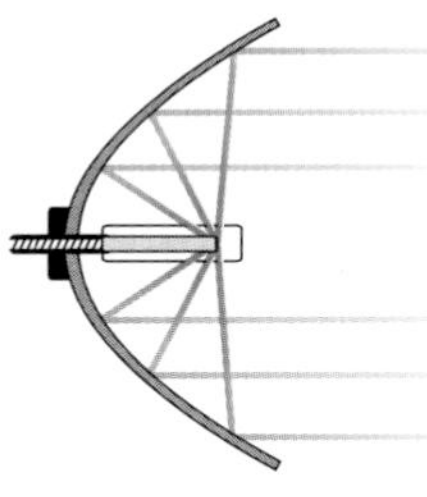

The designs of telescope lenses, spotlights, satellite dishes, and other parabolic reflecting surfaces are based on a remarkable property of parabolas: A ray that travels parallel to the axis of symmetry will strike the surface of the parabola or paraboloid and reflect toward the **focus.** Likewise, when a ray from the focus strikes the curve, it will reflect in a ray that is parallel to the axis of symmetry. A **paraboloid** is a three-dimensional parabola, formed when a parabola is rotated about its line of symmetry.

Science CONNECTION

Satellite dishes, used for television, radio, and other communications, are always parabolic. A satellite dish is set up to aim directly at a satellite. As the satellite transmits signals to a dish, the signals are reflected off the dish surface and toward the receiver, which is located at the focus of the paraboloid. In this way, every signal that hits a parabolic dish can be directed into the receiver.

A large satellite dish

NCTM STANDARDS

CONTENT		PROCESS	
	Number	✓	Problem Solving
✓	Algebra		Reasoning
✓	Geometry	✓	Communication
✓	Measurement	✓	Connections
	Data/Probability	✓	Representation

LESSON OBJECTIVES

- Introduce the locus definition of *parabola* and new vocabulary associated with a parabola
- Understand the relationship between the locus definition of *parabola* and applications to paraboloids and parabolic mirrors
- Determine the location of the parabola's focus, directrix, and vertex from its equation and graph the parabola
- Find the equation of a parabola from its graph

LESSON

9.3

PLANNING

LESSON OUTLINE

One day:

10 min Example

15 min Investigation

10 min Sharing

10 min Exercises

MATERIALS

- patty paper, wax paper, or tracing paper
- graph paper
- Definition of Parabola (T), *optional*
- Ellipse in a Cone (T), *optional*
- Sketchpad demonstration Definition of Parabola, *optional*

TEACHING

In this lesson students broaden their understanding of parabolas to include the focus-and-directrix locus definition and parametric equations. If your class has not studied parametric equations, students can disregard references to them in this lesson.

One Step

Hand out patty paper and graph paper, and pose this problem, based on the investigation: "Fold the patty paper parallel to one edge to form a line called the *directrix.* On the larger portion of the paper, mark a point called the *focus.* Repeatedly fold and crease the paper so that the focus lies at different points on the directrix, unfolding each time. Sketch in the shape outlined by the creases. Then lay the patty paper on top of a sheet of graph paper. Derive an equation for the shape you just sketched. See how that equation relates to the focus and the directrix." Encourage a variety of approaches.

One Step (continued)

As needed, **[Ask]** "Do you have any distances to which you could apply the distance formula as you did for ellipses?" You might wonder aloud which points on the directrix correspond to various points on the curve, to help students see that the segment connecting the points is perpendicular to the directrix. During Sharing, explore how to find the focus and the directrix from a parabola's equation.

INTRODUCTION

You might want to use the Sketchpad demonstration Definition of Parabola or the Definition of Parabola transparency to help introduce this lesson.

Students can explore rotated parabolas in the Exploration The Rotation Matrix on page 534.

[Ask] "In the equation $y^2 = 4fx$, where will the focus be?" [to the right of the vertex if $f > 0$ and to the left of the vertex if $f < 0$] "Where will the directrix be?" [to the left of the parabola if $f > 0$ and to the right of the parabola if $f < 0$]

[Alert] Students might have forgotten the meaning of *axis of symmetry.* **[Ask]** "Where is the axis of symmetry for a parabola?"

This reflective property of parabolas can be proved based on the locus definition of a parabola. You'll see how in the exercises. Compare this locus definition of a parabola to the locus definition of an ellipse.

Definition of a Parabola

A **parabola** is a locus of points P in a plane, whose distance from a fixed point, F, is the same as the distance from a fixed line, ℓ. That is, $d_1 = d_2$. The fixed point, F, is called the **focus.** The line, ℓ, is called the **directrix.**

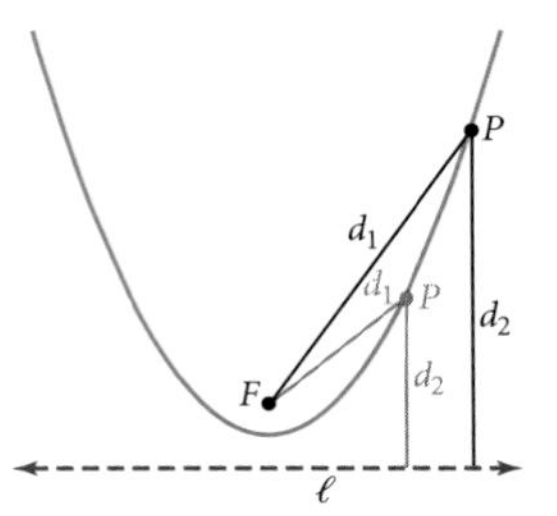

A parabola is the set of points for which the distances d_1 and d_2 are equal. If the directrix is a horizontal line, the parabola is vertically oriented, like the one in the definition box above. If the directrix is a vertical line, the parabola is horizontally oriented, like the one at left. The directrix can also be neither horizontal nor vertical, creating a parabola that is rotated at an angle.

How can you locate the focus of a given parabola? Suppose the parabola is horizontally oriented, with vertex (0, 0). It has a focus inside the curve at a point, $(f, 0)$, as shown in the first diagram below. The vertex is on the curve and will be the same distance from the focus as it is from the directrix, as shown in the second diagram. This means the equation of the directrix is $x = -f$. You can use this information, and the distance formula, to find the value of f when the vertex is the origin, as shown in the third diagram.

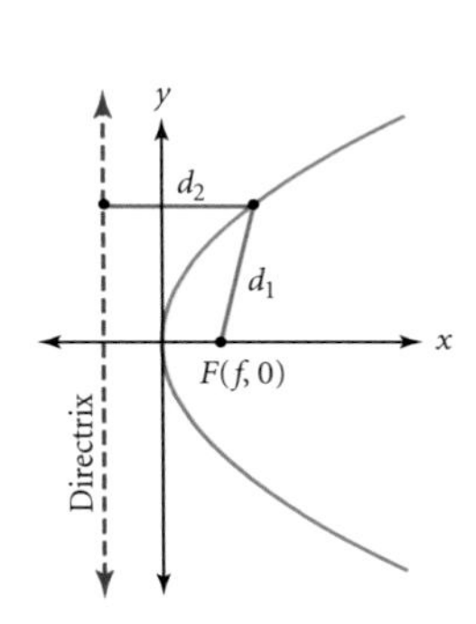

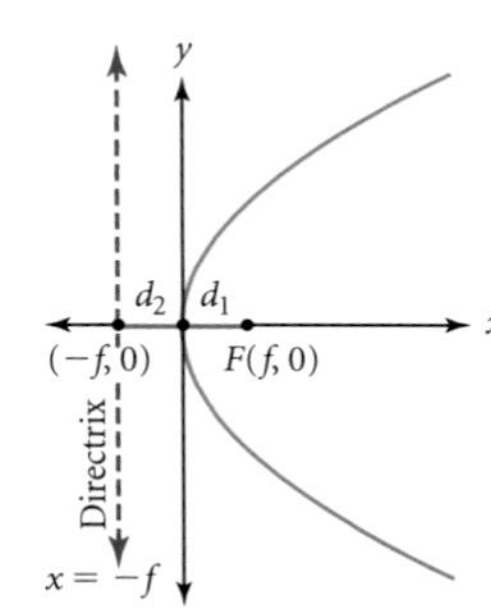

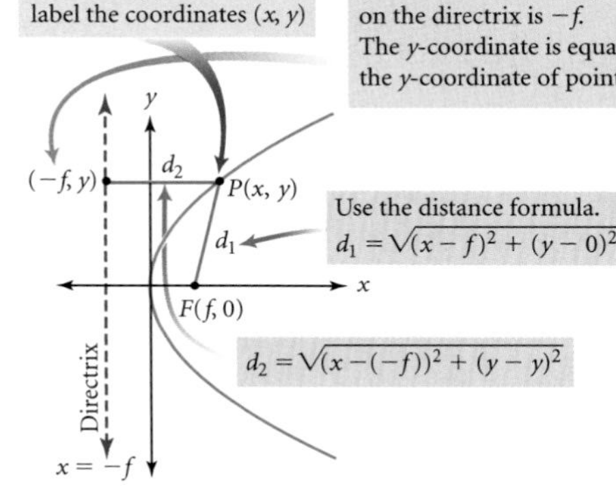

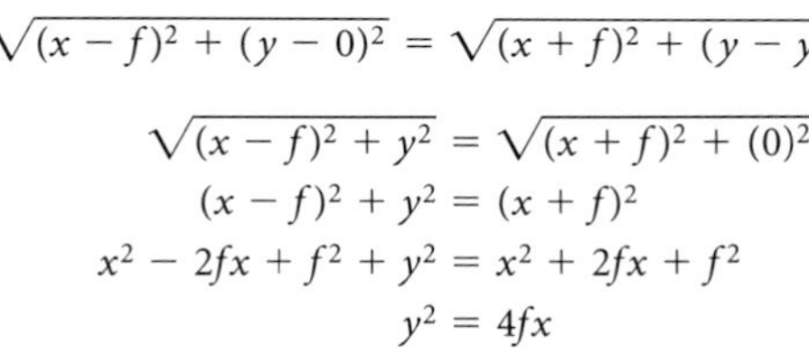

$\sqrt{(x - f)^2 + (y - 0)^2} = \sqrt{(x + f)^2 + (y - y)^2}$	Definition of parabola states that $d_1 = d_2$.
$\sqrt{(x - f)^2 + y^2} = \sqrt{(x + f)^2 + (0)^2}$	Subtract.
$(x - f)^2 + y^2 = (x + f)^2$	Square both sides.
$x^2 - 2fx + f^2 + y^2 = x^2 + 2fx + f^2$	Expand.
$y^2 = 4fx$	Combine like terms.

This result means that the coefficient of the variable x is $4f$, where f is the distance from the vertex to the focus. What do you think it means if f is negative?

The parabola opens to the left.

If the parabola is vertically oriented, the x- and y-coordinates are exchanged, for a final equation of $x^2 = 4fy$, or $y = \frac{1}{4f}x^2$.

Designed in 1960, the Theme Building at Los Angeles International Airport in California uses double parabolic arches.

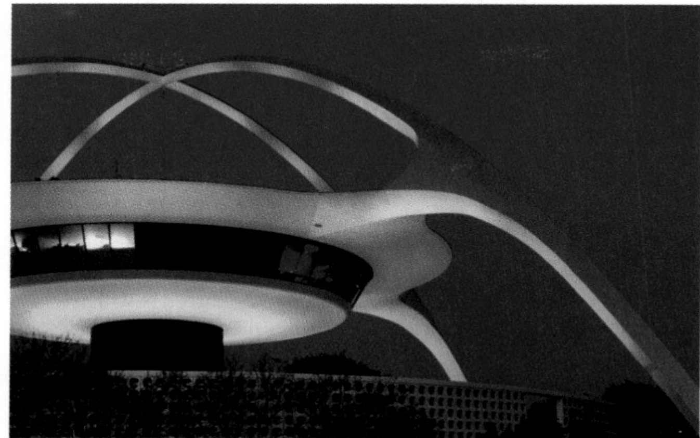

EXAMPLE

Consider the parent equation of a horizontally oriented parabola, $y^2 = x$.

a. Write the equation of the image of this graph after the following transformations have been performed, in order: a vertical stretch by a factor of 3, a translation right 2 units, and then a translation down 1 unit. Graph the new equation.

b. Where is the focus of $y^2 = x$? Where is the directrix?

c. Where is the focus of the transformed parabola? Where is its directrix?

► ***Solution***

Recall the transformations of functions that you studied in Chapter 4.

a. Begin with the parent equation, and perform the specified transformations.

$$y^2 = x \qquad \text{Original equation.}$$

$$\left(\frac{y}{3}\right)^2 = x \qquad \text{Stretch vertically by a factor of 3.}$$

$$\left(\frac{y+1}{3}\right)^2 = x - 2 \qquad \text{Translate right 2 units and down 1 unit.}$$

Graph the transformed parabola.

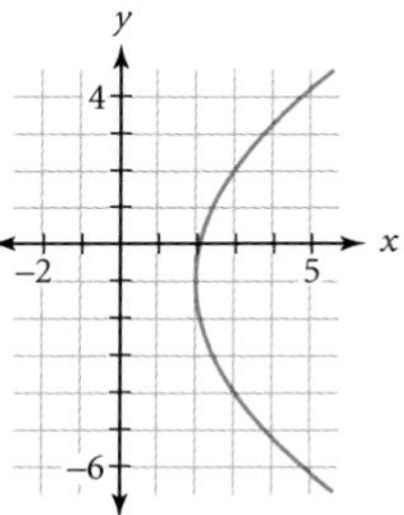

► ***EXAMPLE***

Point out that students must write the equation in standard form before they can see the value of $4f$ (and then f).

The dynamic model of a geometric construction of a parabola at www.keymath.com/DAA can be used to extend this lesson.

Guiding the Investigation

The folding could be completed as a whole class. You might do the folding along with your students and show your result on the overhead, where students can see the folds. The closer together the folds, the more detailed the parabola. Encourage students to lay the focus atop points all the way to the corners of the paper. This construction is an *envelope* of lines.

Once each student has a parabola, groups can work together to find equations of all of them, or students can work individually. As you circulate, try to encourage a mix of equations for both vertically and horizontally oriented parabolas. You might also have students measure distances to see how the definition of a parabola applies to their own creations.

Sample answer: Suppose this parabola was overlaid on graph paper and traced, with focus (3, 0) and directrix $x = 1$. The general form of the parabola is $y^2 = 4fx$. Because the distance from the focus to the vertex is 1, $f = 1$, and the general equation of the parabola is $y^2 = 4x$. However, the parabola is translated right 2 units, so the final equation is $y^2 = 4(x - 2)$.

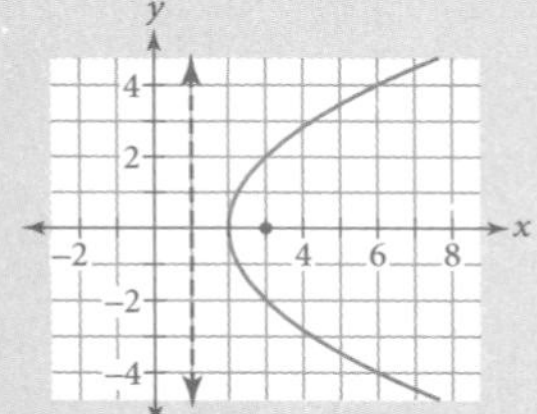

b. Use the general form, $y^2 = 4fx$, to locate the focus and the directrix of the graph of the equation $y^2 = x$. The coefficient of x is $4f$ in the general form, and 1 in the equation $y^2 = x$. So, $4f = 1$, or $f = \frac{1}{4}$. Recall that f is the distance from the vertex to the focus and from the vertex to the directrix. The vertex is (0, 0), so the focus is $\left(\frac{1}{4}, 0\right)$ and the directrix is the line $x = -\frac{1}{4}$.

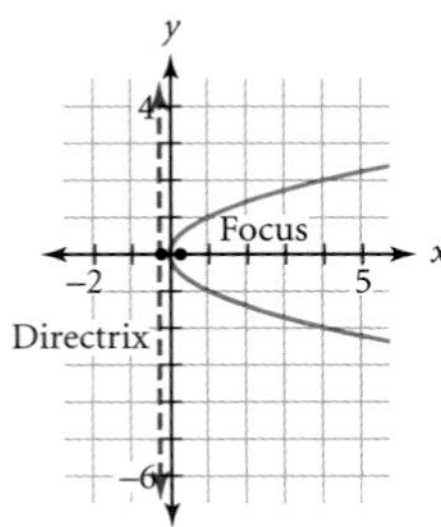

c. To locate the focus and the directrix of $\left(\frac{y+1}{3}\right)^2 = x - 2$, first rewrite the equation as $(y + 1)^2 = 9(x - 2)$. The coefficient of x in this equation is 9, so $4f = 9$, or $f = 2.25$. The focus and the directrix will both be 2.25 units from the vertex in the horizontal direction. The vertex is $(2, -1)$, so the focus is $(4.25, -1)$ and the directrix is the line $x = -0.25$.

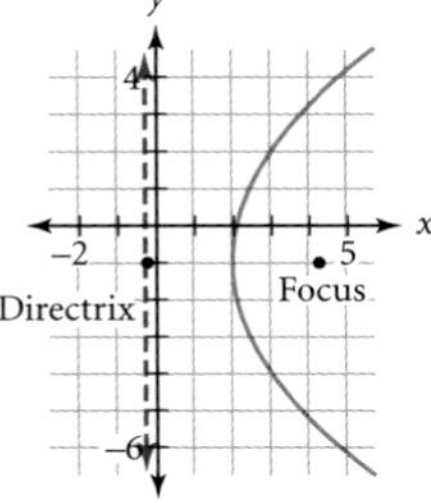

Equation of a Parabola

The standard form of the equation of a vertically oriented parabola with vertex (h, k), horizontal scale factor of a, and vertical scale factor of b is

$$\frac{y-k}{b} = \left(\frac{x-h}{a}\right)^2$$

or, in parametric form,

$$x = at + h$$
$$y = bt^2 + k$$

The focus of a vertically oriented parabola is $(h, k + f)$, where $\frac{a^2}{b} = 4f$, and the directrix is the line $y = k - f$.

The standard form of the equation of a horizontally oriented parabola with vertex (h, k), horizontal scale factor of a, and vertical scale factor of b is

$$\left(\frac{y-k}{b}\right)^2 = \frac{x-h}{a}$$

or, in parametric form,

$$x = at^2 + h$$
$$y = bt + k$$

The focus of a horizontally oriented parabola is $(h + f, k)$, where $\frac{b^2}{a} = 4f$, and the directrix is the line $x = h - f$.

In the investigation you will construct a parabola. As you create your model, think about how your process relates to the locus definition of a parabola.

SHARING IDEAS

As students present equations, help them see that for either of the two parabolas $y = kx^2$ and $x = ky^2$, the value of k is $\frac{1}{4f}$, where f is the distance from the vertex to the focus and to the directrix.

To help prepare students for Exercises 10 and 11, remind them of the reflection property of an ellipse: A signal (light, whisper, pool ball) sent through one focus reflects off the ellipse and back through the other focus. **[Ask]** "What happens if one focus goes to infinity as the ellipse becomes a parabola?" [All signals starting at the remaining focus are reflected out of the parabola along parallel paths.]

[Ask] "Where are the parabola's focus and directrix on a cone?" Show Ellipse in a Cone from Lesson 9.2 as a transparency; the intersection points F_1 and F_2 are foci of the ellipse. Have students imagine what happens to point F_2 as the plane tilts so that it is parallel to one edge of the cone and the section becomes a parabola. The directrix of the parabola is the intersection of the plane of the parabola with the plane of the circle of intersection between the sphere and the cone. (Only one inscribed sphere is now tangent to the plane of the parabola.)

Ask whether an ellipse has a directrix—or perhaps two, one for each focus. It does have two directrices—intersections of the plane of the ellipse with the planes of the circles of intersection of the cone with the two spheres. Each point on the ellipse is

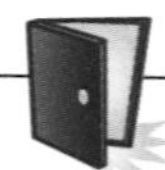

Investigation
Fold a Parabola

You will need
- patty paper
- graph paper

Fold the patty paper parallel to one edge to form the directrix for a parabola. Mark a point on the larger portion of the paper to serve as the focus for your parabola. Fold the paper so that the focus lies on the directrix. Unfold, and then fold again, so that the focus is at another point on the directrix. Repeat this many times. The creases from these folds should create a parabola. Lay the patty paper on top of a sheet of graph paper. Identify the coordinates of the focus and the equation of the directrix, and write an equation for your parabola.

EXERCISES

Practice Your Skills

1. For each parabola described, use the information given to find the location of the missing feature. It may help to draw a sketch.

a. If the focus is (1, 4), and the directrix is $y = -3$, where is the vertex? (1, 0.5)

b. If the vertex is $(-2, 2)$, and the focus is $(-2, -4)$, what is the equation of the directrix? $y = 8$

c. If the directrix is $x = 3$, and the vertex is (6, 2), where is the focus? (9, 2)

2. Sketch each parabola, and label the vertex and line of symmetry.

a. $\left(\frac{x}{2}\right)^2 + 5 = y$ **b.** $(y + 2)^2 - 2 = x$ **c.** $-(x + 3)^2 + 1 = 2y$

d. $2y^2 = -x + 4$ **e.** $x = 4t - 1$, $y = 2t^2 + 3$ **f.** $x = 3t^2 + 2$, $y = 5t$

3. Locate the focus and directrix for each graph in Exercise 2.

4. Write an equation in standard form for each parabola.

a.

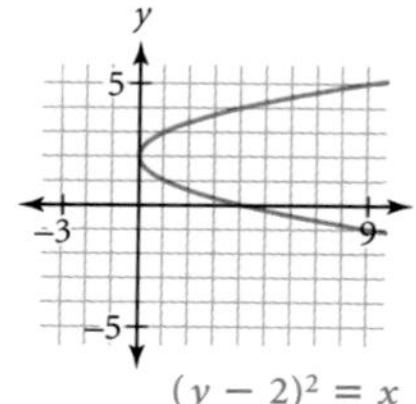

$(y - 2)^2 = x$

b.

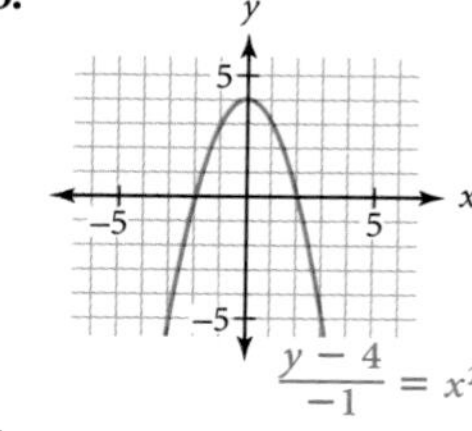

$\frac{y - 4}{-1} = x^2$

c.

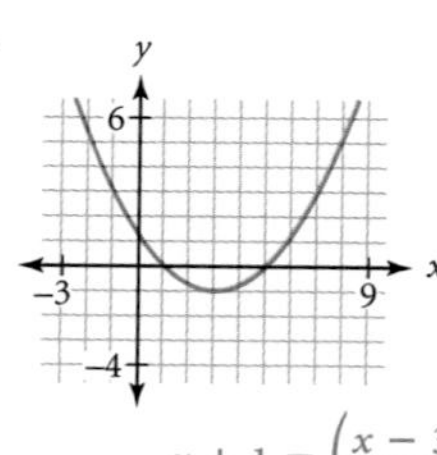

$y + 1 = \left(\frac{x - 3}{2}\right)^2$

d.

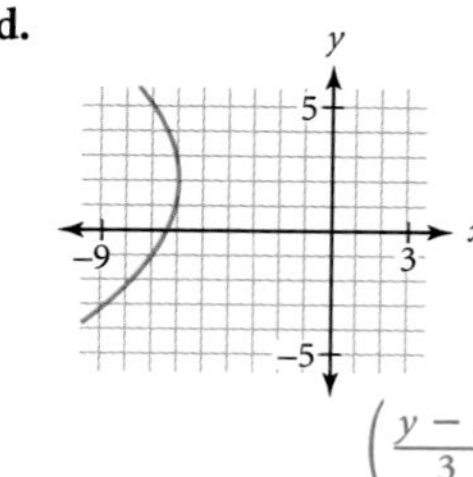

$\left(\frac{y - 2}{3}\right)^2 = \frac{x + 6}{-1}$

Sharing Ideas (continued)
closer to the focus than to the directrices, so an ellipse can be defined as a locus of points whose distances from a fixed point (focus) and line (directrix) have a constant ratio less than 1. This ratio is the eccentricity of the ellipse; the more eccentric (closer to a parabola) the ellipse is, the closer the eccentricity is to 1. Suggest that students conjecture about the directrix, focus, and eccentricity of a hyperbola as the plane continues to tilt. Hyperbolas are the topic of the next lesson.

BUILDING UNDERSTANDING

Students apply the definition of a parabola and its rectangular and parametric equations. If your students have not studied parametric equations, do not assign Exercises 2e, 2f, 3e, 3f, and 5.

ASSIGNING HOMEWORK

Essential	1–5
Performance assessment	6–11
Portfolio	10
Journal	8
Group	7, 11
Review	12–16

MATERIALS

- graph paper

Assessing Progress
Check students' skills at measuring and following directions and their familiarity with the shape and equations of parabolas.

Closing the Lesson

Reiterate that a **parabola** can be defined as a locus of points that are equidistant from a given point (the parabola's **focus**) and a given line (its **directrix**). Also restate the equations.

3a. focus: (0, 6); directrix: $y = 4$
3b. focus: $(-1.75, -2)$; directrix: $x = -2.25$
3c. focus: $(-3, 0)$; directrix: $y = 1$
3d. focus: (3.875, 0); directrix: $x = 4.125$
3e. focus: $(-1, 5)$; directrix: $y = 1$
3f. focus: $\left(\frac{61}{12}, 0\right)$; directrix: $x = \frac{11}{12}$

See page 894 for answers to Exercise 2.

Helping with the Exercises

5a. $x = t^2, y = t + 2$

5b. $x = t, y = -t^2 + 4$

5c. $x = 2t + 3, y = t^2 - 1$

5d. $x = -t^2 - 6, y = 3t + 2$

7. The path is parabolic. If you locate the rock at (0, 2) and the shoreline at $y = 0$, the equation is $y = \frac{1}{4}x^2 + 1$.

8a. $y = \frac{1}{8}x^2 + 1$

8b. The graph is a parabola with vertex at (0, 1), focus at (0, 3), and directrix $y = -1$.

9. $y = \frac{1}{8}(x - 1)^2 + 1$

Exercise 10 Urge students to sketch the parabola to scale on their graph paper.

MAKING THE CONNECTION

Concentrating solar collectors, which reflect solar energy into a single point, have applications far beyond solar cookers. For example, they are used in solar furnaces because they are more effective at producing high temperatures than solar panels. Solar collectors are also the least expensive means of large-scale solar energy generation. Some energy plants use the collectors to turn water into steam, which then drives turbines to produce electricity.

5. Write parametric equations for each parabola in Exercise 4.

Reason and Apply

6. Find the equation of the parabola with directrix $x = 3$ and vertex (0, 0). $y^2 = -12x$

7. The pilot of a small boat charts a course such that the boat will always be equidistant from an upcoming rock and the shoreline. Describe the path of the boat. If the rock is 2 miles offshore, write an equation for the path of the boat.

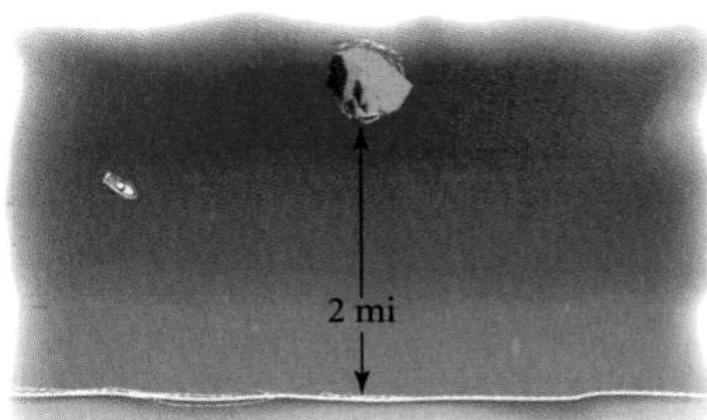

8. Consider the graph at right.

a. Because $d_1 = d_2$, you can write the equation

$$\sqrt{(x-0)^2 + (y-3)^2} = \sqrt{(x-x)^2 + (y+1)^2}$$

Rewrite this equation by solving for y.

b. Describe the graph represented by your equation from 8a.

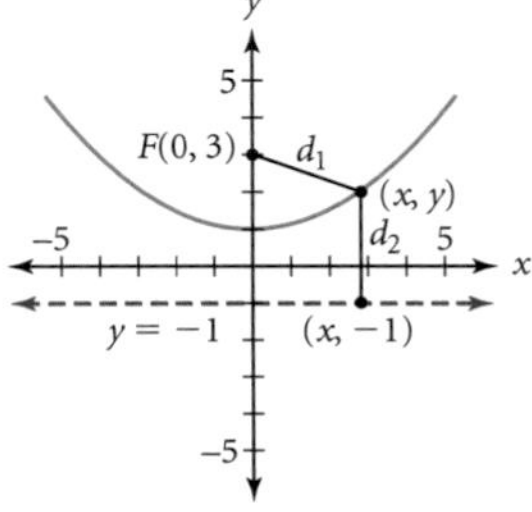

9. Write the equation of the parabola with focus (1, 3) and directrix $y = -1$.

10. APPLICATION Sheila is designing a parabolic dish to use for cooking on a camping trip. She plans to make the dish 40 cm wide and 20 cm deep. Where should she locate the cooking grill so that all of the light that enters the parabolic dish will be reflected toward the food? The grill should be located 5 cm from the center of the dish.

Environmental CONNECTION

Solar cookers focus the heat of the sun into a single spot, in order to boil water or cook food. A well-designed cooker can create heat up to 400°C. Solar cookers can be created with minimal materials, and can help save natural resources, particularly firewood. Inexpensive solar cookers are now being designed and distributed for use in developing countries. For more information on solar cookers, see the links at www.keymath.com/DAA .

A solar cooker fries an omelette.

11. The diagram at right shows the reflection of a ray of light in a parabolic reflector. The angles A and B are equal. Follow these steps to verify this property of parabolas.

a. Sketch the parabola $y^2 = 8x$.

b. What are the coordinates of the focus of this parabola? (2, 0)

c. On the same graph, sketch the line $y = 2x + 1$, tangent to the parabola. Find the coordinates of the point of tangency. What is the slope of this line?

d. Sketch a ray through the point of tangency parallel to the axis of symmetry. What is the slope of this line?

e. Draw the segment from the point of intersection to the focus. What is the slope of this segment?

f. The formula $\tan A = \frac{m_2 - m_1}{1 + m_2 m_1}$ applies when $\angle A$ is the angle between two lines with slopes m_1 and m_2. Use this formula to find the angle between the tangent line and the horizontal line. Then find the angle between the tangent line and the segment joining the focus and the point of tangency. What do you notice about the angles? 63.4°; 63.4°; the angles are congruent.

Technology CONNECTION

The reflective backing in a flashlight is in the shape of a paraboloid. The light source is at the focus, and the light rays reflect off the backing and travel outward parallel to the axis of symmetry. But not all light backings are parabolic. Next time you're sitting in the dentist's chair, see if you can determine the shape of the reflective surface of the light used. It may be a parabola, but it could also be an ellipse. A light source at the focus of an elliptical reflector travels to the other focus of the ellipse, illuminating an area smaller than the area that would be illuminated by a parabolic reflector.

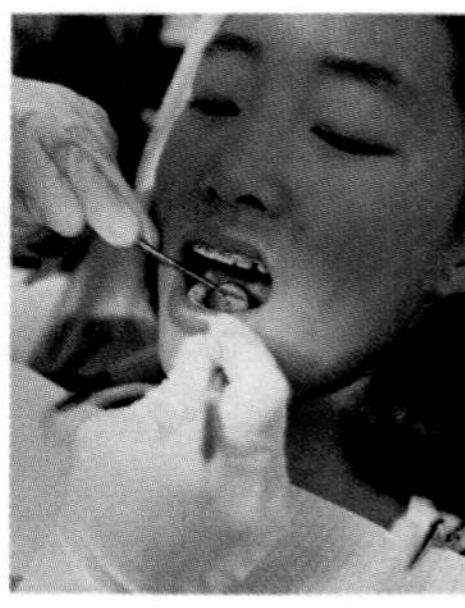

Review

6.3 **12.** Find the equation that describes a parabola containing the points (3.6, 0.764), (5, 1.436), and (5.8, −2.404). $y = -2.4x^2 + 21.12x - 44.164$

9.1 **13.** Find the minimum distance from the origin to the parabola $y = -x^2 + 1$. What point(s) on the parabola is closest to the origin?

9.2 **14.** Find the equation of the ellipse with foci (−6, 1) and (10, 1) that passes through the point (10, 13).

7.8 **15.** Consider the polynomial function $f(x) = 2x^3 - 5x^2 + 22x - 10$.

a. What are the possible rational roots of $f(x)$? $\pm1, \pm2, \pm5, \pm10, \pm\frac{1}{2}, \pm\frac{5}{2}$

b. Find all rational roots. $\frac{1}{2}$ is the only rational root.

c. Write the equation in factored form. $f(x) = (2x - 1)(x - 1 + 3i)(x - 1 - 3i)$

6.4 **16.** On a three-dimensional coordinate system with variables x, y, and z, the standard equation of a plane is in the form $ax + by + cz = d$. Find the intersection of the three planes described by $3x + y + 2z = -11$, $-4x + 3y + 3z = -2$, and $x - 2y - z = -3$. $x = -1, y = 4, z = -6$

Exercise 11 [Language] A *point of tangency* is the point at which a tangent line intersects a curve.

Exercise 13 [Alert] Students probably will not find exact answers to this exercise. Exact answers can be found by completing the square for the equation $0 = x^4 - x^2 + 1$.

13. $\frac{\sqrt{3}}{2}$ or approximately 0.8660; $\left(\pm\frac{\sqrt{2}}{2}, \frac{1}{2}\right)$ or approximately (±0.7071, 0.5)

Exercise 14 Encourage students to graph the ellipse before finding its equation.

14. $\left(\frac{x-2}{16}\right)^2 + \left(\frac{y-1}{\sqrt{192}}\right)^2 = 1$ or $\left(\frac{x-2}{16}\right)^2 + \left(\frac{y-1}{8\sqrt{3}}\right)^2 = 1$

Exercise 16 If students are having trouble getting started, **[Ask]** "Is finding the intersection of three planes analogous to finding the intersection of two lines?" [In both cases, students solve a system of equations.]

EXTENSIONS

A. If you did not use the Sketchpad demonstration Definition of Parabola, ask students to explore the demonstration on their own.

B. Ask students to use geometry software to complete Exercise 11.

C. You might have students research applications of parabolic reflectors.

11a, c.

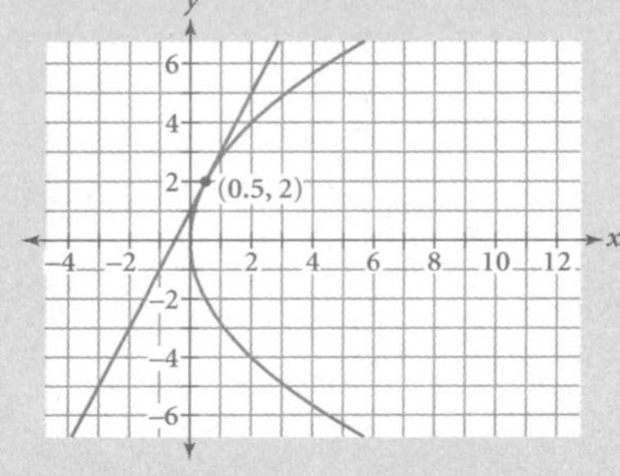

(0.5, 2); $m = 2$

11d.

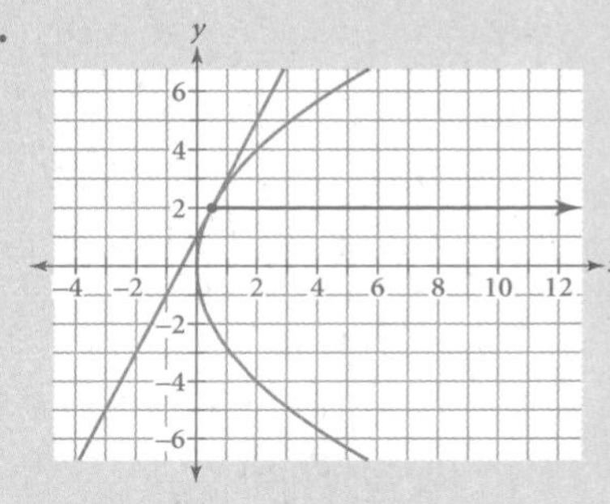

$m = 0$

11e.

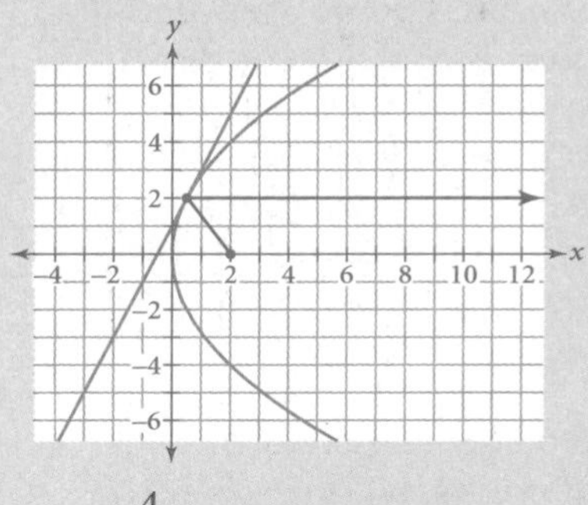

$m = -\frac{4}{3}$

LESSON
9.4

PLANNING

LESSON OUTLINE

First day:

10 min Example A

10 min Example B

15 min Investigation

10 min Exercises

Second day:

10 min Investigation

10 min Sharing

10 min Example C

15 min Exercises

MATERIALS

- motion sensors
- Hyperbola in a Cone (W) for One Step
- Passing By Sample Data (T), *optional*
- Definition of Hyperbola (T), *optional*
- Sketchpad demonstration Definition of Hyperbola, *optional*

TEACHING

In this lesson students learn about the fourth conic section, the hyperbola. If you have only one day to spend on this lesson, you might skip Example A and the investigation.

One Step

Hand out the Hyperbola in a Cone worksheet and ask students to investigate whether hyperbolas have a property analogous to the constant-sum property of ellipses. As needed, remind them that for ellipses they used the fact that the tangent segments to a circle from a point have the same length. Challenge groups that quickly find the constant-difference property to use it to find the equation of a hyperbola centered at the origin. Even if they don't succeed, they'll be able to contribute to its derivation during Sharing, at which time you can also point out the asymptotes.

LESSON
9.4 Hyperbolas

The best paths usually lead to the most remote places.

SUSAN ALLEN TOTH

The fourth, and final, conic section is the hyperbola. Comets travel in orbits that are parabolic, elliptical, or hyperbolic. A comet that comes close to another object, but never returns, is on a hyperbolic path. The two light shadows on a wall next to a cylindrical lampshade form two branches of a hyperbola. And a sonic-boom shock wave formed along the ground by a plane traveling faster than sound is one branch of a hyperbola.

Acqua Alle Funi stands before Wilson Hall at the Fermi National Accelerator Laboratory in Batavia, Illinois. The 32 ft sculpture is a hyperbolic obelisk designed by physicist and sculptor Robert Wilson (1914–2000), founder of the laboratory.

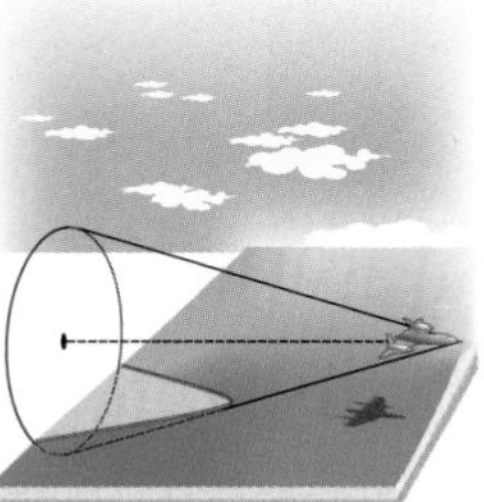

Science CONNECTION

When an aircraft reaches the speed of its own sound, the airflow around the craft changes significantly, causing a disturbance in the air particles. If an aircraft catches up with its own noise, which travels ahead of it at a limited speed, the sound then compresses the air and piles up at the nose of the aircraft. This air causes a shock wave against the craft, which may cause it to vibrate or lock its controls. If the aircraft moves past the speed of sound, the shock waves fall behind the vehicle and cause a sonic boom. Because sonic booms are powerful enough to damage property on land and cause noise pollution, most supersonic flights take place above ocean waters. For more information on sonic booms, see the weblinks at www.keymath.com/DAA .

Definition of a Hyperbola

A **hyperbola** is a locus of points P in a plane, the difference of whose distances, d_1 and d_2, from two fixed points, F_1 and F_2, is always a constant, d. That is, $|d_2 - d_1| = d$, or $|F_2P - F_1P| = d$. The two fixed points, F_1 and F_2, are called **foci.** The points where the two branches of a hyperbola are closest to each other are called **vertices.** The **center** of a hyperbola is midway between the vertices.

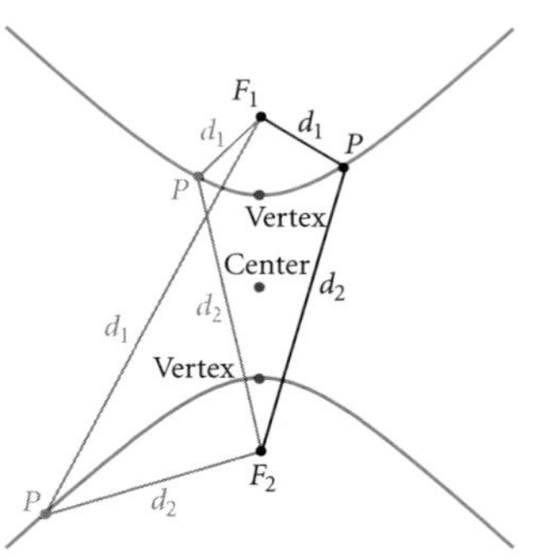

INTRODUCTION

[Ask] "Why does the constant equal the distance between the two vertices?" [The vertices are the same distance from their closer foci.]

[Context] The photograph title translates to "Water of the Rope," referring to a time when an obelisk was being erected by pulleys. The obelisk threatened to topple so water was used to stiffen the ropes.

LESSON OBJECTIVES

- Introduce the locus definition of *hyperbola* and new vocabulary associated with a hyperbola
- Understand the relationship between the locus definition, the equation, and the graph of a hyperbola
- Determine the location of the asymptotes, vertices, and foci of a hyperbola from its equation
- Graph a hyperbola by hand and on a calculator

Regardless of where a point is on a hyperbola, the difference in the distances from the point to the two foci is constant. Notice that this constant is equal to the distance between the two vertices of the hyperbola. The hyperbola shown is oriented vertically. In Example A, you will see a hyperbola that is oriented horizontally.

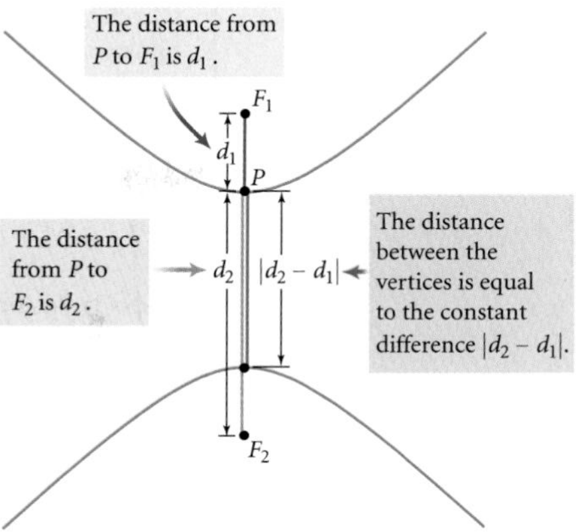

EXAMPLE A

Just as the parent equation of any circle is a unit circle, $x^2 + y^2 = 1$, the parent equation of a hyperbola is called a **unit hyperbola.** The horizontally oriented unit hyperbola has vertices (1, 0) and (−1, 0), and foci $(\sqrt{2}, 0)$ and $(-\sqrt{2}, 0)$. The distance between the vertices is 2, so the difference in the distances from any point on the hyperbola to the two foci is 2. Find the equation of a unit hyperbola.

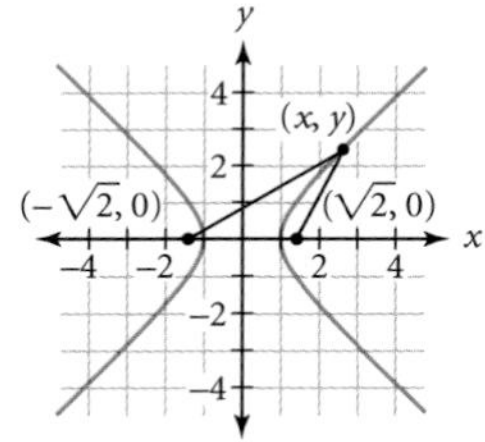

▶ EXAMPLE A

If time is limited, you might skip this example and state the general form of the unit hyperbola without its derivation.

The derivation begins with writing the difference of distances from the point (x, y) to the foci $(-\sqrt{2}, 0)$ and $(\sqrt{2}, 0)$.

The dynamic model of a geometric construction of a hyperbola at www.keymath.com/DAA can be used to extend this lesson.

▶ Solution

Label a point on the hyperbola (x, y). Then use the definition of a hyperbola.

$\left\lvert\sqrt{(x+\sqrt{2})^2+y^2}-\sqrt{(x-\sqrt{2})^2+y^2}\right\rvert = 2$	Definition of hyperbola states that $\lvert d_2 - d_1\rvert$ is a constant, in this case 2.
$\sqrt{(x+\sqrt{2})^2+y^2}-\sqrt{(x-\sqrt{2})^2+y^2} = 2$	Consider the case $d_2 > d_1$.
$\sqrt{(x+\sqrt{2})^2+y^2}=\sqrt{(x-\sqrt{2})^2+y^2} + 2$	Add $\sqrt{(x-\sqrt{2})^2+y^2}$ to both sides.
$(x+\sqrt{2})^2+y^2=(x-\sqrt{2})^2+y^2+4\sqrt{(x-\sqrt{2})^2+y^2}+4$	Square both sides.
$x^2+2x\sqrt{2}+2+y^2=x^2-2x\sqrt{2}+2+y^2+4\sqrt{(x-\sqrt{2})^2+y^2}+4$	Expand.
$2x\sqrt{2}=-2x\sqrt{2}+4\sqrt{(x-\sqrt{2})^2+y^2}+4$	Subtract x^2, y^2, and 2 from both sides.
$4x\sqrt{2}-4=4\sqrt{(x-\sqrt{2})^2+y^2}$	Isolate the radical.
$x\sqrt{2}-1=\sqrt{(x-\sqrt{2})^2+y^2}$	Divide by 4.
$2x^2-2x\sqrt{2}+1=x^2-2x\sqrt{2}+2+y^2$	Square both sides and expand.
$x^2-y^2=1$	Combine like terms, and collect variables on one side of the equation.

If you consider the case $d_1 > d_2$ you find the same equation for the unit hyperbola.

NCTM STANDARDS

CONTENT		PROCESS	
	Number		Problem Solving
✓	Algebra	✓	Reasoning
✓	Geometry	✓	Communication
	Measurement	✓	Connections
✓	Data/Probability	✓	Representation

[Ask] "Do parabolas have asymptotes?" [No; they never approach a constant value.]

Check your answer by graphing on a calculator. First you must solve for y.

$$\begin{aligned} x^2 - y^2 &= 1 \\ -y^2 &= 1 - x^2 \\ y^2 &= x^2 - 1 \\ y &= \pm\sqrt{x^2 - 1} \end{aligned}$$

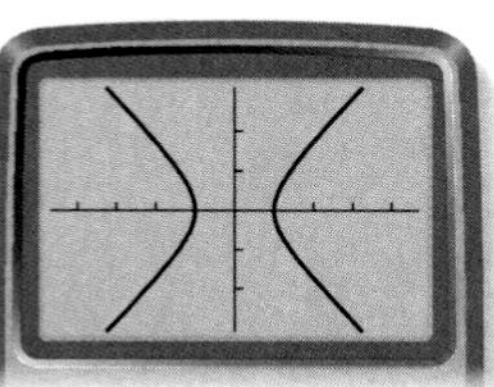

[–4.7, 4.7, 1, –3.1, 3.1, 1]

One special feature of a hyperbola is that each branch approaches two lines called **asymptotes.** Asymptotes are lines that a graph approaches as x- or y-values increase in the positive or negative direction. If you include the graphs of $y = x$ and $y = -x$ on the same coordinate axes, you will notice that they pass through the vertices of a square with corners at $(1, 1)$, $(1, -1)$, $(-1, -1)$, and $(-1, 1)$. The asymptotes are not a part of the hyperbola, but sometimes they are shown to help you see the behavior of the curve. Sketching asymptotes will help you graph hyperbolas more accurately.

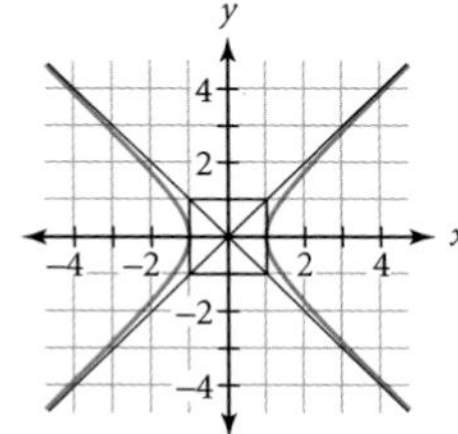

The equation $y^2 - x^2 = 1$ also defines a hyperbola, shown at right. Look at the similarities to, and the differences from, the graph of $x^2 - y^2 = 1$. The features are similar, but the hyperbola is oriented vertically.

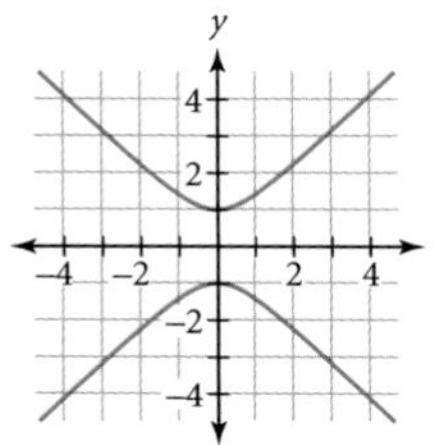

The equation of a hyperbola is similar to the equation of an ellipse, except that the terms are subtracted, rather than added. For example, the equation $\left(\frac{y}{4}\right)^2 - \left(\frac{x}{3}\right)^2 = 1$ describes a hyperbola, whereas $\left(\frac{y}{4}\right)^2 + \left(\frac{x}{3}\right)^2 = 1$ describes an ellipse. The standard form of the equation of a hyperbola centered at the origin is

$$\left(\frac{x}{a}\right)^2 - \left(\frac{y}{b}\right)^2 = 1 \text{ or } \left(\frac{y}{b}\right)^2 - \left(\frac{x}{a}\right)^2 = 1$$

where a is the horizontal scale factor and b is the vertical scale factor.

► ***EXAMPLE B***

The best way to get an accurate sketch by hand is to first determine the rectangle and then sketch in the asymptotes before actually graphing the hyperbola.

[Ask] "How do you know that this hyperbola is vertically oriented?" [The x^2-term is subtracted from the y^2-term. If $x = 0$, then y is defined; but if $y = 0$, x isn't defined, because a negative number would have to equal a positive number. Therefore the figure has y-intercepts but not x-intercepts.]

[Ask] "Is there a way to check the reasonableness of the asymptote equations?" [Choose a large value for x, and show that the hyperbola is very near an asymptote at that point.]

EXAMPLE B Graph $\left(\frac{y}{4}\right)^2 - \left(\frac{x}{3}\right)^2 = 1$.

► ***Solution***

From the equation, you can tell that this is a vertically oriented hyperbola with a vertical scale factor of 4 and a horizontal scale factor of 3. The hyperbola is not translated, so its center is at the origin. To graph it on your calculator, you must solve for y.

$$\begin{aligned} \left(\frac{y}{4}\right)^2 - \left(\frac{x}{3}\right)^2 &= 1 \\ \left(\frac{y}{4}\right)^2 &= 1 + \left(\frac{x}{3}\right)^2 \\ \left(\frac{y}{4}\right) &= \pm\sqrt{1 + \left(\frac{x}{3}\right)^2} \\ y &= \pm 4\sqrt{1 + \left(\frac{x}{3}\right)^2} \end{aligned}$$

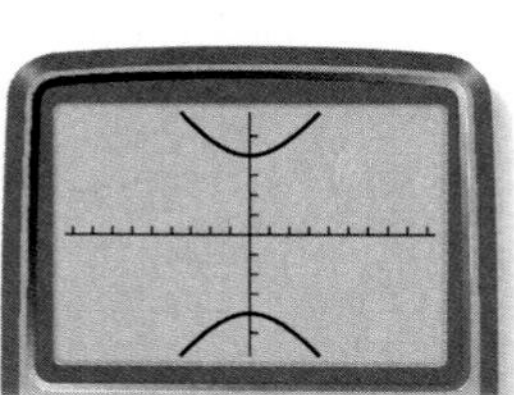

[–9.4, 9.4, 1, –6.2, 6.2, 1]

To sketch a hyperbola by hand, it is easiest if you begin by sketching the asymptotes. Start by drawing a rectangle centered at the origin that measures $2a$, or 6, units horizontally and $2b$, or 8, units vertically. The unit hyperbola begins with a 2-by-2 rectangle. Because this hyperbola is stretched horizontally and vertically, it begins with a 6-by-8 rectangle.

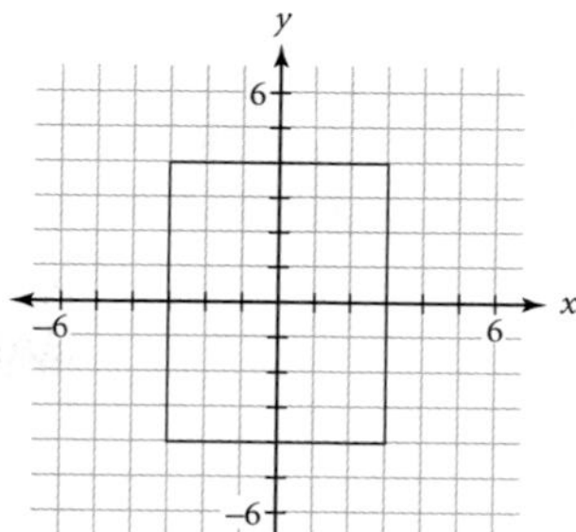

Draw the diagonals of this rectangle, and extend them outside the rectangle. These lines, with equations $y = \pm\frac{4}{3}x$, are the asymptotes of the hyperbola. In general, the slopes of the asymptotes of a hyperbola are $\pm\frac{b}{a}$.

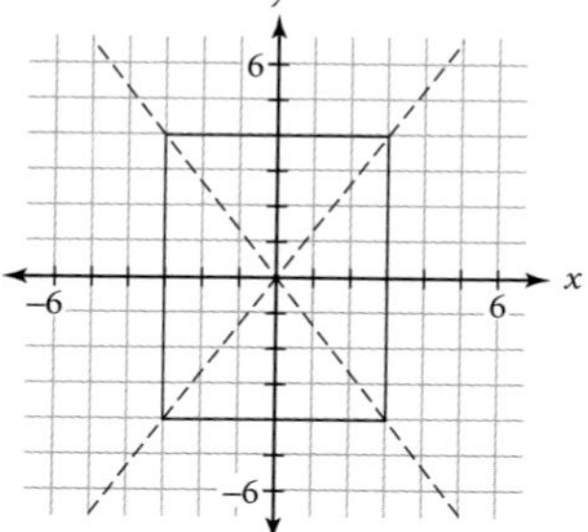

Because this is a vertically oriented hyperbola, the vertices will lie on the top and bottom sides of the rectangle, at (0, 4) and (0, −4). Add two curves such that each one touches a vertex and extends outward, approaching the asymptotes. You can graph the two asymptotes on your calculator to confirm that the hyperbola does approach them asymptotically.

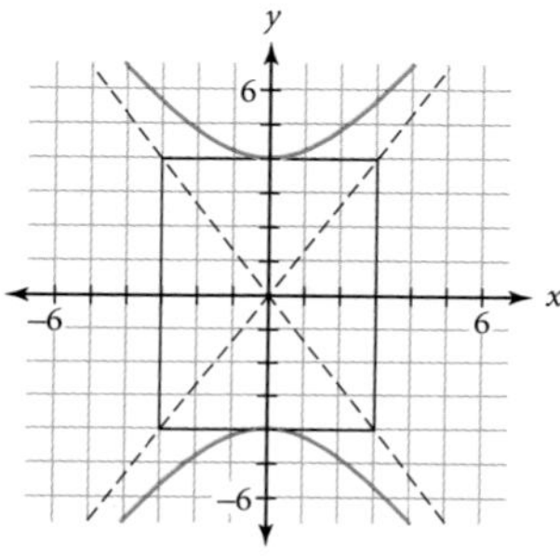

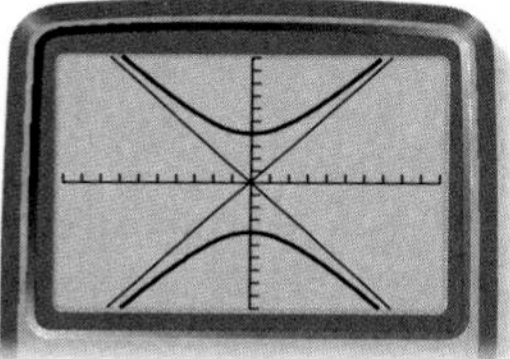

[−10, 10, 1, −10, 10, 1]

The location of foci in a hyperbola is related to a circle that can be drawn through the four corners of the asymptote rectangle. The distance from the center of the hyperbola to the foci is equal to the radius of the circle.

To locate the foci in a hyperbola, you can use the relationship $a^2 + b^2 = c^2$, where a and b are the horizontal and vertical scale factors. In the hyperbola from Example B, shown at right, $3^2 + 4^2 = c^2$, so $c = 5$, and the foci are 5 units above and below the center of the hyperbola at (0, 5) and (0, −5).

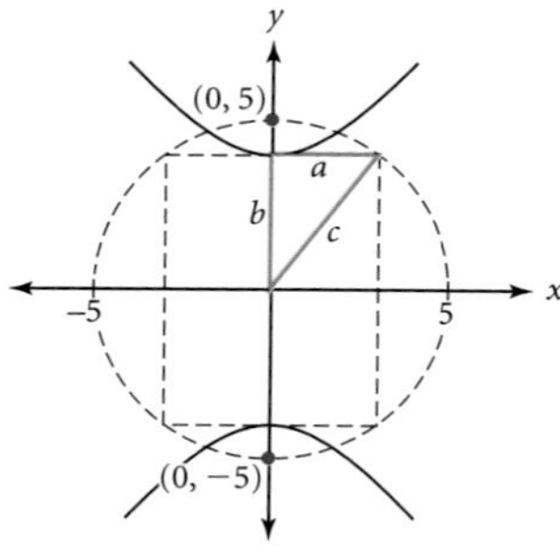

In the investigation you will explore a situation that produces hyperbolic data and find a curve to fit your data.

Slope of the Asymptotes
To guide students in understanding why the slope of the asymptotes is $\pm\frac{b}{a}$, rewrite the equation $\left(\frac{x}{a}\right)^2 - \left(\frac{y}{b}\right)^2 = 1$ in the equivalent form $y = \pm b\sqrt{\left(\frac{x}{a}\right)^2 - 1}$. As x gets increasingly large in magnitude, -1 in this equation becomes less and less significant. So the hyperbola $y = \pm b\sqrt{\left(\frac{x}{a}\right)^2 - 1}$ becomes increasingly close to $y = \pm b\sqrt{\left(\frac{x}{a}\right)^2}$, or $y = \pm b \cdot \frac{x}{a} = \pm\frac{b}{a}x$. A horizontal or vertical translation will translate these asymptotes but will not change their slopes.

The window used for the calculator graph gives a good picture of the hyperbola. However, the graph of the related circle would not look good in the nonfriendly window.

Once the vertices and asymptotes are known, you can substitute in several values of x and find the corresponding values of y to accurately draw the hyperbola.

Guiding the Investigation

You might use the Passing By Sample Data transparency to allow you to skip the first two steps and to provide common data to discuss during Sharing. (All sample data are available on the Calculator Programs and Data CD.)

Step 1 Acquiring adequate data may require several attempts. It is important that the walker walks at a steady pace.

Step 2 [Ask] "Where will the asymptotes intersect?" [at the origin] Students may want to transfer their data to graph paper at this step. Once they graph both branches of the hyperbola, it will be easier for them to visualize the asymptotes. After they have found the asymptotes on graph paper and used them to write the equation, they can graph it on their calculators to compare its graph with the data.

Step 2 Experiment to find asymptotes. $y = 1.3(x - 3.8)$ and $y = -1.3(x - 3.8)$ work well for the sample data.

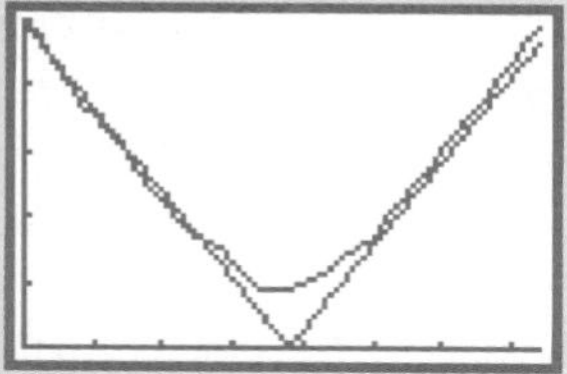

[0, 7.4, 1, 0, 5, 1]

Asymptotes have slope $\pm\frac{b}{a}$, so $\frac{b}{a} = 1.3$. The center of the hyperbola is (3.8, 0), and, according to the sample data, the vertex is approximately (3.8, 0.9). So the value of b, the vertical stretch, is 0.9. So $a = \frac{0.9}{1.3}$, or approximately 0.7. The equation for the vertically oriented hyperbola is $\left(\frac{y}{0.9}\right)^2 - \left(\frac{x-3.8}{0.7}\right)^2 = 1$.

Step 3 The distances from the center to the foci are determined by $0.9^2 + 0.7^2 = c^2$, so $c = 1.14$, and the foci are (3.8, 1.14) and (3.8, −1.14).

See page 894 for answers to Step 1.

Investigation
Passing By

You will need

- a motion sensor

Procedure Note

1. One member of your group will use a motion sensor to measure the distance to the walker for 10 s. The motion sensor must be kept pointed at the walker.
2. The walker should start about 5 m to the left of the sensor holder. He or she should walk at a steady pace, continuing past the sensor holder, and stop about 5 m to the right of the sensor holder. Be sure the walker stays at least 0.5 meter in front of the sensor holder.

Step 1 Collect data as described in the procedure note. Transfer these data from the motion sensor to each calculator in the group, and graph your data. They should form one branch of a hyperbola.

Step 2 Assume the sensor was held at the center of the hyperbola, and find an equation to fit your data. You may want to try to graph the asymptotes first.

Step 3 Transfer your graph to paper, and add the foci and the other branch of the hyperbola. To verify your equation, choose at least two points on the curve and measure their distances from the foci. Calculate the differences between the distances from each focus. What do you notice? Why?

Equation of a Hyperbola

The standard form of the equation of a horizontally oriented hyperbola with center (h, k), horizontal scale factor of a, and vertical scale factor of b is

$$\left(\frac{x-h}{a}\right)^2 - \left(\frac{y-k}{b}\right)^2 = 1$$

or, in parametric form,

$$x = \frac{a}{\cos t} + h$$
$$y = b\tan t + k$$

The equation of a vertically oriented hyperbola under the same conditions is

$$\left(\frac{y-k}{b}\right)^2 - \left(\frac{x-h}{a}\right)^2 = 1$$

or, in parametric form,

$$x = a\tan t + h$$
$$y = \frac{b}{\cos t} + k$$

The foci are located c units from the center, where $a^2 + b^2 = c^2$. The asymptotes pass through the center and have slope $\pm\frac{b}{a}$.

Calculating $d_2 - d_1$ for two different points gives approximately 1.8 units. The differences in the distances are the same. This is the locus definition of a hyperbola.

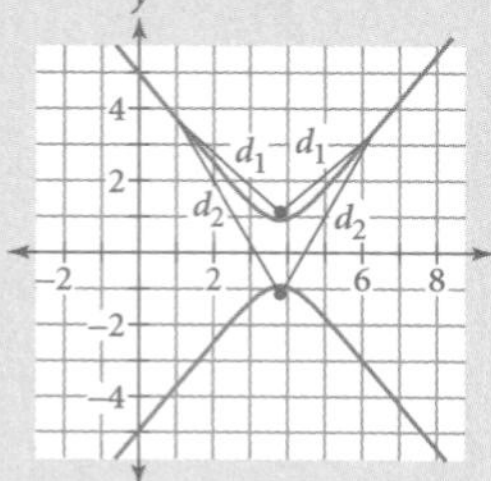

Assessing Progress

As students present their ideas, you can assess their ability to follow instructions, to make careful measurements, and to see patterns in data.

EXAMPLE C

Write the equation of this hyperbola in standard form, and find the foci.

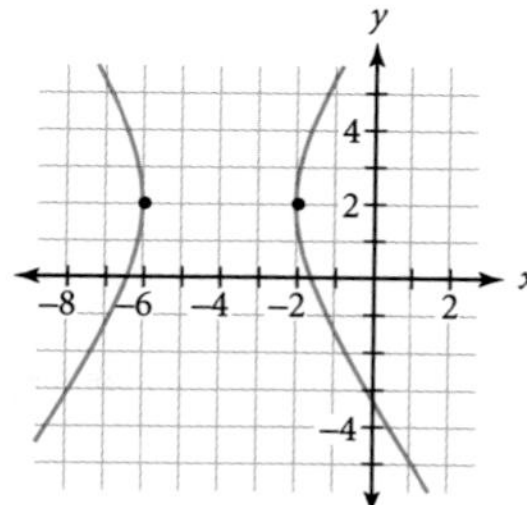

▶ Solution

The center is halfway between the vertices, at the point $(-4, 2)$. The horizontal distance from the center to the vertex, a, is 2. If you knew the location of the asymptotes, you could find the value of b using the fact that the slopes of asymptotes of a hyperbola are $\pm\frac{b}{a}$. In this case, the value of b is not as easy to find. Write the equation, substituting the values you know.

$$\left(\frac{x+4}{2}\right)^2 - \left(\frac{y-2}{b}\right)^2 = 1$$

To solve for b, choose another point on the curve and substitute. It appears that the point $(0, -3.2)$ is on the curve. Because this is an estimate, your value of b will be an approximation.

$$\left(\frac{0+4}{2}\right)^2 - \left(\frac{-3.2-2}{b}\right)^2 = 1$$ Substitute 0 for x and -3.2 for y.

$$(2)^2 - \left(\frac{-5.2}{b}\right)^2 = 1$$ Add and divide.

$$4 - \frac{27.04}{b^2} = 1$$ Square.

$$-\frac{27.04}{b^2} = -3$$ Subtract 4 from both sides.

$$9.013 = b^2$$ Multiply by b^2 and divide by -3 on both sides.

$$3.002 \approx b$$ Take the square root of both sides.

The value of b is approximately 3, so the equation of the hyperbola is close to

$$\left(\frac{x+4}{2}\right)^2 - \left(\frac{y-2}{3}\right)^2 = 1$$

To write the equation in parametric form, you can simply substitute the values of a, b, h, and k, to get $x = \frac{2}{\cos t} - 4$ and $y = 3\tan t + 2$.

You can find the distance to the foci by using the equation $a^2 + b^2 = c^2$.

$$2^2 + 3^2 = c^2$$
$$13 = c^2$$
$$13 = c^2$$
$$\pm\sqrt{13} = c$$

So, the foci are $\sqrt{13}$ to the right and left of the center at $(-4 + \sqrt{13}, 2)$ and $(-4 - \sqrt{13}, 2)$, or approximately $(-0.39, 2)$ and $(-7.6, 2)$.

You will continue to explore the relationship between the equation and graph of a hyperbola in the exercises.

▶ EXAMPLE C

You might use the Definition of Hyperbola transparency as you discuss this example. Encourage students to follow the process shown in the book, but with other values. **[Ask]** "Could you use the point $(-6, 2)$ to find b?" [No; any value of b satisfies the equation $\left(\frac{-2}{2}\right)^2 + \left(\frac{0}{b}\right)^2 = 1$, because infinitely many hyperbolas have these two vertices.]

SHARING IDEAS

As students present ideas from the investigation, ask why these data form one branch of a hyperbola. After all, the physical movement is steady along a line, not hyperbolic. If you diagram the situation, you see that the variables satisfy the equation $y^2 = x^2 + L^2$, or $y^2 - x^2 = L^2$, the equation of a hyperbola.

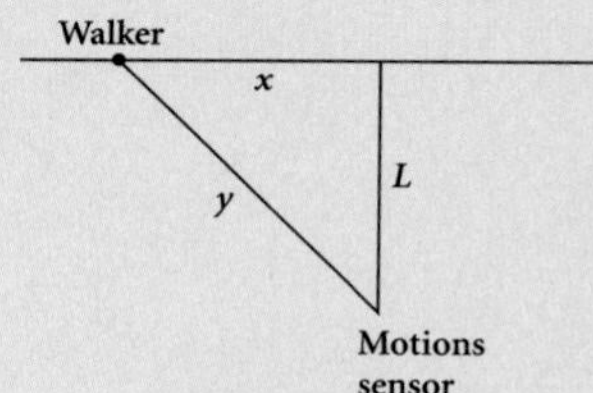

Remind students that the conic sections are all sections of a double cone, and ask how their equations relate. The equation $y^2 = px + kx^2$ shows the relationship: If $k < 0$, the equation represents an ellipse; if $k = 0$, it represents a horizontal parabola; and if $k > 0$, it represents a hyperbola. In fact, the geometric representation of these equations might be why the Greeks decided on the names they did. **[Language]** An ellipse is something lacking (as in the word *ellipsis*); *parabola* means "equal" (as in the phrase *on a par with*); and a hyperbola means an excess (as in *being hyper* or *hyperbole*).

[Ask] "Does a hyperbola have directrices and eccentricity?" Show Hyperbola in a Cone as a transparency. Try to avoid judging students' initial ideas; let the discussion itself convince them of the rightness or wrongness of

Sharing Ideas (continued)

their conjectures. The foci are still at the points of tangency of the spheres and the plane of the section. The directrices are still at the intersections of that plane with the circles of intersection between the cone and the spheres. The directrices lie between the two branches of the hyperbola. Points on the hyperbola are farther from the foci than from the directrices, so the eccentricity (the ratio of these distances) is more than 1. Students may be able to see from the diagram that the difference of the distances of point P from the foci, as with the ellipse, equals the constant distance between the two circles of intersection.

You might show the Sketchpad demonstration Definition of a Hyperbola and talk about the Sketchpad construction of a hyperbola.

Closing the Lesson

Summarize by saying that a **hyperbola** can be defined as the points on a plane whose distances from two fixed points, its **foci,** have a constant difference. Also restate the equations.

BUILDING UNDERSTANDING

If your students have not studied parametric equations, do not assign Exercises 1e, 1f, 2e, 2f, 4, and 16c.

ASSIGNING HOMEWORK

Essential	1–5
Performance assessment	6–12
Portfolio	6, 10
Journal	10, 12
Group	9–11
Review	13–18

MATERIALS

- graph paper

Helping with the Exercises

2a. $(\sqrt{20}, 0)$ and $(-\sqrt{20}, 0)$ or $(2\sqrt{5}, 0)$ and $(-2\sqrt{5}, 0)$

2b. $(2, -2 + \sqrt{10})$ and $(2, -2 - \sqrt{10})$

2c. $(4 + \sqrt{18}, 1)$ and $(4 - \sqrt{18}, 1)$

2d. $(-2, -1 + \sqrt{13})$ and $(-2, -1 - \sqrt{13})$

2e. $(-1 + \sqrt{20}, 3)$ and $(-1 - \sqrt{20}, 3)$

2f. $(3, \sqrt{34})$ and $(3, -\sqrt{34})$

3a. $\left(\frac{x}{2}\right)^2 - \left(\frac{y}{1}\right)^2 = 1$

3b. $\left(\frac{y+3}{2}\right)^2 - \left(\frac{x-3}{2}\right)^2 = 1$

3c. $\left(\frac{x+2}{3}\right)^2 - \left(\frac{y-1}{4}\right)^2 = 1$

3d. $\left(\frac{y-1}{4}\right)^2 - \left(\frac{x+2}{3}\right)^2 = 1$

4a. $x = \frac{2}{\cos t}, y = \tan t$

4b. $x = 2\tan t + 3$, $y = \frac{2}{\cos t} - 3$

See pages 894–895 for answers to Exercise 1.

EXERCISES

Practice Your Skills

1. Sketch each hyperbola on your paper. Write the coordinates of each vertex and the equation of each asymptote.

a. $\left(\frac{x}{2}\right)^2 - \left(\frac{y}{4}\right)^2 = 1$ **b.** $\left(\frac{y+2}{1}\right)^2 - \left(\frac{x-2}{3}\right)^2 = 1$ **c.** $\left(\frac{x-4}{3}\right)^2 - \left(\frac{y-1}{3}\right)^2 = 1$

d. $y = \pm 2\sqrt{1 + \left(\frac{x+2}{3}\right)^2} - 1$ **e.** $x = \frac{4}{\cos t} - 1$, $y = 2\tan t + 3$ **f.** $x = 3\tan t + 3$, $y = \frac{5}{\cos t}$

2. What are the coordinates of the foci of each hyperbola in Exercise 1?

3. Write an equation in standard form for each graph.

a.

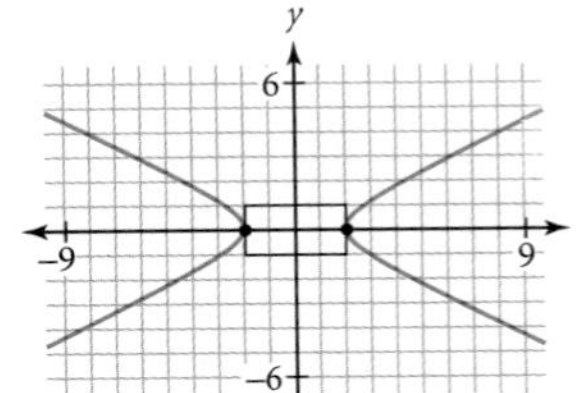

b.

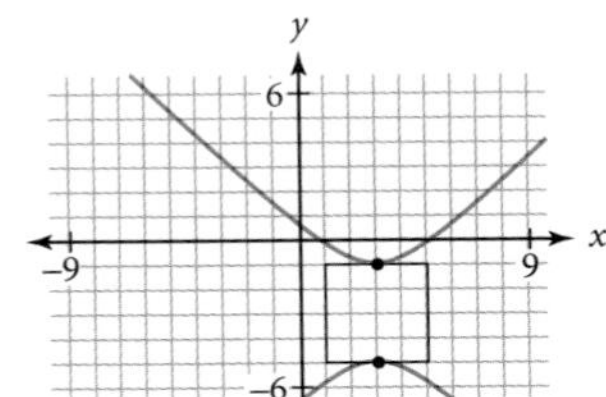

c.

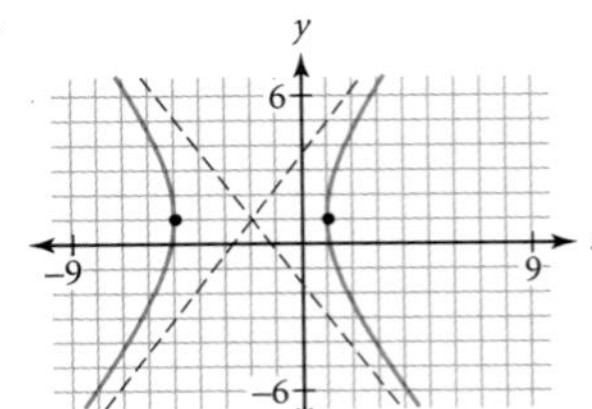

d.

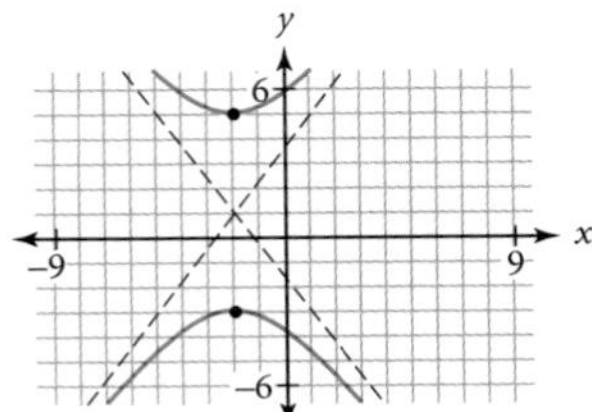

4. Write parametric equations for each graph in Exercise 3.

5. Write the equations of the asymptotes for each hyperbola in Exercise 3.

Reason and Apply

6. Another way to locate the foci of a hyperbola is by rotating the asymptote rectangle about its center so that opposite corners lie on the line of symmetry that contains the vertices of the hyperbola. From the diagram, you can see that the distance from the origin to a focus is one-half the length of the diagonal of the rectangle.

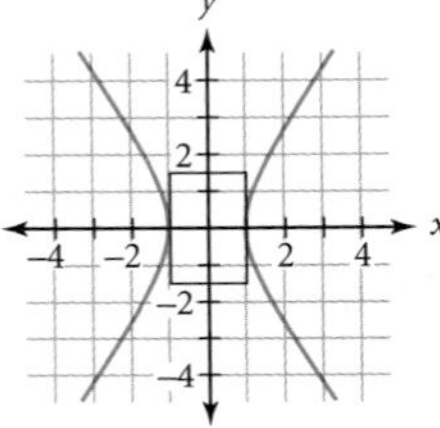

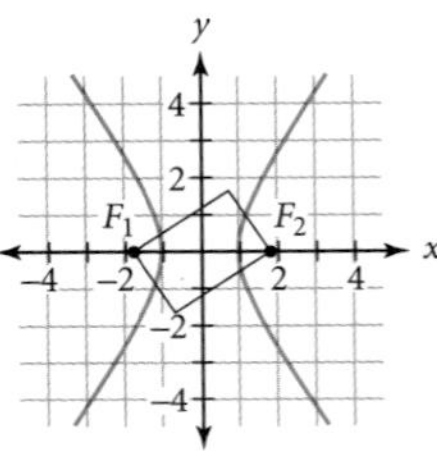

a. Show that this distance is $\sqrt{a^2 + b^2}$.

b. Find the coordinates of the foci for $\left(\frac{y+2}{1}\right)^2 - \left(\frac{x-2}{3}\right)^2 = 1$.

4c. $x = \frac{3}{\cos t} - 2, y = 4\tan t + 1$

4d. $x = 3\tan t - 2, y = \frac{4}{\cos t} + 1$

5a. $y = \pm 0.5x$

5b. $y = x - 6$ and $y = -x$

5c. $y = \frac{4}{3}x + \frac{11}{3}$ and $y = -\frac{4}{3}x - \frac{5}{3}$

5d. $y = \frac{4}{3}x + \frac{11}{3}$ and $y = -\frac{4}{3}x - \frac{5}{3}$

Exercise 6 [Ask] "The distance $\sqrt{a^2 + b^2}$ looks like the Pythagorean Theorem or maybe the equation of a circle. Can you use a circle to find the foci of a hyperbola?" [Construct a circle from the center of the asymptote rectangle to one of its vertices. The foci will be the points where the circle intersects the line of symmetry.]

6a. The lengths of the sides of the asymptote rectangle are $2a$ and $2b$. Using the Pythagorean Theorem, the length of the diagonal is $\sqrt{(2a)^2 + (2b)^2} = \sqrt{4a^2 + 4b^2} = \sqrt{4(a^2 + b^2)} = 2\sqrt{a^2 + b^2}$. Half this distance is $\sqrt{a^2 + b^2}$.

6b. $\left(2, -2 + \frac{\sqrt{10}}{2}\right)$ and $\left(2, -2 - \frac{\sqrt{10}}{2}\right)$

7. A point moves in a plane so that the difference of its distances from $(-5, 1)$ and $(7, 1)$ is always 10 units. What is the equation of the path of this point?

8. Graph and write the equation of a hyperbola that has an upper vertex at $(-2.35, 1.46)$ and has an asymptote of $y = 1.5x + 1.035$.

9. Approximate the equation of each hyperbola shown.

a.

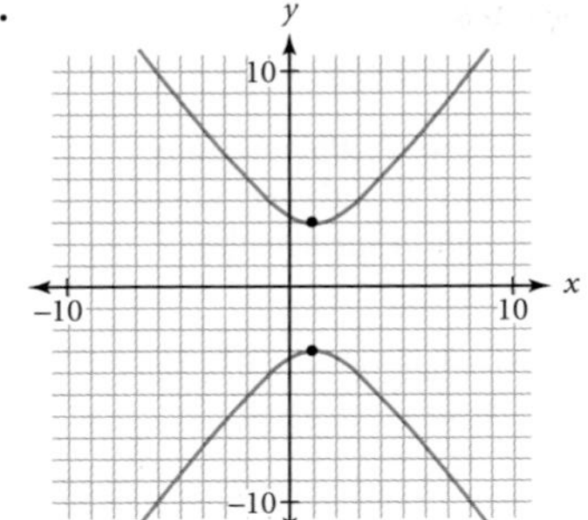

b.

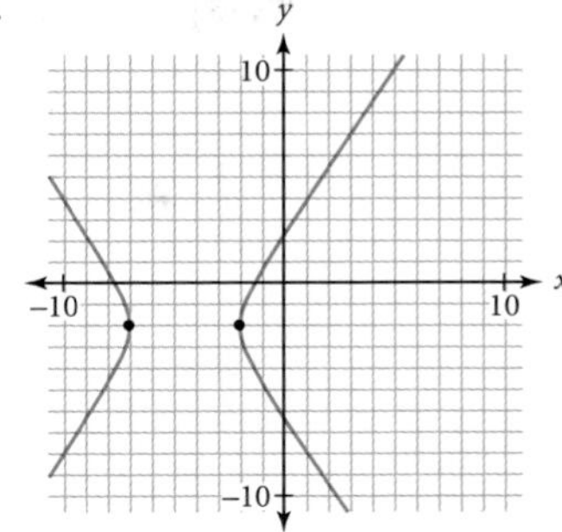

10. APPLICATION A receiver can determine the distance to a homing transmitter by its signal strength. These signal strengths were measured using a receiver in a car traveling due north.

Distance (mi)	0.0	2.0	4.0	6.0	8.0	10.0	12.0	14.0	16.0
Signal strength (W/m²)	9.82	7.91	6.04	4.30	2.92	2.55	3.54	5.15	6.96

a. Find the equation of the hyperbola that best fits the data.

b. Name the center of this hyperbola. What does this point tell you?

c. What are the possible locations of the homing transmitter?
2.5 mi east or west of the road at mile 9.5.

11. Sketch the graphs of the conic sections in 11a–d.

a. $y = x^2$ b. $x^2 + y^2 = 9$ c. $\frac{x^2}{9} + \frac{y^2}{16} = 1$ d. $\frac{x^2}{9} - \frac{y^2}{16} = 1$

e. If each of the curves in 11a–d is rotated about the y-axis, describe the shape that is formed. Include a sketch.

Mathematics CONNECTION

One area in the study of calculus is the analysis of three-dimensional solids formed by revolving a curve about an axis. Revolving a hyperbola about the line through its foci or about the perpendicular bisector of the segment connecting the foci produces a hyperboloid. The hyperboloid is used in the design of cooling towers because the concrete shell can be relatively thin for its large size. Also, the structure of the hyperboloid allows cooling towers to use a natural draft design to bring air into the cooling process.

Cooling towers in Middletown, Pennsylvania

MAKING THE CONNECTION

The hyperboloids in the picture are *one-sheet hyperboloids* created by revolving the curve about the perpendicular bisector of the segment connecting the foci. A hyperboloid of two sheets is created when the curve is revolved around the line through the foci.

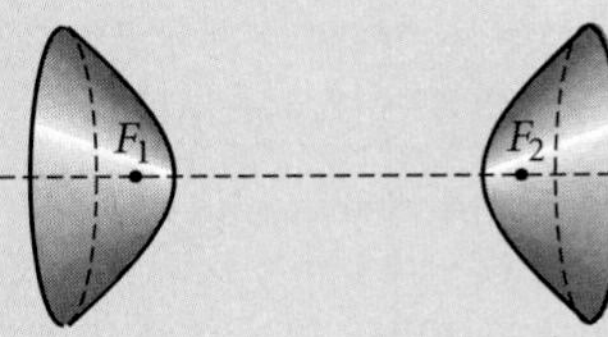

Exercise 7 Once students have graphed the two points, they'll see that the center of the hyperbola is at the point halfway between them, (1, 1). Because the length of the major axis is 10, a is 5. Students can follow the technique of Example C to find the value of b. **[Ask]** "How can you tell that this hyperbola is horizontally oriented?" [If y is 1, x is 6 or -4, but if x is 1, no values of y solve the equation.]

7. $\left(\frac{x-1}{5}\right)^2 - \left(\frac{y-1}{\sqrt{11}}\right)^2 = 1$

8. $\left(\frac{y+2.49}{3.95}\right)^2 - \left(\frac{x+2.35}{2.63}\right)^2 = 1$

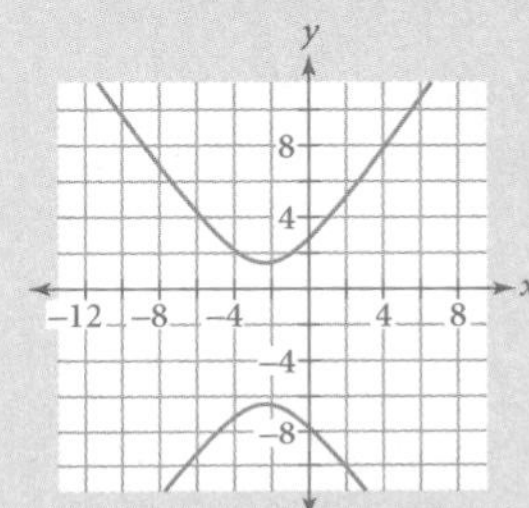

Exercise 9 In this exercise students are not given the asymptotes, so they can only approximate a point on the curve, as in Example C.

9a. possible answer: $\left(\frac{y}{3}\right)^2 - \left(\frac{x-1}{2}\right)^2 = 1$

9b. possible answer: $\left(\frac{x+4.5}{2.5}\right)^2 - \left(\frac{y+2}{3}\right)^2 = 1$

Exercise 10 As needed, remind students that a curve gets closer to an asymptote as x-values increase. Once students have the equation, you might ask them to try even larger x-values and negative x-values.

10a. possible answer: $\left(\frac{y}{2.5}\right)^2 - \left(\frac{x-9.5}{2.5}\right)^2 = 1$

10b. (9.5, 0) When the car has traveled 9.5 mi, it is 2.5 mi from the transmitter and will not get any closer.

See pages 895–896 for answers to Exercise 11.

Exercise 13 The method of completing the square will be used extensively in Lesson 9.5.

Exercise 15 [Language] In volleyball, a *setter* hits the ball up to get it into a position where a *hitter* on the team can jump and *spike* the ball directly toward the floor on the other side of the net.

17a. $s = s_0\left(\frac{1}{2}\right)^{t/1620}$

EXTENSIONS

A. Ask students to use the Sketchpad demonstration Definition of Hyperbola.

B. Ask students to use geometry software to model Exercise 6.

C. Have students create three-dimensional models of the conic sections.

D. Use Take Another Look activity 3 on page 563.

Sketches for Slicing a Cone
The first four sections are pictured on page 497.

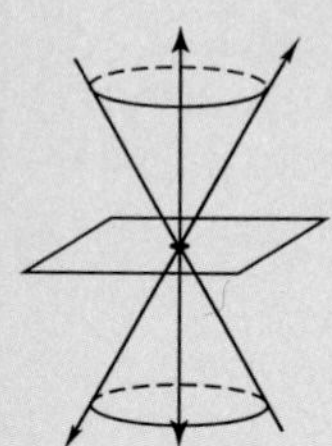

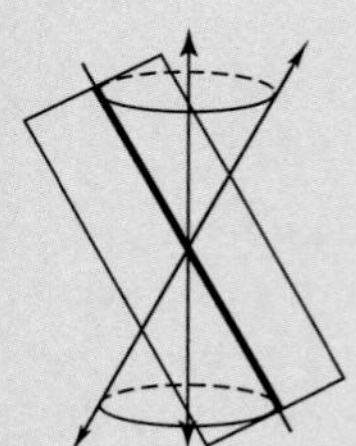

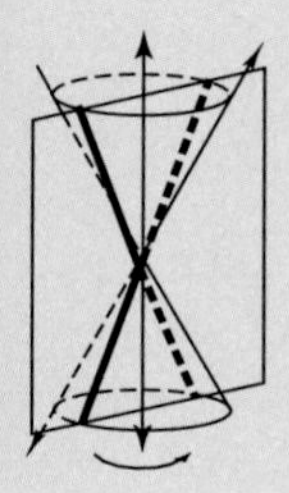

See page 896 for answers to Exercises 14 and 16.

12. Find the vertical distance between a point on the hyperbola $\left(\frac{y+1}{2}\right)^2 - \left(\frac{x-2}{3}\right)^2 = 1$ and its nearest asymptote for each x-value shown at right.

x-value	5	10	20	40
Distance	0.83	0.36	0.17	0.08

Review

7.3 **13.** Solve the quadratic equation $0 = -x^2 + 6x - 5$ by completing the square. $0 = 4 - (x - 3)^2$; $x = 1$ or $x = 5$

9.2 **14.** Mercury's orbit is an ellipse with the Sun at one focus, eccentricity 0.206, and major axis approximately 1.158×10^8 km. If you consider Mercury's orbit with the Sun at the origin and the other focus on the positive x-axis, what equation models the orbit?

4.6 **15.** The setter on a volleyball team makes contact with the ball at a height of 5 ft. The parabolic path of the ball reaches a maximum height of 17.5 ft when the ball is 10 ft from the setter.

a. Find an equation that models the ball's path. possible answer: $y = -\frac{1}{8}(x - 10)^2 + 17.5$

b. A hitter can spike the ball when it is 8.5 feet off the floor. How far from the setter is the hitter when she makes contact? approximately 18.5 ft or 1.5 ft

9.3 **16.** Sketch the graph of each parabola. Give the coordinates of each vertex and focus, and the equation of each directrix.

a. $y = -(x + 1)^2 - 2$ **b.** $y = \frac{1}{2}x^2 - 3x + 5$ **c.** $x = \frac{1}{2}t^2 - 6$, $y = t$

5.6 **17.** The half-life of radium-226 is 1620 yr.

a. Write a function that relates the amount s of a sample of radium-226 remaining after t years.

b. After 1000 yr, how much of a 500 g sample of radium-226 will remain? 326 g

c. How long will it take for a 3 kg sample of radium-226 to decay so that only 10 g remains? 13,331 yr

7.1 **18.** Use finite differences to write an equation for the nth term of the sequence $-20, -14, -6, 4, 16, \ldots$. $n^2 + 3n - 24$

IMPROVING YOUR VISUAL THINKING SKILLS

Slicing a Cone

Describe how to slice a double cone to produce each of these geometric shapes: a circle, an ellipse, a parabola, a hyperbola, a point, one line, and two lines. Be sure to describe at what angle and where the plane must slice the cone. Sketch a diagram of each slicing. (*Hint:* Look back at the illustrations on page 497 for help.)

IMPROVING VISUAL THINKING SKILLS

Circle: The slice is perpendicular to the cone's axis. Ellipse: The slice intersects only one branch of the cone and is not perpendicular to the axis or parallel to an edge. Parabola: The slice intersects only one branch of the cone and is parallel to an edge. Hyperbola: The slice intersects both branches of the cone but does not contain the cone's vertex. Point: The slice intersects only at the cone's vertex. One line: The slice is along an edge. Two lines: The slice intersects both branches of the cone through the vertex, but not along an edge.

EXPLORATION

Constructing the Conic Sections

In geometry class you probably used a compass and straightedge to construct polygons, such as triangles and squares. You also know that a compass can easily construct a circle, one of the conic sections.

What about the other conic sections—the ellipse, the parabola, and the hyperbola? How could you possibly construct these complex curves? In this chapter you learned locus definitions for these shapes, but they may seem impossible to construct geometrically.

Actually, there are many different ways to construct the conic sections. Geometry software, such as The Geometer's Sketchpad, makes these constructions even easier. In the activity you will learn one way to construct an ellipse. The follow-up questions then challenge you to construct a parabola and a hyperbola.

History CONNECTION

In 1646, Dutch mathematician Frans van Schooten (1615–1660) wrote *Sive de Organica Conicarum Sectionum in Plano Descriptione, Tractatus,* which translates to *A Treatise on Devices for Drawing Conic Sections.* This book describes several different ways to construct each of the conic sections. Some of the constructions used unique mechanical devices.

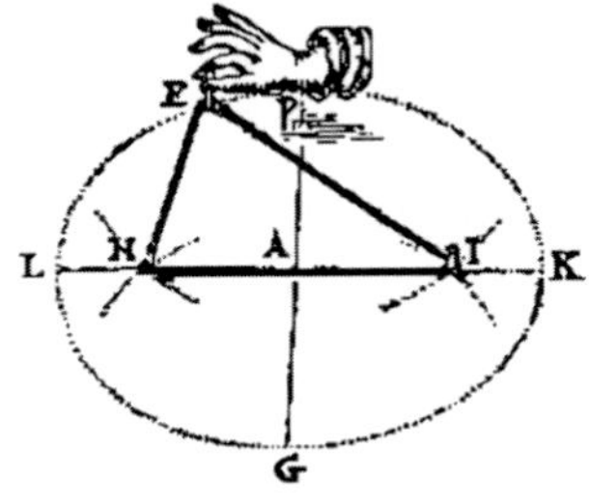

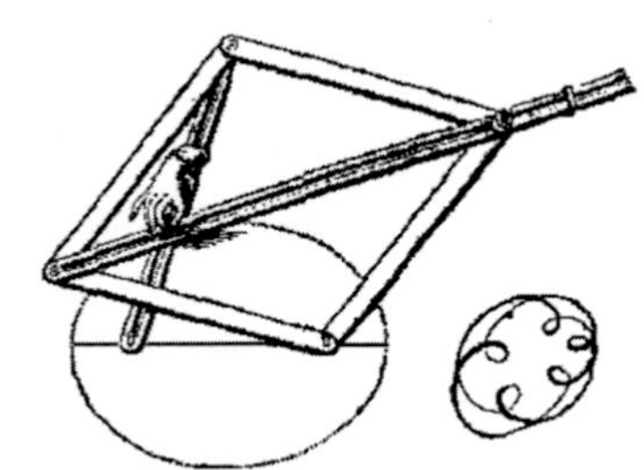

These illustrations from van Schooten's *Sive de Organica Conicarum Sectionum in Plano Descriptione, Tractatus* show two ways of constructing an ellipse.

Activity
From Circles to the Ellipse

Steps 1–5 result in the diagram at right.

Step 1 In a new sketch, construct a segment and label the endpoints *A* and *B*.

Step 2 Construct a point on $\overline{AB}$. Label this point *C*.

Step 3 Construct segments *AC* and *CB*. What is true about $AC + CB$?

Step 3 The sum $AC + CB$ is constant.

Step 4 Construct and label points F_1 and F_2, not on $\overline{AB}$. These will be the foci of your ellipse.

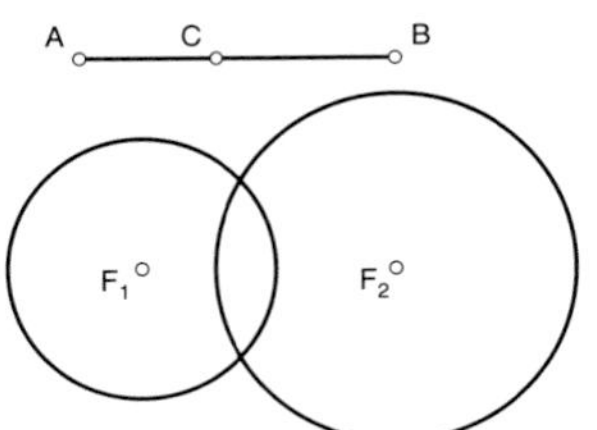

EXPLORATION

PLANNING

LESSON OUTLINE

One day:

5 min	Introduction
15 min	Activity
5 min	Sharing
20 min	Questions

MATERIALS

- The Geometer's Sketchpad
- Sketchpad demonstration From Circles to the Ellipse, *optional*

TEACHING

This exploration shows students how Sketchpad's tools allow construction of the conic sections. If your class has only one computer available, you can use the Sketchpad demonstration From Circles to the Ellipse.

See *Exploring Conic Sections with The Geometer's Sketchpad* for more activities. Additional resources include the dynamic algebra explorations on constructing an ellipse, constructing a parabola, and constructing a hyperbola at www.keymath.com/DAA.

Guiding the Activity

Step 3 [Alert] Students may not realize that the question is asking what is true regardless of where point *C* is located on $\overline{AB}$.

Step 4 These two points can be anywhere on the sketch except on $\overline{AB}$. To create subscripts as point labels, students can type F[1] and F[2], in the Properties of Point box. Or you might have them use F1 and F2, without subscripts, instead.

NCTM STANDARDS

CONTENT		PROCESS	
	Number		Problem Solving
✓	Algebra	✓	Reasoning
✓	Geometry	✓	Communication
	Measurement	✓	Connections
	Data/Probability	✓	Representation

LESSON OBJECTIVES

- Construct conic sections using The Geometer's Sketchpad
- Investigate properties of conic sections

Step 5 If students find that the construction choice isn't available, ask whether they have accidentally selected more than the specified items.

Step 6 To adjust the model, drag point C along $\overline{AB}$ until the circles intersect.

Step 8 To deselect **Trace Intersections,** select it again to remove the check mark.

Step 9 Students can change the color of the ellipse by selecting the ellipse and choosing **Color** from the Display menu.

SHARING IDEAS

The noncircular conic sections can't be constructed with straightedge and compass. **[Ask]** "Why is this construction possible with Sketchpad?" [Sketchpad includes the additional tools **Trace Intersections** and **Locus.**]

In Sketchpad, it is possible to construct points on the loci. Students can then construct rays and measure angles to verify that signals (such as light or sound) emitted from one focus of an ellipse are reflected to the other focus, that rays emitted from the focus of a parabola are reflected perpendicular to the directrix (as in the picture in the book), and that rays emitted from the focus of a hyperbola are reflected in a dispersed pattern.

▶ Helping with the Questions

Questions 1, 2 Mathematically, changing the distance between the foci or changing the distance AB (technically the length of the major axis) changes the eccentricity.

Question 2 [Language] Conic sections that share the same foci are called *confocular.* As point B is dragged, confocular ellipses are formed. **[Ask]** "What happens as you drag point C?"

See page 896 for answers to Steps 7 and 9 and to Questions 1, 3, and 4.

Step 5 Select F_1 and $\overline{AC}$, and choose **Circle By Center+Radius** from the Construct menu. Construct another circle with F_2 and $\overline{CB}$.

Step 6 If necessary, adjust your model so that the circles intersect. Select the two circles and choose **Intersections** from the Construct menu. What is the distance from either intersection to F_1? What is the distance from either intersection to F_2? What is true about the sum of these distances?

Step 6 The distance from either intersection to F_1 is equivalent to AC. The distance from either intersection to F_2 is equivalent to BC. The sum of these distances is a constant AB.

Step 7 Select the two intersections and choose **Trace Intersections** from the Display menu. Slowly drag point C back and forth along $\overline{AB}$. Describe the shape of the trace. Explain why this happens.

In this chapter you learned about loci. In Step 7 you traced a locus of points. Depending on how slowly you dragged point C, your ellipse may be smooth or it may have gaps. Sketchpad also allows you to see the locus as a smooth curve.

Step 8 Choose **Erase Traces** from the Display menu. Then select the two intersections and deselect **Trace Intersections** from the Display menu.

Step 9 Select point C and one of the intersections, and choose **Locus** from the Construct menu. You should see one half of your ellipse. Repeat this process with the other intersection to see both halves.

When you construct a locus, you can experiment by dragging objects and seeing how the locus changes.

Questions

1. Experiment by dragging one focus. How does the ellipse change? How far apart can the foci be before you no longer have an ellipse? What happens when both foci are at the same point?
2. Experiment by dragging point B. How does the ellipse change? Based on the locus definition of an ellipse, what is changing?
3. The illustration at right shows one method of constructing a parabola based on the geometric definition. Use Sketchpad to construct this locus. Explain how the construction satisfies the definition. (Note that $\overleftrightarrow{PA} \perp \overline{FB}$.)
4. Find a way to construct a hyperbola with Sketchpad. (*Hint:* One possible construction is similar to the ellipse construction, except you want the difference $AC - BC$ to have a constant value.)

2. As AB increases, both the major and minor axes become longer.

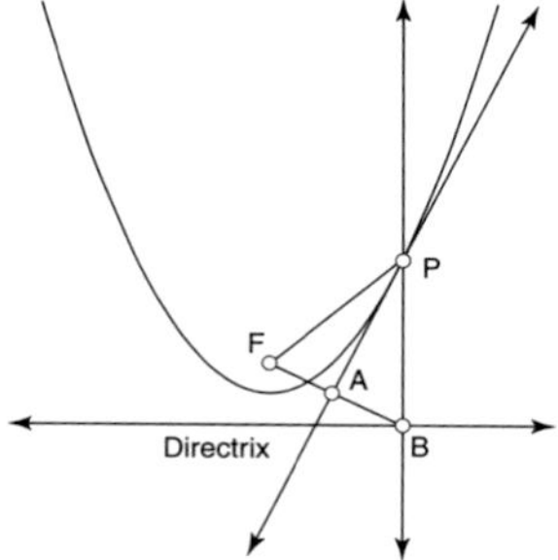

Question 3 After students have completed the construction, encourage them to experiment with moving the focus and to describe the result.

Question 4 After students have completed the hyperbola construction, suggest that they experiment by changing the distance between the foci and the distance between points A and B. **[Ask]** "What happens when point B is dragged to the right of point C?" [The construction becomes an ellipse.] "What happens when points A and B are on top of each other?" [The construction becomes a line.]

Assessing Progress

Check students' facility with Sketchpad and with following detailed instructions, as well as their understanding of the properties of the conic sections.

Closing the Lesson

Reiterate that, of the conic sections, only the circle can be constructed with straightedge and compass, but Sketchpad's **Locus** and **Trace Intersections** tools can construct large sets of points that appear to form conic sections.

LESSON

9.5

The General Quadratic

A complex system that works is invariably found to have evolved from a simple system that works.

JOHN GAULE

Circles, parabolas, ellipses, and hyperbolas are called **quadratic curves,** or second-degree curves, because the highest power of any of the variables is 2. Although the curves look very different, all conic sections are closely related. All of the standard forms you have seen can be converted into one general equation.

General Quadratic Equation

The **general quadratic equation** in two variables, x and y, is

$$Ax^2 + Bxy + Cy^2 + Dx + Ey + F = 0$$

where A, B, and C are not all zero.

In this lesson you will learn how to convert the general quadratic equation into standard form. You will also learn how to solve for y so that you can use your calculator to graph the curves.

In all the relationships you have seen so far in this chapter, B is equal to zero. When B does not equal zero, the graph of the equation will be a rotated conic section. You can explore these rotated curves in the exploration that follows this lesson.

Astronomy CONNECTION

When a comet passes through the solar system, its motion is influenced by the Sun's gravity. Some comets swing around the Sun and leave the solar system, never to return. The paths are described by one branch of a hyperbola with the Sun at one focus. However, if a comet is moving more slowly, it will be captured into an elliptical orbit with the Sun at one focus. The outcome depends on the speed of the comet and the angle at which it approaches the Sun. Some orbits appear parabolic, but are probably very long ellipses. To have a parabolic orbit, a comet would have to start with a velocity of 0, at an infinite distance from the Sun. A circular orbit is possible, but unlikely.

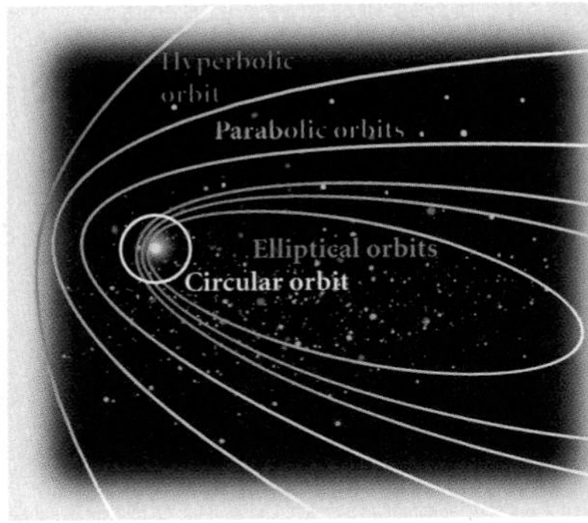

In 1997, the comet Hale-Bopp passed by Earth and was one of the brightest comets seen in the 20th century. Hale-Bopp has an elliptical orbit.

LESSON

9.5

PLANNING

LESSON OUTLINE

First day:

30 min	Examples A–C
15 min	Exercises

Second day:

10 min	Example D
10 min	Investigation
5 min	Example E
10 min	Sharing
10 min	Exercises

MATERIALS

- graph paper
- geometry software, *optional*
- Calculator Note 9A, *optional*

TEACHING

In this lesson students see the general form of the quadratic equation and the conic sections it represents. If you don't need to review the process of completing the square, this lesson may take only one day.

[Ask] "What's the difference between the general form of a quadratic equation given here and the standard forms we saw before?" [The standard forms of the equation of conic sections vary, but none has an expression that equals 0.] In Lesson 7.2, students also saw the general form of a quadratic function in one variable, $y = ax^2 + bx + c$.

You can begin with the one-step investigation on page 526, or start with a discussion of Example A.

NCTM STANDARDS

CONTENT		PROCESS	
	Number	✓	Problem Solving
✓	Algebra		Reasoning
✓	Geometry	✓	Communication
	Measurement	✓	Connections
	Data/Probability	✓	Representation

LESSON OBJECTIVES

- Explore the general quadratic equation
- Convert a general quadratic equation to standard form for a conic section
- Find the solution to a system of quadratic equations in two variables

One Step
Introduce the general quadratic equation and ask students to make rules for looking at the coefficients and deciding what kind of conic section the equation describes. As students work, encourage them to work backward from the standard forms and look for patterns. (For example, the parabola is the only conic section with either an x^2-term or a y^2-term but not both). As the question arises of how the xy-term comes into play, suggest that students first classify all cases in which $B = 0$. Students will examine the xy-term again in the Exploration The Rotation Matrix and in Lesson 9.6.

▸ *EXAMPLE A*

[Ask] "Could the equation in this example represent a parabola?" [No; it includes squared terms of both x and y.]

Graphing this equation on a calculator is not essential to the lesson.

[Context] Remind students that they saw their first Robert Wilson–designed sculpture on page 514. Each tube in *Tractricious* weighs 550 lb, and the entire structure can withstand winds of up to 80 mi/h.

EXAMPLE A Convert the equation $4x^2 - 9y^2 + 144 = 0$ to standard form. Then name the shape and graph it. Solve for y and graph on your calculator to confirm your answer.

▸ *Solution* Put the equation in standard form:

$4x^2 - 9y^2 = -144$ — Subtract 144 from both sides.

$\dfrac{4x^2 - 9y^2}{-144} = 1$ — Divide by -144.

$-\dfrac{x^2}{36} + \dfrac{y^2}{16} = 1$ — Divide each term by -144 and reduce the fractions.

$\dfrac{y^2}{16} - \dfrac{x^2}{36} = 1$ — Reorder to put in standard form.

Tractricious, another Robert Wilson–designed sculpture at the Fermi National Accelerator Laboratory, is a free-standing hyperboloid of stainless steel tubes.

This equation is the standard form of a vertically oriented hyperbola. It is centered at the origin and has values $a = \sqrt{36} = 6$ and $b = \sqrt{16} = 4$. Sketch the asymptote rectangle and the asymptotes, then plot the vertices and draw the curve.

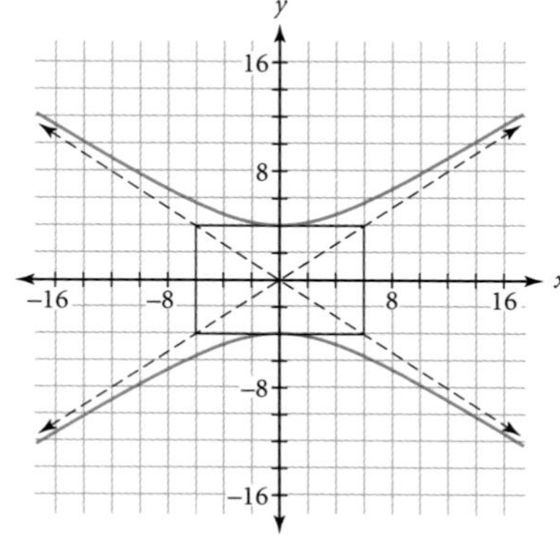

Now solve for y:

$\dfrac{y^2}{16} - \dfrac{x^2}{36} = 1$ — The equation in standard form.

$\dfrac{y^2}{16} = 1 + \dfrac{x^2}{36}$ — Add $\frac{x^2}{36}$ to both sides.

$y^2 = 16\left(1 + \dfrac{x^2}{36}\right)$ — Multiply by 16.

$y = \pm 4\sqrt{1 + \dfrac{x^2}{36}}$ — Take the square root of both sides.

Graph this equation on your calculator to confirm the sketch.

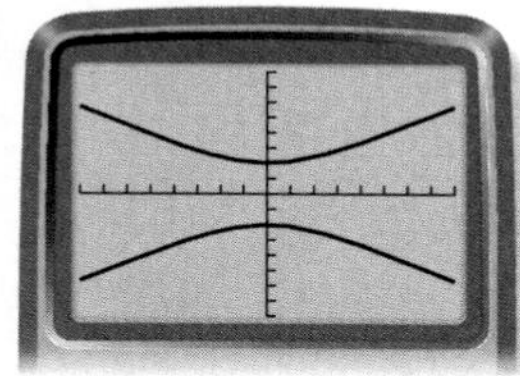

$[-16, 16, 2, -16, 16, 2]$

The equation in Example A was relatively easy to work with because the values of B, D, and E in the general equation were zero. When D or E is nonzero, you must use the process of completing the square to convert the equation to standard form.

EXAMPLE B | Describe the shape determined by the equation $x^2 + 4y^2 - 14x + 33 = 0$.

▶ Solution

Complete the square to convert from general form to standard form.

$x^2 + 4y^2 - 14x + 33 = 0$	Original equation.
$(x^2 - 14x) + (4y^2) = -33$	Group x-terms and y-terms and isolate constants on the other side.
$(x^2 - 14x + 49) + (4y^2) = -33 + 49$	To complete the square for x, add $\left(-\frac{14}{2}\right)^2$, or 49, to both sides.
$(x - 7)^2 + 4y^2 = 16$	Write the equation in perfect-square form.
$\frac{(x-7)^2}{16} + \frac{y^2}{4} = 1$	Divide by 16 and reduce.
$\left(\frac{x-7}{4}\right)^2 + \left(\frac{y}{2}\right)^2 = 1$	Write the equation in standard form.

In this form, it is clear that this is the equation of an ellipse. The center is (7, 0), the horizontal stretch factor is 4, and the vertical stretch factor is 2.

Look back at the original equation in Example B. How might you have known that this equation described an ellipse? The coefficients of x^2 and y^2 are both positive.

EXAMPLE C | Graph the equation $y^2 - 4x + 6y + 1 = 0$.

▶ Solution

Begin by completing the square.

$(y^2 + 6y) - (4x) = -1$	Group x-terms and y-terms and isolate constants on the other side.
$(y^2 + 6y + 9) - (4x) = -1 + 9$	To complete the square for y, add 9 to both sides.
$(y + 3)^2 - 4x = 8$	Write in perfect-square form.

This equation describes a parabola, because only one of the variables has an exponent of 2. You can now choose whether to convert this equation to standard form to graph it, or solve for y. Let's solve for y.

$(y + 3)^2 = 4x + 8$	Add $4x$ to both sides.
$(y + 3)^2 = 4(x + 2)$	Factor.
$y + 3 = \pm\sqrt{4(x + 2)}$	Take the square root of both sides.
$y = \pm 2\sqrt{x + 2} - 3$	Subtract 3 from both sides.

This equation indicates a horizontally oriented parabola with vertex $(-2, -3)$ and a vertical scale factor of 2.

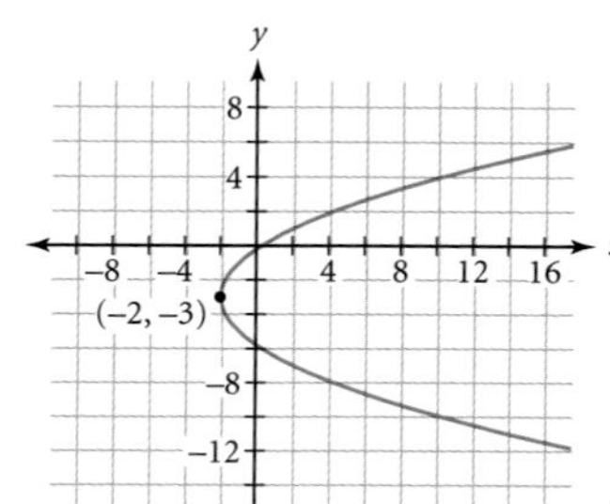

▶ EXAMPLE B

You might want to review the process of completing the square. When students first saw this technique in Lesson 7.3, they worked with a single expression, adding and subtracting the same amount. Here students have an equation. Because they eventually want the constants combined on one side of the equation, they add the same constant to both sides of the equation.

The equation is an ellipse, because in the general form B equals 0 and A and C have the same sign.

▶ EXAMPLE C

Before beginning this example, **[Ask]** "Can you tell what type of conic section this equation represents?" [a parabola, because y is squared but not x] "What is this equation in standard form?" $\left[(y + 3)^2 = 4(x + 2)\right]$

You could tell that the original equation in Example C described a parabola, because only one of the variables has an exponent of 2. The standard form of a parabola gives you information about the focus and directrix. However, if you only want to graph a parabola, you can solve for y quickly by using the quadratic formula. Recall that the quadratic formula states that the solutions of $ax^2 + bx + c = 0$ are $x = \frac{-b \pm \sqrt{b^2 - 4ac}}{2a}$.

▸ *EXAMPLE D*

This example demonstrates another method of solving the equation in Example C.

Students may find this method easier than completing the square.

EXAMPLE D | Use the quadratic formula to solve the equation $y^2 - 4x + 6y + 1 = 0$ for y.

▸ *Solution*

In this case the variable y is the quadratic term, so rewrite the equation in the form $ay^2 + by + c = 0$.

$y^2 - 4x + 6y + 1 = 0$ Original equation.

$y^2 + 6y - 4x + 1 = 0$ Write the equation as $ay^2 + by + c = 0$.

So $a = 1$, $b = 6$, and $c = -4x + 1$. Substitute these values into the quadratic formula.

$$y = \frac{-b \pm \sqrt{b^2 - 4ac}}{2a}$$

$$= \frac{-6 \pm \sqrt{6^2 - 4(1)(-4x + 1)}}{(2)(1)}$$

$$= \frac{-6 \pm \sqrt{36 + 16x - 4}}{2}$$

$$= \frac{-6 \pm \sqrt{32 + 16x}}{2}$$

$$= \frac{-6 \pm \sqrt{16(2 + x)}}{2}$$

$$= \frac{-6 \pm 4\sqrt{2 + x}}{2}$$

$$y = -3 \pm 2\sqrt{2 + x}$$

The solution gives the equation $y = -3 \pm 2\sqrt{2 + x}$.

This equation is equivalent to the equation you found in Example C by completing the square.

String Art

Curved figures that are created with intersecting straight lines, such as this string art, are called *envelopes.* Students created an envelope for a parabola in the Lesson 9.3 investigation.

In this sculpture, the strings appear to create the envelope of a parabola or perhaps a hyperbola. To determine whether the curve created by the string is a conic section, you would need to know the curve of the frame. The sculpture on page 526 is another example of an envelope.

Solve a system of equations.

How can you find the points of intersection of two conic sections? In this investigation you'll begin by exploring how many intersection points are possible for various combinations of curves.

Stringed Figure (Curlew) (1956) was designed by British abstract sculptor Barbara Hepworth (1903–1975). What conic sections appear to be created by the intersecting strings? parabolas

Investigation
Systems of Conic Equations

If you graph two conic sections on the same graph, in how many ways could they intersect?

There are four conic sections: circles, ellipses, parabolas, and hyperbolas. Among the members of your group, investigate the possible numbers of intersection points for all ten pairs of shapes. For example, an ellipse and a hyperbola could intersect in 0, 1, 2, 3, or 4 points, as shown below. For each pair of conic sections, list the possible numbers of intersection points.

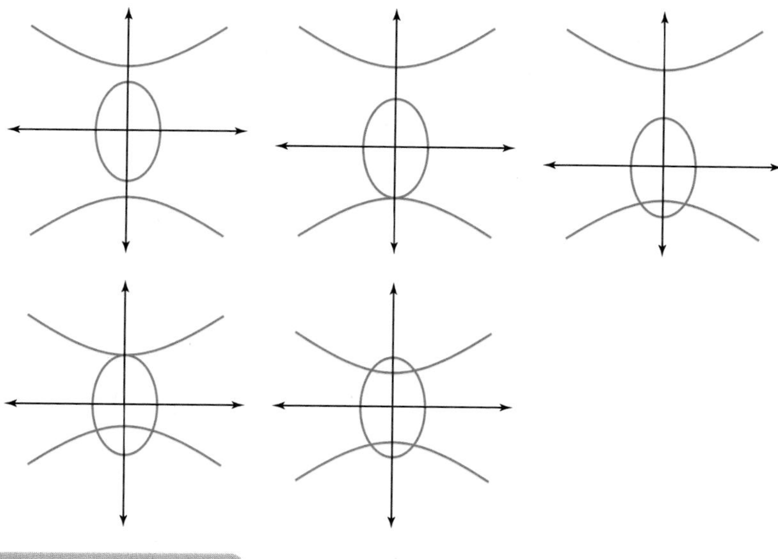

History CONNECTION

A method of constructing an ellipse was discovered by Abū Ali Al-Hasan ibn al-Haytham (or Alhazen), who lived from about 965 to 1041 C.E. in Basra, Iraq, and Alexandria, Egypt. His book *Optics* explained light and vision using geometry. He posed a problem, still famous today as "Alhazen's problem," about the reflection of light rays on a spherical surface. The solution can be found geometrically as the intersection of a great circle of the sphere and a hyperbola that passes through the center of the circle.

EXAMPLE E | Find the points of intersection of $\frac{(x-5)^2}{4} + y^2 = 1$ and $x = y^2 + 5$.

▶ ***Solution*** | First, graph the curves and estimate the points of intersection. Then you can solve the system algebraically.

▶ ***EXAMPLE E***

Encourage students to use both algebraic and graphical techniques to find solutions. If you want to emphasize the general form of a quadratic equation, you might suggest that students write each conic section in that form and solve the system by eliminating y^2.

Students can find intersection points more accurately using the calculator's Intersect command; see Calculator Note 9A. If you prefer to use the trace method, you might want to ask students to substitute their estimated solution points into the original equations to see how accurate they are.

Guiding the Investigation

[Alert] Students may doubt that an ellipse and a hyperbola can intersect in only five ways. Help them see that two ways are considered to be the same if they are translations, reflections, or rotations of each other.

Students may miss the intersection of two parabolas in three or four points. **[Ask]** "If the axes of two parabolas are parallel or the same line, how many points of intersection can there be?" [0, 1, 2, or infinitely many] "What if the axes are distinct and not parallel?" [also 3 or 4]

Students may sketch their solutions on paper or use geometry software.

circle and circle: 0, 1, 2, infinitely many

ellipse and ellipse: 0, 1, 2, 3, 4, infinitely many

parabola and parabola: 0, 1, 2, 3, 4, infinitely many

hyperbola and hyperbola: 0, 1, 2, 3, 4, infinitely many

all other combinations: 0, 1, 2, 3, 4

Answers will show sketches for each of the pairs similar to the sketches for the ellipse and hyperbola.

MAKING THE CONNECTION

Alhazen's problem is "Given a light source and a spherical mirror, find the point on the mirror where the light will be reflected to the eye of an observer." It is also known as "Alhazen's billiard problem" because it can also be stated as "Find the point on the edge of a circular billiard table at which a cue ball at a given point must be aimed in order to bounce off the edge of the table and hit another ball at a second given point."

Students can find more information about the solution to this problem through links at www.keymath.com.

SHARING IDEAS

As students finish presenting ideas about the investigation, **[Ask]** "Can there be intersections of a conic section with another conic section of the same shape?" [Yes, many. Circles can intersect circles in one or two points, for example.]

For the curves studied in Lessons 9.2–9.4, A and C cannot both be 0. In Lesson 9.6, students will see the curve defined by $xy = 1$, a rotated hyperbola. **[Ask]** "What happens when B, C, and E are all 0?" [The equation is the general quadratic equation in one variable.]

Assessing Progress
You can assess students' understanding of the equations of conic sections and their skill at solving systems of equations.

Closing the Lesson

The main point of this lesson is that, if $B = 0$, you can tell from the general form of the quadratic equation, $Ax^2 + Bxy + Cy^2 + Dx + Ey + F = 0$, which conic section is represented. If either A or C is 0 (but not both), the equation represents a parabola. Otherwise, if the product AC is positive the equation represents an ellipse, and if the product AC is negative it represents a hyperbola. You can put the equation into the appropriate standard form by completing the square.

You can graph these equations using your knowledge of transformations, or by solving for y and graphing on your calculator. Graphing on the calculator provides the advantage that you can trace the curves to approximate the points of intersection. First, solve for y in both equations.

$$\frac{(x-5)^2}{4} + y^2 = 1 \qquad \text{The first equation.}$$

$$y^2 = 1 - \frac{(x-5)^2}{4} \qquad \text{Solve for } y^2.$$

$$y = \pm\sqrt{1 - \frac{(x-5)^2}{4}} \qquad \text{Solve for } y.$$

$$x = y^2 + 5 \qquad \text{The second equation.}$$

$$y^2 = x - 5 \qquad \text{Solve for } y^2.$$

$$y = \pm\sqrt{x-5} \qquad \text{Solve for } y.$$

Graph the two equations, and trace to approximate the points of intersection.

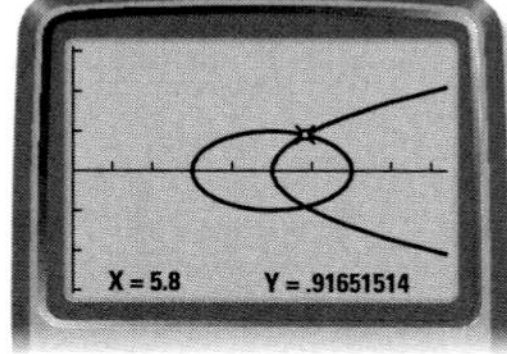

[0, 9.4, 1, −3.1, 3.1, 1]

There are two points of intersection, approximately (5.8, 0.9) and (5.8, −0.9). You can use algebraic methods to find the intersection points more accurately. To solve algebraically, you can use the two equations that are solved for y and the substitution method. Or, in this case, you can use the two original equations and the substitution or elimination method. Notice that both equations have a y^2 term. Solve for y^2 in the second equation, and substitute.

$$\frac{(x-5)^2}{4} + y^2 = 1 \text{ and } x = y^2 + 5 \qquad \text{Original equations.}$$

$$y^2 = x - 5 \qquad \text{Solve the second equation for } y^2.$$

$$\frac{(x-5)^2}{4} + x - 5 = 1 \qquad \text{Substitute } (x-5) \text{ for } y^2 \text{ in the first equation.}$$

$$(x-5)^2 + 4x - 20 = 4 \qquad \text{Multiply both sides by 4 to eliminate the denominator.}$$

$$x^2 - 10x + 25 + 4x - 20 = 4 \qquad \text{Square.}$$

$$x^2 - 6x + 1 = 0 \qquad \text{Combine like terms.}$$

$$x = \frac{6 \pm \sqrt{36 - 4 \cdot 1 \cdot 1}}{2 \cdot 1} \approx 5.828 \text{ and } 0.172 \qquad \text{Use the quadratic equation to solve for } x.$$

Now substitute these two values into one of the equations relating x and y, and solve for y.

$$y = \pm\sqrt{x-5} = \pm\sqrt{5.828-5} = \pm 0.910$$

$$y = \pm\sqrt{x-5} = \pm\sqrt{0.172-5} = \pm\sqrt{-4.828} = \pm 2.197i$$

The points of intersection are (5.828, 0.910) and (5.828, −0.910). When you substitute 0.172 for x, you find two imaginary values for y. These nonreal numbers are solutions, but they are not points of intersection. The intersection points you estimated by graphing are close to the two real solutions.

You can always use graphing to estimate real solutions. Graphing is valuable even if you are finding solutions algebraically, because a graph will tell you how many intersection points to look for. It can also help confirm whether your algebraic solutions are correct.

EXERCISES

You will need

Geometry software for Exercise **9**

Practice Your Skills

1. Rewrite each equation in the form $Ax^2 + Bxy + Cy^2 + Dx + Ey + F = 0$. See below.

a. $(x + 7)^2 = 9(y - 11)$

b. $\frac{(x-7)^2}{9} + \frac{(y+11)^2}{1} = 1$

c. $(x - 1)^2 + (y + 3)^2 = 5$

d. $\frac{(x-2)^2}{4} - \frac{(y+3)^2}{9} = 1$

2. Find the values for a, b, c, and d as you follow these steps to complete the square for $15x^2 + 21x$. $a = 1.4$; $b = 0.49$; $c = 7.35$; $d = 0.7$

$15x^2 + 21x$

$15(x^2 + ax)$

$15(x^2 + ax + b) - 15b$

$15(x^2 + ax + b) - c$

$15(x + d)^2 - c$

3. Convert each equation to the standard form of a conic section. Name the shape described by each equation. See below.

a. $x^2 - y^2 + 8x + 10y + 2 = 0$

b. $2x^2 + y^2 - 12x - 16y + 10 = 0$

c. $3x^2 + 30x + 5y - 4 = 0$

d. $5x^2 + 5y^2 + 20x - 6 = 0$

4. Identify each equation as true or false. If it is false, correct it to make it true.

a. $y^2 + 11y + 121 = (y + 11)^2$

b. $x^2 - 18x + 81 = (x - 9)^2$ true

c. $5y^2 + 10y + 5 = 5(y + 1)^2$ true

d. $4x^2 + 24x + 36 = 4(x + 6)^2$
false; possible answer: $4x^2 + 48x + 144 = 4(x + 6)^2$

Reason and Apply

5. Use the quadratic formula to solve each equation for y. Graph each curve.

a. $25x^2 - 4y^2 + 100 = 0$

b. $4y^2 - 10x + 16y + 36 = 0$

c. $4x^2 + 4y^2 + 24x - 8y + 39 = 0$

d. $3x^2 + 5y^2 - 12x + 20y + 8 = 0$

6. Solve each system of equations algebraically, using the substitution or elimination method.

a. $\begin{cases} y = x^2 + 4 \\ y = (x-2)^2 + 3 \end{cases}$

b. $\begin{cases} 3x^2 + 9y^2 = 9 \\ 3x^2 + 5y^2 = 8 \end{cases}$

c. $\begin{cases} x^2 - \frac{y^2}{4} = 1 \\ x^2 + (y+4)^2 = 9 \end{cases}$

7. **APPLICATION** Two seismic monitoring stations recorded the vibrations of an earthquake. The second monitoring station is 50 mi due east of the first. The epicenter was determined to be 30 mi from the first station and 27 mi from the second station. Where could the epicenter of the earthquake be located?

1a. $x^2 + 14x - 9y + 148 = 0$

1b. $x^2 + 9y^2 - 14x + 198y + 1129 = 0$

1c. $x^2 + y^2 - 2x + 6y + 5 = 0$

1d. $9x^2 - 4y^2 - 36x - 24y - 36 = 0$

3a. $\left(\frac{y-5}{\sqrt{11}}\right)^2 - \left(\frac{x+4}{\sqrt{11}}\right)^2 = 1$; hyperbola

3b. $\left(\frac{x-3}{6}\right)^2 + \left(\frac{y-8}{\sqrt{72}}\right)^2 = 1$, or

$\left(\frac{x-3}{6}\right)^2 + \left(\frac{y-8}{6\sqrt{2}}\right)^2 = 1$; ellipse

3c. $\left(\frac{x+5}{\sqrt{5}}\right)^2 = \frac{(y-15.8)}{-3}$; parabola

3d. $(x + 2)^2 + y^2 = 5.2$; circle

7. approximately 26.7 mi east and 13.7 mi north of the first station, or approximately 26.7 mi east and 13.7 mi south of the first station

BUILDING UNDERSTANDING

If you are spending two days on this lesson, you might assign Exercises 1–5 and some review exercises on the first day. If your students have not studied parametric equations, do not assign Exercise 13b.

ASSIGNING HOMEWORK

Essential	1–3
Performance assessment	5–11
Portfolio	10
Journal	9
Group	6, 9
Review	4, 12–17

MATERIALS

- Sketchpad demonstration A Conic Construction, *optional*

Helping with the Exercises

Exercise 1 [Alert] Students may forget the middle term when they square a binomial.

In 1b and 1d, students can either find a common denominator on the left or first multiply through by the product of the denominators.

Exercise 3 [Ask] "How can you determine which conic section the equation represents without graphing?" The rules are stated in Closing the Lesson.

4a. false; possible answer: $y^2 + 22y + 121 = (y + 11)^2$

Exercise 5 [Ask] "Without graphing, name each curve." [a. hyperbola; b. parabola; c. circle; d. ellipse]

Exercise 7 Although the methods are algebraic, many students will benefit from making a graph. Students can use either geometry software or a compass and a ruler to make an accurate scale drawing.

See page 897 for answers to Exercises 5 and 6.

8. Match each equation to one of the graphs.

a. $9x^2 + 4y^2 - 36 = 0$ D

b. $x^2 - 4y^2 - 8x = 0$ B

c. $3x^2 - 30x + 5y + 55 = 0$ C

d. $x^2 + y^2 + 2x - 6y - 15 = 0$ A

A.

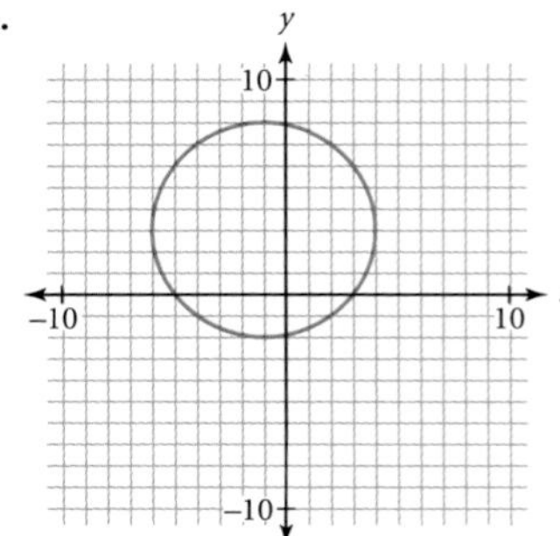

B.

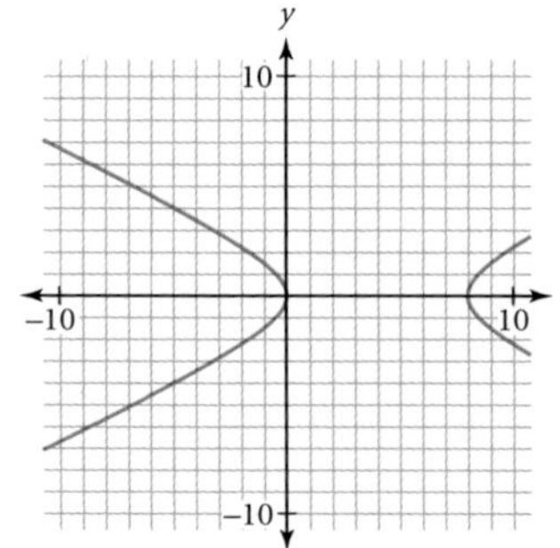

C.

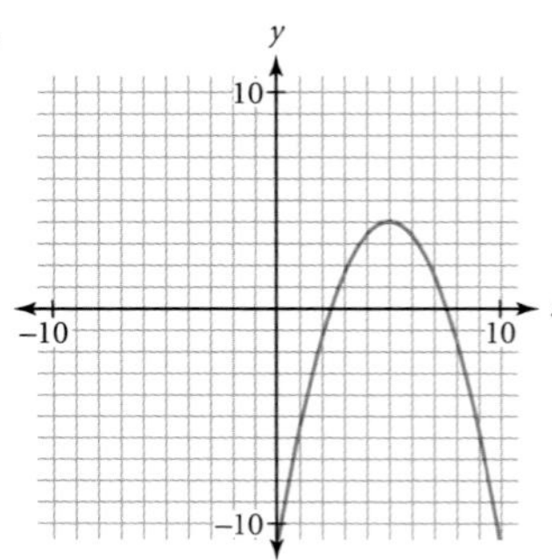

D.

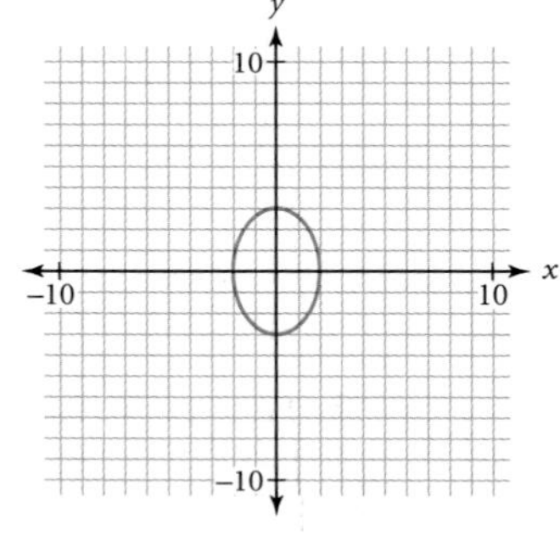

Exercise 9 In 9a, point A can be any point on the circle except the point that determines the radius. In 9e, rather than tracing the point, students might construct a locus by selecting points A and P and choosing **Locus** from the Construct menu.

Instead of asking students to do this exercise, you might show the Sketchpad demonstration A Conic Construction.

9a, b. These constructions will result in a diagram similar to the one shown in the book.

9c. $\triangle PAG$ is an isosceles triangle, so $PA = PG$. So $FP + GP$ remains constant because they sum to the radius.

9d. An ellipse. The sum of the distances to two points remains constant.

9e. Moving G within the circle creates other ellipses. The closer P is to G, the less eccentric the ellipse. Locations outside the circle produce hyperbolas.

9. ***Technology*** Use geometry software to construct and explore this sketch.

a. Construct a circle F. Pick a point A on the circle, and another point G inside the circle. Construct $\overline{GA}$.

b. Construct the perpendicular bisector of $\overline{GA}$ and label it ℓ. Construct $\overrightarrow{FA}$. Label the intersection of ℓ and $\overrightarrow{FA}$ as P.

c. Explain why the sum of the distances FP and GP is constant.

d. Trace point P as you drag point A. What shape is traced? Why?

e. Now move G to a different location within the circle and repeat 9d. Describe how the shape changes. What happens when you move G outside the circle?

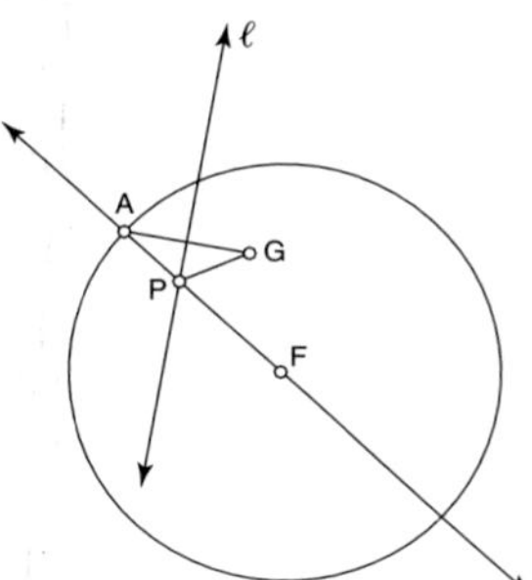

10. **APPLICATION** Three LORAN radio transmitters, A, B, and C, are located 200 miles apart along a straight coastline. They simultaneously transmit radio signals at regular intervals. The signals travel at a speed of 980 feet per microsecond. A ship, at S, first receives a signal from transmitter B. After 264 microseconds, the ship receives the signal from transmitter C, and then another 264 microseconds later it receives the signal from transmitter A. Use the diagram at right to answer these questions to find the location of the ship.

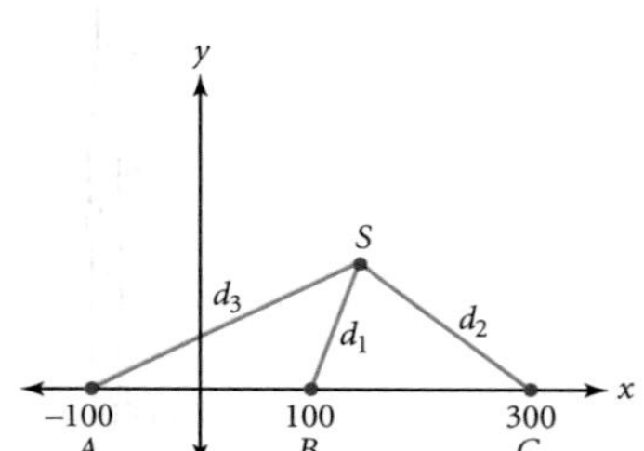

a. Find $d_2 - d_1$. Express your answer in miles (1 mi = 5280 ft). 49 mi

b. Find $d_3 - d_1$. Express your answer in miles. 98 mi

c. Use the fact that $d_2 - d_1$ is constant to write the equation of the hyperbola represented in 10a. Note that transmitters B and C are located at the foci.

d. Write the equation of the hyperbola represented in 10b.

e. Graph the hyperbolas and find the coordinates of the location of the ship. How can you be sure which of the intersection points represents the ship?

During World War II, LORAN, a long-range navigation system developed at MIT, used radio waves and the definition of a hyperbola to determine the exact location of ships. Today, LORAN-C is operated by the U.S. Coast Guard to monitor U.S. coastal waters. Civil and military air, land, and marine users are provided navigation, location, and timing services by the Coast Guard. Although today global positioning satellites can provide accurate locations, LORAN is a lower-cost alternative because it does not require the launch of satellites.

A technician performs a system check at the LORAN Station at Kodiak, Alaska.

11. Find the equation of the circle that passes through the four intersection points of the ellipses $\frac{x^2}{16} + \frac{y^2}{9} = 1$ and $\frac{x^2}{9} + \frac{y^2}{16} = 1$. $x^2 + y^2 = 11.52$

Review

6.3 **12.** Find the equations of two parabolas that pass through the points (2, 5), (0, 9), and (−6, 7). Sketch each parabola.

9.2 **13.** Find the coordinates of the foci of each ellipse.

a. $\left(\frac{x+2}{4}\right)^2 + \left(\frac{y-5}{6}\right)^2 = 1$

b. $x = \cos t + 1$
$y = 0.5 \sin t - 2$

9.4 **14.** Find the equations of the asymptotes of the hyperbola with vertices (5, 8.5) and (5, 3.5), and foci (5, 12.5) and (5, −0.5). $y = \frac{5}{12}x + \frac{47}{12}$ and $y = -\frac{5}{12}x + \frac{97}{12}$

9.1 **15.** If the vertices of a triangle are $A(10, 16)$, $B(4, 9)$, and $C(8, 1)$, find $m\angle ABC$. 113°

7.6 **16.** Write the polynomial expression $x^4 - 3x^3 + 4x^2 - 6x + 4$ in factored form. $(x-1)(x-2)\left(x - i\sqrt{2}\right)\left(x + i\sqrt{2}\right)$

17. You have seen that a double cone can be intersected with a plane to form a circle, an ellipse, a parabola, and a hyperbola. What shapes can be formed by the intersection of a plane and a square-based pyramid? Draw a sketch of each possibility.

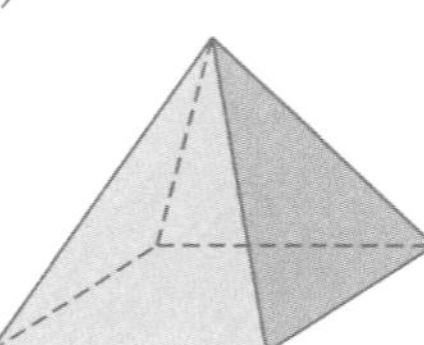

Extensions (continued)

B. Ask students to extend Exercise 9 by using their sketch to verify the reflection property of an ellipse.

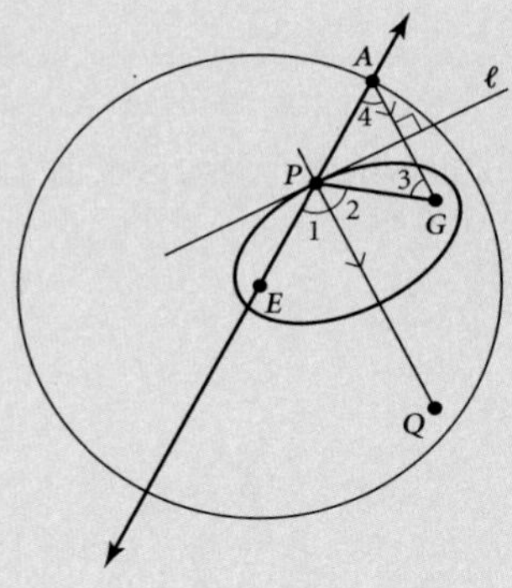

[Construct $\overline{PQ}$ parallel to $\overline{AG}$. Then $\angle 1 \cong \angle 4$ (corresponding angles), $\angle 2 \cong \angle 3$ (alternate interior angles), and $\angle 3 \cong \angle 4$ (ℓ is the perpendicular bisector of $\overline{AG}$). Therefore $\angle 1 \cong \angle 2$; that is, the angle of incidence is congruent to the angle of reflection.]

10c. $\frac{(x-200)^2}{600.25} - \frac{y^2}{9399.75} = 1$

10d. $\frac{x^2}{2401} - \frac{y^2}{7599} = 1$

10e.

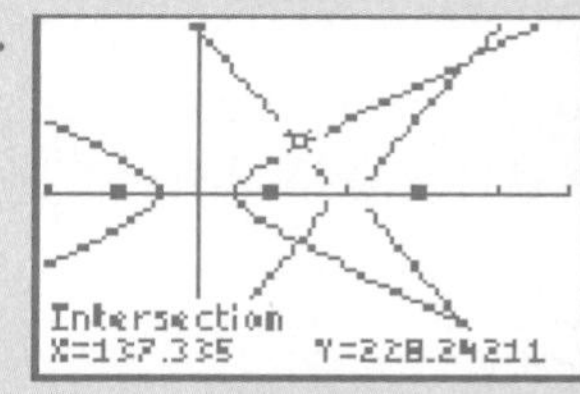

[−200, 500, 100, −800, 800, 800]

Because the three transmitters are on the shoreline, the points below the x-axis are on land, so they are excluded. The point in the upper right is excluded because it is closer to transmitter C. The intersection point closest to B is the location of the ship. The ship is at approximately (137.3, 228.2).

13a. $\left(-2, 5 + 2\sqrt{5}\right)$ and $\left(-2, 5 - 2\sqrt{5}\right)$ or approximately (−2, 0.53) and (−2, 9.47)

13b. $\left(1 + \frac{\sqrt{3}}{2}, -2\right)$ and $\left(1 - \frac{\sqrt{3}}{2}, -2\right)$ or approximately (0.13, −2) and (1.87, −2)

17. square, trapezoid, kite, triangle, pentagon

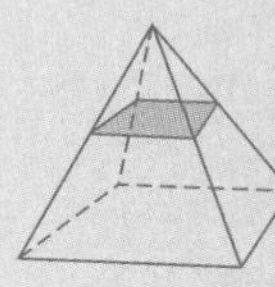

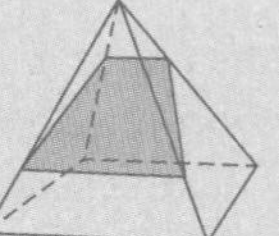

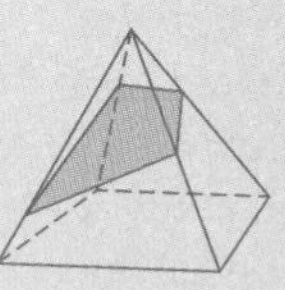

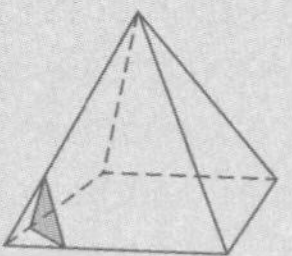

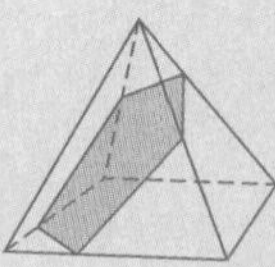

EXTENSIONS

A. Use Take Another Look activity 4 on page 563.

See page 897 for answer to Exercise 12.

EXPLORATION

PLANNING

LESSON OUTLINE

One day:

25 min Activity

5 min Sharing

15 min Questions

MATERIALS

- graph paper
- protractors
- compasses or rulers
- geometry software, *optional*
- Calculator Note 9B

TEACHING

Students can draw the rotations using geometry software.

It is possible to do this exploration if you have not included parametric equations, but students might need extra help with Questions 2 and 4 (or you can skip these questions).

Students have studied the inverse variation function $y = \frac{c}{x}$, or $xy = c$, which is a hyperbola rotated 45°. **[Link]** Quadratic functions that are not horizontally or vertically oriented have general equations with an xy-term. Students will study these functions further in precalculus.

Guiding the Activity

Step 1 Students within a group should work with the same points A and B but on separate sheets of paper. To minimize error, points A and B should not be too close to the origin.

E X P L O R A T I O N

The Rotation Matrix

Nearly all of the conic sections you have studied have been either horizontally or vertically oriented. You know how to translate and stretch or shrink their graphs. It is also possible to rotate their graphs.

In this exploration you will use rotation matrices to rotate points. This will allow you to graph a rotation of any function or relation.

Activity
Around We Go

You will need

- graph paper
- a protractor
- a compass or ruler

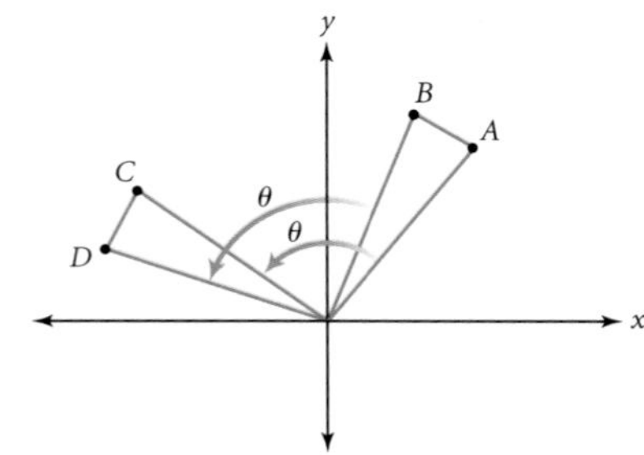

Step 1 Draw coordinate axes such that the origin is near the center of your graph paper. Mark two points, A and B, in the first quadrant. Draw $\overline{AB}$, and draw a segment from each point to the origin. Each member of your group must use the same points A and B.

Step 2 Choose an angle of rotation, θ, between 0° and 180°. Every member of your group must use a different angle. Locate points C and D, the images of points A and B after they are rotated $\theta°$ counterclockwise about the origin. Draw $\overline{CD}$. Find the coordinates of points C and D as accurately as you can.

Step 3 Answers will vary depending on θ.

Step 3 You can also rotate segment $\overline{AB}$ by multiplying a rotation matrix by the coordinate matrix of $\overline{AB}$. To find the rotation matrix for your value of θ, substitute the coordinates of the points A, B, C, and D into the second and third matrices shown below. (A_x denotes the x-coordinate of point A.) Use an inverse matrix to find the entries of the rotation matrix, the first matrix shown below. Multiply to check your answer.

$$\begin{bmatrix} e & f \\ g & h \end{bmatrix}\begin{bmatrix} A_x & B_x \\ A_y & B_y \end{bmatrix} = \begin{bmatrix} C_x & D_x \\ C_y & D_y \end{bmatrix}$$

Step 3 Geometry software can't help with this step. You might want to review solving matrices using inverses: To find the matrix $[X]$ that satisfies the matrix equation $[X][A] = [B]$, you can multiply matrix $[B]$ by $[A]^{-1}$. Have students check by doing the multiplication $[X][A]$.

Step 4 This step can be done in Sketchpad by choosing **Calculate** from the Measure menu. However, if students are using a calculator for Step 3, they will probably prefer to do the trigonometric calculations on their calculator as well.

LESSON OBJECTIVES

- Use a rotation matrix to rotate a function
- Understand the entries of the rotation matrix for a rotation angle θ

Step 4 $\begin{bmatrix} \cos\theta & -\sin\theta \\ \sin\theta & \cos\theta \end{bmatrix}$

Step 5 $(y\cos(90-\theta), y\sin(90-\theta))$, or $(-y\sin\theta, y\cos\theta)$; the rotation matrix has to transform $(x, 0)$ to $(x\cos\theta, x\sin\theta)$. So the entries in the first column must be $\cos\theta$ and $\sin\theta$. It also has to transform $(0, y)$ to $(-y\sin\theta, y\cos\theta)$, so the second column entries must be $-\sin\theta$ and $\cos\theta$.

Step 6 $\begin{bmatrix} x\cos\theta - y\sin\theta \\ x\sin\theta + y\cos\theta \end{bmatrix}$

Step 4 Find the sine and cosine of your rotation angle θ. What is the connection between the entries of your rotation matrix and your sine and cosine values? Compare results with your group. Write a conjecture about a matrix that will rotate a graph $\theta°$ counterclockwise about the origin.

Step 5 To see why the rotation matrix has those entries, look at the effect of rotation on each coordinate. The diagram at right shows the images of points $(x, 0)$ and $(0, y)$ after rotating $\theta°$ counterclockwise about the origin. Identify the lengths, in terms of x, of all three sides of the triangle on the right. Do you see why the point $(x, 0)$ rotates to $(x\cos\theta, x\sin\theta)$? Write the coordinates of the point (a, b) in terms of $\cos\theta$ and $\sin\theta$. Then explain why the entries of the rotation matrix make sense.

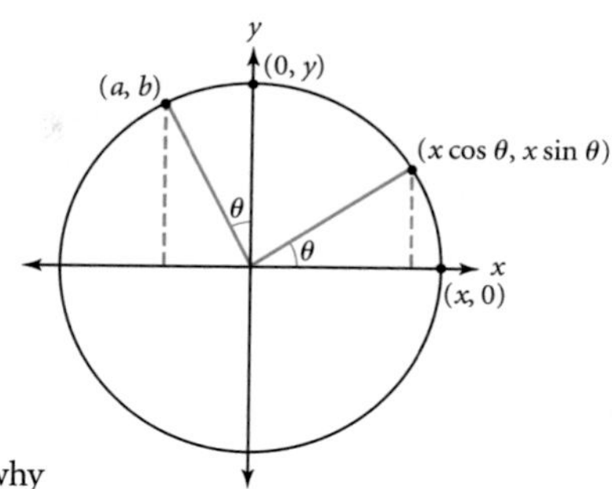

Step 6 Multiply the rotation matrix you found in Step 4 by the point $\begin{bmatrix} x \\ y \end{bmatrix}$ to find the coordinates of a point (x, y) that has been rotated $\theta°$.

Questions

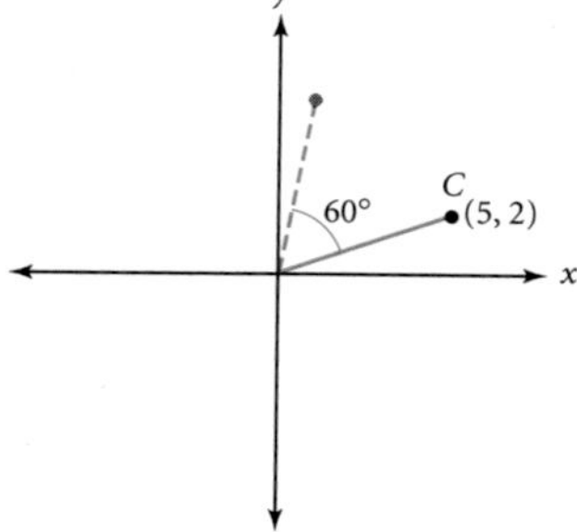

1. Point C is rotated 60° counterclockwise about the origin. Find the coordinates of the new point. (0.77, 5.33)
2. The parametric equations of a parabola are $x = 3t^2 + 3$ and $y = 5t$. Rotate the parabola 135° counterclockwise. Write the parametric equations for the new parabola. Verify your results by graphing the original parabola and its rotated image.
3. Rotate the hyperbola $x^2 - y^2 = 1$ counterclockwise 45° about the origin. Verify your result by graphing the original hyperbola and its rotated image.
4. Consider the parametric equations $x_1 = \tan t$ and $y_1 = \frac{1}{\cos t}$.
   a. Predict what the graph will look like.
   b. Predict what the graph of $x_2 = x_1\cos\theta - y_1\sin\theta$ and $y_2 = x_1\sin\theta + y_1\cos\theta$ will be when θ equals 50°. [▶ See **Calculator Note 9B** to use functions within functions in Parametric mode. ◀]
   c. Draw the graphs to check your predictions.

▶ Helping with the Questions

Question 2 Students can find several points on the parabola and transform the points or transform the parametric expressions.

Question 3 Students may think they should substitute 45° for θ, but just as you replace x with $(x - 2)$ to translate a graph to the right, you must substitute $-45°$ to rotate the graph counterclockwise (in the positive direction).

SHARING IDEAS

Ask students whether they can justify geometrically the rotation equations and matrix they derived. You might show them this picture of rotated axes (with the point fixed) and ask whether rotating the axes is equivalent to rotating the point. [Rotating the axes counterclockwise through $\angle\theta$ is equivalent to rotating the point clockwise through $\angle\theta$.]

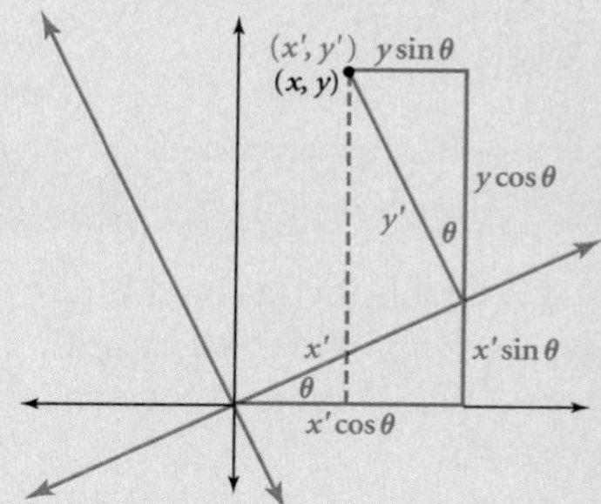

EXTENSION

Show this screen and ask students to write parametric equations for x_1 and y_1 that will draw the larger equilateral triangle on the calculator."

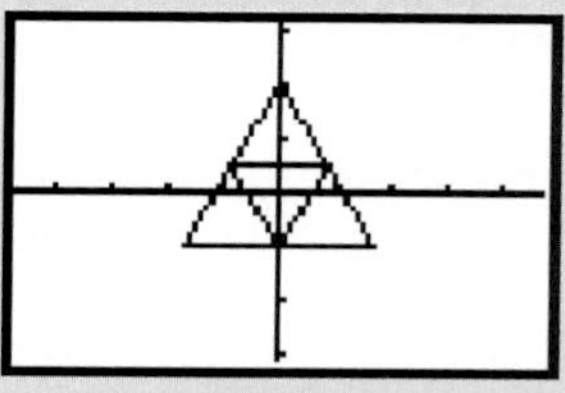

[−4.7, 4.7, 1, −3.1, 3.1, 1]

Then have them write a set of parametric equations in terms of x_1 and y_1 that will transform the large triangle into the small triangle."

See pages 897–898 for answers to the Extension and Questions 2–4.

NCTM STANDARDS

CONTENT		PROCESS	
	Number		Problem Solving
✓	Algebra	✓	Reasoning
	Geometry	✓	Communication
✓	Measurement		Connections
	Data/Probability	✓	Representation

Assessing Progress
You can check students' skills at measuring angles, multiplying matrices, finding trigonometric ratios, and seeing patterns.

Closing the Lesson

The matrix $[X] = \begin{bmatrix} \cos\theta & -\sin\theta \\ \sin\theta & \cos\theta \end{bmatrix}$ represents a rotation. If matrix $[A]$ represents a point, then the matrix product $[X][A]$ represents the image of that point under a counterclockwise rotation through $\angle\theta$.

LESSON

9.6

PLANNING

LESSON OUTLINE

One day:

- 20 min Investigation
- 10 min Sharing
- 10 min Examples
- 5 min Exercises

MATERIALS

- dry linguine, fettuccine, or spaghetti
- small film canisters
- string
- small weights
- rulers
- tape
- Piston Pressure (W), *optional*
- Calculator Note 9C

TEACHING

In this lesson the rational function $y = \frac{1}{x}$ provides a transition from conic sections to rational functions.

One Step

Pose this problem, taken from Example B: "Suppose you have 100 mL of a solution that is 30% acid and 70% water. How many milliliters of acid do you need to add to make a solution that is 60% acid? To make it a 90% acid solution? What's the long-run value of the percentage as acid is added?" For the third question, suggest that students use long or synthetic division to rewrite the function as $y = -\frac{70}{x + 100} + 1$. During Sharing, elicit the fact that this is a transformation of the parent function $y = \frac{1}{x}$ and that the graphs of these functions are hyperbolas rotated 45° from the hyperbolas they studied in the previous lesson.

LESSON 9.6

Introduction to Rational Functions

You probably know that a lighter tree climber can crawl farther out on a branch than a heavier climber can, before the branch is in danger of breaking. What do you think the graph of (*length, mass*) data will look like when mass is added to a length of pole until it breaks? Is the relationship linear, like line *A*, or does it resemble one of the curves, *B* or *C*?

Engineers study problems like this because they need to know the weight that a beam can safely support. In the next investigation you will collect data and experiment with this relationship.

The Louise M. Davies Symphony Hall, built in 1980, is part of the Civic Center in San Francisco, California. The design of both the balcony and the covered entrance rely upon cantilevers—projecting beams that are supported at only one end.

Investigation
The Breaking Point

You will need

- several pieces of dry spaghetti
- a small film canister
- string
- some weights (pennies, beans, or other small units of mass)
- a ruler
- tape

Procedure Note

1. Lay a piece of spaghetti on a table so that its length is perpendicular to one side of the table and the end extends over the edge of the table.
2. Measure the length of the spaghetti that extends beyond the edge of the table. (See the photo on the next page.) Record this information in a table of (*length, mass*) data.
3. Tie the string to the film canister so that you can hang it from the end of the spaghetti. (You may need to use tape to hold the string in place.)
4. Place mass units into the container one at a time until the spaghetti breaks. Record the maximum number of weights that the length of spaghetti was able to support.

LESSON OBJECTIVES

- Investigate inverse variations
- Define *rational function*
- Graph and find the equations of transformations of the parent function $y = \frac{1}{x}$
- Use rational functions to solve mixture problems and for other applications

NCTM STANDARDS

CONTENT	PROCESS
Number	✓ Problem Solving
✓ Algebra	Reasoning
Geometry	✓ Communication
✓ Measurement	✓ Connections
✓ Data/Probability	Representation

Step 1 Work with a partner. Follow the procedure note to record at least five data points and then compile your results with those of other group members.

Step 2 Make a graph of your data with length as the independent variable, x, and mass as the dependent variable, y. Does the relationship appear to be linear? If not, describe the appearance of the graph.

Step 3 $y = \frac{90}{x}$

Step 3 Write an equation that is a good fit with the plotted data.

The relationship between length and mass in the investigation is an **inverse variation.** The parent function for an inverse variation curve, $f(x) = \frac{1}{x}$, is the simplest **rational function.**

Rational Function

A **rational function** is one that can be written as a quotient, $f(x) = \frac{p(x)}{q(x)}$, where $p(x)$ and $q(x)$ are both polynomial expressions. The denominator polynomial must be of degree 1 or higher.

This type of function can be transformed just like all the other functions you have previously studied. The function you found in the investigation was probably a transformation of $f(x) = \frac{1}{x}$.

Graph the function $f(x) = \frac{1}{x}$ on your calculator and observe some of its special characteristics. The graph is made up of two branches. One part occurs where x is negative and the other where x is positive. There is no value for this function when $x = 0$. What happens when you try to evaluate $f(0)$? Notice that the graph is a hyperbola that has been rotated 45°, and has vertices (1, 1) and (−1, −1). The x- and y-axes are the asymptotes. As x gets closer to zero, the y-values become increasingly large in absolute value.

$f(0)$ is undefined.

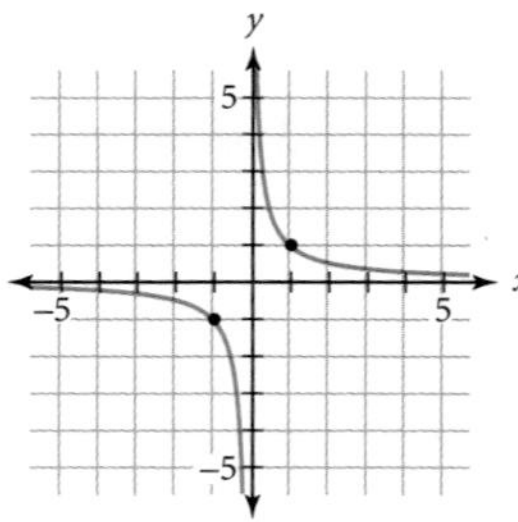

Step 2

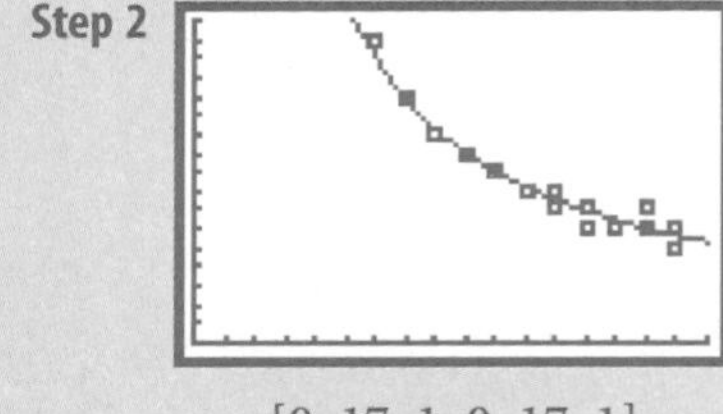

[0, 17, 1, 0, 17, 1]

The graph does not appear to be linear. It is a curve that decreases quickly at first, and then more slowly.

Rational Functions

[Ask] "For $f(x) = \frac{1}{x}$, what is the numerator function?" [$p(x) = 1$] "What is its degree?" [0] "What are the denominator function and its degree?" [$q(x) = x$; 1]

In the investigation, x had no negative values, so the graph was only one branch of the hyperbola given by the equation $y = \frac{1}{x}$. **[Language]** Students may recall from *Discovering Algebra,* Chapter 3, that x and y satisfy the *inverse variation* $y = \frac{k}{x}$.

Guiding the Investigation

You might use the Piston Pressure worksheet as an alternative to this investigation. Teacher notes for that alternative investigation are on page 538.

[Language] A beam that supports a weight at one end is called a *cantilever* ['kan-tə-lē-vər] *beam.*

Test the procedure first. The type of weights and the size canister you choose will depend on the strength of the pasta. Flat pastas, such as linguine or fettuccine, work best. Pennies or equivalent masses are about the right weight.

Step 1 As students follow Procedure Note 3, caution them to make sure they hang the film canister the same distance from the end of each piece of pasta.

Cupped hands are best for catching the film canister when the pasta breaks.

Students should use a new piece of pasta, rather than part of the broken pasta, for each data point. Encourage students to collect data from a wide domain of lengths.

As they work, students may suggest that the amount of pasta on the table, not just the amount extending beyond the table, affects the breaking point. Let them check this hypothesis by breaking some of the pasta into shorter pieces and recording a third variable. **[Ask]** "What do you observe about the influence of the length of pasta on the table?"

Step 3 Students can use guess-and-check to try different models. The function $f(x) = 1 - x$ decreases but is linear. Students may also try an exponential function.

See page 898 for answers to Step 1.

Using the Piston Pressure Investigation
You can find syringes at a farm animal feed store; they are often used to give medicine to animals. You can cap the end of the syringe by drilling a hole partway into a rubber stopper that is 50% smaller than the opening at the end of the syringe. Then fill the hole with superglue before you force the syringe into the hole. (You might design some support system to support the weight. Clamping the syringe to a heavy ring stand works.)

This function should be a strict inverse function $y = \frac{k}{x}$. If the pressure were zero, then the volume would be infinite. If the y-value or the volume were zero, then all the molecules of air would be pressed into nothing.

Consider these values of the function $f(x) = \frac{1}{x}$.

x	-1	-0.1	-0.01	-0.001	0	0.001	0.01	0.1	1
y	-1	-10	-100	-1000	undefined	1000	100	10	1

As x approaches zero from the negative side, the y-values have an increasingly large absolute value.

So $x = 0$ is a vertical asymptote.

As x approaches zero from the positive side, the y-values have an increasingly large absolute value.

The behavior of the y-values as x gets closer to zero shows that the y-axis is a vertical asymptote for this function.

x	-10000	-1000	-100	-10	0	10	100	1000	10000
y	-0.0001	-0.001	-0.01	-0.1	undefined	0.1	0.01	0.001	0.0001

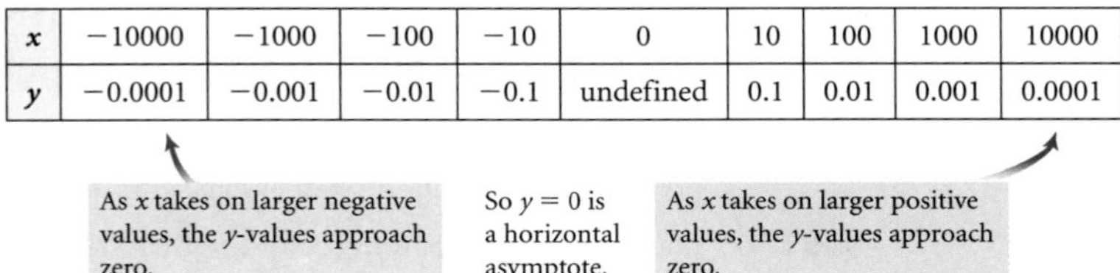

As x takes on larger negative values, the y-values approach zero.

So $y = 0$ is a horizontal asymptote.

As x takes on larger positive values, the y-values approach zero.

As x approaches the extreme values at the left and right ends of the x-axis, the curve approaches the y-axis. The horizontal line $y = 0$, then, is a horizontal asymptote. This asymptote is called an end behavior model of the function. In general, the end behavior of a function is its behavior for x-values that are large in absolute value.

If you think of $y = \frac{1}{x}$ as a parent function, then $y = \frac{1}{x} + 1$, $y = \frac{1}{x-2}$, and $y = 3\left(\frac{1}{x}\right)$ are examples of transformed rational functions. What happens to a function when x is replaced with $(x - 2)$? The function $y = \frac{1}{x-2}$ is shown at right. The graph is translated right 2 units.

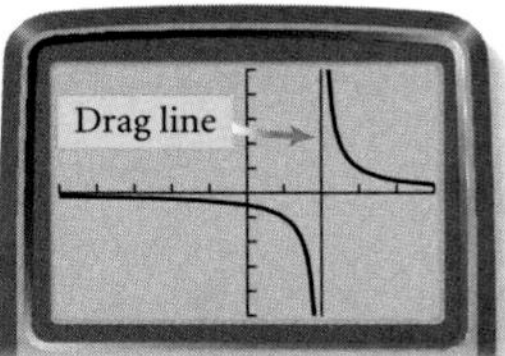

$[-5, 5, 1, -5, 5, 1]$

Frequently, rational function graphs on the calculator include a nearly vertical drag line. The drag line is not part of the graph! However, it will look much like the graph of the vertical asymptote. [► See **Calculator Note 9C** to learn how to eliminate this line from your graph. ◄]

► *EXAMPLE A*
This example shows how to rewrite a ratio of linear functions to see how it's a transformation of the function $f(x) = \frac{1}{x}$. Students will do this in Exercise 9. Another way to change the form of the function is by division, which leads to the quotient 2 remainder -3. Rather than focusing on the mechanics of the process, you might emphasize interpreting the rewritten function $f(x) = 2 - \frac{3}{x-1}$. Students may see the transformation more clearly if you replace $f(x)$ with y.

EXAMPLE A

Describe the function $f(x) = \frac{2x-5}{x-1}$ as a transformation of the parent function, $f(x) = \frac{1}{x}$. Then sketch a graph.

► *Solution*

You can change the form of the equation so that the transformations are more obvious. Because the denominator is $(x - 1)$, rather than x, try to get the expression $(x - 1)$ in the numerator as well.

$$f(x) = \frac{2x-5}{x-1}$$ Original equation.

$$f(x) = \frac{2(x-1)-3}{x-1}$$ Consider the numerator to be $2x - 2 - 3$, and then factor to get $2(x - 1) - 3$.

Now you want to look for a scale factor and an added term. Separate the rational expression into two fractions:

$$f(x) = \frac{2(x-1)}{x-1} - \frac{3}{x-1}$$ Separate the numerator into two numerators over the same denominator.

$$f(x) = 2 - \frac{3}{x-1}$$ Reduce.

Now you can see that the parent function has been vertically stretched by a factor of -3, then translated right 1 unit and up 2 units.

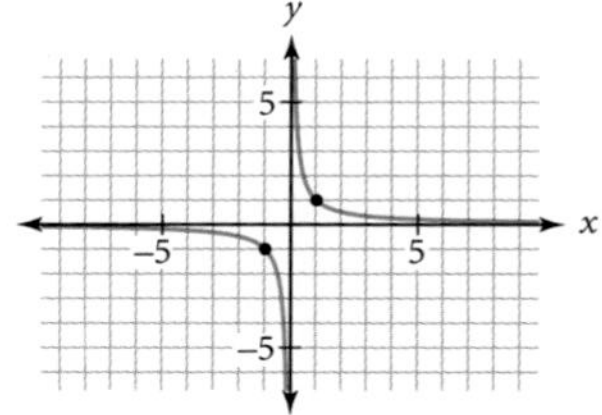

$y = \frac{1}{x}$

The parent rational function, $y = \frac{1}{x}$, has vertices $(1, 1)$ and $(-1, -1)$.

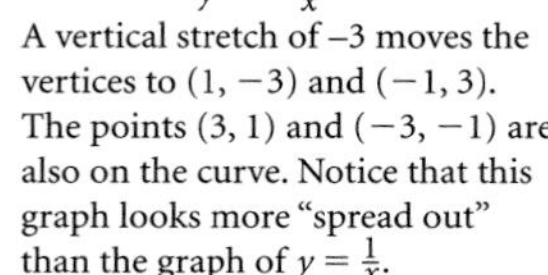

$y = -\frac{3}{x}$

A vertical stretch of -3 moves the vertices to $(1, -3)$ and $(-1, 3)$. The points $(3, 1)$ and $(-3, -1)$ are also on the curve. Notice that this graph looks more "spread out" than the graph of $y = \frac{1}{x}$.

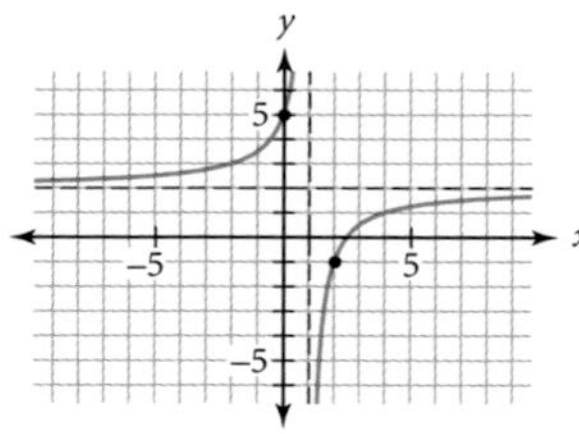

$y = 2 - \frac{3}{x-1}$

A translation right 1 unit and up 2 units moves the vertices to $(2, -1)$ and $(0, 5)$. The asymptotes are also translated to $x = 1$ and $y = 2$.

Notice that the asymptotes have been translated. How are the equations of the asymptotes related to your final equation above?

The asymptotes are translated right 1 unit and up 2 units.

To identify an equation that will produce a given graph, do the procedure you used to graph Example A in reverse. You can identify translations by simply looking at the translations of the asymptotes. To identify stretch factors, pick a point, such as a vertex, whose coordinates you would know after the translation of $f(x) = \frac{1}{x}$. Then find a point on the stretched graph that has the same x-coordinate. The ratio of the vertical distances from the horizontal asymptote to those two points is the vertical scale factor.

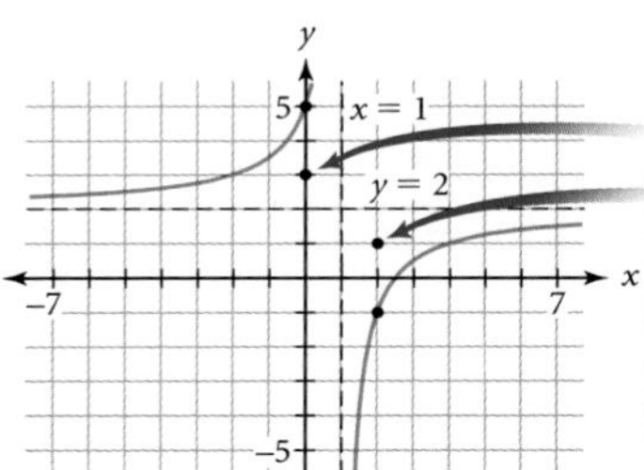

An unstretched (but reflected) inverse variation function with these translations would have vertices $(2, 1)$ and $(0, 3)$, 1 horizontal unit and 1 vertical unit away from the center. Because the distance is now 3 vertical units from the center, include a vertical stretch of 3 to get the equation $y = 2 - \frac{3}{x-1}$

Rational expressions are very useful in chemistry. Scientists use them to model many situations, including the concentration of a solution or mixture as it is diluted.

Example A (continued)

[Ask] "How are the equations of the asymptotes related to the equation $y = 2 - \frac{3}{x-1}$?" [If a rational function is translated right 1 unit and up 2 units, so are the asymptotes; the asymptotes can be found simply by looking at the translations in the equation.]

▶ **EXAMPLE B**

In this example students see an application of a rational function in which the numerator and denominator are linear polynomials. **[Alert]** Students may wonder how a percentage P can have a denominator of $100 + x$ rather than 100. P is the ratio of the volume of acid to the volume of water, and $100 + x$ is the new total amount.

Students can also solve the equation by graphing.

[Ask] "Is there a situation in which you could want P to represent the portion of water?" [yes, if water instead of acid is being added]

[Ask] "Where else have you seen a long-run value?" [in Chapter 1, with concentrations expressed by sequences; in Chapter 5, in conjunction with exponential decay; and in Chapter 6, in the context of transition matrices]

SHARING IDEAS

As students present, you might want to review transformations of the inverse function on a graphing calculator.

[Ask] "The graph of the function $y = \frac{1}{x}$ is a rotation of what hyperbola?" [It's a rotation of infinitely many hyperbolas. The most familiar to students are the horizontally oriented hyperbola, which is rotated 45° counterclockwise, and the vertically oriented hyperbola, which is rotated 45° clockwise.]

[Ask] "Is the horizontally oriented hyperbola the hyperbola with the equation $x^2 - y^2 = 1$?" [No; this hyperbola's vertices are 1 unit from the center, whereas the vertices of the hyperbola with the equation $y = \frac{1}{x}$ are $\sqrt{2}$ units from the center.] **[Link]** The study of rotations of the hyperbola (and of other conic sections) through other angles is a topic of precalculus.

See page 898 for answers to Exercise 1.

EXAMPLE B Suppose you have 100 mL of a solution that is 30% acid and 70% water. How many mL of acid do you need to add to make a solution that is 60% acid? To make it a 90% acid solution? Can it ever be 100% acid?

▶ **Solution**

Of the 100 mL of solution, 30%, or 30 mL, is acid. The percentage, P, can be written as $P = \frac{30}{100}$. If x milliliters of acid are added, there will be more acid, but also more solution. The concentration of acid will be

$$P = \frac{30 + x}{100 + x}$$

To find when the solution is 60% acid, substitute 0.6 for P and solve the equation.

$$0.6 = \frac{30 + x}{100 + x} \qquad \text{Substitute 0.6 for } P.$$
$$0.6(100 + x) = 30 + x \qquad \text{Multiply both sides by } (100 + x).$$
$$60 + 0.6x = 30 + x \qquad \text{Distribute.}$$
$$30 = 0.4x \qquad \text{Collect like terms.}$$
$$75 = x \qquad \text{Divide by 0.4.}$$

Adding 75 mL of acid will make a 60% acid solution.

To find when the solution is 90% acid, solve the equation $0.9 = \frac{30 + x}{100 + x}$. You will find that 600 mL of acid must be added.

The graph of $P = \frac{30 + x}{100 + x}$ shows horizontal asymptote $y = 1$. No matter now many milliliters of acid you add, you will never have a mixture that is 100% acid. This is because the original 70 mL of water will remain, even though it is a smaller and smaller percentage of the entire solution as you continue to add acid.

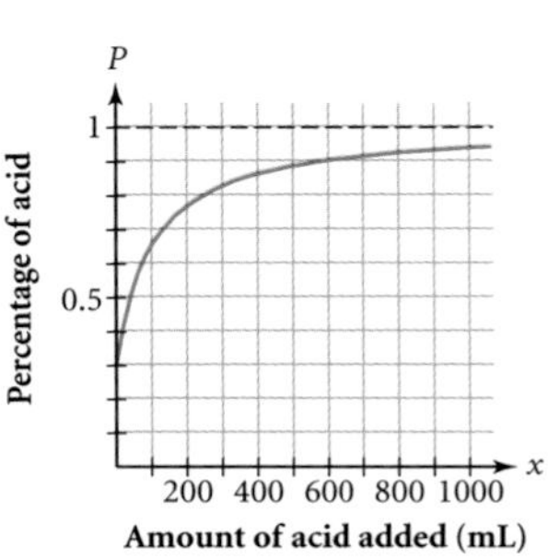

EXERCISES

You will need

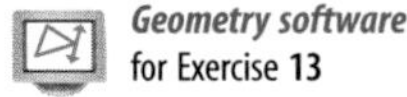

Practice Your Skills

1. Write an equation and graph each transformation of the parent function $f(x) = \frac{1}{x}$.
   a. Translate the graph up 2 units.
   b. Translate the graph right 3 units.
   c. Translate the graph down 1 unit and left 4 units.
   d. Vertically stretch the graph by a scale factor of 2.
   e. Horizontally stretch the graph by a factor of 3, and translate it up 1 unit.

2. What are the equations of the asymptotes for each hyperbola?
   a. $y = \frac{2}{x} + 1$ — $y = 1, x = 0$
   b. $y = \frac{3}{x - 4}$ — $y = 0, x = 4$
   c. $y = \frac{4}{x + 2} - 1$ — $y = -1, x = -2$
   d. $y = \frac{-2}{x + 3} - 4$ — $y = -4, x = -3$

Assessing Progress

You can assess students' knowledge of decreasing functions such as linear functions, exponential functions, and power functions.

Closing the Lesson

The main point of this lesson is that the rational function $y = \frac{1}{x}$ is the parent function of rational functions consisting of a linear function divided by another linear function. These functions' graphs are hyperbolas rotated 45° from horizontally or vertically oriented hyperbolas.

3. Solve.

a. $12 = \frac{x - 8}{x + 3}$ $x = -4$

b. $21 = \frac{3x + 8}{x - 5}$

c. $3 = \frac{2x + 5}{4x - 7}$ $x = 2.6$

d. $-4 = \frac{-6x + 5}{2x + 3}$ $x = -8.5$

4. As the rational function $y = \frac{1}{x}$ is translated, its asymptotes are translated also. Write an equation for the translation of $y = \frac{1}{x}$ that has the asymptotes described.

a. horizontal asymptote $y = 2$ and vertical asymptote $x = 0$

b. horizontal asymptote $y = -4$ and vertical asymptote $x = 2$

c. horizontal asymptote $y = 3$ and vertical asymptote $x = -4$

5. If a basketball team's present record is 42 wins and 36 losses, how many consecutive games must it win so that its winning record reaches 60%? 12 games

Reason and Apply

6. Write a rational equation to describe each graph. Some equations will need scale factors.

a. $y = \frac{-1}{x + 5}$

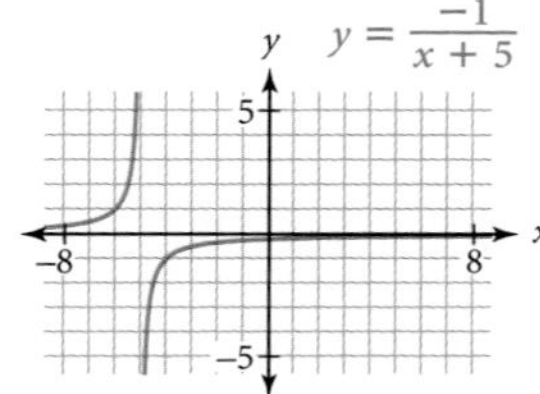

b. $y = \frac{1}{x - 6} - 2$

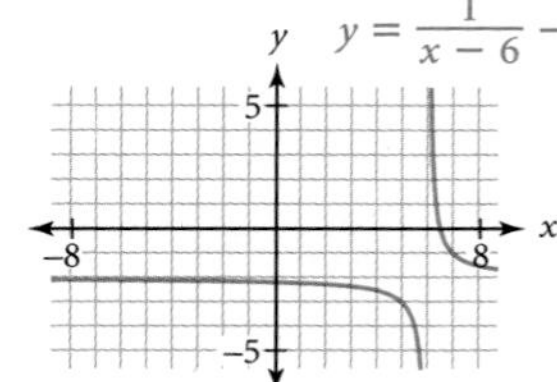

c. $y = \frac{4}{x}$

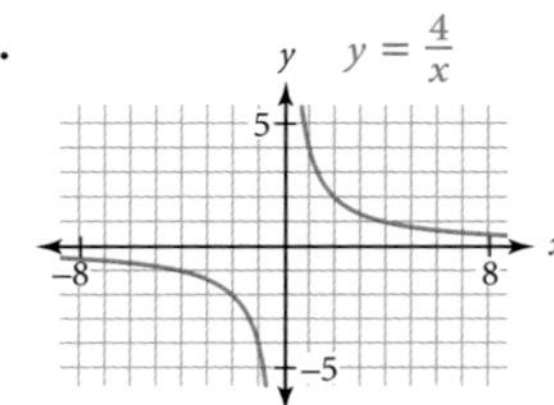

d. $y = \frac{9}{x + 4}$

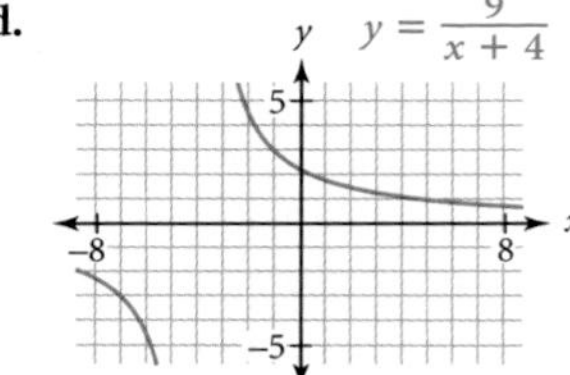

7. APPLICATION The graph at right shows the concentration of acid in a solution as pure acid is added. The solution began as 55 mL of a 38% acid solution.

a. How many milliliters of pure acid were in the original solution? 20.9 mL

b. Write an equation for $f(x)$.

c. Find the amount of pure acid that must be added to create a solution that is 64% acid. 39.72 mL

d. Describe the end behavior of $f(x)$. The graph approaches $y = 1$.

Percentage of acid; Amount of acid added (mL); $y = f(x)$

8. APPLICATION In a container of 2% milk, 2% of the mixture is fat. How much of the liquid in a 1 gal container of 2% milk would need to be emptied and replaced with pure fat so that the container could be labeled as whole (3.25%) milk? approximately 0.013 gal

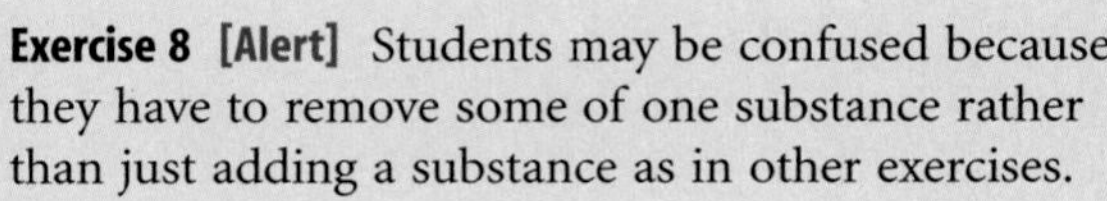

Exercise 8 [Alert] Students may be confused because they have to remove some of one substance rather than just adding a substance as in other exercises.

BUILDING UNDERSTANDING

Do not assign Exercise 17c if you are not teaching parametric equations.

ASSIGNING HOMEWORK

Essential	1, 2, 4, 5
Performance assessment	6–13
Portfolio	10
Journal	7
Group	9, 10, 13
Review	3, 14–19

MATERIALS

- graph paper
- Sketchpad demonstration Inverse Variation, *optional*

Helping with the Exercises

Exercise 3 To help students deepen their understanding of rational functions, you might encourage them to solve these equations by graphing.

3b. $x = \frac{113}{18}$ or $x = 6.2\overline{7}$

Exercise 4 It may be useful for students to sketch graphs of these situations.

4a. $y = \frac{1}{x} + 2$

4b. $y = \frac{1}{x - 2} - 4$

4c. $y = \frac{1}{x + 4} + 3$

Exercise 5 Students can let P represent the portion of wins and let x represent the number of consecutive wins.

Exercise 7d [Ask] "What is the real-world meaning of this end behavior?" [The solution will never be 100% acid.]

7b. $f(x) = \frac{20.9 + x}{55 + x}$

Exercise 9 Students can either use the method described in Example A or graph and use guess-and-check to find the transformed equations.

9a. i. $y = 2 + \frac{-3}{x-5}$

9a. ii. $y = 3 + \frac{2}{x+3}$

9b. i. For $y = 2 + \frac{-3}{x-5}$, stretch vertically by a factor of −3, and translate right 5 units and up 2 units.

9b. ii. For $y = 3 + \frac{2}{x+3}$, stretch vertically by a factor of 2, and translate left 3 units and up 3 units.

9c. i.

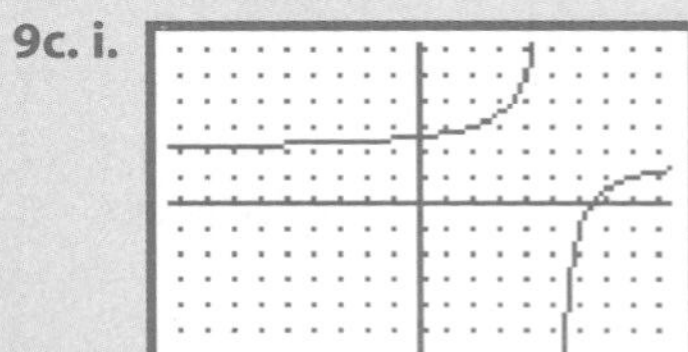

[−9.4, 9.4, 1, −6.2, 6.2, 1]

9c. ii.

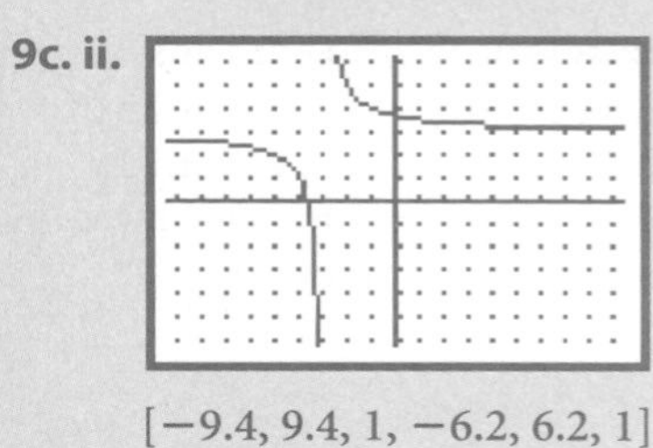

[−9.4, 9.4, 1, −6.2, 6.2, 1]

Exercises 10, 13 You might use the Sketchpad demonstration Inverse Variation to explore these exercises with your students.

Exercise 10 For 10b **[Ask]** "Can you construct the rectangular box that has the asymptotes as its diagonals with straightedge and compass?" [Construct the line of symmetry through the vertices. Construct the perpendicular to the line of symmetry at each vertex. Connect the intersections of these perpendiculars with the x- and y-axes to form the rectangle.] For 10d **[Ask]** "Can you construct the foci geometrically?" [Construct a circle with center at the origin and radius through a vertex of the rectangle. The intersections of the circle with the line of symmetry are the foci.]

9. Consider these functions.

i. $y = \frac{2x - 13}{x - 5}$ ii. $y = \frac{3x + 11}{x + 3}$

a. Rewrite each rational function to show how it is a transformation of $y = \frac{1}{x}$.

b. Describe the transformations of the graph of $y = \frac{1}{x}$ that will produce graphs of the equations in 9a.

c. Graph each equation on your calculator to confirm your answers to 9b.

10. Draw the graph of $y = \frac{1}{x}$.

a. Label the vertices of the hyperbola.

b. The x- and y-axes are the asymptotes for this hyperbola. Draw the box between the two branches of the hyperbola that has the asymptotes as its diagonals. The vertices should lie on the box.

c. The dimensions of the box are $2a$ and $2b$. Find the values of a and b. $a = b = \sqrt{2}$

d. The foci of the hyperbola lie on the line passing through the two vertices. In this case, that line is $y = x$. The foci are c units from the center of the hyperbola where $a^2 + b^2 = c^2$. Find the value of c and the coordinates of the two foci. $c = 2$; foci: $(\sqrt{2}, \sqrt{2})$ and $(-\sqrt{2}, -\sqrt{2})$

11. Recall that the general quadratic equation is $Ax^2 + Bxy + Cy^2 + Dx + Ey + F = 0$. Let $A = 0, B = 4, C = 0, D = 0, E = 0$, and $F = -1$. See page 543 for 11b and 11c.

a. Graph this equation. What type of conic section is formed?

b. What is the relationship between the inverse variation function, $y = \frac{1}{x}$, and the conic sections?

c. Convert the rational function $y = \frac{1}{x-2} + 3$ to general quadratic form. What are the values of A, B, C, D, E, and F in the general quadratic equation?

12. APPLICATION Ohm's law states that $I = \frac{V}{R}$. This law can be used to determine the amount of current I, in amps, flowing in the circuit when a voltage V, in volts, is applied to a resistance R, in ohms.

a. If a hairdryer set on high is using a maximum of 8.33 amps on a 120-volt line, what is the resistance in the heating coils? 14.4 ohms

b. In the United Kingdom, power lines use 240 volts. If a traveler were to plug in a hairdryer, and the resistance in the hairdryer was the same as in 12a, what would be the flow of current? 16.7 amps

c. The additional current flowing through the hairdryer would cause a meltdown of the coils and the motor wires. In order to reduce the current flow in 12b back to the value in 12a, how much resistance would be needed? 28.8 ohms

Consumer CONNECTION

Many travel appliances, such as hairdryers and shavers, are made with a voltage switch that provides the resistance necessary for the appliance to work properly in different countries. In the United States, a voltage of about 120V is standard, whereas in Europe about 240V is typical. A dimmer switch on a light fixture works in a similar way. When the dimmer switch is set low, there is higher resistance, causing less current to flow, and less illumination is produced. As the dimmer switch is turned, there is less resistance, allowing more current to flow, and more illumination is produced. The volume control on a stereo system works the same way.

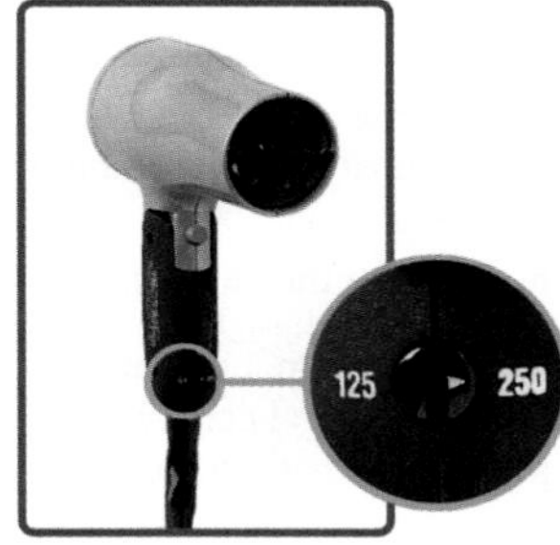

10a.

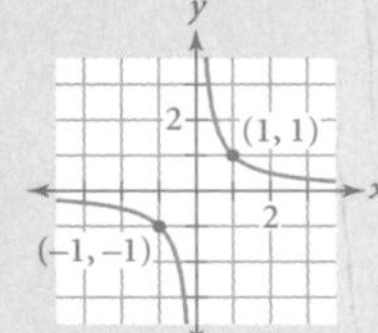

10b.

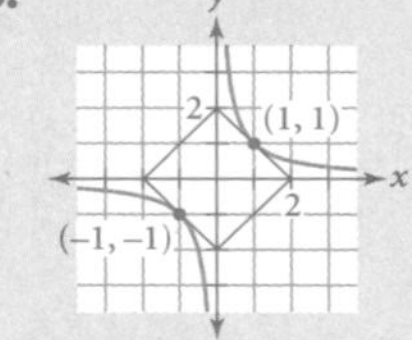

11a. a rotated hyperbola

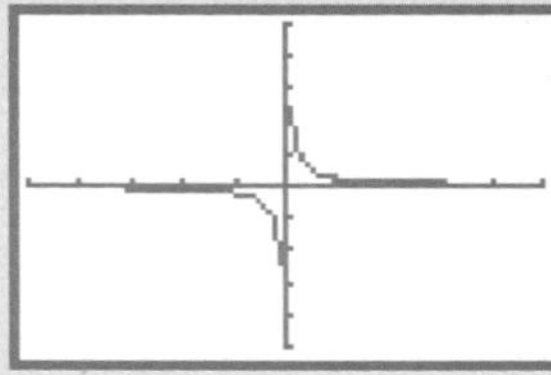

[−5, 5, 1, −5, 5, 1]

13. *Technology* Using geometry software, draw the curve $y = \frac{1}{x}$ and plot the foci you found in Exercise 10d. Use measurement tools to verify that $y = \frac{1}{x}$ satisfies the locus definition of a hyperbola.

Review

7.6 **14.** Factor each expression completely.

a. $x^2 - 7x + 10$ $(x - 5)(x - 2)$

b. $x^3 - 9x$ $x(x - 3)(x + 3)$

9.2 **15.** Write the equation of the circle with center (2, −3) and radius 4. $(x - 2)^2 + (y + 3)^2 = 16$

9.1 **16.** A 2 m rod and a 5 m rod are mounted vertically 10 m apart. One end of a 15 m wire is attached to the top of each rod. Suppose the wire is stretched taut and fastened to the ground between the two rods. How far from the base of the 2 m rod is the wire fastened? 9.8 m

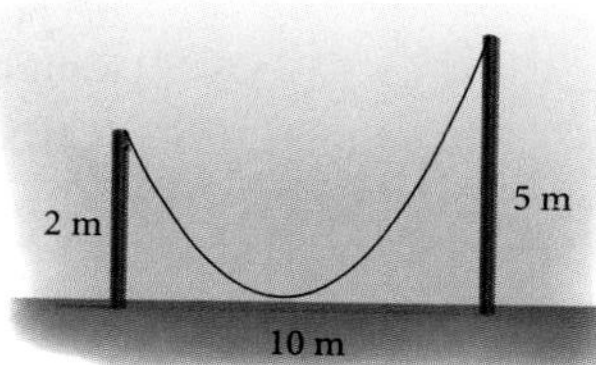

8.4 **17.** Sarah would like to row her boat directly across a river 500 m wide. The current flows 3 km/h and she is able to row 5 km/h.

a. At what angle to the riverbank should she point her boat?

b. As she starts, how far upstream on the opposite bank should she head?

c. Write parametric equations to simulate Sarah's crossing.

500 m

9.5 **18.** Write the general quadratic equations of two concentric circles with center (6, −4) and radii 5 and 8.

19. Find exact values of missing side lengths for 19a–d.

a.

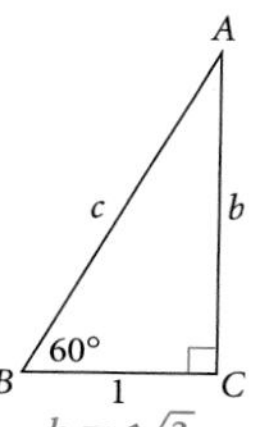

$b = \sqrt{3}, c = 2$

b.

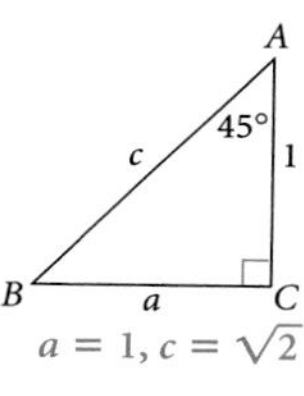

$a = 1, c = \sqrt{2}$

c.

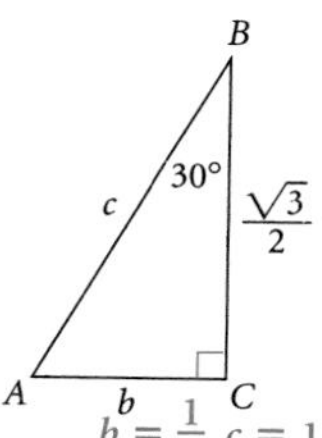

$b = \frac{1}{2}, c = 1$

d.

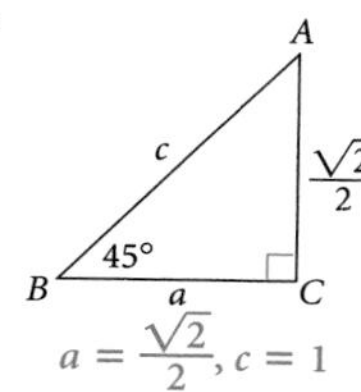

$a = \frac{\sqrt{2}}{2}, c = 1$

e. What is the ratio of side lengths in a 45°-45°-90° triangle? A 30°-60°-90° triangle?

$\frac{\sqrt{2}}{2} : \frac{\sqrt{2}}{2} : 1; \frac{1}{2} : \frac{\sqrt{3}}{2} : 1$

11b. The inverse variation function, $y = \frac{1}{x}$, can be converted to the form $xy = 1$, which is a conic section. Its graph is a rotated hyperbola.

11c. $xy - 3x - 2y + 5 = 0$; $A = 0, B = 1, C = 0, D = -3, E = -2, F = 5$

13.

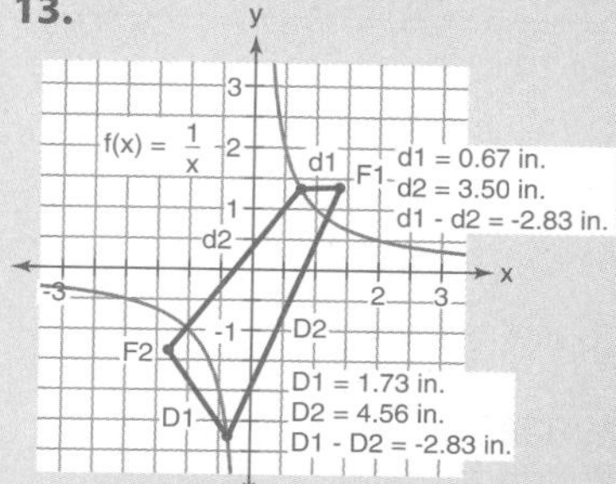

17a. 53° to the riverbank

17b. 375 m

17c. $x = 5t \cos 37°$, $y = 5t \sin 37° - 3t$

18. $x^2 + y^2 + 12x - 8y + 27 = 0$, $x^2 + y^2 + 12x - 8y - 12 = 0$

LESSON

9.7

PLANNING

LESSON OUTLINE

One day:

15 min Investigation

10 min Sharing

15 min Examples

5 min Exercises

MATERIALS

- none

TEACHING

This lesson extends the study of rational functions beyond the family of functions with parent function $y = \frac{1}{x}$.

One Step

Display the function

$$y = \frac{x^3 + 3x^2 - x - 3}{x^2 + x - 6}$$

and ask students to find intercepts and asymptotes exactly, using a calculator only to check their work approximately. As students work, encourage factoring and long or synthetic division. Press faster groups to state a general method for finding intercepts and asymptotes of rational functions. During Sharing, use the term *slant asymptote* to describe the line $y = x + 2$ for this function. Be sure the idea of a hole arises, and lead students toward a general rule that includes consideration of holes.

LESSON 9.7

Graphs of Rational Functions

Besides learning to see, there is another art to be learned—to see what is not.

MARIA MITCHELL

Some rational functions create very different kinds of graphs from those you have studied previously. The graphs of these functions are often in two or more parts. This is because the denominator, a polynomial function, may be equal to zero at some point, so the function will be undefined at that point. Sometimes it's difficult to see the different parts of the graph because they may be separated by only one missing point, called a **hole.** At other times you will see two parts that look very similar—one part may look like a reflection or rotation of the other part. Or you might get multiple parts that look totally different from each other. Look for these features in the graphs below.

$$y = \frac{x^3 + 2x^2 - 5x - 6}{x - 2}$$

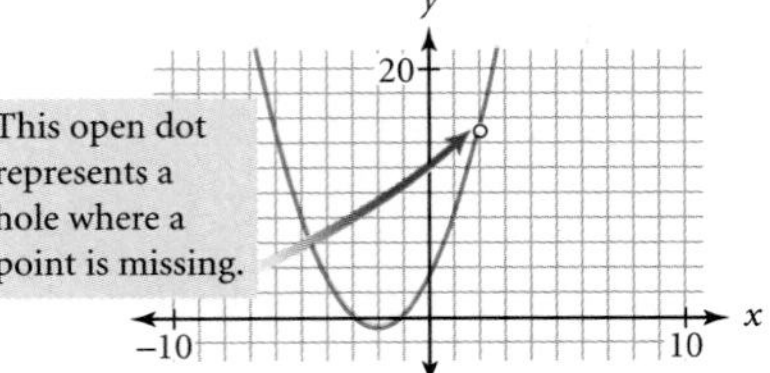

$$y = \frac{1}{x - 2}$$

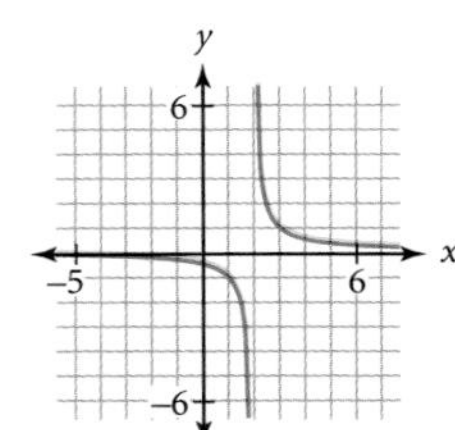

$$y = \frac{x^3 - x^2 - 8x + 12}{6x^2 + 6x - 12}$$

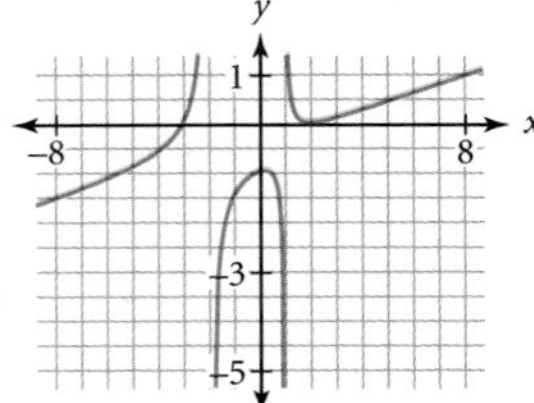

$$y = \frac{1}{x^2 + 1}$$

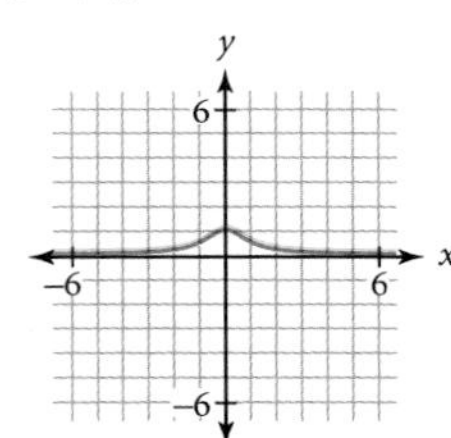

$$y = \frac{x - 1}{x^2 + 4}$$

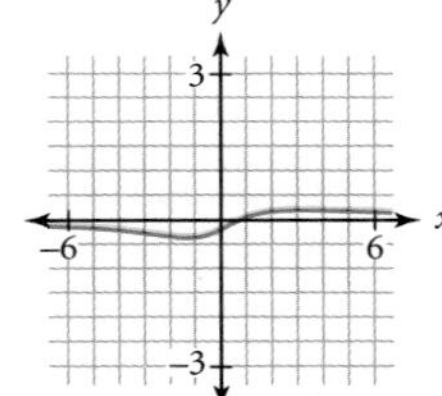

In this lesson you will explore local and end behavior of rational functions, and you will learn how to predict some of the features of a rational function's graph by studying its equation. When examining a rational function, you will often find it helpful to look at the equation in factored form.

LESSON OBJECTIVES

- Identify characteristics of the graph of a rational function from its equation
- Learn to write the equation of a rational function from its graph
- Rewrite a function as a rational function
- Review factoring
- Identify holes, vertical asymptotes, x-intercepts, y-intercepts, and horizontal asymptotes of rational functions

NCTM STANDARDS

	CONTENT		PROCESS
	Number	✓	Problem Solving
✓	Algebra	✓	Reasoning
✓	Geometry	✓	Communication
	Measurement	✓	Connections
	Data/Probability		Representation

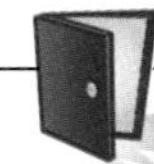

Investigation
Predicting Asymptotes and Holes

In this investigation you will consider the graphs of four rational functions.

Step 1 Match each rational function with a graph. Use a friendly window as you graph and trace the equations on your calculator. Describe the unusual occurrences at and near $x = 2$, and try to explain what feature in the equation makes the graph look the way it does. (You will not actually see the hole pictured in graph d unless you turn off the coordinate axes on your calculator.)

a. 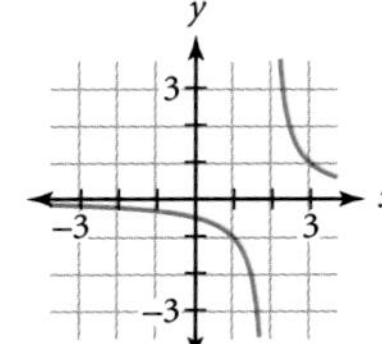
b. 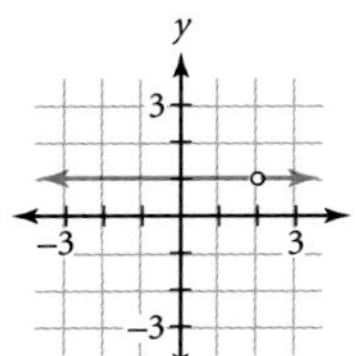
c. 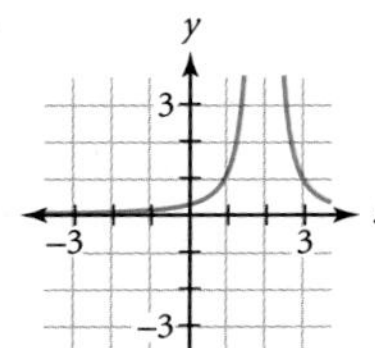
d. 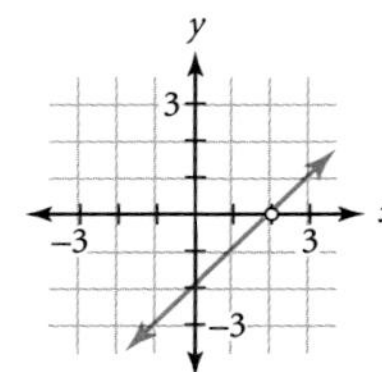

A. $y = \dfrac{1}{(x-2)^2}$ **B.** $y = \dfrac{1}{x-2}$ **C.** $y = \dfrac{(x-2)^2}{x-2}$ **D.** $y = \dfrac{x-2}{x-2}$

Step 2 Have each group member choose one of the graphs below. Find a rational function equation for your graph, and write a few sentences that explain the appearance of your graph. Share your answers with your group.

a. 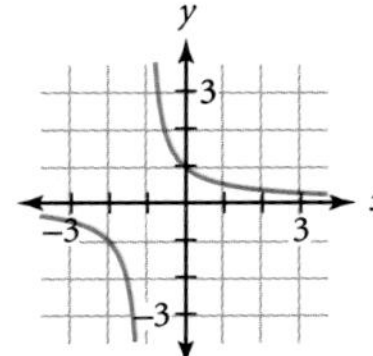
b. 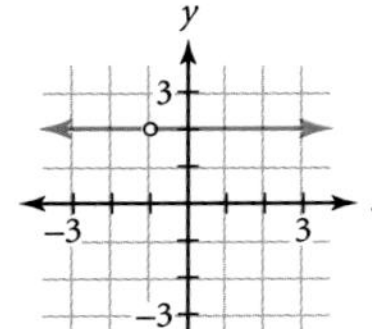
c. 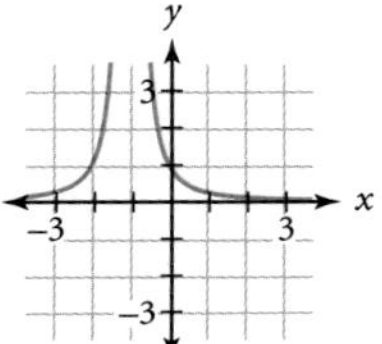
d. 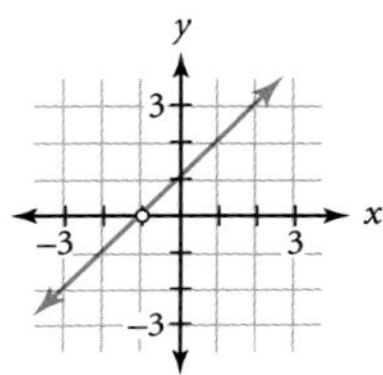

Step 3 Write a paragraph explaining how you can use an equation to predict where holes and asymptotes will occur, and how you can use these features in a graph to write an equation.

Step 4 Consider the graph of $y = \frac{x-2}{(x-2)^2}$. What features does it have? What can you generalize about the graph of a function that has a factor that occurs more times in the denominator than in the numerator?

You have seen transformations of the function $y = \frac{1}{x}$ and observed some of the peculiarities involving graphs of more complicated rational functions. You have seen that $y = \frac{1}{x}$ has both horizontal and vertical asymptotes, as shown at right. What do you think the graph would look like if you added x to $\frac{1}{x}$? Reflect on this question for a moment. Then graph $y = x + \frac{1}{x}$ on your calculator.

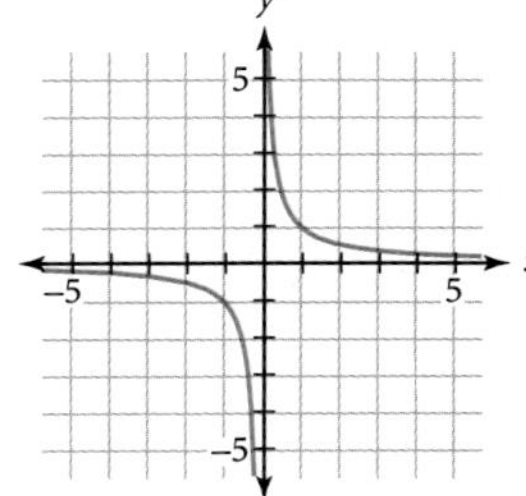

Guiding the Investigation

Geometry software is not appropriate for this investigation because it may not leave holes in the graphs.

Step 1a B; vertical asymptote $x = 2$. $x = 2$ makes the denominator 0.

Step 1b D; hole at $x = 2$. $x = 2$ makes both the numerator and denominator 0.

Step 1c A; vertical asymptote $x = 2$. $x = 2$ makes the denominator 0, and the denominator is squared so all values become positive.

Step 1d C; hole at $x = 2$. $x = 2$ makes both the numerator and denominator 0. If you reduce the equation, you get $y = x - 2$, which produces the graph shown, except you get a hole at $x = 2$.

Step 2a $y = \frac{1}{x+1}$. The graphic has asymptote $x = -1$. Other than that, the equation looks like $y = \frac{1}{x}$.

Step 2b $y = \frac{2(x+1)}{x+1}$. There is a hole at $x = -1$, so the denominator is $(x + 1)$. However, when you reduce you get the line $y = 2$, so there must be factors of 2 and an $(x + 1)$ in the numerator.

Step 2c $y = \frac{1}{(x+1)^2}$. There is a vertical asymptote at $x = -1$, so the denominator includes $(x + 1)$. Because all y-values end up positive, the equation must have an even number of factors of $(x + 1)$ in the denominator.

Step 2d $y = \frac{(x+1)^2}{x+1}$. There is a hole at $x = -1$, so the denominator includes $(x + 1)$. When the equation is reduced, it must be $y = x + 1$ to produce the given graph, so the equation must be $y = \frac{(x+1)^2}{x+1}$.

Step 3 Paragraph should include

- A vertical asymptote occurs at zeros that appear only in the denominator, or zeros that appear more times in the denominator than the numerator.
- A hole occurs at values that make both the denominator and the numerator 0, provided that there are not vertical asymptotes at these values.

Step 4 The graph has vertical asymptote $x = 2$. When a factor occurs in both the denominator and numerator, but occurs more times in the denominator, it indicates a vertical asymptote rather than a hole.

Step 4 [Alert] Students many think that because the value $x = 2$ makes both the numerator and denominator equal 0, it indicates a hole. Point out that $y = \frac{x-2}{(x-2)^2}$ reduces to $y = \frac{1}{x-2}$. When you reduce a rational expression you may lose information about a value for which the denominator is undefined. In this case, the factor $(x - 2)$ is still represented in the denominator, so $y = \frac{x-2}{(x-2)^2}$ is equivalent to $y = \frac{1}{x-2}$. This function has a vertical asymptote, not a hole.

▶ **EXAMPLE A**

A point value at which a function is undefined could indicate either an asymptote, as in this case, or a hole.

With their books closed, have your students make conjectures about the shape of the graph of the equation $y = x + \frac{1}{x}$. Elicit the idea of graphing the hyperbola $y = \frac{1}{x}$ and then rotating the horizontal asymptote (the x-axis) to the line $y = x$.

As a quick extension, **[Ask]** "Can you guess the shape of the graph of the equation $x = y + \frac{1}{y}$?" [It has slant asymptote $y = x$ and horizontal asymptote $y = 0$.]

▶ **EXAMPLE B**

If you think your students will have difficulty with the factoring, you might do a few factoring exercises for review.

Ask students to conjecture about the features of the graph of the function's factored version before actually graphing. Ask about holes, asymptotes, and x- and y-intercepts. Horizontal asymptotes are a little more difficult to find. Students might substitute values of x far from 0 to investigate end behavior.

[Link] Calculus tools allow more accurate sketching of these curves by determining regions of increase and decrease and of positive and negative concavity.

▶ **EXAMPLE C**

As you work through the solution, you might want to calculate a sum of rational numbers, such as $\frac{3}{2} + 5$, alongside the solution steps to show the similarities. In Lesson 9.8, students will see more details about addition of rational expressions.

EXAMPLE A | Describe the graph of $y = x + \frac{1}{x}$.

▶ **Solution**

There is a vertical asymptote or hole at $x = 0$ because the function is undefined when $x = 0$. The graph shows that the feature at $x = 0$ is a vertical asymptote. The values of $\frac{1}{x}$ are added to the values of x. This means that as the absolute value of x increases, the absolute value of $y = x + \frac{1}{x}$ also increases. If you graph the curve and the line $y = x$, you see that the function approaches the line $y = x$ instead of the x-axis. The line $y = x$ is called a slant asymptote, because it is a diagonal line that the function approaches as x-values increase in the positive and negative directions. This slant asymptote describes the end behavior for this function.

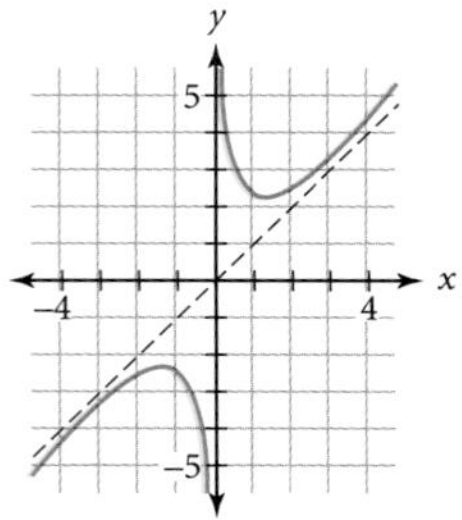

Often you can determine the features of a rational function graph before you actually graph it. Values that make the denominator or numerator equal to zero give you important clues about the appearance of the graph.

EXAMPLE B | Describe the features of the graph of $y = \frac{x^2 + 2x - 3}{x^2 - 2x - 8}$.

▶ **Solution**

Features of rational functions are apparent when the numerator and denominator are factored.

$$y = \frac{x^2 + 2x - 3}{x^2 - 2x - 8} = \frac{(x + 3)(x - 1)}{(x - 4)(x + 2)}$$

No common factors occur in both the numerator and denominator, so there are no holes.

If $x = 4$ or $x = -2$, then the denominator is 0 and the function is undefined. There are vertical asymptotes at these values.

If $x = -3$ or $x = 1$, then the numerator is 0, so the x-intercepts are -3 and 1.

If $x = 0$, then $y = 0.375$. This is the y-intercept.

To find any horizontal asymptotes, consider what happens to y-values as x-values get increasingly large in absolute value.

x	−10000	−1000	−100	100	1000	10000
y	0.9996001	0.9960129	0.9612441	1.0413603	1.0040131	1.0004001

A table shows that the y-values get closer and closer to 1 as x gets farther from 0. So, $y = 1$ is a horizontal asymptote. Note that for large positive values of x, y-values decrease to 1, whereas for large negative values of x, y-values increase to 1.

A graph of the function confirms these features.

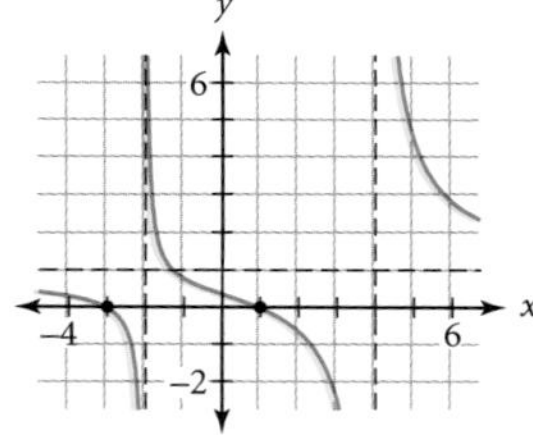

SHARING IDEAS

After students have presented ideas, **[Ask]** "Can you describe a method for finding the vertical asymptotes and x-intercepts of rational functions?" Students may conjecture that vertical asymptotes occur where the denominator is 0 and x-intercepts occur where the numerator is 0. You might put forth the example $y = \frac{(x + 3)(x - 1)}{(x - 4)(x + 3)}$ for testing the conjecture. Points at which both the numerator and the denominator are 0 indicate potential holes, or possibly vertical asymptotes.

Refer to Example C and **[Ask]** "Are the asymptotes and intercepts related to the graph of the parent function?" The parent function $y = \frac{1}{x}$ has asymptotes $x = 0$ and $y = 0$ and no x-intercept. A translation right 2 units and down 4 units will move the asymptotes to $x = 2$ and $y = -4$. This translation to the right and down will introduce intercepts, but their exact values can't be seen easily from the translation.

[Ask] "Which rational functions have graphs that are hyperbolas?" [those whose parent function is $y = \frac{1}{x}$]

Rational functions can be written in different forms. The factored form is convenient for locating asymptotes and intercepts. And you saw in the previous lesson how rational functions can be written in a form that shows you clearly how the parent function has been transformed. You can use properties of arithmetic with fractions to convert from one form to another.

EXAMPLE C | Rewrite $f(x) = \frac{3}{x-2} - 4$ as a rational function.

▶ Solution

The original form shows that this function is related to the parent function, $f(x) = \frac{1}{x}$. It has been vertically stretched by a factor of 3 and translated right 2 units and down 4 units. To change to rational function form, you must add the two parts to form a single fraction.

$$f(x) = \frac{3}{x-2} - 4 \qquad \text{Original equation.}$$

$$= \frac{3}{x-2} - \frac{4}{1} \cdot \frac{x-2}{x-2} \qquad \text{Create a common denominator of } (x-2).$$

$$= \frac{3}{x-2} - \frac{4x-8}{x-2} \qquad \text{Rewrite second fraction.}$$

$$= \frac{3-4x+8}{x-2} \qquad \text{Combine the two fractions.}$$

$$f(x) = \frac{11-4x}{x-2} \qquad \text{Add like terms.}$$

There are no common factors in both the numerator and denominator, so there are no holes.

In this form you can see that $x = 2$ is a vertical asymptote, because this value makes the denominator equal to zero. You can also see that the x-intercept is $\frac{11}{4}$, because this x-value makes the numerator equal to zero. Evaluating the function for large values shows that $y = -4$ is a horizontal asymptote.

x	−10000	−1000	−100	100	1000	10000
y	−4.0002999	−4.0029940	−4.0294118	−3.9693878	−3.9969940	−3.9996999

EXERCISES

Practice Your Skills

1. Rewrite each rational expression in factored form.

a. $\frac{x^2+7x+12}{x^2-4}$ $\frac{(x+3)(x+4)}{(x+2)(x-2)}$

b. $\frac{x^3-5x^2-14x}{x^2+2x+1}$ $\frac{x(x-7)(x+2)}{(x+1)(x+1)}$

2. Identify the vertical asymptotes for each equation.

a. $y = \frac{x^2+7x+12}{x^2-4}$ $x = 2$ and $x = -2$

b. $y = \frac{x^3-5x^2-14x}{x^2+2x+1}$ $x = -1$

3. Rewrite each expression in rational form (as the quotient of two polynomials).

a. $3 + \frac{4x-1}{x-2}$ $\frac{7x-7}{x-2}$

b. $\frac{3x+7}{2x-1} - 5$ $\frac{-7x+12}{2x-1}$

Assessing Progress

You can check students' familiarity with factoring, addition and subtraction of fractions, and the hyperbola $y = \frac{1}{x}$.

BUILDING UNDERSTANDING

The exercises provide students with practice in working with rational functions and their graphs.

ASSIGNING HOMEWORK

Essential	1–4
Performance assessment	5–13
Portfolio	7
Journal	6
Group	8, 13
Review	14–16

▶ Helping with the Exercises

Exercise 2 It's important for students to make sure zeros of the denominator are not also zeros of the numerator before deciding that they mark vertical asymptotes.

Closing the Lesson

You can find the x-intercepts and vertical asymptotes of a rational function by finding zeros of the numerator and denominator, perhaps by factoring. A zero of both the numerator and the denominator may indicate a hole or a vertical asymptote in the graph, a zero of only the numerator indicates an x-intercept, and a zero of only the denominator indicates a vertical asymptote. Any horizontal asymptotes can be estimated by evaluating the function at extremely large and extremely small numbers. You can graph the sum of a function with no asymptotes and a function in the family with parent function $y = \frac{1}{x}$ by imagining the second graph and then rotating the horizontal asymptote to become the graph of the first function. The new asymptote is a **slant asymptote.**

Exercise 4 [Ask] "Can you simply cancel the common factors from the numerator and the denominator?" [The original function and the reduced function may not be equivalent if the common factor can equal 0; the graph of the function with common factors has a hole.]

6. 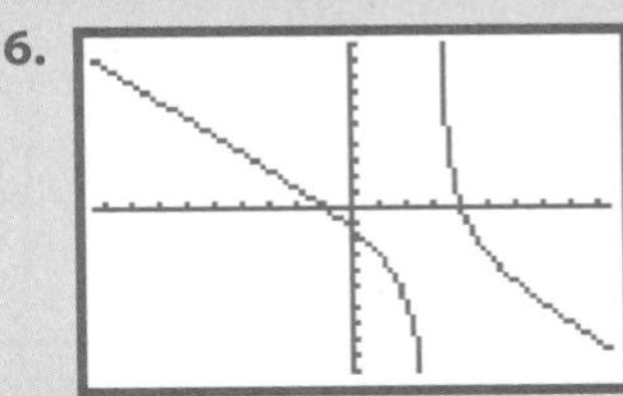

$[-9.4, 9.4, 1, -10, 10, 1]$

6b. The graph gets closer and closer to both sides of the vertical line $x = 3$.

6d. $y = -\frac{(x-4)(x+1)}{x-3}$. The x-intercepts are 4 and -1, and the vertical asymptote is $x = 3$.

7a. 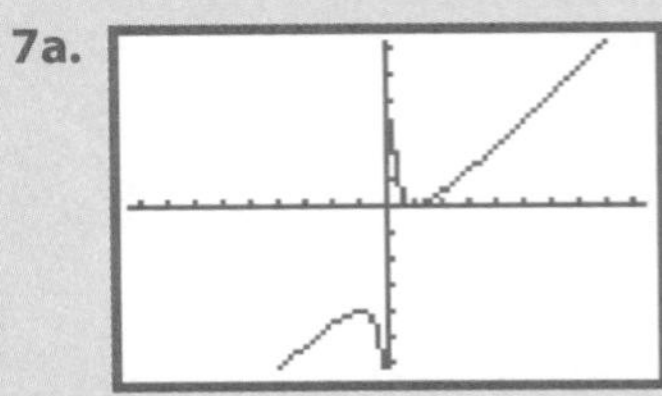

$[-9.4, 9.4, 1, -6.2, 6.2, 1]$

vertical asymptote $x = 0$, slant asymptote $y = x - 2$

7b. 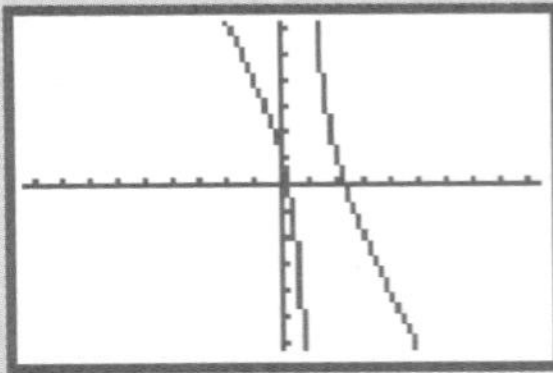

$[-9.4, 9.4, 1, -6.2, 6.2, 1]$

vertical asymptote $x = 1$, slant asymptote $y = -2x + 3$

7c. 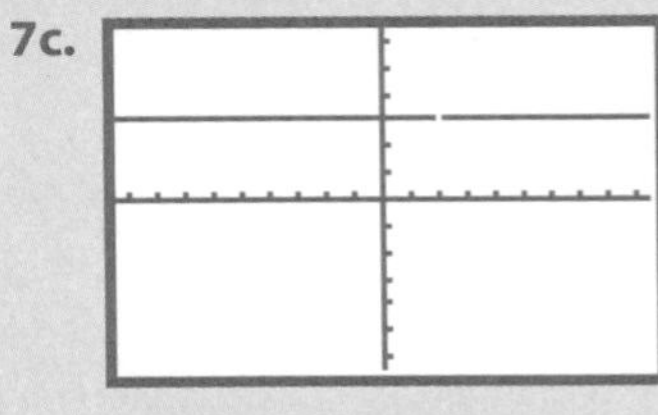

$[-9.4, 9.4, 1, -6.2, 6.2, 1]$

hole at $x = 2$

See pages 898–899 for answers to Exercises 4a–c and 5.

4. Graph each equation on your calculator, and make a sketch of the graph on your paper. Use a friendly graphing window. Indicate any holes on your sketches.

a. $y = \frac{5 - x}{x - 5}$ **b.** $y = \frac{3x + 6}{x + 2}$ **c.** $y = \frac{(x + 3)(x - 4)}{x - 4}$

d. What causes a hole to appear in the graph? A hole occurs when both the numerator and denominator are 0 for a value of x, and the zero appears more times in the denominator than in the numerator.

Reason and Apply

5. Write an equation for each graph.

a. 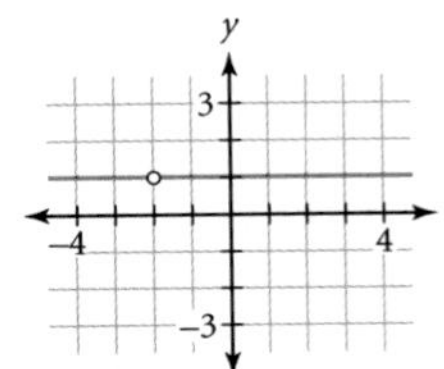

b. 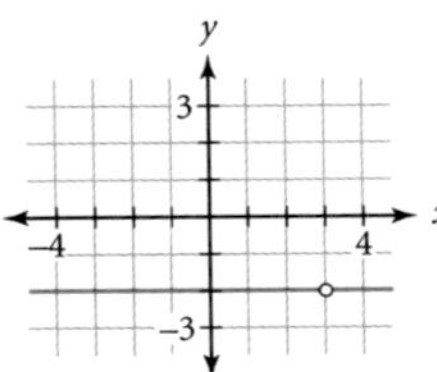

c. 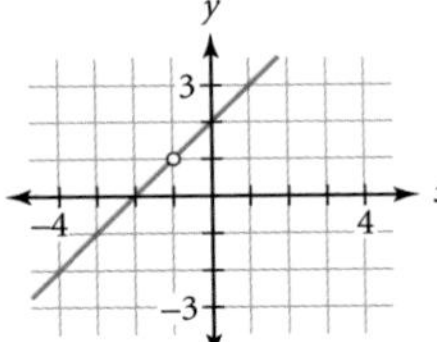

6. Graph $y = -x + \frac{4}{x-3}$.

a. Describe the end behavior of the graph. It has slant asymptote $y = -x$.

b. Describe the behavior of the graph near $x = 3$.

c. Rewrite $y = -x + \frac{4}{x-3}$ in rational function form. $y = \frac{-x^2 + 3x + 4}{x - 3}$

d. Factor your answer from 6c. What do the factors tell you about the graph?

7. Graph each function on your calculator. List all holes and asymptotes, including slant asymptotes.

a. $y = x - 2 + \frac{1}{x}$ **b.** $y = -2x + 3 + \frac{2}{x - 1}$ **c.** $y = 7 + \frac{8 - 4x}{x - 2}$

d. Convert each equation in 7a–c to rational function form. Use the rational function form to help you verify the location of the holes and vertical asymptotes you found.

8. The two graphs below show the same function.

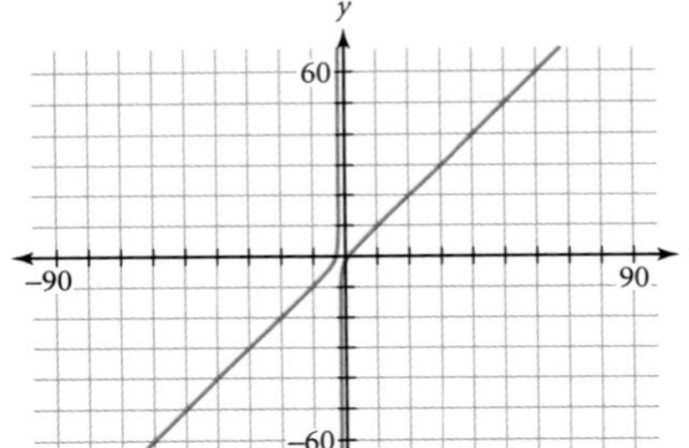

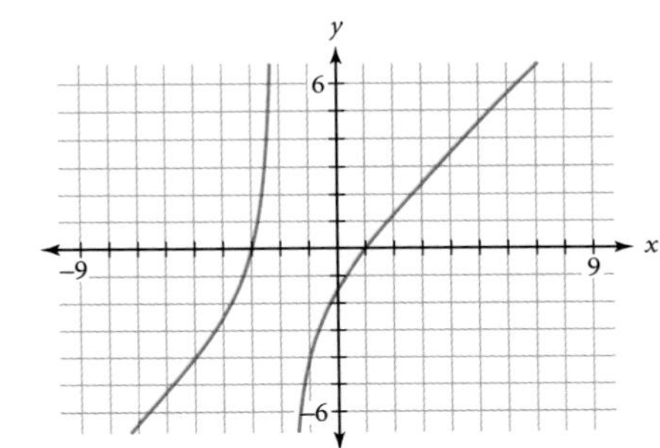

a. List all the important facts you can about the graph.

b. Find the equation of the slant asymptote in the first graph. $y = x$

c. Give an example of an equation with asymptote $x = -2$. possible answer: $y = \frac{1}{x + 2}$

7d. For 7a: $y = \frac{x^2 - 2x + 1}{x}$. The denominator is 0 and the numerator is nonzero when $x = 0$, so the vertical asymptote is $x = 0$.

For 7b: $y = \frac{-2x^2 + 5x - 1}{x - 1}$. The denominator is 0 and the numerator is nonzero when $x = 1$, so the vertical asymptote is $x = 1$.

For 7c: $y = \frac{3x - 6}{x - 2}$. A zero occurs once in both the numerator and denominator when $x = 2$. This causes a hole in the graph.

Exercises 8, 9 [Ask] "What are the advantages and disadvantages of a larger window?" [You can see the slant asymptote more clearly, but it is difficult to see the vertical asymptote.]

8a. The graph has slant asymptote $y = x$, vertical asymptote $x = -2$, and x-intercepts 1 and -3.

d. Name a polynomial with zeros $x = -3$ and $x = 1$. possible answer: $y = (x + 3)(x - 1)$

e. Write an equation for the function shown in the graphs. Graph the function to check your answer. $y = \frac{(x + 3)(x - 1)}{x + 2}$ or $y = x + \frac{-3}{x + 2}$

9. The two graphs below show the same function. Write an equation for this function.

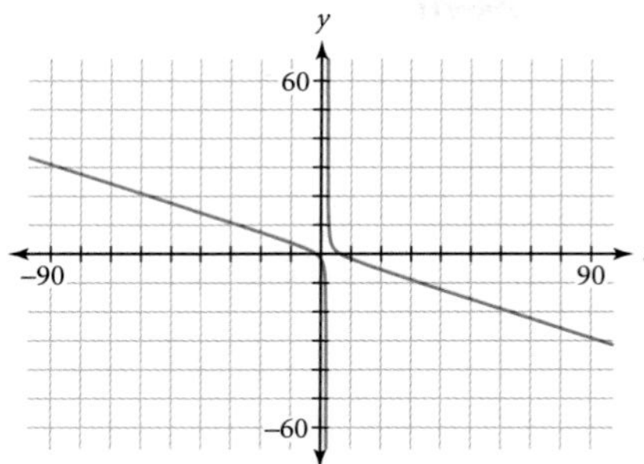

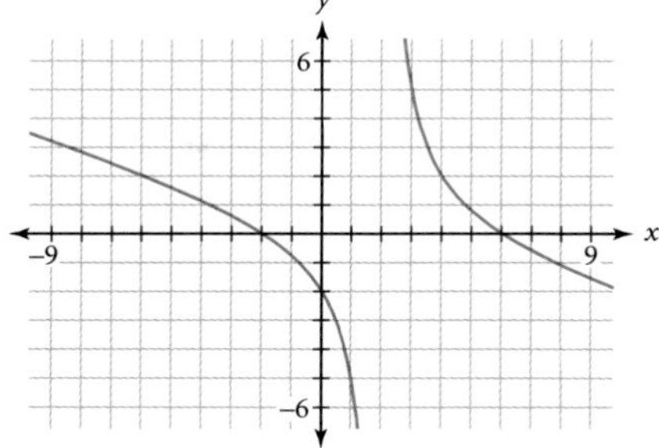

10. Consider the equation $y = \frac{(x - 1)(x + 4)}{(x - 2)(x + 3)}$.

a. Describe the features of the graph of this function.

b. Describe the end behavior of the graph. The graph approaches horizontal asymptote $y = 1$.

c. Sketch the graph.

11. Solve. Give exact solutions.

a. $\frac{2}{x - 1} + x = 5$ $x = 3 \pm \sqrt{2}$

b. $\frac{2}{x - 1} + x = 2$ no real solutions; $x = \frac{3 \pm i\sqrt{7}}{2}$

12. APPLICATION The functional response curve given by the function $y = \frac{60x}{1 + 0.625x}$ models the number of moose attacked by wolves as the density of moose in an area increases. In this model, x represents the number of moose per 1000 km^2, and y represents the number of moose attacked every 100 days.

a. How many moose are attacked every 100 days if there is a herd containing 260 moose in a land preserve with area 1000 km^2? 95

b. Graph the function.

c. What are the asymptotes for this function?

d. Describe the significance of the asymptotes in this problem.

Environmental CONNECTION

Ecologists often look for a mathematical model to describe the interrelationship of organisms. C. S. Holling, a Canadian researcher, came up with an equation in the late 1950s for what he called a Type II functional response curve. The equation describes the relationship between the number of prey attacked by a predator and the density of the prey. For example, the wolf population increases through reproduction as moose density increases. Eventually, wolf populations stabilize at about 40 per 1000 km^2, which is the optimum size of their range based on defense of their territories.

The functional response curve applies to all species of animals. It could be larvae-eating insects and mosquito larvae, fishers and a particular species of fish, or panda and amount of bamboo in a forest.

A moose rises from the surface of a pond in Baxter State Park, Maine.

EXTENSION

Use Take Another Look activity 2 on page 562.

Exercise 9 As needed, encourage students to follow steps similar to those followed in Exercise 8.

9. $y = \frac{-(x + 2)(x - 6)}{3(x - 2)}$

10a. The graph has x-intercepts 1 and -4, vertical asymptotes $x = 2$ and $x = -3$, and y-intercept $\frac{2}{3}$.

10c.

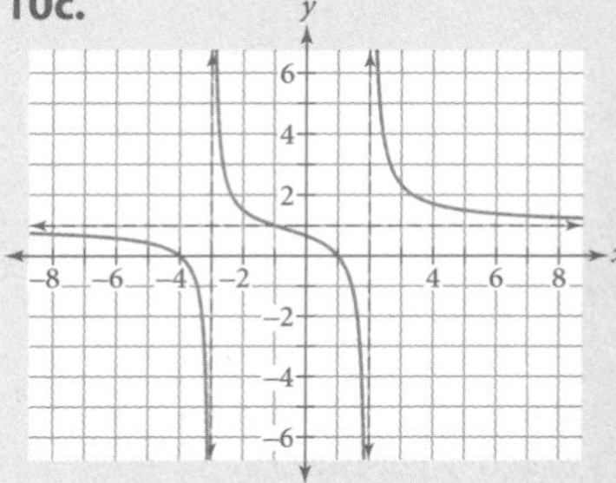

12b.

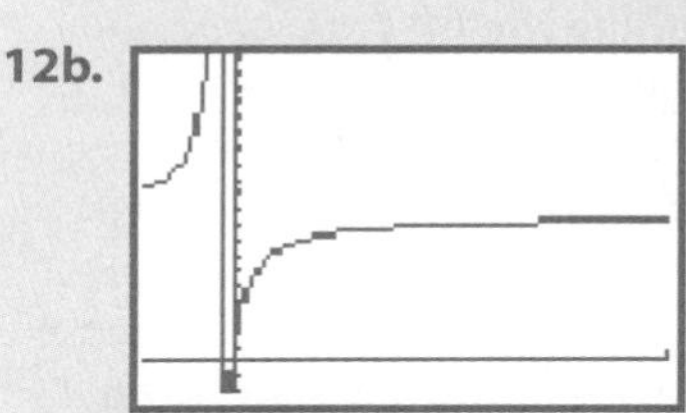

[−10, 50, 50, −20, 200, 10]

12c. vertical asymptote $x = -1.6$ and horizontal asymptote $y = 96$.

12d. The vertical asymptote is meaningless because there cannot be a negative number of moose. The horizontal asymptote means that as the density of the moose increases, more will be attacked, up to a maximum of 96 during 100 days. This is the maximum number that the wolves can eat.

MAKING THE CONNECTION

Mathematical modeling of population change has helped ecologists better understand ecological *niches.* Niches are the unique roles that various species play in an *ecosystem,* or natural community. These roles depend on a variety of factors, such as an animal's eating habits, its predators, and the amount of heat and moisture it needs to survive. The niches of the various species in an ecosystem help maintain a fragile population balance that may be disturbed by human activity.

Exercise 13 [Alert] Students might miss the word *any* in *any cylinder.* No matter what cylinder is used, the same amount of material is to remain after drilling.

13a.

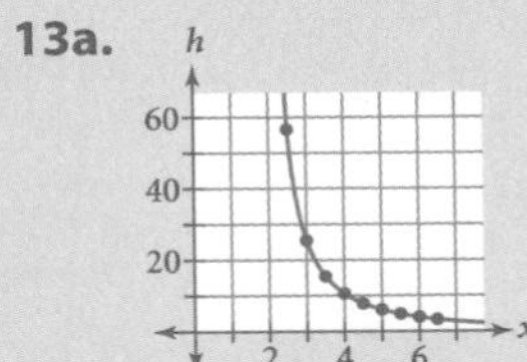

Exercise 16 Methods can include graphing, factoring, the quadratic formula, and completing the square.

The Physics of Going Downhill Fast

The physics of the situation in the project implies that if friction is ignored, then the ball on the incline will have an acceleration equal to the sine of the angle times the acceleration due to gravity. This means that a ball starting at rest would travel a distance of $0.5gt^2 \sin\theta$ in t seconds. Because the distance is constant, say 8 ft, you have the equation $8 = 0.5(32)t^2 \sin\theta$. Solving this equation for t gives you $t = \sqrt{0.5 \csc\theta}$ s.

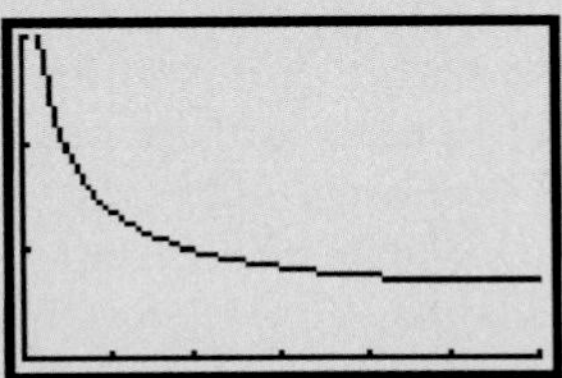

[0, 90, 15, 0, 3, 1]

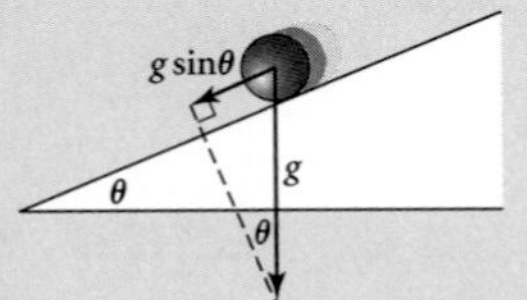

13. A machine drill removes a core from any cylinder. Suppose you want the amount of material left after the core is removed to remain constant. The table below compares the height and radius needed if the volume of the hollow cylinder is to remain constant.

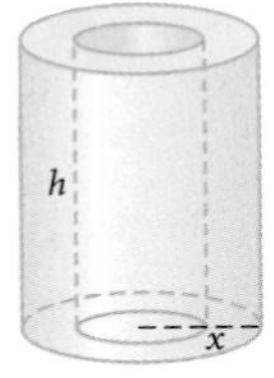

Radius x	2.5	3.0	3.5	4.0	4.5	5.0	5.5	6.0	6.5
Height h	56.6	25.5	15.4	10.6	7.8	6.1	4.9	4.0	3.3

a. Plot the data points, (x, h), and draw a smooth curve through them.

b. Explain what happens to the height of the figure as the radius gets smaller. How small can x be? The height gets larger as the radius gets smaller. The radius must be greater than 2.

c. Write a formula for the volume of the hollow cylinder, V, in terms of x and h. $V = \pi x^2 h - 4\pi h$

d. Solve the formula in 13c for h to get a function that describes the height as a function of the radius. $h = \dfrac{V}{\pi(x^2 - 4)}$

e. What is the constant volume? approximately 400 units^3

Review

9.5 **14.** Find the points of intersection, if any, of the circle with center (2, 1) and radius 5 and the line $x - 7y + 30 = 0$. $(-2, 4)$ and $(5, 5)$

9.6 **15.** A 500 g jar of mixed nuts contains 30% cashews, 20% almonds, and 50% peanuts.

a. How many grams of cashews must you add to the mixture to increase the percentage of cashews to 40%? What is the new percentage of almonds and peanuts? $83\frac{1}{3}$ g; approximately 17% almonds and 43% peanuts

b. How many grams of almonds must you add to the original mixture to make the percentage of almonds the same as the percentage of cashews? Now what is the percentage of each type of nut? 50 g; approximately 27.3% almonds, 27.3% cashews, and 45.5% peanuts

7.4 **16.** Solve each quadratic equation.

a. $2x^2 - 5x - 3 = 0$ $x = -\frac{1}{2}$ or $x = 3$

b. $x^2 + 4x - 4 = 0$ $x = -2 \pm 2\sqrt{2}$

c. $x^2 + 4x + 1 = 0$ $x = -2 \pm \sqrt{3}$

Project

GOING DOWNHILL FAST

Design an investigation to determine a relationship between the angle of elevation of a long tube and the time it takes a ball to travel the length of the tube.

Your project should include

- A description of your investigation and the data you collect.
- A graph that shows the relationship between the tube's angle and the ball's time.
- The domain and range of the relationship. Include a description of what happens to the time as the angle approaches the extreme values of the domain.
- A description of the features of the graph. Attach real-world meaning to each feature.

Supporting the Project

If you skipped parametric equations, your students may not be familiar enough with the ideas of motion to benefit from this project.

A cardboard carpet tube is ideal. At least two people are needed to conduct this experiment. A graph of the data will look like the graph of a rational function, but it is not.

OUTCOMES

- The report includes a description of experimental procedure along with the several data points and their graph.
- The graph is explained in real-world terms. For example: The graph has no x- or y-intercepts (no angle for which the time is zero and no ball movement for a horizontal tube).
- The student makes a conjecture about the shape of the curve formed by the graph of the data.
- The report analyzes problems that arose during the experiment.
- The physics is explained.

LESSON

9.8 Operations with Rational Expressions

Images/split the truth/ in fractions.

DENISE LEVERTOV

In this lesson you will learn to add, subtract, multiply, and divide rational expressions. In the previous lesson you combined a rational expression with a single constant or variable by finding a common denominator. That process was much like adding a fraction to a whole number. Likewise, all of the other arithmetic operations you will do with rational expressions have their counterparts in working with fractions. Keeping the operations with fractions in mind will help you understand the procedures.

Recall that to add $\frac{7}{12} + \frac{3}{10}$, you need a common denominator. The smallest number that has both 12 and 10 as factors is 60. So, use 60 as the common denominator.

$\frac{7}{12} + \frac{3}{10}$	Original expression.
$\frac{7}{12} \cdot \frac{5}{5} + \frac{3}{10} \cdot \frac{6}{6}$	Multiply each fraction by an equivalent of 1 to get a denominator of 60.
$\frac{35}{60} + \frac{18}{60}$	Multiply.
$\frac{53}{60}$	Add.

You could use other numbers, such as 120, as a common denominator, but using the least common denominator keeps the numbers as small as possible and eliminates some of the reducing afterward. Recall that you can find the least common denominator by factoring the denominators to see which factors they share and are unique to each one. In this example, 12 factors to $2 \cdot 2 \cdot 3$ and 10 factors to $2 \cdot 5$. The least common denominator must include factors that multiply to give each denominator, with no extras. So, in this case you need two 2's, a 3, and a 5. You can use this same process to add two rational expressions.

Rational expressions can be combined, just like fractions, to express the sum of parts. *Circles* (1916–1923) by Johannes Itten (1888–1967) shows many circles divided into fractional parts.

EXAMPLE A Add rational expressions to rewrite the right side of this equation as a single rational expression in factored form.

$$y = \frac{x-3}{(x+1)(x-2)} + \frac{2x+1}{(x+2)(x-2)}$$

NCTM STANDARDS

CONTENT		PROCESS	
✓	Number		Problem Solving
✓	Algebra		Reasoning
	Geometry	✓	Communication
	Measurement	✓	Connections
	Data/Probability		Representation

LESSON OBJECTIVES

- Learn to add, subtract, multiply, and divide rational expressions
- Review factoring
- Simplify rational expressions in order to find x-intercepts, vertical asymptotes, and holes

LESSON 9.8

PLANNING

LESSON OUTLINE

One day:

10 min	Example A
20 min	Examples B–D
15 min	Exercises

MATERIALS

- Calculator Note 5D (for project)

TEACHING

In this lesson students see the four arithmetic operations applied to rational functions. Many schools are moving away from this kind of algebraic manipulation. You might skip the lesson unless your state standards require it. If you include it, keep referring back to arithmetic fractions, such as those illustrating the sum in the introduction, so that students realize they're extending familiar ideas. **[Alert]** You may want to review the concept *least common denominator.*

One Step

Pose this problem: "Make up some rational expressions that have holes, vertical asymptotes, and/or x-intercepts. Experiment with adding, subtracting, multiplying, and dividing them, and describe where holes, vertical asymptotes, and x-intercepts will be in the results. For example, one rule (perhaps not true) might be 'If a rational expression has a hole at $x = a$, then its sum with any other rational expression has a hole where $x = a$.'" If students are having difficulty thinking of rational expressions, refer them to the examples. As needed, encourage students to review the operations on fractions when deciding how to combine rational expressions.

▶ EXAMPLE A

[Ask] "Why would you want to factor the end result?" [From the factored form, you can identify holes, x-intercepts, and vertical asymptotes.]

▶ Solution

First, identify the least common denominator. It must contain all of the factors of each denominator. The factors $(x + 1)$ and $(x - 2)$ are needed to create the first denominator, and an additional $(x + 2)$ is needed for the second denominator. So, use the common denominator $(x + 1)(x - 2)(x + 2)$.

$y = \dfrac{x - 3}{(x + 1)(x - 2)} + \dfrac{2x + 1}{(x + 2)(x - 2)}$	Original equation.
$y = \dfrac{x - 3}{(x + 1)(x - 2)} \cdot \dfrac{(x + 2)}{(x + 2)} + \dfrac{2x + 1}{(x + 2)(x - 2)} \cdot \dfrac{(x + 1)}{(x + 1)}$	Multiply each fraction by an equivalent of 1 to get a common denominator.
$y = \dfrac{x^2 - x - 6}{(x + 1)(x - 2)(x + 2)} + \dfrac{2x^2 + 3x + 1}{(x + 2)(x - 2)(x + 1)}$	Multiply and expand the numerators.
$y = \dfrac{3x^2 + 2x - 5}{(x + 1)(x - 2)(x + 2)}$	Add the two fractions and combine like terms in the numerator.
$y = \dfrac{(3x + 5)(x - 1)}{(x + 1)(x - 2)(x + 2)}$	Factor the numerator.

In this case, the numerator factors. Often, however, it will not.

Expressing a rational function as a single rational expression in factored form helps you identify some features of the graph. An x-value that makes the expression equal to zero is an x-intercept. Here, 1 and $-\frac{5}{3}$ are the x-intercepts. An x-value that leads to division by zero makes the expression undefined. This results in a vertical asymptote (when the associated factor appears more times in the denominator than in the numerator) or a hole (when the factor appears in both the numerator and denominator, and the factor does not represent a vertical asymptote). The graph of the equation above has vertical asymptotes $x = -1$, $x = 2$, and $x = -2$, as shown.

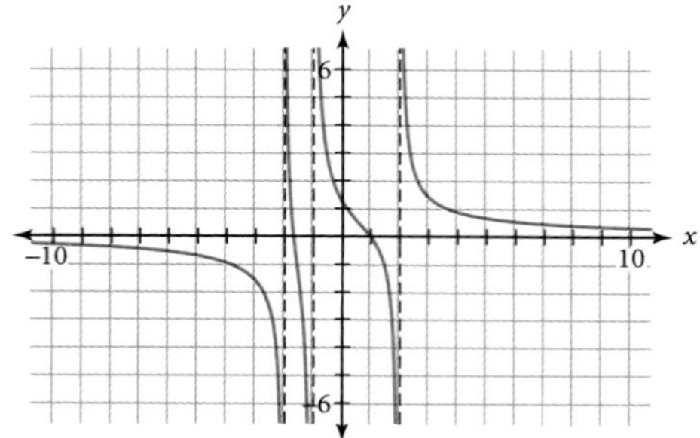

Subtraction of rational expressions is much like addition.

▶ EXAMPLE B

In the next-to-last step, **[Ask]** "Why is the expression in the numerator $-5x + 60$ instead of $+5x - 60$?" [The negative sign has been distributed.]

[Ask] "Why are there no holes?" [The numerator and denominator have no polynomial factors in common.]

EXAMPLE B

Find any x-intercepts, vertical asymptotes, or holes in the graph of

$$y = \frac{x + 2}{(x - 3)(x + 4)} - \frac{5}{x + 1}$$

▶ Solution

Begin by finding a common denominator so that you can write the expression on the right side as a single rational expression in factored form. The common denominator is $(x - 3)(x + 4)(x + 1)$.

$$y = \frac{(x+2)}{(x-3)(x+4)} \cdot \frac{(x+1)}{(x+1)} - \frac{5}{(x+1)} \cdot \frac{(x-3)(x+4)}{(x-3)(x+4)}$$ Multiply each fraction by an equivalent of 1 to get a common denominator.

$$y = \frac{x^2 + 3x + 2}{(x-3)(x+4)(x+1)} - \frac{5(x^2 + x - 12)}{(x+1)(x-3)(x+4)}$$ Expand the numerators.

$$y = \frac{x^2 + 3x + 2 - 5(x^2 + x - 12)}{(x-3)(x+4)(x+1)}$$ Write with a single denominator.

$$y = \frac{x^2 + 3x + 2 - 5x^2 - 5x + 60}{(x-3)(x+4)(x+1)}$$ Use the distributive property.

$$y = \frac{-4x^2 - 2x + 62}{(x-3)(x+4)(x+1)}$$ Combine like terms.

Check to see whether the numerator factors. There is a common factor of -2 in the numerator, so you may rewrite it as $y = \frac{-2(2x^2 + x - 31)}{(x-3)(x+4)(x+1)}$. The equation is undefined when $x = 3$, $x = -4$, or $x = -1$, so these are the vertical asymptotes. Because the numerator cannot be factored further, the x-intercepts are not obvious. But you can use the quadratic formula to find the values that make the expression in the numerator equal to zero.

$$x = \frac{-1 \pm \sqrt{1 - 4(2)(-31)}}{2(2)}$$

$$x \approx 3.695 \text{ or } x \approx -4.195$$

Because there are no common factors in the numerator and denominator, there are no holes. Check the graph to confirm the features you've identified.

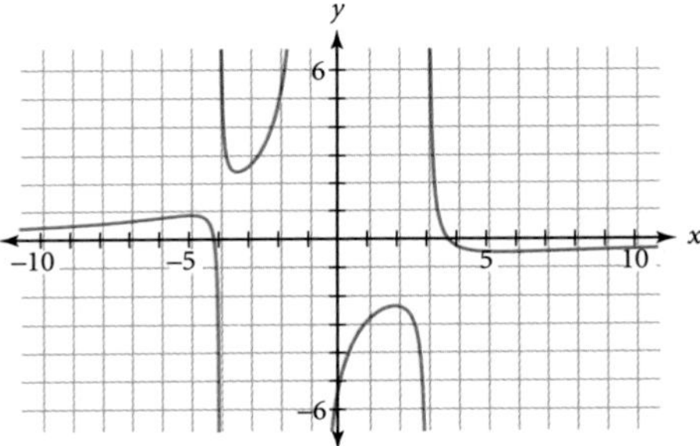

To multiply and divide rational expressions, you don't need to find a common denominator. Look at the following problems to remind yourself how multiplication and division work with fractions.

$$\frac{5}{12} \cdot \frac{3}{4} = \frac{5 \cdot 3}{12 \cdot 4} = \frac{5}{4 \cdot 4} = \frac{5}{16}$$ Multiply straight across. Reduce common factors if any appear.

$$\frac{\frac{2}{5}}{\frac{6}{7}} = \frac{2}{5} \cdot \frac{7}{6} = \frac{2 \cdot 7}{5 \cdot 6} = \frac{7}{5 \cdot 3} = \frac{7}{15}$$ To divide, multiply by the reciprocal of the denominator.

In multiplication and division problems with rational expressions, it is best to factor all expressions first. This will make it easy to reduce common factors and identify x-intercepts, holes, and vertical asymptotes.

▶ **EXAMPLE C**

[Ask] "Why is there no $y =$ in this example, as there was in the previous examples?" [This and the next example deal with expressions, not entire functions or equations.] You might want to remind students of the difference between an expression and an equation. To encourage critical thinking, **[Ask]** "Why does the book say the expressions are equivalent even though the graph of one has a hole and the graph of the other doesn't?" [The expressions are equivalent; the graphs are of functions, which aren't equivalent because the functions have different domains. The function $y = \frac{(x+1)}{(x-1)(x-2)}$ has domain all real numbers except 1 and 2, whereas the function from the original expression, even after it is reduced, has domain all real numbers except -2, 1, 2, and 3.]

▶ **EXAMPLE D**

You might **[Ask]** "Why do you invert and multiply when you divide fractions?" Encourage students to explain in ways that show understanding. You might have students use lengths of line segments or pie slices to demonstrate the quotients $\frac{1}{\frac{1}{4}}$, $\frac{5}{\frac{1}{4}}$, $\frac{5}{\frac{3}{4}}$, and $\frac{\frac{5}{2}}{\frac{3}{4}}$.

SHARING IDEAS

[Ask] "Why do the rules for fractions apply to rational algebraic expressions?" [because the variables represent numbers]

Tell students you suspect there's something wrong with the equations $\frac{3}{x+2} + \frac{4}{x+5} = \frac{9}{x^2+7x+10}$ and $\frac{6x^2}{3x^2+x} + \frac{2}{3x+1} = \frac{1}{x}$. **[Ask]** "What is wrong with these equations?" [Standard manipulation of each equation produces a result that doesn't check because it makes at least one denominator 0.]

EXAMPLE C Multiply $\frac{(x+2)}{(x-3)} \cdot \frac{(x+1)(x-3)}{(x-1)\left(x^2-4\right)}$.

▶ **Solution**

$\frac{(x+2)}{(x-3)} \cdot \frac{(x+1)(x-3)}{(x-1)(x-2)(x+2)}$ — Factor any expressions that you can. $\left(x^2-4\right)$ factors to $(x-2)(x+2)$.

$\frac{(x+2)(x+1)(x-3)}{(x-3)(x-1)(x-2)(x+2)}$ — Combine the two expressions.

$\frac{\cancel{(x+2)}(x+1)\cancel{(x-3)}}{\cancel{(x-3)}(x-1)(x-2)\cancel{(x+2)}}$ — Reduce common factors.

$\frac{(x+1)}{(x-1)(x-2)}$ — Rewrite.

The expression $\frac{(x+2)}{(x-3)} \cdot \frac{(x+1)(x-3)}{(x-1)\left(x^2-4\right)}$ reduces to $\frac{(x+1)}{(x-1)(x-2)}$, but their graphs are slightly different. The original multiplication expression had two factors, $(x-3)$ and $(x+2)$, that were eventually reduced. When a factor can be reduced, and the factor no longer appears in the denominator after being reduced, it represents a hole. So the graph of $y = \frac{(x+2)}{(x-3)} \cdot \frac{(x+1)(x-3)}{(x-1)\left(x^2-4\right)}$ has holes at $x = 3$ and $x = -2$, whereas the graph of $y = \frac{(x+1)}{(x-1)(x-2)}$ does not. Both graphs have vertical asymptotes $x = 1$ and $x = 2$ and x-intercept -1.

$$y = \frac{(x+1)}{(x-1)(x-2)}$$

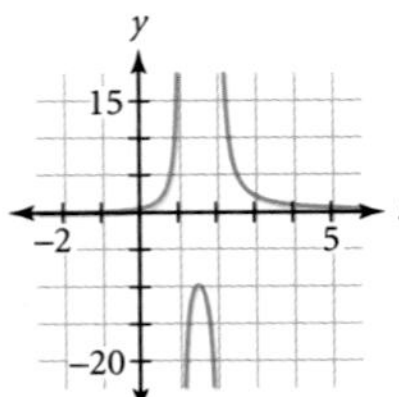

Multiplication and division with rational expressions will give you a good chance to practice your factoring skills.

EXAMPLE D Divide $\frac{\frac{x^2-1}{x^2+5x+6}}{\frac{x^2-3x+2}{x+3}}$.

▶ **Solution**

$\frac{x^2-1}{x^2+5x+6} \cdot \frac{x+3}{x^2-3x+2}$ — Invert the fraction in the denominator and multiply.

$\frac{(x+1)(x-1)}{(x+2)(x+3)} \cdot \frac{(x+3)}{(x-2)(x-1)}$ — Factor all expressions.

$\frac{(x+1)(x-1)(x+3)}{(x+2)(x+3)(x-2)(x-1)}$ — Multiply.

$\frac{(x+1)}{(x+2)(x-2)}$ — Reduce all common factors.

Assessing Progress

You can assess students' skills at manipulating fractions and factoring polynomials.

Closing the Lesson

Sums, differences, products, and quotients of rational functions and expressions follow the same rules as their fraction counterparts.

Rational expressions like those in Example D can look intimidating. However, the rules are the same as for regular fraction arithmetic. Work carefully and stay organized. Check the graph of the original problem and any step along the way to see whether you have made an error. The graphs should be identical except for holes after you have reduced common factors.

EXERCISES

Practice Your Skills

1. Factor each expression completely and reduce common factors.

a. $\dfrac{x^2+2x}{x^2-4}$ b. $\dfrac{x^2-5x+4}{x^2-1}$ c. $\dfrac{3x^2-6x}{x^2-6x+8}$ d. $\dfrac{x^2+3x-10}{x^2-25}$

2. What is the least common denominator for each pair of rational expressions?

a. $\dfrac{x}{(x+3)(x-2)}, \dfrac{x-1}{(x-3)(x-2)}$ b. $\dfrac{x^2}{(2x+1)(x-4)}, \dfrac{x}{(x+1)(x-2)}$

c. $\dfrac{2}{x^2-4}, \dfrac{x}{(x+3)(x-2)}$ d. $\dfrac{x+1}{(x-3)(x+2)}, \dfrac{x-2}{x^2+5x+6}$

3. Add or subtract as indicated.

a. $\dfrac{x}{(x+3)(x-2)}+\dfrac{x-1}{(x-3)(x-2)}$ b. $\dfrac{2}{x^2-4}-\dfrac{x}{(x+3)(x-2)}$

c. $\dfrac{x+1}{(x-3)(x+2)}+\dfrac{x-2}{x^2+5x+6}$ d. $\dfrac{2x}{(x+1)(x-2)}-\dfrac{3}{x^2-1}$

4. Multiply or divide as indicated. Reduce any common factors to simplify.

a. $\dfrac{x+1}{(x+2)(x-3)}\cdot\dfrac{x^2-4}{x^2-x-2}$ $\dfrac{1}{x-3}$ b. $\dfrac{x^2-16}{x+5}\div\dfrac{x^2+8x+16}{x^2+3x-10}$ $\dfrac{(x-4)(x-2)}{x+4}$

c. $\dfrac{x^2+7x+6}{x^2+5x-6}\cdot\dfrac{2x^2-2x}{x+1}$ $2x$ d. $\dfrac{\dfrac{x+3}{x^2-8x+15}}{\dfrac{x^2-9}{x^2-4x-5}}$ $\dfrac{x+1}{(x-3)^2}$

Reason and Apply

5. Rewrite as a single rational expression.

a. $\dfrac{1-\dfrac{x}{x+2}}{\dfrac{x+1}{x^2-4}}$ $\dfrac{2(x-2)}{x+1}$ b. $\dfrac{\dfrac{1}{x-1}+\dfrac{1}{x+1}}{\dfrac{x}{x-1}-\dfrac{x}{x+1}}$ 1

6. Graph $y=\frac{x+1}{x^2-7x-8}-\frac{x}{2(x-8)}$ on your calculator.

a. List all asymptotes, holes, and intercepts based on your calculator's graph.

b. Rewrite the right side of the equation as a single rational expression. $\frac{2-x}{2(x-8)}$

c. Use your answer from 6b to verify your observations in 6a. Explain.

6.

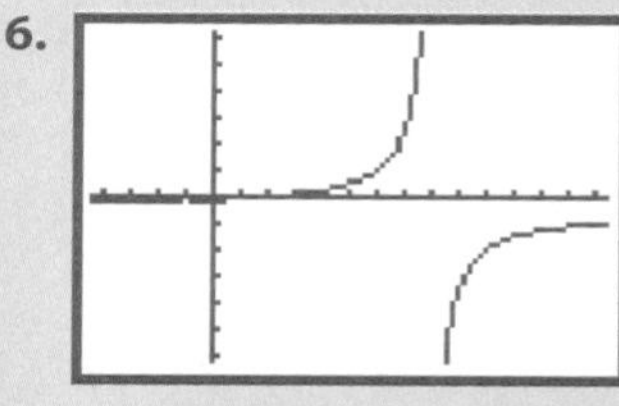

$[-4.4, 14.4, 1, -6.2, 6.2, 1]$

6a. vertical asymptote $x = 8$; horizontal asymptote $y = -0.5$; hole at $x = -1$; y-intercept: -0.125; x-intercept: 2

6c. The expression is undefined at $x = 8$, and the numerator is nonzero at $x = 8$, causing the vertical asymptote. The factor $(x + 1)$ was canceled and there are no more factors of $(x + 1)$ in the denominator after reducing; this causes a hole. When $x = 0$ the expression has the value $-\frac{1}{8}$ or -0.125, the y-intercept. The numerator is 0 when $x = 2$; this is the x-intercept. For large values of x the expression approaches the value -0.5, the horizontal asymptote.

BUILDING UNDERSTANDING

Students practice operating on rational expressions and functions.

ASSIGNING HOMEWORK

Essential	1–4
Performance assessment	5–8, 10
Portfolio	10
Journal	6
Group	8, 10
Review	9, 11–13

Helping with the Exercises

1a. $\dfrac{x(x+2)}{(x-2)(x+2)}=\dfrac{x}{x-2}$

1b. $\dfrac{(x-1)(x-4)}{(x+1)(x-1)}=\dfrac{x-4}{x+1}$

1c. $\dfrac{3x(x-2)}{(x-4)(x-2)}=\dfrac{3x}{x-4}$

1d. $\dfrac{(x+5)(x-2)}{(x+5)(x-5)}=\dfrac{x-2}{x-5}$

Exercises 2, 3 [Alert] If students are not finding the least common denominator, help them remember to factor first.

2a. $(x+3)(x-3)(x-2)$

2b. $(2x+1)(x-4)(x+1)(x-2)$

2c. $(x+2)(x-2)(x+3)$

2d. $(x-3)(x+2)(x+3)$

3a. $\dfrac{(2x-3)(x+1)}{(x+3)(x-2)(x-3)}$

3b. $\dfrac{-x^2+6}{(x+2)(x+3)(x-2)}$

3c. $\dfrac{2x^2-x+9}{(x-3)(x+2)(x+3)}$

3d. $\dfrac{2x^2-5x+6}{(x+1)(x-2)(x-1)}$

Exercise 5 As needed, suggest that students work in stages, first combining the terms in the numerators and denominators separately and then reducing the quotient.

7. Consider the equation $y = \frac{x-3}{x^2-4}$.

a. Without graphing, identify the zeros and asymptotes of the graph of the equation. Explain your methods.

b. Verify your answers by graphing the function.

8. Consider the equation $y = x + 1 + \frac{1}{x-1}$.

a. Without graphing, name the asymptotes of the function.

b. Rewrite the equation as a single rational function. $y = \frac{x^2}{x-1}$

c. Sketch a graph of the function without using your calculator.

d. Confirm your work by graphing the function with your calculator.

9. ***Mini-Investigation*** You saw in Lesson 9.7 that a transformation of the parent function $f(x) = \frac{1}{x}$ is a rotated hyperbola. Are there other kinds of rational functions that are also rotated hyperbolas? Recall that any conic section can be written in the general quadratic form, $Ax^2 + Bxy + Cy^2 + Dx + Ey + F = 0$.

a. Look back at your graph of $y = x + 1 + \frac{1}{x-1}$ from Exercise 8. Does the graph appear to be a rotated hyperbola? Answers will vary.

b. Rewrite the equation $y = x + 1 + \frac{1}{x-1}$ in general quadratic form, if possible. Is the graph actually a rotated hyperbola? $-x^2 + xy - y = 0$; yes

c. Look back at your graph of $y = \frac{x-3}{x^2-4}$ from Exercise 7. Does the graph appear to be a rotated hyperbola? no

d. Rewrite the equation $y = \frac{x-3}{x^2-4}$ in general quadratic form, if possible. Is the graph actually a rotated hyperbola? not possible; no

e. Write a conjecture that describes how you can tell, based on an equation, what rational functions are rotated hyperbolas. After reducing common factors, the degree of the numerator must be less than or equal to 2, and the degree of the denominator must be 1.

10. **APPLICATION** How long should a traffic light stay yellow before turning red? One study suggests that for a car approaching a 40 ft wide intersection under normal driving conditions, the length of time, y, that a light should stay yellow, in seconds, is given by the equation $y = 1 + \frac{v}{25} + \frac{50}{v}$, where v is the velocity of an approaching car in feet per second.

a. Rewrite the equation in rational function form. $y = \frac{v^2 + 25v + 1250}{25v}$

b. Enter the original equation as Y_1 and your simplified equation as Y_2 into your calculator. Check using the table feature that the values of both functions are the same. What does this tell you?

c. If the speed limit at a particular intersection is 45 mi/h, how long should the light stay yellow? 4.4 s

d. If cars typically travel at speeds ranging from 25 mi/h to 55 mi/h at that intersection, what is the possible range of times that a light should stay yellow? 3.8 s to 4.8 s

Career CONNECTION

Traffic engineers time traffic signals to minimize the "dilemma zone." The dilemma zone occurs when a driver has to decide to brake hard to stop or to accelerate to get through the intersection. Either decision can be risky. It is estimated that 22% of traffic accidents occur when a driver runs a red light.

7a. $x = 3$ is a zero, because that value causes the numerator to be 0. The vertical asymptotes are $x = 2$ and $x = -2$, because these values make the denominator 0 and do not also make the numerator 0. The horizontal asymptote is $x = 0$, because this is the value that y approaches when $|x|$ is large.

7b.

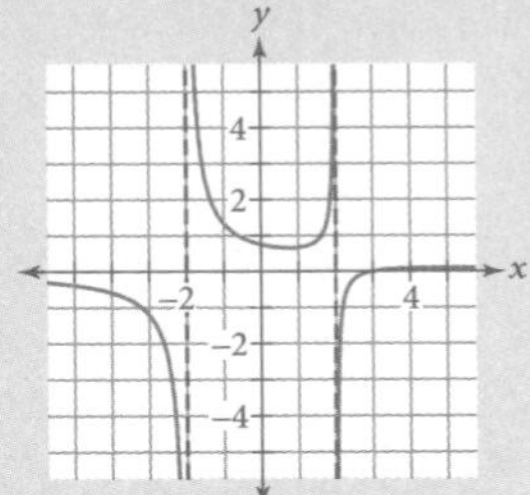

8a. $y = x + 1$ is a slant asymptote; $x = 1$ is a vertical asymptote.

8d.

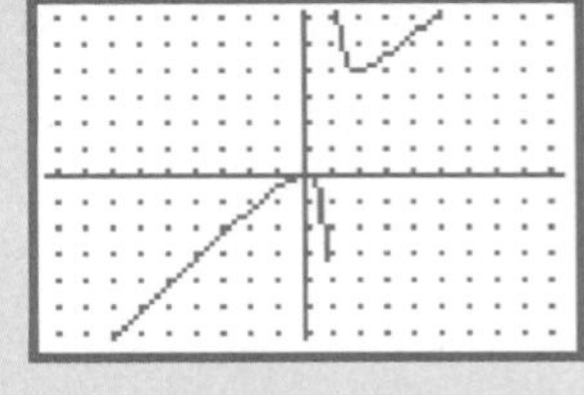

[−9.4, 9.4, 1, −6.2, 6.2, 1]

Exercise 9 [Alert] Students may not understand that every conic section can be represented by an equation that can be put in general quadratic form and that every equation in this form with nonzero A, B, or C represents a conic section.

Exercise 10 This formula is valid only for speeds over approximately 25 mi/h. Students must convert mi/h to ft/s to complete 10c and 10d.

MAKING THE CONNECTION

States use a number of variables to determine the length of the yellow light. In California, for example, the yellow light interval is determined by the equation $T = r + \frac{V}{d}$, where T is the yellow light interval in seconds, V is the speed limit in meters per second, d is the deceleration rate (presumed to be 3.05 m/s²), and r is the driver's reaction time (presumed to be 1 s).

8c.

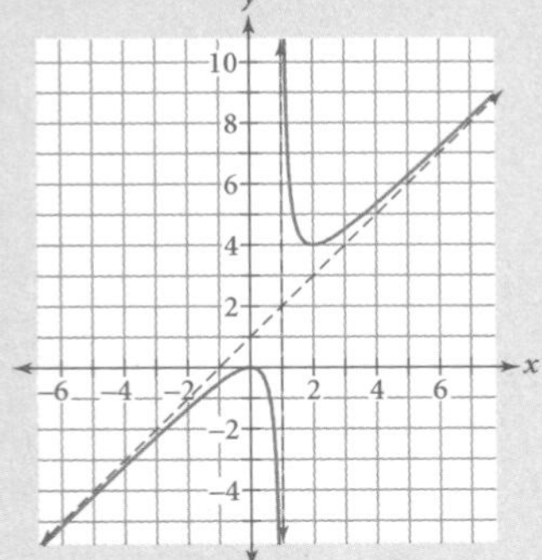

10b.

X	Y1	Y2
1	51.04	51.04
2	26.08	26.08
3	17.787	17.787
4	13.66	13.66
5	11.2	11.2
6	9.5733	9.5733
7	8.4229	8.4229

X=1

The equations are the same, so it was simplified correctly.

Review

9.7 **11.** The graph at right is the image of $y = \frac{1}{x}$ after a transformation.

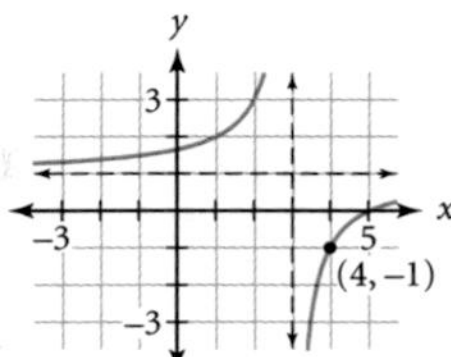

a. Write an equation for each asymptote. $x = 3, y = 1$

b. What translations are involved in transforming $y = \frac{1}{x}$ to its image? translation right 3 units and up 1 unit

c. The point $(4, -1)$ is on the image. What is the vertical scale factor in the transformation? -2

d. Write an equation of the image. $y = 1 - \frac{2}{x-3}$ or $y = \frac{x-5}{x-3}$

e. Name the intercepts. x-intercept: 5; y-intercept: $\frac{5}{3}$

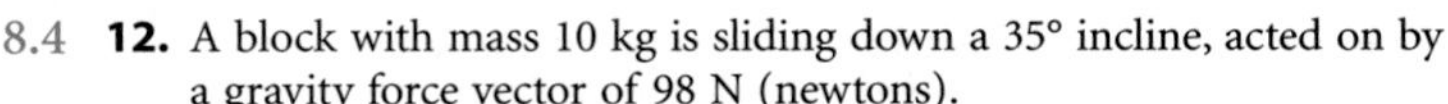

8.4 **12.** A block with mass 10 kg is sliding down a 35° incline, acted on by a gravity force vector of 98 N (newtons).

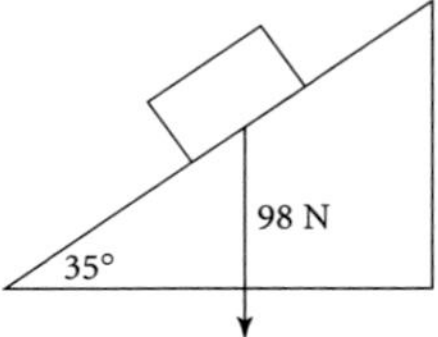

a. Sketch this gravity vector in two components, one parallel to the incline, v_i, and one perpendicular to the incline, v_n.

b. Find the magnitude of each component.
$v_i = 98 \sin 35° \approx 56$ N, $v_n = 98 \cos 35° \approx 80$ N

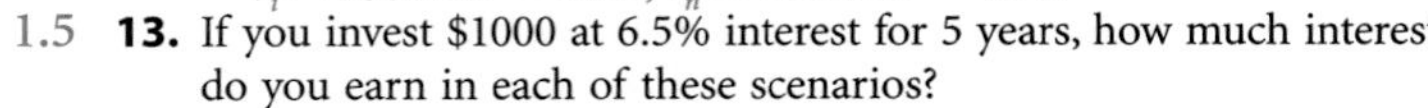

1.5 **13.** If you invest \$1000 at 6.5% interest for 5 years, how much interest do you earn in each of these scenarios?

a. The interest is compounded annually. \$370.09

b. The interest is compounded monthly. \$382.82

c. The interest is compounded weekly. \$383.75

d. The interest is compounded daily. \$383.99

Project

CYCLIC HYPERBOLAS

Consider the rational function $f(x) = \frac{x-3}{x+1}$, whose graph is a hyperbola. You can use this function as a recursive formula. Choose any starting value for x and find the first six terms of the sequence. The values should repeat. Choose another value for x. Does the same thing happen? Graph the function using web graphs and explore what happens for various values of x. [► **See Calculator Note 5D to learn how to make a web graph.** ◄] Then use function composition to prove that such repetition always happens for this function. Hyperbolas with this property are called *cyclic hyperbolas.*

Your project is to explore what can happen when you use a rational function whose graph is a hyperbola as a recursive rule and to look for other cyclic hyperbolas. You might also explore what happens when you use other functions you've studied as a recursive rule. Are any of them cyclic?

Your project should include

- Your calculations and web graphs for $f(x) = \frac{x-3}{x+1}$, and other functions you explore.
- Any other cyclic hyperbolas you find, including a proof that they are cyclic.
- Any research you do about recursive sequences on hyperbolas or other functions.

12a.

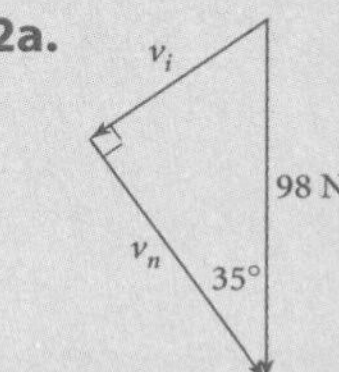

Web Graph for Project

This example is for the function $f(x) = \frac{x-3}{x+1}$, with a starting value of $x = 5$.

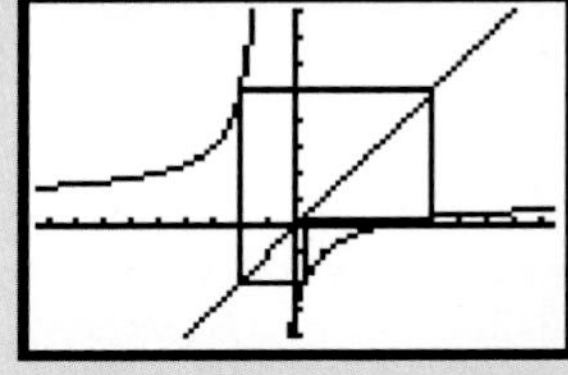

$[-9.4, 9.4, 1, -6.2, 6.2, 1]$

Proof That the Function Is Cyclic

Prove: The function $f(x) = \frac{x-3}{x+1}$ is cyclic.

$$f(f(x)) = \frac{\frac{x-3}{x+1} - 3}{\frac{x-3}{x+1} + 1} = \frac{\frac{x-3-3(x+1)}{x+1}}{\frac{x-3+1(x+1)}{x+1}} = \frac{-2x-6}{2x-2} = \frac{-x-3}{x-1}$$

$$f(f(f(x))) = \frac{\frac{-x-3}{x-1} - 3}{\frac{-x-3}{x-1} + 1} = \frac{\frac{-x-3-3(x-1)}{x-1}}{\frac{-x-3+1(x-1)}{x-1}} = \frac{-4x}{-4} = x$$

Therefore $f(f(f(x))) = x$.

Supporting the Project

Students can use home-screen recursion to find the six terms. If they begin with a starting value $u(1) = 1$, they'll get an undefined value for $u(3)$; for other starting values, the entire sequence will be defined. Help students understand how to adjust the window to include all points being traced.

OUTCOMES

- From several sequences, the student observes and proves that each sequence repeats after exactly three numbers.
- The report includes at least one web graph diagram.
- The report includes other cyclic hyperbolas. Possibilities include $f(x) = \frac{x+7}{-x+2}$, with period 3; $f(x) = \frac{2x+2}{-x}$, with period 4; $f(x) = \frac{x-1}{x+1}$, with period 4; $f(x) = \frac{2x + 8\sqrt{5} + 20}{-x+2}$, with period 5; and $f(x) = \frac{3x-1}{3x+3}$, with period 6.
- The report includes sequences created from other functions and starting values.
- The student makes a conjecture about conditions that make a hyperbola cyclic.

PLANNING

LESSON OUTLINE

One day:

15 min Reviewing

20 min Exercises

10 min Student self-assessment

REVIEWING

Remind students that, because the equation $y = \frac{1}{x}$ represents a hyperbola, points of the form $\left(x, \frac{1}{x}\right)$ satisfy the constant difference property: The difference of their distances from the foci $\left(\sqrt{2}, \sqrt{2}\right)$ and $\left(-\sqrt{2}, -\sqrt{2}\right)$ must be constant. Ask what this constant is. Use the distance formula and operations on rational functions to get $2\sqrt{2}$. To verify the constant, review the idea of the hyperbola's vertices and asymptotes and why the constant equals the distance between the vertices. Then ask students about the constant sum of the ellipse represented by the equation $9x^2 + 25y^2 - 225 = 0$ and the constant ratio of the parabola represented by $y = 4x^2$, reviewing relevant concepts about conic sections as you go.

Helping with the Exercises

2a. $\left(\frac{x-5}{3}\right)^2 + \left(\frac{y+2}{4}\right)^2 = 1$

Exercise 2b This exercise requires knowledge of parametric functions.

2b. $x = 3\cos t + 5$ and $y = 4\sin t - 2$

2c. $(5, -2)$; $\left(5, -2 + \sqrt{7}\right)$ and $\left(5, -2 - \sqrt{7}\right)$

See page 899 for answers to Exercise 1.

CHAPTER 9 REVIEW

In this chapter you saw some special relations. Each relation was described as a set of points, or **locus,** that satisfied some criteria. These relations are called **conic sections** because the shapes can be formed by slicing a double cone at various angles. The simplest of the conic sections is the **circle,** the set of points a fixed distance from a fixed point called the **center.** Closely related to the circle is the **ellipse.** The ellipse can be defined as the set of points such that the sum of their distances from two fixed points, the **foci,** is a constant. The **parabola** is another conic section, which you studied in earlier chapters. It can be defined as the set of points that are equidistant from a fixed point called the focus and a fixed line called the **directrix.** The last of the conic sections is the **hyperbola.** The definition of a hyperbola is similar to the definition of an ellipse, except that the difference between the distances from the foci remains constant. The equations for these conic sections can be written parametrically or in standard form, or as a general quadratic equation. And each of these conic sections can be either vertically oriented or horizontally oriented. You learned how to convert between the general quadratic equation and standard form, and how to solve systems of quadratic equations to find the intersections of two conic sections.

You were also introduced to **rational functions** in the form $y = \frac{p(x)}{q(x)}$, where $p(x)$ and $q(x)$ are polynomial expressions and the degree of $q(x)$ is at least 1. The graphs of rational functions contain **vertical asymptotes** or **holes** when the denominator is undefined. You also learned how to do arithmetic with rational expressions.

EXERCISES

1. Sketch the graph of each equation. Label foci when appropriate.

a. $\frac{x-3}{-2} = (y-2)^2$

b. $x^2 + (y-2)^2 = 16$

c. $\left(\frac{y+2.5}{3}\right)^2 - \left(\frac{x-1}{4}\right)^2 = 1$

d. $\left(\frac{x}{5}\right)^2 + 3y^2 = 1$

2. Consider this ellipse.

a. Write the equation for the graph shown in standard form.

b. Write the parametric equations for this graph.

c. Name the coordinates of the center and foci.

d. Write the general quadratic form of the equation for this graph.

$16x^2 + 9y^2 - 160x + 36y + 292 = 0$

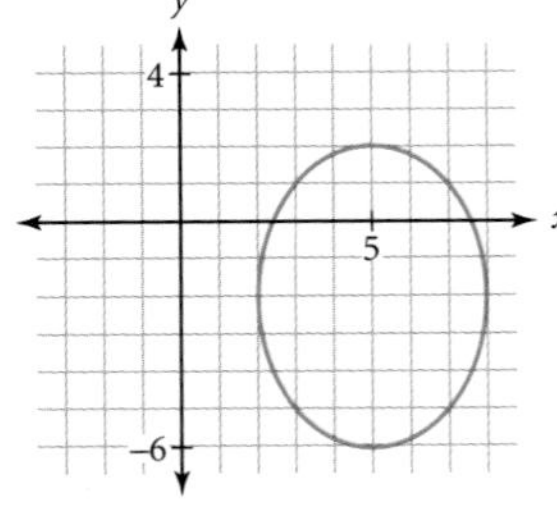

ASSIGNING HOMEWORK

The exercises include the Chapter 9 review and the mixed review. To review the chapter you might suggest that students work in groups on the odd-numbered exercises (1–11) and complete the even-numbered exercises (2–12) for homework. Students might work together on the mixed review, with each student doing part of each problem and working with group members when the parts depend on each other.

3. Consider the hyperbola graphed at right.

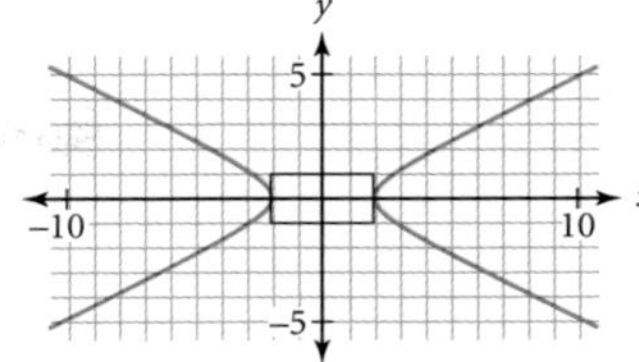
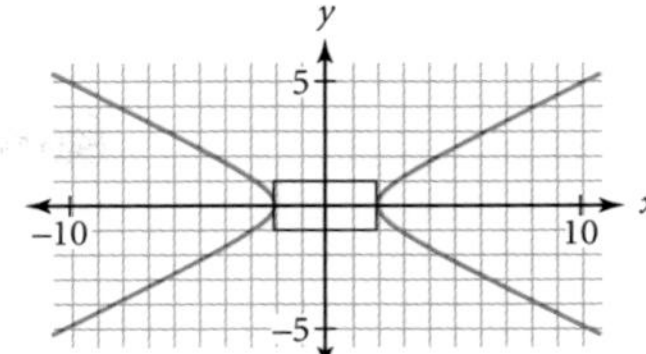

a. Write the equations of the asymptotes for this hyperbola.

b. Write the general quadratic equation for this hyperbola.

c. Write an equation that will give the vertical distance, d, between the asymptote with positive slope and a point on the upper portion of the right branch of the hyperbola as a function of the point's x-coordinate, x.

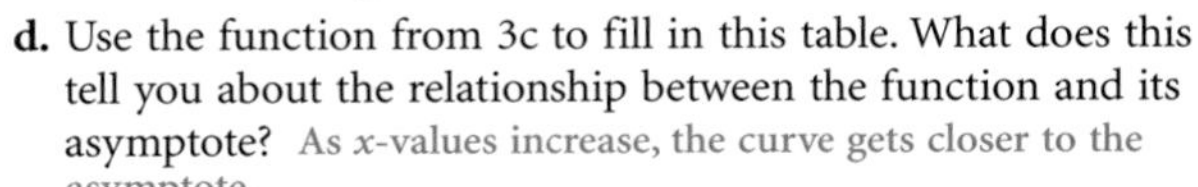

d. Use the function from 3c to fill in this table. What does this tell you about the relationship between the function and its asymptote? As x-values increase, the curve gets closer to the asymptote.

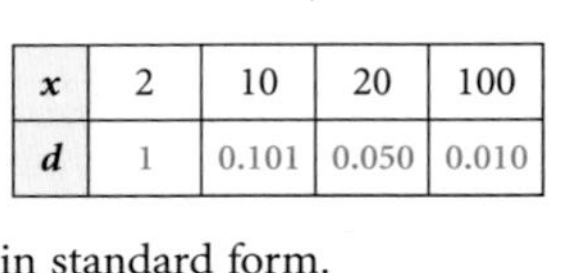

x	2	10	20	100
d	1	0.101	0.050	0.010

4. Write the general quadratic equation $x^2 + y^2 + 8x - 2y - 8 = 0$ in standard form. Identify the shape described by the equation and describe its features. $(x + 4)^2 + (y - 1)^2 = 25$. The graph is a circle with center $(-4, 1)$ and radius 5.

5. Write the general quadratic equation $y^2 - 8y - 4x + 28 = 0$ in standard form. Determine the vertex, focus, and directrix of the parabola defined by this equation. Sketch a graph.

6. **APPLICATION** Pure gold is too soft to be used for jewelry, so gold is always mixed with other metals. 18-karat gold is 75% gold and 25% other metals. How much pure gold must be mixed with 5 oz of 18-karat gold to make a 22-karat (91.7%) gold mixture? 10 oz

7. Write an equation of each rational function described as a translation of the graph of $y = \frac{1}{x}$.

a. The rational function has asymptotes $x = -2$ and $y = 1$. $y = 1 + \frac{1}{x + 2}$ or $y = \frac{x + 3}{x + 2}$

b. The rational function has asymptotes $x = 0$ and $y = -4$. $y = -4 + \frac{1}{x}$ or $y = \frac{-4x + 1}{x}$

8. Graph $y = \frac{2x - 14}{x - 5}$. Write equations for the horizontal and vertical asymptotes.

9. How can you modify the equation $y = \frac{2x - 14}{x - 5}$ so that the graph of the new equation is the same as the original graph except for a hole at $x = -3$? Verify your new equation by graphing it on your calculator.

10. On her way to school, Ellen drives at a steady speed for the first 2 mi. After glancing at her watch, she drives 20 mi/h faster during the remaining 3.5 mi. How fast does she drive during the two portions of this trip if the total time of her trip is 10 min? 23.3 mi/h and then 43.3 mi/h

11. Rewrite each expression as a single rational expression in factored form.

a. $\frac{2x}{(x - 2)(x + 1)} + \frac{x + 3}{x^2 - 4}$ **b.** $\frac{x^2}{x + 1} \cdot \frac{3x - 6}{x^2 - 2x}$ **c.** $\frac{x^2 - 5x - 6}{x} \div \frac{x^2 - 8x + 12}{x^2 - 1}$

12. Solve this system of equations algebraically, then confirm your answer graphically.

$$\begin{cases} x^2 + y^2 = 4 \\ (x + 1)^2 - \frac{y^2}{3} = 1 \end{cases}$$

12. $(0.5, 1.936)$, $(0.5, -1.936)$, $(-2, 0)$

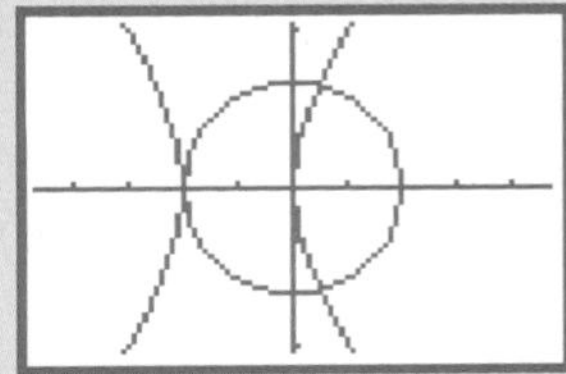

$[-4.7, 4.7, 1, -3.1, 3.1, 1]$

3a. $y = \pm 0.5x$

3b. $x^2 - 4y^2 - 4 = 0$

3c. $d = 0.5x - \sqrt{\frac{x^2}{4} - 1}$

5. $(y - 4)^2 = \frac{x - 3}{0.25}$; vertex: $(3, 4)$, focus: $(4, 4)$, directrix: $x = 2$

8.

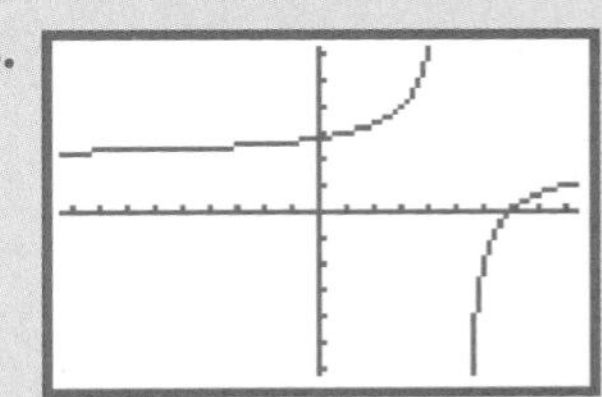

$[-9.4, 9.4, 1\ -6.2, 6.2, 1]$

horizontal asymptote $y = 2$, vertical asymptote $x = 5$

9. Multiply the numerator and denominator by the factor $(x + 3)$.

$$y = \frac{(2x - 14)(x + 3)}{(x - 5)(x + 3)}$$

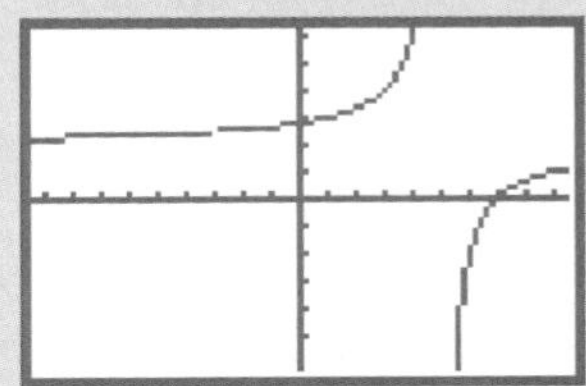

$[-9.4, 9.4, 1\ -6.2, 6.2, 1]$

Exercise 11 This exercise requires operations on rational functions, practiced in Lesson 9.8.

11a. $\frac{3x^2 + 8x + 3}{(x - 2)(x + 1)(x + 2)}$

11b. $\frac{3x}{x + 1}$

11c. $\frac{(x + 1)^2(x - 1)}{x(x - 2)}$

13.

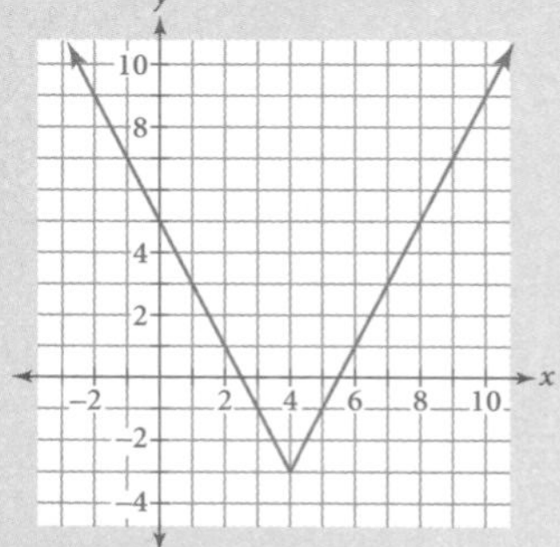

14a. 91.45 million mi

14b. 94.55 million mi

14c. 93 million mi

14d. 1.55 million mi

14e. 92.99 million mi

14f. $\left(\frac{x}{93}\right)^2 + \left(\frac{y}{92.99}\right)^2 = 1$

Snow Sculptures
[Ask] "What portion of the circle of ice bricks is supported with ground beneath it? [Reasonable answers: $\frac{135}{360}$, 35–40%, a little more than $\frac{1}{3}$] "What will happen as the circles sag?" [Perhaps they'll look more like ellipses.]

MIXED REVIEW

4.6 **13.** Write an equation of the image of the absolute-value function, $y = |x|$, after performing each of the following transformations in order. Sketch a graph of your final equation.

a. Stretch vertically by a factor of 2. $y = 2|x|$  **b.** Then translate right 4 units. $y = 2|x - 4|$

c. Then translate down 3 units. $y = 2|x - 4| - 3$

9.2 **14.** Earth's orbit is an ellipse with the Sun at one of the foci. Perihelion is the point at which Earth is closest to the Sun, and aphelion is the point at which it is farthest from the Sun. The distances from perihelion to the Sun and from the Sun to aphelion are in an approximate ratio of 59:61. If the total distance from aphelion to perihelion along the major axis is about 186 million miles, approximate

a. The distance from perihelion to the Sun.

b. The distance from aphelion to the Sun.

c. The distance from aphelion to the center.

d. The distance from the center to the Sun.

e. In this ellipse it can be shown that the distance from the Sun to point P equals the distance from aphelion to the center. Using this information, find the distance from the center to P.

f. Write an equation that models the orbit of Earth around the Sun.

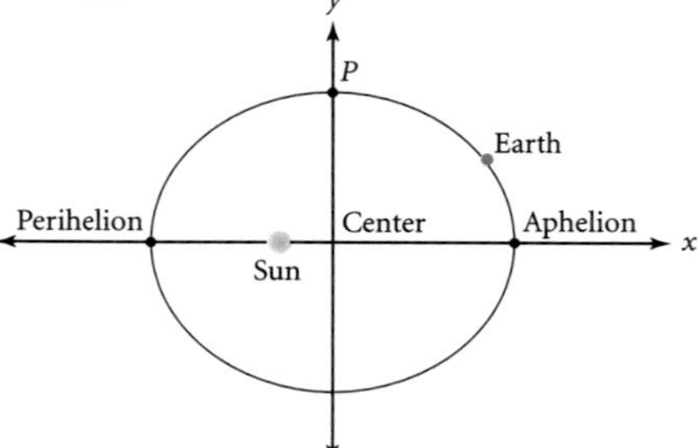

These four circular snow sculptures by British environmental sculptor Andy Goldsworthy (b 1956) were made from bricks of packed snow at the Arctic Circle.

6.2 **15.** Perform the following matrix computations. If a computation is not possible, explain why.

$[A] = \begin{bmatrix} -2 & 0 \\ 1 & -3 \end{bmatrix}$ $[B] = \begin{bmatrix} 0 & -2 \\ 5 & 0 \\ 3 & -1 \end{bmatrix}$ $[C] = \begin{bmatrix} 1 & -1 \\ 0 & 2 \end{bmatrix}$

a. $[A][B]$ **b.** $[A] + [B]$ **c.** $[A] - [C]$ **d.** $[B][A]$ **e.** $3[C] - [A]$

15a. Not possible. The number of columns in $[A]$ must match the number of rows in $[B]$.

15b. Not possible. To add matrices, they must have the same dimensions.

15c. $\begin{bmatrix} -3 & 1 \\ 1 & -5 \end{bmatrix}$

15d. $\begin{bmatrix} -2 & 6 \\ -10 & 0 \\ -7 & 3 \end{bmatrix}$

15e. $\begin{bmatrix} 5 & -3 \\ -1 & 9 \end{bmatrix}$

1.2 **16.** Identify each sequence as arithmetic, geometric, or neither. State the next three terms, and then write a recursive formula to generate each sequence.

a. 9, 12, 15, 18, . . . **b.** 1, 1, 2, 3, 5, 8, 13, . . . **c.** −3, 6, −12, 24, . . .

8.3 **17.** Evan is standing at one corner of the football field when he sees his dog, Spot, start to run diagonally across the field as shown. Evan knows that Spot can run to the opposite corner in 15 s. The dimensions of the football field are 100 yd by 52 yd.

a. What is Spot's rate in yards per second? 7.5 yd/s

b. What is Spot's angle with the horizontal axis? 27.5°

c. Write equations that model the motion of Spot running from corner to corner.

d. Write equations that show Evan running at the same rate as Spot from one corner to an opposite corner as shown in the diagram above.

e. If Spot and Evan both start at the same time, when and where do they meet?
midfield (50, 26), after 7.5 s

2.2 **18.** D'Andre surveyed a randomly chosen group of 15 teachers at his school and asked them how many students were enrolled in their third-period classes. Here is the data set he collected.

{27, 29, 18, 34, 42, 38, 34, 33, 25, 28, 45, 35, 32, 19, 36}

a. List the mean, median, and mode. $\bar{x} = 31.\bar{6}$; *median* = 33; *mode* = 34

b. Make a box plot of the data.

c. Calculate the standard deviation. What does this tell you about the data? If the standard deviation were smaller, what would it tell you about the data?

9.5 **19.** Rewrite each equation in standard form, and identify the type of curve.

a. $25x^2 - 4y^2 + 100 = 0$ **b.** $4y^2 - 10x + 16y + 36 = 0$

c. $4x^2 + 4y^2 + 24x - 8y + 39 = 0$ **d.** $3x^2 + 5y^2 - 12x + 20y + 8 = 0$

6.3 **20.** The towers of a parabolic suspension bridge are 400 m apart and reach 50 m above the suspended roadway. The cable is 4 m above the roadway at the halfway point. Write an equation that models the shape of the cable. Assume the origin, (0, 0), is located at the halfway point of the roadway.

$y = 0.00115x^2 + 4$

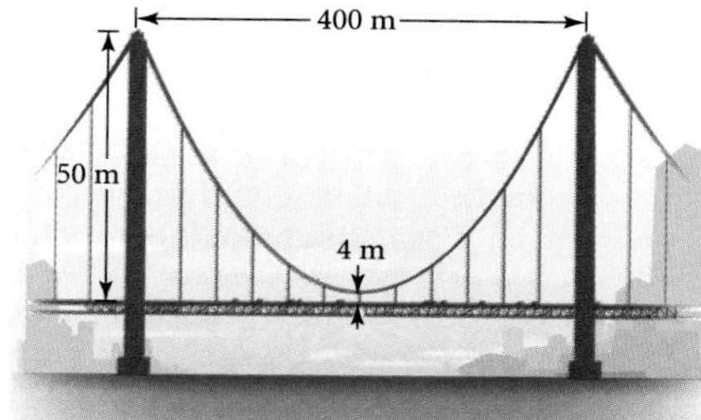

5.7 **21.** Solve algebraically. Round answers to the nearest hundredth.

a. $4 + 5^x = 18$ $x \approx 1.64$ **b.** $12(0.5)^{2x} = 30$ $x \approx -0.66$ **c.** $\log_3 15 = \dfrac{\log x}{\log 3}$ $x = 15$

d. $\log_6 100 = x$ $x \approx 2.57$ **e.** $2\log x = 2.5$ $x \approx 17.78$ **f.** $\log_5 5^3 = x$ $x = 3$

g. $4\log x = \log 16$ $x = 2$ **h.** $\log(5 + x) - \log 5 = 2$ $x = 495$ **i.** $x\log 5^x = 12$ $x \approx \pm 4.14$

16a. arithmetic; 21, 24, 27; $u_1 = 9$ and $u_n = u_{n-1} + 3$ where $n \geq 2$

Exercise 16b This is the Fibonacci sequence, which students saw in the exploration on page 59.

16b. neither; 21, 34, 55; $u_1 = 1$, $u_2 = 1$ and $u_n = u_{n-1} + u_{n-2}$ where $n \geq 3$

16c. geometric; −48, 96, −192; $u_1 = -3$ and $u_n = -2u_{n-1}$ where $n \geq 2$

Exercises 17, 23 These exercises review parametric equations.

17c. $x = 7.5t\cos 27.5°$, $y = 7.5t\sin 27.5°$

17d. $x = 100 - 7.5t\cos 27.5°$, $y = 7.5t\sin 27.5°$

18b.

0 10 20 30 40 50
Number of students

18c. $s = 7.57$. The data are fairly spread out from the mean. If the standard deviation were smaller, the data would be more closely grouped around 33 students per class.

19a. $\left(\frac{y}{5}\right)^2 - \left(\frac{x}{2}\right)^2 = 1$; hyperbola

19b. $(y + 2)^2 = \dfrac{(x - 2)}{\frac{2}{5}}$; parabola

19c. $(x + 3)^2 + (y - 1)^2 = \frac{1}{4}$; circle

19d. $\left(\dfrac{x - 2}{\sqrt{8}}\right)^2 + \left(\dfrac{y + 2}{\sqrt{4.8}}\right)^2 = 1$ or $\left(\dfrac{x - 2}{2\sqrt{2}}\right)^2 + \left(\dfrac{y + 2}{2\sqrt{1.2}}\right)^2 = 1$; ellipse

3.5 **22.** The chart below shows average fuel efficiency of new U.S. passenger cars.

Average Fuel Efficiency

Year	1970	1975	1980	1985	1990	1995	1998	1999
Fuel efficiency (mi/gal)	14.1	15.1	22.6	26.3	26.9	27.7	28.1	28.2

(*The New York Times Almanac 2002*)

a. Find the median-median line for the data. $\hat{y} = 0.565x - 1100$

b. What is the root mean square error for the median-median line model? $s = \sqrt{\frac{48.61}{6}} \approx 2.8$

c. What is the real-world meaning of the root mean square error in 22b?

d. Is the median-median line a good model to use to predict fuel efficiency in the future?

8.3 **23.** The bases on a baseball diamond form a square that is 90 ft on each side. Deanna has a 12 ft lead and can run the remaining 78 ft from first to second base at 28 ft/s. The catcher releases the ball from home plate toward second base 1.5 s after Deanna starts to steal the base, and the ball travels 125 ft/s. Write parametric equations to simulate this situation and determine whether Deanna is successful. Explain your solution.

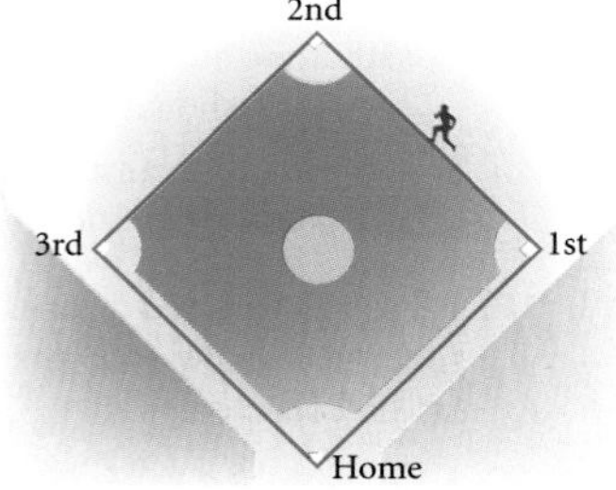

7.5 **24.** Use $P = 1 + 3i$, $Q = -2 + i$, and $R = 3 - 5i$ to evaluate each expression. Give answers in the form $a + bi$.

a. $P + Q - R$ $-4 + 9i$ **b.** PQ $-5 - 5i$ **c.** Q^2 $3 - 4i$ **d.** $P \div Q$ $\frac{1}{5} - \frac{7}{5}i$

TAKE ANOTHER LOOK

1. The equation $\left(\frac{x}{a}\right)^2 + \left(\frac{y}{b}\right)^2 = 1$ is the standard form of an ellipse. What shape will the equations $\left(\frac{x}{a}\right)^3 + \left(\frac{y}{b}\right)^3 = 1$, $\left(\frac{x}{a}\right)^4 + \left(\frac{y}{b}\right)^4 = 1$, or generally $\left(\frac{x}{a}\right)^n + \left(\frac{y}{b}\right)^n = 1$ create? These equations are called Lamé curves, or superellipses, when $n > 2$. Investigate several Lamé curve graphs in a friendly graphing window. Assume that $a > 0$ and $b > 0$. You already know what effect the values of a and b have on an ellipse. Do they have the same effect on a Lamé curve? For fixed values of a and b, try different n-values, including positive, negative, whole-number, and rational values. Explore the graph shapes and properties for different values of n. Summarize your discoveries.

2. How can you find the horizontal asymptote of a rational function without graphing or using a table? Use a calculator to explore these functions, and look for patterns. Some equations may not have horizontal asymptotes. Make a conjecture about how to determine the equation of a horizontal asymptote just by looking at the equation.

$y = \frac{3x^2 + 4x - 5}{2x^4 + 2}$ $\quad y = \frac{4x^4 - 2x^3 - 2}{x^5 - 5x}$ $\quad y = \frac{3x^2 + 4x - 5}{2x^2}$

$y = \frac{4x^5 - 2x^3 - 2}{x^5 - 5x}$ $\quad y = \frac{-x^3}{x^2 - 2x + 5}$ $\quad y = \frac{3x^4 + 2x}{5x^2 - 1}$ See page 563.

22c. In general, the median-median line model predicts results within 2.8 mi/gal of the actual results.

22d. Answers will vary. The model is likely a good model for the next few years at least. Eventually, however, alternative forms of fuel will make the model obsolete.

Exercise 23 [ESL] In baseball *stealing a base* means running to that base without the batter hitting the ball and without being touched by the ball. Deanna is "successful" if she steals the base.

23. Bases are home (0, 0), first (90, 0), second (90, 90), and third (0, 90).

Deanna: $x = 90$
$y = 28t + 12$

ball: $x = 125(t - 1.5)\cos 45°$
$y = 125(t - 1.5)\sin 45°$

Deanna reaches second base after 2.79 s, ball reaches second after 2.52 s. Deanna is out.

Take Another Look

1. To investigate the graph on their calculators, students can solve the equation $\left(\frac{x}{a}\right)^n + \left(\frac{y}{b}\right)^n = 1$ for y and enter $Y_1 = b\sqrt[n]{1 - \left(\frac{x}{a}\right)^n}$ and, if n is even, $Y_2 = -Y_1$. Then, on the Home screen, they can store values for a, b, and n.

For $n = 1$, the graph is a line. When n is odd and greater than 1, the graph is similar to the ones shown. As n gets larger, the curve has "sharper" corners.

When n equals 2, the graph of the equation is an ellipse with x-intercepts a and $-a$, and y-intercepts b and $-b$. As the even powers of n get larger, the graph looks more like a rectangle.

These graphs use window $[-4.7, 4.7, 1, -3.1, 3.1, 1]$.

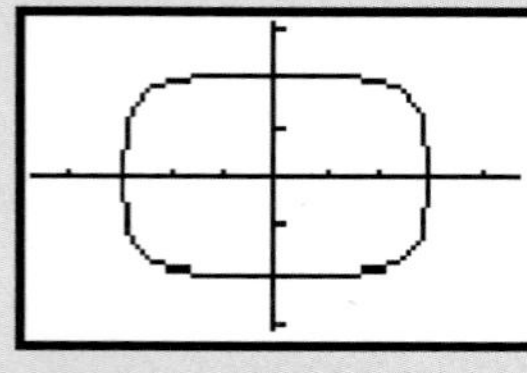
$n = 4$

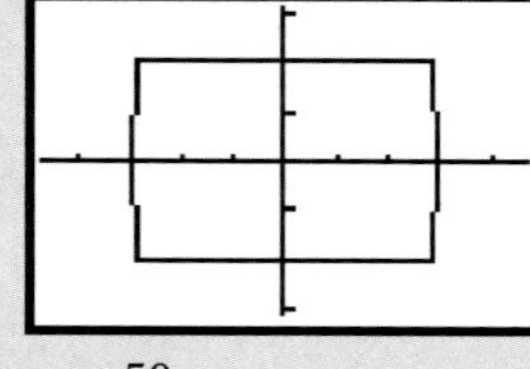
$n = 50$

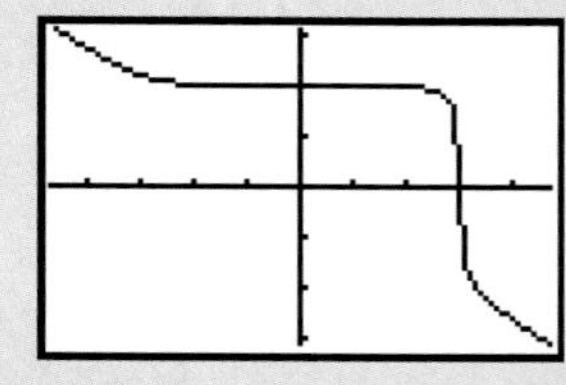
$n = 7$

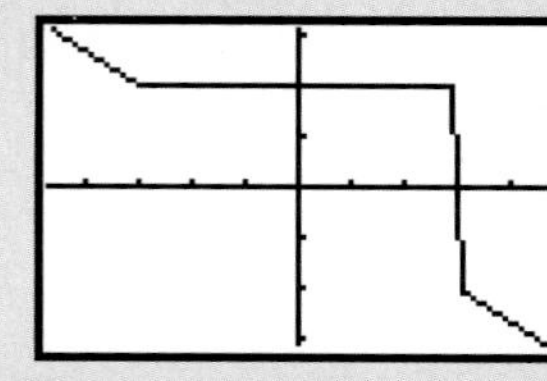
$n = 51$

3. You have seen that for an ellipse, the sum of the distances from any point to the two foci is constant. For a hyperbola, the difference of the distances from any point to the two foci is constant. What shape is created if the product of the distances is constant? What if the ratio of the distances is constant? You may want to use geometry software to explore these patterns.

4. In Lesson 9.5, you explored the number of points of intersection of two conic sections. You saw that, for example, a hyperbola and an ellipse can intersect 0, 1, 2, 3, or 4 times. However, points of intersection on a coordinate plane only include the real solutions to a system of equations. If you include nonreal answers, how many solutions can a system of conic sections have? Consider each pair of the four conic sections. Explain how the number of solutions is related to the exponents in the original equations.

Assessing What You've Learned

GIVE A PRESENTATION By yourself or with a group, demonstrate how to factor the equation of a rational function. Then describe how to find asymptotes, holes, and intercepts, and graph the equation. Or present your solution to a project or Take Another Look activity from this chapter.

PERFORMANCE ASSESSMENT While a classmate, teacher, or family member observes, demonstrate how to convert the equation of a conic section in general quadratic form to standard form. Describe the features of the conic section, then draw a graph of the equation.

ORGANIZE YOUR NOTEBOOK Update your notebook to include the equations for the four conic sections. Include methods of graphing and how to find foci, vertices, centers, and asymptotes.

2. When the degree of the numerator is less than the degree of the denominator, the horizontal asymptote is the line $y = 0$. When the degree of the numerator is greater than the degree of the denominator, there is no horizontal asymptote. When the degree of the numerator equals the degree of the denominator, the horizontal asymptote is determined by the ratio of the leading coefficients.

3. A constant product gives a family of shapes called *Cassini ovals* such as these.

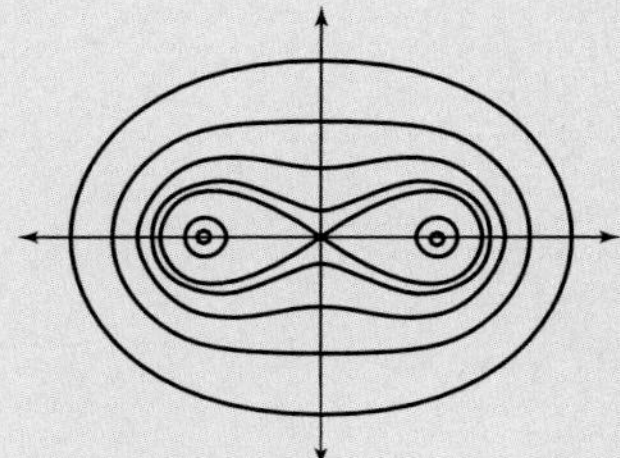

To explore this activity in Sketchpad, students can begin by graphing a curve given by an equation of the form $y = \frac{a}{x}$, where a is a constant, and measuring the distances from a point on the curve to the x- and y-axes. These two measurements will have a constant product regardless of the location of the point on the curve. The rest of the construction is similar to the construction of the ellipse in the Exploration Constructing the Conic Sections.

When the ratio is constant, you get a circle around one of the foci. This can be demonstrated similarly in Sketchpad, beginning with the function $y = ax$. This family of circles is called the *Apollonius circles.*

4. The highest degree on a variable determines the number of solutions for that variable. If a system of equations contains an x^2-term and a y^2-term, there are two solutions for x and two corresponding solutions for y, making a total of four solutions. These solutions may be real or nonreal. If a system of equations contains an x^2-term and a y-term, there are two solutions for x but only one corresponding solution for y, for a total of two solutions (real or nonreal). When the system contains a y^2-term and an x-term, the reverse is true, and there are still two solutions.

ASSESSING

If you choose to give a unit exam at this time, you might use a performance assessment for the chapter test, as well as items from the parts of this chapter that are important for meeting your school's standards.

FACILITATING SELF-ASSESSMENT

If you would like your students to give presentations, you might want to divide the topics covered in the chapter and spend a couple of days reviewing as each group gives its presentation.

Items that students might add to their portfolios include Lesson 9.1, Exercise 8 or 10; Lesson 9.2, Exercise 8; Lesson 9.3, Exercise 10; Lesson 9.4, Exercise 6 or 11; Lesson 9.5, Exercise 10; Lesson 9.6, Exercise 10; Lesson 9.7, Exercise 7; and Lesson 9.8, Exercise 10.

CHAPTER

10 Trigonometric Functions

Overview

Lesson 10.1 expands students' understanding of trigonometric ratios by defining the trigonometric functions for angle measures greater than 90°. Students are introduced to radian measure in **Lesson 10.2,** where they explore angular speed. In **Lesson 10.3,** students apply their knowledge of transformations to the graphs of trigonometric functions and learn vocabulary associated with sinusoidal graphs, including *amplitude* and *phase shift.* The graphs in **Lesson 10.4** help students understand the inverse trigonometric functions as functions that give only one of infinitely many angles whose measures have a specific trigonometric ratio. In **Lesson 10.5,** students fit real-world data to trigonometric functions. **Lesson 10.6** introduces students to the cotangent, cosecant, and secant functions and to trigonometric identities and their proofs. In **Lesson 10.7,** students combine sinusoidal graphs to create periodic functions, and they use trigonometric identities to find exact values of trigonometric ratios. The **exploration** that ends the chapter introduces polar coordinates and gives students a chance to explore rose curves, cardioids, and spirals.

The Mathematics

Many phenomena, both natural and human-made, are cyclic, or *periodic,* and many cyclic situations can be represented by wavelike graphs called *sinusoids.* The corresponding family of functions, *sinusoidal functions,* consists of extensions of the sine and cosine ratios, now defined for numbers other than those representing angle measures. The extension is based on the unit circle: As a point moves around the unit circle, its y-coordinate is the value of sine and its x-coordinate is the value of cosine. Therefore the parent sine and cosine functions are often called *circular functions.*

To move beyond angles and degrees, we often consider the independent variable of the trigonometric functions to be the distance traveled by a point moving around the unit circle. The independent variable's units are *radians.* Radian units thus are tied more closely to the structure of a circle than are degree units. Moreover, the formulas for arc length and the area of a sector (as well as formulas for derivatives in calculus) are simpler if the angle measure is given in radians.

To find a sinusoidal function that models periodic data, you can use either the sine or the cosine function as the parent function. The parent function $y = \cos x$, for example, has a maximum at point $(0, 1)$, period 2π, and amplitude 1. You can find the period of the data, a, by calculating the distance between peaks. The amplitude of the data, b, is half the difference between the maximum and the minimum. The values of a and b are stretch factors, so the function $y = \cos x$ is stretched to $\frac{y}{b} = \cos\left(\frac{x}{a}\right)$, or $y = b\cos\left(\frac{x}{a}\right)$. Next you consider translations: The x-coordinate of the first data maximum to the right of the y-axis is the amount h of the horizontal translation. The average of the data's maximum and minimum values is the vertical shift k. The resulting sinusoidal model is $y = b\cos\left(\frac{x-h}{a}\right) + k$.

Modeling with the parent function $y = \sin x$ is the same except that you consider the horizontal translation of the maximum from $x = \frac{\pi}{2}$ instead of from $x = 0$, or the horizontal translation of the starting point of a cycle of $y = \sin x$ from $x = 0$.

The tangent ratio can also be extended to a function, whose graph has vertical asymptotes $x = \frac{\pi}{2} \pm 2\pi n$. Other trigonometric functions can be useful in modeling periodic phenomena: $\sec x = \frac{1}{\cos x}$ and the cofunctions $\cot x$ $\left(\text{the complement's tangent, } \tan\left(\frac{\pi}{2} - x\right)\right)$ and $\csc x$ $\left(\text{the complement's secant, } \sec\left(\frac{\pi}{2} - x\right)\right)$.

Because of the periodic nature of trigonometric functions, their inverse relations are not functions. However, if you restrict the domain of a trigonometric function to an interval of increase or decrease, the inverse relation is a function. These functions are the inverse trigonometric functions, such as $y = \sin^{-1} x$ and $y = \tan^{-1} x$, which are extensions of the inverse trigonometric ratios.

Numerous equations relate trigonometric functions. For example, for any value of x, $\sin^2 x + \cos^2 x = 1$ and $\tan 2x = \frac{2\tan x}{1 - \tan^2 x}$. An equation that is true for all values of x for which it's defined is called an *identity.* Proving trigonometric identities is a good exercise in logical reasoning.

Using This Chapter

Lessons 10.6 and 10.7 might be optional depending on your state standards.

Resources

Discovering Advanced Algebra Resources

Teaching and Worksheet Masters
  Lessons 10.1–10.3, 10.5–10.7
  Exploration: Polar Coordinates

Calculator Notes 3B, 3C, 5B, 8A, 9A, 9C, 10A–E

Sketchpad Demonstrations
  Lesson 10.1
  Exploration: Polar Coordinates

Fathom Demonstration
  Lesson 10.3

Assessment Resources A and B
  Quiz 1 (Lessons 10.1, 10.2)
  Quiz 2 (Lessons 10.3–10.5)
  Quiz 3 (Lessons 10.6, 10.7)
  Chapter 10 Test
  Chapter 10 Constructive Assessment Options

More Practice Your Skills for Chapter 10

Condensed Lessons for Chapter 10

Other Resources

www.keypress.com/DAA

Materials

- compasses or circle templates
- washers
- string
- motion sensors
- graph paper
- springs
- masses of 50–100 g
- support stands, *optional*
- calculator-based sensors with microphone probes
- tuning forks
- musical instrument, *optional*

Pacing Guide

	day 1	day 2	day 3	day 4	day 5	day 6	day 7	day 8	day 9	day 10
standard	10.1	10.2	quiz, 10.3	10.4	10.5	quiz, 10.6	10.7	quiz, exploration	review	review
enriched	10.1	10.2	quiz, 10.3, 10.4	10.4, project	10.5, project	quiz, 10.6	10.7	quiz, exploration	review, TAL	review
block	10.1, 10.2	quiz, 10.3, 10.4	10.5, projects	quiz, 10.6	10.7, exploration	quiz, review	TAL, assessment			

	day 11
standard	assessment
enriched	assessment

CHAPTER 10 OBJECTIVES

- Introduce angle measure in radians and convert between radians and degrees
- Use the unit circle to extend trigonometric ratios to the circular, or sinusoidal, functions
- Evaluate trigonometric functions through reference angles and reference triangles
- Apply knowledge of transformations to find the period, amplitude, phase shift, vertical translation, and average value of a data set or sinusoidal function from an equation or graph
- Understand the inverse trigonometric functions as functions that give only one of infinitely many angle measures that have a specific trigonometric ratio
- Use graphs to help find solutions to inverse trigonometric functions other than the principal value
- Use trigonometric functions to model real-world data
- Define the other trigonometric functions through identities
- Discover, prove, and apply the Pythagorean identities and the sum and difference identities
- Combine sinusoidal graphs to create periodic functions

CHAPTER 10 Trigonometric Functions

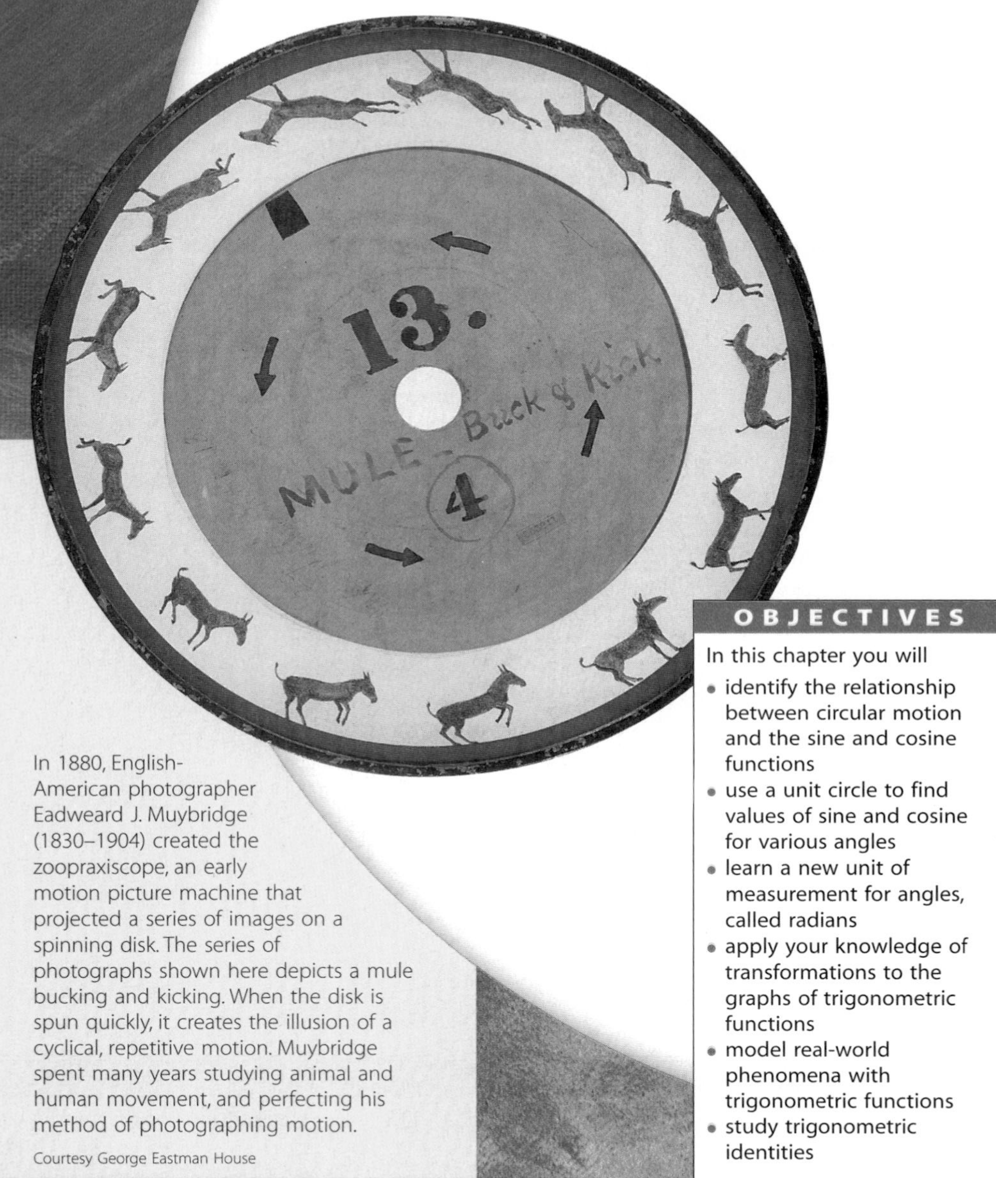

In 1880, English-American photographer Eadweard J. Muybridge (1830–1904) created the zoopraxiscope, an early motion picture machine that projected a series of images on a spinning disk. The series of photographs shown here depicts a mule bucking and kicking. When the disk is spun quickly, it creates the illusion of a cyclical, repetitive motion. Muybridge spent many years studying animal and human movement, and perfecting his method of photographing motion.

Courtesy George Eastman House

OBJECTIVES

In this chapter you will

- identify the relationship between circular motion and the sine and cosine functions
- use a unit circle to find values of sine and cosine for various angles
- learn a new unit of measurement for angles, called radians
- apply your knowledge of transformations to the graphs of trigonometric functions
- model real-world phenomena with trigonometric functions
- study trigonometric identities

To understand the word *zoopraxiscope,* break it down into parts. *Zoo-* means "animal," *praxis* means "action," and *-scope* means "instrument for viewing." So the word *zoopraxiscope* means "instrument for viewing an animal in action."

The machine was invented after Leland Stanford (1824–1893), former governor of California and founder of Stanford University, commissioned Muybridge to photograph his horse. As legend has it, Stanford wanted to settle a bet that a galloping horse lifts all hooves off the ground at the same time. After showing that a horse does indeed lift all four hooves off the ground, Muybridge continued to photograph things in motion. He eventually had the idea to transfer a series of photographs onto a disk that could be rotated, and he created the zoopraxiscope, one of the first motion picture machines.

[Ask] "How does the zoopraxiscope relate to the sine function?" [Like a sinusoidal function, the machine's motion picture is cyclic.] "What is the period of the zoopraxiscope?" [one cycle through the photographs, or 360°]

LESSON

10.1 Defining the Circular Functions

It is by will alone I set my mind in motion.

MENTAT CHANT

Many phenomena are predictable because they are repetitive, or cyclical. The water depths caused by the tides, the motion of a person on a swing, your height above ground as you ride a Ferris wheel, and the number of hours of daylight each day throughout the year are all examples of cyclical patterns. In this lesson you will discover how to model phenomena like these with the sine and cosine functions.

In *Light Graphs: Winter Solstice 2000,* American photographer Erika Blumenfeld (b 1971) used Polaroid photos, placed together in a grid pattern, to show the amount of light present every minute, from sunrise to sunset, on the shortest day of the year.

Science CONNECTION

High and low ocean tides repeat in a continuous cycle, with two high tides and two low tides every 24.84 hours. The highest tide is an effect of the gravitational pull of the Moon, which causes a dome of water to travel under the Moon as it orbits Earth. The entire Earth experiences the Moon's gravitational pull, but because water is less rigid than land, it flows more easily in response to this force. The lowest tide occurs when this dome of water moves away from the shoreline. There are several theories about what causes the second high tide each day. For more information about tides, see the links at www.keymath.com/DAA .

The circle at right has radius r and center at the origin. A central angle of t degrees is shown. You can use your knowledge of right triangle trigonometry to write the equations $\sin t = \frac{y}{r}$ and $\cos t = \frac{x}{r}$.

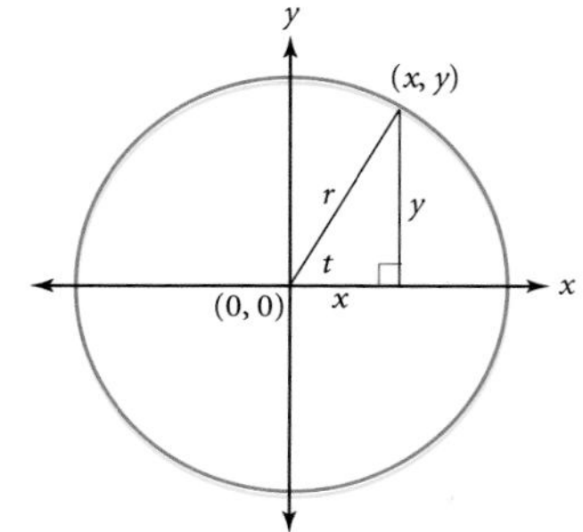

In this investigation you'll see how to use the sine and cosine functions to model circular motion.

NCTM STANDARDS

CONTENT		PROCESS	
✓	Number		Problem Solving
✓	Algebra	✓	Reasoning
✓	Geometry	✓	Communication
✓	Measurement	✓	Connections
	Data/Probability	✓	Representation

LESSON OBJECTIVES

- Identify the relationships between trigonometric ratios and the circular functions
- Use the unit circle to find the values of sine and cosine functions for various angles, including those with measures greater than 90°
- Find the reference angle and draw the reference triangle
- Identify a periodic function and find its period
- Understand that coterminal angles have the same trigonometric value

LESSON 10.1

PLANNING

LESSON OUTLINE

One day:

20 min	Investigation
5 min	Example A
5 min	Example B
5 min	Sharing
10 min	Exercises

MATERIALS

- Defining Circular Functions (T), *optional*
- Calculator Notes 3B, 8A, 10A
- Sketchpad demonstration Sine and Cosine, *optional*

TEACHING

This lesson introduces functions that extend the sine and cosine ratios to all real numbers. Exercise 16, which reviews trigonometric ratios, might serve as a warm-up.

INTRODUCTION

You might use the Defining Circular Functions transparency, the Sketchpad demonstration Sine and Cosine, or Calculator Note 10A.

[ESL] A *phenomenon* (plural *phenomena*) is an observable fact or event.

One Step

Pose this problem: "A huge Ferris wheel has a 100-meter diameter, takes 15 minutes to complete a full rotation, and reaches a maximum height of 112.5 meters. Sketch a graph showing the height of a rider as a function of time. Exactly how high will the rider be after 10 minutes? When will the rider be at $\frac{2}{3}$ the maximum height?" To find the exact

One Step (continued)
height, students can use triangle trigonometry. **[Alert]** Students might not recognize that the height as you ride a Ferris wheel corresponds to the y-coordinate.

During Sharing, bring out how the unit circle can be used to extend sine and cosine ratios to functions in order to model periodic phenomena. Define a *periodic function* and its *period.*

Guiding the Investigation

These parametric equations require no previous experience. If you skipped Lessons 8.1 and 8.2, however, you might demonstrate how to use Parametric mode on graphing calculators or hand out Calculator Note 8A.

[Alert] Students thinking of bearings may want to measure angles clockwise from the vertical rather than counterclockwise from the positive ray of the horizontal axis.

Step 2 x- and y-values can be found by tracing on the calculator or by substituting values of t into the equations for x and y.

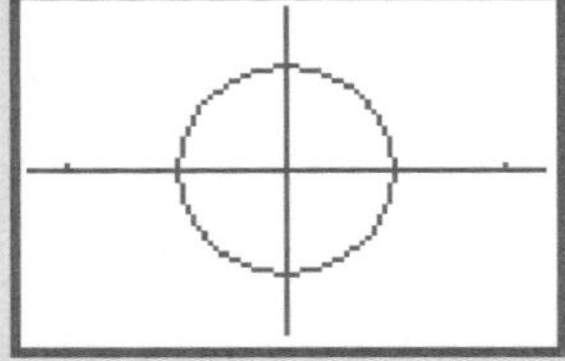

$[-2.35, 2.35, 1, -1.55, 1.55, 1]$

Step 3 After 360°, the table values repeat. The x- and y-values are cyclical. For degree values in Quadrant I, the x- and y-values are positive, in Quadrant II, the x-values are negative and y-values are positive, in Quadrant III, the x-values are negative and y-values are negative, and in Quadrant IV, the x-values ar positive and y-values are negative. As x-values increase, y-values decrease, and vice versa. The pairing of x- and y-values is always the same. That is, ± 0.866 is always paired with ± 0.5, and so on.

Investigation
Paddle Wheel

Procedure Note

1. Set your calculator in *degree* and *parametric* modes.
2. Graph the equations in a friendly window with a factor of $\frac{1}{2}$. Use t-values of $0° \le t \le 900°$ and t-step 15°. [▸ See **Calculator Note 10A.** ◂]

While swimming along, a frog reaches out and grabs onto the rim of a paddle wheel with radius 1 m. The center of the wheel is at water level. The frog, clinging tightly to the wheel, is immediately lifted from the surface of the river.

Step 1 60° each minute, 1° each second

Step 1 The wheel spins slowly counterclockwise at a rate of one rotation every 6 minutes. Through how many degrees does the frog rotate each minute? Each second?

Step 2 Follow the procedure note to graph the parametric equations $x = \cos t$ and $y = \sin t$. Sketch this graph, and explain how to find the x- and y-values of any point on the graph.

Step 3 Create a table recording the frog's x- and y-positions every 15°, relative to the center of the wheel. Use domain $0° \le t \le 510°$. Note that the wheel is turning through 1° per second, so the number of degrees equals the number of seconds. Explain any patterns you find in your table values.

Step 4a $(-0.707, 0.707)$; 135 s, 495 s, 855 s

Step 4b 210 s, 330 s, 570 s, 690 s, 930 s, 1050 s

Step 4c $-1 \le y \le 1$, $-1 \le x \le 1$

Step 4 Answer these questions by looking for patterns in your table.

a. What is the frog's location after 1215°, or 1215 s? When, during the first three rotations of the wheel, is the frog at that same location?

b. When is the frog at a height of -0.5 m during the first three rotations?

c. What are the maximum and minimum x- and y-values?

Step 5 Plot data in the form (t, x) to create a graph of the function $x = \cos t$. Use domain $0° \le t \le 360°$. Plot data in the form (t, y) on a different graph to create a graph of the function $y = \sin t$. How do these graphs compare? How can you use these graphs to find the frog's position at any time? Why do you think the sine and cosine functions are sometimes called circular functions?

A circle with radius 1 unit centered at the origin is called a unit circle. While using the unit circle created during the investigation, you discovered that values for sine and cosine repeat in a regular pattern. When output values of a function repeat at regular intervals, the function is **periodic.** The **period** of a function is the smallest distance between values of the independent variable before the cycle begins to repeat.

t	x	y	t	x	y	t	x	y	t	x	y
0	1	0	135	−0.707	0.707	270	0	−1	405	0.707	0.707
15	0.966	0.259	150	−0.866	0.5	285	0.259	−0.966	420	0.5	0.866
30	0.866	0.5	165	−0.966	0.259	300	0.5	−0.866	435	0.259	0.966
45	0.707	0.707	180	−1	0	315	0.707	−0.707	450	0	1
60	0.5	0.866	195	−0.966	−0.259	330	0.866	−0.5	465	−0.259	0.966
75	0.259	0.966	210	−0.866	−0.5	345	0.966	−0.259	480	−0.5	0.866
90	0	1	225	−0.707	−0.707	360	1	0	495	−0.707	0.707
105	−0.259	0.966	240	−0.5	−0.866	375	0.966	0.259	510	−0.866	0.5
120	−0.5	0.866	255	−0.259	−0.966	390	0.866	0.5			

EXAMPLE A | Find the period of the cosine function.

▶ Solution

In the investigation the frog returned to the same position each time the paddle wheel made one complete rotation, or every 360°. So, a period of 360° seems reasonable. You can verify this guess by looking at a graph of $y = \cos x$.

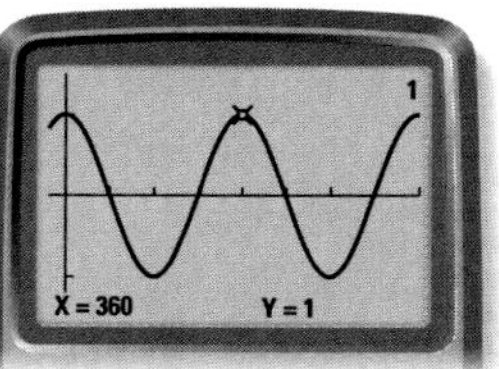

[−30, 720, 90, −1.5, 1.5, 1]

The graph shows that from $x = 0°$ to $x = 360°$, the function completes one full cycle.

Notice that the graphs of $y = \cos x$ and $y = \cos(x + 360°)$, shown below, are the same. And the table shows that $\cos 0° = \cos 360°$, $\cos 15° = \cos 375°$, and so on. So the period of cosine is 360°.

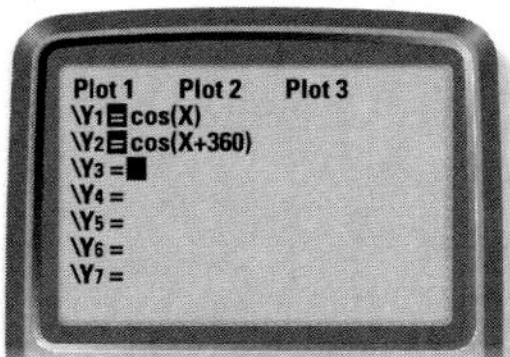

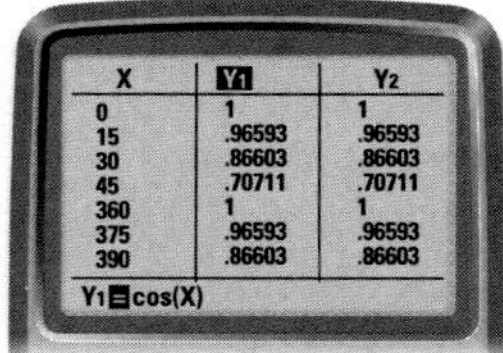

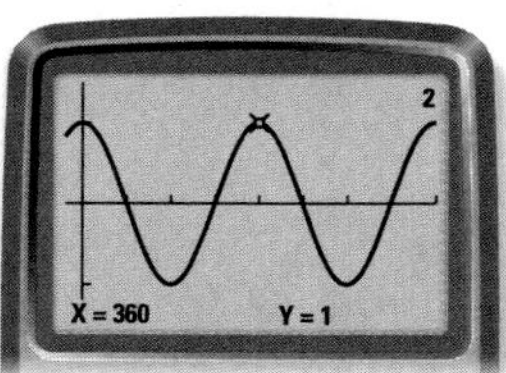

You can also verify that the sine function has a period of 360°. Use the table and graph below to convince yourself that this is true.

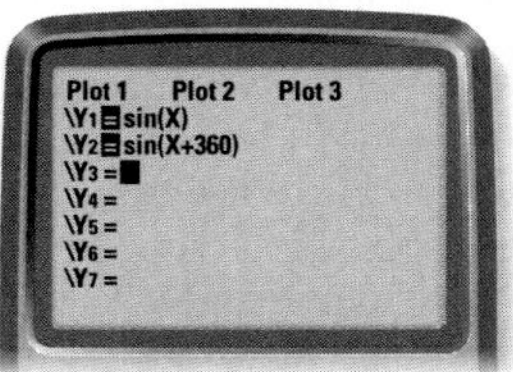

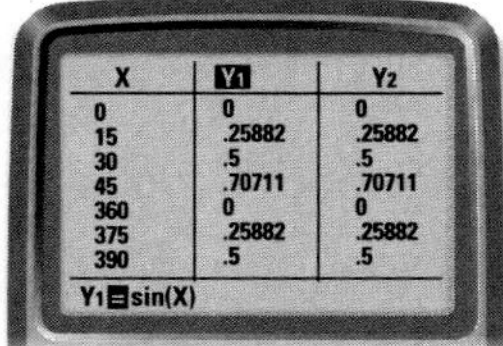

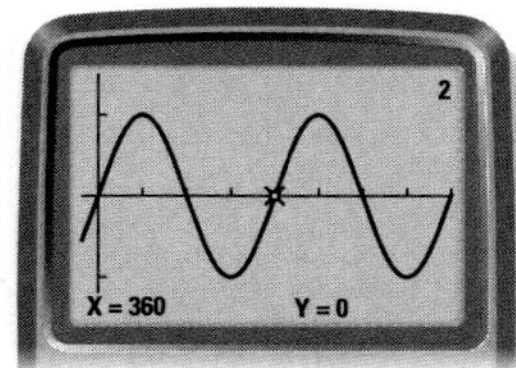

[−30, 720, 90, −1.5, 1.5, 1]

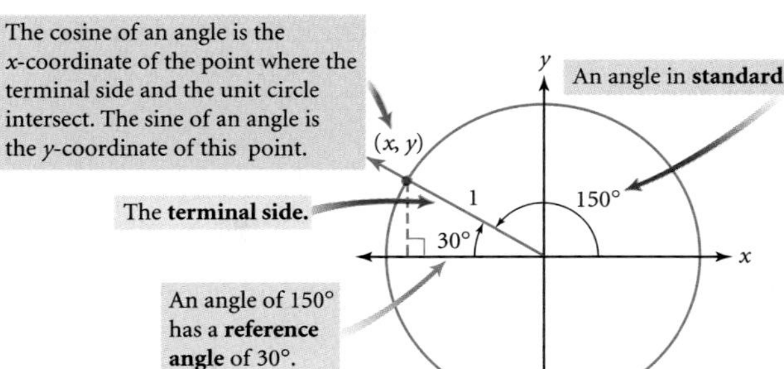

Notice that the domains of the sine and cosine functions include all positive and negative numbers. In a unit circle, angles are measured from the positive x-axis. Positive angles are measured in a counterclockwise direction, and negative angles are measured in a clockwise direction. An angle in **standard position** has one side on the positive x-axis, and the other side is called the **terminal side.**

The x- and y-coordinates of the point where the terminal side touches the unit circle determine the values of the cosine and sine of the angle. Identifying a **reference angle,** the acute angle between the terminal side and the x-axis, and drawing a **reference triangle** can help you find these values.

Guiding the Investigation (continued)

Step 3 Students can use calculator tables to obtain these values. They should then copy these values into their group's table. As needed, refer them to Calculator Note 3B for how to create tables.

Step 4 If students are consulting the graph rather than the table, point out that the instructions ask them to look for patterns in the table. For parts a and b, students can adjust the maximum calculator value of t or apply a pattern to determine the position at times outside those their graphs provide.

Step 5 The independent variable is t, the time or angle measure. Because Function mode on the calculator uses x as the independent variable, students will be more accustomed to seeing $y = \sin x$ than $y = \sin t$.

▶ EXAMPLE A

If students want to graph these equations on calculators, they'll need to change to Function mode and adjust the window. It is also possible to graph these functions in Parametric mode. For example, let $x = t$ and $y = \cos t$ with t-step 15°.

You might show students that they could determine the period by measuring from maximum to maximum or from minimum to minimum but that measuring between the x-intercepts is easier.

Sine and Cosine on the Unit Circle

[Alert] Students may not understand why the coordinates on the unit circle determine the cosine and the sine. Point out that $\cos t = \frac{y}{r}$; $r = 1$, therefore $\cos t = y$.

The dynamic algebra exploration at www.keymath.com/DAA can give students a deeper understanding of the definitions and graphs of the circular functions sine and cosine.

Step 5

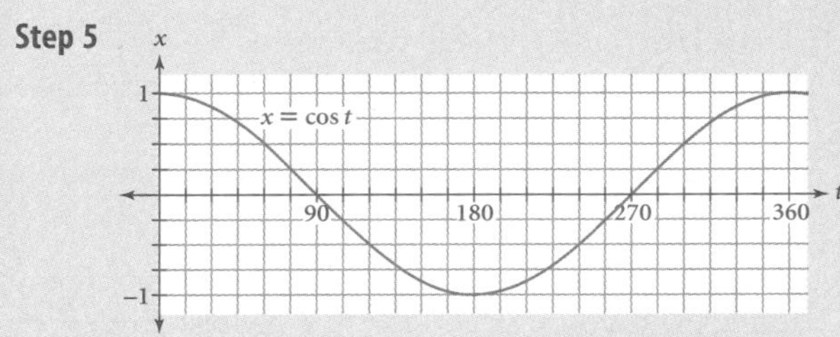

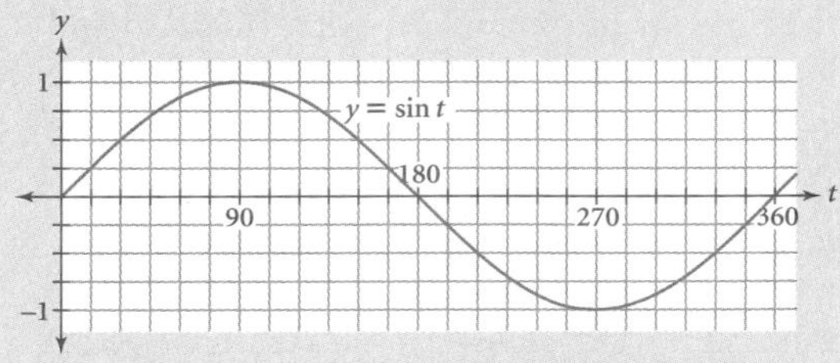

The graphs both show cyclical motion, in the same pattern. However, $\cos t$ starts at 1 and $\sin t$ starts at 0. They both pass through 1 full cycle and return to the starting location after 360°. To find the frog's position at time t, find the corresponding x-value on the first graph and y-value on the second graph.

EXAMPLE B

Find the value of the sine or cosine for each angle. Explain your process.

a. sin 150° **b.** cos 150° **c.** sin 210° **d.** cos 320°

▶ Solution

For each angle in a–d, rotate the terminal side counterclockwise from the positive x-axis, then draw a right triangle by dropping a line perpendicular to the x-axis. Then identify the reference angle.

a. For 150°, the reference angle measures 30°.

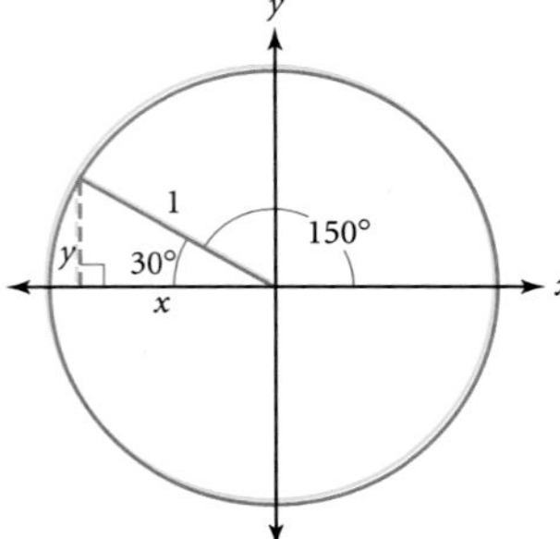

The value of y determines the sine of the angle. Use your knowledge of the ratios of side lengths in a 30°-60°-90° triangle to find the value of y. The sides have ratio $\frac{1}{2}:\frac{\sqrt{3}}{2}:1$. So, the length, y, of the leg opposite the 30° angle is $\frac{1}{2}$, and the length, x, of the adjacent leg is $\frac{\sqrt{3}}{2}$. Therefore

$$y = \sin 150° = \frac{1}{2}$$

Notice that y remains positive in Quadrant II. Use your calculator to verify that sin 150° equals 0.5.

b. You can use the same unit circle diagram as above. To find the value of cos 150°, find the value of x. As stated in part a, the length of the adjacent leg is $\frac{\sqrt{3}}{2}$. However, in the second quadrant x is negative, so

$$x = \sin 150° = -\frac{\sqrt{3}}{2}$$

The calculator gives -0.866, which is approximately equal to $-\frac{\sqrt{3}}{2}$, as a decimal approximation of cos 150°.

c. Rotate the terminal side counterclockwise 210°, then draw a right triangle by drawing a line perpendicular to the x-axis. The reference angle in this triangle again measures 30°. Because this angle is in Quadrant III, the y-value is negative, so

$$\sin 210° = -\frac{1}{2}$$

Use your calculator to verify this result.

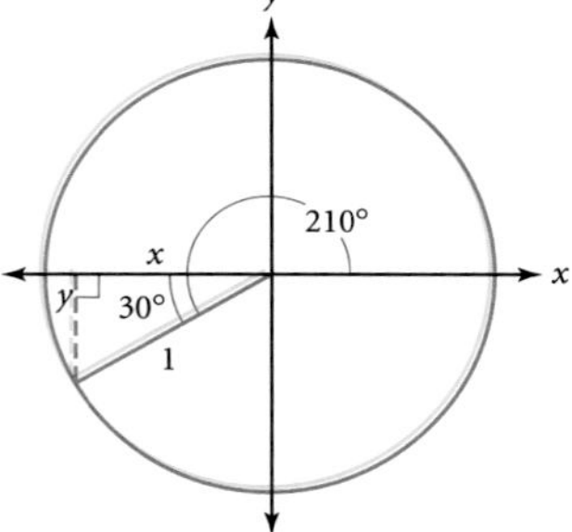

▶ EXAMPLE B

Urge students to sketch these reference angles in preparation for later lessons. Students do not have to use the quadrant numbers, but they do need to know the location of the triangles. Measures of sides along the negative axes are considered negative.

You can also show students how to trace a sine or cosine graph on a calculator to find approximate values of the functions and to check that sin 30° = sin 150° and that cos 150° = −cos 30°. You may want to discuss the difference between exact values and values estimated on the calculator.

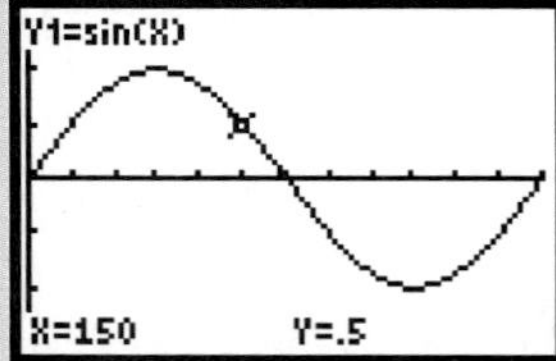

[0, 360, 30, −1.5, 1.5, 0.5]

Students can find the value in part d by tracing to 320° on a unit circle in Parametric mode. As needed, remind students that cos 320° is the x-coordinate of the point on the unit circle.

SHARING IDEAS

As students present the results of Step 5 of the investigation, ask why the graphs of the sine and cosine functions are horizontal translations of each other. The fact that *cosine* means *complement's sine* leads to the equation $\cos t = \sin(90° - t) = \sin(-(t - 90°))$, technically a reflection as well as a horizontal translation by 90°.

To give students a glimpse of the value and excitement of posing problems, encourage them to anticipate questions you might ask about the lesson, such as these.

[Ask] "Does the period of a periodic function have anything to do with the period of a pendulum?" As needed, refer students back to Lesson 4.6, where they saw the period of a pendulum—the time for one complete swing (forward and back). The location of a swinging pendulum bob (without dampening) is indeed described by a periodic function, as addressed in Lesson 10.3.

[Ask] "Are sin t and cos t ratios of side lengths of a triangle, or are they x- and y-values of points on the unit circle?" [They can be seen from either perspective. For measuring distances, they're most useful as ratios; for modeling periodic phenomena, the extension to functions is more appropriate.]

"What are some periodic phenomena besides rotating circles and pendulums?" [average rainfalls, amounts of daylight, distances of Earth from the Sun, tides, the bounce of a spring, musical sounds, gear-driven mechanisms]

To lay the groundwork for future lessons as well as to review trigonometry, **[Ask]** "What else from the study of trigonometric ratios might be extended to functions?" A good list would include the tangent ratio and the inverse functions.

d. If you draw a reference triangle for 320°, you will find a reference angle of 40°, in Quadrant IV. In this quadrant, x-values are positive. So, $\cos 320° = \cos 40°$. An angle measuring 40° is not a special angle, so you don't know its exact trigonometric values. According to the calculator, either $\cos 320°$ or $\cos 40°$ is approximately 0.766.

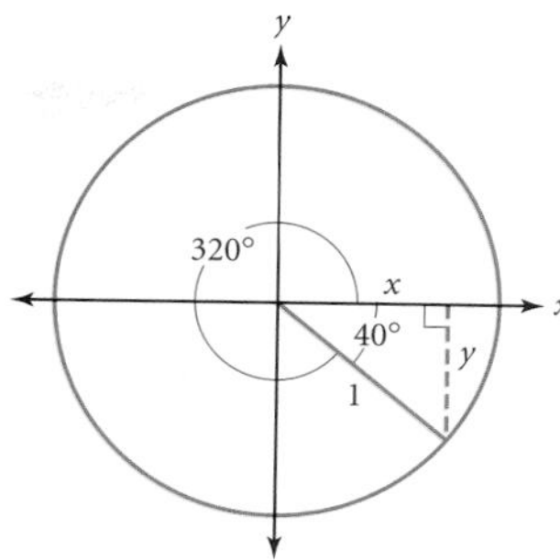

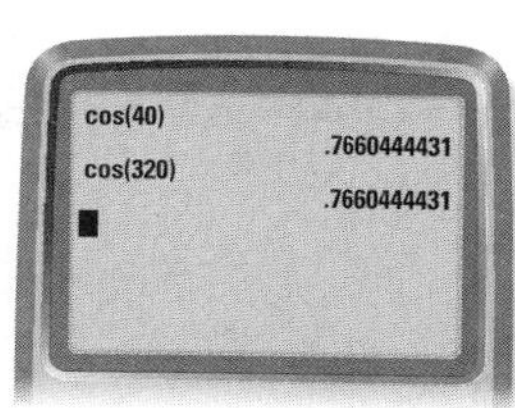

Angles in standard position are **coterminal** if they share the same terminal side. For example, the angles measuring −145°, 215°, and 575° are coterminal, as shown. Coterminal angles have the same trigonometric values. When a variable is chosen to represent the measure of an unknown angle, it is common to use a Greek letter. When you see a Greek letter like θ (theta) or α (alpha), it is likely that the variable quantity is an angle measure.

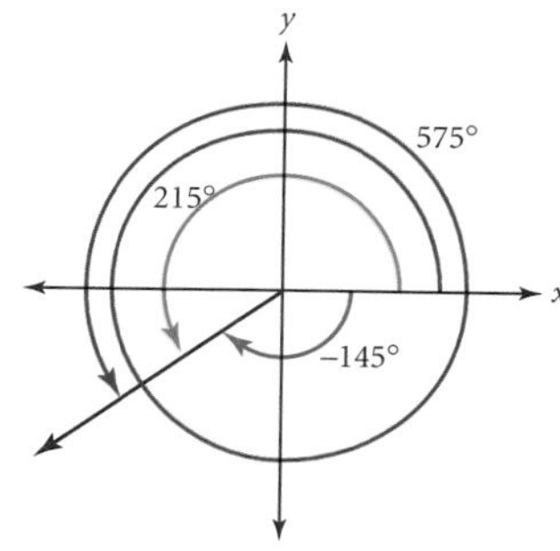

Exercises

Practice Your Skills

1. After 300 s, the paddle wheel in the investigation has rotated 300°. Draw a reference triangle and find the frog's height at this time.

2. Use your calculator to find each value, approximated to four decimal places. Then draw diagrams in a unit circle to show the meaning of the value. Name the reference angle.

   a. $\sin(-175°)$ b. $\cos 147°$ c. $\sin 280°$ d. $\cos 310°$ e. $\sin(-47°)$

3. The functions $y = \sin x$ and $y = \cos x$ are periodic. How many cycles of each function are pictured?

   a. 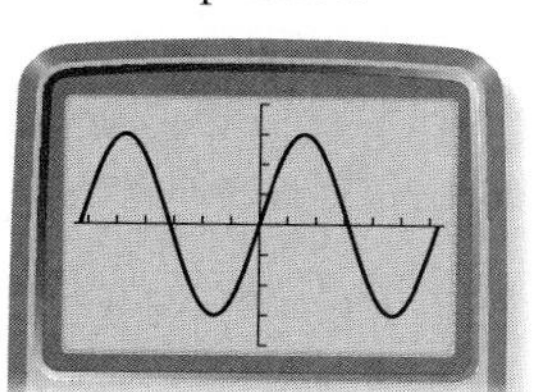 2

   b. 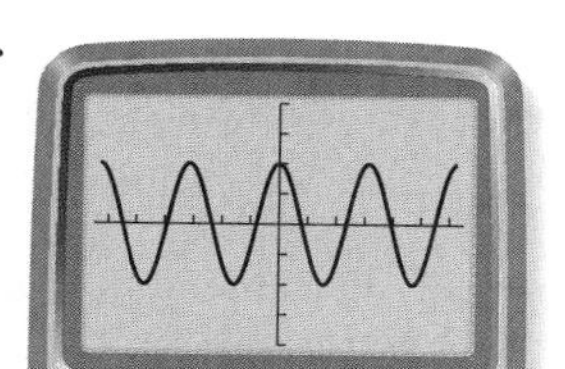 4

Assessing Progress
You can assess students' understanding of the trigonometric ratios and their ability to plot points and to follow detailed instructions.

Closing the Lesson

The sine and cosine functions are extensions of the trigonometric ratios and are used to model **periodic** phenomena. The period of one of these functions is the distance between corresponding points in the cycles, for example, between maximums. Because both $y = \sin t$ and $y = \cos t$ have period 360°, the period of a function that cycles n times in 360° is $\frac{360°}{n}$. You can evaluate the functions by drawing **reference triangles** in standard position and finding the trigonometric ratio of the angle at the origin.

BUILDING UNDERSTANDING

Students practice evaluating and applying the circular functions.

ASSIGNING HOMEWORK

Essential	1–6
Performance assessment	7–15
Portfolio	15
Group	13, 14
Review	16–20

MATERIALS

- compasses or circle templates

Helping with the Exercises

Exercise 1 This exercise relies on students' knowledge of the investigation.

1.

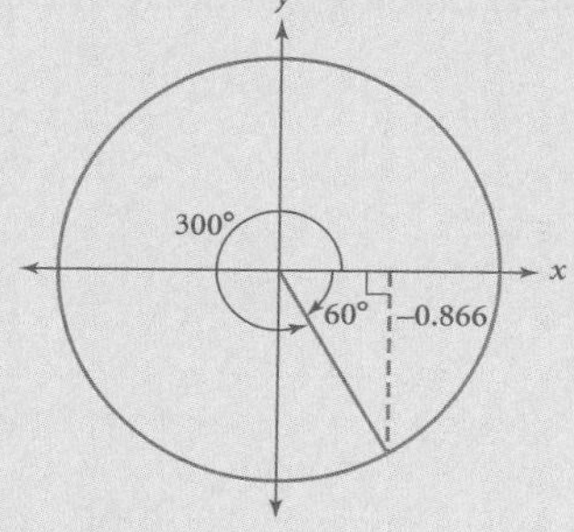

approximately −0.866 m

2a. −0.0872; $\sin(-175°) = -\sin 5°$; reference angle 5°

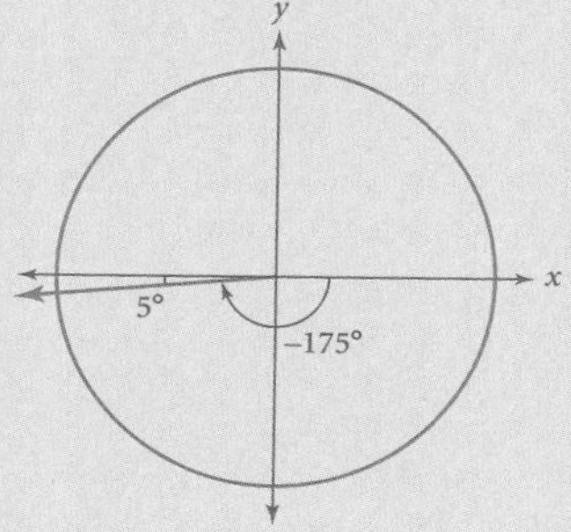

See page 899 for answers to Exercise 2b–e.

4. Create a sine or cosine graph, and trace to find the value of each expression.

a. sin 120° **b.** sin (−120°) **c.** cos (−150°) **d.** cos 150°

5. Which of the following functions are periodic? For each periodic function, identify the period.

a. periodic, 180°

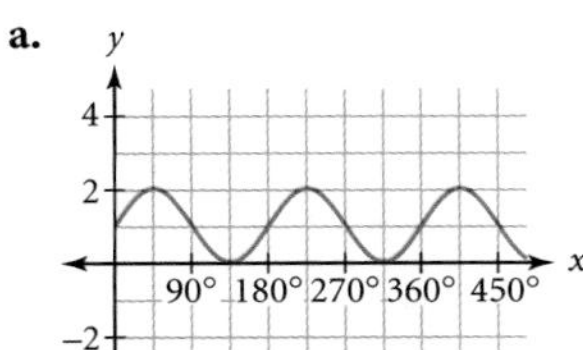

b. not periodic

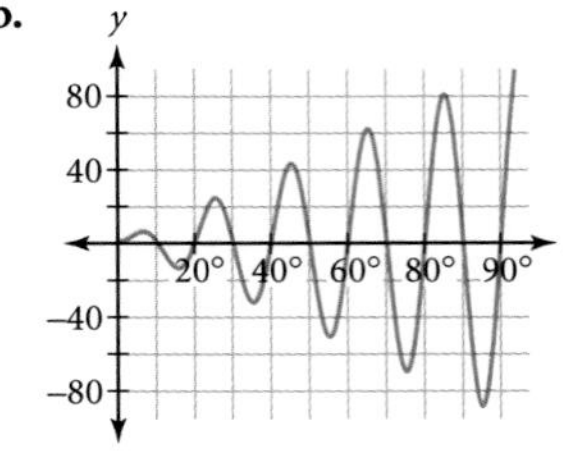

c. periodic, 90°

y; 4; 2; −2; −4; x; 90° 180° 270° 360° 450°

d. periodic, 180°

y; 4; 2; −2; −4; x; 90° 180° 270° 360° 450°

Reason and Apply

6. Identify an angle θ that is coterminal with the given angle. Use domain $0° \le \theta \le 360°$.

a. −25° $\theta = 335°$ **b.** −430° $\theta = 290°$ **c.** 435° $\theta = 75°$ **d.** 1195° $\theta = 115°$

7. For each Quadrant, I–IV, shown at right, identify whether the values of $\cos\theta$ and $\sin\theta$ are positive or negative.

Quadrant II; Quadrant I; Quadrant III; Quadrant IV; x; y

8. Carefully sketch a graph of the function $y = \sin x$ over the domain $-360° \le x \le 360°$. Identify all values of x in this interval for which $\sin x = 0$.

9. Carefully sketch a graph of the function $y = \cos x$ over the domain $-360° \le x \le 360°$. Identify all values of x in this interval for which $\cos x = 0$.

10. Suppose $\sin\theta \approx -0.7314$ and $180° \le \theta \le 270°$.

a. Locate the point where the terminal side of θ intersects the unit circle.

b. Find θ and $\cos\theta$. $\theta \approx 227°$; $\cos\theta = -0.682$

c. What other angle α has the same cosine value? Use domain $0° \le \alpha \le 360°$. $\alpha = 360° - \theta \approx 133°$

11. Find an angle in standard position, θ, for a plane flying on these bearings. Use domain $-180° \le \theta \le 180°$.

a. 105° $\theta = -15°$ **b.** 325° $\theta = 125°$ **c.** 180° $\theta = -90°$ **d.** 42° $\theta = 48°$

Exercise 4 You might ask students to draw the reference triangles. Be tolerant if a student interprets the instructions as accepting a sine or cosine graph for any of the functions. The property $\cos x = \sin\left(\frac{\pi}{2} - x\right)$ allows you to find a value of either the sine or the cosine function from the other function.

4a.

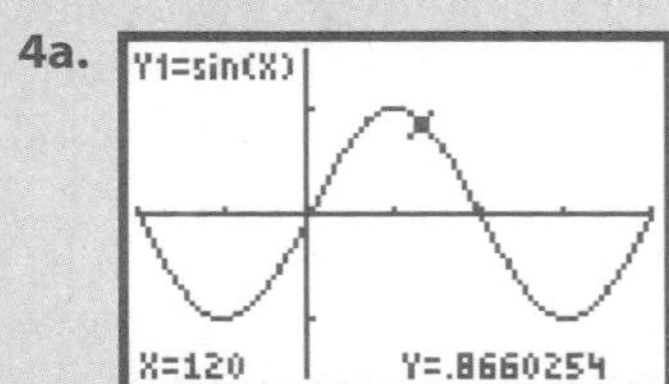

[−180, 360, 90, −1.55, 1.55, 1]

4b.

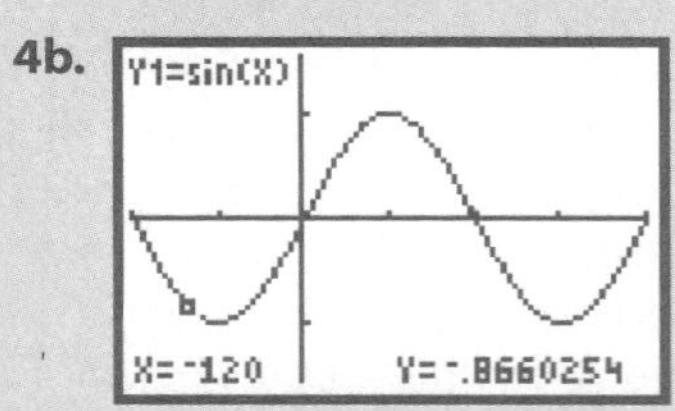

[−180, 360, 90, −1.55, 1.55, 1]

4c.

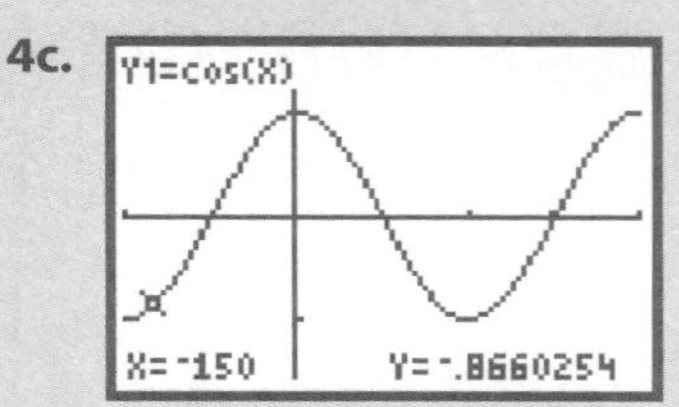

[−180, 360, 90, −1.55, 1.55, 1]

4d.

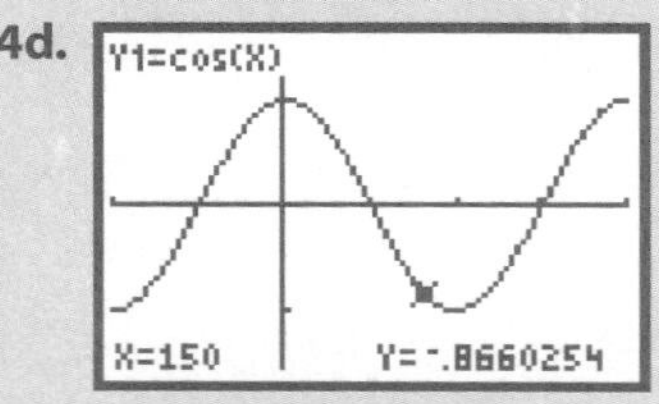

[−180, 360, 90, −1.55, 1.55, 1]

Exercise 5 If students are having difficulty, ask what the period would be if the curve cycled twice in 360° or three times in 360°. [The period is 360° divided by the number of cycles.]

7. Quadrant I: $\cos\theta$ and $\sin\theta$ are positive; Quadrant II: $\cos\theta$ is negative and $\sin\theta$ is positive; Quadrant III: $\cos\theta$ and $\sin\theta$ are negative; Quadrant IV: $\cos\theta$ is positive and $\sin\theta$ is negative.

Exercise 8 [Ask] "What is the range of the function $y = \sin x$?" $[-1 \le y \le 1]$

8.

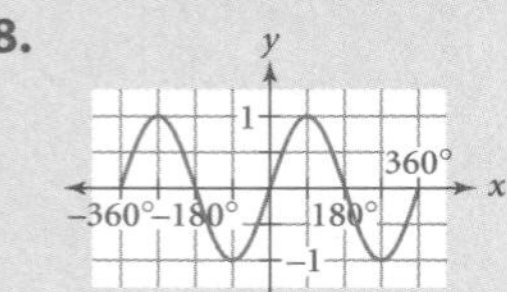

$x = \{-360°, -180°, 0°, 180°, 360°\}$

Exercise 9 [Ask] "What is the range of the function $y = \cos x$?" $[-1 \le y \le 1]$

9.

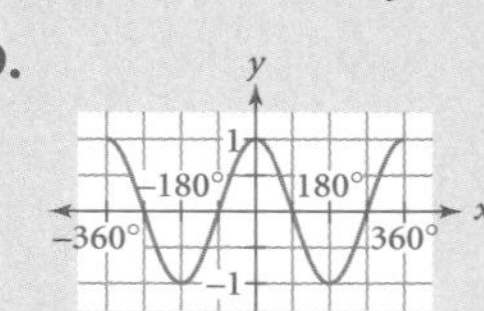

$x = \{-270°, -90°, 90°, 270°\}$

12. Find $\sin\theta$ and $\cos\theta$ for each angle in standard position described. (*Hint:* You may want to use the Pythagorean Theorem.)

a. The terminal side of angle θ passes through the point (2, 3).

b. The terminal side of angle θ passes through the point (−2, 3).

13. Find each angle θ with the given trigonometric value. Use domain $0 \le \theta \le 360°$.

a. $\cos\theta = -\frac{\sqrt{3}}{2}$ b. $\cos\theta = -\frac{\sqrt{2}}{2}$ c. $\sin\theta = -\frac{3}{5}$ d. $\sin\theta = 1$

14. ***Mini-Investigation*** Make a table of the values of $\sin\theta$, $\cos\theta$, $\tan\theta$, and $\frac{\sin\theta}{\cos\theta}$, using values of θ at intervals of 30° over the domain $0° \le \theta \le 360°$. What do you notice? Use the definitions of trigonometric ratios to explain your conjecture.

15. **APPLICATION** For the past several hundred years, astronomers have kept track of the number of sunspots. This table shows the average number of sunspots each year from 1972 to 1999.

Year	Number of sunspots	Year	Number of sunspots	Year	Number of sunspots
1972	68.9	1982	115.9	1992	94.3
1973	38.0	1983	66.6	1993	54.6
1974	34.5	1984	45.9	1994	29.9
1975	15.5	1985	17.9	1995	17.5
1976	12.6	1986	3.4	1996	8.6
1977	27.5	1987	29.4	1997	21.5
1978	92.5	1988	100.2	1998	64.3
1979	155.4	1989	157.6	1999	93.3
1980	154.6	1990	142.6		
1981	140.4	1991	145.7		

(*www.solarmovie.com*)

a. Make a scatter plot of the data and describe any patterns that you notice.

b. Estimate the length of a cycle.

c. Predict the next period of maximum solar activity after 1999.

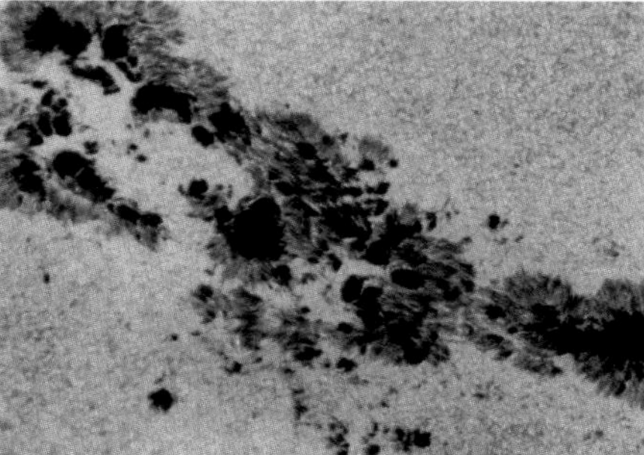

This photo of several sunspots shows powerful eruptions occurring on the Sun's surface.

Science CONNECTION

Sunspots are dark regions on the Sun's surface that are cooler than the surrounding areas. They are caused by magnetic fields on the Sun and seem to follow short-term and long-term cycles.

Sunspot activity affects conditions on Earth. The particles emitted by the Sun during periods of high sunspot activity disrupt radio communications, and have an impact on Earth's magnetic field and climate. Some scientists theorize that ice ages are caused by relatively low solar activity over a period of time.

Exercise 10a Students may consult a calculator table, trace on the unit circle in Parametric mode, or use the Pythagorean Theorem.

10a.

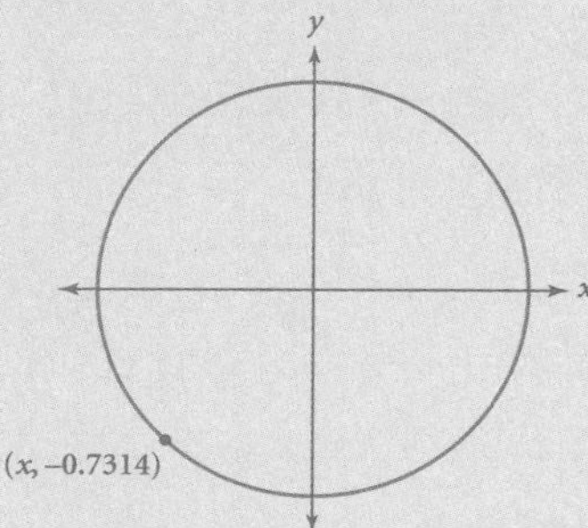

Exercise 11 [Alert] Students may not remember that a bearing is an angle measured clockwise from north.

12a. $\sin A = \frac{3}{\sqrt{13}}$, $\cos A = \frac{2}{\sqrt{13}}$

12b. $\sin A = \frac{3}{\sqrt{13}}$, $\cos A = \frac{-2}{\sqrt{13}}$

Exercise 13 These angle measures can be found by drawing the reference triangle in the appropriate quadrant, recognizing the special triangle, and finding the angle with respect to the positive x-axis. Inverses of trigonometric functions are a topic of Lesson 10.4.

13a. $\theta = 150°$ and $\theta = 210°$

13b. $\theta = 135°$ and $\theta = 225°$

13c. $\theta \approx 217°$ and $\theta \approx 323°$

13d. $\theta = 90°$

15a.

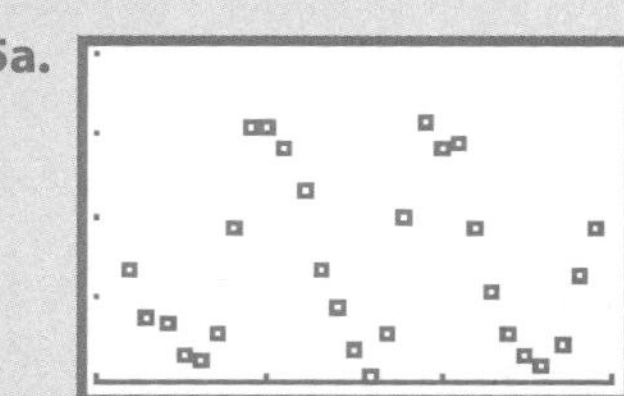

[1970, 2000, 10, 0, 200, 50]

The data are cyclical and appear to have a shape like a sine or cosine curve.

15b. 10–11 yr

Exercise 15c [Language] The phrase *maximum solar activity* refers to a period in the solar cycle with a large number of sunspots, such as occurred in 1979–1982 and 1988–1991.

15c. 2001

MAKING THE CONNECTION

The number and position of sunspots varies according to the approximately 11-year solar cycle. At the point in the cycle with the minimum number of sunspots, sunspots appear close to the solar equator. At the high point in the cycle, sunspots appear closer to the poles. The magnetic activity in the sunspots, however, has a 22-year cycle. Most sunspots have one magnetic polarity for a period of 11 years and then switch to the opposite polarity for 11 years. Scientists do not yet know why sunspots follow this cycle.

See page 899 for answer to Exercise 14.

Exercise 16 You might use this exercise to review trigonometric ratios as a warm-up for this lesson.

16a. $h = 1.5 + 20 \tan A$

16b. 33.5 m

16c. 16.0 m and 18.3 m

16d. 23°

17a. 43,200 s

17b. 4.4 ft/s

18. $C \approx 29.7$ units, $A \approx 70.1$ square units

Exercise 19 This exercise reviews Lesson 9.8, which was optional.

19a. $\frac{3}{x-4}$

19b. 2

19c. $\frac{2(3+a)}{6-a}$

20. $f(x) = \frac{2(x+2)(x-5)}{(x+4)(x-1)}$

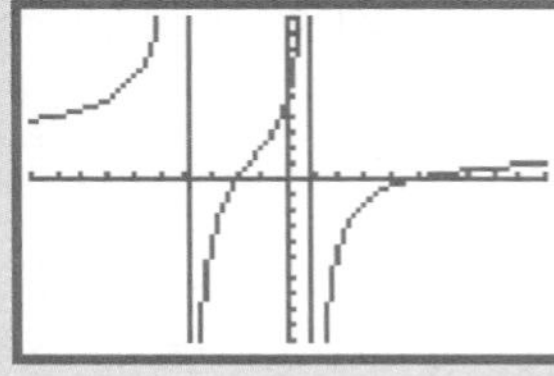

[−10, 10, 1, −10, 10, 1]

EXTENSIONS

A. Use Take Another Look activity 1 on page 627.

B. If you didn't use it in class, ask students to explore and answer the questions on the Sketchpad demonstration Sine and Cosine.

Review

8.3 **16.** Annie is standing on a canyon floor 20 m from the base of a cliff. Looking through her binoculars, she sees the remains of ancient cliff dwellings in the cliff face. Annie holds her binoculars at eye level, 1.5 m above the ground.

a. Write an equation that relates the angle at which she holds the binoculars to the height above ground of the object she sees.

b. The top of the cliff is at an angle of 58° above horizontal when viewed from where Annie is standing. How high is the cliff, to the nearest tenth of a meter?

c. Lower on the cliff, Annie sees ruins at angles of 36° and 40° from the horizontal. How high are the ruins?

d. There is a nest of cliff swallows in the cliff face, 10 m above the canyon floor. At what angle should Annie point her binoculars to observe the nest? Round your answer to the nearest degree.

The Cliff Palace in Mesa Verde National Park, Colorado, was constructed by Ancestral Puebloan people around 1200 C.E.

0.3 **17.** Convert to the specified units using ratios. For example, to convert 0.17 meter to inches:

$$0.17 \not{m} \cdot \frac{100 \not{cm}}{1 \not{m}} \cdot \frac{1 \text{ in.}}{2.54 \not{cm}} \approx 6.7 \text{ in.}$$

a. 0.500 day to seconds

b. 3.0 mi/h to ft/s (There are 5280 feet per mile.)

9.5 **18.** Find the circumference and area of the circle with equation $2x^2 + 2y^2 - 2x + 7y - 38 = 0$.

9.8 **19.** Rewrite each expression as a single rational expression in factored form.

a. $\frac{x+1}{x-4} - \frac{x+2}{x+4} + \frac{4x}{16-x^2}$

b. $\frac{2x^2-2}{x^2+3x+2} \cdot \frac{x^2-x-6}{x^2-4x+3}$

c. $\frac{1+\frac{a}{3}}{1-\frac{a}{6}}$

9.8 **20.** Write an equation for a rational function, $f(x)$, that has vertical asymptotes $x = -4$ and $x = 1$, horizontal asymptote $y = 2$, and zeros $x = -2$ and $x = 5$. Check your answer by graphing the equation on your calculator.

LESSON

10.2

Radian Measure and Arc Length

The measure of our intellectual capacity is the capacity to feel less and less satisfied with our answers to better and better problems.

C. WEST CHURCHMAN

The choice to divide a circle into 360 degrees is rooted in the history of mathematics. The number 360 actually has no connection to any fundamental properties of a circle. In this lesson you will learn about a different angle measure.

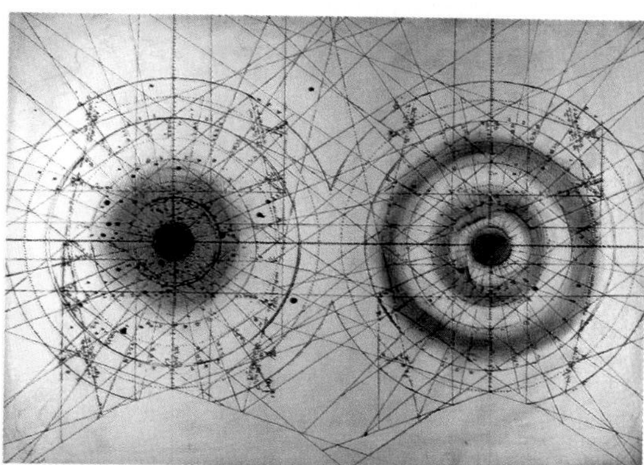

American artist Penny Cerling (b 1946) created this piece, titled *Black Hole and Big Bang* (1999), using pen, ink, and oil on wood. Cerling explores themes of science and nature in many of her works.

History CONNECTION

Over 5000 years ago, the Sumerians in Mesopotamia used a base-60 number system. They may have chosen this system because numbers like 30, 60, and 360 can be evenly divided by many numbers. The Babylonians and Egyptians then borrowed this system and divided the circle into 360 degrees. The Egyptians also devised the symbol for degrees and went on to divide both the Earth's equator and north-south great circles into 360 degrees, inventing latitude and longitude lines. The Greek astronomer and mathematican Hipparchus of Rhodes (ca. 190–120 B.C.E.) is credited with introducing the Babylonian division of the circle to Greece and producing a table of chords, the earliest known trigonometric table. Hipparchus is often called the "founder of trigonometry."

Investigation

A Circle of Radians

Recall from geometry that the measure of an arc is not the same as the length of an arc. For example, all 90° arcs have the same measure, but they can have different lengths.

To find the length of an arc, you need to know the radius of the circle, as well as the measure of the central angle intercepted by the arc.

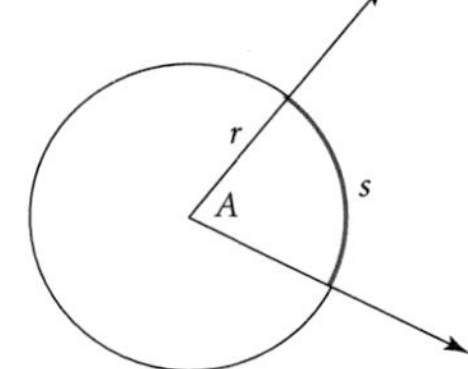

LESSON

10.2

PLANNING

LESSON OUTLINE

One day:

15 min	Investigation
10 min	Sharing
5 min	Examples A, B
5 min	Example C
10 min	Exercises

MATERIALS

- Arcs and Radii (W) for One Step
- Calculator Note 10B

TEACHING

In the investigation students learn the concept of radians and discover formulas for arc length and the area of a sector.

One Step

Hand out the Arcs and Radii worksheet and pose this problem: "A 40° angle has its vertex at the center of several circles. Is there a relationship between the radii of the arcs intercepted by the angle and the number of radius lengths in those arcs?" As students decide that the number of radii in the arcs' lengths is the same for all the circles, ask for that number $\left(\frac{2\pi}{9}\right)$ and encourage them to generalize to angles of all measures. During Sharing, define *radian measure* and point out that it counts the number of radii (as opposed to the number of degrees).

NCTM STANDARDS

CONTENT		PROCESS	
✓	Number	✓	Problem Solving
✓	Algebra	✓	Reasoning
✓	Geometry	✓	Communication
✓	Measurement	✓	Connections
	Data/Probability		Representation

LESSON OBJECTIVES

- Introduce angle measure in radians and convert between radians and degrees
- Understand a 1-radian angle as the angle whose intercepted arc is the length of the radius
- Find angular speed, the amount of rotation in radians (or degrees) per unit of time
- Learn formulas for arc length and the area of a sector in terms of radians

Guiding the Investigation

[Language] You might need to review the definition of *intercepted arc* as the arc of a circle whose endpoints are on the sides of a central angle.

Step 1 To save time, you might assign different groups different figures and have them share their results.

As needed, help students make the connection that the ratio of the central angle measure to 360° is the ratio of the arc length to the circumference. That is, $\frac{A}{360°} = \frac{s}{c}$. Help students notice the instruction to give exact answers in terms of π rather than multiplying out by a decimal approximation.

Steps 1 and 2

A (deg)	r (cm)	s (cm)	θ (radians)
90	3	$\frac{6\pi}{4} = \frac{3\pi}{2}$	$\frac{\pi}{2}$
90	6	$\frac{12\pi}{4} = 3\pi$	$\frac{\pi}{2}$
180	2	$\frac{4\pi}{2} = 2\pi$	π
180	4	$\frac{8\pi}{2} = 4\pi$	π
45	4	$\frac{8\pi}{8} = \pi$	$\frac{\pi}{4}$
45	8	$\frac{16\pi}{8} = 2\pi$	$\frac{\pi}{4}$
60	4	$\frac{8\pi}{6} = \frac{4\pi}{3}$	$\frac{\pi}{3}$
60	6	$\frac{12\pi}{6} = 2\pi$	$\frac{\pi}{3}$

Step 1 Make a table to record angle degree measure A, radius r, arc length s, and radian measure θ. You will not need to fill in the last column until Step 2.

A (deg)	r (cm)	s (cm)	θ (radians)

For each figure, use the radius to calculate the circumference of the circle. Then use the angle measure and the circumference to determine the arc length. Give exact answers in terms of π. Record your results in your table.

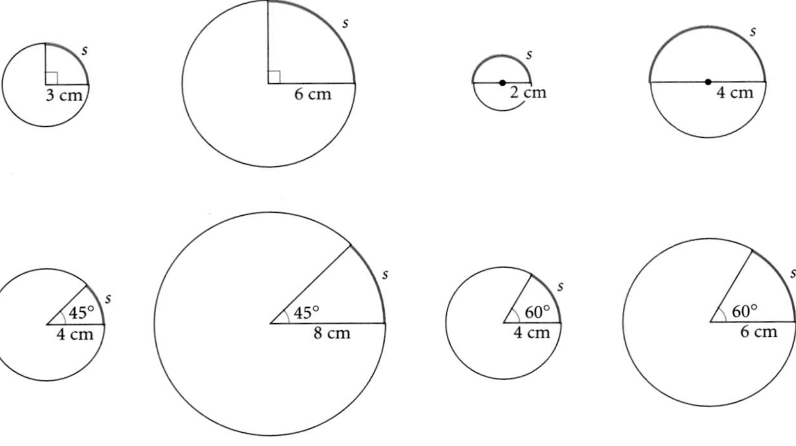

Using degrees, a full circle, or one rotation, is 360°. A half circle, or a half rotation, is 180°. A quarter rotation is 90°, and so on.

Suppose you divide a circle a different way so that one full rotation is 2π. Then a half rotation is π. A quarter rotation is $\frac{\pi}{2}$. These measures are called **radians.** As you will see in the next part of the investigation, radians have certain advantages over degrees.

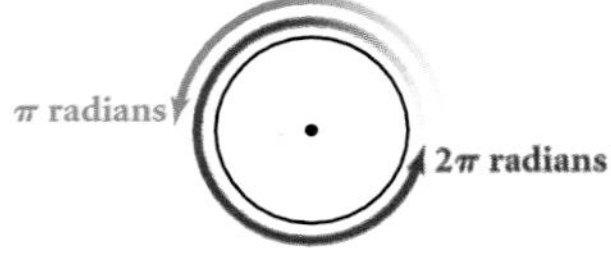

The conversion formula

$$\frac{\textit{angle in degrees}}{360} = \frac{\textit{angle in radians}}{2\pi}$$

is based on the full circle, or one rotation. You can also use an equivalent formula based on a half rotation.

$$\frac{\textit{angle in degrees}}{180} = \frac{\textit{angle in radians}}{\pi}$$

Radian measures of some common angles are irrational numbers, but you can express them as exact values in terms of π.

Step 2 Find a formula to convert degrees to radians. Convert the degree measures in your table to radians, and fill in the last column of your table. Give exact values in terms of π.

Step 3 Look for a relationship between r, s, and θ in your table. Express s in terms of r and θ. Check a few values from your table to make sure your relationship works.

Step 4 What is the advantage of radians over degrees in calculating arc length?

Radian measure is based on the properties of a circle. For this reason, it is often preferred in advanced mathematics and in physics. You can learn to recognize, compare, and use radians and degrees, just as in the past you have worked with inches and centimeters and Fahrenheit and Celsius.

Degree measures are always labeled with the symbol °. Radian measures do not need to be labeled, but they can be labeled for clarity.

EXAMPLE A Convert degrees to radians or radians to degrees.

a. $\frac{2\pi}{3}$ **b.** n radians

c. 225° **d.** $n°$

▶ Solution You can use either conversion formula. Here we will use the equivalence $180° = \pi$ radians.

a. You can think of $\frac{2\pi}{3}$ as $\frac{2}{3}(\pi)$ or $\frac{(2\pi)}{3}$. Although no units are given, it is clear that these are radians.

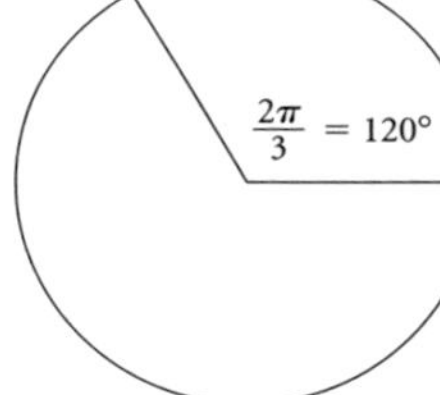

$$\frac{x}{180} = \frac{\frac{2\pi}{3}}{\pi} \text{ or } \frac{x}{180} = \frac{2}{3}$$

So, $x = 120°$. Therefore $\frac{2\pi}{3} = 120°$.

b. $\frac{x}{180} = \frac{n}{\pi}$ or $x = \frac{n}{\pi} \cdot 180$, so n radians $= \left(\frac{180n}{\pi}\right)°$.

c. $\frac{225}{180} = \frac{x}{\pi}$ or $x = \frac{225}{180} \cdot \pi = \frac{5\pi}{4}$, so $225° = \frac{5\pi}{4}$ radians.

d. $\frac{n}{180} = \frac{x}{\pi}$ or $x = \frac{n}{180} \cdot \pi$, so $n° = \frac{\pi n}{180}$ radians.

You can use the relations you found in parts b and d in Example A to convert easily between radians and degrees.

Step 2 *angle in degrees* $\cdot \frac{\pi}{180} =$ *angle in radians*

Step 3 $s = r\theta$

Step 4 The full circumference of a circle with radius 1 measures 2π. A full rotation of 360° is also 2π in radians.

Step 4 Radian measure allows immediate calculation of the length of an arc, whereas degree measure does not.

▶ EXAMPLE A

In part a, **[Ask]** "What happened to pi?"
$\left[\frac{\frac{2\pi}{3}}{\pi} = \frac{2\pi}{3} \cdot \frac{1}{\pi} = \frac{2}{3}\right]$

In part c, help students resist the urge to use a decimal approximation.

Another way to convert between degrees and radians is dimensional analysis. Dimensional analysis is a procedure based on multiplying by fractions formed of conversion factors to change units. For example, to convert 140° to radian measure, you write it as a fraction over 1 and multiply it by $\frac{\pi \text{ radians}}{180°}$, which is a fraction equal to 1.

$$\frac{140 \text{ \sout{degrees}}}{1} \cdot \frac{\pi \text{ radians}}{180 \text{ \sout{degrees}}} = \frac{140\pi \text{ radians}}{180} = \frac{7\pi}{9} \text{ radians}$$

You can use your calculator to check or approximate conversions between radians and degrees. [► See **Calculator Note 10B.** ◄]

You can also write the relationship $s = r\theta$ as $\theta = \frac{s}{r}$. So, the radian measure of a central angle, θ, is the quotient $\frac{s}{r}$, where s is the arc length and r is the radius. You can use this equation to find the length of an arc of a circle. You can also use radian measure to write a simple formula for the area of a sector.

► EXAMPLE B

The formula for arc length is the formula derived in the investigation.

[Ask] "What is the area of the remainder of the circle?" $\left[25\pi - 17.5 \approx 61.04 \text{ m}^2\right]$

EXAMPLE B

Circle O has diameter 10 m. The measure of central angle BOC is 1.4 radians. What is the length of its intercepted arc, $\overset{\frown}{BC}$? What is the area of the shaded sector?

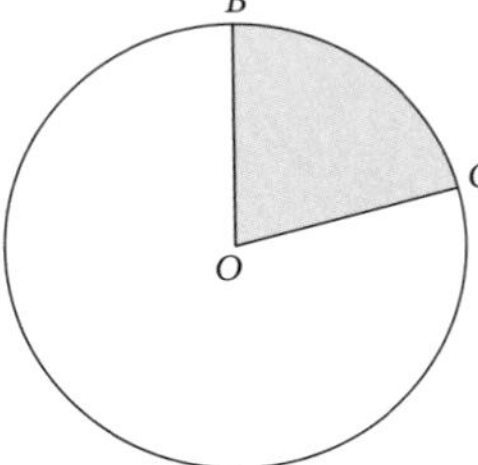

► Solution

In the formula $s = r\theta$, substitute 5 for r and 1.4 for θ, and solve for s. The length of $\overset{\frown}{BC}$ is $5 \cdot 1.4$, or 7 m.

The ratio of the area of the sector to the total area of the circle is the same as the ratio of the measure of $\angle BOC$ to 2π radians.

$$\frac{A_{\text{sector}}}{A_{\text{circle}}} = \frac{1.4}{2\pi}$$

The area of the circle is πr^2, or 25π m^2.

$$\frac{A_{\text{sector}}}{25\pi} = \frac{1.4}{2\pi}$$

Solving the equation, you find that the area of the sector is 17.5 m^2.

As you saw in the example, the area of a sector with radius r and central angle θ can be found using the proportion

$$\frac{A_{\text{sector}}}{\pi r^2} = \frac{\theta}{2\pi}$$

You can rewrite this relationship as

$$A_{\text{sector}} = \frac{\pi r^2 \theta}{2\pi} = \frac{r^2\theta}{2} = \frac{1}{2}r^2\theta$$

Length of an Arc and Area of a Sector

When a central angle, θ, of a circle with radius r is measured in radians, the length of the intercepted arc, s, is given by the equation

$$s = r\theta$$

and the area of the intercepted sector, A, is given by the equation

$$A = \frac{1}{2}r^2\theta$$

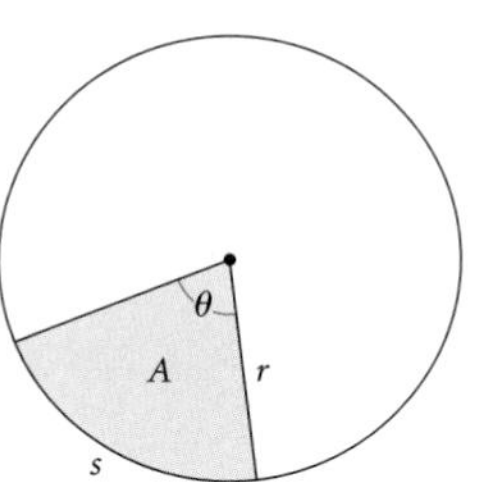

When an object follows a circular path, the distance it travels is the arc length. You can calculate its speed as distance traveled per unit of time. The amount of rotation, or angle traveled per unit of time, is called the **angular speed.**

EXAMPLE C

The Cosmo Clock 21 Ferris wheel at the Cosmo World amusement park in Yokohama, Japan, has a 100 m diameter. This giant Ferris wheel, with 60 gondolas and 8 people per gondola, makes one complete rotation every 15 minutes. The wheel reaches a maximum height of 112.5 m from the ground.

a. Find the speed of a person on this Ferris wheel as it is turning.

b. Find the angular speed of this person.

The Cosmo Clock 21 Ferris wheel is the world's largest Ferris wheel and also a giant clock.

▶ Solution

The speed is the distance traveled per unit of time, measured in units such as meters per second. The angular speed is the rate of rotation, measured in units like radians per second or degrees per second.

a. The person travels one complete circumference every 15 min or

$$\frac{2\pi r \text{ m}}{15 \text{ min}} = \frac{2\pi \cdot 50 \text{ m}}{15 \text{ min}} \approx 20.94 \frac{\text{m}}{\text{min}}$$

So, the person travels at about 21 m/min. You can also use dimensional analysis to express this speed as approximately 1.26 km/h.

$$\frac{20.94 \cancel{\text{m}}}{1 \cancel{\text{min}}} \cdot \frac{60 \cancel{\text{min}}}{1 \text{ h}} \cdot \frac{1 \text{ km}}{1000 \cancel{\text{m}}} \approx \frac{1.26 \text{ km}}{1 \text{ h}}$$

b. The person completes one rotation, or 2π radians, every 15 min.

$$\frac{2\pi \text{ radians}}{15 \text{ min}} \approx 0.42 \text{ radian/min}$$

So, the person's angular speed is 0.42 radian/min.

Sharing Ideas (continued)

[Ask] "What units do the variables have in the arc length formulas?" [The variables r and s have length units, so in the degree formula 2π must have no units and in the radian formula θ must have no units.] Arc length provides an example of why radians are not considered to have units. Having no units makes them especially valuable in applications in which the independent variable does not represent an angle at all, but a quantity such as time.

▶ EXAMPLE C

In part a, students can use dimensional analysis again to find the speed in miles per hour. Their thinking might go like this: "I know the number of $\frac{\text{m}}{\text{min}}$, and I want $\frac{\text{m}}{\text{h}}$. I need to get rid of min and introduce h. So I need to multiply $\frac{\text{m}}{\text{min}}$ by min in the numerator to cancel out min, and I need to multiply by h in the denominator to introduce h. That is, I need to multiply by $\frac{60 \text{ min}}{1 \text{ h}}$."

SHARING IDEAS

As students present ideas, ask whether the number of radii in the arcs intercepted by an angle is really always the same no matter the size of the circle that includes those arcs. Bring out the idea that, because all circles are similar to one another, the ratio of arc length to radius is always the same.

Note that radian measures often involve π, and ask why. [Angles are parts of the full angle of a circle, so their radian measures are related to 2π.]

To help students appreciate the value of posing problems, encourage them to ask questions you yourself might ask about the lesson, such as those below. Be open to a variety of questions.

[Ask] "Why are radians useful? Why not continue to use degrees, which are so familiar?" [Radians relate to a basic part of the circle's structure, its radius, so you don't have to convert between units when you use them.] Students have already seen the difference in formulas for arc length and area of a sector. In degrees, arc length s is $\frac{2\pi\theta}{360°}r$. In radians, arc length s is θr, because 360° becomes 2π. In degrees, the area A of a sector is $\frac{\pi\theta}{360°}r^2$, whereas in radians $A = \frac{\theta}{2}r^2$. **[Link]** You might also mention that rate-of-change formulas in calculus are simpler if radian measure is used.

Assessing Progress
As students work and present, you can assess their understanding of arc length and their comfort level in working with ratios and proportions.

Closing the Lesson

The number of **radians** in an angle is the number of radii that can be laid out along the arc the angle intercepts, where the radii are those of a circle centered at the angle's vertex and containing the arc. Because a 360° angle intercepts a full circle, which has arc length 2π radii, 2π radians corresponds to 360°. The length of an arc intercepted by an angle of θ radians is θr: θ radii times r units of length per radius. The area of a sector with angle θ is $\frac{\theta}{2}r^2$ square units.

BUILDING UNDERSTANDING

The exercises give students practice with radian measure and with converting between radians and degrees.

ASSIGNING HOMEWORK

Essential	1–4, 7, 8
Performance assessment	5–15
Portfolio	9
Journal	5
Group	7, 8, 14, 15
Review	10, 16–22

MATERIALS

- compasses or circle templates
- Exercise 3 (W), *optional*
- Exercises 7 and 8 Solutions (T), *optional*

Helping with the Exercises

Exercise 1 Encourage students to think about ratios instead of applying formulas.

Using dimensional analysis, you can convert between units to express answers in any form.

$$\frac{2\pi\ \text{radians}}{15\ \text{min}} \cdot \frac{360°}{2\pi\ \text{radians}} = \frac{24°}{1\ \text{min}}$$

So, you can also express the angular speed as 24°/min.

A central angle has a measure of 1 radian when its intercepted arc is the same length as the radius. Similarly, the number of radians in an angle measure is the number of radii in the arc length of its intercepted arc. One radian is $\frac{180°}{\pi}$, or approximately 57.3°.

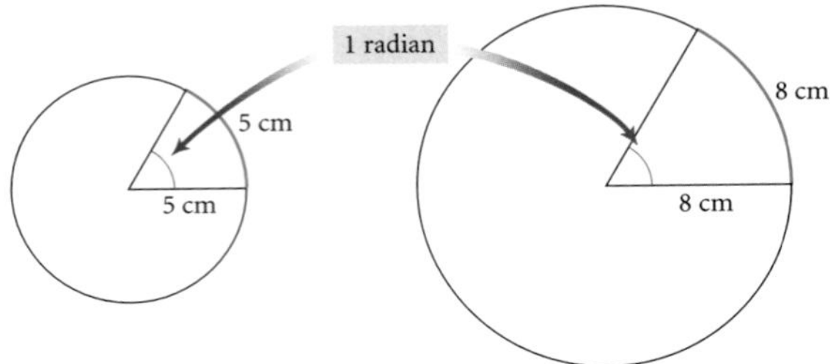

EXERCISES

Practice Your Skills

1. Convert between radians and degrees. Give exact answers. (Remember that degree measures are always labeled °, and radians generally are not labeled.)

a. 80° $\frac{4\pi}{9}$ b. 570° $\frac{19\pi}{6}$ c. $-\frac{4\pi}{3}$ −240° d. $\frac{11\pi}{9}$ 220°

e. $-\frac{3\pi}{4}$ −135° f. 3π 540° g. −900° -5π h. $\frac{5\pi}{6}$ 150°

2. Find the length of the intercepted arc for each central angle.

a. $r = 3$ and $\theta = \frac{2\pi}{3}$ 2π

b. $r = 1$ and $\theta = 1$ 1

c. $d = 5$ and $\theta = \frac{\pi}{6}$ $\frac{5\pi}{12}$

3. Draw a large copy of this diagram on your paper. Each angle shown has a reference angle of 0°, 30°, 45°, 60°, or 90°.

a. Find the counterclockwise degree rotation of each segment from the positive x-axis. Write your answers in both degrees and radians.

b. Find the exact coordinates of points A–N.

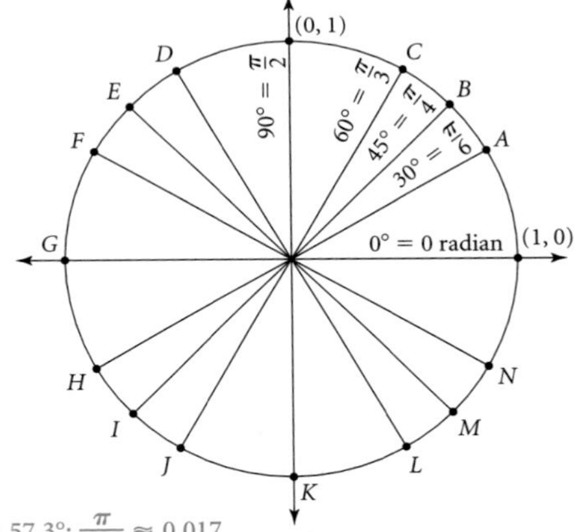

4. One radian is equivalent to how many degrees? One degree is equivalent to how many radians? $\frac{180}{\pi} \approx 57.3°$; $\frac{\pi}{180} \approx 0.017$

Exercise 2 Suggest that students sketch these angles and arcs.

Exercise 3 You might provide the Exercise 3 worksheet or use it as a transparency and fill it in with the class. Once completed, the diagram will be a useful tool for students for the rest of the chapter. You can use the Exercises 7 and 8 Solutions transparency to talk about how the solution to this exercise relates to Exercises 7 and 8.

3a, b.

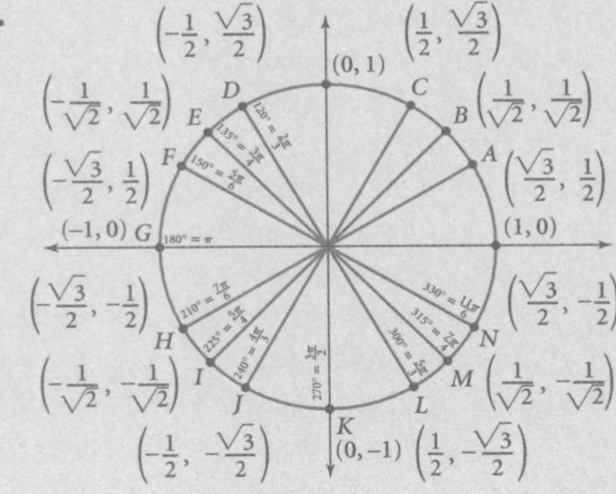

Reason and Apply

5. Are 6 radians more than, less than, or the same as one rotation about a circle? Explain.

6. The minute hand of a clock is 15.2 cm long.

a. What is the distance the tip of the minute hand travels during 40 minutes?

b. At what speed is the tip moving, in cm/min?

c. What is the angular speed of the tip in radians/minute?

American actor Harold Lloyd (1893–1971), shown here hanging from a clock in the film *Safety Last* (1923), often performed daring physical feats in his more than 500 comedic films.

7. ***Mini-Investigation*** On your paper, graph $y = \sin x$ over the domain $0 \le x \le 2\pi$.

a. On the x-axis, label all the x-values that are multiples of $\frac{\pi}{6}$.

b. On the x-axis, label all the x-values that are multiples of $\frac{\pi}{4}$.

c. What x-values in this domain correspond to a maximum value of $\sin x$? A minimum value of $\sin x$? $\sin x = 0$?

8. ***Mini-Investigation*** On your paper, graph $y = \cos x$ over the domain $0 \le x \le 2\pi$.

a. On the x-axis, label all the x-values that are multiples of $\frac{\pi}{6}$.

b. On the x-axis, label all the x-values that are multiples of $\frac{\pi}{4}$.

c. What x-values in this domain correspond to a maximum value of $\cos x$? A minimum value of $\cos x$? $\cos x = 0$?

9. ***Mini-Investigation*** Follow these steps to explore the relationship between the tangent ratio and the slope of a line. For 9a and b, find $\tan\theta$ and the slope of the line.

a.

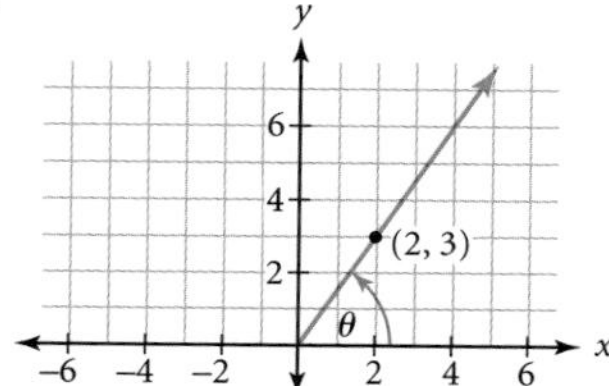

b.

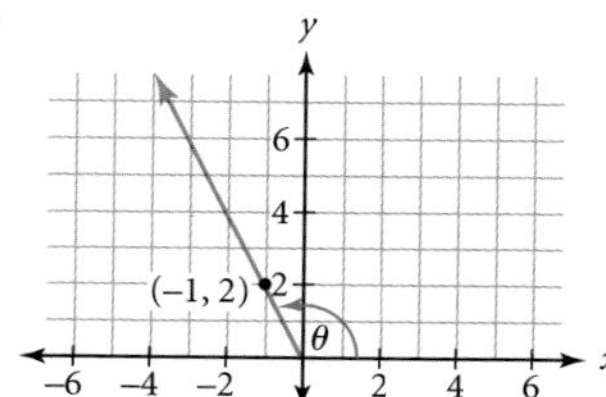

c. What is the relationship between the tangent of an angle in standard position, and the slope of its terminal side?

d. Find the slope of this line.

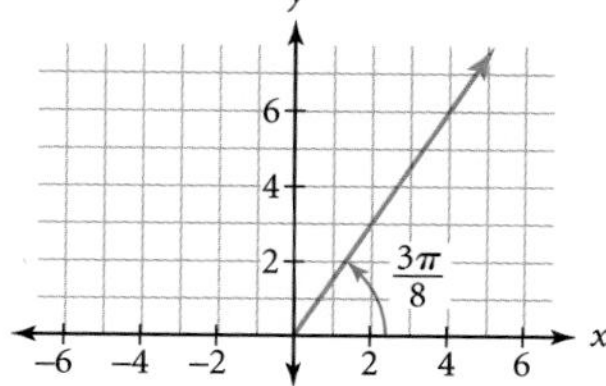

5. Less than; one rotation is 2π, which is more than 6.

6a. 63.7 cm

6b. 1.6 cm/min

6c. 0.105 radian/min

Exercises 7, 8 If students want to check their results on a calculator, they will need to change to Radian mode. You might use the Exercises 7 and 8 Solutions transparency.

Exercise 7 You might suggest that students first mark off π and 2π and then divide each section into six sections for $\frac{\pi}{6}$ and into four sections for $\frac{\pi}{4}$. **[Ask]** "Do any of these values coincide?" $\left[\text{Yes; } \frac{3\pi}{6} = \frac{2\pi}{4}, \text{ and } \frac{9\pi}{6} = \frac{6\pi}{4}.\right]$

7a, b. See below.

7c. $\frac{\pi}{2}$; $\frac{3\pi}{2}$; 0, π, and 2π

8a, b. See below.

8c. 0 and 2π; π; $\frac{\pi}{2}$ and $\frac{3\pi}{2}$

9a. $\frac{3}{2}$; $\frac{3}{2}$

9b. −2; −2

9c. They are equal.

9d. approximately 2.414

7a, b.

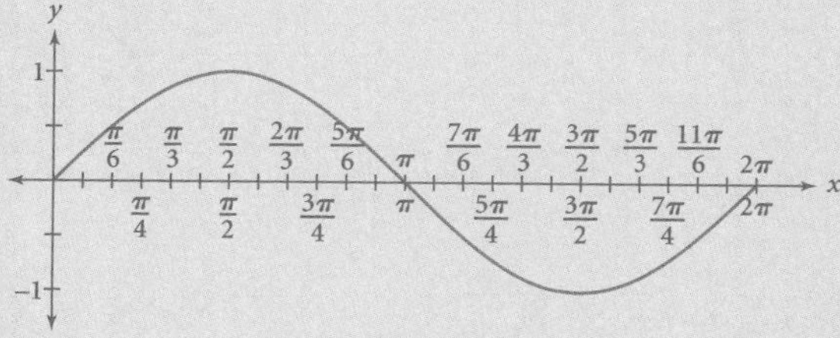

8a, b.

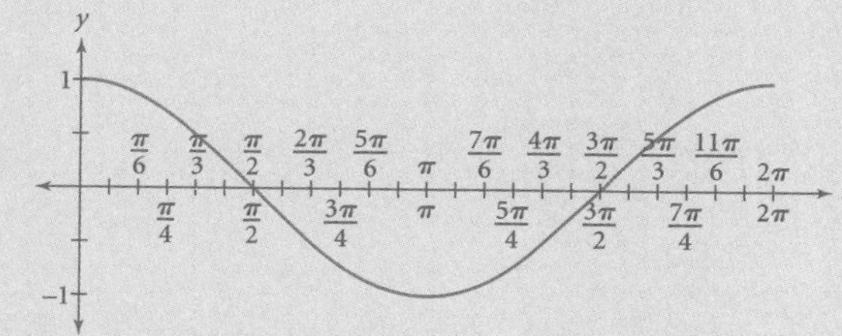

Exercise 11 Suggest that students sketch these reference triangles in the appropriate quadrant. They will need to recall the ratios of sides of 30°-60°-90° and 45°-45°-90° triangles. If students are stuck on 11c, ask whether they know another name for $\frac{\sin\theta}{\cos\theta}$. [$\tan\theta$]

Exercise 12 If students are having difficulty, you might wonder aloud whether they can find revolutions per second more easily than radians per second.

13a. $A \approx 57.54 \text{ cm}^2$

13b. $\frac{A}{64\pi} = \frac{\frac{4\pi}{7}}{2\pi}$

13c.

$A = 64\pi \cdot \frac{\frac{4\pi}{7}}{2\pi} \approx 57.54 \text{ cm}^2$

Exercise 14 If students want to convert kilometers to miles, they can either multiply by 0.62 or divide by 1.61.

Exercise 15 In 15a and 15c, the distances are measured on the surface of Earth. That is, they are arc lengths, not lengths of the shortest paths, which would go through the planet.

On TI calculators, students can enter degrees and minutes by pressing (2nd) Angle. Pressing (ENTER) will produce the decimal value.

10. Find the value of r in the circle at right. $r = 48$

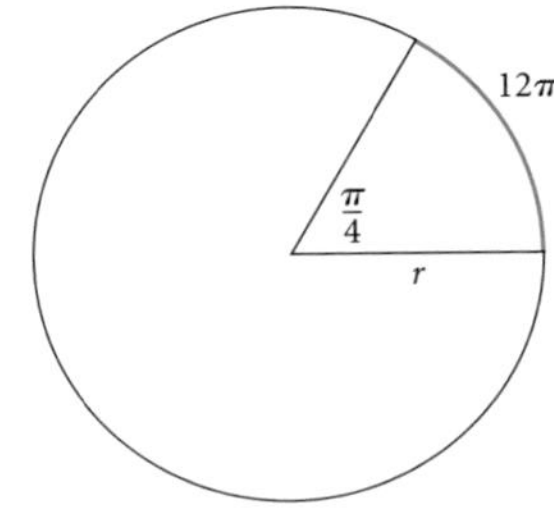

11. Solve for θ. Express your answers in radians.

a. $\cos\theta = -\frac{1}{2}$ and $\pi \le \theta \le \frac{3\pi}{2}$ $\frac{4\pi}{3}$

b. $\cos\theta = \frac{\sqrt{2}}{2}$ and $\frac{3\pi}{2} \le \theta \le 2\pi$ $\frac{7\pi}{4}$

c. $\frac{\sin\theta}{\cos\theta} = \sqrt{3}$ and $0 \le \theta \le \frac{\pi}{2}$ $\frac{\pi}{3}$

12. Suppose you are biking down a hill at 24 mi/h. What is the angular speed, in radians per second, of your 27-inch-diameter bicycle wheel? 31.3 radians/s

Recreation CONNECTION

Fred Rompelberg of the Netherlands broke the world record in 1995 for the fastest recorded bicycle speed, 167.043 mi/h. He rode a lead bicycle behind a race car, which propelled him forward by slipstream, an airstream that reduces air pressure. The record-breaking event took place at Bonneville Salt Flats in Utah.

Dutch cyclist Fred Rompelberg (b 1945)

13. A sector of a circle with radius 8 cm has central angle $\frac{4\pi}{7}$.

a. Find the area of the sector.

b. Set up a proportion of the area of the sector to the total area of the circle, and a proportion of the central angle of the sector to the total central angle measure.

c. Solve your proportion from 13b to show that the formula you used in 13a is correct.

14. Sitting at your desk, you are approximately 6350 km from the center of Earth. Consider your motion relative to the center of Earth, as Earth rotates on its axis.

a. What is your angular speed? 2π radians/day or 0.26 radian/h

b. What is your speed in km/h? 1660 km/h

c. What is your speed in mi/h? 1040 mi/h

15. APPLICATION The two cities Minneapolis, Minnesota, and Lake Charles, Louisiana, lie on the 93° W longitudinal line. The latitude of Minneapolis is 45° N (45° north of the equator) whereas the latitude of Lake Charles is 30° N. The radius of Earth is approximately 3960 mi.

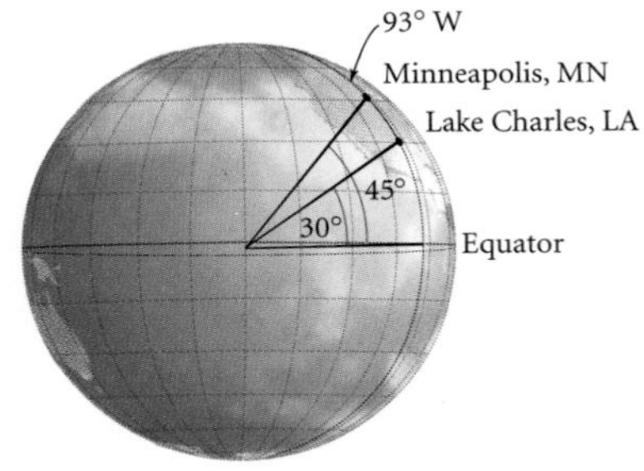

a. Calculate the distance between the two cities. 1037 mi

b. Like hours, degrees can be divided into minutes and seconds for more precision. (There are 60 seconds in a minute and 60 minutes in a degree.) For example, 61°10′ means 61 degrees 10 minutes. Write this measurement as a decimal. 61.17°

c. If you know the latitudes and longitudes of two cities, you can find the distance in miles between them, D, using this formula:

$$D = \frac{\pi \cdot r}{180}\cos^{-1}\left(\sin\phi_A \sin\phi_B + \cos\phi_A \cos\phi_B \cos\left(\theta_A - \theta_B\right)\right)$$

In the formula, r is the radius of Earth in miles, ϕ_A and θ_A are the latitude and longitude of city A in degrees, and ϕ_B and θ_B are the latitude and longitude of city B in degrees. North and east are considered positive angles, and south and west are considered negative. Using this formula, find the distance between Anchorage, Alaska (61°10′ N, 150°1′ W), and Tucson, Arizona (32°7′ N, 110°56′ W). 2660 mi

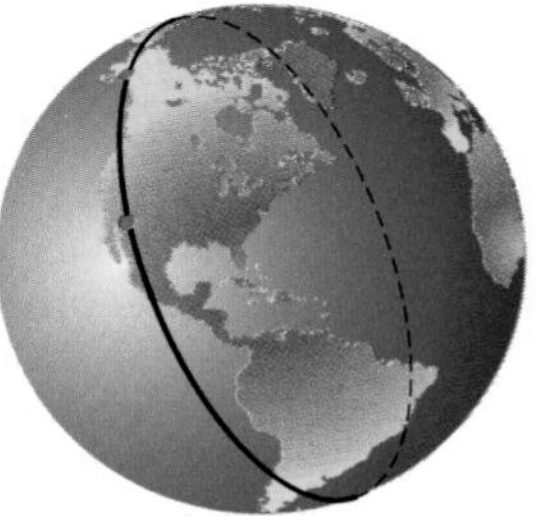

Exercise 15c The formula calculates the great arc connecting the cities (see the history connection). To demonstrate the idea of a great arc, use a globe, ball, or balloon and pull a string tight between two points on the surface.

History CONNECTION

To find the shortest path between two points on a sphere, you connect the two points with a great arc, an arc of a circle that has the same center as the center of Earth. Pilots fly along great circle routes to save time and fuel. Charles Lindbergh's carefully planned 1927 flight across the Atlantic was along a great circle route that saved about 473 miles compared to flying due east.

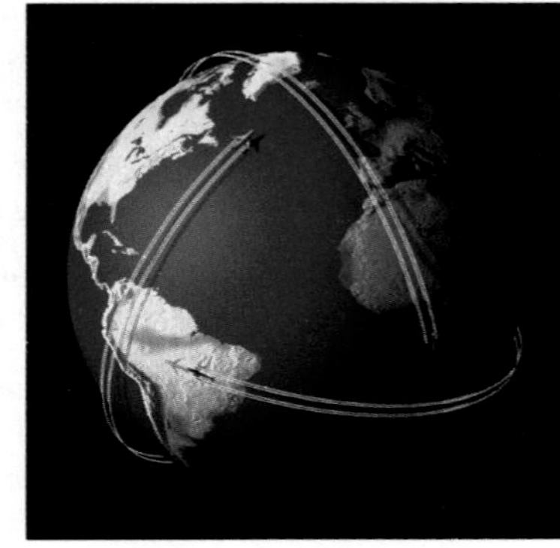

MAKING THE CONNECTION

Two-dimensional maps are deceptive for purposes of navigation. Drawing a straight line between two points, for example, appears to be shorter than following a plane's curved flight path. Flat maps also present a distorted representation of the rounded surface of Earth. This distortion is especially significant on most world maps, where distances are greatly exaggerated near the poles. Globes are useful when an accurate representation of Earth is needed. In addition to helping plot great-circle routes, globes are useful for tracing earthquake shocks, tidal-wave paths, and satellite movement.

Review

4.6 **16.** List the transformations of each graph from its parent function.

a. $y = 2 + (x + 4)^2$

b. $\frac{y}{3} = \left(\frac{x-5}{4}\right)^2$

c. $y + 1 = |x - 3|$

d. $y = 3 - 2|x + 1|$

4.6 **17.** Write an equation for each graph.

a.

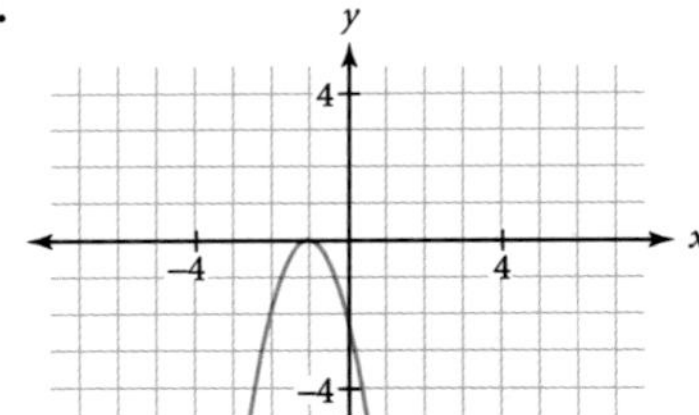

b.

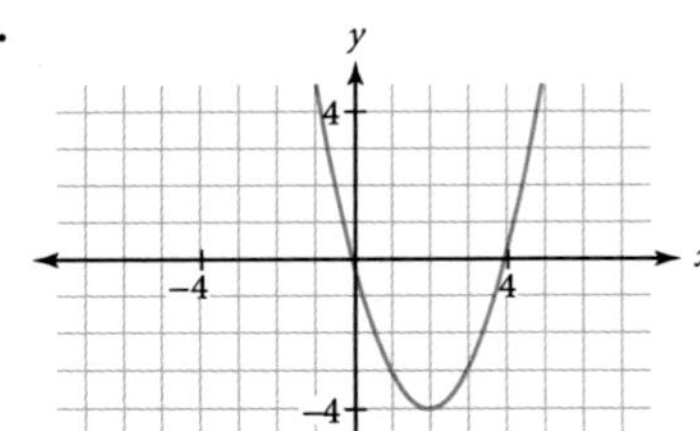

c.

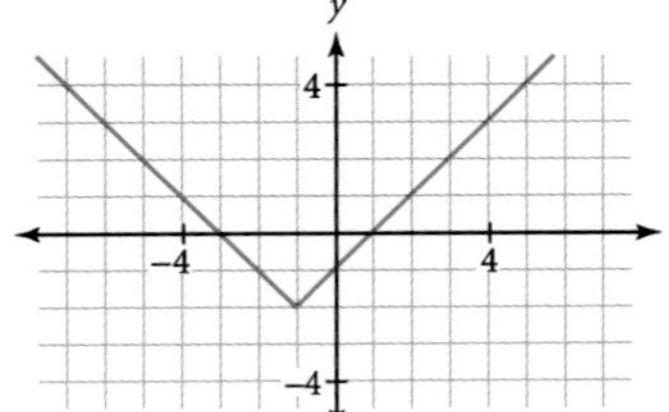

d.

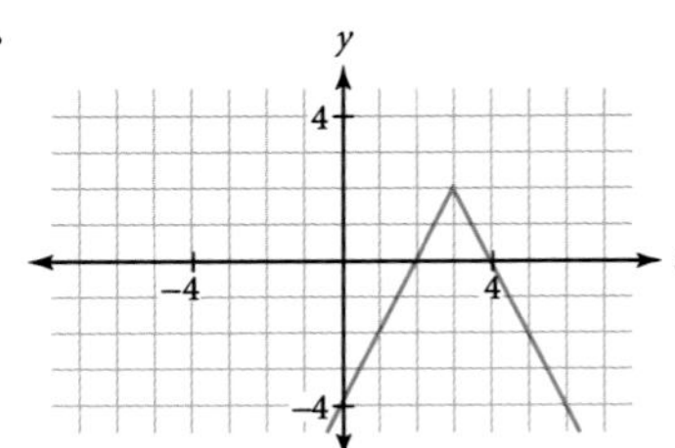

16a. translated up 2 units and left 4 units

16b. stretched vertically by a factor of 3 and horizontally by a factor of 4 and translated right 5 units

16c. translated down 1 unit and right 3 units

16d. stretched vertically by a factor 2, reflected, and translated up 3 units and left 1 unit

17a. $y = -2(x + 1)^2$

17b. $y + 4 = (x - 2)^2$ or $y = (x - 2)^2 - 4$

17c. $y + 2 = |x + 1|$ or $y = |x + 1| - 2$

17d. $-\frac{y-2}{2} = |x - 3|$ or $y = -2|x - 3| + 2$

Exercise 18 As needed, suggest that students use the unit circle and reference angles to find these values.

20.

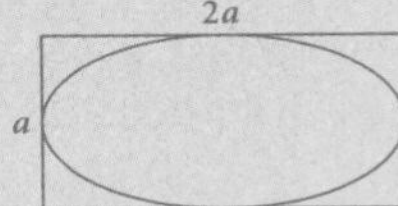

$\frac{\sqrt{3}}{2}$; the major axis is a, the minor axis is and $\frac{a}{2}$, so the foci are $\frac{\sqrt{3}}{2}a$ units from the center. Therefore the eccentricity is $\frac{\frac{\sqrt{3}}{2}a}{a} = \frac{\sqrt{3}}{2}$.

21. Possible answer: Construct $\overline{AP}$, $\overline{BP}$, and $\overline{CP}$. $\triangle APC$ is isosceles because $\overline{AP}$ and $\overline{CP}$ are radii of the same circle. $\angle A \cong \angle C$ because they are base angles of an isosceles triangle. $\angle ABP$ measures 90° because the angle is inscribed in a semicircle. $\angle PBC = 90°$ because it is supplementary to $\angle APB$. $\triangle APB \cong \triangle CPB$ by AAS. Therefore, $AB = BC$ because corresponding parts of congruent triangles are congruent.

Exercise 22 This exercise asks for parametric equations; 22c can also be done with projectile motion and linear speed equations, but not as easily.

22a. $x = 1.5t$, $y = 80 - 4.9t^2$

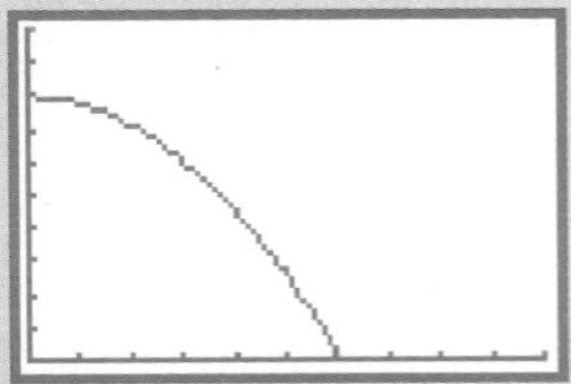

[0, 10, 1, 0, 10, 1]
$0 \le t \le 100$

EXTENSION

Use Take Another Look activity 3 or 4 on pages 627 and 628.

10.1 **18.** Find a second value of θ that gives the same trigonometric value as the angle given. Use domain $0° \le \theta \le 360°$.

a. $\sin 23° = \sin\theta$ 157°

b. $\sin 216° = \sin\theta$ 324°

c. $\cos 342° = \cos\theta$ 18°

d. $\cos 246° = \cos\theta$ 114°

10.1 **19.** While Yolanda was parked at her back steps, a slug climbed onto the wheel of her go-cart just above where the wheel makes contact with the ground. When Yolanda hopped in and started to pull away, she did not notice the slug until her wheels had rotated $2\frac{1}{3}$ times. Yolanda's wheels have a 12 cm radius.

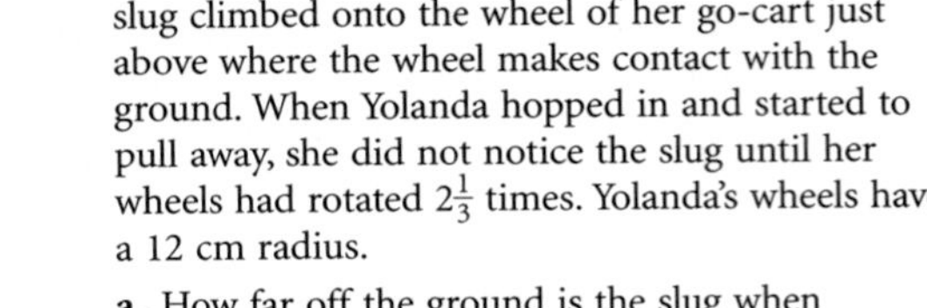

a. How far off the ground is the slug when Yolanda notices it? 18 cm

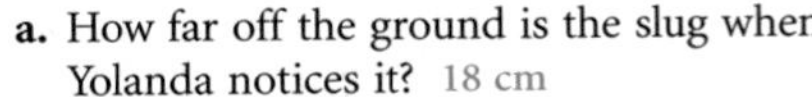

b. How far horizontally has the slug moved? 169 cm

9.2 **20.** Sketch a rectangle with length a and width $2a$. Inscribe an ellipse in the rectangle. What is the eccentricity of the ellipse? Why?

21. Circles O and P, shown at right, are tangent at A. Explain why $AB = BC$. (*Hint:* One method uses congruence.)

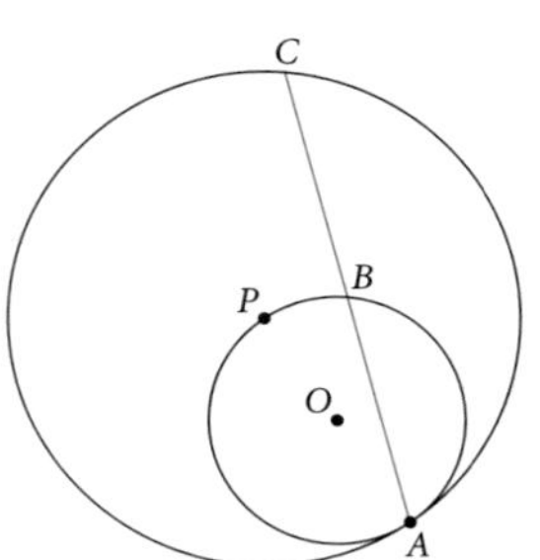

8.5 **22.** A river flowing at 1.50 m/s runs over an 80 m high cliff and into a lake below.

a. Write and graph parametric equations to model the water's path from the cliff to the lake.

b. Use the trace feature to approximate the time it takes for the water to reach the surface of the lake. Then find the distance from the bottom of the cliff to the bottom of the waterfall. about 4 s; about 6 m

c. Write an equation and solve it to find the time and distance in 22b. $0 = 80 - 4.9t^2$, $t \approx 4.04$, $x \approx 6.06$ m

LESSON

10.3 Graphing Trigonometric Functions

The best way to predict the future is to invent it.

BENJAMIN PIMENTEL

Graphs of the functions $y = \sin x$ and $y = \cos x$, and transformations of these graphs, are collectively called **sine waves** or **sinusoids.** You will find that reflecting, translating, and stretching or shrinking sinusoidal functions and other **trigonometric functions** is very much like transforming any other function. In this lesson you will explore many real-world situations in which two variables can be modeled by a sinusoidal function in the form $y = k + b\sin\left(\frac{x-h}{a}\right)$ or $\frac{y-k}{b} = \sin\left(\frac{x-h}{a}\right)$.

The wavy terraces of the Hsinbyume Pagoda in Mingum, Myanmar, may represent the seven surrounding hills or the seven seas of the universe.

EXAMPLE A

The graph of one cycle ($0 \le x \le 2\pi$) of $y = \sin x$ is shown at right. Sketch the graph of one cycle of

a. $y = 2 + \sin x$

b. $y = \sin(x - \pi)$

c. $y = 3 + 2\sin(x + \pi)$

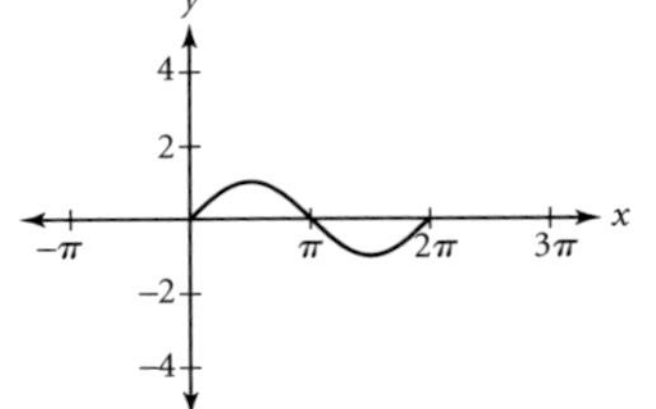

▶ Solution

Use your knowledge of transformations of functions.

a. In relation to the graph of any parent function, $y = f(x)$, the graph of $y = 2 + f(x)$ is a translation up 2 units. The graph of one cycle of $y = 2 + \sin x$ is therefore a translation up 2 units from the graph of $y = \sin x$.

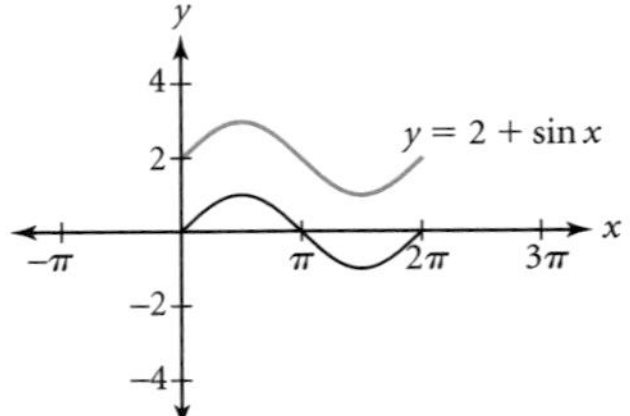

LESSON

10.3

PLANNING

LESSON OUTLINE

One day:

5 min	Example A
15 min	Investigation
10 min	Sharing
10 min	Examples B, C
5 min	Exercises

MATERIALS

- washers or other small weights
- string
- motion sensors
- Pendulum II Sample Data (W), *optional*
- Calculator Note 3C, *optional*

TEACHING

In this lesson students see how the period, amplitude, and phase shift of sinusoidal and tangent functions relate to transformations. The one-step investigation is on page 584.

[Language] A *sinusoid* is a curve shaped like the graph of the sine (or cosine) function.

[Alert] The variable a is associated with the horizontal direction, as in Chapter 9 on conic sections, rather than with the vertical direction, as in Chapter 4 on polynomials (in which the leading coefficient of the polynomial equation $y = ax^2 + bx + c = a(x - h)^2 + k$ was the vertical scale factor). If you skipped Chapter 9, students might initially be confused.

▶ EXAMPLE A

Before going over the solution, ask students to predict, without using graphing calculators, how the graphs will differ from the graph of the parent function.

NCTM STANDARDS

CONTENT		PROCESS	
	Number		Problem Solving
✔	Algebra		Reasoning
	Geometry	✔	Communication
✔	Measurement	✔	Connections
✔	Data/Probability	✔	Representation

LESSON OBJECTIVES

- Apply knowledge of transformations to the graphs of trigonometric functions
- Learn vocabulary associated with sinusoidal graphs, including *amplitude* and *phase shift*
- Model real-world data with sine and cosine functions

One Step

Ask students to do the investigation, or hand out the Pendulum II Sample Data worksheet. As they work to find functions to model the data, encourage them to consider horizontal and vertical stretches and horizontal translations of the parent functions. During Sharing, introduce the tangent function and the terms *sinusoid, sinusoidal function, amplitude,* and *phase shift.* Ask students to save their data for the one-step investigation in Lesson 10.4.

b. When x is replaced by $(x - \pi)$ in any function, the graph translates right π units.

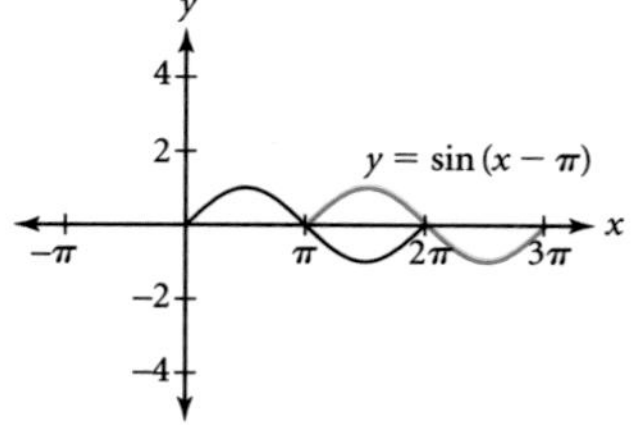

c. The coefficient 2 means the graph $y = \sin x$ must be stretched vertically by a factor of 2. The graph must also be translated left π units and up 3 units.

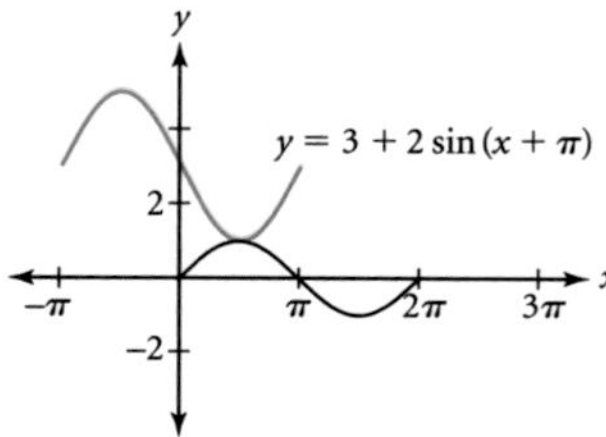

Recall that the period of a function is the smallest distance between values of the independent variable before the cycle begins to repeat. In Lesson 10.1, you discovered that the period of both $y = \sin x$ and $y = \cos x$ is 2π, or 360°. The period of each of the three functions in Example A is also 2π, because they were not stretched horizontally.

The **amplitude** of a sinusoid is half the difference of the maximum and minimum function values, or $\frac{maximum - minimum}{2}$. This is the same as the absolute value of the vertical scale factor, or $|b|$. The amplitude of $y = \sin x$ and $y = \cos x$ is 1 unit. In Example A, the amplitude of $y = 2 + \sin x$ and $y = \sin(x - \pi)$ is also 1. The amplitude of $y = 3 + 2\sin(x + \pi)$, however, is 2.

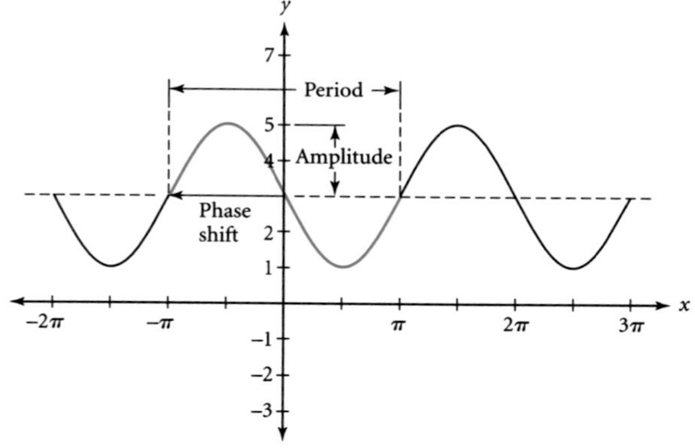

The horizontal translation of a sine or cosine graph is called the **phase shift.** In Example A, the phase shift of $y = 3 + 2\sin(x + \pi)$ is $-\pi$.

Cosine function sinusoids are transformed in the same way as sine function sinusoids. In fact, a cosine function is simply a horizontal translation of a sine function. Below is the graph of one cycle of two cosine functions:

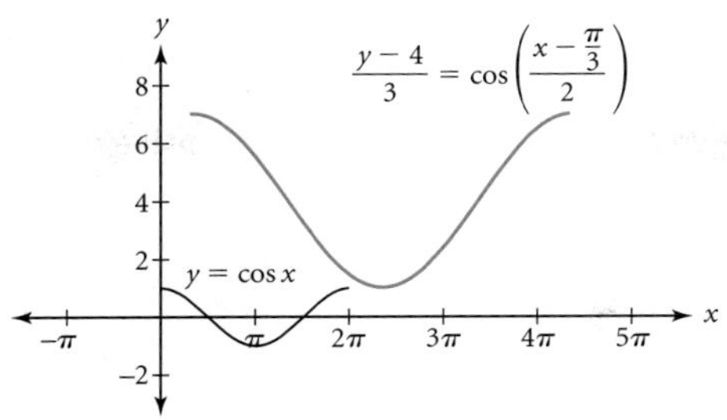

The parent cosine function is shown in black. In relation to the parent cosine function, the graph of the second function has been stretched vertically by a factor of 3, stretched horizontally by a factor of 2, translated right $\frac{\pi}{3}$ units, and translated up 4 units.

Values of the second function vary from a minimum of 1 to a maximum of 7, so it has amplitude 3. The horizontal scale factor 2 means its period is stretched to 4π. The horizontal translation makes the phase shift $\frac{\pi}{3}$, so that the cycle of this graph starts at $\frac{\pi}{3}$ and ends at $4\pi + \frac{\pi}{3}$, or $\frac{13\pi}{3}$.

In the investigation you will transform sinusoidal functions to fit real-world, periodic data.

Investigation
The Pendulum II

You will need

- a washer
- string
- a motion sensor

Suspend a washer from two strings so that it hangs 10 to 15 cm from the floor between two tables or desks. Place the motion sensor on the floor about 1 m in front of the washer hanging at rest. Pull the washer back about 20 to 30 cm and let it swing. Collect data points for 2 s of time. Model your data with both a sine function and a cosine function. Give real-world meanings for all numerical values in each equation.

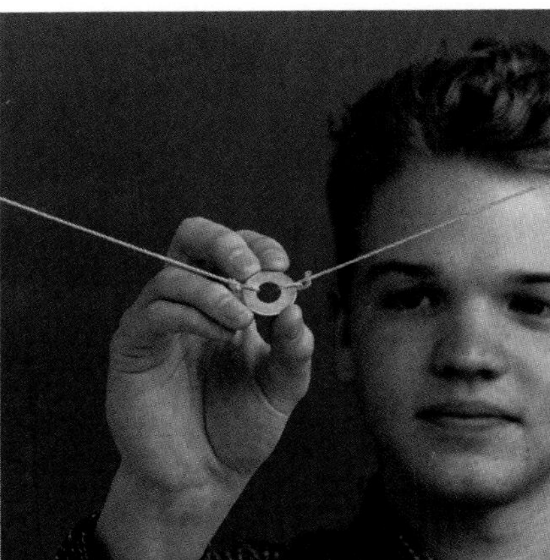

Guiding the Investigation

Students first investigated the pendulum in Lesson 4.6, where they related period to length. This investigation looks for a periodic function that describes the location of the swinging bob. The bob might be a metal washer, a ring, a spool of tape, or a water bottle partly filled with water.

Students might use the Pendulum II Sample Data worksheet if they do not have time to gather their own data.

As students saw earlier, the length of the pendulum's string determines the period. Different lengths will thus yield different sinusoidal function models.

You might have copies of Calculator Note 3C available for students who want to review using the calculator with a motion sensor.

As needed, encourage students to think about how to transform the parent function to fit the data. Students may find it easier to model the data with a cosine function, because the cosine function has a peak at $x = 0$. The sine model can be derived through the relationship $\sin x = \cos\left(\frac{\pi}{2} - x\right)$, because *cosine* means "complement's sine."

Investigation

See page 900 for the sample data.

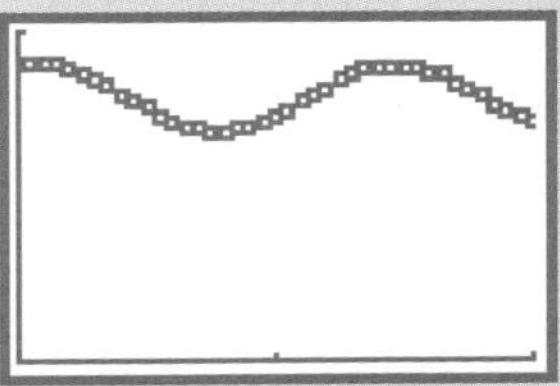

[0, 2, 1, 0, 1, 1]

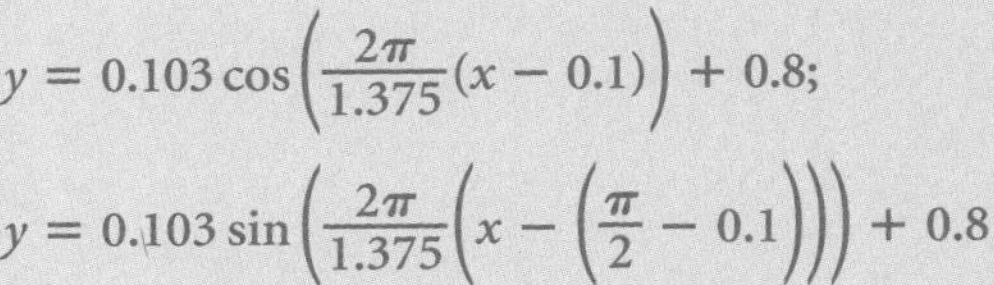

$$y = 0.103\cos\left(\frac{2\pi}{1.375}(x - 0.1)\right) + 0.8;$$

$$y = 0.103\sin\left(\frac{2\pi}{1.375}\left(x - \left(\frac{\pi}{2} - 0.1\right)\right)\right) + 0.8$$

For the sample data, 0.8 is the average distance from the motion sensor; 0.103 is the distance from the average value to the minimum or maximum value of the swing; 0.1 is the number of seconds before the first maximum value occurs; 1.375 is the number of seconds it takes to complete one cycle; x is measured in radians.

MAKING THE CONNECTION

Galileo's discovery that the periods for pendulums of the same length are constant holds true if tested on pendulums in the same room. The periods may vary, however, when pendulums of the same length are tested in different locations. Gravity plays a role in determining a pendulum's oscillation. Because the acceleration due to gravity differs depending on latitude and altitude, a pendulum on an ocean beach will have a longer period than a pendulum on a mountaintop. This property is used by devices that measure the force of gravity.

▶ EXAMPLE B

Students may benefit from seeing this function written first as

$$y = 300 + 10\cos\left(\frac{x}{\frac{15}{2\pi}}\right)$$

This form shows clearly that the value of a is $\frac{15}{2\pi}$.

[Ask] "Why does the book use the cosine function rather than the sine function for the model?" [The data have a peak at $x = 0$.]

SHARING IDEAS

As students present their ideas, **[Ask]** "Is a sinusoid a graph or a function?" [A sinusoid is a graph; a sinusoidal function is a transformation of the parent function $y = \sin x$.] Terms that are defined for graphs, such as *amplitude* and *phase shift,* are often also applied to functions as well. Likewise, terms such as *period,* defined for functions in Lesson 10.1, are also applied to graphs.

Encourage students to ask questions, such as those on the next page, that probe the deeper meanings of the lesson. Showing extra respect for all questions will help your students feel comfortable about asking creative questions. Rather than trying to answer students' questions yourself, turn them over to the class.

History CONNECTION

Italian scientist Galileo Galilei (1564–1642) studied pendulums of the same length, but with different amplitudes of motion. He found that the back-and-forth motion occurred at a set period of time, regardless of the amplitude. Called isochronism, this principle made way for devices, such as clocks, that rely on the pendulum as a regulator.

Russian-French painter Marc Chagall's (1887–1985) style, with its multiple points of view and geometric shapes, was partially influenced by the Cubist movement, but originated independently out of his own spiritual interests and works of poetry.

You can use sinusoidal functions to model many kinds of situations.

EXAMPLE B

After flying 300 mi west from Detroit to Chicago, a plane is put in a circular holding pattern above Chicago's O'Hare International Airport. The plane flies an additional 10 mi west past the airport and then starts flying in a circle with diameter 20 mi. The plane completes one circle every 15 min. Model the east-west component of the plane's distance from Detroit as a function of time.

▶ Solution

To help understand the situation, first sketch a diagram. The plane flies 300 mi to Chicago and then 10 mi past Chicago. At this time, call it 0 min, the plane begins to make a circle every 15 minutes. The diagram helps you see at least five data points, recorded in the table.

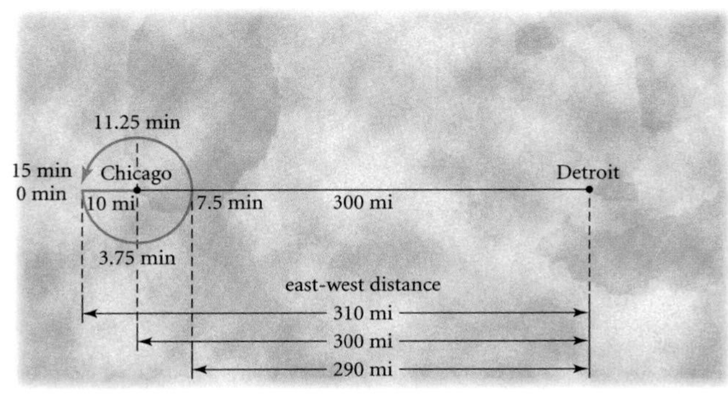

Time from beginning of circle (min) x	East-west distance from Detroit (mi) y
0	310
3.75	300
7.5	290
11.25	300
15	310

A quick plot of these points suggests that a cosine function might be a good model.

The period of $y = \cos x$ is 2π (from 0 to 2π). The period of this model should be 15 s (from 0 to 15). The horizontal scale factor that stretches 2π to 15 is $a = \frac{15}{2\pi}$.

The amplitude of the model should be 10 mi, so use the vertical scale factor $b = 10$.

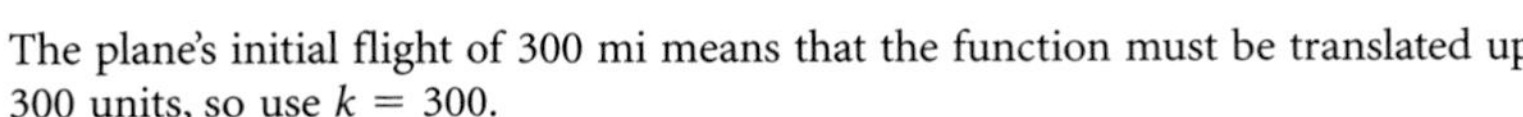

The plane's initial flight of 300 mi means that the function must be translated up 300 units, so use $k = 300$.

One possible model is

$$y = 300 + 10\cos\left(\frac{2\pi x}{15}\right)$$

Although the sine and cosine functions describe many periodic phenomena, such as the motion of a pendulum or the number of hours of daylight each day, there are other periodic functions that you can create from the unit circle.

You may recall studying the tangent ratio for right triangles. In right triangle trigonometry, the tangent of angle A is the ratio of the length of the opposite leg to the length of the adjacent leg.

$$\tan A = \frac{a}{b}$$

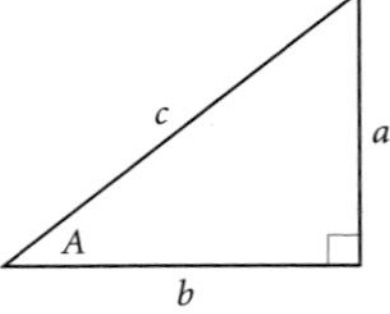

Sharing Ideas (continued)

[Ask] "How do you think the values of h, k, a, and b will affect the graphs of the sine and cosine functions?" You might need to point out that a represents not amplitude but rather the horizontal stretch factor, which is associated with the period. You may want to ask students to write equations relating the period to a and 2π, the period of the parent sinusoidal functions. For example, they might write the equation $period = 2\pi a$ or $a = \frac{period}{2\pi}$. The period of any periodic function is the period of the parent function times the horizontal stretch factor.

Now that students are working primarily with radians, you might ask them how the labels (scale) on the x-axis differ for radians and degrees. Elicit the idea that the graph doesn't need to change if the scale changes appropriately, with 360° replacing 2π.

[Ask] "Is it true that the functions $y = \sin x$ and $y = \cos x$ are related to each other by phase shifts?" [Yes; *cosine* means "complement's sine," so the relationship $y = \cos x = \cos(-x)$ is equivalent to $y = \sin\left(\frac{\pi}{2} - (-x)\right) = \sin\left(x + \frac{\pi}{2}\right)$, a phase shift of $-\frac{\pi}{2}$ from the graph of $y = \sin x$.]

[Ask] "Is the tangent function sinusoidal?" [It's periodic with period π, but its graph doesn't have the same shape as that of the sine function, so it's not sinusoidal.]

The definition of tangent can be extended to apply to any angle. Here, the tangent of angle A is the ratio of the y-coordinate to the x-coordinate of a point rotated $A°$ (or radians) counterclockwise about the origin from the positive ray of the x-axis.

$$\tan A = \frac{y\text{-coordinate}}{x\text{-coordinate}}$$

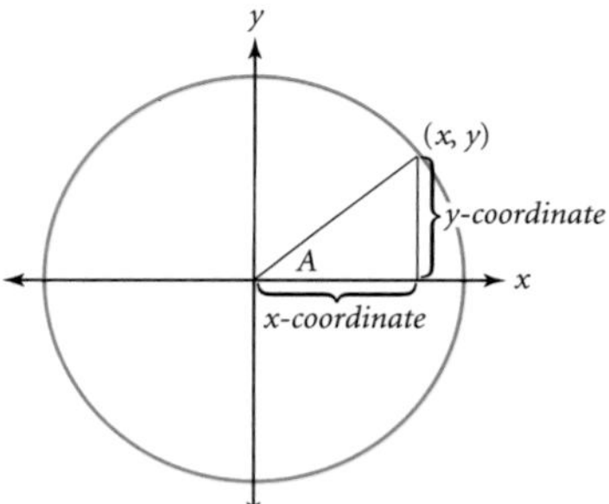

The tangent ratio describes the slope of the segment that connects the origin to any point on a circle centered at the origin. For example, the unit circle at right shows the point (0.8, 0.6) on the circle, which is rotated 0.6435 radian. The slope of the segment is $\frac{0.6}{0.8}$, or 0.75. This slope is equivalent to $\tan 0.6435$, which is also 0.75.

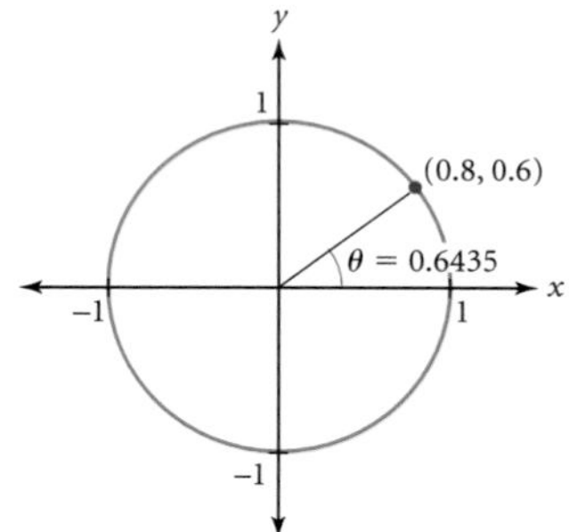

You can transform the graph of the tangent function in the same way as you transform sinusoidal functions.

EXAMPLE C The graph of $y = \tan x$ is shown in black. Find an equation for the red curve, which is a transformation of the graph of $y = \tan x$.

▶ Solution Notice that the parent tangent curve, $y = \tan x$, has a period of π $\left(\text{from } -\frac{\pi}{2} \text{ to } \frac{\pi}{2}\right)$. The red curve appears to run from $-\pi$ to 2π, a distance of 3π, so the horizontal scale factor is 3.

Notice how the parent curve bends as it passes through the origin, (0, 0). The red curve appears to bend in the same way at $\left(\frac{\pi}{2}, 1\right)$. That is a translation right $\frac{\pi}{2}$ units and up 1 unit. So an equation for the red curve is

$$y = 1 + \tan\left(\frac{x - \frac{\pi}{2}}{3}\right)$$

In Example C, the point $\left(\frac{\pi}{2}, 1\right)$ on the red curve could have been considered the image of $(\pi, 0)$, rather than (0, 0). This would indicate a translation *left* $\frac{\pi}{2}$ units and up 1 unit. So the equation

$$y = 1 + \tan\left(\frac{x + \frac{\pi}{2}}{3}\right)$$

will also model the red curve. Periodic graphs can always be modeled with many different, but equivalent, equations.

▶ *EXAMPLE C*

[Language] You may want to define the points at which the graph of the tangent function changes the direction of curving (at $x = 0$, $x = \pm 2\pi$, and so on) to be *inflection points.* This term is revisited in Chapter 13, in which students find the inflection points on the normal curve.

Students will see the identity $\tan A = \frac{\sin A}{\cos A}$ in Lesson 10.6. You may prefer to introduce it here.

You might **[Ask]** "Will the denominator of the tangent function ever be 0, making the function undefined?" [The value of x (or $\cos A$) is 0 when A is $\frac{\pi}{2} \pm \pi n$. At these points the graph of the tangent function has a vertical asymptote.] Students will explore the tangent function further in Exercise 10.

Assessing Progress

You can check students' understanding of the sine and cosine functions and the period of a periodic function.

Closing the Lesson

The period of any periodic function—including the **tangent function,** $y = \tan x$, and the **sinusoidal functions,** transformations of the functions $y = \sin x$ and $y = \cos x$—is the period of the parent function times the horizontal stretch factor of its graph. For the sinusoidal functions, the parent function's period is 2π and the stretch factor is represented by a, so the period is $2\pi a$. The **phase shift** of a periodic function is the amount of horizontal translation of the parent function, usually represented by h. The **amplitude** of a sinusoidal function is the vertical stretch factor, often represented by b.

EXERCISES

Practice Your Skills

1. For 1a–f, write an equation for each sinusoid as a transformation of the graph of either $y = \sin x$ or $y = \cos x$. More than one answer is possible.

a. $y = \sin x + 1$

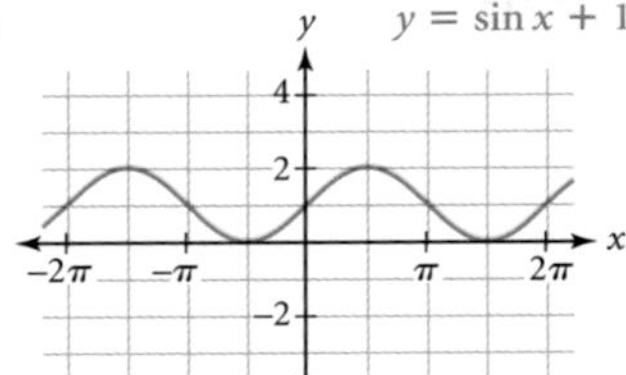

b. $y = \cos x - 2$

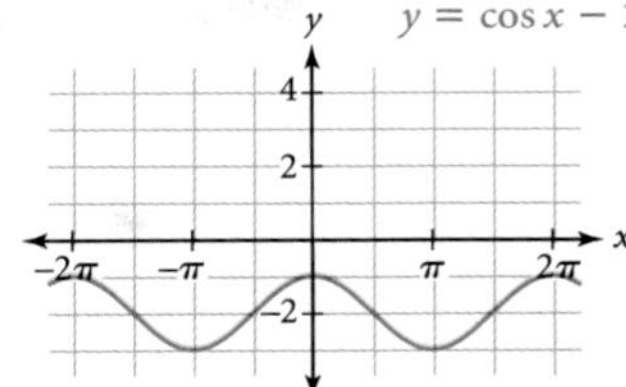

c. $y = \sin x - 0.5$

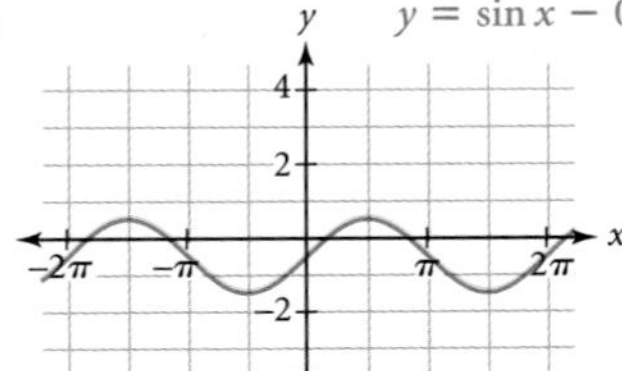

d. $y = -3\cos x$

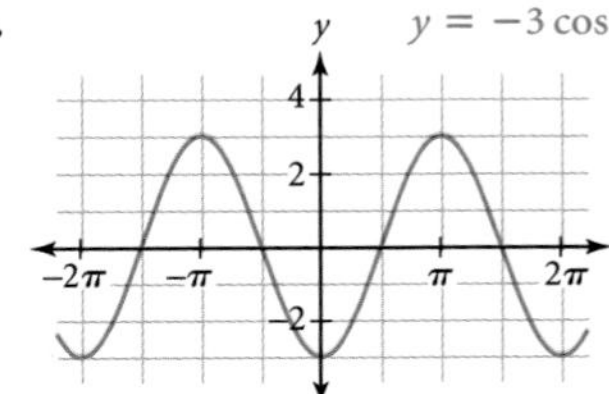

e. $y = -2\sin x$

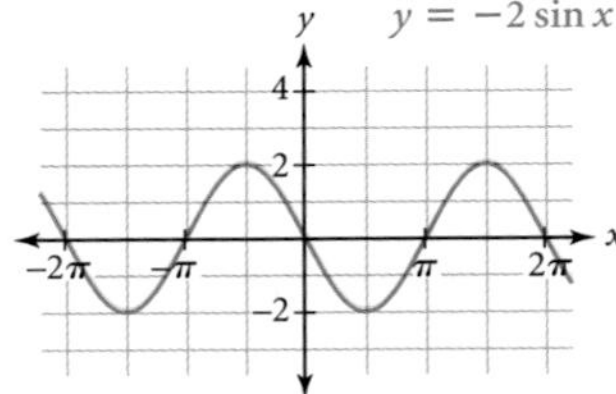

f. $y = 2\cos x + 1$

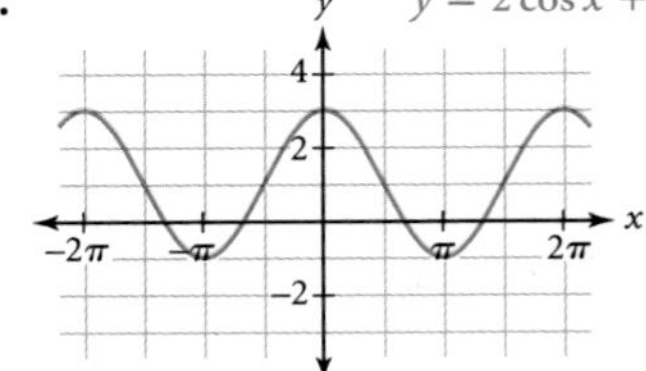

2. For 2a–f, write an equation for each sinusoid as a transformation of the graph of either $y = \sin x$ or $y = \cos x$. More than one answer is possible.

a. $y = \cos\frac{x}{0.5}$ or $y = \cos 2x$

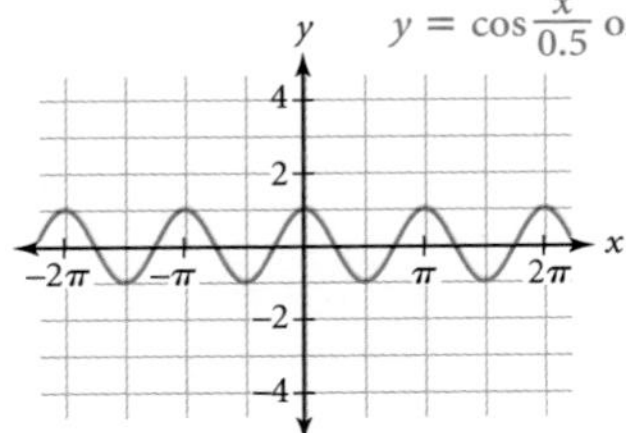

b. $y = \sin\left(\frac{x}{2}\right) - 1$

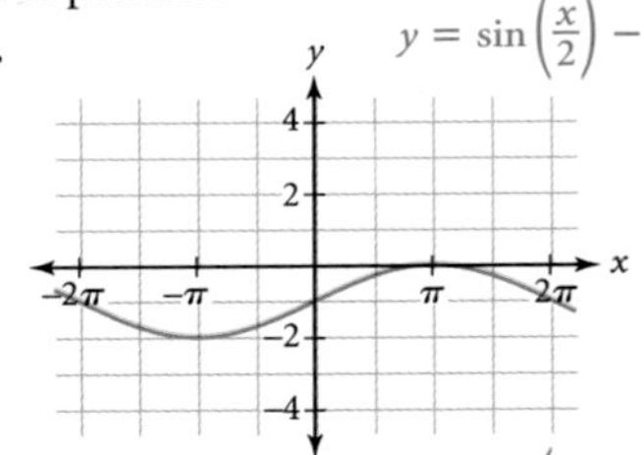

c. $y = -2\sin 3x$

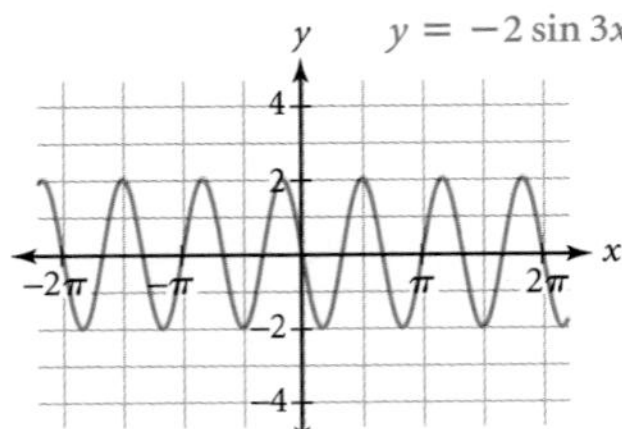

d. $y = \sin\left(x - \frac{\pi}{4}\right) + 1$

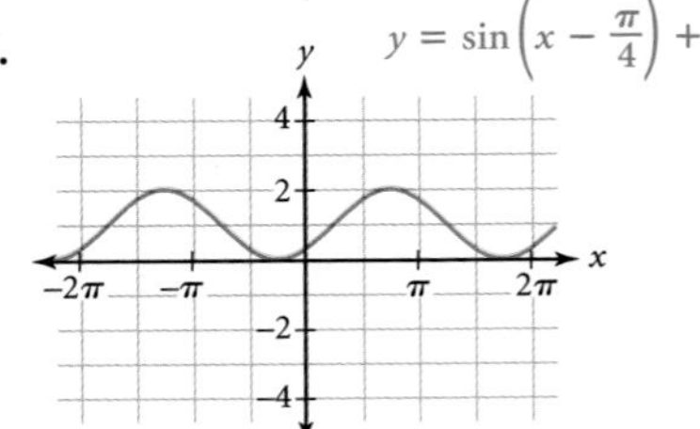

BUILDING UNDERSTANDING

The answers for most of the exercises are sample answers. Students now know about phase shifts and that every sinusoidal function can be written as infinitely many transformations of the sine or cosine function.

ASSIGNING HOMEWORK

Essential	**1–3, 10, 11**
Performance assessment	**4–9, 12, 13**
Portfolio	**8, 10**
Journal	**3, 5**
Group	**9, 13**
Review	**14–18**

MATERIALS

- graph paper
- Coordinate Axes for Periodic Functions (W), *optional*
- Calculator Note 9C, *optional*
- Fathom demonstration Day Times, *optional*

Helping with the Exercises

3a. The k-value vertically translates the graph of the function.

3b. The b-value vertically stretches or shrinks the graph of the function. The absolute value of b represents the amplitude. When b is negative, the curve is reflected across the x-axis.

3c. The a-value horizontally stretches or shrinks the graph of the function. It also determines the period with the relationship $2\pi a = \text{period}$.

3d. The h-value horizontally translates the graph of the function. It represents the phase shift.

Exercise 4 You might specify that an acceptable sketch would contain axes and the correct shape with clearly labeled maximums, minimums, and x- and y-intercepts.

4.

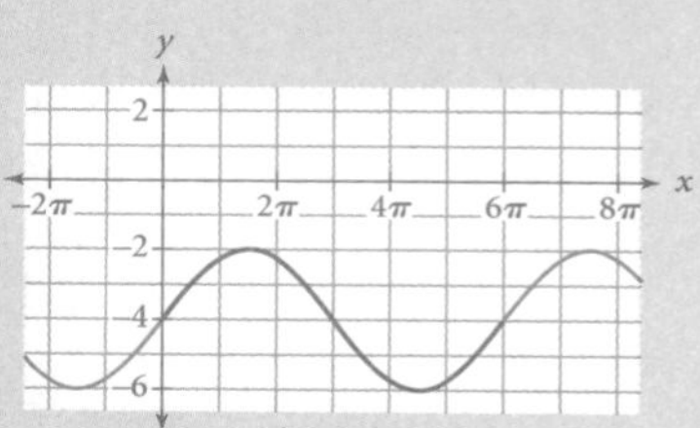

5. horizontal translation $\frac{\pi}{2}$ units left $\left(\text{phase shift of } -\frac{\pi}{2} \text{ units}\right)$; $y = \sin\left(x + \frac{\pi}{2}\right)$

6. possible answer:

$y = \sin\left(x - \frac{\pi}{2}\right)$,

$y = -\sin\left(x + \frac{\pi}{2}\right)$, or

$y = -\cos x$

Exercise 7 **[Ask]** "What are the independent and dependent variables?" [The independent variable is time; the dependent variable is the percentage of the surface that is lit.] "What are the domain and range?" [The domain is unbounded; the range is $0 \leq y \leq 100$.]

e. $y = -\cos\frac{x}{0.5}$ or $y = -\cos 2x$

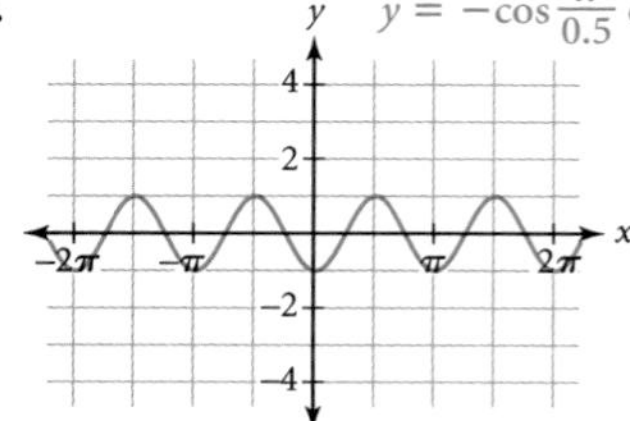

f. $y = \sin\frac{x + \frac{\pi}{2}}{2}$

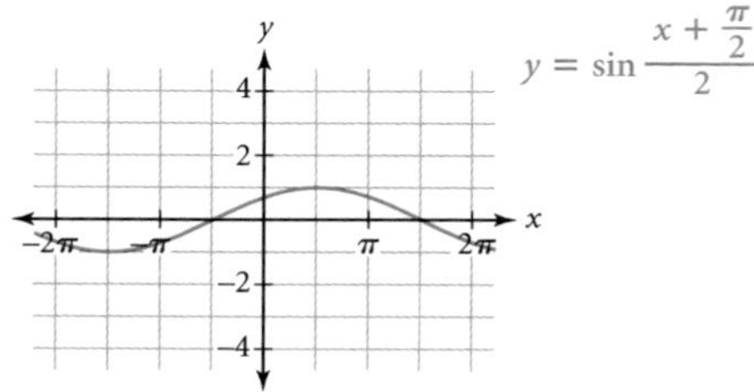

3. Consider the graph of $y = k + b\sin\left(\frac{x-h}{a}\right)$.

a. What effect does k have on the graph of $y = k + \sin x$?

b. What effect does b have on the graph of $y = b\sin x$? What is the effect if b is negative?

c. What effect does a have on the graph of $y = \sin\left(\frac{x}{a}\right)$?

d. What effect does h have on the graph of $y = \sin(x - h)$?

Reason and Apply

4. Sketch the graph of $y = 2\sin\left(\frac{x}{3}\right) - 4$. Use a calculator to check your sketch.

5. Describe a transformation of the graph of $y = \sin x$ to obtain an image that is equivalent to the graph of $y = \cos x$.

6. Write three different equations for the graph at right.

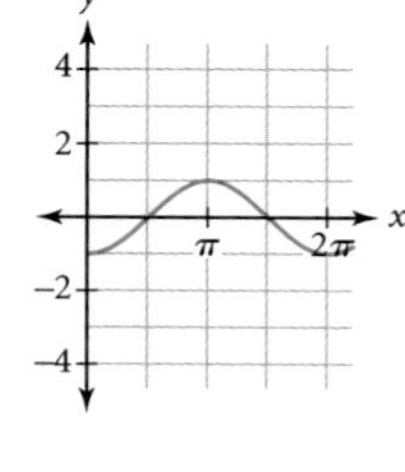

7. APPLICATION The percentage of the lighted surface of the Moon that is visible from Earth can be modeled with a sinusoid. Assume that tonight the Moon is full (100%) and in 14 days it will be a new moon (0%).

a. Define variables and find a sinusoidal function that models this situation.

b. What percentage will be visible 23 days after the full moon? 72%

c. What is the first day after a full moon that shows less than 75% of the lit surface? day 5

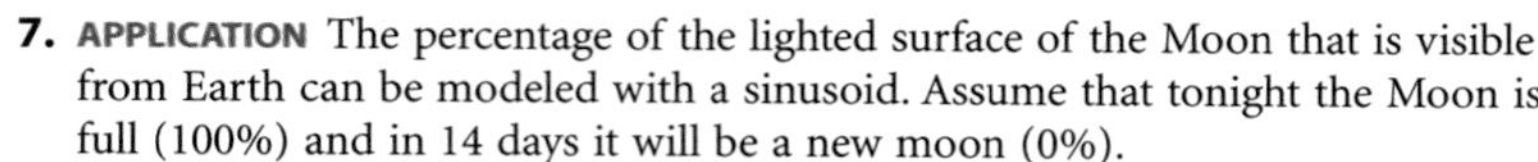

Science CONNECTION

Half of the Moon's surface is always lit by the Sun. The phases of the Moon, as visible from Earth, result from the Moon's orientation changing as it orbits Earth. A full moon occurs when the Moon is farther away from the Sun than Earth, and the lighted side faces Earth. A new moon is mostly dark because its far side is receiving the sunlight, and only a thin crescent of the lighted side is visible from Earth. For more information about the phases of the Moon, see the links at www.keymath.com/DAA .

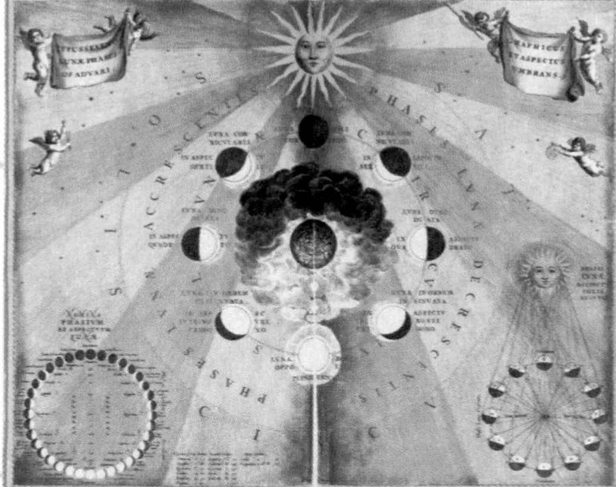

This engraving from the *Harmonia Macrocosmica Atlas* (ca. 1661) by Dutch-German mathematician Andreas Cellarius (ca. 1596–1665) depicts how astronomers of the 17th century interpreted the phases of the Moon.

7a. Let x represent the number of days after a full moon (today), and let y represent the percentage of lit surface that is visible.

$y = 0.5 + 0.5\cos\left(\frac{2\pi x}{28}\right)$

8. You may have noticed that a fluorescent light flickers, especially when it is about to blow out. Fluorescent lights do not produce constant illumination like incandescent lights. Ideally, fluorescent light cycles sinusoidally from dim to bright 60 times per second. At a certain distance from the light, the maximum brightness is measured at 50 watts per square centimeter (W/cm²) and the minimum brightness at 20 W/cm².

a. To collect data on light brightness from three complete cycles, how much total time should you record data? 0.05 s

b. Sketch a graph of the sinusoidal model for the data collected in 8a if the light climbed to its mean value of 35 W/cm² at 0.003 s. See below.

c. Write an equation for the sinusoidal model. $y = 35 + 15\sin 120\pi(x - 0.003)$

9. Imagine a unit circle in which a point is rotated A radians counterclockwise about the origin from the positive x-axis. Copy this table and record the x-coordinate and y-coordinate for each angle. Then use the definition of tangent to find the slope of the segment that connects the origin to each point.

Angle A	0	$\frac{\pi}{6}$	$\frac{\pi}{4}$	$\frac{\pi}{2}$	$\frac{3\pi}{4}$	π	$\frac{4\pi}{3}$	$\frac{5\pi}{3}$	$\frac{11\pi}{6}$
x-coordinate	1	$\frac{\sqrt{3}}{2}$	$\frac{\sqrt{2}}{2}$	0	$-\frac{\sqrt{2}}{2}$	-1	$-\frac{1}{2}$	$\frac{1}{2}$	$\frac{\sqrt{3}}{2}$
y-coordinate	0	$\frac{1}{2}$	$\frac{\sqrt{2}}{2}$	1	$\frac{\sqrt{2}}{2}$	0	$-\frac{\sqrt{3}}{2}$	$-\frac{\sqrt{3}}{2}$	$-\frac{1}{2}$
Slope or tan A	0	$\frac{1}{\sqrt{3}}$	1	↑ undefined	-1	0	$\sqrt{3}$	$-\sqrt{3}$	$-\frac{1}{\sqrt{3}}$

10. Graph $y = \tan x$ on your calculator. Use Radian mode with $-2\pi \le x \le 2\pi$ and $-5 \le y \le 5$.

a. What happens at $x = \frac{\pi}{2}$? Explain why this is so, and name other values when this occurs.

b. What is the period of $y = \tan x$? π

c. Explain, in terms of the definition of tangent, why the values of $\tan\frac{\pi}{5}$ and $\tan\frac{6\pi}{5}$ are the same.

d. Carefully graph two cycles of $y = \tan x$ on paper. Include vertical asymptotes at x-values where the graph is undefined.

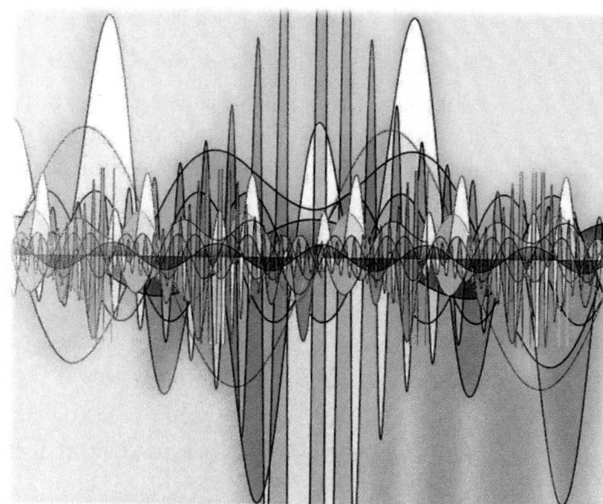

11. Write equations for sinusoids with these characteristics:

a. a cosine function with amplitude 1.5, period π, and phase shift $-\frac{\pi}{2}$

b. a sine function with minimum value -5, maximum value -1, and one cycle starting at $x = \frac{\pi}{4}$ and ending at $x = \frac{3\pi}{4}$

c. a cosine function with period 6π, phase shift π, vertical translation 3, and amplitude 2 $y = 3 + 2\cos\frac{x - \pi}{3}$

Exercise 8 [Ask] "What are the independent and dependent variables?" [The independent variable is time; the dependent variable is brightness.] "What are the domain and range?" [The domain is unbounded; the range is $20 \le y \le 50$.]

Exercise 10 You might suggest that students follow the instructions given in Calculator Note 9C to eliminate the drag lines; however, the graph will then appear broken.

10.

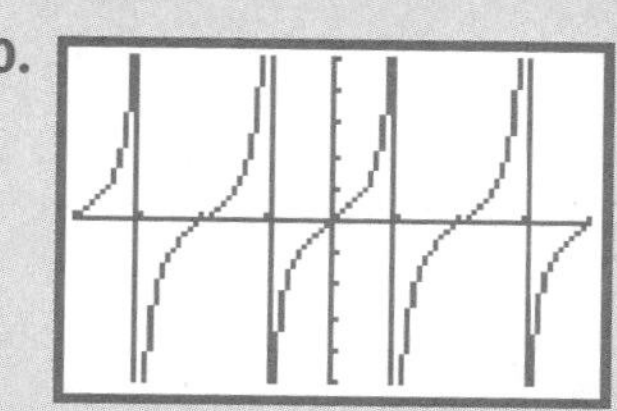

$[-2\pi, 2\pi, \pi/2, -5, 5, 1]$

10a. A drag line appears. The value of $\tan\frac{\pi}{2}$ is undefined, so $x = \frac{\pi}{2}$ is a vertical asymptote. The vertical asymptotes are $x = \ldots -\frac{3\pi}{2}, -\frac{\pi}{2}, \frac{\pi}{2}, \frac{3\pi}{2}, \ldots$, or in general, $x = \frac{\pi}{2} + \pi n$, where n is an integer.

10c. On a unit circle, the point rotated $\frac{\pi}{5}$, the origin, and the point rotated $\frac{6\pi}{5}$ are collinear. So, the segment from the origin to the point rotated $\frac{\pi}{5}$ has the same slope as the segment from the origin to the point rotated $\frac{6\pi}{5}$.

10d.

8b.

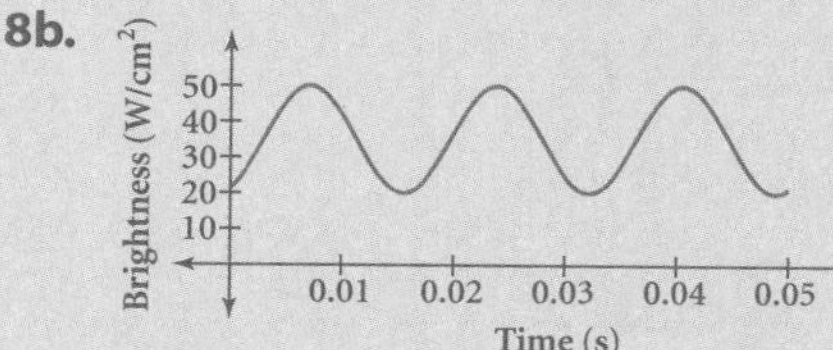

11a. $y = 1.5\cos 2\left(x + \frac{\pi}{2}\right)$

11b. $y = -3 + 2\sin 4\left(x - \frac{\pi}{4}\right)$

Exercise 12 Students can download these data from the Calculator Programs and Data CD or from www.keymath.com/DAA. You might use the Fathom demonstration Day Times.

12a.

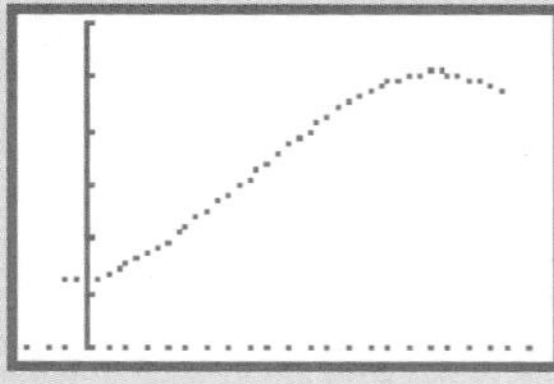

$[-30, 225, 10, 9, 15, 1]$

$$y = 2\sin\frac{2\pi(x - 80)}{365} + 12.15$$

12b. According to the equation, the least amount of daylight, 10.15 h, occurred on December 20.

12c. The graph should be similar in shape but with a greater amplitude.

Exercise 13 The connection at the top of page 593 explains this phenomenon.

MAKING THE CONNECTION

Doppler radar is a key weather-forecasting tool. It takes advantage of the Doppler effect by measuring frequency change in radio waves sent out. Waves reflected by a weather front moving away from the antenna change to a lower frequency. Waves reflected by a front moving toward the antenna change to a higher frequency. A computer uses the frequency changes to show the directions and speeds of the weather front, producing the Doppler radar images seen on television and on the Internet.

12. **APPLICATION** The table gives the number of hours between sunrise and sunset for the period between December 21, 1995, and July 29, 1996, in New Orleans, Louisiana, which is located at approximately 30° N latitude.

Date	Hours	Date	Hours	Date	Hours	Date	Hours	Date	Hours
21 Dec	10.217	30 Jan	10.717	11 Mar	11.833	20 May	13.750	29 June	14.050
26 Dec	10.233	4 Feb	10.850	16 Mar	11.983	25 May	13.833	4 July	14.017
31 Dec	10.250	9 Feb	10.967	21 Mar	12.133	30 May	13.917	9 July	13.983
5 Jan	10.283	14 Feb	11.100	26 Mar	12.283	4 June	13.983	14 July	13.900
10 Jan	10.350	19 Feb	11.250	31 Mar	12.433	9 June	14.017	24 July	13.833
15 Jan	10.417	24 Feb	11.400	5 Apr	12.583	14 June	14.050	29 July	13.750
20 Jan	10.517	1 Mar	11.533	10 Apr	12.733	19 June	14.083		
25 Jan	10.617	6 Mar	11.683	15 Apr	12.833	24 June	14.083		

a. Assign December 31 as day zero, let x represent the number of days after December 31, and let y represent the number of hours between sunrise and sunset. Graph these data and find a sinusoidal model.

b. Which day had the least amount of daylight? How many hours of daylight were there on this day?

c. For locations that are far north, the tilt of the Earth as it orbits the Sun causes days to be very long in summer and very short in winter. (For more information, see the links at **www.keymath.com/DAA**.) Homer, Alaska, is located at approximately 60° N latitude. How does its daylight graph compare to your graph in 12a?

The Mississippi River Bridge in New Orleans, Louisiana, at sunset

13. A train whistle produces a sound at 440 Hz.

a. When the train is not moving, the sound waves emanate evenly in all directions. This diagram shows how the sound waves travel toward persons A and B. If the sound wave completes 8 cycles over a distance of 2π meters, what is its wavelength (period)? 0.79 m

b. When the train heads east at 20 m/s, the sound waves are more compressed in the direction of motion. This diagram shows how the sound waves travel toward persons A and B in this situation. What is the approximate wavelength of the sound wave traveling toward person A if it completes 8.5 cycles in 2π meters? 0.74 m

c. In the situation in 13b, what is the approximate wavelength of the sound wave traveling toward person B if it completes 7.75 cycles in 2π meters? 0.81 m

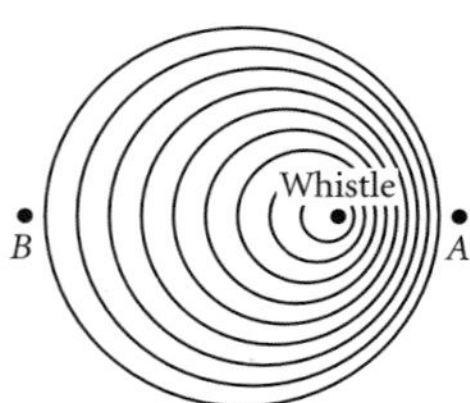

15.

Degrees	0°	15°	30°	45°	60°	75°	90°	105°	120°	135°	150°	165°	180°
Radians	0	$\frac{\pi}{12}$	$\frac{\pi}{6}$	$\frac{\pi}{4}$	$\frac{\pi}{3}$	$\frac{5\pi}{12}$	$\frac{\pi}{2}$	$\frac{7\pi}{12}$	$\frac{2\pi}{3}$	$\frac{3\pi}{4}$	$\frac{5\pi}{6}$	$\frac{11\pi}{12}$	π

Degrees	195°	210°	225°	240°	255°	270°	285°	300°	315°	330°	345°	360°
Radians	$\frac{13\pi}{12}$	$\frac{7\pi}{6}$	$\frac{5\pi}{4}$	$\frac{4\pi}{3}$	$\frac{17\pi}{12}$	$\frac{3\pi}{2}$	$\frac{19\pi}{12}$	$\frac{5\pi}{3}$	$\frac{7\pi}{4}$	$\frac{11\pi}{6}$	$\frac{23\pi}{12}$	2π

Science
CONNECTION

As a vehicle speeds toward you, the sound of its horn, whistle, or engine is high in pitch. This is because the sound waves in front of the vehicle are being compressed as it moves. This motion causes more vibrations to reach your ear per second, resulting in a higher pitched sound. As the vehicle moves away from you, there are fewer vibrations per second, and thus you hear a lower pitched sound. This change in pitch is known as the Doppler effect, discovered by the Austrian mathematician and physicist Christian Doppler (1803–1853).

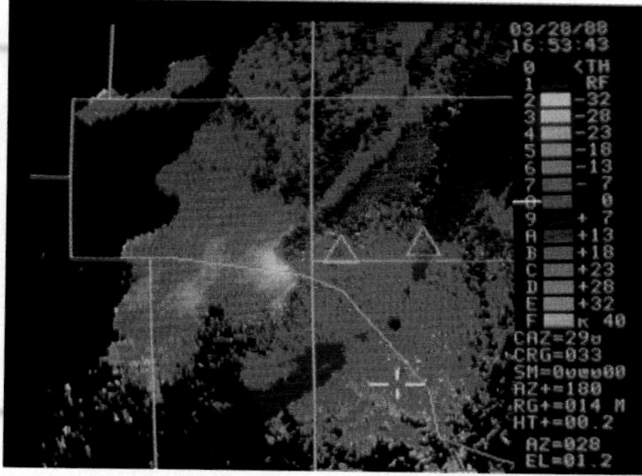

The Doppler effect applies to light and radio waves, as well as sound waves. This effect is the principle behind Doppler radar, shown here recording wind velocity. Doppler radar has been used to forecast weather patterns since the 1970s.

Review

8.6 **14.** Find the measure of the labeled angle in each triangle.

a. 40°, 7, 4.7, A

$A \approx 73.2°$ or $A \approx 106.8°$

b.

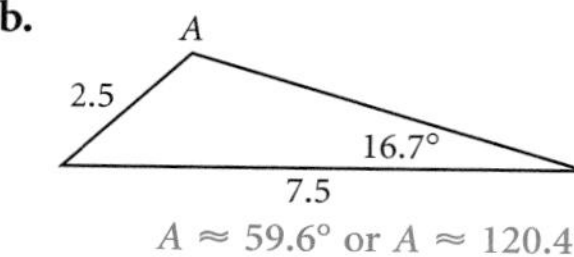

$A \approx 59.6°$ or $A \approx 120.4°$

10.2 **15.** Make a table of angle measures from 0° to 360° by 15° increments. Then find the radian measure of each angle. Express the radian measure as a multiple of π. See page 592.

10.2 **16.** The second hand of a wristwatch is 0.5 cm long.

a. What is the speed, in meters per hour, of the tip of the second hand? 1.884 m/h

b. How long would the minute hand of the same watch have to be for its tip to have the same speed as the second hand? 30 cm

c. How long would the hour hand of the same watch have to be for its tip to have the same speed as the second hand? 360 cm

d. What is the angular speed, in radians per hour, of the three hands in 16a–c?

e. Make an observation about the speeds you found.

5.5 **17.** Consider these three functions:

i. $f(x) = -\frac{3}{2}x + 6$ **ii.** $g(x) = (x + 2)^2 - 4$ **iii.** $h(x) = 1.3^{x+6} - 8$

a. Find the inverse of each function.

b. Graph each function and its inverse.

c. Which of the inverses, if any, are functions?

18. Use what you know about the unit circle to find possible values of θ in each equation. Use domain $0° \le \theta \le 360°$ or $0 \le \theta < 2\pi$.

a. $\cos\theta = \sin 86°$
$\theta = 4°$ and $\theta = 356°$

b. $\sin\theta = \cos\frac{19\pi}{12}$
$\theta = \frac{\pi}{12}$ and $\theta = \frac{11\pi}{12}$

c. $\sin\theta = \cos 123°$
$\theta = 213°$ and $\theta = 327°$

d. $\cos\theta = \sin\frac{7\pi}{6}$
$\theta = \frac{2\pi}{3}$ and $\theta = \frac{4\pi}{3}$

EXTENSIONS

A. Example B ignores the relatively small north-south component of the motion. Ask students to find an equation for the distance that includes both the east-west and the north-south components.
$\left[y = \sqrt{\left(300 + 10\cos\left(\frac{2\pi x}{15}\right)\right)^2 + \left(10\sin\left(\frac{2\pi x}{15}\right)\right)^2}\right]$
Then have them compare the total distance to just the east-west component. Discuss whether a maximum difference of 0.16 mi is really small enough to be ignored in this context.

B. Ask students to use a photometer (light sensor) to collect real data for Exercise 8 or a microphone probe to collect data for Exercise 13.

Exercise 14 Students might legitimately find the measure of only the acute angle for 14a and only the obtuse angle for 14b because they can see from the sketches which angles are requested. **[Ask]** "If the side lengths and angle measures were listed rather than displayed on sketches, would your answers be the same?" [No; without the sketches this would be the ambiguous case (SSA), and each angle could have one of two measures. For the triangles not drawn: In 14a, $A \approx 106.8°$; in 14b, $A \approx 59.6°$.] Discussion of the ambiguous case previews issues that will arise in Lesson 10.4, Example A.

Students might give both answers to each part of the exercise, considering the case ambiguous. **[Alert]** Rounding in 14b can be tricky. To the nearest hundredth of a degree, the answers are 59.55° and 120.45°, both of which could be rounded up to angle measures that wouldn't sum to 180°. However, if the second supplementary angle is found by subtracting 59.6° from 180°, its measure will be 120.4°.

Exercise 16c The hour hand completes one revolution in 12 hours. It takes 12 times as long as the minute hand, so to have the same speed it would have to be 12 times as long.

16d. second hand: 377 radians/h; minute hand: 6.28 radians/h; hour hand: 0.52 radian/h

16e. The speed of the tip of a clock hand varies directly with the length of the hand. Angular speed is independent of the length of the hand.

17a. i. $y = -\frac{2}{3}x + 4$

17a. ii. $y = \pm\sqrt{x + 4} - 2$

17a. iii. $y = \frac{\log(x + 8)}{\log 1.3} - 6$

17c. The inverses of i and iii are functions.

See page 900 for answers to Exercise 17b.

LESSON
10.4

PLANNING

LESSON OUTLINE

One day:

5 min	Example A
10 min	Investigation
10 min	Example B
10 min	Sharing
10 min	Exercises

MATERIALS

- graph paper
- Coordinate Axes for Periodic Functions (W), *optional*
- Calculator Note 5B, *optional*

TEACHING

In Lesson 5.5, students studied inverse relations and determined when inverses of functions are also functions. In Lesson 5.6, they applied these ideas to develop logarithmic functions as inverses of exponential functions. In this lesson they extend inverse trigonometric ratios (Lesson 8.3) to inverse trigonometric functions. In Lesson 8.6 (The Law of Sines), students encountered a difficulty with inverse trigonometric ratios that must be surmounted here: More than one angle can have the same sine. If your students have not encountered parametric equations, you can skip the discussion of the graph of inverse relations at the end of the lesson or use the calculator's draw function to draw the inverse function. (See Calculator Note 5B.)

LESSON 10.4

Inverses of Trigonometric Functions

As you learned in Chapter 8, trigonometric functions of an angle in a right triangle give the ratios of sides when you know an angle. The inverses of these functions give the measure of the angle when you know the ratio of sides.

$$\sin^{-1}\left(\frac{a}{c}\right) = A$$

$$\cos^{-1}\left(\frac{b}{c}\right) = A$$

$$\tan^{-1}\left(\frac{a}{b}\right) = A$$

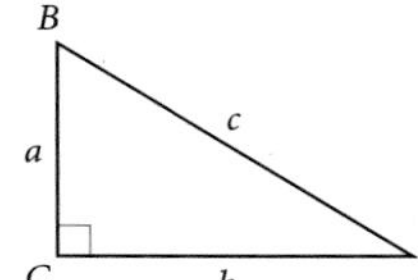

In Lesson 10.1, you learned that the trigonometric ratios apply to any angle measure, not just acute measures. The sine, cosine, and tangent functions have repeating values. So, if you want to find an angle whose sine is 0.5, there will be many answers. For this reason, the calculator answer for an inverse trigonometric function is not always the angle that you're looking for.

EXAMPLE A Find the measure of $\angle B$.

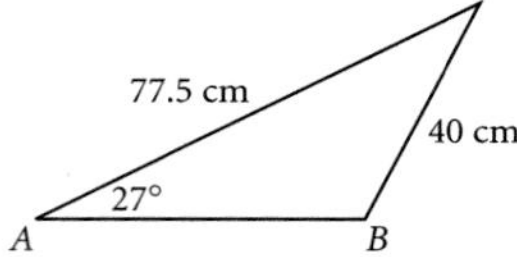

▶ Solution This is not a right triangle, but you can use the Law of Sines to find $m\angle B$.

$$\frac{\sin 27°}{40} = \frac{\sin B}{77.5}$$

$$\sin B = \frac{77.5 \sin 27°}{40}$$

$$B = \sin^{-1}\left(\frac{77.5 \sin 27°}{40}\right) \approx 61.6°$$

Recall from geometry that two sides and a non-included angle do not determine a specific triangle. This situation is an ambiguous case. So, two different triangles can be constructed with the information given in the diagram. In one of these cases, $\angle B$ is acute; in the other, $\angle B$ is obtuse. The calculator has given you the reference angle, or the acute angle. The obtuse angle with the same sine as 61.6° measures 180° − 61.6°, or 118.4°.

$$\sin 118.4° = \sin 61.6° \approx 0.8796$$

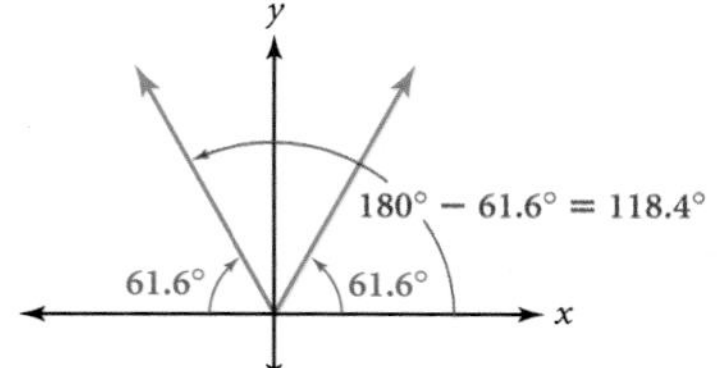

One Step

Have students refer to their data from the pendulum investigation in Lesson 10.3. **[Ask]** "When will the pendulum be $\frac{2}{3}$ of the way from the end of its swing to the bottom of its swing?" The question is intentionally ambiguous so students will consider both ends of all the pendulum's swings. During Sharing, ask students how to restrict their modeling function so that the inverse relation will be a function and how to define the inverse trigonometric functions.

▶ EXAMPLE A

This example revisits the ambiguous case of Lesson 8.6 from the point of view of trigonometric functions.

As needed, remind students that to find angle measures and side lengths of nonright triangles they can use the Law of Sines or the Law of Cosines. Students saw the ambiguous case on page 471.

As students look at the graph at the top of page 595, check that they understand what they are looking at. **[Ask]** "What is the blue line?" $\left[y = \frac{77.5 \sin 27°}{40}\right]$

Shown at right are the graphs of $y = \sin x$ and $y = \frac{77.5 \sin 27°}{40}$. In the interval $0° \leq x \leq 180°$, the graphs intersect at 61.6° and again at 118.4°. The two solutions are based on the symmetry of the sine graph—118.4° is the same distance from the x-intercept at 180° as 61.6° is from the x-intercept at 0°.

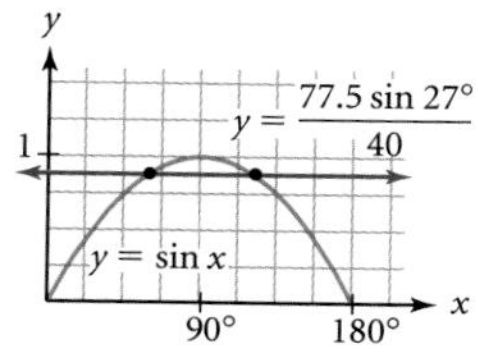

When you evaluate an inverse trigonometric function with your calculator, you only get one answer. A graph can help you make sense of a situation that has more than one solution.

You may recall that the inverse of a relation maps every point (x, y) to a point (y, x). You get the inverse of a relation by exchanging the x- and y-coordinates of all points. That's why a graph and its inverse are reflections of each other across the line $y = x$.

At right are the graphs of the exponential function $y = b^x$ and its inverse, $x = b^y$, which you've learned to call $y = \log_b x$. Notice that each is a function.

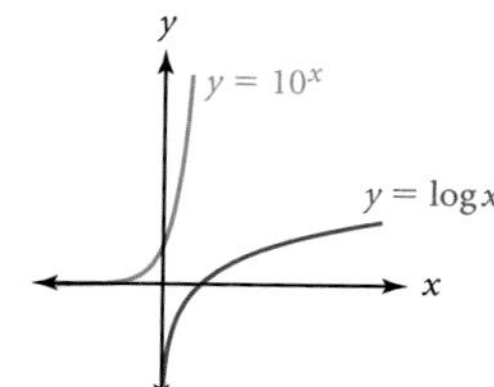

The graphs of the equation $y = x^2$ and its inverse, $x = y^2$, are also shown. Notice that in this case the inverse is not a function. When you solve the equation $4 = y^2$, how many solutions do you find?

two

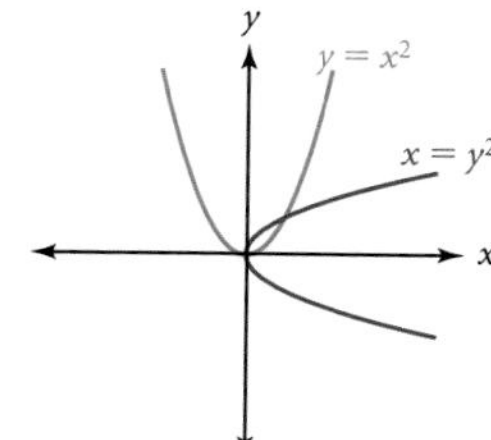

Investigation

Exploring the Inverses

In this investigation you will explore the graphs of trigonometric functions and their inverses.

Step 1 On graph paper, carefully graph $y = \sin x$ on x- and y-axes ranging from -10 to 10. Mark the x-axis at intervals of $\frac{\pi}{2}$, and mark the y-axis at intervals of 1. Use the same scale for both axes. That is, the distance from 0 to 3.14 on your y-axis should be the same as the distance from 0 to π on your x-axis. Test a few points on your graph to make sure they fit the sine function.

Step 2 Add the line $y = x$ to your graph. Fold your paper along this line, and then trace the image of $y = \sin x$ onto your paper.

Verify that this transformation maps the point $\left(\frac{\pi}{2}, 1\right)$ onto $\left(1, \frac{\pi}{2}\right)$, $(\pi, 0)$ onto $(0, \pi)$, and $\left(\frac{3\pi}{2}, -1\right)$ onto $\left(-1, \frac{3\pi}{2}\right)$. In general, every point (x, y) should map onto (y, x).

Guiding the Investigation

Students might use The Geometer's Sketchpad to complete this investigation. Instructions for drawing the same graphs on calculators (with parametric equations) appear at the end of the lesson. If students work by hand, they can use the top half of a sheet of graph paper for Steps 1–4 and the bottom half for Step 5. Or you can hand out the Coordinate Axes for Periodic Functions worksheet from Lesson 10.3.

Step 2 Students might use a pencil to draw the curve with a heavy line, fold the paper, and then retrace the curve on the back of the paper. Some of the penciled curve will be reflected across the line.

Steps 1, 2, 4

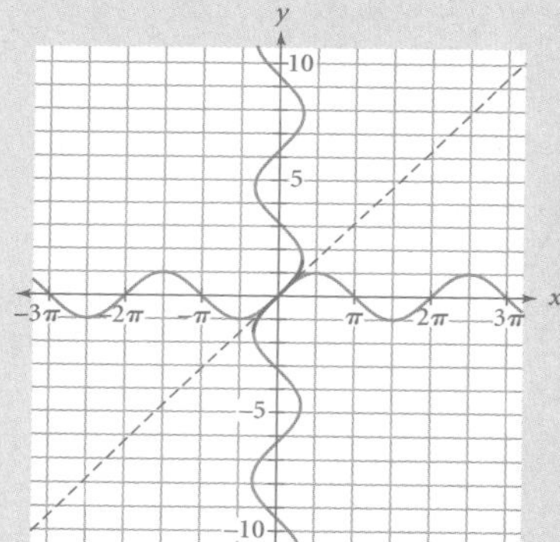

LESSON OBJECTIVES

- Understand the inverse trigonometric functions as functions that give only one of infinitely many angles whose measures have a specific trigonometric ratio
- Define *principal value*
- Use graphs to solve trigonometric equations for values other than the principal value
- Distinguish between the equations $x = \cos^{-1} 0.5$ and $\cos x = 0.5$

NCTM STANDARDS

	CONTENT		PROCESS
	Number		Problem Solving
✓	Algebra	✓	Reasoning
	Geometry	✓	Communication
	Measurement		Connections
	Data/Probability		Representation

Step 3 $x = \sin y$ is not a function. There is more than one y-value for each x-value.

Steps 4, 5 [Ask] "Why do you think the book says to darken part of the inverse?" [The undarkened part of the inverse relation is not a function. Only when the inverse is restricted to the darkened part can it be considered a function.]

Step 4 The notation $\sin^{-1} x$ is sometimes written as $\arcsin x$, meaning "the arc whose sine is x." (Trigonometric functions can be considered as functions of arcs, or chords, rather than of angles.) It can be read as "inverse sine of x" or "arc sine x" or "the angle whose sine is x." The last phrasing will help students understand the meaning.

Step 4 The portion of $x = \sin y$ for $-\frac{\pi}{2} \leq y \leq \frac{\pi}{2}$ is a function. There is only one y-value for each x-value.

Step 5 $0 \leq y \leq \pi$

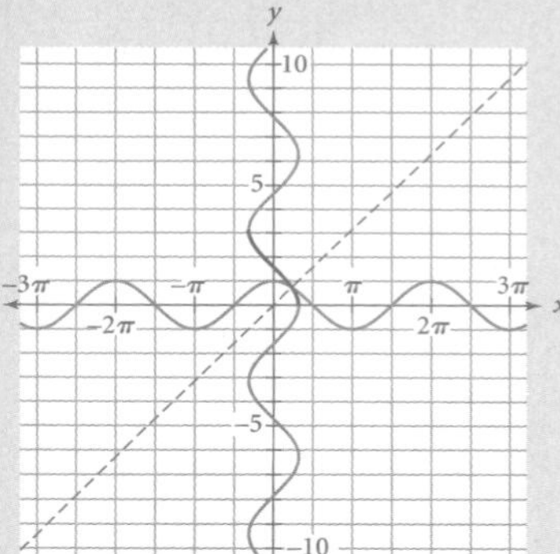

▸ EXAMPLE B

Encourage students to sketch the reference triangles when they solve equations involving inverse trigonometric functions.

[Ask] "Geometrically, what does subtracting $\frac{\pi}{2}$ do to the solution x?" [In terms of angles, it rotates the solution 90° clockwise. On the number line, it shifts x to the left.]

Step 3 — If your original graph is $y = \sin x$, then the equation of the inverse, when x and y are switched, is $x = \sin y$. Is the inverse of $y = \sin x$ a function? Why or why not?

Step 4 — Darken the portion of the curve $x = \sin y$, between $y = -\frac{\pi}{2}$ and $y = \frac{\pi}{2}$. Is this portion of the graph a function? Why or why not?

Step 5 — Carefully sketch graphs of $y = \cos x$ and its inverse, $x = \cos y$, on axes similar to those you used in Step 1. Then darken the portion of the curve $x = \cos y$ that is a function. What domain did you select?

When you solve an equation like $x^2 = 7$ with your calculator, the square root function gives only one value. But there are actually two solutions. This is because the inverse of the parabola $y = x^2$ is not a function.

Similarly, the calculator command $\sin^{-1}$ is a function—it gives only one answer. However, the actual inverse of the sine function is not a function but a relation. So, the equation $\sin x = 0.7$ has many solutions, because x can be any angle whose sine is 0.7.

EXAMPLE B Find the first four positive values of x for which $3 + 2\cos\left(x + \frac{\pi}{2}\right) = 2$.

▸ Solution Graphically, this is equivalent to finding the first four intersections of the equations $y = 3 + 2\cos\left(x + \frac{\pi}{2}\right)$ and $y = 2$ for positive values of x. Examine this graph.

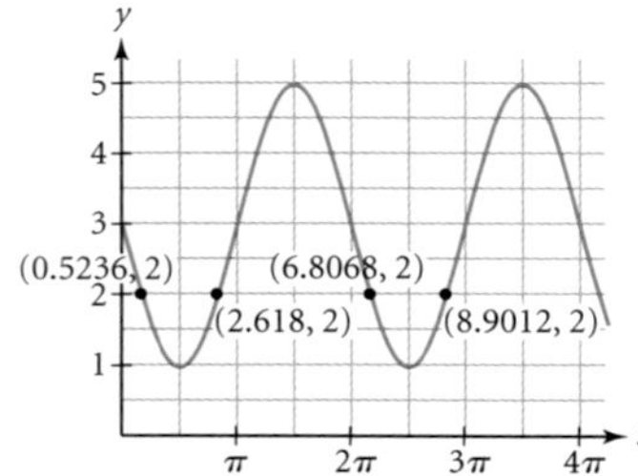

Solving the system of equations symbolically, you will find one answer.

$$3 + 2\cos\left(x + \frac{\pi}{2}\right) = 2$$

$$2\cos\left(x + \frac{\pi}{2}\right) = -1$$

$$\cos\left(x + \frac{\pi}{2}\right) = -\frac{1}{2}$$

$$x + \frac{\pi}{2} = \cos^{-1}\left(-\frac{1}{2}\right)$$

$$x = \cos^{-1}\left(-\frac{1}{2}\right) - \frac{\pi}{2}$$

The unit circle shows that the first positive solution for $\cos x = -\frac{1}{2}$ is $\frac{2\pi}{3}$. Substitute $\frac{2\pi}{3}$ for $\cos^{-1}\left(-\frac{1}{2}\right)$ and continue solving.

$$x = \cos^{-1}\left(-\frac{1}{2}\right) - \frac{\pi}{2}$$

$$x = \frac{2\pi}{3} - \frac{\pi}{2}$$

$$x = \frac{\pi}{6} \approx 0.5236$$

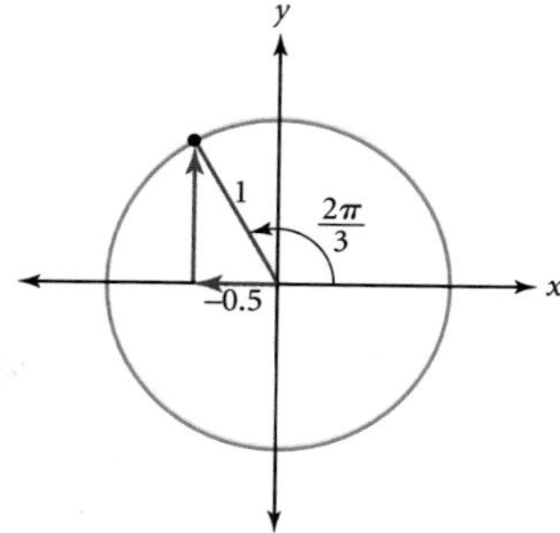

So, one solution is $x = \frac{\pi}{6}$, or approximately 0.5236. Graphs of trigonometric functions follow a pattern and have certain symmetries. You can look at the graph to find the other solutions.

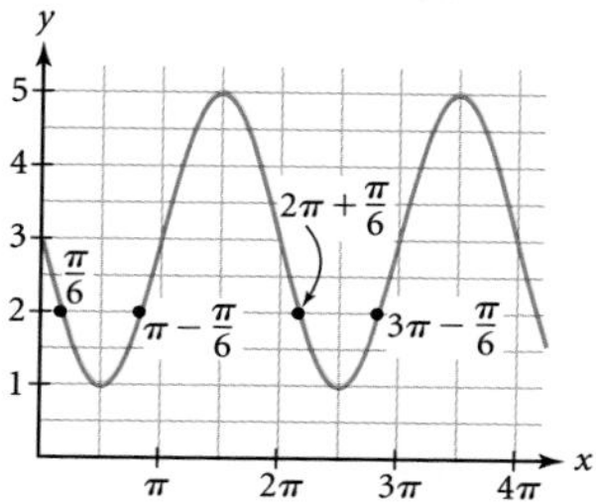

So, the next solutions are

$$x = \pi - \frac{\pi}{6} = \frac{5\pi}{6} \approx 2.6180$$

$$x = 2\pi + \frac{\pi}{6} = \frac{13\pi}{6} \approx 6.8068$$

$$x = 3\pi - \frac{\pi}{6} = \frac{17\pi}{6} \approx 8.9012$$

Consider the graphs of $y = \sin x$ and its inverse relation, $x = \sin y$. You can graph these on your calculator using the parametric equations $x_1 = t$ and $y_1 = \sin t$, and $x_2 = \sin t$ and $y_2 = t$. The graph of the relation $x = \sin y$ extends infinitely in the y-direction.

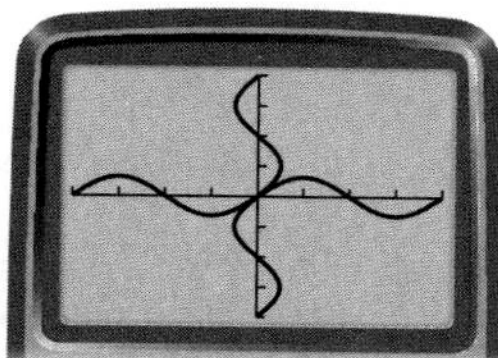

$[-2\pi, 2\pi, \pi/2, -2\pi, 2\pi, \pi/2]$

The function $y = \sin^{-1} x$ is the portion of the graph of $x = \sin y$ such that $-\frac{\pi}{2} \leq y \leq \frac{\pi}{2}$ (or $-90° \leq y \leq 90°$).

Similarly, the function $y = \cos^{-1} x$ is the portion of the graph of $x = \cos y$, such that $0 \leq y \leq \pi$ (or $0° \leq y \leq 180°$).

Because inverse cosine is defined as a function, the equation $x = \cos^{-1} 0.5$ has only one solution, whereas $\cos x = 0.5$ has infinitely many solutions. As you saw in Example B, some problems may have multiple solutions, but the inverse cosine and inverse sine functions on your calculator will give you only the value within the ranges given above. This value is called the **principal value.**

SHARING IDEAS

If your students have not encountered parametric equations, you can de-emphasize the point that the relation at the end of the lesson was graphed parametrically. You could instead graph two functions in Y1 and Y2 and find the intersections on the graph.

Continue to encourage students to ask questions that probe the deeper meaning of the lesson. You might focus attention beyond "how" and "what" questions to "why" questions by asking whether students encountered any surprises.

[Ask] "What are the ranges of the inverse trigonometric functions, according to your calculator?" Students can experiment by graphing or by using guess-and-check. Standard ranges are: for $\sin^{-1}$, from $-\frac{\pi}{2}$ to $\frac{\pi}{2}$; for $\cos^{-1}$, from 0 to π; for $\tan^{-1}$, from $-\frac{\pi}{2}$ to $\frac{\pi}{2}$. Follow up by asking the question "Why?" [Over these domains, the sine, cosine, and tangent functions are only increasing or decreasing and therefore take on each value only once, so their inverse relations are functions. The inverse trigonometric functions, then, are inverses of the trigonometric functions restricted to these domains.]

Ask students about any previously encountered functions whose inverse relations were not functions, and ask how they found the inverses. [They restricted the domain of the function $y = x^2$ to nonnegative values of x so that the inverse relation was the function $y = \sqrt{x}$.]

Assessing Progress

You can evaluate students' ability to graph sine and cosine functions and to tell whether a graph is the graph of a function.

Closing the Lesson

The inverse relations of trigonometric functions aren't themselves functions, but sections of their graphs are graphs of functions. The domains of $y = \sin^{-1} x$ and $y = \cos^{-1} x$ are from −1 to 1; the domain of $y = \tan^{-1} x$ consists of all real numbers. The values of x in the range of the inverse function are called the **principal values.**

BUILDING UNDERSTANDING

Students practice evaluating and applying the inverse trigonometric functions. If you are not teaching parametric equations, assign only the nonparametric equation of 19b and 19d of Exercise 19.

ASSIGNING HOMEWORK

Essential	1–4, 11
Performance assessment	5–15
Portfolio	11
Journal	5, 8
Group	11, 15
Review	16–19

MATERIALS

- compasses or circle templates

Helping with the Exercises

Remind students to check whether their calculators are in Degree mode or Radian mode.

Exercise 2 Students can use either the unit circle or a graph in Function mode.

2a. $\frac{\pi}{6}, \frac{5\pi}{6}, -\frac{11\pi}{6}, -\frac{7\pi}{6}$

2b. $\frac{3\pi}{8}, \frac{13\pi}{8}, -\frac{13\pi}{8}, -\frac{3\pi}{8}$

2c. 0.47, 5.81, −5.81, −0.47

2d. 1.47, 1.67, −4.81, −4.61

6.

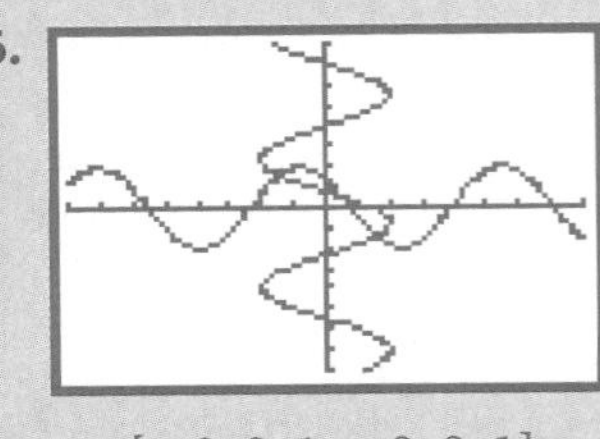

[−8, 8, 1, −8, 8, 1]

Exercise 8 As needed, help students see that the first three cycles refer to the domain $0 \leq x \leq 6\pi$.

See page 900 for answers to Exercise 4.

EXERCISES

Practice Your Skills

1. Find the principal value of each expression to the nearest tenth of a degree and then to the nearest hundredth of a radian.

a. $\sin^{-1} 0.4665$ 27.8° and 0.49 **b.** $\sin^{-1}(-0.2471)$ −14.3° and −0.25 **c.** $\cos^{-1}(-0.8113)$ 144.2° and 2.52 **d.** $\cos^{-1} 0.9805$ 11.3° and 0.20

2. Find all four values of x between -2π and 2π that satisfy each equation.

a. $\sin x = \sin\frac{\pi}{6}$ **b.** $\cos x = \cos\frac{3\pi}{8}$ **c.** $\cos x = \cos 0.47$ **d.** $\sin x = \sin 1.47$

3. Illustrate the answers to Exercise 2 by plotting the points on the graph of the sine or cosine curve. See page 599.

4. Illustrate the answers to Exercise 2 by drawing segments on a graph of the unit circle.

Reason and Apply

5. Explain why your calculator can't find $\sin^{-1} 1.28$. $-1 \leq \sin x \leq 1$. There is no angle whose sine is 1.28.

6. On the same coordinate axes, create graphs of $y = 2\cos\left(x + \frac{\pi}{4}\right)$ and its inverse.

7. Find values of x that satisfy the conditions given.

a. Find the first two positive solutions of $0.4665 = \sin x$. $x \approx 0.485$ or $x \approx 2.656$

b. Find the two negative solutions closest to zero of $-0.8113 = \cos x$. $x \approx -2.517$ or $x \approx -3.766$

8. How many solutions to the equation $-2.6 = 3\sin x$ occur in the first three positive cycles of the function $y = 3\sin x$? Explain your answer.

9. Find the measure of the largest angle of a triangle with sides 4.66 m, 5.93 m, and 8.54 m. 106.9°

10. In $\triangle ABC$, $AB = 7$ cm, $CA = 3.9$ cm, and $m\angle B = 27°$. Find the two possible measurements for $\angle C$. 55° or 125°

11. *Mini-Investigation* Consider the inverse of the tangent function.

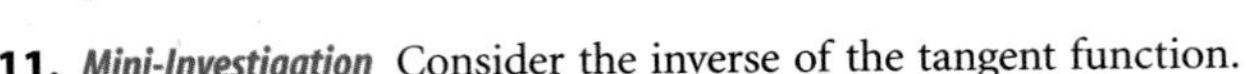

a. Find the values of $\tan^{-1} x$ for several positive and negative values of x. possible answer (using radians): (10, 1.471), (1, 0.785), (0, 0), (−1, −0.785), (−10, −1.471)

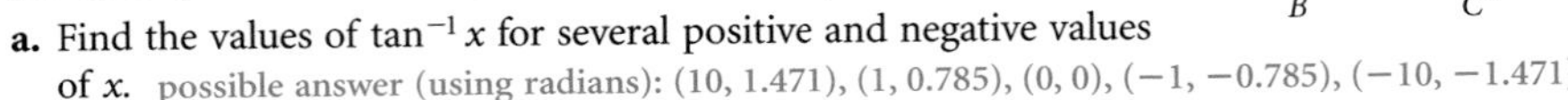

b. Based on these answers, predict what the graph of $y = \tan^{-1} x$ will look like. Sketch your prediction. See page 599.

c. How does the graph of $y = \tan^{-1} x$ compare to the graph of $x = \tan y$? See page 599.

d. Use your calculator to verify your graph of the function $y = \tan^{-1} x$. See page 599.

12. Shown at right are a constant function and two cycles of a cosine graph over the domain $0° \leq x \leq 720°$. The first intersection point is shown. What are the next three intersection values? 306.4°, 413.6°, 666.4°

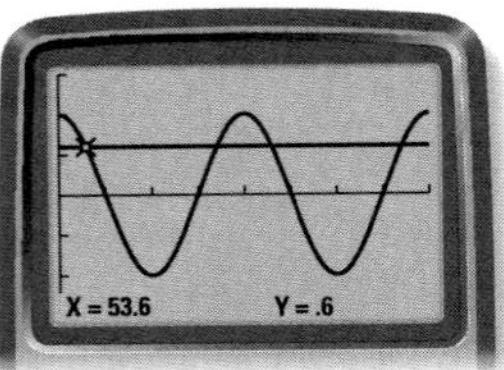

[0, 720, 90, −1.5, 1.5, 0.5]

8. 6 solutions. See the six intersections of $y = -2.6$ and $y = 3\sin x$ in the interval $0 \leq x \leq 6\pi$.

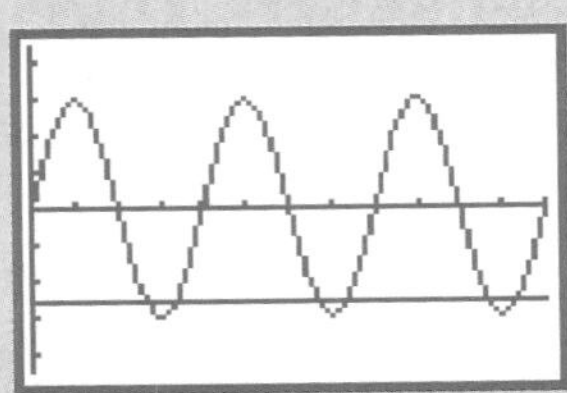

[0, 6π, π/2, −4.5, 4.5, 1]

Exercises 9, 10 Encourage students to sketch the triangles. They can then use the Law of Cosines or the Law of Sines.

Exercise 11 Students might use either Degree mode or Radian mode. The general observations will be the same no matter what the units, but the ranges, domains, and specific points depend on which mode students use.

13. The cosine graph at right shows two maximum values, at 50° and 770°. If the first point of intersection with the constant function occurs when $x = 170°$, what is the value of x at the second point of intersection? 650°

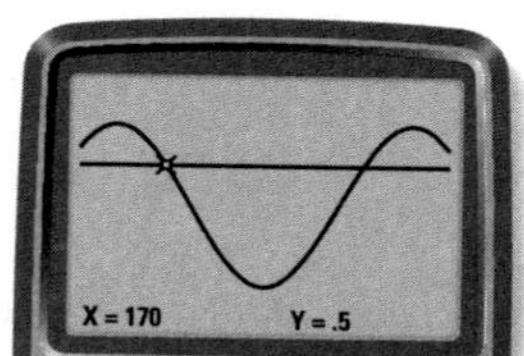

14. Find the exact value of each expression.

a. $\sin\left(\sin^{-1}\frac{4}{5}\right)$ $\frac{4}{5}$ **b.** $\sin\left(\sin^{-1}\left(-\frac{2}{3}\right)\right)$ $-\frac{2}{3}$

c. $\sin^{-1}\left(\sin\frac{2\pi}{3}\right)$ $\frac{\pi}{3}$ **d.** $\cos^{-1}(\cos(-45°))$ 45°

15. **APPLICATION** When a beam of light passes through a polarized lens, its intensity is cut in half, or $I_1 = 0.5I_0$. To further reduce the intensity, you can place another polarized lens in front of it. The intensity of the beam after passing through the second lens depends on the angle of the second filter to the first. For instance, if the second lens is polarized in the same direction, it will have little or no additional effect on the beam of light. If the second lens is rotated so that its axis is $\theta°$ from the first lens's axis, then the intensity in watts per square meter $\left(\text{W/m}^2\right)$ of the transmitted beam, I_2, is

$$I_2 = I_1 \cos^2\theta$$

where I_1 is the intensity in watts per square meter of the incoming beam.

I_0 Unpolarized light I_1 I_2 θ

a. A beam of light passes successively through two polarized sheets. The angle between the polarization axes of the filters is 30°. If the intensity of the incoming beam is 16.0×10^{-4} W/m², what is the intensity of the beam after passing through the first filter? The second filter? 8.0×10^{-4} W/m²; 6.0×10^{-4} W/m²

b. A polarized beam of light has intensity 3 W/m². The beam then passes through a second polarized lens and intensity drops to 1.5 W/m². What is the angle between the polarization axes? $\theta = 45°$

c. At what angle should the axes of two polarized lenses be placed to cut the intensity of a transmitted beam to 0 W/m²? $\theta = 90°$

Technology CONNECTION

Skiers, boaters, and photographers know that ordinary sunglasses reduce brightness but do not remove glare. Polarized lenses will eliminate the glare from reflective surfaces such as snow, water, sand, and roads. This is because glare is the effect of reflected light being polarized parallel to the reflective surface. Polarized lenses will filter, or block out, this polarized light. You can think of a polarized lens as a set of tiny slits. The slits block light at certain angles, while allowing light to pass through select angles.

The photo on the left was taken without a polarized lens and the one on the right was taken with a polarized lens. Notice how the polarized lens reduces glare.

3a.

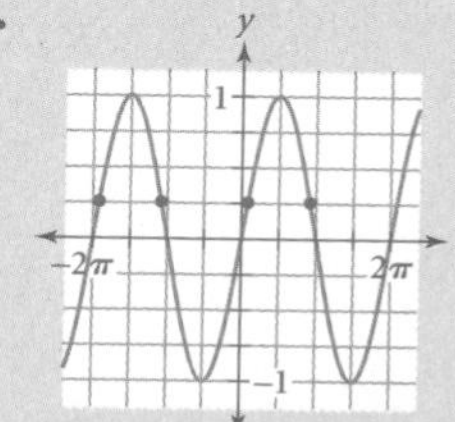

3b.

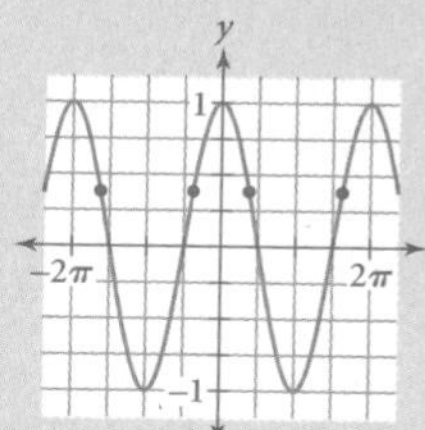

3c.

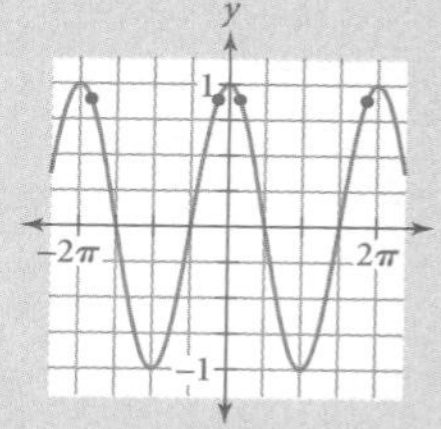

3d.

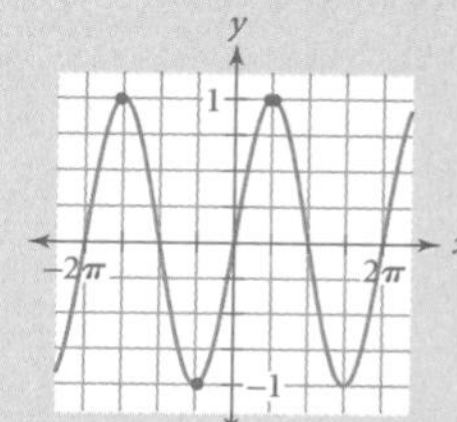

11b. The domain is all real numbers. The range is $-\frac{\pi}{2} < y < \frac{\pi}{2}$ (or $-90° < y < 90°$). Sketches will vary.

11c. The function $y = \tan^{-1} x$ is the portion of $x = \tan y$, such that $-\frac{\pi}{2} < y < \frac{\pi}{2}$ (or $-90° < y < 90°$).

11d.

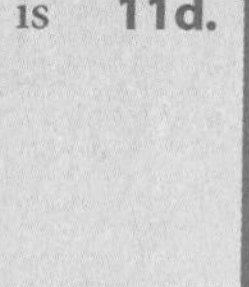

$[-20, 20, 5, -3\pi/2, 3\pi/2, \pi/2]$

18a. $x = \frac{6 \pm \sqrt{12}}{4}$ or $x = \frac{3 \pm \sqrt{3}}{2}$

18b. $x = \frac{1}{2}$ or $x = 6$

18c. $x = -\frac{2}{3} \pm \frac{\sqrt{32}}{2}i$ or $x = -\frac{2}{3} \pm \frac{2\sqrt{2}}{3}i$

Exercise 19 Students can do this exercise in either Degree mode or Radian mode. The answers will be the same except for the t-values, t-step, and t-range.

19a. Ellipse with center at origin, horizontal major axis of length 6 units, and vertical minor axis of length 4 units. The parametric equations are $x = 3\cos t$ and $y = 2\sin t$.

19b. $\left(\frac{x+1}{3}\right)^2 + \left(\frac{y-2}{2}\right)^2 = 1$; $x = 3\cos t - 1$ and $y = 2\sin t + 2$

19c. (1.9, 1.5) and (−2.9, 0.5) (t-values are shown in degrees.)

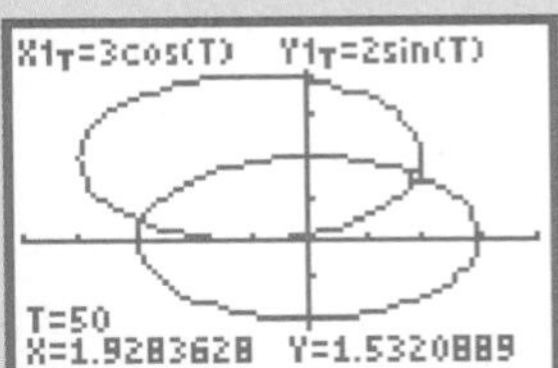

[−5, 4, 1, −3, 5, 1]
$0 \leq t \leq 360$

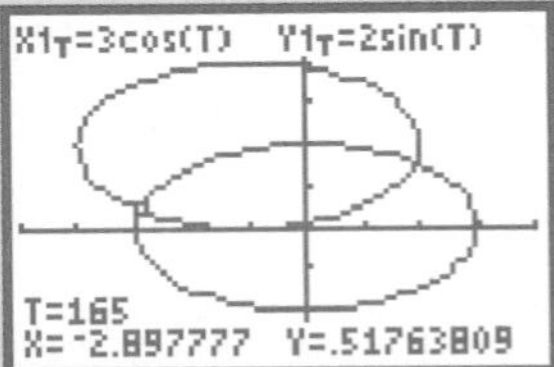

[−5, 4, 1, −3, 5, 1]
$0 \leq t \leq 360$

19d. (1.92, 1.54) and (−2.92, 0.46)

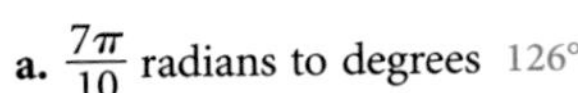

Review

10.2 **16.** Convert

a. $\frac{7\pi}{10}$ radians to degrees 126°

b. −205° to radians $-\frac{41\pi}{36}$

c. 5π radians per hour to degrees per minute 15°/min

10.3 **17.** Write an equation for each graph.

a. $y = \tan\frac{x + \frac{\pi}{2}}{2}$

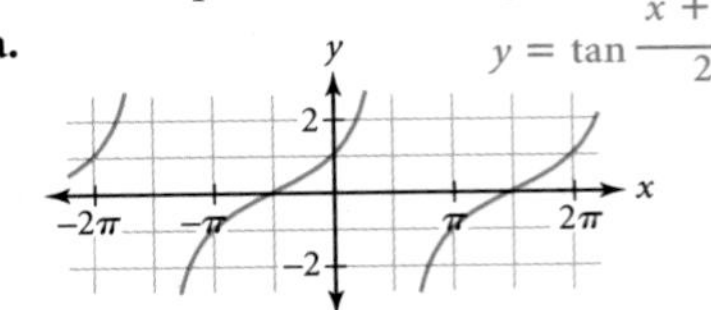

b. $y = 1 - 0.5\tan\left(x - \frac{\pi}{2}\right)$

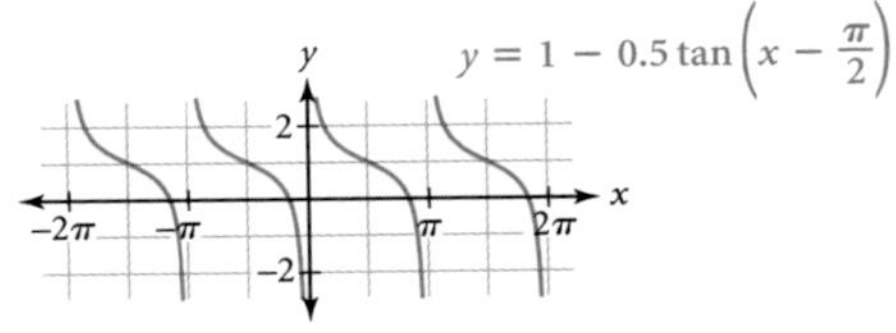

7.6 **18.** Find all roots, real or nonreal. Give exact answers.

a. $2x^2 - 6x + 3 = 0$

b. $13x - 2x^2 = 6$

c. $3x^2 + 4x + 4 = 0$

9.5 **19.** Consider the equation $\left(\frac{x}{3}\right)^2 + \left(\frac{y}{2}\right)^2 = 1$.

a. Describe the shape defined by the equation and write the equation in parametric form.

b. Write the nonparametric and parametric equations of the given equation after a translation left 1 unit and up 2 units.

c. Graph both sets of parametric equations on your calculator, and trace to approximate the coordinates of the intersection point(s).

d. Solve a system of equations to find the points of intersection.

Project

DESIGN A PICNIC TABLE

A well-made piece of wood furniture is carefully designed so that the pieces fit together perfectly. If the design is not perfect, assembly will be more difficult, and the furniture may not be stable.

Your task is to design a picnic table and draw the plans for it. Decide on the shape and size of your table. Make scale drawings showing your design. Then make a separate drawing of each piece, labeling all the lengths and all the angle measures.

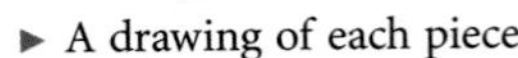

Your project should include

- Scale drawings of your table showing the front view, side view, and top view.
- A drawing of each piece.
- The calculations you made to determine the lengths and angles, clearly labeled and organized.
- A description of your design process, including any problems you encountered and how you solved them.

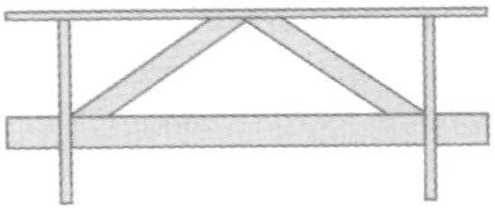

Supporting the Project

Students might design a different piece of furniture, as long as the design includes some nonright angles. Calculations can be time-consuming, so discourage students from choosing anything too complicated. If students get frustrated trying to visualize the different pieces, you might suggest that they build a model.

OUTCOMES

- The scale drawings are accurate.
- Measurements and perspective are consistent with each other.
- The report includes a description of difficulties encountered and their resolution.
- The design is original and appealing.
- The student uses angle measures other than 30°, 45°, 60°, and 90°.

LESSON

10.5 Modeling with Trigonometric Equations

Language exerts hidden power, like the moon on the tides.

RITA MAE BROWN

Tides are caused by gravitational forces, or attractions, between the Earth, Moon, and Sun as the Moon circles Earth. You can model the height of the ocean level in a seaport with a combination of sinusoidal functions of different phase shifts, periods, and amplitudes.

The wooden pillars below, shown at low tide, protect land in Winchelsea, East Sussex, England, from high waters.

The tide-predicting machine shown above records the times and heights of high and low tides. Designed in 1910, it combines sine functions to produce a graph that predicts tide levels over a period of time.

Science CONNECTION

The Moon's gravitational pull causes ocean tides, and tidal bores in rivers. Tidal bores occur during new and full moons when ocean waves rush upstream into a river passage, sometimes at speeds of more than 40 mi/h. The highest recorded river bore was 15 ft high, in China's Fu-ch'un River. To learn more about tides, see the links at www.keymath.com/DAA.

EXAMPLE A

The height of water at the mouth of a certain river varies during the tide cycle. The time in hours since midnight, t, and the height in feet, h, are related by the equation

$$h = 15 + 7.5\cos\left(\frac{2\pi(t-3)}{12}\right)$$

a. What is the length of a period modeled by this equation?

b. When is the first time the height of the water is 11.5 ft?

c. When will the water be at that height again?

LESSON 10.5

PLANNING

LESSON OUTLINE

One day:

10 min	Example A
15 min	Investigation
5 min	Example B
10 min	Sharing
5 min	Exercises

MATERIALS

- motion sensors
- springs
- masses of 50–100 g
- support stands, *optional*
- Bouncing Spring Sample Data (W), *optional*
- Calculator Notes 3C, 9A, *optional*

TEACHING

In this lesson students apply the characteristics of sinusoidal functions to modeling real-world situations. The Geometer's Sketchpad is excellent for graphing the somewhat complicated functions that arise. If you want to start with the one-step investigation, you will find it on page 602.

► EXAMPLE A

This example illustrates the interpretation of data that can be modeled by a trigonometric function. **[ESL]** The *mouth of a river* is the place where the river empties into another body of water such as a lake or an ocean.

From previous lessons most students will have acquired enough knowledge to complete the investigation without first working through Example A.

NCTM STANDARDS

CONTENT		PROCESS	
	Number		Problem Solving
✓	Algebra	✓	Reasoning
	Geometry	✓	Communication
✓	Measurement	✓	Connections
✓	Data/Probability	✓	Representation

LESSON OBJECTIVES

- Use trigonometric equations to model real-world phenomena
- Define *frequency* and calculate it
- Find the average value of a sine or cosine function

Example A (continued)

A slightly different approach to part c is to think about the symmetry of the function. If the period of this function is 12 h and the cycle pictured is considered an example, the middle time will be 6 h, so the maximum will occur at 3 h and the minimum at 9 h. Therefore, if the height was 11.6 at 6.9 h, which is 2.1 h before the minimum, the height must be 11.6 again 2.1 h after the minimum, or at 11.2 h.

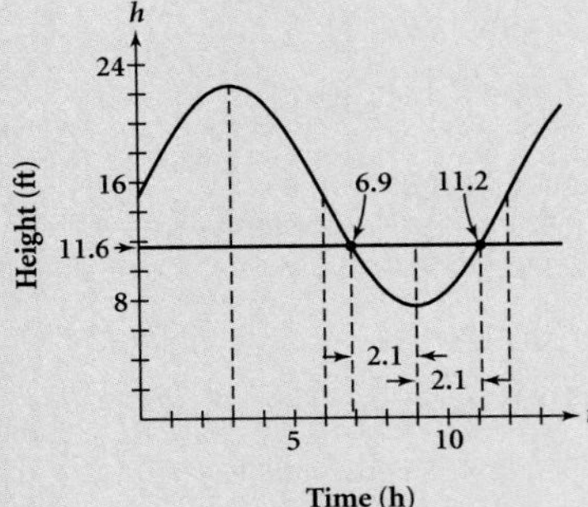

One Step

Pose this problem, based on Exercise 8: "The time between high and low tides in a river harbor is approximately 7 h. The high-tide depth of 16 ft has just occurred at noon today, and the average river depth is 11 ft. What are the next two time periods when a boat requiring at least 9 ft of water will not be able to enter the harbor?" As students work, encourage them to draw diagrams and graphs and to use the terminology of sinusoidal functions and their inverses. Introduce the term *frequency* as appropriate, during Sharing if not before.

► ***Solution***

One cycle of the parent cosine function has length 2π.

a. The cosine function in the height equation has been stretched horizontally by a scale factor of $\frac{12}{2\pi}$. So, the length of the cycle is $\frac{12}{2\pi} \cdot 2\pi = 12$ h.

b. To find when the height of the water is 11.5 ft, substitute 11.5 for h.

$$11.5 = 15 + 7.5\cos\left(\frac{2\pi(t-3)}{12}\right) \quad \text{Substitute 11.5 for } h.$$

$$\frac{-3.5}{7.5} = \cos\left(\frac{\pi(t-3)}{6}\right) \quad \text{Subtract 15, and divide by 7.5.}$$

$$\cos^{-1}\left(\frac{-3.5}{7.5}\right) = \frac{\pi(t-3)}{6} \quad \text{Take the inverse cosine of both sides.}$$

$$\frac{6}{\pi}\cdot\cos^{-1}\left(\frac{-3.5}{7.5}\right) + 3 = t \quad \text{Multiply by } \tfrac{6}{\pi}\text{, and add 3.}$$

$$t \approx 6.9 \text{ h}$$

So, the water height will be 11.5 ft after approximately 6.9 h, or at 6:54 A.M.

You can also find this answer by graphing the height function and the line $h = 11.5$ and by approximating the point of intersection. The graph verifies your solution. (*Note:* On your calculator, use x in place of t and y in place of h.)

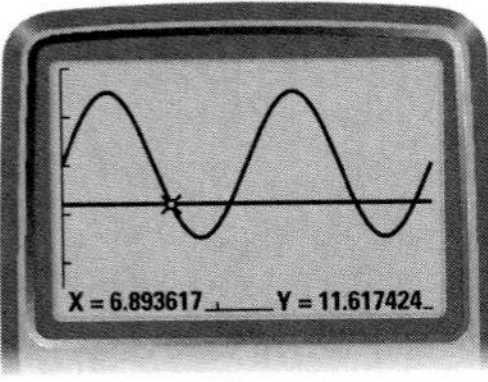

[0, 24, 5, 0, 25, 5]

c. The graph in part b shows several different times when the water depth is 11.5 ft. The third occurrence is 12 hours after the first, because each cycle is 12 hours in length. So the third occurrence is at 6:54 P.M. But how can you find the second occurrence? First, consider that the graph is shifted left 3 units, so the cycle begins at $t = 3$. It has a period of 12, so it ends at $t = 15$.

The first height of 11.5 ft occurred when $t = 6.9$, or 3.9 h after the cycle's start. The next solution will be 3.9 h before the end of the cycle, that is, at $15 - 3.9 = 11.1$ h, or 11:01 A.M. This value will also repeat every 12 h. A graph confirms this approximation.

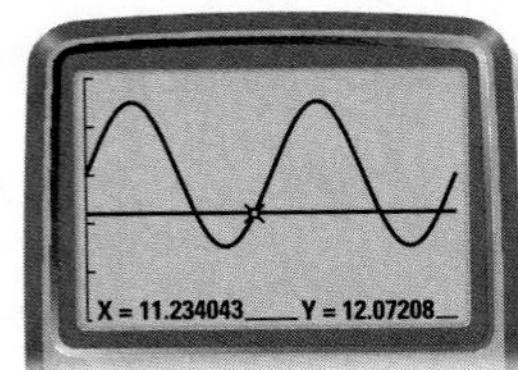

[0, 24, 5, 0, 25, 5]

You can use both sine and cosine functions to model sinusoidal patterns because they are just horizontal translations of each other. Often it is easier to use a cosine function, because you can identify the maximum value as the start value of a cycle.

In Example A, the height of the river has a cycle length, or period, of 12 hours. Sometimes it is useful to discuss the **frequency** of a function as well. Whereas a period tells you how long it takes to complete one cycle, the frequency tells you how many cycles are completed in one unit of time. The frequency is the reciprocal of the period. It is more useful to talk about frequency in motion with a short cycle. For example, if a wave has a period of 0.01 second, then it has a frequency of 100 cycles per second. In Example A, the period is 12 h, so the frequency is $\frac{1}{12}$ cycle per hour.

$$\textit{frequency} = \frac{1}{\textit{period}}$$

Investigation
A Bouncing Spring

You will need

- a motion sensor
- a spring
- a mass of 50 to 100 g
- a support stand

In this experiment you will suspend a mass from a spring. When you pull down on the mass slightly, and release, the mass will move up and down. In reality, the amount of motion gradually decreases, and eventually the mass returns to rest. However, if the initial motion is small, then the decrease in the motion occurs more slowly and can be ignored during the first few seconds.

Procedure Note

1. Attach a mass to the bottom of a spring. Position the motion sensor directly below the spring, so it is always at least 0.5 m from the mass.
2. Set the motion sensor to collect about 5 s of data. Pull the mass down slightly, and release at the same moment as you begin gathering data.

Step 1 Follow the procedure note to collect data on the height of the bouncing spring for a few seconds.

Step 2 Delete values from your lists to limit your data to about four cycles. Identify the phase shift, amplitude, period, frequency, and vertical shift of your function.

Step 3 Write a sine or cosine function that models the data.

Step 4 Answer these questions, based on your equation and your observations.

a. How does each of the numbers in your equation from Step 3 correspond to the motion of the spring?

b. How would your equation change if you moved the motion sensor 1 m farther away?

c. How would your equation change if you pulled the spring slightly lower when you started?

Step 4b The vertical translation would increase by 1. All other values would remain the same.

Step 4c The amplitude would increase. The period might change too.

This car is performing in a car dance competition in Los Angeles, California. Springs are often used as shock absorbers.

Guiding the Investigation

Have Calculator Note 3C available to help students with gathering data from motion sensors.

A Slinky Jr. cut in half works well as the spring, and a heavy washer works well as the mass. Students might use a ruler between two desks as the support stand. If time is limited, you could collect a set of class data and link it to a calculator in each group. Or students can use the Bouncing Spring Sample Data worksheet.

Step 1 How far students pull down the mass does not matter as long as they are consistent.

Step 2 Students can report average values of the numbers characterizing the function.

Step 2 Sample data is on page 900. Answers for sample data:

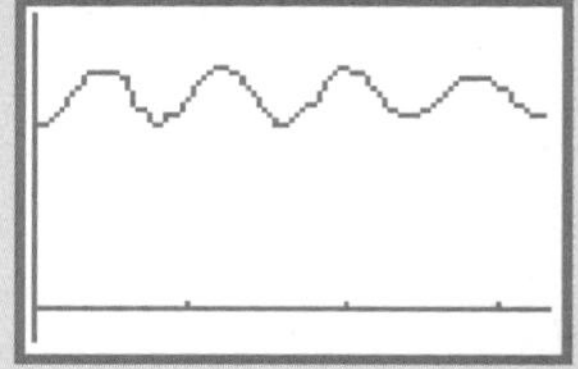

[0, 3.3, 1, −0.1, 0.9, 1]

The average maximum is 0.728, and the average minimum is 0.575, so amplitude is $\frac{0.153}{2} \approx 0.077$. The average value, the vertical translation, is 0.652. The periods are 0.808, 0.805, 0.806, and 0.860, so 0.807 may be a good choice for the period. The frequency is $\frac{1}{0.807}$, or 1.239 cycles per second. The first maximum occurs at $t = 0.43$, so if you choose a cosine function, it has been translated right 0.43.

Step 3 $h = 0.652 + 0.077\cos\left(\frac{2\pi(t - 0.43)}{0.807}\right)$

A graph of the curve with the data shows a good fit.

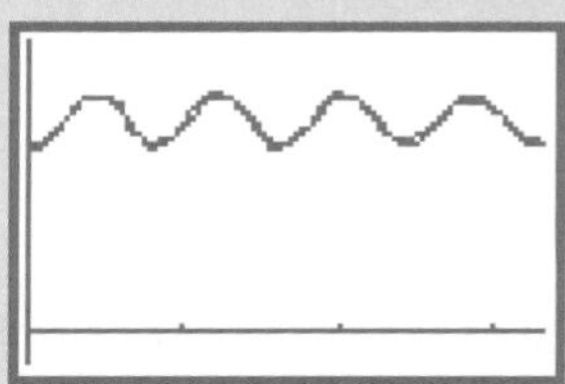

[0, 3.3, 1, −0.1, 0.9, 1]

Step 4 If needed, help students see that the length of one cycle is the same as the period. In 4b, students can assume that t starts at zero. To use a calculator to find the point of intersection, refer students to Calculator Note 9A.

Step 4a 0.652 m is the average height of the spring. 0.077 m is the amount up and down from the average value the spring moves. 0.807 s is the length of time it takes to complete one cycle. 0.43 s is the time when the first maximum occurs.

▶ ***EXAMPLE B***

This example shows how to set up a trigonometric function model. This Ferris wheel first appeared in Lesson 10.2, Example C.

[Ask] "Why does the average height of the parent sinusoid curve equal zero?" [Each positive value is matched with a negative value, so the average is zero.] "Why is the average height of a point on the Ferris wheel 62.5 m?" [The maximum height is 112.5 m and the wheel is 100 m in diameter, so the minimum height is 12.5 m and the average height is 62.5 m.]

[Ask] "Why will the function have a value of 47 m before the maximum point?" [The symmetry of the cosine function guarantees that, if the function reaches 47 m after the maximum, it must also reach that value before the maximum.]

SHARING IDEAS

After students present their ideas, **[Ask]** "What steps would you write up for how to use a sinusoidal function to model a data set that appears to be periodic?" Steps should include (not necessarily in this order):

- Subtract the minimum from the maximum and divide by 2 to get the amplitude, or vertical stretch, *b*.
- Find the average of the maximum and minimum values to determine the amount of vertical translation, *k*.
- Subtract the *x*-values of consecutive maximums (or minimums) to calculate the period, *a*.
- Find the *x*-value of the maximum with the smallest positive *x*-coordinate. For a cosine model, that number is the phase shift, *h;* for a sine model, the phase shift *h* is $\frac{\pi}{2}$ minus that number.
- Write the function as $y = b\cos\left(\frac{2\pi(x-h)}{a}\right) + k$ or $y = b\sin\left(\frac{2\pi(x-h)}{a}\right) + k$, depending on how you calculated *h*.

Students need not memorize these steps as long as they can find the function. To check the algebra, they should continually refer back to the physical characteristics represented by the various numbers.

Continue soliciting probing questions from the class and turning the questions back to the class for discussion. Many students grasp the meaning of what they've learned by thinking aloud with their peers; give them this opportunity to deepen their understanding.

[Ask] "What are the units of frequency?" [They are the reciprocal of the units of the period. For example, if the period is 15 minutes per cycle, then the frequency is $\frac{1}{15}$ cycle per minute.]

In the investigation, you modeled cyclical motion with a sine or cosine function. As you read the next example, think about how the process of finding an equation based on given measurements compares to your process in the investigation.

EXAMPLE B

On page 577 you learned that the Cosmo Clock 21 Ferris wheel has a 100 m diameter, takes 15 min to rotate, and reaches a maximum height of 112.5 m.

Find an equation that models the height in meters, *h,* of a seat on the perimeter of the wheel as a function of time in minutes, *t.* Then determine when, in the first 30 min, a given seat is 47 m from the ground, if the seat is at its maximum height 10 min after the wheel begins rotating.

▶ ***Solution***

The parent sinusoid curve has an amplitude of 1. The diameter of the Ferris wheel is 100 m, so the vertical stretch, or amplitude, is 50. The period of a parent sinusoid is 2π and the period of the Ferris wheel is 15 min, so the horizontal stretch is $\frac{15}{2\pi}$. The average value of the parent sinusoid is 0, but the average height of the wheel is 62.5 m, so the vertical translation is 62.5. The top of a sinusoid corresponds to the maximum height of a seat. The cosine curve starts at a maximum point, so it will be easiest to use a cosine function. Because the first maximum of the Ferris wheel occurs after 10 min, the phase shift of its equation is 10 to the right. Incorporate these values into a cosine function.

$$h = 50\cos\left(\frac{2\pi(t-10)}{15}\right) + 62.5$$

Now, to find when the height is 47 m, substitute 47 for *h*.

$50\cos\left(\frac{2\pi(t-10)}{15}\right) + 62.5 = 47$	Substitute 47 for *h*.
$\cos\left(\frac{2\pi(t-10)}{15}\right) = \frac{47-62.5}{50} = -0.31$	Subtract 62.5 and divide by 50. Evaluate.
$\frac{2\pi(t-10)}{15} = \cos^{-1}(-0.31)$	Take the inverse cosine of both sides.
$t - 10 = \frac{15}{2\pi} \cdot \cos^{-1}(-0.31)$	Multiply by $\frac{15}{2\pi}$ on both sides.
$t = \frac{15}{2\pi} \cdot \cos^{-1}(-0.31) + 10$	Add 10.
$t \approx 14.5$	Approximate the principal value of *t*.

So, the given seat is at a height of 47 m approximately 14.5 min after it starts rotating. But this is not the only time. The period is 15 min, so the seat will also reach 47 m after 29.5 min. Also, the height is 47 m once on the way up and once on the way down. The seat is at 47 m 4.5 min after its maximum point, which is at 10 min. It will also be at the same height 4.5 min before its maximum point, at 5.5 min, and 15 min after that, at 20.5 min.

So, in the first 30 min, the seat reaches a height of 47 m after 5.5, 14.5, 20.5, and 29.5 min. A graph confirms this.

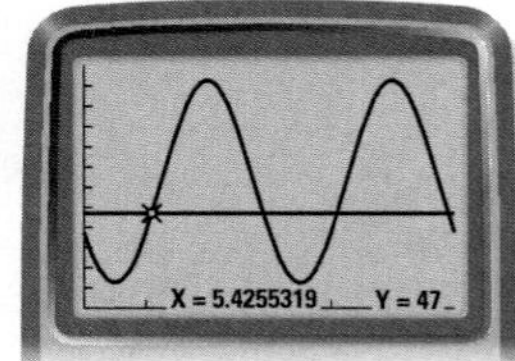

[0, 30, 5, 0, 120, 10]

Using sinusoidal models, you can easily find y when given an x-value. As you saw in the examples, the more difficult task is finding x when given a y-value. There will be multiple answers, because the graphs are periodic. You should always check the values and number of solutions with a calculator graph.

This mural is painted in the style of *The Great Wave,* by Japanese artist Hokusai (1760–1849). Like tides, the motion of waves can be modeled with trigonometric functions.

EXERCISES

You will need

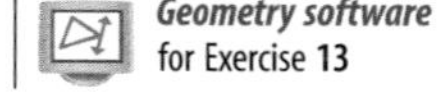

Geometry software for Exercise 13

Practice Your Skills

1. Find the first four positive solutions. Give exact values in radians.

a. $\cos x = 0.5$ $x = \left\{\frac{\pi}{3}, \frac{5\pi}{3}, \frac{7\pi}{3}, \frac{11\pi}{3}\right\}$

b. $\sin x = -0.5$ $x = \left\{\frac{7\pi}{6}, \frac{11\pi}{6}, \frac{19\pi}{6}, \frac{23\pi}{6}\right\}$

2. Find all solutions for $0 \leq x < 2\pi$, rounded to the nearest thousandth.

a. $2\sin(x + 1.2) - 4.22 = -4$ $x = \{1.831, 5.193\}$

b. $7.4\cos(x - 0.8) + 12.3 = 16.4$ $x = \{1.784, 6.100\}$

3. Consider the graph of the function $h = 5 + 7\sin\left(\frac{2\pi(t-9)}{11}\right)$.

a. What are the vertical translation and average value? 5; 5

b. What are the vertical stretch factor, minimum and maximum values, and amplitude? 7; −2; 12; 7

c. What are the horizontal stretch factor and period? $\frac{11}{2\pi}$; 11

d. What are the horizontal translation and phase shift? 9; 9

4. Consider the graph of the function $h = 18 - 17\cos\left(\frac{2\pi(t+16)}{15}\right)$.

a. What are the vertical translation and average value? 18; 18

b. What are the vertical stretch factor, minimum and maximum values, and amplitude? −17; 1; 35; 17

c. What are the horizontal stretch factor and period? $\frac{15}{2\pi}$; 15

d. What are the horizontal translation and phase shift? −16; −16

Reason and Apply

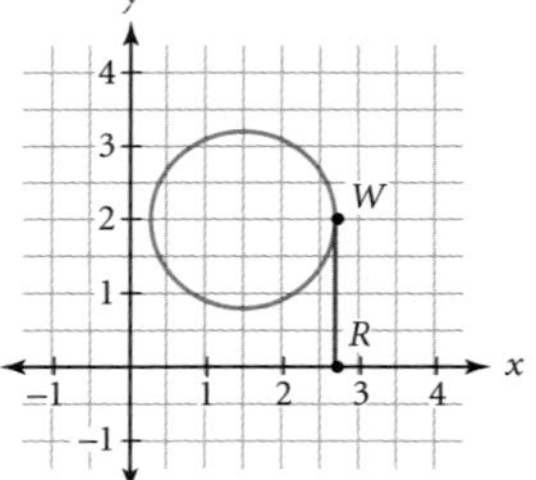

5. A walker moves counterclockwise around a circle with center (1.5, 2) and radius 1.2 m and completes a cycle in 8 s. A recorder walks back and forth along the x-axis, staying even with the walker, with a motion sensor pointed toward the walker. What equation models the (*time, distance*) relationship? Assume the walker starts at point (2.7, 2). $y = 1.2\sin\frac{2\pi t}{8} + 2$ or $y = 1.2\sin\frac{\pi t}{4} + 2$

Assessing Progress

You can assess students' understanding of and ability to work with the phase shift, amplitude, period, and vertical translation of a periodic function.

Closing the Lesson

Reiterate the steps needed to model a situation with a sinusoidal function, and remind students that the **frequency** is the reciprocal of the period.

BUILDING UNDERSTANDING

Students practice modeling with sinusoidal functions.

ASSIGNING HOMEWORK

Essential	3–5
Performance assessment	6–13
Portfolio	7
Group	5, 9, 12
Review	1, 2, 14–18

Helping with the Exercises

Exercise 1 An equation such as $\cos x = 0.5$ has infinitely many solutions. The first positive solution is $\frac{\pi}{3}$. The equation $y = \cos x$ is periodic with a period of 2π, so $\frac{\pi}{3} + 2\pi, \frac{\pi}{3} + 4\pi, \frac{\pi}{3} + 6\pi$, and so on are all solutions. These solutions can be generated by $\frac{\pi}{3} + 2\pi n$, where n is any integer. The second positive solution is $\frac{5\pi}{3}$, so values generated by $\frac{5\pi}{3} + 2\pi n$ are also solutions. **[Link]** This method of representing solutions to trigonometric equations is used in precalculus and higher mathematics.

Exercises 3a, 4a **[Language]** *Average value* refers to the average value of the function. For sinusoidal functions, the average value is the mean of the maximum and minimum values.

Exercise 5 Students may want to walk through this exercise before starting to solve it. **[Ask]** "What is the real-world meaning of each part of the equation?" Although y-coordinates usually are given by sines, students might choose to model the phenomenon with a cosine function, leading to the equation

$$y = 1.2\cos\left(\frac{2\pi(x-2)}{8}\right) + 2$$

Exercise 6 Experience gained in the investigation will help students visualize this exercise.

6. 0.267 s, 0.533 s, 1.067 s, 1.333 s, 1.867 s

Exercise 7 Students can assume that the function has a phase shift of 0.

7a. possible answer: $v = 110\sqrt{2}\sin(120\pi t)$

7b.

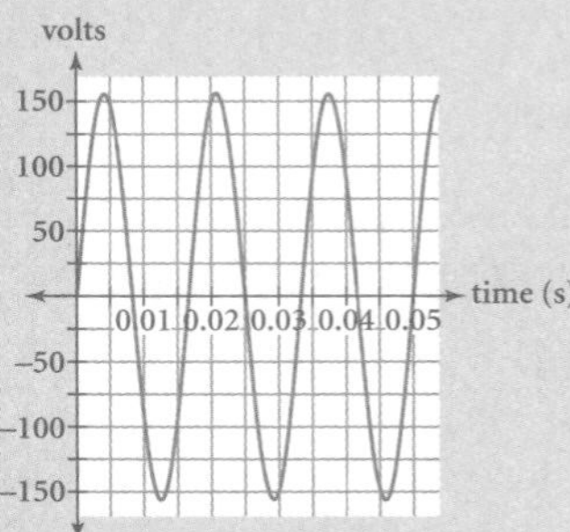

8a. possible answer: $d = 11 + 5\cos\frac{\pi t}{7}$

8b. between 4:25 P.M. and 9:35 P.M., and between 6:25 A.M. and 11:35 A.M. the next day

6. A mass attached to a string is pulled down 3 cm from its resting position and then released. It makes ten complete bounces in 8 s. At what times during the first 2 s was the mass 1.5 cm above its resting position?

7. Household appliances are typically powered by electricity through wall outlets. The voltage provided varies sinusoidally between $-110\sqrt{2}$ volts and $110\sqrt{2}$ volts, with a frequency of 60 cycles per second.

a. Use a sine or cosine function to write an equation for (*time, voltage*).

b. Sketch and label a graph picturing three complete cycles.

8. The time between high and low tide in a river harbor is approximately 7 h. The high-tide depth of 16 ft occurs at noon and the average harbor depth is 11 ft.

a. Write an equation modeling this relationship.

b. If a boat requires a harbor depth of at least 9 ft, find the next two time periods when the boat will not be able to enter the harbor.

9. Two masses are suspended from springs, as shown. The first mass is pulled down 3 cm from its resting position and released. A second mass is pulled down 4 cm from its resting position. It is released just as the first mass passes its resting position on its way up. When released, each mass makes 12 bounces in 8 s.

a. Write a function for the height of each mass. Use the moment the second mass is released as $t = 0$.

b. At what times during the first 2 s will the two masses be at the same height? Solve graphically, and state your answers to the nearest 0.1 s.

10. **APPLICATION** An AM radio transmitter generates a radio wave given by a function in the form $f(t) = A\sin 2000\pi nt$. The variable n represents the location on the broadcast dial, $550 \le n \le 1600$, and t is the time in seconds.

a. For radio station WINS, located at 1010 on the AM radio dial, what is the period of the function that models its radio waves?

b. What is the frequency of your function from 10a?

c. Find a function that models the radio waves of an AM radio station near you. Find the period and frequency.

Amplitude modulation, or AM, is one way that a radio transmitter can send information over large distances. By varying the amplitude of a continuous wave, the transmitter adds audio information to the signal. The wave's amplitude is adjusted simply by changing the amount of energy put in. More energy causes a larger amplitude, whereas less energy causes a smaller amplitude. One problem with AM (as opposed to FM, or frequency modulation) is that the signal is affected by electrical fields, such as lighting. The resulting static and clicks decrease sound quality.

A radio transmitter from the early 1900s used electric pulses or vacuum tubes to create radio waves.

9a.

$$y_1 = -3\cos\left(\frac{2\pi(t+0.17)}{\frac{2}{3}}\right),\ y_2 = -4\cos\left(\frac{2\pi t}{\frac{2}{3}}\right),$$

or $y_1 = 3\sin 3\pi t,\ y_2 = -4\cos 3\pi t$

9b. at 0.2, 0.6, 0.9, 1.2, 1.6, 1.9 s

10a. $\frac{1}{1010000}$

10b. 1,010,000 cycles/s

10c. Answers will vary. Find the dial number of an AM radio station and substitute it for n. Period will be $\frac{1}{1000n}$. Frequency will be $1000n$.

11. The number of hours of daylight, y, on any day of the year in Philadelphia can be modeled using the equation $y = 12 + 2.4\sin\left(\frac{2\pi(x - 80)}{365}\right)$, where x represents the day number (with January 1 as day 1).

a. Find the amount of sunlight in Philadelphia on day 354, the shortest day of the year (the winter solstice).

b. Find the dates on which Philadelphia has exactly 12 hours of daylight.

12. A popular amusement park ride is the double Ferris wheel. Each small wheel takes 20 s to make a single rotation. The two-wheel set takes 30 s to rotate once. The dimensions of the ride are given in the diagram.

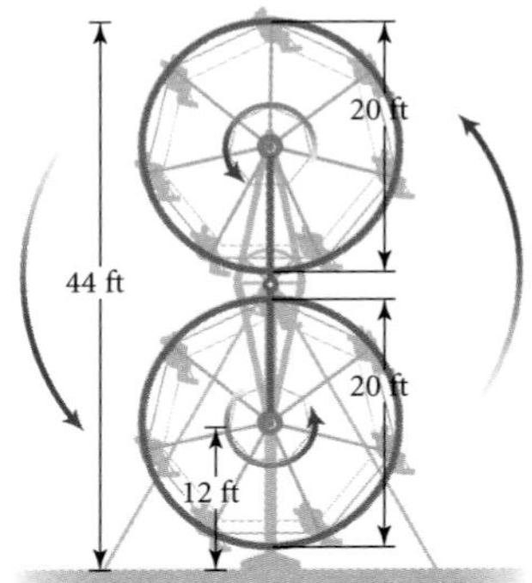

The Sky Wheel, a double Ferris wheel, operated at the Cedar Point theme park in Sandusky, Ohio, from 1962 to 1981.

a. Sandra gets on at the foot of the bottom wheel. Write an equation that will model her height above the center of this wheel as the wheels rotate.

b. The entire ride (the two-wheel set) starts revolving at the same time that the two smaller wheels begin to rotate. Write an equation that models the height of the center of Sandra's wheel as the entire ride rotates.

c. Because the two motions occur simultaneously, you can add the two equations to write a final equation for Sandra's position. Write this equation.

d. During a 5 min ride, during how many distinct time periods is Sandra within 6 ft of the ground?

13. ***Technology*** Use geometry software to simulate Sandra's ride on the double ferris wheel in Exercise 12. Describe your steps.

Review

10.3 **14.** Solve $\tan\theta = -1.111$ graphically. Use domain $-180° \le \theta \le 360°$. Round answers to the nearest degree.

15. Which has the larger area, an equilateral triangle with side 5 cm or a sector of a circle with radius 5 cm and arc length 5 cm? Give the area of each shape to the nearest 0.1 cm.

9.2 **16.** Find the equation of the circle with center $(-2, 4)$ that has tangent line $2x - 3y - 6 = 0$.

11a. about 9.6 h

11b. day 80, March 21, the spring equinox; and day 262.5, September 21 or 22, the autumn equinox

Exercise 12 This exercise illustrates how the sum of two periodic functions is also a periodic function. Sound waves provide other examples of sums of sinusoidal functions.

The visualization of the motion of a double Ferris wheel at www.keymath.com/DAA can help students solve this exercise.

12a. possible answer: $h = -10\cos\left(\frac{2\pi t}{20}\right)$

12b. possible answer: $h = 23 - 11\cos\left(\frac{2\pi t}{30}\right)$

12c. possible answer: $h = 23 - 11\cos\left(\frac{2\pi t}{30}\right) - 10\cos\left(\frac{2\pi t}{20}\right)$

12d. 6

Exercise 13 An exploration found at www.keymath.com/DAA can give students some ideas for how to create their own simulation.

13. Construct a circle and its diameter for the main rotating arm. Construct a circle with a fixed radius at each end of the diameter. Make a point on each of these two circles. Animate them and one endpoint of the diameter.

14.

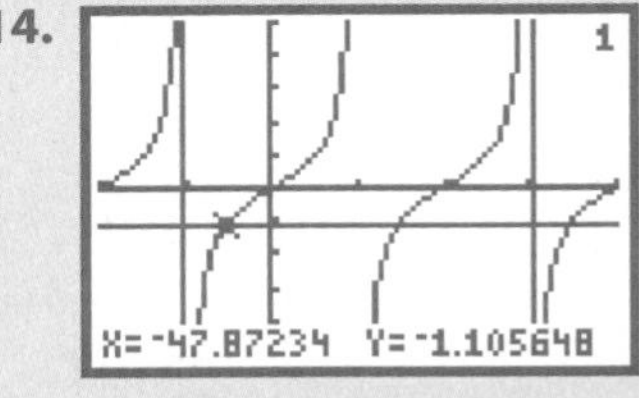

$[-180, 360, 90, -5, 5, 1]$

$\theta = \{-48°, 132°, 312°\}$

15. The sector has the larger area. The triangle's area is 10.8 cm^2; the sector's area is 12.5 cm^2.

Exercise 16 [Language] A *tangent line* to a circle has exactly one point in common with the circle.

16. $(x + 2)^2 + (y - 4)^2 = \frac{484}{13}$

17a. $\pm 1, \pm 5, \pm\frac{1}{2}, \pm\frac{5}{2}$

17b. $x = \frac{1}{2}$

17c. $x = \pm\sqrt{5}$

17d. $P(x) = 2\left(x - \frac{1}{2}\right)\left(x + \sqrt{5}\right)\left(x - \sqrt{5}\right)$ or $P(x) = (2x - 1)\left(x + \sqrt{5}\right)\left(x - \sqrt{5}\right)$

Exercise 18 You may want to help students see that the length of the hypotenuse of each right triangle is twice the radius, so the distance from the angle's vertex to the closest point on any circle equals the radius of that circle.

18a. The radius of C_2 is 18. The radius of C_3 is 54.

18b. The radius of C_n is $6(3^{n-1})$.

EXTENSIONS

A. Suggest that students research how springs are used in machinery. [For example, they are used as shock absorbers, as energy devices, and as a part of weight scales.]

B. You might suggest that students find a time-lapse or other photograph that shows a curve, import that image into The Geometer's Sketchpad, and determine whether a trigonometric function models that curve.

7.6 **17.** Consider the equation $P(x) = 2x^3 - x^2 - 10x + 5$.

a. List all possible rational roots of $P(x)$.

b. Find any actual rational roots.

c. Find exact values for all other roots.

d. Write $P(x)$ in factored form.

18. Circles $C_1, C_2, \ldots$ are tangent to the sides of $\angle P$ and to the adjacent circle(s). The radius of circle C_1 is 6. The measure of $\angle P$ is 60°.

a. What are the radii of C_2 and C_3? (*Hint:* One method uses similar right triangles.)

b. What is the radius of C_n?

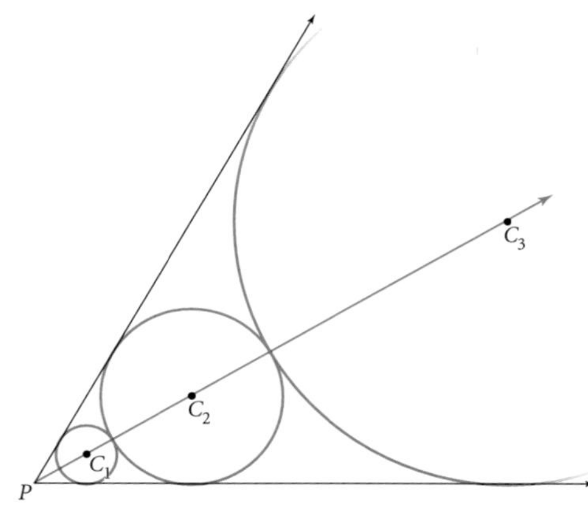

Project

A DAMPENED SINE CURVE

You have modeled the motion of springs and pendulums using sinusoidal curves. In each case, you assumed that the amplitude of the motion did not decrease over time. In reality, forces of friction dampen, or reduce, the amplitude of the motion over time, until the object comes to rest. In this project you will investigate this phenomenon.

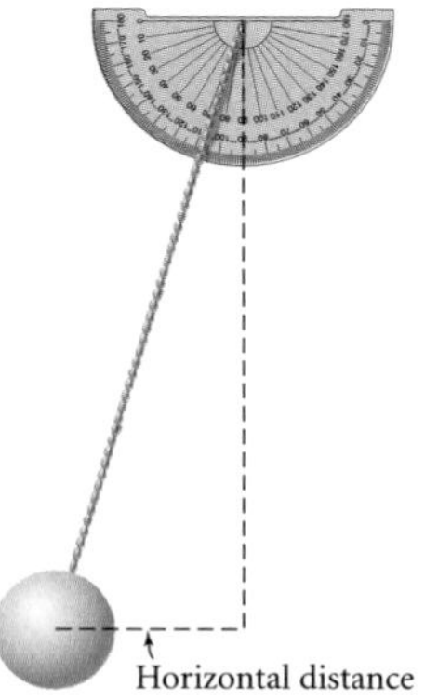

Set up a pendulum with a protractor at the top. Hold the string at a 20° angle from the center, and release. Time the first few swings and determine the period of your pendulum. Begin the experiment again and record the angle of the swing after each swing, or at regular intervals of swings, until the pendulum is nearly at rest. Use these angles and the length of the pendulum to calculate the horizontal distance of the pendulum from the center at the end of each swing.

Because the period of the pendulum is constant throughout the experiment, you can assign time values for each swing. Plot the data (*time, distance*), and draw a smooth sinusoidal curve that peaks at each of these points. Draw a second curve that just passes through these maximum points. Find an equation that models this second curve. Then use this equation as the amplitude for the sine curve that models the entire motion. Write an equation for your dampened sine function.

Your project should include

- A description of your experimental process.
- Tables showing all of the data you collected.
- The equation you found for the amplitude.
- An equation for your final dampened sine curve.

Supporting the Project

Students have probably noticed that the motion of a pendulum or a spring does not continue forever but rather decays, or dampens. In this project, students explore how to find a more accurate model for pendulum motion.

OUTCOMES

- The report includes a description of the experimental process and tables of the data the student gathered.
- The student provides an equation for amplitude, probably an exponential function.
- The final dampened sine curve equation is likely of the form $y = bc^x \sin\left(\frac{2\pi(x-h)}{a}\right) + k$, where a, h, b, and k have the same meanings as in the lesson and c is approximately 0.94, depending on the length of the string.
- The report includes a graph of the curve.

LESSON 10.6 Fundamental Trigonometric Identities

In this lesson you will discover several equations that express relationships among trigonometric functions. When an equation is true for all values of the variables for which the expressions are defined, the equation is called an **identity.**

You've already learned that $\tan A = \frac{y\text{-coordinate}}{x\text{-coordinate}}$ when a point $P(x, y)$ is rotated $A°$ counterclockwise about the origin from the positive x-axis. You've also seen that the y-coordinate is equivalent to $r\sin A$, where r is the distance between the point and the origin, and the x-coordinate is equivalent to $r\cos A$. You can use these relationships to develop an identity that relates $\tan A$, $\sin A$, and $\cos A$.

$\tan A = \frac{y}{x}$ — Definition of tangent.

$\tan A = \frac{r\sin A}{r\cos A}$ — Substitute $r\sin A$ for y and $r\cos A$ for x.

$\tan A = \frac{\sin A}{\cos A}$ — Reduce.

The reciprocals of the tangent, sine, and cosine functions are also trigonometric functions. The reciprocal of tangent is called **cotangent,** abbreviated cot. The reciprocal of sine is called **cosecant,** abbreviated csc. The reciprocal of cosine is called **secant,** abbreviated sec. These definitions lead to six more identities.

History CONNECTION

The reciprocal trigonometric functions were introduced by Muslim astronomers in the 9th and 10th centuries C.E. Before there were calculating machines, these astronomers developed remarkably precise trigonometric tables based on earlier Greek and Indian findings. They used these tables to record planetary motion, to keep time, and to locate their religious center of Mecca. Western Europeans began studying trigonometry when Arabic astronomy handbooks were translated in the 12th century.

Reciprocal Identities

$\csc A = \frac{1}{\sin A}$ or $\sin A = \frac{1}{\csc A}$

$\sec A = \frac{1}{\cos A}$ or $\cos A = \frac{1}{\sec A}$

$\cot A = \frac{1}{\tan A}$ or $\tan A = \frac{1}{\cot A}$

Your calculator does not have special keys for secant, cosecant, and cotangent. Instead, you must use the reciprocal identities in order to enter them into your calculator. For example, to graph $y = \csc x$, you use $y = \frac{1}{\sin x}$. The calculator screen at right shows the graphs of the principal cycles of the parent sine and cosecant functions.

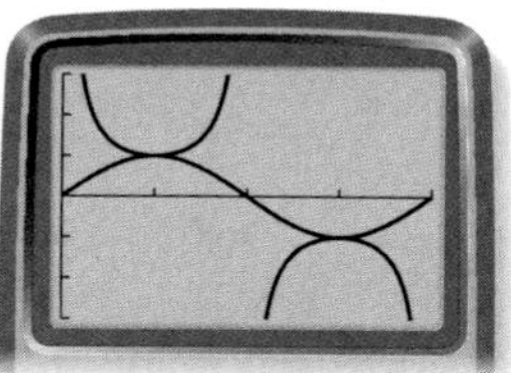

$[0, 2\pi, \pi/2, -3, 3, 1]$

[► See **Calculator Note 10C** for more information about using secant, cosecant, and cotangent on your calculator. ◄]

Once you know a few identities, you can use them to prove other identities. One strategy for proving that an equation is an identity is to verify that both sides of the equation are always equivalent. You can do this by writing equivalent expressions for one side of the equation until it is the same as the other side.

EXAMPLE | Prove algebraically that $\cot A = \frac{\cos A}{\sin A}$ is an identity. (Assume $\sin A \neq 0$.)

NCTM STANDARDS

CONTENT		PROCESS	
	Number		Problem Solving
✓	Algebra	✓	Reasoning
	Geometry	✓	Communication
	Measurement	✓	Connections
	Data/Probability	✓	Representation

LESSON OBJECTIVES

- Define the trigonometric functions secant, cotangent, and cosecant
- Understand the reciprocal relationships among the trigonometric functions
- Discover Pythagorean identities
- Prove trigonometric identities

LESSON 10.6

PLANNING

LESSON OUTLINE

One day:

10 min Example

15 min Investigation

10 min Sharing

10 min Exercises

MATERIALS

- Calculator Note 10C

TEACHING

In this lesson students see and prove reciprocal identities and Pythagorean identities. The material might be optional for your school. If you choose to use the one-step investigation, you'll find it on page 610.

As needed, caution students that $\frac{1}{\sin A}$ is not the $\sin^{-1}$ function on the calculator. They can either divide 1 by $\sin A$ or use the x^{-1} button, entering $\sin(A)^{-1}$.

Reciprocal Identities

[Ask] "For what values are these identities undefined?" [$\csc A$ is undefined when $\sin A = 0$, or $A = \pi n$ for any integer n; $\sec A$ is undefined when $\cos A = 0$, or $A = \frac{\pi}{2} + \pi n$; $\cot A$ is undefined when $\tan A = 0$, or $A = \pi n$; $\tan A$ is undefined when $\cot A = 0$, or $A = \frac{\pi}{2} + \pi n$. The identities for $\sin A$ and $\cos A$ are defined everywhere, because $\csc A$ and $\sec A$ never equal 0.]

► ***EXAMPLE***

You might suggest that students rewrite everything in terms of sine and cosine when they are proving identities. In this case, that advice implies that they should work on the left side of the equation.

Example A (continued)
Working on only one side of an equation is essential for a valid proof. A proof must go from what is known to what is being proved. If you start with the assumption that $\cot A$ equals $\frac{\cos A}{\sin A}$ and conclude that $\frac{\cos A}{\sin A}$ equals $\frac{\cos A}{\sin A}$, you must show that the steps are reversible. That's why question marks appear until the last step. For example, the steps

$3 \stackrel{?}{=} 17$

$0 \cdot 3 \stackrel{?}{=} 0 \cdot 17$

$0 = 0$

don't prove that $3 = 17$, because you can't go backward from the known $(0 = 0)$ and divide by 0. Working with only one side of the equation helps students avoid irreversible steps.

[Ask] "Is the graphing at the end of the solution a proof?" [Graphing might be more persuasive to students than the logical reasoning, but verification by graphing is not a proof.]

One Step
Challenge students to write a convincing argument that the equation $1 + \frac{\cos^2 A}{\sin^2 A} = \frac{1}{\sin^2 A}$ is valid. As students try a variety of approaches, keep stressing that to be convincing the argument must clearly state assumptions and work from known facts to what is to be proved. During Sharing, introduce the idea of identity; the functions $\cot A$, $\sec A$, and $\csc A$; and the standard method for writing proofs of trigonometric identities. Then challenge students to try dividing the identity $\sin^2 A + \cos^2 A = 1$ by $\cos^2 A$. [$\tan^2 A + 1 = \sec^2 A$]

Guiding the Investigation

Step 1 A squared trigonometric function can be written as $\sin^2 x$ or $(\sin x)^2$. When referring to graphing on the calculator, the book uses argument x instead of argument A.

See page 901 for answers to Steps 1–3 and 5.

▶ ***Solution***

Use definitions and identities that you know in order to show that both sides of the equation are equivalent. Be sure to work on only one side of the equation.

$\cot A \stackrel{?}{=} \frac{\cos A}{\sin A}$	Original identity.
$\frac{1}{\tan A} \stackrel{?}{=} \frac{\cos A}{\sin A}$	Use the reciprocal identity to replace $\cot A$ with $\frac{1}{\tan A}$.
$\frac{1}{\frac{\sin A}{\cos A}} \stackrel{?}{=} \frac{\cos A}{\sin A}$	Replace $\tan A$ with $\frac{\sin A}{\cos A}$.
$\frac{\cos A}{\sin A} = \frac{\cos A}{\sin A}$	$1 \div \frac{\sin A}{\cos A}$ is equivalent to $1 \cdot \frac{\cos A}{\sin A}$, or simply $\frac{\cos A}{\sin A}$.

Therefore, $\cot A = \frac{\cos A}{\sin A}$ is an identity. To verify this, you can graph the two equations $y = \cot x$ and $y = \frac{\cos x}{\sin x}$, and check that they give the same graph. Now that you have proved this identity, you can use it to prove other identities.

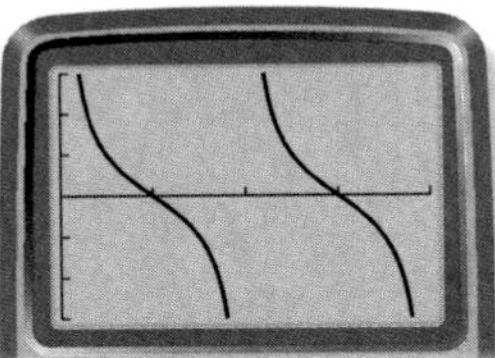

$[0, 2\pi, \pi/2, -3, 3, 1]$

In the investigation you will discover a set of trigonometric identities that are collectively called the Pythagorean identities. To prove a new identity, you can use any previously proved identity.

Investigation
Pythagorean Identities

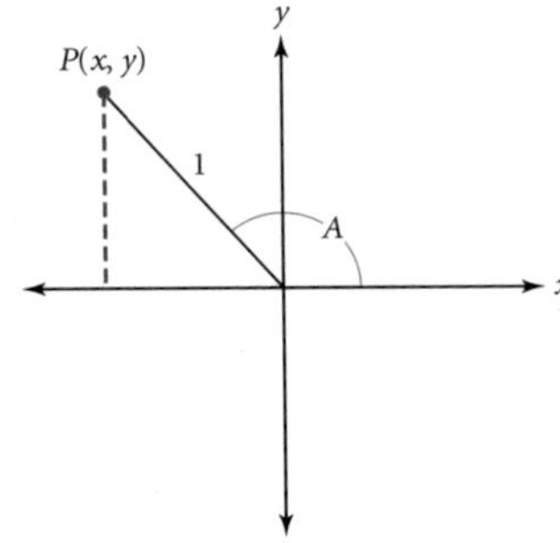

Step 1 Use your calculator to graph the equation $y = \sin^2 x + \cos^2 x$. (You'll probably have to enter this as $y = (\sin x)^2 + (\cos x)^2$.) Does this graph look familiar? Use your graph to write an identity.

Step 2 Use the definitions for $\sin A$, $\cos A$, and the diagram at right to prove your identity.

Step 3 Explain why you think this identity is called a Pythagorean identity.

Step 4 Solve the identity from Step 1 for $\cos^2 x$ to get another identity. Then solve for $\sin^2 x$ to get another variation.

$\cos^2 x = \underline{\ ?\ }$ $1 - \sin^2 x$

$\sin^2 x = \underline{\ ?\ }$ $1 - \cos^2 x$

Step 5 Divide both sides of the identity from Step 1 by $\cos^2 x$ to develop a new identity. Simplify so that there are no trigonometric functions in the denominator.

Step 5 By dividing both sides of a known identity by $\cos^2 x$, students have a proof of the new identity. This proof has the single reason "If equals are divided by equals, the quotients are equal." The book asks for a proof that follows the more generalizable method of the example. In writing this kind of proof, a possible first step is to rewrite $\frac{\sin^2 x}{\cos^2 x}$ as $\tan^2 x$.

Step 7 In the standard identity the quotient $\frac{\cos^2 x}{\sin^2 x}$ is simplified to $\cot^2 x$. Again, the intention is for students to use the form of the example. A good first step is to rewrite $\frac{\cos^2 x}{\sin^2 x}$ as $\cot^2 x$.

SHARING IDEAS

As students present, **[Ask]** "If the cotangent is the reciprocal of the tangent, why isn't the cosine the reciprocal of the sine?" Elicit the idea that cofunctions are different from reciprocal functions. As graphs show, cofunctions are functions of complements. The fact that cotangent is also the reciprocal of the tangent is an anomaly.

Continue to focus on having students ask questions for class discussion.

Step 6 | Verify your identity from Step 5 with a graph. Name any domain values for which the identity is undefined.

Step 7 | Divide both sides of the identity from Step 1 by $\sin^2 x$ to develop a new identity. Simplify so that there are no trigonometric functions in the denominator.

Step 8 | Verify the identity from Step 7 with a graph. Name any domain values for which the identity is undefined.

You have verified identities by setting each side of the equation equal to y and graphing. If the graphs and table values match, you may have an identity. You should always use an algebraic proof to be certain. You may have used your calculator in this way to verify the Pythagorean identities in the investigation. If not, try it now on one of the three identities below.

Pythagorean Identities

$\sin^2 A + \cos^2 A = 1$

$1 + \tan^2 A = \sec^2 A$

$1 + \cot^2 A = \csc^2 A$

Exercises

Practice Your Skills

1. Because the cotangent function is not built into your calculator, explain how you would graph $y = \cot x$ on your calculator. Graph $y = \frac{1}{\tan x}$.

2. Use graphs to determine which of these equations may be identities.

   a. $\cos x = \sin\left(\frac{\pi}{2} - x\right)$ yes
   b. $\cos x = \sin\left(x - \frac{\pi}{2}\right)$ no
   c. $(\csc x - \cot x)(\sec x + 1) = 1$ no
   d. $\tan x(\cot x + \tan x) = \sec^2 x$ yes

3. Prove algebraically that the equation in Exercise 2d is an identity.

4. Evaluate.

   a. $\sec\frac{\pi}{6}$ $\frac{2}{\sqrt{3}}$ or $\frac{2\sqrt{3}}{3}$
   b. $\csc\frac{5\pi}{6}$ 2
   c. $\csc\frac{2\pi}{3}$ $\frac{2}{\sqrt{3}}$ or $\frac{2\sqrt{3}}{3}$
   d. $\sec\frac{3\pi}{2}$ undefined
   e. $\cot\frac{5\pi}{3}$ $-\frac{1}{\sqrt{3}}$ or $-\frac{\sqrt{3}}{3}$
   f. $\csc\frac{4\pi}{3}$ $-\frac{2}{\sqrt{3}}$ or $-\frac{2\sqrt{3}}{3}$

Reason and Apply

5. In your own words, explain the difference between a trigonometric equation and a trigonometric identity. A trigonometric equation may be true for some, all, or none of the defined values of the variable. A trigonometric identity is a trigonometric equation that is true for all defined values of the variable.

Sharing Ideas (continued)

To encourage familiarity with the identities, ask students which few identities they should remember because others can be derived from them. It is not important which identities students choose to remember and which they choose to derive, though you might want to ensure that their answers are valid.

[Ask] "Does the equal sign in the trigonometric identities mean that they are trigonometric equations?" Like words, equal signs have different meanings in different contexts. The word *identity* is used if the equation is satisfied for all values of the variable (for which the two sides are defined). Otherwise, the equation is called a *trigonometric equation.*

[Ask] "Are you comfortable proving these identities?" Students who are method-oriented may be uncomfortable with proving trigonometric identities. They may remember from a geometry course that proving is an art, not a science. It's an art they can master with some creativity.

Assessing Progress

You can check students' ability to write a logical proof and their familiarity with the Pythagorean Theorem.

Closing the Lesson

Restate the identity $\tan A = \frac{\sin A}{\cos A}$, the reciprocal identities, and the Pythagorean identities. Reiterate that a proof of a trigonometric identity involves changing only one side of the equation (typically the more complicated side), usually by rewriting all functions on that side in terms of sines and cosines.

Helping with the Exercises

Exercise 3 As needed, suggest that students rewrite the left side of the equation in terms of sines and cosines.

Exercise 4 [Alert] Students might use calculators to get approximate values. If you want them to find exact values, ask them to draw reference triangles on the unit circle.

BUILDING UNDERSTANDING

In the exercises students apply the identities of the lesson and prove a few identities.

ASSIGNING HOMEWORK

Essential	1–4
Performance assessment	5, 7–14
Portfolio	11, 14
Journal	5
Group	6, 8, 12, 15
Review	14–18

MATERIALS

- graph paper
- Exercise 8 (W), *optional*

See pages 901–902 for answers to Steps 6–8 and Exercise 3.

Exercise 6 This exercise introduces even and odd functions. As needed, remind students of the equalities $\cos(-x) = \cos x$ and $\sin(-x) = -\sin x$. You might ask students to draw their own even and odd functions and trade with their partners to determine whether each function is odd or even. **[Ask]** "Why might these functions be called odd and even?" [The function $y = x^n$ is an odd function if n is odd and an even function if n is even. Another possible origin of the terms is that the functions satisfy properties similar to those of odd and even integers: An odd times an odd is odd, and any product of an even with an odd or an even function is even.] "What kinds of symmetry do the graphs of odd and even functions have?" [even: reflective symmetry across the y-axis; odd: point symmetry or 2-fold rotational symmetry]

Exercise 8 You might hand out the Exercise 8 worksheet.

8a.

8b.

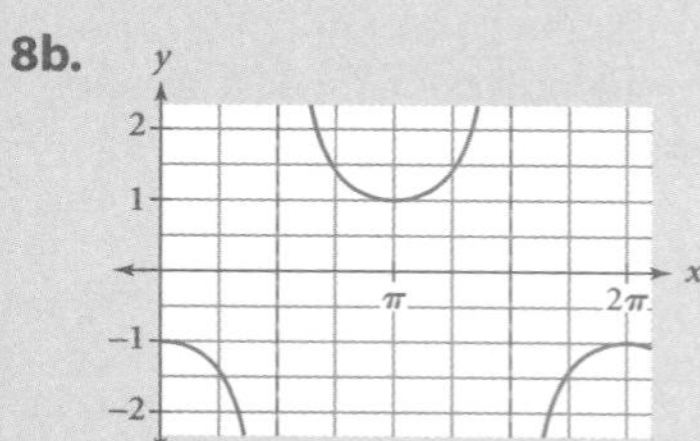

Exercise 9 Encourage students to graph the functions. You might have them find two other functions that share each graph.

Exercise 10 Encourage students to use a combination of graphing and inverse trigonometric functions rather than the calculator's solve function.

See page 902 for answers to Exercise 11.

6. A function f is **even** if $f(-x) = f(x)$ for all x-values in its domain. It is **odd** if $f(-x) = -f(x)$ for all x-values in its domain. Determine whether each function is even, odd, or neither.

a. $f(x) = \sin x$ odd | **b.** $f(x) = \cos x$ even | **c.** $f(x) = \tan x$ odd

d. $f(x) = \cot x$ odd | **e.** $f(x) = \sec x$ even | **f.** $f(x) = \csc x$ odd

7. In the next lesson, you'll see that $\cos 2A = \cos^2 A - \sin^2 A$ is an identity. Use this identity and the identities from this lesson to prove that

a. $\cos 2A = 1 - 2\sin^2 A$ | **b.** $\cos 2A = 2\cos^2 A - 1$

8. Sketch the graph of $y = \frac{1}{f(x)}$ for each function.

a.

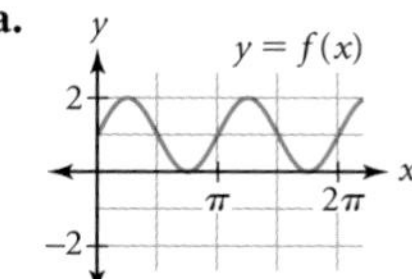

b.

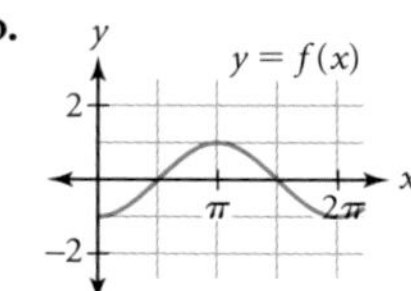

9. Find another function that has the same graph as each function named below. More than one answer is possible.

a. $y = \cos\left(\frac{\pi}{2} - x\right)$ $y = \sin x$ | **b.** $y = \sin\left(\frac{\pi}{2} - x\right)$ $y = \cos x$ | **c.** $y = \tan\left(\frac{\pi}{2} - x\right)$ $y = \cot x$

d. $y = \cos(-x)$ $y = \cos x$ | **e.** $y = \sin(-x)$ $y = -\sin x$ | **f.** $y = \tan(-x)$ $y = -\tan x$

g. $y = \sin(x + 2\pi)$ $y = \sin x$ | **h.** $y = \cos\left(\frac{\pi}{2} + x\right)$ $y = -\sin x$ | **i.** $y = \tan(x + \pi)$ $y = \tan x$

10. Find the first three positive x-values that make each equation true.

a. $\sec x = -2.5$ 1.98, 4.30, 8.27 | **b.** $\csc x = 0.4$ no such values

11. Sketch a graph for each equation with domain $0 \le x < 4\pi$. Include any asymptotes and state the x-values at which the asymptotes occur.

a. $y = \csc x$ | **b.** $y = \sec x$ | **c.** $y = \cot x$

12. Write an equation for each graph. More than one answer is possible. Use your calculator to check your work.

a. $y = \tan 2x - 1$

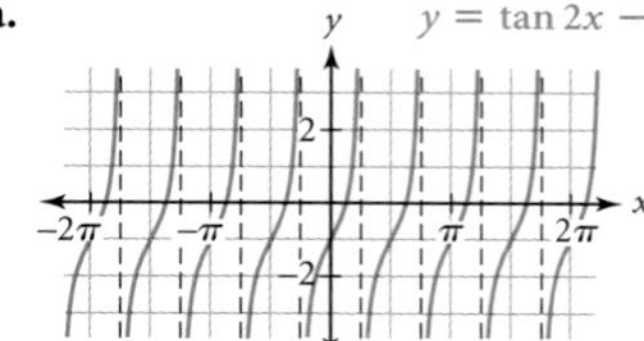

b. $y = \cot\left(x + \frac{\pi}{2}\right) + 1$

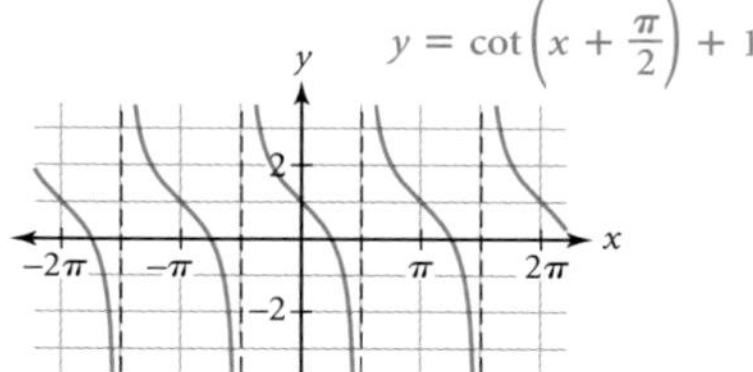

c. $y = 0.5\csc x + 1$

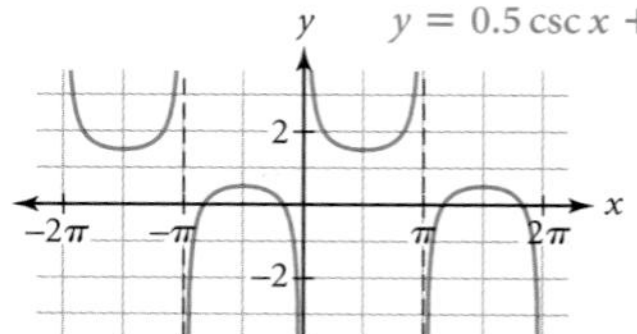

d. $y = \tan\frac{1}{3}x$

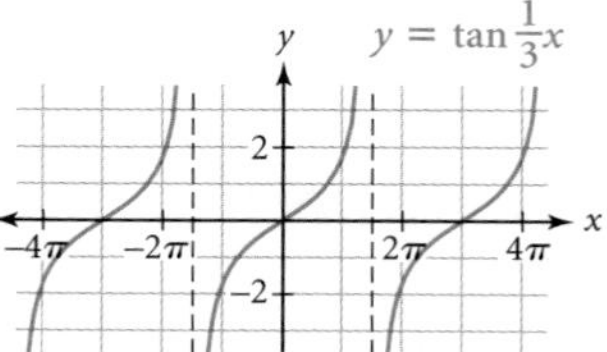

7a. Proof:

$$\cos 2A \stackrel{?}{=} 1 - 2\sin^2 A$$
$$\cos^2 A - \sin^2 A \stackrel{?}{=} 1 - 2\sin^2 A$$
$$1 - \sin^2 A - \sin^2 A \stackrel{?}{=} 1 - 2\sin^2 A$$
$$1 - 2\sin^2 A = 1 - 2\sin^2 A$$

7b. Proof:

$$\cos 2A \stackrel{?}{=} 2\cos^2 A - 1$$
$$\cos^2 A - \sin^2 A \stackrel{?}{=} 2\cos^2 A - 1$$
$$\cos^2 A - (1 - \cos^2 A) \stackrel{?}{=} 2\cos^2 A - 1$$
$$\cos^2 A - 1 + \cos^2 A \stackrel{?}{=} 2\cos^2 A - 1$$
$$2\cos^2 A - 1 = 2\cos^2 A - 1$$

13. Use the trigonometric identities to rewrite each expression in a simplified form that contains only one type of trigonometric function. For each expression, give values of θ for which the expression is undefined. Use domain $0 \le \theta < 2\pi$.

a. $2\cos^2\theta + \dfrac{\sin\theta}{\csc\theta} + \sin^2\theta$

b. $(\sec\theta)(2\cos^2\theta) + (\cot\theta)(\sin\theta)$

c. $\sec^2\theta + \dfrac{1}{\cot\theta} + \dfrac{\sin^2\theta - 1}{\cos^2\theta}$

d. $\sin\theta(\cot\theta + \tan\theta)$

Review

10.5 **14.** APPLICATION Tidal changes can be modeled with a sinusoidal curve. This table gives the time and height of the low and high tides for Burntcoat Head, Nova Scotia, on June 10 and 11, 1999.

High and Low Tides for Burntcoat Head, Nova Scotia, 1999

	Low	High	Low	High
	Time (AST)/Height (m)	Time (AST)/Height (m)	Time (AST)/Height (m)	Time (AST)/Height (m)
June 10	04:13/1.60	10:22/13.61	16:40/1.42	22:49/14.15
June 11	05:12/1.01	11:19/14.09	17:38/0.94	23:45/14.71

(*www.ldeo.columbia.edu*)

a. Select one time value as the starting time and assign it time 0. Reassign the other time values in minutes relative to the starting time.

b. Let x represent time in minutes relative to the starting time, and let y represent the tide height in meters. Make a scatter plot of the eight data points.

c. Find mean values for

i. Height of the low tide.

ii. Height of the high tide.

iii. Height of "no tide," or the mean water level.

iv. Time in minutes of a tide change between high and low tide.

d. Write an equation to model these data.

e. Graph your equation with the scatter plot in order to check the fit.

f. Predict the water height at 12:00 on June 10, 1999.

g. Predict when the high tide(s) occurred on June 12, 1999.

The Bay of Fundy borders Maine and the Canadian provinces of New Brunswick and Nova Scotia. This bay experiences some of the most dramatic tides on Earth, with water depths fluctuating up to 18 m.

1.5 **15.** APPLICATION Juan's parents bought a \$500 savings bond for him when he was born. Interest has compounded monthly at an annual fixed rate of 6.5%.

a. Juan just turned 17, and he is considering using the bond to pay for college. How much is his bond currently worth?

b. Juan also considers saving the bond and using it to buy a used car after he graduates. If he would need about \$4000, how long would he have to wait?

Exercise 13 The result when 13a is simplified is not a trigonometric ratio.

$2(\cos^2\theta + \sin^2\theta) = 2$

13a. 2; undefined when θ equals 0 or π

13b. $3\cos\theta$; undefined when θ equals $0, \frac{\pi}{2}, \pi$, or $\frac{3\pi}{2}$

13c. $\tan^2\theta + \tan\theta$; undefined when θ equals $\frac{\pi}{2}$ or $\frac{3\pi}{2}$

13d. $\sec\theta$; undefined when θ equals $0, \frac{\pi}{2}, \pi, \frac{3\pi}{2}$, or 2π

Exercise 14 AST is Atlantic standard time, the time zone directly east of eastern standard time. **[Alert]** If students are confused by times such as 16:40, explain that these are times on a 24-hour clock; thus 16:40 is 4:40 P.M.

14a. Sample answer: Select the second time value, 10:22, as time 0. The new time values are −369, 0, 378, 747, 1130, 1497, 1876, 2243.

14b.

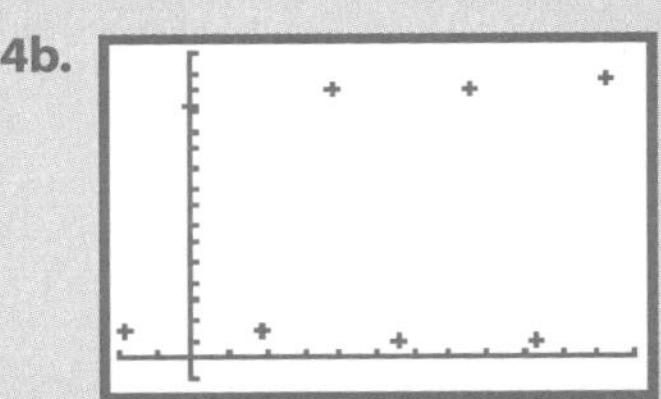

[−400, 2400, 200, −1, 16, 1]

14c. i. 1.24 m

14c. ii. 14.14 m

14c. iii. 7.69 m

14c. iv. 373 min

14d. possible answer:

$y = 6.45\cos\left(\frac{2\pi}{746}x\right) + 7.69$

14e.

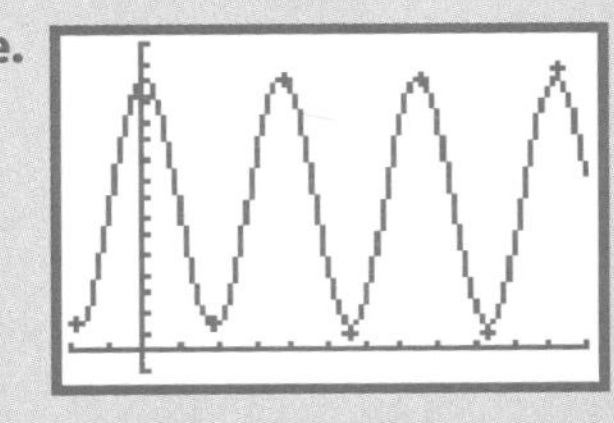

[−400, 2400, 200, −1, 16, 1]

14f. 12.06 m

14g. only one high tide at 12:11

15a. \$1505.12

15b. another 15 years, or until he's 32

16a. $d(x) = \dfrac{60}{100 + x}$

16d.

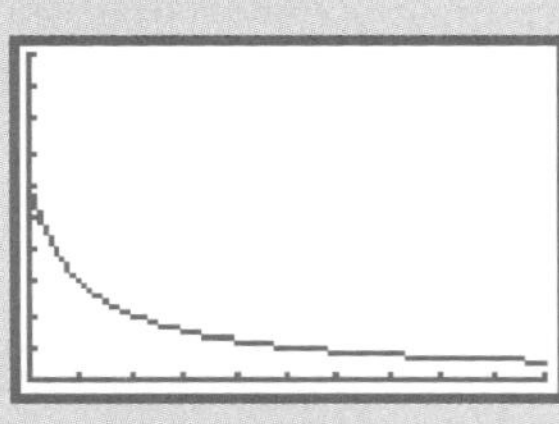

[0, 1000, 100, 0, 1, 0.1]

The asymptote is the x-axis, $y = 0$. The more water that is added the closer the concentration will get to 0%, but it will never actually become 0%.

17d.

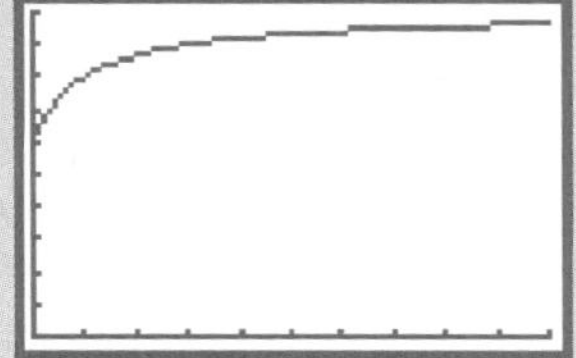

[0, 1000, 100, 0, 1, 0.1]

The asymptote is the line $y = 1$. The more pure medicine that is added the closer the concentration will get to 100%, but it will never actually become 100%.

EXTENSIONS

A. Use Take Another Look activity 1 or 2 on page 627.

B. If students remember secant lines from geometry, have them investigate the connection between secant lines and the secant function.

9.7 **16.** **APPLICATION** A pharmacist has 100 mL of a liquid medication that is 60% concentrated. This means that in 100 mL of the medication, 60 mL is pure medicine and 40 mL is water. She alters the concentration when filling a specific prescription. Suppose she alters the medication by adding water.

a. Write a function that gives the concentration of the medication, $d(x)$, as a function of the amount of water added in milliliters.

b. What is the concentration if the pharmacist adds 20 mL of water? 50%

c. How much water should she add if she needs a 30% concentration? 100 mL

d. Graph $y = d(x)$. Explain the meaning of the asymptote.

9.7 **17.** **APPLICATION** The pharmacist in Exercise 16 could also alter the medication by increasing the amount of pure medicine.

a. Write a function that gives the concentration of the medication, $c(x)$, as a function of the amount of pure medicine added in milliliters. $c(x) = \dfrac{60 + x}{100 + x}$

b. What is the concentration if the pharmacist adds 20 mL of pure medicine? $66\frac{2}{3}\%$

c. How much pure medicine should she add if she needs a 90% concentration? 300 mL

d. Graph $c(x)$. Explain the meaning of the asymptote.

e. Under what circumstances should the pharmacist use the function $d(x)$? When should she use the function $c(x)$? Use the diluting function to obtain concentrations less than 60%. Use the concentrating function to obtain concentrations greater than 60%.

5.7 **18.** Solve. Give each answer correct to the nearest 0.01.

a. $4 + 5^x = 18$ $x = 1.64$

b. $\log_3 15 = \dfrac{\log x}{\log 3}$ $x = 15$

c. $120(0.5)^{2x} = 30$ $x = 1$

d. $\log_6 100 = x$ $x = 2.57$

e. $2\log x = 2.5$ $x = 17.78$

f. $\log_5 5^3 = x$ $x = 3$

g. $4\log x = \log 16$ $x = 2$

h. $\log(5 + x) - \log 5 = 2$ $x = 495$

IMPROVING YOUR VISUAL THINKING SKILLS

An Equation is Worth a Thousand Words

You have learned to model real-world data with a variety of equations. You've also seen that many types of equations have real-world manifestations. For example the path of a fountain of water is parabolic because its projectile-motion equation is quadratic.

Look for a photo of a phenomenon that suggests the graph of an equation. Impose coordinate axes, and find the equation that models the photo. If you have geometry software, you can import an electronic version of your photo and graph your function over it.

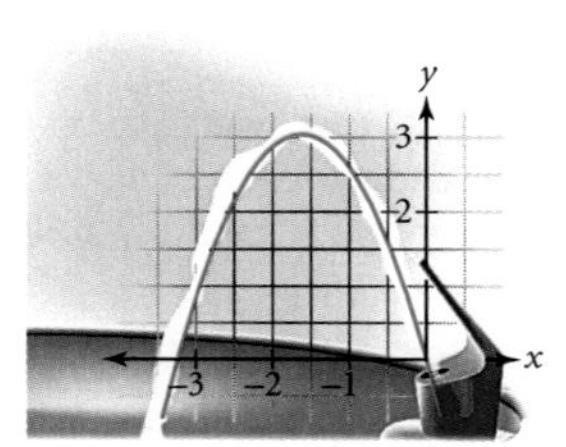

IMPROVING VISUAL THINKING SKILLS

Students could find photos that represent linear, quadratic, polynomial, exponential, logarithmic, conic section, or trigonometric equations. For the illustration in the book, a sample equation that models the water fountain is $y = -1.15x(x + 3.25)$.

LESSON

10.7 Combining Trigonometric Functions

Music is the pleasure that the human soul experiences from counting without being aware that it is counting.

GOTTFRIED LEIBNIZ

When you add sinusoidal functions, your result is still a periodic function. Two periods of the graph of $y = \sin 2x + \sin 3x$ are shown below.

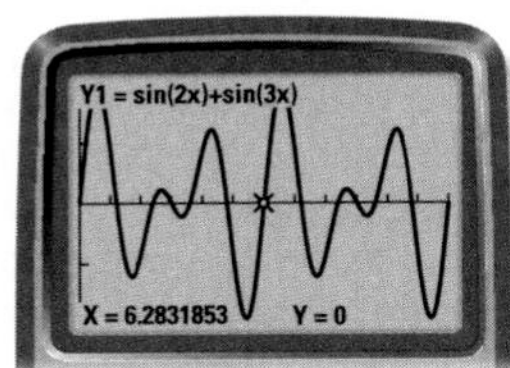

$[0, 4\pi, \pi/3, -2, 2, 1]$

American cellist Yo Yo Ma (b 1955) is one of the world's most renowned classical musicians. He has released more than 50 albums and won 14 Grammy awards.

For many applications you'll need to combine several functions to get a realistic model. When a musician plays a note, the sound produced by a musical instrument is actually the sum of several different tones. Different musical instruments have different characteristic sounds. Flutes and violins sound very different, even when they play the same note. As each instrument plays an A note at a frequency of 440 cycles per second, for example, it also sounds the next higher A at 880 cycles per second and several other tones. These additional tones form the "overtone series" of the note and contribute to the distinctive sound of each instrument. Overtones are present in varying degrees of loudness for different instruments. The graphs and equations below show a flute and a violin playing the same A above middle C.

The coefficient of a term represents the loudness of the tone. The coefficients in this equation are relatively small compared to the leading coefficient of 16. This is why a flute has a pure sound.

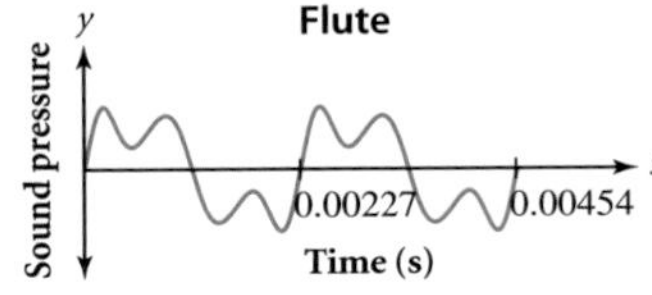

$$y = 16\sin(440\cdot 2\pi x) + 9\sin(880\cdot 2\pi x) + 3\sin(1320\cdot 2\pi x) + 2.5\sin(1760\cdot 2\pi x) + 1.0\sin(2200\cdot 2\pi x)$$

Some of the coefficients in this equation are quite large relative to the leading coefficient of 19. This causes its graph to be more "bumpy," reflecting a violin's complex sound.

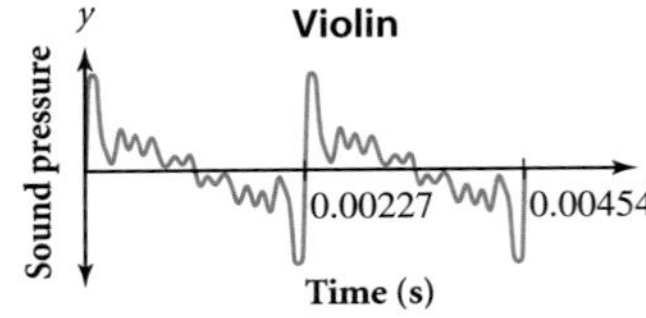

$$y = 19\sin(440\cdot 2\pi x) + 9\sin(880\cdot 2\pi x) + 8\sin(1320\cdot 2\pi x) + 9\sin(1760\cdot 2\pi x) + 12.5\sin(2200\cdot 2\pi x) + 10.5\sin(2640\cdot 2\pi x) + 14\sin(3080\cdot 2\pi x) + 11\sin(3520\cdot 2\pi x) + 8\sin(3960\cdot 2\pi x) + 7\sin(4400\cdot 2\pi x) + 5.5\sin(4840\cdot 2\pi x) + 1.0\sin(5280\cdot 2\pi x) + 4.5\sin(5720\cdot 2\pi x) + 4.0\sin(6160\cdot 2\pi x) + 3\sin(6600\cdot 2\pi x)$$

NCTM STANDARDS

CONTENT		PROCESS	
	Number		Problem Solving
✓	Algebra		Reasoning
	Geometry	✓	Communication
✓	Measurement	✓	Connections
✓	Data/Probability	✓	Representation

LESSON OBJECTIVES

- Combine sinusoidal graphs to create periodic functions
- Derive and apply identities for $\cos(A - B)$ and $\cos(A + B)$
- Use trigonometric identities to find exact values of trigonometric ratios

LESSON 10.7

PLANNING

LESSON OUTLINE

One day:

20 min	Investigation
5 min	Example A
5 min	Example B
10 min	Sharing
5 min	Exercises

MATERIALS

- microphone probes
- tuning forks
- musical instrument, *optional*
- Two Ways to c (W) for One Step
- Sound Wave Sample Data (W), *optional*
- Calculator Note 10D

TEACHING

This lesson concerns sums of sinusoidal functions, the sum and difference identities, the double-angle identities, and the half-angle identities. If you do not want to study the trigonometric identities in this lesson, you might limit attention to the investigation, which looks at sums of sinusoidal functions.

One Step

Hand out the Two Ways to c worksheet and ask students to express the length c in two ways, set the expressions equal, and derive a new trigonometric identity. As needed, encourage the use of the distance formula and the Law of Cosines. If students get stuck after they have arrived at a simple expression in angles A, B, and C, wonder aloud whether they can simplify even further by expressing one angle in terms of the other two. Challenge groups that finish first to derive other identities from this one.

INTRODUCTION

[Language] *Combining* functions typically refers to adding them. Make sure students don't confuse this with *composing* functions, which refers to using the output of one function as the input of another.

[Ask] "Why is the fundamental frequency represented by the equation $y = \sin(440 \cdot 2\pi x)$?" [The function $y = \sin 440x$ has period $\frac{2\pi}{440}$ s. To change it to a function with period $\frac{1}{440}$ s, you shrink it horizontally by a factor of 2π. Then its equation will be $y = \sin(440 \cdot 2\pi x)$.]

Guiding the Investigation

If you don't have tuning forks, you may be able to borrow some from a physics teacher or a music teacher. The microphone probe converts small changes in air pressure to voltage, using a magnet and a wire coil. An equation in the data-collection device converts voltage to numbers. The probe measures sound pressure with a relative scale, with no particular units.

You might want to show your students the Sound Wave Sample Data worksheets so they know approximately what their data should look like. They can also use these worksheets if you do not have the equipment to conduct the investigation.

The sample data printed on the worksheets is only part of the data found on the Calculator Programs and Data CD. Graphs from the larger data sets will show the shape of the data more clearly.

[Alert] Students might be confused about the difference between the procedure note, which says to collect frequency, and what the microphone probe is measuring, which is actually pressure. Assure them that measurement of pressure gives the same results as a measurement of frequency would give.

The periods of both graphs on the preceding page are the same, and are determined by the coefficient of the argument of the leading term, 440, which represents the primary A tone or fundamental frequency above middle C. The "bumps" in the graphs are caused by the overtones, which are described by the remaining terms in each equation. The coefficients of these terms indicate the loudness of each overtone. The numbers 440, 880, 1320, 1760, and so on, are the frequencies of the tones. Each of these frequencies is a multiple of the primary frequency, 440 cycles per second. One cycle is completed in $\frac{1}{440}$ of a second, or approximately 0.00227 s.

When the frequency increases, the period decreases, and you hear a higher sound. When frequency decreases, you hear a lower sound. The amplitude determines the loudness of a tone.

Each musical instrument has its own typical sound and its own graph for the sound of a particular note. A musician can only slightly affect the sound of the note and the shape of the graph it produces. Try entering the flute and violin equations on page 615 into your calculator to reproduce the graphs. Then change the coefficients of some of the terms and observe how the graph is affected.

Technology CONNECTION

Producing music electronically on a synthesizer involves a series of steps. First a sequencer creates the electronic equivalent of sheet music. This information is sent to the synthesizer using a digital code called MIDI (Musical Instrument Digital Interface). The synthesizer then reproduces each instrument's sound accurately by producing the correct strength of each individual overtone frequency. Some early synthesizers did this by adding together sine waves. Methods now used include adapting recordings of real instruments! Programs called wave editors let you create your own new "instruments" by specifying what their waves will look like.

Investigation
Sound Wave

You will need

- a microphone probe
- two tuning forks

In this investigation you'll explore the frequency of some tones and combinations of tones.

Procedure Note

1. Set up your calculator and microphone probe to collect sound frequency data. [► See **Calculator Note 10D.** ◄]
2. To ring a tuning fork, rap it sharply on a semisoft surface like a book or the heel of your shoe. Hold the fork close to the microphone and begin collecting data. When you use more than one fork, be sure to hold them equidistant from the microphone.

Step 1 Choose a tuning fork and collect data as described in the procedure note. Find an equation to fit the data. Repeat this process with a second tuning fork.

You might encourage students to use three different calculators to collect the data—two for Step 1 and one for Step 2.

Step 1 Noise in the room will not necessarily contaminate the data. If students rap the tuning fork sharply to get a clear note and the group members don't yell, the data should be fine.

Step 1 See pages 902–903 for sample data. To find the equation, average the maximums and average the minimums. Use these mean values to find the amplitude and the vertical translation. Then find the period by averaging the time intervals between minimums. Find the phase shift by approximating the first minimums of the function—it will fall between data values.

Equation for a single G-392 Hz tuning fork:

$$y = 0.116 \sin\left(\frac{2\pi}{0.0025}(x - 0.0027)\right) + 2.681$$

Equation for a single C-256 Hz tuning fork:

$$y = 0.0828 \sin\left(\frac{2\pi}{0.0038}(x - 0.0012)\right) + 2.6815$$

Step 2 Using the same two tuning forks that you used in Step 1, ring both forks simultaneously, and collect frequency data. You should see a combination of sinusoids, rather than a simple sinusoid. Model the data with an equation that is the sum of two simple sinusoid equations.

Step 3 Select a musical instrument, perhaps a flute, violin, piano, timpani, or your voice. Play one note (or string) and collect data. You should see a complex wave, probably too complex for you to write an equation. Identify the fundamental frequency. See if you can identify the frequencies of some of the overtones as well.

Relationships modeled by adding sinusoids are not limited to music and sound. These patterns occur in the motion of moons, planets, tides, and satellites, and in any gear-driven mechanism, from a wristwatch to a car.

You can write a horizontally translated sinusoid as a sum of two untranslated curves, for example, $y = \cos(x - 0.6435)$ is equivalent to $y = 0.8\cos x + 0.6\sin x$. (Check this on your calculator.) Here is a proof that $\cos(A - B) = \cos A \cos B + \sin A \sin B$.

The diagram at right shows the terminal sides of $\angle A$ and $\angle B$ with $m\angle A - m\angle B = m\angle C$. Note the coordinates of the intersections of the terminal sides with the unit circle. The distance c between those points can be determined by two equations, one using the distance formula, and one using the Law of Cosines.

$$c = \sqrt{(\cos A - \cos B)^2 + (\sin A - \sin B)^2}$$

and

$$c = \sqrt{1 + 1 - 2\cos C}.$$

$\sqrt{2 - 2\cos C} = \sqrt{(\cos A - \cos B)^2 + (\sin A - \sin B)^2}$	Set the expressions for c equal to each other.
$2 - 2\cos C = (\cos A - \cos B)^2 + (\sin A - \sin B)^2$	Square both sides.
$2 - 2\cos C = \cos^2 A - 2\cos A\cos B + \cos^2 B + \sin^2 A - 2\sin A\sin B + \sin^2 B$	Expand.
$2 - 2\cos C = (\sin^2 A + \cos^2 A) + (\sin^2 B + \cos^2 B) - 2\cos A\cos B - 2\sin A\sin B$	Reorder terms.
$2 - 2\cos C = 1 + 1 - 2\cos A\cos B - 2\sin A\sin B$	Use the Pythagorean identity, $\sin^2 A + \cos^2 A = 1$.
$-2\cos C = -2\cos A\cos B - 2\sin A\sin B$	Subtract 2 from both sides.
$\cos C = \cos A\cos B + \sin A\sin B$	Divide both sides by -2.
$\cos(A - B) = \cos A\cos B + \sin A\sin B$	Substitute $(A - B)$ for C.

So, $\cos(A - B) = \cos A\cos B + \sin A\sin B$ is an identity. You can use this identity to find exact cosine values for some new angles, using values you already know.

Step 2 (continued)

Equation for the combination of G and C tuning forks:

$$y = 0.116\sin\left(\frac{2\pi}{0.0025}(x - 0.0027)\right) + 2.681 + 0.0828\sin\left(\frac{2\pi}{0.0038}(x - 0.0012)\right)$$

Step 2 Make sure the two tuning forks do not collide when students are collecting these data. Students can add the equations they found in Step 1.

The vertical translation of 2.6815 in the equation for the sample data has no real-world meaning. It is simply an artifact of the CBL2 data-collection device. Students can make clearer graphs using Sketchpad, especially if they use the full data set from the Calculator Programs and Data CD.

Step 2 See page 903 for sample data. If you add the equations of the two tuning forks, you get a close approximation of the wave formed by ringing the two forks together. However, the curve is translated up because the two vertical translations are combined.

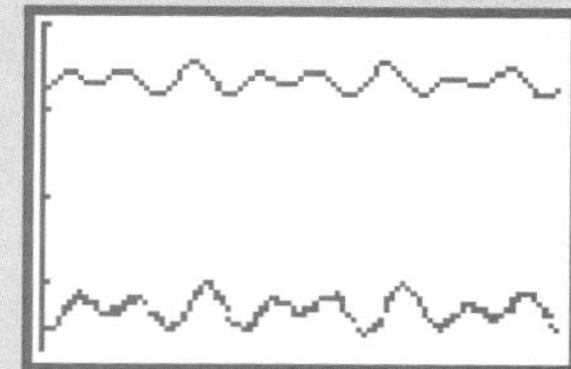

[0, 0.02, 1, 2.2, 6, 1]

Subtract 2.6815 from the sum of the equations to account for the vertical translation of the new data. The equation is below.

Step 3 Students are to find the fundamental frequency (period) from the graph of the collected data.

Proof of Identity

[Ask] "Is it acceptable that this proof manipulates both sides of the equation?" [Yes; this proof begins with what's known and ends with the identity that is to be proved, so it avoids question marks and concerns about the reversibility of steps.]

See page 903 for the answer to Step 3.

▶ EXAMPLE A

You might want to refer to the unit circle and discuss which angles are associated with exact values of sine and cosine. By identifying these values, students can then search for values whose difference is $\frac{\pi}{12}$. **[Alert]** Students may need to convert $\frac{\pi}{12}$ to 15° in order to see how to express it as a difference.

▶ EXAMPLE B

If time is limited, you might skip this derivation. Alternatively, you might ask students to close their books and assign it as a follow-up to the derivation of $\cos(A - B)$.

SHARING IDEAS

As students present, wonder aloud whether they've seen sums or differences of functions before. [They saw sums of rational functions in Chapter 9; they may recall how each part of the function $y = x + \frac{1}{x}$ influenced its graph.]

Again, allow students to ask questions and discuss the answers.

[Language] Some students will remember the term *Hertz* from Chapter 5. The equivalent term *cycles per second* is used in this lesson to emphasize that sound waves are periodic.

[Ask] "What can you use these new identities for?" [Before, students knew the sines and cosines of integer multiples of $\frac{\pi}{6}$ and $\frac{\pi}{4}$. Now they can find the sines and cosines of sums and differences of these multiples.] "Why bother if you can find these sines and cosines on a calculator?" [The calculator gives only approximations for the values of the trigonometric functions of most angles.]

EXAMPLE A | Find the exact value of $\cos\frac{\pi}{12}$.

▶ Solution

You know exact values of the sine and cosine of $0, \frac{\pi}{6}, \frac{\pi}{4}, \frac{\pi}{3}$, and π. So rewrite $\frac{\pi}{12}$ as a difference of these values.

$$\cos\frac{\pi}{12} = \cos\left(\frac{3\pi}{12} - \frac{2\pi}{12}\right) = \cos\left(\frac{\pi}{4} - \frac{\pi}{6}\right)$$ Rewrite $\frac{\pi}{12}$ as a difference of two fractions, and reduce.

$$\cos\frac{\pi}{12} = \cos\frac{\pi}{4}\cdot\cos\frac{\pi}{6} + \sin\frac{\pi}{4}\cdot\sin\frac{\pi}{6}$$ Rewrite $\cos\left(\frac{\pi}{4} - \frac{\pi}{6}\right)$ using the identity $\cos(A - B) = \cos A\cos B + \sin A\sin B$.

$$\cos\frac{\pi}{12} = \frac{\sqrt{2}}{2}\cdot\frac{\sqrt{3}}{2} + \frac{\sqrt{2}}{2}\cdot\frac{1}{2}$$ Substitute exact values for sine and cosine of $\frac{\pi}{4}$ and $\frac{\pi}{6}$.

$$\cos\frac{\pi}{12} = \frac{\sqrt{6} + \sqrt{2}}{4}$$ Combine into one rational expression.

So the exact value of $\cos\frac{\pi}{12}$ is $\frac{\sqrt{6}+\sqrt{2}}{4}$. You can check your work by evaluating $\frac{\sqrt{6}+\sqrt{2}}{4}$ and $\cos\frac{\pi}{12}$ with your calculator.

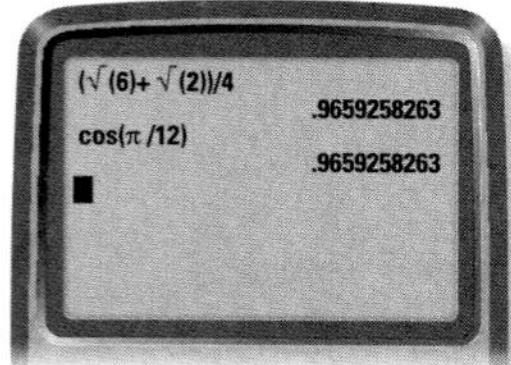

The next example shows you how to develop another identity based on identities that you already know.

EXAMPLE B | Develop an identity for $\cos(A + B)$.

▶ Solution

Notice that $\cos(A + B)$ is similar to $\cos(A - B)$, except the sign of B is changed. Start with the identity $\cos(A - B) = \cos A\cos B + \sin A\sin B$, and replace B with $-B$.

$$\cos(A - (-B)) = \cos A\cos(-B) + \sin A\sin(-B)$$ Replace B with $-B$.

$$\cos(A + B) = \cos A\cos(-B) + \sin A\sin(-B)$$ Rewrite $A - (-B)$ as $A + B$.

Earlier in this chapter, you found that $\cos(-x) = \cos x$ and that $\sin(-x) = -\sin x$.

$$\cos(A + B) = \cos A\cos B - \sin A\sin B$$ Replace $\cos(-B)$ with $\cos B$ and $\sin(-B)$ with $-\sin B$.

So, $\cos(A + B) = \cos A\cos B - \sin A\sin B$ is an identity.

There are many other trigonometric identities that can be useful in calculations or for simplifying expressions. As in Example B, you will be asked to prove new identities using existing identities. The box on the next page includes several relationships you have already seen and a few new ones.

Ask students how they might remember these identities. Some students find it easier to remember the special cases of the double-angle identities only (Exercises 8 and 9) and then work backward to the general cases (proved in Exercises 6 and 7) if needed. Or they might combine the four sum and difference identities into just two:

$$\cos(A \pm B) = \cos A\cos B \mp \sin A\sin B$$

$$\sin(A \pm B) = \sin A\cos B \pm \cos A\sin B$$

In the symbol $\mp$, the minus sign on top goes with the plus sign on top of the $\pm$ symbol in the same equation. For $\cos(A \pm B)$, the sign on the right of the equal sign is the opposite of the sign on the left. For $\sin(A \pm B)$, the sign is the same on both sides of the equal sign.

Sum and Difference Identities

$$\cos(A - B) = \cos A \cos B + \sin A \sin B$$
$$\cos(A + B) = \cos A \cos B - \sin A \sin B$$
$$\sin(A - B) = \sin A \cos B - \cos A \sin B$$
$$\sin(A + B) = \sin A \cos B + \cos A \sin B$$
$$\tan(A - B) = \frac{\tan A - \tan B}{1 + \tan A \tan B}$$
$$\tan(A + B) = \frac{\tan A + \tan B}{1 - \tan A \tan B}$$

Double-Angle Identities

$$\cos 2A = \cos^2 A - \sin^2 A = 1 - 2\sin^2 A = 2\cos^2 A - 1$$
$$\sin 2A = 2 \sin A \cos A$$
$$\tan 2A = \frac{2\tan A}{1 - \tan^2 A}$$

Half-Angle Identities

$$\sin\frac{A}{2} = \pm\sqrt{\frac{1 - \cos A}{2}}$$
$$\cos\frac{A}{2} = \pm\sqrt{\frac{1 + \cos A}{2}}$$
$$\tan\frac{A}{2} = \pm\sqrt{\frac{1 - \cos A}{1 + \cos A}} = \frac{\sin A}{1 + \cos A} = \frac{1 - \cos A}{\sin A}$$

For the half-angle identities, the sign of the answer is determined by the quadrant in which the terminal side of the given angle lies.

In the exercises you will be asked to prove some of these identities. As you do so, remember to only work on one side of the equation.

EXERCISES

Practice Your Skills

1. Decide whether each expression is an identity by substituting values for A and B.
   a. $\cos(A + B) = \cos A + \cos B$ not an identity
   b. $\sin(A + B) = \sin A + \sin B$ not an identity
   c. $\cos(2A) = 2\cos A$ not an identity
   d. $\sin(2A) = 2\sin A$ not an identity

2. Prove each identity. The sum and difference identities will be helpful.
   a. $\cos(2\pi - A) = \cos A$
   b. $\sin\left(\frac{3\pi}{2} - A\right) = -\cos A$

3. Rewrite each expression with a single sine or cosine.
   a. $\cos 1.5 \cos 0.4 + \sin 1.5 \sin 0.4$ $\cos 1.1$
   b. $\cos 2.6 \cos 0.2 - \sin 2.6 \sin 0.2$ $\cos 2.8$
   c. $\sin 3.1 \cos 1.4 - \cos 3.1 \sin 1.4$ $\sin 1.7$
   d. $\sin 0.2 \cos 0.5 + \cos 0.2 \sin 0.5$ $\sin 0.7$

Assessing Progress

You can assess students' ability to gather data systematically, to model periodic data with sinusoids, and to identify the period.

Closing the Lesson

Reiterate the sum and difference identities, and the double-angle identities. Remind students that trigonometric identities can be derived from other identities.

BUILDING UNDERSTANDING

If students did the investigation but not the examples, assign Exercises 14–16.

ASSIGNING HOMEWORK

Essential	1–4
Performance assessment	5–16
Portfolio	16
Journal	10, 14
Group	14, 15
Review	17–19

Helping with the Exercises

Exercise 1 Encourage students to substitute more than one value for A and B into each expression.

Exercise 2 [Alert] Students might think of 2π and $\frac{3\pi}{2}$ as symbols rather than numbers at which they can evaluate sine and cosine.

2a. $\cos(2\pi - A) = \cos(2\pi)\cos A + \sin(2\pi)\sin A = 1 \cdot \cos A + 0 \cdot \sin A = \cos A$

2b. $\sin\left(\frac{3\pi}{2} - A\right) = \sin\frac{3\pi}{2}\cos A - \cos\frac{3\pi}{2}\sin A = -1 \cdot \cos A - 0 \cdot \sin A = -\cos A$

Exercise 5 Students can start with the double-angle identity for $\sin 2x$, but they may get stuck finding $\cos x$. Using the calculator to find x and then its cosine leads to approximations. Suggest that they draw a reference triangle in the appropriate quadrant. They can then use the Pythagorean Theorem to find the length of the third side of the triangle and hence the cosine.

Exercise 7 As needed, remind students that $\sin(-A) = -\sin(A)$.

Exercise 11 Students can substitute numerical values for A and B to show that the equation is not an identity. Rewriting $\tan(A + B)$ in terms of sine and cosine can help. As an extension, point out that because $\tan A + \tan B = \tan(A + B)$ is not an identity, it is a trigonometric equation, and ask what values of A and B satisfy it. [values of A and B for which $\tan A = 0$ or $\tan B = 0$ or $\tan A = -\tan B$]

12. $\tan 2A = \tan(A + A) = \dfrac{\tan A + \tan A}{1 - \tan A \tan A} = \dfrac{2\tan A}{1 - \tan^2 A}$

13a. $\cos 2A = 1 - 2\sin^2 A$
$2\sin^2 A = 1 - \cos 2A$
$\sin^2 A = \dfrac{1 - \cos 2A}{2}$

13b. $\cos 2A = 2\cos^2 A - 1$
$2\cos^2 A = \cos 2A + 1$
$\cos^2 A = \dfrac{\cos 2A + 1}{2}$

14a. sample graph when $a = 3$ and $b = 4$:

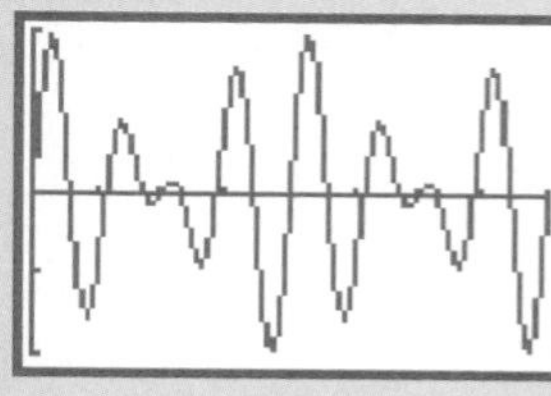

$[0, 4\pi, \pi/2, -2, 2, 1]$

Exercise 15 With the realization that $\frac{x}{a} = \frac{1}{a}x$, students can apply the results of Exercise 14.

See pages 903–904 for answers to Exercises 6–9.

4. Use identities to find the exact value of each expression.

a. $\sin\dfrac{-11\pi}{12}$ $\dfrac{-\sqrt{6} + \sqrt{2}}{4}$ **b.** $\sin\dfrac{7\pi}{12}$ $\dfrac{\sqrt{6} + \sqrt{2}}{4}$ **c.** $\tan\dfrac{\pi}{12}$ $2 - \sqrt{3}$ **d.** $\cos\dfrac{\pi}{8}$ $\sqrt{\dfrac{1}{2} + \dfrac{\sqrt{2}}{4}}$

Reason and Apply

5. Given $\pi \le x \le \frac{3\pi}{2}$ and $\sin x = -\frac{2}{3}$, find the exact value of $\sin 2x$. $\frac{4\sqrt{5}}{9}$

6. Use the identity for $\cos(A - B)$ and the identities $\sin A = \cos\left(\frac{\pi}{2} - A\right)$ and $\cos A = \sin\left(\frac{\pi}{2} - A\right)$ to prove that

$\sin(A + B) = \sin A \cos B + \cos A \sin B$

7. Use the identity for $\sin(A + B)$ from Exercise 6 to prove that

$\sin(A - B) = \sin A \cos B - \cos A \sin B$

8. Use the identity for $\sin(A + B)$ to prove the identity $\sin 2A = 2\sin A \cos A$.

9. Use the identity for $\cos(A + B)$ to prove the identity $\cos 2A = \cos^2 A - \sin^2 A$.

10. What is wrong with this statement?

$\cos(\tan x) = \cos\left(\dfrac{\sin x}{\cos x}\right) = \sin x$

Sample answer: $\cos(\tan x)$ is a composite function, whereas $\cos x(\tan x)$ is a product; $\cos x(\tan x) = \cos x\left(\frac{\sin x}{\cos x}\right) = \sin x$.

11. Show that $\tan(A + B)$ is not equivalent to $\tan A + \tan B$. Then use the identities for $\sin(A + B)$ and $\cos(A + B)$ to develop an identity for $\tan(A + B)$.

12. Use your identity from Exercise 11 to develop an identity for $\tan 2A$.

13. You have seen that $\sin^2 A = 1 - \cos^2 A$ and $\cos^2 A = 1 - \sin^2 A$.

a. Use one of the double-angle identities to develop an expression that is equivalent to $\sin^2 A$ but does not contain the term $\cos^2 A$.

b. Use another double-angle identity to develop an expression equivalent to $\cos^2 A$ that does not contain $\sin^2 A$.

14. ***Mini-Investigation*** Set your graphing window to $0 \le x \le 4\pi$ and $-2 \le y \le 2$.

a	1	2	2	3	3	4	4	4
b	2	3	4	4	6	6	8	12
Period	2π	2π	π	2π	$\frac{2\pi}{3}$	π	$\frac{\pi}{2}$	$\frac{\pi}{2}$

a. Graph equations in the form $y = \sin ax + \sin bx$, using the a- and b-values listed in the table. Record the period for each pair.

b. Explain how to find the period of any function in the form $y = \sin ax + \sin bx$, where a and b are whole numbers. The period is 2π divided by the greatest common factor of a and b.

15. ***Mini-Investigation*** Set your graphing window to $0 \le x \le 24\pi$ and $-2 \le y \le 2$.

a	2	2	2	4	3
b	4	3	5	6	6
Period	8π	12π	20π	24π	12π

11. possible answer: $\tan(1 + 2) \ne \tan 1 + \tan 2$; because $\tan 3 \approx -0.1425$, whereas $\tan 1 + \tan 2 \approx -0.6276$

$$\tan(A + B) = \frac{\sin(A + B)}{\cos(A + B)} = \frac{\sin A\cos B + \cos A\sin B}{\cos A\cos B - \sin A\sin B} =$$

$$\frac{\dfrac{\sin A\cos B + \cos A\sin B}{\cos A\cos B}}{\dfrac{\cos A\cos B - \sin A\sin B}{\cos A\cos B}} = \frac{\dfrac{\sin A}{\cos A} + \dfrac{\sin B}{\cos B}}{1 - \dfrac{\sin A}{\cos A}\cdot\dfrac{\sin B}{\cos B}} = \frac{\tan A + \tan B}{1 - \tan A\tan B}$$

a. Graph equations in the form $y = \sin\frac{x}{a} + \sin\frac{x}{b}$, using the a- and b-values listed in the table. Record the period for each pair.

b. Explain how to find the period of any function in the form $y = \sin\frac{x}{a} + \sin\frac{x}{b}$, where a and b are integers. The period is 2π multiplied by the least common multiple of a and b.

c. Predict the period for $y = \sin\frac{x}{3} + \sin\frac{x}{4} + \sin\frac{x}{8}$. Explain your reasoning. 48π; multiply 2π by the least common multiple of 3, 4, and 8, which is 24.

16. When a tuning fork for middle C is struck, the resulting sound wave has a frequency of 262 cycles per second. The equation $y = \sin(262 \cdot 2\pi x)$ is one possible model for this wave.

a. Identify the period of this wave. Make a graph showing about five complete cycles.

b. Suppose middle C on an out-of-tune piano is played and that the resulting wave has a frequency of 265 cycles per second. Write an equation to model the out-of-tune wave. Identify its period. Then make a graph using the same window as in 16a.

c. A piano tuner plays the out-of-tune C at the same time she uses the tuning fork. The two waves are added to produce a new sound wave. Write the equation that models the sum of the two waves. Graph a 0.5 s interval of this new equation.

Music CONNECTION

The sound waves from an out-of-tune piano and a tuning fork have slightly different frequencies. When they are played together, the resulting wave will vary in amplitude, getting louder and softer in cycles. These periodic variations are called beats. Because the difference between the number of cycles is three (265 − 262), there are three beats per second. The loudness will rise and fall three times per second. Musicians listen for beats to see if their instruments are out of tune. An out-of-tune piano is tuned by adjusting the tension of a string until the beats disappear.

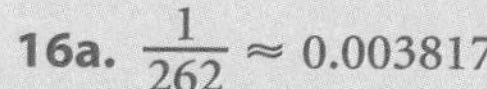

Review

10.6 **17.** Solve.

a. $\sec 144° = x$ $x \approx -1.2361$

b. $\csc\frac{24\pi}{9} = x$ $x \approx 1.1547$

c. $\cot 3.92 = x$ $x \approx 1.0141$

d. $\cot 630° = x$ $x = 0$

10.6 **18.** Find all values of θ that satisfy each equation. Use domain $0° \le \theta < 360°$.

a. $\tan\theta = 0.5317$ $\theta = 28°$ or $\theta = 208°$

b. $\sec\theta = -3.8637$ $\theta = 105°$ or $\theta = 255°$

c. $\csc\theta = 1.1126$ $\theta = 64°$ or $\theta = 116°$

d. $\cot\theta = -4.3315$ $\theta = 167°$ or $\theta = 347°$

10.5 **19.** A fishing boat rides gently up and down, 10 times per minute, on the ocean waves. The boat rises and falls 1.5 m between each wave crest and trough. Assume the boat is on a crest at time 0 min.

a. Sketch a graph of the boat's height above sea level over time.

b. Use a cosine function to model your graph. $y = 0.75\cos\frac{\pi}{3}x$

c. Use a sine function to model your graph. $y = 0.75\sin\left(\frac{\pi}{3}(x + 1.5)\right)$

15a. sample graph when $a = 2$ and $b = 5$:

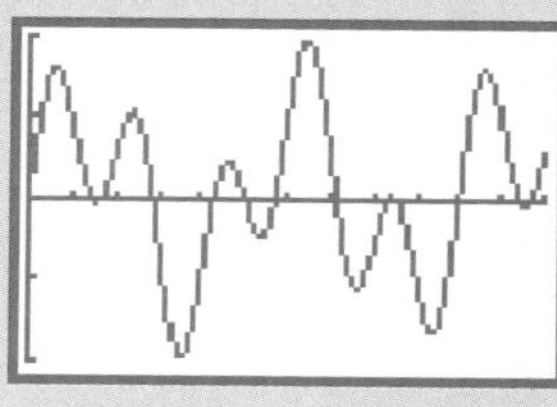

$[0, 24\pi, 2\pi, -2, 2, 1]$

Exercise 17 When students use a calculator to solve 17d, they will get an error message because $\tan 630°$ is undefined and thus $\frac{1}{\tan 630°}$ is undefined. However, $\cot 630°$ is actually $\frac{0}{-1}$, or 0.

Exercise 18 If students are having difficulty finding angles with given secants, cosecants, and cotangents, suggest that they sketch right triangles. Also, if they know, for example, that $\sec\theta \approx -3.8637$, then $\frac{1}{\cos\theta} \approx -3.8637$ and $\cos\theta \approx -\frac{1}{3.8637}$.

19a. Let x represent time in seconds, and let y represent height in meters above the surface of the water if it were calm.

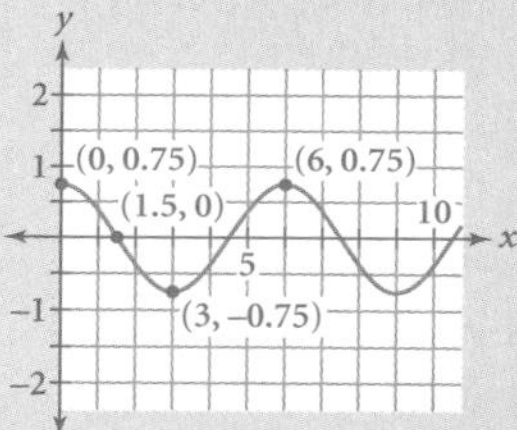

EXTENSIONS

A. Use Take Another Look activity 5 on page 628.

B. Have students explore compositions of trigonometric functions.

16a. $\frac{1}{262} \approx 0.003817$

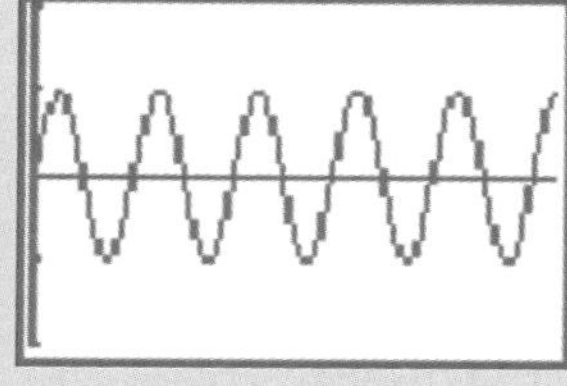

$[0, 0.02, 0, -2, 2, 1]$

16b. $y = \sin(265 \cdot 2\pi x)$ · $\frac{1}{265} \approx 0.003774$

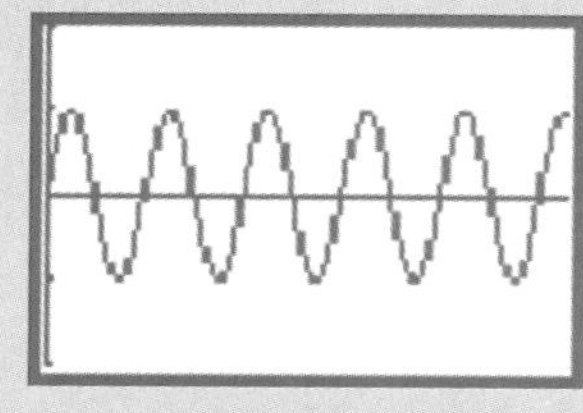

$[0, 0.02, 0, -2, 2, 1]$

16c. $y = \sin(262 \cdot 2\pi x) + \sin(265 \cdot 2\pi x)$

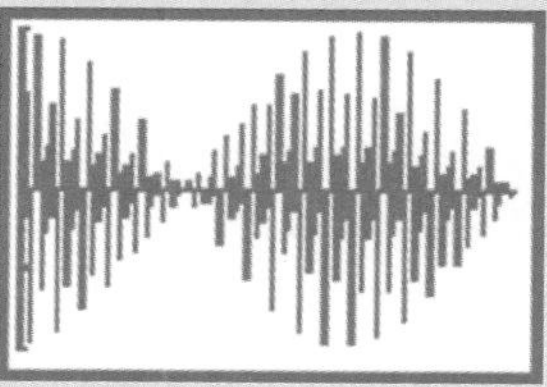

$[0, 0.5, 0, -2, 2, 1]$

EXPLORATION

PLANNING

LESSON OUTLINE

One day:

20 min Activity

10 min Sharing

15 min Questions

MATERIALS

- Polar Graph Paper (W), *optional*
- Calculator Note 10E
- Sketchpad demonstration Rose Curves, *optional*

TEACHING

This exploration gives students some experience with polar coordinates and graphs. **[Language]** You may want to review the definition of *concentric circles* as circles that have the same center.

[Language] The adjective *coordinate* means "equal in importance," as opposed to *subordinate.* Like the *x*- and *y*-coordinates in rectangular coordinate systems, the two numerical values r and θ have equal importance, because both are necessary to determine the location of a point on the coordinate plane. You might point out that at each point the two directions are perpendicular to each other, as with rectangular coordinates.

You might use the Polar Graph Paper worksheet to give students experience in graphing polar curves by hand. Or consider creating a polar grid on your classroom floor with tape and asking students to plot points by rotating by θ and walking r units.

E X P L O R A T I O N

Polar Coordinates

You are very familiar with graphing points on a plane with rectangular coordinates. When you graph points in the form (x, y), you need both the x-coordinate and the y-coordinate to identify the exact location of any point. But this is not the only way to locate points on a plane.

In this chapter you have worked with circles centered at the origin. As you move around a circle, you can identify any point on the circle with coordinates in the form (x, y). However, because the radius of the circle remains constant, you can also identify these points by the radius, r, and the angle of rotation from the positive x-axis, θ.

Imagine infinitely many concentric circles covering a plane, all centered at the origin. You can identify any point on the plane with coordinates in the form (r, θ), called **polar coordinates.** Polar equations in the form $r = f(\theta)$ may lead to familiar or surprising results.

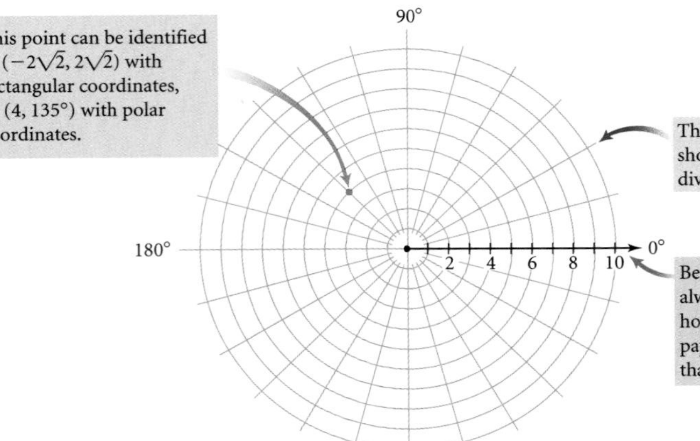

This point can be identified as $(-2\sqrt{2}, 2\sqrt{2})$ with rectangular coordinates, or $(4, 135°)$ with polar coordinates.

The grid on polar graph paper shows concentric circles, often divided into 15° sectors.

Because polar coordinates always relate to the positive horizontal axis, polar graph paper often shows a single axis that is a ray.

For instance, look at the graph of the polar equation $r = 4$, shown at right.

There is no θ in this equation, so r will always be 4. This is the set of all points 4 units from the origin—a circle with radius 4. Notice how much simpler this equation is than the equation of the same circle using rectangular coordinates!

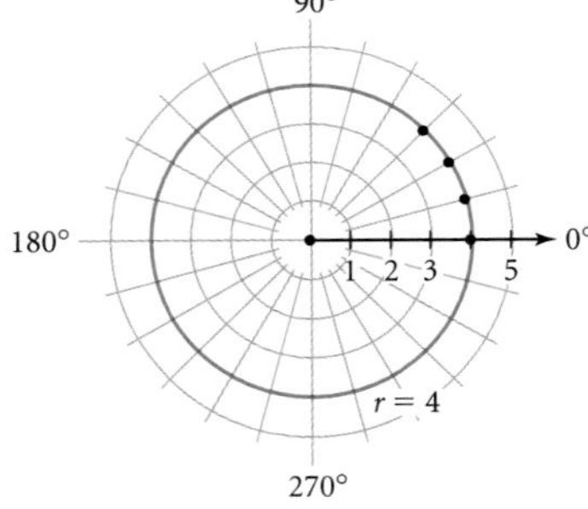

[Alert] With rectangular coordinates, x is customarily the independent variable, functions are written in the form $y = f(x)$, and x appears first in the coordinate pairs. In contrast, with polar coordinates, θ is customarily the independent variable and functions are written in the form $r = f(\theta)$, but r is listed first in the coordinate pairs.

LESSON OBJECTIVES

- Understand graphs that are made using polar coordinates
- Graph polar equations by hand and with the calculator
- Explore rose curves, cardioids, and spirals

Imagine standing at the origin looking in the direction of the positive horizontal axis. First, rotate counterclockwise by the necessary angle. Then, imagine walking straight out from the origin and placing a point at distance r. If r is positive, walk forward. If r is negative, walk backward.

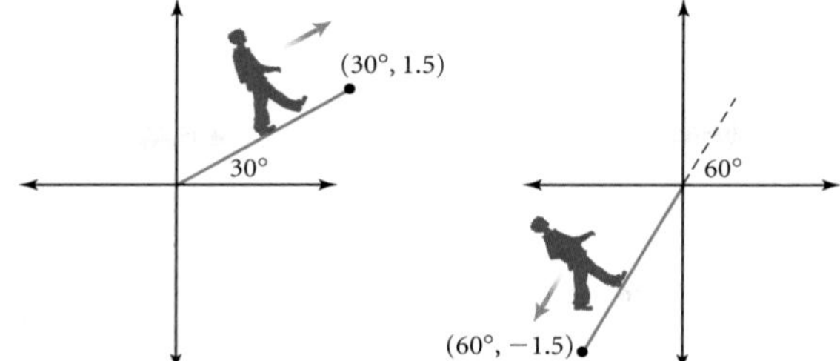

In the activity and questions that follow, you'll explore some of the elegant and complicated-looking graphs that result from polar equations.

Activity

Rose Curves

Use these steps to explore polar equations in the form $r = a\cos n\theta$.

For Steps 1–3, make a table of values, plot the points, and connect them in order with a smooth curve. The results are called rose curves, and each will look like a flower with petals. You can easily check your work with your graphing calculator. [► See **Calculator Note 10E** to learn how to graph polar equations on your calculator. ◄]

Step 1 Graph the family of curves $r = a\cos 2\theta$ with $a = \{1, 2, 3, 4, 5, 6\}$. How does the coefficient a affect the graph?

Step 2 Graph the family of curves $r = 3\cos n\theta$ with $n = \{1, 2, 3, 4, 5, 6\}$. Generalize the effect of the coefficient n. Write statements that describe the curves when n is even and when n is odd.

Step 3 Graph the family of curves $r = 3\sin n\theta$ with $n = \{1, 2, 3, 4, 5, 6\}$. Generalize your results. How do these curves differ from the curves in Step 2?

Step 4 Find a way to graph a rose curve with only two petals. Explain why your method works.

Step 1 The coefficient a affects the size of the petals, or the radius of the circle that encompasses the rose. In effect, a is a dilation scale factor.

Step 2 The coefficient n affects the number of petals. When n is even, the number of petals is $2n$. When n is odd, the number of petals is n.

Questions

1. Find a connection between the graph of the polar equation $r = a\cos n\theta$ and the graph of the associated rectangular equation $y = a\cos nx$. Explain whether or not you can look at the graph of $y = a\cos nx$ and predict the shape and number of petals in the polar graph.

2. The graphs of polar equations in the forms $r = a(\cos\theta + 1)$, $r = a(\cos\theta - 1)$, $r = a(\sin\theta + 1)$, and $r = a(\sin\theta - 1)$ are called cardioids because they resemble hearts. Graph several curves in the cardioid family. Generalize your results by answering the questions at the top of page 624.

Guiding the Activity

Students might do this activity individually and then share results as a group.

This activity is intended for graphing calculators. You might instead use the Sketchpad demonstration Rose Curves.

Students can work in either degrees or radians. It's best if students use the same units and domain to compare or share results. Friendly windows give the best results.

Step 1 As needed, suggest that students enter the function $r = a\cos 2\theta$ on the Y= screen and then enter various values of a on the Home screen. **[Ask]** "What is the domain of θ?" [one rotation around the origin, either $0° \le \theta \le 360°$ or $0 \le \theta \le 2\pi$]

Step 3 Students enter the function $r = a\sin n\theta$ on the Y= screen and then enter various values of a and n on the Home screen.

Step 3 The size and number of petals for $r = a\sin n\theta$ is the same as $r = a\cos n\theta$; however, the graph of $r = a\sin n\theta$ is rotated $\frac{90}{n}°$ counterclockwise from the graph of $r = a\cos n\theta$.

Step 4 Sample answer: $r = 3\sqrt{\cos 2\theta}$, because the square root of a negative number is not real, and thus for angles where the cosine is negative, the graph does not exist, which deletes two petals from the graph.

NCTM STANDARDS

CONTENT		PROCESS	
	Number		Problem Solving
✓	Algebra	✓	Reasoning
	Geometry	✓	Communication
✓	Measurement	✓	Connections
	Data/Probability		Representation

1. The height (y-value) of a point on the graph of $y = a\cos nx$ corresponds to the value of r when $x = \theta$. The number of local maximums and minimums of $y = a\cos nx$ in the domain $0° \le x \le 360°$ corresponds to the number of petals; if n is even, the number of petals is the same as the number of local maximums and minimums in the domain $0° \le x \le 360°$; if n is odd, the number of petals is half the number of local maximums and minimums.

► Helping with the Questions

Question 1 Student groups might want to use several calculators to explore these equations.

Question 2 Students might be interested in how the shape of the graph of the equation $r = a(\cos n\theta + 1)$ differs for various values of n near 1.

2a. The graphs are exactly the same. The difference is where the graph begins.

2b. The graphs created with sine are rotated 90° counterclockwise in relation to the graphs created with cosine.

Question 3 To find these equations, students should use the general forms of equations explored in the activity and in Question 2.

3. possible answers:

3a. $r = 3 \cos \theta$

3b. $r = 3 \cos 2\theta$ and $r = 2 \sin 2\theta$

3c. $r = -2(\cos \theta + 1)$

3d. $r = 2(\cos \theta + 1)$ and $r = -2(\cos \theta + 1)$

Question 4 You might suggest that students plot a spiral on polar graph paper and discuss how they would obtain the points using values of r and θ.

4c. For negative values of θ, the spiral reflects across the vertical axis.

Question 5 If students doubt that polar equations are functions because their graphs don't pass the vertical line test, remind them that, in parametric equations, x and y are functions of t even though values of x might correspond to more than one value of y.

5. Answers will vary. In terms of rectangular coordinates, polar equations are not generally functions; rose curves, cardioids, spirals, and so on, do not pass a vertical line test. In terms of polar coordinates, the polar equations in this exploration are functions, as indicated by the notation $r = f(\theta)$; for any value of θ, there is only one value of r.

Technology CONNECTION

Cardioid microphones are designed to pick up sound at equal intensity levels from any point on a cardioid around the microphone. These microphones are designed so that the dimple of the curve is directed toward the base of the microphone, so that they minimize sound coming from behind. For this reason, cardioid microphones are especially useful for recording sound from a stage because they pick up little noise from the audience.

a. How do the graphs of $r = a(\cos \theta + 1)$ and $r = a(\cos \theta - 1)$ differ?

b. How do the cardioids created with sine differ from those created with cosine?

c. What is the effect of the coefficient a? The coefficient a is a dilation scale factor.

3. Write polar equations to create each graph. For 3b and d, you'll need more than one equation.

a.

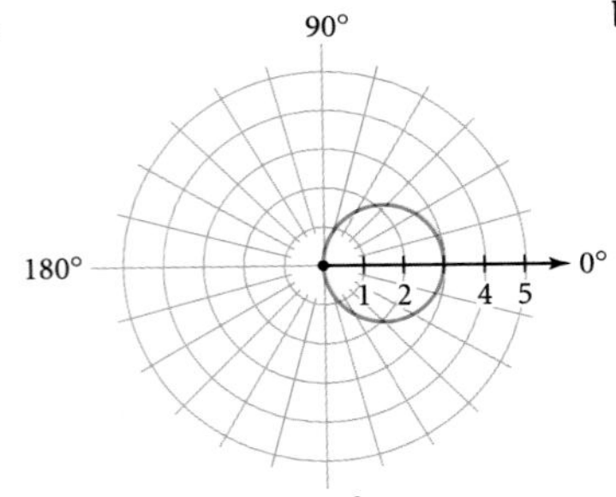

b.

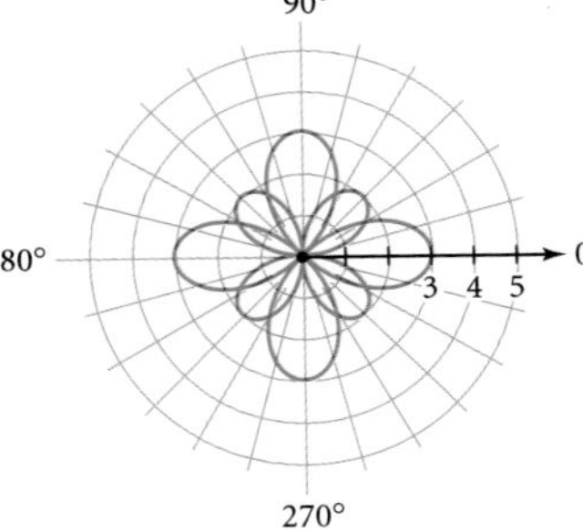

c.

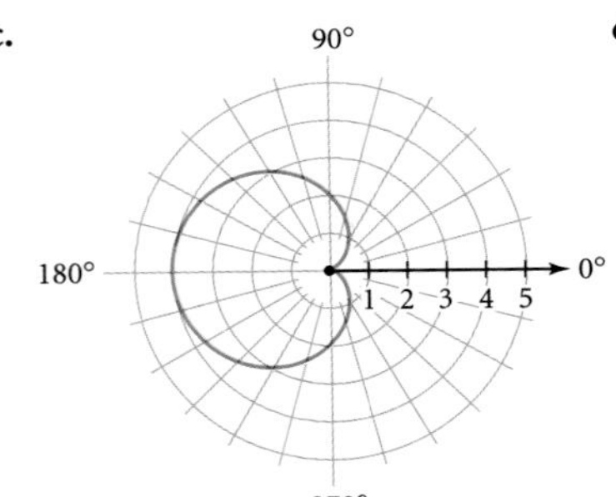

d.

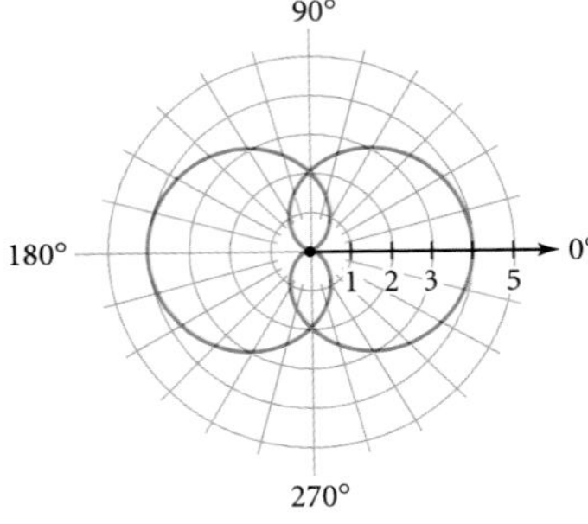

4. Think about what happens in a spiral and how the value of r changes as the value of θ changes.

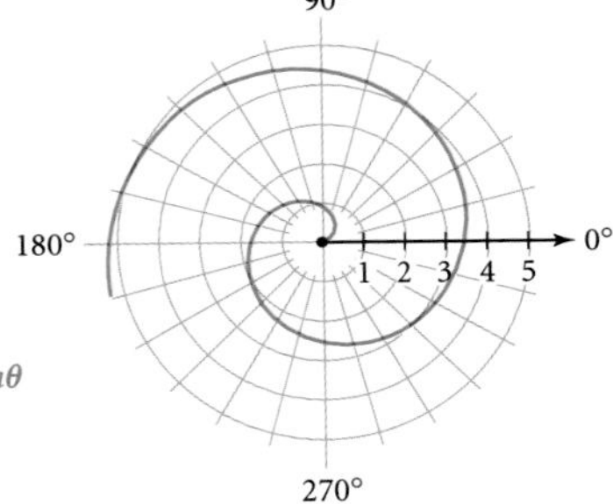

a. Find an equation that creates a spiral. Check your work by graphing on your calculator with the domain $0° \le \theta \le 360°$. What is the general form of the equation that creates a spiral? general form: $r = a\theta$

b. What happens as you extend the domain of θ to values greater than 360°? The spiral continues to grow outward.

c. What happens if you change the domain of θ to include negative values?

5. In general, are polar equations functions? Explain your reasoning.

SHARING IDEAS

[Ask] "How are the graphs in radians different from those in degrees?" [They're the same.]

[Ask] "How are negative values of θ graphed? Negative values of r?"

Assessing Progress

You can assess students' understanding of independent and dependent variables, functions, and radians.

Closing the Lesson

Summarize the polar coordinates (r, θ) and polar equations of the form $r = f(\theta)$. Two kinds of curves with simple polar equations are rose curves of the form $r = a \cos n\theta$ or $r = a \sin n\theta$ and the cardioids $r = a(\cos \theta \pm 1)$ and $r = a(\sin \theta \pm 1)$.

EXTENSION

Have students research or experiment to find other polar graphs.

CHAPTER 10 REVIEW

In this chapter you expanded your understanding of trigonometry to include angles with any real number measure. You learned to measure angles in **radians,** and you then identified relationships among radian measure, arc length, speed, and **angular speed.** You studied circular functions, their graphs, and their applications, and you learned to think of the sine and cosine of an angle as the y- and x-coordinates of a point on the unit circle. This allowed you to identify angles in **standard position** that are **coterminal.** That is, they share the same **terminal side.** Coterminal angles have the same trigonometric values. The remaining **trigonometric functions**—tangent, **cotangent, secant,** and **cosecant**—are also defined either as a ratio involving an x-coordinate and a y-coordinate, or as a ratio of one of these coordinates and the distance from the origin to the point.

Graphs of the trigonometric functions model periodic behavior and have domains that extend in both the positive and negative directions. You worked with many relationships that can be modeled with **sinusoids.** You studied transformations of sinusoidal functions and defined their **amplitude, period, phase shift, vertical translation,** and **frequency.**

You learned the difference between an inverse trigonometric relation and an inverse trigonometric function, and used this distinction to solve equations involving periodic functions. You learned, for example, that $x = \cos y$ provides infinitely many values of y for a given choice of x, whereas the function $y = \cos^{-1}x$ provides exactly one value of y for each value of x, called the **principal value.**

Finally, you discovered several properties and identities involving trigonometric expressions, and you learned how to prove that an equation is an identity.

EXERCISES

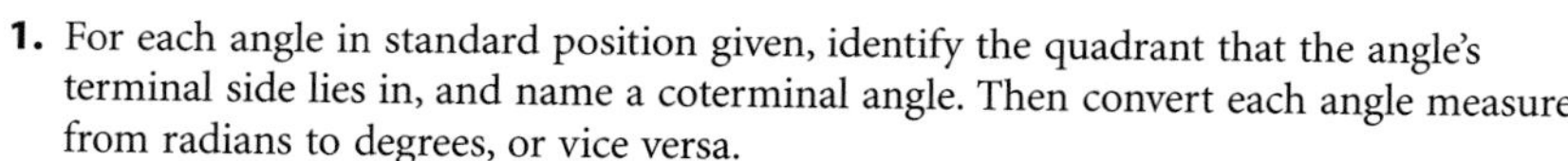

1. For each angle in standard position given, identify the quadrant that the angle's terminal side lies in, and name a coterminal angle. Then convert each angle measure from radians to degrees, or vice versa.

   a. 60° I; 420°; $\frac{\pi}{3}$ b. $\frac{4\pi}{3}$ III; $\frac{10\pi}{3}$; 240° c. 330° IV; −30°; $\frac{11\pi}{6}$ d. $-\frac{\pi}{4}$ IV; $\frac{7\pi}{4}$; −45°

2. Find exact values of the sine and cosine of each angle in Exercise 1.

3. State the period of the graph of each equation, and write one other equation that has the same graph.

   a. $y = 2\sin\left(3\left(x - \frac{\pi}{6}\right)\right)$ b. $y = -3\cos 4x$

   c. $y = \sec 2x$ d. $y = \tan(-2x) + 1$

2a. $\sin 60° = \frac{\sqrt{3}}{2}$; $\cos 60° = \frac{1}{2}$

2b. $\sin\frac{4\pi}{3} = -\frac{\sqrt{3}}{2}$; $\cos\frac{4\pi}{3} = -\frac{1}{2}$

2c. $\sin 330° = -\frac{1}{2}$; $\cos 330° = \frac{\sqrt{3}}{2}$

2d. $\sin\left(-\frac{\pi}{4}\right) = -\frac{\sqrt{2}}{2}$; $\cos\left(-\frac{\pi}{4}\right) = \frac{\sqrt{2}}{2}$

3. Other equations are possible.

3a. period $= \frac{2\pi}{3}$; $y = -2\cos\left(3\left(x - \frac{2\pi}{3}\right)\right)$

3b. period $= \frac{\pi}{2}$; $y = 3\sin\left(4\left(x - \frac{\pi}{8}\right)\right)$

3c. period $= \pi$; $y = \csc\left(2\left(x + \frac{\pi}{4}\right)\right)$

3d. period $= \frac{\pi}{2}$; $y = \cot\left(2\left(x - \frac{\pi}{4}\right)\right) + 1$

PLANNING

LESSON OUTLINE

One day:

15 min	Reviewing
15 min	Exercises
15 min	Student self-assessment

REVIEWING

Ask students to revisit Lesson 10.1, Exercise 15, about sunspots. Pose the problem of predicting the next two years (after 1999) during which the number of sunspots will be about 30. Model the data with both sine and cosine functions, reminding students of the meanings of radians, sinusoids, amplitude, phase shift, vertical translation, period, frequency, and inverse functions. Then remind students of the other trigonometric functions, the inverse trigonometric functions, and how to prove some trigonometric identities.

ASSIGNING HOMEWORK

Challenge students working in groups or with a partner to extend the problems and ask each other further questions.

Helping with the Exercises

Exercise 2 As needed, suggest that students draw reference triangles.

Exercise 3 Looking at the graphs of these equations might help students find other equations.

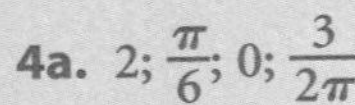

4a. $2; \frac{\pi}{6}; 0; \frac{3}{2\pi}$

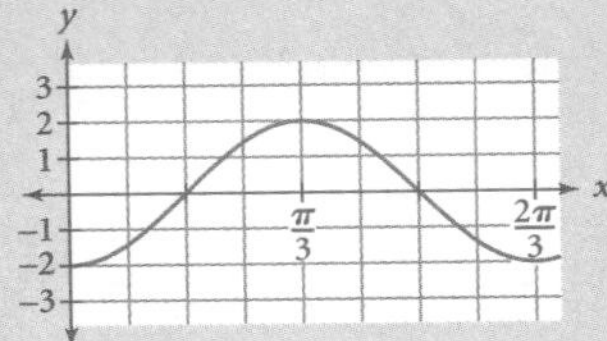

4b. $3; 0; 0; \frac{2}{\pi}$

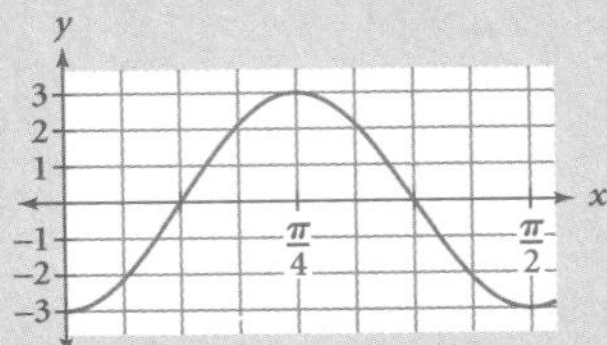

7. $\cos y = x$: domain: $-1 \le x \le 1$; range: all real numbers. $y = \cos^{-1} x$: domain: $-1 \le x \le 1$; range: $0 \le y \le \pi$

Exercise 8 As needed, remind students to draw reference triangles. The values can be found without calculating the angle measures, but finding those angle measures could be an extension.

9. $y = -3\sin\left(\frac{x - \frac{\pi}{2}}{4}\right)$

Exercise 10 This exercise depends on identities from Lessons 10.6 and 10.7.

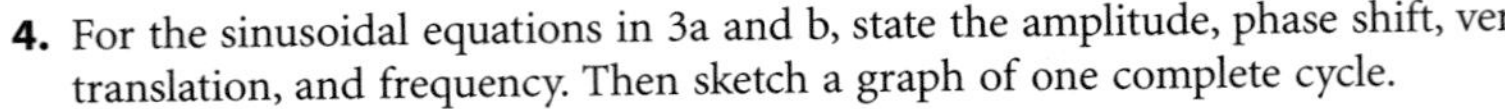

4. For the sinusoidal equations in 3a and b, state the amplitude, phase shift, vertical translation, and frequency. Then sketch a graph of one complete cycle.

5. Write an equation for each graph.

a. $y = -2\sin(2x) - 1$

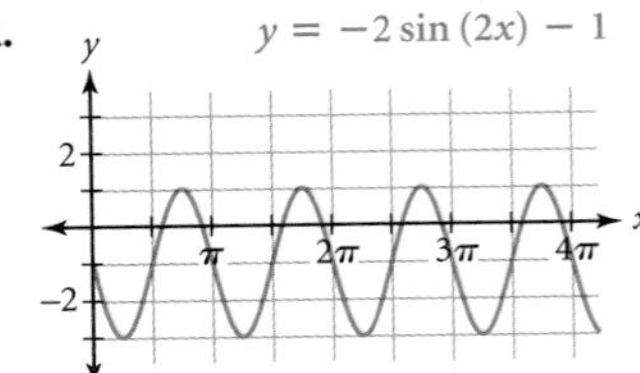

b. $y = \sin(0.5x) + 1.5$

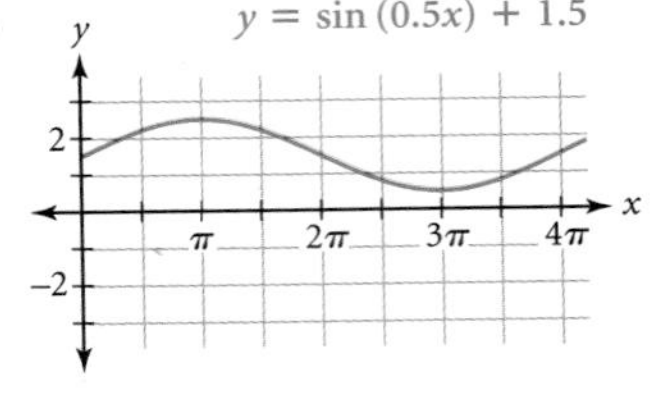

c. $y = 0.5\tan\left(x - \frac{\pi}{4}\right)$

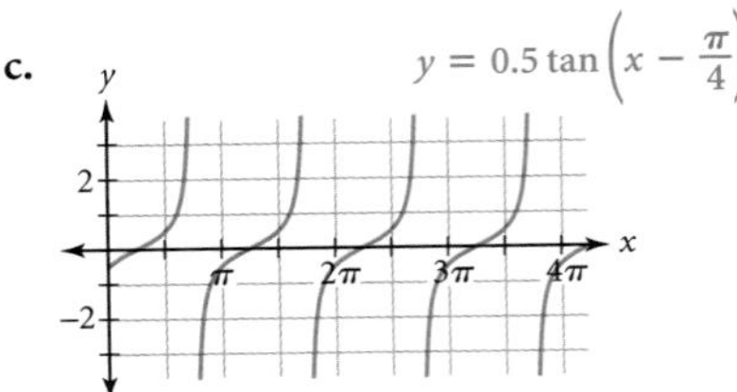

d. $y = 0.5\sec(2x)$

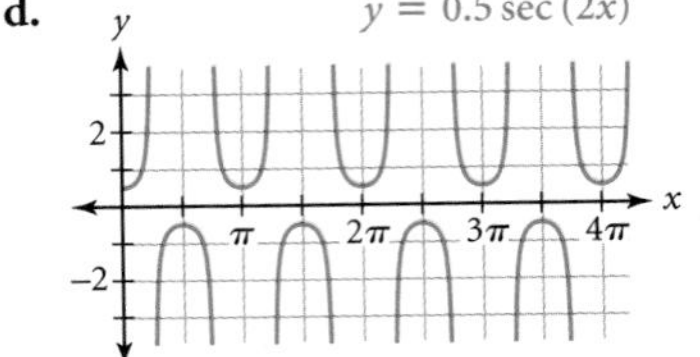

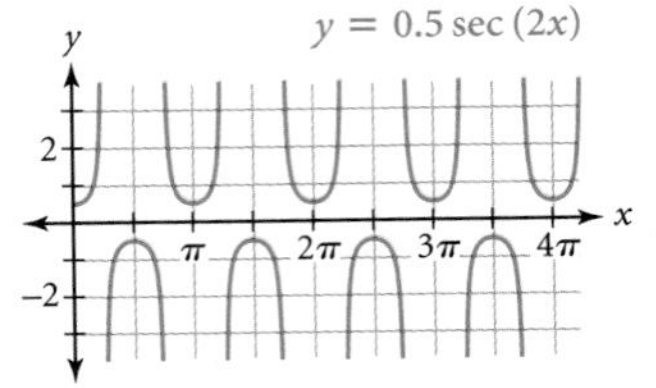

6. Find the area and arc length of a sector of a circle that has radius 3 cm and central angle $\frac{\pi}{4}$. Give exact answers. area $= \frac{9\pi}{8}$ cm^2; arc length $= \frac{3\pi}{4}$ cm

7. Identify the domain and range of $\cos y = x$ and $y = \cos^{-1} x$.

8. Find these values without using your calculator. Then verify your answers with your calculator.

a. $\sin\left(\tan^{-1}\frac{3}{4}\right)$ $\frac{3}{5}$

b. $\cos\left(\sin^{-1}\frac{3}{5}\right)$ $\frac{4}{5}$

c. $\sin\left(\sin^{-1}\frac{8}{17}\right)$ $\frac{8}{17}$

9. Write an equation for a transformation of $y = \sin x$ that has a reflection across the x-axis, amplitude 3, period 8π, and phase shift $\frac{\pi}{2}$.

10. Prove that each of these identities is true. You may use any of the identities that have been proved in this chapter.

a. $\sec A - \sin A \tan A = \cos A$

b. $\frac{1}{\sin^2 A} - \frac{1}{\tan^2 A} = 1$

c. $\frac{\sec A \cos B - \tan A \sin B}{\sec A} = \cos(A + B)$

A detail from American sculptor Ruth Asawa's (b 1926) hourglass-shaped baskets shows her focus on circular patterns as a metaphor for family and community circles. The piece is called *Completing the Circle.*

10a. Proof:

$$\sec A - \sin A \tan A \stackrel{?}{=} \cos A$$
$$\frac{1}{\cos A} - \sin A\left(\frac{\sin A}{\cos A}\right) \stackrel{?}{=} \cos A$$
$$\frac{1 - \sin^2 A}{\cos A} \stackrel{?}{=} \cos A$$
$$\frac{\cos^2 A}{\cos A} \stackrel{?}{=} \cos A$$
$$\cos A = \cos A$$

10b. Proof:

$$\frac{1}{\sin^2 A} - \frac{1}{\tan^2 A} \stackrel{?}{=} 1$$
$$\frac{1}{\sin^2 A} - \frac{\cos^2 A}{\sin^2 A} \stackrel{?}{=} 1$$
$$\frac{1 - \cos^2 A}{\sin^2 A} \stackrel{?}{=} 1$$
$$\frac{\sin^2 A}{\sin^2 A} \stackrel{?}{=} 1$$
$$1 = 1$$

10c. Proof:

$$\frac{\sec A \cos B - \tan A \sin B}{\sec A} \stackrel{?}{=} \cos(A + B)$$
$$\frac{\cos B}{\sec A} - \frac{\tan A \sin B}{\sec A} \stackrel{?}{=} \cos(A + B)$$
$$\cos B \cos A - \frac{\sin A}{\cos A}\sin B \cos A \stackrel{?}{=} \cos(A + B)$$
$$\cos B \cos A - \sin A \sin B \stackrel{?}{=} \cos(A + B)$$
$$\cos(A + B) = \cos(A + B)$$

11. A mass hanging from a spring is pulled down 2 cm from its resting position and released. It makes 12 complete bounces in 10 s. At what times during the first 3 s was the mass 0.5 cm below its resting position? 0.174 s, 0.659 s, 1.008 s, 1.492 s, 1.841 s, 2.325 s, 2.675 s

12. **APPLICATION** These data give the ocean tide heights each hour on November 17, 2002, at Saint John, New Brunswick, Canada.

a. Create a scatter plot of the data.

b. Write a function to model the data, and graph this function on the scatter plot from 12a.

c. What would you estimate the tide height to have been at 3:00 P.M. on November 19, 2002?

d. A ship was due to arrive at Saint John on November 20, 2002. The water had to be at least 5 m for the ship to safely enter the harbor. Between what times on November 20 could the ship have entered the harbor?
between 0:00 and 1:55, between 8:50 and 14:10, and between 21:05 and 23:59

Time	Tide height (m)	Time	Tide height (m)
00:00	5.56	12:00	6.09
01:00	4.12	13:00	4.65
02:00	2.71	14:00	3.08
03:00	1.77	15:00	1.85
04:00	1.56	16:00	1.33
05:00	2.09	17:00	1.60
06:00	3.21	18:00	2.54
07:00	4.70	19:00	3.96
08:00	6.18	20:00	5.51
09:00	7.20	21:00	6.75
10:00	7.50	22:00	7.33
11:00	7.09	23:00	7.17

TAKE ANOTHER LOOK

1. Consider the geometry-software diagram at right. You have seen that in a unit circle, the length AB has the same value as $\cos\theta$. The lengths AF, GI, AD, AI, and CF correspond to other trigonometric values of θ. Decide which segment length equals each of the values $\sin\theta$, $\tan\theta$, $\sec\theta$, $\csc\theta$, and $\cot\theta$. Justify your answers.

2. You have seen how to find the exact value of $\cos\frac{\pi}{12}$ by rewriting the expression as $\cos\left(\frac{\pi}{4}-\frac{\pi}{6}\right)$, and using a trigonometric identity to expand and evaluate. How can you find the exact value of $\sin\frac{11\pi}{12}$? (*Hint:* Write $\frac{11\pi}{12}$ as a sum or difference of three terms.) Find some other exact values of sine, cosine, or tangent using this method.

3. You are now familiar with angle measures in degrees and radians, but have you ever heard of gradians? Research the gradian angle measure. Explain how it compares to radians and degrees, when and where it was used, and any advantages it might have. Can you find any other units that measure angle or slope?

Exercise 12 Remind students that 00:00 is midnight on a 24-hour clock.

12a. Let x represent time in hours, and let y represent tide height in meters.

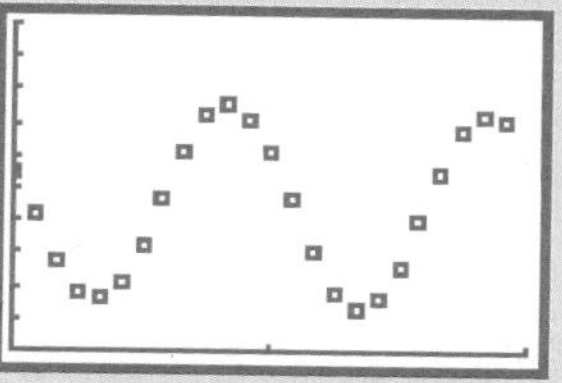

[0, 24, 12, 0, 10, 1]

12b. possible answer:
$y = 3.165\cos\left(\frac{2\pi}{12.25}(x-10)\right) + 4.365$

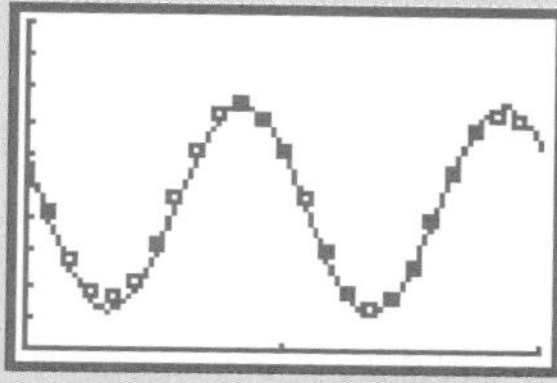

[0, 24, 12, 0, 10, 1]

12c. approximately 2.24 m

Take Another Look

1. $AF = \sec\theta$; $GI = \cot\theta$; $AD = \sin\theta$; $AI = \csc\theta$; and $CF = \tan\theta$

$\sec\theta = \frac{\text{hypotenuse}}{\text{adjacent}} = \frac{AF}{AC} = \frac{AF}{1}$;

$\cot\theta = \frac{\text{adjacent}}{\text{opposite}} = \frac{AJ}{IJ} = \frac{GI}{AG} = \frac{GI}{1}$;

$\sin\theta = \frac{\text{opposite}}{\text{hypotenuse}} = \frac{BE}{AE} = \frac{AD}{AE} = \frac{AD}{1}$; $\csc\theta = \frac{\text{hypotenuse}}{\text{opposite}} = \frac{AI}{IJ} = \frac{AI}{1}$;

$\tan\theta = \frac{CF}{AC} = \frac{CF}{1}$

2. Possible answer:

$\sin\left(\left(\frac{\pi}{3}+\frac{\pi}{4}\right)-\frac{\pi}{6}\right) =$
$\sin\left(\frac{\pi}{3}+\frac{\pi}{4}\right)\cos\frac{\pi}{6} -$
$\cos\left(\frac{\pi}{3}+\frac{\pi}{4}\right)\sin\frac{\pi}{6} =$
$\left(\sin\frac{\pi}{3}\cos\frac{\pi}{4}+\cos\frac{\pi}{3}\sin\frac{\pi}{4}\right)\cos\frac{\pi}{6} -$
$\left(\cos\frac{\pi}{3}\cos\frac{\pi}{4}-\sin\frac{\pi}{3}\sin\frac{\pi}{4}\right)\sin\frac{\pi}{6} =$
$\left(\frac{\sqrt{3}}{2}\cdot\frac{\sqrt{2}}{2}+\frac{1}{2}\cdot\frac{\sqrt{2}}{2}\right)\frac{\sqrt{3}}{2} -$
$\left(\frac{1}{2}\cdot\frac{\sqrt{2}}{2}-\frac{\sqrt{3}}{2}\cdot\frac{\sqrt{2}}{2}\right)\frac{1}{2} =$
$\left(\frac{\sqrt{6}}{4}+\frac{\sqrt{2}}{4}\right)\frac{\sqrt{3}}{2} -$
$\left(\frac{\sqrt{2}}{4}-\frac{\sqrt{6}}{4}\right)\frac{1}{2} = \frac{\sqrt{2}+\sqrt{6}}{4}$

Take Another Look 2 (continued)
Students could also evaluate $\sin\left(\pi+\left(\frac{\pi}{3}+\frac{\pi}{4}\right)\right)$ or $\cos\left(\frac{\pi}{2}-\frac{7\pi}{12}\right)$, which equals $\cos\left(-\frac{\pi}{12}\right)$ or $\cos\left(\frac{\pi}{4}-\frac{\pi}{3}\right)$.
The sine or cosine of any sum or difference of multiples of $\frac{\pi}{4}$ and $\frac{\pi}{3}$ can be evaluated by using the sum or difference identities repeatedly.

3. A circle can be divided into 400 gradians so that a right angle measures 100 gradians. Gradians, used in surveying, were proposed by the French shortly after the French Revolution.

A compass is divided into 32 points. For example, NE is between N and E, and NNE is between N and NE.

A mil is a military unit based on the milliradian $\left(\frac{1}{1000}\text{ radian}\right)$, but instead of the approximately 6283.1583 milliradians in a circle, the U.S. military has standardized 6400 mils in a circle.

Just as a circle can be divided into degrees, radians, and gradians, a sphere can be divided into steradians. There are 4π steradians in a sphere.

4. If your students did not study parametric equations, do not assign this activity. The equations are $x = r(t - \sin t)$ and $y = r(1 - \cos t)$, where r is the radius of the wheel.

5. $\cos^2 A = \frac{1 + \cos 2A}{2} \to$

$\cos A = \pm\sqrt{\frac{1 + \cos 2A}{2}} \to$

$\cos\frac{\theta}{2} = \pm\sqrt{\frac{1 + \cos\theta}{2}}$;

$\sin^2 A = \frac{1 + \cos 2A}{2} \to$

$\sin A = \pm\sqrt{\frac{1 - \cos 2A}{2}} \to$

$\sin\frac{\theta}{2} = \pm\sqrt{\frac{1 - \cos\theta}{2}}$;

$\tan\frac{\theta}{2} = \pm\sqrt{\frac{1 - \cos\theta}{1 + \cos\theta}}$

ASSESSING

FACILITATING SELF-ASSESSMENT

You might have groups demonstrate modeling periodic functions to the geometry classes (or the classes of students who will be studying advanced algebra next year). This will give your current students practice presenting ideas and your future students a taste of what they will be studying next year. If you ask students to make presentations, spend two days on the review.

Exercises that require students to write about the mathematics they are learning include
Lesson 10.1, Exercise 14;
Lesson 10.2, Exercise 5;
Lesson 10.3, Exercises 3 and 5;
Lesson 10.4, Exercises 5 and 8;
Lesson 10.6, Exercise 5; and
Lesson 10.7, Exercises 10 and 14.

4. The path traced by a fixed point, P, on a moving wheel is called a **cycloid** and is shown below. A cycloid can be defined with parametric equations. Use the diagram to derive parametric equations for x and y, the coordinates of point P. Note that the length of arc CP equals the length of segment CO.

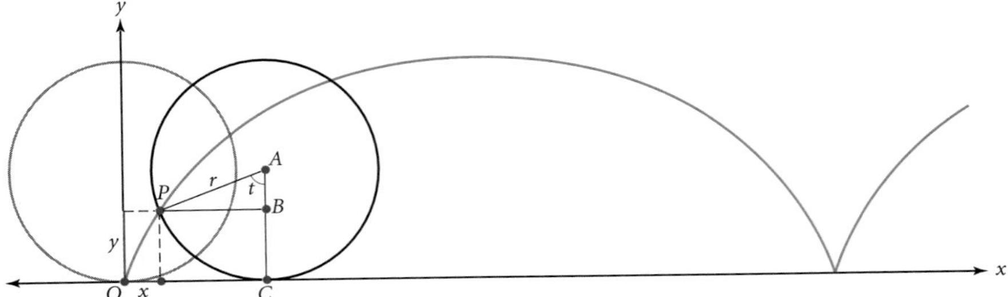

5. In Exercise 13b on page 620, you developed the formula $\cos^2 A = \frac{1 + \cos 2A}{2}$. Use this formula to develop the half-angle formula for cosine. Begin by taking the square root of both sides, then substitute $\frac{\theta}{2}$ for A. Use the formula from Exercise 13a for $\sin^2 A$ and a similar process to develop the half-angle formula for sine. Then use the half-angle formulas for sine and cosine to develop the half-angle formula for tangent.

Assessing What You've Learned

PERFORMANCE ASSESSMENT Demonstrate for a friend or family member how to find an equation that models periodic motion data. Be sure to use the words *amplitude, period, frequency, phase shift,* and *vertical translation.* Describe what each of these values tells you about the data.

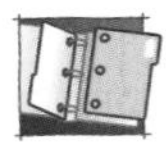

ORGANIZE YOUR NOTEBOOK Check that your notebook is in order. Make sure that you have definitions of all the terminology from this chapter. Include terms related to angles, like *standard position* and *terminal side,* and terms related to sinusoidal graphs, like *amplitude* and *period.* Check that all the trigonometric identities you have learned are in your notes as well.

WRITE IN YOUR JOURNAL Are your understandings of the sine, cosine, and tangent functions different now than they were when you started this chapter? Write a journal entry that describes how your understanding of the trigonometric functions has changed over time.

CHAPTER

11

Series

Overview

Lesson 11.1 introduces students to series and the summation notation used to represent them. Students learn to write recursive and explicit formulas for arithmetic series and find partial sums of arithmetic series. In **Lesson 11.2,** students learn to write recursive and explicit formulas for geometric series and find the sum of a convergent infinite geometric series. In **Lesson 11.3,** students find partial sums of geometric series. In the **exploration** that ends the chapter, students use Sketchpad to explore the sum of geometric series.

The Mathematics

Mathematicians have grappled for centuries with paradoxes that arise from trying to sum infinitely many numbers. Adding the same nonzero number infinitely many times clearly gives an infinite result, but what about the sum $\frac{1}{2} + \frac{1}{4} + \frac{1}{8} + \frac{1}{16} + \cdots$? If you enter the numbers into a calculator, and sum after each entry, the sum seems bounded. In fact, it appears to be 1. The series $1 - \frac{1}{2} + \frac{1}{3} - \frac{1}{4} + \cdots$ also seems to have a finite sum. But what about the series $1 - 1 + 1 - 1 + \cdots$? Is its sum 1 or 0—or maybe, as a compromise, $\frac{1}{2}$?

It is difficult to understand exactly what a series is. Is it a sum? Is the series $\frac{1}{2} + \frac{1}{4} + \frac{1}{8} + \frac{1}{16} + \cdots$ the same as its apparent sum, 1? Is a series equivalent to a sequence? In standard English, the word *series* usually refers to a sequence, but the series $\frac{1}{2} + \frac{1}{4} + \frac{1}{8} + \frac{1}{16} + \cdots$ is different from the sequence $\left\{\frac{1}{2}, \frac{1}{4}, \frac{1}{8}, \frac{1}{16}, \ldots\right\}$.

Students' difficulties with series reflect the historical mathematical struggle. Most students at this level aren't ready to grapple with mathematicians' current definitions: A series is a pair of sequences, a sequence $\{u_i\}$ and a sequence $\{S_n\}$ whose nth term is the sum of the first n terms of the sequence $\{u_i\}$. Each term S_n is called a *partial sum* of the series. The series is represented by $\sum_{i=1}^{\infty} u_i$; the nth partial sum, S_n, can be represented by $\sum_{i=1}^{n} u_i$.

A series is convergent if the sequence of partial sums has a limit—that is, if it approaches a specific number as n increases. This limit is called the *sum* of the series, and we say that the series *converges* to this number. For example, the partial sums of the series $1 - 1 + 1 - 1 + \cdots$ alternate between 1 and 0, so they don't approach a limit, meaning that the series is not convergent. In contrast, the nth partial sum of the series $\frac{1}{2} + \frac{1}{4} + \frac{1}{8} + \frac{1}{16} + \cdots$ is $S_n = 1 - \frac{1}{2^n}$; as n gets larger, $\frac{1}{2^n}$ gets smaller, approaching 0, so the partial sums approach 1. The series therefore converges to 1.

The number to which the partial sums converge is the sum of infinitely many terms but it is not infinite. If it were, the series would not have a sum.

To avoid addressing the idea of a pair of sequences, the book describes a series as a sum of terms of a sequence. It refers to partial sums and their long-run behavior without dwelling on the sequence of partial sums. Although the book considers all series as having infinitely many terms and never uses the term *finite series,* it does introduce the term *infinite geometric series* to stress that infinitely many terms are being summed.

There are many kinds of series. The book considers two of them, based on the two kinds of sequences emphasized in Chapter 1: *arithmetic series* and *geometric series.* Students generate data and use finite differences to find formulas for the nth partial sums of both kinds of series as well as a formula for the sum of a convergent geometric series. Incidentally, if this last formula were used on the geometric series $1 - 1 + 1 - 1 + \cdots$, it would give a sum of $\frac{1}{2}$—but the formula applies only to convergent series, and this series diverges.

Using This Chapter

If your curriculum does not require the study of series, you can skip the chapter; later chapters do not build on it.

Resources

Discovering Advanced Algebra Resources

Teaching and Worksheet Masters
Lesson 11.1

Calculator Note 11A

Sketchpad Demonstrations
Lesson 11.2
Exploration: Seeing the Sum of a Series

Fathom Demonstration
Lesson 11.1

Assessment Resources A and B
Quiz 1 (Lesson 11.1)
Quiz 2 (Lessons 11.2, 11.3)
Chapter 11 Test
Chapter 11 Constructive Assessment Options

More Practice Your Skills for Chapter 11

Condensed Lessons for Chapter 11

Other Resources

www.keypress.com/DAA

Materials

none

Pacing Guide

	day 1	day 2	day 3	day 4	day 5	day 6
standard	11.1	quiz, 11.2	11.3	quiz, review	review	assessment
enriched	11.1	quiz, 11.2	11.3	quiz, exploration	TAL, review	assessment
block	11.1, 11.2	quiz, 11.3, exploration	quiz, TAL, review	TAL, assessment		

CHAPTER

11 Series

Korean artist Do-Ho Suh (b 1962) is perhaps best known for his sculptures that use numerous miniature items that contribute to a greater, larger mass. Shown here is a detail from his installation *Floor* (1997–2000), made of thousands of plastic figurines that support a 40 m^2 floor of glass.

OBJECTIVES

In this chapter you will

- learn about mathematical patterns called series, and distinguish between arithmetic and geometric series
- write recursive and explicit formulas for series
- find the sum of a finite number of terms of an arithmetic or geometric series
- determine when an infinite geometric series has a sum and find the sum if it exists

CHAPTER 11 OBJECTIVES

- Learn about mathematical series and the summation notation used to represent series
- Write recursive and explicit formulas for the terms of arithmetic and geometric series
- Find formulas for the partial sums of arithmetic and geometric series
- Determine when a geometric series converges, and find its sum
- Investigate other types of series

Each of the 2000 polyvinyl chloride (PVC) figures that hold up the floor is only a few centimeters tall, yet the floor can support hundreds of pounds. **[Ask]** "What commentary on the state of humanity do you think Suh is making with this piece?" Be prepared for students to discuss potentially sensitive topics, such as the repression of minorities.

This artwork conveys the idea of the summation of many small things. To preview the chapter, you could pose this problem: "Suppose one of the small figures is 3 cm tall and every time a person steps on it the figure loses $\frac{1}{100}$ of its height. As the figure is repeatedly walked upon, what sequence of heights, in cm, is generated?" [3, 2.97, 2.9403, 2.9109, 2.8818, . . .] "What is the sequence of the changes in height?" [$-0.03, -0.0297, -0.0294, -0.0291, \ldots$] Help students use their knowledge of sequences to write the series that represents the sum of the changes in height: $-\frac{1}{100}(3) - \frac{1}{100}(2.97) - \frac{1}{100}(2.9403) - \frac{1}{100}(2.9109) - \cdots$. **[Ask]** "Will the figure's height ever become 0?" [The sum of infinitely many terms in the series will never equal -3, so the height will never equal 0.]

LESSON

11.1

PLANNING

LESSON OUTLINE

One day:

20 min Investigation

10 min Sharing

5 min Example

10 min Exercises

MATERIALS

- Soup Cans (T) for One Step
- Sigma Notation (W), *optional*
- Calculator Note 11A
- Fathom demonstration Arithmetic Series Formula, *optional*

TEACHING

This lesson introduces the notion of a series and develops a formula for the partial sum of an arithmetic series.

One Step
Show the Soup Cans transparency and pose this problem, based on Exercise 9: "To celebrate the twenty-first birthday of a fellow employee, Jessica wants to arrange a display of soup cans as pictured on the transparency, but 21 rows high. She has 11 cases of 48 cans each. Can she do it?" [No; she needs 693 cans and she has only 528.]

Students may approach the problem in a variety of ways. Challenge those who methodically sum 21 terms to find an easier way. Push some groups to find a formula for the sum of the terms of any finite arithmetic sequence. During Sharing, remind students of how to write their results more compactly using sigma notation, and introduce the terms *series, arithmetic series,* and *partial sum.*

LESSON 11.1

Arithmetic Series

According to the U.S. Environmental Protection Agency, each American produced an average of 978 lb of trash in 1960. This increased to 1336 lb in 1980. By 2000, trash production had risen to 1646 lb/yr per person. You have learned in previous chapters how to write a sequence to describe the amount of trash produced per person each year. If you added the terms in this sequence, you could find the amount of trash a person produced in his or her lifetime.

Environmental CONNECTION

Mount Everest, part of the Himalaya range of southern Asia, reaches an altitude of 29,035 ft and is the world's highest mountain above sea level. It has been nicknamed "the world's highest junkyard" because decades of litter—climbing gear, plastic, glass, and metal—have piled up along Mount Everest's trails and in its camps. An estimated 50 tons of junk remain. Environmental agencies like the World Wildlife Fund have cleared garbage from the mountain's base camp, but removing waste from higher altitudes is more challenging.

A 1998 cleanup of Mt. Everest

Series

A sum of terms of a sequence is a **series.**

The sum of the first n terms in a sequence is represented by S_n. You can calculate S_n by adding the terms $u_1 + u_2 + u_3 + \cdots + u_n$.

History CONNECTION

Chu Shih-chieh (ca. 1280–1303) was a celebrated mathematician from Beijing, China, known for his theories on arithmetic series, geometric series, and finite differences. His two mathematical works, *Introduction to Mathematical Studies* and *Precious Mirror of the Four Elements,* were discovered in the 19th century.

Finding the value of a series is a problem that has intrigued mathematicians for centuries. Chinese mathematician Chu Shih-chieh called the sum $1 + 2 + 3 + \cdots + n$ a "pile of reeds" because it can be pictured like the diagram at right. The diagram shows S_9, the sum of the first nine terms of this sequence, $1 + 2 + 3 + \cdots + 9$. The sum of any **finite,** or limited, number of terms is called a **partial sum** of the series.

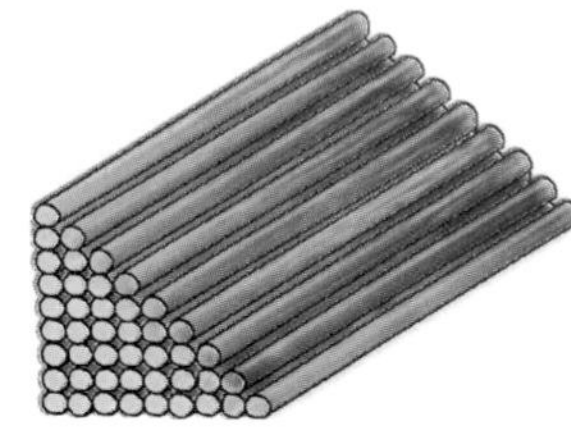

The expressions S_9 and $\sum_{n=1}^{9} u_n$ are shorthand ways of writing

$u_1 + u_2 + u_3 + \cdots + u_9$.

You can express the partial sum S_9 with sigma notation as $\sum_{n=1}^{9} n$.

INTRODUCTION

You might point out that the recursive formula for the series produces terms that form a sequence. The sequence is $\{S_1, S_2, S_3, S_4, \ldots\}$.

Take time to review the recursive formation of arithmetic sequences from Lesson 1.1 and sigma notation from Lesson 2.1.

LESSON OBJECTIVES

- Learn about mathematical series and the summation notation used to represent them
- Write recursive and explicit formulas for the terms of an arithmetic series
- Find formulas for the partial sums of arithmetic series

The expression $\sum_{n=1}^{9} n$ tells you to substitute the integers 1 through 9 for n in the explicit formula $u_n = n$, and then sum the resulting nine values. You get $1 + 2 + 3 + \cdots + 9 = 45$.

How could you find the sum of the integers 1 through 100? The most obvious method is to add the terms, one by one. You can use a recursive formula and a calculator to do this quickly.

First, write the sequence recursively as

$$u_1 = 1$$
$$u_n = u_{n-1} + 1 \quad \text{where } n \geq 2$$

You can write a recursive formula for the series S_n like this:

$$S_1 = 1$$
$$S_n = S_{n-1} + u_n \quad \text{where } n \geq 2$$

This states that the sum of the first n terms is equal to the sum of the first $(n - 1)$ terms, plus the nth term. From the recursive formula for the sequence you know that u_n is equivalent to $u_{n-1} + 1$, so the recursive formula for the series is

$$S_1 = 1$$
$$S_n = S_{n-1} + u_{n-1} + 1 \quad \text{where } n \geq 2$$

Enter the recursive formulas into your calculator as shown. A table shows each term in the sequence and the sequence of partial sums.

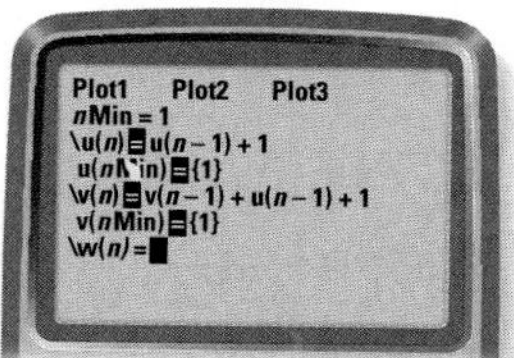

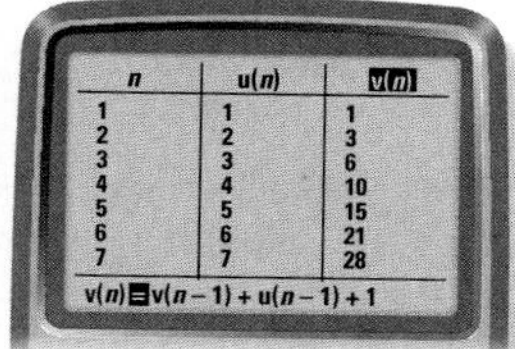

n	u(n)	v(n)
1	1	1
2	2	3
3	3	6
4	4	10
5	5	15
6	6	21
7	7	28

v(n)=v(n−1)+u(n−1)+1

The graph of S_n appears to form a solid curve, but it is actually a discrete set of 100 points representing each partial sum from S_1 through S_{100}. Each point is in the form (n, S_n) for integer values of n, for $1 \leq n \leq 100$. You can trace to find that the sum of the first 100 terms, S_{100}, is 5050. [► See **Calculator Note 11A** for more information on graphing and calculating partial sums. ◄]

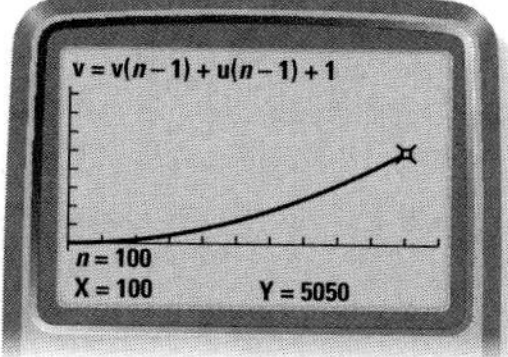

[0, 110, 10, −3000, 10000, 1000]

When you compute this sum recursively, you or the calculator must compute each of the individual terms. The investigation will give you an opportunity to discover at least one explicit formula for calculating the partial sum of an **arithmetic series** without finding all terms and adding.

[Alert] Students working with Calculator Note 11A may not recognize the meaning of each variable. For example, on the TI-83, $u(n)$ represents the nth term, and $v(n)$ represents the nth partial sum.

Sigma Notation Worksheet

If students have forgotten sigma notation, you might use the optional Sigma Notation worksheet now for class review or assign it as homework before students work on the exercises.

The worksheet includes some problems involving geometric series, which students have not yet been exposed to. You can tell them that a geometric series is the sum of a geometric sequence, or you can assign the worksheet in Lesson 11.2 or Lesson 11.3.

Answers for Sigma Notation Worksheet

1a. $5 + 8 + 11 + 14 + 17 + 20 + 23 + 26$; 124; $u_1 = 5$, $d = 3$

1b. $4 + 3.2 + 2.56 + 2.048$; 11.808; $u_1 = 4$, $r = 0.8$

1c. $-2 + 4 - 8 + 16 - 32$; -22; $u_1 = -2$, $r = -2$

1d. $2 - 3 + 4 - 5$; -2; neither

1e. $-9 - 16 - 21 - 24 - 25 - 24 - 21 - 16 - 9 + 0$; -165; neither

2a. $k = 28$

2b. $k = 21$

3a. $\sum_{n=1}^{13} 2n + 1$

3b. $\sum_{n=1}^{7} 2(0.5)^{n-1}$

3c. $\sum_{n=1}^{23} (5 + 10(n - 1))(-1)^{n+1}$

NCTM STANDARDS

CONTENT		PROCESS	
✓	Number		Problem Solving
✓	Algebra	✓	Reasoning
	Geometry	✓	Communication
	Measurement	✓	Connections
✓	Data/Probability	✓	Representation

Guiding the Investigation

You might want to pose the problem in the example to your students as a warm-up before the investigation. The Fathom demonstration Arithmetic Series Formula can be used in place of the investigation.

Ask that group members who have the same starting value u_1 use different common differences d. Students complete Steps 1 and 2 individually.

Step 1 This step assumes that the common difference is added rather than subtracted.

Step 2 If students need to review finite differences, they can look back at Lesson 7.1. The polynomial will always be degree 2, so the second differences will be equal.

Step 4 The partial sum will be in terms of n.

Step 5 The value of the coefficient of n^2 is easy to recognize. If students are finding it impossible to find the coefficient of n, wonder aloud whether they can combine values they already know $\left(u_1, d,\right.$ and the coefficient of $\left.n^2\right)$.

▶ *EXAMPLE*

This method can be used to find the partial sums of other series. You might ask students to use the method to find other sums, such as even numbers from 2 to 100 or multiples of 3 from 3 to 99.

Partial Sum of Reeds

In the expression $\frac{9(1+9)}{2}$, the first 9 represents the width of the rectangular pile and the $1 + 9$ represents the height, so $9(1 + 9)$ represents the area (total number of reeds in the double stack). The product is divided by 2 because the pile of reeds now has twice the number of reeds as the original pile.

See page 904 for answers to Steps 2 and 4.

Investigation
Arithmetic Series Formula

Select three integers between 2 and 9 for your group to use. Each person should write his or her own arithmetic sequence using one of the three values for the first term and another value for the common difference. Make sure that each person uses a different sequence.

Step 1 sample answer: $u_1 = 5$ and $u_n = u_{n-1} + 4$ where $n \geq 2$; sequence: $\{5, 9, 13, 17, 21, 25, 29, 33, 37, 41\}$; series: $\{5, 14, 27, 44, 65, 90, 119, 152, 189, 230\}$

Step 1 Find the first ten terms of your sequence. Then find the first ten partial sums of the corresponding series. For example, using $u_1 = 7$ and $d = 8$, you would write

Sequence: $u_n = \{7, 15, 23, 31, \ldots\}$

Partial Sums: $S_n = \{7, 22, 45, 76, \ldots\}$

Step 2 Use finite differences to find the degree of a polynomial function that would fit data points in the form (n, S_n). Then find a polynomial function to fit the data.

Step 3 Create a new series by replacing either the first term or the common difference with another one of the three integers that your group selected. Repeat Steps 1 and 2.

Step 4 Combine the results from all members of your group into a table like the one below. For the partial sum column, enter the polynomial functions found in Step 2.

First term u_1	Common difference d	Partial sum S_n

Step 5 In general, the coefficient of n^2 is $\frac{d}{2}$, and the coefficient of n is $\left(u_1 - \frac{d}{2}\right)$. $S_n = \left(\frac{d}{2}\right)n^2 + \left(u_1 - \frac{d}{2}\right)n$

Step 5 Look for a relationship between the coefficients of each polynomial and the values of u_1 and d. Then write an explicit formula for S_n in terms of u_1, d, and n.

In the investigation you found a formula for a partial sum of an arithmetic series. Use your formula to check that when you add $1 + 2 + 3 + \cdots + 100$ you get 5050.

History CONNECTION

According to legend, when German mathematician and astronomer Carl Friedrich Gauss (1777–1855) was 9 years old, his teacher asked the class to find the sum of the integers 1 through 100. The teacher was hoping to keep his students busy, but Gauss quickly wrote the correct answer, 5050. The example shows Gauss's solution method.

This stamp of Gauss was issued by Nicaragua in 1994 as part of a series about astronomers.

EXAMPLE | Find the sum of the integers 1 through 100, without using a calculator.

SHARING IDEAS

[Language] The word *series* is often used in everyday English. **[Ask]** "Is the common meaning of the word *series* the same thing as the mathematical meaning?" [In common usage, *series* means a sequence rather than a summation.] You might also point out that the word *series* is both plural and singular.

As the last students present, ask what happens if the common difference or the first term is negative. Let students experiment to see that the formula still applies. Elicit the fact that the partial sums get farther from 0 as n increases, whether the common difference is positive or negative.

If students don't make the observation, show them that the constant second difference of the sequence of sums equals the common difference of the original arithmetic sequence. **[Ask]** "Why?" [The first differences in the sequence of sums are given by the terms of the original sequence; the second differences therefore are the differences between the terms of the

▶ ***Solution***

Carl Friedrich Gauss solved this problem by adding the terms in pairs. Consider the series written in ascending and descending order, as shown.

$$\begin{array}{cccccccccccc} 1 & + & 2 & + & 3 & + \cdots + & 98 & + & 99 & + & 100 & = S_{100} \\ 100 & + & 99 & + & 98 & + \cdots + & 3 & + & 2 & + & 1 & = S_{100} \\ \hline 101 & + & 101 & + & 101 & + \cdots + & 101 & + & 101 & + & 101 & = 2S_{100} \end{array}$$

The sum of every column is 101, and there are 100 columns. Thus, the sum of the integers 1 through 100 is

$$\frac{100(101)}{2} = 5050$$

You must divide the product 100(101) by 2 because the series was added twice.

You can extend the method in the example to any arithmetic series. Before continuing, take a moment to consider why the sum of the reeds in the original pile can be calculated using the expression

$$\frac{9(1+9)}{2}$$

What do the 9, 1, 9, and 2 represent in this context?

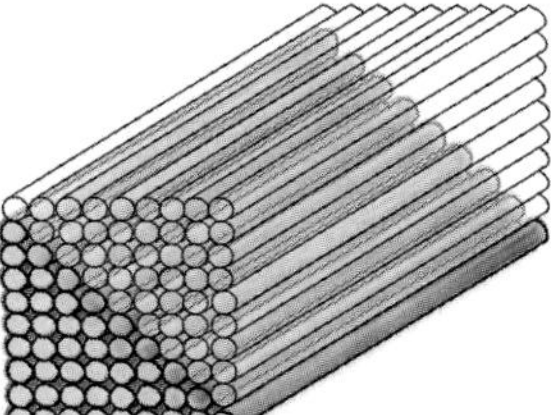

Partial Sum of an Arithmetic Series

The partial sum of an arithmetic series is given by the explicit formula

$$S_n = \left(\frac{d}{2}\right)n^2 + \left(u_1 - \frac{d}{2}\right)n$$

where n is the number of terms, u_1 is the first term, and d is the common difference.

An alternative formula is

$$S_n = \frac{n(u_1 + u_n)}{2}$$

where n is the number of terms, u_1 is the first term, and u_n is the last term.

In the exercises you will use the formulas for partial sums to find the sum of consecutive terms of an arithmetic sequence.

EXERCISES

▶ Practice Your Skills

1. List the first five terms of this sequence. Identify the first term and the common difference. $-3, -1.5, 0, 1.5, 3$; $u_1 = -3, d = 1.5$

$u_1 = -3$
$u_n = u_{n-1} + 1.5 \quad \text{where } n \geq 2$

2. Find S_1, S_2, S_3, S_4, and S_5 for this sequence: 2, 6, 10, 14, 18. $S_1 = 2, S_2 = 8, S_3 = 18, S_4 = 32, S_5 = 50$

Sharing Ideas (continued)
original arithmetic sequence, all of which equal the common difference of that sequence.]

Ask students if they have any questions or problems. Use the questions below only if you have time remaining after discussing questions they have asked.

The second formula for the partial sum of an arithmetic series contains the expression $\frac{u_1 + u_n}{2}$. **[Ask]** "Does considering this expression as the mean of u_1 and u_n give any new insight into the formula?" [The summation can be thought of as adding this mean n times. In fact, this mean is the mean of all n terms in the arithmetic series up to this point, and the sum of any n numbers equals n times their mean.]

[Ask] "Can you also show algebraically that the two formulas for the partial sum of an arithmetic series are equivalent?" [Substitute $u_1 + (n-1)d$ for u_n in the second formula.]

A good opener for new problems is a "what if not" question. **[Ask]** "What if it is not an arithmetic series but a geometric series?" You need not address this question now; it motivates Lesson 11.2. Challenge students to think about it overnight.

BUILDING UNDERSTANDING

If students need help with sigma notation, you might assign the Sigma Notation worksheet.

Assessing Progress
You can assess students' understanding of arithmetic sequences and their ability to use the method of finite differences.

Closing the Lesson

Restate the main points of this lesson: A **series** is a summation of terms in a sequence. An **arithmetic series** is based on an arithmetic sequence. The nth **partial sum** of a series is a sum of the first n terms of the sequence. The nth partial sum of the terms of an arithmetic sequence is given by the formula

$$S_n = \left(\frac{d}{2}\right)n^2 + \left(u_1 - \frac{d}{2}\right)n = \frac{n(u_1 + u_n)}{2}$$

where d is the common difference, u_1 is the first term of the sequence, and u_n is the nth term of the sequence. The partial sums get farther from 0 as n increases.

ASSIGNING HOMEWORK

Essential	2–5
Performance assessment	6–13
Portfolio	12
Journal	12, 14
Group	10, 13, 15
Review	1, 16–20

Helping with the Exercises

Exercise 4 [ESL] *Multiples* of 6 are numbers that are 6 times an integer. In other words, they have 6 as a factor or 6 divides into them without a remainder.

Exercises 4, 5 If students have trouble starting these exercises, ask them to find the values of n, u_1, and the common difference.

Exercise 6 Students can use either formula to evaluate 6b and 6c, or they can apply Gauss's method and avoid using a formula.

7a. $u_{46} = 229$

7b. $u_n = 5n - 1$, or $u_1 = 4$ and $u_n = u_{n-1} + 5$ where $n \geq 2$

7c. $S_{46} = 5359$

Exercise 9 Students can assume that Jessica leaves no gaps in any layer. As needed in 9c, **[Ask]** "What is n?" [47] If students get stuck in solving 9d, you might **[Ask]** "What do you know, and what do you want to find?" [You know that S_n equals 288, and you want to find the number of rows, n.] "Does either formula include just these variables?" [You can use the first formula without calculating u_n; substitute 3 for d and 3 for u_1 and then solve for n.]

9a. 3, 6, 9, 12, 15, 18, 21, 24, 27, 30

9b. $u_1 = 3$ and $u_n = u_{n-1} + 3$ where $n \geq 2$

9c. 3384 cans

9d. 13 rows with 15 cans left over

3. Write each expression as a sum of terms, then calculate the sum.

a. $\sum_{n=1}^{4}(n+2)$ $3 + 4 + 5 + 6; 18$

b. $\sum_{n=1}^{3}(n^2-3)$ $-2 + 1 + 6; 5$

4. Find the sum of the first 50 multiples of 6: $\{6, 12, 18, \ldots, u_{50}\}$. $S_{50} = 7650$

5. Find the sum of the first 75 even numbers, starting with 2. $S_{75} = 5700$

Reason and Apply

6. Find these values.

a. Find u_{75} if $u_n = 2n - 1$. $u_{75} = 149$

b. Find $\sum_{n=1}^{75}(2n-1)$. $S_{75} = 5625$

c. Find $\sum_{n=20}^{75}(2n-1)$. $S_{75} - S_{19} = 5264$

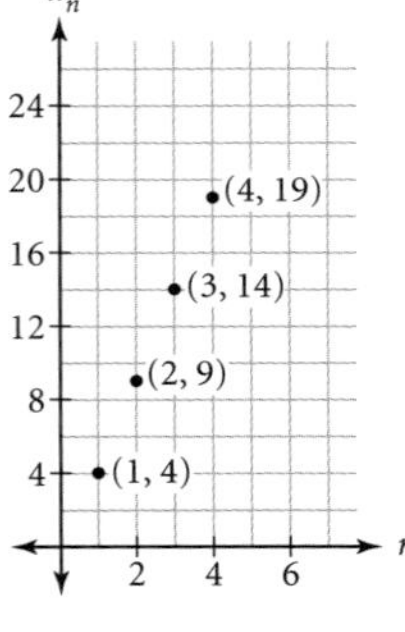

7. Consider the graph of the arithmetic sequence shown at right.

a. What is the 46th term?

b. Write a formula for u_n.

c. Find the sum of the heights from the horizontal axis of the first 46 points of the sequence's graph.

8. Suppose you practice the piano 45 min on the first day of the semester and increase your practice time by 5 min each day. How much total time will you devote to practicing during

a. The first 15 days of the semester? 1200 min, or 20 h

b. The first 35 days of the semester? 4550 min, or 75 h 50 min

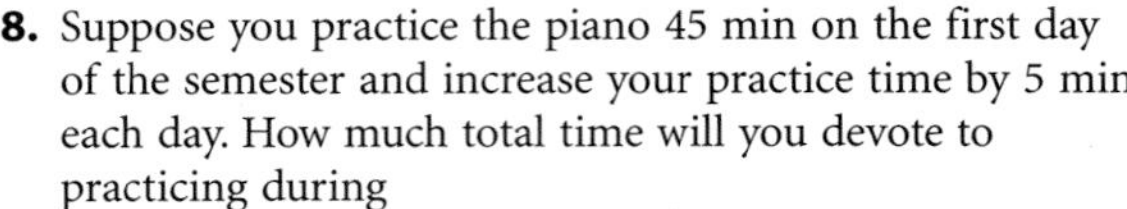

American pianist Van Cliburn (b 1934) caused a sensation by winning the first International Tchaikovsky Competition in Moscow in 1958, during the height of the Cold War. When asked how many hours he practiced per day, he replied, "Mother always told me that if you knew how long you had practiced, you hadn't done anything. She believed you had to become engrossed . . . or it just didn't count for anything. Nothing happens if you watch the clock."

9. Jessica arranges a display of soup cans as shown.

a. List the number of cans in the top row, the second row, the third row, and so on, down to the tenth row.

b. Write a recursive formula for the terms of the sequence in 9a.

c. If the cans are to be stacked 47 rows high, how many cans will it take to build the display?

d. If Jessica uses six cases (288 cans), how tall can she make the display?

10. Find each value.

a. Find the sum of the first 1000 positive integers (the numbers 1 through 1000).

b. Find the sum of the second 1000 positive integers (1001 through 2000).

c. Guess the sum of the third 1000 positive integers (2001 through 3000).

d. Now calculate the sum for 10c.

e. Describe a way to find the sum of the third 1000 positive integers, if you know the sum of the first 1000 positive integers.

11. Suppose $y = 65 + 2(x - 1)$ is an explicit representation of an arithmetic sequence, for integer values $x \geq 1$. Express the partial sum of the arithmetic series as a quadratic expression, with x representing the term number. $S_x = x^2 + 64x$

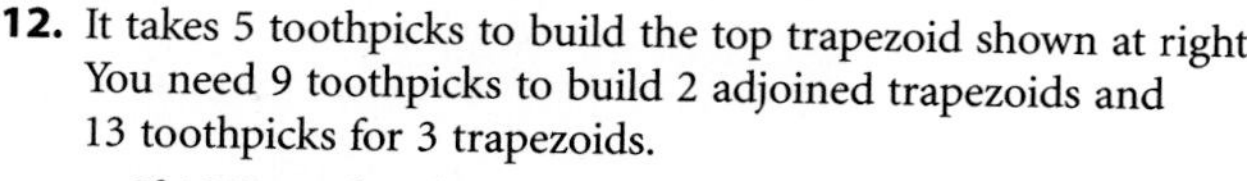

12. It takes 5 toothpicks to build the top trapezoid shown at right. You need 9 toothpicks to build 2 adjoined trapezoids and 13 toothpicks for 3 trapezoids.

a. If 1000 toothpicks are available, how many trapezoids will be in the last complete row?

b. How many complete rows will there be?

c. How many toothpicks will you use to construct these rows?

d. Use the numbers in this problem to carefully describe the difference between a sequence and a series.

13. **APPLICATION** If an object falls from rest, then the distance it falls during the first second is about 4.9 m. In each subsequent second, the object falls 9.8 m farther than in the preceding second.

a. Write a recursive formula to describe the distance the object falls during each second of free fall. $u_1 = 4.9$ and $u_n = u_{n-1} + 9.8$ where $n \geq 2$

b. Find an explicit formula for 13a. $u_n = 9.8n - 4.9$

c. How far will the object fall during the 10th second? 93.1 m

d. How far does the object fall during the first 10 seconds? 490 m

e. Find an explicit formula for the distance an object falls in n seconds. $S_n = 4.9n^2$

f. Suppose you drop a quarter from the Royal Gorge Bridge. How long will it take to reach the Arkansas River 331 m below? approximately 8.2 s

The Royal Gorge Bridge (built 1929) near Cañon City, Colorado, is the world's highest suspension bridge, with length 384 m (1260 ft) and width 5 m (18 ft).

10a. $S_{1000} = 500{,}500$

10b. $S_{2000} - S_{1000} = 1{,}500{,}500$

10c. Answers will vary.

10d. $S_{3000} - S_{2000} = 2{,}500{,}500$

10e. Each of these 1000 values is 2000 more than the corresponding value between 1 and 1000, so add 1000(2000) to the first sum.

Exercise 11 As needed, suggest that students write out the first few terms of the sequence. They can see that d is 2 and u_1 is 65 and apply the first formula, or they may see that u_n equals $u_1 + (x - 1)d$ and use the second formula.

12a. 21 trapezoids

12b. 21 rows

12c. 945 toothpicks

12d. The numbers of toothpicks in each row form a sequence, whereas the total numbers of toothpicks used form a series.

Exercise 13 [Alert] Students may think that 13c and 13d are asking the same question.

Exercises 14, 15 These exercises preview Lesson 11.2.

14a. i. increases without bound; **ii.** 0

14b. i. 2; **ii.** $\frac{1}{2}$

14c. i. The sum will be infinitely large; **ii.** The sum will approach 4.

18a. 0.39, 0.0039, 0.000039, 0.00000039, 0.0000000039, 0.000000000039

18b. $u_n = 39(0.01)^n$

Exercise 19 This exercise reviews Lesson 10.7, which was optional.

EXTENSION

Ask students to explain the first formula for the partial sum of an arithmetic series, rewriting it as needed. Also ask them what makes the two formulas for the partial sum of an arithmetic series equivalent. [The expression $d(n-1)$ is the difference between the first and the last terms in the series.]

14. Consider these two geometric sequences:

i. 2, 4, 8, 16, 32, . . .

ii. $2, 1, \frac{1}{2}, \frac{1}{4}, \frac{1}{8}, \ldots$

a. What is the long-run value of each sequence?

b. What is the common ratio of each sequence?

c. What will happen if you try to sum all of the terms of each sequence?

15. APPLICATION There are 650,000 people in a city. Every 15 minutes, the local radio and television stations broadcast a tornado warning. During each 15-minute time period, 42% of the people who had not yet heard the warning become aware of the approaching tornado. How many people have heard the news

a. After 1 hour? 576,443 people

b. After 2 hours? 641,676 people

In the central United States, an average of 800 to 1000 tornadoes occur each year. Tornado watches, forecasts, and warnings are announced to the public by the National Weather Service.

Review

1.5 **16.** Suppose you invest \$500 in a bank that pays 5.5% annual interest compounded quarterly.

a. How much money will you have after five years? \$657.03

b. Suppose you also deposit an additional \$150 at the end of every three months. How much will you have after five years? \$4,083.21

5.1 **17.** Consider the explicit formula $u_n = 81\left(\frac{1}{3}\right)^{n-1}$.

a. List the first six terms, u_1 to u_6. $81, 27, 9, 3, 1, \frac{1}{3}$

b. Write a recursive formula for the sequence. $u_1 = 81$ and $u_n = \frac{1}{3}u_{n-1}$ where $n \geq 2$

5.1 **18.** Consider the recursive formula

$u_1 = 0.39$

$u_n = 0.01 \cdot u_{n-1}$ where $n \geq 2$

a. List the first six terms.

b. Write an explicit formula for the sequence.

10.7 **19.** Find the exact value for

a. $\cos 15°$ $\frac{\sqrt{6}+\sqrt{2}}{4}$

b. $\cos 75°$ $\frac{\sqrt{6}-\sqrt{2}}{4}$

9.7 **20.** Consider the rational equation $y = \frac{4x+3}{2x-1}$.

a. Rewrite the equation as a transformation of the parent function $y = \frac{1}{x}$. $y = 2 + \frac{\frac{5}{2}}{x - \frac{1}{2}}$

b. What are the asymptotes of $y = \frac{4x+3}{2x-1}$? $x = \frac{1}{2}, y = 2$

c. The point (1, 1) is on the graph of the parent function. What is its image on the transformed function? $\left(\frac{3}{2}, \frac{9}{2}\right)$

LESSON

11.2

Infinite Geometric Series

Beauty itself is but the sensible image of the infinite.

GEORGE BANCROFT

In Lesson 11.1, you developed an explicit formula for a partial sum of an arithmetic series. This formula works when you have a finite, or limited, number of terms. You also saw that as the number of terms, n, increases, the magnitude of the partial sum, S_n, increases in the long run. If the number of terms of an arithmetic series were **infinite,** or unending, then the magnitude of the sum would be infinite.

But some geometric sequences have terms that get smaller. What happens to the partial sums of these sequences?

For example, the geometric sequence

0.4, 0.04, 0.004, . . .

has common ratio $\frac{1}{10}$, so the terms get smaller. Adding the terms creates a **geometric series.** Notice the pattern of repeating decimals that is formed.

These nested photographs represent an infinite sequence.

$S_3 = 0.4 + 0.04 + 0.004 = 0.444$

$S_4 = 0.4 + 0.04 + 0.004 + 0.0004 = 0.4444$

$S_5 = 0.4 + 0.04 + 0.004 + 0.0004 + 0.00004 = 0.44444$

If you sum an infinite number of terms of this sequence, would the result be infinitely large?

An **infinite geometric series** is a geometric series with infinitely many terms. In this lesson you will specifically look at **convergent series,** for which the sequence of partial sums approaches a long-run value as the number of terms increases.

EXAMPLE A

Jack baked a pie and promptly ate one-half of it. Determined to make the pie last, he then decided to eat only one-half of the pie that remained each day.

a. Record the amount of pie eaten each day for the first seven days.

b. For each of the seven days, record the total amount of pie eaten since it was baked.

c. If Jack lives forever, then how much of this pie will he eat?

NCTM STANDARDS

CONTENT	PROCESS
✓ Number	Problem Solving
✓ Algebra	✓ Reasoning
Geometry	✓ Communication
✓ Measurement	✓ Connections
Data/Probability	✓ Representation

LESSON OBJECTIVES

- Learn about geometric series
- Write recursive and explicit formulas for geometric series
- Determine when an infinite geometric series converges
- Find the sum of a convergent infinite geometric series

LESSON

11.2

PLANNING

LESSON OUTLINE

One day:

5 min	Example A
15 min	Investigation
10 min	Sharing
10 min	Examples B, C
5 min	Exercises

MATERIALS

- Calculator Note 11A

TEACHING

Students investigate geometric series and find a formula for the sum of a convergent infinite geometric series. If you are beginning with the one-step investigation, you'll find it on page 638.

INTRODUCTION

If you sum infinitely many terms of the introductory sequence, the sum will be the finite number $0.\overline{4}$, which equals $\frac{4}{9}$.

▶ *EXAMPLE A*

You might represent the pie with a piece of paper. Have one student cut it in half and place one piece on the overhead projector. Another student can halve the remaining half and place one piece on the projector. Continue the process with more students, asking each student to place the new piece of paper on the projector to demonstrate that $\frac{1}{2} + \frac{1}{4} + \frac{1}{8} + \cdots = 1$.

One Step
Pose this problem, based on Exercise 9: "A New Orleans sporting event draws 50,000 visitors, who spend an average of \$500 each. After the event, 60% of the income from the visitors is again spent in the local economy, 60% of that amount is again spent in the local economy, and so on. Over the long run, how much money will be spent in the local economy due to the event?" As needed, suggest that students write out a few terms of the series and look for patterns. Push some groups to find a formula for the sum of infinitely many terms, or the *n*th partial sum, of any geometric series. During Sharing, introduce the terms *geometric series* and *convergent geometric series.*

Guiding the Investigation

[Alert] Students, remembering Lesson 11.1, might use one of the numbers as a common ratio, rather than one-tenth of the number. Students may express the ratio as either a decimal or a fraction.

Step 1 Technically the partial sums are never equivalent, but eventually the calculator rounds all sums to the same value.

Step 3 sample answers:

First term u_1	Common ratio r	Sum S	$\frac{u_1}{S}$
7	0.8	35	0.2
7	0.9	70	0.1
8	0.7	$26.\overline{6}$	0.3
8	0.9	80	0.1
9	0.7	30	0.3
9	0.8	45	0.2

► ***Solution***

The amount of pie eaten each day is a geometric sequence with first term $\frac{1}{2}$ and common ratio $\frac{1}{2}$.

a. The first seven terms of this sequence are

$$\frac{1}{2}, \frac{1}{4}, \frac{1}{8}, \frac{1}{16}, \frac{1}{32}, \frac{1}{64}, \frac{1}{128}$$

b. Find the partial sums, S_1 through S_7, of the terms in part a.

$$\frac{1}{2}, \frac{3}{4}, \frac{7}{8}, \frac{15}{16}, \frac{31}{32}, \frac{63}{64}, \frac{127}{128}$$

c. It may seem that eating pie "forever" would result in eating a lot of pie. However, if you look at the pattern of the partial sums, it seems as though for any finite number of days Jack's total is slightly less than 1. This leads to the conclusion that Jack would eat exactly one pie in the long run. This is a convergent infinite geometric series with long-run value 1.

Recall that a geometric sequence can be represented with an explicit formula in the form $u_n = u_1 \cdot r^{n-1}$ or $u_n = u_0 \cdot r^n$, where r represents the common ratio between the terms. The investigation will help you create an explicit formula for the sum of a convergent infinite geometric series.

Investigation
Infinite Geometric Series Formula

Select three integers between 2 and 9 for your group to use. Each person should write his or her own geometric sequence using one of the three values for the first term and one-tenth of another value for the common ratio. Make sure that each person uses a different sequence.

Step 1 Sample answer: Using the sequence $u_1 = 7$ and $u_n = 0.8u_{n-1}$ where $n \geq 2$, the calculator gives $S_{400} \approx 35$ and $S_{500} \approx 35$.

Step 1 Use your calculator to find the partial sum of the first 400 and the first 500 terms of your sequence. If your calculator rounds these partial sums to the same value, then use this number as the long-run value. If not, then continue summing terms until you find the long-run value. [► Revisit **Calculator Note 11A** to review how to calculate partial sums. ◄]

Step 2 Create a new series by replacing either the first term or the common ratio with another one of the three integers that your group selected. Remember that the common ratio is one-tenth of the integer. Repeat Step 1.

Step 3 Combine the results from all members of your group into a table like the one below. Your long-run value is equivalent to the sum of infinitely many terms, represented by S with no subscript.

First term u_1	Common ratio r	Sum S

Step 4 Find a formula for S in terms of u_1 and r. (*Hint:* Include another column for the ratio $\frac{u_1}{S}$ and look for relationships.) Will your formula work if the ratio is equal to 1? If the ratio is greater than 1? Justify your answers with examples.

Step 4 [Alert] Students may have difficulty with this step. You might have them work on it in groups for a few minutes and then share their ideas with the class. Many students will say that the formula does not apply when the ratio is 1 because you get division by zero, which is undefined. A few students will claim that dividing by zero gives a result of infinity. Because infinity is not a number, this phrasing is shorthand for a statement about limits.

Step 4 $S = \frac{u_1}{1 - r}$

When $r = 1$, for example, $u_1 = 1$ and $u_n = u_{n-1}$ where $n \geq 2$, the sum is infinite and the infinite series does not converge.

When $r > 1$, for example, $u_1 = 1$ and $u_n = 2u_{n-1}$ where $n \geq 2$, the sum is infinite and the infinite series does not converge. The formula does not work because it gives $S = -1$.

Infinity by American sculptor José de Rivera (1904–1985)

In the investigation you used partial sums with large values of n to determine the long-run value of the sum of infinitely many terms. A graph of the sequence of partial sums is another tool you can use.

EXAMPLE B

Consider an ideal (frictionless) ball bouncing after it is dropped. The distances in inches that the ball falls on each bounce are represented by 200, 200(0.8), $200(0.8)^2$, $200(0.8)^3$, and so on. Summing these distances creates a series. Find the total distance the ball falls during an infinite number of bounces.

▶ Solution

The sequence of partial sums is represented by the recursive formula

$$S_1 = 200$$
$$S_n = S_{n-1} + u_n \quad \text{where } n \geq 2$$

The explicit formula for the sequence of terms is $u_n = 200(0.8)^{n-1}$. So, the recursive formula for the series is equivalent to

$$S_1 = 200$$
$$S_n = S_{n-1} + 200(0.8)^{n-1} \quad \text{where } n \geq 2$$

The graph of S_n levels off as the number of bounces increases. This means the total sum of all the distances continues to grow, but seems to approach a long-run value for larger values of n.

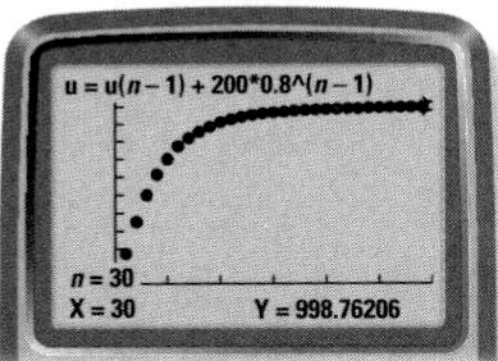

[−5, 30, 5, −200, 1200, 100]

By looking at larger and larger values of n, you'll find the sum of this series is 1000 inches. So, the sum of the distances the ball falls is 1000 inches. Use the formula that you found in the investigation to verify this answer.

▶ EXAMPLE B

[Language] *Ideal* here means "unlike the real world." In an ideal situation, there is nothing for the ball to rub against to slow it down. In reality, air resistance and perhaps other forces will slow the ball down. Moreover, in the real world the ball will stop bouncing when the rebound distance is less than the radius of the ball. This ideal ball is a point.

The approach in this example differs from that of Lesson 11.1 in using the explicit rather than the recursive form for u_n in the equation $S_n = S_{n-1} + 200(0.8)^{n-1}$. The formula found in the investigation gives $\frac{200}{1 - 0.8}$, or 1000.

SHARING IDEAS

[Alert] Watch for students who think the sum of an infinite series must be infinite. Make sure students understand that the sum is finite though the series is infinite. You might suggest that students talk about the sum of infinitely many terms. During and after student presentations, suggest that students ask "why" and "what if not" questions. Prepare for questions like those below.

A crucial question for students first encountering series is "*Why* can the sum of infinitely many numbers be a finite number?" Students' mystification reflects the centuries of investigation by mathematicians exploring the counterintuitive nature of infinity and limits. Be prepared for resistance from students who have difficulty changing their intuition. Also be prepared to encourage those students who find the mysteries of infinity fascinating.

[Language] You may want to define and discuss the term *limit* as a number that, in the long run, a sequence or function comes so close to that you can no longer determine any difference. You might remind students that they first studied long-run values (limits) in Lesson 1.3 and that limits can help define asymptotes.

Sharing Ideas (continued)

[Ask] "Explain the formula $S = \frac{u_1}{1 - r}$ for the sum of a convergent geometric series." [One argument that students find convincing, and indeed might use to derive the formula when they can't recall it, represents the sum with a variable:

$$S = u_1 + u_1r + u_1r^2 + u_1r^3 + \cdots$$
$$rS = u_1r + u_1r^2 + u_1r^3 + u_1r^4 + \cdots$$
$$S - rS = u_1$$
$$S(1 - r) = u_1; S = \frac{u_1}{1 - r}$$]

Make sure this derivation arises if you plan to use the one-step investigation in Lesson 11.3.

[Ask] "Why doesn't a geometric series converge if the constant ratio r is beyond -1 or 1?" Different people have different criteria for answers to "why" questions. Some students will be satisfied by examples, such as $1 + 2 + 4 + 8 + 16 + \cdots$ (with $r = 2$) or $1 - 2 + 4 - 8 + 16 - \cdots$ (with $r = -2$). Others will want to see where the formulas fail, as in Take Another Look activity 2 on page 654. Others will be happier applying the definition of *convergence* by finding

Sharing Ideas (continued)
a formula for the partial sums; partial sums of geometric series are the topic of the next lesson, but you might encourage interested students to find a formula now.

You may want to discuss the series $1 - 1 + 1 - 1 + \cdots$, a geometric series with $r = -1$. If you consider it as $(1 - 1) + (1 - 1) + \cdots$, the sum is 0; if you treat it as $1 + (-1 + 1) + (-1 + 1) + \cdots$, the sum is 1. If you apply the formula $S = \frac{u_1}{1 - r}$, the sum is $\frac{1}{2}$.

[Alert] The formula applies only to convergent geometric series; it should not be used with the series with $r = -1$.

[Language] You might define *divergent series* as a series that is not convergent, or a series whose partial sums do not approach a long-run value. The series $1 - 1 + 1 - 1 + \cdots$ is divergent because its partial sums, $1, 0, 1, 0, 1, 0, \cdots$, don't approach a long-run value.

[Ask] "What if the constant ratio is 0? Does the series really converge?" The series is $u_1 + 0 + 0 + 0 + \cdots$, which has the sum u_1. The formula $S = \frac{u_1}{1 - r}$ still applies.

To foreshadow Lesson 11.3, **[Ask]** "What if we are not talking about the sum of the entire geometric series? What are the partial sums?"

EXAMPLE C

Have students write out the first few terms to see that the first term is 0.3. Display the sigma notation and **[Ask]** "Why is the power $n - 1$ rather than n?" You might have the students derive the generalization that every geometric series can be written as $\sum_{n=1}^{\infty} ar^{n-1}$ or, equivalently, as $\sum_{n=1}^{\infty} u_1 r^{n-1}$ or $\sum_{n=0}^{\infty} ar^{n}$.

[Language] In part c, a *ratio of integers* is a fraction.

You now have several ways to determine the long-run value of an infinite geometric series. If the series is convergent, the formula that you found in the investigation gives you the sum of infinitely many terms.

Convergent Infinite Geometric Series

An infinite geometric series is a convergent series if the absolute value of the common ratio is less than 1, $|r| < 1$. The sum of infinitely many terms, S, of a convergent infinite geometric series is given by the explicit formula

$$S = \frac{u_1}{1 - r}$$

where u_1 is the first term and r is the common ratio ($|r| < 1$).

In mathematics the symbol ∞ is used to represent infinity, or a quantity without bound. You can use ∞ and sigma notation to represent infinite series.

EXAMPLE C Consider the infinite series

$$\sum_{n=1}^{\infty} 0.3(0.1)^{n-1}$$

a. Express this sum of infinitely many terms as a decimal.

b. Identify the first term, u_1, and the common ratio, r.

c. Express the sum as a ratio of integers.

▶ ***Solution*** When you substitute $n = \{1, 2, 3, \ldots\}$ into the expression $0.3(0.1)^{n-1}$, you get

$$0.3 + 0.03 + 0.003 + \cdots$$

a. The sum is the repeating decimal 0.333..., or $0.\overline{3}$.

b. $u_1 = 0.3$ and $r = 0.1$

c. Use the formula for the infinite sum and reduce to a ratio of integers:

$$S = \frac{0.3}{1 - 0.1} = \frac{0.3}{0.9} = \frac{1}{3}$$

You'll work with infinite geometric series and their sums further in the exercises.

EXERCISES

Practice Your Skills

1. Consider the repeating decimal 0.444..., or $0.\overline{4}$.

a. Express this decimal as the sum of terms of an infinite geometric series. $0.4 + 0.04 + 0.004 + \cdots$

b. Identify the first term and the ratio. $u_1 = 0.4, r = 0.1$

c. Use the formula you learned in this lesson to express the sum as a ratio of integers. $S = \frac{4}{9}$

Assessing Progress
You can check students' understanding of series and partial sums, their skill at using calculator sequences, and their ability to collect data and see patterns.

Closing the Lesson

A **geometric series** is a summation of the terms of a geometric sequence. An **infinite** geometric series is **convergent** if its partial sums have a finite long-run value. The **sum** of a convergent geometric series can be found by applying the formula $S = \frac{u_1}{1 - r}$.

2. Repeat the three parts of Exercise 1 with the repeating decimal 0.474747..., or $0.\overline{47}$.

3. Repeat the three parts of Exercise 1 with the repeating decimal 0.123123123..., or $0.\overline{123}$.

4. An infinite geometric sequence has a first term of 20 and a sum of 400. What are the first five terms? 20, 19, 18.05, 17.1475, 16.290125

Reason and Apply

5. An infinite geometric sequence contains the consecutive terms 128, 32, 8, and 2. The sum of the series is $43,690.\overline{6}$. What is the first term? $u_1 = 32768$

6. Consider the sequence $u_1 = 47$ and $u_n = 0.8u_{n-1}$ where $n \geq 2$. Find

   a. $\sum_{n=1}^{10} u_n$ $S_{10} \approx 209.767$

   b. $\sum_{n=1}^{20} u_n$ $S_{20} \approx 232.291$

   c. $\sum_{n=1}^{30} u_n$ $S_{30} \approx 234.709$

   d. $\sum_{n=1}^{\infty} u_n$ $S = 235$

7. Consider the sequence $u_n = 96(0.25)^{n-1}$.

   a. List the first ten terms, u_1 to u_{10}.

   b. Find the sum $\sum_{n=1}^{10} 96(0.25)^{n-1}$. $S_{10} \approx 128.000$

   c. Make a graph of partial sums for $1 \leq n \leq 10$.

   d. Find the sum $\sum_{n=1}^{\infty} 96(0.25)^{n-1}$. $S = 128$

This digitally manipulated photo, depicting a never-ending roller coaster, is titled *Infinite Fun*.

8. A ball is dropped from an initial height of 100 cm. The rebound heights to the nearest centimeter are 80, 64, 51, 41, and so on. What is the total distance the ball will travel, both up and down? 900 cm

9. APPLICATION A sporting event is to be held at the Superdome in New Orleans, Louisiana, which holds about 95,000 people. Suppose 50,000 visitors arrive in New Orleans and spend $500 each. In the month after the event, the people in New Orleans spend 60% of the income from the visitors. The next month, 60% is spent again, and so on.

   a. What is the initial amount the visitors spent? $25,000,000

   b. In the long run, how much money does this sporting event seem to add to the New Orleans economy? $62,500,000

   c. The ratio of the long-run amount to the initial amount is called the economic multiplier. What is the economic multiplier in this example? 2.5

   d. If the initial amount spent by visitors is $10,000,000 and the economic multiplier is 1.8, what percentage of the initial amount is spent again and again in the local economy? 44.4%

Exercise 5 As needed, point out that the terms given are not necessarily at the beginning of the series.

Exercise 6 Students won't see an explicit formula for the partial sums of a geometric series until the next lesson. They can use the calculator method from Lesson 11.1 to find these partial sums.

Infinite Fun

You might **[Ask]** "Why is the photograph titled *Infinite Fun*?" [The track is shaped like an infinity symbol.]

7a. 96, 24, 6, 1.5, 0.375. 0.09375, 0.0234375, 0.005859375, 0.00146484375, 0.0003662109375

Exercise 8 [ESL] The term *rebound height* means "the height of the bounce."

Exercise 9d The exact percentage is $44.\overline{4}\%$, or $44\frac{4}{9}\%$.

BUILDING UNDERSTANDING

Students work with infinite geometric series, determining convergence and finding sums of convergent series.

ASSIGNING HOMEWORK

Essential	1–4, 6
Performance assessment	5, 7–12
Portfolio	11
Group	8, 10
Review	13–16

MATERIALS

- Sketchpad demonstration Fractals, *optional*

Helping with the Exercises

Exercises 1–3 Students may have seen an alternative approach to converting repeating decimals to fractions that didn't rely on series. For example, if they set S equal to $0.123123\overline{123}$, then $1000S$ equals $123.123123\overline{123}$, subtracting $999S$ equals 123. This gives $S = \frac{123}{999}$. This approach is equivalent to the derivation of the formula for the sum of an infinite geometric series discussed during Sharing.

Exercise 1 This series is the one that opened the lesson.

2a. $0.47 + 0.0047 + 0.000047 + \cdots$

2b. $u_1 = 0.47, r = 0.01$

2c. $S = \frac{47}{99}$

3a. $0.123 + 0.000123 + 0.000000123 + \cdots$

3b. $u_1 = 0.123, r = 0.001$

3c. $S = \frac{123}{999} = \frac{41}{333}$

Exercise 4 Students might use guess-and-check, but encourage them to use the formula for the sum and solve for r.

See page 904 for answer to Exercise 7c.

Exercise 11 You might use the Sketchpad demonstration Fractals to show the creation of these squares and the measurement of their perimeter and area.

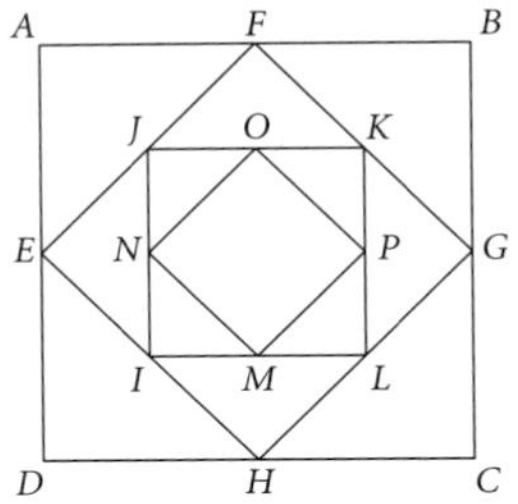

Exercise 12 The Sketchpad demonstration Fractals can also be used for this exercise. Students may have seen in *Discovering Geometry,* Chapter 2, that the perimeter of a Sierpiński triangle grows without bound even though the area approaches a limit.

12a. approaches 0

12b. approaches 0

10. A flea jumps $\frac{1}{2}$ ft right, then $\frac{1}{4}$ ft left, then $\frac{1}{8}$ ft right, and so on. To what point is the flea zooming in? the point $\frac{1}{3}$ ft to the right from its starting point

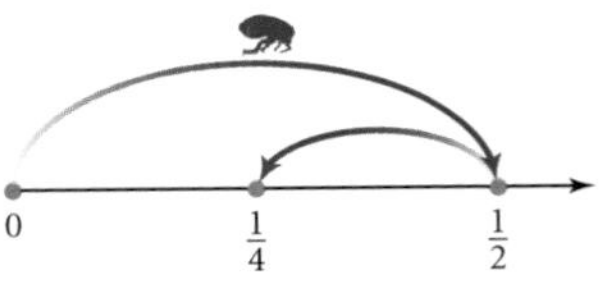

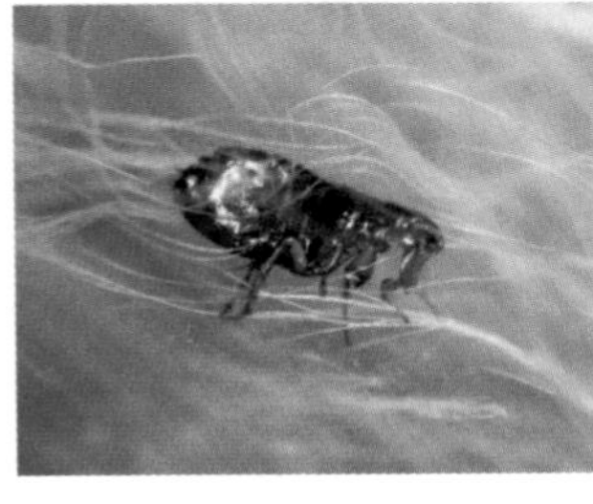

Magnified view of a flea in a dog's fur

11. Suppose square $ABCD$ with side length 8 in. is cut out of paper. Another square, $EFGH$, is placed with its corners at the midpoints of $ABCD$. A third square is placed with its corners at midpoints of $EFGH$, and so on.

a. What is the perimeter of the tenth square? $\sqrt{2}$ in.

b. What is the area of the tenth square? 0.125 in.^{2}

c. If the pattern were repeated infinitely many times, what would be the sum of the perimeters of the squares? approximately 109.25 in.

d. What would be the sum of the areas? 128 in.^{2}

12. The fractal known as the Sierpiński triangle begins as an equilateral triangle with side length 1 unit and area $\frac{\sqrt{3}}{4}$ square units. The fractal is created recursively by replacing the triangle with three smaller congruent equilateral triangles such that each smaller triangle shares a vertex with the larger triangle. This removes the area from the middle of the original triangle.

Stage 0

Stage 1

Stage 2

. . .

Stage 6

In the long run, what happens to

a. The perimeter of each of the smaller triangles?

b. The area of each of the smaller triangles?

c. The sum of the perimeters of the smaller triangles? (*Hint:* You can't use the sum formula from this lesson.) approaches infinity

d. The sum of the areas of the smaller triangles? approaches 0

These Swedish stamps show the Koch snowflake, another fractal design that begins with an equilateral triangle. Can you determine the recursive procedure that creates the snowflake?

Koch Snowflake

The Koch snowflake is made up of three fractals—Koch curves created on the sides of an equilateral triangle. The recursive process involves trisecting a segment and replacing the middle third by two sides of an equilateral triangle. (The replaced third would be the third side of that triangle.) Then each resulting segment is trisected and the middle third is replaced by two sides of an equilateral triangle, and so on. **[Ask]** "In the long run, what happens to the length of each added segment?" [approaches 0] "The number of segments?" [increases without bound] "The perimeter of the fractal?" [increases without bound] "What happens to the area of the fractal?" [It approaches a fixed value that is less than twice the area of the original triangle.]

Review

3.4 **13.** A large barrel contains 12.4 gal of oil 18 min after a drain is opened. How many gallons of oil were in the barrel initially, if it drains at 4.2 gal/min? 88 gal

5.4 **14.** Match each equation to a graph.

A. $y = 10(0.8)^x$ **B.** $y = 10 - 10(0.75)^x$

C. $y = 3 + 7(0.7)^x$ **D.** $y = 10 - 7(0.65)^x$

i. B

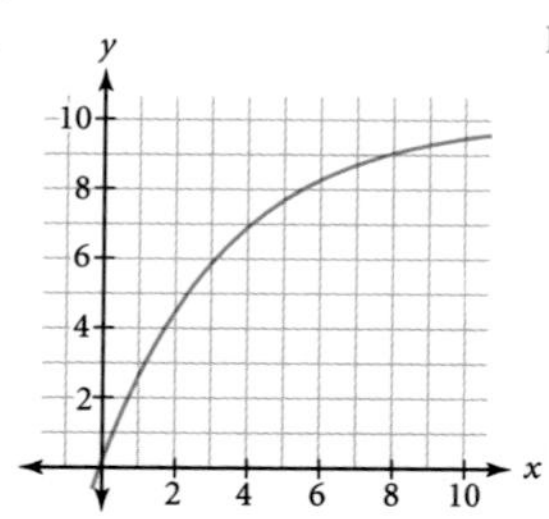

ii. C

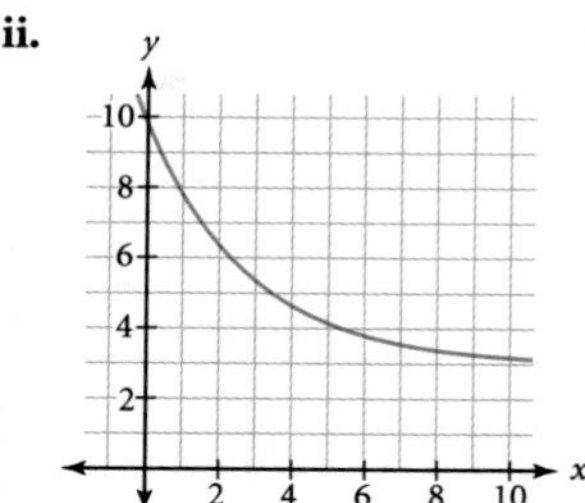

iii. D

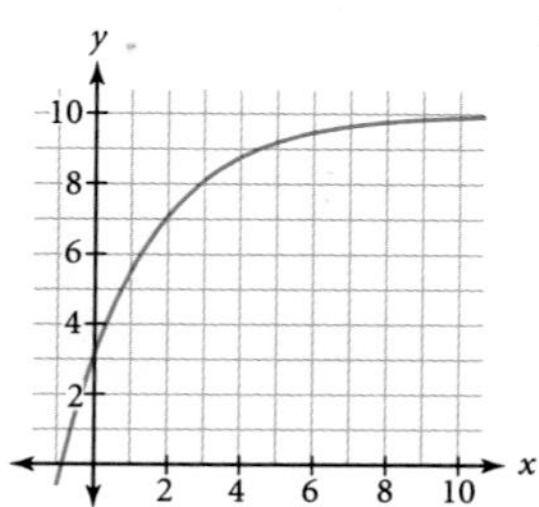

iv. A

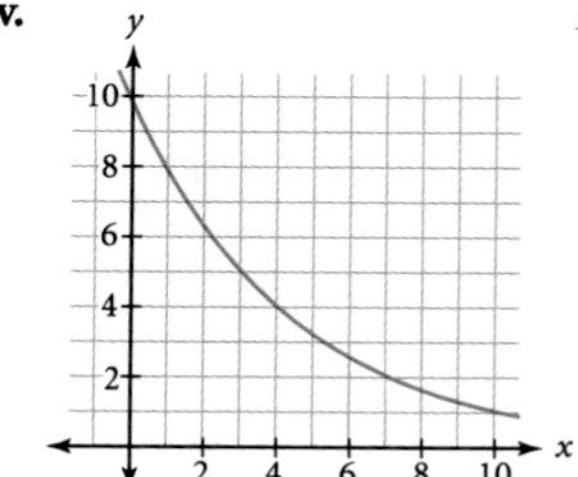

11.1 **15.** APPLICATION A computer software company decides to set aside \$100,000 to develop a new video game. It estimates that development will cost \$955 the first week and that expenses will increase by \$65 each week.

a. After 25 weeks, how much of the development budget will be left? \$56,625

b. How long can the company keep the development phase going before the budget will not support another week of expenses? 43 wk

11.1 **16.** Hans sees a dog. The dog has four puppies. Four cats follow each puppy. Each cat has four kittens. Four mice follow each kitten. How many legs does Hans see? Express your answer using sigma notation. $\sum_{n=1}^{5} 4^n = 1364$

IMPROVING YOUR VISUAL THINKING SKILLS

Toothpicks

You have eight toothpicks—four are short, and four are long. Each of the short toothpicks is one-half the length of any of the long toothpicks. Arrange the toothpicks to make exactly three congruent squares.

IMPROVING VISUAL THINKING SKILLS

A good problem-solving technique when stuck is to ask what assumptions are being made. The assumption that the toothpicks can't overlap is a natural one, but it prevents students from arriving at this solution.

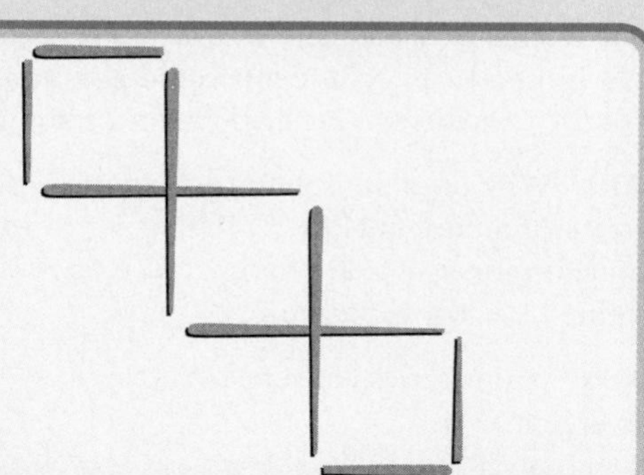

EXTENSIONS

A. Ask students to generalize their results from Exercises 1, 2, and 3. [Any repeating decimal with n repeating digits can be written as a fraction of those digits over n 9's. For example, $0.\overline{1256} = \frac{1256}{9999}$.]

B. Ask students to investigate Zeno's Achilles paradox, which can be thought of in terms of infinite geometric series.

C. If you didn't show the Sketchpad demonstration Fractals to the class, ask students to look at it individually and answer the questions.

D. Use Take Another Look activity 1 on page 653.

E. Have students investigate series that represent properties of other fractals.

LESSON

11.3

PLANNING

LESSON OUTLINE

One day:

10 min Example A

15 min Investigation

5 min Examples B, C

5 min Sharing

10 min Exercises

MATERIALS

- Calculator Note 11A

TEACHING

This lesson addresses the question of the nth partial sum of a geometric series. The solution to the problem that introduces the lesson is 3 minutes.

One Step

Pose this problem, from Example C: "Each day, the imaginary caterpillarsaurus eats 25% more leaves than it did the day before. If a 30-day-old caterpillarsaurus has eaten 151,677 leaves in its brief lifetime, how many will it eat the next day?" As needed, help students see that they need a formula for the nth partial sum of a geometric series, and ponder the possibility of extending the derivation of the formula for the sum of an infinite geometric series (from Lesson 11.2, Sharing Ideas, on page 639).

▸ *EXAMPLE A*

As needed, refer students to Calculator Note 11A for calculating and graphing the partial sums. You might need to remind students that the calculator might use a symbol other than S_n for the partial sums.

LESSON 11.3

Partial Sums of Geometric Series

If a pair of calculators can be linked and a program transferred from one calculator to the other in 20 s, how long will it be before everyone in a lecture hall of 250 students has the program? During the first time period, the program is transferred to one calculator; during the second time period, to two calculators; during the third time period, to four more calculators; and so on. The number of students who have the program doubles every 20 s. To solve this problem, you must determine the maximum value of n before S_n exceeds 250. This problem is an example of a partial sum of a geometric series. It requires the sum of a finite number of terms of a geometric sequence.

EXAMPLE A

Consider the sequence 2, 6, 18, 54, ...

a. Find u_{15}.

b. Graph the partial sums S_1 through S_{15}, and find the partial sum S_{15}.

▸ *Solution*

The sequence is geometric with $u_1 = 2$ and $r = 3$.

a. A recursive formula for the sequence is $u_1 = 2$ and $u_n = 3u_{n-1}$ where $n \geq 2$. The sequence can also be defined explicitly as $u_n = 2(3)^{n-1}$. Substituting 15 for n into either equation gives $u_{15} = 9{,}565{,}938$.

b. Use your calculator to graph the partial sums. (You'll see the data points better if you turn the axes off.) Trace to find that S_{15} is 14,348,906.

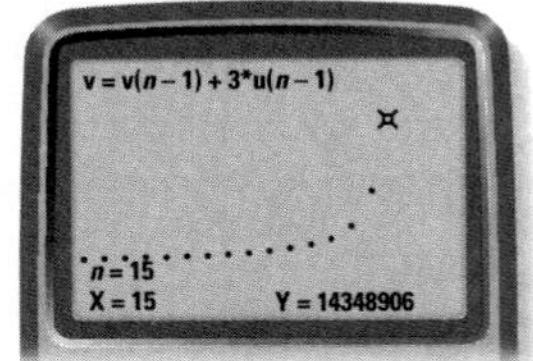

[0, 18, 1, −5000000, 20000000, 5000000]

In the example you used a recursive method to find the partial sum of a geometric series. For some partial sums, especially those involving a large number of terms, it can be faster and easier to use an explicit formula. The investigation will help you develop an explicit formula.

The calculator screen shows a recursive formula like that in Lesson 11.1. Students could also graph $S_n = S_{n-1} + 2(3)^{n-1}$ explicitly, as in Lesson 11.2.

[Ask] "Why does the solution say that n has to be greater than or equal to 2?" [Using $n = 1$ in the equation for u_n would require a u_0 term, which isn't defined for this sequence.]

[Ask] "Is this series convergent?" [No; it is divergent.]

LESSON OBJECTIVES

- Find formulas for the partial sums of geometric series
- Given the partial sum of a geometric series and either the common ratio or the initial value, find the other value
- Distinguish between arithmetic series and geometric series
- Investigate other types of series

Investigation
Geometric Series Formula

Select three integers between 2 and 9 for your group to use. Each person should write his or her own geometric sequence using one of the three values for the first term and one-tenth of another value for the common ratio. Make sure that each person uses a different sequence.

Step 1 Find the first ten terms of your sequence. Then find the first ten partial sums of the corresponding series.

Step 2 Graph data points in the form (n, S_n), and find a translated exponential equation to fit the data. The equation will be in the form $S_n = L - a \cdot b^n$. (*Hint:* L is the long-run value of the partial sums. In Lesson 11.2, how did you find this value?)

Step 3 Rewrite your equation from Step 2 in terms of n, u_1, and r. Use algebraic techniques to write your explicit formula as a single rational expression.

Step 4 Create a new series, this time using an integer for the common ratio. Repeat Step 1.

Step 5 Use your formula to find S_{10}, and compare the result to the partial sum from Step 4. Does your formula work when the ratio is greater than 1? If not, then what changes do you have to make?

Step 4 sample answer: $u_1 = 7$ and $u_n = 2u_{n-1}$ where $n \geq 2$; sequence: {7, 14, 28, 56, 112, 224, 448, 896, 1792, 3584}; series: {7, 21, 49, 105, 217, 441, 889, 1785, 3577, 7161}

Step 5 $S_{10} = \frac{7(1-2^{10})}{1-2} = 7161$

Yes, the same formula works.

In the investigation you found an explicit formula for a partial sum of a geometric series that uses only three pieces of information—the first term, the common ratio, and the number of terms. Now you do not need to write out the terms to find a sum.

EXAMPLE B Find S_{10} for the series $16 + 24 + 36 + \cdots$.

▶ **Solution**

The first term, u_1, is 16. The common ratio, r, is 1.5. The number of terms, n, is 10. Use the formula you developed in the investigation to calculate S_{10}.

$$S_{10} = \frac{16(1 - 1.5^{10})}{1 - 1.5} = 1813.28125$$

EXAMPLE C Each day, the imaginary caterpillarsaurus eats 25% more leaves than it did the day before. If a 30-day-old caterpillarsaurus has eaten 151,677 leaves in its brief lifetime, how many will it eat the next day?

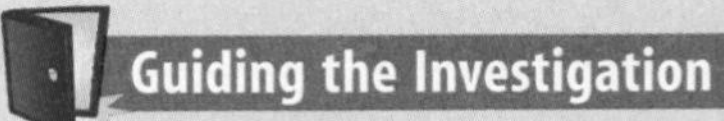

This investigation starts out like the investigation in Lesson 11.2. The difference is that in Lesson 11.2 students were looking for the sum of the entire series, whereas in this investigation they're looking for the partial sum.

Step 1 sample answer: $u_1 = 7$ and $u_n = 0.8u_{n-1}$ where $n \geq 2$; sequence: 7, 5.6, 4.48, 3.584, 2.8672, 2.29376, 1.835008, 1.4680064, 1.17440512, 0.939524096; series: 7, 12.6, 17.08, 20.664, 23.5312, 25.82496, 27.659968, 29.1279744, 30.30237952, 31.241903616

Step 2 As needed, **[Ask]** "In the investigation of the last lesson, how did you find the long-run value?" [by evaluating the formula $S = \frac{u_1}{1-r}$ or in this case, where b is used in place of r, $S = \frac{u_1}{1-b}$]

Step 3 $S_n = \left(\frac{u_1}{1-r}\right) - \left(\frac{u_1}{1-r}\right)r^n$ or $S_n = \frac{u_1(1-r^n)}{1-r}$

Step 5 Students can use their formula from either Step 2 or Step 3. If students had difficulty deriving the formula in this investigation, they might be able to figure it out from the solution in Example B. If not, it's given in the box that follows the examples.

▶ **EXAMPLE B**

[Ask] "Should the result be negative because the denominator is negative?" [No; the numerator is also negative.] In cases where r is greater than 1, the formula is sometimes written $S_n = u_1\frac{r^n - 1}{r - 1}$ to have all quantities positive.

See page 904 for answer to Step 2.

NCTM STANDARDS

CONTENT		PROCESS	
✓	Number		Problem Solving
✓	Algebra	✓	Reasoning
	Geometry	✓	Communication
	Measurement	✓	Connections
	Data/Probability	✓	Representation

▶ **EXAMPLE C**

[Ask] "Why does the book use the value $r = 1.25$ rather than $r = 0.25$?" [The value $r = 1.25$ represents 25% *more than* the number eaten the day before; an r-value of 0.25 would represent 25% *of* the number eaten the day before, and the powers of r would be smaller rather than larger than r.]

SHARING IDEAS

As students present, elicit the idea that S_n is the sum of the first n terms and that the nth term itself is u_1r^{n-1}, not u_1r^n.

Then encourage the class to pose new problems. Be prepared for those given below.

[Ask] "Can you derive the formula for the nth partial sum deductively rather than inductively?"

[You can use the derivation of the formula for the sum of the infinite series for the partial sum as well, although you will get an extra term at the end after subtracting: $S_n(1-r) = u_1 - u_1r^n$, so $S_n = \frac{u_1}{1-r}(1-r^n)$.]

If you won't be assigning Take Another Look activity 2, ask students to explain how you can see from the formulas why the partial sums approach the sum of the infinite series. [Because $|r| \geq 1$, the values of r^n get closer to 0, so $(1-r^n)$ approaches 1. This relationship also shows why the series diverges if $|r| \geq 1$.]

[Ask] "What if the series is not arithmetic or geometric? Are there other kinds of series?" Encourage creativity in students' answers. Two common series that are neither arithmetic nor geometric are the *harmonic series* $1 + \frac{1}{2} + \frac{1}{3} + \frac{1}{4} + \cdots$ and the *alternating harmonic series,* $1 - \frac{1}{2} + \frac{1}{3} - \frac{1}{4} + \cdots$. **[Ask]** "Do you think these series converge?" [The harmonic series does not converge, but the alternating harmonic series does.] **[Link]** Calculus provides tools for analyzing the convergence of such series.

▶ ***Solution***

To solve this problem, you must find u_{31}. The information in the problem tells you that r is $(1 + 0.25)$, or 1.25, and when n equals 30, S_n equals 151,677. Substitute these values into the formula for S_n and solve for the unknown value, u_1.

$$\frac{u_1(1-1.25^{30})}{1-1.25} = 151677$$

$$u_1 = 151677 \cdot \frac{1-1.25}{1-1.25^{30}}$$

$$u_1 \approx 47$$

Now you can write an explicit formula for the terms of the geometric sequence, $u_n = 47(1.25)^{n-1}$. Substitute 31 for n to find that on the 31st day, the caterpillarsaurus will consume 37,966 leaves.

The explicit formula for the sum of a geometric series can be written in several ways, but they are all equivalent. You probably found these two ways during the investigation:

Partial Sum of a Geometric Series

A partial sum of a geometric series is given by the explicit formula

$$S_n = \left(\frac{u_1}{1-r}\right) - \left(\frac{u_1}{1-r}\right)r^n \quad \text{or} \quad S_n = \frac{u_1(1-r^n)}{1-r}$$

where n is the number of terms, u_1 is the first term, and r is the common ratio ($r \neq 1$).

EXERCISES

Practice Your Skills

1. For each partial sum equation, identify the first term, the ratio, and the number of terms.

a. $\frac{12}{1-0.4} - \frac{12}{1-0.4}0.4^8 \approx 19.9869$ $u_1 = 12, r = 0.4, n = 8$

b. $\frac{75(1-1.2^{15})}{1-1.2} \approx 5402.633$ $u_1 = 75, r = 1.2, n = 15$

c. $\frac{40 - 0.46117}{1-0.8} \approx 197.69$ $u_1 = 40, r = 0.8, n = 20$

d. $-40 + 40(2.5)^6 = 9725.625$ $u_1 = 60, r = 2.5, n = 6$

2. Consider the geometric sequence

256, 192, 144, 108, . . .

a. What is the eighth term? $u_8 = 34.171875$

b. Which term is the first one smaller than 20? u_{10}

c. Find u_7. $u_7 = 45.5625$

d. Find S_7. $S_7 = 887.3125$

3. Find each partial sum of this sequence.

$u_1 = 40$

$u_n = 0.6u_{n-1}$ where $n \geq 2$

a. S_5 $S_5 = 92.224$

b. S_{15} $S_{15} \approx 99.952$

c. S_{25} $S_{25} \approx 99.999$

Assessing Progress

Check students' understanding of series, partial sums, translations of graphs, and the formula for the sum of an infinite geometric series.

Closing the Lesson

The nth partial sum of the geometric series $\sum u_1r^n$ is given by the formula $S_n = S - Sr^n = \frac{u_1(1-r^n)}{1-r}$, where the formula $S = \frac{u_1}{1-r}$ gives the sum of the infinite geometric series. The partial sum can be calculated even if the series diverges, but the partial sums approach S (that is, the series converges) only if $|r| < 1$.

4. Identify the first term and the common ratio or common difference of each series. Then find the partial sum.

a. $3.2 + 4.25 + 5.3 + 6.35 + 7.4$
$u_1 = 3.2, d = 1.05, S_5 = 26.5$

b. $3.2 + 4.8 + 7.2 + \cdots + 36.45$
$u_1 = 3.2, r = 1.5, S_7 = 102.95$

c. $\sum_{n=1}^{27} (3.2 + 2.5n)$
$u_1 = 5.7, d = 2.5, S_{27} = 1031.4$

d. $\sum_{n=1}^{10} 3.2(4)^{n-1}$
$u_1 = 3.2, r = 4, S_{10} = 1118480$

Reason and Apply

5. Find the missing value in each set of numbers.

a. $u_1 = 3, r = 2, S_{10} = \underline{?}$ 3069

b. $u_1 = 4, r = 0.6, S_{\underline{?}} \approx 9.999868378$ 22

c. $u_1 = \underline{?}, r = 1.4, S_{15} \approx 1081.976669$
2.8

d. $u_1 = 5.5, r = \underline{?}, S_{18} \approx 66.30642497$
0.95

6. Find the nearest integer value for n if $\frac{3.2(1 - 0.8^n)}{1 - 0.8}$ is approximately 15. $n = 12$

7. Consider the sequence $u_1 = 8$ and $u_n = 0.5u_{n-1}$ where $n \geq 2$. Find

a. $\sum_{n=1}^{10} u_n$

b. $\sum_{n=1}^{20} u_n$

c. $\sum_{n=1}^{30} u_n$

d. Explain what is happening to these partial sums as you add more terms.

8. Suppose you begin a job with an annual salary of \$17,500. Each year, you can expect a 4.2% raise.

a. What is your salary in the tenth year after you start the job? \$25,342.39

b. What is the total amount you earn in ten years? \$212,065.89

c. How long must you work at this job before your total earnings exceed \$1 million? 29 yr 271 days, or about 30 yr

9. An Indian folktale, recounted by Arab historian and geographer Ahmad al-Yaqubi in the 9th century, begins, "It is related by the wise men of India that when Husiya, the daughter of Balhait, was queen . . . ," and goes on to tell how the game of chess was invented. The queen was so delighted with the game that she told the inventor, "Ask what you will." The inventor asked for one grain of wheat on the first square of the chessboard, two grains on the second, four grains on the third, and so on, so that each square contained twice the number of grains as on the square before. (There are 64 squares on a chessboard.)

a. How many grains are needed

i. For the 8th square? 128

ii. For the 64th square?

iii. For the first row? 255

iv. To fill the board?

b. In sigma notation, write the series you used to fill the board.

$\sum_{n=1}^{64} 2^{n-1}$

Sonfonisba Anguissola's (ca. 1531–1625) painting, titled *The Chess Game* (1555), includes a self-portrait of the Italian artist (far left).

BUILDING UNDERSTANDING

Do not assign Exercise 16 if your students did not study parametric equations.

ASSIGNING HOMEWORK

Essential	1–5
Performance assessment	6–14
Portfolio	9
Journal	7
Group	11, 12, 14
Review	15–18

Helping with the Exercises

Exercise 1d As needed, **[Ask]** "What is the value of r?" [2.5]

Exercise 2b Students can solve the inequality by guess-and-check or by home-screen recursion on a calculator. You might also encourage students to use logarithms, because they're solving for an exponent. **[Alert]** Students might follow the inequality $n\log(0.75) < \log\left(\frac{20}{256}\right)$ with the inequality $n < \frac{\log\left(\frac{20}{256}\right)}{\log(0.75)}$, leading to $n < 8.8620$, but the inequality is backward. Although it may not be apparent, they're dividing both sides of the inequality by a number less than 0 (that is, by $\log(0.75)$), so they must switch the direction of the inequality.

7a. $S_{10} = 15.984375$

7b. $S_{20} \approx 15.99998474$

7c. $S_{30} \approx 15.99999999$

7d. They continue to increase, but by a smaller amount each time.

9a. ii. more than 9×10^{18}

9a. iv. more than 1.8×10^{19}

10. The second choice is more profitable by approximately \$4.5 quadrillion.

Exercise 11 [Alert] Students may believe that the formula for the nth partial sum, like the formula for the sum of a series, applies only if the series is convergent. **[Ask]** "Is this series convergent?" [No; it is divergent.]

11a. 5, 15, 35, 75, 155, 315, 635

11b. No, they form a shifted geometric sequence.

11c. not possible

12a. neither

12b. $S_8 \approx 2.717857$

13a. $1 + 4 + 9 + 16 + 25 + 36 + 49 = 140$

13b. $9 + 16 + 25 + 36 + 49 = 135$

14a. 496 games

14b. 31 games

10. As a contest winner, you are given the choice of two prizes. The first choice awards \$1000 the first hour, \$2000 the second hour, \$3000 the third hour, and so on. For one entire year, you will be given \$1000 more each hour than you were given during the previous hour. The second choice awards 1¢ the first week, 2¢ the second week, 4¢ the third week, and so on. For one entire year, you will be given double the amount you received during the previous week. Which of the two prizes will be more profitable, and by how much?

11. Consider the geometric series

$5 + 10 + 20 + 40 + \cdots$

a. Find the first seven partial sums, $S_1, S_2, S_3, \ldots, S_7$.

b. Do the partial sums create a geometric sequence?

c. If u_1 is 5, find value(s) of r such that the partial sums form a geometric sequence.

12. Consider the series

$$\sum_{n=1}^{8} \frac{1}{n} = \frac{1}{1} + \frac{1}{2} + \frac{1}{3} + \frac{1}{4} + \cdots + \frac{1}{8}$$

a. Is this series arithmetic, geometric, or neither?

b. Find the sum of this series.

13. List terms to find

a. $\sum_{n=1}^{7} n^2$ **b.** $\sum_{n=3}^{7} n^2$

14. The 32 members of the Greeley High chess team are going to have a tournament. They need to decide whether to have a round-robin tournament or an elimination tournament. (Read the Recreation Connection.)

a. If the tournament is round-robin, how many games need to be scheduled?

b. If it is an elimination tournament, how many games need to be scheduled?

Recreation CONNECTION

In setting up tournaments, organizers have to decide the type of play. Most intramural sports programs are set up in "round-robin" format, in which every player or team plays every other player or team. Scheduling is different for odd and even numbers of teams, and it can be tricky if there is to be a minimum number of rounds. Another method is the elimination tournament, in which teams or players are paired and only the winners progress to the next round. For this format, scheduling difficulties arise when the initial number of teams is not a power of 2.

Review

1.5 **15.** What monthly payment is required to pay off an $80,000 mortgage at 8.9% interest in 30 years? $637.95

10.6 **16.** Develop the parametric equations of a hyperbola by following these steps.

a. Write the equation of a unit hyperbola in standard form using x and y. $x^2 - y^2 = 1$

b. Replace x with $\frac{1}{\cos t}$ and solve for y in terms of t. You should get a square root equation.

c. Add the terms under the radical by finding a common denominator.

d. Use the identity $(\sin t)^2 + (\cos t)^2 = 1$ to rewrite the numerator under the radical.

e. Use the identity $\tan t = \frac{\sin t}{\cos t}$ to rewrite the equation. $y = \tan t$

f. State the parametric equations for a unit hyperbola. (Look back at 16a to determine the parametric equation for x.) $x = \frac{1}{\cos t}$ and $y = \tan t$

g. Modify the parametric equations in 16f to incorporate horizontal and vertical translations (h and k) and horizontal and vertical scale factors (a and b).

11.2 **17.** The Magic Garden Seed Catalog advertises a bean with unlimited growth. It guarantees that with proper watering, the bean will grow 6 in. the first week and the height increase each subsequent week will be three-fourths of the previous week's height increase. "Pretty soon," the catalog claims, "Your beanstalk will touch the clouds!" Is this misleading advertising? Yes. The long-run height is only 24 in.

7.8 **18.** Write the polynomial equation of least degree that has integer coefficients and zeros $-3 + 2i$ and $\frac{2}{3}$. $f(x) = 3x^3 + 16x^2 + 27x - 26$

IMPROVING YOUR REASONING SKILLS

Planning for the Future

Pamela and Candice are identical 20-year-old twins with identical jobs and identical salaries, and they receive identical bonuses of $2000 yearly.

Pamela is immediately concerned with saving money for her retirement. She invests her $2000 bonus each year at an interest rate of 9% compounded annually. At age 30, when she receives her tenth bonus, she decides it is time to see the world, and from that point on she spends her annual bonus on a trip.

Candice is immediately concerned with enjoying her income while she is young. She spends her $2000 bonus every year until she reaches 30. On her 30th birthday, when she receives her tenth bonus, she starts to worry about what will happen when she retires, so she starts saving her bonus money at an interest rate of 9% compounded annually.

How much will each twin have in her retirement account when she is 30 years old? Compare the value of each investment account when Pamela and Candice are 65 years old.

16b. $y = \pm\sqrt{\left(\frac{1}{\cos t}\right)^2 - 1}$

16c. $y = \pm\sqrt{\frac{1 - (\cos t)^2}{(\cos t)^2}}$

16d. $y = \pm\sqrt{\frac{(\sin t)^2}{(\cos t)^2}}$

16g. $x = \frac{a}{\cos t} + h$ and $y = b\tan t + k$

Exercise 17 [Alert] Students might use the value $r = 0.75$ rather than $r = 1.75$. Refer them to Example C.

Exercise 18 As needed, remind students that for polynomial equations with real coefficients, nonreal roots come in conjugate pairs. Therefore the factored form of the equation is $P(x) = (x + 3 - 2i)(x + 3 + 2i)(3x - 2)$.

EXTENSIONS

A. Use Take Another Look activity 1, 2, or 3 on pages 653 and 654.

B. Have students research the convergence or divergence of the harmonic and alternating harmonic series.

C. Have students research power series for functions they've studied, such as rational functions. [One example is the function $y = \frac{1}{1-x} = 1 + x + x^2 + x^3 + \cdots = \sum_{n=0}^{\infty} x^n$, which is a geometric series.]

IMPROVING REASONING SKILLS

Students might use home-screen recursion or a formula for the partial sum of a geometric series to find that at age 30 Pamela has $35,120.59 (assuming she saves $2,000 at age 20 and again each year until age 30). Candice has $2,000 if she starts saving in her 30th year. Encourage students to use a formula rather than home-screen recursion to find Candice's amount at age 65. To generate the geometric series, they might realize that the $2,000 Candice deposited at age 64 will have grown to $2000(1 + 0.09)$, her deposit at age 63 will have increased to $2000(1 + 0.09)^2$, her previous deposit will have grown to $2000(1 + 0.09)^3$, and so on, down to her deposit at age 30, which will have grown to $2000(1 + 0.09)^{35}$. The sum of the 36 deposits, then, is $2000\left(\frac{1 - 1.09^{36}}{1 - 1.09}\right)$, or $472,249.45. Pamela's $35,120.59 grows exponentially without further deposits, achieving an amount at age 65 of $(35{,}120.59)(1.09)^{35}$, or approximately $716,950.60.

EXPLORATION

PLANNING

LESSON OUTLINE

One day:

20 min Activity

20 min Questions

5 min Closing

MATERIALS

- The Geometer's Sketchpad
- Sketchpad demonstration A Geometric Series, *optional*

TEACHING

Guiding the Activity

You can use the Sketchpad demonstration A Geometric Series in place of the activity.

Step 1 To create a horizontal segment, hold down the Shift key while drawing the segment.

For the second step in the procedure, **[Ask]** "Why do you dilate by a negative scale factor?" [so the image will be on the other side of point *B*] Make sure students dilate by $\frac{-6}{10}$ and not $\frac{6}{10}$.

Step 3 Students may be skeptical, but where they construct point *C* really doesn't matter. Encourage skepticism and experimentation.

EXPLORATION

Seeing the Sum of a Series

The sum of an infinite geometric sequence is sometimes hard to visualize. Some sums clearly converge, whereas other sums do not. In this exploration you will use The Geometer's Sketchpad to simulate the sum of an infinite geometric series.

Activity

A Geometric Series

Step 1 Start Sketchpad. In a new sketch, construct horizontal segment $\overline{AB}$. Follow the procedure note to extend this segment by 60%.

Procedure Note

1. Mark center *B*.
2. Dilate point *A* by $\frac{-6}{10}$ about center *B*. Label the new point *A'*. Construct $\overline{BA'}$.
3. Construct lines perpendicular to $\overline{AA'}$ through point *B* and *A'*. These will help you see how the series develops.

Step 2 Measure the distance between *A* and *B*.

Step 3 Construct point *C*, not on $\overline{AA'}$. Measure the distance between *C* and *B*.

Step 4 Select point *A*, then point *B*. Choose **Iterate** from the Transform menu. Map point *A* to point *B*, and point *B* to point *A'*. When you iterate, you'll get a table of values for *AB* and *CB*. What do the values for *AB* represent? If you move point *C* to coincide with point *A*, what do the values for *CB* represent?

Step 4 The values for *AB* represent the length of the segments constructed, which form a geometric sequence with common ratio 0.6. The values for *CB* represent the length of the whole segment at each iteration. These are the sum of the terms in the geometric sequence, or a geometric series with common ratio 0.6.

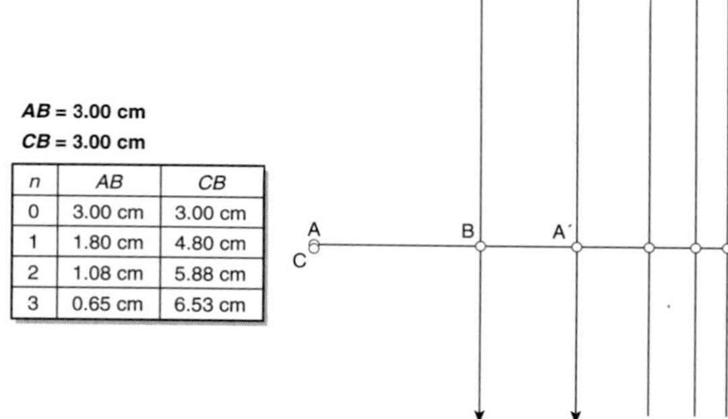

n	AB	CB
0	3.00 cm	3.00 cm
1	1.80 cm	4.80 cm
2	1.08 cm	5.88 cm
3	0.65 cm	6.53 cm

Step 5 Choose **Select All** from the Edit menu. Use the "+" key on your keyboard to add iterations to your sketch. Do approximately 25 iterations. Describe what happens as you add iterations.

Step 5 The growth of the segment is less and less with each new iteration, until it appears to stop growing—it converges. The table values for *AB* approach 0, whereas the values for *CB* approach the long-run value.

Step 4 Students may notice that the table of values does not include the last segment constructed by the iteration. This is because the iteration is based on the construction of $\overline{AB}$ and $\overline{AA'}$, but you measure only the distance *AB*. Hence, in the table of values, *n* represents the number of iterations, not the term number. For the example in the book, the first segment $(u_1 = 3)$ corresponds to iteration 0. If students prefer to think of the first segment as u_0, they can appropriately answer the questions using 0.6^n rather than 0.6^{n-1}.

LESSON OBJECTIVES

- Deepen understanding by visualizing a geometric series

Questions

1. What geometric series does your model represent? Write your answer in sigma notation.
2. According to the table values, what is the sum of your infinite series? Use the explicit formula $S = \frac{u_1}{1-r}$ to confirm this sum.
3. Vary the length of $\overline{AB}$ by dragging point B. What conclusions can you draw? Does the sum always converge for this common ratio?
4. Repeat the activity, but this time extend the segment by 120% (dilate point A by a factor of $\frac{-12}{10}$ about B). What happens with this series model? The figure continues to grow and does not converge.
5. Consider any geometric series in the form $\sum_{n=1}^{\infty} ar^{n-1}$. Explain how to model the series with Sketchpad, using the values a and r. Use a as the initial length of $\overline{AB}$ and $\frac{-r}{1}$ as the dilation factor.

This untitled painting (1965) by French artist Jean-Pierre Yvaral (b 1934) uses geometric forms and symmetry to give the illusion of movement.

▶ Helping with the Questions

Questions 1, 2 AB equals u_1.

1. $\sum_{n=1}^{\infty} AB(0.6)^{n-1}$. For the example shown in the book, $\sum_{n=1}^{\infty} 3(0.6)^{n-1}$.

2. For the example shown in the book, by the 16th iteration the table values suggest that $S = 7.5$. This is confirmed by the explicit formula, $S = \frac{3}{1-0.6} = 7.5$.

3. Varying the length of $\overline{AB}$ reduces or enlarges the entire figure, but the sum is still finite. Yes, the series is always convergent for $r = 0.6$.

Question 5 [Ask] "Can you tell whether the series converges or diverges just by looking at the formula for the sum?" [It will converge if $|r| < 1$.]

Assessing Progress

You can assess students' understanding of geometric series, the condition for convergence, and how partial sums approach the actual sum in the case of convergence.

Closing the Lesson

The value of r in the formula for the sum of a geometric series indicates whether the series converges, when $|r| < 1$, or diverges, when $|r| \geq 1$.

NCTM STANDARDS

CONTENT		PROCESS	
✓	Number		Problem Solving
✓	Algebra	✓	Reasoning
✓	Geometry	✓	Communication
✓	Measurement		Connections
	Data/Probability		Representation

PLANNING

LESSON OUTLINE

One day:

5 min Reviewing

25 min Exercises

15 min Student self-assessment

MATERIALS

- none

REVIEWING

[Ask] "Are any series both arithmetic and geometric?" As students discuss the question and you try to ensure that they defend their answers and communicate them to others, you can review the definitions of geometric and arithmetic series. Then ask whether the only such series, $\sum_{n=1}^{\infty} 0$, converges and review partial sums, the meaning of the convergence of an infinite geometric series, and the condition for convergence.

ASSIGNING HOMEWORK

Exercise 3 is a good group exercise.

▶ Helping with the Exercises

Exercise 3 As needed, suggest that students write out a few terms until they see a pattern. The recursive formula can be thought of as $u_n = 24\left(\frac{u_{n-1}}{2}\right)$ because each of the $\left(\frac{u_{n-1}}{2}\right)$ pairs produces 24 bugs.

CHAPTER 11 REVIEW

A **series** is a sum of terms of a sequence, defined recursively with the rule $S_1 = u_1$ and $S_n = S_{n-1} + u_n$ where $n \geq 2$. Series can also be defined explicitly. With an explicit formula, you can find any **partial sum** of a sequence without knowing the preceding term(s). Explicit formulas for **arithmetic series** are

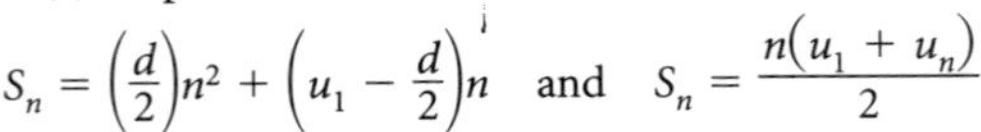

$$S_n = \left(\frac{d}{2}\right)n^2 + \left(u_1 - \frac{d}{2}\right)n \quad \text{and} \quad S_n = \frac{n(u_1 + u_n)}{2}$$

Explicit formulas for **geometric series** are

$$S_n = \left(\frac{u_1}{1-r}\right) - \left(\frac{u_1}{1-r}\right)r^n \quad \text{and} \quad S_n = \frac{u_1(1-r^n)}{1-r}$$

where $r \neq 1$. If a geometric series is **convergent,** then you can calculate the sum of infinitely many terms with the formula $S = \frac{u_1}{1-r}$.

EXERCISES

1. Consider the arithmetic sequence: 3, 7, 11, 15, . . .
   a. What is the 128th term? $u_{128} = 511$
   b. Which term has the value 159? $u_{40} = 159$
   c. Find u_{20}. $u_{20} = 79$
   d. Find S_{20}. $S_{20} = 820$
2. Consider the geometric sequence: 100, 84, 70.56, . . .
   a. Which term is the first one smaller than 20? $u_{11} \approx 17.490$
   b. Find the sum of all the terms that are greater than 20. $S_{10} \approx 515.687$
   c. Find the value of $\sum_{n=1}^{20} u_n$. $S_{20} \approx 605.881$
   d. What happens to S_n as n gets very large? The partial sum approaches 625.
3. Given plenty of food and space, a particular bug species will reproduce geometrically, with each pair hatching 24 young at age 5 days. (Assume that half the newborn bugs are male and half female, and are ready to reproduce in five days. Also assume each female bug can only reproduce once.) Initially, there are 12 bugs, half male and half female.
   a. How many bugs are born on the 5th day? On the 10th day? On the 15th day? On the 35th day?
   b. Write a recursive formula for the sequence in 3a.
   c. Write an explicit formula for the sequence in 3a. $u_n = 12^n$
   d. Find the total number of bugs after 60 days. approximately 1.2×10^{14}
4. Consider the series

   $125.3 + 118.5 + 111.7 + 104.9 + \cdots$

   a. Find S_{67}. -6639.7
   b. Write an expression for S_{67} using sigma notation.

A swarm of ladybugs

3a. 144; 1728; 20,736; 429,981,696

3b. $u_1 = 12$ and $u_n = 12\,u_{n-1}$ where $n \geq 2$ and where $n = \frac{d}{5} + 1$, where d is the number of the day

Exercise 4b Whether or not students actually use the formula $u_n = u_1 + d(n-1)$ (d is negative in this case), their reasoning will reflect the justification for the formula.

4b. $S_{67} = \sum_{n=1}^{67} (125.3 - 6.8(n-1))$

5. Emma's golf ball lies 12 ft from the last hole on the golf course. She putts and, unfortunately, the ball rolls to the other side of the hole, $\frac{2}{3}$ as far away as it was before. On her next putt, the same thing happens.

   a. If this pattern continues, how far will her ball travel in seven putts? approximately 56.49 ft
   b. How far will the ball travel in the long run? 60 ft

6. A flea jumps $\frac{1}{2}$ ft, then $\frac{1}{4}$ ft, then $\frac{1}{8}$ ft, and so on. It always jumps to the right.

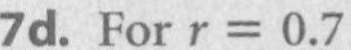

   a. Do the jump lengths form an arithmetic or geometric sequence? What is the common difference or common ratio?
   b. How long is the flea's eighth jump, and how far is the flea from its starting point? 0.0039 ft; 0.996 ft to the right
   c. How long is the flea's 20th jump? Where is it after 20 jumps?
   d. Write explicit formulas for jump length and the flea's location for any jump.
   e. To what point is the flea zooming in? The point 1 ft to the right from its starting point.

7. For 7a–c, use $u_1 = 4$. Round your answers to the nearest thousandth.
   a. For a geometric series with $r = 0.7$, find S_{10} and S_{40}. $S_{10} \approx 12.957$; $S_{40} \approx 13.333$
   b. For $r = 1.3$, find S_{10} and S_{40}. $S_{10} \approx 170.478$; $S_{40} \approx 481571.531$
   c. For $r = 1$, find S_{10} and S_{40}. $S_{10} = 40$; $S_{40} = 160$
   d. Graph the partial sums of the series in 7a–c.
   e. For which value of r (0.7, 1.3, or 1) do you have a convergent series? 0.7

8. Consider the series

   $0.8 + 0.08 + 0.008 + \cdots$

   a. Find S_{10}. 0.8888888888
   b. Find S_{15}. 0.888888888888888
   c. Express the sum of infinitely many terms as a ratio of integers. $\frac{8}{9}$

TAKE ANOTHER LOOK

1. You know how to write the equation of a continuous function that passes through the discrete points of a sequence, (n, u_n). For example, the function $y = 200(0.8)^{x-1}$ passes through the sequence of points representing the distance in inches that a ball falls on each bounce. Write a continuous function that passes through the points representing the *total* distance the ball has fallen on each bounce, (n, S_n). How can you use the function to find any partial sum or the sum of infinitely many terms? In general, what continuous function passes through the points of a geometric series? Through the points of an arithmetic series?

Exercise 5b This question concerns the total distance traveled, not the ultimate location of the ball. The direction traveled is ignored in the summation.

Exercise 6 [Alert] Students may be tempted to copy the work they did on Lesson 11.2, Exercise 10, not realizing that the fleas are acting differently here.

6a. geometric; $r = \frac{1}{2}$

6c. approximately 9.5×10^{-7} ft; approximately 1 ft to the right of its starting point

6d. $u_n = 0.5^n$; $S_n = \dfrac{0.5(1 - 0.5^n)}{1 - 0.5}$

7d. For $r = 0.7$

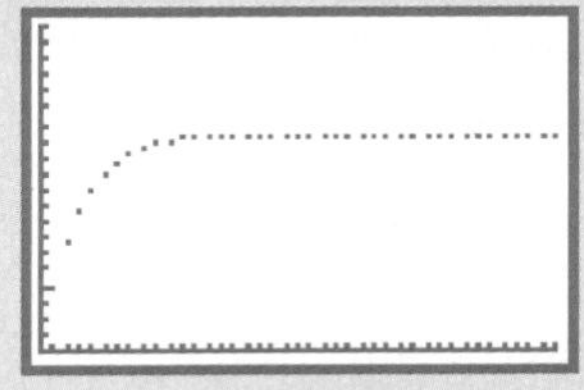

[0, 40, 1, 0, 20, 1]

For $r = 1.3$

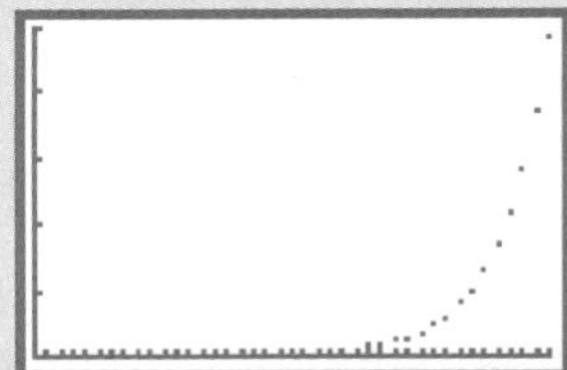

[0, 40, 1, 0, 500000, 100000]

For $r = 1$

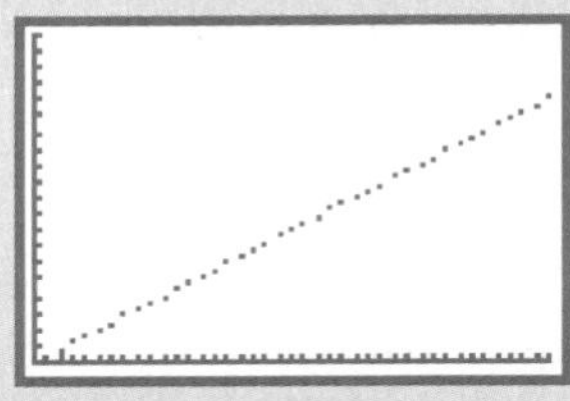

[0, 40, 1, 0, 200, 10]

Take Another Look

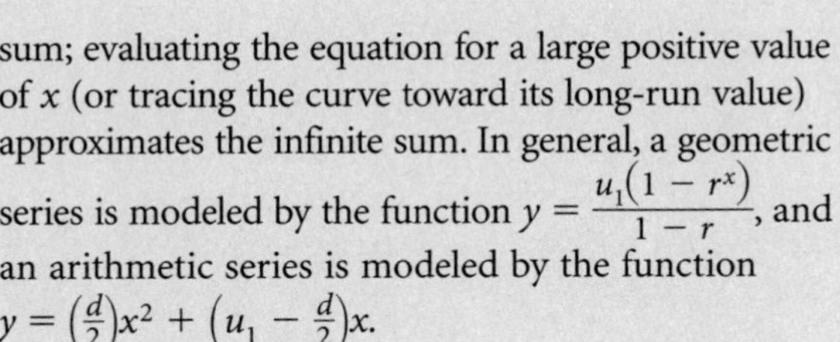

1. The total distance the ball has fallen is modeled by the function $y = \dfrac{200(1 - 0.8^x)}{1 - 0.8}$. A graph of this equation gives a smooth curve that fits the data points representing the partial sums. Evaluating the equation for any integer value of x gives a partial sum; evaluating the equation for a large positive value of x (or tracing the curve toward its long-run value) approximates the infinite sum. In general, a geometric series is modeled by the function $y = \dfrac{u_1(1 - r^x)}{1 - r}$, and an arithmetic series is modeled by the function $y = \left(\frac{d}{2}\right)x^2 + \left(u_1 - \frac{d}{2}\right)x$.

2. If $|r| < 1$, then r^n approaches 0 and $\frac{u_1(1-r^n)}{1-r}$ approaches $\frac{u_1(1-0)}{1-r}$, or $\frac{u_1}{1-r}$. This behavior supports the explicit formula for the infinite sum of a convergent geometric sequence, $S = \frac{u_1}{1-r}$. If $r > 1$, then r^n gets larger without bound, and $1 - r$ will be a fixed negative number; therefore $\frac{u_1(1-r^n)}{1-r}$ also gets larger without bound. If $r < -1$, the expression r^n alternates sign, getting farther from 0, so $\frac{u_1(1-r^n)}{1-r}$ also gets farther from 0.

3. If needed, remind students that they must divide the annual interest rate by 12 to find the monthly percentage rate. The student edition gives the answers to the two questions so students can check their equations.

$A_n = A_0(1+r)^n - P(1+r)^{n-1} - P(1+r)^{n-2} - P(1+r)^{n-3} - \cdots - P(1+r)^1 - P$

The part of the equation with the P's is a geometric series of n terms in reverse order with $u_1 = -P$ and constant ratio $(1 + r)$. By the formula, the partial sum equals $\frac{-P(1-(1+r)^n)}{1-(1+r)}$, or $\frac{P(1-(1+r)^n)}{r}$. The equation for A_n then becomes $A_n = A_0(1+r)^n + \frac{P(1-(1+r)^n)}{r}$. Substituting 0 for A_n and solving for P yields the equation $P = \frac{-A_0r(1+r)^n}{1-(1+2)^n}$, or $P = \frac{A_0r(1+r)^n}{(1+r)^n - 1}$.

ASSESSING

Items for your chapter test can come from students' questions or from any of the assessment resources.

2. The explicit formula for a partial sum of a geometric series is $S_n = \frac{u_1(1-r^n)}{1-r}$. To find the sum of an infinite geometric series, you can imagine substituting ∞ for n. Explain what happens to the expression $\frac{u_1(1-r^n)}{1-r}$ when you do this substitution.

3. Since Chapter 1, you have solved problems about monthly payments, such as auto loans and home mortgages. You've learned how to find the monthly payment, P, required to pay off an initial amount, A_0, over n months with a monthly percentage rate, r. With series, you can find an explicit formula to calculate P. The recursive rule $A_n = A_{n-1}(1 + r) - P$ creates a sequence of the unpaid balances after the nth payment. The expanded equations for the unpaid balances are

$$A_1 = A_0(1 + r) - P$$
$$A_2 = A_0(1 + r)^2 - P(1 + r) - P$$
$$A_3 = A_0(1 + r)^3 - P(1 + r)^2 - P(1 + r) - P$$

and so on. Find the expanded equation for the last unpaid balance, A_n. Look at this equation for a partial sum of a geometric series, and use the explicit formula, $S_n = \frac{u_1(1-r^n)}{1-r}$, to simplify the equation for A_n. Then, substitute 0 for A_n (because after the last payment, the loan balance should be zero) and solve for P. This gives you an explicit formula for P in terms of A_0, n, and r. Test your explicit formula by solving these problems.

a. What monthly payment is required for a 60-month auto loan of $11,000 at an annual interest rate of 4.9% compounded monthly? (Answer: $207.08)

b. What is the maximum home mortgage for which Tina Fetzer can qualify if she can only afford a monthly payment of $620? Assume the annual interest rate is fixed at 7.5%, compounded monthly, and that the loan term is 30 years. (Answer: $88,670.93)

Assessing What You've Learned

WRITE TEST ITEMS Write a few test questions that explore series. You may use sequences that are arithmetic, geometric, or perhaps neither. You may want to include problems that use sigma notation. Be sure to include detailed solution methods and answers.

GIVE A PRESENTATION By yourself or with a partner, do a presentation showing how to find the partial sum of an arithmetic or geometric series using both a recursive formula and an explicit formula. Discuss the advantages and disadvantages of each method. Are there series that can be summed using one method, but not the other?

UPDATE YOUR PORTFOLIO Pick one of the three investigations from this chapter to include in your portfolio. Explain in detail the methods that you explored, and how you derived a formula for the partial sum of an arithmetic series, the partial sum of a geometric series, or the sum of an infinite convergent geometric series.

FACILITATING SELF-ASSESSMENT

You might ask students to write test questions as you finish each lesson. Items from this chapter suitable for student portfolios include Lesson 11.1, Exercise 12; Lesson 11.2, Exercise 11; and Lesson 11.3, Exercise 9.

CHAPTER

12

Probability

Overview

In **Lesson 12.1,** students simulate random processes to compare experimental and theoretical probabilities. In the first **exploration,** students investigate geometric probability. Tree diagrams in **Lesson 12.2** help students break down dependent compound events into independent events and explore conditional probability. In the second **exploration,** students look at the relationship between theoretical probability and experimental probability. In **Lesson 12.3,** students break down events into mutually exclusive events with the aid of Venn diagrams. **Lesson 12.4** introduces random variables and expected value. **Lesson 12.5** applies the counting principle to permutations. The relationship between permutations and combinations is used to count combinations in **Lesson 12.6.** In **Lesson 12.7,** students relate combination numbers to Pascal's triangle and binomial expansion.

The Mathematics

Probability is one of the most difficult mathematical topics to teach because it involves counting discrete quantities, determining ratios, and understanding how events are related.

In mathematics, things that happen are called *events.* Most events are *compound events,* consisting of smaller events. The simplest events are called *outcomes, simple events,* or *cases.*

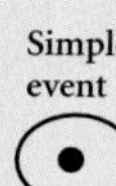

A probability function assigns to each event a number between 0 and 1. The event containing all possible outcomes has probability 1, and the event containing no outcomes has probability 0. The probability of each event is the sum of the probabilities of the outcomes comprising that event.

If the outcomes are all assigned the same probability, they're equally likely. The probability of an event is $\frac{\textit{number of equally likely outcomes in the event}}{\textit{total number of equally likely outcomes possible}}$. This number can be represented as a fraction, a decimal, or a percent.

Many outcomes involve arrangements, called *permutations,* of some objects or people. (Students often find it difficult to list the actual permutations systematically, but doing so is a good exercise in recursive thinking.) For purposes of probability, we want to count these permutations. The number of permutations of n objects chosen r at a time, ${}_nP_r$, can be found by applying the counting principle: $n(n-1)(n-2)\cdots(n-r+1)$. Note that ${}_nP_r$ refers to a number, not to the permutations themselves, so avoid reading it as "the permutation of n things chosen r at a time." ${}_nP_r$ can also be expressed using factorials, as $\frac{n!}{(n-r)!}$.

Often the outcomes to be counted for a probability are groupings, called *combinations.* The number of combinations of n objects chosen r at a time is represented in the book by ${}_nC_r$. (Again, the symbol refers to a number.) If the permutations (arrangements) are partitioned according to which grouping they contain, ${}_nC_r$ will equal $\frac{{}_nP_r}{r!}$, or $\frac{n!}{r!(n-r)!}$.

Textbooks tend to help students decide whether they're counting permutations or combinations by saying that "order matters" with permutations and "order doesn't matter" with combinations. Besides being mechanical rather than deepening understanding, these phrases can be misleading. For examples, see Reviewing and Exercise 4 in Chapter Review.

Another common situation requires calculating the probability of one event under the condition that another event has occurred. (Assume that the events contain some outcomes in common.) If the outcomes are all equally likely, then the probability of event A given event B, written $P(A \mid B)$, is the number of outcomes in both A and B divided by the number of outcomes in B. This gives the same result as $\frac{P(A \text{ and } B)}{P(B)}$.

If $P(A \mid B)$ equals $P(A)$ (with no assumption about B), the events A and B are independent. Tree diagrams are useful for analyzing non-independent, or dependent, events in terms of simpler independent events. Because conditional probability and independent events involve ratios of ratios, they are particularly difficult topics for many students.

A special case of dependent events is mutually exclusive events: If one event occurs, the other doesn't. Venn diagrams break down dependent events into smaller, mutually exclusive events. The Venn diagram represents three mutually exclusive events: the region inside A but outside B, the region inside B but outside A, and the region inside both.

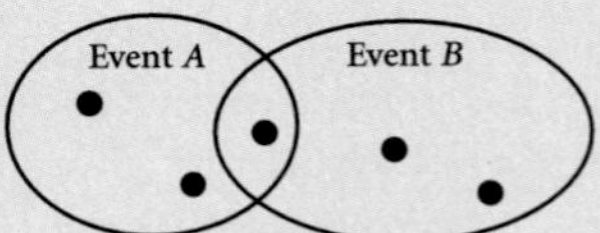

If each outcome is associated with a number, the function representing the association is called a *random variable.* The book shows how to find the average, or expected value, of a random variable assigned to outcomes that are discrete, like those in the diagram above. A standard approach is to multiply the number associated with each outcome by the probability of that outcome and then sum the products.

Using This Chapter

Lesson 12.7, Example C, is optional. This concept is not included in most advanced algebra standards.

Resources

Discovering Advanced Algebra Resources

Teaching and Worksheet Masters
Lessons 12.1, 12.3, 12.7
Exploration: Geometric Probability

Calculator Notes 1L, 2B, 2D, 12A–F

Fathom Demonstrations
Lessons 12.2, 12.4, 12.7
Exploration: The Law of Large Numbers

Assessment Resources A and B
Quiz 1 (Lessons 12.1–12.3)
Quiz 2 (Lessons 12.4, 12.5)
Quiz 3 (Lessons 12.6, 12.7)
Chapter 12 Test
Chapter 12 Constructive Assessment Options

More Practice Your Skills for Chapter 12

Condensed Lessons for Chapter 12

Other Resources

www.keypress.com/DAA

Materials

- coins (pennies, nickels, dimes, quarters)
- model cube, *optional*
- millimeter rulers
- dice (one die per person)
- sets of five distinct objects (one set per group)

Pacing Guide

	day 1	day 2	day 3	day 4	day 5	day 6	day 7	day 8	day 9	day 10
standard	12.1	exploration	12.2	12.2	12.3	quiz, 12.4	12.5	quiz, 12.6	12.7	quiz, review
enriched	12.1	exploration	12.2	exploration	12.3	quiz, 12.4	12.5	quiz, 12.6	12.7	quiz, review
block	12.1, exploration	12.2	exploration, 12.3	quiz, 12.4	12.5, 12.6	quiz, 12.7	quiz, review, TAL	TAL, assessment		

	day 11	day 12
standard	review	assessment
enriched	review, TAL	assessment

CHAPTER

12

Probability

American artist Carmen Lomas Garza (b 1948) created this color etching, *Lotería–Primera Tabla* (1972), which shows one game card in the traditional Mexican game *lotería*. As in bingo, a caller randomly selects one image that may appear on the game cards and players try to cover an entire row, column, diagonal, or all four corners of their game cards. The chance of winning many games, including *lotería,* can be calculated using probability.

OBJECTIVES

In this chapter you will

- learn about randomness and the definition of probability
- count numbers of possibilities to determine probabilities
- determine expected values of random variables
- discover how numbers of combinations relate to binomial probabilities

The artist uses recognizable images from Mexican culture in all her artwork so that Mexican Americans can appreciate it and others can learn from it. This is one piece in a series of pieces that display different game cards.

The game *lotería* is similar to bingo, but there are differences. For instance, the caller may give a riddle whose answer is the image. In *lotería* there is no free space, and covering the four corners makes a winning card. Students can find more information through www.keymath.com/DAA.

Ask students what they observe about the card. Encourage students to come up with questions about probability related to *lotería.* For example, **[Ask]** "If there are 50 images, what is the probability that the first image chosen will be on your card? The second image? What is the probability that the second image chosen will be in the same row or column as the first image?" Questions like this can help you feel out students' comfort level with probability.

CHAPTER 12 OBJECTIVES

- Learn about randomness
- See how experimental probabilities relate to theoretical probabilities
- Define and calculate geometric probability
- Use tree diagrams and conditional probabilities to break down compound events into independent events
- Use the multiplication rule for independent events
- Use Venn diagrams to break down compound events into mutually exclusive events
- Understand the additive rule for mutually exclusive events
- Calculate the expected value of a discrete random variable
- Apply the counting principle to count permutations (arrangements)
- Relate permutations to combinations in order to count combinations
- Relate combination numbers to Pascal's triangle, the binomial theorem, and binomial probabilities

LESSON

12.1

PLANNING

LESSON OUTLINE

One day:

10 min Investigation

15 min Examples

10 min Sharing

10 min Exercises

MATERIALS

- coins
- Flip a Coin (W), *optional*
- Calculator Notes 1L, 2D, 12A, 12A/APP

TEACHING

In this lesson students see the basic concepts of randomness and experimental and theoretical probability. They may have encountered these ideas in *Discovering Algebra.*

One Step

Pose this problem: "What is the probability that, when two dice are rolled, their sum will be 6?" Let students discuss the question in groups. Some may say $\frac{1}{11}$ because there are 11 possible sums, only one of which is 6. Others may say $\frac{3}{21}$ because there are 21 possible pairs of dice, three of which have a sum of 6. Others may say $\frac{5}{36}$ because there are 36 possible pairs of dice, five of which have a sum of 6. Ask groups to experiment with pairs of dice or calculator lists (refer them to Example B as needed). During Sharing, ask why the experimental results differ from all the conjectured results. Introduce the ideas of experimental and theoretical probability and how the latter is the long-run behavior of the former. Also lead the class in articulating definitions of probability in terms of equal likelihood so they can see why $\frac{5}{36}$ fits the definitions better than the other conjectures.

LESSON

12.1

Randomness and Probability

It's choice—not chance—that determines your destiny.

JEAN NIDETCH

"It isn't fair," complains Noah. "My car insurance rates are much higher than yours." Rita replies, "Well, Noah, that's because insurance companies know the chances are good that it will cost them less to insure me."

How much do you think Demolition Derby drivers pay for auto insurance?

Insurance companies can't know for sure what kind of driving record you will have. So they use the driving records for people of your age group, gender, and prior driving experience to determine your chances of an accident and, therefore, your insurance rates. This is just one example of how probability theory and the concept of randomness affect your life.

Career CONNECTION

An actuary uses mathematics to solve financial problems. Actuaries often work for insurance, consulting, and investment companies. They use probability, statistics, and risk theory to decide the cost of a company's employee benefit plan, the cost of a welfare plan, and how much funding an insurance company will need to pay for expected claims.

Probability theory was developed in the 17th century as a means of determining the fairness of games, and it is still used to make sure that casino customers lose more money than they win. Probability is also important in the study of sociological and natural phenomena.

At the heart of probability theory is randomness. Rolling a die, flipping a coin, drawing a card, and spinning a game-board spinner are examples of **random processes.** In a random process, no individual outcome is predictable, even though the long-range pattern of many individual outcomes often is predictable.

LESSON OBJECTIVES

- Learn about randomness
- Define experimental and theoretical probability
- Simulate experimental probability on a calculator
- Define and calculate geometric probability

NCTM STANDARDS

	CONTENT		PROCESS
	Number	✓	Problem Solving
✓	Algebra	✓	Reasoning
✓	Geometry	✓	Communication
	Measurement	✓	Connections
✓	Data/Probability	✓	Representation

History
CONNECTION

Many games are based on random outcomes, or chance. Paintings and excavated material from Egyptian tombs show that games using *astragali* were established by the time of the First Dynasty, around 3500 B.C.E. An *astragalus* is a small bone in the foot and was used in games resembling modern dice games. In the Ptolemaic dynasty (323–30 B.C.E.) games with 6-sided dice became common in Egypt. People in ancient Greece made icosahedral (20-sided) and other polyhedral dice. The Romans were such enthusiastic dice players that laws were passed forbidding gambling except in certain seasons.

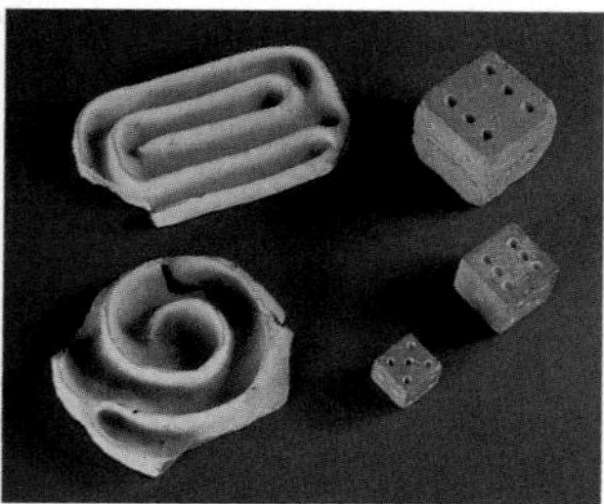

Playing dice, or *tesserae,* was a popular game during the Roman Empire (ca. 1st century B.C.E.–5th century C.E.). The mosaic on the left depicts three men playing *tesserae.* The photo on the right shows ancient Gallo-Roman counters and dice, dating from the second half of the 1st century B.C.E.

Investigation
Flip a Coin

You will need
- a coin

In this investigation you will explore the predictability of random outcomes. You will use a familiar random process, the flip of a coin.

Step 1 Imagine you are flipping a **fair** coin, one that is equally likely to land heads or tails. Without flipping a coin, record a random arrangement of ten H's and T's, as though you were flipping a coin ten times. Label this Sequence A.

Step 2 Now flip a coin ten times and record the results on a second line. Label this Sequence B.

Step 3 How is Sequence A different from the result of your coin flips? Make at least two observations.

Step 4 Find the longest string of consecutive H's or T's in Sequence A. Do the same for Sequence B. Then find the second-longest string. Record these lengths for each person in the class as tally marks in a table.

Longest string	Sequence A	Sequence B	2nd-longest string	Sequence A	Sequence B
1			1		
2			2		
3			3		
4			4		
5 or more			5 or more		

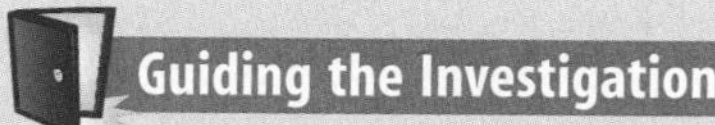

Guiding the Investigation

Students can use the Flip a Coin worksheet to record their outcomes in this investigation.

Step 1 When students invent a list of H's and T's, they are likely to think about what they have already listed in order to decide what to list next. They may try to avoid having many of the same letters in a row or having an unbalanced number of H's and T's.

Although the "random" numbers generated by calculators and computers are called *pseudorandom,* the numbers that students generate in this step are not pseudorandom. The term is generally reserved for numbers generated by computer methods, which, though deterministic, produce results that appear random. The methods embedded in calculators and computers do not take into account numbers generated before the last one.

Step 1 Sample Sequence A: H, T, T, H, T, T, H, H, T, H

Step 2 Sample Sequence B: T, T, T, T, T, H, T, T, T, H

Step 3 Sequence B has more uneven results, with more T's than H's. Sequence B has 5 T's in a row, whereas the most Sequence A has in a row is 2.

Step 4 Answers will vary.

▶ EXAMPLE A

[ESL] The singular of *dice* is *die.* You might discuss several meanings of the word *die.*

The numbers generated by the calculator are pseudorandom, but they serve the purpose.

Calculator Note 12A/App explains how to use Texas Instruments' application called Probability Simulation (available on the *Calculator Programs and Data* CD). Students can use the App as they follow the example.

[Ask] "Could you generate these numbers without using a calculator?" [yes, by rolling a pair of dice or using a random number table] "What advantages are there to using the calculator simulation?" [You can quickly simulate 300 rolls.]

You might refer to Calculator Note 2D for creating the histogram.

[Language] As needed, remind students that a *bin* is one bar on the histogram and that the *bin height* tells how many results fall within the bin. Here each bin represents a single digit, but in many histograms the bin contains numbers over an interval.

You might point out that when a probability is described as a decimal, the custom is to omit a leading 0, writing .5 instead of 0.5 for example, because all probabilities are less than 1.

[Ask] "Which probability, .12 or .138, is the actual probability?" [Neither; the theoretical probability is $\frac{5}{36}$. The value .138 is closer to this, which is to be expected because it's the result of more trials.]

Step 5 Answers will vary.

Step 6 Sample answer: It would include longer runs of H's or T's.

Step 5 Count the number of H's in each set. Record the results of the entire class in a table.

Step 6 If you were asked to write a new random sequence of H's and T's, how would it be different from what you recorded in Sequence A?

Number of H's	Sequence A	Sequence B
0		
1		
2		
3		
4		
5		
6		
7		
8		
9		
10		

You often use a random process to generate **random numbers.** Over the long run, each number is equally likely to occur, and there is no pattern in any sequence of numbers generated. [▶ See **Calculator Note 1L** to learn how to generate random numbers. ◀]

EXAMPLE A Use a calculator's random-number generator to find the probability of rolling a sum of 6 with a pair of dice.

▶ Solution

As you study this solution, follow along on your own calculator. Your results will be slightly different. [▶ To learn how to simulate rolling two dice, see **Calculator Note 12A.** ◀]

To find the probability of the event "the sum is 6," also written as *P*(sum is 6), simulate a large number of rolls of a pair of dice. First, create a list of 300 random integers from 1 to 6 to simulate 300 tosses of the first die. Store it in list L1. Store a second list of 300 outcomes in list L2. Add the two lists to get a list of 300 random sums of two dice. Store it in list L3.

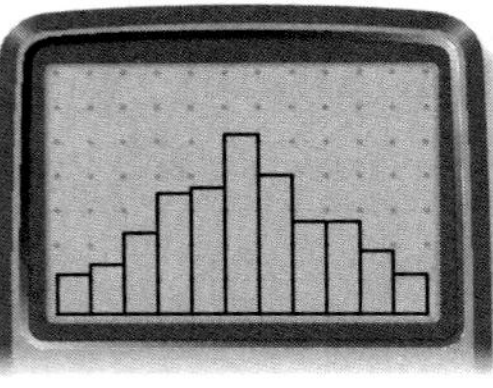

[2, 13, 1, 0, 70, 10]

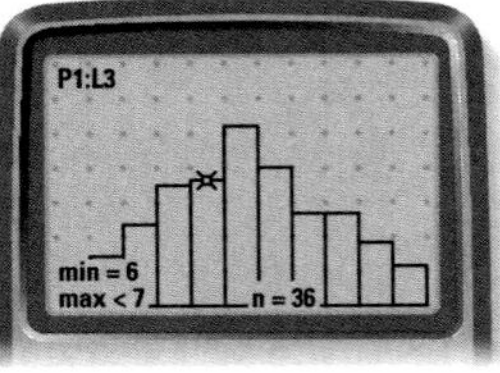

[2, 13, 1, 0, 70, 10]

Create a histogram of the 300 entries in the sum list. The calculator screens above show the number of each of the sums from 2 to 12. (Your lists and histogram will show different entries.) Tracing shows that the bin height of the "6" bin is 36. So, out of 300 simulated rolls, $P(\text{sum is } 6) = \frac{36}{300} = .12$.

Repeating the entire process five times gives slightly different results: $\frac{249}{1800} \approx .138$.

Rather than actually rolling a pair of dice 1800 times in Example A, you performed a **simulation,** representing the random process electronically. You can use dice, coins, spinners or electronic random-number generators to simulate trials and explore the probabilities of different **outcomes,** or results.

An **event** is a set of desired outcomes. You might recall that the probability of an event, such as "the sum of two dice is 6," must be a number between 0 and 1. The probability of an event that is certain to happen is 1. The probability of an impossible event is 0. In Example A, you found that $P(\text{sum is } 6)$ is approximately .14, or 14%.

Probabilities that are based on trials and observations like this are called **experimental probabilities.** A pattern often does not become clear until you observe a large number of trials. Find your own results for 300 or 1800 simulations of a sum of two dice. How do they compare with the outcomes in Example A?

Sometimes you can determine the **theoretical probability** of an event, without conducting an experiment. To find a theoretical probability, you count the number of ways a desired event can happen and compare this number to the total number of equally likely possible outcomes. Outcomes that are "equally likely" have the same chance of occurring. For example, you are equally likely to flip a head or a tail with a fair coin.

Experimental Probability

If $P(E)$ represents the probability of an event, then

$$P(E) = \frac{\textit{number of occurrences of an event}}{\textit{total number of trials}}$$

Theoretical Probability

If $P(E)$ represents the probability of an event, then

$$P(E) = \frac{\textit{number of different ways the event can occur}}{\textit{total number of equally likely outcomes possible}}$$

How can you calculate the theoretical probability of rolling a sum of 6 with two dice? You might at first think that there are 11 possible sums of the two dice (from 2 through 12), so $P(\text{sum is } 6) = \frac{1}{11}$. But the 11 sums are not equally likely. Imagine that one die is green and the other is white, for example. Then you can get a sum of 5 in four ways:

Green	White
1	4
2	3
3	2
4	1

But you get a sum of 12 only if you roll a 6 on both dice. Therefore, a sum of 5 is more likely than a sum of 12.

So, what equally likely outcomes can you use in this situation to find the theoretical probability?

EXAMPLE B | Find the theoretical probability of rolling a sum of 6 with a pair of dice.

▶ **Solution**

The possible equally likely outcomes, or sums, when you roll two dice are represented by the 36 grid points in this diagram. The point in the upper-left corner represents a roll of 1 on the first die and 6 on the second die, for a total of 7.

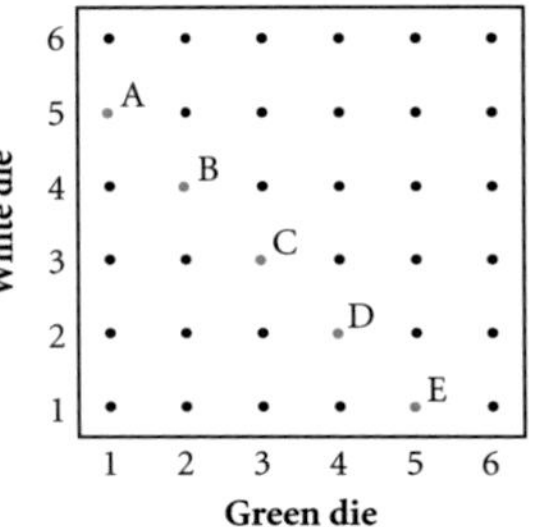

The five possible outcomes with a sum of 6 are labeled A–E in the diagram. Point D, for example, represents an outcome of 4 on the green die and 2 on the white die. What outcome does point A represent? 1 on green die and 5 on white die

The theoretical probability is the number of ways the event can occur, divided by the number of equally likely events possible. So, $P(\text{sum is } 6) = \frac{5}{36} \approx .1389$, or 13.89%.

Before moving on, compare the experimental and theoretical results of this event. Do you think the experimental probability of an event can vary? How about its theoretical probability? yes; no

When you roll dice, the outcomes are whole numbers. What if outcomes could be other kinds of numbers? In those cases, you can often use an area model to find probabilities.

EXAMPLE C | What is the probability that any two numbers you select at random between 0 and 6 have a sum that is less than or equal to 5?

▶ **Solution**

Because the two values are no longer limited to integers, counting would be impossible. The possible outcomes are represented by all points within a 6-by-6 square.

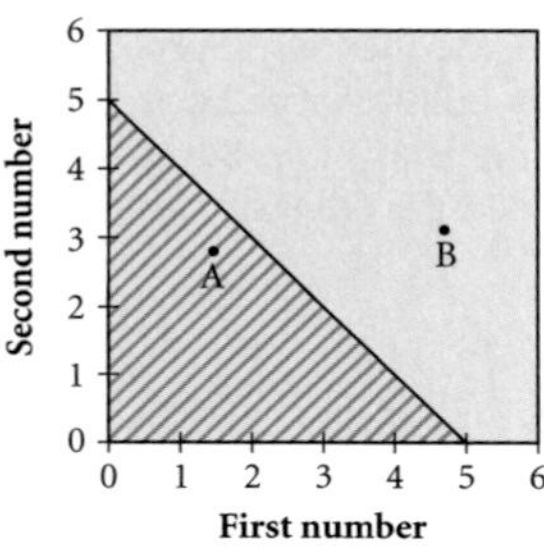

In the diagram, point A represents the outcome $1.47 + 2.8 = 4.27$, and point B represents $4.7 + 3.11 = 7.81$. The points in the triangular shaded region are all those with a sum less than or equal to 5. They satisfy the inequality $n_1 + n_2 \leq 5$, where n_1 is the first number and n_2 is the second number. The area of this triangle is $(0.5)(5)(5) = 12.5$. The area of all possible outcomes is $(6)(6) = 36$. The probability is therefore $\frac{12.5}{36} \approx .347$, or 34.7%.

▶ ***EXAMPLE B***

If students are having difficulty understanding the grid, suggest that they write out all the possible sums. For example: sum of 2: (1, 1); sums of 3: (1, 2), (2, 1); and so on.

[Ask] "What is your interpretation of the upper-rightmost grid point?" [6 on both dice] "Why do you need to consider both point (1, 5) and point (5, 1)?" [All grid points represent equally likely events; point (1, 5) represents 1 on the green die and 5 on the white die and is different from point (5, 1), which represents 5 on the green die and 1 on the white die.]

▶ ***EXAMPLE C***

[Ask] "Can you use inequalities to describe the region representing a sum less than or equal to 5?" [yes; $n_1 \geq 0$, $n_2 \geq 0$, $n_2 \leq 5 - n_1$]

SHARING IDEAS

As students present, **[Ask]** "Can you imagine someone thinking that your sequence was more random than the sequence generated randomly?" Also **[Ask]** "Why do we represent probabilities sometimes as fractions and sometimes as decimals?" [In discrete cases, it's easier to come up with fractions, and often they're more exact; decimals are usually easier to compare.]

Ask why the results of Examples A and B differ. Reiterate the difference between experimental and theoretical probabilities, and emphasize that the former approaches the latter as the number of trials increases. Ponder that this idea sounds familiar, and elicit students' memory of long-run values of sequences.

If students initially thought that the probability of a sum of 6 would be $\frac{1}{11}$ and now understand why it's not, ask whether they can recall other mathematical ideas that have surprised them and whether it's OK to be surprised by mathematics.

Ask students to critique the argument that the probability is $\frac{3}{21}$ because there are 21 outcomes—(1, 1), (1, 2), (1, 3), (1, 4), (1, 5), (1, 6), (2, 2), (2, 3), (2, 4), (2, 5), (2, 6), (3, 3), (3, 4), (3, 5), (3, 6), (4, 4), (4, 5), (4, 6), (5, 5), (5, 6), (6, 6)—three of which have a sum of 6. Students may or may not realize that these outcomes are not equally likely. Indeed, the doubles, such as (3, 3), are half as likely as the other pairings, each of which represents two different pairs. (For example, (2, 4) represents both itself and (4, 2).) If each double counted as only half a possibility here, making all outcomes equally likely, then the probability would be $\frac{2\frac{1}{2}}{18} = \frac{5}{36}$, as found in Example B.

Encourage students to pose "why" and "what if not" problems for the class to discuss. The questions on the facing page are some that might arise.

A probability that is found by calculating a ratio of lengths or areas is called a **geometric probability.**

Experimental probabilities can help you estimate a trend if you have enough cases. But obtaining enough data to observe what happens in the long run is not always feasible. Calculating theoretical probabilities can help you predict these trends. In the rest of this chapter, you'll explore different ways to calculate numbers of outcomes in order to find theoretical probabilities.

In skee ball the probability of getting different point values is based on the geometric area of the regions and their distance from the player.

EXERCISES

Practice Your Skills

1. Nina has observed that her coach does not coordinate the color of his socks to anything else that he wears. Guessing that the color is a random selection, she records these data during three weeks of observation:

   black, white, black, white, black, white, black, red, white, red, white, white, white, black, black

   a. What is the probability that he will wear black socks the next day? $\frac{6}{15} = .4$

   b. What is the probability that he will wear white socks the next day? $\frac{7}{15} \approx .467$

   c. What is the probability that he will wear red socks the next day? $\frac{2}{15} \approx .133$

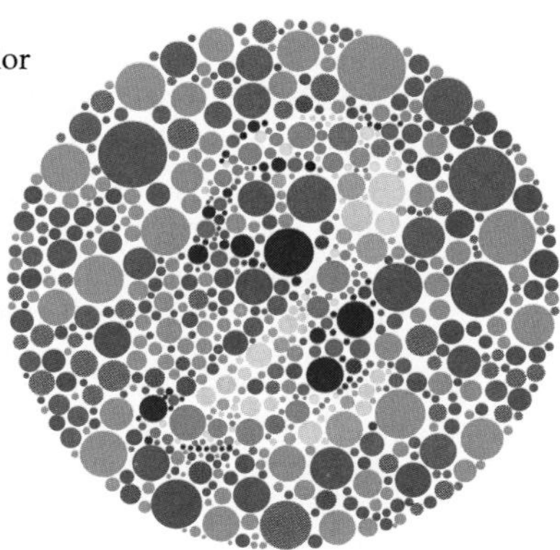

This is a visual test for color blindness, a condition that affects about 8% of men and 0.5% of women. A person with red-green color blindness (the most common type) will see the number 2 more clearly than the number 5 in this image. Dr. Shinobu Ishihara developed this test in 1917.

2. This table shows numbers of students in several categories at Ridgeway High. Find the probabilities described below. Express each answer to the nearest 0.001.

	Male	Female	Total
10th grade	263	249	512
11th grade	235	242	477
12th grade	228	207	435
Total	726	698	1424

   a. What is the probability that a randomly chosen student is female? $\frac{698}{1424} \approx .490$

   b. What is the probability that a randomly chosen student is an 11th grader? $\frac{477}{1424} \approx .335$

   c. What is the probability that a randomly chosen 12th grader is male? $\frac{228}{435} \approx .524$

   d. What is the probability that a randomly chosen male is a 10th grader? $\frac{263}{726} \approx .362$

Sharing Ideas (continued)

[Ask] "What if the two numbers in Example C did have to be integers? Would the result be the same?" [It would be $\frac{21}{49}$, or about .429] "Why are the results different?" [There are infinitely many ways to get a sum of 5 in Example C, but only finitely many ways if two positive integers are being added.]

[Ask] "What if the sum does not have to be less than or equal to 5 in Example C? What if it must be exactly 5?" [The probability is the area of a line, which is 0.] Students will revisit this in Chapter 13.

Assessing Progress

As students work on the investigation, you can assess their ability to follow directions, record data systematically, and work in groups.

Closing the Lesson

Repeat the main points of the lesson: Although no particular outcome of a **random process** is predictable, **probabilities** can be associated with **outcomes** to make overall predictions. Some of these probabilities are determined through **experiments,** such as **simulations;** others are determined **theoretically,** perhaps **geometrically.** Review formulas as needed.

BUILDING UNDERSTANDING

In the exercises students practice working with experimental and theoretical probabilities.

MATERIALS

- dice, *optional*
- model cube, *optional*

Helping with the Exercises

Exercise 2 [Alert] Students who don't easily think about parts of a sentence relative to one another may find it difficult to determine which cell of the table represents the total number of outcomes. You might **[Ask]** "What part of the questions in 2a and 2b refers to the total number of outcomes?" [a randomly chosen student from a total of 1424 students] "Is the same true for the questions in 2c and 2d?" [No; the total is no longer 1424.] You might challenge students to ask and answer a question about a randomly chosen female or 11th grader.

ASSIGNING HOMEWORK

Essential	1, 3–5, 10
Performance assessment	2, 6–9, 11–15
Portfolio	6
Journal	5
Group	6, 8, 9
Review	16–21

3a. $\frac{4}{14} \approx .286$

3b. $\frac{10}{14} \approx .714$

3c. $\frac{7.5}{14} \approx .536$

3d. $\frac{1.5}{14} \approx .107$

3e. $\frac{2}{14} \approx .143$

Exercise 4 4b and 4c preview the notion of complement in Lesson 12.3: *P*(event will not occur) = 1 − *P*(event will occur).

4a. $\frac{5}{30} \approx .167$

4b. $\frac{97.5}{100} = .975$

4c. $\frac{31}{36} \approx .861$

Exercise 6 As needed, warn students not to spend too much time making the guess in 6a. Students might prefer to use a die rather than a calculator for 6c.

6a. Answers will vary.

6b. Possible answer: Use the random integer command on the calculator to simulate rolling a die.

6c. Answers will vary.

6d. Answers will vary. Sum your answers from 6c and divide the answer by 10.

6e. Answers will vary. Long-run averages should tend toward 6 turns in order to roll a 6.

3. The graph of the shaded area at right shows all possible combinations of two numbers, *x* and *y*. Use the graph and basic area formulas to answer each question. Express each answer to the nearest 0.001.

a. What is the probability that *x* is between 0 and 2?

b. What is the probability that *y* is between 0 and 2?

c. What is the probability that *x* is greater than 3?

d. What is the probability that *y* is greater than 3?

e. What is the probability that $x + y$ is less than 2?

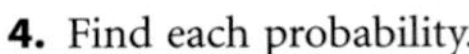

4. Find each probability.

a. Each day, your teacher randomly calls on 5 students in your class of 30. What is the probability you will be called on today?

b. If 2.5% of the items produced by a particular machine are defective, then what is the probability that a randomly selected item will *not* be defective?

c. What is the probability that the sum of two tossed dice will not be 6?

Reason and Apply

5. To prepare necklace-making kits, three camp counselors pull beads out of a box, one at a time. They discuss the probability that the next bead pulled out of the box will be red. Describe each probability as theoretical or experimental.

a. Claire said that $P(\text{red}) = \frac{1}{2}$, because 15 of the last 30 beads she pulled out were red. experimental

b. Sydney said that $P(\text{red}) = \frac{1}{2}$, because the box label says that 1000 of the 2000 beads are red. theoretical

c. Mavis says $P(\text{red}) = \frac{1}{3}$, because 200 of the 600 beads the three of them have pulled out so far have been red. experimental

6. Suppose you are playing a board game for which you need to roll a 6 on a die before you can start playing.

a. Predict the average number of rolls a player should expect to wait before starting to play.

b. Describe a simulation, using random numbers, that you could use to model this problem.

c. Do the simulation ten times and record the number of rolls you need to start playing in each game. (For example, the sequence of rolls 4, 3, 3, 1, 6 means you start playing on the fifth roll.)

d. Find the average number of rolls needed to start during these ten games.

e. Combine your results from 6d with those of three classmates, and approximate the average number of rolls a player should expect to wait.

This watercolor (ca. 1890) by an unknown Indian artist shows men playing dice.

7. Rank i–iii according to the method that will best produce a random integer from 0 to 9. Support your reasoning with complete statements.
   i. the number of heads when you drop nine pennies
   ii. the length, to the nearest inch, of a standard 9 in. pencil belonging to the next person you meet who has a pencil
   iii. the last digit of the page number closest to you after you open a book to a random page and spin it

8. Simulate rolling a fair die 100 times with your calculator's random-number generator. Display the results in a histogram to see the number of 1's, 2's, 3's, and so on. [▶ To learn how to display random numbers in a histogram, see **Calculator Note 12A.** ◀] Do the simulation 12 times.
   a. Make a table storing the results of each simulation. After each 100 rolls, calculate the experimental probability, so far, of rolling a 3.

Simulation number	1's	2's	3's	4's	5's	6's	Ratio of 3's	Cumulative ratio of 3's
1								$\frac{?}{100} = \underline{?}$
2								$\frac{?}{200} = \underline{?}$
3								$\frac{?}{300} = \underline{?}$

   b. What do you think the long-run experimental probability will be?
   c. Make a graph of the cumulative ratio of 3's versus the number of tosses. Plot the points (cumulative number of tosses, cumulative ratio of 3's). Then plot three more points as you extend the domain of the graph to 2400, 3600, and 4800 trials by adding the data from three classmates. Would it make any difference if you were considering 5's instead of 3's? Explain.
   d. What is $P(3)$ for this experiment?
   e. What do you think the theoretical probability, $P(3)$, should be? Explain.

9. Consider rolling a green die and a white die. The roll (1, 5) is different from (5, 1).
   a. How many different outcomes are possible for this two-die experiment?
   b. How many different outcomes are possible in which there is a 4 on the green die? Draw a diagram to show the location of these points. What is the probability of this event?
   c. How many different outcomes are possible in which there is a 2 or a 3 on the white die? What is the probability of this event?
   d. How many different outcomes are possible in which there is an even number on the green die and a 2 on the white die? What is the probability of this event?

10. Find the number of equally likely outcomes of each event described for a two-die roll. Then write the probability of each event.
   a. The dice sum to 9.
   b. The dice sum to 6.
   c. The dice have a difference of 1.
   d. The sum of the dice is 6, and their difference is 2.
   e. The sum of the dice is at most 5.

7. Answers will vary. Each of these procedures has shortcomings.

7. i. Middle numbers (3–7) are more common than getting only 1 or 2 or 8 or 9 heads in one trial of dropping pennies.

7. ii. Very few pencils will be at 0 or 1 in.; students throw away their pencils long before that.

7. iii. This is the best method, although books tend to open to pages that are used more than others.

8a. Answers will vary.

8b. The long-run experimental probability should show that $\frac{1}{6}$ of all rolls are a 3.

8c. Answers will vary. The points should level out to a straight line at $y = 0.1\overline{6}$. If you considered 5's instead of 3's, the data should level out to the same value.

8d. Answers will vary but should be close to $\frac{1}{6}$.

8e. $P(3) = \frac{1}{6} \approx .167$. There are six equally likely outcomes, and 3 is one of them, so the theoretical probability is $\frac{1}{6}$.

9a. 36

9b. 6; $\frac{1}{6} \approx .167$

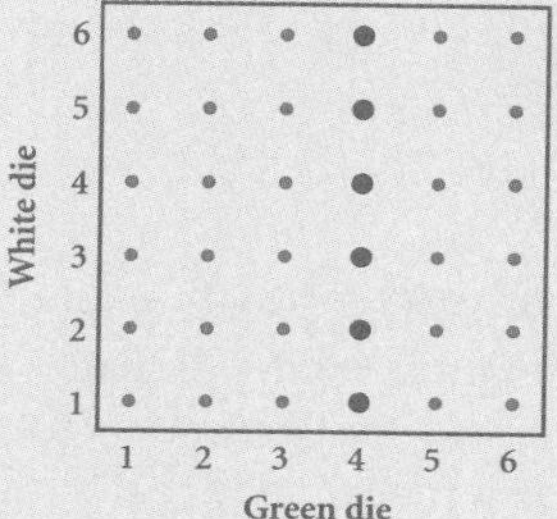

9c. 12; $\frac{12}{36} \approx .333$

9d. 3; $\frac{3}{36} \approx .083$

10a. 4; $\frac{4}{36} \approx .111$

10b. 5; $\frac{5}{36} \approx .139$

10c. 10; $\frac{10}{36} \approx .278$

10d. 2; $\frac{2}{36} \approx .056$

10e. 10; $\frac{10}{36} \approx .278$

11a. 144 square units

11b. 44 square units

11c. $\frac{44}{144}$

11d. $\frac{44}{144} \approx .306$

11e. $\frac{100}{144} \approx .694$

Exercise 11f The probability of hitting a line or a point is 0 because the area of a point or a line is 0. If students are uncomfortable with this, you can describe the probability as *infinitesimally small,* but make it clear that no real numbers other than 0 are that small. **[Link]** You might mention that calculus involves the study of infinitesimally small quantities.

11f. 0; 0

12a. $x + y \leq 6$

12b.

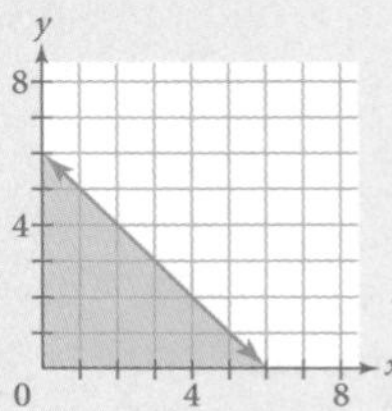

12c. $\frac{18}{64} \approx .281$

13a. 270

13b. 1380

13c. $\frac{270}{1380} \approx .196$

13d. $\frac{1110}{1380} \approx .804$

Exercise 14 [Alert] Visualization of the situation will be difficult for some students. You may want to display a model cube that is marked off with the dimensions 3 by 3 by 3 or have students build a 3-by-3-by-3 cube out of sugar cubes. You might suggest that students check that their answers to 14a–d sum to 1.

14a. $\frac{6}{27} \approx .222$

14b. $\frac{12}{27} \approx .444$

14c. $\frac{8}{27} \approx .296$

11. Consider the diagram at right.

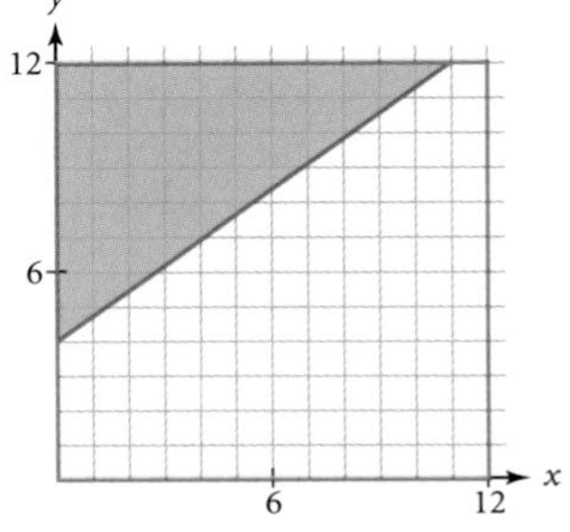

a. What is the total area of the square?

b. What is the area of the shaded region?

c. Suppose the horizontal and vertical coordinates are randomly chosen numbers between 0 and 12, inclusive. Over the long run, what ratio of these points will be in the shaded area?

d. What is the probability that any randomly chosen point within the square will be in the shaded area?

e. What is the probability that the randomly chosen point will *not* land in the shaded area?

f. What is the probability that any point randomly selected within the square will land on a specific point? On a specific line?

12. Suppose x and y are both randomly chosen numbers between 0 and 8. (The numbers are not necessarily integers.)

a. Write a symbolic statement describing the event that the sum of the two numbers is at most 6.

b. Draw a two-dimensional picture of all possible outcomes, and shade the region described in 12a.

c. Determine the probability of the event described in 12a.

13. Use the histogram at right for 13a–d.

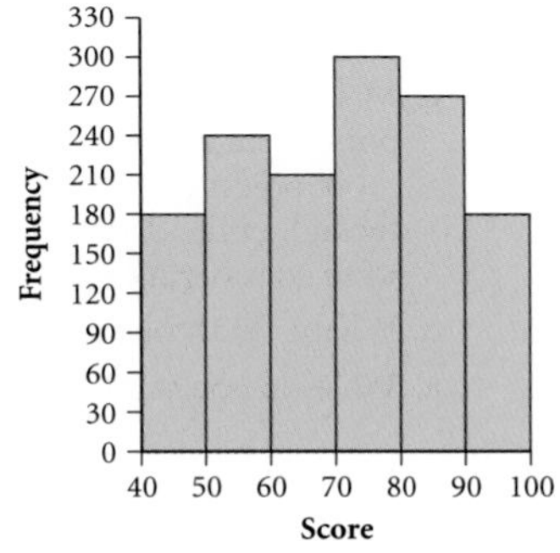

a. Approximate the frequency of scores between 80 and 90.

b. Approximate the sum of all the frequencies.

c. Find P(a score between 80 and 90).

d. Find P(a score that is not between 80 and 90).

14. A 6 in. cube painted on the outside is cut into 27 smaller congruent cubes. Find the probability that one of the smaller cubes, picked at random, will have the specified number of painted faces.

a. exactly one

b. exactly two

c. exactly three

d. no painted face

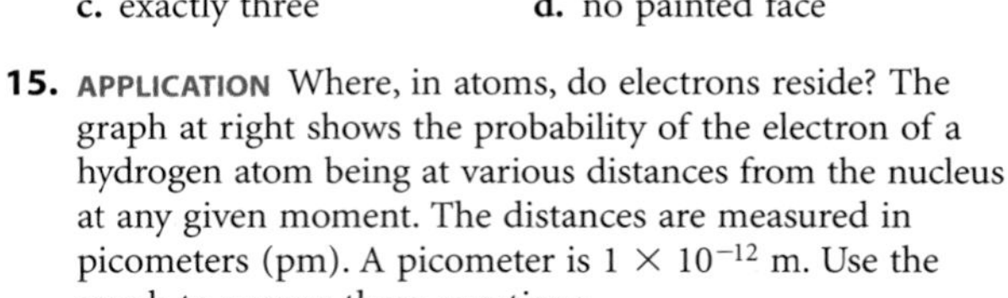

15. APPLICATION Where, in atoms, do electrons reside? The graph at right shows the probability of the electron of a hydrogen atom being at various distances from the nucleus at any given moment. The distances are measured in picometers (pm). A picometer is 1×10^{-12} m. Use the graph to answer these questions.

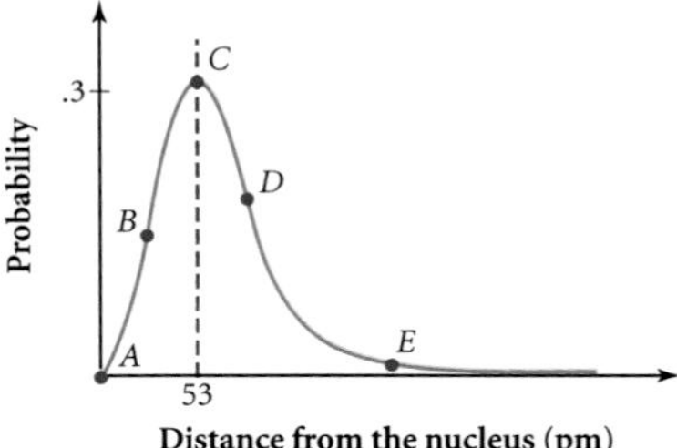

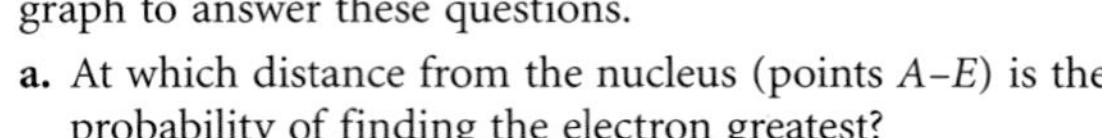

a. At which distance from the nucleus (points A–E) is the probability of finding the electron greatest?

b. At what distance is there zero probability of finding the electron?

c. As the distance from the nucleus increases, describe what happens to the probability of finding an electron.

14d. $\frac{1}{27} \approx .037$

15a. 53 pm, at point C

15b. 0 pm, at point A, the nucleus

15c. The probability starts at zero at the nucleus, increases and peaks at a distance of 53 pm, and then decreases quickly, then more slowly, but never reaches zero.

Science
CONNECTION

Electron position is important to scientists because it lays the foundation for understanding chemical changes at the atomic level and determining how likely it is that particular chemical changes will take place. In the early part of the 20th century, scientists thought that electrons orbit the nucleus of an atom much the way the planets orbit the Sun. Danish physicist Niels Bohr (1885–1962) theorized that the electron of a hydrogen atom always orbits at 53 pm from the nucleus. In the mid-1920s, Austrian physicist Erwin Schrödinger (1887–1961) first proposed using a probability model to describe the electron's position. Instead of a predefined orbit, Schrödinger's work led to the electron cloud model.

This electron cloud model shows possible locations of an electron in a hydrogen molecule. The density of points in a particular region indicates the probability that an electron will be located in that area.

Review

7.7 **16.** Expand $(x - y)^4$. $x^4 - 4x^3y + 6x^2y^2 - 4xy^3 + y^4$

5.7 **17.** Write $\log a - \log b + 2\log c$ as a single logarithmic expression. $\log\left(\frac{ac^2}{b}\right)$

5.7 **18.** Solve $\log 2 + \log x = 4$. $x = 5000$

19. Consider this system of inequalities:

$$\begin{cases} 3x + y \leq 15 \\ x + 6y \geq -12 \\ -5x + 4y \leq 26 \end{cases}$$

a. Graph the triangle defined by this system.

b. Give the coordinates of the vertices of the triangle in 19a.

c. Find the area of the triangle in 19a.

9.5 **20.** Describe the locus of points equidistant from the line $y = 6$ and the point (3, 0). Then write the polynomial equation in general form.

2.2 **21.** Consider these two sets of data.

i. {5, 23, 36, 48, 63} **ii.** {112, 115, 118, 119, 121}

a. Which set would you expect to have the larger standard deviation? Explain your reasoning.

b. Calculate the mean and the standard deviation of each set.

c. Predict how the mean and the standard deviation of each set will be affected if you multiply every data value by 10. Then do calculations to verify your answer. How do these measures compare to those you found in 21b?

d. Predict how the mean and the standard deviation of each set will be affected if you add 10 to every data value. Then do calculations to verify your answer. How do these measures compare to those you found in 21b?

MAKING THE CONNECTION

The atomic models proposed by Niels Bohr and Erwin Schrödinger contributed to the development of quantum theory, which uses probability models to describe the behavior of subatomic particles. The properties of these particles are not accurately described by classical physics, because they follow rules that have a negligible effect in the perceivable world. One such rule is the Heisenberg uncertainty principle, which states that it is impossible to simultaneously determine a subatomic particle's position and its velocity. Probability models describe the possible positions and velocities of the particle. Additionally, quantum theory treats particles both as waves and as matter. Among Schrödinger's contributions to quantum theory was his theory of wave mechanics, which uses the wavelike behavior of electrons to determine the particles' probable location in an atom.

19a.

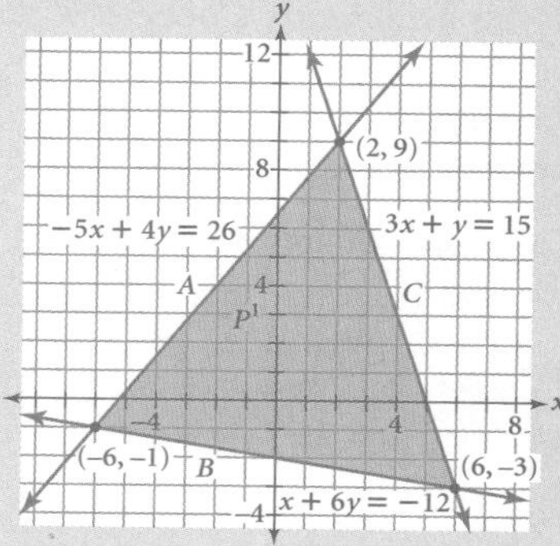

19b. (2, 9), (−6, −1), (6, −3)

Exercise 19c You might suggest that students inscribe the triangle in a square with horizontal and vertical sides.

19c. 68 units^2

20. a parabola with focus (3, 0) and directrix $y = 6$; $y = -\frac{1}{12}x^2 + \frac{1}{2}x + \frac{9}{4}$

21a. Set i should have a larger standard deviation because the values are more spread out.

21b. i. $\bar{x} = 35, s \approx 22.3$

21b. ii. $\bar{x} = 117, s \approx 3.5$

21c. The original values of $\bar{x}$ and s are multiplied by 10.

21c. i. $\bar{x} = 350, s \approx 223.5$

21c. ii. $\bar{x} = 1170, s \approx 35.4$

21d. The original values of $\bar{x}$ are increased by 10, and the original values of s are unchanged.

21d. i. $\bar{x} = 45, s \approx 22.3$

21d. ii. $\bar{x} = 127, s \approx 3.5$

EXTENSION

Have students design and carry out their own simulation of some random process.

EXPLORATION

PLANNING

LESSON OUTLINE

One day:

25 min Activity

5 min Sharing

15 min Questions

MATERIALS

- millimeter rulers
- pennies, nickels, dimes, quarters (one of each per group)
- 20 mm Grid Paper (W)
- 30 mm Grid Paper (W)
- 40 mm Grid Paper (W)
- 40 mm Grid Paper with 5 mm Borders (W)

TEACHING

In this exploration students work with an application of geometric probability. Hand out the four worksheets to each group.

[Language] *Buffon* is pronounced "bə-'fon."

Guiding the Activity

This activity is easiest if students work in groups of four and divide up the experimentation. If you are short on time, students can toss each coin 20–50 times.

Step 1 [Ask] "Do you think the way you toss your coin has an effect on how it lands?"

Step 2 [Ask] "Why are we concerned with just the center of the coin?" [The position of the center determines the area covered by the coin; we can consider each event as a single point.]

See page 904 for answers to Steps 2 and 3.

EXPLORATION 

Geometric Probability

French naturalist Georges Louis Leclerc, Comte de Buffon (1707–1788), posed one of the first geometric probability problems: If a coin is tossed randomly onto a floor of congruent tiles, what is the probability that it will land entirely within a tile, not touching any edges? The answer depends on the size of the coin and the size and shape of the tiles. You'll explore this problem through experimentation, then analyze your results.

Activity
The Coin Toss Problem

You will need

- a millimeter ruler
- a penny, a nickel, a dime, and a quarter
- grid paper in different sizes: 20 mm, 30 mm, 40 mm, and 40 mm with 5 mm borders

Work with your group to investigate Buffon's coin toss problem using different-size grids to simulate different-size tiles. For the first three grids, you can assume the borders around each tile have no thickness. Divide up the experimentation among your group members so that you can collect the data more quickly. Record your results in a table like the one below.

	Coin diameter (mm)	20 mm grid	30 mm grid	40 mm grid	40 mm grid with 5 mm borders
Penny	19	$\frac{1}{400} \approx .003$	$\frac{13}{100} = .13$	$\frac{28}{100} = .28$	$\frac{22}{100} = .22$
Nickel	21	$\frac{0}{100} = 0$	$\frac{9}{100} = .09$	$\frac{23}{100} = .23$	$\frac{18}{100} = .18$
Dime	18	$\frac{1}{100} = .01$	$\frac{16}{100} = .16$	$\frac{30}{100} = .3$	$\frac{24}{100} = .24$
Quarter	24	$\frac{0}{100} = 0$	$\frac{4}{100} = .04$	$\frac{16}{100} = .16$	$\frac{13}{100} = .13$

Step 1 Answers will vary. Approximate theoretical probabilities are given.

Step 1 Measure the diameter of your coin, and record your answer in millimeters in your table. Toss your coin 100 times, and count the number of times the coin lands entirely within a square, not touching any lines. Record your number of successes, and the experimental probability of success. Collect data from your group members to complete the table.

Step 2 Where must the center of a coin fall in order to have a successful outcome? What is the area of this region for each combination of coin and grid paper? You may choose to explore this problem using The Geometer's Sketchpad or other geometry software.

Step 3 Use your answers from Step 2 to calculate the theoretical probability of success for each coin and grid-paper combination. How do these theoretical probabilities compare to your experimental probabilities? If they are significantly different, explain why.

LESSON OBJECTIVE

- Explore one example of geometric probability

NCTM STANDARDS

CONTENT		PROCESS	
	Number		Problem Solving
✓	Algebra	✓	Reasoning
✓	Geometry	✓	Communication
✓	Measurement	✓	Connections
✓	Data/Probability	✓	Representation

Questions

1. Design a grid, different from any you used in the activity, that has a probability of success of .01, for a coin of your choice.
2. Determine a formula that will calculate the theoretical probability of success, given a coin with diameter d and a grid of squares with side length a and line thickness t.
3. What would be the theoretical probability of success if you tossed a coin with diameter 10 mm onto an infinite grid paper tiled with equilateral triangles with side length 40 mm, arranged as shown below?

IMPROVING YOUR REASONING SKILLS

Beating the Odds

Tracy and Trish have two boxes. One box contains 50 blue marbles; the other box contains 50 red marbles. Tracy will blindfold Trish and place the two boxes in front of her. Trish will pick one marble from one of the boxes. If Trish picks a red marble, she wins. If she picks a blue marble, Tracy wins. Before being blindfolded, Trish requests that she be allowed to distribute the marbles between the boxes in any way she likes. Tracy thinks about the request and says, "Sure, as long as all one hundred marbles are there, what difference could it make?" How should Trish distribute the marbles to have the greatest chance of winning? What would be the probability that Trish will win?

IMPROVING REASONING SKILLS

Trish should put 49 of the red marbles into the box with the blue marbles, leaving only 1 red marble in the other box. If the box with 99 marbles is chosen, the probability of choosing a red marble is $\frac{49}{99}$. If the box with 1 marble is chosen, the probability of choosing a red marble is 1. It is equally likely that either box will be chosen, so the overall probability of Trish winning is the average of $\frac{49}{99}$ and 1, or $.\overline{74}$.

Step 3 [Alert] Students may calculate the ratio of the area of the coin to the area of the square. Ask them to justify their reasoning, perhaps referring them back to Step 2. They may still have difficulty seeing that the ratio of the sum of the areas of the small squares (where the center might lie) to the total area is the same as the ratio of the area of one of the small squares to the area of one of the larger ones.

Helping with the Questions

1. Answers will vary. Sample answer: A coin with diameter 8 mm is tossed onto a grid of squares with side length 10 mm and line thickness 10 mm.

Question 2 Try to check each group's results in Step 3 of the activity before students work on this question.

2. $P(\text{success}) = \frac{(a-d)^2}{(a+t)^2}$

Question 3 Students might solve this using manual calculations or geometry software.

3. approximately .321

SHARING IDEAS

As students generalize, you might say that Buffon also posed a problem about dropping a needle rather than a coin. Wonder aloud how the results might be different.

Assessing Progress

You can observe students' ability to gather data systematically, their visualization skills, and their comfort with finding ratios of areas.

Closing the Lesson

Remind students that geometric probabilities are ratios of areas of geometric figures.

LESSON

12.2

PLANNING

LESSON OUTLINE

First day:

10 min Example A

15 min Investigation

5 min Sharing

5 min Example B

10 min Exercises

Second day:

10 min Example C

20 min Sharing

15 min Exercises

MATERIALS

- Fathom demonstration Independent Events, *optional*

TEACHING

Students learn to use tree diagrams to arrive at the multiplication rule for finding probabilities of independent events. If you choose to begin with the one-step investigation, you'll find it at the top of page 669.

▸ EXAMPLE A

[Language] In this situation *distributed equally* means that each type of toy is put into the same number of boxes.

[Ask] "Will Talya collect the toys in a particular order?" [No; there are two possibilities: Toy 1 then Toy 2, or Toy 2 then Toy 1.]

LESSON 12.2

Counting Outcomes and Tree Diagrams

In Lesson 12.1, you determined some theoretical probabilities by finding the ratio of the number of desired outcomes to the number of possible equally likely outcomes. In some cases it can be difficult to count the number of possible or desired outcomes. You can make this easier by organizing information and counting outcomes using a **tree diagram.**

EXAMPLE A A national advertisement says that every puffed-barley cereal box contains a toy and that the toys are distributed equally. Talya wants to collect a complete set of the different toys from cereal boxes.

a. If there are two different toys, what is the probability that she will find both of them in her first two boxes?

b. If there are three different toys, what is the probability that she will have them all after buying her first three boxes?

▸ Solution Draw tree diagrams to organize the possible outcomes.

a. In this tree diagram, the first branching represents the possibilities for the first box and the second branching represents the possibilities for the second box. Thus, the four paths from left to right represent all possibilities for two boxes and two toys. Path 2 and Path 3 contain both toys. If the advertisement is accurate about equal distribution of toys, then the paths are equally likely. So, the probability of getting both toys is $\frac{2}{4}$, or .5.

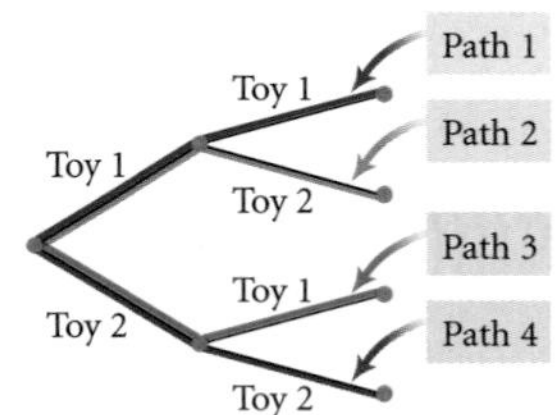

LESSON OBJECTIVES

- Use tree diagrams as an aid to counting possibilities for compound events
- Use the multiplication rule for independent events
- Explore conditional probability

NCTM STANDARDS

CONTENT		PROCESS	
	Number	✓	Problem Solving
✓	Algebra	✓	Reasoning
	Geometry	✓	Communication
	Measurement	✓	Connections
✓	Data/Probability	✓	Representation

b. This tree diagram shows all the toy possibilities for three boxes. There are 27 possible paths. You can determine this quickly by counting the number of branches on the far right. Six of the 27 paths contain all three toys, as shown. Because the paths are equally likely, the probability of having all three toys is $\frac{6}{27}$, or approximately .222.

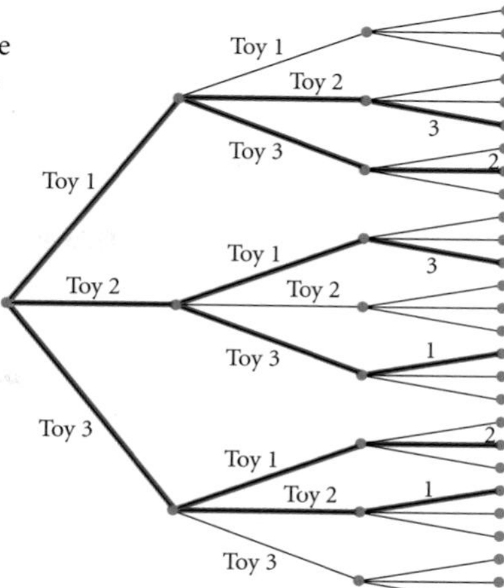

Tree diagrams can represent clearly the total number of different outcomes and can help you to identify those paths representing the desired outcomes. Each single branch of the tree represents a **simple event.** A path, or sequence of simple events, is a **compound event.** Tree diagrams can be helpful for organizing complicated situations.

Investigation
The Multiplication Rule

Step 1 On your paper, redraw the tree diagram for Example A, part a. This time, write the probability of each simple event on each branch. Then find the probability of each path.

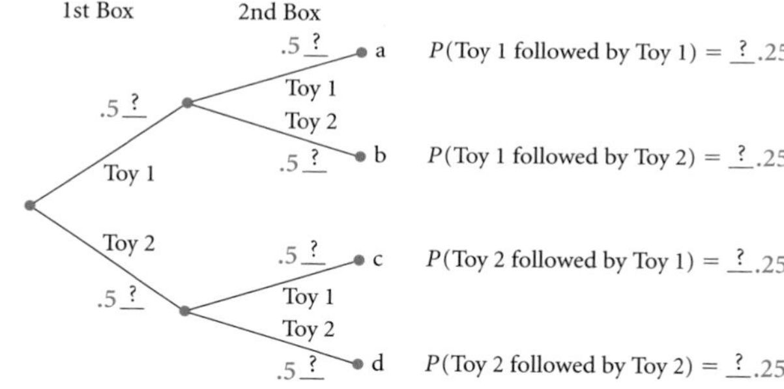

Step 2 Redraw the tree diagram for Example A, part b. Indicate the probability of each simple event, and also write the probability of each path. What is the sum of the probabilities of all possible paths? What is the sum of the probabilities of the highlighted paths?

One Step

Pose this problem: "Each week, one of the four officers of the math club is randomly chosen to write a problem for a club competition. For each of the first three weeks of the competition, Angela's name is drawn. Angela claims that this is not very likely, but Becca argues, 'It is just as likely as any other three names.' Your group needs to defend either Angela's or Becca's point of view. Be sure to use diagrams as you prepare your case." If you see no group using tree diagrams, show at least one group how to use them and ask them to present that approach during Sharing. At that time, introduce the idea of independent events and show how tree diagrams break down compound events into simple independent events, perhaps referring to conditional probabilities.

Guiding the Investigation

Step 1 Students can check their work against Example A.

See page 905 for answer to Step 2.

Step 3 [Alert] Students may need to draw or see the entire tree diagram.

Step 3a .25; .25; .25; .25

Step 3b not significantly

Step 3c $(.25)^4 \approx .004$; 256

Step 4 The probabilities of each branch in a path can be multiplied to find the probability of a particular path.

Step 5 $\frac{24}{256} \approx .094$

Step 3 Suppose the national advertisement in Example A listed four different toys distributed equally in a huge supply of boxes. Draw only as much of a tree diagram as you need to in order to answer these questions:

a. What would be *P*(Toy 2) in Talya's first box? Talya's second box? Third box? *P*(any particular toy in any particular box)?

b. In these situations, does the toy she finds in one box influence the probability of there being a particular toy in the next box?

c. One outcome that includes all four toys is Toy 3, followed by Toy 2, followed by Toy 4, followed by Toy 1. What is the probability of this outcome? How many different equally likely outcomes are there for four boxes of cereal?

Step 4 Write a statement explaining how to use the probabilities of a path's branches to find the probability of the path.

Step 5 What is *P*(obtaining the complete set in the first four boxes)?

In some cases, such as that for four toys and four boxes, a tree diagram with equally likely branches is a lot to draw. In some cases, as you'll see in Example B, a tree with branches of different probabilities may be practical.

► *EXAMPLE B*

Students may realize that they don't need to draw a tree diagram to solve this problem.

EXAMPLE B

Mr. Roark teaches three classes. Each class has 20 students. His first class has 12 sophomores, his second class has 8 sophomores, and his third class has 10 sophomores. If he randomly chooses one student from each class to participate in a competition, what is the probability that he will select three sophomores?

► *Solution*

You could consider drawing a tree with 20 branches representing the students in the first class. This would split into 20 branches for the second class, and each of these paths would split into 20 branches for the third class. This would be a tree with 8000 paths!

Instead, you can draw two branches for each stage of the selection process. One branch represents a choice of a sophomore (S) and one represents a choice of a nonsophomore (NS). This tree shows all eight possible outcomes. However, the outcomes are not equally likely. For the first class, the probability of choosing a sophomore is $\frac{12}{20} = .6$, and the probability of choosing a nonsophomore is $1 - .6 = .4$. Calculate the probabilities for the second and third classes, and represent them on a tree diagram, as shown.

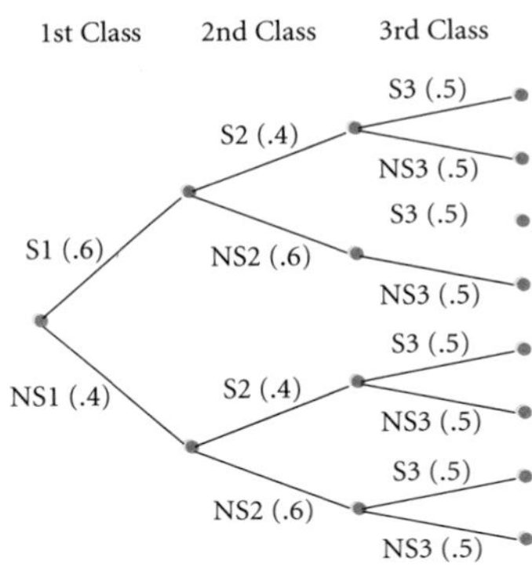

The uppermost path represents a sophomore being chosen from each class. In the investigation you learned to find the probability of a path by multiplying the probabilities of the branches. So, the probability of choosing three sophomores is (.6)(.4)(.5), or .12.

In Example B, the probability of choosing a sophomore in the second class is the same, regardless of whether a sophomore was chosen in the first class. These events are called **independent.** Events are independent when the occurrence of one has no influence on the occurrence of the other.

Probability of a Path (The Multiplication Rule for Independent Events)

If n_1, n_2, n_3, and so, on represent events along a path, then the probability that this sequence of events will occur can be found by multiplying the probabilities of the events.

$$P(n_1 \text{ and } n_2 \text{ and } n_3 \text{ and } \ldots) = P(n_1) \cdot P(n_2) \cdot P(n_3) \cdot \cdots$$

Are there events that aren't independent? If so, how do you calculate their theoretical probabilities? Mr. Roark's situation provides another example.

EXAMPLE C

Consider the situation from Example B again.

a. What is the probability that Mr. Roark will choose only one sophomore to participate in the competition?

b. Suppose you are a sophomore in Mr. Roark's second class, and the competition rules say that only one sophomore can be on the three-person team. What is the probability that you will be selected?

▶ *Solution*

Tree diagrams will help you determine these probabilities.

a. The three highlighted paths represent the different outcomes that include a single sophomore. The first path has probability (.6)(.6)(.5), or .18, the second path has probability (.4)(.4)(.5), or .08, and the last path has probability (.4)(.6)(.5), or .12. The probability of one of these paths occurring is .18 + .08 + .12, or .38. So, 38% of the 8000 total paths contain exactly one sophomore.

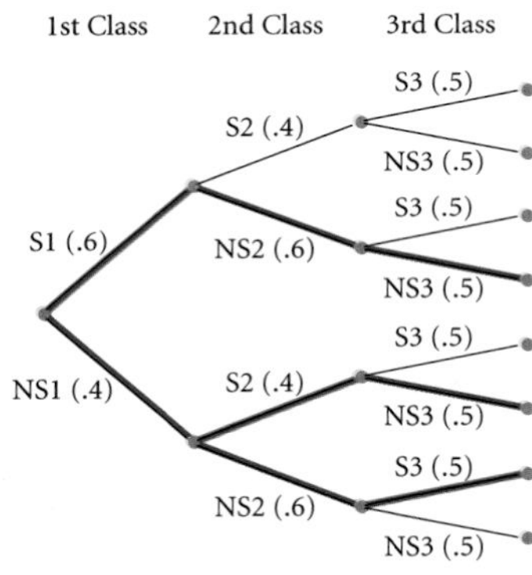

b. If only one sophomore is allowed, then the probability that you are selected depends on what happened in the first class. If a sophomore was selected earlier, then you cannot be chosen. So, $P(\text{you}) = 0$. You have a chance only

Sharing Ideas (continued)

[Alert] Conditional probability is a difficult concept for students who have trouble seeing relative relationships. You might **[Ask]** "What's $P(n_2 | n_1)$ if all the outcomes in events n_2 and n_1 are equally likely?" $\left[\dfrac{\textit{number of outcomes shared by } n_1 \textit{ and } n_2}{\textit{number of outcomes in } n_1}\right]$

▶ *EXAMPLE C*

[Ask] "What would be the probability of your being chosen if one sophomore was randomly selected from the 60 total students?"

SHARING IDEAS

As students present their work on the investigation, **[Ask]** "Are the events independent?" (Introduce the term *independent* as needed.) Theoretically each event has a slight effect on the probability of the next. For example, if the first box contains Toy 1, then the number of Toy 1's in the rest of the boxes decreases by 1. Because the number of boxes is so large and other boxes are being purchased, the effect is minimal.

Encourage students to pose problems of their own, such as those below, for the class to discuss. You might suggest the question opener "What's an example of . . . ." Keep supporting students' efforts even as you challenge them to do better.

[Ask] "What's an example of a simple event? A compound event?" Refer students to the examples and the investigation. In Example A, obtaining one toy is a simple event; obtaining any pair of toys is a compound event.

[Ask] "What's an example of conditional probability?" Example C focuses on tree diagrams for non-independent events. To illustrate a calculation with conditional probability, you might refer to Lesson 12.1, Exercise 2c or 2d; the probability in 2c can be expressed as "the probability that a student is male given that the student is a 12th grader." If conditional probability is a topic in your curriculum, challenge students to write a formula for it. $\left[P(n_2 | n_1) = \dfrac{P(n_1 \text{ and } n_2)}{P(n_1)}\right]$ Tree diagrams provide an informal approach to conditional probability. Each of the 2nd and 3rd probabilities along any path in Example C is an example of a conditional probability.

Independent and Dependent
The Fathom demonstration Independent Events will help students understand the statistical definitions of dependent events and independent events.

Assessing Progress
You can assess students' understanding of equal likelihood and of probability as a ratio of integers.

Closing the Lesson

The main idea of this lesson is that a **tree diagram** allows breaking down **compound events** into **simple events** that are **independent** so that the **multiplication rule** applies: The probability of the compound event is the product of the probabilities of the simple events. If the probability of one of the simple events depends on which path it's on, it's a **conditional probability.**

if a sophomore was not selected earlier. In that case, $P(\text{you}) = \frac{1}{20} = .05$, because there are 20 students in your class. There is a .4 probability that a nonsophomore will be chosen in the first class, and then a .05 probability that you will be chosen in the second class. So, your probability of being chosen for the competition is (.4)(.05), or .02. You might suggest that Mr. Roark use a more fair method of selecting the team!

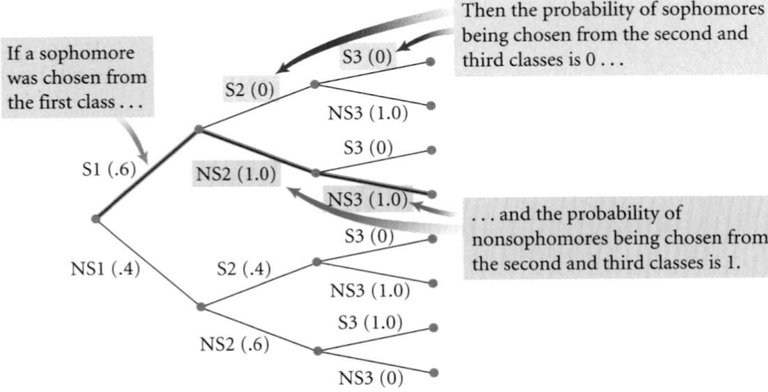

When the probability of an event depends on the occurrence of another event, the events are **dependent.** Independent and dependent events can be described using **conditional probability.** When events *A* and *B* are dependent, the probability of *A* occurring given that *B* occurred is different from the probability of *A* by itself. The probability of *A* given *B* is denoted with a vertical line:

$$P(A \mid B)$$

In Examples B and C, the probability of a sophomore in class 2 given a sophomore in class 1 would be written as $P(\text{S2} \mid \text{S1})$. The fact that events S1 and S2 were dependent in Example C means that $P(\text{S2} \mid \text{S1}) \neq P(\text{S2})$. In Example B, however, S1 and S2 were independent, so $P(\text{S2} \mid \text{S1}) = P(\text{S2})$.

You can use tree diagrams to break up dependent events into independent ones. In the tree diagram for Example C, part b, above, the probabilities of all branches other than the first branch are actually conditional probabilities. Events S1 and (S2 given S1) are independent, as are (S2 given S1) and (S3 given S1 and S2). So, you can use the multiplication rule to find the probabilities of the paths.

The Multiplication Rule (again)

If n_1, n_2, n_3, and so on, represent events along a path, then the probability that this sequence of events will occur can be found by multiplying the probabilities of the events.

$$P(n_1 \text{ and } n_2 \text{ and } n_3 \text{ and} \ldots) = P(n_1) \cdot P(n_2 \mid n_1) \cdot P(n_3 \mid (n_1 \text{ and } n_2)) \cdot \cdots$$

In the case of independent events, this statement is the same as the earlier statement of the multiplication rule, because $P(n_2 \mid n_1) = P(n_2)$, $P(n_3 \mid (n_1 \text{ and } n_2)) = P(n_3)$, and so on. In later lessons you'll see how to calculate the theoretical probabilities of other sorts of events.

EXERCISES

Practice Your Skills

1. Create a tree diagram showing the different outcomes if the cafeteria has three main entrée choices, two vegetable choices, and two dessert choices.

2. Find the probability of each path, a–d, in the tree diagram at right. What is the sum of the values of a, b, c, and d? $P(a) = .675$; $P(b) = .075$; $P(c) = .05$; $P(d) = .2$; 1

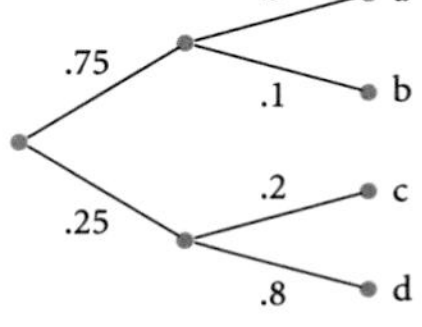

3. Find the probability of each path, a–g, in the tree diagram below. $P(a) = .7$; $P(b) = .3$; $P(c) = .18$; $P(d) = .4$; $P(e) = .8$; $P(f) = .2$; $P(g) = .08$

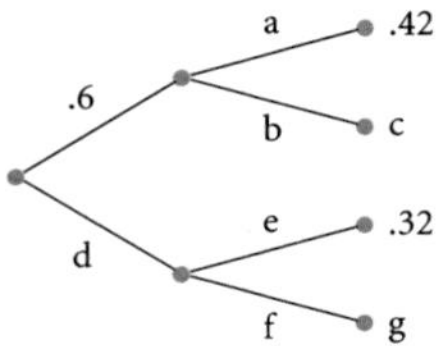

4. Three friends are auditioning for different parts in a comedy show. Each student has a 50% chance of success. Use the tree diagram at right to answer 4a–c.
   a. Find the probability that all three students will be successful. $\frac{1}{8} = .125$
   b. Find the probability that exactly two students will be successful. $\frac{3}{8} = .375$
   c. If you know that exactly two students have been successful, but do not know which pair, what is the probability that Celina was successful? $\frac{2}{3} \approx .667$

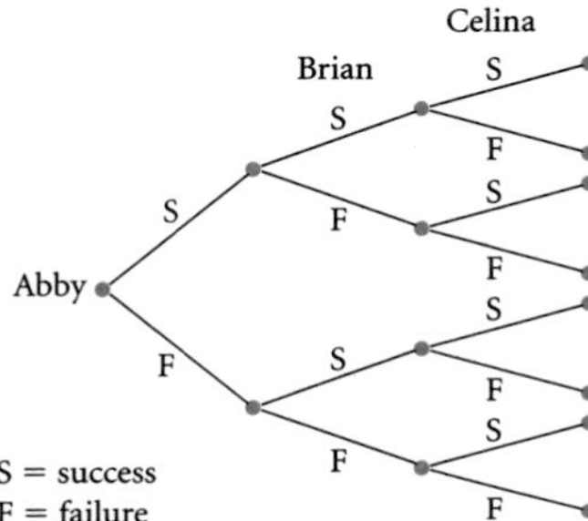

BUILDING UNDERSTANDING

The exercises provide students practice in working with tree diagrams and independent events. If you use two days for this lesson, consider assigning Exercises 1–10 on the first day and Exercises 11–20 on the second day.

ASSIGNING HOMEWORK

Essential	1–4, 11, 13
Performance assessment	5–10, 12
Portfolio	10
Journal	5, 14
Group	11, 15, 16
Review	17–20

Helping with the Exercises

Exercise 1 **[Ask]** "Can you find the number of outcomes without using a tree diagram?" [3(2)(2) = 12]

1.

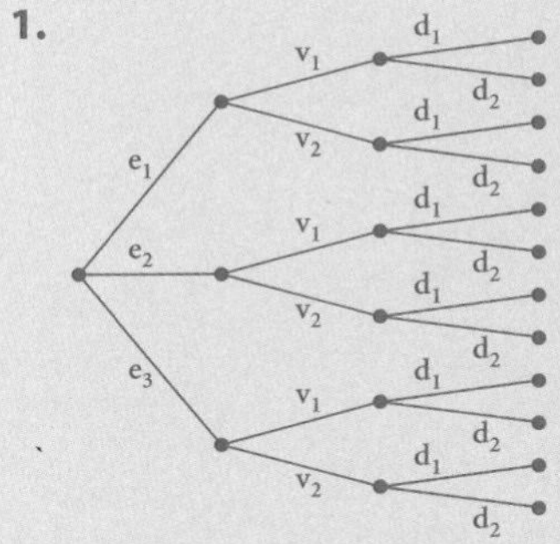

Exercise 4b You may want to discuss the importance of the word *exactly* here, contrasting it with the terms *at least* and *at most.*

Exercise 5 [Ask] "Are the two choices independent events?" [No; the probabilities at the second branch point depend on which branch was chosen first.]

5. For the first choice, the probability of choosing a sophomore is $\frac{14}{21}$, and the probability of choosing a junior is $\frac{7}{21}$. Once the first student is chosen, the class total is reduced by 1 and either the junior or sophomore portion is reduced by 1.

6a. $\frac{182}{420} \approx .433$; $\frac{98}{420} \approx .233$; $\frac{98}{420} \approx .233$; $\frac{42}{420} = .1$

6b. No, because the probabilities of the four paths are not all the same.

6c. $\frac{420}{420} = 1$

8a.

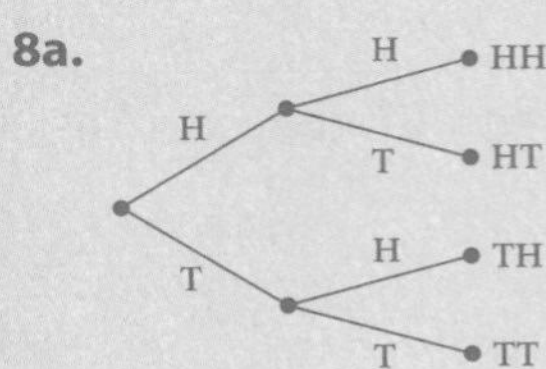

8b.

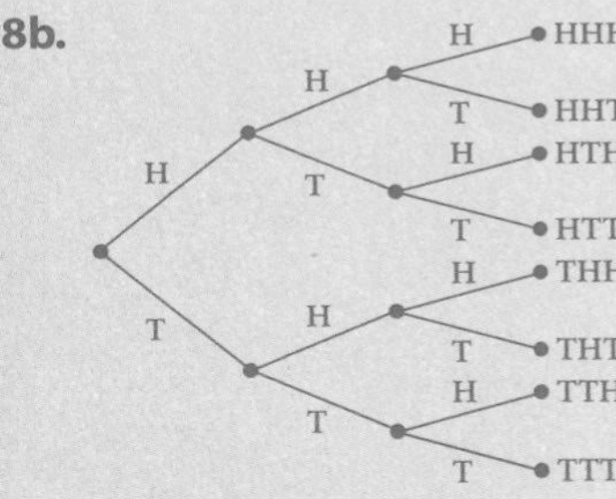

8c.

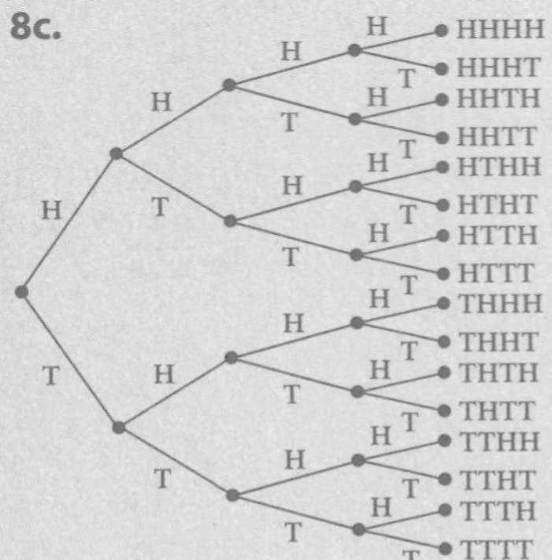

Reason and Apply

5. Explain the branch probabilities listed on this tree diagram, which models the outcomes of selecting two different students from a class of 7 juniors and 14 sophomores.

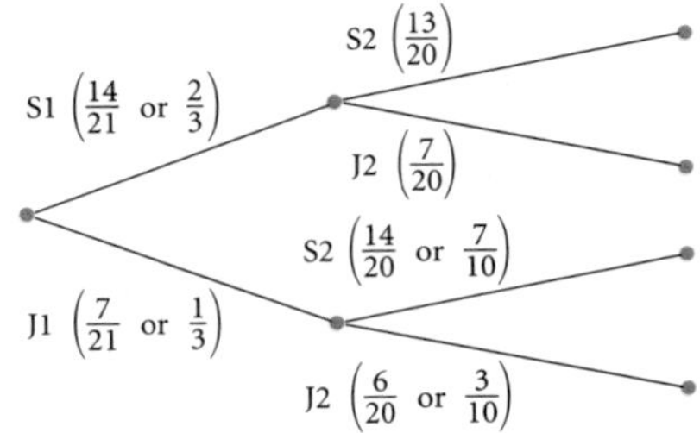

6. Use the diagram from Exercise 5 to answer each question.

a. Use the multiplication rule to find the probability of each path.

b. Are the paths equally likely? Explain.

c. What is the sum of the four answers in 6a?

7. A recipe calls for four ingredients: flour, baking powder, shortening, and milk (F, B, S, M). But there are no directions stating the order in which they should be combined. Chris has never followed a recipe like this before and has no idea which order is best, so he chooses the order at random.

a. How many different possible orders are there? 24

b. What is the probability that milk should be first? .25

c. What is the probability that the correct order includes flour first and shortening second? $\frac{2}{24} \approx .083$

d. What is the probability that the order is FBSM? $\frac{1}{24} \approx .042$

e. What is the probability that the order isn't FBSM? $\frac{23}{24} \approx .958$

f. What is the probability that flour and milk are next to each other? $\frac{12}{24} = .5$

8. Draw a tree diagram that pictures all possible equally likely outcomes if a coin is flipped as specified.

a. two times **b.** three times **c.** four times

9. How many different equally likely outcomes are possible if a coin is flipped as specified?

a. two times 4 **b.** three times 8 **c.** four times 16

d. five times 32 **e.** ten times 1024 **f.** n times 2^n

10. You are totally unprepared for a true-false quiz, so you decide to guess randomly at the answers. There are four questions. Find the probabilities described in 10a–e.

a. P(none correct) $\frac{1}{16} = .0625$

b. P(exactly one correct) $\frac{4}{16} = .25$

$\frac{6}{16} = .375$ **c.** P(exactly two correct)

d. P(exactly three correct) $\frac{4}{16} = .25$

e. P(all four correct) $\frac{1}{16} = .0625$

f. What should be the sum of the five probabilities in 10a–e? 1

g. If a passing grade means you get at least three correct answers, what is the probability that you passed the quiz? .3125

Exercises 9, 10 Help students feel comfortable using tree diagrams only to the extent they need to. Some students will want to use them extensively; others will be able to solve these problems without drawing any diagrams. In either case, make sure students understand what they are doing. Tree diagrams help students think through the situation rather than just working with an expression.

11. APPLICATION The ratios of the number of phones manufactured at three sites, M1, M2, and M3, are 20%, 35%, and 45%, respectively. The diagram at right shows some of the ratios of the numbers of defective (D) and good (G) phones manufactured at each site. The top branch indicates a .20 probability that a phone made by this manufacturer was manufactured at site M1. The ratio of these phones that are defective is .05. Therefore, .95 of these phones are good. The probability that a randomly selected phone is both from site M1 and defective is (.20)(.05), or .01.

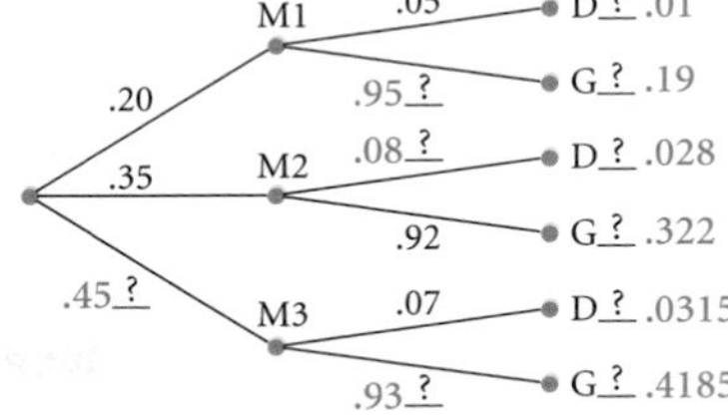

a. Copy the diagram and fill in the missing probabilities.

b. Find *P*(a phone from site M2 is defective).

c. Find *P*(a randomly chosen phone is defective).

d. Find *P*(a phone was manufactured at site M2 if you already know it is defective).

12. The Pistons and the Bulls are tied, and time has run out in the game. However, the Pistons have a player at the free throw line, and he has two shots to make. He generally makes 83% of the free throw shots he attempts. The shots are independent events, so each one has the same probability. Find these probabilities:

a. *P*(he misses both shots) .0289

b. *P*(he makes at least one of the shots) .9711

c. *P*(he makes both shots) .6889

d. *P*(the Pistons win the game) .9711

13. What is the probability that there are exactly two girls in a family with four children? Assume that girls and boys are equally likely. $\frac{6}{16} = .375$

14. The table at right gives numbers of students in several categories. Are the events "10th grade" and "Female" dependent or independent? Explain your reasoning.

	Male	Female	Total
10th grade	263	249	512
11th grade	243	234	477
12th grade	220	215	435
Total	726	698	1424

15. APPLICATION In 1963, the U.S. Postal Service introduced the ZIP code to help process mail more efficiently.

a. A ZIP code contains five digits, 0–9. How many possible ZIP codes are there?

b. In 1983, the U.S. Postal Service introduced ZIP + 4. The extra four digits at the end of the ZIP code help pinpoint the destination of a parcel with greater accuracy and efficiency. How many possible ZIP + 4 codes are there?

The Canadian postal service uses a six-character mailing code of the form

letter, digit, letter, digit, letter, digit

Postal workers sort through bulk mail.

c. How many possible Canadian postal codes are there if no restrictions are placed on the letters and digits?

d. In Canadian postal codes, the letters D, F, I, O, Q, and U are never used and the letters W and Z are not used as the first characters. How many possible postal codes are there now?

11b. .08

11c. .0695

11d. .4029

Exercise 12 Students might be concerned that if the player makes or misses the first shot, the probability of making the second will change. Point out that the problem states that each shot has the same probability. The probability is based on so many trials that the outcome of one trial won't affect it significantly.

Exercise 14 The table is similar to that of Lesson 12.1, Exercise 2, but the question posed is different. The exercise illustrates that independent events are not necessarily as separate as different dice or consecutive coin flips. **[Alert]** Many students find tables like this difficult to deal with because they require thinking about ratios.

14. Dependent; $P(\text{10th grade} \mid \text{female}) = \frac{249}{698} \approx .357$, but $P(\text{female}) = \frac{698}{1424} \approx .490$. So the probability of choosing a female from the 10th grade is less than the probability of choosing a female.

Exercise 15 Some students will need to use tree diagrams, or partial tree diagrams, more than other students. Be sensitive to different needs, but encourage students to be moving away from using tree diagrams if possible.

15a. 100,000

15b. 1,000,000,000

15c. 17,576,000

15d. 7,200,000

Exercise 16 If students assume that the possibility of no raised dots is not a character, the answer is 63.

16. 64

17a. $-3 + 2i$

17b. $2 + 24i$

17c. $\frac{18}{29} + \frac{16}{29}i$

18. $P(\text{orange}) \approx .152$; $P(\text{blue}) \approx .457$

Exercise 19 **[Alert]** Some students will have difficulty thinking about parts relative to the whole. For example, they might interpret the question in 19a as asking "What is the probability that a student is a junior and female?" A mechanical rule of thumb, such as "the whole is usually mentioned first," does not induce understanding and can be misleading. (The question might have been phrased "What is the probability that a student is female if she's a junior?") To focus students on the whole, **[Ask]** "What do you know for sure about the people being referred to?" [They're juniors.] You might also want to **[Ask]** "What do you need to know to answer these questions?" [row totals]

19a. $\frac{50}{110} \approx .455$

19b. $\frac{120}{230} \approx .522$

20. $8\sqrt{2}$

16. Braille is a form of writing for sight-impaired people. Each Braille character consists of a cell containing six positions that can have a raised dot or not have one. How many different Braille characters are possible?

American author and lecturer Helen Keller (1880–1968) was both blind and deaf. This photo shows her with a Braille chart.

History CONNECTION

At age 12, French innovator and teacher Louis Braille (1809–1852) invented a code that enables sight-impaired people to read and write. He got the idea from a former soldier who used a code consisting of up to 12 raised dots that allowed soldiers to share information on a dark battlefield without having to speak. Braille modified the number of dots to 6, and added symbols for math and music. In 1829, he published the first book in Braille.

Review

7.5 **17.** Write each expression in the form $a + bi$.

a. $(2 + 4i) - (5 + 2i)$ **b.** $(2 + 4i)(5 + 2i)$ **c.** $\frac{2 + 4i}{5 + 2i}$

12.1 **18.** What is the probability that a randomly selected point within the rectangle at right is in the orange region? The blue region?

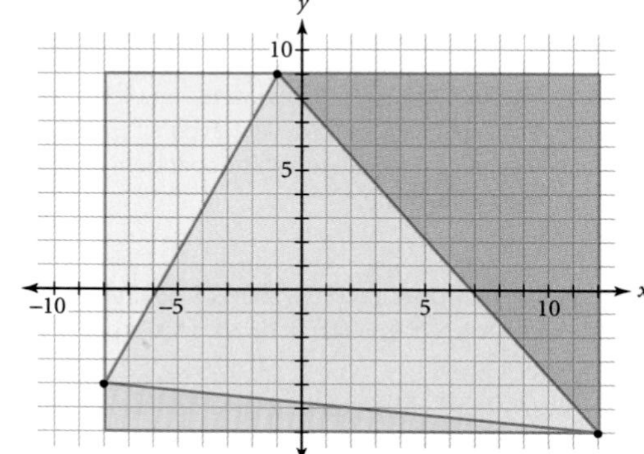

12.1 **19.** A sample of 230 students is categorized as shown.

	Male	Female
Junior	60	50
Senior	70	50

a. What is the probability that a junior is female?

b. What is the probability that a student is a senior?

11.2 **20.** The side of the largest square in the diagram at right is 4. Each new square has side length equal to half of the previous one. If the pattern continues infinitely, what is the long-run length of the spiral made by the diagonals?

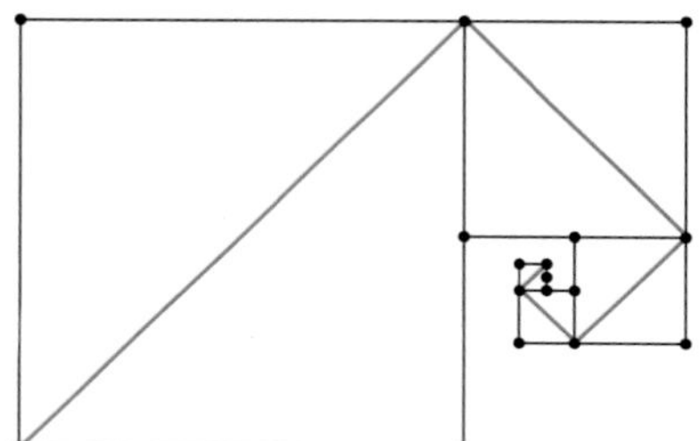

EXPLORATION 

The Law of Large Numbers

You have calculated both experimental and theoretical probabilities of events. In some cases, these probabilities are close. But when might they be different? And how can you predict the outcome of a single random process? In the activity you will explore ways to generalize the probability of an event.

Activity

A Repeat Performance

In this activity you will use a random number generator to simulate the roll of a die. You will then explore the effects of different numbers of trials.

Step 1 Open a new Fathom document. Insert a new case table. Enter the column heading, or attribute, Roll.

Step 2 Click on the attribute Roll. Choose **Edit Formula** from the Edit menu. To simulate the roll of a standard six-sided die, enter **randomPick(1, 2, 3, 4, 5, 6).** This command tells the computer to pick randomly any of the integers 1 through 6.

Step 3 From the Data menu, choose **New Cases.** Enter 10 as the number of new cases. Your case table will fill with 10 randomly chosen integers between 1 and 6. Predict the shape of the histogram of your 10 data items. Then make a histogram and compare it to your prediction. To make a histogram, open a new graph. Drag the attribute Roll to the x-axis of your graph. Then change the graph type to histogram.

Step 4 What is the mode of your data? What are the maximum and minimum number of occurrences of outcomes? What is the difference between these values (the range)?

Step 5 Choose **Rerandomize** from the Analyze menu to generate another set of cases. Does the random generator seem to favor one number over the others? Does the **randomPick** command seem to simulate a fair die? How can you check?

Step 4 The mode is 4. Each outcome occurs 0–3 times, so the range is 3.

Step 5 The random generator doesn't seem to favor one number over the other. If you generate many data sets, you find that there is a lot of variation in the data sets and many sets don't include any rolls of a particular number. You can be sure the random generator is fair by creating many different sets and observing that there is no pattern.

Step 6 Predict the shape of a histogram for 100 cases. How do you think it would compare to a histogram for 10 items?

Step 7 Choose **New Cases** from the Data menu again and add 90 new cases. Your histogram should update automatically. Compare it to your prediction and to the histogram for 10 cases.

Step 8 What are the mode and range of possible outcomes? Rerandomize to generate another set of cases. Does the random generator seem to favor one number over the others?

Step 6 In a histogram showing 100 cases, the bins should be of more even heights. There shouldn't be any numbers that don't ever show up. The height of each of the bins will be larger.

EXPLORATION

PLANNING

LESSON OUTLINE

One day:

20 min Activity

15 min Questions

10 min Sharing

MATERIALS

- Fathom
- Calculator Note 12A/APP, *optional*
- Fathom demonstration A Repeat Performance, *optional*

TEACHING

Depending on their experience with Fathom up to this point, students may need more or less help than that given in the book. If you have only one computer, you might use the Fathom demonstration A Repeat Performance. A similar exploration can be done using a graphing calculator. See Calculator Note 12A/APP.

Guiding the Activity

This activity differs from previous Fathom explorations in that the program generates the data, which are the cases (outcomes).

Step 2 [Alert] Students may have difficulty seeing how the formula can generate data for one attribute without reference to other attributes.

Step 4 The mode can include more than one number.

Step 7 As needed, point out that the case table now holds a total of 100 cases.

See page 905 for answers to Steps 3, 7, and 8.

NCTM STANDARDS

CONTENT		PROCESS	
✓	Number		Problem Solving
✓	Algebra	✓	Reasoning
	Geometry	✓	Communication
	Measurement		Connections
✓	Data/Probability	✓	Representation

LESSON OBJECTIVE

- Explore the effect of a large number of trials on the difference between an event's experimental probability and its theoretical probability

Step 8 As needed, show students how to rerandomize using the keyboard shortcut shown in the menu. The theoretical probabilities are all equal, so over the long run the mode will include all six numbers.

Step 9 To get to 1000, students will add 900 new cases.

Step 10 Students should start over with a new document, using a different formula for rolls. For example, the formula **randomPick(1,1,1,2,3,4,6)** would produce 1 as an outcome $\frac{3}{7}$ of the time, 5 never, and each other integer $\frac{1}{7}$ of the time.

Helping with the Questions

Question 1 The histogram's shape changes less with rerandomizing.

Question 2 The range of the data increases, but not as much as the number of cases increases.

Question 4 The experimental probabilities can be seen in the histogram. Because rerandomizing changes the histogram less for many cases than it does for few cases, the experimental probability is closer to the theoretical probability after many trials.

SHARING IDEAS

As students share their responses to Question 3, make sure they consider that experimental probabilities are rarely equal to the theoretical probabilities. It's quite difficult to be sure whether or not a die is loaded, although if one side dominates many times—considering many cases with lots of rerandomizing—the argument for bias can be convincing.

See page 905 for answer to Step 9.

Step 9 | Predict the histogram for 1000 cases. Then make a histogram and repeat Step 8.

A die that is not fair is called "loaded." A loaded die is designed to roll certain numbers more often.

Steps 10, 11 Answers will vary, but students should be able to determine how the die is loaded more accurately based on 1000 cases than on 10 cases.

Step 10 | Create a loaded die by using **randomPick** and any selection of numbers between 1 and 6. Let a classmate guess how the die is loaded by observing only 10 cases at a time.

Step 11 | Now repeat Step 10, but allow your classmate to use 1000 cases at a time.

Questions

1. How does increasing the number of cases affect the shape of the histogram?
2. How does increasing the number of cases affect the range of data?
3. What strategies did you use to judge whether a die was loaded? Suppose you suspect that a die is loaded. How can you show that it is?
4. The Law of Large Numbers states that if an experiment is repeated many times, the experimental probability will get closer and closer to the theoretical probability. How does the Law of Large Numbers apply to this activity?

1. For more cases, the shape of the histogram is closer to what it theoretically should be.

2. For more cases, the relative range of the data becomes smaller.

3. I rerandomized many times and looked for a pattern. For 1000 cases it was very easy to determine how the die was loaded, but for only 10 cases I couldn't be as sure.

4. The Law of Large Numbers was demonstrated by this exploration. The more cases we looked at, the closer the histogram was to the theoretical probability, for both fair and loaded dice.

IMPROVING YOUR REASONING SKILLS

The Fake Coin

Angelina's grandfather gives her a collection of rare coins. It includes a box with 81 identical-looking coins. He tells her that one coin is fake because it is slightly lighter than all the others, but he does not remember which one it is. Angelina has a pan balance. What is the fewest number of balancings that she needs to make to be sure she will find the fake coin?

IMPROVING REASONING SKILLS

If students are weighing individual coins against each other, suggest that comparing groups of coins might be more efficient. If they're trying to divide the collection into halves repeatedly, wonder aloud whether the number 81 has any special properties.

Angelina can put one-third of the coins into each pan. If they don't balance, the lighter coin is in the lighter third. More difficult for some students to see is that, if they do balance, the omitted third contains the lighter coin. She can then repeat the process with the lighter third and isolate the lighter coin in a total of four balancings.

LESSON

12.3 Mutually Exclusive Events and Venn Diagrams

Of course there is no formula for success except perhaps an unconditional acceptance of life and what it brings.

ARTHUR RUBENSTEIN

Two outcomes or events that cannot both happen are **mutually exclusive.** You already worked with theoretical probabilities and mutually exclusive events when you added probabilities of different paths.

For example, this tree diagram represents the possibilities of success in auditions by Abby, Bonita, and Chih-Lin. One path from left to right represents the outcome that Abby and Chih-Lin are successful but Bonita is not (outcome AC). Another outcome is success by all three (outcome ABC). These two outcomes cannot both take place, so they're mutually exclusive.

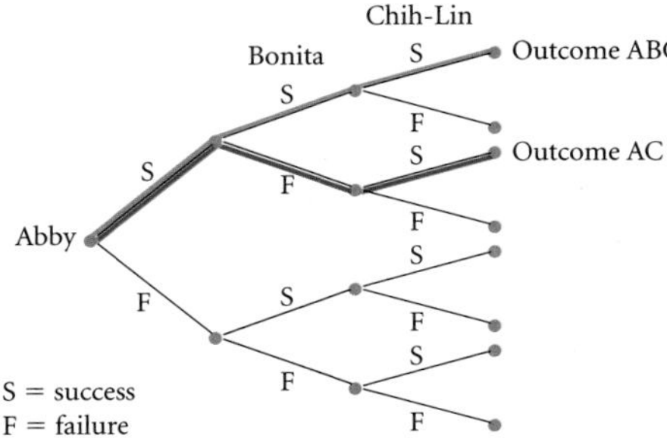

Suppose that each student has a .5 probability of success. Then the probability of any single path in the tree is (.5)(.5)(.5) = .125. So, the probability that either AC or ABC occurs is the sum of the probabilities on two particular paths, .125 + .125, or .25.

Untitled (1988) by British-American artist Judy Pfaff (b 1946) shows overlapping circles similar to Venn diagrams.

NCTM STANDARDS

CONTENT	PROCESS
✓ Number	✓ Problem Solving
✓ Algebra	✓ Reasoning
Geometry	✓ Communication
Measurement	✓ Connections
✓ Data/Probability	✓ Representation

LESSON OBJECTIVES

- Explore mutually exclusive events
- Use Venn diagrams as a tool for breaking down compound events into mutually exclusive events
- Understand the addition rule for finding the probabilities of events described by a Venn diagram
- Differentiate between mutually exclusive events and independent events

LESSON 12.3

PLANNING

LESSON OUTLINE

One day:

5 min	Example A
10 min	Investigation
10 min	Examples B, C
10 min	Sharing
10 min	Exercises

MATERIALS

- New Baby (T) for One Step

TEACHING

Just as tree diagrams help break down compound events into simple independent events, Venn diagrams help break down compound events into mutually exclusive events.

One Step

Display the New Baby transparency and pose this problem: "Reba's parents are going to have a baby, and she wonders about the probability that this child will have some of the same physical traits she has. She does some research and finds the information listed in the table about two traits. What's the probability that the new baby will have both an attached earlobe and a longer second toe?"

As students work, encourage the use of diagrams (Venn or other) to see how the intersection is being double-counted when adding .6 and .7 (or 60 and 70). Be open to a variety of approaches. During Sharing, bring up Venn diagrams, mutually exclusive events, the general addition rule, and complements.

Just as tree diagrams allow breaking down sequences of dependent events into sequences of independent events, there's a tool for breaking down non–mutually exclusive events into mutually exclusive events. This tool is the Venn diagram, consisting of overlapping circles.

▶ ***EXAMPLE A***

[Alert] Students may have difficulty differentiating between the probability that the guitar string breaks and the probability that the guitar string breaking is the only one of the three events that occurs. You might want students to write about or discuss the meaning of each of the eight probabilities.

[Ask] "What do the probabilities add up to?" [1] "What is the probability that at least one of these three events will occur?" [1 − .57, or .43] "Can you find the probability that either there is a math quiz or the guitar string breaks?" [Yes; add all the probabilities of outcomes within those two circles.]

EXAMPLE A

Melissa has been keeping a record of probabilities of events involving

- **i.** Her guitar string breaking during orchestra rehearsal (Event B).
- **ii.** A pop quiz in math (Event Q).
- **iii.** Her team losing in gym class (Event L).

Although the three events are not mutually exclusive, they can be broken into eight mutually exclusive events. These events and their probabilities are shown in the Venn diagram.

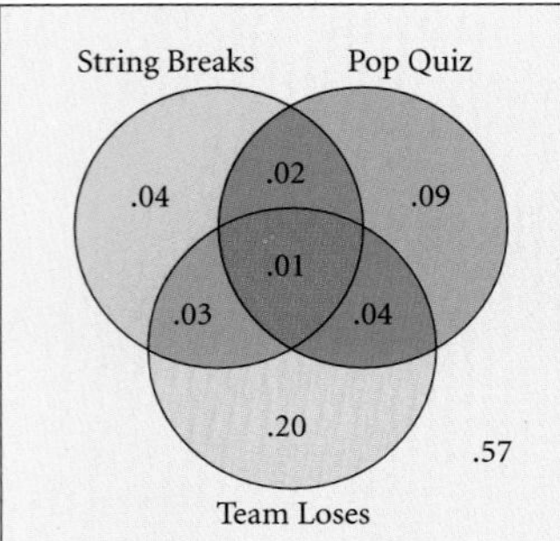

a. What is the meaning of the region labeled .01?

b. What is the meaning of the region labeled .03?

c. What is the probability of a pop quiz, $P(Q)$, today?

d. Find the probability of a pretty good day, $P(\text{not } B \text{ and not } Q \text{ and not } L)$. This means no string breaks and no quiz and no loss.

▶ ***Solution***

The meaning of each region is determined by the circles that contain it.

a. The region labeled .01 represents the probability of a really bad day. In this intersection of all three circles Melissa's string breaks, she gets a pop quiz, and her team loses.

b. The region labeled .03 represents the probability that Melissa's string will break and her team will lose, but there will be no pop quiz in math.

c. You can find the probability of a pop quiz by adding the four areas that are part of the pop-quiz circle: $.02 + .09 + .01 + .04 = .16$.

d. The probability of a pretty good day, $P(\text{not } B \text{ and not } Q \text{ and not } L)$ is pictured by the region outside the circles, and is .57.

In general, the probability that one of a set of of mutually exclusive events will occur is the sum of the probabilities of the individual events.

The Addition Rule for Mutually Exclusive Events

If n_1, n_2, n_3, and so on represent mutually exclusive events, then the probability that any event in this collection of mutually exclusive events will occur is the sum of the probabilities of the individual events.

$$P(n_1 \text{ or } n_2 \text{ or } n_3 \text{ or} \ldots) = P(n_1) + P(n_2) + P(n_3) + \cdots$$

But what if you don't know all the probabilities that Melissa knew? In the investigation you'll discover one way to figure out probabilities of mutually exclusive events when you know probabilities of non-mutually exclusive events.

Investigation
Addition Rule

Of the 100 students in 12th grade, 70 are enrolled in mathematics, 50 are in science, 30 are in both subjects, and 10 are in neither subject.

Step 1 "A student takes mathematics" and "a student takes science" are two events. Are these events mutually exclusive? Explain.

Step 2 Complete a Venn diagram, similar to the one below, that shows enrollments in mathematics and science courses.

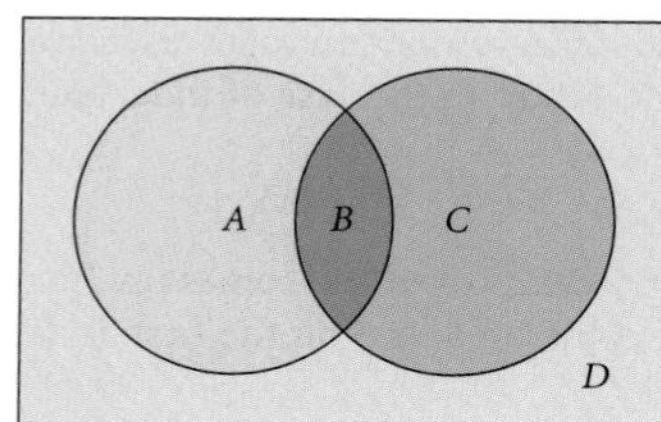

Step 3 Use the numbers of students in your Venn diagram to calculate probabilities.

Step 4 Explain why the probability that a randomly chosen student takes mathematics or science, $P(\text{M or S})$, does not equal $P(\text{M}) + P(\text{S})$.

Step 5 Create a formula for calculating $P(\text{M or S})$ that includes the expressions $P(\text{M})$, $P(\text{S})$, and $P(\text{M and S})$.

Step 6 Suppose two dice are tossed. Draw a Venn diagram to represent the events

A = "sum is 7"

B = "both dice > 2"

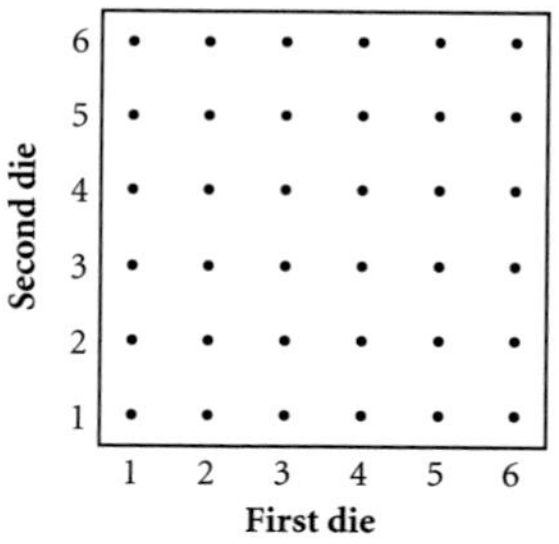

Find the probabilities in parts a–e by counting dots:

a. $P(\text{A})$

b. $P(\text{B})$

c. $P(\text{A and B})$

d. $P(\text{A or B})$

e. $P(\text{not A and not B})$

f. Find $P(\text{A or B})$ by using a rule or formula similar to your response in Step 5.

Second die: 1–6; First die: 1–6 (6 × 6 grid of dots)

Step 7 Complete the statement: For any two events A and B, $P(\text{A or B}) = \underline{?}$.

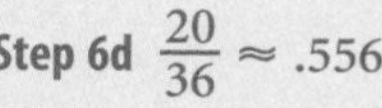

Guiding the Investigation

Step 2 **[Ask]** "Can you know when you have accounted for all 100 students?" [Yes; the sum of the numbers of all four events equals 100.] **[Alert]** Students may put 50 into the region representing science only rather than making it the sum of the numbers in the entire science circle.

Step 1 No; a student can take both.

Step 2

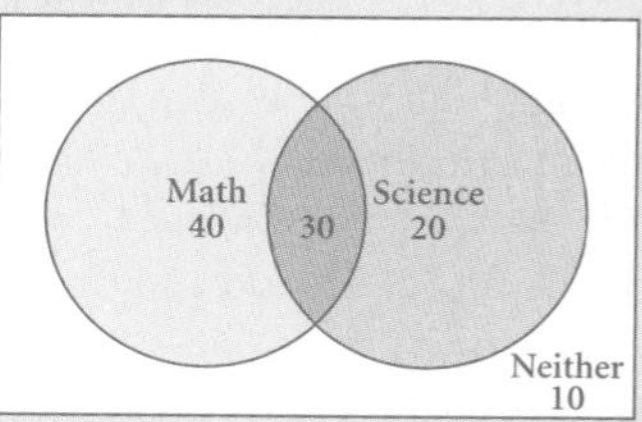

Step 3

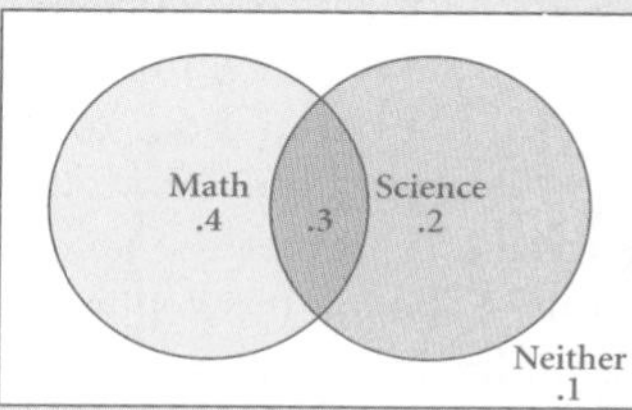

Step 4 As needed, remind students that $P(\text{M})$ is the probability for the entire mathematics circle and $P(\text{S})$ is the probability for the entire science circle.

Step 4 $P(\text{M}) + P(\text{S})$ counts the intersection twice.

Step 5 $P(\text{M or S}) = P(\text{M}) + P(\text{S}) - P(\text{M and S})$

Step 6

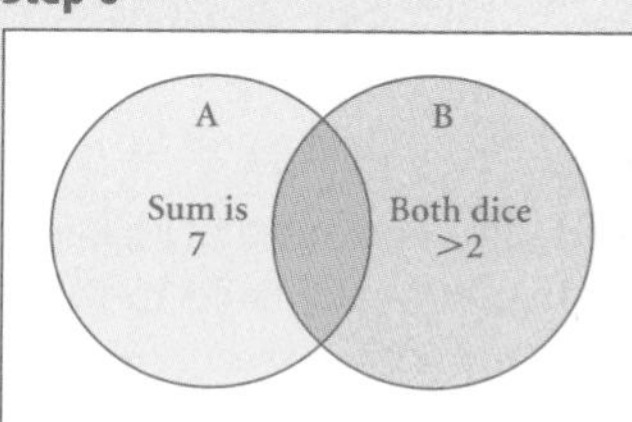

Step 6a $\frac{6}{36} \approx .167$

Step 6b $\frac{16}{36} \approx .444$

Step 6c $\frac{2}{36} \approx .056$

Step 6d $\frac{20}{36} \approx .556$

Step 6e $\frac{16}{36} \approx .444$

Step 6f $\frac{6}{36} + \frac{16}{36} - \frac{2}{36} = \frac{20}{36} \approx .556$

Step 7 $P(\text{A or B}) = P(\text{A}) + P(\text{B}) - P(\text{A and B})$

▸ EXAMPLE B

[Language] The phrase *and/or* expresses that 3 or 6 can come up on the first roll, the second roll, or both rolls.

If students are bothered by the use of fractions for probabilities, remind them that probabilities can be expressed as fractions, decimals, or percents.

To help deepen students' understanding of the ideas, **[Ask]** "What are all the possibilities of having a 3 or a 6 on the first roll and the second roll? What is the probability? How does this probability fit into the Venn diagram?" [There are four possibilities: (6, 3), (3, 6), (3, 3), and (6, 6). The probability is $\frac{4}{36}$. Put the number 4 in the intersection of the circles in the Venn diagram.] "What are all the possibilities of having a 3 or a 6 on the first or second roll but not on both rolls? What is the probability? How does this probability fit into the Venn diagram?" [There are two possibilities of having either a 3 or a 6 on the first roll and four possibilities of having neither on the second roll, for a total of eight possibilities. The same is true if you reverse the first and second rolls. Thus the probability of having a 3 or a 6 come up on only one roll is $\frac{2}{6} \cdot \frac{4}{6} + \frac{2}{6} \cdot \frac{4}{6} = \frac{16}{36}$. You can put the number 8 in each circle (outside the intersection) to represent this probability.] "What is the sum of the probability that 3 and 6 will come up and the probability that 3 or 6 will come up?" $\left[\frac{4}{36} + \frac{16}{36} = \frac{20}{36} = \frac{5}{9}\right]$ As needed, point out that this is the probability calculated in the example, expressed as *and/or.*

A general form of the addition rule allows you to find the probability of an "or" statement even when two events are not mutually exclusive.

The General Addition Rule

If n_1 and n_2 represent event 1 and event 2, then the probability that at least one of the events will occur can be found by adding the probabilities of the events and subtracting the probability that both will occur.

$$P(n_1 \text{ or } n_2) = P(n_1) + P(n_2) - P(n_1 \text{ and } n_2)$$

You might wonder whether independent events and mutually exclusive events are the same. Independent events don't affect the probabilities of each other. Mutually exclusive events affect each other dramatically: If one occurs, the probability of the other occurring is 0.

But there is a connection between independent and mutually exclusive events. In calculating probabilities of non–mutually exclusive events, you use the probability that they both will occur. In the case of independent events, you know this probability.

EXAMPLE B The probability that a rolled die comes up 3 or 6 is $\frac{1}{3}$. What's the probability that a die will come up 3 or 6 on the first and/or second roll?

▸ Solution

Let F represent getting a 3 or 6 on the first roll, regardless of what happens on the second roll. Let S represent getting a 3 or 6 on the second roll, regardless of what happens on the first roll. Notice that both F and S include the possibility of getting a 3 or 6 on both rolls, as shown by the overlap in the Venn diagram. To account for the overlap, the general addition rule subtracts $P(\text{F and S})$ once.

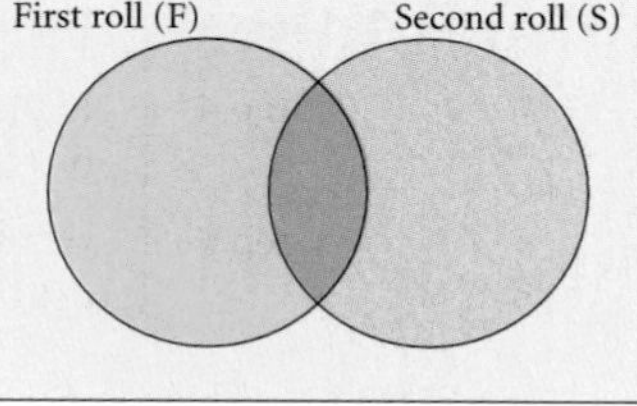

$P(\text{F or S}) = P(\text{F}) + P(\text{S}) - P(\text{F and S})$	The general addition rule.
$P(\text{F or S}) = P(\text{F}) + P(\text{S}) - P(\text{F}) \cdot P(\text{S})$	F and S are independent, so $P(\text{F and S}) = P(\text{F}) \cdot P(\text{S})$.
$P(\text{F or S}) = \frac{1}{3} + \frac{1}{3} - \left(\frac{1}{3}\right)\left(\frac{1}{3}\right)$	Substitute the probability.
$P(\text{F or S}) = \frac{5}{9}$.	Multiply and add.

The probability of getting a 3 or 6 on the first and/or second roll is $\frac{5}{9}$.

When two events are mutually exclusive and make up all possible outcomes, they are referred to as **complements.** The complement of "a 1 or a 3 on the first roll" is "not a 1 and not a 3 on the first roll," an outcome that is represented by the regions outside the F circle. Because $P(\text{F})$ is $\frac{1}{3}$, the probability of the complement, $P(\text{not F})$, is $1 - \frac{1}{3}$, or $\frac{2}{3}$.

EXAMPLE C

Every student in the school music program is backstage, and no other students are present. Use O to represent the event that a student is in the orchestra, C to represent the event that a student is in the choir, and B to represent the event that a student is in the band. A reporter who approaches a student at random backstage knows these probabilities:

i. P(B or C) = .8

ii. P(not O) = .6

iii. P(C and not O and not B) = .1

iv. O and C are independent

v. O and B are mutually exclusive

a. Turn each of these statements into a statement about percentage in plain English.

b. Create a Venn diagram of probabilities describing this situation.

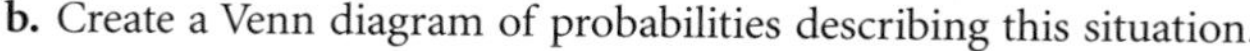

▶ Solution

a. Convert each probablility statement to a percentage statement.

i. P(B or C) = .8 means that 80% of the students are in band or in choir.

ii. P(not O) = .6 means that 60% of the students are not in orchestra.

iii. P(C and not O and not B) = .1 means that 10% of the students are in choir only.

iv. "O and C are independent" means that the percentage of students in choir is the same as the percentage of orchestra students in choir. Being in orchestra does not make a student any more or less likely to be in choir, and vice versa.

v. "O and B are mutually exclusive" means that there are no students in both orchestra and band.

b. Start with a general Venn diagram showing the overlap of 3 events.

Because every student backstage is in the music program, the probability P(not C and not O and not B) is 0. So, the region Z in the Venn diagram below has a probability of 0.

Because O and B are mutually exclusive, $T = 0$ and $V = 0$.

P(C and not O and not B) = .1 means that $Y = .1$.

P(B or C) = .8 means that $U + W + X + Y = .8$.

P(not O) = .6 means that $U + X + Y = .6$.

The difference in the last two statements, $(U + W + X + Y) - (U + X + Y)$, is W, so $W = .8 - .6 = .2$.

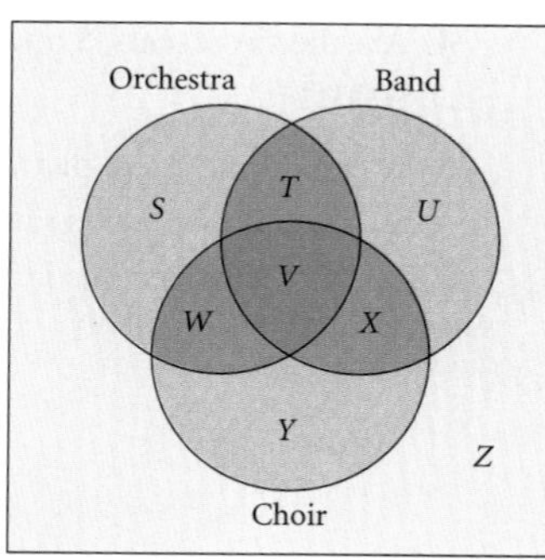

[Ask] "Is it possible to tell from a Venn diagram whether events are independent?" [Not directly, but by calculation; if the ratio of the number of outcomes in the intersection to the number of outcomes in one event is the same as the ratio of the number of outcomes in that same event to the total number of outcomes, then the events are independent. In this diagram, for example, $P(B \mid A) = \frac{3}{6}$ and $P(B) = \frac{8}{16}$; because these probabilities are equal, the events are independent.]

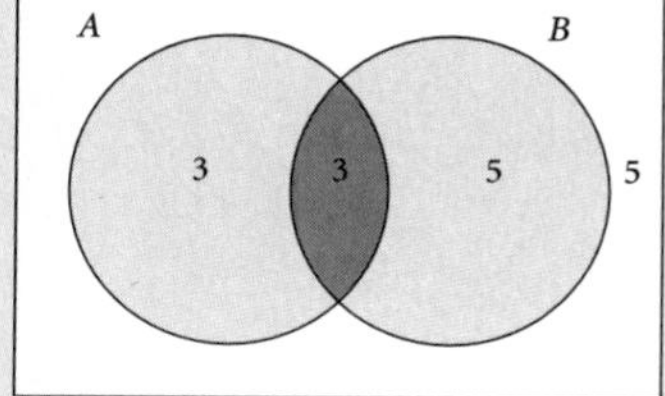

▶ EXAMPLE C

Because regions T and V are both 0, the Venn diagram could be drawn like this.

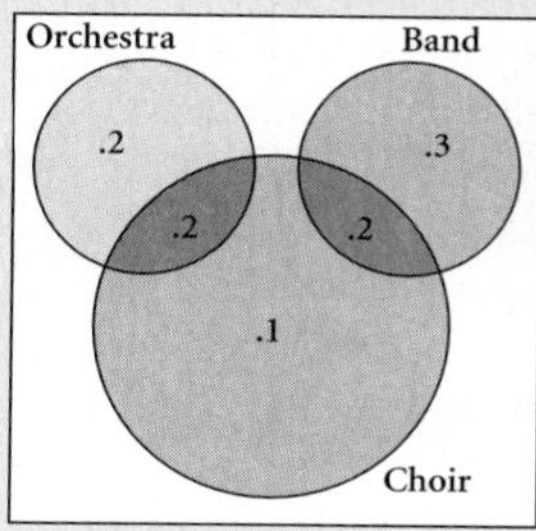

SHARING IDEAS

After students present the results of their investigation, [Ask] "If the number of students who are enrolled in mathematics had not been given, could you have found it?" [Yes. Subtract the other values from 100 to get 40, the number of students taking only mathematics. Then add 40 to the number of students taking both mathematics and science, 30, to get 70 students.]

Suggest that students open questions with "In general . . . " or "Is it possible . . . ." (See examples below.) Listen carefully to students' questions; you can learn a great deal from your students.

[Ask] "In general, are mutually exclusive events the same as independent events?" Help students rephrase the explanation in the book in their own words. Emphasize the idea that mutually exclusive events are dependent unless one event is always impossible. The occurrence of one event definitely affects the probability of the other (making it 0). Algebraically, if events A and B are mutually exclusive, then $P(A \text{ and } B) = 0$; this probability can't equal $P(A) \cdot P(B)$ unless either $P(A)$ or $P(B)$ is 0, so except in this special case the events aren't independent.

Assessing Progress
You can check students' comfort level with seeing parts of wholes, such as seeing students who take only mathematics as a part of students who take mathematics. You can also assess students' ability to express probabilities as fractions and to generalize from data to formulas.

Closing the Lesson

The main idea of this lesson is that a **Venn diagram** allows you to break down events into **mutually exclusive events.** For events n_1 and n_2, $P(n_1 \text{ or } n_2) = P(n_1) + P(n_2) - P(n_1 \text{ and } n_2)$. If the events are mutually exclusive, then $P(n_1 \text{ and } n_2) = 0$, so $P(n_1 \text{ or } n_2)$ equals the sum of the probabilities.

BUILDING UNDERSTANDING

Students practice working with mutually exclusive events and the addition rule.

ASSIGNING HOMEWORK

Essential	1–4
Performance assessment	5–11
Portfolio	8
Journal	5, 8
Group	6–8
Review	12–16

$P(\text{not O}) = .6$ means $P(\text{O}) = .4$. Therefore, $S + W + T + V$ equals .4. Substituting the known values of W, T, and V, gives $S + .2 = .4$, so $S = .2$.

Because O and C are independent,

$$P(\text{O}) \cdot P(\text{C}) = P(\text{O and C})$$
$$(S + W)(W + X + Y) = W$$
$$.4(.2 + .1 + X) = .2$$
$$.3 + X = \frac{.2}{.4} = .5$$
$$X = .2$$

Finally returning to $U + X + Y = .6$, substitute the values of X and Y to get $U = .3$.

Write the probabilities in your Venn diagram.

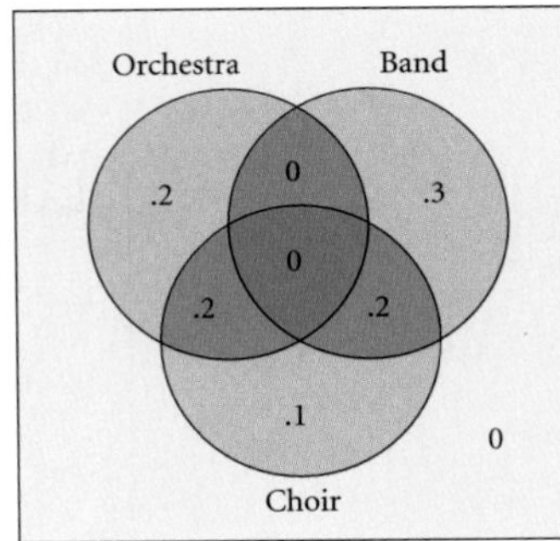

You should take the time to check that the sum of the probabilities in all the areas is 1. Solving this kind of puzzle exercises your understanding of probabilities and the properties of *and, or, independent,* and *mutually exclusive.*

EXERCISES

Practice Your Skills

Exercises 1–4 refer to the diagram at right. Let S represent the event that a student is a sophomore, and A represent the event that a student takes advanced algebra.

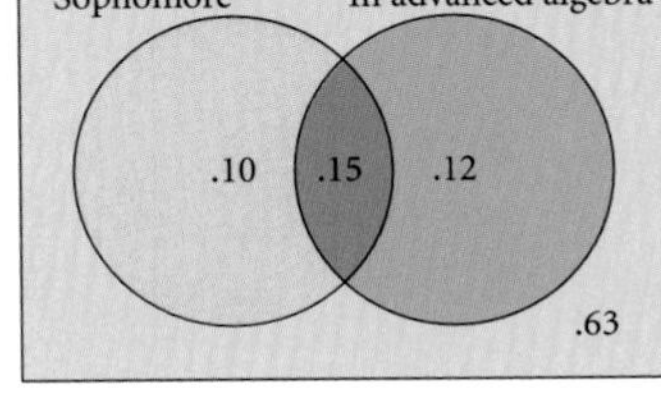

1. Describe the events represented by each of the four regions.

2. Find the probability of each event.

a. $P(\text{S})$ .25 **b.** $P(\text{A and not S})$ .12

c. $P(\text{S} \mid \text{A})$ $\frac{.15}{.15 + .12} \approx .56$ **d.** $P(\text{S or A})$ .37

3. Suppose the diagram refers to a high school with 500 students. Change each probability into a frequency (number of students).

4. Are the two events, S and A, independent? Show mathematically that you are correct.

5. Events A and B are pictured in the Venn diagram at right.

a. Are the two events mutually exclusive? Explain.

b. Are the two events independent? Assume $P(A) \neq 0$ and $P(B) \neq 0$. Explain.

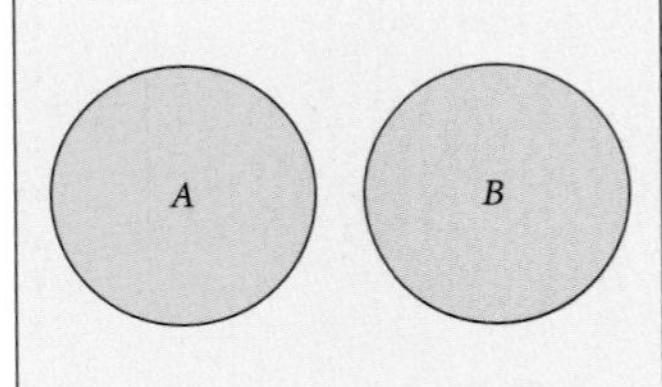

Helping with the Exercises

1. 10% of the students are sophomores and not in advanced algebra. 15% are sophomores in advanced algebra. 12% are in advanced algebra but are not sophomores. 63% are neither sophomores nor in advanced algebra.

Exercise 3 [Alert] Students may neglect to convert one or more of the four probabilities to a frequency.

3.

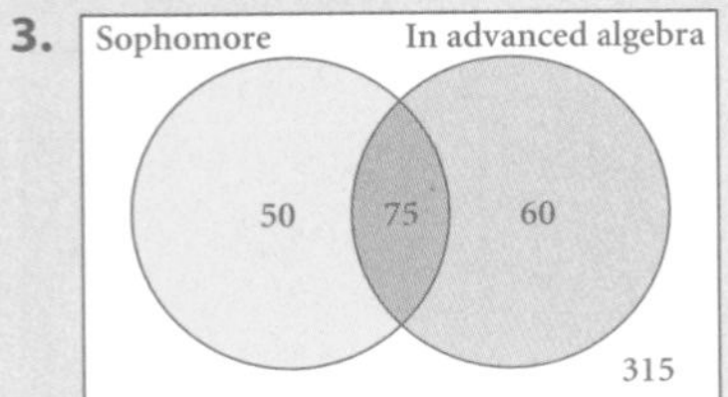

4. No. $P(\text{S}) \cdot P(\text{A}) = .25 \cdot .27 = .0675$, $P(\text{S and A}) = .15$. These must be equal if the events are independent.

Exercise 5 [Alert] Students may think that this is not a Venn diagram because it doesn't look like those they've seen before. Circles in a Venn diagram can be drawn as non-intersecting to represent that it is not possible for both events to occur. They can also be drawn as concentric to indicate that if one occurs, the other must occur. Alternatively, they can be drawn overlapping, with impossible regions labeled with 0.

5a. Yes, because they do not overlap.

5b. No. $P(\text{A and B}) = 0$. This would be the same as $P(\text{A}) \cdot P(\text{B})$ if they were independent.

Reason and Apply

6. Of the 420 students at Middletown High School, 126 study French and 275 study music. Twenty percent of the music students take French.

a. Create a Venn diagram of this situation.

b. What percentage of the students take both French and music?

c. How many students take neither French nor music?

7. Two events, A and B, have probabilities $P(A) = .2$, $P(B) = .4$, $P(A \mid B) = .2$.

a. Create a Venn diagram of this situation.

b. Find the value of each probability indicated.

i. $P(A \text{ and } B)$ .08

ii. $P(\text{not } B)$ .60

iii. $P(\text{not } (A \text{ or } B))$ .48

8. If $P(A) = .4$ and $P(B) = .5$, what range of values is possible for $P(A \text{ and } B)$? What range of values is possible for $P(A \text{ or } B)$? Use a Venn diagram to help explain how each range is possible.

9. Assume that the diagram for Exercises 1–4 refers to a high school with 800 students. Draw a new diagram showing the probabilities if 20 sophomores moved from geometry to advanced algebra.

10. At right are two color wheels. Figure A represents the mixing of light, and Figure B represents the mixing of pigments.

Figure A Figure B

Using Figure A, what color is produced when equal amounts of

a. Red and green light are mixed? yellow

b. Blue and green light are mixed? cyan

c. Red, green, and blue light are mixed? white

Using Figure B, what color is produced when equal amounts of

d. Magenta and cyan pigments are mixed? blue

e. Yellow and cyan pigments are mixed? green

f. Magenta, cyan, and yellow pigments are mixed? black

Science CONNECTION

The three primary colors of light are red, green, and blue, each having its own range of wavelengths. When these waves reach our eyes, we see the color associated with the wave. These colors are also used to project images on TV screens and computer monitors and in lighting performances on stage. In the mixing of colors involving paint, ink, or dyes, the primary colors are cyan (greenish-blue), magenta (purplish-red), and yellow. Mixing other pigment colors cannot duplicate these three colors. Pigment color mixing is important in the textile industry as well as in art, design, and printing.

This magnified image shows how the color in a printed photograph appears on paper. The colors are combinations of cyan, magenta, yellow, and black. These four colors can be blended in varying amounts to create any color.

Exercise 10 It might help students to read the Science Connection before completing this exercise.

[Language] *Cyan* is pronounced "'sī-an."

6a.

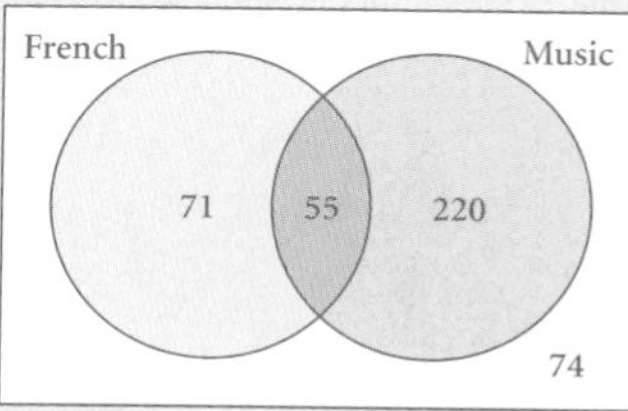

6b. approximately 13%

6c. 74

Exercise 7 [Ask] "What meaning would $P(A \mid B)$ have in this situation?" [It is the portion of B that is also in A.]

7a.

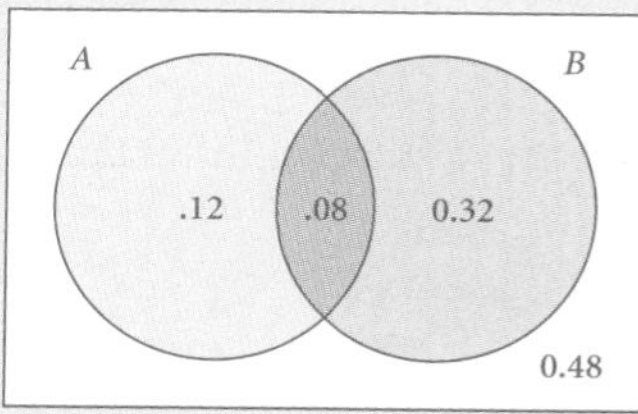

8. $0 \leq P(A \text{ and } B) \leq .4$, $.5 \leq P(A \text{ or } B) \leq .9$. The first diagram shows $P(A \text{ and } B) = 0$ and $P(A \text{ or } B) = .9$. The second diagram shows $P(A \text{ and } B) = .4$ and $P(A \text{ or } B) = .5$.

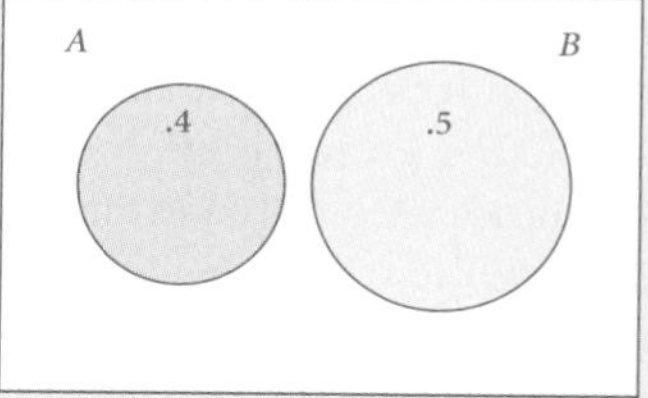

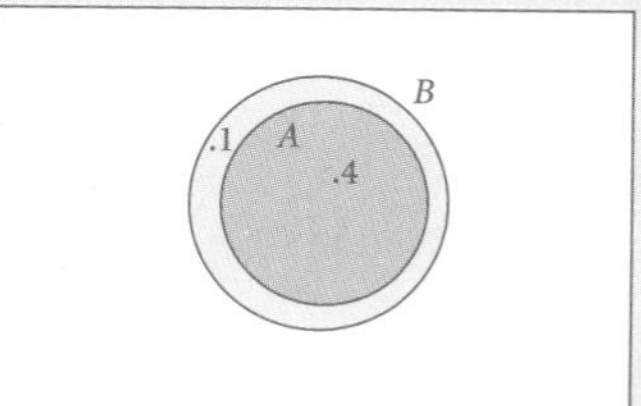

9.

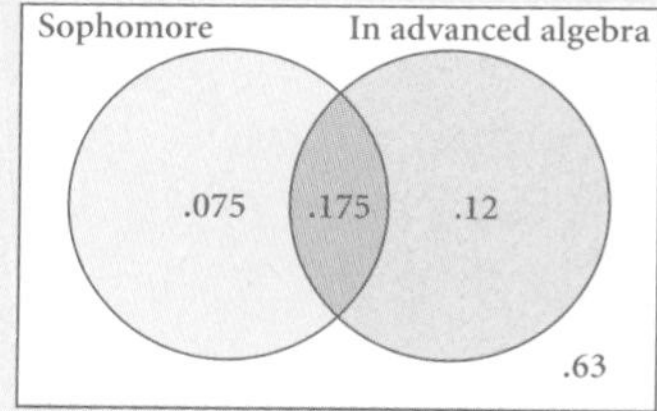

11. Kendra needs help on her math homework and decides to call one of her friends—Amber, Bob, or Carol. Kendra knows that Amber is on the phone 30% of the time, Bob is on the phone 20% of the time, and Carol is on the phone 25% of the time.

a. If the three friends' phone usage is independent, make a Venn diagram of the situation.

b. What is the probability that all three of her friends will be on the phone when she calls?

c. What is the probability that none of her friends will be on the phone when she calls?

Review

12.1 **12.** The registered voters represented in the table have been interviewed and rated. Assume that this sample is representative of the voting public in a particular town. Find each probability.

	Liberal	Conservative
Age under 30	210	145
Age 30–45	235	220
Age over 45	280	410

a. P(a randomly chosen voter is over 45 yr old and liberal)

b. P(a randomly chosen voter is conservative)

c. P(a randomly chosen voter is conservative if under 30 yr old)

d. P(a randomly chosen voter is under 30 yr old if conservative)

2.1 **13.** The most recent test scores in a chemistry class were

$\{74, 71, 87, 89, 73, 82, 55, 78, 80, 83, 72\}$

What was the average (mean) score?

12.2 **14.** If an unfair coin has $P(\text{H}) = \frac{2}{5}$ and $P(\text{T}) = \frac{3}{5}$, then what is the probability that six flips come up with H, T, T, T, H, T in exactly this order?

15. Rewrite each expression in the form $a\sqrt{b}$, such that b contains no factors that are perfect squares.

a. $\sqrt{18}$ **b.** $\sqrt{54}$ **c.** $\sqrt{60x^3y^5}$

16. Port Charles and Turner Lake are 860 km apart. At 6:15 A.M., Patrick and Ben start driving from Port Charles to Turner Lake at an average speed of 80 km/h. At 9:30 A.M., Carl and Louis decide to meet them. They leave Turner Lake and drive at 95 km/h toward Port Charles. When and where do the two parties meet?

11a.

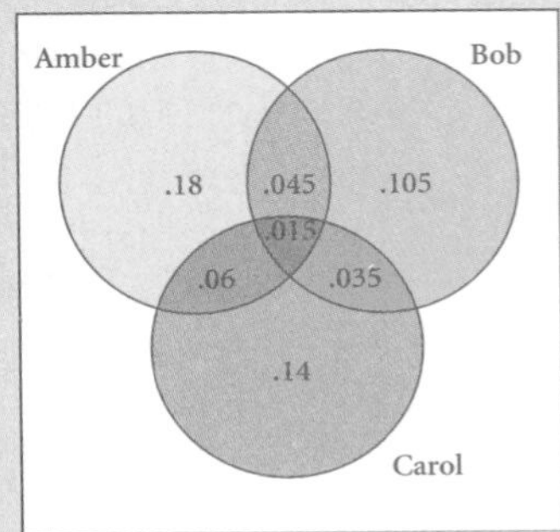

11b. .015

11c. .42

Exercise 12 If students are having difficulty, ask them what information they are missing in order to help them see that they need to find row and column totals.

12a. $\frac{280}{1500} \approx .187$

12b. $\frac{775}{1500} \approx .517$

12c. $\frac{145}{355} \approx .408$

12d. $\frac{145}{775} \approx .187$

13. approximately 77

Exercise 14 **[Ask]** "Are the results of the coin flips independent events?" [Yes; even though the probabilities are not the same, as they would be with a fair coin, the result of one flip doesn't affect the probability associated with the next.]

14. $\frac{324}{15{,}625} \approx .02$

15a. $3\sqrt{2}$

15b. $3\sqrt{6}$

15c. $2xy^2\sqrt{15xy}$

16. They meet 6.68 h after Patrick and Ben leave, or at 12:56 P.M., 534 km from Port Charles.

LESSON

12.4 Random Variables and Expected Value

The real measure of your wealth is how much you'd be worth if you lost all your money.

ANONYMOUS

Imagine that you are sitting near the rapids on the bank of a rushing river. Salmon are attempting to swim upstream. They must jump out of the water to pass the rapids. While sitting on the bank, you observe 100 salmon jumps and, of those, 35 are successful. Having no other information, you can estimate that the probability of success is 35% for each jump.

What is the probability that a salmon will make it on its second attempt? Note that this situation requires that two conditions be met: that the salmon fails on the first jump, and that it succeeds on the second jump. In the diagram, you see that this probability is $(.65)(.35) = .2275$, or about 23%. To determine the probability that the salmon makes it on the first or second jump, you sum the probabilities of the two mutually exclusive events: making it on the first jump and making it on the second jump. The sum is $.35 + .2275 = .5775$, or about 58%.

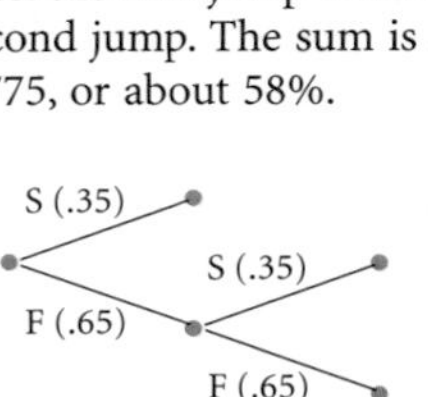

Sockeye salmon swim upstream to spawn.

Probabilities of success such as these are often used to predict the number of independent trials required before the first success (or failure) is achieved. The salmon situation gave experimental probabilities. In the investigation you'll explore theoretical probabilities associated with dice.

Investigation
"Dieing" for a Four

Each person will need a single die. [▶ See **Calculator Note 1L** to simulate rolling a die if you don't have one.◀] Imagine that you're about to play a board game in which you must roll a 4 on your die before taking your first turn.

Step 1 Answers will vary. The mean should be approximately 6.

Step 1 Record the number of rolls it takes for you to get a 4. Repeat this a total of ten times. Combine your results with those of your group and find the mean of all values. Then find the mean of all the group results in the class.

Step 2 6

Step 2 Based on this experiment, how many rolls would you expect to make on average before a 4 comes up?

NCTM STANDARDS

CONTENT		PROCESS	
	Number	✓	Problem Solving
✓	Algebra	✓	Reasoning
	Geometry	✓	Communication
	Measurement	✓	Connections
✓	Data/Probability	✓	Representation

LESSON OBJECTIVES

- Understand a random variable as a quantity whose value depends on an outcome
- Calculate the expected value of a discrete random variable

LESSON 12.4

PLANNING

LESSON OUTLINE

One day:

15 min Investigation
5 min Example A
5 min Example B
5 min Sharing
15 min Exercises

MATERIALS

- dice (one die per person)
- Calculator Notes 1L, 2B, 12B
- Fathom demonstration Expected Value, *optional*

TEACHING

This lesson introduces the concept of a random variable and derives methods for finding the expected value of a discrete random variable.

One Step

Pose this problem: "A national sweepstakes awards one prize of \$1 million, 10 prizes of \$100,000, and 1,000 prizes of \$1,000. If 10 million people enter the sweepstakes, what's a fair amount to pay for a ticket?" As needed, encourage students to think about means. During Sharing, introduce the phrase *expected value of a discrete random variable* and derive the method of calculating the expected value as a sum of products. Refer students to Example B, where they will see that even experiments that occur only once can have an expected value.

Guiding the Investigation

Step 1 Because all of the groups' means come from the same number of trials, the class mean will be the mean of the group means.

Step 3 6

Step 4 **[Alert]** Students may not realize that for the first 4 to appear on the second roll, a 4 must not appear on the first roll. Also, you may need to **[Ask]** "What's the probability that a 4 *won't* appear on a particular roll?" $\left[1 - \frac{1}{6}, \text{ or } \frac{5}{6}\right]$

Step 4 $\frac{1}{6} \approx .167; \frac{5}{36} \approx .139;$ $\frac{25}{216} \approx .116; \frac{125}{1296} \approx .096$

Step 5 $\frac{5^{n-1}}{6^n}$

Step 6 Students might use a spreadsheet for this step.

Step 6 The sum should be about 6. This is the average number of rolls it will take to roll a 4.

Step 7 The two numbers should be close.

► EXAMPLE A

To encourage critical thinking, express skepticism about the fractional expression for the mean being equivalent to the sum of products.

The student book uses x to represent both the random variable and values of the random variable. The standard mathematical convention is to use a capital letter, such as X, to represent the random variable and x_i to denote a possible value of X. Because this notation can be confusing, this book uses lower case to represent the random variable in all instances. In Example A, the random variable x takes on the values $x = 1, 2, 3, \ldots, 12$.

Step 3 To calculate the result more theoretically, imagine a "perfect" sequence of rolls, with the results 1, 2, 3, 4, 5, 6, 1, 2, 3, 4, 5, 6, and so on. On average, how many rolls do you need after each 4 to get the next 4?

Step 4 Another theoretical approach uses the fact that the probability of success is $\frac{1}{6}$. Calculate the probability of rolling the first 4 on the first roll, the first 4 on the second roll, the first 4 on the third roll, and the first 4 on the fourth roll. (A tree diagram might help you do the calculations.)

Step 5 Find a formula for the probability of rolling the first 4 on the nth roll.

Step 6 Create a calculator list with the numbers 1 through 100. [► See **Calculator Note 12B** for a quick way to enter sequences into lists. ◄] Use your formula from Step 5 to make a second list of the probabilities of rolling the first 4 on the first roll, the second roll, the third roll, and so on, up to the 100th roll. Create a third list that is the product of these two lists. Calculate the sum of this third list. [► See **Calculator Note 2B.** ◄]

Step 7 How close is the sum you found in Step 6 to your estimates in Steps 2 and 3?

The average value you found in Steps 2, 3, and 6 is called the **expected value.** It is also known as the long-run value, or mean value.

But it's the expected value of what? A numerical quantity whose value depends on the outcome of a chance experiment is called a **random variable.** In the investigation the random variable gave the number of rolls before getting a 4 on a die. You found the expected value of that random variable. The number of jumps a salmon makes before succeeding is another example of a random variable. Both of these variables are **discrete random variables** because their values are integers. They're also called **geometric random variables** because they are a count of the number of independent trials before something happens (success or failure). You will discover why these variables can be called *geometric* in the exercise set for this lesson.

The following example shows discrete random variables that are not geometric.

EXAMPLE A When two fair dice are rolled, the sum of the results varies.

a. What are the possible values of the random variable, and what probabilities are associated with those values?

b. What is the expected value of this random variable?

► Solution The random variable x has as its values all possible sums of the two dice.

a. The values of x are the integers such that $2 \le x \le 12$. The table shows each value and its probability, computed by counting numbers of outcomes.

x	2	3	4	5	6	7	8	9	10	11	12
Probability $P(x)$	$\frac{1}{36}$	$\frac{2}{36}$	$\frac{3}{36}$	$\frac{4}{36}$	$\frac{5}{36}$	$\frac{6}{36}$	$\frac{5}{36}$	$\frac{4}{36}$	$\frac{3}{36}$	$\frac{2}{36}$	$\frac{1}{36}$

b. The expected value of x is the theoretical average you'd expect to have after many rolls of the dice. Your intuition may tell you that the expected value is 7. One way of finding this weighted average is to imagine 36 "perfect" rolls, so every possible outcome occurs exactly once. The mean of the values is

$$\frac{2+3+3+4+4+4+\cdots+11+11+12}{36}=7$$

If you distribute the denominator over the terms in the numerator, and group like outcomes, you get an equivalent expression that uses the probabilities:

$$\frac{1}{36}\cdot 2+\frac{2}{36}\cdot 3+\frac{3}{36}\cdot 4+\frac{4}{36}\cdot 5+\frac{5}{36}\cdot 6+\frac{6}{36}\cdot 7+\frac{5}{36}\cdot 8+\frac{4}{36}\cdot 9+\frac{3}{36}\cdot 10+\frac{2}{36}\cdot 11+\frac{1}{36}\cdot 12=7$$

Note that each term in this expression is equivalent to the product of a value of x and the corresponding probability, $P(x)$, in the table on page 688.

Expected Value

The expected value of a random variable is an average value found by multiplying the value of each event by its probability and then summing all of the products. If $P(x)$ is the probability of an event with a value of x, then the expected value, $E(x)$, is given by the formula

$E(x) = \Sigma xP(x)$

Even if a random variable is discrete, its expected value may not be an integer.

EXAMPLE B

When Nate goes to visit his grandfather, his grandfather always gives him a piece of advice and a bill from his wallet. Grandpa closes his eyes and takes out one bill and gives it to Nate. On this visit he sends Nate to get his wallet. Nate peeks inside and sees 8 bills: 2 one-dollar bills, 3 five-dollar bills, 2 ten-dollar bills, and 1 twenty-dollar bill. What is the expected value of the bill Nate will receive?

Solution

The random variable x takes on 4 possible values, and each has a known probability.

Outcome x	\$1	\$5	\$10	\$20	
Probability $P(x)$	.25	.375	.25	.125	**Sum**
Product $x \cdot P(x)$	0.25	1.875	2.5	2.5	7.125

The expected value is \$7.125.

Expected Value

In earlier chapters students have seen summation expressions in sigma notation with the lower and upper values indicated. When these values are not specified, as in $\Sigma xP(x)$, it means that the summation is over all the possible values of x.

EXAMPLE B

[Ask] "How does the book find $P(x)$?" [by dividing the number of bills of a given denomination by the total of eight bills]

SHARING IDEAS

As students complete presentations of the investigation, **[Ask]** "Why didn't the instructions say to find 1000 values instead of 100? Wouldn't that expected value be closer to the theoretical value?" [The probability of rolling the die 100 times before a 6 is rolled is very close to 0; the probability of rolling the die more times than that will be even closer to 0 and will not significantly affect the sum.]

[Ask] "Why do you multiply the first list by the second list?" [You're looking for the average number of rolls, so you need to multiply each number of rolls by the probability that it will take that many rolls.]

To lay the groundwork for Chapter 13, **[Ask]** "Can you think of an example of a random variable that is not discrete?" [Examples: wait time on hold, height of a 5-year-old, weight of your backpack. Values of these variables are not limited to integers or even to rational numbers, even though practical measurements of the values may be limited.]

Assessing Progress
You can assess students' ability to follow instructions, find means, express patterns as formulas, and work with calculator lists.

Closing the Lesson

The main points of this lesson are that numbers might be associated with outcomes by a **random variable** and that the **expected value** of a discrete random variable can be found by multiplying the number and probability associated with each outcome and then summing these products.

BUILDING UNDERSTANDING

Students practice finding expected values.

ASSIGNING HOMEWORK

Essential	1–4
Performance assessment	5–12
Portfolio	5, 11
Journal	8
Group	5, 6, 9
Review	13–17

The other approach, using division, gives the same result:

$$\frac{1+1+5+5+5+10+10+20}{8} = \frac{57}{8} = 7.125$$

Nate doesn't actually expect Grandpa to pull out a $7.125 bill. But if Grandpa did the activity over and over again, with the same bills, the value of the bill would average $7.125. The expected value applies to a single trial, but it's based on an average over many imagined trials.

In Example B, suppose Nate always had the same choice of bills and that he had to pay his grandfather $7 for the privilege of receiving a bill. Over the long run, he'd make $0.125 per trial. On the other hand, if Nate had to pay $8 each time, his grandfather would make $0.875 on average per trial. This is the principle behind the way that raffles and casinos make money. Sometimes gamblers win, but on average gamblers lose.

Consumer CONNECTION

Casinos make money because on average gamblers bet more than they win. The amount by which the casino is favored is called the "house edge," calculated by finding the ratio of the casino's expected earnings to the player's initial wager. There are two ways that a casino creates an edge. In some games, like Blackjack, the probability is simply higher that the dealer will win. In a game like Roulette, the casino pays a winner at a rate less than the actual odds of winning. Either way, the casino always profits in the long run.

The name Roulette is derived from the Old French word *roelete,* meaning little wheel.

You can use either the mean or the probability approach to find the expected value if the random variable takes on a finite number of values. But there's no theoretical limit to the number of times you might have to roll a die before getting a 4. If the random variable has infinitely many values, you must use the probability approach to find the expected value.

EXERCISES

Practice Your Skills

1. Which of these numbers comes from a discrete random variable? Explain.
   a. the number of children who will be born to members of your class
   b. the length of your pencil in inches
   c. the number of pieces of mail in your mailbox today

1a. Yes; the number of children will be an integer, and it is based on a random process.

1b. No; the length may be a non-integer.

1c. Yes; there will be an integer number of pieces of mail, and it is based on random processes of who sends mail when.

2. Which of these numbers comes from a geometric random variable? Explain.
   a. the number of phone calls a telemarketer makes until she makes a sale
   b. the number of cats in the home of a cat owner
   c. the number of minutes until the radio plays your favorite song

3. You have learned that 8% of the students in your school are left-handed. Suppose you stop students at random and ask whether they are left-handed.
   a. What is the probability that the first left-handed person you find is on your third try? approximately .068
   b. What is the probability that you will find exactly one left-handed person in three tries? approximately .221

4. Suppose you are taking a multiple-choice test for fun. Each question has five choices (A–E). You roll a six-sided die and mark the answer according to the number on the die and leave the answer blank if the die is a 6. Each question is scored one point for a right answer, minus one-quarter point for a wrong answer, and no points for a question left blank.
   a. What is the expected value for each question? 0
   b. What is the expected value for a 30-question test? 0

Reason and Apply

5. Sly asks Andy to play a game with him. They each roll a die. If the sum is greater than 7, Andy scores 5 points. If the sum is less than 8, Sly scores 4 points.
   a. Find a friend and play the game ten times. [▶ See **Calculator Note 1L** if you have no dice. ◀] Record the final score.
   b. What is the experimental probability that Andy will have a higher score after ten games?
   c. Draw a tree diagram of this situation showing the theoretical probabilities.
   d. If you consider this game from Andy's point of view, his winning value is +5 and his losing value is −4. What is the expected value of the game from his point of view?
   e. Suggest a different distribution of points that would favor neither player.

6. Suppose each box of a certain kind of cereal contains a card with one letter from the word CHAMPION. The letters have been equally distributed in the boxes. You win a prize when you send in all eight letters.
   a. Predict the number of boxes you would expect to buy to get all eight letters. Answers will vary.
   b. Describe a method of modeling this problem using the random-number generator in your calculator.
   c. Use your method to simulate winning the prize. Do this five times. Record your results. Answers will vary.
   d. What is the average number of boxes you will have to buy to win the prize?
   e. Combine your results with those of several classmates. What seems to be the overall average number of boxes needed to win the prize?

Helping with the Exercises

2a. Yes; the result of each call is independent of other calls, and you stop counting when she is successful.

2b. No; the number of cats is a discrete random variable, but you don't stop counting when you get the first cat, it is not geometric.

2c. No; you are counting minutes until you hear a song, but because not all songs are the same length and minutes are not equivalent to songs, you are working with two different types of variables.

Exercise 4 [Ask] "Is it a good strategy to guess on this test?" [No; your expected score will be zero.]

5a. Answers will vary. Theoretically, after 10 games Sly should get about 23 points, and Andy should get about 21.

5b. Answers will vary. Theoretically, it should be close to .41.

5c.

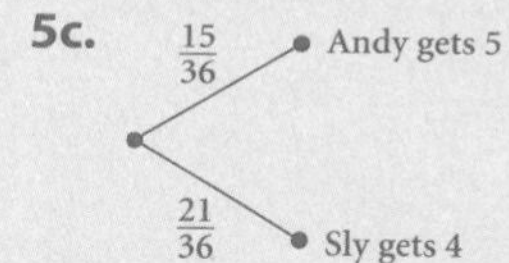

5d. −0.25

5e. Answers will vary. One possible answer is 5 points for Sly if the sum of the dice is less than 8 and 7 points for Andy if the sum of the dice is greater than 7.

6b. Sample answer: Assign each of the letters in the word CHAMPION a different number from 1 to 8. Randomly generate numbers between 1 and 8. Count how many digits you must generate until you have at least one of each number.

6d. Answers will vary. Theoretically, it should be about 22 boxes.

6e. Answers will vary. Average numbers of boxes should be about 22 boxes.

Exercise 7 [Alert] Students might ignore the conditional probability in 7c and calculate $(.16)(\$35) + (.32)(\$25) = \$13.60$. Ask whether this answer makes sense, given that the ticket is for section A or C. [No, the expected value should be between \$25 and \$35.] In 7b the probability that the ticket is from section C given that it's from section A or C is $\frac{.32}{.16 + .32} = \frac{2}{3}$.

Exercise 8 [ESL] In this context a *spinner* is a pointer fastened to the center of a circle so that it can rotate and point randomly to one of the marked sectors of the circle.

9a. .2

9b. .12

9c.

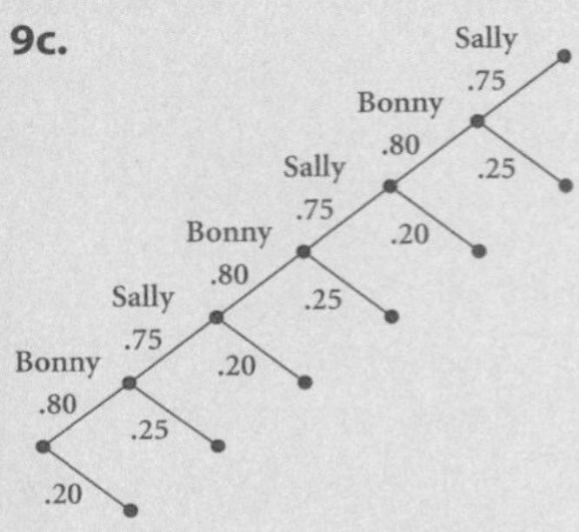

.072

9d. .392

Exercise 9e Because the sequence is geometric, random variables of this type are called *geometric random variables.*

9e. geometric; $u_1 = .20, r = .6$

9f. .476672

9g. .5

7. In a concert hall, 16% of seats are in section A, 24% are in section B, 32% are in section C, and 28% are in section D. Section A seats sell for \$35, section B for \$30, section C for \$25, and section D for \$15. You see a ticket stuck high in a tree.

a. What is the expected value of the ticket? \$25

b. The markings on the ticket look like either section A or C. If this is true, then what is the probability that the ticket is for section C? .67

c. If the ticket is for section A or C, then what is the expected value of the ticket? \$28.33

8. The tree diagram at right represents a game played by two players.

a. Find a value of x that gives approximately the same expected value for each player. approximately 7 points

b. Design a game that could be described with this tree diagram. (You may use coins, dice, spinners, or some other device.) Explain the rules of the game and the scoring of points. Answers will vary.

9. APPLICATION Bonny and Sally are playing in a tennis tournament. On average, Bonny makes 80% of her shots, whereas Sally makes 75% of hers. Bonny serves first. At right are tree diagrams depicting possible sequences of events for one and two volleys of the ball. (A volley is a single sequence of Bonny hitting the ball and Sally returning it.) Note that once a ball is missed, that branch ends.

a. What is the probability that Bonny will win the point after just one volley?

b. What is the probability that Bonny will win the point in exactly two volleys?

c. Make a tree diagram to represent three volleys. What is the probability that Bonny will win the point in exactly three volleys?

d. What is the probability that Bonny will win the point in at most three volleys?

e. What kind of sequence do the answers to 9a–c form? Explain.

f. What is the probability that Bonny will win the point in at most six volleys?

g. In the long run, what is the probability that Bonny will win the point?

Technology CONNECTION

In computer simulations of sporting events, software designers enter all the data and statistics they can find so that they can model the game as accurately as possible. In tennis, for instance, individual statistics on serves, backhand shots and forehand shots, and positions on the court are taken into account. When setting up a fantasy team or match, programmers base their formulas on actual probabilities, and even the best players or teams will lose some of the time.

American tennis players Venus and Serena Williams are shown here playing in the Women's Doubles at the 2003 Australian Open Tennis Championship in Melbourne, Australia.

10. A group of friends has a huge bag of red and blue candies, with approximately the same number of each color. Each of them picks out candies, one at a time, until he or she gets a red candy. The bag is then passed on to a friend.

a. Devise and describe a simulation for this problem. Use your simulation to approximate the long-run average number of candies each person pulled out in one turn.

b. What is the long-run average number of blue candies each person pulled out in one turn?

11. **APPLICATION** A quality-control engineer randomly selects five radios from an assembly line. Experience has shown that the probabilities of finding 0, 1, 2, 3, 4, or 5 defective radios are as shown in the table.

Number of defective radios x	Probability $P(x)$	$x \cdot P(x)$
0	.420	0
1	.312	0.312
2	.173	0.346
3	.064	0.192
4	.031	0.124
5	.000	0

a. What is the probability the engineer will find at least one defective radio in a random sample of five?

b. Make a copy of this table on your paper, and complete the entries for the column titled $x \cdot P(x)$.

c. Find the sum of the entries in the column titled $x \cdot P(x)$.

d. What is the real-world meaning of your answer in 11c?

12. What is the probability that a 6 will not appear until the eighth roll of a fair die? approximately .0465

Review

12.3 **13.** Find $P(E_1 \text{ or } E_2)$ if E_1 and E_2 are mutually exclusive and complementary. 1

12.3 **14.** Two varieties of flu spread through a school one winter. The probability that a student gets both varieties is .18. The probability that a student gets neither variety is .42. Having one variety of flu does not make a student more or less likely to get the other variety. What is the probability that a student gets exactly one of the flu varieties? .4

12.3 **15.** This table gives counts of different types of paperclips in Maricela's paperclip holder.

	Small	Large
Metal & oval	47	23
Plastic & oval	25	10
Metal & triangular	18	6
Plastic & triangular	10	5

a. Create a Venn diagram of the probabilities of picking each kind of clip if one is selected at random. Use metal, oval, and small as the categories for the three circles on your diagram.

b. Create a tree diagram of the outcomes and their probabilities. Use size on the first branch, shape on the second, and material on the third.

16. Solve $\left(\frac{1}{2}\right)^n \leq 10^{-5}$.

12.2 **17.** Suppose the probability of winning a single game of chance is .9. How many wins in a row would it take before the likelihood of such a string of wins would be less than 1%? 44

10a. Answers will vary. In the long run, the average should tend toward 2 candies.

10b. The long-run average for number of blue candies should be 1.

Exercise 11a As needed, remind students that it is sometimes easier to find $1 - P(0)$ than to find $P(1) + P(2) + P(3) + P(4) + P(5)$.

11a. .580

11c. 0.974

11d. On average, the engineer should expect to find 0.974 defective radio in a sample of 5.

Exercise 13 [Language] *Complementary* events are events that are complements (see Lesson 12.3, page 682). The probability of an event or its complement is 1.

15a.

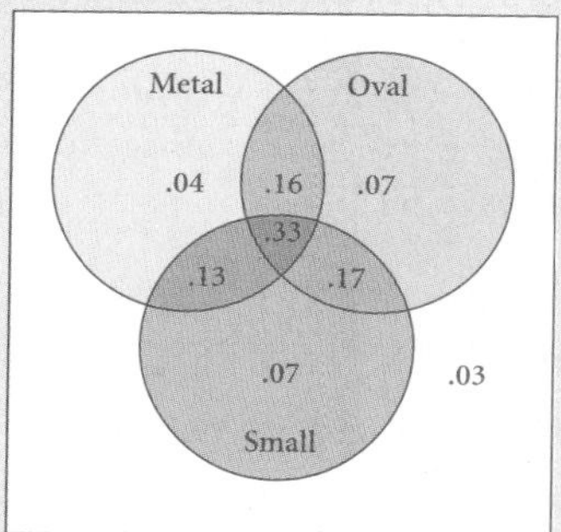

15b. Calculated using the actual frequencies:

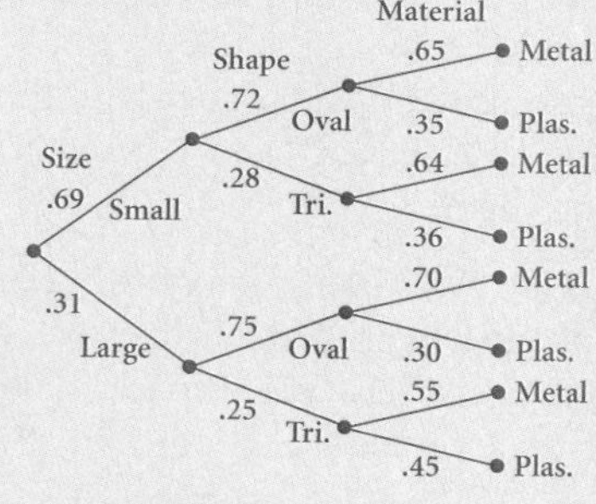

16. $n \geq \frac{5}{\log 2}$ or $n \geq 16.61$

EXTENSION

Have students design a simulation for Example B.

LESSON

12.5

PLANNING

LESSON OUTLINE

One day:

10 min Investigation

15 min Examples A and B

5 min Sharing

15 min Exercises

MATERIALS

- sets of five distinct objects
- Calculator Notes 12C, 12D

TEACHING

The counting principle is used for calculating probabilities, including the special case of counting numbers of permutations. The one-step investigation is on page 695.

Guiding the Investigation

Step 1 You might use pencils, blocks, or paper clips of different colors for the sets of objects each group is given, or you could give groups distinct items, such as a coin, a pencil, a paper clip, a book, and a pen. Students can also use scraps of paper with the letters A, B, C, D, and E printed on them.

[Ask] "Why are some of the cells of the table shaded?" [In those cases you have more spaces than puzzle pieces.]

[Alert] Some students will have difficulty finding a system for listing arrangements of four or more items, even if they could list arrangements of three items systematically. Encourage group discussion about methods of listing, not just about the numbers of arrangements.

LESSON 12.5

Permutations and Probability

Never say never. . . . Never is a long, undependable time, and life is too full of rich possibilities to have restrictions placed upon it.

GLORIA SWANSON

The numerator and denominator of a theoretical probability are numbers of possibilities. Sometimes those possibilities follow regular patterns that allow you to "count" them.

Investigation
Order and Arrange

You will need

- five different objects

Suppose you are working on a jigsaw puzzle. You get to a section of the puzzle where there are five spaces to be filled. Unfortunately, it looks as though they are all nearly the same shape and color. You grab a handful of the remaining pieces and start trying them. How many different ways could you try to fit the remaining pieces into the remaining spaces? If you try different random arrangements, how many arrangements are there to try?

Step 1 Investigate this problem using different objects to represent the puzzle pieces. Let n represent the number of objects and r the number of spaces, or slots, you need to fill. For example, $n = 3$ and $r = 2$ represents the number of different ways three pieces can fill two spaces.

In this case the order matters, so object A followed by object B is different from object B followed by object A. Copy and complete the table on the next page for different values of n and r.

LESSON OBJECTIVES

- Understand permutations as arrangements
- Use the counting principle to count permutations
- Learn factorial notation as a way to express the number of permutations of n objects chosen r at a time

NCTM STANDARDS

CONTENT		PROCESS	
✓	Number		Problem Solving
✓	Algebra	✓	Reasoning
	Geometry	✓	Communication
	Measurement	✓	Connections
✓	Data/Probability	✓	Representation

		Number of items, n				
		$n = 1$	$n = 2$	$n = 3$	$n = 4$	$n = 5$
Number of spaces, r	$r = 1$	1	2	3	4	5
	$r = 2$		2	6	12	20
	$r = 3$			6	24	60
	$r = 4$				24	120
	$r = 5$					120

Step 2 Compare your results with those of your group. Describe any patterns you found in either the rows or columns of the table.

There are many patterns you might have seen in the investigation. One pattern can be described as a product of the numbers of outcomes that fill the slots. For example, for $n = 4$ and $r = 3$, you would make three slots because $r = 3$, and then fill the first slot with four choices and decrease by one choice for each slot as you go: 4 3 2. The product of those numbers is 24, the number in the third row, fourth column of the table you completed.

Why do you multiply the numbers in the slots? The problem might remind you of a familiar situation. How many different outfits—consisting of a sweater, pants, and shoes—could you wear if you were to select from four sweaters, six pairs of pants, and two pairs of shoes?

You can visualize a tree diagram with four choices of sweaters. For each of those sweaters, you can select six different pants. Each of those sweater and pants outfits can be matched with two pairs of shoes. (Actually drawing all of the paths would be difficult and messy.) Each different outfit is represented by a path of three segments representing a sweater *and* a pair of pants *and* a pair of shoes. The paths represent all the possible outcomes, or the different ways in which the entire sequence of choices can be made.

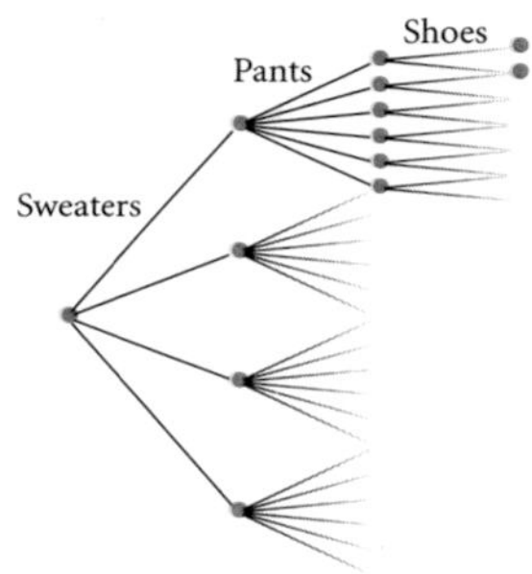

How many outfits are there? From the tree you're imagining, you can see that the total number of outfits with four choices, then six choices, and then two choices can be found by multiplying $4 \cdot 6 \cdot 2$. You are using the **counting principle.**

Counting Principle

Suppose there are n_1 ways to make a choice, and for each of these there are n_2 ways to make a second choice, and for each of these there are n_3 ways to make a third choice, and so on. The product $n_1 \cdot n_2 \cdot n_3 \cdot \cdots$ is the number of possible outcomes.

Step 2 Answers will vary and may include 1st row: consecutive integers; 2nd row: increase by consecutive even numbers; 3rd row: increase by multiples of 18; results are the same for $r = n$ and $r = n - 1$, because there is only one way to place the last object.

One Step

Pose this problem, adapted from the investigation and Example B: "Flute players Alfie, Bryce, Carrie, Drew, and Evelyn are in the pit orchestra for a musical. Only four of them are needed for each performance. If the four are chosen and lined up randomly, what's the probability that they will be sitting in alphabetical order?" As students work, watch carefully to see how systematic their listings are. Students who can list three players systematically may become more arbitrary when listing four; help them work recursively. Begin to call the arrangements *permutations.* As groups finish, challenge them to generalize their results to finding the number of arrangements of n flute players chosen r at a time.

The counting principle provides a quick method for calculating numbers of outcomes, using multiplication. Rather than memorizing the formula, you can look for patterns, and sketch or visualize a representative tree diagram.

▶ **EXAMPLE A**

[Ask] "How many different license plates are possible if the first letter can't be Z and none of the numbers can be 0?" [$\underline{25} \cdot \underline{26} \cdot \underline{26} \cdot \underline{9} \cdot \underline{9} \cdot \underline{9} = 12{,}320{,}100$]

EXAMPLE A

Suppose a set of license plates has any three letters from the alphabet, followed by any three digits.

a. How many different license plates are possible?

b. What is the probability that a license plate has no repeated letters or numbers?

▶ ***Solution***

To better understand the problem, fill in some slots.

a. There are 26 possible letters for each of the first three slots and 10 possible digits for each of the last three slots. Remember that letters and digits can repeat. Using the counting principle, you can multiply the number of possibilities:

$$\underline{26} \cdot \underline{26} \cdot \underline{26} \cdot \underline{10} \cdot \underline{10} \cdot \underline{10} = 17{,}576{,}000$$

There are 17,576,000 possible license plates.

b. Once the first letter is chosen, there are only 25 ways of choosing the second letter to avoid repetition. This pattern continues for the third letter and for the digits. Filling slots gives the product $\underline{26} \cdot \underline{25} \cdot \underline{24} \cdot \underline{10} \cdot \underline{9} \cdot \underline{8} = 11{,}232{,}000$. The probability that a license plate will be one of these arrangements is this number divided by the total number of possible outcomes:

$$\frac{11232000}{17576000} \approx .639$$

This means that about 63.9% of license plates would not have repeated letters or numbers.

This building is decorated with Colorado license plates.

When the objects cannot be used more than once, the number of possibilities decreases at each step. These are called "arrangements without replacement." In other words, once an item is chosen, that same item cannot be used again in the same arrangement.

An arrangement of some or all of the objects from a set, without replacement, is called a **permutation.** The notation ${}_nP_r$ is read "the number of permutations of n things chosen r at a time." As in the investigation and part b of Example A, you can calculate ${}_nP_r$ by multiplying $n(n-1)(n-2)(n-3)\cdots(n-r+1)$. [▶ See **Calculator Note 12C** to learn how to compute ${}_nP_r$ on a calculator.◀]

EXAMPLE B

Seven flute players are performing in an ensemble.

a. The names of all seven players are listed in the program in random order. What is the probability that the names are in alphabetical order?

b. After the performance, the players are backstage. There is a bench with only room for four to sit. How many possible seating arrangements are there?

c. What is the probability that the group of four players is sitting in alphabetical order?

▶ Solution

You can find numbers of permutations by filling in slots.

a. There are seven choices for the first name on the list, six choices remaining for the second name, five for the third name, and so on.

$${}_7P_7 = \underline{7} \cdot \underline{6} \cdot \underline{5} \cdot \underline{4} \cdot \underline{3} \cdot \underline{2} \cdot \underline{1} = 5040$$

Only one of these arrangements is in alphabetical order. The probability is $\frac{1}{5040}$, or approximately .0002.

b. In this case there are only four slots to fill. There are seven choices for the first seat, six choices remaining for the second seat, five for the third seat, and four for the fourth seat.

$${}_7P_4 = \underline{7} \cdot \underline{6} \cdot \underline{5} \cdot \underline{4} = 840$$

c. With each arrangement of 4, there is only one correct order:

$${}_4P_4 = 4 \cdot 3 \cdot 2 \cdot 1 = 24$$

There are 24 ways to arrange each grouping of 4 players, so the probability is $\frac{1}{24}$, or approximately .04167.

Notice that the answer to part c does not depend on the answer to part b.

When $r = n$, as in parts a and c of Example B, you can see that ${}_nP_r$ equals the product of integers from n all the way down to 1. A product like this is called a **factorial** and is written with an exclamation point. For example, 7 factorial, or 7!, is $7 \cdot 6 \cdot 5 \cdot 4 \cdot 3 \cdot 2 \cdot 1$, or 5040. [▶ See **Calculator Note 12D** to learn how to evaluate factorials on a calculator.◀]

Look again at Example B. You can write the solution to part a as

$${}_7P_7 = 7! = 5040$$

[Ask] "How do you express ${}_nP_r$ in words?" Students may say something like "the permutations of n objects chosen r at a time." Stress that the permutations are arrangements and that ${}_nP_r$ refers to the *number* of those arrangements.

[Ask] "Is it always true that ${}_nP_r$ equals $\frac{n!}{(n-r)!}$? What if $r = n$? Aren't you dividing by zero?" [When r equals n you are dividing by 0!. When r equals n, the quotient should be $n!$, because ${}_nP_n$ equals $n!$.] There are two choices: Every time you write ${}_nP_r = \frac{n!}{(n-r)!}$, you can add "except when $r = n$." Alternatively, you can define 0! to be 1 and not have to keep qualifying your statement. Mathematicians define 0! to be 1 to avoid the extra writing.

Ask what happens if r equals 0. The formula then yields ${}_nP_r = 1$. Is this correct? That is, is there one way to arrange none of n objects? Students may think this is strange and say that there is no way to arrange zero objects. Generally the formula is restricted to positive values of r and n.

▶ EXAMPLE B

If students are having difficulty visualizing this situation, ask seven students to stand up and get in alphabetical order. **[Ask]** "How many ways can these seven students stand in alphabetical order?" Then have the seven move into some other orders.

[Alert] You might need to remind students that in part c they are considering only four students, not the entire group of seven.

SHARING IDEAS

As students present the results of the investigation, ask them to describe their methods of systematic listing. One method for listing arrangements of four items is the recursive method, which builds on lists of arrangements of three items:

a followed by bcd, bdc, cbd, cdb, dbc, dcb

b followed by all six arrangements of acd

c followed by all six arrangements of abd

d followed by all six arrangements of abc

Elicit the idea that the six arrangements of three items can also be thought of recursively: Each item is followed by the two arrangements of the other two items.

Other methods are possible. If nobody mentions any and you want to encourage creative thinking, you might mention a "switching adjacent" method:

abcd, acbd, cadb, cdab, dcba, dbca, bdac, badc

abdc, bacd, bcad, cbda, cdba, dcab, dacb, adbc

dabc, adcb, acdb, cabd, cbad, bcda, bdca, dbac

Suggest that students pose new problems that begin with "How do you . . . ," "Is it always true that . . . ," "Why . . . ," "What if not . . . ," and "In general . . . ." Some examples follow.

For part b, you need only the product of integers from 7 down to 4. You can write this as $\frac{7!}{3!}$.

$$\frac{7!}{(7-4)!} = \frac{7!}{3!} = \frac{7 \cdot 6 \cdot 5 \cdot 4 \cdot \cancel{3} \cdot \cancel{2} \cdot \cancel{1}}{\cancel{3} \cdot \cancel{2} \cdot \cancel{1}} = 7 \cdot 6 \cdot 5 \cdot 4 = 840$$

You can use this idea to write a formula for any number of permutations, ${}_nP_r$. As you saw above, you can write the number as $\frac{n!}{(n-r)!}$.

To avoid division by 0 when $r = n$, we define 0! as equal to 1. So, when r and n are equal,

$${}_nP_r = \frac{n!}{0!} = \frac{n!}{1} = n!$$

Permutations

A **permutation** is an arrangement of some or all of the objects from a set, without replacement.

The number of permutations of n objects chosen r at a time ($r \leq n$) is

$${}_nP_r = n(n-1)(n-2) \cdots (n-r+1) = \frac{n!}{(n-r)!}$$

Verify that the formula above gives you the same values you found in the investigation.

In this lesson you used tree diagrams, the counting principle, your calculator, and perhaps other ways to count permutations. As you do the exercises, consider which strategy is best for each particular problem.

EXERCISES

Practice Your Skills

1. Screamers Ice Cream Parlor sells a triple-scoop cone. Which of these situations are permutations? For those that are not, tell why.
   a. the different cones if all three scoops are different flavors and vanilla, then lemon, then mint is considered different from vanilla, then mint, then lemon
   b. the different cones if all three scoops are different flavors and vanilla, then lemon, then mint is considered the same as vanilla, then mint, then lemon
   c. the different cones if you can repeat a flavor two or three times and vanilla, then lemon, then lemon is different from lemon, then vanilla, then lemon
   d. the different cones if you can repeat a flavor two or three times and vanilla, then lemon, then lemon is the same as lemon, then vanilla, then lemon

1b. No. We are not counting different arrangements separately.

1c. No. Repetition is not allowed in permutations.

1d. No. Repetition is not allowed in permutations.

Definition of 0!
The definition of 0! as 1 is not completely arbitrary; it is made to keep the mathematics consistent. ${}_nP_n = n!$, so if $n = r$, ${}_nP_r = \frac{n!}{0!}$ must equal $n!$, so 0! is defined as equal to 1.

Assessing Progress
As students work, you can assess their ability to make systematic lists and to find probabilities as ratios.

Closing the Lesson

The **counting principle** can be applied to counting possibilities needed for calculating probabilities. In the special case of arrangements, it is used to calculate the **number of permutations.** In the special case of arrangements of all objects in a set, the number of permutations is a **factorial.** In fact, the number of permutations of n objects chosen r at a time, designated ${}_nP_r$, can be expressed in terms of factorials even if r does not equal n.

BUILDING UNDERSTANDING

The exercises provide practice with the counting principle, counting permutations, and using factorials.

ASSIGNING HOMEWORK

Essential	1–4
Performance assessment	5–12
Portfolio	5, 11
Journal	8
Group	9, 11, 12
Review	13–17

Helping with the Exercises

1a. Yes. Different arrangements of scoops are different.

Exercise 1b These are combinations, the subject of the next lesson.

2. Evaluate the factorial expressions. (Some answers will be in terms of n.)

a. $\frac{12!}{11!}$ 12

b. $\frac{7!}{6!}$ 7

c. $\frac{(n+1)!}{n!}$ $n+1$

d. $\frac{n!}{(n-1)!}$ n

e. $\frac{120!}{118!}$ 14,280

f. $\frac{n!}{(n-2)!}$ $n(n-1)$

g. Find n if $\frac{(n+1)!}{n!} = 15$. $n = 14$

3. Evaluate each expression. (Some answers will be in terms of n.)

a. ${}_7P_3$ 210

b. ${}_7P_6$ 5040

c. ${}_{n+2}P_n$ $\frac{(n+2)!}{2}$

d. ${}_nP_{n-2}$ $\frac{n!}{2}$

4. Consider making a four-digit I.D. number using the digits 3, 5, 8, and 0.

a. How many I.D. numbers can be formed using each digit once? 24

b. How many can be formed using each digit once and not using 0 first? 18

c. How many can be formed if repetition is allowed and any digit can be first? 256

d. How many can be formed if repetition is allowed but 0 is not used first? 192

5. **APPLICATION** A combination lock has four dials. On each dial are the digits 0 to 9.

a. Suppose you forget the correct combination to open the lock. How many combinations do you have to try? If it takes 10 s to enter each combination, how long will it take you to try every possibility?

b. Suppose you replace your lock with one that has five dials, each with the digits 0 to 9. How many combinations are possible? If it still takes 10 s to enter each combination, how long will it take to try every possibility?

c. For a lock to be secure, it has to be difficult for someone to guess the correct combination. How many times as secure as a 4-dial lock is a 5-dial lock?

Consumer CONNECTION

Gaining access to personal bank, telephone, or e-mail accounts often requires using a password, usually a minimum of 4 digits and/or letters. Most businesses recommend that consumers change their passwords frequently and choose a password with more than six characters, in combinations of digits and upper- and lowercase letters, to increase the safety of their accounts. In addition, password programs are designed to automatically shut down after a certain number of consecutive incorrect passwords have been entered.

Login

User name: XXXXXXXXXX

Password: ●●●●●●

Need to change your password?

Reasoning and Apply

6. For what value(s) of n and r does ${}_nP_r = 720$? Is there more than one answer?

7. How many factors are in the expression $n(n-1)(n-2)(n-3)\cdots(n-r+1)$? r factors

8. Suppose each student in a school is assigned one locker. How many ways can three new students be assigned to five available lockers? 60

Exercise 4 [Ask] "Are any or all of these questions asking you to count permutations?" [yes; 4a and 4b]

Exercise 5 [Language] Although it is called a *combination lock*, such a lock actually uses permutations. In 5b, students can estimate the time it will take to try one combination.

5a. 10,000; $27.\overline{7}$ hr

5b. 100,000; approximately 11.57 days

5c. 10

Exercise 6 [Ask] "Why are these two permutation numbers the same for $r = 5$ and $r = 6$?" [Once you've arranged five of six objects, the place of the last object is determined, so the number of ways of arranging five of six objects is the same as the number of ways of arranging all six.]

6. $n = r = 6$, or $n = 6$ and $r = 5$, or $n = 10$ and $r = 3$, $n = 720$ and $r = 1$

9a. 40,320

9b. 5040

9c. .125

9d. Sample answer: There are eight possible positions for Volume 5, all equally likely. So $P(5 \text{ in rightmost slot}) = \frac{1}{8} = .125$.

9e. .5; sample answer: there are four even-numbered books that can be in the rightmost position out of the eight books. So the probability of an even-numbered book being on the right is $\frac{4}{8}$ or .5.

9f. 1

9g. 40,319

9h. $\frac{1}{40320} \approx .000025$

Exercise 10 A permutation of N items is an arrangement of all those items, so students are to find ${}_NP_N$.

9. An eight-volume set of reference books is kept on a shelf. The books are used frequently and put back in random order.

a. How many ways can the eight books be arranged on the shelf?

b. How many ways can the books be arranged so that Volume 5 will be the rightmost book?

c. Use the answers from 9a and b to find the probability that Volume 5 will be the rightmost book if the books are arranged at random.

d. Explain how to compute the probability in 9c using another method.

e. If the books are arranged randomly, what is the probability that the last book on the right is an even-numbered volume? Explain how you determined this probability.

f. How many ways can the books be arranged so that they are in the correct order, with volume numbers increasing from left to right?

g. How many ways can the books be arranged so that they are out of order?

h. What is the probability that the books happen to be in the correct order?

10. Suppose a computer is programmed to list all permutations of N items. Use the values given in the table below to figure out how long it will take for the computer to list all of the permutations for the remaining values of N listed. Use an appropriate time unit for each answer (minutes, hours, days, or years).

N	Number of permutations of N items	Time
5	120	0.00012 s
10	3,628,800	3.6288 s
12	479,001,600	≈ 8 min
13	6,227,020,800	≈ 1.7 h
15	$\approx 1.31 \cdot 10^{12}$	≈ 15 d
20	$\approx 2.43 \cdot 10^{18}$	≈ 77100 yr

Computers are programmed to play games such as chess by considering all possible moves. By working with a tree diagram of possible moves, a computer can choose from millions of board positions in a matter of seconds. A person, on the other hand, usually plays the game by remembering and visualizing previous winning moves. It usually takes many minutes for a human to decide which move to make.

Photographed here in 1997, champion chess player Garry Kasparov plays against IBM's chess-playing computer, Deep Blue. Kasparov lost the match.

11. You have purchased four tickets to a charity raffle. Only 50 tickets were sold. Three tickets will be drawn, and first, second, and third prizes will be awarded.

a. What is the probability that you win the first prize (and no other prize)?

b. What is the probability that you win both the first and second prizes, but not the third prize?

c. What is the probability that you win the second or third prize?

d. If the first, second, and third prizes are gift certificates for $25, $10, and $5, respectively, what is the expected value of your winnings?

12. **APPLICATION** Biologists use Punnett squares to represent the ways that genes can be passed from parent to offspring. In the Punnett squares at right, B stands for brown eyes, a dominant trait, whereas b stands for blue eyes, a recessive trait. E represents brown hair, the dominant trait, whereas e represents the recessive trait, blonde hair. If a dominant gene is present, a recessive trait will be hidden. The first row and column represent the parents' genes. The rest of the squares represent the possible pairs of genes the parents could pass on to their offspring.

a. In Table 1, both parents are brown-eyed, but one parent has a Bb gene combination, whereas the other has a BB gene combination. What is the probability of a blue-eyed (bb) offspring?

b. In Table 2, both parents are brown-eyed, each having the Bb gene combination. What is the probability of a blue-eyed (bb) offspring?

c. In Table 3, one parent is blue-eyed (bb), whereas the other is brown-eyed (Bb). What is the probability of a blue-eyed (bb) offspring?

d. According to Table 4, is it possible for two blue-eyed parents to have a child with brown eyes? Explain.

e. In Table 5, one parent is brown-eyed and brown-haired (BbEE). The other parent is brown-eyed and blonde-haired (Bbee). What is the probability of a blue-eyed, brown-haired child?

Table 1

	B	b
B	BB	Bb
B	BB	Bb

Table 2

	B	b
B	BB	Bb
b	Bb	bb

Table 3

	b	b
B	Bb	Bb
b	bb	bb

Table 4

	b	b
b	bb	bb
b	bb	bb

Table 5

	BE	BE	bE	bE
Be	BBEe	BBEe	BbEe	BbEe
Be	BBEe	BBEe	BbEe	BbEe
be	BbEe	BbEe	bbEe	bbEe
be	BbEe	BbEe	bbEe	bbEe

This photo shows an image of a karyotype, all 23 pairs of chromosomes found in every human cell. The genes in these chromosomes determine individual characteristics.

Science CONNECTION

Genetics helps predict the likelihood of inheriting particular traits. Genetics can help animal breeders develop breeds with more desirable qualities than existing breeds have. And new strains of disease-resistant crops can be developed by crossbreeding existing plants. Genetic counselors can test the genes of human parents to see whether they are carriers of genetic diseases, such as sickle-cell anemia, Tay-Sachs disease, or hemophilia, which are passed on from generation to generation. To learn more about the science of genetics, visit the weblinks at www.keymath.com/DAA .

11a. $\frac{4 \cdot 46 \cdot 45}{50 \cdot 49 \cdot 48} \approx .070$

11b. $\frac{4 \cdot 3 \cdot 46}{50 \cdot 49 \cdot 48} \approx .005$

11c. $1 - \frac{46 \cdot 45}{50 \cdot 49} \approx .155$

11d. $3.20

Exercise 12 Students can assume that the genes from each parent are equally likely.

12a. 0

12b. $\frac{1}{4} = .25$

12c. $\frac{2}{4} = .5$

12d. It is not possible because there are no brown-eyed (B) genes in the mixture.

12e. $\frac{4}{16} = .25$

13a. $\frac{30}{50} = .6$

13b. $\frac{16}{30} \approx .533$

14a. -0.5

14b. You would expect to lose 0.50 point on each of the ten tosses, or a total of -5 points.

15a. $\frac{1}{8} = .125$

15b. $\frac{3}{8} = .375$

15c. $\frac{1}{2} = .5$

16a. $y = -0.25x^2 + 2.5x - 3.25$

16b. $y = -0.25(x - 5)^2 + 3$

16c. $y = -0.25\left(x - 5 + 2\sqrt{3}\right) \cdot \left(x - 5 - 2\sqrt{3}\right)$

17a. 41

17b. about 808.3 in.^{2}

EXTENSION

Ask students to investigate methods of systematic listing used in the change ringing of bells. (Change ringing is the art of ringing tuned bells, usually in a bell tower, in continually varying order.)

Review

12.3 **13.** In a gym class of 50 students, 28 are sophomores and 30 are athletes.

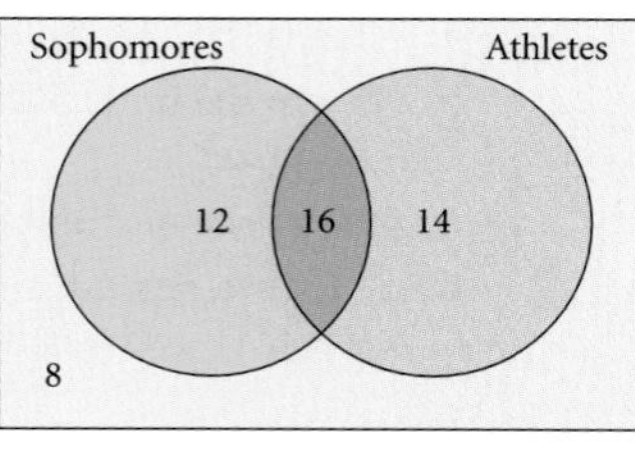

a. What is the probability that a randomly selected member of the class is an athlete?

b. If you already know a randomly selected member is an athlete, what is the probability that this student is a sophomore?

12.4 **14.** A fair six-sided die is rolled. If the number showing is even, you lose a point for each dot showing. If the number showing is odd, you win a point for each dot showing.

a. Find $E(x)$ for one roll if x represents the number of points you win.

b. Find the expected winnings for ten rolls.

15. Assume that boys and girls are equally likely to be born.

a. If there are three consecutive births, what is the probability of two girls and one boy being born, in that order?

b. What is the probability that two girls and one boy are born in any order?

c. Given that the first two babies born are girls, what is the probability that the third will be a boy?

7.4 **16.** Write the equation of the parabola at right in

a. Polynomial form. **b.** Vertex form. **c.** Factored form.

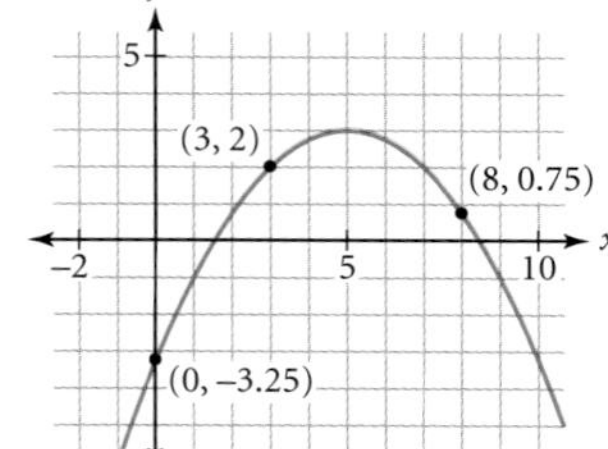

11.3 **17.** As an art project, Jesse is planning to make a set of nesting boxes (boxes that fit inside each other). Each box requires five squares that will fold into an open box with no lid. The largest box will measure 4 in. on each side. The side length of each successive box is 95% of the previous box. Jesse wants the smallest box to be no less than 0.5 in. on a side.

a. How many boxes can Jesse make in one set?

b. What is the total amount of paper needed for one set of open boxes?

IMPROVING YOUR VISUAL THINKING SKILLS

A Perfect Arrangement

Craig has a summer landscape business planting trees and shrubs. His neighbor, Mr. Malone, contracted with him to plant 5 rows of fruit trees with 4 trees in each row. He said that he had all the trees ready for him to plant. When Craig arrived to do the planting, he found 10 trees. He was about to point out the mistake, but just completed the job instead. What did he do?

IMPROVING VISUAL THINKING SKILLS

To help students overcome the tendency to assume that each tree is in only one row, you might **[Ask]** "On average, how many rows must each tree be in?" [2] "Are there any figures that are made with five lines?" [pentagons, five-pointed stars]

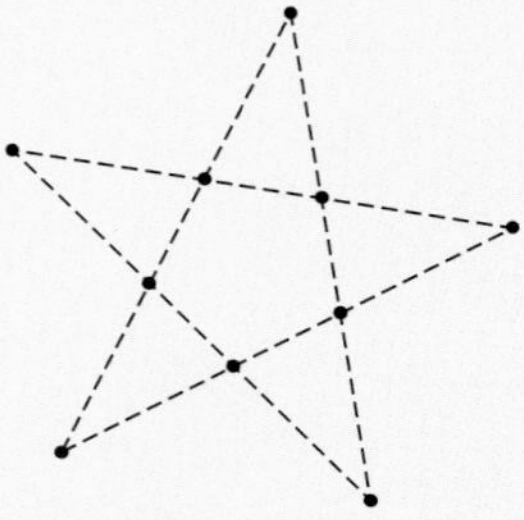

LESSON

12.6 Combinations and Probability

Math is like love—a simple idea but it can get complicated.

R. DRABEK

If three coins are flipped, a tree diagram and the counting principle both indicate that there are $\underline{2} \cdot \underline{2} \cdot \underline{2}$, or 8, equally likely outcomes: 2 choices, then 2 choices, then 2 choices. But if you are not concerned about the order in which the heads and tails occur, then you can describe paths 2, 3, and 5 as "2 heads and 1 tail," and paths 4, 6, and 7 as "1 head and 2 tails." So, if you're not concerned about order, there are only 4 outcomes, which are not equally likely:

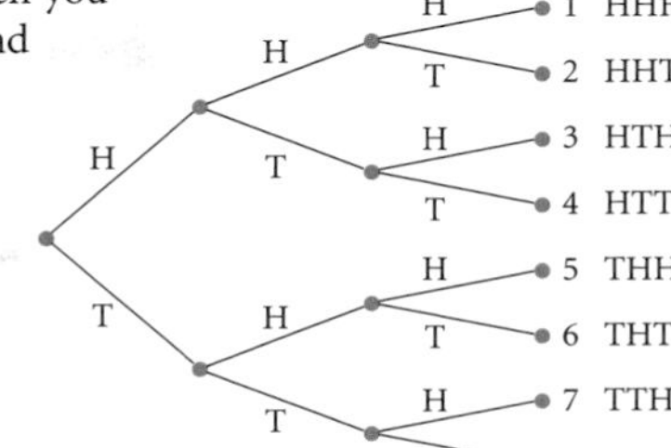

3 heads (one path)

2 heads and 1 tail (three paths)

1 head and 2 tails (three paths)

3 tails (one path)

In this lesson you will learn about counting outcomes and calculating theoretical probabilities when order doesn't matter. There are generally fewer possibilities if order doesn't matter than there are if order is important.

EXAMPLE A

At the first meeting of the International Club, the members get acquainted by introducing themselves and shaking hands. Each member shakes hands with every other member exactly once. How many handshakes are there in each of the situations listed below?

a. Three people meet.

b. Four people meet.

c. Five people meet.

d. Fifteen people meet.

LESSON

12.6

PLANNING

LESSON OUTLINE

One day:

10 min Examples

20 min Investigation

10 min Sharing

5 min Exercises

MATERIALS

- Calculator Note 12E

TEACHING

In this lesson students study how to count combinations through counting permutations and use the results to find probabilities. If you decide to start with the one-step investigation, you will find it on page 704.

[Ask] "Why are there fewer possibilities if order doesn't matter than if order is important?" [because, for example, if order doesn't matter, then HHT, HTH, and THH are the same outcome, whereas if order matters they are three distinct outcomes]

▸ ***EXAMPLE A***

You might want to have a few students demonstrate the handshaking situation for the class.

NCTM STANDARDS

CONTENT		PROCESS	
✓	Number	✓	Problem Solving
✓	Algebra	✓	Reasoning
	Geometry	✓	Communication
	Measurement	✓	Connections
✓	Data/Probability	✓	Representation

LESSON OBJECTIVES

- Learn the notation and the formula for the number of combinations
- Understand the relationships between permutations and combinations
- Use combination numbers to calculate probabilities

One Step

Pose this problem, adapted from Example B: "Five students, including you and your friend, have volunteered to be on a committee of the International Club. The committee will consist of only three members, chosen randomly from these five. What's the probability that both you and your friend will be chosen for the committee?" As students work, have them list the possibilities systematically. If they count permutations, help them see that their result doesn't make sense. During Sharing, introduce the term *combination* and help students formalize a definition of ${}_nC_r$.

▶ ***Solution***

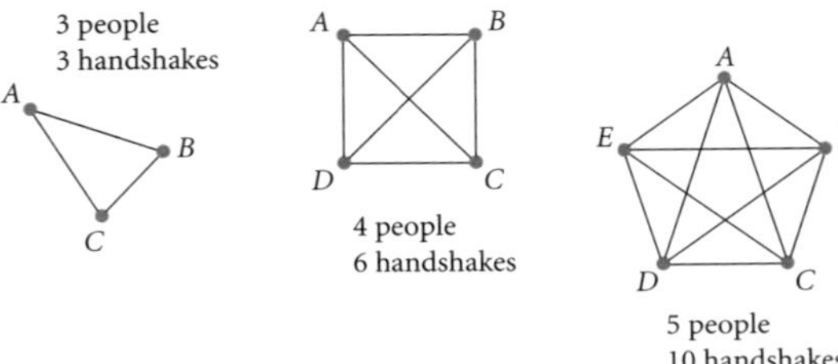

The points (vertices) pictured in the diagram above can represent the three, four, or five people in a room, and the lines (edges) can represent the handshakes. The diagrams show that there are 3 handshakes between 3 people, 6 handshakes between 4 people, and 10 handshakes between 5 people. You can find the number of handshakes by counting edges, but as you add more people to the group, it will become more difficult to draw and count. So, look for patterns to determine the number of handshakes between 15 people.

The four edges at each vertex in the five-person handshake diagram might suggest that there are $5 \cdot 4$ edges. However, if you use this method to count edges, then an edge like $\overline{DB}$ will be counted at vertex D and again at vertex B. Because $\overline{DB}$ is the same as $\overline{BD}$, you are counting twice as many edges as the actual total. The number of possibilities in which order doesn't matter is only half the number in which order does matter. Therefore, if 15 people are in the room, there are $\frac{15 \cdot 14}{2}$, or 105 handshakes.

You can think of each handshake as a pairing of two of the people in the room, or two of the vertices. When you count collections of people or objects, without regard to order, you are counting **combinations.**

The number of combinations of 5 people taken 2 at a time is symbolized by ${}_5C_2$. (The notation ${}_5C_2$ can be read as "five choose two.") Although there are ${}_5P_2$, or 20, permutations of 5 vertices taken 2 at a time, you have only half as many combinations:

$${}_5C_2 = \frac{{}_5P_2}{2} = \frac{20}{2} = 10$$

You can calculate the number of handshakes in Example A in the same way:

$${}_{15}C_2 = \frac{{}_5P_2}{2} = \frac{15 \cdot 14}{2} = 15 \cdot 7 = 105$$

There are 105 handshakes.

▶ ***EXAMPLE B***

[Ask] "Would the arrangement of members ever be important in forming a committee?" [yes, if you needed to select officers or if committee members were assigned seats]

EXAMPLE B Anna, Ben, Chang, and Dena are members of the International Club, and they have volunteered to be on a committee that will arrange a reception for exchange students. Usually there are only three students on the committee. How many different three-member committees could be formed with these four students?

▶ ***Solution*** Note that order isn't important in these committees. ABD and BDA are the same committee and shouldn't be counted more than once. The number of different committee combinations will be fewer than the number of permutations, ${}_4P_3$, or 24, listed on the next page.

ABC	**ABD**	**ACD**	**BCD**
ACB	ADB	ADC	BDC
BAC	BAD	CAD	CBD
BCA	BDA	CDA	CDB
CAB	DAB	DAC	DBC
CBA	DBA	DCA	DCB

The four committees listed in the top row can represent all of the 3!, or 6, permutations listed in each column. Therefore, the number of combinations, ${}_4C_3$, is one-sixth the number of permutations. That is, ${}_4C_3 = \frac{{}_4P_3}{3!}$. You can evaluate ${}_4C_3$ using the factorial definition of ${}_nP_r$:

$${}_4C_3 = \frac{{}_4P_3}{3!} = \frac{4!}{3!(4-3)!} = \frac{4!}{3!\,1!} = \frac{4 \cdot \not{3} \cdot \not{2} \cdot \not{1}}{\not{3} \cdot \not{2} \cdot \not{1} \cdot 1} = 4$$

Combinations

A **combination** is a grouping of some or all of the objects from a set without regard to order.

The number of combinations of n objects chosen r at a time $(r \leq n)$ is

$${}_nC_r = \frac{{}_nP_r}{r!} = \frac{n!}{r!\,(n-r)!}$$

Rather than simply memorizing the formula given above, try to understand how numbers of combinations relate to numbers of permutations and to a tree diagram. You may want to draw a representation of each problem you investigate.

You can count combinations to calculate theoretical probabilities.

EXAMPLE C

Suppose a coin is flipped 10 times.

a. What is the probability that it will land heads exactly five times?

b. What is the probability that it will land heads exactly five times, including on the third flip?

► ***EXAMPLE C***

[Ask] "How would the probability change in part b if the coin landed heads on the first and third flip?" [Rather than finding ${}_9C_4$, you would find ${}_8C_3$.]

► ***Solution***

The tree diagram for this problem has ten stages (one for each flip) and splits into two possibilities (heads or tails) at each point on the path. It's not necessary to draw the entire tree diagram. By the counting principle there are 2^{10} or 1024 possibilities.

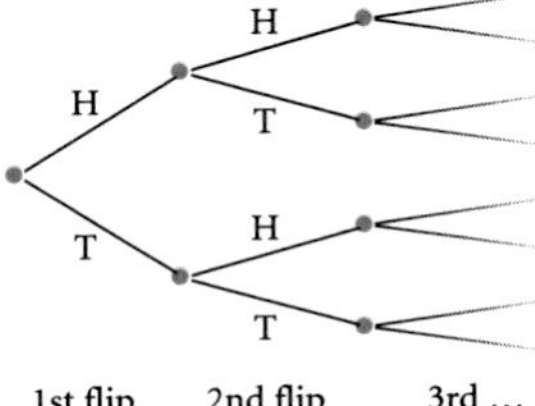

a. To find the numerator of the probability ratio, you must determine how many of the 1024 separate paths contain 5 heads. Because order is not important, you can find the number of paths that fit this description by counting combinations. There are ${}_{10}C_5 = \frac{10!}{5!\,5!} = 252$ ways of choosing 5 of the 10 flips to contain H's. [► See **Calculator Note 12E** to learn how to find numbers of combinations on a calculator. ◄] That is, 252 of the 1024 paths will contain exactly 5 heads.

Guiding the Investigation

Step 1 Students write numbers between 1 and 47 inclusive, meaning they include the numbers on the ends, 1 and 47. Although the numbers in each set are all different, the sets may overlap. If time is limited, you can reduce the number of minutes that students write down numbers.

You can use a calculator to generate random integers. You might delegate the task to students who have sat down, to give them practice and keep them involved. **[Alert]** Give students enough time to go through their list of numbers to see whether they have the winning combination.

Step 1 Answers will vary. Everyone will probably be seated before three or four numbers are generated.

Step 2 $\frac{1}{_{47}C_6} = \frac{1}{10737573} \approx .0000000931$

Step 3 Answers will vary. Multiply $1 by the number of sets that each person wrote, and then sum these products.

Step 4 Answers will vary. Students may find the average expenditure per person in their group and multiply that by the number of students in the class.

SHARING IDEAS

As students present, repeatedly **[Ask]** "What's the difference between permutations and combinations?" If students give formulas, remind them that the formulas give numbers of permutations and combinations, not the permutations or combinations themselves. The phrases *order matters* and *order doesn't matter* can be misleading in applications, such as Exercise 12, so encourage the use of the word *arrangement* for permutation and the word *committee, grouping,* or *collection* for combination.

Therefore, the probability that you will get exactly 5 heads and 5 tails is $\frac{252}{1024}$, or approximately .246.

b. If there's a head on the third flip, then the other four heads must be chosen from the other nine flips. There are $_9C_4 = \frac{9!}{5!\,4!}$ or 126 ways of making that choice. Therefore, the probability of this event is $\frac{126}{1024}$, or approximately .123.

In the investigation you'll count combinations to discover mathematical reasons why playing the lottery is a losing proposition.

Investigation
Winning the Lottery

You will do Step 1 of this investigation with the whole class. Then, in Steps 2–8, you will work with your group to analyze the results.

Consider a state lottery called Lotto 47. Twice a week, players select six different numbers between 1 and 47. The state lottery commission also selects six numbers between 1 and 47. Selection order doesn't matter, but a player needs to match all six numbers to win Lotto 47.

Step 1 Follow these directions with your class to simulate playing Lotto 47.

a. For five minutes, write down as many sets of six different numbers as you can. Write only integers between 1 and 47.

b. After five minutes of writing, everyone stands up.

c. Your teacher will generate a random integer, 1–47. Cross out all of your sets of six numbers that do not contain the given number. If you cross out all of your sets, sit down.

d. Your teacher will generate a second number, 1–47. (If it's the same number as before, it will be skipped.) Again, cross out all of your sets that do not contain this number. If you cross out all of your sets, sit down.

e. Your teacher will continue generating different random numbers until no one is still standing, or six numbers have been generated.

Work together with your group to answer the questions in Steps 2–8.

Step 2 What is the probability that any one set of six numbers wins?

Step 3 At $1 for each set of six numbers, how much did each of your group members invest during the first five minutes? What was the total group investment?

Step 4 Estimate the total amount invested by the entire class during the first five minutes. Explain how you determined this estimate.

Ask students to try to understand the formula for $_nC_r$ by figuring out where it comes from. Help them see that it is $\frac{_nP_r}{r!}$, as illustrated in Example B.

Although it's important not to override student questions with your own, demonstrate your own curiosity as an investigator. For example, a good problem opener is "Is there . . . ." You might **[Ask]** "Is there a method for listing combinations? For example, what are all the combinations of three of the letters A, B, C, D, E, and F?" As with permutations, students may have difficulty devising a system that includes all cases. The "finger method" might be helpful, especially for kinesthetic learners. Put a finger on each of A, B, and C, and then move the finger on C down the line to D, E, and F. Then move the second finger from B to C and move the third finger through D, E, and F, and so on.

Step 5 Estimate the probability that someone in your class wins. Explain how you determined this estimate.

Step 6 Estimate the probability that someone in your school would win if everyone in the school participated in this activity. Explain how you determined this estimate.

Step 7 If each possible set of six numbers were written on a 1-inch chip, and if all the chips were laid end to end, how long would the line of chips be? Convert your answer to an appropriate unit.

Step 8 Write a paragraph comparing Lotto 47 with some other event whose probability is approximately the same. Answers will vary.

Step 5 Answers will vary. Divide the answer to Step 4 (not including the $ sign) by ${}_{47}C_6$.

Step 6 Answers will vary. Multiply the average number of sets per person by the number of students in the school, and then divide by ${}_{47}C_6$.

Step 7 approximately 169 mi

Assessing Progress
You can assess students' understanding of probability and their ability to estimate and convert distance measurements.

EXERCISES

Practice Your Skills

1. Evaluate each expression without using your calculator.

a. $\frac{10!}{3!\,7!}$ 120 b. $\frac{7!}{4!\,3!}$ 35 c. $\frac{15!}{13!\,2!}$ 105 d. $\frac{7!}{7!\,0!}$ 1

2. Evaluate each expression.

a. ${}_{10}C_7$ 120 b. ${}_{7}C_3$ 35 c. ${}_{15}C_2$ 105 d. ${}_{7}C_0$ 1

3. Consider each expression in the form ${}_nP_r$ and ${}_nC_r$.

a. What is the relationship between ${}_7P_2$ and ${}_7C_2$? $\frac{{}_7P_2}{2!} = {}_7C_2$

b. What is the relationship between ${}_7P_3$ and ${}_7C_3$? $\frac{{}_7P_3}{3!} = {}_7C_3$

c. What is the relationship between ${}_7P_4$ and ${}_7C_4$? $\frac{{}_7P_4}{4!} = {}_7C_4$

d. What is the relationship between ${}_7P_7$ and ${}_7C_7$? $\frac{{}_7P_7}{7!} = {}_7C_7$

e. Describe how you can find ${}_nC_r$ if you know ${}_nP_r$. $\frac{{}_nP_r}{r!} = {}_nC_r$

4. Which is larger, ${}_{18}C_2$ or ${}_{18}C_{16}$? Explain. Neither; they are the same.

Reason and Apply

5. For what value(s) of n and r does ${}_nC_r$ equal 35?

6. Find a number r, $r \neq 4$, such that ${}_{10}C_r = {}_{10}C_4$. Explain why your answer makes sense.

7. Suppose you need to answer any four of seven essay questions on a history test and you can answer them in any order.

a. How many different question combinations are possible? 35

b. What is the probability that you include Essay Question 5 if you randomly select your combination? $\frac{20}{35} \approx .571$

Closing the Lesson

The number of possibilities in some probabilities is a number of **combinations,** or groupings. **Combination numbers** ${}_nC_r$ are smaller than the corresponding permutation numbers ${}_nP_r$ by a factor of $r!$; that is, ${}_nC_r = \frac{{}_nP_r}{r!}$, or, equivalently, ${}_nC_r = \frac{n!}{r!(n-r)!}$.

BUILDING UNDERSTANDING

Students practice counting combinations and distinguishing combinations from permutations.

ASSIGNING HOMEWORK

Essential	1–4, 7
Performance assessment	5, 6, 8–12
Portfolio	8
Journal	3, 6
Group	11
Review	13–18

Exercise 4 After students determine that the numbers are the same, ask why. [The number of ways of choosing 2 of 18 people to be on a committee is the same as the number of ways of choosing 16 of 18 people not to be on the committee.]

Exercises 5, 6 From Exercise 4, students may have grasped the idea that different pairs (n, r) can have the same value of ${}_nC_r$.

5. $n = 7$ and $r = 3$, or $n = 7$ and $r = 4$, or $n = 35$ and $r = 1$, or $n = 35$ and $r = 34$

6. $r = 6$; $\frac{10!}{4!\,6!} = \frac{10!}{6!\,4!}$; the number of 10 things taken 4 at a time is equal to the number of 10 things omitted 6 at a time.

Helping with the Exercises

Exercise 1 [Alert] Students may try to use multiplication and long division rather than cancellation.

8. Sample answer: In a true "combination" lock, the order in which the numbers are entered would not matter. In combination locks, the order of the numbers does matter, so they are more like permutation locks. However, in a true "permutation lock," repeated numbers would not be allowed.

Exercise 9d Students may wonder why this pattern holds. The sum of the combination numbers is the number of all subsets (groupings) of all sizes. A different way to count the groupings is to think of a list of all n objects and put check marks by those in a subset. There are two possibilities for each object: a check mark or no check mark. By the counting principle, the total number of possibilities (which is the number of subsets) is 2^n.

9d. The sum of all possible combinations of n things is 2^n; $2^5 = 32$.

Exercise 10b [Ask] "How long would it take to fill out 1000 tickets?" [about 2.8 hr]

Exercise 11 [Language] A *chord* of a circle is a line segment connecting two points on the circle.

Exercise 12 This is one kind of situation in which it's confusing to ask whether order matters. It doesn't matter for choosing the 12 jurors; in 12a that can be done in ${}_{30}C_{12}$ ways. Order does matter for choosing the alternates; in 12a, for each choice of 12 jurors there are 18 choices for a first alternate and, for each of these 18 choices, 17 choices for the second alternate, so the total number of ways is ${}_{30}C_{12} \cdot 18 \cdot 17$.

8. Does a "combination lock" really use combinations of numbers? Should it be called a "permutation lock?" Explain.

9. Find the following sums.

a. ${}_2C_0 + {}_2C_1 + {}_2C_2$ 4

b. ${}_3C_0 + {}_3C_1 + {}_3C_2 + {}_3C_3$ 8

c. ${}_4C_0 + {}_4C_1 + {}_4C_2 + {}_4C_3 + {}_4C_4$ 16

d. Make a conjecture about the sum of ${}_nC_0 + {}_nC_1 + \cdots + {}_nC_n$. Test it by finding the sum for all possible combinations of five things.

10. Consider the Lotto 47 game, which you simulated in the Investigation Winning the Lottery.

a. If it takes someone 10 seconds to fill out a Lotto 47 ticket, how long would it take him or her to fill out all possible tickets? approximately 3.4 yr

b. If someone fills out 1000 tickets, what is his or her probability of winning Lotto 47? $\frac{1000}{{}_{47}C_6} \approx .000093$

11. Draw a circle and space points equally on its circumference. Draw chords to connect all pairs of points. How many chords are there if you place

a. 4 points? 6

b. 5 points? 10

c. 9 points? 36

d. n points? ${}_nC_2 = \frac{n!}{2(n-2)!}$

12. In most state and local courts, 12 jurors and 2 alternates are chosen from a pool of 30 prospective jurors. The order of the alternates is specified. If a juror is unable to serve, then the first alternate will replace that juror. The second alternate will be called on if another juror is dismissed.

a. In how many ways can 12 jurors and first and second alternates be chosen from 30 people? 26,466,926,850

b. In federal court cases, 12 jurors and 4 alternates are usually selected from a pool of 64 prospective jurors. In how many ways can this be done? approximately 2.134×10^{19}

Social Science
CONNECTION

The U.S. Constitution guarantees a person accused of a crime the right to a speedy and public trial by an impartial jury. In the jury selection process, both the defense and the prosecution can "challenge" (request that the judge dismiss) potential jurors. Each side tries to seat a jury they feel will benefit their case. Often, jury consultants are brought in to evaluate prospective jurors and to investigate community and individual attitudes and biases.

A jury box

Review

7.7 **13.** Expand each expression.

a. $(x+y)^2$ $x^2+2xy+y^2$ **b.** $(x+y)^3$ $x^3+3x^2y+3xy^2+y^3$ **c.** $(x+y)^4$ $x^4+4x^3y+6x^2y^2+4xy^3+y^4$

12.2 **14.** How many speeds, or combinations of gears, does a bicycle have if it has three gears in front and five gears in the rear? 15 speeds

12.2 **15.** Use the tree diagram at right. Find each probability and explain its meaning.

a. $P(\text{H and P})$ **b.** $P(\text{P}\mid\text{H})$

c. $P(\text{P})$ **d.** $P(\text{H}\mid\text{P})$

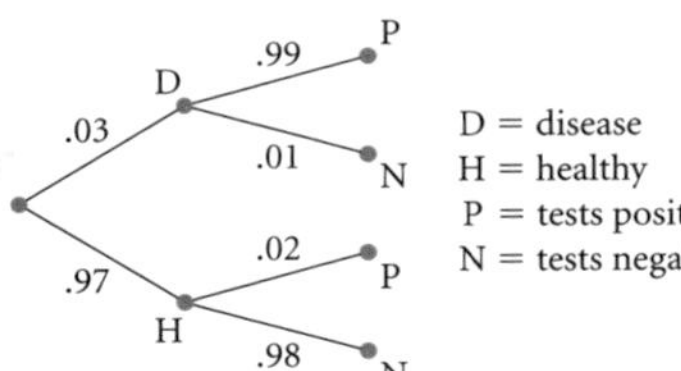

9.5 **16.** If the equation $x^2+y^2+6x-11y+C=0$ describes a circle, give the range of possible values for C. $C<\frac{157}{4}$, or $C<39.25$

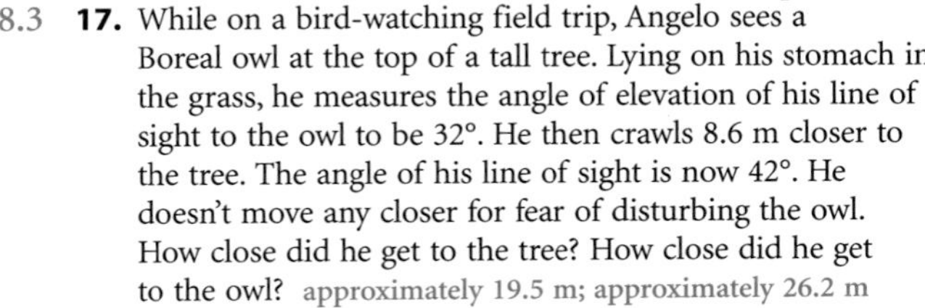

8.3 **17.** While on a bird-watching field trip, Angelo sees a Boreal owl at the top of a tall tree. Lying on his stomach in the grass, he measures the angle of elevation of his line of sight to the owl to be 32°. He then crawls 8.6 m closer to the tree. The angle of his line of sight is now 42°. He doesn't move any closer for fear of disturbing the owl. How close did he get to the tree? How close did he get to the owl? approximately 19.5 m; approximately 26.2 m

John James Audubon (1785–1851) engraved this image of a Tengmalm's night owl, known as a Boreal owl in North America.

5.6 **18.** Suppose the value of a certain building depreciates at a rate of 6% per year. When new, the building was worth $36,500.

a. How much is the building worth after 5 years and 3 months? $26,376.31

b. To the nearest month, when will the building be worth less than $10,000? 20 years 11 months

IMPROVING YOUR REASONING SKILLS

A Change of Plans

Angelo takes the train into the city for his weekly guitar lesson. After his lesson his mother picks him up at the train station knowing he will be on the 2:00 P.M. train. She always gets to the station just as the train arrives. This week when Angelo arrived for his lesson, he found out that his teacher was ill and had to cancel the lesson. Angelo went back to the train station and just managed to get the 1:00 P.M. train. He didn't have time to call his mother about the change. When he arrived at his station, he decided to start walking home until he met his mother en route to the station. When he saw her, he flagged his mother down, hopped into the car, and they arrived home 20 min ahead of their usual time. How long did Angelo walk before he met his mother?

IMPROVING REASONING SKILLS

Because motion is involved, students may use velocities and distances or temporarily assume that the train trip takes, say, 30 minutes and the car trip takes, say, 25 minutes. Another possibility is a time line as shown at right.

Students may reason if Angelo had waited for his mother, his trip from the time he arrived at the station until the time he arrived home would have been an hour longer than usual. Because he walked, he cut off 20 minutes—10 minutes off his mother's driving time each way. He was with her for 10 of those minutes; the other 10 came off the hour he was early, so he must have walked for 50 minutes.

Exercise 13 This exercise previews Lesson 12.7.

Exercise 14 Students can use a tree diagram or the counting principle.

15a. .0194 is the probability that someone is healthy but tests positive.

15b. .02 is the probability that a healthy person tests positive.

15c. .0491 is the probability that a person tests positive.

15d. .395 is the probability that a person who tests positive is healthy.

Example 17 As needed, remind students of what the angle of elevation is. If students are stuck, wonder aloud whether finding the height of the owl would help.

A Change of Plans
If students sketch a picture with variables representing the times, expressed in the same time units (minutes or hours), they might derive equations such as $2t_1-2t_2=20$ min, so $t_1-t_2=10$ min and $t_3+t_2=(60-t_1)+t_2=60-10=50$ min.

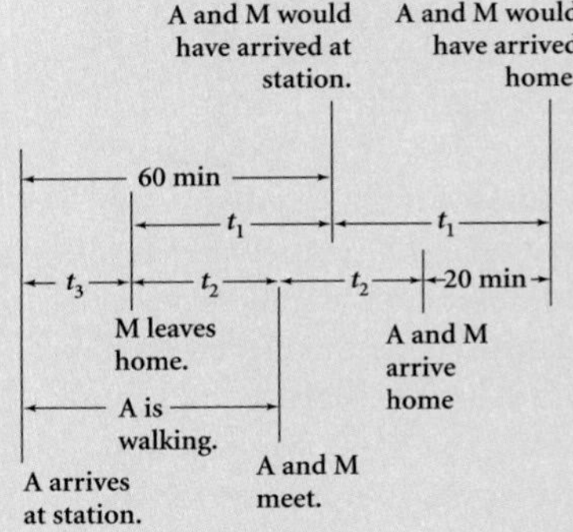

LESSON

12.7

PLANNING

LESSON OUTLINE

One day:

15 min Investigation

15 min Examples

10 min Sharing

5 min Exercises

MATERIALS

- Pascal's Triangle (T), *optional*
- Fathom demonstration Sapsuckers, *optional*

TEACHING

If your students are unfamiliar with Pascal's triangle, you might use the Pascal's Triangle transparency as you introduce this lesson.

One Step

Pose this problem, adapted from Example B: "A hatching yellow-bellied sapsucker has a .58 probability of surviving to adulthood. If a nest has 6 eggs, what are the probabilities that exactly 0, 1, 2, 3, 4, 5, and 6 birds will survive?" If students are calculating the probability that r of the birds survive as $(.58)^r$ or $(.58)^r\,(.42)^{6-r}$, let them finish and then ask whether the probabilities should sum to 1. As needed, help them see why they also need to consider the ${}_6C_n$ choices of which r birds survive. Push groups that finish first to generalize their results. If students see the relationship to binomial coefficients or Pascal's triangle, have them present their ideas during Sharing; otherwise, raise these ideas yourself and investigate the reasons for the relationships.

LESSON 12.7

The Binomial Theorem and Pascal's Triangle

Mathematics is the science of patterns.

LYNN ARTHUR STEEN

1

1 1

1 2 1

1 3 3 1

1 4 6 4 1

1 5 10 10 5 1

Probability is an area of mathematics that is rich with patterns. Many random processes, such as flipping coins, involve patterns in which there are two possible outcomes. In this lesson you will learn about using the binomial theorem and Pascal's triangle to find probabilities in those cases.

Shown at left is **Pascal's triangle.** It contains many different patterns that have been studied for centuries. The triangle begins with a 1, then there are two 1's below it. Each successive row is filled in with numbers formed by adding the two numbers above it. For example, each of the 4's is the sum of a 1 and a 3 in the previous row. Every row begins and ends with a 1.

In Lesson 12.6, you studied numbers of combinations. These numbers occur in the rows of Pascal's triangle. For example, the numbers 1, 5, 10, 10, 5, and 1 in the sixth row are the values of ${}_5C_r$:

$${}_5C_0 = 1 \quad {}_5C_1 = 5 \quad {}_5C_2 = 10 \quad {}_5C_3 = 10 \quad {}_5C_4 = 5 \quad {}_5C_5 = 1$$

Is this the case in all rows? If so, why? In the investigation you'll explore these questions.

Investigation
Pascal's Triangle and Combination Numbers

A group of five students regularly eats lunch together, but each day only three of them can show up.

Step 1 How many groups of three students could there be? Express your answer in the form ${}_nC_r$ and as a numeral.

Step 2 If Leora is definitely at the table, how many other students are at the table? How many students are there to choose from? Find the number of combinations of students possible in this instance. Express your answer in the form ${}_nC_r$ and as a numeral.

Step 3 How many combinations are there that don't include Leora? Consider how many students there are to select from and how many are to be chosen. Express your answer in the form ${}_nC_r$ and as a numeral.

Step 4 Repeat Steps 1–3 for groups of four of the five students.

Step 1 ${}_5C_3 = 10$

Step 2 2; 4; ${}_4C_2 = 6$

Step 3 ${}_4C_3 = 4$

Step 4 ${}_5C_4 = 5$; ${}_4C_3 = 4$; ${}_4C_4 = 1$

LESSON OBJECTIVES

- Relate Pascal's triangle to combination numbers
- Relate Pascal's triangle and combination numbers to binomial expansions
- Use the Binomial Theorem to represent probabilities when there are only two outcomes
- Explore the probability of an outcome in a population when the probability of that outcome in a given sample is known

Step 5 What patterns do you notice in your answers to Steps 1–3 for groups of three students and four students? Write a general rule that expresses ${}_nC_r$ as a sum of other combination numbers.

Step 6 How does this rule relate to Pascal's triangle?

Pascal's triangle can provide a shortcut for expanding binomials. An **expansion** of a binomial raised to a power is the power expressed as a single polynomial. For example, the expansion of $(x + y)^3$ is $1x^3 + 3x^2y + 3xy^2 + 1y^3$. Note that the coefficients of this expansion are the numbers in the fourth row of Pascal's triangle.

Why are the numbers in Pascal's triangle equal to the coefficients of a binomial expansion? Remember that the numbers in Pascal's triangle are evaluations of ${}_nC_r$. So, the question could also be asked, why are the coefficients of a binomial expansion equal to values of ${}_nC_r$?

EXAMPLE A Expand $(\text{H} + \text{T})^3$. Relate the coefficients in the expansion to combinations.

▶ ***Solution***

You can write $(\text{H} + \text{T})^3$ as (H + T)(H + T)(H + T). To expand this product, multiply in steps. First you multiply the first binomial, (H + T), by the second binomial, (H + T):

$$(\text{H} + \text{T})(\text{H} + \text{T}) = (\text{HH} + \text{HT} + \text{TH} + \text{TT})$$

Then you multiply each term of that result with the H and the T in the third binomial:

$$(\text{HH} + \text{HT} + \text{TH} + \text{TT})(\text{H} + \text{T}) =$$
$$\text{HHH} + \text{HHT} + \text{HTH} + \text{HTT} + \text{THH} + \text{THT} + \text{TTH} + \text{TTT}$$

Notice that if H represents flipping a head, and T represents flipping a tail, this result shows you all the possible outcomes of flipping a coin three times. If the order does not matter, you can also write this expression as

$$1\text{H}^3 + 3\text{H}^2\text{T} + 3\text{HT}^2 + 1\text{T}^3$$

This expression shows that there is one way of getting three heads, there are three ways of getting two heads and a tail, and so on. You can also express these numbers of combinations as ${}_3C_3$, ${}_3C_2$, and so on.

Here are binomial expansions of the first few powers of (H + T). Notice that the coefficients are the same as the rows in Pascal's triangle. Think about what these expansions tell you about the results of flipping a coin 0, 1, 2, and 3 times.

$(\text{H} + \text{T})^0 =$	1	1st row
$(\text{H} + \text{T})^1 =$	$1\text{H} + 1\text{T}$	2nd row
$(\text{H} + \text{T})^2 =$	$1\text{H}^2 + 2\text{HT} + 1\text{T}^2$	3rd row
$(\text{H} + \text{T})^3 =$	$1\text{H}^3 + 3\text{H}^2\text{T} + 3\text{HT}^2 + 1\text{T}^3$	4th row

Notice the pattern in the coefficients. You can use Pascal's triangle, or the values of ${}_nC_r$, to expand binomials without multiplying all the terms together.

Guiding the Investigation

Step 5 Students might benefit from first writing out the sums for Steps 1–4 $\left({}_5C_3 = {}_4C_2 + {}_4C_3\right.$ and $\left.{}_5C_4 = {}_4C_3 + {}_4C_4\right)$ before generalizing to n and r.

Step 5 The answer to Step 1 is equal to the sum of the answers to Steps 2 and 3.
${}_nC_r = {}_{n-1}C_{r-1} + {}_{n-1}C_r$

Step 6 Each number (except a 1) is the sum of the two numbers above it in the preceding row.

▶ ***EXAMPLE A***

To emphasize why the binomial coefficients are combination numbers, you might write (H + T)(H + T)(H + T) on the board or the overhead and use two fingers to point to where the H's and T's are coming from. For example, to get two H's and one T, you can take H's from the first two factors and a T from the third factor, or H's from the first and third factors and a T from the middle factor, or H's from the last two factors and a T from the first factor. Thus there are ${}_3C_2$ ways of choosing two of the three H's (or one of the three T's) to appear in the product; that is, the coefficient of HHT, or H^2T, is ${}_3C_2$.

NCTM STANDARDS

CONTENT		PROCESS	
✓	Number		Problem Solving
✓	Algebra	✓	Reasoning
	Geometry	✓	Communication
	Measurement	✓	Connections
✓	Data/Probability	✓	Representation

The Binomial Theorem

If a binomial $(p + q)$ is raised to a whole number power, n, the coefficients of the expansion are the combination numbers ${}_nC_n$ to ${}_nC_0$, as shown:

$$(p + q)^n = {}_nC_np^nq^0 + {}_nC_{(n-1)}p^{n-1}q^1 + {}_nC_{(n-2)}p^{n-2}q^2 + \cdots + {}_nC_0p^0q^n$$

or

$$(p + q)^n = \sum_{j=0}^{n} {}_nC_{(n-j)} \cdot p^{n-j}q^j$$

You can use binomial expansions to represent results of random processes with two possible outcomes. In Example A, you saw that if a coin is flipped three times, these outcomes are possible: 1 outcome of 3 heads, 3 outcomes of 2 heads and 1 tail, 3 outcomes of 1 head and 2 tails, and 1 outcome of 3 tails.

When you flip a fair coin, the outcomes H and T are equally likely. Example B shows how you can use a binomial expansion to find probabilities of outcomes that are not equally likely.

► ***EXAMPLE B***

[Language] You may need to review the meaning of *at most* and *at least*. For example, at least 6 means 6 or more survivals, and at most 6 means 0, 1, 2, 3, 4, 5, or 6 survivals.

You're looking for individual probabilities, so you consider the terms rather than the sum of the binomial expansion.

Creating a tree diagram might help some students, but only if they remember to take into account that these are combinations (that is, SSSSSN is the same as SNSSSS).

You can use the Fathom demonstration Sapsuckers instead of Example B.

EXAMPLE B

Suppose that a hatching yellow-bellied sapsucker has a .58 probability of surviving to adulthood. If a nest has 6 eggs, what are the probabilities that 0, 1, 2, 3, 4, 5, and 6 birds will survive?

A yellow-bellied sapsucker

► ***Solution***

Represent the event of survival, or success, with S and the event of nonsurvival with N. Then let s represent $P(\text{S})$, the probability of a bird's survival, and let n represent $P(\text{N})$. The outcome that 4 of the 6 birds survive and the other 2 do not survive is given by S^4N^2. The number of combinations in which 4 birds survive is given by ${}_6C_4$. You can see the expression ${}_6C_4\text{S}^4\text{N}^2$ in the expansion of $(\text{S} + \text{N})^6$.

$$(\text{S} + \text{N})^6 = {}_6C_6\text{S}^6\text{N}^0 + {}_6C_5\text{S}^5\text{N}^1 + {}_6C_4\text{S}^4\text{N}^2 + {}_6C_3\text{S}^3\text{N}^3 + {}_6C_2\text{S}^2\text{N}^4 + {}_6C_1\text{S}^1\text{N}^5 + {}_6C_0\text{S}^0\text{N}^6$$

In fact, each term of the binomial expansion gives a number of ways that a certain number of birds will survive and the others will not. You can write a similar expansion using s and n to find the probability of each of those combinations. You can then substitute .58 for s and .42 for n to find the probability of each outcome.

$$\begin{aligned}(s + n)^6 &= {}_6C_6s^6n^0 + {}_6C_5s^5n^1 + {}_6C_4s^4n^2 + {}_6C_3s^3n^3 + {}_6C_2s^2n^4 + {}_6C_1s^1n^5 + {}_6C_0s^0n^6 \\ &= 1(.58)^6(.42)^0 + 6(.58)^5(.42)^1 + 15(.58)^4(.42)^2 + 20(.58)^3(.42)^3 + 15(.58)^2(.42)^4 + 6(.58)^1(.42)^5 + 1(.58)^0(.42)^6 \\ &\approx .038 + .165 + .299 + .289 + .157 + .045 + .005\end{aligned}$$

You can put these numbers into a table to organize the information.

Number of birds that survive x	6	5	4	3	2	1	0
Probability $P(x)$	.038	.165	.299	.289	.157	.045	.005

So, it is most likely that 4 birds survive and very unlikely that 0 will survive.

You could show these probabilities with a histogram, as shown at right. This display allows you to compare the probabilities of different outcomes quickly. Notice the general shape of the histogram. You'll learn more about probability diagrams like these in Chapter 13.

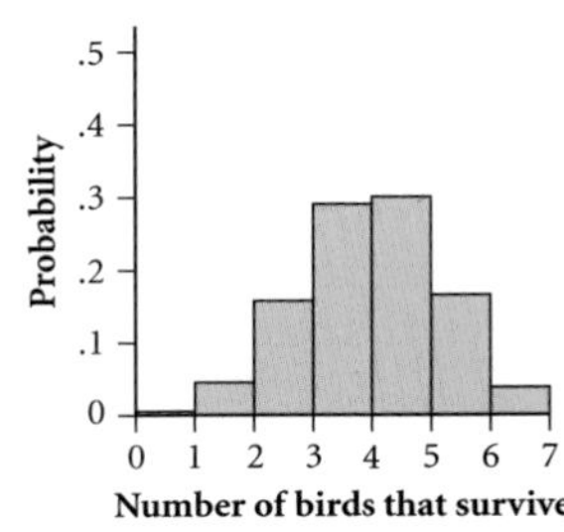

In a situation like Example B, sometimes you want to know the probability that at most 4 birds survive or that at least 4 birds survive. How could you calculate the values in this expanded table? You will calculate the missing table values in Exercise 3.

	6 birds	5 birds	4 birds	3 birds	2 birds	1 bird	0 birds
Exactly	.038	.165		.289	.157	.045	.005
At most	1	.962			.207	.050	.005
At least	.038				.949	.995	1

You can think of the 6 birds as a **sample** taken from a **population** of many birds. You know the probability of success in the population, and you want to calculate various probabilities of success in the sample. You saw in Example B that a survival rate of 4 birds was most likely.

What if the situation is reversed? Suppose you don't know what the probability of success in the population is, but you do know that on average 4 out of 6 birds survive to adulthood. This ratio would indicate a population success probability of $\frac{4}{6}$, or .67; but you saw in the example that this ratio is also highly likely with a population success probability of .58. What range of population success probabilities would have the highest probability of 4 survivors out of 6?

This kind of problem often presents itself when voters are polled. A pollster questions a sample of voters, not the entire population. Statisticians then have to interpret the data from that sample to make predictions about the population.

Example B (continued)

[Ask] "What is the expected number of birds that will survive?" [3.48 birds] **[Ask]** "Should the probabilities in the table sum to 1?" Let students discuss this question and decide that the probabilities should sum to 1 but don't. Rounding off often creates this kind of discrepancy in analyzing data.

Probability of Survival Table

Values in the "at most" and "at least" rows can be calculated in two different ways. Because values are rounded, the answers are slightly different. For example, you can find the probability that at most 5 birds survive by subtracting the probability that 6 birds survive from 1: $1 - .038 = .962$. Or you could add the probabilities that 0, 1, 2, 3, 4, or 5 birds survive: $.005 + .045 + .157 + .289 + .299 + .165 = .960$.

▶ EXAMPLE C

[Alert] Students may have difficulty understanding that this problem is the reverse of the previous example: Here a sample probability is known and a population probability is being sought. The task is to find what population probabilities of support would make it more likely that a sample would include exactly 24 supporters (as this one did) rather than 23 or 25 supporters.

[Alert] Students may get lost in the algebraic calculations when the factorial signs disappear. **[Ask]** "What is $\frac{24!}{23!}$?" [24] "What is $\frac{9!}{8!}$?" [9] You might suggest that they find numerals for 24! 8! and 23! 9! and work out the rest of the steps using those numbers.

Referring to the graph on page 715, **[Ask]** "Why does the book replace $\frac{25}{33}$ with 75% when the fraction rounds to 76%?" [One condition on p that ensures that the sample probability .75 is the most likely probability is that p be less than $.\overline{75}$. You can't conclude this condition from the statement $p < .7576$, which allows possibilities of p larger than $.\overline{75}$, but you can conclude that p is less than $.\overline{75}$ from the statement $p < .7575$.]

Students will solve the second inequality in Exercise 5.

SHARING IDEAS

As students present their ideas about the investigation, keep asking them to explain in their own words why the rule ${}_nC_r = {}_{n-1}C_{r-1} + {}_{n-1}C_r$ holds. Then encourage them to pose their own problems. Good question openers might include "What patterns . . ." and "Under what conditions . . ." as in the following questions. Be open to all questions, and take advantage of teachable moments. Feel free to deviate from your plans as you practice the craft of teaching.

EXAMPLE C

A random sample of 32 voters is taken from a large population. In the sample, 24 voters favor passing a proposal. What is the probability that a randomly selected member of the whole population favors the proposal? What can you predict about the whole population?

▶ Solution

The ratio of supporters to voters in the sample is $\frac{24}{32}$, or 0.75. This ratio of support in the sample is highly likely if the probability that a randomly chosen member of the population supports the proposal is also .75. But it could also occur for other probabilities of success in the population.

You can represent the unknown probability of support in the population with p and the probability of nonsupport with q. Because p and q are complements, the value of q is $1 - p$. The probability that exactly n people in a sample of 32 will be supporters is ${}_{32}C_n p^n q^{32-n}$.

If $n = 24$, as in the sample taken, then the most likely value of p is .75. In fact, if you graph $y = {}_{32}C_{24}p^{24}(1-p)^8$, the maximum value of the function is at $p = .75$.

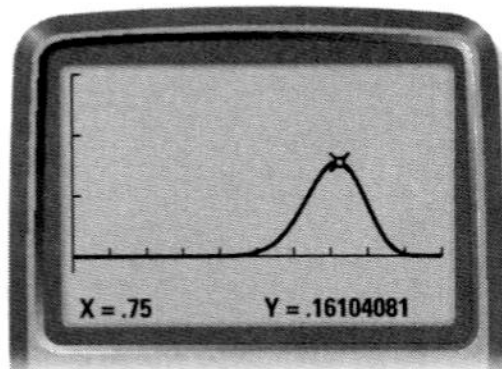

But there may be other values of p for which 24 supporters are likely. What other values of p give a higher probability of 24 supporters than of 23 or 25 supporters? That is, what values of p will satisfy these two inequalities?

$${}_{32}C_{24}p^{24}q^8 > {}_{32}C_{23}p^{23}q^9 \quad \text{and} \quad {}_{32}C_{24}p^{24}q^8 > {}_{32}C_{25}p^{25}q^7$$

You can solve the first inequality using algebra.

${}_{32}C_{24}p^{24}q^8 > {}_{32}C_{23}p^{23}q^9$	Original inequality.
${}_{32}C_{24}p > {}_{32}C_{23}q$	Divide both sides by p^{23} and by q^8.
$\frac{32!}{24!\,8!}p > \frac{32!}{23!\,9!}q$	Substitute numbers of combinations for ${}_{32}C_{24}$ and ${}_{32}C_{23}$.
$\frac{p}{24!\,8!} > \frac{q}{23!\,9!}$	Divide both sides by 32!.
$9p > 24q$	Multiply both sides by 24! and by 9!.
$9p > 24(1-p)$	Replace q with $1 - p$.
$33p > 24$	Add $24p$ to both sides.
$p > \frac{24}{33}$	Divide both sides by 33.

Solving the other inequality in the same way gives

$$p < \frac{25}{33}$$

[Ask] "What patterns do you see in the binomial expansion?" [Some examples: Powers of p decrease by 1 as powers of q increase by 1; there are n terms; the exponents of p and q always sum to n; the numerical coefficients in the rows are symmetric.] Because of the symmetry, it doesn't matter whether the coefficients are given from ${}_nC_0$ to ${}_nC_n$ or from ${}_nC_n$ to ${}_nC_0$. For notational purposes and for clarity in most problem scenarios, r matches the exponent on p in the book.

Direct students' attention to Example C and **[Ask]** "Under what conditions would you ever want to know the population probability?" This kind of information is especially interesting when polls indicate that slightly more or less than 50% of a sample will vote in a particular way. Finding the likely probability of votes in the general population tells you how much confidence you can have in the sample.

You can then say that

$\frac{24}{33} < p < \frac{25}{33}$, or $.7273 < p < .7576$

Compare the graph on page 714 with the graphs of $y = {}_{32}C_{23}p^{23}(1-p)^9$ and $y = {}_{32}C_{25}p^{25}(1-p)^7$, shown below. You find that the inequality corresponds to the portion of the graph where the value of the original function is higher than either of these two functions.

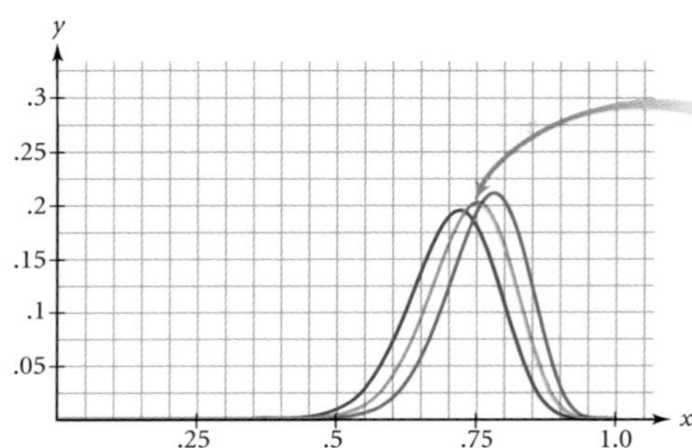

Over the domain $.7273 < p < .7576$, the probability of 24 supporters in the sample is higher than the probablity of 23 or 25.

So, a random member of the population is most likely to have a probability between about 73% and 75% of favoring the proposal. The proposal is likely to pass.

In Example C, you found an interval for a population probability. In Chapter 13, you will learn about another type of interval based on probability.

EXERCISES

You will need

Statistics software for Exercise **18**

Practice Your Skills

1. Given the expression $(x + y)^{47}$, find the terms below.

a. 1st term x^{47} **b.** 11th term $5{,}178{,}066{,}751x^{37}y^{10}$ **c.** 41st term $62{,}891{,}499x^7y^{40}$ **d.** 47th term $47xy^{46}$

2. If the probability of success for each trial is .25 and all trials are independent, then

a. What is the probability of failure for a single trial? .75

b. What is the probability of two successes in two trials? .0625

c. What is the probability of n successes in n trials? $(.25)^n$

d. What is the probability that there will be some combination of two successes and three failures in five trials? approximately .264

3. Return to the expanded table after Example B on page 713.

a. Fill in the missing probability in the "exactly" row. .299

b. Find the two missing probabilities in the "at most" row. For example, to find the probability that *at most* 2 birds survive, you could find the sum of the probabilities of 0, 1, and 2 birds surviving. .795, .496

c. Find the three missing probabilities in the "at least" row. .203, .502, .791

d. Why don't the "at most" and "at least" values for each number of birds sum to 1?

e. Make a statement about birds that incorporates the 20.3% entry in the "at least" row.

Assessing Progress
From students' work on the investigation, you can assess their understanding of counting combinations.

Closing the Lesson

The numbers in Pascal's triangle are combination numbers, leading to a new rule for combination numbers that makes sense in terms of groupings: ${}_nC_r = {}_{n-1}C_{r-1} + {}_{n-1}C_r$. Combination numbers also appear in the binomial theorem, which can be applied to analyzing random processes with two possible outcomes.

BUILDING UNDERSTANDING

Students work with Pascal's triangle, the Binomial Theorem, and combination numbers.

ASSIGNING HOMEWORK

Essential	1–5
Performance assessment	6–16
Portfolio	12
Journal	3, 6, 13
Group	15
Review	17–19

MATERIALS

- Calculator Note 12F

Exercise 3 Answers for 3b and 3c may vary slightly, based on students' method of calculation. (See the note on the Probability of Survival Table on page 713.)

3d. Both the "at most" and "at least" numbers include the case of "exactly." For example, if "exactly" 5 birds (.165) is subtracted from "at least" 5 birds (.203), the result (.038) is the same as 1 − .962 ("at most" 5 birds).

3e. The probability that at least 5 birds survive is 20.3%.

Helping with the Exercises

Exercise 5 This is the second inequality in Example C.

6a. HH, HT, TH, TT

6b. HH, HT, TH, TT

6c. Both diagrams would look the same.

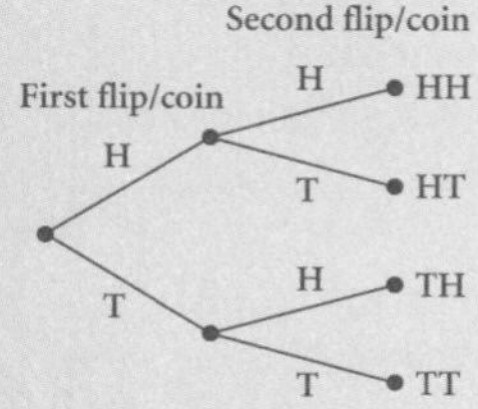

6d. ${}_2C_0 = 1$ is the number of ways of getting 0 tails, ${}_2C_1 = 2$ is the number of ways of getting 1 tail, and ${}_2C_2 = 1$ is the number of ways of getting 2 tails.

6e. There is 1 way of getting 2 heads; there are 2 ways of getting 1 head and 1 tail; and there is 1 way of getting 2 tails.

7a. $x^4 + 4x^3y + 6x^2y^2 + 4xy^3 + y^4$

7b. $p^5 + 5p^4q + 10p^3q^2 + 10p^2q^3 + 5pq^4 + q^5$

7c. $8x^3 + 36x^2 + 54x + 27$

7d. $81x^4 - 432x^3 + 864x^2 - 768x + 256$

8a. ${}_{50}C_{40} \cdot p^{10}q^{40}$ or ${}_{50}C_{10} \cdot p^{10}q^{40}$

8b. ${}_{50}C_{10}p^{10}q^{40} > {}_{50}C_{11}p^{11}q^{39}$

8c. ${}_{50}C_{10}p^{10}q^{40} > {}_{50}C_{9}p^{9}q^{41}$

8d. $\frac{10}{51} < p < \frac{11}{51}$ or $.1961 < p < .2157$

Exercise 9a As needed, **[Ask]** "Which term in the binomial expansion would represent this probability?" $\left[{}_{30}C_0(.97)^{30}(.03)^0\right]$

9a. .401

9b. .940

9c. $Y_1 = {}_{30}C_x(.97)^{30-x}(.03)^x$

9d. .940

4. Suppose that the probability of success is .62. What is the probability that there are 35 successes in 50 trials? .0606

5. Solve for p: ${}_{32}C_{24}p^{24}q^8 > {}_{32}C_{25}p^{25}q^7$ $p < \frac{25}{33}$

Reason and Apply

6. Answer each probability question.

a. List the equally likely outcomes if a coin is tossed twice.

b. List the equally likely outcomes if two coins are tossed once.

c. Draw tree diagrams that illustrate the answers to 6a and b.

d. Describe the connection between the expressions ${}_2C_0 = 1$, ${}_2C_1 = 2$, and ${}_2C_2 = 1$, and the results of your answers to 6a–c.

e. Give a real-world meaning to the equation

$$(H + T)^2 = 1H^2 + 2HT + 1T^2$$

7. Expand each binomial expression.

a. $(x + y)^4$ **b.** $(p + q)^5$ **c.** $(2x + 3)^3$ **d.** $(3x - 4)^4$

8. **APPLICATION** A survey of 50 people shows that only 10 support a new traffic circle.

a. Which term of $(p + q)^{50}$ would correspond to the results of this sample?

b. What inequality does p satisfy if the probability that 10 of the 50 are supporters is more than the probability that 11 are supporters?

c. What inequality does p satisfy if the probability that 10 of the 50 are supporters is more than the probability that 9 are supporters?

d. Solve these inequalities to find an interval for p.

9. Dr. Miller is using a method of treatment that is 97% effective.

a. What is the probability that there will be no failure in 30 treatments?

b. What is the probability that there will be fewer than 3 failures in 30 treatments?

c. Let x represent the number of failures in 30 treatments. Write an equation that will provide a table of values representing the probability $P(x)$ for any value of x.

d. Use the equation and table from 9c to find the probability that there will be fewer than 3 failures in 30 treatments.

10. A university medical research team has developed a new test that is 88% effective at detecting a disease in its early stages. What is the probability that there will be more than 20 incorrect readings in 100 applications of the test on subjects known to have the disease? [See **Calculator Note 12F** to learn how to find the terms of a binomial expansion.] .007

11. Suppose the probability is .12 that a randomly chosen penny was minted before 1975. What is the probability that you will find 25 or more such coins in

a. A roll of 100 pennies? .000257

b. Two rolls of 100 pennies each? .446

c. Three rolls of 100 pennies each? .983

Exercise 10 **[Ask]** "Before looking at Calculator Note 12F, what calculation would you want to make?" [Let F represent an incorrect reading. $P(F > 20) = P(F = 21) + P(F = 22) + \cdots + P(F = 100)$, which is the same as $1 - (P(F = 0) + P(F = 1) + \cdots + P(F = 20))$.]

Exercise 11 **[ESL]** *Minted* means "made" when speaking of coins.

12. Suppose that a blue-footed booby has a 47% chance of surviving from egg to adulthood. For a nest of four eggs

a. What is the probability that all four birds will hatch and survive to adulthood?

b. What is the probability that none of the four birds will hatch and survive to adulthood?

c. How many birds would you expect to survive?

A pair of blue-footed boobies

13. A fair coin is tossed five times and comes up heads four out of five times. In your opinion, is this event a rare occurrence? Defend your position.

14. Data collected over the last ten years show that, in a particular town, it will rain sometime during 30% of the days in the spring. How likely is it that there will be a week with

a. Exactly five rainy days?

b. Exactly six rainy days?

c. Exactly seven rainy days?

d. At least five rainy days?

15. Consider the function $y = f(x) = \left(1 + \frac{1}{x}\right)^x$. Note that the right side of the equation is a binomial raised to a power.

a. Fill in the table below using the Binomial Theorem or Pascal's triangle. Verify using your calculator.

x	1	2	3	4
y	2	2.25	≈ 2.370	≈ 2.441

b. Using your calculator, find $f(10), f(100), f(1000)$, and $f(10000)$.

c. Describe what happens to the values of $f(x)$ as you use larger and larger values of x.

Mathematics
CONNECTION

The real number e is a mathematical constant whose value is 2.718... . When a quantity changes at a rate proportional to the quantity present, the growth can be modeled using an exponential function with base e. This kind of change occurs when money is continuously compounded, when a capacitor discharges, and when a radioactive compound decays. In statistics, e is part of the equation that gives us the normal distribution curve, and in engineering, e is part of the equation of a *catenary,* a hanging cable. In the study of calculus, e is used most often in the study of exponents and logarithms.

16. Mrs. Gutierrez has 25 students and she sends 4 or 5 students at random to the board each day to solve a homework problem. You can calculate that there are ${}_{25}C_4$, or 12,650, ways that 4 students could be selected, and ${}_{25}C_5$, or 53,130, ways that 5 students could be selected. Suppose the class has grown to 26 students. Without using a calculator, determine how many ways 5 students can be selected now. Explain your solution method.

12a. .049

12b. .079

Exercise 12c As needed, remind students to find the probabilities of all the cases in order to calculate the expected value.

12c. 1.88 birds, or approximately 2 birds

13. Answers will vary. This event will happen in 15.6% of trials.

Exercise 14 On a rainy day, rain falls sometime during the day.

14a. .02500

14b. .00357

14c. .00022

14d. .02880

15b. $f(10) \approx 2.5937$, $f(100) \approx 2.7048$, $f(1000) \approx 2.7169$, $f(10000) \approx 2.7181$

15c. There is a long-run value of about 2.718.

16. 65,780. Sample answer: Either the group of five students selected includes the new student or it doesn't. If the new student is included, then the other 4 are selected from the remaining 25 class members and this can be done ${}_{25}C_4 = 12{,}650$ ways. If the new student is not selected, then all 5 are selected from the 25 original members and this can be done ${}_{25}C_5 = 53{,}130$ ways. This means there are 12,650 ways that the new student is part of the group and 53,130 ways that he or she is not. This makes $12{,}650 + 53{,}130 = 65{,}780$ ways to select 5 students.

Exercise 18 In Fathom use the formula **randomPick(1,2),** where 1 represents heads and 2 represents tails, or use the formula **randomPick("H","T"),** where H represents heads and T represents tails.

19a. (*distance, period*)

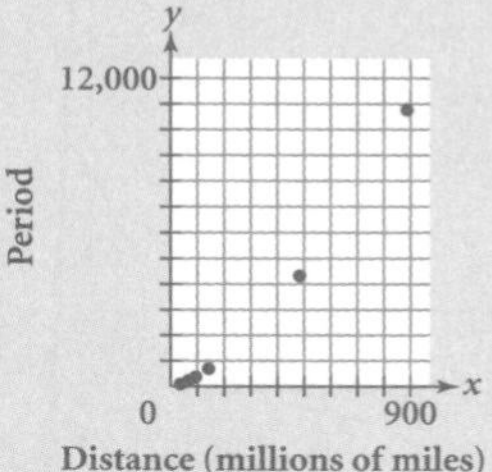

(log (*distance*), *period*)

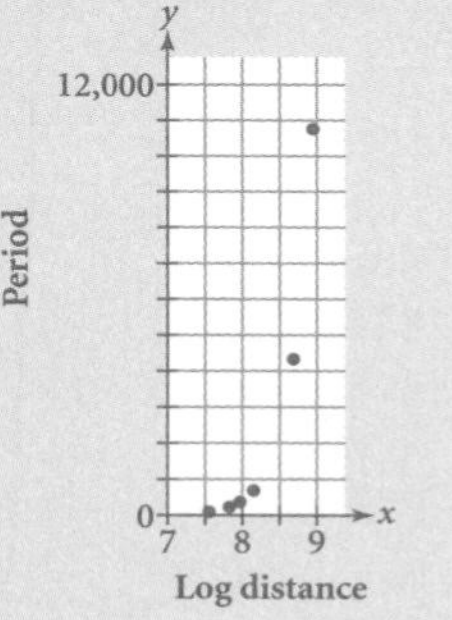

(*distance*, log (*period*))

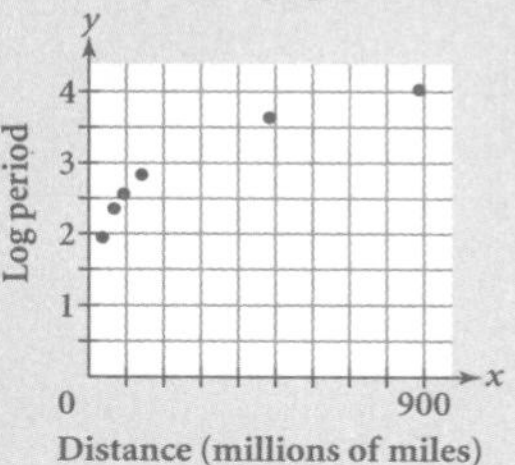

(log (*distance*), log (*period*))

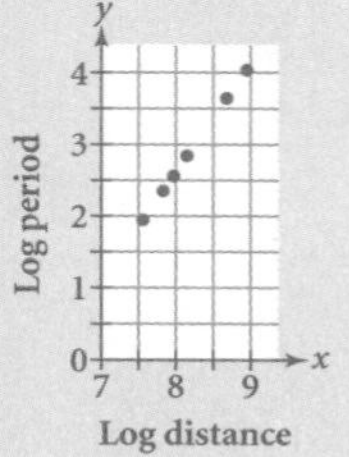

(log (*distance*), log (*period*)) is the most linear of the four, so use the median-median line to find an equation to fit these points; $y = 1.50x - 9.38$; $\log(period) = 1.50 \log(distance) - 9.38$; $10^{\log(period)} = 10^{1.50 \log(distance) - 9.38}$; $period = distance^{1.50} \times 10^{-9.38}$.

See page 905 for answers to Exercise 18.

Review

12.1 **17.** Suppose that 350 points are randomly selected within the rectangle at right and 156 of them fall within the closed curve. What is an estimate of the area within the curve?
37.44 cm²

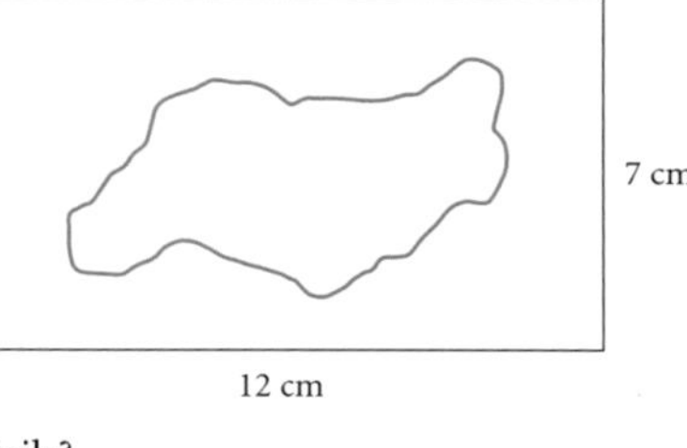

12.1 **18.** ***Technology*** Use statistics software to simulate flipping a coin. (See the Exploration The Law of Large Numbers on page 677 for help creating a simulation.)

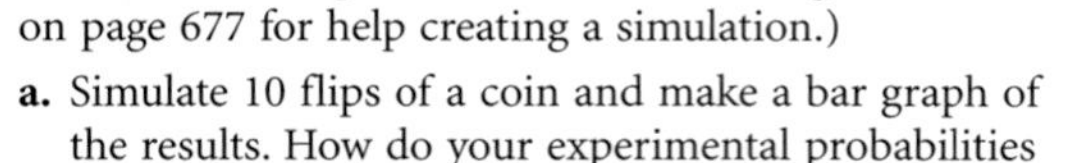

a. Simulate 10 flips of a coin and make a bar graph of the results. How do your experimental probabilities compare to the theoretical probabilities of getting heads or tails?

b. Simulate 1000 flips of a coin by adding 990 more trials to your simulation. How do the experimental probabilities now compare to the theoretical probabilities?

c. Explain how you could modify your simulation to model an unfair coin that comes up heads more frequently than tails. Make the necessary modifications and test whether or not your simulation produces appropriate experimental results.

5.8 **19.** APPLICATION Kepler's third law of planetary motion states that the square of a planet's period is proportional to the cube of its average distance to the Sun. Planetary data are given in the table.

Planet	Average distance from Sun (miles)	Period of revolution (days)
Mercury	35,900,000	88
Venus	67,200,000	224.7
Earth	92,960,000	365.26
Mars	141,600,000	687
Jupiter	483,600,000	4,332.6
Saturn	886,700,000	10,759.2

a. Use logarithms and curve straightening to find an equation that fits data in the form (*distance, period*). Show all steps leading to your answer.

b. Use your equation to verify the data for Uranus, Neptune, or Pluto. How can you explain any errors?

Planet	Average distance from Sun (miles)	Period of revolution (days)
Uranus	1,783,000,000	30,685.4
Neptune	2,794,000,000	60,189
Pluto	3,666,100,000	90,465

c. Rewrite your equation from 19a in the form $p^2 = ka^3$. $period^2 = 10^{-18.76}\, distance^3$

Science CONNECTION

In 1618, after working for over 10 years with the data, German astronomer Johannes Kepler (1571–1630) suddenly realized that "the proportion between the periodic times of any two planets is precisely one and a half times the proportion of the mean distances." English physicist and mathematician Sir Isaac Newton (1642–1727) later restated Kepler's third law to include the masses of the planets. Newton was then able to calculate the masses of the planets relative to the mass of Earth.

19b. 31,385; 61,566; 92,535; errors may be due to rounding. For more accurate results, the *a*- and *b*-values found from regression can be stored in variables in the calculator.

EXTENSIONS

A. Use Take Another Look activity 1 or 2 on page 722.

B. Ask students to use the formula for a trinomial expansion from Take Another Look activity 2 to solve this problem: "Suppose the probability of a passenger buying a first-class airline ticket is .05 and the probability that a passenger will buy a business-class ticket is .08. The probability that a passenger will buy a coach ticket, then, is .87. If 81 seats are sold, what is the probability that exactly 4 seats are sold in first class, 6 in business class, and 71 in coach?" [.03283] "If a plane has 100 seats, with 10 in first class, 10 in business class, and 80 in coach, find the probability that any of the three sections will be oversold if 81 seats are sold." [.06] "What is the probability that both first class and business class will be oversold?" [.000071]

CHAPTER 12 REVIEW

In this chapter you were introduced to the concept of randomness and you learned how to generate random numbers on your calculator. Random numbers should all have an equal chance of occurring and should, in the long run, occur equally frequently. You can use random-number procedures to simulate situations and to determine the **experimental probability** of an **event.** You can determine **theoretical probability** by comparing the number of successful **outcomes** to the total number of possible outcomes. You represented situations involving probability with Venn diagrams and learned the meaning of events that are **dependent, independent,** and **mutually exclusive.** You used **tree diagrams** to help you count possibilities, and learned that sometimes probability situations can be represented geometrically. Using what you learned about theoretical probability, you were able to calculate **expected value,** by multiplying the value of each event by its probability and then summing all the products.

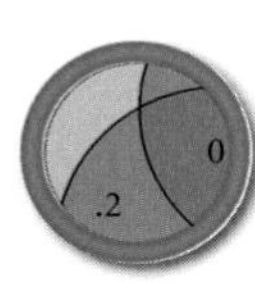

To help find theoretical probabilities, you were introduced to some formal counting techniques. The **counting principle** states that when there are n_1 ways to make the first choice, n_2 ways to make the second choice, n_3 ways to make the third choice, and so on, the product $n_1 \cdot n_2 \cdot n_3 \cdot \cdots$ represents the total number of different ways in which the entire sequence of choices can be made. These arrangements of choices, in which the order is important, are called **permutations.** The notation ${}_nP_r$ indicates the number of ways of choosing r things out of n possible choices. If the order is unimportant, then arrangements are called **combinations** and the notation ${}_nC_r$ represents the number of combinations of r things from a set of n choices. Your calculator can calculate permutation numbers and combination numbers, but before you use the calculator, be sure that you understand the situation and can visualize the possibilities. Combinations also appear in **Pascal's triangle** and as coefficients in **binomial expansions** that you can use to help calculate probabilities when there are two possible outcomes.

EXERCISES

1. Name two different ways to generate random numbers from 0 to 10.
2. Suppose you roll two octahedral (eight-sided) dice, numbered 1–8.
   a. Draw a diagram that shows all possible outcomes of this experiment.
   b. Indicate on your diagram all the possible outcomes for which the sum of the dice is less than 6.
   c. What is the probability that the sum is less than 6? $\frac{10}{64} \approx .156$
   d. What is the probability that the sum is more than 6? $\frac{49}{64} \approx .766$

1. Answers will vary depending upon whether you interpret the problem to imply random decimal numbers (between 0 and 10, non-inclusive) or random integers (0 to 10, inclusive). To generate random decimal numbers, you might look at a random-number table and place the decimal point after the first digit in each group of numbers. Alternatively, you could use a calculator command, such as 10*rand on the TI-83 Plus. To generate random integers, you might number 11 chips or slips of paper and randomly select one. Alternatively, you could use a calculator command, such as randInt(0,10) on the TI-83 Plus.

2a, b.

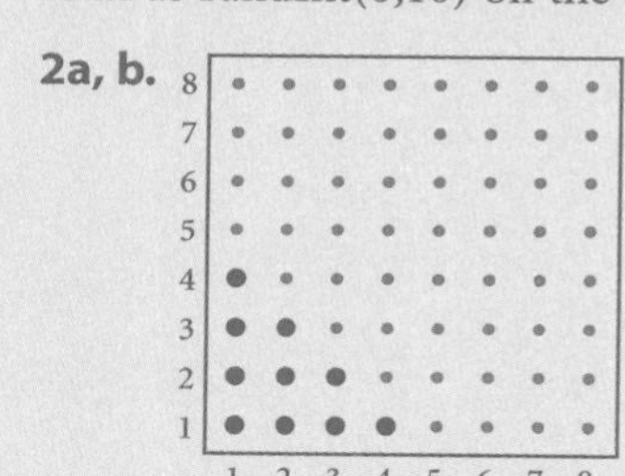

CHAPTER REVIEW 12

PLANNING

LESSON OUTLINE

One day:

15 min	Reviewing
15 min	Exercises
15 min	Student self-assessment

REVIEWING

Pose this problem: "Suppose your school is three blocks east and two blocks north of your home, and the library is one block east and one block north of your home. If you randomly choose a route from home to school, going east or north along the grid of streets, what is the probability that the route will go by the library?" [For the answer see page 720.] As you work this problem with your students, review the definition of probability, the counting principle, and the formulas for counting combinations, with reference to organizing permutations into combinations. Continue with this problem: "Going past the library is event A; going past the post office, which is two blocks east and one block north of home, is event B; and going past a friend's house, zero blocks east and two blocks north of home, is event C. Are any two of these three events independent or mutually exclusive?" [See page 720.]

ASSIGNING HOMEWORK

You might have groups work together on Exercises 1, 5, 8, and 9.

Helping with the Exercises

Exercise 2 An 8-by-8 table is preferable to a tree diagram.

Review Problem Answers
If strings such as EEENN and EENEN designate paths, the number of routes is the number of ways to choose two of five characters to be N (or three of five characters to be E). Therefore there are ${}_5C_2$ or 10 routes from home to school. To get to the library from home there are two routes, and for each of these there are three routes to continue on to school, so six of the ten routes go by the library. The probability of choosing a route past the library is thus $\frac{6}{10}$.

$P(B \mid A) = \frac{2}{3}$, which doesn't equal $P(B) = \frac{6}{10}$, or $\frac{3}{5}$, so A and B are dependent. $P(C \mid A) = 0$ and $P(C \mid B) = 0$, so C and any other event are mutually exclusive.

Exercise 4 [Alert] Students may think that, because "order matters" (different orders of T's and F's make different tests), they should count permutations rather than combinations. If students get stuck on 4d, refer them to their tree diagram.

4a.

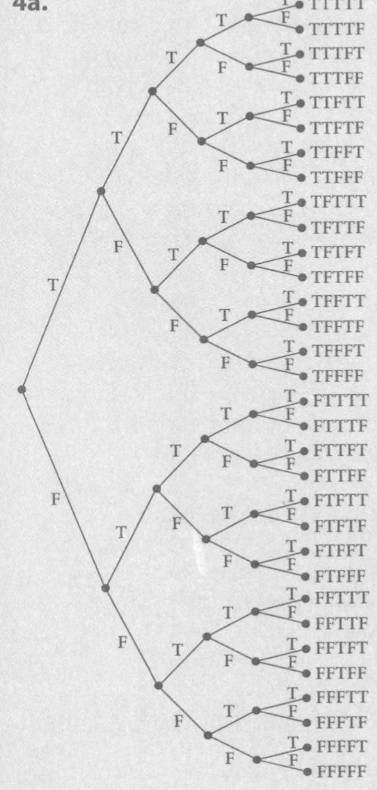

3. Answer each geometric probability problem.

a. What is the probability that a randomly plotted point will land in the shaded region pictured at right? .5

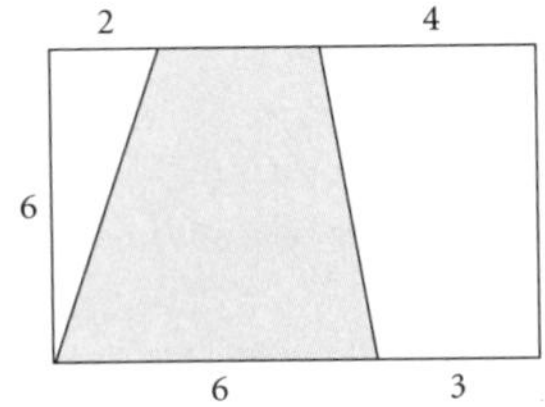

b. One thousand points are randomly plotted in the rectangular region shown below. Suppose that 374 of the points land in the shaded portion of the rectangle. What is an approximation of the area of the shaded portion? 17.765 units²

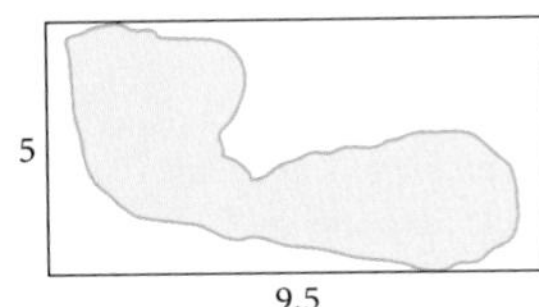

4. A true-false test has five questions.

a. Draw a tree diagram representing all of the possible results. (Assume all five questions are answered.)

b. How many possible ways are there of getting three true and two false answers?

c. How could you use combinations or permutations to answer 4b?

d. Suppose you are sure that the answers to the first two questions on the test are true, and you write these answers down. Then you guess the answers to the remaining three questions at random. What is the probability that there will be three true and two false answers on the test?

5. The local outlet of Frankfurter Franchise sells three types of hot dogs: plain, with chili, and veggie. The owners know that 47% of their sales are chili dogs, 36% are plain, and the rest are veggie. They also offer three types of buns: plain, rye, and multigrain. Sixty-two percent of their sales are plain buns, 27% are multigrain, and the rest are rye. Assume that the choice of bun is independent of the choice of type of hot dog.

a. Make a tree diagram showing this information.

b. What is the probability that the next customer will order a chili dog on rye?

c. What is the probability that the next customer will *not* order a veggie dog on a plain bun?

d. What is the probability that the next customer will order either a plain hot dog on a plain bun or a chili dog on a multigrain bun?

4b. 10

4c. Because the order in which the true and false answers occur doesn't matter, use combinations. ${}_5C_3 = 10$.

4d. $\frac{3}{8} = .375$

5a.

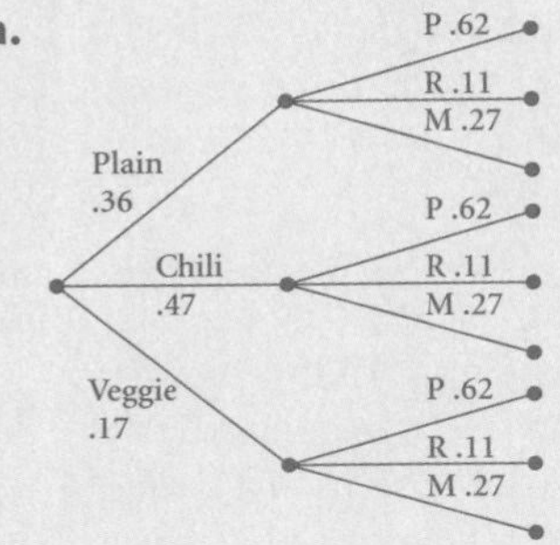

5b. .0517

5c. .8946

5d. .3501

6. All students in a school were surveyed regarding their preference for whipped cream or ice cream to be served with chocolate cake. The results, tabulated by grade level, are reported in the table.

	9th grade	10th grade	11th grade	12th grade	Total
Ice cream	18	37	85	114	254
Whipped cream	5	18	37	58	118
Total	23	55	122	172	372

a. Copy and complete the table.

b. What is the probability that a randomly chosen 10th grader will prefer ice cream?

c. What is the probability that a randomly chosen 11th grader will prefer whipped cream?

d. What is the probability that someone who prefers ice cream is a 9th grader?

e. What is the probability that a randomly chosen student will prefer whipped cream?

7. Rita is practicing darts. On this particular dartboard, she can score 20 points for a bull's-eye and 10 points, 5 points, or 1 point for the other regions. Although Rita doesn't know exactly where her five darts will land, she has been a fairly consistent dart player over the years. She figures that she hits the bull's-eye 30% of the time, the 10-point circle 40% of the time, the 5-point circle 20% of the time, and the 1-point circle 5% of the time. What is the expected value of her score if she throws a dart ten times? 110.5

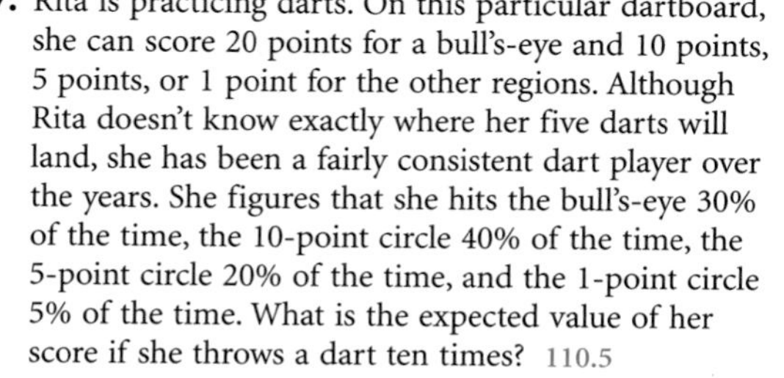

1
5
10
20

8. Misty polls residents of her neighborhood about the types of pets they have: cat, dog, other, or none. She determines these facts:

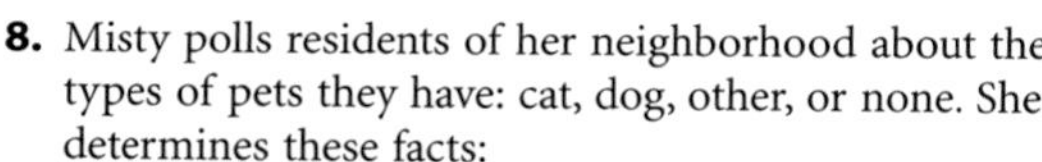

Ownership of cats and dogs is mutually exclusive.

32% of homes have dogs.

54% of homes have a dog or a cat.

16% of homes have only a cat.

42% of homes have no pets.

22% of homes have pets that are not cats or dogs.

Draw a Venn diagram of these data. Label each region with the probability of each outcome.

9. Elliott has time to take exactly 20 more pizza orders before closing. He has enough pepperoni for 16 more pizzas. On a typical night, 65% of orders are for pepperoni pizzas. What is the probability that Elliott will run short on pepperoni? .044

Exercise 6 [Alert] Some students at this point will still be unsure of what constitutes the whole. In 6b, for example, is the whole the number of 10th graders or the number of students who prefer ice cream? To help students focus on the whole, **[Ask]** "What do you know for sure about the people being referred to?" [They're 10th graders.]

6b. $\frac{37}{55} \approx .673$

6c. $\frac{37}{122} \approx .303$

6d. $\frac{18}{254} \approx .071$

6e. $\frac{118}{372} \approx .317$

Exercise 8 [Alert] Students may want to add a circle for no pets. Remind them that this event is represented by the region outside the other three circles. They also may believe that having dogs means having only dogs because these homes won't also have cats (ignoring the possibility of other). A solution depends on the fact that 58% of homes have at least one pet.

8.

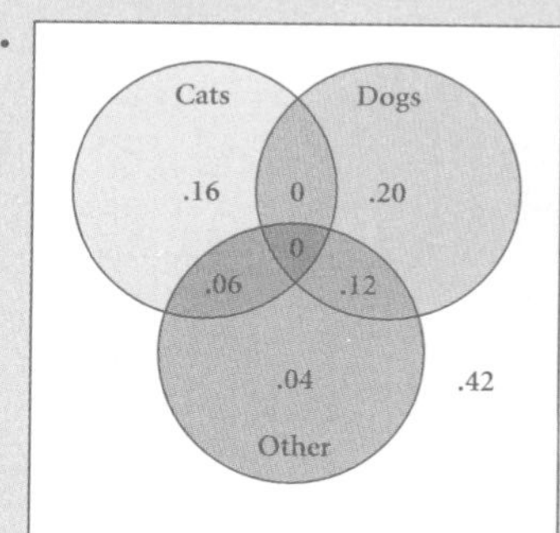

Exercise 9 As needed, **[Ask]** "How many possibilities of pepperoni pizza orders would cause Elliott to run out of pepperoni?" $\left[{}_{20}C_{17}\right.$ ways of getting 17 pepperoni orders, ${}_{20}C_{18}$ ways of getting 18 orders, ${}_{20}C_{19}$ ways of getting 19 orders, plus ${}_{20}C_{20}$ ways of getting 20 orders$\left.\right]$

10. Find the term specified for each binomial expansion.

a. the first term of $\left(1 + \frac{x}{12}\right)^{99}$ 1

b. the last term of $\left(1 + \frac{x}{12}\right)^{99}$ $\frac{x^{99}}{12^{99}}$

c. the tenth term of $(a + b)^{21}$ $293{,}930a^{12}b^9$

TAKE ANOTHER LOOK

1. Pascal's triangle is filled with patterns. Write the first ten rows of Pascal's triangle, and look for as many relationships as you can among the numbers. You may want to consider numerical patterns, sums of numbers in particular locations, and patterns of even or odd numbers, or numbers that share a factor.

2. In this chapter you have seen that a binomial expansion can help you find the probability of an outcome of a series of events when each event has only two possible results (such as success or failure). When there are three possible results instead of two, you can use trinomials in a similar way. Expand each trinomial given below. The first answer will have 6 terms, the second will have 10 terms, and the third will have 15 terms.

$(x + y + z)^2 \qquad (x + y + z)^3 \qquad (x + y + z)^4$

Write a formula for the expansion of $(x + y + z)^n$.

Assessing What You've Learned

GIVE A PRESENTATION By yourself or with a group, write and present a probability exercise. Detail the outcome you want to find the probability of, and tell how to solve the problem. If possible, explain how to find both experimental and theoretical probabilities of the outcome occurring. You may even want to do a simulation with the class. Or, present your work on a Project or Take Another Look from this chapter.

WRITE IN YOUR JOURNAL You have seen how to represent situations involving probabilities using tree diagrams and Venn diagrams. Describe situations in which each of these approaches would be appropriate, and explain how each method can help you solve problems. Specify the kinds of questions that can be answered with each type of diagram.

UPDATE YOUR PORTFOLIO Choose a couple of investigations or exercises from this chapter that you are particularly proud of. Write a paragraph about each piece of work. Describe the objective of the problem, how you demonstrated understanding in your solution, and anything you might have done differently.

Take Another Look

1. Sample patterns: The first and last digits in every row are 1; the second and second-to-last digits are equal to the row number (if the row with only one 1 is called row 0); the next numbers in row n are ${}_nC_2$; numbers in each row are symmetric. If you shade even numbers one color and odd numbers another color, you get a pattern that resembles a Sierpiński triangle. (Similar patterns appear when you color multiples of other factors as well.) Adding the numbers in rows gives powers of 2. Adding numbers next to each other in the diagonal starting with 1, 3 gives square numbers. Looking at the numbers in a row as digits in a number gives powers of 11 (with a procedure to deal with numbers of more than two digits). Fibonacci numbers can be found as sums of diagonals parallel to the one starting in row 3, which contains 1, 6, 5, 1.

2. $(x + y + z)^2 = x^2 + y^2 + z^2 + 2xy + 2xz + 2yz$

$(x + y + z)^3 = x^3 + y^3 + z^3 + 3x^2y + 3x^2z + 3xy^2 + 3xz^2 + 3y^2z + 3yz^2 + 6xyz$

$(x + y + z)^4 = x^4 + y^4 + z^4 + 4x^3y + 4x^3z + 4xy^3 + 4xz^3 + 4y^3z + 4yz^3 + 6x^2y^2 + 6x^2z^2 + 6y^2z^2 + 12x^2yz + 12xy^2z + 12xyz^2$

$(x + y + z)^n = \sum_{i=0}^{n}\sum_{j=0}^{n-i} \frac{n!}{i!j!(n-i-j)!} x^i y^j z^{(n-i-j)}$

ASSESSING

You can use items from any of the assessment resources for a chapter test. Student portfolios might count as part of the chapter assessment grade.

FACILITATING SELF-ASSESSMENT

If you ask students to create and solve their own probability problem, be aware that many difficult probability problems are easy to state. If the problem involves conditional probability or there is a question about whether events are dependent or independent, student solutions may not be correct. If students can't solve their problems with the techniques they've learned, encourage them to think critically about what information or methods they would need to solve the problem.

Exercises with prompts that require students to explain the mathematics and thus make good journal entries include Lesson 12.1, Exercise 5; Lesson 12.2, Exercises 5 and 14; Lesson 12.3, Exercises 5 and 8; Lesson 12.4, Exercise 8; Lesson 12.5, Exercise 8; Lesson 12.6, Exercises 3 and 6; and Lesson 12.7, Exercises 3, 6, and 13.

Exercises that would make good portfolio entries include Lesson 12.1, Exercise 6; Lesson 12.2, Exercise 10; Lesson 12.3, Exercise 8; Lesson 12.4, Exercises 5 and 11; Lesson 12.5, Exercises 5 and 11; Lesson 12.6, Exercise 8; and Lesson 12.7, Exercise 12.

CHAPTER

13

Applications of Statistics

Overview

Lesson 13.1 opens the discussion of making predictions about a population by considering relative frequency histograms and probability distributions. In **Lesson 13.2,** students are introduced to normal distributions and learn to find the equation of a normal curve whose mean and standard deviation are known. Students investigate normally distributed data in the first **exploration.** As students continue to study the normal curve in **Lesson 13.3,** they learn the 68-95-99.7 rule and find confidence intervals. The importance of random samples to reducing bias is discussed in **Lesson 13.4,** where students learn the Central Limit Theorem and principles of inference. The second **exploration** uses Fathom to look again at confidence intervals. **Lesson 13.5** introduces correlation. Students study linear regression in **Lesson 13.6** and explore nonlinear regression in **Lesson 13.7.**

The Mathematics

Many applications of statistics involve prediction. You might be trying to predict how a large group of people will vote based on a survey of some of the people, or you might want to predict the height of an oak tree from its circumference.

Inferential Statistics

In inference, predictions about a large group (the population) are made from a smaller group (a sample). You collect a sample, calculate numbers describing it (statistics), and then find corresponding numbers (parameters) describing the population.

This chapter assumes that the sample collected is representative by virtue of being a simple random sample—each member of the population is equally likely to be chosen, as is each same-size group.

The second step of inference is descriptive statistics. In Chapter 2, students described discrete samples by their central tendency, spread, and shape. This chapter introduces ways to describe continuous data through probability distributions, with emphasis on the normal distribution. In particular, students learn the 68-95-99.7 rule.

Because parameters can rarely be known with certainty, the third step of inference requires the application of probability. Loosely, the question is "How probable is it that these sample statistics are close to the population parameters?" To answer this question, you imagine taking many (simple random) samples of size n, even though you usually have only one sample. The Central Limit Theorem says that, if you did have many samples, the sample means would be approximately normally distributed; the mean of these sample means would approximate the population mean, μ; and the standard deviation of the sample means (the standard error) would be about $\frac{\sigma}{\sqrt{n}}$, where σ is the population's standard deviation. (The approximations are closer with larger values of n.)

The Central Limit Theorem is applied in two ways to describe parameters from the statistics of a single sample. One way is by estimation. By knowing that 95% of the data in a normal distribution lie within two standard deviations of the mean, you can say that 95% of the imagined sample means would lie within $\frac{2\sigma}{\sqrt{n}}$ of the population mean. Therefore you can be "95% confident" that the mean $\bar{x}$ of the single sample you obtained is within this distance of the population mean. Equivalently, the population mean is within this distance of the sample mean, $\bar{x}$. Thus the 95% confidence interval for the population mean is from $\bar{x} - \frac{2\sigma}{\sqrt{n}}$ to $\bar{x} + \frac{2\sigma}{\sqrt{n}}$.

The Central Limit Theorem is also applied to the third step of inference through hypothesis testing. You decide to accept your hypothesis if the sample result is quite probable. Actually, you reject the null hypothesis, the opposite of your hypothesis, if it would imply that the sample result was very improbable. For example, you might decide to reject the null hypothesis that living in a certain area does not increase the incidence of cancer if the sample mean of cancer levels among those living in this area was more than two standard deviations above the population mean of cancer levels. In this case, the hypothesis that living in a certain area increases the incidence of cancer would be accepted at a 95% level of confidence.

Bivariate Statistics

To make predictions about one characteristic from another, you use bivariate statistics. Pearson's correlation coefficient is calculated as the mean of products of z-values, the number of standard deviations of each of the two variables from their means. It can be used to find the slope of the least squares line, which passes through a point determined by those means. Predictions for nonlinear data can often be made by finding the least squares line after the data are straightened through logarithmic processes.

Using This Chapter

If your standards require nothing from this chapter besides least squares regression, you can use Lessons 13.5 and 13.6, perhaps teaching them along with Chapter 3. Lessons 13.1 and 13.2 could also be used alone to study normal distributions. You can omit hypothesis testing in Lesson 13.4 by skipping Example B and Exercises 6 and 9; if you don't omit any material, spend two days on the lesson.

Resources

Discovering Advanced Algebra Resources

Teaching and Worksheet Masters
Lessons 13.1, 13.2, 13.4–13.7, Chapter Review

Calculator Notes 2B, 3B, 13A–I

Sketchpad Demonstration
Chapter Review

Fathom Demonstrations
Lessons 13.1, 13.6
Exploration: Normally Distributed Data
Exploration: Confidence Intervals for Binary Data

Assessment Resources A and B
Quiz 1 (Lessons 13.1, 13.2)
Quiz 2 (Lessons 13.3, 13.4)
Quiz 3 (Lessons 13.5–13.7)
Chapter 13 Test
Chapter 13 Constructive Assessment Options
Chapters 11–13 Exam
Final Exam

More Practice Your Skills for Chapter 13

Condensed Lessons for Chapter 13

Other Resources

Statistics by David Freedman et al.

Data in Depth by Tim Erickson.

For complete references to these and other resources see www.keypress.com/DAA.

Materials

- centimeter rulers
- pencils (a few per group)
- graph paper
- pieces of rope (one per group)
- metersticks or tape measures
- plastic water containers (one per group)
- tape
- timing devices
- water
- food coloring

Pacing Guide

	day 1	day 2	day 3	day 4	day 5	day 6	day 7	day 8	day 9	day 10
standard	13.1	13.2	quiz, 13.3	13.4	13.4	quiz, 13.5	13.6	13.7	13.7	quiz, review
enriched	13.1, project	13.2, exploration	quiz, 13.3	13.4	quiz, exploration	13.5, project	13.6	13.7	13.7, project	quiz, review, TAL
block	13.1, 13.2	exploration, quiz, 13.3	13.4	exploration, quiz, 13.5	13.6, 13.7	13.7, quiz, review	TAL, assessment	review, exam	review	final exam

	day 11	day 12	day 13	day 14	day 15
standard	assessment	review	exam	review	final exam
enriched	assessment	review	exam	review	final exam

CHAPTER

13 Applications of Statistics

This untitled painting (1990) by Japanese-born artist Naoki Okamoto creates a "crowd" of faces. In this chapter you'll explore how numerical data about a population can be represented with a few summary numbers. You'll also explore whether data about a small but random group of people can lead to valid generalizations about a whole population.

OBJECTIVES

In this chapter you will

- learn methods for making predictions about a population based on a random sample
- discover the association between the statistics of a sample and the parameters of an entire population
- study population distributions, including normal distributions
- fit functions to data and make predictions using least squares lines and other regression equations

The collage of faces in this painting might represent a small sample from a larger population. In this chapter, students will be learning about what constitutes a random sample; you might ask students if they think that this painting depicts a sample and what it might be a sample of. To encourage creativity, you can also **[Ask]** "Can you give this untitled painting a title that relates to the ideas of statistics?"

Naoki Okamoto also works in photography. He uses a method called street shooting, in which the photographer takes pictures of everyday objects and activities on the street. Street shooting might also be used to sample a population. **[Ask]** "Are there ways that photography can be used to gather data?" [For example, aerial photos can be used to estimate crowd size.] "How would you choose a random sample? How would you make sure that your sample was representative of the population?" Students might wonder whether a photograph can really be trusted to gather data, especially with advanced technologies that can alter photographs after they are taken.

CHAPTER 13 OBJECTIVES

- Understand the difference between a population parameter and a sample statistic
- Learn about relative frequency histograms and probability distributions
- Find the mean, median, and mode of probability distributions
- Investigate the graph and equation of the normal curve
- Learn the 68-95-99.7 rule and its relationship to the area under the normal curve
- Find confidence intervals of the population mean
- Find and understand z-values
- Understand the Central Limit Theorem
- Apply the Central Limit Theorem to hypothesis testing
- Find and interpret the correlation coefficient
- Find the equation and properties of the least squares line
- Find exponential, power, and polynomial models to fit nonlinear data sets

LESSON

13.1

PLANNING

LESSON OUTLINE

One day:

15 min Investigation

5 min Example A

10 min Example B

5 min Sharing

10 min Exercises

MATERIALS

- centimeter rulers
- pencils
- graph paper
- Random-Number Generator (T), *optional*
- Puzzle Time (T), *optional*

TEACHING

This lesson begins a study of inference, which involves using samples to make predictions about populations. It considers relative frequencies of infinite or very large populations.

One Step

Pose this problem: "How could you estimate, in the next 15 minutes, the mean and median length of all the pencils in this state?" As in the investigation, have groups measure their own pencils to the nearest tenth of a centimeter. Each group should keep its sample data separate and also add its data to a frequency chart for the class. Rather than settle for the mean and median of the compiled data, encourage at least one group to make a relative frequency histogram, imagine extending it to represent the lengths of all the pencils in the state, and find the median and mean in terms of areas.

LESSON

13.1

Probability Distributions

Statistical thinking will one day be as necessary for efficient citizenship as the ability to read and write.

H. G. WELLS

"I did a survey and 22 percent of the kids in this school have blue eyes, so 22 percent of the people in this neighborhood must have blue eyes," claims Sean. "Exactly 22 percent?" asks Yiscah.

One of the main uses of statistics is to find out about large collections, such as the residents of a city, by looking at smaller collections, such as the students in the school. The larger collection is called a **population,** and the smaller collection is a **sample** of that population.

You've seen in earlier chapters that statistics are numbers, such as mean or standard deviation, that describe a sample. The corresponding numbers describing the entire population are called **parameters.** The larger the sample, the closer its statistics will be to the parameters.

When you examined probabilities in Chapter 12, you used discrete random variables. The data had integer values, such as 5 heads, 3 tails, or 454 students. However, sometimes data can take on any real value within an interval. This is represented by a **continuous random variable.** For example, the ages of all the students in your class are continuous. You might say that everyone is 15 or 16 years old; but actually no one is exactly 16, because a person is exactly 16 at only one instant. Your age is a continuous variable, and there are infinitely many of these ages.

This 14-meter installation, shown here in two views, is called *100 edition of 12* (1995). To create this piece, American artist Paul Ramirez Jonas (b 1965) chronologically arranged 100 photos of people aged 0–99.

During Sharing, introduce the terms *sample, population, statistic,* and *parameter.* Elicit the idea of describing an infinite or very large population with a continuous random variable and a probability distribution. Save the data from the groups and the compiled data for the one-step investigation in Lesson 13.3.

LESSON OBJECTIVES

- Understand the difference between a parameter and a statistic
- Create and read relative frequency histograms
- Distinguish between discrete variables and continuous random variables
- Find the mean, median, and mode of probability distributions

Investigation
Pencil Lengths

You will need

- centimeter rulers
- a few pencils
- graph paper

In this investigation you'll explore the difference between discrete and continuous random variables.

Begin by collecting all the pencils that your group has.

Step 1 Measure your pencils accurate to a tenth of a centimeter. Before you share data with other groups, predict the shape of a histogram of the class data.

Step 2 Share all measurements so that the class has one set of data. On graph paper, draw a histogram with bins representing 1 cm increments in pencil length.

Step 3 Divide the number of pencils in each bin by the total number of pencils. Make a new histogram, using these quotients as the values on the y-axis.

Step 4 Check that the area of your second histogram is 1. Why must this be true?

Step 5 Imagine that you collect more and more pencils and draw a histogram using the method described in Step 3. Sketch what this histogram of increasingly many pencil lengths would look like. Give reasons for your answer.

Step 6 Imagine doing a very complete and precise survey of all the pencils in the world. Assume that their distribution is about the same as the distribution of pencils in your sample. Also assume that you use infinitely many very narrow bins. What will this histogram look like?

To approximate this plot, sketch over the top of your histogram with a smooth curve, as shown at right. Make the area between the curve and the horizontal axis about the same as the area of the histogram. Make sure that the extra area enclosed by the curve above the histogram is about the same as the area cut off the corners of the bins as you smooth out the shape.

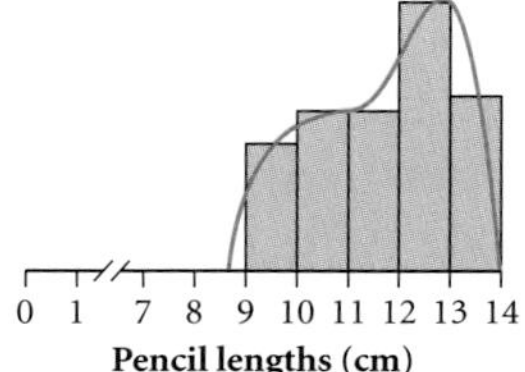

Step 7 Let x represent pencil length. Use your histogram from Step 6 to estimate the areas of various regions between the curve and the x-axis that satisfy these conditions:

a. $x < 10$

b. $11 < x < 12$

c. $x > 12.5$

d. $x = 11$

Step 1 Pencil lengths will vary between approximately 4 cm and 19 cm. Sample answer: The histogram will have bars of approximately the same heights from 12 cm through 19 cm, and shorter bars between 4 cm and 12 cm.

Step 4 Multiply the width, 1, by the height of each bar, and add the results to find that the total area is 1. The area of each bar represents the fraction of the total, so these fractions must sum to 1.

Step 7a–c Answers will vary but should sum to less than 1.

Step 7d 0

The histogram you made in Step 3 of the investigation, giving the proportions of pencils in the bins, is a **relative frequency histogram.** It shows what fraction of the time the value of a discrete random variable falls within each bin. The continuous curve you drew in Step 6 approximates a continuous random variable for the infinite set of measurements. This graph represents a function called a **probability distribution.**

Guiding the Investigation

As a class, try to collect about a hundred data points. **[Alert]** A large number of unsharpened pencils or mechanical pencils may create spikes in the data.

Instead of using pencils, you can use leaves taken from the branch of a tree or spaghetti strands taken from a somewhat battered box.

Step 1 As needed, review histograms from Chapter 2.

Step 2 You might ask groups to record their data in a table on the board or on a transparency. Have them use a method that allows them to count the number of measurements that lie in various intervals.

Step 2 Data sets will vary. Sample histogram:

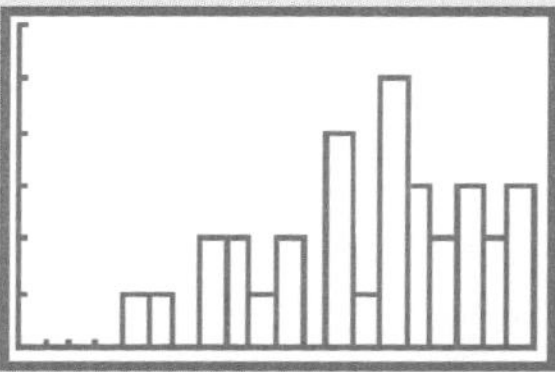

[0, 20, 1, 0, 6, 1]

Step 4 To find the total area, students will find the area of each bar and then sum all the areas.

Step 5 If it were possible to have infinitely many data points, the histogram would have infinitely many bins that were infinitely thin—that is, line segments.

Step 5 Histograms will vary but will probably be similar to the histogram in Step 3. The bins may be more even, and the range may be larger. If answers differ greatly, rationale should be provided. Sample histogram:

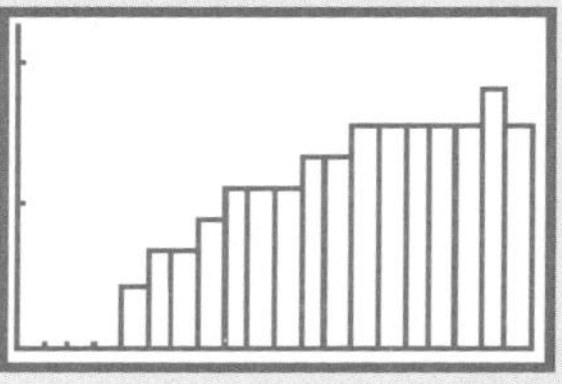

[0, 20, 1, 0, 0.11, 0.05]

See page 906 for answer to Step 3.

NCTM STANDARDS

CONTENT		PROCESS	
	Number	✓	Problem Solving
✓	Algebra	✓	Reasoning
	Geometry	✓	Communication
✓	Measurement	✓	Connections
✓	Data/Probability	✓	Representation

Step 6 If students don't understand the term *distribution* in this context, you can say that it's represented by the shape of the histogram.

Step 6

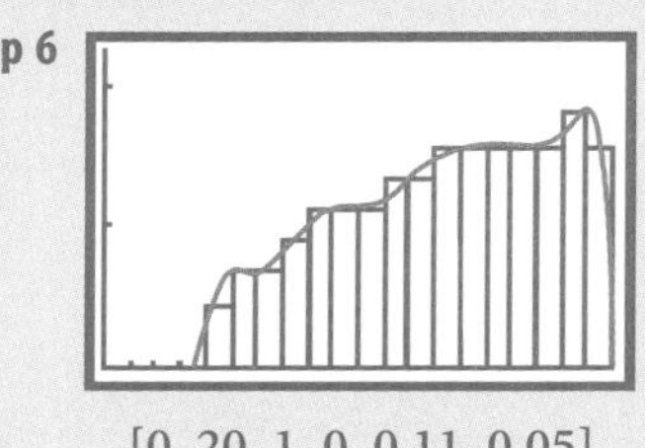

[0, 20, 1, 0, 0.11, 0.05]

The areas you found in Step 7 of the investigation give probabilities that a randomly chosen pencil length will satisfy a condition. As with geometric probabilities in Lesson 12.1, these probabilities are given by areas. If x represents the continuous random variable giving the pencil lengths in centimeters, then you can write these areas as

$$P(x < 10 \text{ cm}),\ P(11 \text{ cm} < x < 12 \text{ cm}),\ P(x > 12.5 \text{ cm}),\ \text{and } P(x = 11 \text{ cm})$$

In a continuous probability distribution, the probability of any single outcome, such as the probability that x is exactly 11 centimeters, is the area of a line segment, which is 0. It is possible for a pencil to be exactly 11 cm long, but the probability of choosing any one value from infinitely many values is theoretically 0. As you learned in geometry, a single point or line has no area.

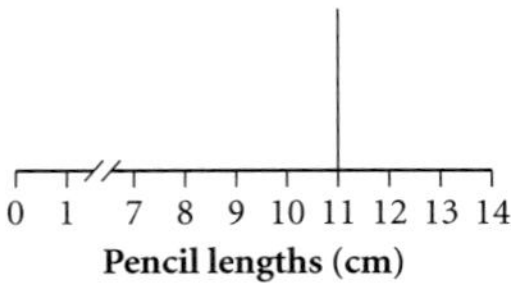

In the following example, you'll see how areas represent probabilities for a continuous random variable.

► EXAMPLE A

You can show the Random-Number Generator transparency as you go over this example. You might challenge students to find the total area of the distribution in as many ways as they can. For example, they can think of the shape as a triangle appended to a rectangle, as a trapezoid, or as a rectangle with a triangle removed.

[Ask] "Why don't the three answers sum to 1?" [They don't include the sections over the intervals $2 \leq x \leq 2.5$ and $3.5 \leq x \leq 4$.]

EXAMPLE A

A random-number generator selects a number between 0 and 6 according to the probability distribution at right. Because the random number can be any value of x with $0 \leq x \leq 6$, the graph is a continuous graph. Find the probability that a selected number is

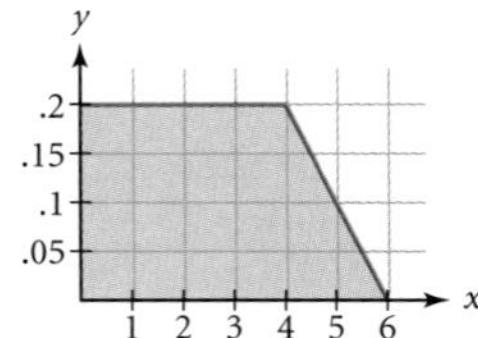

a. Less than 2.

b. Between 2.5 and 3.5.

c. More than 4.

► Solution

First, note that the region shaded for the entire distribution has area 1. To find the probability of a particular set of outcomes, find the area of the region that corresponds to it.

a. The region between 0 and 2 is a rectangle with width 2 and height .2. Its area is $2 \cdot .2$, or .4. So, the probability is .4 that a randomly selected number is between 0 and 2.

b. The region between 2.5 and 3.5 is a rectangle with width 1 and height .2. The area of this rectangle is $1 \cdot .2$, or .2. So, the probability is .2 that a number is between 2.5 and 3.5.

c. The region between 4 and 6 is a triangle with width 2 and height .2. The area of the triangle is $0.5 \cdot 2 \cdot .2 = .2$, so the probability is .2.

In Chapter 2 you learned three measures of center to describe a data set—mean, median, and mode. With a probability distribution you don't have a finite set of data. So these statistics must be defined and calculated in a slightly different way.

Measures of Center for Probability Distributions

Mode

The value or values of x at which the graph reaches its maximum value.

Median

The number d such that the line $x = d$ divides the area into two parts with equal areas.

Mean

The sum of each value of x times its probability. Also, the x-coordinate of the centroid, or balance point, of the region.

EXAMPLE B

A large number of people were asked to complete a puzzle. The time it took each person was recorded. The data are shown in the probability distribution graph at right, with times ranging between 0 and 8 seconds.

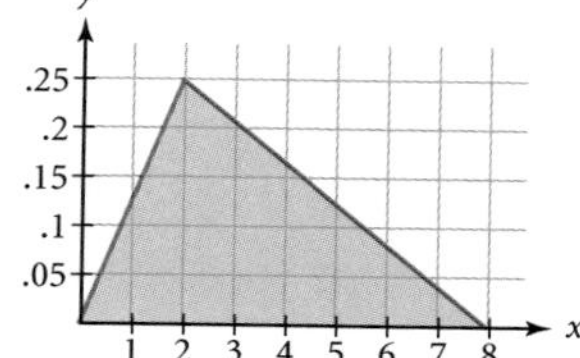

a. Find the mode.

b. Find the median.

c. Find the mean.

▶ Solution

Note that the shaded region has area 1.

a. The mode is the x-coordinate of the highest point, 2 seconds.

b. Find the vertical line that divides the triangle into two regions each having area .5. Some trial and error shows the median is about 3 s. The smaller triangle has base 5 and height about .2.

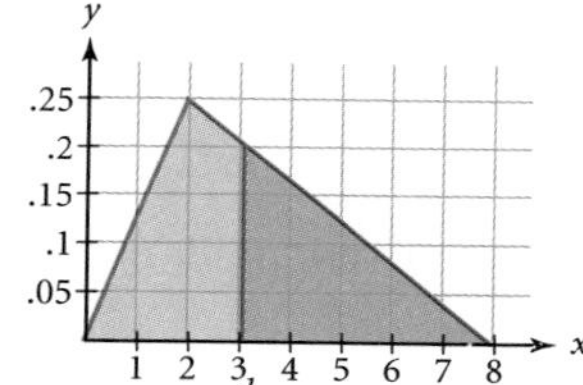

$A \approx 0.5 \cdot (5)(.2) \approx .5$

So about half the area of the larger triangle falls after 3. To calculate the median exactly, you can use equations of the lines that form boundaries of the region. The equation of the line through (2, .25) and (8, 0) is $y = -\frac{1}{24}(x - 8)$. Use this equation to find the value of the median, d, so that the area of the triangle to the right of the median is .5.

$A = 0.5bh = 0.5(8 - d)\left(\frac{-1}{24}(d - 8)\right)$	The area of a triangle is half the product of the base $(8 - d)$ and height. The height is the y-value at $x = d$.
$0.5 = 0.5(8 - d)\left(\frac{-1}{24}(d - 8)\right)$	Solve for d when the area is 0.5.
$1 = \frac{-1}{24}\left(-d^2 + 16d - 64\right)$	Divide both sides by 0.5 and multiply the binomials.
$-24 = -d^2 + 16d - 64$	Multiply both sides by -24.
$d^2 - 16d + 40 = 0$	Write the quadratic equation in general form.
$d \approx 3.101, 12.899$	Use the quadratic formula to solve for d.

Sharing Ideas (continued)

Add a column or row to the table to record relative frequencies, and label them as probabilities. Like the histogram, this table represents the distribution.

Check students' understanding by asking why the probability that a pencil will be exactly 11 cm long is 0. From a real-world point of view, measurement is exact. Theoretically a pencil has an exact length and the length could be exactly 11 cm, but no measurement of the length can be exact. Thus the probability of choosing a pencil measuring exactly 11 cm is 0.

From a graphical perspective, the portion of pencils exactly 11 cm long is represented by a line segment, which has width 0 and therefore area 0.

[Ask] "In the investigation, what's the sample and what's the population?" [The population is all pencils; each group measured a sample, and all the pencils in the class make up a larger sample.] Learning about a population from sample data is a theme of this chapter.

Refer students to the definition of *mean* and **[Ask]** "Does this sum of each value times probability

▶ EXAMPLE B

If time is short, you can limit the class's focus to approximating the median through calculating areas. You might use the Puzzle Time transparency.

[Alert] Students may confuse the median of a probability distribution with the medians of a triangle, which are cited in this example as a way to find the *mean* of the distribution.

[Language] The *centroid* of a triangle is the point of intersection of the three medians. A *median* is a line segment from a vertex to the midpoint of the opposite side.

SHARING IDEAS

As students present ideas about Step 3 of the investigation, ask about the mean and median of the data. One difficulty students have with histograms is recognizing that the bin heights represent frequencies (counts) of data points. As needed, remind the class how to find the mean and median of data represented by a simple histogram. Students tend to think that these values are within the bins rather than points on the horizontal axis. This confusion will increase with relative frequency histograms, in which the bins represent ratios. The mean and median of the data are found the same way as before and are still represented by points on the horizontal axis.

In discussing Steps 5 and 6 of the investigation, **[Ask]** "If there were infinitely many data points, would the bins be infinitely high?" [Only if the bins continued to have width, but they are getting increasingly narrow as the number of data points increase without bound. In a relative frequency histogram no bin height (ratio) will exceed 1.]

[Ask] "Do probability distributions have to be represented by histograms?" As needed, remind students that they first represented the pencil-length data in a table.

Sharing Ideas (continued)

seem familiar?" As needed, review the definition of the *expected value* of a *discrete random variable.* Then point out that, with a continuous random variable, the probability of each value of x is 0. **[Ask]** "Aren't we only adding up a bunch of 0's, so the sum will be 0? Do all probability distributions have a mean of 0?" If possible, let students grapple with these questions in groups for a while. You might suggest students think of integration as splitting a region into many thin vertical strips, multiplying the width and length of each strip to get its area, and taking the limit as the widths of the strips approach 0. In extending this to finding the mean of a distribution, the x-value for each strip is also a factor because we extend the discrete definition $\Sigma x \cdot P(x)$ to the continuous definition $\int x \cdot P(x)$, where $P(x) = f(x)dx$, the area of the strip. Mechanical shortcuts for integrating can verify the mean of this distribution. The two functions that make up the Example B graph are $y = \frac{1}{8}x$ and $y = -\frac{1}{24}(x - 8)$, so the mean equals

$$\int_0^2 x\left(\tfrac{1}{8}x\right)dx + \int_2^8 x\left(-\tfrac{1}{24}(x - 8)\right)dx,$$

or $\frac{10}{3}$.

[Link] The idea of "adding infinitely many 0's" yet getting a nonzero number is the basis of integral calculus.

Assessing Progress

During the investigation you can assess students' understanding of histograms, their ability to collect measurement data systematically, and their skill at thinking about areas.

Closing the Lesson

A major goal of probability and statistics is to learn about **population parameters** from **sample statistics.** If a population is infinite or very large, corresponding data might be assigned numbers in such a way that every real number, not only integers or decimals, is a potential data point (such as a length or an age). This assignment is a **continuous random variable.** The **relative frequency histogram** of such data is a continuous curve, or very close to one. The continuous function whose graph goes through the tops of these bins is a **probability distribution.** The region under the curve has area 1, and the probabilities of intervals of data are given by the areas of regions under the curve and above the interval. The **median** and **mean** of a distribution can sometimes be determined through areas, although the mean of the distribution (and the expected value of the random variable) can best be determined as a sum of products of outcomes (values of the random variable) and their probabilities.

The second value, 12.899, is outside of the domain, so the median of this distribution is about 3.101.

c. By cutting out the triangle and balancing it on the eraser end of a pencil, you can get a pretty good estimate that the mean is 3.33 in.

Because the distribution forms a triangle, you can find its centroid using geometric construction or algebra. You might find the intersection of two medians of the triangle. Or you might recall from geometry that the coordinates of the centroid are the means of the coordinates of the vertices. The x-coordinate of the centroid, then, is the mean of the x-coordinates:

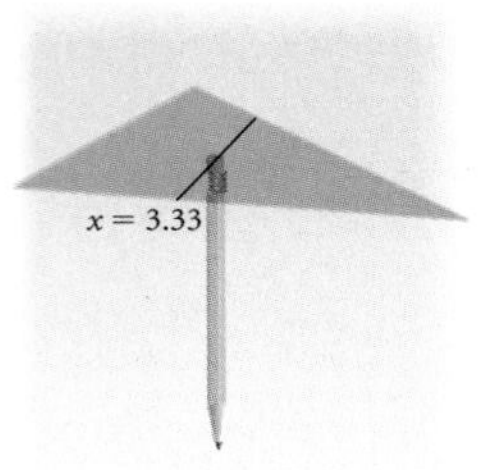

$$\frac{0 + 2 + 8}{3} = \frac{10}{3} = 3\frac{1}{3}$$

Calculus can be used to find the measures of center of some more-complicated regions. But for most probability distributions, finding the exact values of these parameters is almost impossible. They must be estimated using methods such as the balancing approach.

EXERCISES

You will need

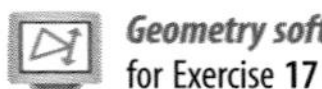

Geometry software for Exercise 17

Practice Your Skills

Answer Exercises 1–4 on page 729 for each probability distribution below.

Distribution A

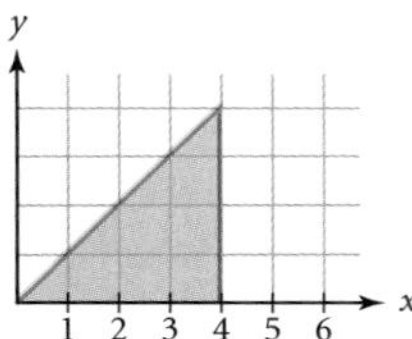

Distribution B

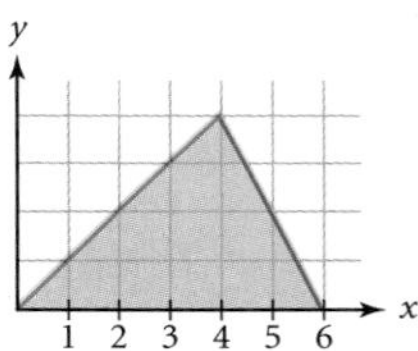

Distribution C

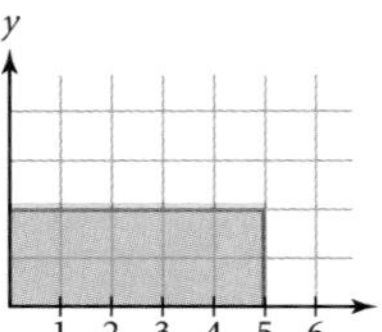

Distribution D

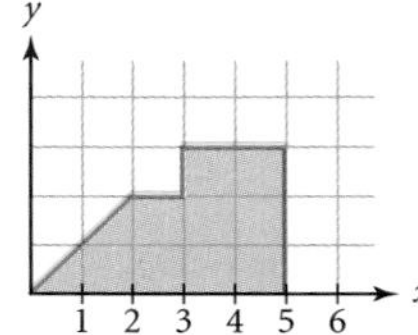

1. Find the height of one grid box on the y-scale so that the area is 1.

2. Find the probability that a randomly chosen value will be less than 3.

3. Estimate the median.

4. Estimate the mean.

5. Draw a probability distribution for each histogram below. Try to keep the area under the curve the same as the area under the histogram.

a. 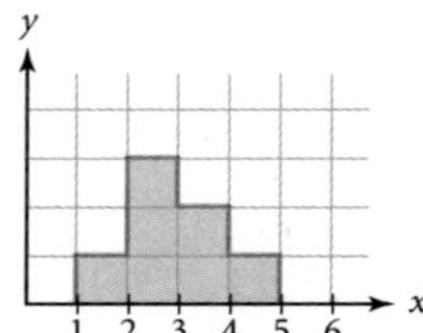

b. 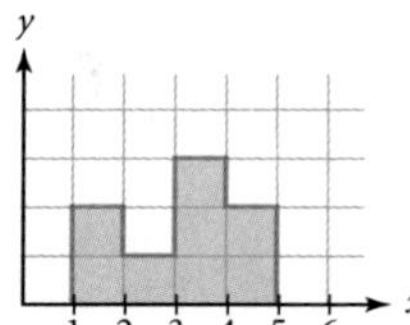

Reason and Apply

6. Suppose each person in your class selects a set of four numbers from 1 to 8 (repeats are allowed) and that each person calculates the mean of his or her own set.
   a. Sketch a possible histogram of these mean values. Explain the reasoning behind your histogram.
   b. Based on your histogram, estimate the mode and median of your distribution.

7. Classify each statement as true or false and if false, explain why.
   a. The y-value of the mode in a probability distribution can never be more than 1. true
   b. It is impossible to tell how many data values were used to create a probability distribution. true
   c. The mean, median, and mode of a continuous distribution can never all be the same value. False; if the distribution is symmetric, then they can all be the same.

8. Imagine finding many random numbers from 0 to 1 and substituting them into each expression below. Sketch what you think the relative frequency histograms or probability distributions of the results would look like, and explain your reasoning.
   a. $(random\ number)^2$ b. $(random\ number)^4$ c. $\sqrt{random\ number}$

9. ***Technology*** Use statistics software or lists on your graphing calculator to investigate Exercise 8.

10. Sketch a relative frequency histogram to fit each set of conditions. You may want to sketch these using the squares on graph paper to be certain you have a total area of 1. Label each axis with an appropriate scale.
    a. The data values are continuous from 0 to 10. The mean and median are the same value.
    b. The data values are continuous from 10 to 15. The mean is larger than the median.

BUILDING UNDERSTANDING

Students work with relative frequency and probability distributions.

ASSIGNING HOMEWORK

Essential	1–5
Performance assessment	6–13
Portfolio	13
Journal	7, 8
Group	8, 19
Review	14–19

MATERIALS

- Fathom demonstration Ages, *optional*

Helping with the Exercises

Exercises 1, 2 As needed, remind students of how to find the area of a triangle.

1. A: $\frac{1}{8}$; B: $\frac{1}{12}$; C: $\frac{1}{10}$; D: $\frac{1}{10}$

2. A: $\frac{9}{16}$; B: $\frac{3}{8}$; C: $\frac{3}{5}$; D: $\frac{2}{5}$

3. Answers will vary. A: $\sqrt{8} = 2\sqrt{2}$; B: $\sqrt{12} = 2\sqrt{3}$; C: 2.5; D: $3\frac{1}{3}$

Exercise 4 For Distribution D, students might trace the figure, cut it out, and balance it. For a more exact answer, they can use the sum of products of heights and values of the midpoints of unit intervals: $0.5(.05) + 1.5(.15) + 2.5(.2) + 3.5(.3) + 4.5(.3) = 3.15$.

4. Answers will vary. A: approximately 2.7; B: approximately 3.3; C: 2.5; D: approximately 3.2

Exercise 5 The purpose here is to approximate the sample with a continuous random variable.

5a. 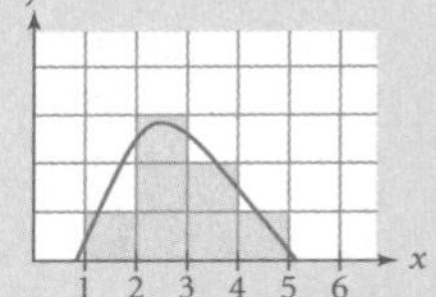

5b. 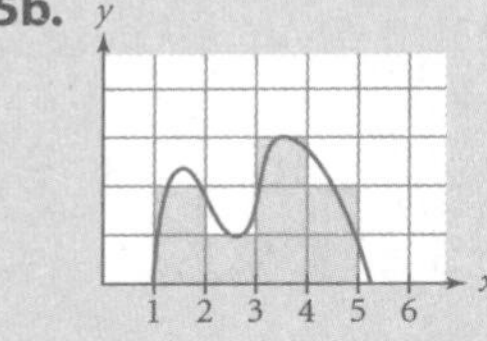

6a. Answers will vary, but the values range from 1 to 8, and mean values 1 and 8 are very rare.

Sample histogram:

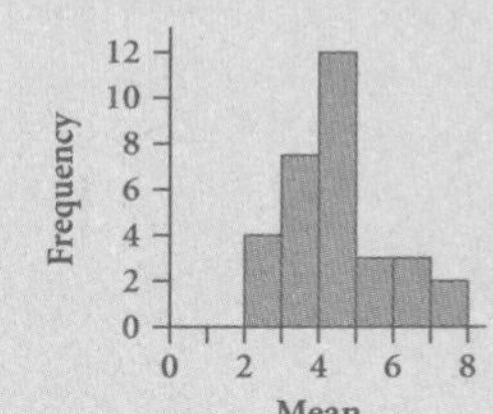

See page 906 for answers to Exercises 6b and 8–10.

Exercise 12 The data for this exercise are on the Calculator Programs and Data CD and in the Fathom demonstration Ages. You might show the Fathom demonstration and discuss its questions instead of assigning this exercise.

[Context] Anyone who meets the criteria specified in the U.S. Constitution can run for president, but roadblocks limit the diversity of people who run. Candidates need millions of dollars to conduct a successful campaign. They must also receive the backing of one of the two major political parties, although some third-party candidates, such as Ross Perot in 1992, have made strong showings. John F. Kennedy, a Catholic, was the only non-Protestant president. No woman has ever received a major party nomination, although Geraldine Ferraro received the Democratic nomination for vice president in 1984. Despite Jesse Jackson's strong showing in the Democratic primaries in 1984 and 1988, no African American has received a major-party nomination.

12a. President: $\bar{x} = 54.8$, $s = 6.3$, median $= 54.5$, $IQR = 7$

VP: $\bar{x} = 54.0$, $s = 8.5$, median $= 53$, $IQR = 11$

The mean and median ages are close, but there is more spread in the vice presidents' ages.

12b. President

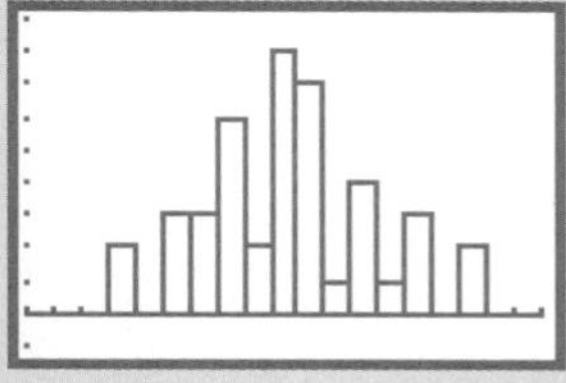

[36, 74, 2, −1, 9, 1]

Vice President

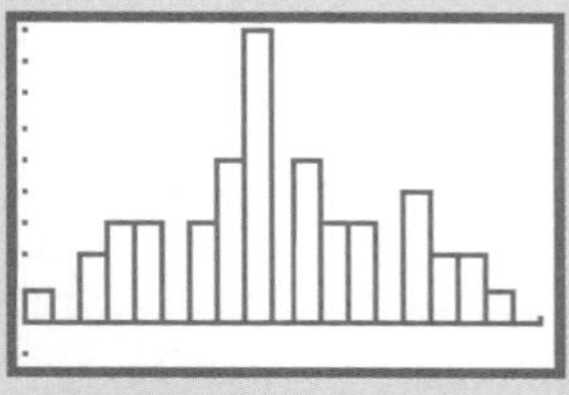

[36, 74, 2, −1, 9, 1]

11. Describe a data set that might produce each of these continuous distribution graphs. Indicate the range of values on the x-axis. Answers will vary.

a.

b.

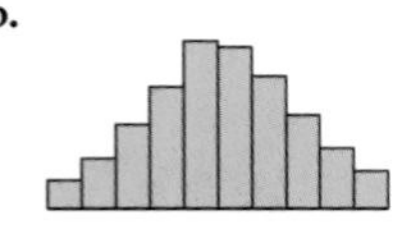

c.

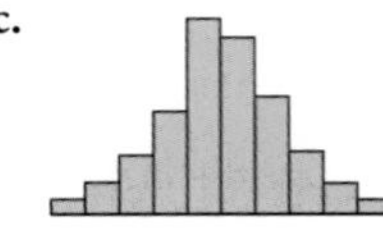

12. This table lists the ages of the presidents and vice presidents of the United States when they first took office.

President	Age
Washington	57
J. Adams	61
Jefferson	57
Madison	57
Monroe	58
J. Q. Adams	57
Jackson	61
Van Buren	54
W. Harrison	68
Tyler	51
Polk	49
Taylor	64
Fillmore	50
Pierce	48
Buchanan	65
Lincoln	52
A. Johnson	56
Grant	46
Hayes	54
Garfield	49
Arthur	50
Cleveland	47
B. Harrison	55

President	Age
McKinley	54
T. Roosevelt	42
Taft	51
Wilson	56
Harding	55
Coolidge	51
Hoover	54
F. D. Roosevelt	51
Truman	60
Eisenhower	62
Kennedy	43
L. B. Johnson	55
Nixon	56
Ford	61
Carter	52
Reagan	69
G. H. W. Bush	64
W. Clinton	46
G. W. Bush	54

Vice president	Age
J. Adams	53
Jefferson	53
Burr	45
G. H. Clinton	65
Gerry	68
Tompkins	42
Calhoun	42
Van Buren	50
R. M. Johnson	56
Tyler	50
Dallas	52
Fillmore	49
King	66
Breckinridge	36
Hamlin	51
A. Johnson	56
Colfax	45
Wilson	61
Wheeler	57
Arthur	51
Hendricks	65
Morton	64
Stevenson	57

Vice president	Age
Hobart	52
T. Roosevelt	42
Fairbanks	52
Sherman	53
Marshall	58
Coolidge	48
Dawes	59
Curtis	69
Garner	64
Wallace	52
Truman	60
Barkley	71
Nixon	40
L. B. Johnson	52
Humphrey	53
Agnew	50
Ford	60
Rockefeller	66
Mondale	49
G. H. W. Bush	56
Quayle	41
Gore	44
Cheney	59

(*The World Almanac and Book of Facts 2003*)

a. Enter the two separate lists of data into your calculator and calculate the mean, $\bar{x}$, the standard deviation, s, the median, and the IQR for each list. Compare the data sets based on these statistics.

b. Graph a histogram for each data set. Use the same range and scale for each graph. Describe how the histograms reflect the statistics of each data set.

c. Calculate $\frac{x_i - \bar{x}}{s}$ for each entry, and create two new lists to convert the ages in each list to a standardized scale.

The histogram for presidents' ages has less spread, so more presidents' ages are clustered around the mean and median. The histogram for vice presidents' ages is more spread out, resulting in a larger IQR and standard deviation.

12c. Create these lists on a calculator. For example, if L1 contains presidents' ages, enter (L1 − 54.8)/6.3 in the header of L2 to create a list of standardized values.

d. What is the range of values in each of the new distributions? Explain what the new distributions represent.

e. Graph a histogram for each of these standardized distributions. Use domain $-3.5 \leq x \leq 3.5$.

f. Compare and describe the graphs.

The U.S. Constitution specifies that presidents must be natural-born citizens, have lived in the United States for at least 14 years, and be at least 35 years old. The 26th U.S. president, Theodore Roosevelt (1858–1919), was the youngest president, whereas the 40th president, Ronald Reagan (b 1911), was the oldest. Roosevelt became president when William McKinley (1843–1901) was assassinated. John F. Kennedy was the youngest president to be elected.

13. **APPLICATION** In order to provide better service, a customer service call center investigated the hang-up rates of people who called in for help on a recent evening. These data were collected.

Hang-Up Rates

Duration of call before hanging up (min)	0–3	3–6	6–9	9–12	12–15	15–18
Number of customers	1	3	4	6	13	9

Duration of call before hanging up (min)	18–21	21–24	24–27	27–30	30–33
Number of customers	8	10	6	4	1

a. Make a table showing the probability distribution of the random variable x, where x represents the duration of the call in three-minute intervals.

b. Construct a relative frequency histogram for the probability distribution.

c. What is the median length of time a customer waited before hanging up? 15–18 min

d. Draw a smooth curve on your histogram, so that the area under the curve is approximately the same as the area of the histogram.

Consumer CONNECTION

Customers often get frustrated when put on hold, and lost calls can mean lost business. Companies perform queue-time case studies to see how long a customer will wait on hold before abandoning a phone call. They can reschedule their staff to be available during high calling periods.

13a.

x	0–3	3–6	6–9	9–12	12–15	15–18	18–21	21–24	24–27	27–30	30–33
$P(x)$	.015	.046	.062	.092	.2	.138	.123	.154	.092	.062	.015

13b, d.

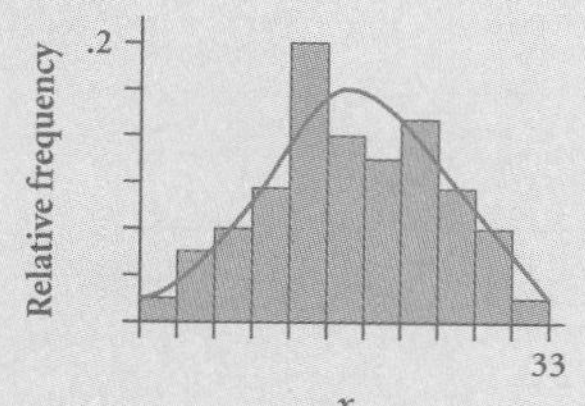

12d. Range for standardized age of president: -2.0 to 2.3; range for standardized age of VP: -2.1 to 2.0. They represent how many standard deviations above or below the mean the presidents' ages or vice presidents' ages are.

12e. President

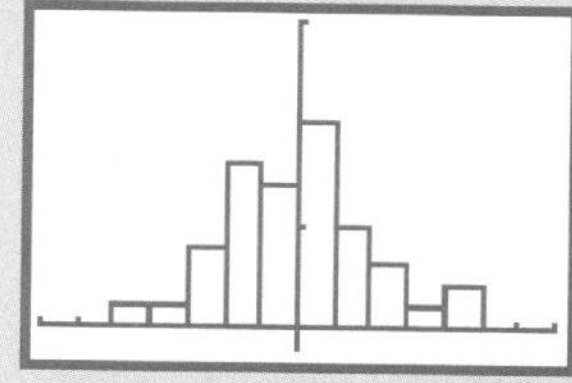

[−3.5, 3.5, 0.5, −1, 15, 5]

Vice President

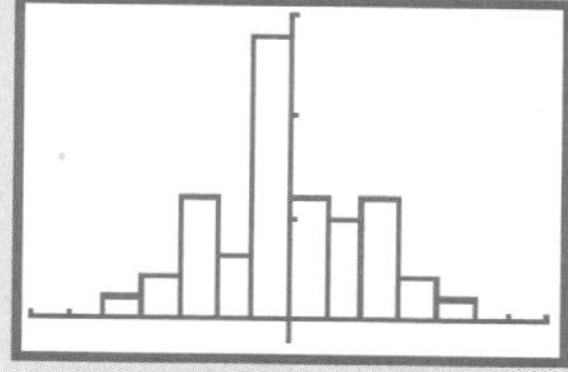

[−3.5, 3.5, 0.5, −1, 15, 5]

12f. Responses will vary. The graphs are reasonably symmetric with most values near the y-axis. All values are within the $-3.5 \leq x \leq 3.5$ domain, and most are within $-2.0 \leq x \leq 2.0$.

Exercise 13a [Alert] Students may think that the distribution is given in the table or that they need to make a histogram, in which case 13b is redundant. A probability distribution can be described by a table if the numbers are relative frequencies rather than the frequencies themselves.

The standard deviation is a number that describes a data set, but it can also be thought of as a distance from the mean. For example, you can count how many standard deviations from the mean a data point is.

MAKING THE CONNECTION

[Language] A *queue* is a waiting line.

Exercise 14 Be prepared to review the idea of standard deviation. This exercise is a preview of the 68-95-99.7 rule for normal distributions, introduced in Lesson 13.3.

14b.

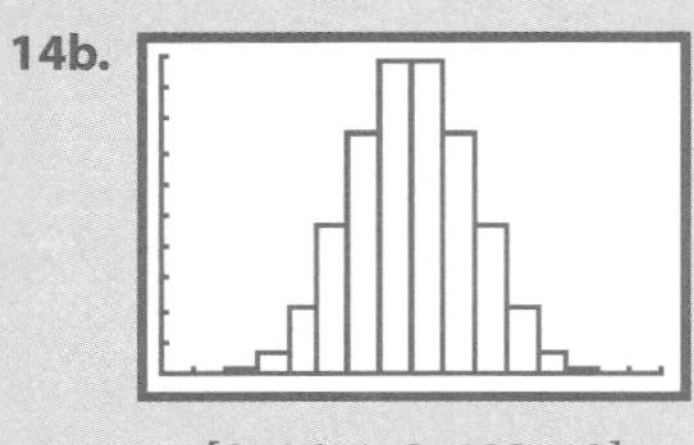

[0, 16, 1, 0, 100, 10]

16a. $d = \left|\tan\left(\frac{\pi}{10}t\right)\right|, 0 \leq t \leq 60$ where t is in seconds and d is in units.

16b.

[0, 60, 5, −2, 10, 1]

(*Note:* Distance is always positive.)

17. *QR* is 0 when *P* overlaps *R*, then grows larger and larger without bound until *P* reaches the *y*-axis, at which point *Q* is undefined because $\overrightarrow{PO}$ and $\overleftrightarrow{RT}$ are parallel and do not intersect. As *P* moves through Quadrant II, *QR* decreases to 0. Then, as *P* moves through Quadrant III, *QR* increases again without bound. When *P* reaches the *y*-axis, point *Q* is again undefined. As *P* moves through Quadrant IV, *QR* again decreases to 0. These patterns correspond to the zeros and vertical asymptotes of the graph in Exercise 16.

Exercise 18 If needed, **[Ask]** "What's the expected point value of each spin?" [0.5]

18. The expected value of points per spin is +0.5, so the game should last 100 spins.

Review

12.7 **14.** Consider the number of heads, x, when 15 fair coins are all tossed at once.

a. Use binomial expansion to find the probability distribution for $P(x)$. Then calculate the theoretical results for 500 trials of this experiment. Copy and complete the table below. Round off the frequencies in row 3 to whole-number values.

Heads (x)	0	1	2	. . .	14	15	Total
$P(x)$	(0.5^{15})						1
Frequency	$500(0.5^{15}) = \underline{?}$			. . .			500

b. Create a histogram showing the probability distribution for $P(x)$.

c. Find the mean and standard deviation of the number of heads. $\bar{x} = 7.5, s = 1.94$

d. How many of the 500 trials are within one standard deviation of the mean? 348

e. What percentage of the data is within one standard deviation of the mean? 69.6%

f. What percentage of the data is within two standard deviations of the mean? 96.4%

g. What percentage of the data is within three standard deviations of the mean? 100%

12.2 **15.** Suppose you roll a pair of standard six-sided dice five times. What is the probability of rolling a sum of 8 at least three times? .022

10.5 **16.** The line *RT* is tangent to a unit circle, and $\overrightarrow{PO}$ intersects $\overleftrightarrow{RT}$ at *Q*. Point *P* makes one rotation around the unit circle every 20 seconds.

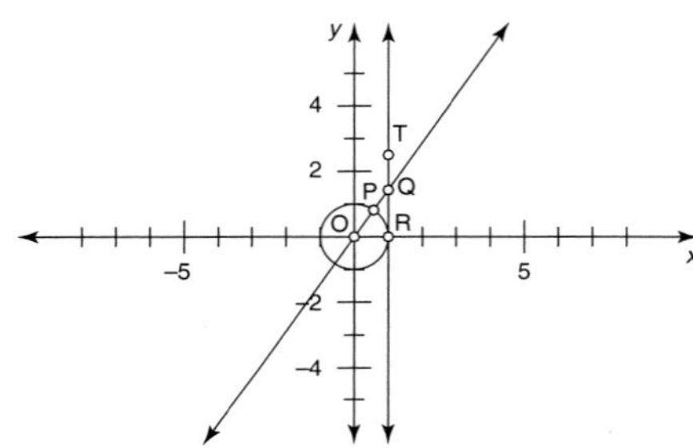

a. Find an equation to model the distance *QR* over a 1-minute period, starting when point *P* overlaps point *R*.

b. Graph the equation you found in 16a on your calculator.

10.5 **17.** ***Technology*** Use geometry software to construct the sketch in Exercise 16. Measure the distance *QR*, and animate point *P*. Describe the range of values of *QR* as *P* moves along the circle. Explain how these values relate to your answer to Exercise 16.

12.4 **18.** A spinner is divided into ten equal sectors numbered 1 through 10 in random order. If you get an even number, you add that number to your score. If you get an odd number, you subtract that number from your score. The game is over when your score reaches either +50 or −50. How many spins do you expect a typical game to last?

14a.

Heads (x)	0	1	2	3	4	5	6	7
$P(x)$	0.00003	0.0005	0.003	0.014	0.042	0.092	0.153	0.196
Frequency	0	0	2	7	21	46	76	98

Heads (x)	8	9	10	11	12	13	14	15
$P(x)$	0.196	0.153	0.092	0.042	0.014	0.003	0.0005	0.00003
Frequency	98	76	46	21	7	2	0	0

19. How is the area of a rectangle affected when its length is doubled and its width is halved? How is the area of a triangle affected when its base is doubled and its height is halved? How are the area of a rectangle and triangle affected when their horizontal dimensions are multiplied by 3 and their vertical dimensions are multiplied by one-third? Do you think this relationship is true for any two-dimensional figure?

Exercise 19 This exercise previews an idea that students will use in Lesson 13.2: If you stretch a normal curve horizontally (to get the desired standard deviation), you must shrink it vertically to keep the area under the curve equal to 1.

19. In all cases, the area remains the same. The relationship holds for all two-dimensional figures.

Project

SIMPSON'S PARADOX

This table shows the number of male and female applicants, and the percentages admitted, to the six largest graduate school majors at the University of California, Berkeley, in Fall 1973.

	Men		Women		Total	
	Number of applicants	Percentage admitted	Number of applicants	Percentage admitted	Number of applicants	Percentage admitted
A	825	62	108	82	933	64
B	560	63	25	68	585	67
C	325	37	593	34	918	35
D	417	33	375	35	792	34
E	191	28	393	24	584	25
F	373	6	341	7	714	6

(D. Freedman, R. Pisani, R. Purves, and A. Adhikari (1991), *Statistics*, 2d ed., New York: Norton, p. 17)

Compare the percentages for men, women, and total admitted. Does it seem as though there is a bias in favor of men or women in admissions? Why or why not?

Now calculate the total number of men and women admitted to these six majors. (You'll need to use the data given for number of applicants and admission rate for each major.) Then calculate the overall percentages of men and of women admitted. Does it appear that there is a bias in favor of men or women? What happened?

Your project should include

- Answers to the questions above.
- Any additional research you do on Simpson's paradox, including examples of other problems you find or one you make up yourself.

Supporting the Project

Simpson's paradox is a dramatic example of a biased researcher manipulating statistics. The paradoxical nature of these data is analyzed in the 1991 book *Statistics,* by David Freedman et al. Simpson's paradox was first described by British statistician E. H. Simpson in his 1951 article "The Interpretation of Interaction in Contingency Tables."

OUTCOMES

- The student finds that, for the data given, the admission rates of women, men, and all applicants are very close. There may be a slight bias in favor of women.
- The student finds that, when numbers are combined, approximately 45% of men were admitted compared to approximately 30% of women, indicating a strong bias in favor of men.
- The report includes possible reasons for the different statistical results.
- The report includes research on Simpson's paradox.
- The student includes another example of a situation illustrating Simpson's paradox.

LESSON

13.2

PLANNING

LESSON OUTLINE

One day:

15 min Investigation

10 min Example A

5 min Example B

10 min Sharing

5 min Exercises

MATERIALS

- Penny Weights (T), *optional*
- Calculator Notes 2B, 3B, 13A–C

TEACHING

In this lesson students see what it means for a continuous distribution representing a population to be a normal distribution.

Example A refers to the number *e*, the subject of the Exploration The Number *e* in Chapter 5. It's not necessary for students to have done the exploration first, but if they didn't do it earlier you might have them do it now if you have time.

The one-step investigation is on page 735.

Guiding the Investigation

If time is limited, you can do this investigation as a class demonstration.

Step 1 As needed, refer students to Calculator Note 3B for creating function tables.

Step 1 $p = .5$; 7 or 8

See page 906 for answers to Steps 2 and 3.

LESSON

13.2

Normal Distributions

In Chapter 12, you studied the binomial distribution, $(p + q)^n$, for discrete random variables. The number of trials is represented by n, and p and q represent the only two possible outcomes of each event. In this lesson you will discover some properties of this probability distribution.

This 10-foot-tall machine drops balls through a grid of pins. The balls land in a bell-shaped curve—a visual representation of their probability distribution.

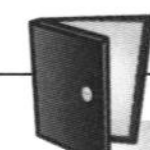

Investigation
The Bell

Consider the number of heads, x, when 15 fair coins are all tossed at once. The probability distribution, $P(x)$, is a binomial distribution, because there are exactly two possible outcomes for each toss—heads or tails.

Step 1 The binomial probability distribution for this theoretical experiment is $P(x) = {}_{15}C_x p^x(1 - p)^{15-x}$, where p is the probability of a head for each coin toss. Create a calculator table of this function with table entries at integer values of x from 0 to 15. What value should you use for p? What x-value gives the maximum for $P(x)$?

Step 2 Create two lists, L_1 and L_2. The entries in list L_1 should contain all the possible values of x. Enter the corresponding values of $P(x)$ in list L_2. You can do this quickly by defining L_2 as the expression $Y_1(L_1)$. Complete the table below. What is the sum of values in list L_2? Why does this answer make sense?

Heads (x)	0	1	2	. . .	15
$P(x)$					

Step 3 Create a relative frequency histogram showing the distribution of heads. Use list L_2 as the frequency. Describe the shape and range of this histogram. What is the maximum value?

LESSON OBJECTIVES

- Investigate the graph of the normal curve
- Use the equation of a normal distribution to determine characteristics of normally distributed populations

NCTM STANDARDS

CONTENT		PROCESS	
	Number	✓	Problem Solving
✓	Algebra	✓	Reasoning
	Geometry	✓	Communication
✓	Measurement	✓	Connections
✓	Data/Probability	✓	Representation

Step 4 Graph $P(x)$ using a window with friendly domain, such as [0, 18.8, 1, −0.01, 0.25, 0.1]. You may choose to turn off the axes to see all the points. For what values of x is the function defined? Write a short description of this graph. Include the shape and your estimates of the mode, median, and mean of the distribution. How does this graph differ from the histogram in Step 3?

Step 5 Graph $P(x) = {}_{45}C_x p^x(1-p)^{45-x}$ using a window with friendly domain, such as [0, 47, 1, −0.01, 0.25, 0.1]. What theoretical experiment does this equation describe? Again, write a short description of the graph that includes the shape, the domain and range, and your estimate of the mode, median, and mean of the distribution. Compare this graph with the one in Step 4.

Step 6 Enter the defined values of x and $P(x)$ in lists L1 and L2. Then find the mean and standard deviation of the distribution. [▶ See **Calculator Note 2B** to learn how to find statistics of frequency tables. ◀] $\bar{x} = 22.5$, $s \approx 3.354$

Step 7 If the number of coins increased, how would the answers to Steps 5 and 6 change? Write your predictions and then verify them.

Step 7 The domain would increase, the range would decrease, and the shape would be roughly the same, but wider and flatter. Mean, median, and mode would all move up to $\frac{n}{2}$, where n is the number of coins. Standard deviation would be larger due to larger spread.

As n grows increasingly large, the binomial distribution $(p+q)^n$ looks more and more like the continuous bell-shaped curve at right. Distributions for large populations often have this shape. Heights, clothing sizes, and test scores are a few examples. In fact, the bell-shaped curve is so common that it is called a **normal curve,** and a bell-shaped distribution is called a **normal distribution.**

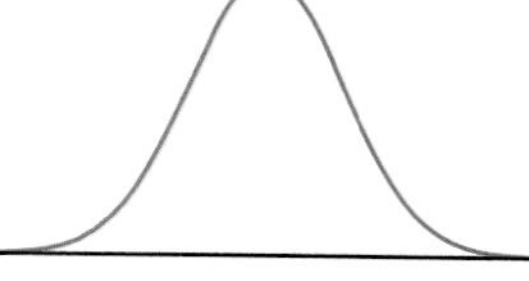

Normal curves can describe the distribution of a sample or an entire population. You use $\bar{x}$ and s to represent the mean and standard deviation of a sample, but you use μ and σ (pronounced "mew" and "sigma") to represent the mean and standard deviation of an entire population.

In this lesson you'll see some properties of normal distributions. The general equation for a normal distribution curve is in the form $y = ab^{-x^2}$. If you graph a function like $y = 3^{-x^2}$, you'll get a bell-shaped curve that is symmetric about the vertical axis. To describe a particular distribution of data, you translate the curve horizontally to be centered at the mean of the data, and you stretch it horizontally to match the standard deviation of the data. Then you shrink it vertically so that the area is 1. These steps are shown graphically below. You'll want to begin with a parent function that has standard deviation 1.

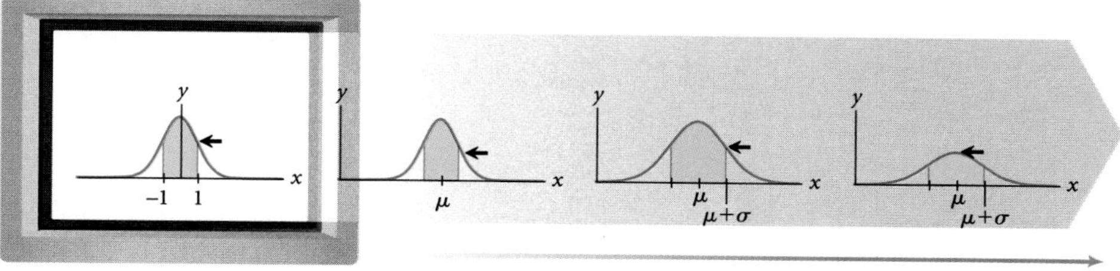

Step 4 If students don't want to use lists for this step, they can enter the function into the Y= screen and graph; another window with a friendly domain is [0, 47, 5, −0.05, 0.20, 0.1]. However, most students will probably have to use lists to find the standard deviation in Step 6.

Step 4

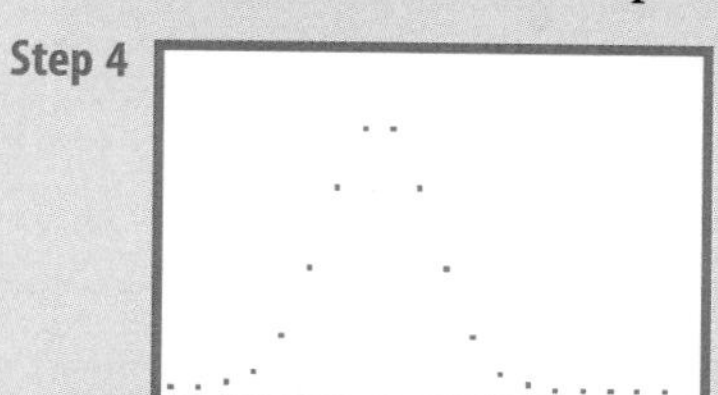

[0, 18.8, 1, −0.01, 0.25, 0.1]

The function is defined for integer values from 0 to 15. The graph consists of discrete points that form a mound-shaped, symmetric graph, with the same shape as the histogram in Step 3. The mean, median, and mode are all 7.5.

Step 5

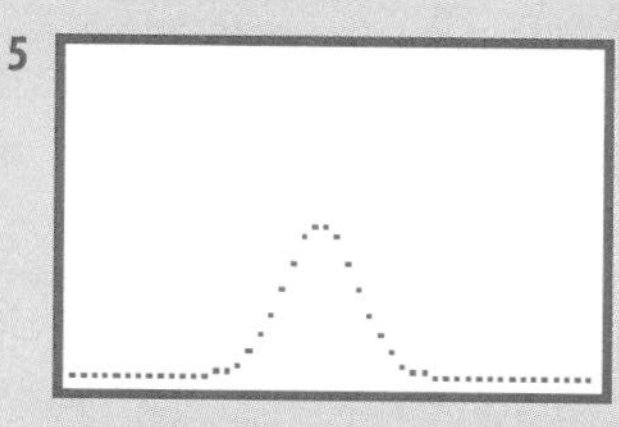

[0, 47, 1, −0.01, 0.25, 0.1]

The function describes the probability distribution when 45 coins are flipped at once. The shape is the same as Step 4, but wider and shorter. The domain is integer values from 0 to 45, and the range is 0 to .117. The mean, median and mode are all 22.5.

Step 7 You might encourage at least one group to try setting n equal to 90 in the equation and save the results for use in Example A.

Normal Distribution Viewing Window
A graphing window of $0 \leq y \leq \frac{0.4}{\sigma}$ will always contain the full range of the normal curve. When $\sigma = 1$, the maximum y-value is less than 0.4. For larger values of σ, the graph is more spread out, and therefore the maximum y-value is even smaller.

One Step
Pose this problem, adapted from the investigation: "Choose a probability p for a head to come up when a coin is flipped. Graph the binomial probability distribution $P(x) = {}_{15}C_x p^x(1-p)^{(15-x)}$, representing the probability that various numbers of coins will come up heads when 15 coins are flipped. Then transform the function $y = e^{x^2}$ to fit those data points." Challenge groups that finish first to repeat the problem for larger numbers of coins, such as 90.

During Sharing, introduce the terminology and equation of a standard normal distribution, derive the equation of a normal distribution with mean μ and standard deviation σ, and have students figure out (from Calculator Notes 13B and 13C) how to graph the function quickly and find probabilities as areas.

Standard Normal Distribution

You might want to lead students to guess the formula for the parent function, symmetric about the y-axis. **[Ask]** "What properties does the graph of the parent function, symmetric about the y-axis, have?" [$y(0) = 1$; the function is even; the x-axis is an asymptote.] "What functions have some of these properties?" [Exponential functions have y-intercept 1 and the x-axis as an asymptote.] "Can you adjust the exponential function to be symmetric about the y-axis?" [The graph of the function $y = b^{x^2}$ doesn't have the asymptote, but the graph of $y = b^{-x^2}$ does, and this is the parent function of the standard normal distribution.]

You might check on student understanding by asking, "What does x represent?" [data values] "What does y represent?" [frequencies of the data values] "What does the area under the curve represent?" [the probability] "What is the total area under the curve? Why?" [1; because the sum of the probabilities for all possible outcomes must be one.]

[Link] The values of a and b can be found with calculus using a double integral and trigonometric substitution. The constant is related to e because e^x is the standard exponential function. (You could use other bases and get slightly more complicated results.) The constant a is related to π as a result of the trigonometric substitution.

MAKING THE CONNECTION

Although Carl Gauss developed the idea of the normal curve, the curve was first invented by French mathematician Abraham de Moivre (1667–1754) in his 1718 book *Doctrine of Chances.* De Moivre also introduced the use of mortality statistics to calculate the maturation of insurance policies and successfully predicted the exact date of his own death.

History CONNECTION

German mathematician Carl Gauss (1777–1855) developed the idea of a normal distribution to describe the variation in the measurements made by surveyors and astronomers as they remeasured the same distances.

The parent function of a probability distribution has standard deviation 1, and is called the **standard normal distribution.** To meet the conditions for the standard normal distribution, statisticians have used advanced mathematics to determine the values of a and b in the equation $y = ab^{-x^2}$. The value of a is related to the number π.

$$a = \sqrt{\frac{1}{2\pi}} \approx 0.399$$

The value of b is related to another common mathematical constant, the transcendental number e.

$$b = \sqrt{e} \approx 1.649$$

Calculators allow you to work with these numbers fairly easily.

EXAMPLE A

The general equation for a normal curve is in the form $y = ab^{-x^2}$.

a. Write the equation for a standard normal curve, using $a = \sqrt{\frac{1}{2\pi}}$ and $b = \sqrt{e}$. Find a good graphing window for this equation and describe the graph. [▶ To learn how to enter the value of e, see **Calculator Note 13A.** ◀]

b. Write the equation for a normal distribution with mean μ and standard deviation σ.

c. Write the equation for the normal curve that fits the binomial distribution $P(x) = {}_{90}C_x\, p^x(1-p)^{90-x}$, where $p = .5$.

▶ ***Solution***

Substitute the values given for the constants a and b into the general equation for a normal curve.

a. The equation for a standard normal curve is

$$y = \sqrt{\frac{1}{2\pi}}\left(\sqrt{e}\right)^{-x^2}$$

Note that $\sqrt{\frac{1}{2\pi}}$ is the same as $\frac{1}{\sqrt{2\pi}}$.

A good window for this graph is [−3.5, 3.5, 1, −0.1, 0.5, 0.25]. The graph is bell-shaped and symmetric about $x = 0$. So the mean, median, and mode are all 0. Almost all of the data are in the interval $-3 \leq x \leq 3$.

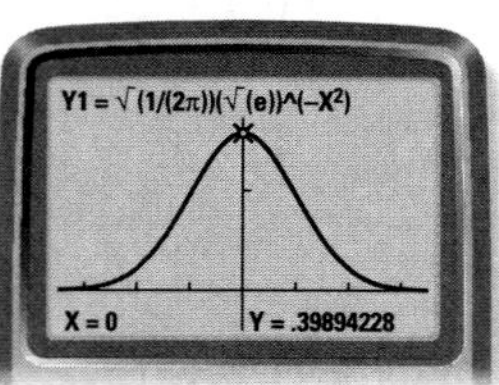

[−3.5, 3.5, 1, −0.1, 0.5, 0.25]

Another history connection about Gauss is on page 623.

▶ ***EXAMPLE A***

As needed, make it clear that the standard normal distribution is the parent function. **[Ask]** "Why is the range of the function so small?" [Because the y-value is the probability of the x-value, it will never be greater than 1 or less than 0. In addition, the area under the entire graph is 1, so its maximum height will be less than 1.]

Transcendental numbers were introduced in the Exploration The Number e on page 293. If your students did not do that exploration, you may wish to tell them that $e \approx 2.718$ and that, like π, e is an irrational number (a number that cannot be expressed as a ratio of two integers and that, when expressed as a decimal, does not repeat). Like π, e is also a transcendental number (a number that is not the root of any algebraic equation).

b. Translate the curve horizontally to shift the mean from 0 to μ. And stretch the curve horizontally to change the standard deviation from 1 to σ. The area under a probability distribution must be 1. A horizontal stretch will increase the area, so it must be accompanied by a vertical shrink.

$$y = \sqrt{\frac{1}{2\pi}}\left(\sqrt{e}\right)^{-x^2}$$ Start with the parent function.

$$y = \sqrt{\frac{1}{2\pi}}\left(\sqrt{e}\right)^{-(x-\mu)^2}$$ Substitute $(x - \mu)$ for x to translate the mean horizontally to μ.

$$y = \frac{1}{\sqrt{2\pi}}\left(\sqrt{e}\right)^{-((x-\mu)/\sigma)^2}$$ Divide $(x - \mu)$ by the horizontal scale factor, σ, so the curve reflects the correct standard deviation.

$$y = \frac{1}{\sigma\sqrt{2\pi}}\left(\sqrt{e}\right)^{-((x-\mu)/\sigma)^2}$$ Divide the right side of the equation by the vertical scale factor, σ, to keep the area under the curve equal to 1.

c. To write the equation for the normal curve that fits this distribution, you must first find the values of μ and σ. You can do this by entering values of x and $P(x)$ in lists L1 and L2, then using your calculator as shown below. For this distribution, $\mu = 45$ and $\sigma \approx 4.7434$, so the equation is

$$y = \frac{1}{4.7434\sqrt{2\pi}}\left(\sqrt{e}\right)^{-((x-45)/4.7434)^2} \approx (0.084)(1.649)^{-((x-45)/4.7434)^2}$$

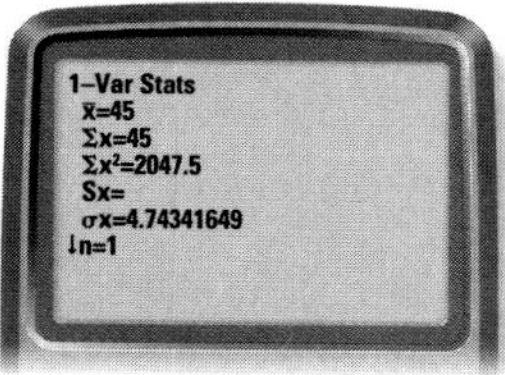

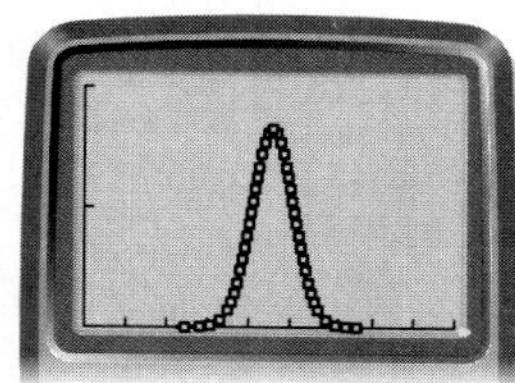

[0, 90, 10, 0, 0.1, 0.05]

You can see that the graph of this normal curve fits the discrete points of the binomial distribution graph.

The Normal Distribution

The equation for a **normal distribution** with mean μ and standard deviation σ is

$$y = \frac{1}{\sigma\sqrt{2\pi}}\left(\sqrt{e}\right)^{-((x-\mu)/\sigma)^2}$$

You can view the graph of a normal distribution well in the window

$$\mu - 3\sigma \le x \le \mu + 3\sigma \quad \text{and} \quad 0 \le y \le \frac{0.4}{\sigma}$$

This window will show 3 standard deviations above and below the mean, and the minimum and maximum frequencies of the distribution.

In the equation for a normal distribution, the data values are represented by x and their relative frequencies by y. The area under a section of the curve gives the probability that a data value will fall in that interval.

Example A (continued)

In part b, **[Ask]** "Why are we transforming the graph here?" [The parent graph is translated horizontally to move the mean from 0, it is stretched or shrunk horizontally to adjust the standard deviation, and the graph is shrunk or stretched vertically to keep the area 1.]

In part c, if possible, use the result of the investigation for n equal to 90 to find the values of μ and σ. **[Alert]** The trickiest part of entering the function is correctly placing the parentheses. Storing the constant values first and then using their names while entering the functions can help.

Dynamic Normal Curve

A dynamic version of the illustration at the bottom of page 735 showing how the mean and standard deviation impact the bell-shaped normal curve can be found at www.keymath.com/DAA.

▶ **EXAMPLE B**

This example demonstrates how to use a graphing calculator to find probabilities within a normal distribution. The pennies these students used are not representative of U.S. pennies in general.

[Alert] Students may replicate these results on their calculators without understanding what each number represents. You might display the Penny Weights transparency as you discuss the significance of each number.

As you discuss part c **[Ask]** "If you want the penny's weight to be between 3.3 g and some upper bound, what's the smallest upper bound that gives the same answer to seven decimal places?" [An upper bound of 3.94 gives the same answer.]

SHARING IDEAS

As students report on their investigation results, keep asking them about the concept of a normal distribution, to help them move beyond the calculator.

You might tell students that the normal curve has also been called the *curve of error,* the *curve of facility of error, das Fehlerkurve* (the defect curve), the *Gaussian curve,* the *Laplace-Gaussian curve,* and the *probability curve.* Francis Galton (1822–1911) was probably the first to call it the *normal curve.*

If you didn't get a chance to discuss Lesson 13.1, Exercise 19, remind students of the stretching and shrinking in Example A, and **[Ask]** "If you stretch a figure horizontally by a factor and then shrink it vertically by the same factor, will the area always be unchanged?" Let students experiment with rectangles and triangles until they understand the idea.

[Ask] "Is it really possible for the unbounded region under this graph to have a finite area?" As students discuss this question, help them make the connection to finite sums of convergent series.

Most graphing calculators provide the normal distribution equation as a built-in function, and you have to provide only the mean and standard deviation. In this chapter we will use the notation $n(x)$ to indicate a standard normal distribution function with mean 0 and standard deviation 1. Using this notation, a nonstandard normal distribution is written

$n(x,$ *mean, standard deviation*$)$

For example, a normal distribution with mean 3.1 and standard deviation 0.14 is written $n(x, 3.1, 0.14)$. [▶ To learn how to graph a normal distribution on your calculator, see **Calculator Note 13B.** ◀] The area under a portion of a normal curve is written

$N($*lower, upper, mean, standard deviation*$)$

This notation indicates the lower and upper endpoints of the interval, and the mean and standard deviation of the distribution. [▶ To learn how to find this value on your calculator, see **Calculator Note 13C.** ◀] This area determines the probability that a value in a normal distribution will fall within a particular range.

EXAMPLE B

A group of students weighs 500 U.S. pennies. They find that the pennies have normally distributed weights with a mean of 3.1 g and a standard deviation of 0.14 g.

a. Use your calculator to create a graph of this normal curve.

b. What is the probability that a randomly selected penny will weigh between 3.2 and 3.4 g?

c. What is the probability that a randomly selected penny will weigh more than 3.3 g?

d. What is the probability that the weight of a penny will be within one standard deviation of the mean? Two standard deviations of the mean? Three standard deviations of the mean?

▶ **Solution**

The mean is 3.1, and the standard deviation is 0.14 g.

a. You can graph the probability curve using $n(x, 3.1, 0.14)$.

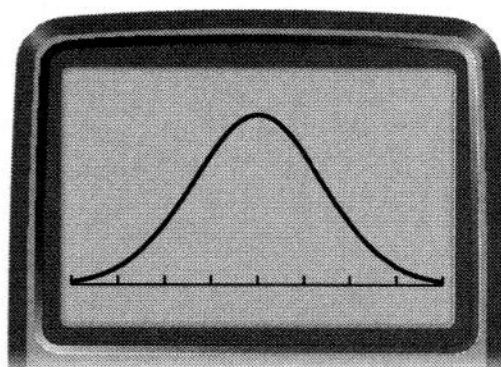

[2.7, 3.5, 0.1, –0.5, 3, 0]

b. The probability that a randomly selected penny will weigh between 3.2 and 3.4 g is equal to the area under the normal curve between 3.2 and 3.4 g.

You can find this area on your calculator using $N(3.2, 3.4, 3.1, 0.14)$. The area is about .22, so there is a 22% chance that a randomly selected penny will have a mass between 3.2 and 3.4 g.

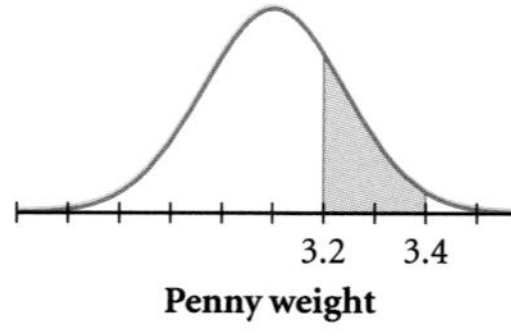

c. You want to find the area under the curve to the right of 3.3 g. However, this interval has no upper limit. (Theoretically, there is no upper limit for the mass. Although a penny with a mass over 5 or 6 g would be extremely unlikely, it is not impossible.) How high should you set the upper bound? Whether you use 100 or 1000, you find the same answer, accurate to eight digits:

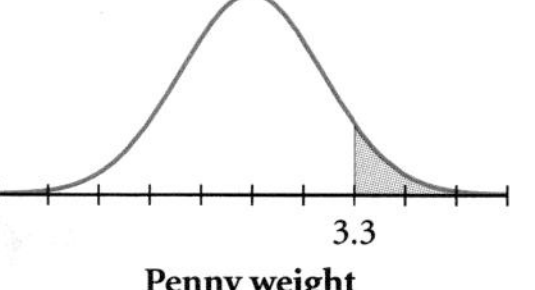

$N(3.3, 100, 3.1, 0.14) = .0765637714$

$N(3.3, 1000, 3.1, 0.14) = .0765637714$

So, you can use any fairly large number for the upper limit.

The probability that a penny will weigh more than 3.3g is approximately .07.

d. The probability that the mass will be within one standard deviation of the mean is $N(3.1 - 0.14, 3.1 + 0.14, 3.1, 0.14)$, or approximately .683. The probability that the mass will be within two standard deviations of the mean is $N(3.1 - 0.28, 3.1 + 0.28, 3.1, 0.14)$, or approximately .955. The probability that the mass will be within three standard deviations of the mean is $N(3.1 - 0.42, 3.1 + 0.42, 3.1, 0.14)$, or approximately .997.

Look at the curvature of a normal curve. At the points that are exactly one standard deviation from the mean, the curve changes between curving downward (the part of the curve with decreasing slope) and curving upward (the parts of the curve with increasing slope). These points are called **inflection points.** You can estimate the standard deviation of any normal distribution by locating the inflection points of its graph.

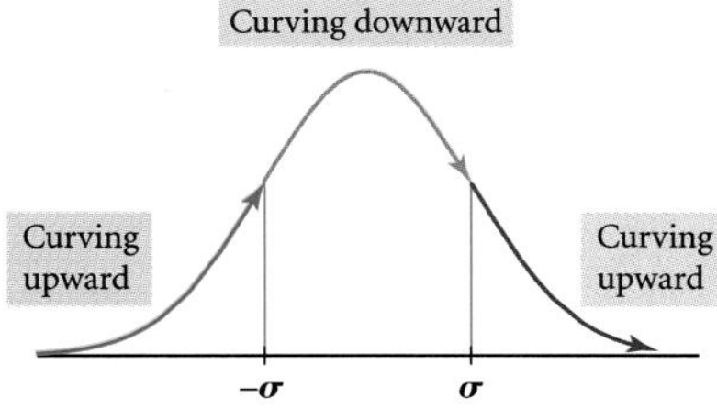

History CONNECTION

English nurse Florence Nightingale (1820–1910) contributed to the field of applied statistics by collecting and analyzing data during the Crimean War (1853–1856). While stationed in Turkey, she systematized data collection and record keeping at military hospitals and created a new type of graph, the polar-area diagram. Nightingale used statistics to show that improved sanitation in hospitals resulted in fewer deaths. For more information about Nightingale's contributions, see the web links at www.keymath.com/DAA .

Florence Nightingale

Sharing Ideas (continued)

[Ask] "What might be a good way to find inflection points on a graph?" Be open to a variety of ideas. One way is to cover the right (or left) part of the graph until the visible curve is the largest part that appears concave up. A line drawn to the x-axis will locate the inflection point.

[Ask] "Can the curve be increasing but concave down?" [Yes, between $-\sigma$ and the mean the curve is increasing at a decreasing rate.] "Where is the curve decreasing at an increasing rate?" [from the mean to σ] "Where is the curve decreasing but curving up?" [above σ]

After discussing inflection points, you might ask students to sketch by hand normal curves with given means and standard deviations.

Assessing Progress

You can assess students' understanding of binomial probability, relative frequency histograms, and probability distributions and their means and standard deviations.

Closing the Lesson

Reiterate the main point of this lesson: The probability distributions of many populations are normal. Their equations have the parent function $y = ab^{-x^2}$, where $a = \frac{1}{\sqrt{2\pi}}$ and $b = \sqrt{e}$. The graph of the standard normal curve is mound-shaped, is symmetric about the y-axis, has a maximum at the point (0, 1), has inflection points one standard deviation from the mean (at $x = \pm 1$), and (because it's a probability distribution) bounds (with the x-axis) a region with area 1. Transformations adjust the mean with a horizontal shift, adjust the standard deviation with a horizontal stretch, and keep the total area 1 with a vertical shrink by the same factor.

BUILDING UNDERSTANDING

The exercises provide practice with normal distributions and the probabilities given by areas under the curves.

ASSIGNING HOMEWORK

Essential	1–6
Performance assessment	7–12
Portfolio	10
Journal	7, 11
Group	10
Review	13–16

Helping with the Exercises

1a. The tables and graphs of both functions agree.

X	Y2	Y3
-3	.00443	.00443
-2	.05399	.05399
-1	.24197	.24197
0	.39894	.39894
1	.24197	.24197
2	.05399	.05399
3	.00443	.00443

Y3=A*B^(-X²)

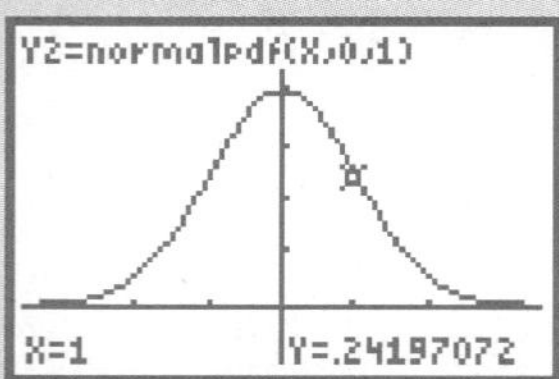

Exercise 2 Students can determine the exact value of the mean from each equation. To approximate the standard deviation in 2c and d, they can use the fact that the coefficient c in cb^d must be $\frac{1}{\sigma\sqrt{2\pi}}$.

Exercise 3 On graphs the standard deviation is estimated by finding inflection points.

4a. $y = \frac{1}{2.5\sqrt{2\pi}}\left(\sqrt{e}\right)^{-((x-18)/2.5)^2}$

4b. $y = \frac{1}{0.8\sqrt{2\pi}}\left(\sqrt{e}\right)^{-((x-10)/0.8)^2}$

4c. $y = \frac{1}{6\sqrt{2\pi}}\left(\sqrt{e}\right)^{-((x-68)/6)^2}$

EXERCISES

Practice Your Skills

1. The standard normal distribution equation, $y = ab^{-x^2}$, where $a = \sqrt{\frac{1}{2\pi}}$ and $b = \sqrt{e}$, is equivalent to the calculator's built-in function $n(x, 0, 1)$.

a. Use a table or graph to verify that these functions are equivalent.

b. Evaluate each function at $x = 1$. $y \approx .242$ and $n(x, 0, 1) \approx .242$

2. From each equation, estimate the mean and standard deviation.

a. $y = \frac{1}{5\sqrt{2\pi}}\left(\sqrt{e}\right)^{-((x-47)/5)^2}$ $\mu = 47, \sigma = 5$

b. $y = \frac{0.4}{23}0.60653^{((x-250)/23)^2}$ $\mu = 250, \sigma = 23$

c. $y = 1.29e^{-((x-5.5)^2/0.1922)}$ $\mu = 5.5, \sigma = 0.31$

d. $y = 0.054(0.99091)^{(x-83)^2}$ $\mu = 83, \sigma = 7.4$

3. From each graph, estimate the mean and standard deviation. Estimates will vary.

a.

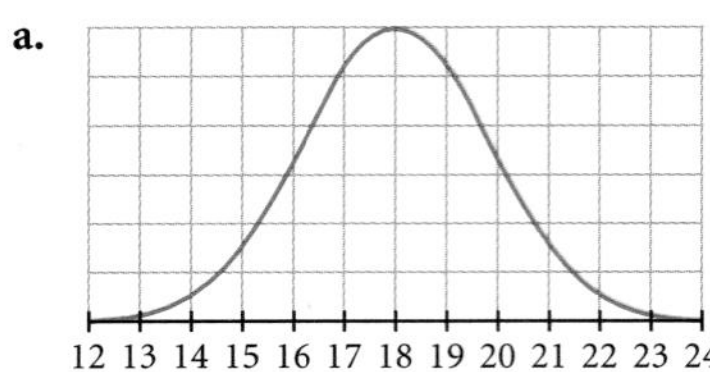
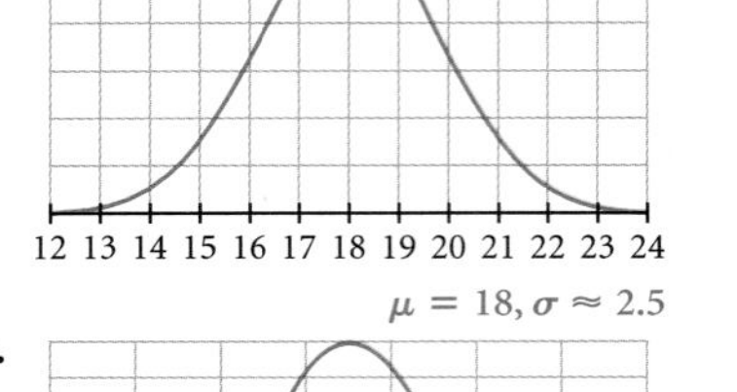

$\mu = 18, \sigma \approx 2.5$

b.

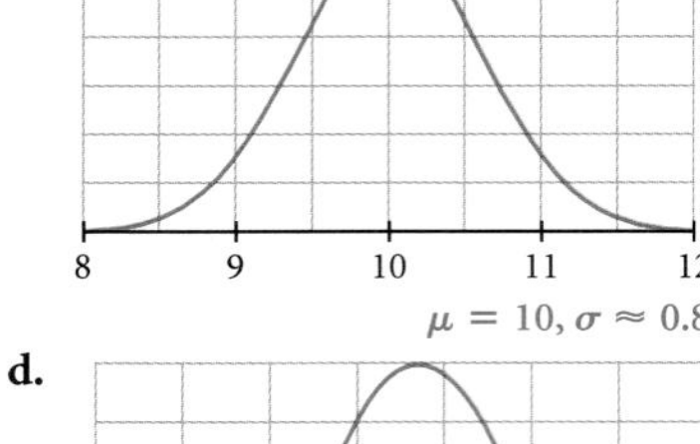

$\mu = 10, \sigma \approx 0.8$

c.

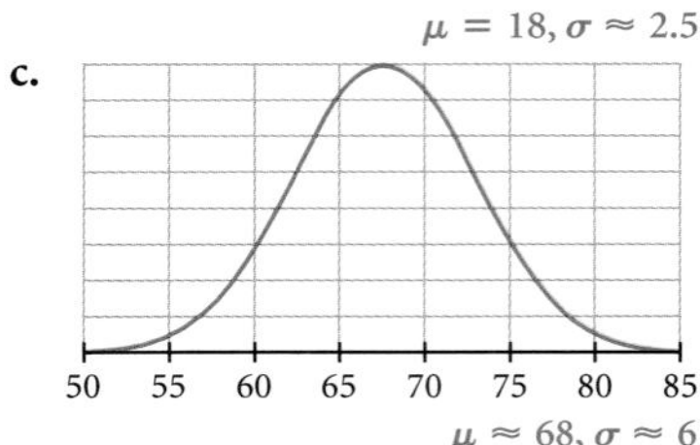

$\mu \approx 68, \sigma \approx 6$

d.

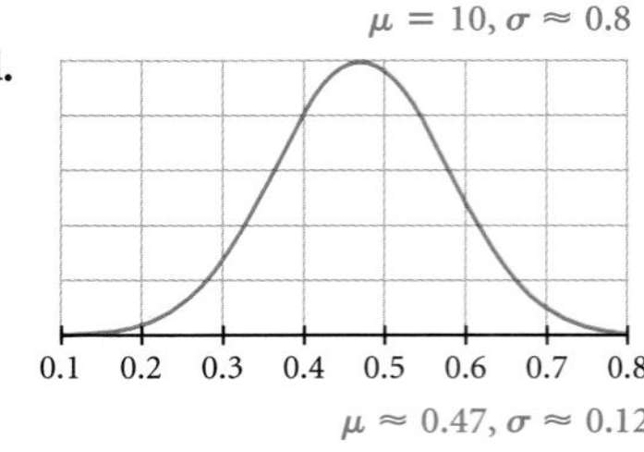

$\mu \approx 0.47, \sigma \approx 0.12$

4. Estimate the equation of each graph in Exercise 3.

Reason and Apply

5. The life spans of wild tribbles are normally distributed with a mean value of 1.8 years and a standard deviation of 0.8 year. Sketch the normal curve, and shade the portion of the graph showing tribble life spans of 1.0 to 1.8 years.

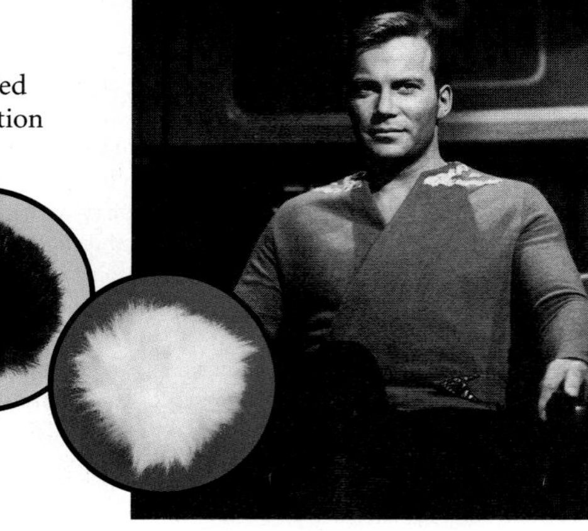

William Shatner (b 1931) played Captain James T. Kirk in the television series *Star Trek* (1966–1969). Captain Kirk and two fictional alien creatures called tribbles are shown here.

4d. $y = \frac{1}{0.12\sqrt{2\pi}}\left(\sqrt{e}\right)^{-((x-0.47)/0.12)^2}$

Exercise 5 As needed, remind students to put the maximum at the mean and inflection points one standard deviation above and below the mean. Ask them to label the mean and standard deviations. **[Alert]** Some students will think that the mean is at the maximum point on the curve rather than on the x-axis.

5.

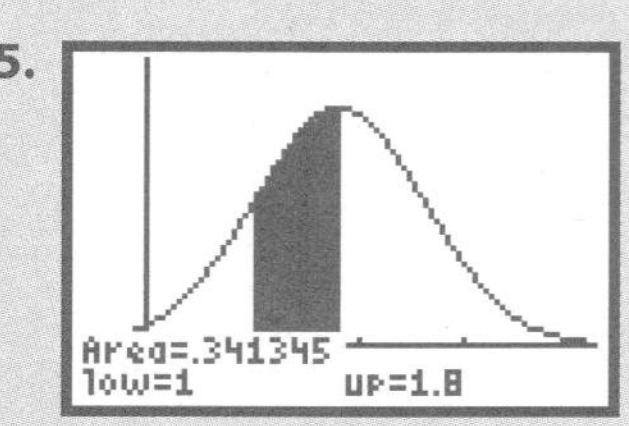

$[-0.6, 4.2, 1, -0.1, 0.6, 0]$

6. Assume that the mean height of an adult male gorilla is 5 ft 8 in., with a standard deviation of 7.2 in.

a. Sketch the graph of the normal distribution of gorilla heights.

b. Sketch the graph if, instead, the standard deviation were 4.3 in.

c. Shade the portion of each graph representing heights greater than 6 ft. Compare your sketches and explain your reasoning.

7. Frosted Sugar Squishies are packaged in boxes labeled "Net weight: 16 oz." The filling machine is set to put 16.8 oz in the box, with a standard deviation of 0.7 oz.

a. Sketch a graph of the normal distribution of package weights. Shade the portion of the graph representing boxes that are below the advertised weight.

b. What percentage of boxes does the shading represent? Is this acceptable? Why?

8. Makers of Sweet Sips 100% fruit drink have found that their filling machine will fill a bottle with a standard deviation of 0.75 oz. The control on the machine will change the mean value but will not affect the standard deviation.

a. Where should they set the mean so that 90% of the bottles have at least 12 oz of fruit drink in them?

b. If a fruit drink bottle can hold 13.5 oz before overflowing, what percentage of the bottles will overflow at the setting suggested in 8a?

9. The pH scale measures the acidity or alkalinity of a solution. Water samples from different locations and depths of a lake usually have normally distributed pH values. The mean of those pH values, plus or minus one standard deviation, is defined to be the pH range of the lake.

Lake Fishbegon has a pH range of 5.8 to 7.2. Sketch the normal curve, and shade those portions that are outside the pH range of the lake.

10. Data collected from 493 women are summarized in the table.

Height (cm)	148–50	150–52	152–54	154–56	156–58	158–60	160–62	162–64	164–66
Frequency	2	5	9	15	27	40	52	63	66

Height (cm)	166–68	168–70	170–72	172–74	174–76	176–78	178–80	180–82	182–84
Frequency	64	53	39	28	15	8	4	1	2

a. Find the mean and standard deviation of the heights, and sketch a histogram of the data.

b. Write an equation based on the model $y = ab^{-x^2}$ that approximates the histogram. $y = 66(0.99)^{(x-165)^2}$

c. Find the equation for a normal curve using the height data. $y = \frac{1}{5.90\sqrt{2\pi}}\left(\sqrt{e}\right)^{-((x-165)/5.90)^2}$

11. The data at right show the pulse rates of 50 people.

a. Find the mean and standard deviation of the data and sketch a histogram.

b. Sketch a distribution that approximates the histogram.

c. Find the equation of a normal curve using the pulse-rate data.

d. Are these pulse rates normally distributed? Why or why not?

66	75	83	73	87	94	79	93	87	64
80	72	84	82	80	73	74	80	83	68
86	70	73	62	77	90	82	85	84	80
80	79	81	82	76	95	76	82	79	91
82	66	78	73	72	77	71	79	82	88

9.

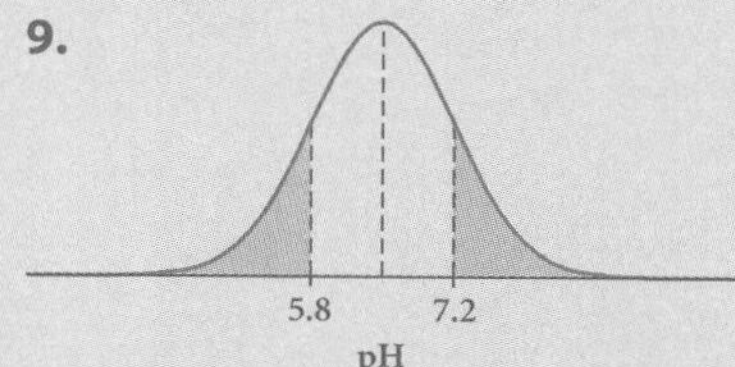

Shade the area greater than or less than one standard deviation away from the mean.

10a. $\mu \approx 165$; $\sigma \approx 5.90$

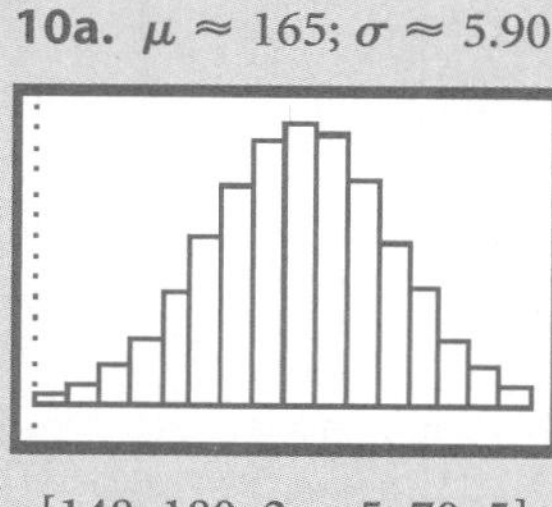

[148, 180, 2, −5, 70, 5]

Exercise 6 [Alert] Students may try to determine the inflection points by taking one standard deviation above and below 0 rather than above and below the mean. Remind them to find the values of the points one and two standard deviations away from the mean.

6a, c.

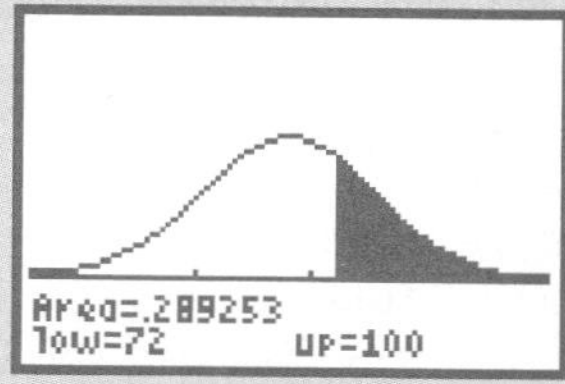

[46.4, 89.6, 10, −0.03, 0.1, 0]

6b, c.

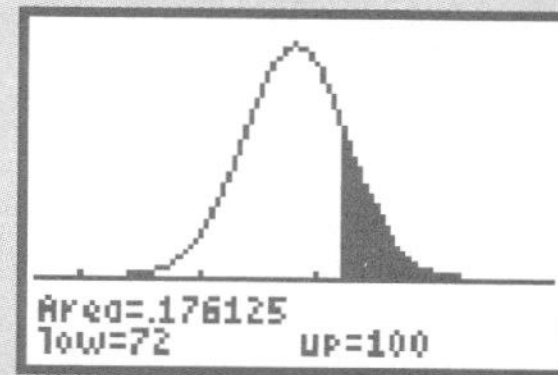

[46.4, 89.6, 10, −0.03, 0.1, 0]

6c. The first graph is sketched in the domain $m - 3s \leq x \leq m + 3s$. The second graph displays less spread because the standard deviation is smaller; because there is more area under the central portion of the curve, there is less area under the tail where $x > 72$ in.

Exercise 10 In 10a, advise students as needed to use the midpoint of each bin for list L1. Because the area of the histogram is not 1, the continuous distribution approximating the histogram in 10b will also have an area other than 1, so this distribution is not a probability distribution and hence not the normal distribution requested in 10c. Even if the heights of the histogram bins are adjusted to give portions of the total, the area is still not 1, because the bins have width 2. The normal curve of 10c includes the bottom half of this relative frequency histogram.

See page 907 for answers to Exercises 7, 8, and 11.

MAKING THE CONNECTION

For law enforcement officers, fingerprint identification is vital for the investigation of crimes. At a crime scene, investigators examine smooth, hard surfaces for fingerprints that are made by the oily secretions of the skin. Powder or chemicals are used to make the prints visible so that they can be photographed or preserved. Law enforcement agencies keep databases of fingerprints that they compare with the fingerprints found at the crime scene to identify potential suspects.

13a. Possible answers: The means for both the French and Spanish tests are lower than that for the Mandarin test, which may indicate more difficult tests. Also, the larger standard deviation on the French exam indicates that there is a larger variation in scores, meaning that more students did worse. However, it is difficult to compare three completely different exams.

13b. the French exam, because it has the greatest standard deviation

Exercise 13c This exercise previews *z*-values, discussed in Lesson 13.3.

13c. Determine how many standard deviations each student's score is from the mean.

Paul: 1.88σ above
Kenyatta: 2.07σ above
Rosanna: 0.98σ above

Kenyatta's score is better than Paul's and Rosanna's because her score is 2.07 standard deviations above the mean.

16a. possible answers:

$y = \frac{37}{56}x^2 + \frac{95}{56}x - \frac{197}{28}$ or

$x = \frac{37}{30}y^2 - \frac{7}{2}y - \frac{41}{15}$

12. Ridge counts in fingerprints are approximately normally distributed with a mean of about 150 and a standard deviation of about 50. Find the probability that a randomly chosen individual has a ridge count

a. between 100 and 200 approximately .68

b. of more than 200 approximately .16

c. of less than 100 approximately .16

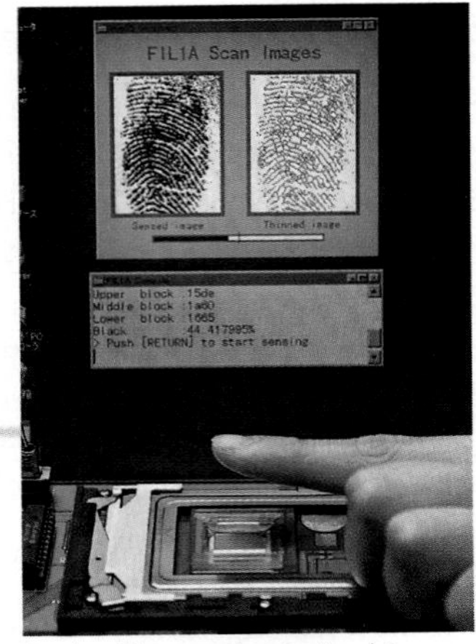

Developed by researchers in Atsugi, Japan, a microchip scans a finger to identify a fingerprint with 99% accuracy in half a second.

Science CONNECTION

Dactyloscopy is the comparison of fingerprints for identification. Francis Galton (1822–1911), an English anthropologist, demonstrated that fingerprints do not change over the course of an individual's lifetime, and that no two fingerprints are exactly the same. Even identical twins, triplets, and quadruplets have completely different prints. According to Galton's calculations, the odds of two individual fingerprints being the same are 1 in 64 billion. For more information on fingerprint identification, see the weblinks at www.keymath.com/DAA .

Review

13. Paul, Kenyatta, and Rosanna each took one national language exam. Paul took the French exam and scored 88. Kenyatta took the Spanish exam and scored 84. Rosanna took the Mandarin exam and scored 91. The national means and standard deviations for the tests are as follows:

French: $\mu = 72, \sigma = 8.5$
Spanish: $\mu = 72, \sigma = 5.8$
Mandarin: $\mu = 85, \sigma = 6.1$

a. Can you determine which test is most difficult? Why or why not?

b. Which test had the widest range of scores nationally? Explain your reasoning.

c. Which of the three friends did best when compared to the national norms? Explain your reasoning.

12.6 **14.** Mr. Hamilton gave his history class an exam in which a student must choose 3 out of 6 parts and complete 2 out of 4 questions in each part selected. How many different ways are there to complete the exam? 120

12.7 **15.** In the expansion of $(2x + y)^{12}$, what is the coefficient of the term containing y^7? 25344

9.3 **16.** Find the equation of a conic section that passes through the three points given at right if the conic section is

a. A parabola. b. A circle.

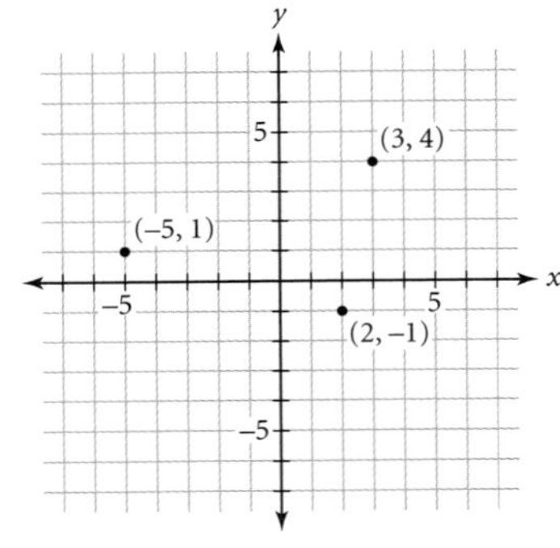

16b. possible answers:

$\left(x + \frac{65}{74}\right)^2 + \left(y - \frac{161}{74}\right)^2 = \frac{50297}{2738}$,

or $(x + 0.878)^2 + (y - 2.176)^2 = 18.369$

EXTENSION

Use Take Another Look activity 3 or 4 on page 795.

EXPLORATION

Normally Distributed Data

What kinds of data are normally distributed? In this exploration you'll use census data and Fathom Dynamic Statistics software to explore what attributes of the population of the United States are distributed normally.

Activity

Is This Normal?

Step 1 Start Fathom. From the File menu choose **Open.** Open one of the census data files in the **Sample Documents** folder. You'll see a box of gold balls, called a collection, that holds data about a group of individuals.

Step 2 Click on the collection, and then choose **Case Table** from the Insert menu. Scroll through the table. What numerical attributes are included? Which ones do you think might be normally distributed?

Step 3 A histogram can show whether a set of data is approximately normally distributed. To create a histogram, choose **Graph** from the Insert menu. Drag and drop an attribute onto the horizontal axis, and then choose **Histogram** from the pull-down menu in the corner of the graph window.

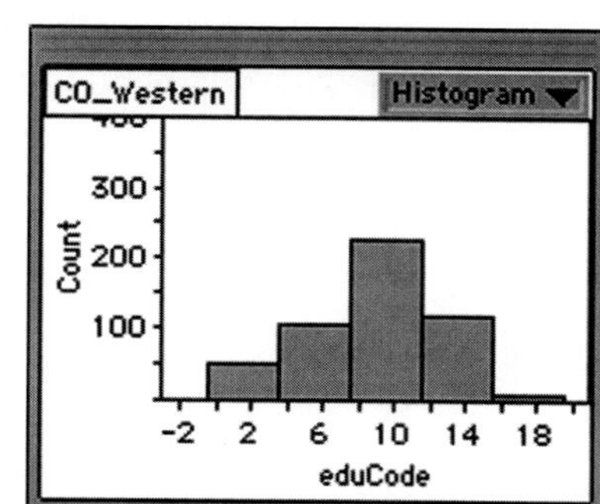

To experiment with different bin widths, double-click on any number on the horizontal axis. You will see a new window describing the bin width and axes scales. Click on any of the numbers in blue to modify them. What bin width makes it easiest to see patterns for each of the numerical attributes?

Information about this graph:
Histogram: Bin width: **4.0000**
starting at: **−0.50000**
The **eduCode** axis is horizontal from **−3.0000** to **21.000**
The **Count** axis is vertical from 0 to **402.15**

NCTM STANDARDS

CONTENT		PROCESS	
	Number		Problem Solving
✓	Algebra	✓	Reasoning
	Geometry	✓	Communication
	Measurement		Connections
✓	Data/Probability	✓	Representation

LESSON OBJECTIVE

- Look for and study data that are normally distributed

EXPLORATION

PLANNING

LESSON OUTLINE

One day:

25 min Activity

20 min Questions

MATERIALS

- Fathom
- Fathom demonstration Is This Normal?, *optional*

TEACHING

In this exploration students use Fathom to work with normal distributions they studied in the previous lesson. If you have only one computer, you might do the Fathom demonstration Is This Normal? with the class.

Guiding the Activity

Step 1 The **Sample Documents** folder is located in the Fathom program folder.

Step 2 age, education code, and income; sample answer: age and income

Step 3 Real data will rarely be exactly normally distributed. Encourage students to look for histograms that indicate an approximately normal distribution. They can use their judgment in deciding whether a histogram looks normal enough.

Step 3 Sample answer: age: 5; education code: 4; income: 4000

Step 4 Sample answer: Age is usually normally distributed in urban areas, but not in rural areas. If you separate age by marital status, age remains normally distributed only for married people. Income is not normally distributed, even if you filter out people under 20 and over 65. However, if you look at income for men only (with young and old people filtered out), it is normally distributed for some regions. When you use a bin width of about 4, educational code appears normally distributed.

▶Helping with the Questions

1. Sample answer: Rural areas tend to have more young people. This could be either because people in rural areas have more children than people in urban areas or because more adults leave rural areas and move to urban areas. Income is not normally distributed because many young and old people have no income, and some adults also have no income. If you look at men only, it is more normally distributed, but there is still a relatively large number of men with no income. Educational code was normally distributed with a peak at 8–12 years. This implies that most people attend high school, with fewer people having lower or higher levels of schooling.

Question 2 As needed, remind students of the terms *skewed left, skewed right,* and *bimodal.*

2. Data sets that are not normally distributed are usually skewed right and occasionally skewed left.

Step 4 Experiment with different attributes, bin widths, and regional data files to find data that are approximately normally distributed. You may want to filter your data. For example, income will not appear to be normally distributed because there are many people who have an income of $0. Many of these people are younger than 20 or older than 65. Choose **Add Filter** from the Data menu. Type "(age > 20) and (age < 65)". Click **Apply.** People younger than 20 and older than 65 will be removed from the case table and histogram. You may also want to separate histograms into categories, such as male and female. To do this, drag and drop a second attribute onto the vertical axis of the histogram.

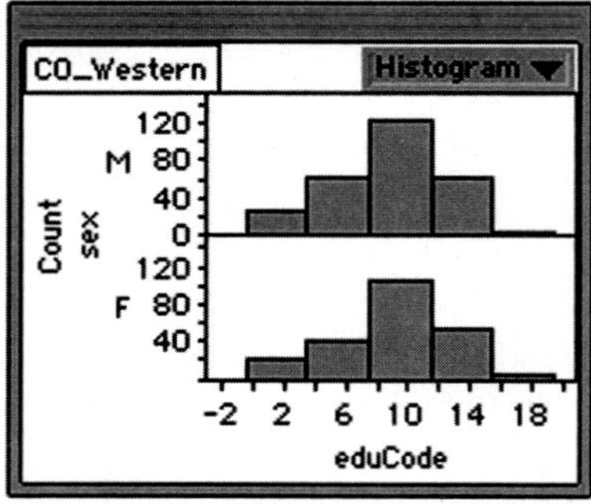

What normally distributed data do you find? What data are not normally distributed that you thought might be? What regional differences are there?

Questions

1. Make conjectures about why specific attributes in the census data that you explored are or are not normally distributed.
2. For census data that are not normally distributed, what histogram shape is most common?

LESSON 13.3

z-Values and Confidence Intervals

The way to do research is to attack the facts at the point of greatest astonishment.

CELIA GREEN

In Lesson 13.2, you learned about normally distributed populations and the probability that a randomly chosen item from such a population will fall in various intervals. That is, you knew something about the population and you saw how to find information about a sample.

In most real-life situations, however, you have statistics from one or more samples and want to estimate parameters of the population, which can be quite large. For example, suppose you know the mean height and standard deviation of 50 students that you survey, and you want to know the mean height and standard deviation of the entire population of students in your school. In this lesson you'll see how to describe some population parameters based on sample statistics.

First, it will be useful to learn a new method for describing a data value in a normal distribution. Knowing how a value relates to the mean value is important, but it does not tell you how typical the value is. For instance, to say that a penny's weight is 0.4 g less than the mean does not tell you whether this measurement is a rare event or a common event. But if you state how many standard deviations a value is from the mean, you have a much better idea of how unusual the value is.

Chinese-American artist Diana Ong (b 1940) titled this watercolor *So Very Crowded.*

Investigation
Areas and Distributions

You will need

- a piece of rope
- a meterstick or tape measure

Any measurement of an object's length is an approximation of the actual length. Typically, the measurements made by several people will be normally distributed. You'll use this idea to explore areas under the normal curve.

Step 1 Measurements will vary, but the results in Step 2 are independent of the measurements.

Step 1 Measure a length of rope, accurate to 0.1 cm. Assume that your measurement is the mean of all measurements and the standard deviation is 0.8 cm. Sketch a normal curve based on your measurement.

NCTM STANDARDS

CONTENT		PROCESS	
	Number	✓	Problem Solving
✓	Algebra	✓	Reasoning
	Geometry	✓	Communication
	Measurement		Connections
✓	Data/Probability		Representation

LESSON OBJECTIVES

- Learn the 68-95-99.7 rule and its relationship to the area under the normal curve
- Find confidence intervals of the population mean given the population standard deviation
- Find and understand z-values

LESSON 13.3

PLANNING

LESSON OUTLINE

One day:

10 min	Investigation
5 min	Example A
10 min	Example B
10 min	Sharing
10 min	Exercises

MATERIALS

- pieces of rope (one per group)
- metersticks or tape measures
- Calculator Note 13C

TEACHING

In the previous lesson students studied properties of samples from populations that were normally distributed. In real life we want to go in the other direction: We know about a sample and want to learn about the population. We can make nonstandard normal distributions normal through z-values and estimate the population mean within confidence intervals.

If you will be using the one-step investigation, you'll find it on page 746.

Guiding the Investigation

To dramatize the fact that measurements will give different results, use a rope that is longer than the measuring stick or measuring tape, or use a rope with some stretch to it. Point out as needed that students are to work alone until Step 3.

Step 2 Refer to Calculator Note 13C for finding area.

Step 3 Students may ask why .683 is rounded to 68% and .954 is rounded to 95%, but .997 is given as 99.7%. Ask them what they think 99.7 should be rounded to. [Rounding to 99% gives a percentage that is not close enough, and it's false to say that 100% of the data lie within three standard deviations of the mean.]

Step 3 The 68-95-99.7 rule states that, for a normal distribution, there is a 68% probability that a value will be within one standard deviation of the mean; there is a 95% probability that a value will be within two standard deviations of the mean; and there is a 99.7% probability that a value will be within three standard deviations of the mean.

[Language] Other names for *z*-values are *z-scores, standard scores,* and *z-statistics.*

One Step

Display both the group and the class data from the one-step investigation in Lesson 13.1 (describing the lengths of all pencils in the state), and pose this problem: "What is the probability that a randomly chosen pencil will have a length within one standard deviation of the sample mean? Within two standard deviations? Within three standard deviations?" Ask groups that finish first what the probability is that the mean length of a group's sample will lie within one, two, or three standard deviations of the population mean. Help them see that the numbers are different, even if they can't find the relationship. During Sharing, bring out the idea of *z*-values and the concepts associated with confidence intervals.

Step 2 Use the area under your normal curve to find the probability that a new measurement will be

a. within one standard deviation of your length. (That is, find the area between *your length* − 0.8 and *your length* + 0.8.) .683, or about 68%

b. within two standard deviations of your length. .954, or about 95%

c. within three standard deviations of your length. .997, or about 99.7%

Step 3 There is a rule in statistics known as the "68-95-99.7 rule." Compare your results from Step 2 with those of your group members, and write a rule that might go by this name.

To say that a penny's weight is 0.4 g less than the mean does not tell you whether or not this is a rare event. But to say that a penny's weight is 2.86 standard deviations from the mean does indicate that this measurement is a rare event.

In the investigation, you focused on adding and subtracting some number of standard deviations to or from the mean. The number of standard deviations that a normally distributed variable x is from the mean is called its **z-value.** In terms of z-values, the investigation asked for the probabilities that a new measurement would have a z-value between -1 and 1, between -2 and 2, and between -3 and 3. The 68-95-99.7 rule says that answers to these questions are about 68%, 95%, and 99.7%.

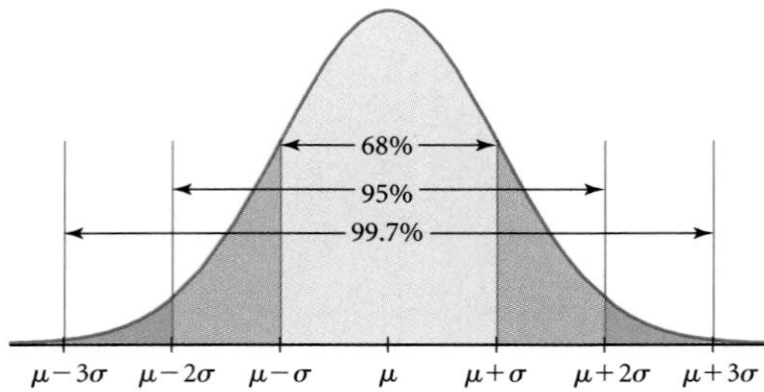

By the 68-95-99.7 rule, 68% of the area under a normal curve falls within one standard deviation of the mean, 95% within two standard deviations, and 99.7% within three standard deviations.

You can think of the z-value of x as the image of x under a transformation that translates and either shrinks or stretches the normal distribution to the standard normal distribution $n(x)$, with mean $\mu = 0$ and standard deviation $\sigma = 1$. This transformation from x-value to z-value is called **standardizing the variable** and can be calculated with the equation $z = \frac{x - \mu}{\sigma}$. The following example illustrates how to standardize values of a variable.

EXAMPLE A The heights of a large group of men are distributed normally with mean 70 in. and standard deviation 2.5 in.

a. Find the z-values for 67.5 in. and 72.5 in.

b. What is the probability that a randomly chosen member of this group has height x between 65 and 75 in.?

c. Find an interval of x-values, symmetric about the mean, that contains 90% of the heights.

► Solution

For this population, $\mu = 70$ and $\sigma = 2.5$.

a. Use the formula $z = \frac{x - \mu}{\sigma}$ to standardize the variable.

$$z = \frac{67.5 - 70}{2.5} = -1 \quad \text{and} \quad z = \frac{72.5 - 70}{2.5} = 1$$

In this distribution, 67.5 in. corresponds to a z-value of -1, which means the value is one standard deviation below the mean. The height 72.5 in. corresponds to a z-value of 1, or one standard deviation above the mean.

b. The z-value of 65 in. is $\frac{65 - 70}{2.5}$, or -2, and the z-value of 75 in. is $\frac{75 - 70}{2.5}$, or 2. There is a 95% probability that a randomly chosen value is within two standard deviations of the mean. A calculator graph confirms this prediction. [► See **Calculator Note 13C** to recall how to draw a normal curve with an area shaded. ◄]

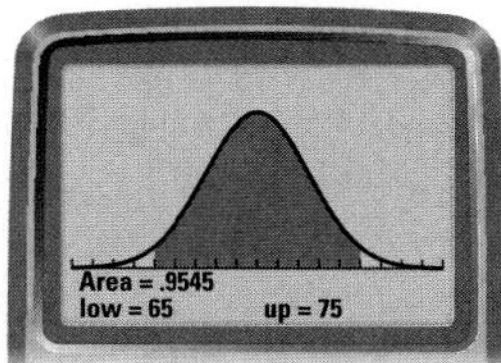

[61, 79, 1, –0.05, 0.2, 0.05]

c. You already know that 68% of the heights fall in the interval $-1 \le z \le 1$, which corresponds to $67.5 \le x \le 72.5$. You also know that 95% of the heights fall in the interval $65 \le x \le 75$. So, you can guess that an interval of about $66 \le x \le 74$ will contain 90% of the heights. Use your calculator and trial and error to obtain more precise endpoints. The calculator screen below shows that the interval $65.8875 \le x \le 74.1125$ contains 90.003% of the data.

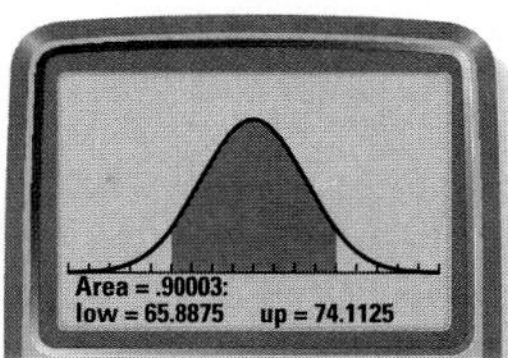

[61, 79, 1, –0.05, 0.2, 0.05]

Do z-values and the 68-95-99.7 rule help you learn about a population from a normally distributed sample taken from that population? Can you conclude, for example, that the probability is 68% that a rope's actual length—the mean of the population—is within one standard deviation of the sample mean? Not really. The population mean either is or isn't in this interval, so the probability that it is there is either 1 or 0; you just don't know which. But you can describe how confident you are that the population mean lies in a particular interval.

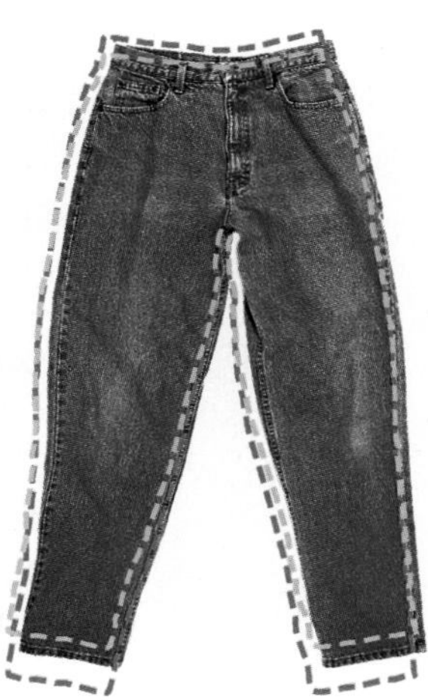

Clothing sizes are usually normally distributed.

► EXAMPLE A

In part c, students can use guess-and-check and the area method described in Calculator Note 13C.

Confidence Interval

[Alert] Students may confuse the interval notation with the notation for a point's coordinates. Make sure they know that confidence intervals can use parentheses and can look like coordinates once they are evaluated. You might point out that if the endpoints are included in the interval, the notation uses brackets rather than parentheses.

▸ EXAMPLE B

The assumption is that 0.28 s is the standard deviation of the population.

SHARING IDEAS

As students present, work toward a more formal statement of the 68-95-99.7 rule.

In the normal distribution with mean μ and standard deviation σ:

About 68% of the data fall within σ of the mean μ.

About 95% of the data fall within 2σ of the mean μ.

About 99.7% of the data fall within 3σ of the mean μ.

[Alert] Students may make statements such as "The probability that the population mean is within one standard deviation of the sample mean is 68%." Actually, the population mean either is or isn't in that interval, so the probability that it lies there is either 0 or 1. Not knowing which, we say that we're 68% confident that it's there, because it would be there for 68% of samples if we took many samples.

Encourage students to pose problems and ask questions, such as those below.

[Ask] "What's the 68-95-99.7 rule in terms of z-values?" [In a normal distribution, about 68% of the z-values lie between -1 and 1, about 95% between -2 and 2, and about 99.7 between -3 and 3. That is, the mean of the z-values is 0, and their standard deviation is 1.]

Confidence Interval

Suppose a sample from a normally distributed population has size n and mean $\bar{x}$, and the population standard deviation is σ. Then the p% **confidence interval** is an interval about $\bar{x}$ in which you can be p% confident that the population mean, μ, lies. If z is the number of standard deviations from the mean within which p% of normally distributed data lie, the p% confidence interval is

$$\bar{x} - \frac{z\sigma}{\sqrt{n}} < \mu < \bar{x} + \frac{z\sigma}{\sqrt{n}}$$

The confidence interval may also be expressed as $\mu = \bar{x} \pm \frac{z\sigma}{\sqrt{n}}$ or $\mu = \left(\bar{x} - \frac{z\sigma}{\sqrt{n}}, \bar{x} + \frac{z\sigma}{\sqrt{n}}\right)$.

In real-world situations, you may not know the population standard deviation. However, if the sample size is large enough, generally $n > 30$, you may use the sample standard deviation, s, in place of σ when calculating confidence intervals.

For example, suppose your class obtained a sample of 30 measurements of a rope's length, with mean 32.4 cm and standard deviation 0.8 cm. You can't say that the population mean is exactly 32.4 cm. But you can describe your confidence that the population mean (the rope's actual length) lies in an interval. For instance, knowing that 95% of normally distributed data have a z-value between -2 and 2, you can say that you're 95% confident that the population mean lies in the interval $\left(32.4 - \frac{2(0.8)}{\sqrt{30}}, 32.4 + \frac{2(0.8)}{\sqrt{30}}\right)$, or about (32.1, 32.7).

The 68-95-99.7 rule is useful in cases like these, but sometimes you want to be confident by a percentage other than 68%, 95%, or 99.7%. You can find the associated z-values by experimenting with a normal curve and trying to find an area symmetric to the mean that has the desired percentage of the total area. Here are the z-values associated with some other commonly used confidence intervals:

Confidence interval	90%	99%	99.9%
z-value	1.645	2.576	3.291

In the next example, confidence intervals are calculated using z-values from this table.

EXAMPLE B

Jackson is training for the 100 m race. His coach timed his last run at 11.47 s. Experience in previous training sessions indicates that the standard deviation for timing this race is 0.28 s.

a. Find the 95% confidence interval.

b. What confidence interval corresponds to ± 2.3 standard deviations?

c. Find the 90% confidence interval.

▸ Solution

Because only one run time is known, the value for n is 1. A confidence interval is given as $\left(11.47 - \frac{z(0.28)}{\sqrt{1}}, 11.47 + \frac{z(0.28)}{\sqrt{1}}\right)$. This is the interval with endpoints $11.47 \pm 0.28z$.

[Ask] "Is the z-value associated with 95% of the data exactly 2?" [It's really closer to 1.96, but the 68-95-99.7 rule is easy to remember and good enough for most purposes.] You might have students rework Example B, part a, with the more exact value.

[Ask] "What's the sum of the z-values?" [The sum of the n values in any data set is n times the mean, and the mean of the z-values is 0, so their sum is 0.]

[Ask] "What does confidence really mean?" [It refers to a ratio. 95% of samples this size from this population will have means in this interval. You can also show that 95% of the populations from which this sample could have come have means in this interval.]

[Ask] "What do these symbols mean in the confidence interval definition: n, $\bar{x}$, μ, s, σ?" [n is the number of data points in the sample; $\bar{x}$ and μ are the sample and population means, respectively; s and σ are the sample and population standard deviations, respectively. English letters refer to the sample statistics, and Greek letters refer to the population parameters.]

a. By the 68-95-99.7 rule, the z-value for 95% is about 2 standard deviations. The endpoints of the confidence interval, then, are $11.47 \pm 0.28(2)$. The coach is 95% confident that the actual time is between approximately 10.91 and 12.03 s.

b. By guess-and-check, the interval with endpoints $11.47 \pm 0.28(2.3)$, that is or between 10.826 and 12.114 s, has a probability of $N(10.826, 12.114, 11.47, 0.28)$, or .9786. That is, a z-value of 2.3 standard deviations corresponds to about a 98% confidence interval.

c. Using the table on page 748, the coach is 90% confident that the actual time is in the interval $11.47 \pm 0.28(1.645)$, or between 11.01 and 11.93 s.

Men race in the 100-meter final at the 2000 Olympic Games in Sydney, Australia.

In Example B, the coach had to rely on only one time measurement. If four people, instead of only one, had timed the run, and the mean of those times had been 11.47 s, then the 95% interval would have had endpoints $11.47 \pm \frac{2(0.28)}{\sqrt{4}}$, making it between 11.19 and 11.75 s. In general, the larger the sample size, the narrower the interval in which you can be confident that the population mean lies.

EXERCISES

Practice Your Skills

1. Trace the normal curve at right onto your paper. Add vertical lines demonstrating the 68-95-99.7 rule.

2. A set of normally distributed data has mean 63 and standard deviation 1.4. Find the z-value for each of these data values.

a. 64.4 $z = 1$ **b.** 58.8 $z = -3$ **c.** 65.2 $z \approx 1.57$ **d.** 62 $z \approx -0.71$

3. A set of normally distributed data has mean 125 and standard deviation 2.4. Find the data value for each of these z-values.

a. $z = -1$ 122.6 **b.** $z = 2$ 129.8 **c.** $z = 2.9$ 131.96 **d.** $z = -0.5$ 123.8

4. Complete these statements.

a. 95% of all data values in a normal distribution are within _?_ standard deviations of the mean. 2

b. 90% of all data values in a normal distribution are within _?_ standard deviations of the mean. 1.645

c. 99% of all data values in a normal distribution are within _?_ standard deviations of the mean. 2.576

Closing the Lesson

Summarize the main points of the lesson: In a normally distributed population, the 68-95-99.7 rule indicates what percentage of the data lies within one, two, and three standard deviations of the mean. We can use confidence intervals to make predictions about the population mean; for example, we can say that we are 95% confident that the population mean lies in a particular interval about the sample mean.

1.

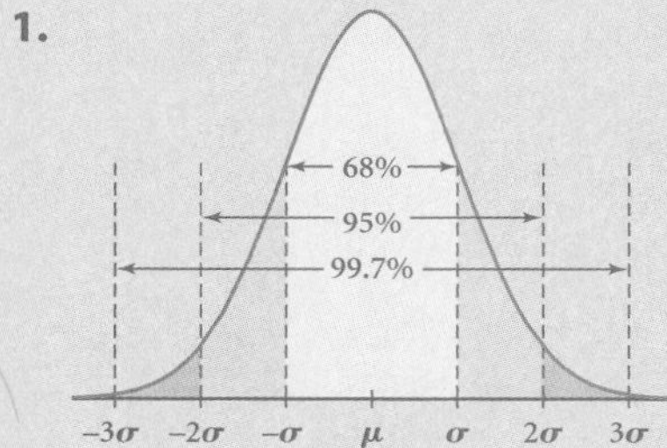

Sharing Ideas (continued)

[Ask] "Why do we use $\frac{\sigma}{\sqrt{n}}$ rather than just s?" Point out some sample data, indicate that the size of the interval should vary inversely with the size of the sample, and add that the derivation of this number is beyond the scope of this course, though students will see more about it in Lesson 13.4.

[Ask] "If the population is not normally distributed, can you still calculate confidence intervals?" You need not answer this question; it motivates Lesson 13.4.

[Ask] "Is the z in the confidence interval definition a z-value?" [It's not the z-value of any particular data point, but rather the number of standard deviations from the mean within which p% of the data lie. Statistics books often call it by another name, such as z^* or $z_{\alpha/2}$, to emphasize the difference.]

Students may ask what they should do if they don't know the population standard deviation but the size of the sample is less than 30. When the sample standard deviation is substituted for the population standard deviation, the scores are called t-values rather than z-values. When the sample size is less than 30, t-values are pretty far from z-values, and a special test called a t-test is used. The number 30 is not a magic number; the accuracy of the sample depends on how normally distributed the population is as well as on the size of the sample.

[Ask] "Would z-values affect what you did in Lesson 13.2, Example B, part d?" [Standardizing the scores will not affect the results.]

Assessing Progress

Assess students' understanding of the mean and standard deviation of a normal distribution and their ability to find probabilities related to normal distributions.

BUILDING UNDERSTANDING

Students practice working with the 68-95-99.7 rule and confidence intervals.

ASSIGNING HOMEWORK

Essential	1–5, 7
Performance assessment	6, 8–12
Portfolio	12
Group	12
Review	13–15

Helping with the Exercises

Exercise 1 As needed, remind students to look for the inflection points on the curve to find $\pm\sigma$.

Exercise 4 For 4b and c, students can consult the table on page 748.

8a. (3.077, 3.123)

8b. (3.072, 3.128)

8c. (3.064, 3.136)

Exercise 9 If students are having difficulty, you might suggest that they use sample data and change the variables for each step.

Exercise 12c [ESL] *Retooling* is the process of updating equipment by getting new tools or refurbishing old tools.

Reason and Apply

5. The mean travel time between two bus stops is 58 min with standard deviation 4.5 min.

a. Find the z-value for a trip that takes 66.1 min. $z = 1.8$

b. Find the z-value for a trip that takes 55 min. $z = -0.67$

c. Find the probability that the bus trip takes between 55 and 66.1 min. approximately .71

Created by American sculptor Richard Beyer (b 1925), *Waiting for the Interurban* is a cluster of statues at a bus stop in Seattle, Washington. Local residents frequently change the statues' clothes. In this photo, they are wearing Batman costumes.

6. A set of normally distributed data has mean 47 s and standard deviation 0.6 s. Find the percentage of data within these intervals:

a. between 45 and 47 s approximately 50%

b. greater than 1.5 s above or below the mean approximately 1.2%

7. A sample has mean 3.1 and standard deviation 0.14. Find each confidence interval, and round values to the nearest 0.001. Assume $n = 30$ in each case.

a. 90% confidence interval (3.058, 3.142)

b. 95% confidence interval (3.049, 3.151)

c. 99% confidence interval (3.034, 3.166)

8. Repeat Exercise 7 assuming $n = 100$.

9. Make a statement about the change in size of each new confidence interval.

a. If you increase the size of your sample, then the confidence interval will __?__. decrease

b. If you increase your confidence from 90% to 99%, then the interval will __?__. increase

c. If your sample has a larger mean, then the interval will __?__. stay the same size

d. If your sample has a larger standard deviation, then the interval will __?__. increase

10. APPLICATION Fifty recent tests of an automobile's mileage indicate it averages 31 mi/gal with standard deviation 2.6 mi/gal. Assuming the distribution is normal, find the 95% confidence interval. between 30.3 and 31.7 mi/gal

11. APPLICATION A commercial airline finds that, over the last 60 days, a mean of 207.5 ticketed passengers actually show up for a particular 7:24 A.M. flight. The standard deviation of their data is 12 passengers.

a. Assuming this distribution is normal, find the 95% confidence interval. between 204.4 and 210.6 passengers

b. If the plane seats 225 passengers, what is the probability the plane will be overbooked? .07

12. APPLICATION The BB Manufacturing Company mass-produces ball bearings. The optimum diameter of a bearing is 45 mm, but records show that the diameters follow a normal distribution with mean 45 mm and standard deviation 0.05 mm. A diameter between 44.95 and 45.05 mm is acceptable.

a. What percentage of the output is acceptable? 68%

b. What percentage of the output is unacceptable? 32%

c. After retooling some of the equipment, the standard deviation is cut in half. What percentage of the output is now unacceptable? 5%

d. If the engineers at the company want a 99.7% acceptability rate, what should their target standard deviation be? $\frac{.05}{3}$, or $0.1\overline{6}$

Consumer CONNECTION

Most manufacturers practice quality control. The strength of materials, sizes of parts, and reliability of the product are constantly monitored. In mass production and assembly lines, companies measure randomly chosen samples and compare the measurements to the desired mean and standard deviation. Using sampling, manufacturers can determine whether or not they are operating consistently, and they can determine when adjustments or improvements are necessary.

Quality control in plastics manufacturing

MAKING THE CONNECTION

If companies do not maintain good quality control, they may not only invite the anger of their customers but also come under the watchful eyes of independent product testers. The Consumers Union is a nonprofit organization that represents the interests of consumers and performs tests on a wide range of consumer goods. The results of their tests are reported in the organization's magazine, on its website, and to the news media.

Review

12.1 **13.** A random-number generator selects a real number between 0 and 50, inclusive, according to the probability distribution at right. Find each value described.

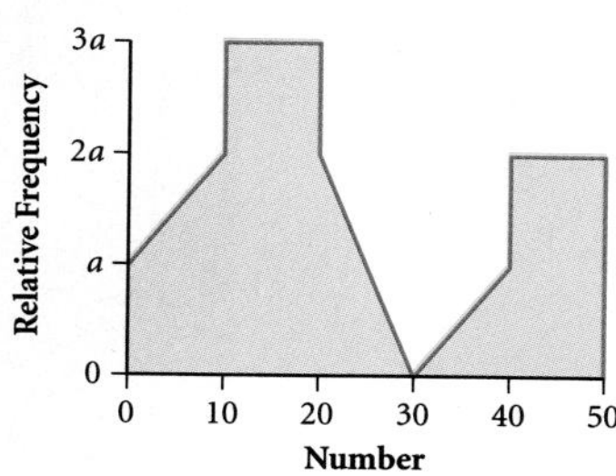

a. a $a = 0.0125$

b. P(a number is less than 30) .6875

c. P(a number is between 20 and 40) .1875

d. P(a number is 30) 0

e. P(a number is 15) 0

f. the median value $18\frac{1}{3}$

12.4 **14.** Five hundred integer values, −3 through 3, are randomly selected (and replaced) from a hat containing tens of thousands of integers. The frequency table at right lists the results. Find these values.

Value	Frequency
−3	32
−2	60
−1	153
0	92
1	45
2	90
3	28

a. $P(-3)$ .064

b. P(less than 0) .49

c. P(not 2) .82

d. the expected sum of the next ten selected values −1.2

11.2 **15.** You are about to sign a long-term rental agreement for an apartment. You are given two options:

Plan 1: Pay $400 the first month with a $4 increase each month.
Plan 2: Pay $75 the first month with a 2.5% increase each month.

a. Write a function to model the accumulated total you will pay over time for each plan.

b. Use your calculator to graph both functions on the same screen.

c. Which rental plan would you choose? Explain your reasoning.

15a. Let n represent the number of months, and let S_n represent the cumulated total.
Plan 1: $S_n = 398n + 2n^2$;
Plan 2: $S_n = \dfrac{75(1 - 1.025^n)}{1 - 1.025}$

15b.

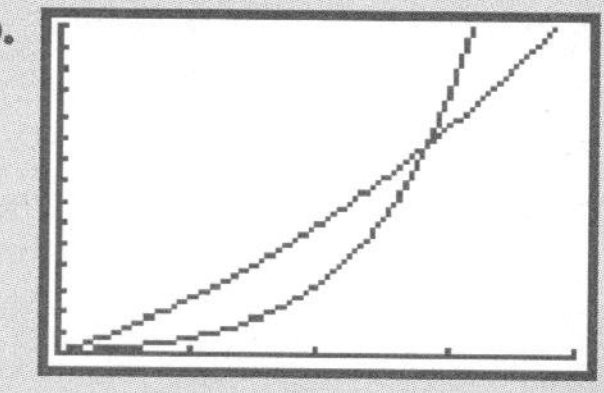

[0, 200, 50, 0, 150000, 10000]

15c. If you stay 11 years 9 months or less, choose Plan 2. If you stay longer, choose Plan 1.

LESSON

13.4

PLANNING

LESSON OUTLINE

First day:

20 min Investigation

5 min Example A

10 min Sharing

10 min Exercises

Second day:

15 min Hypothesis testing

15 min Example B

15 min Exercises

MATERIALS

- Sample Means (T) for One Step
- Calculator Notes 13B, 13D, 13E

TEACHING

In this lesson students generalize confidence intervals to skewed populations and apply properties of normal distributions to hypothesis testing. The lesson may take two days if you want to bring about deep understanding of hypothesis testing. In this case, use the section Hypothesis Testing on page 755 as the investigation for the second day. The one-step investigation that you can use instead of the investigation is on page 753.

Guiding the Investigation

Step 1 The terms *skewed left* and *skewed right* were defined in Chapter 2.

Step 2 On many calculators μ will be represented by $\bar{x}$. Because the calculator can't distinguish between population data and sample data, it may give both kinds of standard deviations.

LESSON 13.4

The Central Limit Theorem

You can use all the quantitative data you can get, but you still have to distrust it and use your own intelligence and judgment.

ALVIN TOFFLER

In the previous lesson, you saw how to use sample statistics to estimate some parameters of a normally distributed population. But what if you don't know whether or not the population is normally distributed? Can you still learn about population parameters from samples? In this lesson you'll explore this question.

Perhaps it will surprise you to learn that you can check how well a single sample predicts population parameters by imagining what would happen if you took lots of samples. For example, to determine the yield of a new variety of corn, a seed company runs a test with an experimental group of farmers. It collects a random sample of ears of corn from each farm and finds the mean number of kernels on the ears from each sample. These means help determine the mean and standard deviation of the entire population of corn, no matter how that population is skewed.

Investigation
Means of Samples

In this investigation you'll explore how the mean of a sample compares to the mean of a population.

Steps 1 and 2 Results will vary depending on the type of distribution and the random numbers that are generated.

Step 1 Each person in your group will create a population. Each group member's population should have a different type of distribution, as listed below. Make a histogram of your population to check that it is distributed appropriately.
[▶ See **Calculator Note 13D** to create a list of 200 values, each between 20 and 50, for your population. ◀]

a. uniform **b.** normal **c.** skewed left **d.** skewed right

Step 2 Calculate the mean, μ, and standard deviation, σ, of your population.

Step 3 Answers will vary, but students should find that the sample means are fairly close to the population mean.

Step 3 Devise a way to choose values randomly from your list. Select three values from your population, and calculate the mean of this small sample. Then select two more values, add them to the sample, and recalculate the mean. Add another two values and recalculate. How do these sample means compare to the actual mean?

Step 3 Students are to append values, not replace them. There are many methods for choosing values randomly. The simplest might be to recognize that the calculator commands used in Calculator Note 13D already randomly generate the numbers. Students may also create a random number routine that picks two or three numbers from 1 to 200 and then selects the values at those positions in the list.

LESSON OBJECTIVES

- Learn the importance of a simple random sample
- Understand the Central Limit Theorem
- Apply the Central Limit Theorem to hypothesis testing
- Begin to understand and apply the principles of inference

Step 4 Graph the equations $y = \mu$, $y = \mu - \frac{2\sigma}{\sqrt{x}}$, and $y = \mu + \frac{2\sigma}{\sqrt{x}}$, where μ and σ are the values of your population mean and standard deviation. Use the graphing window $[0, 50, 5, \mu - 2\sigma, \mu + 2\sigma, 5]$. These graphs will help you see a trend in your sample means from Step 3.

Step 5 Create a recursive routine that adds one randomly chosen value at a time to a sample from your population and plots the mean of the new sample. Plot each point in the form (*number sampled, mean*). [▶ See **Calculator Note 13E** for help with this routine. ◀] Make a rough sketch of what you see.

Step 6 Clear the graph, reset the counters N and T to 0, and repeat Step 5 three more times. What do you notice?

Step 7 Compare your results to those of your group members who used a different type of population distribution. In general, explain how the means of your samples compare to the mean of the entire population.

Step 4 Results will vary depending on the type of distribution and the random numbers that are generated. See Calculator Note 13E for sample calculator screen captures.

Step 7 Regardless of the shape of the distribution, the sample mean is a good predictor of the population mean. As the sample size increases, the deviation of the sample mean from the population mean decreases.

Your work on the investigation shows that, although the mean number of kernels per ear is different on each farm, the mean of a sample approximates the population mean, and the approximation is better for larger samples. In fact, given several different samples from a population, the sample means themselves are normally distributed, even if the population is not. Moreover, from the sample means, you can even predict the standard deviation of the population. These observations are summarized by the **Central Limit Theorem.**

The Central Limit Theorem

If several samples, each containing n data values, are taken from a population (with any distribution):

1. The means of the samples form a distribution that is approximately normal.
2. The population mean is approximately the mean of the distribution of sample means.
3. The standard deviation of the sample means is approximately the population's standard deviation divided by the square root of n, or $\frac{\sigma}{\sqrt{n}}$.

Each approximation is better for larger values of n.

In most real-life situations, you have only one sample rather than many. But you can still use information about the theoretical possibilities of many samples. For instance, many statements are made about "average" American teens—the amount of money they spend weekly, their consumption of various foods, the amount of time they spend on the Internet. These "averages" usually come not from asking every teen in the country but, instead, from sampling them. The Central Limit Theorem says that the sample mean is not much different from the mean of the population, no matter how skewed the population distribution is. If pollsters choose a large enough sample or several samples, they can confidently estimate the parameters of the entire population.

The Central Limit Theorem can also be applied to evaluate a claim about a population mean, as in the next example.

Step 4 Students can substitute the values of μ and σ in several ways. They can enter them manually as decimal approximations, or they can use the calculator's storage of the statistics. See Calculator Note 13B.

By the Central Limit Theorem, the standard deviation of the sample means is $\frac{\sigma}{\sqrt{n}}$. When students graph the equation $y = \mu \pm \frac{2\sigma}{\sqrt{n}}$, they create an upper and lower bound within two standard deviations of the mean, corresponding to a 95% confidence interval. Statisticians would consider values outside the 95% interval "significant at a 95% level."

Steps 5 and 6 Answers will vary, but students should find that as the sample size increases, the points (which represent the sample mean) get closer and closer to the line $y = \mu$, and are usually within the lower and upper bounds $y = \mu - \frac{2\sigma}{\sqrt{x}}$ and $y = \mu + \frac{2\sigma}{\sqrt{x}}$. In other words, for sample size n, the sample mean is within $-\frac{2\sigma}{\sqrt{n}}$ and $\frac{2\sigma}{\sqrt{n}}$ of the population mean.

Step 6 The counters N and T are used in Calculator Note 13E.

One Step

Display the Sample Means transparency and ask students what patterns they see. Elicit the first two parts of the Central Limit Theorem. Then **[Ask]** "What's the standard deviation of the collection of many sample means?" As needed, draw students' attention to confidence intervals.

During Sharing, compile a complete statement of the Central Limit Theorem. Bring out the idea that confidence intervals can apply to populations that are not normally distributed.

NCTM STANDARDS

CONTENT		PROCESS	
	Number	✓	Problem Solving
✓	Algebra	✓	Reasoning
	Geometry	✓	Communication
	Measurement	✓	Connections
✓	Data/Probability		Representation

Career CONNECTION

Demographers collect statistics to determine how the number of people in a location changes from year to year. They also study factors that cause population changes and use this information to predict future population trends. Having a detailed understanding of a population's development helps people working in government and public and private organizations to initiate policies on education, health, unemployment, and other community services.

A demographic study can determine what health issues are of concern in a particular community, allowing resources to be used in the most effective way.

EXAMPLE A

A pharmaceutical company claims that its antacid contains an average of 324 mg of its active ingredient in each tablet. Students in a chemistry class analyzed 25 tablets to determine the amount of active ingredient. Their results, in milligrams, are at right. If the company's claim is correct, what is the probability of getting these results?

314	338	330	328	319
326	307	319	313	315
335	351	308	333	316
318	317	306	300	321
294	325	314	317	335

▶ Solution

The mean of the students' sample is 319.96 mg. You want to know the probability that a sample will have a mean of 319.96 mg or less if the population mean is 324 mg.

The first part of the Central Limit Theorem says that, if you took many samples, their means would form a normal distribution. Therefore, if you knew the mean and standard deviation of that distribution of means, you could use properties of the normal distribution to determine the probability of a range of means, such as 319.96 mg or less.

The second part of the Central Limit Theorem says that the mean of the means is the same as the population mean, which the company says is 324 mg. And the third part of the Central Limit Theorem says that the standard deviation of the distribution of means is the population standard deviation divided by the square root of the sample size, or $\frac{\sigma}{\sqrt{n}}$. You don't know the standard deviation of the population, but you can assume it's the same as the standard deviation of the sample, which is 12.75 mg. Then the standard deviation of the distribution of means is $\frac{12.75}{\sqrt{25}}$, or 2.55 mg.

Putting all this together, you see that the probability of a mean of 319.96 mg or less is $N(0, 319.96, 324, 2.55)$, or .057. There is only a 5.7% chance that a sample's mean would be 319.96 mg or less. So, actually collecting a sample with a mean of 319.96 mg is a fairly rare event, and the company's claim of 324 mg is open to question.

▶ *EXAMPLE A*

[Ask] "What does the value 324 mg represent?" [the population mean]

The assumption that the sample standard deviation equals the population standard deviation is made only because the latter isn't known. For samples this small, if statisticians don't know that the population is normally distributed, they usually use other measures.

[Ask] "What is $\frac{12.75}{\sqrt{25}}$ the standard deviation of?" [It is the standard deviation of the distribution of many (imagined) sample means; it's not the standard deviation of either the sample or the population.]

[Alert] The conclusion of this example may be difficult for students to grasp. You might ask them to summarize it in their own words. If the population mean is really 324 mg, as the company claims, then a sample mean of 319.96 mg should occur only 5.7% of the time. Therefore, the company's claim of 324 mg may be too high, and more samples should be taken to check the claim. **[ESL]** A *fairly rare event* is an event that does not happen very often.

Example A illustrates **inference.** Inference involves creating a hypothesis about one or more population parameters ("The mean is 324 mg"), deciding on what would make the hypothesis "improbable," collecting data, and either rejecting the hypothesis or letting it stand, based on probabilities. This **hypothesis testing** is the basis of research in many areas, including the medical field.

EXAMPLE B

A routine company medical exam performed on a worker suggests that a new product used for cleaning might be causing a reduction in the amount of white blood cells in the blood. How should the company proceed?

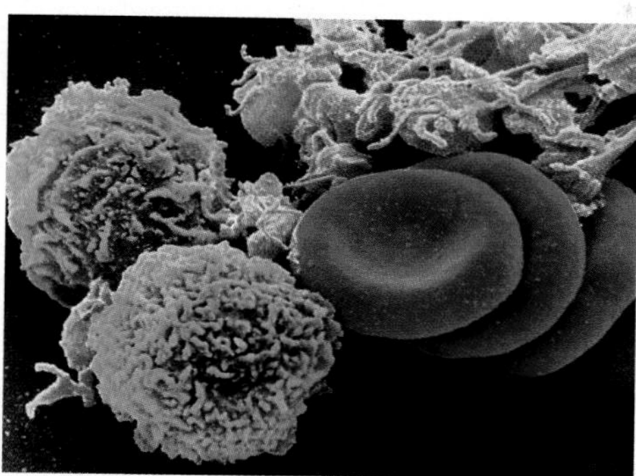

This magnified photo of blood cells uses color scanning to show white blood cells (blue), red blood cells (red), and platelets (pink). White blood cells function in the immune system, red blood cells carry oxygen through the body, and platelets help heal wounds.

▸ Solution

The company can follow these steps to decide whether they should be concerned about the effect of the cleaning product.

Step 1 With statistics you cannot decide for sure whether the cleaning product has an effect on the number of white blood cells. You can decide only whether or not it "probably" has an effect. Actually, you want to decide whether or not a resulting sample statistic is "improbable." To do that, you state as your hypothesis that the cleaning product has *no* effect; this is called the **null hypothesis.** Then you decide what would make the hypothesis "improbable." Suppose you decide that if the mean number of white blood cells you get from sample data is less than 5% probable, then you'll reject the null hypothesis.

Step 2 You take a random sample of 36 workers and find they have a mean white blood cell count of 7075 cells per cubic millimeter $\left(\text{cells/mm}^3\right)$. You look up medical information and find that a population of healthy adults has a mean white blood cell count of 7500 cells/mm^3 and a standard deviation of 1250 cells/mm^3.

Step 3 By the central limit theorem, the mean of many sample means would be 7500 cells/mm^3 with a standard deviation of $\frac{1250}{\sqrt{36}}$, or 208 cells/mm^3. The probability that a sample will have a mean of 7075 or less is therefore $N(0, 7075, 7500, 208)$, or .0205. This means that there is a 2% chance that, if the population mean were 7500 cells, a sample would have a mean of 7075 cells or less.

Step 4 Because the probability of the hypothesis is below your cutoff of 5%, the null hypothesis—that the cleaning product has no effect—is improbable and you reject it. The company should stop using the cleaning product and consider doing more conclusive testing.

Hypothesis Testing

To help students understand hypothesis testing, pose this problem, adapted from Example A: "A brand of antacid claims to contain 324 mg of its active ingredient in each tablet. Students in a chemistry class analyzed 36 tablets. They found that the amounts of the active ingredient in the tablets had a mean of 319.96 mg and a standard deviation of 12.75 mg. What can you conclude?" As needed, tell students that they may assume the population standard deviation equals the sample standard deviation. [The company's claim is suspect. The probability that a sample of 36 would have this mean is only about 2.9%.]

During Sharing, formalize students' reasoning into the steps of hypothesis testing (inference).

▸ EXAMPLE B

This example is a quick introduction to the extensive topic of hypothesis testing. If your curriculum doesn't include hypothesis testing and you are short on time, omit this example and Exercises 6 and 9.

Step 1 [ESL] A *hypothesis* is an assumption that you make temporarily while you check its truth.

You may want to discuss the 5% criterion for this example and mention that, as statisticians, students can choose any significance level they wish. The most common significance levels are 1%, 5%, and 10%.

Step 2 With this example, the null hypothesis would state that the cleaning product has no effect—that is, that the mean white blood cell count of its users is 7500 cells/mm^3. The alternative hypothesis would state that the mean white blood cell count will be less than 7500 cells/mm^3, because the cleaning product is reducing the number of white blood cells.

Example B (continued)

Step 3 In this step we check to see whether 7075 is an unusually low number of white blood cells. In other words, if we took a sample of 36 workers, is the probability of getting a sample mean of 7075 greater than 5%?

Step 4 Because the probability that we would get a sample mean as low as 7075 is only 2%, we reject the hypothesis that the cleaning product does not affect the number of blood cells.

SHARING IDEAS

Students may be skeptical about the importance of a bunch of sample means when you usually have only one sample. As an analogy, remind them of expected value, which tells you something about a single situation even though it's based on the results of many imagined occurrences.

You might illustrate this analogy by relating ratios and probabilities. For example, only 5% of a collection of sample means would lie outside $\frac{2\sigma}{\sqrt{n}}$

Sharing Ideas (continued)
(that is, two standard deviations) of the population mean, so the probability that the one sample mean under consideration will be in this interval is .05.

Encourage students to pose good problems and ask insightful questions, like those below.

[Ask] "Because $\frac{\sigma}{\sqrt{n}}$ appeared with confidence intervals, are these intervals related to the Central Limit Theorem?" [Yes; 95% of sample means lie within $\frac{2\sigma}{\sqrt{n}}$, or two standard deviations, of the population mean, so you can be 95% confident that the particular sample mean at hand lies in that interval.]

[Ask] "Is the normal distribution of sample means supposed to be obvious?" Students may well be surprised at this phenomenon, especially if the population itself is not normally distributed. You might ask whether they recall other non-intuitive results in mathematics and whether they reconciled their intuition with the apparent paradoxes.

[Ask] "Isn't the example of selecting two boys and four girls a random sample?" [Yes, but it's not a simple random sample.] Stratified random sampling is often used; the population is divided into strata (such as states, ages, or genders), and then the strata are sampled in a way that is representative of the whole population. Have students imagine impediments to the process.

Assessing Progress
You can check students' understanding of populations and samples, histograms, means, and standard deviations as well as their skill at calculator use.

If you had decided in advance that you would reject the null hypothesis if the statistic were less than 1% probable, you couldn't reject the hypothesis here. Not being able to reject the null hypothesis doesn't mean the hypothesis is true, only that it's not what you decided to call false. Most hypothesis testing rejects null hypotheses if the sample statistic has a probability less than 5% or 10%. When the null hypothesis is rejected, statisticians call it a "significant event."

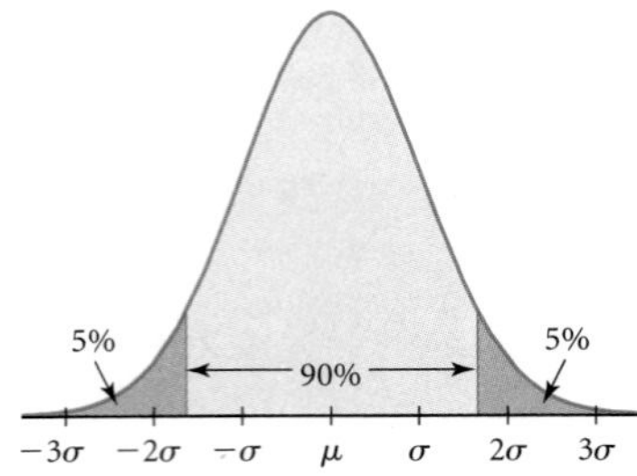

As you learned on page 748, 90% of the data in a normal curve falls within 1.645σ of the mean. So 5% is less than 1.645σ below the mean and 5% is more than 1.645σ above the mean.

In this chapter the problems and examples have noted that the data collected were from a random sample. A sample in which not only each person is equally likely but all groups of persons are equally likely is called a **simple random sample.** For instance, suppose a class consists of 20 girls and 10 boys. If you put everyone's name in a hat and randomly draw any 6 names, you have a simple random sample. In contrast, if you separate the names by gender and randomly select 4 girls and 2 boys, you do not have a simple random sample because not all groups of 6 persons are equally likely. For example, a group of 6 girls will never be selected.

The random samples throughout this book are actually simple random samples. In particular, the samples in the Central Limit Theorem must be simple random samples. The probability formulas you learned in Chapter 12 also depend on working with a simple random sample.

If you do not have a simple random sample, then you need to find different formulas that do not assume simple random sampling, accept the fact that your answer is approximate at best, or realize that you can draw no conclusion. You'll get the most benefit from starting with a simple random sample.

EXERCISES

Practice Your Skills

1. From a population with mean 200 and standard deviation 12, find the probability of

a. A value of 195 or less. 33.85%

b. A sample of size $n = 4$ with mean 195 or less. 20.23%

c. A sample of size $n = 9$ with mean 195 or less. 10.56%

d. A sample of size $n = 36$ with mean 195 or less. 0.6210%

2. For each population and sample, determine what value of sample means would indicate a significant event two standard deviations from the population mean.

a. $\mu = 80, \sigma = 10$, sample size $n = 25$

b. $\mu = 130, \sigma = 6$, sample size $n = 36$

c. $\mu = 18, \sigma = 2$, sample size $n = 64$

d. $\mu = 0.52, \sigma = 0.1$, sample size $n = 100$

Closing the Lesson

The **Central Limit Theorem** states that if several **simple random samples,** each containing n data points, are taken from a population, no matter how skewed, the sample means will be approximately normally distributed with a mean about at the population mean and a standard deviation of about $\frac{\sigma}{\sqrt{n}}$, where σ is the population standard deviation. (The approximations are better for large values of n.) This theorem extends confidence intervals to general populations and allows **hypothesis testing.**

2a. $\bar{x} \leq 76$ or $\bar{x} \geq 84$

2b. $\bar{x} \leq 128$ or $\bar{x} \geq 132$

2c. $\bar{x} \leq 17.5$ or $\bar{x} \geq 18.5$

2d. $\bar{x} \leq 0.50$ or $\bar{x} \geq 0.54$

Reason and Apply

3. Penny Adler has worked for many years as an actuary in the same office. By her calculations, it takes her an average of 23 min to get to work every day, with a standard deviation of 4.1 min. As she leaves her home one day, she notes that she must be at the office in 25 min. What is the probability that she will be late? 31.28%

4. The "You Gotta Be Nutz" candy bar has mean weight 75.3 g and standard deviation 4.7 g. The manufacturer wants to avoid complaints that any single candy bar weighs far too little, so it decides to advertise a "minimum guaranteed weight."

   a. What weight should the manufacturer advertise if they want 80% of the candy bars to meet or exceed the minimum weight? (Sketch a normal curve with shading, and write a complete sentence using your numerical answer.)

   b. What weight should the manufacturer advertise if they want 90% of the candy bars to meet or exceed the minimum weight? (Sketch a normal curve with shading, and write a complete sentence using your numerical answer.)

   c. What weight should the manufacturer advertise if they want 95% of the candy bars to meet or exceed the minimum weight? (Sketch a normal curve with shading, and write a complete sentence using your numerical answer.)

5. A random sample of Brand X medication has a mean of 230 mg of its active ingredient. The standard deviation of the sample is 12 mg. Using the sample standard deviation as the population standard deviation, make a prediction of the actual population mean with a 95% confidence interval given these sample sizes:

   a. $n = 16$ $224 < \mu < 236$ b. $n = 100$ $227.6 < \mu < 232.4$ c. $n = 144$ $228 < \mu < 232$

6. A cookie company boasts an average of 20 chips per chocolate chip cookie. You doubt this claim, so you decide to test it. To start, you collect a random sample of 30 cookies and count the number of chips in each cookie. Your results are shown at right.

13	24	13	12	16	18
21	16	20	19	17	24
16	20	19	17	24	20
10	16	17	17	9	15
17	17	19	21	13	20

   a. Make a mathematical statement of what you are trying to disprove. This is your null hypothesis.

   b. Find the mean and standard deviation of your sample.

   c. Use the standard deviation of the sample as a population parameter and find the probability that a population with mean 20 would produce a sample mean less than or equal to your statistic in 6b. 0.006%

   d. Use numbers and context to state a conclusion. If the probability from 6c is small (less than 5%), then state a rejection of the null hypothesis. If the probability is larger (more than 5%), then state that you fail to reject the hypothesis. There is significant evidence to reject the claim of 20 chips per cookie.

7. A biologist takes 300 water samples from a lake. He uses an indicator solution to find that 225 of the samples are in the pH range between 5.5 and 6.5. The mean pH is calculated to be 6.0. Estimate the standard deviation of the samples. Then sketch a graph of the pH distribution of the lake.

BUILDING UNDERSTANDING

Many of these exercises are new only in the sense that students are asked to apply sample statistics to predict population parameters.

ASSIGNING HOMEWORK

Essential	1, 2
Performance assessment	3–9
Portfolio	4
Journal	4, 8
Group	6, 9
Review	10–14

Helping with the Exercises

Encourage your students to draw and shade a normal curve for most of these exercises.

Exercise 1 Students are expected to use calculators for this exercise.

4a. 80% of the time the candy bars will weigh at least 71.3 g, so advertise this as the weight.

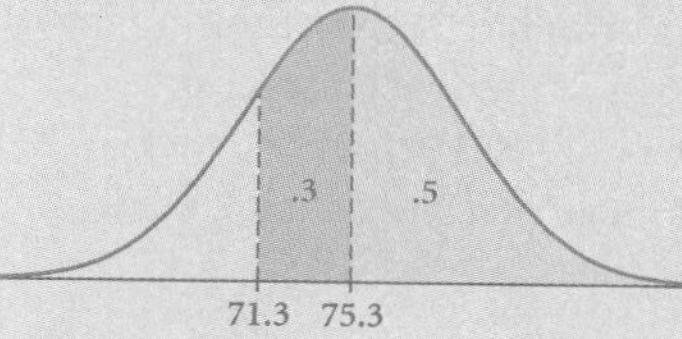

4b. 90% of the time the candy bars will weigh at least 69.2 g, so advertise this as the weight.

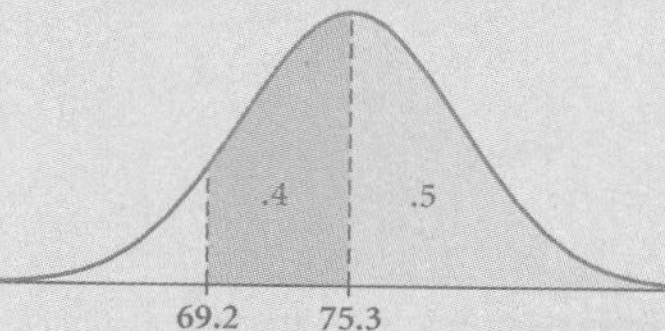

4c. 95% of the time the candy bars will weigh at least 67.5 g, so advertise this as the weight.

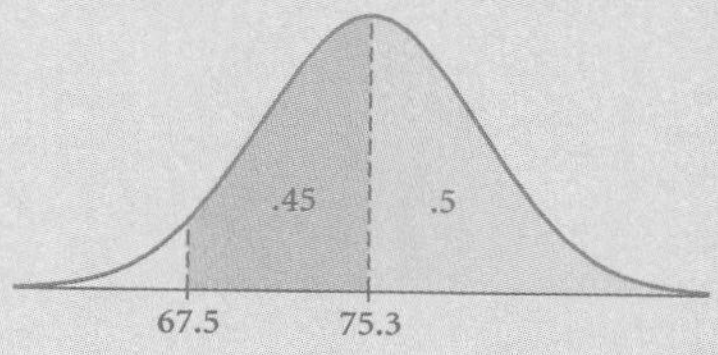

Exercise 4 Students can find these answers by guess-and-check or by graphing.

Exercises 6, 9 These exercises concern hypothesis testing as in Example B.

6a. The mean number of chips is equal to 20.

6b. $\bar{x} = 17.33, s = 3.80$

7. $s = 0.43$

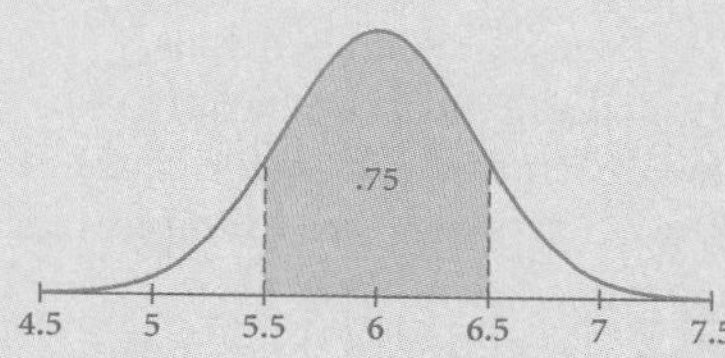

Exercise 8 As needed, remind students that 8b, unlike 8a, is a skewed distribution. If they claim that they can't answer the question without knowing the direction of skew, suggest that they figure out in what direction the distribution could be skewed.

8a. $\bar{x} = 2.5, s \approx 2.53$

8b. $\bar{x} = s = median = 2.5$

8c. The mean is the same, but the median and mode are less than the mean. The median will always be less than the mean for a skewed-right distribution.

9b. $\bar{x} = 0.56, s = 0.20$

9d. probably, because these results are highly unlikely if the site is contaminated

10. The graph appears to sit on a horizontal line and has a line of symmetry at $x = 10$.

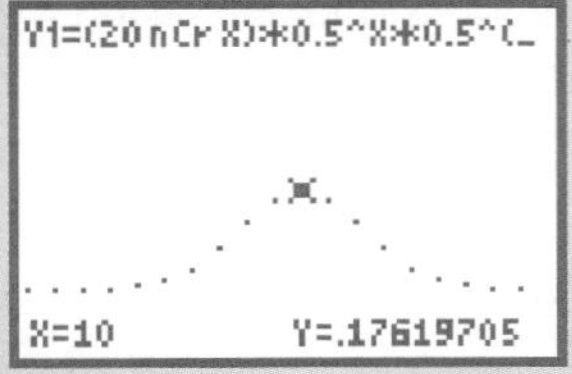

[0, 18.8, 5, −0.1, 0.5, 0.1]

Exercise 11 It is difficult to see that the graph is skewed. You might suggest students also graph $y = {}_{20}C_x(0.1)^x(0.9)^{(20-x)}$ where it is clear that the data are skewed.

11. The graph appears to sit on a horizontal line. The graph is skewed; it doesn't have a line of symmetry.

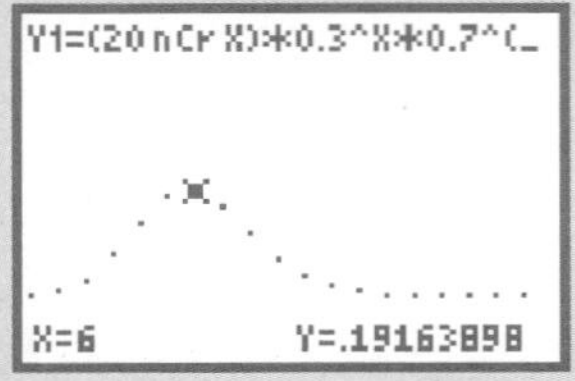

[0, 18.8, 5, −0.1, 0.5, 0.1]

8. The number of automobile accidents per week in a small city were recorded for the first half of the year. The data collected are:

{4, 2, 0, 2, 3, 2, 0, 10, 3, 1, 2, 3, 1, 6, 1, 1, 2, 2, 3, 0, 1, 4, 0, 0, 9, 3}

a. Calculate the mean and standard deviation of these data. Is the accident data normally distributed? If not, how is it skewed?

b. What are the mean, median, and mode of a normal distribution with the mean and standard deviation you found in 8a?

c. How do the mean, median, and mode of the accident data compare to your answers to 8b? Will the mean and median always be in this order for a distribution that is skewed right?

9. APPLICATION A real estate development corporation wants to demolish an abandoned factory and build condominiums in its place. Before proceeding with this plan, the corporation tests the site for toxic contaminants. Fifty core samples are randomly collected from various locations around the site and analyzed for cadmium (Cd). If the average concentration of cadmium in the soil is 0.8 mg/kg or higher, the site is declared contaminated and the developer will scrap its plans because the project will be too costly. The results of the sampling are shown in the table at right.

Concentration of Cd (mg/kg)					
0.89	0.4	0.56	0.29	0.51	0.30
0.53	0.71	0.79	0.61	0.77	0.36
0.24	0.62	0.55	0.63	0.40	0.43
0.63	0.89	0.47	0.33	0.32	0.22
0.71	0.57	0.50	0.98	0.66	0.72
0.43	0.54	0.65	0.95	0.11	
0.78	0.75	0.45	0.69	0.77	
0.62	0.88	0.36	0.71	0.58	
0.36	0.61	0.37	0.39	0.53	

a. How many samples are contaminated? 5 samples

b. Find the mean and standard deviation of these data.

c. If the true concentration of cadmium in the soil is 0.8 mg/kg, what is the probability of these results? approximately 0

d. Will the developer build the condominiums?

Environmental CONNECTION

Soil samples are often tested for toxic chemicals, but soil can also be tested for soil pH, nutrient or element breakdown, and particular physical characteristics. Many laboratories—public, private, and university—will carry out soil testing for farmers and home gardeners. Using the test results, farmers and gardeners can improve plant production by implementing a soil treatment plan.

An employee of an energy company records a core sampling test of the soil.

Review

12.7 **10.** Graph the equation $y = {}_{20}C_x\,(0.5)^x(0.5)^{(20-x)}$ on your calculator in a graphing window with friendly x-values, and turn off the axes. Describe this graph.

12.7 **11.** Graph the equation $y = {}_{20}C_x\,(0.3)^x(0.7)^{(20-x)}$ on your calculator in a graphing window with friendly x-values, and turn off the axes. Describe this graph.

MAKING THE CONNECTION

Soil pollution—in the form of toxic chemicals, radioactive materials, and salt—can be harmful to plant and animal life. Agriculture is a major cause of soil pollution. The use of fertilizers, for example, can interfere with natural processes in the soil by killing organisms beneficial to plant life and thus causing the soil to become sterile. Irrigation and rainfall wash these fertilizers into lakes and streams, threatening aquatic life. Heavy irrigation can lead to a buildup of salt in the soil, causing crop failure.

4.3 **12.** Consider the linear function $f(x) = 16.8x + 405$.

a. Find $f(-19.5)$. 77.4

b. Find x such that $f(x) = 501.096$. 5.72

c. Write the equations of the two parallel lines that are 2.4 units above and below the line $y = f(x)$. $y = 16.8x + 407.4$, $y = 16.8x + 402.6$

3.5 **13.** Find the median-median line for these data, and determine the root mean square error. $y = 4.53x + 12.98$; 6.2

x	1	2	3.5	5	5.5	7	8.5	9.5	10
y	17	23	32	30	36	52	57	55	70

13.3 **14.** Every student in a large school measures the distance from the front door of the school to the flagpole using a meterstick. The results are normally distributed with mean 12.45 m and standard deviation 0.36 m.

a. Find the z-value that corresponds to a measurement of 12.00 m. $z = -1.25$

b. What is the probability that a randomly chosen measurement is between 12.30 and 12.60 m? 32%

c. Nine students, who were absent on measurement day, measured the distance the next day. What is the probability that the mean of their measurements is between 12.30 and 12.60 m? 79%

d. Find the 95% confidence interval for a single measure. (11.73, 13.17)

e. Find the 95% confidence interval for the mean of nine measurements. (12.21, 12.69)

IMPROVING YOUR VISUAL THINKING SKILLS

Acorns

Acorns fall around the base of a particular tree in an approximately normal distribution with standard deviation 20 ft away from the base.

1. What is the probability that any 1 acorn will land more than 10 ft from the tree?

2. What is the probability that any 4 randomly chosen acorns will land an average of more than 10 ft from the tree?

3. What is the probability that any 16 randomly chosen acorns will land an average of more than 10 ft from the tree?

IMPROVING VISUAL THINKING SKILLS

[Alert] Students might forget that "more than 10 ft from the tree" can be on either tail of the normal distribution.

1. .6171

2. .3178

3. .0455

EXPLORATION

PLANNING

LESSON OUTLINE

One day:

25 min Activity

20 min Questions

MATERIALS

- Fathom
- Fathom file **Polling.ftm**
- Fathom demonstration Polling Voters, *optional*

TEACHING

This exploration continues the work begun in Lesson 12.7, Example C. There students found the values of the population ratio p for which a particular polling (sample) result was most likely. Here they adjust a slider, representing the population percentage, and look at how the statistics from many samples bracket that parameter. **[Alert]** Students may have difficulty thinking of a confidence interval as a ratio of a discrete random variable rather than as the mean of a continuous random variable. The 95% confidence interval is the interval in which 95% of the samples will have whatever measure you're considering.

This exploration is based on the activity "Pennies and Polling" from *Data in Depth* by Tim Erickson.

You might use the Fathom demonstration Polling Voters instead of this activity.

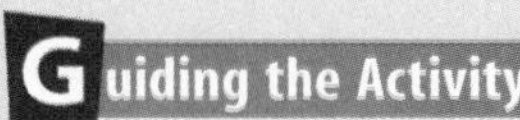

Step 1 Students can download the file **Polling.ftm** at www.keymath.com/DAA. Alternatively, students can start from scratch, setting up a slider p and generating the values of the opinion attribute with this formula:

$$\textbf{if (random( ) < p)} \begin{cases} \text{"yes"} \\ \text{"no"} \end{cases}$$

They can then open the case table, set up the measure result with the formula **100proportion(opinion="yes")**, and collect 100 measures.

[Ask] "How does the horizontal scale of the histogram change when you change the value of the population percentage?"

EXPLORATION

Confidence Intervals for Binary Data

Suppose you take a poll of 50 randomly chosen voters in your state and find that 53% would vote "yes" on a proposition that would increase taxes in order to support schools. Is it possible that the proposition will fail? How likely is it that the proposition will pass? (If a proposition is to pass, at least 50% of the population must vote "yes.") What if your poll shows that 78% of your sample supports the proposition? Then how certain can you be that the proposition will pass?

You learned about confidence intervals in Lesson 13.4, and explored continuous variable data, such as age and height. In this voting situation, however, the data are *binary.* That is, there are two possible values for each data value, "yes" or "no." In this exploration you'll use Fathom to simulate the results of 100 random polls of 50 voters and make hypotheses about what the results of a sample poll allow you to conclude about a population's opinion.

Activity

Polling Voters

Step 1 Start Fathom. From the File menu, choose **Open,** and open the file **Polling.ftm.** You will see a window similar to the one shown below.

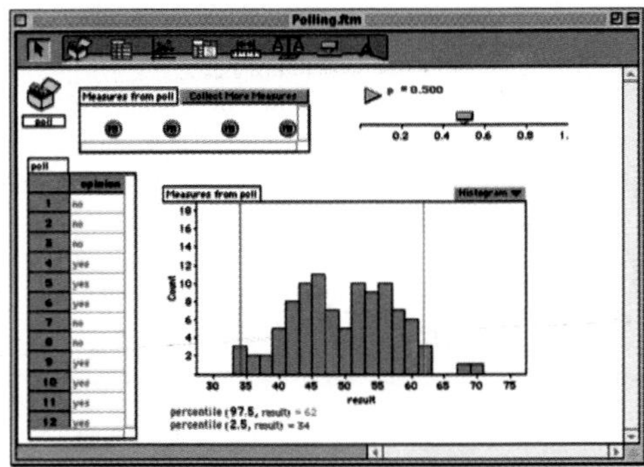

There are two collections: **poll,** which contains 50 opinions (either "yes" or "no"), and **Measures from poll,** which contains the results (the percentage who said "yes") from each of 100 polls of a random sample of 50 voters. The case table on the left shows the results of one poll, and the histogram shows the distribution of the percentage results from the 100 polls. The histogram also shows the 2.5th percentile and the 97.5th percentile of the 100 results, so 95% of the results lie between the blue and red lines—the equivalent of the 95% confidence interval.

Step 2 [Alert] Students may confuse the three uses of percentages here: 95% indicates the confidence interval, 50% is the support in the population (set with the slider p), and 53% and 78% are the level of support in the samples. As needed, help students articulate what the 95% confidence interval means here. [The percentage of "yes" votes for 95% of samples is in the interval 53% to 78%.]

Step 6 Be open to some variation in results. With guess-and-check, students might begin to see 53% included in 95% of most sample collections when p equals 39% or even 38%, up to p equals about 66.5%. They may find 78% of most samples included when p is between 67% and 89%, with the endpoints showing some variation. Emphasize the meaning of what they're doing rather than the results: With changes in the level of support in the population, the confidence interval changes to increase or diminish the chance that 53% or 78% of a sample will be supportive.

Step 6 Because it is probable to get a polling result of 53% when the true percentage of support in the population ranges between 39% and 67%, the proposal may or may not pass. Since it is probable to get a polling result of 78% when the true percentage of support in the population ranges between 67% and 89%, it is very likely that the proposition will pass.

The slider, p, controls the true percentage of voters in the population who support the proposal.

To use the simulation, change the value of p by using the slider or typing in a value. Then click **Collect More Measures** to simulate conducting 100 polls of 50 randomly chosen voters. You should see the case table, the histogram, and the percentile values change.

Step 2 A result of 53% falls within the 95% confidence interval, so it is probable. A result of 78% falls outside the 95% confidence, so it's not probable.

Step 2 Look at the Fathom window on page 760, which shows results for a population with $p = .5$. Is a polling result of 53% probable if exactly 50% of the population support the proposal? Would a result of 78% be probable? (For this exploration, consider a result probable if it falls within the 95% confidence interval.)

Step 3 Work with a partner to estimate the 2.5th and 97.5th percentile values for $p = 0, .1, .2$, and so on, to 1. For each value of p, set the slider, collect a new set of measures, and enter the percentile values into a table like the one below. Then enter "yes" or "no" in the third and fourth columns, depending on whether or not results of 53% and 78% fall within the 95% confidence interval.

p	2.5th percentile	97.5th percentile	Is a result of 53% probable?	Is a result of 78% probable?
0	0	0	no	no
.1				
.2				

Step 4 Copy the graphs below for results of 53% and 78%. Make one point for each row in the table above. The points (0, no) are already filled in.

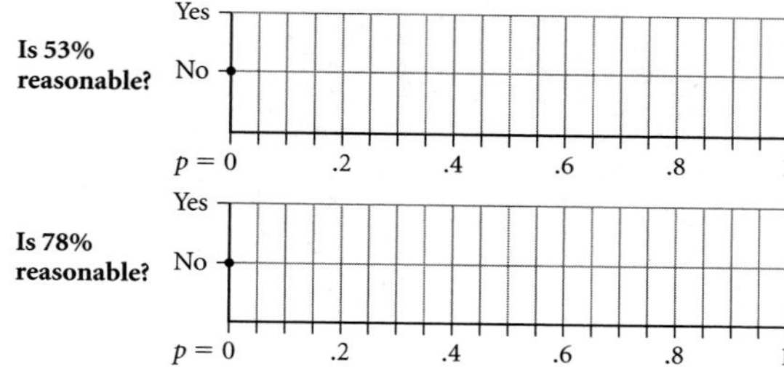

Step 5 Analyze your graphs from Step 4 and figure out, as accurately as possible, where the points change from "no" to "yes" and back again. Explore p-values between those in your table, such as .35, if necessary. Plot any additional points on your graphs. For which values of p are poll results of 53% and 78% probable?

Step 6 You've now examined what kind of poll results are probable, given that you know the actual percentage of the population that will vote "yes." Use your observations to make a reverse hypothesis. That is, is a proposition likely to pass if a poll shows 53% support? 78% support? Explain your reasoning.

NCTM STANDARDS

CONTENT		PROCESS	
	Number		Problem Solving
✓	Algebra	✓	Reasoning
	Geometry	✓	Communication
	Measurement		Connections
✓	Data/Probability	✓	Representation

LESSON OBJECTIVE

- Learn to determine confidence intervals for proportions in polling results

See page 907 for answers to Steps 3, 4, and 5.

Helping with the Questions

Question 1 The randomness of the sample leads to variation in the results. More accurate values can be approximated with larger samples. For example, if students change the sample size to 650 and collect 100 measures, they will see that the confidence interval narrows to about the ±4 percentage points cited in many professional polls.

1. The percentiles vary because each time you use Collect More Measures you are dealing with new samples, and every sample or set of samples from a population will vary slightly. To more precisely determine the percentiles, you could collect the measures multiple times and average the results for the 2.5 and 97.5 percentiles, or you could increase the number of sample polls that are simulated.

Question 2 The theoretical intervals are from 39.2% to 66.8% and from 66.5% to 89.5%.

Notice that here the formula is stated using 1.96 instead of 2. As mentioned in Lesson 13.3, Sharing Ideas, although the z-value associated with a 95% confidence interval is very close to 1.96, it's often rounded to 2.

2. The formula gives values between .39 and .67 for a poll result of 53%, and between .67 and .89 for a poll result of 78%. These answers are close to experimental results found in Step 5.

Questions

1. If you use **Collect More Measures** several times, while holding p constant, the values of the 2.5 and 97.5 percentiles change slightly. Why does this happen? How might you determine more precisely the 2.5 and 97.5 percentiles?
2. For binary data, the formula that determines a 95% confidence interval is

$$CI = \hat{p} \pm 1.96\sqrt{\frac{\hat{p}(1-\hat{p})}{n}}$$

where $\hat{p}$ is the sample percentage and n is the number in the sample. Calculate the confidence interval for sample results of 53% and 78% from a survey of 50 voters. How do these calculations compare to your experimental results in Step 5?

EXTENSIONS

A. Now that students know the formula for the 95% confidence interval for binary data, ask them to use it to answer questions about a voting situation. For example, "If a poll finds that 65% of voters favor a proposition, is the proposition likely to pass with at least 50% support? If a poll finds that 45% of voters favor a proposition, you can be 95% confident that the actual percentage of voters that favor the proposition is between what two percentages?"

B. You might ask students to modify the Fathom file **Polling.ftm** to simulate results for continuous variable data. Students will input sample mean and sample standard deviation data in order to create sample polling results.

LESSON

13.5 Bivariate Data and Correlation

It is a capital mistake to theorize before one has data. Insensibly one begins to twist facts to suit theories, instead of theories to suit facts.

SIR ARTHUR CONAN DOYLE

Dr. Aviles and Dr. Scott collected data on tree diameters and heights. Dr. Aviles thought that the height was closely associated with the diameter, but Dr. Scott claimed that the height was more closely associated with the square of the diameter. Which model is better? Each researcher plotted data and found a good line of fit. Their graphs are shown here.

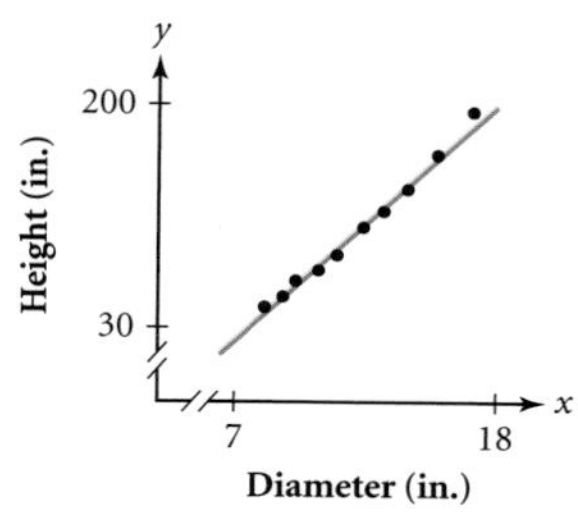

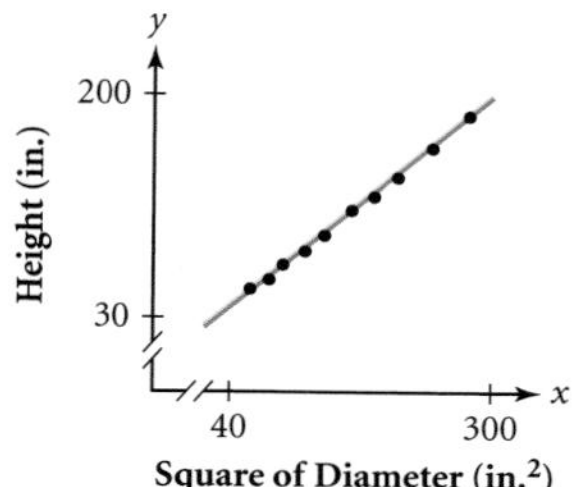

Does it appear that a line is the appropriate model? If so, is there a better linear relationship in Dr. Aviles's data or in Dr. Scott's data? How good is the fit for each line? In this lesson you'll learn how to answer questions like these.

In Lesson 13.4, you learned how to make predictions about population parameters from sample statistics. You can also predict associations between parameters, such as height and diameter or height and the squares of diameter, for a large population, such as all trees. You can even apply this method to populations that are infinitely large. The process of collecting data on two possibly related variables is called **bivariate sampling.** How can you measure the strength of the association in the sample?

A commonly used statistical measure of linear association is called the **correlation coefficient.** A linear association between two variables is called **correlation.** In the investigation you'll use a calculator to explore properties of the correlation coefficient for a bivariate sample.

A giant Sequoia tree in Yosemite National Park, California.

NCTM STANDARDS

CONTENT		PROCESS	
	Number	✓	Problem Solving
✓	Algebra	✓	Reasoning
	Geometry	✓	Communication
	Measurement	✓	Connections
✓	Data/Probability	✓	Representation

LESSON OBJECTIVES

- Learn the language and concept of bivariate sampling
- Find and interpret the coefficient of correlation to measure association
- Understand the difference between correlation and causation

LESSON

13.5

PLANNING

LESSON OUTLINE

One day:

20 min	Investigation
10 min	Examples
10 min	Sharing
5 min	Exercises

MATERIALS

- Sunburn and Ice Cream (T) for One Step
- Looking for Connections Sample Data (W), *optional*
- Calculator Note 13F

TEACHING

In previous lessons students saw how to make predictions about a population from a sample. Now they turn to making predictions about one characteristic from another in a sample or population.

One Step

Show the Sunburn and Ice Cream transparency and ask students to predict the number of visits to the nurse from knowing the number of ice cream sales. As needed, emphasize that the values displayed are z-values. Students might use something like the median-median line to make predictions. Ask groups that finish first to devise a way to measure how accurate the predictions can be, compared to data whose scatter plots seem less linear. Remind them that the correlation between one data set and itself will be perfect. Even if they don't come up with the Pearson correlation coefficient, they'll be open to understanding it when you describe it during Sharing. At that point ask whether buying ice cream causes sunburn, to bring out the difference between correlation and causation.

Guiding the Investigation

To save time, you might want to collect data on the same set of five questions from the whole class and post these data for groups to analyze, or use the Looking for Connections Sample Data worksheet.

Step 1 One way to enter data from question 4 numerically into the calculator is to enter the number of minutes past 8 P.M.

Step 1 Sample data provided are for the survey described in the text. The answer to question 4 is recorded in minutes past 8 P.M.

Step 2 **[ESL]** To *conjecture* means to make a statement that you think is true but you have not yet proved. Some students will include 1 and 3, 1 and 4, 3 and 5, or 4 and 5 as negative rather than weak.

Step 2 Possible answers:

i. positive: 1 and 5; 3 and 4

ii. negative: 1 and 2; 2 and 5

iii. weak: 1 and 3; 1 and 4; 2 and 3; 2 and 4; 3 and 5; 4 and 5

Step 3 You may want to have the class critique various methods of data collection. Students can poll one another or anonymously answer the questions on a piece of paper. If each student in a group asks a separate question and makes one list, remind group members to make sure they enter data for students in the same order. Putting answers to Question n into list Ln might also help avoid confusion.

Investigation
Looking for Connections

Step 1 Work with your group to create a survey with five questions that are all answered with a number, or use the sample survey here.

1. How many minutes of homework did you do last night?
2. How many minutes did you spend talking, calling, e-mailing, or writing to friends?
3. How many minutes did you spend just watching TV or listening to music?
4. At what time did you go to bed?
5. How many academic classes do you have?

Step 2 Conjecture with your group about the strengths of correlations between pairs of variables. For example, you may decide that the number of minutes of homework is strongly correlated with the number of academic classes. Consider each of the ten pairs of variables and identify which combinations you believe will have

i. A positive correlation (as one increases, the other tends to increase).

ii. A negative correlation (as one increases, the other tends to decrease).

iii. A weak correlation.

Step 3 Gather data from each student in your class. Then enter the data into five calculator lists. Plot points for each pair of lists, and find the correlation coefficients. [► See **Calculator Note 13F** to learn how to find the correlation coefficient. ◄] You may want to divide this work among members of your group. Describe the relationship between the appearance of the graph and the value of the correlation coefficient.

Step 4 Write a paragraph describing the correlations you discover. Include any pairs that are not correlated that you find surprising. You have collected a small and not very random sample; do you think these relationships would still be present if you collected answers from a random sample of your entire school population?

In 1896, English mathematician Karl Pearson (1857–1936) proposed the correlation coefficient, now abbreviated r. To compute the correlation coefficient, Pearson replaced each x- and y-value in a data set with its corresponding z-value. If a particular x- or y-value is larger than the mean value for that variable, then its z-value is positive. And if a particular x- or y-value is smaller than the mean value for that variable, then its z-value is negative. Pearson then found the product of z_x and z_y for each data point, and summed these products. In a data set that is generally increasing, the products of z_x and z_y are positive. This is because for every point, either both x and y are above the mean, or both x and y are below the mean. In a data set that is generally decreasing, usually either z_x is positive and z_y is negative, or z_x is negative and z_y is positive. Therefore, the products will be negative. After summing the products, Pearson divided by $(n - 1)$ to get a number between -1 and 1. So, he defined the correlation coefficient as $\frac{\Sigma z_x z_y}{n-1}$. But what do values of this coefficient mean?

Step 3 See page 908 for sample data.

1 and 2: $r \approx -.521$

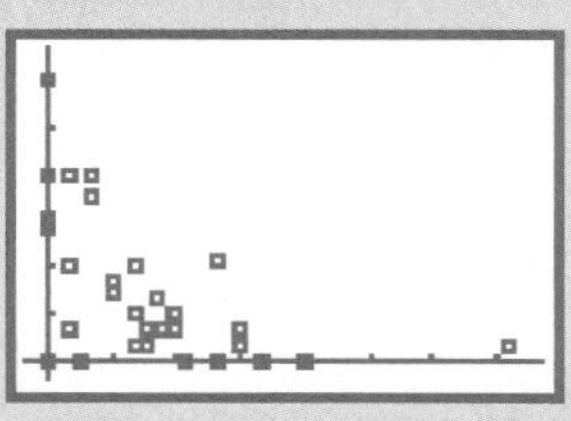

[−10, 230, 30, −10, 200, 30]

1 and 3: $r \approx -.320$

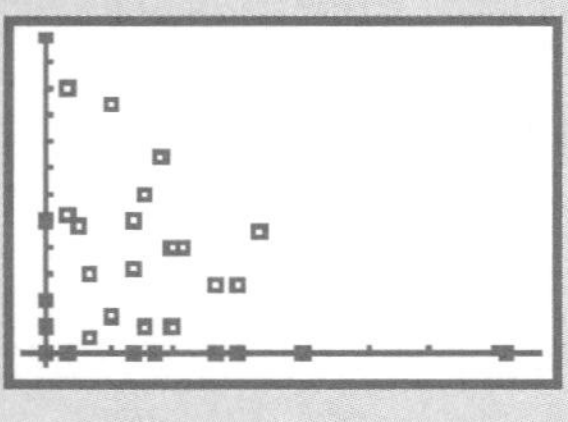

[−10, 230, 30, −10, 360, 30]

1 and 4: $r \approx -.206$

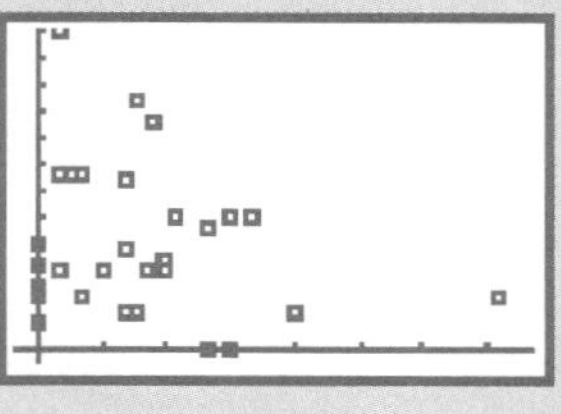

[−10, 230, 30, −10, 250, 30]

1 and 5: $r \approx .771$

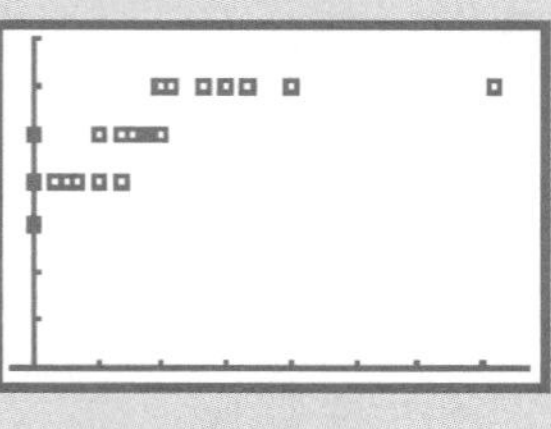

[−10, 230, 30, 0, 7, 1]

You may have noticed in the investigation that values of r can range from -1 to 1. A value of 1 means the x-values are positively correlated with the y-values in the strongest possible way. That is, as x-values increase, y-values increase proportionally. A value of -1 means the x-values are negatively correlated with the y-values in the strongest possible way. That is, as x-values increase, y-values decrease proportionally. A value of 0 means there's no linear correlation between the values of x and y.

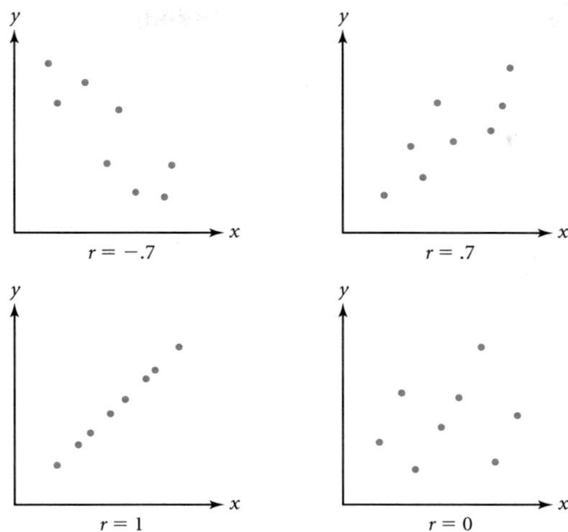

If data are highly correlated, a straight line will model the data points well.

For Dr. Aviles's data in the tree example at the beginning of this lesson, the correlation coefficient is .992. So, his data are very close to linear. For Dr. Scott's data, the correlation coefficient is .999. That's even better. This means that for the trees measured, the squares of diameters are better predictors of the heights than are the diameters themselves.

The Correlation Coefficient

The correlation coefficient, r, can be calculated with the formula

$$r = \frac{\Sigma z_x z_y}{n-1} = \frac{\Sigma(x-\bar{x})(y-\bar{y})}{s_x s_y (n-1)}$$

A value of r close to ± 1 indicates a strong correlation, whereas a value of r close to 0 indicates no correlation.

Note that the definition of the correlation coefficient includes no reference to any particular line, though it describes how well a line fits a bivariate data set. In contrast, the root mean square error you studied in Chapter 3 describes how well a *particular* line fits a data set.

Often, bivariate data are collected from a study or an experiment in which one variable represents some condition and the other represents measurements based on that condition, as shown in the next example. In statistics, the x- and y-variables are often called the **explanatory** and **response** variables instead of the independent and dependent variables.

Step 3 (continued)
2 and 3: $r \approx -.191$

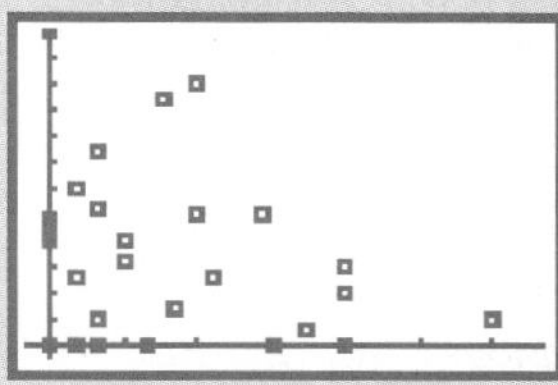

[−10, 200, 30, −10, 360, 30]

2 and 4: $r \approx -.059$

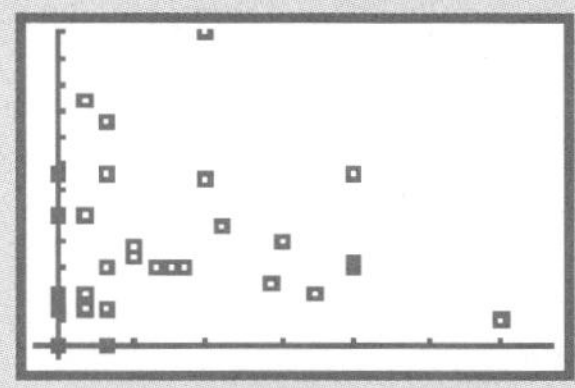

[−10, 200, 30, −10, 360, 30]

2 and 5: $r \approx -.632$

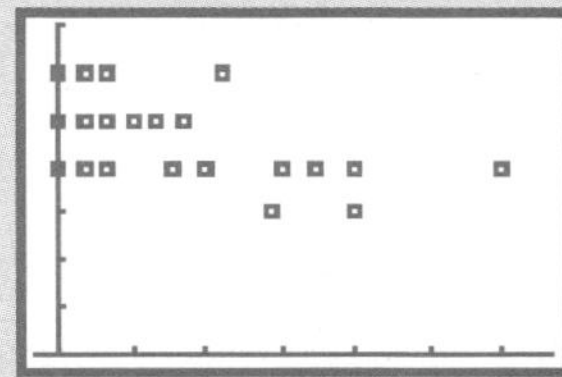

[−10, 200, 30, 0, 7, 1]

3 and 4: $r \approx .576$

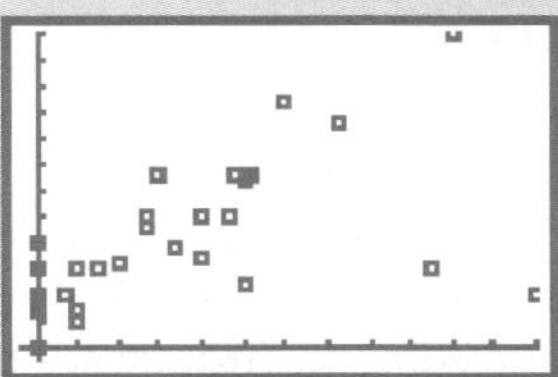

[−10, 360, 30, −10, 360, 30]

3 and 5: $r \approx -.207$

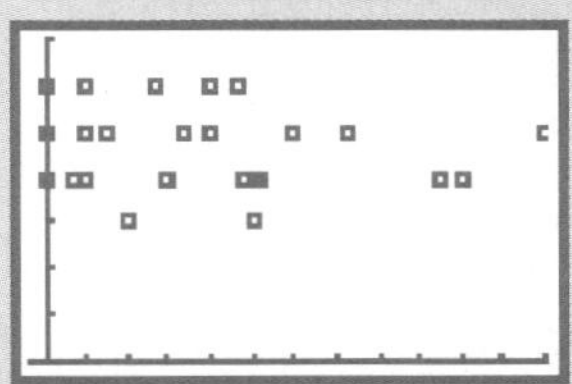

[−10, 360, 30, 0, 7, 1]

4 and 5: $r \approx -.185$

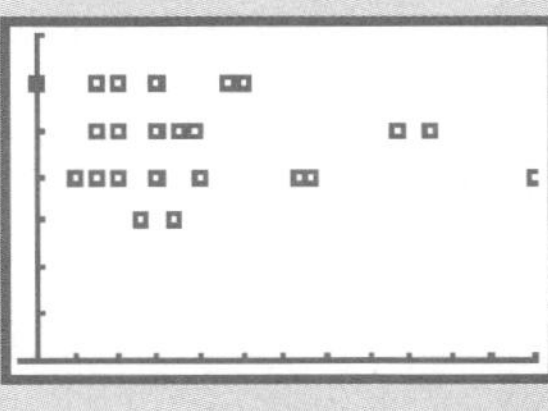

[−10, 360, 30, 0, 7, 1]

Step 3 (continued)
The graphs that increase have positive correlation coefficients, and the graphs that decrease have negative correlation coefficients. When the relationship is strong, the correlation coefficient is closer to ± 1, and when the relationship is weak, the correlation coefficient is close to 0.

Step 4 The correlations between time spent on homework and number of academic classes, and time watching TV and bedtime, are relatively strong, and positive. The correlations between time talking to friends and number of academic classes, and time spent on homework and time talking to friends, are relatively strong and negative. The other pairs of variables do not appear to be correlated. These results do not necessarily represent the school, because people in this class are not a random sample of the school.

▶ EXAMPLE A

If you are short on time, you need not show students how to use the formula, because they can find the correlation coefficient easily on their calculator. What is important is that students understand what the correlation coefficient means.

Causation

As you discuss causation, you might want to refer back to the investigation and **[Ask]** "Would you say there is a causal relationship between any two of the five things studied in the investigation.

▶ EXAMPLE B

[Ask] "What other types of data might appear to be correlated but instead may be affected by lurking variables?" Almost any correlation might be attributed to lurking variables. Even the now well-established causal relationship between smoking and lung cancer was challenged as being only a correlation, with genetic disposition proposed as a possible lurking variable. There might also be correlation with no clear lurking variable, such as a correlation between fire fighters' salaries and the amount of ozone in the atmosphere.

EXAMPLE A

Kiane belongs to many committees and notices that different groups take different amounts of time to make decisions. She wonders if the time it takes to make a decision is linearly related to the size of the committee. So, she collects some data. Find the correlation coefficient of this data set and interpret your result.

Size (people)	4	6	7	9	9	11	15	15	18	20	21	24	25
Time (min)	5.2	3.8	8.2	8.5	12.0	10.8	14.7	15.5	22.0	19.1	35.3	29.2	32.1

▶ Solution

In this instance, it makes sense to let the explanatory variable, x, represent the committee size and the response variable, y, represent the time it takes to make a decision. When plotted, the data show an approximately linear pattern.

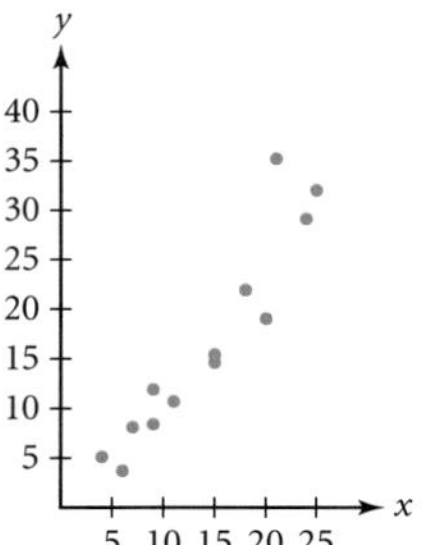

You can find the value of r directly using a calculator, but you should also try to use the formula—assisted by a calculator, of course. First, enter the data into lists and verify these statistics:

$\bar{x} \approx 14.15$ people, $s_x \approx 7.0456$ people

$\bar{y} \approx 16.65$ minutes, $s_y \approx 10.302$ minutes

Then use the lists in the formula:

$$\frac{\Sigma(x - 14.15)(y - 16.65)}{(7.0456)(10.302)(13 - 1)} \approx .9380$$

A correlation coefficient of $r \approx .9380$ means there is a strong positive correlation between the size of a committee and the time it takes to reach a decision. This means that as the size of a committee increases, the time it takes to reach a decision increases proportionately.

Be careful that you don't confuse the ideas of correlation and causation. A strong correlation may exist between two sets of data, but this does not necessarily imply a causal relationship. For instance, in Example A, Kiane found a strong correlation between committee size and decision-making time. But this does not necessarily mean that the size of the committee *caused* the decision to take longer. Whether it did or did not can be proved only by a carefully controlled experiment.

EXAMPLE B

The director of a summer camp has collected data for two weeks on both daily ice cream sales from the camp store and visits to the camp nurse for treatment of sunburn. What conclusions, if any, can you make?

Ice cream sales	\$245.10	\$45.25	\$17.85	\$205.00	\$276.35	\$428.25	\$312.15
Visits to nurse	66	17	1	65	72	131	93

Ice cream sales	\$288.25	\$267.95	\$74.10	\$111.50	\$371.55	\$244.45	\$115.75
Visits to nurse	81	99	2	84	113	78	79

SHARING IDEAS

As students present their results, ask them to make sense of the correlation coefficient, $r = \frac{\Sigma z_x z_y}{n - 1}$. (You might want to remind students of the meaning of z-values as the number of standard deviations from the mean, as discussed in Lesson 13.3. The sum of the z-values of a data set is 0, and their standard deviation is 1.)

Encourage students to make sense of the idea of the correlation coefficient by asking questions such as these.

[Ask] "If all the data points were three standard deviations above the mean, could both z_x and z_y for each point be 3, making the numerator about $9n$ and the fraction about 9?" [You can't have all data points three standard deviations above the mean; in fact, the sum of the z-values in each data set is 0.]

Solution Graph the data and calculate the correlation coefficient. The graph of the data shows a clear upward trend. The correlation coefficient of .866 indicates a fairly strong correlation.

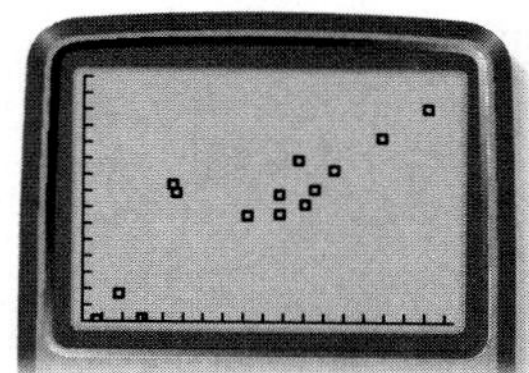

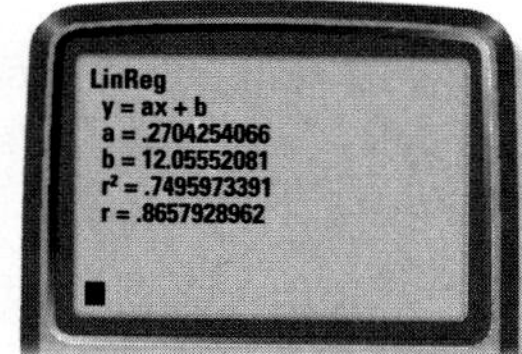

[0, 450, 25, 0, 150, 10]

So, can you conclude that buying ice cream causes a sunburn? Or does getting a sunburn cause ice cream buying? There is most likely another variable causing both of these effects. Perhaps the daily temperature might be a **lurking variable** behind both of these results.

So, you can conclude that sunburn and ice cream sales are correlated, but not that one of these occurrences causes the other.

EXERCISES

Practice Your Skills

1. Approximate the correlation coefficient for each data set.

a. 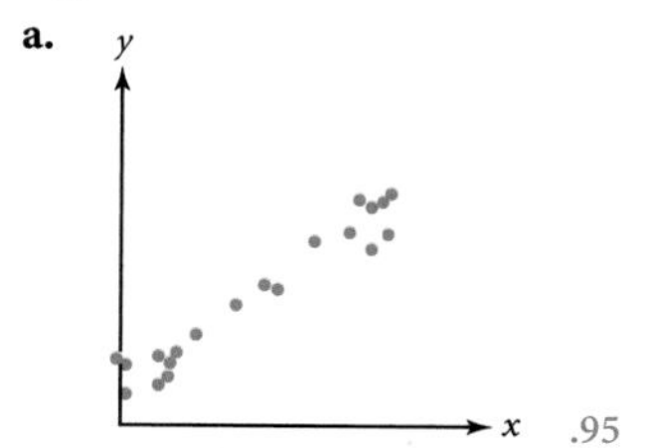 .95

b. 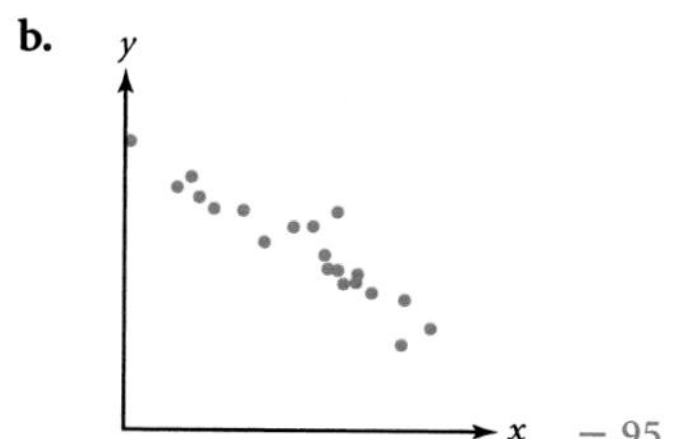 −.95

c. 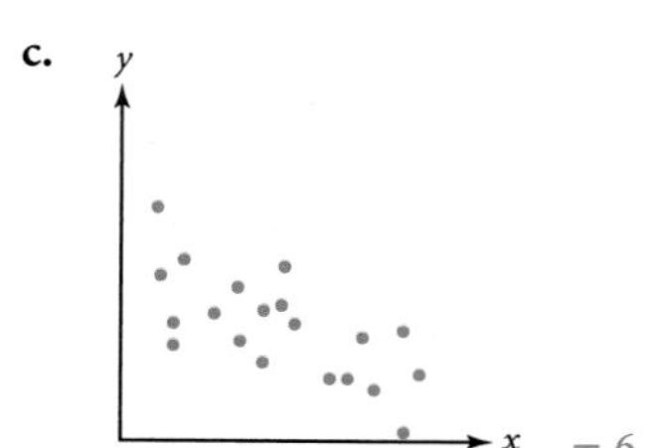 −.6

d. 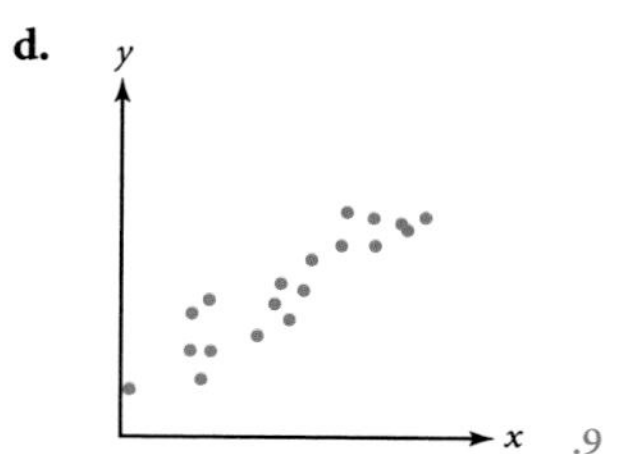 .9

Sharing Ideas (continued)

[Ask] "Is correlation about samples or about populations?" [In this lesson the correlation coefficient is being treated as a sample statistic; it can be used to predict a corresponding population parameter, usually indicated by the Greek letter ρ (rho).]

[Ask] "Is the correlation coefficient r like variance, dividing by $(n - 1)$?" Indeed, the correlation coefficient is a generalization of the variance; if only one sample is involved, corresponding perfectly to itself, then r equals the variance of the sample's z-values, which is 1. In fact, as with variance, to find the correlation coefficient of a population you use denominator N (the population size) rather than $(n - 1)$, where n is the sample size.

[Ask] "How does r relate to the straight line through the data?" [The sign of r will be the same as the sign of the slope of a line through the data.]

[Ask] "Which indicates more correlation, a correlation coefficient of 0.94 or one of −0.94?" [The correlations are equally strong, though one is negative.] You might be prepared to illustrate this idea with various graphs and correlation coefficients.

BUILDING UNDERSTANDING

Students work with correlation coefficients and their limitations.

ASSIGNING HOMEWORK

Essential	1, 2, 4, 5
Performance assessment	3, 8
Portfolio	6
Journal	7
Group	9, 10
Review	11–16

Assessing Progress

You can assess students' understanding of the mean, standard deviation, and probabilities associated with normal curves.

Closing the Lesson

The point of this lesson is that you can make predictions about one characteristic from knowledge about another. This is **bivariate sampling.** The **correlation coefficient,** $r = \frac{\Sigma z_x z_y}{n - 1}$, indicates how strong the association between the samples is.

Helping with the Exercises

Exercise 1 The answers given are only estimates. A range of answers is acceptable.

2. Possible answers:

2a.

2b.

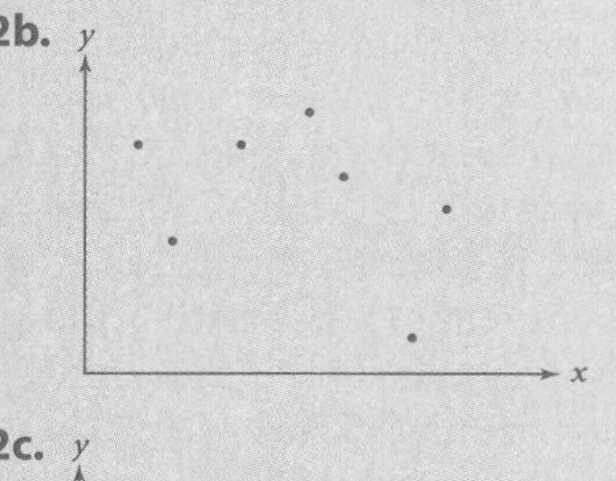

2c.

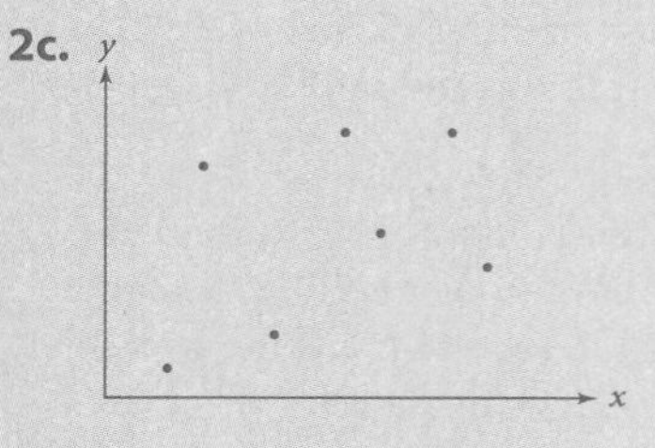

2d.

3f.

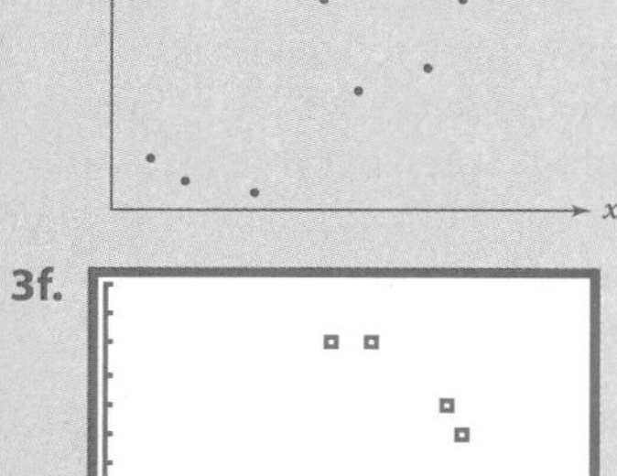

[0, 25, 1, 0, 10, 1]

5a. Correlation; weight gain probably has more to do with amount of physical activity than with television ownership.

5b. Correlation; the age of the children may be the variable controlling both size of feet and reading ability.

5c. Correlation; the size of a fire may be the variable controlling both the number of firefighers and the length of time.

2. Sketch a graph of a data set with approximately these correlation coefficients.

a. $r = -.8$ **b.** $r = -.4$

c. $r = .4$ **d.** $r = .8$

3. Copy and complete the table at right. Then answer 3a–d to calculate the correlation coefficient.

x	y	$x - \bar{x}$	$y - \bar{y}$	$(x - \bar{x})(y - \bar{y})$
12	8	−5	2	−10
14	8	−3	2	−6
18	6	1	0	0
19	5	2	−1	−2
22	3	5	−3	−15

a. What is the sum of the values for $(x - \bar{x})(y - \bar{y})$? −33

b. What are $\bar{x}$ and s_x? 17; 4

c. What are $\bar{y}$ and s_y? 6; 2.1213

d. Calculate $r = \dfrac{\Sigma(x - \bar{x})(y - \bar{y})}{s_x s_y (n-1)}$. −.9723

e. What does this value of r tell you about the data? There is a strong negative correlation in the data.

f. Draw a scatter plot to confirm your conclusion in 3e.

4. In each study described, identify the explanatory and response variables.

a. Doctors measured how well students learned finger-tapping patterns after various amounts of sleep. explanatory variable: amount of sleep; response variable: ability to learn the finger-tapping pattern

b. Scientists investigated the relationship between the weight of a mammal and the weight of its brain. explanatory variable: weight of mammal; response variable: weight of brain

c. A university mathematics department collected data on the number of students enrolled each year in the school and the number of students who signed up for a basic algebra class. explanatory variable: university enrollment; response variable: algebra class enrollment

5. For each research finding, decide whether there is evidence of causation, correlation, or both. If it is only a correlation, name a possible lurking variable that may be the cause of the results.

a. As the sales of television sets has increased, so has the number of overweight adults. Does television cause weight gain?

b. A study in an elementary school found that children with larger shoe sizes were better readers than those with smaller shoe sizes. Do big feet make children read better?

c. The more firefighters sent to a fire, the longer it takes to put out the fire. Does sending more firefighters cause a fire to burn longer?

Reason and Apply

6. An environmental science class conducted a research project to determine whether there was a relationship between the soil pH, x, and the percent dieback of new growth, y, for a particular type of tree. The table below contains the data the class collected.

x	3.3	3.4	3.5	3.6	3.7	3.8	3.9	4.0	4.1	4.2	4.3	4.5	5.0	5.1
y	7.3	10.8	10.4	9.3	12.4	11.2	6.6	10.0	9.2	12.4	2.3	4.3	1.6	1.0

a. Make a scatter plot of the data.

b. Describe the relationship between the two variables. Possible answer: The variables appear to have a negative correlation. As the soil pH increases, the percent of dieback decreases.

6a.

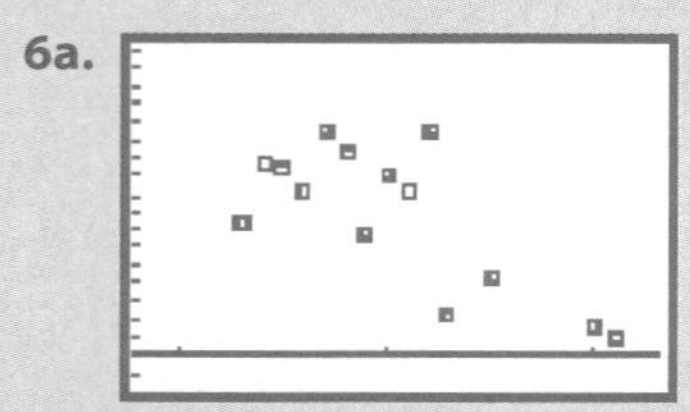

[2.8, 5.4, 1, −2, 17, 1]

c. Find the correlation coefficient. Does this confirm or refute your answer to 6b? How can you tell?

d. Can you conclude that higher soil pH causes less dieback of new growth?

Environmental CONNECTION

Trees take in carbon dioxide from the air which helps offset carbon dioxide emissions caused by cars and industry. Destruction of forests has contributed to an increase in the amount of carbon dioxide in the atmosphere, leading to global warming and other problems. Although nature can eventually reforest most areas on its own, we can speed the process by improving soil quality and selecting the best species for a particular area.

Deforestation from logging and pasture clearing over the past 30 years have reduced the size of the Amazon rain forest in Brazil by 15 percent.

7. The table contains information from a selection of four-year colleges and universities for the 2000–2001 school year. Describe the correlation between the number of students and the number of faculty.

Four-Year Colleges

College	Number of students	Number of faculty
Alfred University	2,433	208
Brandeis University	4,753	461
Brown University	7,723	737
Bryn Mawr College	1,784	167
California College of Arts & Crafts	1,213	326
Carleton College	1,936	214
College of William & Mary	7,530	718
DePauw University	2,225	234
Drake University	5,126	293
Duquesne University	9,667	847
Gallaudet University	1,661	221
Hampshire College	1,172	114
Illinois Wesleyan University	2,102	183
Lehigh University	6,509	457
Maryland Institute, College of Art	1,302	220
Miami University of Ohio	16,290	975

College	Number of students	Number of faculty
Mills College	1,070	154
Morehouse College	2,970	235
Mt. Holyoke College	2,089	228
Princeton University	6,547	914
Rhode Island School of Design	2,086	399
Rhodes College	1,554	156
Saint John's University	2,020	190
St. Olaf College	3,014	315
Spelman College	1,897	147
Swarthmore College	1,428	201
Syracuse University	14,478	1,395
Tufts University	8,933	1,097
Tuskegee University	2,826	262
University of Tulsa	4,158	414
Wesleyan University	3,158	308
Wheaton College	2,827	244

(*The World Almanac and Book of Facts 2002*)

Exercise 6c [ESL] To *refute* an answer means to show it is wrong.

6c. $r \approx -.740$. Answers will vary. A value of $-.740$ confirms a fairly strong negative correlation.

6d. There is a correlation, but you cannot assume it is causation. Other variables, such as temperature, location, and amount of sunlight, would also have to be considered.

MAKING THE CONNECTION

Scientists, environmentalists, and some economists estimate that conserving rain forests has a far greater economic value than deforestation for lumber or agriculture. The rain forests provide numerous environmental services. They absorb carbon dioxide, a greenhouse gas, thus helping to fend off global warming. Rain forests cycle nutrients that are essential to life, such as phosphorus and nitrogen. Thanks to the forests' high biodiversity, researchers often discover the ingredients for new pharmaceuticals in rain forest plants.

Exercises 7, 8 Data for these exercises are on the Calculator Programs and Data CD.

7. $r \approx .915$. There is a strong positive correlation between the number of students and the number of faculty.

Exercises 9, 10 These exercises are intended to emphasize the importance of looking at a plot of data to confirm or refute a correlation implied by an r-value. Like most statistics, the correlation coefficient is a valuable tool only when it is used in appropriate circumstances. Reliance on a statistic can never replace common sense.

9a.

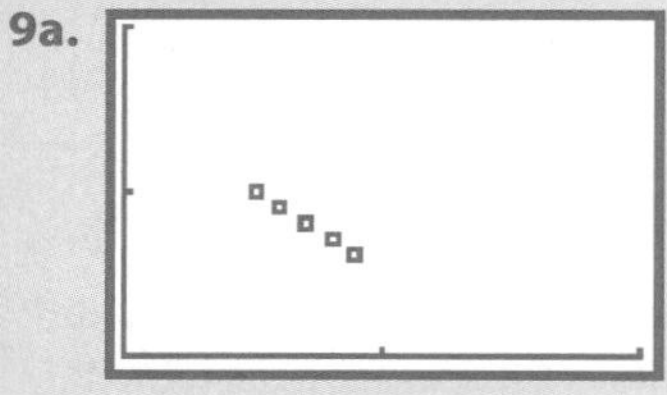

[0, 2, 1, 0, 2, 1]

$r = -1$. This value of r implies perfect negative correlation consistent with the plot.

9b.

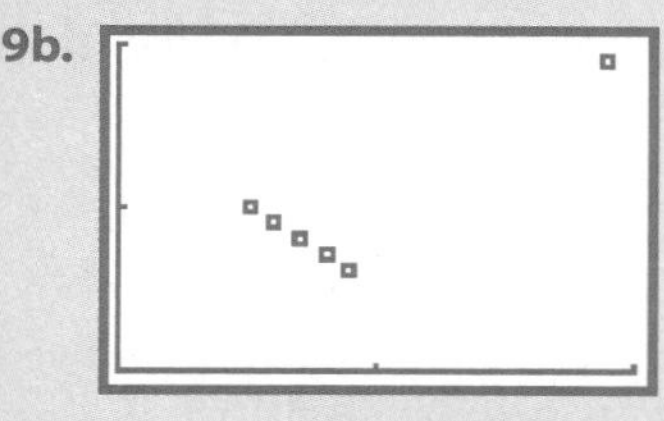

[0, 2, 1, 0, 2, 1]

$r \approx .833$. This value of r implies strong positive correlation, but the plot suggests negative correlation with one outlier.

9c.

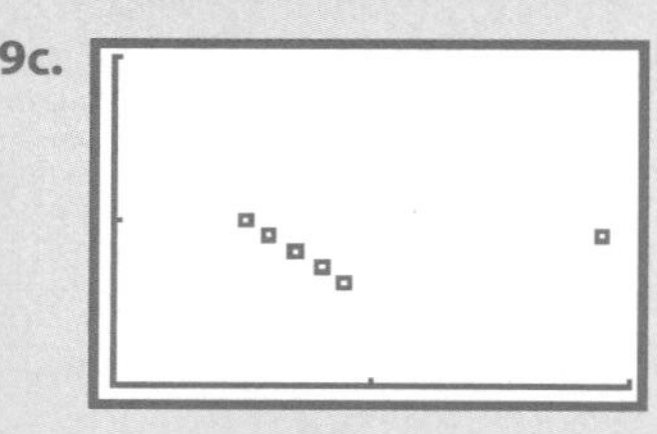

[0, 2, 1, 0, 2, 1]

$r = 0$. This value of r implies no correlation, but the plot suggests negative correlation with one outlier.

8. These data list the number of bound volumes, the annual circulation (the number of books that are checked out), and the annual operating cost for randomly selected public libraries in 2002. Each number in the table is in thousands.

Public Libraries in Selected Cities

City	Volumes	Circulation	Cost ($)
Atlanta, GA	1,960	2,704	19,500
Baton Rouge, LA	1,232	2,449	13,000
Boston, MA	6,582	3,500	30,100
Buffalo, NY	5,241	8,998	29,000
Cleveland, OH	5,380	3,782	48,600
Dallas, TX	3,000	3,807	19,200
Denver, CO	4,224	7,448	23,700
Detroit, MI	2,808	1,513	27,400
Kansas City, MO	2,215	2,224	14,800
Memphis, TN	1,849	3,702	14,700
Omaha, NE	917	2,474	9,090
Philadelphia, PA	7,892	6,067	46,800
Seattle, WA	1,777	4,580	24,500
St. Paul, MN	1,051	2,401	7,800

(*www.infoplease.com*)

Library: Homage to Marcel Proust is a mixed media installation box constructed by French artist Charles Matton (b 1933). The miniature work (15.8 in. wide) evokes the world of French writer Marcel Proust (1871–1922).

a. What is the correlation coefficient for number of volumes and operating cost, and for circulation and operating cost? .862; .419

b. Is number of volumes or circulation more strongly correlated with operating cost? Explain your reasoning. The number of volumes is more strongly correlated to the operating costs.

9. ***Mini-Investigation*** For each data set given in 9a–c, draw a scatter plot and find the correlation coefficient, r. State what this value of r implies about the data, and note any surprising results you find.

a. {(0.5, 1), (0.6, 0.9), (0.7, 0.8), (0.8, 0.7), (0.9, 0.6)}

b. {(0.5, 1), (0.6, 0.9), (0.7, 0.8), (0.8, 0.7), (0.9, 0.6), (1.9, 1.9)}

c. {(0.5, 1), (0.6, 0.9), (0.7, 0.8), (0.8, 0.7), (0.9, 0.6), (1.9, 0.9)}

d. Based on your answers to 9a–c, do you think the correlation coefficient is strongly affected by outliers? Yes, one outlier can drastically affect the value of r.

10. ***Mini-Investigation*** For each data set given in 10a and b, draw a scatter plot and find the correlation coefficient, r. State what this value of r implies about the data.

a. {(0.3, 0.9), (0.4, 0.6), (0.6, 0.4), (1, 0.3), (1.4, 0.4), (1.6, 0.6), (1.7, 0.9), (0.3, 1.1), (0.4, 1.4), (0.6, 1.6), (1, 1.7), (1.4, 1.6), (1.6, 1.4), (1.7, 1.1)}

b. {(0.4, 1.4), (0.6, 1.1), (0.8, 0.8), (1, 0.5), (1.2, 0.8), (1.4, 1.1), (1.6, 1.4)}

c. For the data sets in 10a and b, does there appear to be a relationship between x- and y-values? Is this reflected in the values you found for r? In 10a, the data are circular, and in 10b the data appear to fit an absolute-value function. However, the values of r are 0, implying that there is no correlation. This is because there is no *linear* correlation, although there is in fact a strong relationship in the data.

10a.

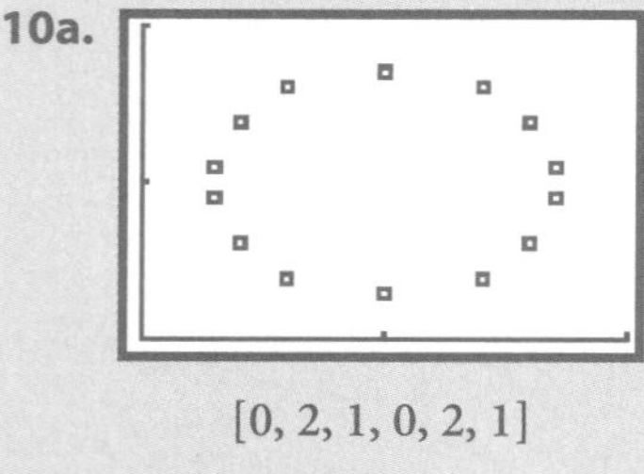

[0, 2, 1, 0, 2, 1]

$r = 0$; no correlation

10b.

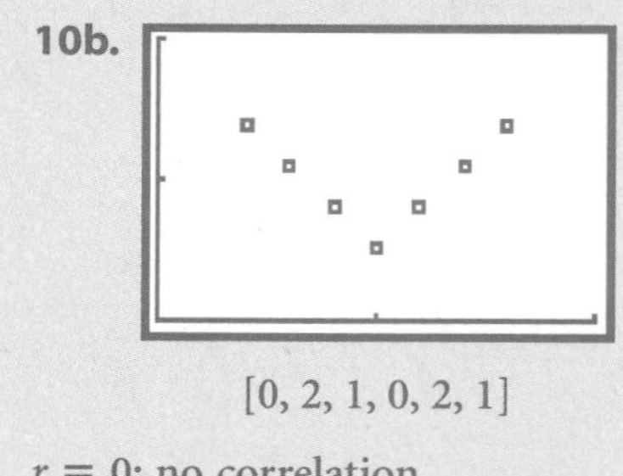

[0, 2, 1, 0, 2, 1]

$r = 0$; no correlation

Review

3.3 **11.** What is the slope of the line that passes through the point (4, 7) and is parallel to the line $y = 12(x - 5) + 21$? 12

3.5 **12.** The data at right give the reaction times of ten people who were administered different dosages of a drug. Find the median-median line for these data and determine the root mean square error. $y = 0.045x - 3.497$; 0.475

Dosage (mg)	Reaction time (s)
85	0.5
89	0.6
90	0.2
95	1.2
95	1.6
103	0.6
107	1.0
110	1.8
111	1.0
115	1.5

3.3 **13.** Find an equation of the line passing through (4, 0) and (6, −3).

5.6 **14.** Graph the equation $y = \log_5 x$.

0.3 **15.** On a car trip, your speed averages 50 km/h as you drive to your destination. You return by the same route and average 75 km/h. What's your average speed for the entire trip? 60 km/h

16. David wants to send his nephew a new 5-foot fishing pole. David wraps up the pole and takes it to Bob's Courier Service. But Bob's has a policy of not accepting any parcels longer than 4 feet. David returns an hour later with the fishing pole wrapped and sends it with no problem. How did he do it? (Assume the pole is not broken into pieces.)

Project

CORRELATION VS. CAUSATION

Think of a relationship someone claims involves causation, but you think might only involve correlation. Your claim can be about anything—science, popular beliefs, sociology—but it must be something that can be tested. First, research data related to the claim and determine whether or not the data seem to show a correlation between the two variables. Then, think about whether or not one event really causes the other. What other factors might be involved? Might the data you found be misleading in some way? If you can, find the data for any other factors and see how these data are related to your claim. Write a report on your findings.

Your project should include

- The claim you researched and the data and analyses you found.
- Any graphs, tables, or equations that you used while analyzing the data.
- A summary of other factors that might be involved.
- Your own conclusion on the relationship of the data.

Fathom™

With Fathom Dynamic Statistics you can plot data related to different pairs of variables. You can also compare the fit of different equations through your data points.

13. $y = 0 - 1.5(x - 4)$ or $y = -3 - 1.5(x - 6)$ or $y = -1.5x + 6$.

14. Graph $y = \frac{\log x}{\log 5}$.

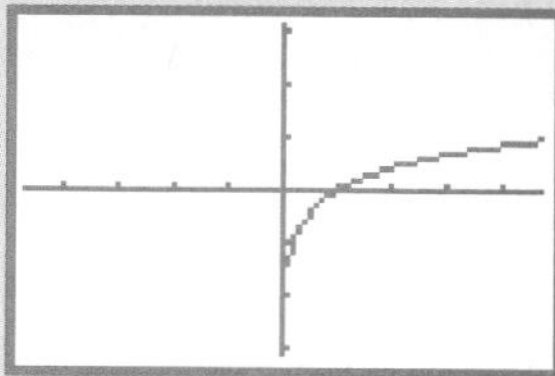

[−4.7, 4.7, 1, −3.1, 3.1, 1]

Exercise 15 [Alert] Students may still want to average the averages—that is, find the mean of 50 and 75. As needed, remind them that these are average speeds over different amounts of time and thus can't be averaged to find the mean speed.

Exercise 16 Students can assume that the fishing pole cannot be separated into pieces or bent.

If students need help you might suggest that the new package has a larger volume but a shorter length.

16. David got a thin box 4 feet long and 3 feet wide. He fit the fishing rod into the box along the diagonal.

Supporting the Project

To illustrate a correlation that does not suggest causation, you might **[Ask]** "What would you think of an article that reported a strong negative correlation between foot size and hours of cartoon watching and concluded that cartoon watching causes small feet?"

OUTCOMES

- The report includes a clear statement of the claim and relevant data.
- The analysis relates the data to the claim.
- Graphs, tables, and equations are clearly explained.
- The student demonstrates understanding in summarizing factors and drawing conclusions.

LESSON

13.6

PLANNING

LESSON OUTLINE

One day:

10 min Example A

15 min Investigation

5 min Example B

5 min Sharing

10 min Exercises

MATERIALS

- rulers or metersticks
- Relating Variables Blank Chart (W), *optional*
- Relating Variables Sample Data (W), *optional*
- Calculator Notes 13G, 13H

TEACHING

The correlation coefficient and the standard deviation of a bivariate sample give the least squares line of fit, from which you can make predictions about the population. You might use the Exploration Residual Plots and Least Squares on page 149 to introduce the topic.

One Step

Pose this problem: "You can use the median-median line to predict the value of one variable from another. It is based on medians. Can you devise a line based on means and the correlation coefficient to make similar predictions?" If students saw the Q-point method of finding a line of fit in *Discovering Algebra,* you might review that. As needed, also remind students that, in describing spread, quartiles go with medians and standard deviations go with means. During Sharing, elicit the formal definition of the least squares line and why it is called that; include reference to minimizing the root mean square error.

LESSON 13.6

The Least Squares Line

In Lesson 13.5, you saw how the correlation coefficient could be used to determine how closely two variables in a sample are linearly related. In this lesson you'll learn how to use the correlation coefficient of a sample to determine a line of fit, from which you can make predictions about the population.

History CONNECTION

In the late 1800s, English anthropologist Francis Galton studied correlations among various measurements, including heights of fathers and sons. He found that sons' heights tended to be closer to the mean height for men than to their fathers' heights. This phenomenon is known today as "regression toward the mean." The term **regression analysis** now refers to finding a model with which to make predictions about one variable from another.

From a family of politicians, brothers John, Robert, and Edward Kennedy stand together in 1960.

In Chapter 3, you saw one line of fit for bivariate data, the median-median line. In this lesson you'll learn about the **least squares line.** You find the least squares line by first standardizing both variables—the x-values and the y-values—which gives the bivariate data center (0, 0) and standard deviation 1 in both the horizontal and vertical directions. Then fit a line that passes through the origin and has slope equal to the correlation coefficient, r. In terms of z-values for x and y, the equation of the least squares line is $z_y = rz_x$. In the extreme case where the data are all perfectly linear, the value of r is $+1$ or -1, so the equation is $z_y = z_x$ or $z_y = -z_x$. In the other extreme, when the data are very scattered, the value of r is 0 and the equation is $z_y = 0$, a horizontal line through the origin.

In practice, you don't want to standardize every piece of sample data. Instead, you can rewrite the equation using means and standard deviations. By the definition of z-values, the equation $z_y = rz_x$ is equivalent to $\frac{y-\bar{y}}{s_y} = r\left(\frac{x-\bar{x}}{s_x}\right)$, or, solving for y, $y = \bar{y} + r\left(\frac{s_y}{s_x}\right)(x - \bar{x})$. Notice that this equation represents a translation of the center from the origin to $(\bar{x}, \bar{y})$.

Finding a Least Squares Line

1. Find the values of r, s_x, s_y, $\bar{x}$, and $\bar{y}$ for the data set.
2. Calculate the slope, $b = r\left(\frac{s_y}{s_x}\right)$.
3. Substitute values of b, $\bar{x}$, and $\bar{y}$ to write the equation for the least squares line, $\hat{y} = \bar{y} + b(x - \bar{x})$.

Introduction

[Context] John F. Kennedy (1917–1963) was elected president in 1960. He was assassinated November 22, 1963. Robert F. Kennedy (1925–1968) was a U.S. senator. He as was assassinated while campaigning for the Democratic presidential nomination. Edward M. Kennedy (b 1932) has been a U.S. senator since 1962.

MAKING THE CONNECTION

In 1805, the French mathematician Adrien-Marie Legendre (1752–1833) first published a mathematical criterion of least squares deviations and derived a system of equations for finding least squares lines. Because Gauss had previously developed the method and had used it for computing the orbits of planets, the method is known as Gauss's method. It is used today to track satellites.

EXAMPLE A

A photography studio offers several packages to students who pose for yearbook photos.

Number of pictures (x)	44	31	24	15
Total cost (y)	\$19.00	\$16.00	\$13.00	\$10.00

Find an equation of the least squares line. Use your line to decide how much a package of two photographs should cost.

▶ Solution

Begin by finding the mean and standard deviation of both the x- and y-values.

$\bar{x} = 28.5 \quad \bar{y} = 14.5 \quad s_x = 12.23 \quad s_y = 3.873$

Then create a table to calculate values of $(x - \bar{x})(y - \bar{y})$.

x	y	$x - \bar{x}$	$y - \bar{y}$	$(x - \bar{x})(y - \bar{y})$
44	19	15.5	4.5	69.75
31	16	2.5	1.5	2.25
24	13	−4.5	−1.5	6.75
15	10	−13.5	−4.5	60.75

So, $\Sigma(x - \bar{x})(y - \bar{y})$ is 141. Use the formula $r = \frac{\Sigma(x - \bar{x})(y - \bar{y})}{s_x s_y (n-1)}$ to find $r \approx .992$.

The slope of the least squares line is $r\left(\frac{s_y}{s_x}\right) = \frac{.992 \cdot 3.873}{12.23} = 0.314$ dollar per photo.

So, the equation of the least squares line is $\hat{y} = 14.5 + 0.314(x - 28.5)$, or $\hat{y} = 5.55 + 0.314x$.

To find the cost of two photographs, substitute 2 for x. You get $y = 6.178$, so according to the model the package should cost \$6.18.

The least squares line has some interesting properties. You'll discover some of them in the investigation.

Investigation
Relating Variables

You will need

- rulers or metersticks

Your class will collect data on the measurements listed below and look for correlations. Then you'll explore a property of the least squares line.

Step 1 Take these measurements in centimeters. Choose one member of your group to post the measurements for your group.

hand span	length of cubit (from tip of middle finger to elbow)
foot length	length of lower leg (from knee to floor)
length of little finger	length of upper arm (from shoulder to elbow)
height	width of thumbnail

▶ EXAMPLE A

Many students will understand the process more deeply if they go through it by hand before using the linear regression function on their calculators.

[Ask] "Do you think the photography studio will actually charge \$6.18 for two photographs? Why?" You might bring out the idea that 2 is a long way from the other values.

Guiding the Investigation

Be aware that students may be sensitive to sharing measurements of parts of their body. Allow students to decline to post their measurements if they don't want to. You may also choose to omit some body parts from the list. Alternatively, consider measuring books: Collect data on length, width, thickness, number of pages, weight, copyright date, and so on. You can also use the Relating Variables Sample Data worksheet.

Step 1 As needed, remind students to keep each person's measurements together. The Relating Variables Blank Chart worksheet can help students organize their data.

See page 908 for answer to Step 1.

NCTM STANDARDS

CONTENT		PROCESS	
	Number		Problem Solving
✓	Algebra		Reasoning
	Geometry	✓	Communication
✓	Measurement	✓	Connections
✓	Data/Probability		Representation

LESSON OBJECTIVES

- Understand the concept of regression analysis
- Review the root mean square error
- Find the equation and properties of the least squares line

Step 2 [Language] *Linearly related* means having a correlation coefficient close to 1 or −1. If you don't want to leave the selection completely open-ended, you might give students a choice among pairs such as foot length and height, distance from ankle to knee and height, or forearm length and height.

Step 3 Clarify whether you'd like students to find this equation using the calculator or by hand using the formulas. If you have Fathom, you can graph a moveable line and show the squares, as in the Exploration Residual Plots and Least Squares on page 149.

Step 3 $\hat{y} = 2.981 + 0.158x$. The line appears to be a good fit.

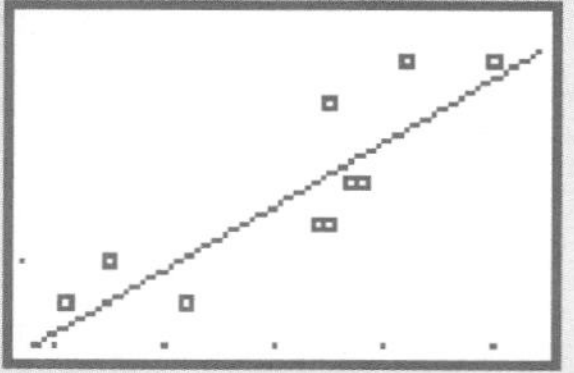

[17.71, 22.39, 1, 5.798, 6.602, 1]

Step 4

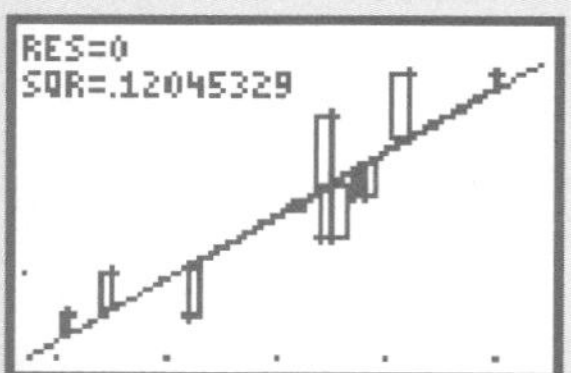

[17.71, 22.39, 1, 5.798, 6.602, 1]

▶ EXAMPLE B

In part b, you may want to review how to find the median-median line, perhaps on the calculator.

In part c, the method for calculating the root mean square error shown on the calculator screen is different from the method taught in Calculator Note 3E. The method used here is better when you have two equations. The answer shown is calculated by pasting the entire line equations into Y_1 and Y_2. If you use rounded values, the root mean square error will be slightly different.

Step 2 Sample answers are given for hand span and length of little finger. $r \approx .858$, so the data are linearly related.

Step 2 As a group, decide on two of the measurements that you think might be linearly related. Enter the data for these measurements into list L_1 and list L_2 on your calculator, and find the correlation coefficient. Are the data linearly related? If not, try another pair of measurements until you find data that are related linearly.

Step 3 Find the equation of the least squares line for your data, and graph the line with your data. Does the line appear to be a good fit?

Step 4c The least squares line is the line for which the sum of the squares of the residuals is as small as possible, and the sum of the residuals is 0.

Step 4d As hand span increases, so does the length of the little finger. The data are modeled pretty well by a straight line.

Step 4 Run the LSL program. [▶ See **Calculator Note 13G.** ◀] Adjust the line produced by your calculator until the sum of the squares of the residuals is as small as possible. Then answer these questions.

a. How does the line you found using the LSL program compare to the least squares line you found in Step 3? It is the same line.

b. What is the sum of the residuals? The sum of the residuals is 0.

c. What property of the line do you think gives it its name?

d. Write a sentence or two describing the relationship between the measurements you analyzed.

You can measure the accuracy of the least squares line using the typical spread of the residuals, as calculated by the root mean square error.

EXAMPLE B

In Chapter 3, you estimated a line of fit for data on the concentration of CO_2 in the atmosphere around Mauna Loa in Hawaii as a function of time. Refer back to the table on page 129 to find

a. The least squares line for the data given.

b. The median-median line for the data given.

c. The root mean square error of both models.

▶ Solution

Enter the data into lists in your calculator and find each model. [▶ See **Calculator Note 13H** to learn how to find the equation of the least squares line. ◀]

a. The equation for the least squares line is $\hat{y} = -2744.562 + 1.557x$. Notice that $r \approx .998$, so a linear model is a good fit for these data.

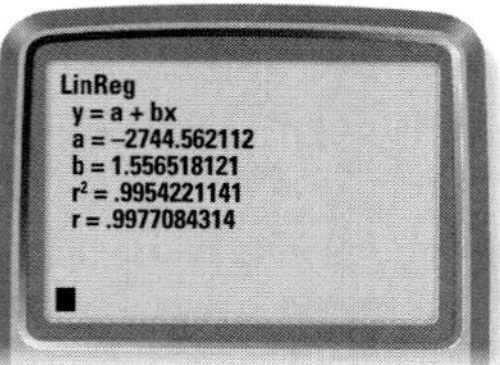

b. The equation of the median-median line is $\hat{y} = -2742.075 + 1.555x$.

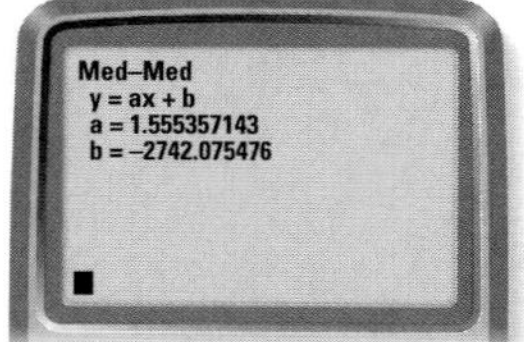

SHARING IDEAS

As students present, press them to make sense of the formula for the least squares line. Thinking about normalizing the data to obtain z-values might help. For normalized data, the equation is $\hat{y} = 0 + r\left(\frac{s_y}{s_x}\right)x$. Thinking in terms of extreme cases can also help understanding: If the correlation is perfect, then r is 1 and s_x equals s_y, so $\hat{y}$ equals x. One way to think of the slope is to imagine that the line given by the equation $\hat{y} = \left(\frac{s_y}{s_x}\right)x$ would climb one standard deviation of the y-values for each standard deviation of the x-values. Multiplying by the correlation coefficient r pulls the line toward the horizontal according to the amount the data are scattered.

[Ask] "Is this about sample or population data?" The use of s_x, s_y, $\bar{x}$, and $\bar{y}$ instead of Greek letters indicates that we're dealing with sample data here. The goal is to make predictions about population values outside the sample.

c. To calculate the root mean square error, find the differences between the y-values in the data and the y-values predicted by the model. Then square the differences and sum the squares. Next, divide by two less than the number of data values, and finally, take the square root. Enter your equations for the least squares line and the median-median line into your calculator as Y1 and Y2. Then calculate the root mean square error as shown.

The root mean square error for the least squares line is 0.666 ppm and for the median-median line is 0.690 ppm. The root mean square error is smaller for the least squares line, so predictions you make with this model are likely to have smaller errors than predictions you make with the median-median line. In all cases, though, you should be careful not to predict too far in the future. Just because the trend has been quite linear in the past does not mean it will be so in the future.

There are many procedures to find lines of fit for linear data. Some, such as the median-median line, distill the data into a few points and are relatively unaffected by one or two outliers. Others, like the least squares line, place equal importance on each point. The least squares procedure produces the line that has the smallest sum of squares of errors between data points and predictions from the line. It is often called the "best-fit line" because of this property. However, when fitting a line to data, always check the line visually; you may sometimes find that a procedure that ignores outliers gives a line that models the overall trend better than the least squares line.

EXERCISES

Practice Your Skills

1. Use these data to find the values specified.

Year x	1950	1960	1970	1980	1990	2000
Percentage y	29.6	33.4	38.1	42.5	45.3	52.0

a. $\bar{x}$ $\bar{x} = 1975$ **b.** $\bar{y}$ $\bar{y} = 40.15$ **c.** s_x $s_x = 18.71$ **d.** s_y $s_y = 8.17$ **e.** r $r \approx .9954$

2. Use the following sets of statistics to calculate the least squares line for each data set described.

a. $\bar{x} = 18, s_x = 2, \bar{y} = 54, s_y = 5, r = .8$
b. $\bar{x} = 0.31, s_x = 0.04, \bar{y} = 5, s_y = 1.2, r = -.75$
c. $\bar{x} = 88, s_x = 5, \bar{y} = 6, s_y = 2, r = -.9$
d. $\bar{x} = 1975, s_x = 18.7, \bar{y} = 40, s_y = 7.88, r = .9975$

Assessing Progress

You can assess students' understanding of how correlation coefficients measure the strength of a relationship.

Closing the Lesson

The **least squares line** through data with points (x, y) has the equation $\hat{y} = \bar{y} + r\left(\frac{s_y}{s_x}\right)(x - \bar{x})$ or, if standardized, $y = r\left(\frac{s_y}{s_x}\right)x$. If r equals ± 1, the line rises or falls one standard deviation in y for each standard deviation in x. The correlation coefficient r rotates the line toward the horizontal depending on how much the data are scattered.

BUILDING UNDERSTANDING

The exercises offer students opportunities to practice working with least squares lines and residuals.

ASSIGNING HOMEWORK

Essential	1, 2, 6
Performance assessment	7–10
Portfolio	5
Journal	9, 10
Group	8
Review	3, 4, 11–15

MATERIALS

- Fathom demonstration SAT Scores, *optional*

2a. $\hat{y} = 54 + 2(x - 18)$, or $\hat{y} = 18 + 2x$

2b. $\hat{y} = 5 - 22.5(x - 0.31)$, or $\hat{y} = 11.975 - 22.5x$

2c. $\hat{y} = 6 - 0.36(x - 88)$, or $\hat{y} = 37.68 - 0.36x$

2d. $\hat{y} = 40 + 0.4203(x - 1975)$, or $\hat{y} = -790.1 + 0.4203x$

Helping with the Exercises

Exercise 3 Students worked with residuals in the investigation, but you might also want to refer them to Lesson 3.5.

3c. 0.1002, 0.0525, 0.0157, 0.0322, 1.8667, 0.9761

Exercise 5 This exercise offers a good example of why extrapolating data to make predictions can be inaccurate.

[Context] The Montreal Protocol has led to a decline in worldwide emissions of ozone-depleting chlorofluorocarbons, or CFCs. The ozone hole, however, was still increasing in size even a decade after the treaty's passage. In 2000, the hole over the South Pole reached a record 29.6 million square miles, an area the size of Canada, the United States, and Mexico combined. Ozone depletion continued to increase because CFCs persist in the atmosphere for several decades. Scientists estimate that CFC levels will not drop low enough for the ozone layer to repair itself until 2050.

5a.

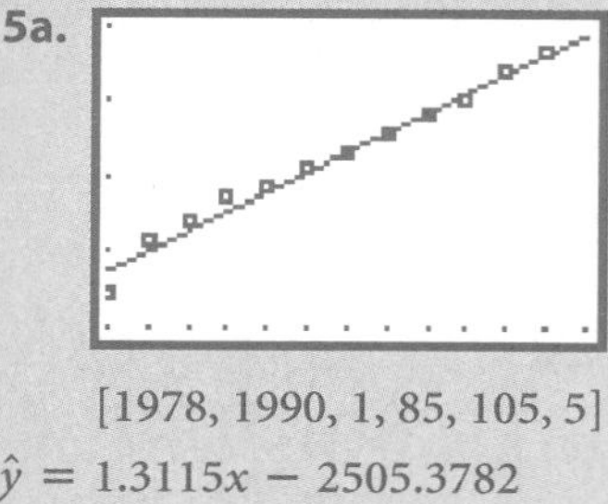

[1978, 1990, 1, 85, 105, 5]

$\hat{y} = 1.3115x - 2505.3782$

5b. 124.2 ppt

5c.

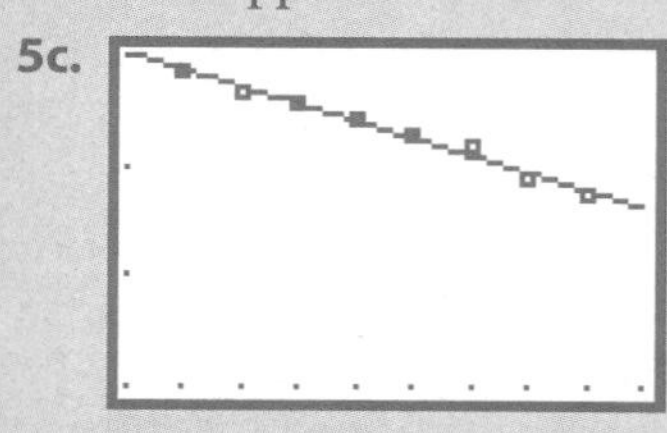

[1989, 1998, 1, 90, 105, 5]

$\hat{y} = -0.7714x + 1639.4179$

5d. 92.8 ppt. This is 31.4 ppt lower than the amount predicted in 5b.

3. Use the data from Exercise 1 and the equation $\hat{y} = -818.13 + 0.434571x$ to calculate

a. the residuals 0.3166, −0.2292, 0.1251, 0.1794, −1.3663, 0.9880

b. the sum of the residuals 0.01365

c. the squares of the residuals

d. the sum of the squares of the residuals 3.0435

e. the root mean square error 0.8689

4. Use the equation $\hat{y} = -818.13 + 0.434571x$ to predict a y-value for each x-value.

a. $x = 1954$ 31.02%

b. $x = 1978$ 41.45%

c. $x = 1989$ 46.23%

d. $x = 2004$ 52.75%

Reason and Apply

5. APPLICATION Carbon tetrachloride is an ozone-depleting chemical found in the atmosphere. The table below shows the concentration of the chemical in parts per trillion (ppt) measured in the European Union.

Year x	1978	1979	1980	1981	1982	1983	1984	1985	1986	1987	1988	1989
Carbon tetrachloride (ppt) y	87.3	90.7	92.1	93.6	94.3	95.5	96.5	97.8	99.3	100.3	102.0	103.3

a. Make a scatter plot of the data, and find the least squares line to fit the data.

b. Use your model to predict the amount of carbon tetrachloride present in 2005.

c. In 1987, 22 countries and the European Economic Community agreed on the Montreal Protocol to reduce ozone-depleting chemicals in the atmosphere. In 1989, the protocol went into effect. The data below represent the levels of carbon tetrachloride from 1990 to 1997. Make a scatter plot of the data, and find the least squares line to fit the data.

Year	1990	1991	1992	1993	1994	1995	1996	1997
Carbon tetrachloride (ppt)	104.2	103.2	102.9	102.1	101.3	100.8	99.5	98.6

(*http://dataservice.eea.eu.int/dataservice/*)

d. Use the model you found in 5c to predict the amount of carbon tetrachloride in 2005. How does this compare to your answer in 5b?

Environmental CONNECTION

Ozone depletion is a worldwide environmental concern that has been addressed by several international agreements. The ozone in the stratosphere (from 11 to 50 km above Earth's surface) protects us by blocking the Sun's ultraviolet (UV) radiation. Exposure to too much UV radiation has been linked to skin cancer, eye problems, and immune-system suppression. When ozone is depleted in the stratosphere, it can build up closer to the Earth's surface, where it acts as a pollutant and contributes to lung damage. For more information on ozone depletion, see the links at **www.keymath.com/DAA**.

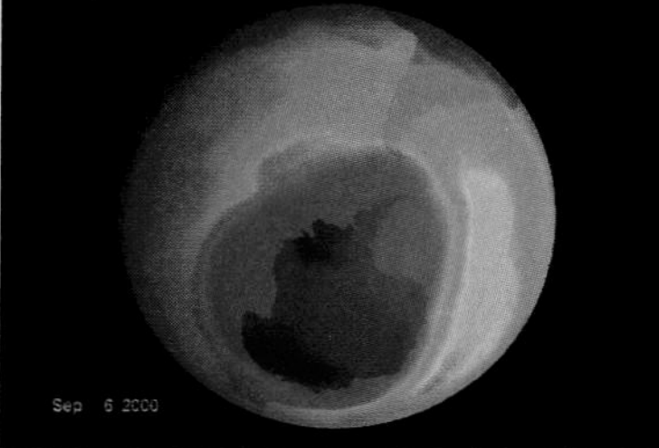

This color-coded image of Earth shows a hole in the ozone layer above Antarctica. Blue and purple indicate low ozone levels, and yellow and orange indicate higher ozone.

6. In the 1990s, an upward trend was noticed in mean SAT math scores of college-bound seniors.

Year	1991	1992	1993	1995	1996	1997	1998	1999	2000
Score	500	501	503	506	508	511	512	511	514

(*The World Almanac and Book of Facts 2002*)

a. Find the equation of the least squares line. Let x represent the year, and let y represent the mean SAT score.

b. Is a linear model a good fit for these data? Justify your answer.

c. Verify that the least squares line passes through the mean x-value and the mean y-value.

d. What does the equation predict for the year 1994? How does this compare with the actual mean score of 504?

e. What does the equation predict for the year 2010? How reasonable is this prediction?

7. These data give the average daily maximum temperatures in April for various cities in North America, and the corresponding latitudes in degrees and minutes north.

City	Lat.	Temp. (°F)	City	Lat.	Temp. (°F)
Acapulco, Mex.	16°51′	87	Mexico City, Mex.	19°25′	78
Bakersfield, CA	35°26′	73	Miami, FL	25°49′	81
Caribou, ME	46°52′	50	New Orleans, LA	29°59′	77
Charleston, SC	32°54′	74	New York City, NY	40°47′	60
Chicago, IL	41°59′	55	Ottawa, Ont.	46°26′	51
Dallas, TX	32°54′	75	Phoenix, AZ	33°26′	83
Denver, CO	39°46′	54	Quebec, Que.	46°48′	45
Duluth, MN	46°50′	52	Salt Lake City, UT	40°47′	58
Great Falls, MT	47°29′	56	San Francisco, CA	37°37′	65
Juneau, AK	58°18′	39	Seattle, WA	47°27′	56
Kansas City, MO	39°19′	59	Vancouver, BC	49°18′	58
Los Angeles, CA	33°56′	69	Washington, DC	38°51′	64

a. Find the equation of the least squares line. Let x represent the latitude, and let y represent the temperature. (You will need to convert the latitudes to decimal degrees; for example, $35°26' = 35\frac{26}{60}° \approx 35.43°$.)

b. What is an appropriate domain for this model?

c. Which cities do not appear to follow the pattern? Give a reason for each of these cases.

d. Choose two cities not on the list, and find the latitude of each. Use your model to predict the average daily maximum temperature in April for each city. Compare your result with the official average April temperature for the city. (An almanac is a good source for this information.)

Exercise 6 The Fathom demonstration SAT Scores can be shown to the class in place of assigning this exercise. Or individual students might work through the demonstration and its questions.

6a. $\hat{y} = -2660.8 + 1.5875x$

6b. $r \approx .985$, so a linear model is a good fit.

6c. $\bar{x} = 1995.67$; $\bar{y} = 507.33$; $\hat{y} = -2660.8 + 1.5875(1995.67) = 507.33$. The point is on the line.

6d. 504.675. This is within one point of the actual value.

6e. 530.075. This is possible, but because it is ten years beyond the current data, it is difficult to know whether the trend will continue.

Exercise 7 These data (with latitudes converted to decimals) are on the Calculator Programs and Data CD.

7a. $\hat{y} = -1.212x + 110.2$

7b. possible answer: 10°N to 60°N

7c. The cities that appear not to follow the pattern are Denver, which is a high mountainous city; Mexico City, which is also a high mountainous city; Phoenix, which is in desert terrain; Quebec, which is subject to the Atlantic currents; and Vancouver, which is subject to the Pacific currents.

7d. Answers will vary.

Exercise 8 Using 1900 as the reference year means that an x-value of 0 represents 1900; a value of 50 then represents 1950.

8b. Each year, 0.435% more of the U.S. labor force was female. The y-intercept, 7.56, means that in 1900, 7.56% of the labor force was female.

8c. Answers will vary. For 2003, $x = 103$, the model predicts about 52.3% of the labor force is female.

9. Answers will vary. The least squares equation for the line uses all of the data; the median-median equation for the line uses only three summary points. The least squares line minimizes the residuals, whereas the median-median line ignores outliers. The least squares equation gives you other values useful for fitting a line; the median-median equation can be found easily even without a calculator.

Exercise 10 Students may want to use sample data in their reasoning.

10. The root mean square error is the square root of the average of the squares of the residuals and the average is proportional to the sum. If one is minimized, the other is as well.

12a. $r \approx -.95$. As the population increased, the number of daily papers decreased.

12b. $r \approx .91$. The high, positive correlation indicates that as the circulation increased, the population increased.

12c. 20%, 26%, 31%, 33%, 27%, 22%. Answers will vary. Midway through the century almost a third of the population read a daily paper. Perhaps in recent years the decline in the percentage reading is due to TV or Internet news coverage. The average circulation per paper is increasing, whereas the number of papers is decreasing. Maybe this is due to people moving to cities and small rural papers going out of business.

8. This table shows the percentage of females in the U.S. labor force at various times.

Year	1950	1960	1970	1980	1990	2000
Percentage	29.6	33.4	38.1	42.5	45.3	52.0

A firefighter manages a controlled fire in New Jersey.

a. Find the least squares line for these data. Let x represent the year, and let y represent the percentage. (Use 1900 as the reference year.) $\hat{y} = 7.56 + 0.4346x$

b. What is the real-world meaning of the slope? Of the y-intercept?

c. According to your model, what percentage of the current labor force is female? Check an almanac to see how accurate your prediction is.

9. Name at least two major differences between the median-median method and the least squares method for finding a line of fit.

10. Explain how the root mean square error is related to the sum of the squares that is minimized by the least squares procedure. If the root mean square error is minimized, is the sum of the squares minimized as well?

Review

5.7 **11.** Solve each equation for y.

a. $\log y = 3$ $y = 1000$

b. $\log x + 2\log y = 4$ $y = \frac{100}{\sqrt{x}}$

13.5 **12.** This table shows the number of daily newspapers in the United States, the daily circulation, and the total U.S. population, for selected years.

Daily Newspapers in the United States

Year	Number of daily papers	Daily circulation (millions)	Total population (millions)
1900	2226	15.1	76.2
1920	2042	27.8	106.0
1940	1878	41.1	132.1
1960	1763	58.9	179.3
1980	1745	62.2	226.5
2000	1480	55.8	248.7

(*The New York Times Almanac 2002*)

a. What is the correlation coefficient between the number of daily newspapers and the population? What does this mean?

b. What is the correlation between daily circulation and the total population?

c. For each year, what percentage of the population reads a daily paper? What does this mean? What are the trends? What are the implications of the data?

7.7 **13.** Write an equation that will produce the graph shown at right, with intercepts $(-5, 0)$, $(-2, 0)$, $(1, 0)$, and $(0, 60)$.

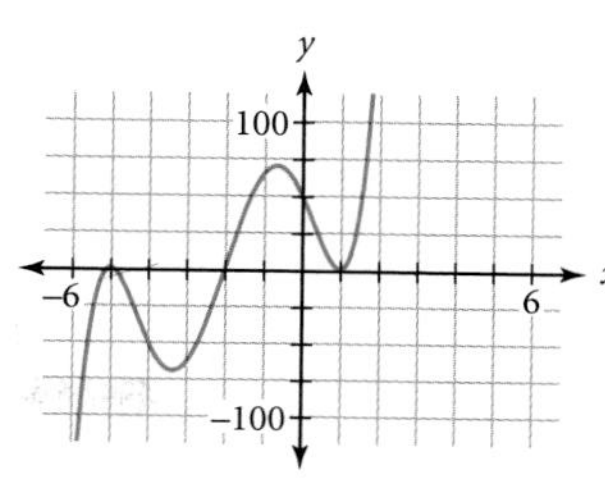

12.4 **14.** If you spin this spinner ten times, what is your expected score?

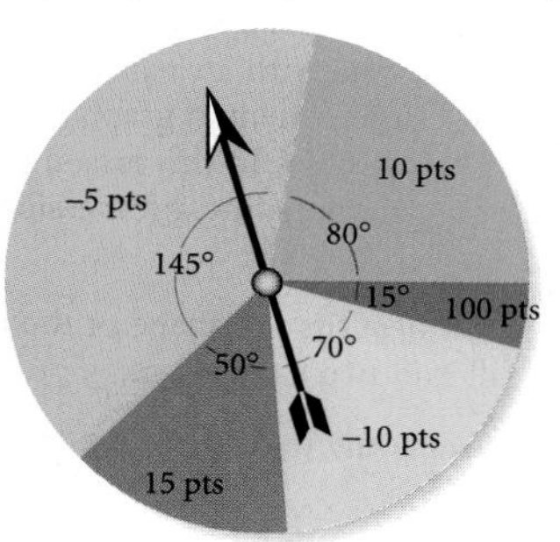

13. $y = -6(x - 1)(x + 2)(x + 5)$

14. 45

1.3 **15.** The Koch curve is a famous fractal introduced in 1906 by Swedish mathematician Niels Fabian Helge von Koch (1870–1924). To create a Koch curve, follow these steps:

i. Draw a segment and divide it into thirds.
ii. Make a bottomless triangle on the middle portion, with each side the length of the missing bottom.
iii. Repeat steps i and ii with each shorter segment.

If the original segment is 18 cm and the process continues through infinitely many steps, how long will the Koch curve become?

15. The length will increase without bound.

IMPROVING YOUR REASONING SKILLS

A Set of Weights

You have a 40-ounce bag of sand, a balance scale, and many blocks of wood with unknown weights. How can you divide the sand into four smaller bags so that you can then use the smaller bags to weigh any block of wood with a whole-number weight between 1 and 40 ounces?

IMPROVING REASONING SKILLS

Students' reasoning might go something like this: We need a 1 oz bag to measure a 1 oz block. We could use a second 1 oz bag to measure a 2 oz block, but we could also measure the 2 oz block if we put it on the same side as the 1 oz bag and had a 3 oz bag on the other side. With the 1 oz and 3 oz bags, we can measure every size block up through 4 oz; if we put the 1 oz bag and the 3 oz bag on the side with a 5 oz block, we can balance them against a 9 oz bag. With 1, 3, and 9 oz bags, we can measure every size block up through 13 oz. By similar reasoning, we can make a 27 oz bag and measure blocks up to $27 + 9 + 3 + 1$ or 40 oz. For example, if a block together with the 3 oz bag balances with the 27 oz bag, we know the block weighs 24 oz.

LESSON 13.7

PLANNING

LESSON OUTLINE

First day:

20 min Examples A, B

10 min Example C

15 min Exercises

Second day:

30 min Investigation

10 min Sharing

5 min Exercises

MATERIALS

- plastic water containers with a hole in the bottom (one per group)
- metric rulers
- tape
- timing devices
- tinted water
- Time and Distance (T) for One Step
- A Leaky Bottle Experiment Sample Data (W), *optional*
- Calculator Note 13I

TEACHING

This lesson extends the notion of least squares to nonlinear data. Some nonlinear relationships between two variables can be found by linearizing; calculators can do this as well as other kinds of curve fitting. Part of this lesson extends the curve straightening of Lesson 5.8, although the earlier lesson is not a prerequisite for this one.

As students look at the power curve graph, you might mention that for most values of b the graph of the equation $y = ax^b$ is defined only for $x \geq 0$. For integer values of b, though, a portion of the graph will lie in the second or third quadrant.

LESSON 13.7

Nonlinear Regression

Telling the future by looking at the past assumes that conditions remain constant. This is like driving a car by looking in the rearview mirror.

HERB BRODY

You have seen how to do regression analysis when bivariate sample data have a strong linear correlation. But what about bivariate data with a clear trend that isn't linear? Can you find the equation of a parabolic or exponential graph such that the sum of the squares of the residuals is as small as possible? In this lesson you'll see how to modify some data like these so that you can apply linear regression techniques.

The first task is to decide what type of function best fits the shape of the data. Standard shapes you've seen in this course fall into two categories.

In the first type of model, the variable, x, appears only once. Here are the most common of these functions:

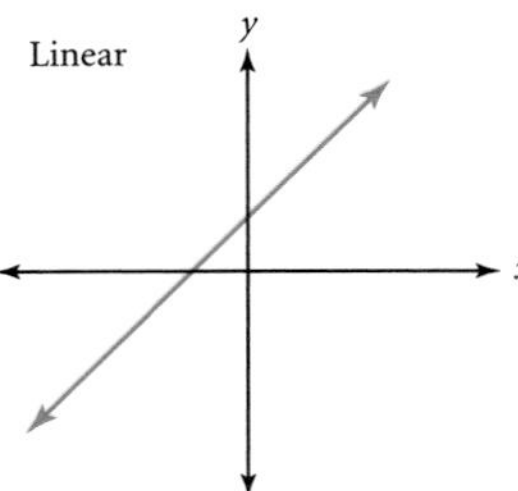

General form: $y = a + bx$

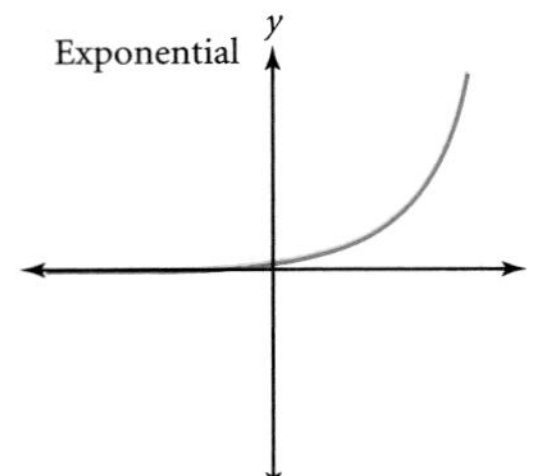

General form: $y = ab^x$

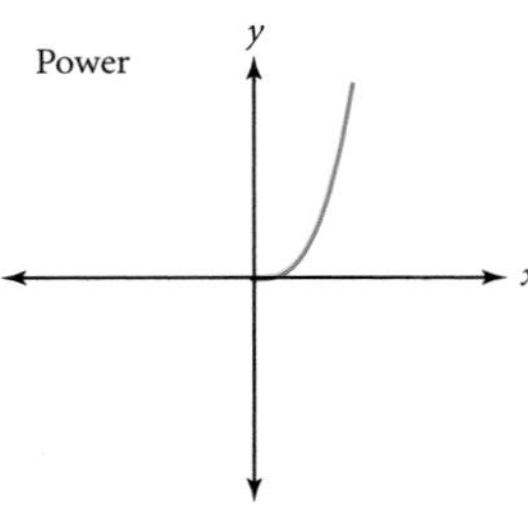

General form: $y = ax^b$

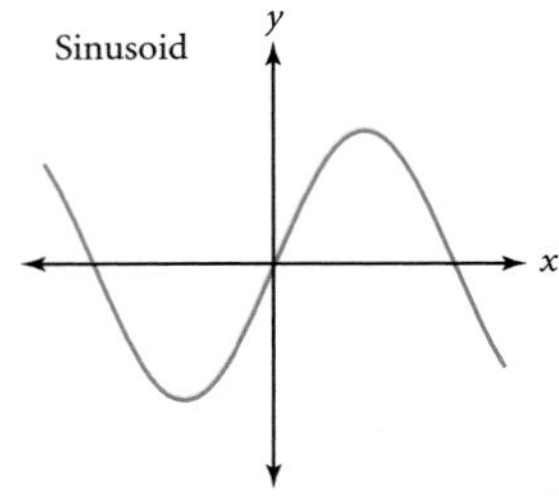

General form: $y = a\sin\left(\frac{x-h}{b}\right) + k$

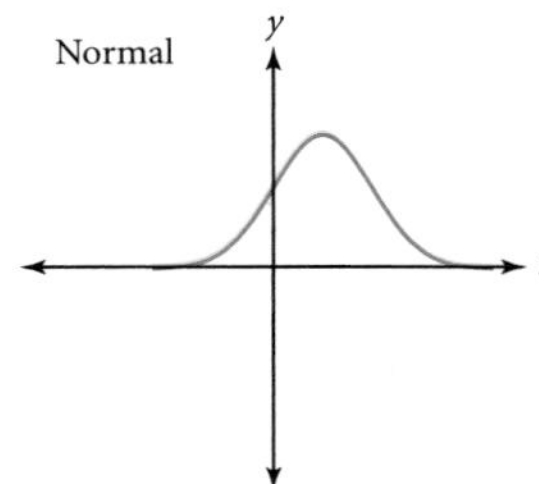

General form: $y = ae^{-((x-c)/b)^2}$

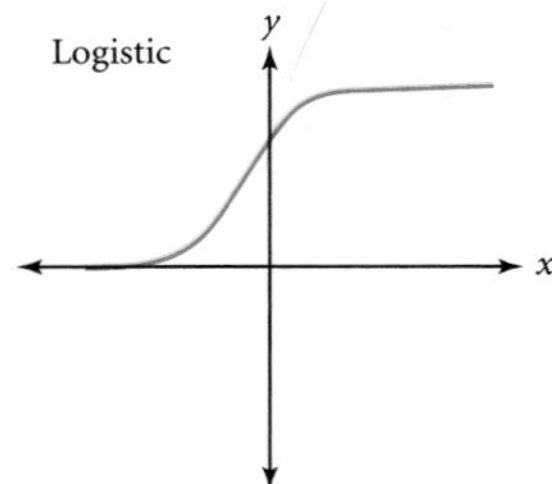

General form: $y = \frac{c}{1 + ab^x}$

If students did not do the Exploration Refining the Growth Model in Chapter 1, you might want to briefly introduce the logistic function.

One Step

Display the Time and Distance transparency and pose this problem, adapted from Examples A and B: "These data points (x, y) aren't linear, but can you find a function that fits them by finding a least squares line modeling the points $(x, \log y)$ or $(\log x, \log y)$?" As needed, help students review properties of logarithms as they work. During Sharing, demonstrate how to use the calculator to do this and other kinds of regression analysis.

In the second type of model, there is more than one independent variable or the variable appears more than one time. Here are some examples of these functions:

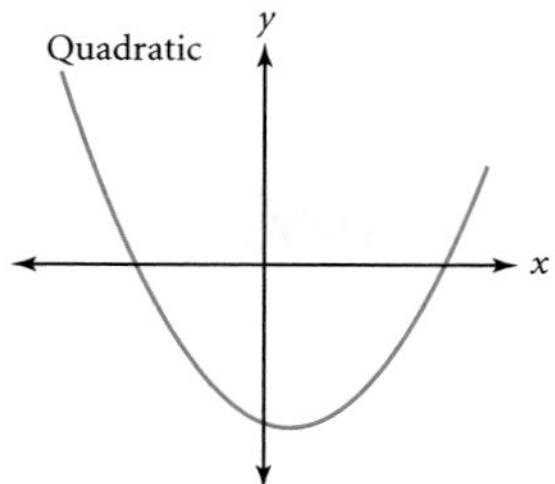

General form: $y = ax^2 + bx + c$

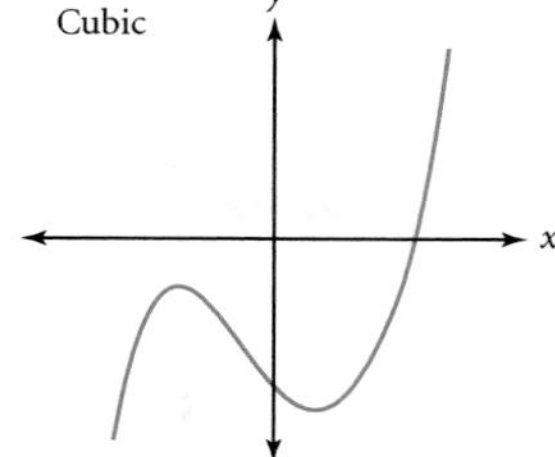

General form: $y = ax^3 + bx^2 + cx + d$

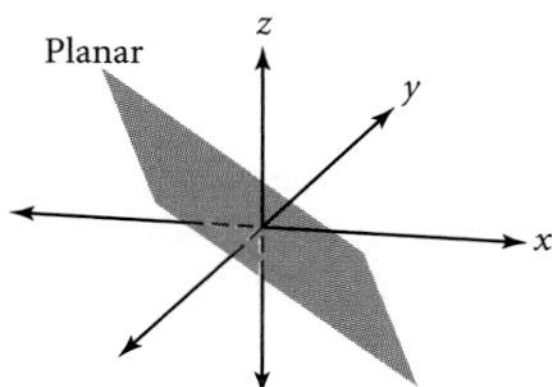

General form: $z = ax + by + c$

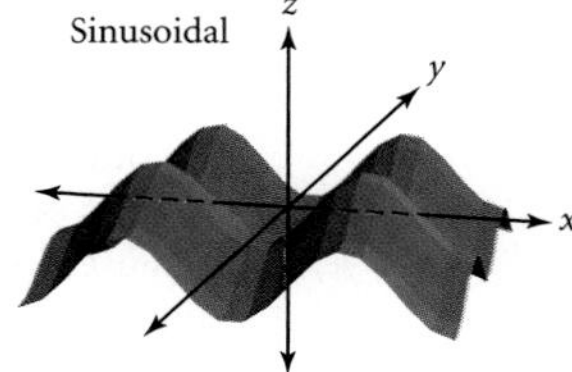

General form: $z = a\sin(bx + cy)$

Some equations of the second type can be transformed into equations of the first type; others will be left to later courses. Be aware that you may not yet have all the tools you need to model every data set in the best way possible.

EXAMPLE A

What kind of functions might fit these data?

Time (s) x	2	4	6	8	10	12	14	16
Distance (cm) y	7.5	48.5	151	337.5	631	1059	1626	2360

► Solution

By looking at a graph of the data, you can determine that an exponential function, a power function, or a polynomial function (such as a quadratic function) might provide the best fit.

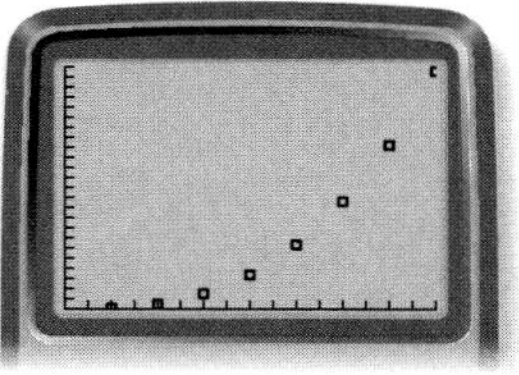

[0, 16, 1, 0, 2400, 100]

At this point, you might try using the finite difference method to see whether a polynomial function fits the data. You would find that a set of constant finite differences never occurs, so a polynomial function is not a good fit.

If your data seem to fit exponential and power models, you can check whether or not these are good models by **linearizing** the data. If the fit is good, then you can extend the linear regression techniques of Lesson 13.6.

► EXAMPLE A

This example involves making a guess at what kinds of functions might fit data, not finding an equation for such a function.

NCTM STANDARDS

	CONTENT		PROCESS
	Number		Problem Solving
✓	Algebra	✓	Reasoning
	Geometry	✓	Communication
✓	Measurement	✓	Connections
✓	Data/Probability	✓	Representation

LESSON OBJECTIVES

- Apply the techniques of linearization of a data set
- Introduce multivariate regression and work specifically with polynomial regression
- Find exponential, power, and polynomial models to fit nonlinear data sets

► EXAMPLE B

This example illustrates actually finding a model while providing a context for reviewing properties of logarithms.

[Ask] "Why would we want to change the exponential equation to a linear equation?" [to use a least squares line for fitting the data]

[Ask] "How do you get $\log y$ to be only y on the left side of the solution?" [by taking the antilog, 10^x, of both sides]

► EXAMPLE C

Encourage students to look at all the data as well as the trends of the data. Part of the data may appear quadratic, but the entire set may be less symmetric. **[Alert]** Students may want to take finite differences to see whether they are ever equal. Although third differences for the cubic model will be equal, they won't be for the actual data. **[Alert]** Once students see how to do various kinds of regression on calculators, they may want to try other curves. They might see that a quartic function also fits these data. Encourage them to work Example B using exponential and power regression. To determine the quality of fit, urge them to consider graphs and sums of residuals, not just values of r (for linear or linearized data) or the coefficient of determination R^2 (as described in Exercise 7).

EXAMPLE B What exponential or power function provides the best fit for the data in Example A?

► Solution

If the data are exponential, an equation in the form $y = ab^x$ will be a good fit. You can use the rules of logarithms to show that $y = ab^x$ is equivalent to $\log y = \log a + x \log b$. Because a and b are constants, $\log a$ and $\log b$ are also constants. So the equation $\log y = (\log a) + x(\log b)$ is a linear equation, where the variables are x and $(\log y)$. Thus, the graph of $(x, \log y)$ should be linear.

A graph shows that $(x, \log y)$ isn't linear, so an exponential function must not be a good fit. Can you fit the data better with a power function?

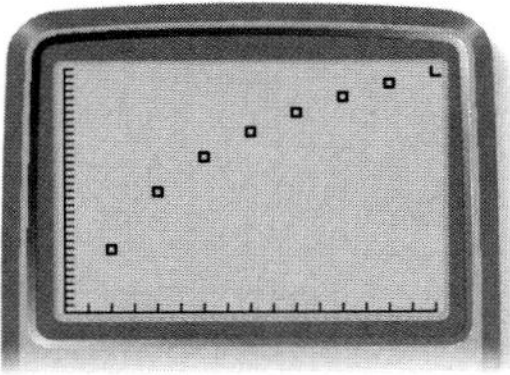

[0, 16, 1, 0, 3.4, 0.1]

If a power function, $y = ax^b$, fits these data, then by rules of logarithms, $\log y = \log a + b \log x$. Because $\log a$ and b are constants, this is a linear equation with variables $(\log x)$ and $(\log y)$. Thus, a graph of $(\log x, \log y)$ should be linear if the data can be modeled by a power function.

The plot of $(\log x, \log y)$ looks linear. The equation of the least squares line for these data is $\hat{y} = 2.77x + 0.03$.

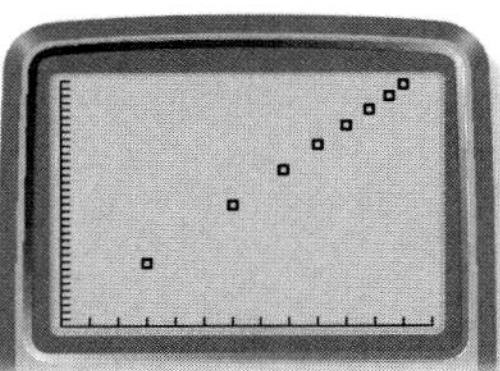

[0, 1.3, 0.1, 0, 3.4, 0.1]

Now replace $\hat{y}$ with $(\log y)$ and x with $(\log x)$, then solve for y.

$$\begin{aligned} \log y &= 2.77 \log x + 0.03 \\ &= 10^{2.77 \log x + 0.03} \\ &= 10^{2.77 \log x} \cdot 10^{0.03} \\ &= \left(10^{\log x}\right)^{2.77} \cdot 10^{0.03} \\ &= x^{2.77} \cdot 10^{0.03} \\ y &= 1.07x^{2.77} \end{aligned}$$

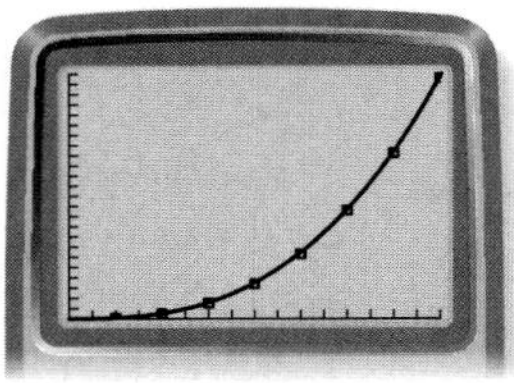

[0, 16, 1, 0, 2400, 100]

The function that fits the data is the power function $\hat{y} = 1.07x^{2.77}$. Using this equation, the root mean square error is approximately 21.7, which is small considering the size of the data values.

The linearization process you use to fit power or exponential curves is built into most graphing technology. [► See **Calculator Note 13I.** ◄] You can use a calculator to verify your answer to Example B.

PwrReg
y=a*x^b
a=1.065395396
b=2.774107427
r²=.9999147872
r=.9999573927

Your calculator can also find polynomial equations that fit data with the smallest sum of the residuals squared. You can use the finite differences method to find a polynomial curve that passes through *selected* data points, but regression techniques will find a curve that is a good fit for the whole data set.

EXAMPLE C Enter these data into lists and graph them. Then identify what types of curves may be good models.

Base (in.)	1	2	3	4	5	6	7	8
Area (in.^{2})	2.1	4.0	5.6	6.6	6.9	6.4	4.8	1.9

▶ Solution The data do not appear symmetric, so a quadratic function is not a good option. It appears that a cubic function may be a good fit.

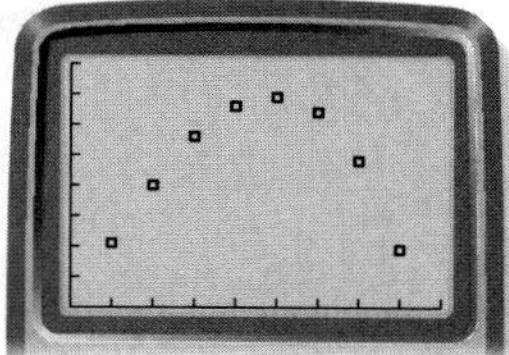

Use the cubic regression command to find a third-degree polynomial that is a good fit.

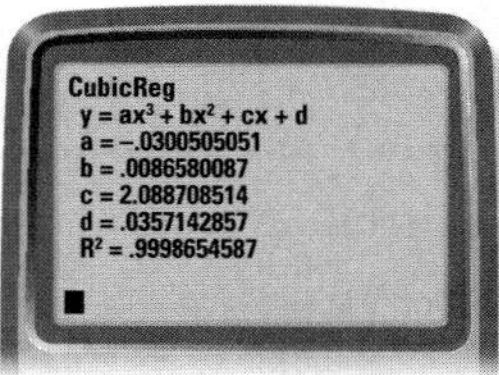

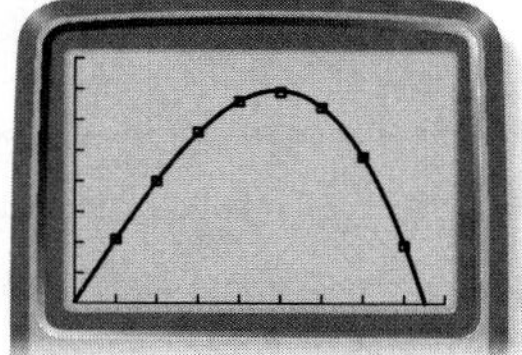

The equation that models these data is $\hat{y} = -0.030x^3 + 0.009x^2 + 2.089x + 0.036$.

In this investigation you will collect data and find a function that fits the data.

Investigation
A Leaky Bottle Experiment

You will need

- a plastic water container with a hole near the bottom
- a metric ruler
- tape
- a timing device
- water (with a bit of food coloring if available)

Procedure Note

1. Assign each group member a role: bottle holder, timekeeper, water-level reader, or recorder.
2. Attach the ruler to the container with tape so that 0 cm is at the bottom of the bottle.
3. Fill the container with water to the 15 cm mark, keeping a finger on the hole.
4. When the timekeeper begins timing, the bottle holder removes his or her finger from the hole and lets the water run out freely.
5. The timekeeper calls out the time every ten seconds.
6. The water-level reader reads aloud the water level to the nearest millimeter.
7. The recorder records the data.
8. Stop measuring the water level before it reaches the curved bottom of the bottle.

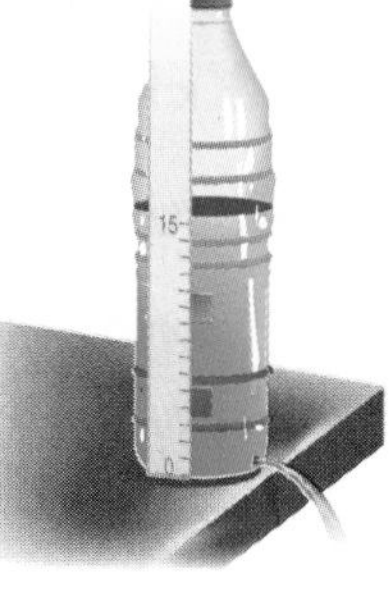

Step 1 Follow the procedure note to collect data.

Step 2 Sketch a graph of the data. Look at the graph and make a conjecture about the type of functions that might fit the data.

Guiding the Investigation

This investigation may take an entire class period, or you may elect to collect the data in class one day and then let students work on the investigation as a project over several days to find the best model. You can also use the worksheet A Leaky Bottle Experiment Sample Data.

Step 1 A one-gallon plastic bleach bottle or a two-liter soda bottle will work well. The hole need not be very large.

If students cannot work on this investigation outside, have a container available to collect the water running out of the bottle.

Step 1 sample data:

Time (s)	Height of water (mm)
0	150
10	134
20	120
30	109
40	97
50	86
60	77
70	68
80	60
90	54
100	48
110	43
120	39

Step 2

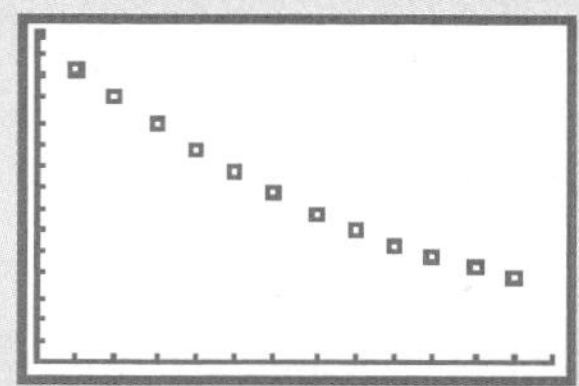

[0, 130, 10, 0, 150, 10]

exponential, quadratic, cubic

Steps 3–5 If students use unrounded values in their regression models in Step 3, they will find that the cubic model has the smallest residuals and root mean square error.

SHARING IDEAS

As students present, ask them to justify their models.

[Ask] "Would it ever help to take the logarithm of only the x-variable, to get the pairs $(\log x, y)$?" [If these pairs are linear, so that y equals $a \log x + b$, then the data are logarithmic.]

Refer students to the data in Example A and **[Ask]** "What if the data were translated 2 units left, so that the distance 7.5 corresponded to time 0 instead of time 2 and the distance 2360 corresponded to time 14 rather than time 16?" Students know from the result that the best model would be a horizontal translation of the graph of $y = 1.07x^{2.77}$ to the graph of $y = 1.07(x - 2)^{2.77}$, but what if they didn't know the result? Linearizing for a power function would require taking the logarithm of 0, which is undefined. One approach is to remove the first data point from consideration. A better fit comes from translating all the points so that none has a coordinate of 0, finding the regression function, and then translating back.

Sharing Ideas (continued)
You might mention that polynomial regression involves treating x, x^2, x^3, and so on as different variables. The formulas for this type of regression involve sums of lists, sums of lists raised to powers, and sums of products of lists. Using calculators, students can find some polynomial models for data, as in the project on page 787.

Assessing Progress
As students work on the investigation, you can assess their familiarity with the graphs of various functions, their ability to transform a graph and its equation to fit data, and their understanding of the root mean square error.

Closing the Lesson

Least squares techniques can be used even if the data (x, y) are not linear as long as the pairs $(x, \log y)$ or $(\log x, \log y)$ are linear. In the former case, manipulations with logarithms determine an exponential function fitting the original data; in the latter case, they determine a power function that fits the data. Other nonlinear data can be fit by polynomial functions. Calculator operations can do these and other kinds of regression fairly quickly.

BUILDING UNDERSTANDING

The exercises involve fitting nonlinear data and provide guidance as to the types of curves that might fit particular data sets. If you want your students to work on something more open-ended, assign the project Making It Fit on page 787.

If you are taking two days for this lesson, assign Exercises 1–5 and some of the review problems the first day.

See page 909 for answers to Steps 4 and 5 and Exercise 1a–d.

Step 3 Find equations of several different types that fit the data well.

Step 4 Create a separate graph of the residuals of each equation, and calculate the root mean square error.

Step 5 Select the best equation, and add its graph to your data plot from Step 2.

Step 6 Use your model to predict when the container would be empty.

If your model fits the data very well, then the residuals will not increase or decrease in any noticeable pattern. But sometimes it can be difficult to fit a curve to data even when you've guessed a good function. In science and in industry, it may be sufficient to find a relatively simple function that produces results that are "close enough." For example, it is common in industry to use polynomial models—even though they may not provide the best fit, they are usually quick to find and fit well enough to predict data in the near future.

EXERCISES

Practice Your Skills

1. Sketch scatter plots of transformed data in the form specified.

Time (h) x	1	2	3	4	5
Percentage y	65.0	50.0	42.5	38.0	35.0

a. (x, y) **b.** $(\log x, y)$ **c.** $(x, \log y)$ **d.** $(\log x, \log y)$

e. Which data appear to be the most linear? It is difficult to tell visually. But $(\log x, \log y)$ has the strongest correlation coefficient, $r \approx -.99994$.

ASSIGNING HOMEWORK

Essential	1–4
Performance assessment	5–8
Portfolio	5, 8
Group	7
Review	9–12

Step 3 $y = 151.234(0.989)^x$;
$y = 0.005x^2 - 1.500x + 149.110$;
$y = -0.000005x^3 + 0.006x^2 - 1.544x + 149.456$

Step 6 None of the equations gives a reasonable answer for when the bottle will be empty. In particular, the quadratic equation predicts that the bottle will *never* be empty. So none of the models are good for predicting data values outside of the domain given.

2. The data from Exercise 1 were gathered again the next day. After the experiment had run 24 hours, the y-values had dropped by nearly 20%. Subtract 20 from each y-value and create a scatter plot of

a. (x, y) **b.** $(\log x, y)$ **c.** $(x, \log y)$ **d.** $(\log x, \log y)$

e. Which data appear to be the most linear?

3. Solve each equation for $\hat{y}$, and rewrite the function in one of these forms:

$\hat{y} = a + bx$ $\quad \hat{y} = ab^x + c$ $\quad \hat{y} = ax^b + c$ $\quad \hat{y} = a + b\log x$

a. $\hat{y} - 20 = 47.7 - 7.2x$ $\hat{y} = 67.7 - 7.2x$

b. $\hat{y} - 20 = 44 - 43.25\log x$ $\hat{y} = 64 - 43.25\log x$

c. $\log(\hat{y} - 20) = 1.7356 - 0.227690x$ $\hat{y} = 54.4 \cdot 0.592^x + 20$

d. $\log(\hat{y} - 20) = 1.66586 - 0.68076\log x$ $\hat{y} = 46.33x^{-0.68076} + 20$

4. Use the data from Exercise 1 and find

a. A quadratic (2nd degree) regression.

b. A cubic (3rd degree) regression.

c. A quartic (4th degree) regression.

d. The root mean square error for each regression.

Reason and Apply

5. APPLICATION A cylindrical tanker truck has a volume of 50 m³ when it is full. The driver can use a stick to find the depth of the contents. The following information is known:

Depth (m)	0	0.5	1.0	1.5	2.0	2.5
Volume (m³)	0	7.12	18.68	31.32	42.88	50

a. Find a cubic model to estimate the volume for different depths.

b. What is the root mean square error for the cubic model from 5a?

c. Predict the volume when the depth is 0.75 m.

d. What kind of accuracy do you expect for this value?

6. APPLICATION An additive to puppy food is shown to increase weight gain in underweight puppies when it is mixed with standard food. What mixture results in highest weight gain for the average puppy? Data are collected from a study of eight puppies fed with different percentages of additive.

Percentage additive x	20%	20%	40%	40%	60%	60%	80%	80%
Weight gain (kg) y	4.1	6.2	6.5	7.3	3.1	4.8	0.5	1.2

a. Find quadratic and cubic models for these data.

b. Use each model to find the predicted percentage that produces the greatest weight gain.

c. How much difference is there in each of these predictions?

Helping with the Exercises

2a.

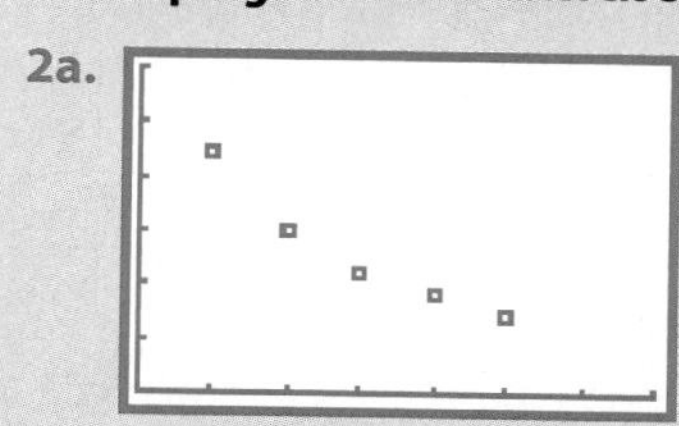

[0, 7, 1, 0, 60, 10]

2b.

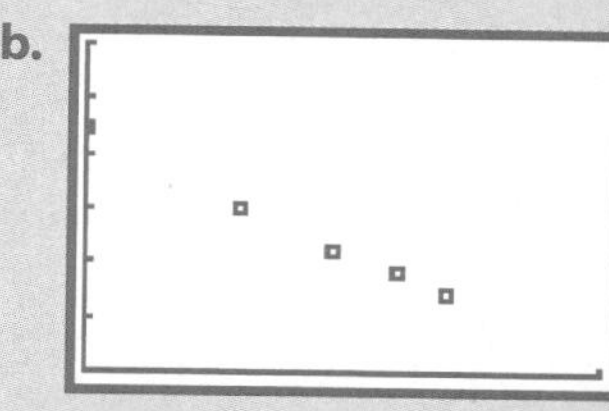

[0, 1, 1, 0, 60, 10]

2c.

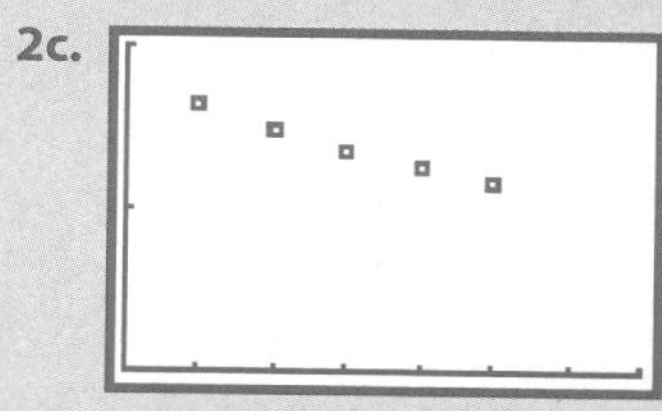

[0, 7, 1, 0, 2, 1]

2d.

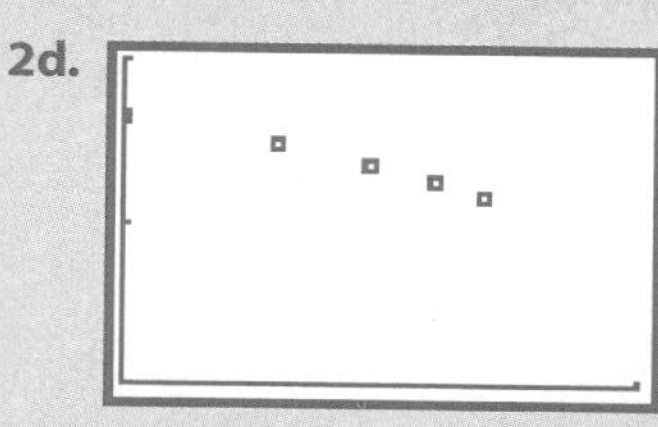

[0, 1, 1, 0, 2, 1]

2e. It is difficult to tell visually. But $(\log x, \log y)$ has the strongest correlation coefficient, $r \approx -.9974$.

Exercise 3 [Alert] This exercise requires using properties of logarithms.

Exercise 4 Students are expected to use calculators for polynomial regression.

4a. $\hat{y} = 1.93x^2 - 18.77x + 81.2$

4b. $\hat{y} = -0.5x^3 + 6.43x^2 - 30.57x + 89.6$

4c. $\hat{y} = 0.125x^4 - 2x^3 + 12.625x^2 - 40.75x + 95$

4d. 1.115; 0.209; 0

Exercise 5 Although one data point has coordinates (0, 0), no translation is needed because the instructions say to find a cubic rather than an exponential or a power function.

5a. $\hat{y} = -3.77x^3 + 14.13x^2 + 8.23x - 0.01$

5b. 0.079

5c. 12.52 m³

5d. Because the root mean square is 0.079, you can expect the predicted volume to be within approximately 0.079 cubic meter of the true value.

6a. $\hat{y} = -0.00303125x^2 + 0.223875x + 2.1125$; $\hat{y} = 0.0000947917x^3 - 0.01725x^2 + 0.85708x - 5.85$

6b. quadratic: approximately 37%; cubic: approximately 35%

6c. The difference is only about 2%.

Exercise 7 This is the only exercise that involves the coefficient of determination R^2, which the calculator reports for polynomial regression. As with the correlation coefficient, r, values of R^2 closer to 1 indicate better fits.

7e. .90236; the cubic model is a better fit.

7f. $\hat{y} = -0.07925x + 8.175$; $R^2 \approx .582$. The values of R^2 and r^2 are equal for the linear model.

8a.

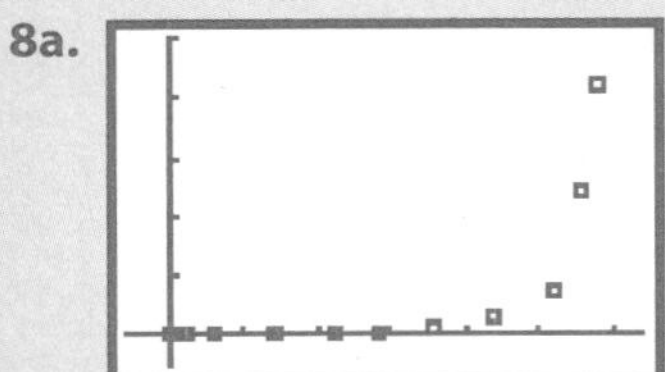

[−3, 32, 5, −7000000, 50000000, 10000000]

The data are not linear.

8b. $(x, \log y)$ is the most linear.

$(\log x, y)$

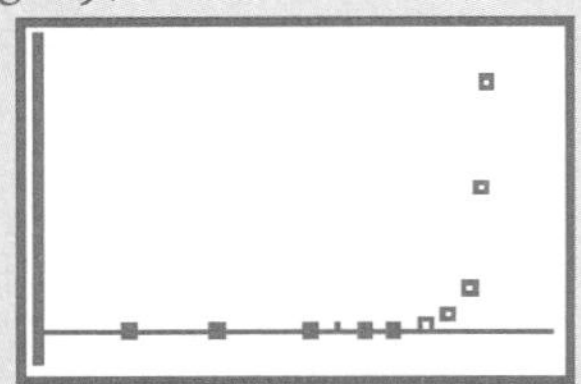

[0, 1.7, 1, −5000000, 50000000, 1]

$(x, \log y)$

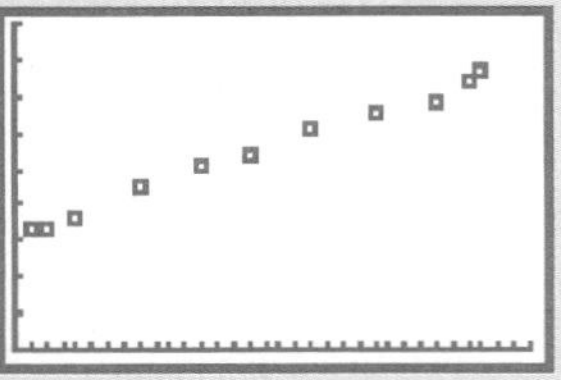

[0, 33, 1, 0, 9, 1]

$(\log x, \log y)$

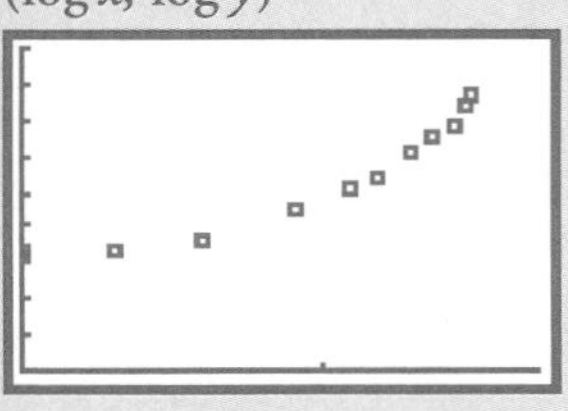

[0, 1.7, 1, 0, 9, 1]

7. ***Mini-Investigation*** For nonlinear data that cannot be linearized (such as polynomial functions), you cannot calculate the coefficient of correlation, r. Instead, you can calculate the **coefficient of determination,** R^2. A value of R^2 close to ±1 indicates a good fit. Use the data and answers from Exercise 6.

a. Calculate the mean y-value of the data. 4.2125

b. Calculate the sum of the squares of the deviations for the y-values, $\Sigma(y_i - \bar{y})^2$. 43.16875

c. Calculate the sum of the squares of the residuals predicted by the quadratic model, $\Sigma(y_i - \hat{y})^2$. 6.28525

d. Find the proportion of change in these values:

$$R^2 = \frac{\Sigma(y_i - \bar{y})^2 - \Sigma(y_i - \hat{y})^2}{\Sigma(y_i - \bar{y})^2} \quad .8544$$

e. Repeat these calculations for the cubic model. Which is a better fit?

f. Find a linear model for the data, and repeat the calculations to find R^2. How does the value of R^2 for the linear model compare with the value of r^2?

8. **APPLICATION** The speed of a computer has increased with time in a consistent way. In 1965, Dr. Gordon Moore (b 1929), a co-founder of Intel, noted that the number of transistors per square inch on integrated circuits seems to double approximately every 18 months. The table below shows the year of introduction of a new chip and the number of transistors on that chip.

a. Make a scatter plot of the data. (Let $x = 0$ represent 1970.) Is the data linear?

b. Make a scatter plot of $(\log x, y)$, $(x, \log y)$, and $(\log x, \log y)$. Which is most linear?

c. Find a least squares line to model the most linear data you found in 8b. $y = 0.144x + 3.217$

d. Using the least squares line in 8c, write an equation to model the data. $y = 10^{0.144x+3.217}$ or $y = 1648.162(1.393)^x$

e. Use your model to make a prediction about the number of transistors on a microchip in 2011. approximately 1,320,000,000

Year of introduction x	Number of transistors y
1971	2,250
1972	2,500
1974	5,000
1978	29,000
1982	120,000
1985	275,000
1989	1,180,000
1993	3,100,000
1997	7,500,000
1999	24,000,000
2000	42,000,000

(www.intel.com)

Technology CONNECTION

As microchips are made smaller and smaller, more and more transistors can fit onto a chip. The chip's speed increases because the distance between the transistors is decreased, resulting in an increase in computer performance. Is Moore's Law limitless? In 1997, Moore said that the physical limitations of silicon chips could be reached by 2017. Researchers are now experimenting with replacing silicon transistors with carbon nanotubes to fit more transistors on a chip.

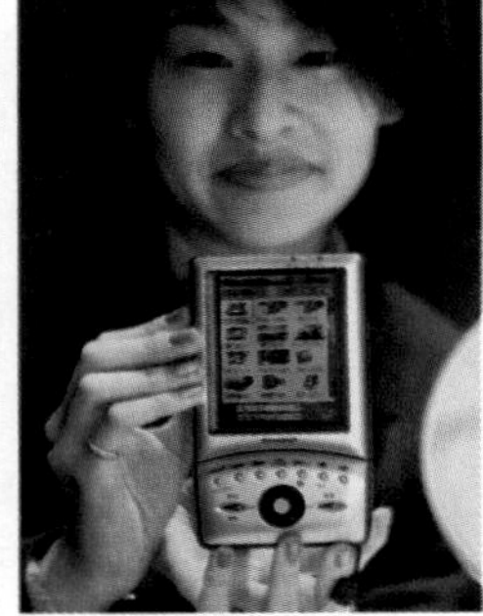

A 1984 IBM AT computer (left) compared to a 2000 Sharp handheld computer shows how computer sizes have decreased with time and technological advances.

MAKING THE CONNECTION

Another way scientists may speed up computers beyond the limitations of the computer chip is through quantum computing. Using subatomic properties, quantum computers would use simple molecules such as chloroform as transistors. Quantum computers would be able to explore all possible answers to a problem simultaneously, instead of testing one at a time. Theoretically, a quantum computer could be millions of times faster than modern-day computers and would be able to make computations that are currently impossible.

Review

13.3 **9.** A set of data with a mean of 83 and a standard deviation of 3.2 is normally distributed. Find each value.

a. one standard deviation above the mean 86.2

b. one standard deviation below the mean 79.8

c. two standard deviations above the mean 89.4

12.4 **10.** A poll shows 47% of voters favor Proposition B. What is the probability that exactly 11 of 20 voters end up voting in favor of the proposal? approximately .137

3.3 **11.** These data show numbers of country radio stations and numbers of oldies radio stations for several years. Assuming the trends in the data continue, answer the questions that follow.

Year	1994	1995	1996	1997	1998	1999	2001
Country	2642	2613	2525	2491	2368	2306	2190
Oldies	714	710	738	755	799	766	785

(*The World Almanac and Book of Facts 2002*)

a. How many country stations will there be in 2005? approximately 1910

b. How many oldies stations will there be in 2005? approximately 847

c. When the number of country stations reaches 1500, how many oldies stations are there likely to be? approximately 919

12.6 **12.** In your class, if three students are picked at random, what is the probability that

a. all were born on a Wednesday?

b. at least one was born on a Wednesday?

c. each was born on a different day of the week?

Singer Patsy Cline's (1932–1963) (top) recordings are considered some of the greatest in country music. Between 1998 and 2003, the Dixie Chicks (bottom) recorded three albums and have released seven number-one singles.

Project

MAKING IT FIT

Find any bivariate data that you think might be related. You might look in an almanac, or search the library or the internet. Then use techniques from this chapter to find a function that fits the data well.

Your project should include

- Your data and its source.
- A graph of your data with the equation you found to model it.
- A description of your process and an analysis of how well your curve fits the data.

EXTENSIONS

A. Ask students to find models to fit any of the nonlinear data from the investigation of Lesson 13.6.

B. Using the data from the investigation in this lesson, you might ask students to calculate the volume for each height recorded and find an equation to model data of the form (*time, volume*).

12a. $\frac{1}{343} \approx .003$

12b. $\frac{127}{343} \approx .370$

12c. $\frac{30}{49} \approx .612$

Supporting the Project

Students have been exploring how to fit a function to data. This project is an opportunity for them to test their skill by finding their own data and fitting a curve to it.

OUTCOMES

- Data sources are included.
- A graph of the data and an equation that models them reasonably well are shown.
- Students' work displays the various types of models that were explored and an evaluation of why the one chosen fits best.
- Values of r, r^2, or R^2 are given.
- The report includes a discussion of any outliers or peculiarities with the data or model.

PLANNING

LESSON OUTLINE

One day:

15 min Reviewing

15 min Exercises

15 min Student self-assessment

MATERIALS

- Age and Income (W)
- Sketchpad demonstration Normal Curve and Approximation, *optional*

REVIEWING

To review the entire chapter, hand out the Age and Income worksheet. The data, which are also available as lists on the Calculator Programs and Data CD, are taken from a sample of census data such as those used in the Exploration Normally Distributed Data. Ask what the corresponding population is, and remind students of the meaning of a normal distribution. Find the mean and median of the age, point out that these numbers are statistics, and remind students that the corresponding numbers for the population are called parameters. Find the z-values of the ages and a 95% confidence interval for the population mean. Test the hypothesis that the mean income of the entire population is $27,000, demonstrating how it's rejected at a 5% level of significance but accepted at a 10% level. Then ask how well age and income correlate, and find the equation of the least squares line. Point out that age would be considered the explanatory variable and income the response variable.

CHAPTER 13 REVIEW

In this chapter you saw some statistical tools for estimating **parameters** of a very large (perhaps infinite) population from **statistics** of samples taken from that population. Many large populations can be described by **probability distributions** of **continuous random variables.** The area under the graph of a probability distribution is always 1. When using any probability distribution, you do not find the probability of a single exact value; you find the probability of a range of values.

The probability distributions of many sets of data are **normal.** Their graphs, called **normal curves,** are bell-shaped. To write an equation of a normal distribution curve, you need to know the mean and standard deviation of the data set. To make predictions about a population based on a sample, you can make a nonstandard normal distribution standard by using **z-values,** and you can predict things about the population mean with a **confidence interval.**

Even if the population is not normal, the **Central Limit Theorem** allows you to discuss its mean and standard deviation based on sample statistics. This theorem also allows you to perform **hypothesis testing** about a population parameter.

You can also make predictions by collecting **bivariate data** and analyzing the relationship between two variables. The **correlation coefficient,** r, tells whether or not the variables have a linear relationship. If two variables are linearly related, the **least squares line** of fit, which passes through $(\bar{x}, \bar{y})$ and has slope $r\left(\frac{s_y}{s_x}\right)$, can help you make predictions about the population. You can also find curves to fit some nonlinear data by linearizing those data and finding a least squares line, or by using your calculator to perform other **regression analysis** techniques.

EXERCISES

Practice Your Skills

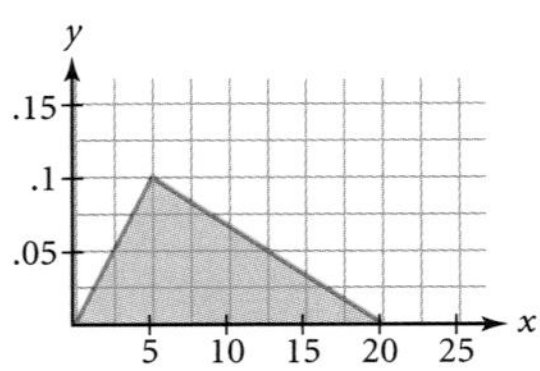

1. A graph of a probability distribution consists of two segments. The first segment connects the points (0, 0) and (5, .1), and the second segment connects the points (5, .1) and (20, 0), as shown.
   a. Verify that the area under the segments is equal to 1. $0.5(20)(.1) = 1$
   b. Find the median. 7.75
   c. What is the probability that a data value will be less than 3? .09
   d. What is the probability that a data value will be between 3 and 6? $\frac{77}{300} \approx .257$

ASSIGNING HOMEWORK

Student groups might do Exercises 4, 6, and 8.

2. Suppose a probability distribution has the shape of a semicircle. What is the radius of the semicircle? $\sqrt{\frac{2}{\pi}}$

3. The 68% confidence interval for the weight of a house cat in northern Michigan is between 8.4 and 12.7 lb.

a. What are the mean and standard deviation for the weight of a house cat in northern Michigan? $\bar{x} = 10.55$ lb; $s = 2.15$ lb

b. What is the 95% confidence interval for the weight of a house cat in northern Michigan? 6.25 lb to 14.85 lb

4. At a maple tree nursery, a grower selects a random sample of 5-year-old trees. He measures their heights to the nearest inch.

Height (in.)	60	61	62	63	64	65	66	67	68	69	70	71	72	73	74	75
Frequency	1	1	4	6	8	10	9	8	13	10	5	6	6	3	6	3

a. Find the mean and the standard deviation of the heights. Make a statement about the meaning of the standard deviation in this problem.

b. Make a histogram of these data and describe the shape of the distribution.

5. Recently, Adam put larger wheels on his skateboard and noticed it would coast farther. He decided to test this relationship. He collected some skateboards, attached wheels of various sizes to them, and rolled them to see how far they would roll on their own. He collected the data shown in the table.

Wheel diameter (in.) x	Rolling distance (in.) y
1	17
2	23
3.5	32
5	30
5.5	36
7	52
8.5	57
9.5	55
10	70

Dirtboards use wheels up to 10 inches in diameter.

a. Make a scatter plot of these data.

b. Does there appear to be a linear relationship between the variables? Find the correlation coefficient, and use this value to justify your answer.

c. Find the equation of the least squares line that models these data. $\hat{y} = 5.322x + 10.585$

d. Describe the real-world meaning of the slope and the y-intercept of your line.

e. Use your model to determine the size of wheel of a skateboard that rolls 50.5 in. 7.5 in.

Helping with the Exercises

Exercise 2 As needed, suggest that students use what they know about the area of a circle.

Exercise 3 If students are having difficulty, remind them that the mean is the midpoint of the confidence interval. They can also apply the 68-95-99.7 rule.

4a. $\bar{x} \approx 67.8$; $s \approx 3.6$. Approximately 68% of the 5-year-old trees are between 64.2 and 71.4 in. tall.

4b.

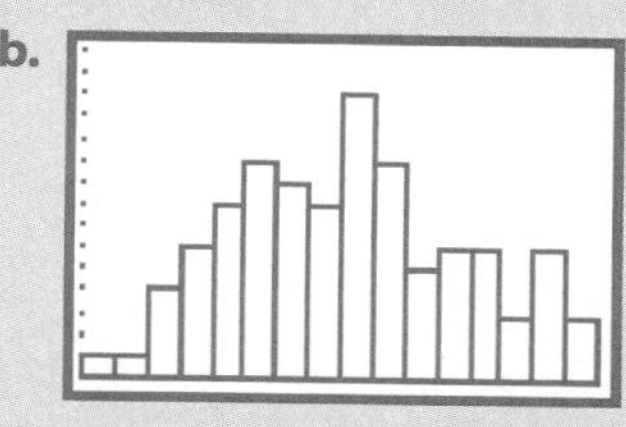

[60, 76, 1, 0, 15, 1]

The distribution is approximately normal, although slightly skewed to the right.

5a.

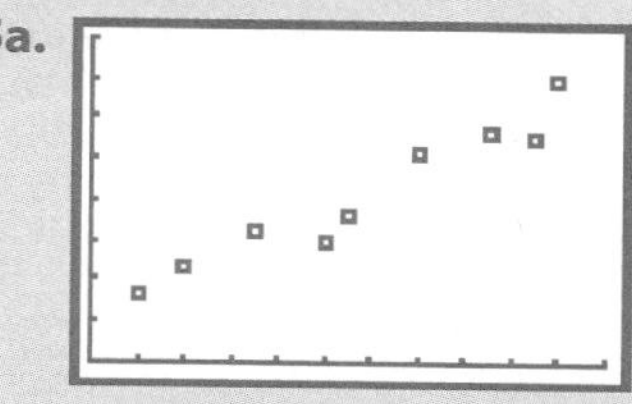

[0, 11, 1, 0, 80, 10]

5b. yes; $r \approx .965$, indicating a relationship that is close to linear

5d. The rolling distance increases 5.322 in. for every additional inch of wheel diameter. The skateboard will skid approximately 10.585 in. even if it doesn't have any wheels.

8b.

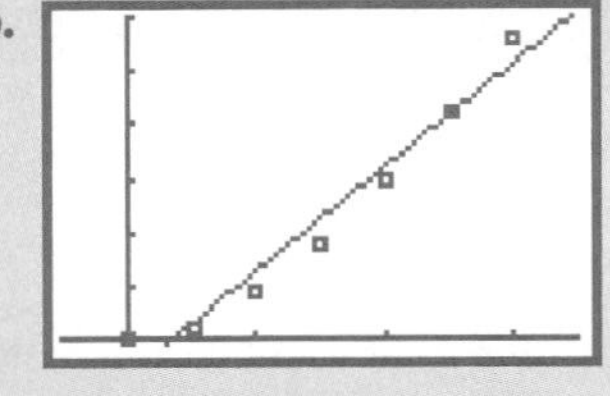

$[-0.5, 3.5, 1, -1, 60, 10]$

It looks like a fairly close fit, but there is a distinct pattern to the residuals.

8c. $r \approx .978$, $r^2 \approx .956$. The value of r is close to 1, so a linear model is a good fit.

8d. $\hat{y} = 4.712x^2 + 5.236x - 0.785$;
$\hat{y} = -1.047x^3 + 9.424x^2 + 0.0003x$

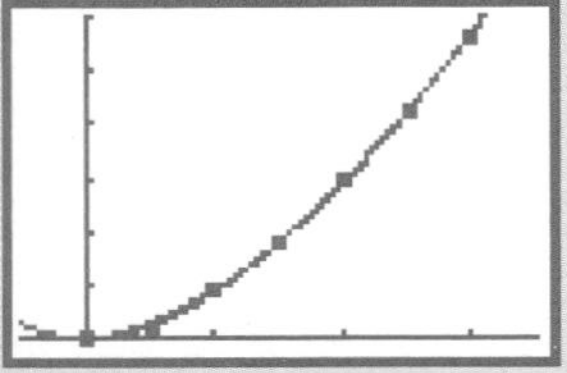

$[-0.5, 3.5, 1, -1, 60, 10]$

Exercise 8f This exercise uses the coefficient of determination, discussed in Lesson 13.7, Exercise 7.

8f. $R^2 \approx .999$, $R^2 \approx 1.000$. The value of R^2 for the cubic model is closer to 1 than the value of R^2 for the quadratic model, or r^2 for the linear model, so the cubic model is the best fit.

9a. hyperbola

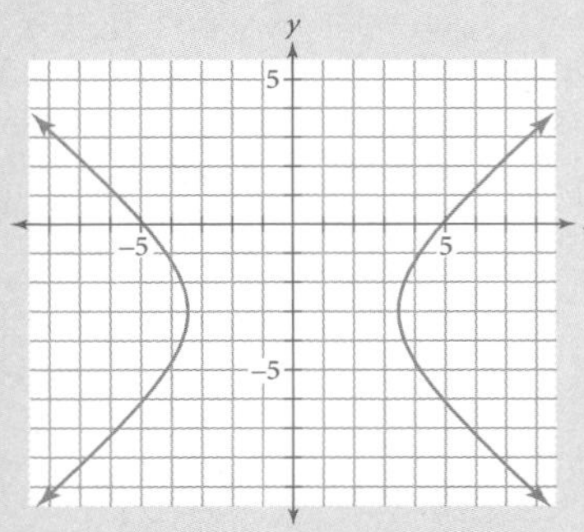

6. Suppose the weights of all male baseball players who are 6 ft tall and between the ages of 18 and 24 are normally distributed. The mean is 175 lb, and the standard deviation is 14 lb.

a. What percentage of these males weigh between 180 and 200 lb? approximately 32.3%

b. What percentage of these males weigh less than 160 lb? approximately 14.2%

c. Find the 90% confidence interval. between 152 and 198 lb

d. Find the equation of a normal curve that provides a probability distribution for this information. $y = \frac{1}{14\sqrt{2\pi}}\left(\sqrt{e}\right)^{-((x-175)/14)^2}$

7. The length of an algebra book is measured by many people. The measurements have mean 284 mm and standard deviation 1.3 mm. If four students measure the book, what is the probability that the mean of their measurements will be less than 283 mm? approximately .062

8. A 3 ft deep fish pond in the shape of a hemisphere has a volume of 56.549 ft³ when it is full. These data have been collected relating depth to volume in the pond:

Depth (ft)	0	0.5	1.0	1.5	2.0	2.5	3.0
Volume (ft³)	0	2.225	8.378	17.671	29.322	42.542	56.549

a. Find the equation of the least squares line that estimates the volume as a function of depth. $\hat{y} = 19.373x - 6.676$

b. Plot your equation from 8a with the data points, and decide whether you think it is a good fit.

c. Calculate the values of r and r^2 for a linear model. What do they tell you about whether or not the least squares line is a good fit?

d. Find quadratic and cubic models to estimate the volume for different depths. Graph these curves with the data.

e. Which of the three regression models (linear, quadratic, or cubic) appears to fit the data best? The cubic model fits best.

f. What are the values of R^2 for the quadratic and cubic models? How does this confirm or refute your answer to 8e?

MIXED REVIEW

9. Sketch a graph of each equation, and identify the shape formed.

9.5 **a.** $\frac{x^2}{12} - \frac{(y+3)^2}{9} = 1$ **b.** $\left(\frac{x-1}{5}\right)^2 + \left(\frac{y-1}{4}\right)^2 = 1$

c. $(y-3)^2 = \frac{(x-4)}{3}$ **d.** $-4x^2 - 24x + y^2 + 2y = 39$

12.3 **10.** If the probability of a snowstorm in July is .004, and the probability you will score an A in algebra is .75, then what is the probability of a snowstorm in July or an A in algebra? .751

9b. ellipse

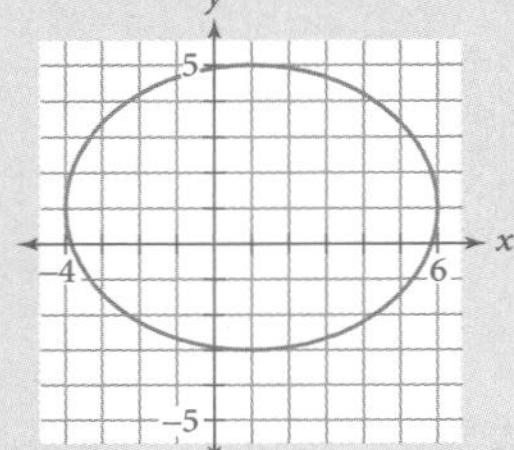

9c. parabola

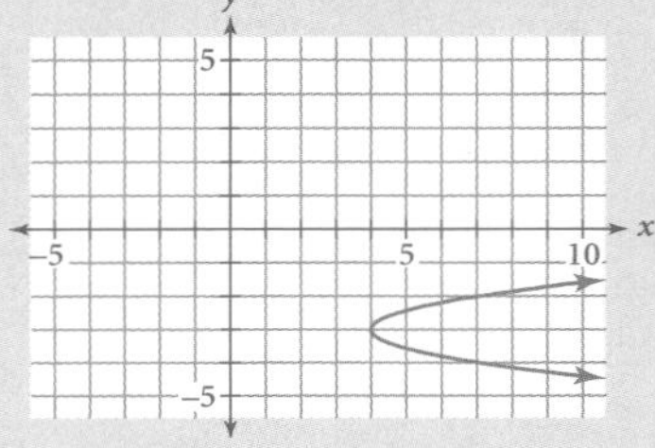

9d. hyperbola

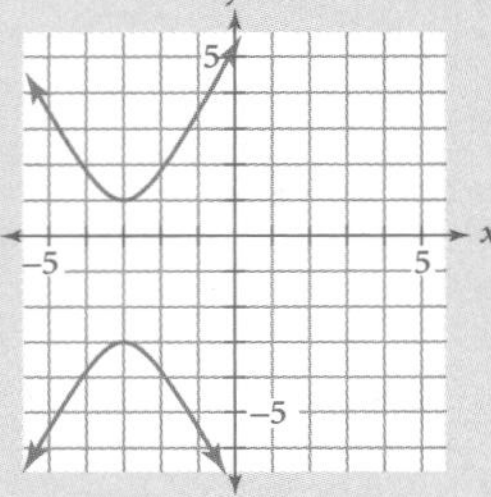

11.1 **11.** Find the sums of each series.

a. Find the sum of the first 12 odd positive integers. $S_{12} = 144$

b. Find the sum of the first 20 odd positive integers. $S_{20} = 400$

c. Find the sum of the first n odd positive integers. (*Hint:* Try several choices for n until you see a pattern.) $S_n = n^2$

6.2 **12. APPLICATION** A Detroit car rental business has a second outlet in Chicago. The company allows customers to make local rentals or one-way rentals to the other location. At the end of each month, one-eighth of the cars that start the month in Detroit will end up in Chicago, and one-twelfth of the cars that start the month in Chicago will end up in Detroit.

a. Write a transition matrix to represent this situation.

b. If there are 500 cars in each city at the start of operations, what would you expect the distribution to be four months later? In the long run?

7.3 **13. APPLICATION** A store in Yosemite National Park charges \$6.60 for a flashlight. Approximately 200 of them are sold each week. A survey indicates that the sales will decrease by 10 flashlights per week for each \$0.50 increase in price.

a. Write a function that describes the weekly revenue in dollars, y, as a function of selling price in dollars, x. $y = -20x^2 + 332x$

b. What selling price provides maximum weekly revenue? What is the maximum revenue? \$8.30; \$1377.80

Camping at Glacier Point, Yosemite National Park, California

10.3 **14.** Consider the function $y = \cos x$.

a. Write the equation of the image after the function is reflected across the x-axis, shrunk by a vertical scale factor of $\frac{1}{2}$, stretched by a horizontal scale factor of 2, and translated up 6 units.

b. What is the period of the image, in radians? What are the amplitude and phase shift? period: 4π; amplitude: $\frac{1}{2}$; phase shift: none

c. Graph the function and its image on the same graph.

12.2 **15. APPLICATION** Lily and Philip both go to their doctor, complaining of the same symptoms. The doctor tests them for a rare disease. Data have shown that 20% of the people with these symptoms actually have the disease. The test the doctor uses is correct 90% of the time. Calculate the probabilities in the table below, and explain the meaning of the results.

		Test results	
		Accurate	**Inaccurate**
Patient's condition	Doesn't have the disease	.72	.08
	Has the disease	.18	.02

12a. $\begin{bmatrix} \frac{7}{8} & \frac{1}{8} \\ \frac{1}{12} & \frac{11}{12} \end{bmatrix}$

12b. approximately 439 cars in Detroit and 561 in Chicago; approximately 400 cars in Detroit and 600 in Chicago

14a. $y = -\frac{1}{2}\cos\left(\frac{1}{2}x\right) + 6$

14c.

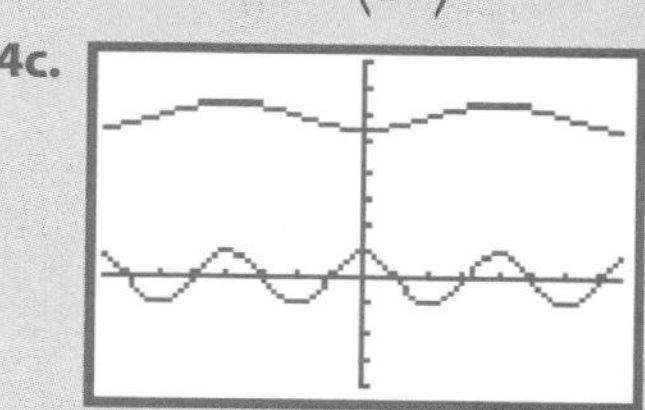

$[-4\pi, 4\pi, \pi/2, -4, 8, 1]$

15. Out of 100 people with the symptoms, the test will accurately confirm that 72 do not have the disease while mistakenly suggesting 8 do have the disease. The test will accurately indicate 18 do have the disease and make a mistake by suggesting 2 do not have the disease who actually have the disease.

Exercise 13 [Alert] Students may still find this kind of problem quite difficult. Encourage them to use dimensional analysis and to test points until they see a pattern.

$$revenue = \left(x\,\frac{\text{dollars}}{\text{flashlight}}\right)\left(200 \text{ flashlights} - 10\,\frac{\text{flashlights}}{\text{increment}} \cdot \frac{(x - 6.6)\text{ dollars}}{0.5\,\frac{\text{dollars}}{\text{increment}}}\right)$$

5.3 **16.** The population of Bombay, India, at various times is given in the table below.

Year	1950	1970	1990	2000
Population (in millions)	2.9	5.8	12.2	18.1

(The New York Times Almanac 2002)

Bombay, India

a. The population roughly doubled in the 20 years between 1950 and 1970 and slightly more than doubled again between 1970 and 1990. What is a good estimate of the growth rate?

b. Find an exponential equation to model Bombay's population.

c. Use your model to predict the population in 2015.

d. *The New York Times Almanac 2002* predicts that the population in 2015 will be 26.1 million. How does this compare with your prediction?

16a. possible answer: 3.5% per year

16b. possible answer: $\hat{y} = 5.8(1 + 0.035)^{x-1970}$

16c. possible answer: 27.3 million

16d. The population predicted by the equation is somewhat higher.

Exercises 17, 20 These data are on the Calculator Programs and Data CD.

13.5 **17.** This table shows the number of seats on various types of airplanes, the planes' cruising speed, and their operating cost per hour.

Plane	Seats	Speed (mi/h)	Operating cost ($/h)
B747-400	369	537	8,158
B747-200/300	357	522	8,080
L-1011	339	493	8,721
DC-10-10	309	513	5,000
DC-10-40	284	491	6,544
DC-10-30	273	520	6,388
MD-11	270	525	7,474
B-777	266	525	4,878
A300-600	228	479	5,145
B767-300ER	207	499	3,823
B767-200ER	176	487	4,406
MD-90	149	441	2,590
B737-800	148	454	2,255
B727-200	147	439	3,435
A320-100/200	146	454	2,492

Plane	Seats	Speed (mi/h)	Operating cost ($/h)
B737-400	141	407	2,948
MD-80	135	431	2,725
B737-300/700	131	408	2,417
DC-9-50	126	365	1,954
A319	122	445	1,987
B737-100/200	117	401	2,601
DC-9-40	111	380	1,845
B737-500	109	410	2,397
B717-200	106	374	2,212
DC-9-30	97	392	2,218
F-100	88	380	3,015
DC-9-10	69	389	2,227
CRJ-145	50	389	1,033
ERJ-145	50	362	1,151
ERJ-135	37	363	1,028

(The World Almanac and Book of Facts 2003)

a. How strongly is the number of seats related to operating cost? How strongly is the speed related to operating cost?

b. Does the number of seats or the speed have the stronger correlation to operating cost? Why might that correlation be stronger?

17a. seats versus cost: $r = .9493$; speed versus cost: $r = .8501$

17b. The number of seats is more strongly correlated to cost. Sample answer: The increase in number of seats will cause an increase in weight (both passengers and luggage) and thus cause an increase in the amount of fuel needed.

5.1 **18.** Identify each sequence as arithmetic, geometric, or neither. Then write both a recursive and explicit formula to describe the pattern, if possible.

a. 3, 9, 27, 81, 243, . . .

b. $-1, -3, -5, -7, -9, \ldots$

c. 2, 5, 10, 17, 26, . . .

d. $1, -\frac{1}{2}, \frac{1}{4}, -\frac{1}{8}, \frac{1}{16}, \ldots$

10.2 **19.** The circle at right has radius 4 cm, and the measure of central angle *ACB* is 55°.

a. What is the measure of $\angle ACB$ in radians?

b. What is the length of $\overset{\frown}{AB}$?

c. What is the area of sector *ACB*?

2.2 **20.** The lengths in feet of the main spans of 38 notable suspension bridges in North America are

{4260, 4200, 3800, 3500, 2800, 2800, 2310, 2300, 2190, 2150, 2000, 1850, 1800, 1750, 1632, 1600, 1600, 1600, 1595, 1550, 1500, 1500, 1470, 1447, 1400, 1380, 1207, 1200, 1150, 1108, 1105, 1080, 1060, 1059, 1057, 1050, 1030, 1010}

(*The World Almanac and Book of Facts 2003*)

a. What are the mean, median, and mode of these data? See below.

b. Make a box plot of these data. Describe the shape.

c. What is the standard deviation?

New York's Manhattan Bridge was constructed from 1901 to 1909 over the East River.

3.7 **21.** Solve each system of equations.

a. $\begin{cases} 3x - y = -1 \\ 2x + y = 6 \end{cases}$

b. $\begin{cases} 2x + 4y = -9 \\ x - y = -6 \end{cases}$

11.3 **22.** Consider this series.

$$\frac{1}{10} + \frac{1}{30} + \frac{1}{90} + \frac{1}{270} + \cdots$$

a. What is the sum of the first five terms?

b. What is the sum of the first ten terms?

c. What is the sum of infinitely many terms?

20a. mean: approximately 1818.4 ft; median: 1572.5 ft; mode: 1600 ft

20b. The data are skewed right.

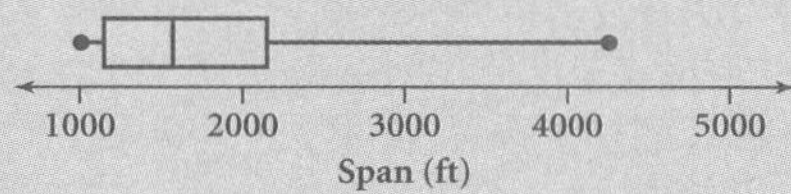

20c. approximately 878.6 ft

21a. (1, 4)

21b. $(-5.5, 0.5)$ or $\left(-\frac{11}{2}, \frac{1}{2}\right)$

22a. $S_5 = \frac{121}{810} \approx 0.149$

22b. $S_{10} \approx 0.150$

22c. $S = \frac{3}{20}$ or 0.15

18a. geometric; $u_1 = 3$ and $u_n = 3u_{n-1}$ where $n \geq 2$; $u_n = 3(3)^{n-1}$ or $u_n = 3^n$

18b. arithmetic; $u_1 = -1$ and $u_n = u_{n-1} - 2$ where $n \geq 2$; $u_n = -2n + 1$

Exercise 18c The pattern is neither arithmetic nor geometric, so students should not be expected to generate a recursive rule. However, the sequence could be modeled with $u_1 = 2$ and $u_n = u_{n-1} + 2n - 1$ where $n \geq 2$.

18c. neither; students are not expected to write a recursive formula; $u_n = n^2 + 1$

18d. geometric; $u_1 = 1$ and $u_n = -\frac{1}{2}u_{n-1}$ where $n \geq 2$; $u_n = \left(-\frac{1}{2}\right)^{n-1}$

19a. $\frac{11\pi}{36}$

19b. approximately 3.84 cm

19c. approximately 7.68 cm^2

4.8 **23.** Consider the functions $f(x) = \sqrt{2x - 3}$ and $g(x) = 6x^2$.

a. What are the domain and range of $f(x)$?
b. What are the domain and range of $g(x)$?
c. Find $f(2)$. $f(2) = 1$
d. Find x such that $g(x) = 2$.
e. Find $g(f(3))$. $g(f(3)) = 18$
f. Find $f(g(x))$. $f(g(x)) = \sqrt{12x^2 - 3}$

8.1 **24.** Two people begin 400 m apart and jog toward each other. One person jogs 2.4 m/s, and the other jogs 1.8 m/s. When they meet, they stop.

a. Write parametric equations to simulate the movement of the joggers. What range of t-values do you need? possible answer: $x = 2.4t$, $y = 1$ and $x = 400 - 1.8t$, $y = 2$; $0 \le t \le 95.24$
b. Use your graph to find how far each person runs before they meet.
c. How long does it take for them to meet? 95.24 s

13.2 **25.** The heights of all adults in Bigtown are normally distributed with a mean of 167 cm and a standard deviation of 8.5 cm.

a. Sketch a graph of the normal distribution of these heights.
b. Shade the portion of that graph showing the percentage of people who are shorter than 155 cm.
c. What percentage of people are shorter than 155 cm? approximately 7.9%

TAKE ANOTHER LOOK

1. The least squares method minimizes the sum of the squares of the residuals. Why is this important? Try to think of another method you could use to find a line of fit. Explain what advantage or disadvantage the method of minimizing squares of residuals has that this other method does not have.

2. As you add to the degree of a polynomial function that models data, the value of the coefficient of determination, R^2, will increase. But increasing the degree of a polynomial doesn't necessarily *significantly* improve how well a function fits data. The formula below adjusts for the increase in accuracy that comes from increasing the degree of a polynomial function. The adjusted value of R^2, R_A^2, allows you to judge whether the model has a significant improvement. The variable n represents the number of data points, and p represents the number of parameters in the model. There are two parameters in a linear, exponential, or power model (a and b), there are three in a quadratic model (a, b, and c), four in a cubic model (a, b, c, and d), and so on.

$$R_A^2 = 1 - \left(1 - R^2\right)\left(\frac{n-1}{n-p}\right)$$

Consider these data, the depth of water in a leaking bucket at various times.

Time (s) x	0	10	20	30	40	50	60	70	80	90
Depth (cm) y	15	12.5	10.5	8.5	6.5	5.0	3.5	2.5	1.5	1.0

23a. domain: $x \ge \frac{3}{2}$; range: $y \ge 0$

23b. domain: any real number; range: $y \ge 0$

23d. $x = \pm\sqrt{\frac{1}{3}}$ or $x \approx \pm 0.577$

24b. The faster person runs approximately 229 m; the slower person runs approximately 171 m.

25a and b.

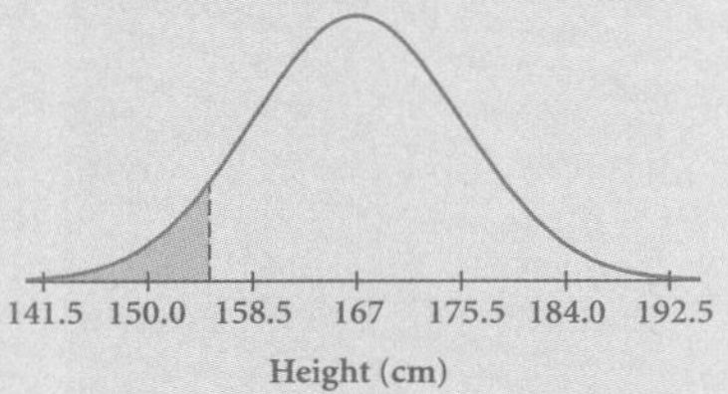

Take Another Look

1. Answers will vary. Squaring the residuals makes them all positive, so the minimum sum is an indicator of a better fit. If one line has two residuals 1 and 5 and another line has residuals 3 and 3, the sum of the residuals would be the same (6) in both cases, but the sum of the squares of the residuals would be 26 and 18, respectively.

2. The coefficient of determination is introduced in Lesson 13.7, Exercise 7.

Equations

linear: $y = 13.727 - 0.15727x$

quadratic: $y = 0.00110x^2 - 0.25614x + 15.045$

cubic: $y = 0.0000036908x^3 + 0.00060023x^2 - 0.23912x + 14.952$

quartic: $y = 0.000000029138x^4 - 0.0000015540x^3 + 0.00089452x^2 - 0.24437x + 14.965$

Coefficient of Determination

linear: $R^2 = 0.96930$

quadratic: $R^2 = 0.99956$

cubic: $R^2 = 0.99976$

quartic: $R^2 = 0.99977$

Adjusted Coefficient of Determination

linear: $R_A^2 = 0.96546$

quadratic: $R_A^2 = 0.99943$

cubic: $R_A^2 = 0.99964$

quartic: $R_A^2 = 0.99959$

It appears that the cubic model has the best value of the adjusted coefficient of determination.

3. You might use the Sketchpad demonstration Normal Curve and Approximation instead of having students work on this activity and Take Another Look activity 4. Summaries should emphasize that the width and height of the normal curve vary inversely, so the area under the curve always remains 1. That is, as σ increases, the curve widens and gets shorter; as σ decreases, the curve narrows and gets taller.

Suggest that students using graphing calculators graph in the same window several equations of the form $y = \frac{1}{\sigma\sqrt{2\pi}}\left(\sqrt{e}\right)^{-(x/\sigma)^2}$ and change the value of

Find several polynomial equations to model these data, state the value of R^2 that your calculator gives for each model, and use the formula to find R_A^2 for each model. What is the best model to describe these data?

3. Consider a normal distribution with mean 0. Use your graphing calculator or geometry software to explore how the standard deviation, σ, affects the graph of the normal curve,

$$y = \frac{1}{\sigma\sqrt{2\pi}}\left(\sqrt{e}\right)^{-(x/\sigma)^2}$$

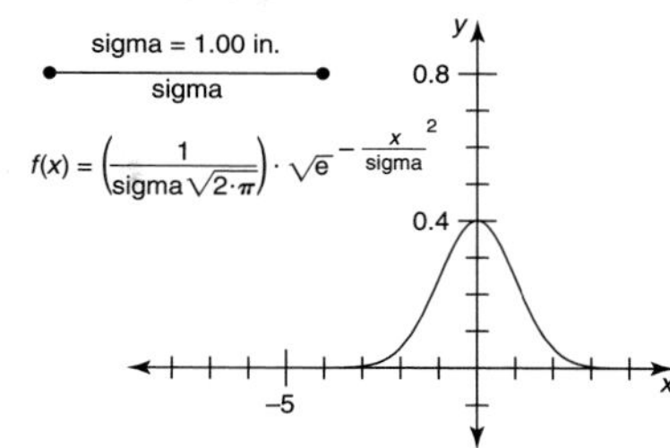

Summarize how the normal curve changes as the value of σ changes.

4. Consider a normal distribution with mean 0. You've already seen that the equation of the normal curve is

$$y = \frac{1}{\sigma\sqrt{2\pi}}\left(\sqrt{e}\right)^{-(x/\sigma)^2}$$

To avoid using e, you can use another equation that approximates the normal curve:

$$y = \frac{1}{\sigma\sqrt{2\pi}}\left(1 - \frac{1}{2\sigma^2}\right)^{x^2}$$

Use your graphing calculator or geometry software to explore how the graphs of these two equations compare for different values of σ. For which values of σ is the second equation a good approximation, a poor approximation, or even undefined?

Assessing What You've Learned

WRITING TEST QUESTIONS Write a few test questions that reflect the topics of this chapter. You may want to include questions on probability distributions, confidence intervals, or bivariate data and correlation. Include detailed solutions.

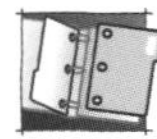

ORGANIZE YOUR NOTEBOOK Make sure that your notebook has complete notes on all of the statistical tools and formulas that you have learned. Specify which statistical measures apply to populations and which apply to samples, and explain which tools allow you to make conclusions about a population based on a sample, and vice versa. Be sure you know when to use the various statistical measures and exactly what each one allows you to predict.

PERFORMANCE ASSESSMENT As a friend, family member, or teacher watches, solve a problem from this chapter that deals with fitting a line or curve to data and analyzing how well the function fits. Explain the various tools for analyzing how well a function fits data. Include a description of what values of r and/or R^2 tell you about a function's fit.

the curves. Students using geometry software should use a rectangular coordinate grid in which the scale of the x-axis can be adjusted independent of the y-axis.

ASSESSING

Test items can include problems students wrote along with items from any of the assessment resources. The exams in Assessment Resources A and Assessment Resources B cover Chapters 10–13. Consider grading students' portfolios as part of the unit grade.

FACILITATING SELF-ASSESSMENT

As you encourage students to organize their notebooks to include the statistical measures, emphasize the importance of including descriptions of how the statistics are used.

σ slightly in each (such as $\sigma = \{0.5, 1.0, 1.5, 2.0\}$). Suggest that students using geometry software create a slider whose length represents the value of σ and then define and graph the function $f(x) = \frac{1}{\sigma\sqrt{2\pi}}\left(\sqrt{e}\right)^{-(x/\sigma)^2}$. Changing the length of the segment will dynamically change the curve. Students using geometry software should use a rectangular coordinate grid in which the scale of the x-axis can be adjusted independent of the y-axis.

4. You might use the Sketchpad demonstration Normal Curve and Approximation instead of having students work on Take Another Look activity 3 and this activity. Students may find that the equation $y = \frac{1}{\sigma\sqrt{2\pi}}\left(1 - \frac{1}{2\sigma^2}\right)^{x^2}$ is a particularly good approximation when σ is greater than 2. For the interval $\sqrt{0.5} < \sigma \leq 2$, the curve is narrower than the actual normal curve. For σ less than or equal to $\sqrt{0.5}$ (or $\frac{\sqrt{2}}{2}$, or approximately 0.7), the function is undefined.

If you previously used *Advanced Algebra Through Data Exploration,* you may recognize the equation $y = \frac{1}{\sigma\sqrt{2\pi}}\left(1 - \frac{1}{2\sigma^2}\right)^{x^2}$ as the formula that was taught in Section 11.6 of that book.

Suggest that students using graphing calculators graph the equations $y = \frac{1}{\sigma\sqrt{2\pi}}\left(\sqrt{e}\right)^{-(x/\sigma)^2}$ and $y = \frac{1}{\sigma\sqrt{2\pi}}\left(1 - \frac{1}{2\sigma^2}\right)^{x^2}$ in the same window and change the value of σ in both equations to see how they compare (such as $\sigma = \{0.4, 0.5, 0.6, 0.7, 0.8, 0.9, 1.0, 1.1, \ldots\}$). Suggest that students using geometry software create a slider whose length represents the value of σ and then define and graph the functions $f(x) = \frac{1}{\sigma\sqrt{2\pi}}\left(\sqrt{e}\right)^{-(x/\sigma)^2}$ and $g(x) = \frac{1}{\sigma\sqrt{2\pi}}\left(1 - \frac{1}{2\sigma^2}\right)^{x^2}$. Changing the length of the segment will dynamically change

Selected Answers

This section contains answers for the odd-numbered problems in each set of Exercises. When a problem has many possible answers, you are given only one sample solution or a hint on how to begin.

CHAPTER 0 • CHAPTER  CHAPTER 0 • CHAPTER

LESSON 0.1

1a. Begin with a 10-liter bucket and a 7-liter bucket. Find a way to get exactly 4 liters in the 10-liter bucket.

1b. Begin with a 10-liter bucket and a 7-liter bucket. Find a way to get exactly 2 liters in the 10-liter bucket.

3. one possible answer: (14, 13)

5. *Hint:* Your strategy could include using objects to act out the problem and/or using pictures to show a sequence of steps leading to a solution.

7a.

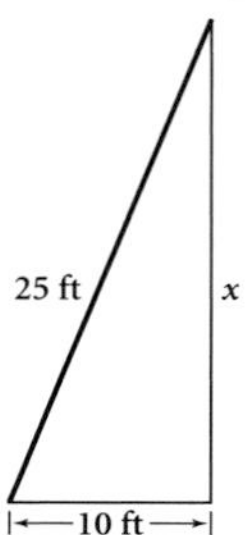

7b.

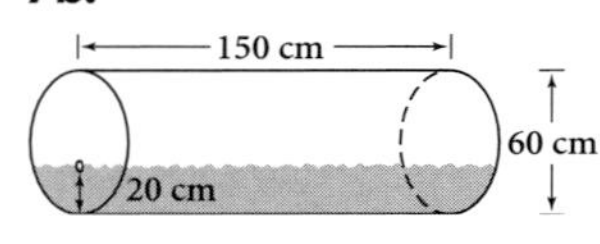

7c.

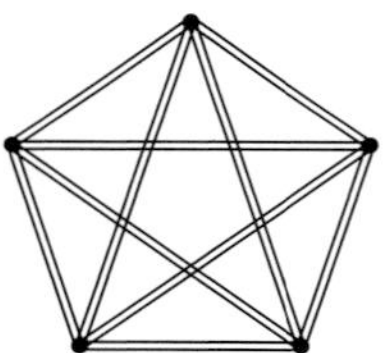

9. *Hint:* Try using a sequence of pictures similar to those on page 2.

11a. $x^2 + 4x + 7x + 28$

	x	4
x	x^2	$4x$
7	$7x$	28

11b. $x^2 + 5x + 5x + 25$

	x	5
x	x^2	$5x$
5	$5x$	25

11c. $xy + 2y + 6x + 12$

	x	2
y	xy	$2y$
6	$6x$	12

11d. $x^2 + 3x - x - 3$

	x	-1
x	x^2	$-1x$
3	$3x$	-3

13a. $n + 3$, where n represents the number

13b. $v = m + 24.3$, where v represents Venus's distance from the Sun in millions of miles and m represents Mercury's distance from the Sun in millions of miles.

13c. $s = 2e$, where s represents the number of CDs owned by Seth and e represents the number of CDs owned by Erin.

15a. $\frac{375}{1000} = \frac{3}{8}$ **15b.** $\frac{142}{100} = \frac{71}{50} = 1\frac{21}{50}$

15c. $\frac{2}{9}$ **15d.** $\frac{35}{99}$

LESSON 0.2

1a. Subtract 12 from both sides.

1b. Divide both sides by 5.

1c. Add 18 to both sides.

1d. Multiply both sides by -15.

3a. $c = 27$ **3b.** $c = 5.8$ **3c.** $c = 9$

5a. $x = 72$ **5b.** $x = 24$ **5c.** $x = 36$

7a. $-12L - 40S = -540$

7b. $12L + 75S = 855$

7c. $35S = 315$

7d. $S = 9$. The small beads cost 9¢ each.

7e. $L = 15$. The large beads cost 15¢ each.

7f. $J = 264$. Jill will pay $2.64 for her beads.

9a. Solve Equation 1 for a. Substitute the result, $5b - 42$, for a in Equation 2 to get $b + 5 = 7((5b - 42) - 5)$.

9b. $b = \frac{167}{17}$ **9c.** $a = \frac{121}{17}$

9d. A has $\frac{121}{17}$ or about 7 denarii, and B has $\frac{167}{17}$ or about 10 denarii.

11a. Draw a 45° angle, then subtract a 30° angle.

11b. Draw a 45° angle, then add a 30° angle.

11c. Draw a 45° angle, then add a 60° angle.

13a. 98 **13b.** -273

15. *Hint:* Try using a sequence of pictures similar to those on page 2. Also be sure to convert all measurements to cups.

LESSON 0.3

1a. approximately 4.3 s

1b. 762 cm **1c.** 480 mi

3. 150 mi/h

5a. $a = 12.8$ **5b.** $b = \frac{4}{3} = 1.\overline{3}$

5c. $c = 10$ **5d.** $d = 8$

7a. 54 in.^{2} **7b.** 1.44 m^3

7c. 1.20 ft **7d.** 24 cm

9a. Equation iii. Explanations will vary.

9b. i. $t \approx 0.03$ **9b. ii.** $t \approx 0.03$ **9b. iii.** $t \approx 8.57$

9c. It would take approximately 9 minutes.

11a. r^{12} **11b.** $\frac{s^4}{3}$

11c. t^{-4} or $\frac{1}{t^4}$ **11d.** $48u^8$

13a. $x^2 + 1x + 5x + 5$

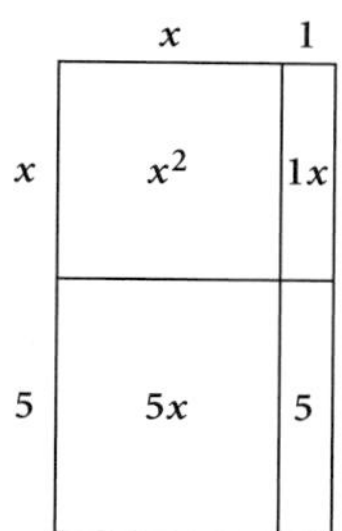

13b. $x^2 + 3x + 3x + 9$

	x	3
x	x^2	$3x$
3	$3x$	9

13c. $x^2 + 3x - 3x - 9$

	x	-3
x	x^2	$-3x$
3	$3x$	-9

CHAPTER 0 REVIEW

1. *Hint:* Try using a sequence of pictures similar to those on page 2.

3a. $x = \sqrt{18}$ cm $= 3\sqrt{2}$ cm ≈ 4.2 cm

3b. $y = 5$ in.

5a. $x = 13$ **5b.** $y = -2.5$

7a. $c = 19.95 + 0.35m$

7b. possible answer: \$61.25

7c. \$8.40

9. 17 years old

11a. $h = 0$. Before the ball is hit, it is on the ground.

11b. $h = 32$. Two seconds after being hit, the ball is 32 feet above the ground.

11c. $h = 0$. After three seconds, the ball lands on the ground.

13a. $y = 1$ **13b.** $y = 8$

13c. $y = \frac{1}{4}$ **13d.** $x = 5$

15. *Hint:* Mr. Mendoza is meeting with Mr. Green in the conference room at 9:00 A.M.

LESSON 1.1

1a. 20, 26, 32, 38 **1b.** 47, 44, 41, 38

1c. 32, 48, 72, 108 **1d.** $-18, -13.7, -9.4, -5.1$

3. $u_1 = 40$ and $u_n = u_{n-1} - 3.45$ where $n \geq 2$; $u_5 = 26.2$; $u_9 = 12.4$

5a. $u_1 = 2$ and $u_n = u_{n-1} + 4$ where $n \geq 2$; $u_{15} = 58$

5b. $u_1 = 10$ and $u_n = u_{n-1} - 5$ where $n \geq 2$; $u_{12} = -45$

5c. $u_1 = 0.4$ and $u_n = 0.1 \cdot u_{n-1}$ where $n \geq 2$; $u_{10} = 0.0000000004$

5d. $u_1 = -2$ and $u_n = u_{n-1} - 6$ where $n \geq 2$; $u_{30} = -176$

5e. $u_1 = 1.56$ and $u_n = u_{n-1} + 3.29$ where $n \geq 2$; $u_{14} = 44.33$

5f. $u_1 = -6.24$ and $u_n = u_{n-1} + 2.21$ where $n \geq 2$; $u_{20} = 35.75$

7. $u_1 = 4$ and $u_n = u_{n-1} + 6$ where $n \geq 2$; $u_4 = 22$; $u_5 = 28$; $u_{12} = 70$; $u_{32} = 190$

9a. 399 km

9b. 10 hours after the first car starts, or 8 hours after the second car starts

11a. \$60 **11b.** \$33.75

11c. during the ninth week

13. *Hint:* Construct two intersecting lines, and then construct several lines that are perpendicular to one of the lines and equally spaced from each other starting from the point of intersection.

15a. $\frac{70}{100} = \frac{a}{65}$; $a = 45.5$

15b. $\frac{115}{100} = \frac{b}{37}$; $b = 42.55$

15c. $\frac{c}{100} = \frac{110}{90}$; $c \approx 122.2\%$

15d. $\frac{d}{100} = \frac{0.5}{18}$; $d \approx 2.78\%$

17. the 7% offer at \$417.30 per week

LESSON 1.2

1a. 1.5 **1b.** 0.4 **1c.** 1.03 **1d.** 0.92

3a. $u_1 = 100$ and $u_n = 1.5u_{n-1}$ where $n \geq 2$; $u_{10} = 3844.3$

3b. $u_1 = 73.4375$ and $u_n = 0.4u_{n-1}$ where $n \geq 2$; $u_{10} = 0.020$

3c. $u_1 = 80$ and $u_n = 1.03u_{n-1}$ where $n \geq 2$; $u_{10} = 104.38$

3d. $u_1 = 208$ and $u_n = 0.92u_{n-1}$ where $n \geq 2$; $u_{10} = 98.21$

5a. $(1 + 0.07)u_{n-1}$ or $1.07u_{n-1}$

5b. $(1 - 0.18)A$ or $0.82A$

5c. $(1 + 0.08125)x$ or $1.08125x$

5d. $(2 - 0.85)u_{n-1}$ or $1.15u_{n-1}$

7. 100 is the initial height, but the units are unknown. 0.20 is the percent loss, so the ball loses 20% of its height with each rebound.

9a. number of new hires for next five years: 2, 3, 3 (or 4), 4, and 5

9b. about 30 employees

11. $u_0 = 1$ and $u_n = 0.8855u_{n-1}$ where $n \geq 1$
$u_{25} = 0.048$, or 4.8%. It would take about 25,000 years to reduce to 5%.

13a. 0.542% **13b.** \$502.71

13c. \$533.49 **13d.** \$584.80

15a. 3 **15b.** $2, 6, \ldots, 54, \ldots, 486, 1458, \ldots, 13122$

15c. 118,098

17a. 4 m/s **17b.** 10 s

17c.

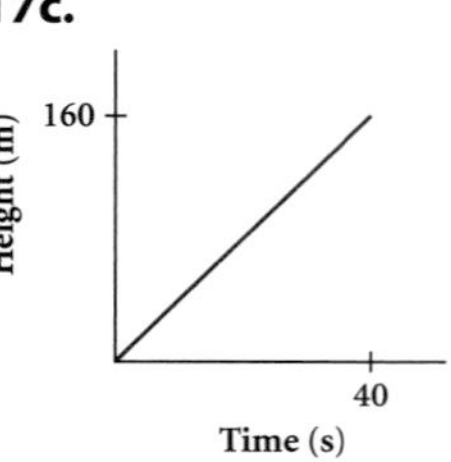

17d.

160
Height (m)
40
Time (s)

17e.

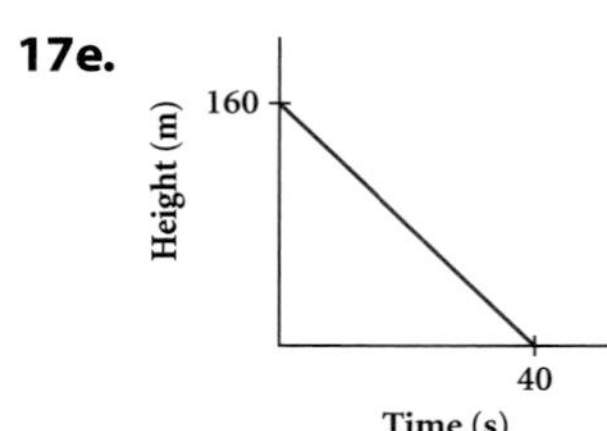

19a. $x \approx 43.34$ **19b.** $x = -681.5$

19c. $x \approx 0.853$ **19d.** $x = 8$

LESSON 1.3

1a. 31.2, 45.64, 59.358; shifted geometric, increasing

1b. 776, 753.2, 731.54; shifted geometric, decreasing

1c. 45, 40.5, 36.45; geometric, decreasing

1d. 40, 40, 40; arithmetic or shifted geometric, neither increasing nor decreasing

3a. 320 **3b.** 320 **3c.** 0 **3d.** 40

5a. The first day, 300 grams of chlorine were added. Each day, 15% disappears, and 30 more grams are added.

5b. It levels off at 200 g.

7a. The account balance will continue to decrease (slowly at first, but faster after a while). It does not level off, but it eventually reaches 0 and stops decreasing.

7b. \$68

9. $u_0 = 20$ and $u_n = (1 - 0.25)u_{n-1}$ where $n \geq 1$; 11 days

11a. Sample answer: After 9 hours there are only 8 mg, after 18 hours there are 4 mg, after 27 hours there are still 2 mg left.

11b.

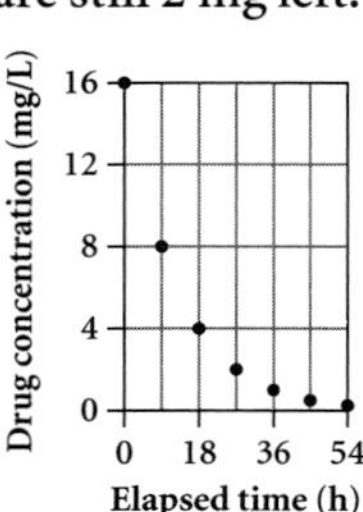

11c. 8 mg

13a. $u_2 = -96, u_5 = 240$ **13b.** $u_2 = 2, u_5 = 1024$

15. 23 times

LESSON 1.4

1a. 0 to 9 for n and 0 to 16 for u_n

1b. 0 to 19 for n and 0 to 400 for u_n

1c. 0 to 29 for n and -178 to 25 for u_n

1d. 0 to 69 for n and 0 to 3037 for u_n

3a. geometric, nonlinear, decreasing

3b. arithmetic, linear, decreasing

3c. geometric, nonlinear, increasing

3d. arithmetic, linear, increasing

5. i. C **5. ii.** B **5. iii.** A

7. The graph of an arithmetic sequence is always linear. The graph increases when the common difference is positive and decreases when the common difference is negative. The steepness of the graph relates to the common difference.

9a.

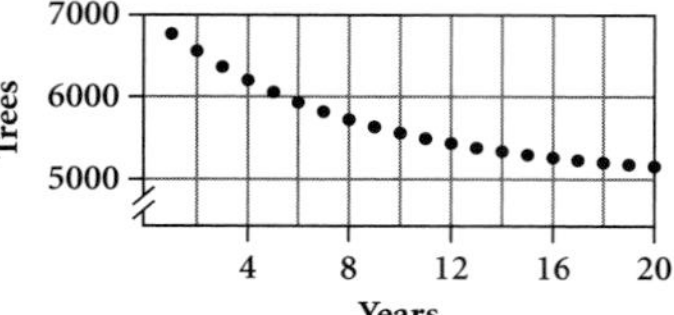

9b. The graph appears to have a long-run value of 5000 trees, which agrees with the long-run value found in Exercise 8b in Lesson 1.3.

11. possible answer: $u_{50} = 40$ and $u_n = u_{n-1} + 4$ where $n \geq 51$

13a. 547.5, 620.6, 675.5, 716.6, 747.5

13b. $\dfrac{547.5 - 210}{0.75} = 450$; subtract 210 and divide the difference by 0.75.

13c. $u_0 = 747.5$ and $u_n = \dfrac{u_{n-1} - 210}{0.75}$ where $n \geq 1$

15a. $33\frac{1}{3}$ **15b.** $66\frac{2}{3}$ **15c.** 100

15d. The long-run value grows in proportion to the added constant. $7 \cdot 33\frac{1}{3} = 233\frac{1}{3}$

LESSON 1.5

1a. investment, because a deposit is added

1b. \$450 **1c.** \$50 **1d.** 3.9%

1e. annually (once a year)

3a. \$130.67 **3b.** \$157.33 **3c.** \$184.00 **3d.** \$210.67

5. \$588.09

7a. \$1877.14 **7b.** \$1912.18 **7c.** \$1915.43

7d. The more frequently the interest is compounded, the more quickly the balance will grow.

9a. \$123.98

9b. for $u_0 = 5000$ and

$u_n = \left(1 + \frac{0.085}{12}\right)u_{n-1} + 123.98$ where $n \geq 1$

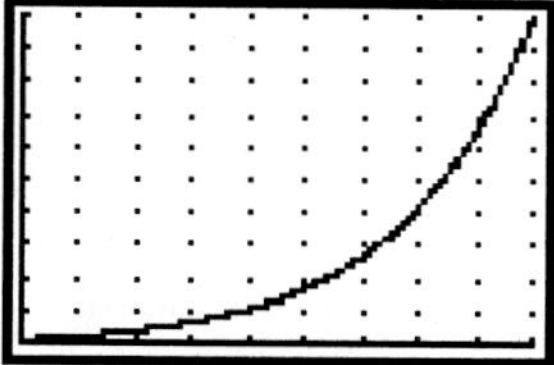

[0, 540, 60, 0, 900000, 100000]

11a. \$528.39

11b. for $u_0 = 60000$ and

$u_n = \left(1 + \frac{0.096}{12}\right)u_{n-1} - 528.39$ where $n \geq 1$

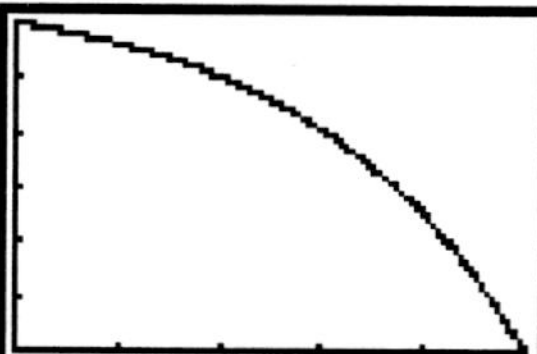

[0, 300, 60, 0, 60000, 10000]

13. something else

15a. 30.48 cm **15b.** 320 km **15c.** 129.64 m

CHAPTER 1 REVIEW

1a. geometric

1b. $u_1 = 256$ and $u_n = 0.75u_{n-1}$ where $n \geq 2$

1c. $u_8 \approx 34.2$ **1d.** $u_{10} \approx 19.2$ **1e.** $u_{17} \approx 2.57$

3a. $-3, -1.5, 0, 1.5, 3$; 0 to 6 for n and -4 to 4 for u_n

3b. 2, 4, 10, 28, 82; 0 to 6 for n and 0 to 100 for u_n

5.i. C **5.ii.** D **5.iii.** B **5.iv.** A

7. approximately 5300; approximately 5200; $u_0 = 5678$ and $u_n = (1 - 0.24)u_{n-1} + 1250$ where $n \geq 1$

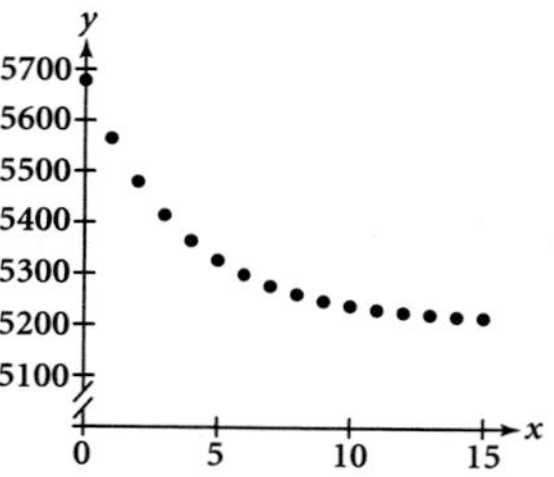

9. $u_{1970} = 34$ and $u_n = (1 + 0.075)u_{n-1}$ where $n \geq 1971$

LESSON 2.1

1a. mean: 29.2 min; median: 28 min; mode: 26 min

1b. mean: 17.35 cm; median: 17.95 cm; mode: 17.4 cm

1c. mean: \$2.38; median: \$2.38; mode: none

1d. mean: 2; median: 2; modes: 1 and 3

3. minimum: 1.25 days; first quartile: 2.5 days; median: 3.25 days; third quartile: 4 days; maximum: 4.75 days

5. D

7. *Hint:* Consider the definitions of each of the values in the five-number summary.

9a. Connie: *range* = 4, *IQR* = 3; Oscar: *range* = 24, *IQR* = 18

9b. *range* = 47; *IQR* = 14

11. *Hint:* Choose three values above 65 and three values below 65.

13a. juniors: $\bar{x} \approx 12.3$ lb; seniors: $\bar{x} \approx 8.6$ lb

13b. juniors: *median* = 10 lb; seniors: *median* = 8 lb

13c. Each mean is greater than the corresponding median.

15a. chemical: 2.29816, 2.29869, 2.29915, 2.30074, 2.30182; atmospheric: 2.30956, 2.309935, 2.31010, 2.3026, 2.31163

15b.

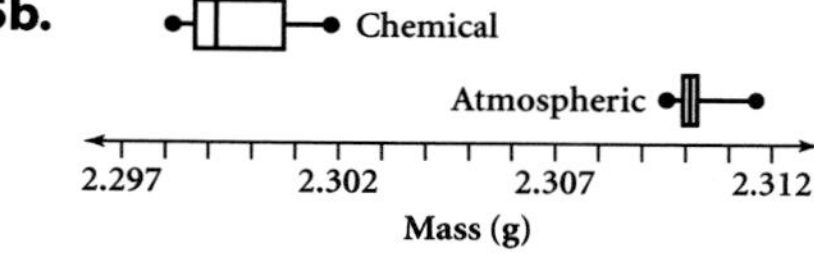

15c. *Hint:* Compare the range, *IQR*, and how the data are skewed. If you conclude that the data are significantly different, then Rayleigh's conjecture is supported.

17a. $6\sqrt{2} \approx 8.5$ **17b.** $\sqrt{89} \approx 9.4$

Selected Answers

17c. $\frac{\sqrt{367}}{2} \approx 9.6$

19a. $x = 7$ **19b.** $x = 5$

19c. $x = \frac{7}{3} = 2.\overline{3}$

LESSON 2.2

1a. 47.0 **1b.** $-6, 8, 1, -3$ **1c.** 6.1

3a. 9, 10, 14, 17, 21 **3b.** $range = 12$; $IQR = 7$

3c. centimeters

5. *Hint:* The number in the middle is 84. Choose three numbers on either side that also have a mean of 84, and check that the other criteria are satisfied. Adjust data values as necessary.

7. 20.8 and 22.1. These are the same outliers found by the interquartile range.

9a. *Hint:* The two box plots must have the same endpoints and *IQR*. The data that is skewed left should have a median value to the right of the center.

9b. The skewed data set will have a greater standard deviation because the data to the left (below the median) will be spread farther from the mean.

9c. *Hint:* The highest and lowest values for each set must be equal, and the skewed data will have a higher median value.

9d. Answers will vary, depending on 9c, but should support 9b.

11a. First period appears to have pulse rates most alike because that class had the smallest standard deviation.

11b. Sixth period might have the fastest pulse rates because that class has both the highest mean and the greatest standard deviation.

13a. $median = 75$ packages; $IQR = 19$ packages

13b. $\bar{x} \approx 80.9$ packages; $s \approx 24.6$ packages

13c. Hot Chocolate Mix

40 60 80 100 120 140 160
Packages

five-number summary: 44, 67.5, 75, 86.5, 158; outliers: 147, 158

13d. Hot Chocolate Mix

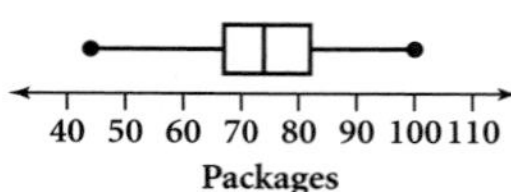

five-number summary: 44, 67, 74, 82, 100

13e. $median = 74$ packages; $IQR = 15$ packages; $\bar{x} \approx 74.7$ packages; $s \approx 12.4$ packages

13f. The mean and standard deviation are calculated from all data values, so outliers affect these statistics significantly. The median and *IQR*, in contrast, are defined by position and not greatly affected by outliers.

15a. mean: \$80.52; median: \$75.00; modes: \$71.00, \$74.00, \$76.00, \$102.50

15b. CD Players

60 80 100 120 140
Price (\$)

five-number summary: 51, 71, 75, 87, 135.5

The box plot is skewed right.

15c. $IQR = \$16$; outliers: \$112.50 and \$135.50

15d. The median will be less affected because the relative positions of the middle numbers will be changed less than the sum of the numbers.

15e. CD Players

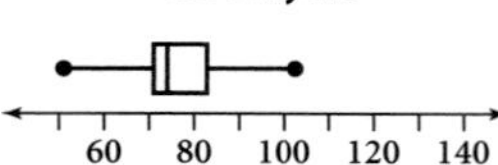

five-number summary: 51, 71, 74, 82.87, 102.5
The median of the new data set is \$74.00 and is relatively unchanged.

15f. *Hint:* Consider whether your decision should be based on the data with or without outliers included. Decide upon a reasonable first bid, and the maximum you would pay.

17a. $x = 59$ **17b.** $y = 20$

LESSON 2.3

1a. 2 **1b.** 9

1c. *Hint:* Choose values that reflect the number of backpacks within each bin.

3a. 5 values

3b. 25th percentile **3c.** 95th percentile

5a. The numbers of acres planted by farmers who plant more than the median number of acres vary more than the numbers of acres planted by farmers who plant fewer than the median number of acres.

5b.

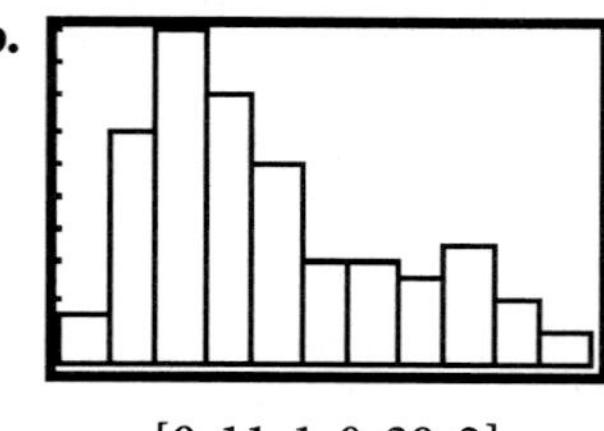

[0, 11, 1, 0, 20, 2]

5c. In a box plot, the part of the box to the left of the median would be smaller than the part to the right because there are more values close to 3 on the left than on the right.

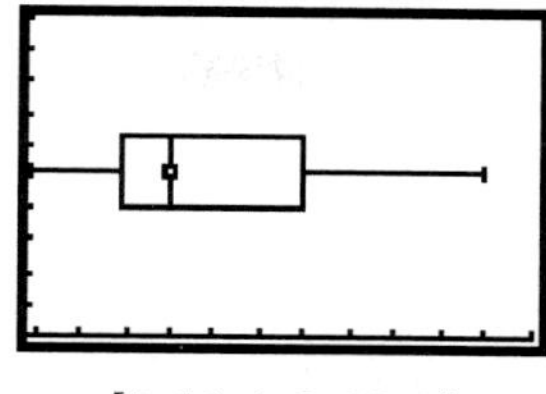

[0, 11, 1, 0, 20, 2]

7a.

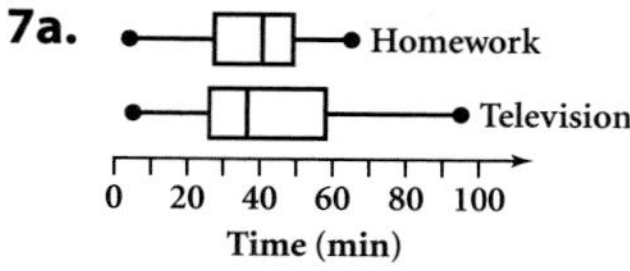

Television has the greater spread.

7b. Television will be skewed right. Neither will be mound shaped.

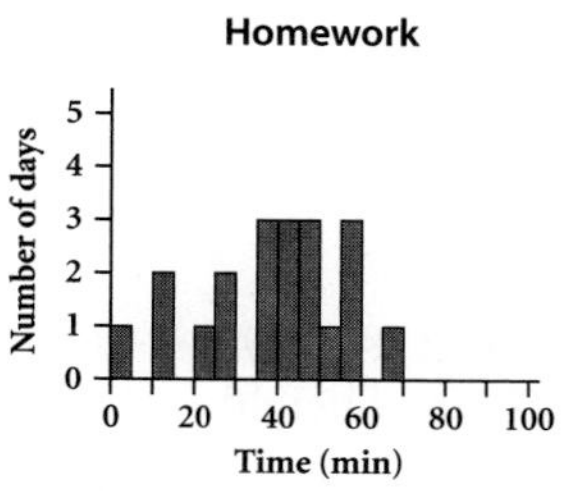

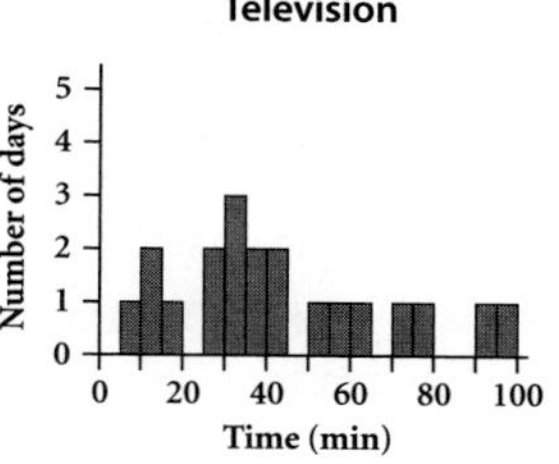

7c. Homework: *median* = 40.5 min; *IQR* = 21.5 min; $\bar{x} \approx 38.4$ min; $s \approx 16.7$ min.
Television: *median* = 36.5 min; *IQR* = 32 min; $\bar{x} = 42.2$ min; $s \approx 26.0$ min. Answers will vary.

9a.

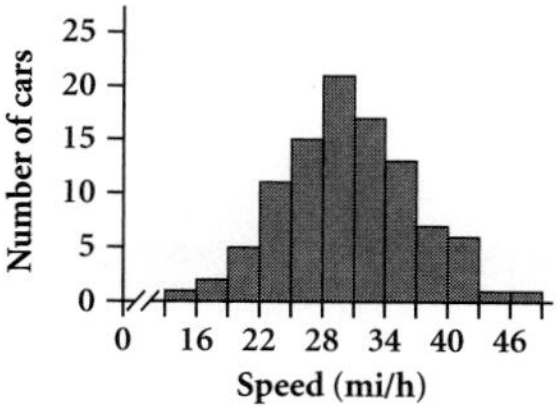

9b. between 37 mi/h and 39 mi/h

9c. possible answer: 35 mi/h

9d. Answers will vary.

11a. The sum of the deviations is 13, not 0.

11b. 20

11c.i. {747, 707, 669, 676, 767, 783, 789, 838}; $s \approx 59.1$; *median* = 757; *IQR* = 94.5

11c.ii. {850, 810, 772, 779, 870, 886, 892, 941}; $s \approx 59.1$; *median* = 860; *IQR* = 94.5

11d. *Hint:* How does translating the data affect the standard deviation and *IQR*?

13. Marissa runs faster.

CHAPTER 2 REVIEW

1. Plot B has the greater standard deviation, because the data have more spread.

3a. mean: 553.6 points; median: 460 points; mode: none

3b. 5, 167, 460, 645, 2019

3c. skewed right

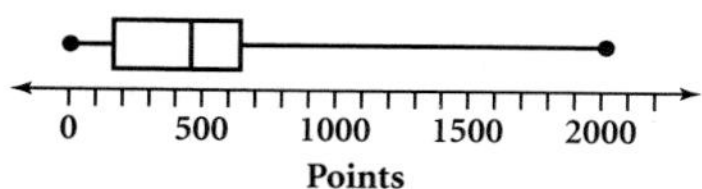

3d. 478 points

3e. Kobe Bryant (2019 points) and Shaquille O'Neal (1822 points)

5a. $\bar{x} \approx 118.3$°F; $s \approx 26.8$°F

5b. $\bar{x} = -60.0$°F; $s \approx 45.7$°F

5c. Antarctica (59°F) is an outlier for the high temperatures. There are no outliers for the low temperatures.

7. Answers will vary. In general, the theory is supported by the statistics and graphs.

CHAPTER 3

LESSON 3.1

1a.

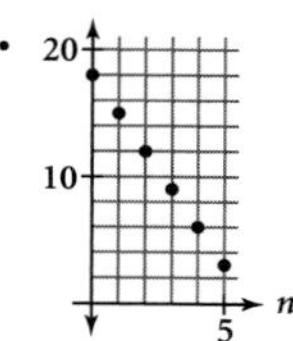

1b. −3; The common difference is the same as the slope.

1c. 18; The y-intercept is the u_0-term of the sequence.

1d. $y = 18 - 3x$

3. $y = 7 + 3x$

5a. 1.7 **5b.** 1 **5c.** −4.5 **5d.** 0

7a. 190 mi **7b.** $y = 82 + 54x$

7c.

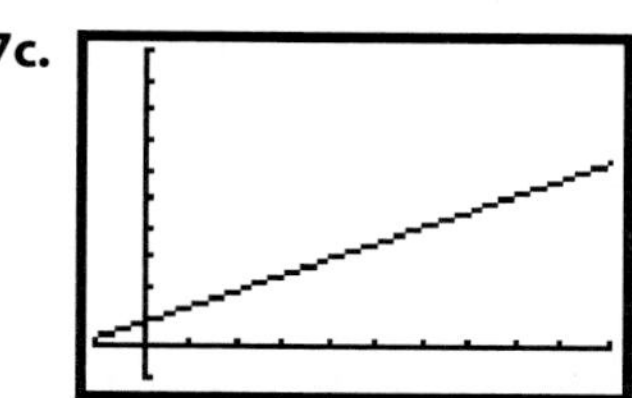

[−1, 10, 1, −100, 1000, 100]

7d. Yes, if only distances on the hour are considered. A line is continuous, whereas an arithmetic sequence is discrete.

9a. $u_0 = -2$ **9b.** 5 **9c.** 50

9d. because you need to add 50 d's to the original height of u_0

9e. $u_n = u_0 + nd$

11a. *Hint:* The x-values must have a difference of 5.

11b. Graphs will vary; 4

11c. 7, 11, 15, 19, 23, 27

11d. *Hint:* The linear equation will have slope of 4. Find the y-intercept.

13. Although the total earnings are different at the end of the odd-numbered six-month periods, the total yearly income is always the same.

15a. \$93.49; \$96.80; \$7.55

15b. The median and mean prices indicate the mid-price and average price, respectively. The standard deviation indicates the amount of variation in prices. The median tells trend of prices better than the mean, which can be affected by outliers.

LESSON 3.2

1a. $\frac{3}{2} = 1.5$ **1b.** $-\frac{2}{3} \approx -0.67$ **1c.** -55

3a. $y = 14.3$ **3b.** $x = 6.5625$

3c. $a = -24$ **3d.** $b = -0.25$

5a. The equations have the same constant, -2. The lines share the same y-intercept. The lines are perpendicular, and their slopes are reciprocals with opposite signs.

5b. The equations have the same x-coefficient, -1.5. The lines have the same slope. The lines are parallel.

7a. Answer depends on data points used. Approximately 1.47 volts/battery.

7b. Answers will vary. The voltage increases by about 1.47 volts for every additional battery.

7c. Yes. There is no voltage produced from zero batteries, so the y-intercept should be 0.

9a. \$20,497; \$17,109 **9b.** \$847 per year

9c. in her 17th year

11a. Answer depends on data points used. Each additional ticket sold brings in about \$7.62 more in revenue.

11b. Answers will vary. Use points that are not too close together.

13a. $-10 + 3x$ **13b.** $1 - 11x$ **13c.** $28.59 + 5.4x$

15a. 71.7 beats/min

15b. 6.47 beats/min. The majority of the data falls within 6.47 beats/min of the mean.

17a. $a > 0, b < 0$ **17b.** $a < 0, b > 0$

17c. $a > 0, b = 0$ **17d.** $a = 0, b < 0$

LESSON 3.3

1a. $y = 1 + \frac{2}{3}(x - 4)$ **1b.** $y = 2 - \frac{1}{5}(x - 1)$

3a. $u_n = 31$ **3b.** $t = -41.5$ **3c.** $x = 1.5$

5a.

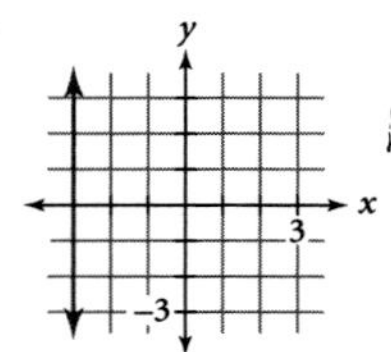

possible answer: $(-3, 0), (-3, 2)$

5b. undefined **5c.** $x = 3$

5d. *Hint:* What can you say about the slope and the x- and y-intercepts of a vertical line?

7a. The y-intercept is about 1.7; (5, 4.6); $\hat{y} = 1.7 + 0.58x$.

7b. The y-intercept is about 7.5; (5, 3.75); $\hat{y} = 7.5 - 0.75x$.

7c. The y-intercept is about 8.6; (5, 3.9); $\hat{y} = 8.6 - 0.94x$.

9a. possible answer: [145, 200, 5, 40, 52, 1]

9b. possible answer: $\hat{y} = 0.26x + 0.71$

9c. On average, a student's forearm length increases by 0.26 cm for each additional 1 cm of height.

9d. The y-intercept is meaningless because a height of 0 cm should not predict a forearm length of 0.71 cm. The domain should be specified.

9e. 189.58 cm; 41.79 cm

11. 102

13a. 16

13b. Add 19.5 and any three numbers greater than 19.5.

LESSON 3.4

1a. 17, 17, 17 **1b.** 17, 16, 17

1c. 16, 15, 16 **1d.** 13, 12, 13

3. $y = 0.9 + 0.75(x - 14.4)$

5. $y = 3.15 + 4.7x$

7. Answers will vary. If the residuals are small and have no pattern, as shown by the box plot and histogram, then the model is good.

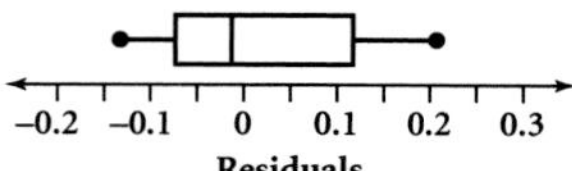

9a. $\hat{y} = 997.12 - 0.389x$

9b. The world record for the 1-mile run is reduced by 0.389 s every year.

9c. 3:57.014. This prediction is 2.3 s faster than Roger Bannister actually ran.

9d. 4:27.745. This prediction is about 3.2 s slower than Walter Slade actually ran.

9e. This suggests that a world record for the mile in the year 0 would have been about 16.6 minutes. This is doubtful because a fast walker can walk a mile in about 15 minutes. The data are only approximately linear and only over a limited domain.

9f. A record of 3:43.13, 3.61 s slower than predicted was set by Hicham El Guerrouj in 1999.

11a.

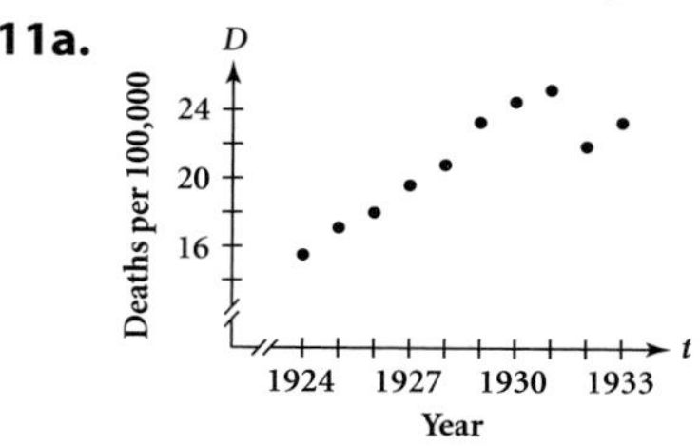

11b. $M_1(1925, 17.1), M_2(1928.5, 22.05), M_3(1932, 23.3)$

11c. $\hat{D} = -1687.83 + 0.886t$

11d. For each additional year, the number of deaths by automobile increases by 0.886 per hundred thousand population.

11e. Answers might include the fact that the United States was in the Great Depression and fewer people were driving.

11f. It probably would not be a good idea to extrapolate because a lot has changed in the automotive industry in the past 75 years. Many safety features
are now standard.

13. $y = 7 - 3x$

15. 2.3 g, 3.0 g, 3.0 g, 3.4 g, 3.6 g, 3.9 g

LESSON 3.5

1a. -0.2 **1b.** -0.4 **1c.** 0.6

3a. $-2.74; -1.2; -0.56; -0.42; -0.18; 0.66; 2.3; 1.74; 0.98; 0.02; -0.84; -0.3; -0.26; -0.22; -0.78; -1.24; -0.536$

3b. 1.22 yr

3c. In general, the life expectancy values predicted by the median-median line will be within 1.23 yr of the actual data values.

5a. Let x represent age in years, and let y represent height in cm; $\hat{y} = 82.5 + 5.6x$.

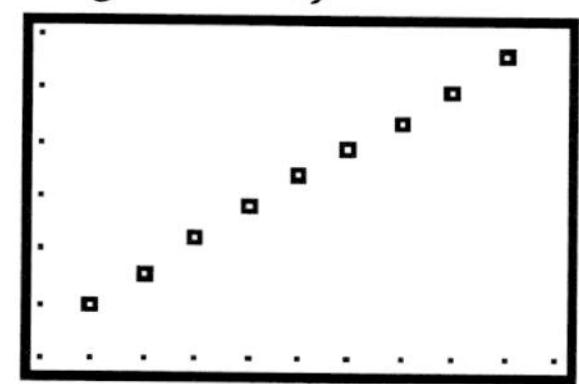

[4, 14, 1, 100, 160, 10]

5b. $-1.3, -0.4, 0.3, 0.8, 0.8, 0.3, -0.4, -0.4, 1.1$

5c. 0.83 cm

5d. In general, the mean height of boys ages 5 to 13 will be within 0.83 cm of the values predicted by the median-median line.

5e. between 165.7 cm and 167.3 cm

7. $\hat{y} = 29.8 + 2.4x$

9. Alex's method: 3.67; root mean square error method: approximately 3.21. Both methods give answers around 3, so Alex's method could be used as an alternate measure of accuracy.

11a.

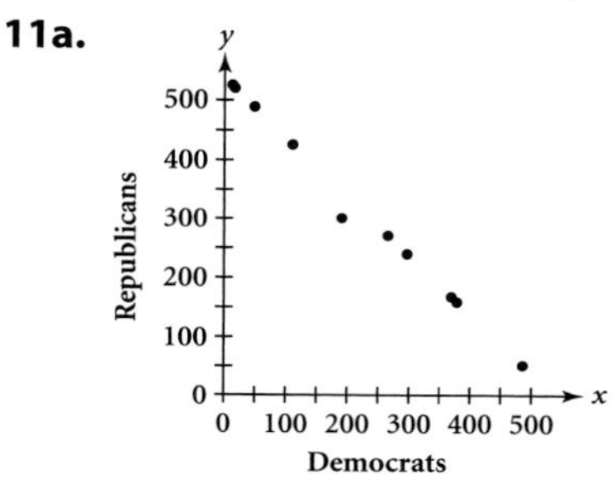

11b. The points are nearly linear because the sum of electoral votes should be 538. The data are not perfectly linear because in a few of the elections, candidates other than the Democrats and Republicans received some electoral votes.

11c.

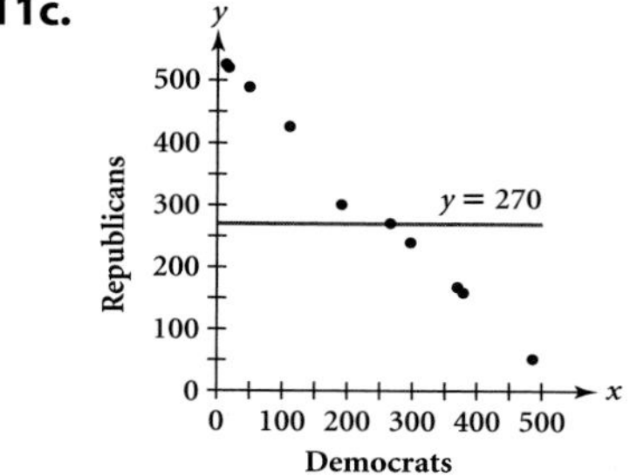

The points above the line are the elections in which the Republican Party's presidential candidate won.

11d. $-218, 31, 250, -30, 219, 255, 156, -102, -111, 1$
A negative residual means that the Democratic Party's presidential candidate won.

11e. a close election

13. *Hint:* The difference between the 2nd and 6th values is 12.

15a. $u_0 = 30$ and $u_n = u_{n-1}\left(1 + \frac{0.07}{12}\right) + 30$ where $n \geq 1$

15b. i. deposited: \$360; interest: \$11.78

15b. ii. deposited: \$3,600; interest: \$1,592.54

15b. iii. deposited: \$9,000; interest: \$15,302.15

15b. iv. deposited: \$18,000; interest: \$145,442.13

15c. Sample answer: If you earn compound interest, in the long run the interest earned will far exceed the total amount deposited.

LESSON 3.6

1a. $(1.8, -11.6)$ **1b.** $(3.7, 31.9)$

3. $y = 5 + 0.4(x - 1)$

5a. $(4.125, -10.625)$ **5b.** $(-3.16, 8.27)$

5c. They intersect at every point; they are the same line.

7a. No. At $x = 25$, the cost line is above the income line.

7b. Yes. The profit is approximately \$120.

7c. About 120 pogo sticks. Look for the point where the cost and income lines intersect.

9a. Phrequent Phoner Plan: $y = 20 + 17([x] - 1)$; Small Business Plan: $y = 50 + 11([x] - 1)$

9b.

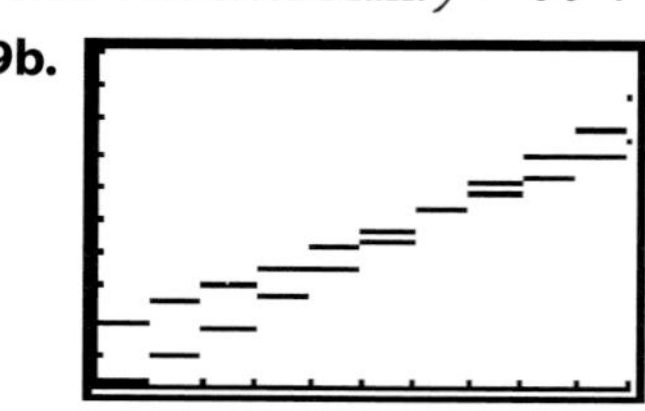

$[0, 10, 1, 0, 200, 20]$

9c. If the time of the phone call is less than 6 min, PPP is less expensive. For times between 6 and 7 min, the plans charge the same rate. If the time of the phone call is greater than or equal to 7 min, PPP is more expensive than SBP. (You could look at the calculator table to see these results.)

11a. Let l represent length in centimeters, and let w represent width in centimeters; $2l + 2w = 44$, $l = 2 + 2w$; $w = \frac{20}{3}$ cm, $l = \frac{46}{3}$ cm.

11b. Let l represent length of leg in centimeters, and let b represent length of base in centimeters; $2l + b = 40$, $b = l - 2$; $l = 14$ cm, $b = 12$ cm.

11c. Let f represent temperature in degrees Fahrenheit, and let c represent temperature in degrees Celsius; $f = 3c - 0.4$, $f = 1.8c + 32$; $c = 27°C$, $f = 80.6°F$.

13a. 51 **13b.** 3rd bin **13c.** 35%

LESSON 3.7

1a. $w = 11 + r$ **1b.** $h = \frac{18 - 2p}{3} = 6 - \frac{2}{3}p$

1c. $r = w - 11$ **1d.** $p = \frac{18 - 3h}{2} = 9 - \frac{3}{2}p$

3a. $5x - 2y = 12$; passes through the point of intersection of the original pair

3b. $-4y = 8$; passes through the point of intersection of the original pair and is horizontal

5a. $\left(-\frac{97}{182}, \frac{19}{7}\right) \approx (-0.5330, 2.7143)$

5b. $\left(8, -\frac{5}{2}\right) \approx (8, -2.5)$

5c. $\left(\frac{186}{59}, -\frac{4}{59}\right) \approx (3.1525, -0.0678)$

5d. $n = 26, s = -71$ **5e.** $d = -18, f = -49$

5f. $\left(\frac{44}{7}, -\frac{95}{14}\right) \approx (6.2857, -6.7857)$

5g. no solution

7. 80°F

9. *Hint:* Write two equations that pass through the point $(-1.4, 3.6)$.

11a. $A = \frac{d^2}{2}$ **11b.** $P = I^2R$ **11c.** $A = \frac{C^2}{4\pi}$

13a. true **13b.** false; $(x - 4)(x + 4)$

15a.

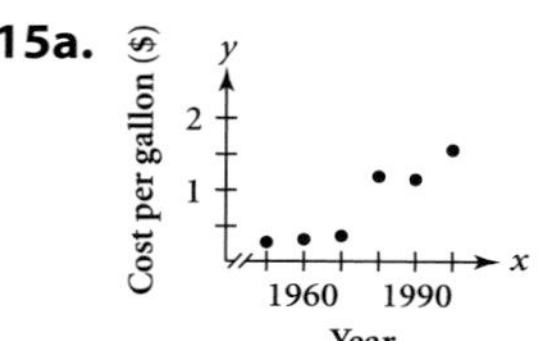

15b. $\hat{y} = \frac{213}{8000}x - 51.78$ or $\hat{y} = 0.027x - 51.78$

15c. If the same trend continues, the cost of gasoline in 2010 will be \$1.74. Answers will vary.

17a. i. 768, –1024; **ii.** 52, 61; **iii.** 32.75, 34.5

17b. i. geometric; **ii.** other; **iii.** arithmetic

17c. i. $u_1 = 243$ and $u_n = \left(-\frac{4}{3}\right)u_{n-1}$ where $n \geq 2$

17c. iii. $u_1 = 24$ and $u_n = u_{n-1} + 1.75$ where $n \geq 2$

17d. iii. $u_n = 1.75n + 22.25$

CHAPTER 3 REVIEW

1. $-\frac{975}{19}$

3a. approximately $(19.9, 740.0)$

3b. approximately $(177.0, 740.0)$

5a. Poor fit; there are too many points above the line.

5b. Reasonably good fit; the points are well-distributed above and below the line, and not clumped.

5c. Poor fit; there are an equal number of points above and below the line, but they are clumped to the left and to the right, respectively.

7a. $(1, 0)$

7b. every point; same line

7c. No intersection; the lines are parallel.

9a.

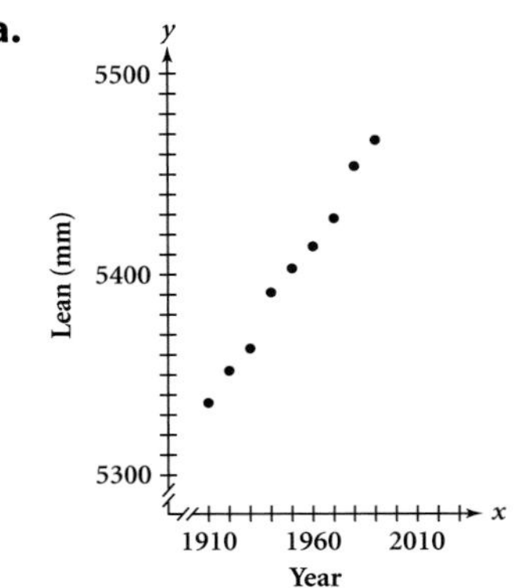

9b. $\hat{y} = 2088 + 1.7x$

9c. 1.7; for every additional year, the tower leans another 1.7 mm.

9d. 5474.4 mm

9e. Approximately 5.3 mm; the prediction in 9d is probably accurate within 5.3 mm. So the actual value will probably be between 5469.1 and 5479.7.

9f. $1173 \leq \text{domain} \leq 1992$ (year built to year retrofit began); $0 \leq \text{range} \leq 5474.4$ mm

11a. geometric; curved; 4, 12, 36, 108, 324

11b. shifted geometric; curved; 20, 47, 101, 209, 425

13a. Possible answer: $u_{2005} = 6486915022$ and $u_n = (1 + 0.015)u_{n-1}$ where $n \geq 2006$. The sequence is geometric.

13b. possible answer: 6,988,249,788 people

13c. On January 1, 2035, the population will be just above 10 billion. So the population will first exceed 10 billion late in 2034.

13d. Answers will vary. An increasing geometric sequence has no limit. But the model will not work for the distant future because there is a physical limit to how many people will fit on Earth.

15.

0 5 10 15 20

15a. skewed left **15b.** 12 **15c.** 6

15d. 50%; 25%; 0%

17a. $\left(\frac{110}{71}, -\frac{53}{213}\right)$ **17b.** $\left(-\frac{27}{20}, \frac{91}{20}\right)$

17c. $\left(\frac{46}{13}, \frac{9}{26}\right)$

19a. $u_1 = 6$ and $u_n = u_{n-1} + 7$ where $n \geq 1$

19b. $y = 6 + 7x$

19c. The slope is 7. The slope of the line is the same as the common difference of the sequence.

19d. 230; It's probably easier to use the equation from 19b.

CHAPTER 4 • CHAPTER 4 CHAPTER 4 • CHAPTER

LESSON 4.1

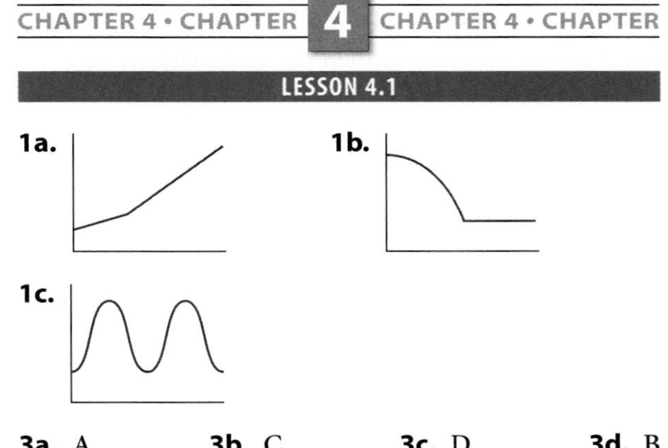

3a. A **3b.** C **3c.** D **3d.** B

5. *Hint:* Consider the rate and direction of change (increasing, decreasing, constant) of the various segments of the graph.

7a. Time in years is the independent variable; the amount of money in dollars is the dependent variable. The graph will be a series of discontinuous segments.

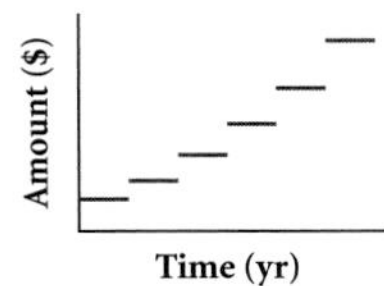

7b. Time in years is the independent variable; the amount of money in dollars is the dependent variable. The graph will be a continuous horizontal segment because the amount never changes.

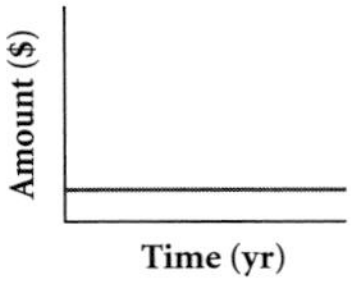

7c. Foot length in inches is the independent variable; shoe size is the dependent variable. The graph will be a series of discontinuous horizontal segments because shoe sizes are discrete.

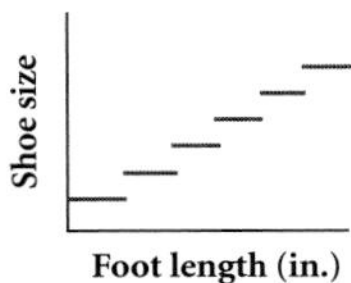

7d. Time in hours is the independent variable; distance in miles is the dependent variable. The graph will be continuous because distance is changing continuously over time.

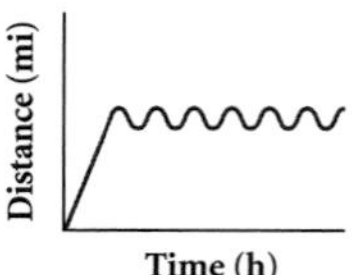

7e. The day of the month is the independent variable; the maximum temperature in degrees Fahrenheit is the dependent variable. The graph will be discrete points because there is just one temperature reading per day.

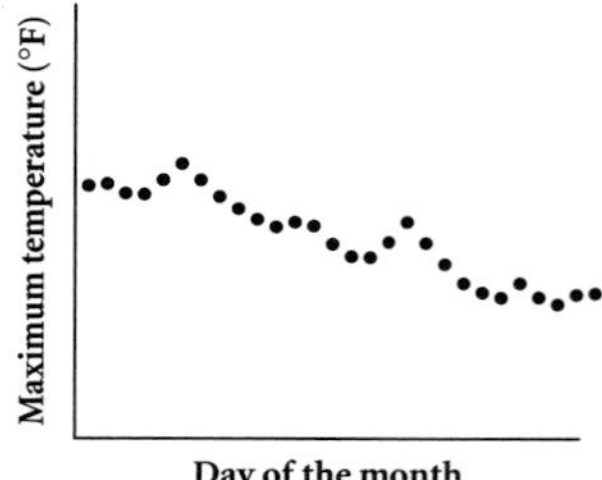

9a. Car A speeds up quickly at first and then less quickly until it reaches 60 mi/h. Car B speeds up slowly at first and then quickly until it reaches 60 mi/h.

9b. Car A will be in the lead because it is always going faster than Car B, which means it has covered more distance.

11a. Let x represent the number of pictures and let y represent the amount of money (either cost or income) in dollars; $y = 155 + 15x$.

11b. $y = 27x$

11c. 13 pictures

13a. $3x + 5y = -9$

13b. $6x - 3y = 21$

13c. $x = 2, y = -3$

13d. $x = 2, y = -3, z = 1$

LESSON 4.2

1a. Function; each x-value has only one y-value.

1b. Not a function; there are x-values that are paired with two y-values.

1c. Function; each x-value has only one y-value.

3. B

5a. The price of the calculator is the independent variable; function.

5b. The time the money has been in the bank is the independent variable; function.

5c. The amount of time since your last haircut is the independent variable; function.

5d. The distance you have driven since your last fill-up is the independent variable; function.

7a, c, d.

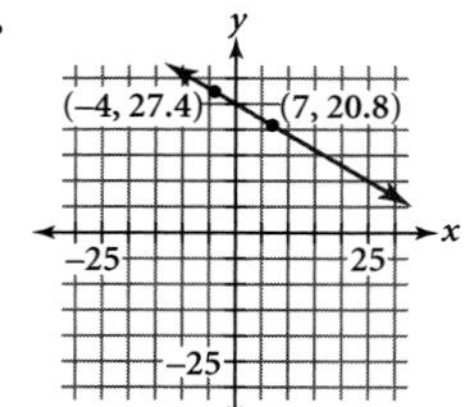

7b. 20.8

7d. −4

9a. possible answer:

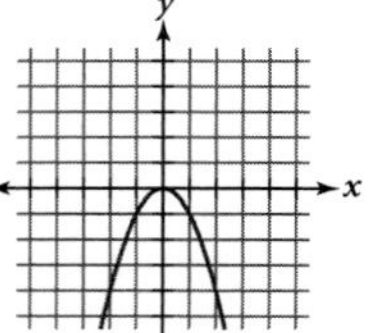

9b. possible answer:

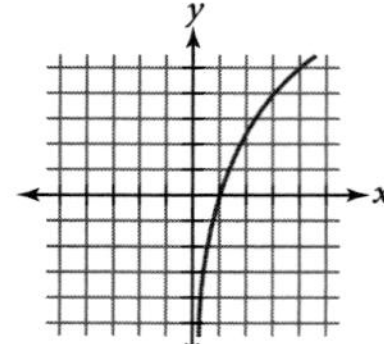

9c.

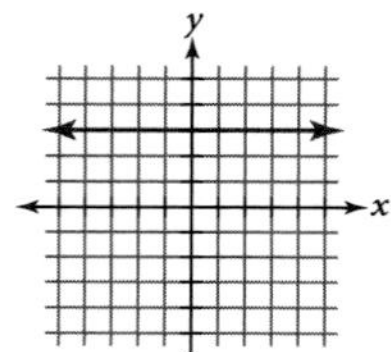

11. Let x represent the time since Kendall started moving and y represent his distance from the motion sensor. The graph is a function; Kendall can be at only one position at each moment in time, so there is only one y-value for each x-value.

13a. 54 diagonals

13b. 20 sides

15. *Hint:* Determine how many students fall into each quartile, and an average value for each quartile.

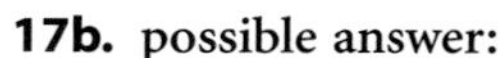

17a. possible answer:

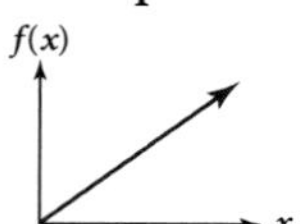

17b. possible answer:

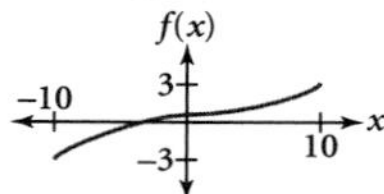

17c. possible answer:

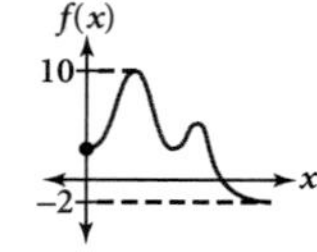

LESSON 4.3

1. $y = -3 + \frac{2}{3}(x - 5)$

3a. $-2(x + 3)$ or $-2x - 6$

3b. $-3 + (-2)(x - 2)$ or $-2x + 1$

3c. $5 + (-2)(x + 1)$ or $-2x + 3$

5a. $y = -3 + 4.7x$ **5b.** $y = -2.8(x - 2)$

5c. $y = 4 - (x + 1.5)$ or $y = 2.5 - x$

7. $y = 47 - 6.3(x - 3)$

9a. $(1400, 733.\bar{3})$ **9b.** $(x + 400, y + 233.\bar{3})$

9c. 20 steps

11a. 12,500; The original value of the equipment is \$12,500.

11b. 10; After 10 years the equipment has no value.

11c. -1250; Every year the value of the equipment decreases by \$1250.

11d. $y = 12500 - 1250x$ **11e.** after 4.8 yr

13a. $x = 15$ **13b.** $x = 31$

13c. $x = -21$ **13d.** $x = 17.6$

LESSON 4.4

1a. $y = x^2 + 2$ **1b.** $y = x^2 - 6$

1c. $y = (x - 4)^2$ **1d.** $y = (x + 8)^2$

3a. translated down 3 units

3b. translated up 4 units

3c. translated right 2 units

3d. translated left 4 units

5a. $x = 2$ or $x = -2$ **5b.** $x = 4$ or $x = -4$

5c. $x = 7$ or $x = -3$

7a. $y = (x - 5)^2 - 3$ **7b.** $(5, -3)$

7c. $(6, -2), (4, -2), (7, 1), (3, 1)$. If (x, y) are the coordinates of any point on the black parabola, then the coordinates of the corresponding point on the red parabola are $(x + 5, y - 3)$.

7d. 1 unit; 4 units

9a.

Number of teams (x)	1	2	3	4	5	6	7	8	9	10
Number of games (y)	0	2	6	12	20	30	42	56	72	90

9b. The points appear to be part of a parabola.

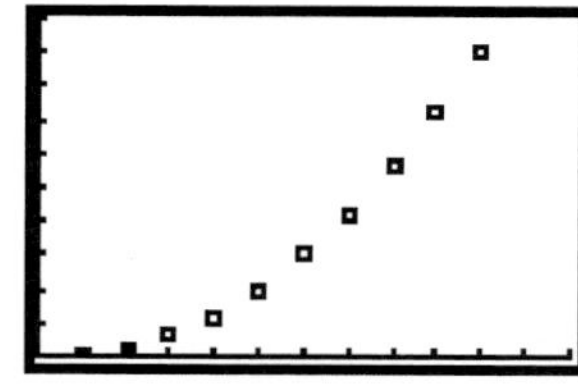

[0, 12, 1, 0, 100, 10]

9c. $y = (x - 0.5)^2 - 0.25$

9d. 870 games

11a.

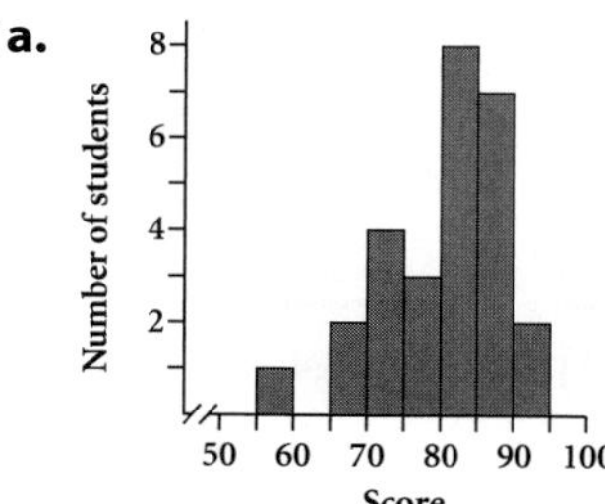

11b.

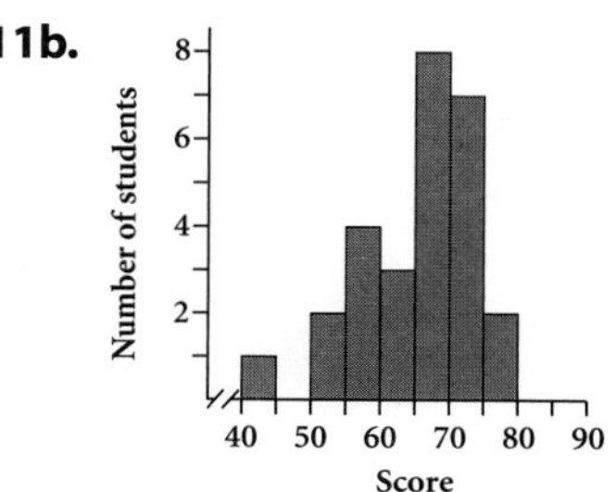

13a. Let m represent the miles driven and let C represent the cost of the one-day rental. Mertz: $C = 32 + 0.1m$; Saver: $C = 24 + 0.18m$; Luxury: $C = 51$.

13b.

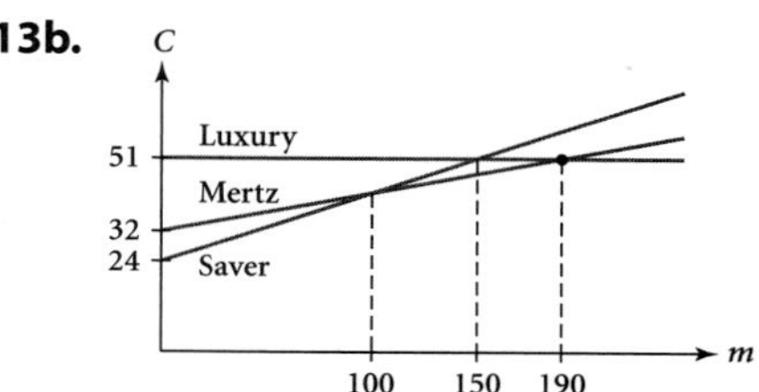

13c. If you plan to drive less than 100 miles, then rent Saver. At exactly 100 miles, Mertz and Saver are the same. If you plan to drive between 100 miles and 190 miles, then rent Mertz. At exactly 190 miles, Mertz and Luxury are the same. If you plan to drive more than 190 miles, then rent Luxury.

15. Answers will vary.

LESSON 4.5

1a. $y = \sqrt{x} + 3$ **1b.** $y = \sqrt{x + 5}$

1c. $y = \sqrt{x + 5} + 2$ **1d.** $y = \sqrt{x - 3} + 1$

1e. $y = \sqrt{x - 1} - 4$

3a. $y = -\sqrt{x}$ **3b.** $y = -\sqrt{x} - 3$

3c. $y = -\sqrt{x + 6} + 5$ **3d.** $y = \sqrt{-x}$

3e. $y = \sqrt{-(x - 2)} - 3$, or $y = \sqrt{-x + 2} - 3$

5a. possible answers: $(-4, -2)$, $(-3, -1)$, and $(0, 0)$

5b. $y = \sqrt{x+4} - 2$

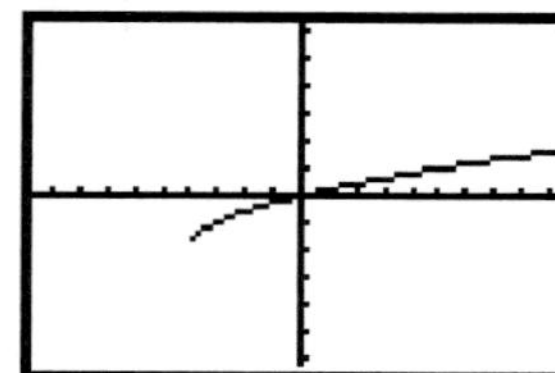

$[-9.4, 9.4, 1, -6.2, 6.2, 1]$

5c. $y = -\sqrt{x-2} + 3$

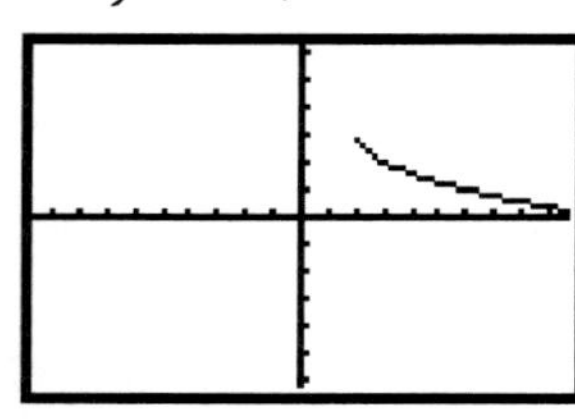

$[-9.4, 9.4, 1, -6.2, 6.2, 1]$

7a. Neither parabola passes the vertical line test.

7b. i. $y = \pm\sqrt{x+4}$ **7b. ii.** $y = \pm\sqrt{x} + 2$

7c. i. $y^2 = x + 4$ **7c. ii.** $(y-2)^2 = x$

9a. $y = -x^2$ **9b.** $y = -x^2 + 2$

9c. $y = -(x-6)^2$ **9d.** $y = -(x-6)^2 - 3$

11a. $S = 5.5\sqrt{0.7D}$

11b.

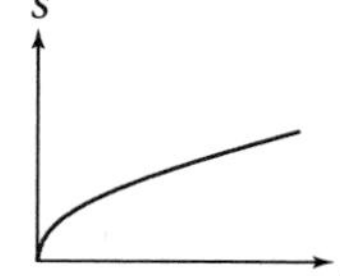

11c. approximately 36 mi/h

11d. $D = \frac{1}{0.7}\left(\frac{S}{5.5}\right)^2$; the minimum braking distance, when the speed is known.

11e.

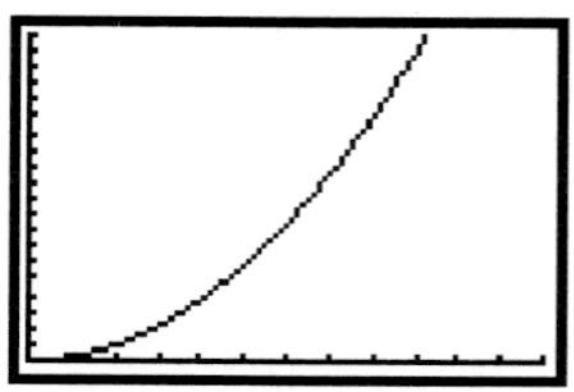

$[0, 60, 5, 0, 100, 5]$

It is a parabola, but the negative half is not used because the distance cannot be negative.

11f. approximately 199.5 ft

13a. $x = 293$ **13b.** no solution

13c. $x = 7$ or $x = -3$ **13d.** $x = -13$

15a. $y = \frac{1}{2}x + 5$

15b. $y = \frac{1}{2}(x-8) + 5$

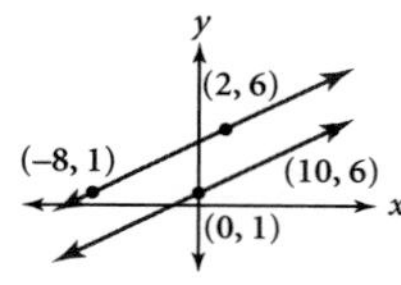

15c. $y = \left(\frac{1}{2}x + 5\right) - 4$ or $y + 4 = \frac{1}{2}x + 5$

15d. Both equations are equivalent to $y = \frac{1}{2}x + 1$.

LESSON 4.6

1a. $y = |x| + 2$ **1b.** $y = |x| - 5$

1c. $y = |x+4|$ **1d.** $y = |x-3|$

1e. $y = |x| - 1$ **1f.** $y = |x-4| + 1$

1g. $y = |x+5| - 3$ **1h.** $y = 3|x-6|$

1i. $y = -\left|\frac{x}{4}\right|$ **1j.** $y = (x-5)^2$

1k. $y = -\frac{1}{2}|x+4|$ **1l.** $y = -|x+4| + 3$

1m. $y = -(x+3)^2 + 5$ **1n.** $y = \pm\sqrt{x-4} + 4$

1p. $y = -2\left|\frac{x-3}{3}\right|$

3a. $y = 2(x-5)^2 - 3$

3b. $y = 2\left|\frac{x+1}{3}\right| - 5$ **3c.** $y = -2\sqrt{\frac{x-6}{-3}} - 7$

5a. 1 and 7; $x = 1$ and $x = 7$

5b. $x = -8$ and $x = 2$

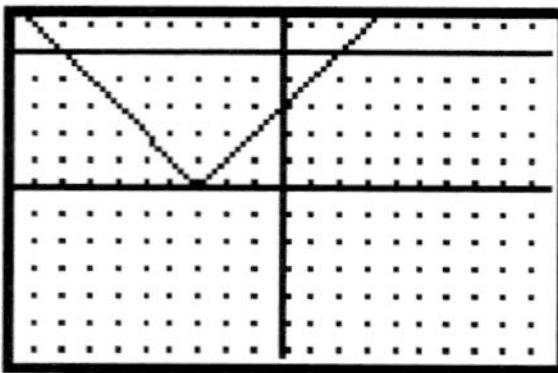

$[-9.4, 9.4, 1, -6.2, 6.2, 1]$

7a. $(6, -2)$

7b. $(2, -3)$ and $(8, -3)$

7c. $(2, -2)$ and $(8, -2)$

9a. possible answers: $x = 4.7$ or $y = 5$

9b. possible answers: $y = 4\left(\frac{x-4.7}{1.9}\right)^2 + 5$ or $\left(\frac{y-5}{4}\right)^2 = \frac{x-4.7}{-1.9}$

9c. There are at least two parabolas. One is oriented horizontally, and another is oriented vertically.

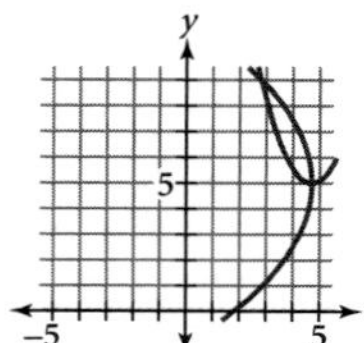

11a.

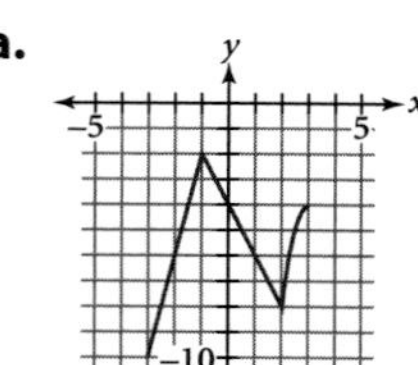

11b.

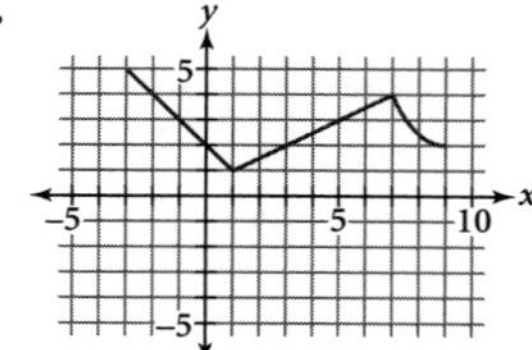

11c.

13a. $\bar{x} = 83.75, s = 7.45$

13b. $\bar{x} = 89.75, s = 7.45$

13c. By adding 6 points to each rating, the mean increases by 6, but the standard deviation remains the same.

LESSON 4.7

1. 2nd row: Reflection, Across x-axis, N/A; 3rd row: Stretch, Horizontal, 4; 4th row: Shrink, Vertical, 0.4; 5th row: Translation, Right, 2; 6th row: Reflection, Across y-axis, N/A

3a.

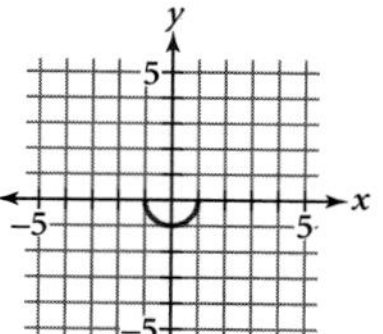

3b.

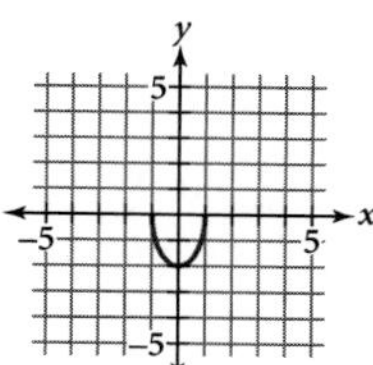

3c.

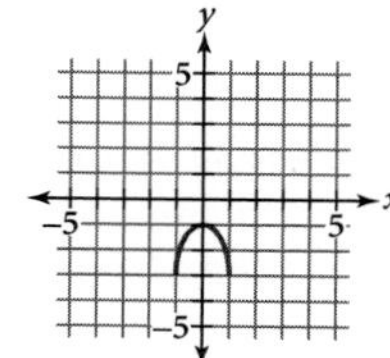

5a.

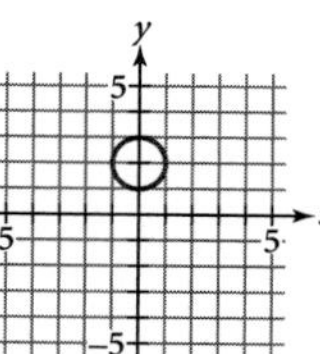

$y = \pm\sqrt{1 - x^2} + 2$ or $x^2 + (y - 2)^2 = 1$

5b.

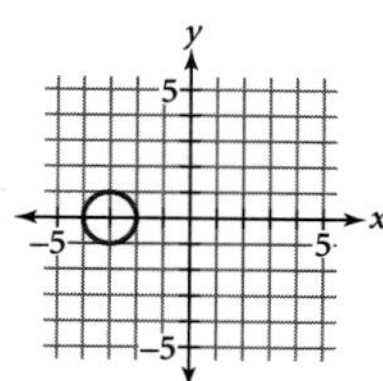

$y = \pm\sqrt{1 - (x + 3)^2}$ or $(x + 3)^2 + y^2 = 1$

5c.

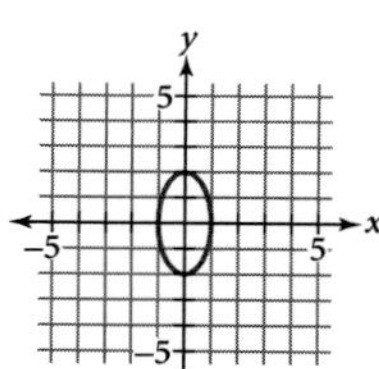

$y = \pm2\sqrt{1 - x^2}$ or $x^2 + \left(\frac{y}{2}\right)^2 = 1$

5d.

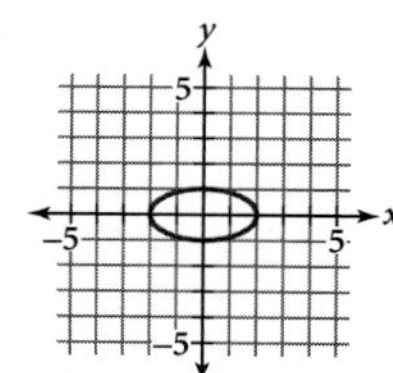

$y = \pm\sqrt{1 - \left(\frac{x}{2}\right)^2}$ or $\frac{x^2}{4} + y^2 = 1$

7a. $x^2 + (2y)^2 = 1$

7b. $(2x)^2 + y^2 = 1$

7c. $\left(\frac{x}{2}\right)^2 + (2y)^2 = 1$

9a.

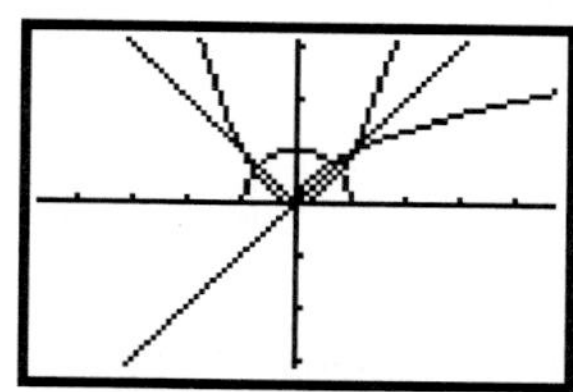

[−4.7, 4.7, 1, −3.1, 3.1, 1]

(0, 0) and (1, 1)

9b. The rectangle has width 1 and height 1. The width is the difference in x-coordinates, and the height is the difference in y-coordinates.

9c.

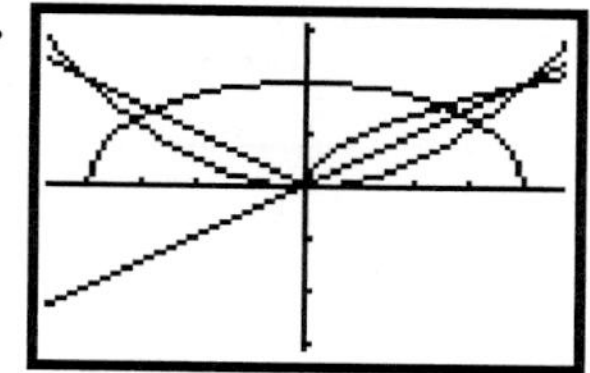

[−4.7, 4.7, 1, −3.1, 3.1, 1]

(0, 0) and (4, 2)

9d. The rectangle has width 4 and height 2. The width is the difference in x-coordinates, and the height is the difference in y-coordinates.

9e.

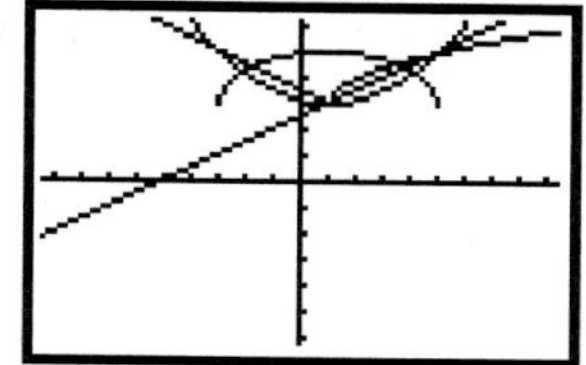

[−9.4, 9.4, 1, −6.2, 6.2, 1]

(1, 3) and (5, 5)

9f. The rectangle has width 4 and height 2. The difference in x-coordinates is 4, and the difference in y-coordinates is 2.

9g. The x-coordinate is the location of the right endpoint, and the y-coordinate is the location of the top of the transformed semicircle.

11. 625, 1562.5, 3906.25

13a.

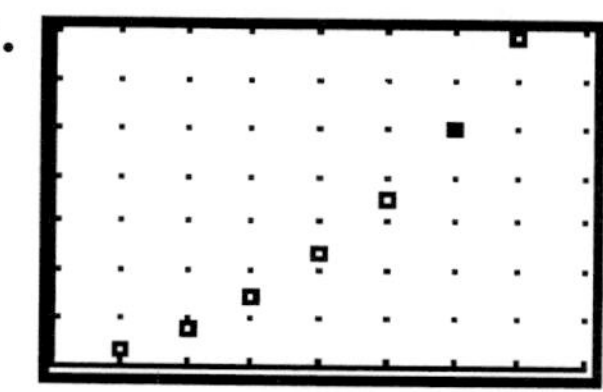

[0, 80, 10, 0, 350, 50]

13b. Sample answer: $\hat{y} = 0.07(x - 3)^2 + 21$.

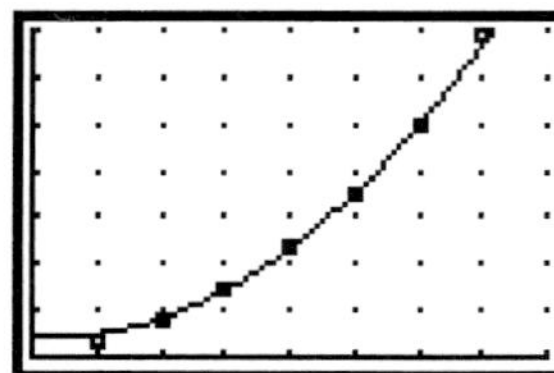

[0, 80, 10, 0, 350, 50]

13c. For the sample answer: residuals: $-5.43, 0.77, 0.97, -0.83, -2.63, -0.43, 7.77$; $s = 4.45$

13d. approximately 221 ft

13e. 13d should be correct ± 4.45 ft.

15a. $y = -3x - 1$ **15b.** $y = -3x + 1$

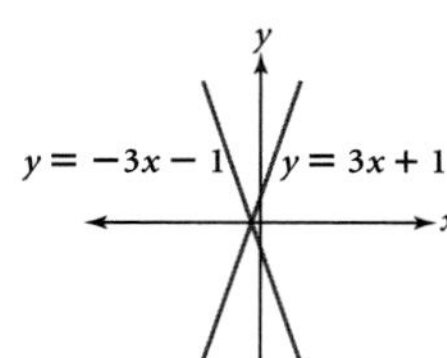

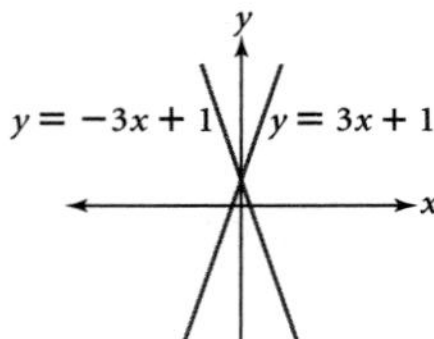

15c. $y = 3x - 1$

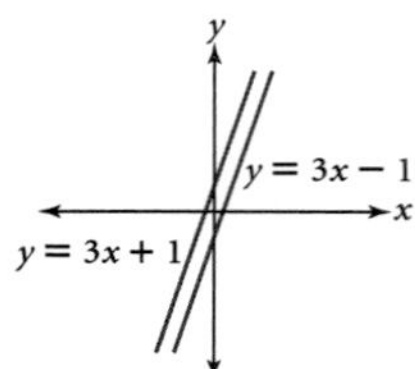

15d. The two lines are parallel.

LESSON 4.8

1a. 6 **1b.** 7 **1c.** 6 **1d.** 18

3a. approximately 1.5 m/s

3b. approximately 12 L/min

3c. approximately 15 L/min

5a. $y = |(x - 3)^2 - 1|$

5b. $f(x) = |x|$ and $g(x) = (x - 3)^2 - 1$

7a.

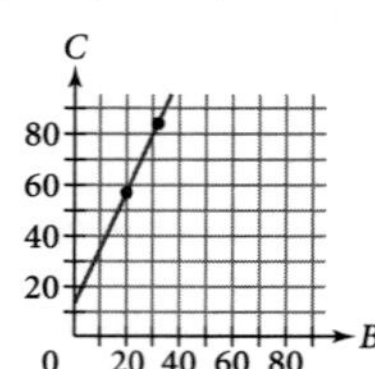

7b. approximately 41

7c. $B = \frac{2}{3}(A - 12) + 13$

7d. $C = \frac{9}{4}(B - 20) + 57$

7e. $C = \frac{9}{4}\left(\frac{2}{3}A + 5\right) + 12 = 1.5A + 23.25$

9a. 2 **9b.** -1

9c. $g(f(x)) = x$ **9d.** $f(g(x)) = x$

9e. The two functions "undo" the effects of each other and thus give back the original value.

11. *Hint:* Use two points to find both parabola and semicircle equations for the curve. Then substitute a third point into your equations and decide which is most accurate.

13a. $x = -5$ or $x = 13$

13b. $x = -1$ or $x = 23$

13c. $x = 64$

13d. $x = \pm\sqrt{1.5} \approx \pm 1.22$

15a. $\left(\frac{x}{3}\right)^2 + \left(\frac{y}{3}\right)^2 = 1$ or $x^2 + y^2 = 9$

15b.

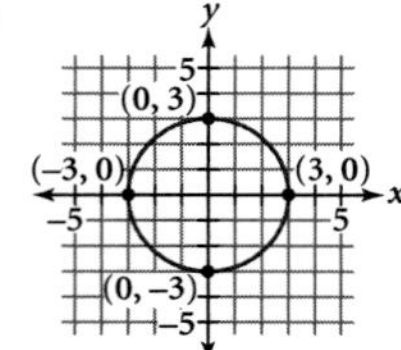

CHAPTER 4 REVIEW

1. Sample answer: For a time there are no pops. Then the popping rate slowly increases. When the popping reaches a furious intensity, it seems to level out. Then the number of pops per second drops quickly until the last pop is heard.

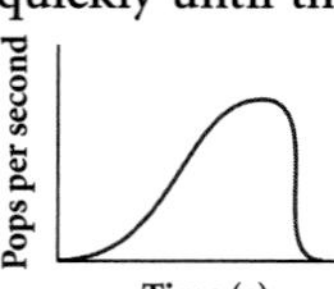

3a.

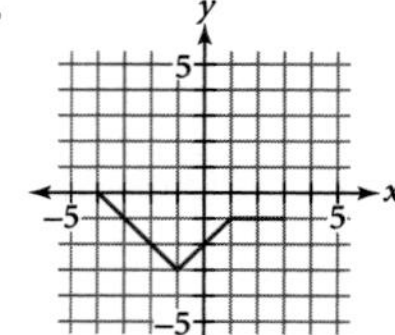

3b.

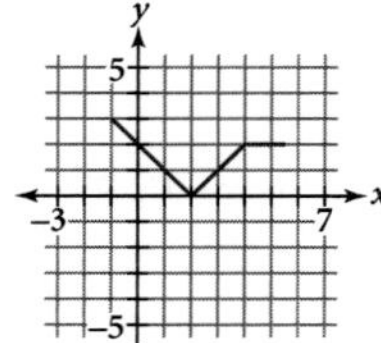

3c.

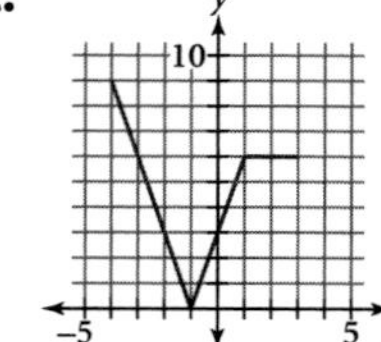

3d.

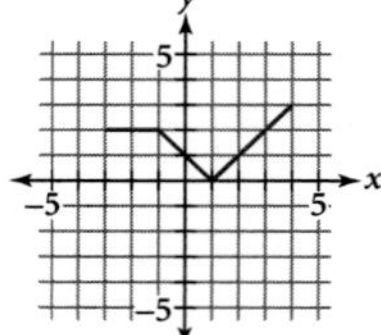

5a.

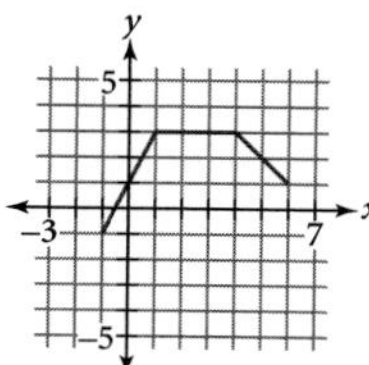

5b.

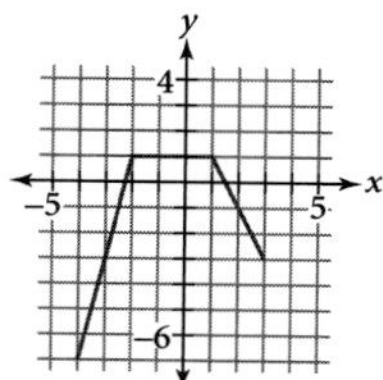

5c.

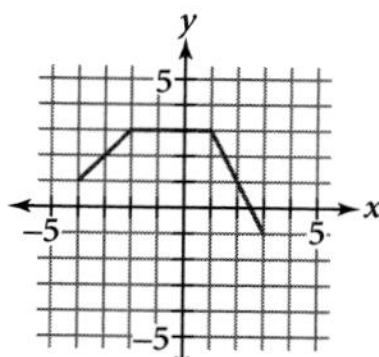

5d.

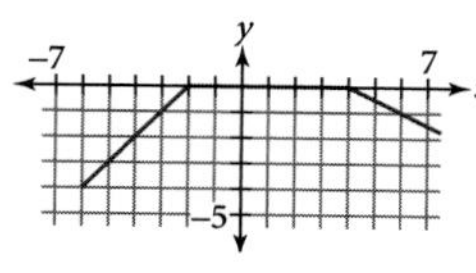

5e.

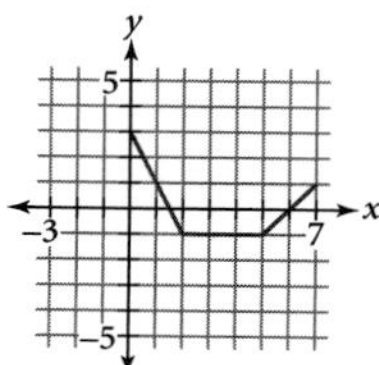

5f.

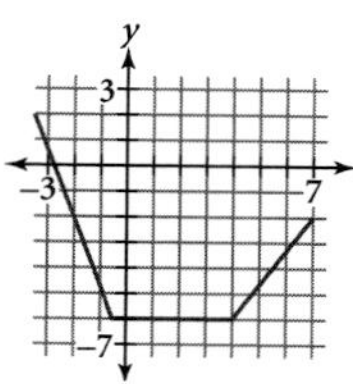

7a. $y = \frac{2}{3}x - 2$

7b. $y = \pm\sqrt{x+3} - 1$

7c. $y = \pm\sqrt{-(x-2)^2 + 1}$

9a. Number of passengers: 17000, 16000, 15000, 14000, 13000, 12000, 11000, 10000; Revenue: 18700, 19200, 19500, 19600, 19200, 18700, 18000

9b.

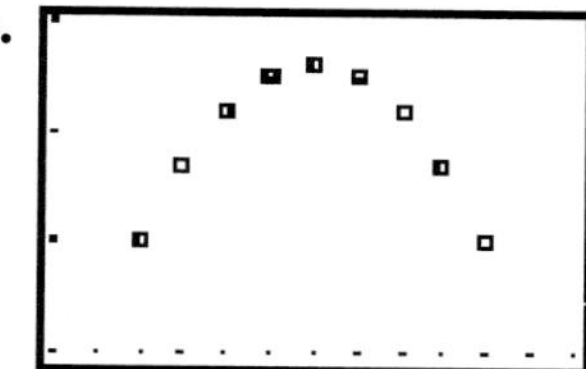

[0.8, 2, 0.1, 17000, 20000, 1000]

9c. (1.40, 19600). By charging $1.40 per ride, the company achieves the maximum revenue, $19,600.

9d. $\hat{y} = -10000(x - 1.4)^2 + 19600$

9d. i. $16,000 **9d. ii.** $0 or $2.80

LESSON 5.1

1a. $f(5) \approx 3.52738$ **1b.** $g(14) \approx 19{,}528.32$

1c. $h(24) \approx 22.9242$ **1d.** $j(37) \approx 3332.20$

3a. $f(0) = 125, f(1) = 75, f(2) = 45$; $u_0 = 125$ and $u_n = 0.6u_{n-1}$ where $n \geq 1$

3b. $f(0) = 3, f(1) = 6, f(2) = 12$; $u_0 = 3$ and $u_n = 2u_{n-1}$ where $n \geq 1$

5a. $u_0 = 1.151$ and $u_n = (1 + 0.015)u_{n-1}$ where $n \geq 1$

5b.

Year	Population (in billions)
1991	1.151
1992	1.168
1993	1.186
1994	1.204
1995	1.222
1996	1.240
1997	1.259
1998	1.277
1999	1.297
2000	1.316

5c. Let x represent the number of years since 1991, and let y represent the population in billions. $y = 1.151(1 + 0.015)^x$

5d. $y = 1.151(1 + 0.015)^{10} \approx 1.336$; the equation gives a population that is greater than the actual population. Sample answer: the growth rate of China's population has slowed since 1991.

7a–d.

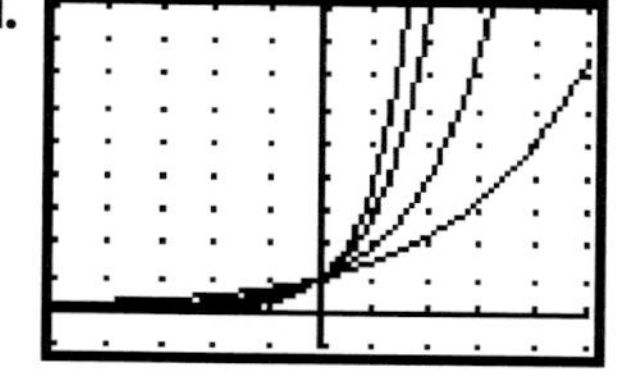

[−5, 5, 1, −1, 9, 1]

7e. As the base increases, the graph becomes steeper. The curves all intersect the y-axis at (0, 1).

7f. The graph of $y = 6^x$ should be the steepest of all of these. It will contain the points (0, 1) and (1, 6).

[−5, 5, 1, −1, 9, 1]

9a–d.

[−5, 5, 1, −1, 9, 1]

9e. As the base increases, the graph flattens out. The curves all intersect the y-axis at (0, 1).

Selected Answers

9f. The graph of $y = 0.1^x$ should be the steepest of all of these. It will contain the points (0, 1) and (−1, 10).

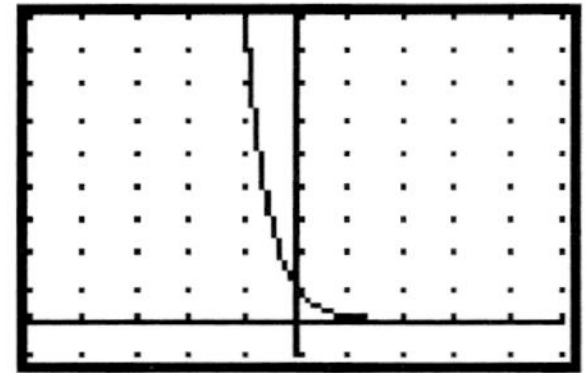

[−5, 5, 1, −1, 9, 1]

11a. $\frac{27}{30} = 0.9$

11b. $f(x) = 30(0.9)^x$

11c.

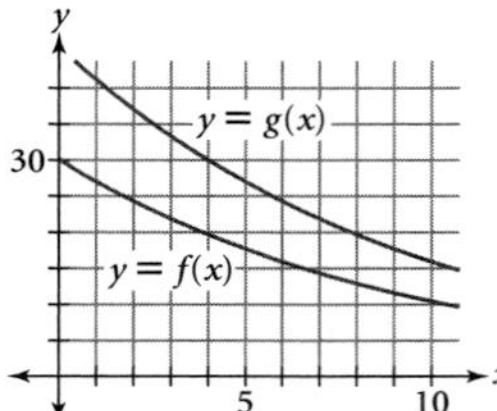

11d. $g(4) = 30$

11e. possible answer: $g(x) = 30(0.9)^{x-4}$

11f. *Hint:* Think about what x_1, y_1, and b represent.

13a. Let x represent time in seconds, and let y represent distance in meters.

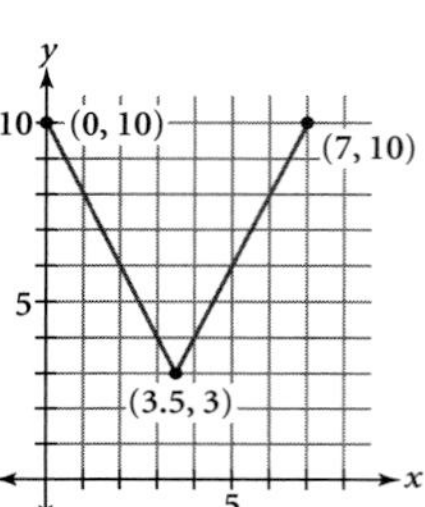

13b. domain: $0 \leq x \leq 7$; range: $3 \leq y \leq 10$

13c. $y = 2|x - 3.5| + 3$

15a–c. *Hint:* One way to construct the circles is to duplicate circle M and change the radius in order to get the correct area.

15d. *Hint:* Recall that the area of a circle is given by the formula $A = \pi r^2$.

LESSON 5.2

1a. $\frac{1}{125}$ **1b.** -36 **1c.** $-\frac{1}{81}$

1d. $\frac{1}{144}$ **1e.** $\frac{16}{9}$ **1f.** $\frac{7}{2}$

3a. false **3b.** false

3c. false **3d.** true

5a. $x \approx 3.27$ **5b.** $x = 784$

5c. $x \approx 0.16$ **5d.** $x \approx 0.50$

5e. $x \approx 1.07$ **5f.** $x = 1$

7. *Hint:* Is $(2 + 3)^2$ equivalent to $2^2 + 3^3$? Is $(2 + 3)^1$ equivalent to $2^1 + 3^1$? Is $(2 - 2)^3$ equivalent to $2^3 + (-2)^3$? Is $(2 - 2)^2$ equivalent to $2^2 + (-2)^2$?

9a–d.

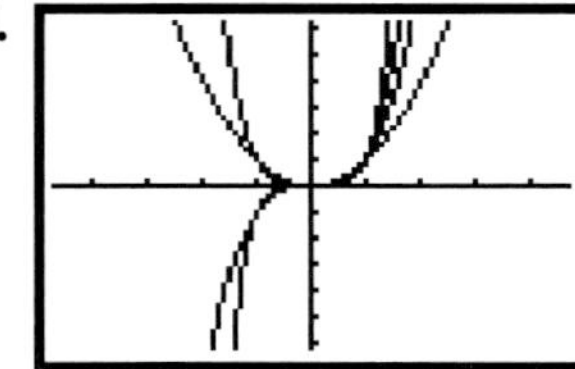

[−4.7, 4.7, 1, −6.2, 6.2, 1]

9e. Sample answer: As the exponents increase, the graphs get narrower horizontally. The even-power functions are U-shaped and always in the first and second quadrants, whereas the odd-power functions have only the right half of the U, with the left half pointed down in the third quadrant. They all pass through (0, 0) and (1, 1).

9f. Sample answer: The graph of $y = x^6$ will be U-shaped, will be narrower than $y = x^4$, and will pass through (0, 0), (1, 1), (−1, 1), (2, 64), and (−2, 64).

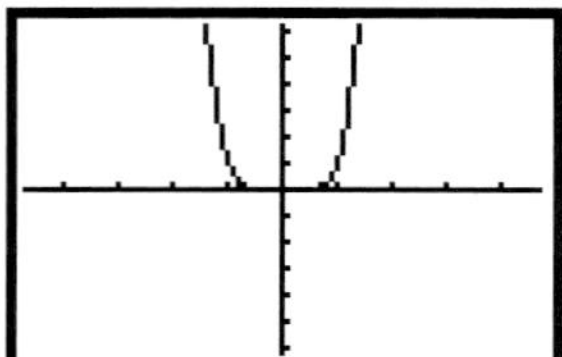

[−4.7, 4.7, 1, −6.2, 6.2, 1]

9g. Sample answer: The graph of $y = x^7$ will fall in the first and third quadrants, will be narrower than $y = x^3$ or $y = x^5$, and will pass through (0, 0), (1, 1), (−1, −1), (2, 128), and (−2, −128).

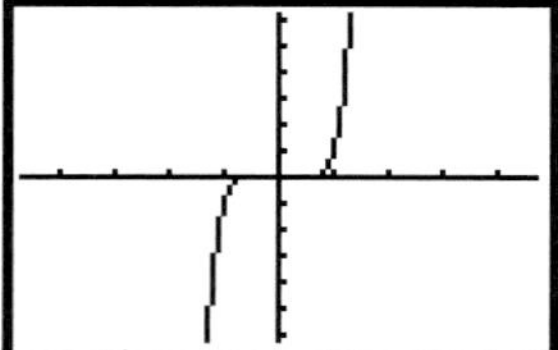

[−4.7, 4.7, 1, −6.2, 6.2, 1]

11a. $47(0.9)(0.9)^{x-1} = 47(0.9)^1(0.9)^{x-1} = 47(0.9)^x$ by the product property of exponents; $42.3(0.9)^{x-1}$.

11b. $38.07(0.9)^{x-2}$

11c. The coefficients are equal to the values of Y1 corresponding to the number subtracted from x in the exponent. If (x_1, y_1) is on the curve, then any equation $y = y_1 \cdot b^{(x-x_1)}$ is an exponential equation for the curve.

13a. $x = 7$ **13b.** $x = -\frac{1}{2}$ **13c.** $x = 0$

15a. $x = 7$ **15b.** $x = -4$

15c. $x = 4$ **15d.** $x = 4.61$

17a. Let x represent time in seconds, and let y represent distance in meters.

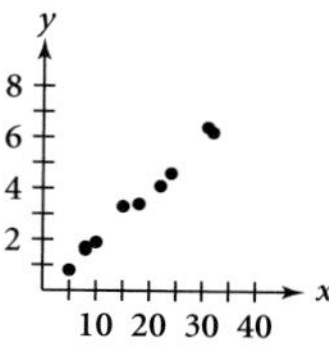

17b. All you need is the slope of the median-median line, which is determined by $M_1(8, 1.6)$ and $M_3(31, 6.2)$. The slope is 0.2. The speed is approximately 0.2 m/s.

LESSON 5.3

1. a—e—j; b—d—g; c—i; f—h

3a. $a^{1/6}$ **3b.** $b^{4/5}$, $b^{8/10}$, or $b^{0.8}$

3c. $c^{-1/2}$ or $c^{-0.5}$ **3d.** $d^{7/5}$ or $d^{1.4}$

5. 490 W/cm^2

7a–d. 

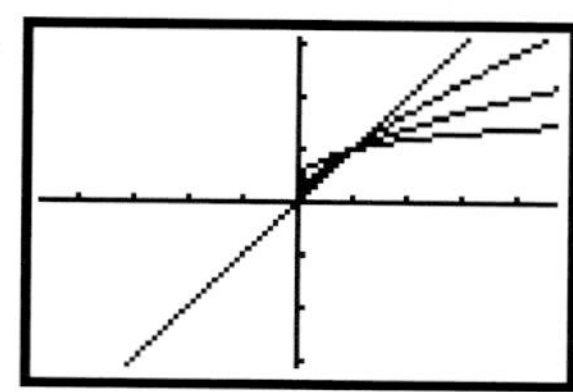

$[-4.7, 4.7, 1, -3.1, 3.1, 1]$

7e. Each graph is steeper and less curved than the previous one. All of the functions go through $(0, 0)$ and $(1, 1)$.

7f. $y = x^{5/4}$ should be steeper and curve upward.

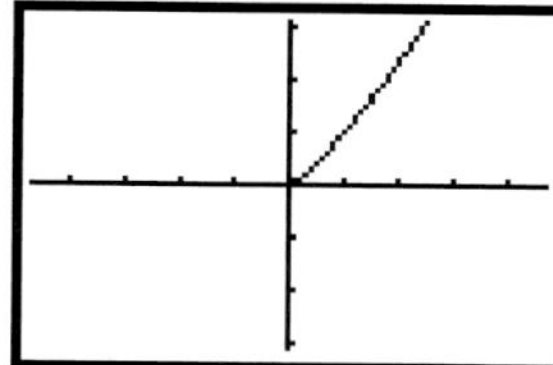

$[-4.7, 4.7, 1, -3.1, 3.1, 1]$

9a. exponential **9b.** neither

9c. exponential **9d.** power

11a. $x = \left(\frac{13}{9}\right)^5 \approx 6.29$ **11b.** $x = 180^{1/4} \approx 3.66$

11c. $x = \left(\frac{\sqrt{35}}{4}\right)^{3/2} \approx 1.80$

13a. *Hint:* Solve for k. **13b.** $k = (40)(12.3) = 492$

13c. 8.2 L **13d.** 32.8 mm Hg

15a. $y = (x + 4)^2$ **15b.** $y = x^2 + 1$

15c. $y = -(x + 5)^2 + 2$ **15d.** $y = (x - 3)^2 - 4$

15e. $y = \sqrt{x + 3}$ **15f.** $y = \sqrt{x} - 1$

15g. $y = \sqrt{x + 2} + 1$ **15h.** $y = -\sqrt{x - 1} - 1$

17a. $u_1 = 20$ and $u_n = 1.2u_{n-1}$ where $n \geq 2$

17b. $u_9 \approx 86$; about 86 rats

17c. Let x represent the year number, and let y represent the number of rats. $y = 20(1.2)^{x-1}$

LESSON 5.4

1a. $x = 50^{1/5} \approx 2.187$ **1b.** $x = 29.791$

1c. no real solution

3a. $9x^4$ **3b.** $8x^6$ **3c.** $216x^{-18}$

5a. She must replace y with $y - 7$ and y_1 with $y_1 - 7$; $y - 7 = (y_1 - 7) \cdot b^{x-x_1}$.

5b. $y - 7 = (105 - 7)b^{x-1}$; $\left(\frac{y-7}{98}\right)^{1/(x-1)} = b$

5c.

x	0	2	3	4	5	6
y	200	57	31	18	14	12
b	0.508	0.510	0.495	0.482	0.517	0.552

5d. Possible answer: The mean of the b-values is 0.511. $y = 7 + 98(0.511)^{x-1}$.

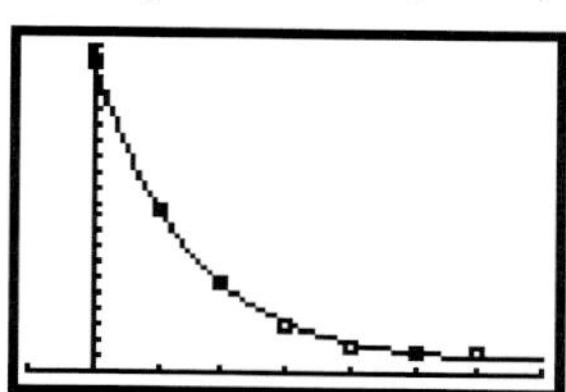

$[-1, 7, 1, 0, 210, 10]$

7a. 68.63 tons **7b.** 63.75 ft

9a. 1.9 g **9b.** 12.8%

11a. 0.9534, or 95.34% per year

11b. 6.6 g **11c.** $y = 6.6(0.9534)^x$

11d. 0.6 g **11e.** 14.5 yr

13. $x = -4.5, y = 2, z = 2.75$

LESSON 5.5

1. $(-3, -2), (-1, 0), (2, 2), (6, 4)$

3. Graph c is the inverse because the x- and y-coordinates have been switched from the original graph so that the graphs are symmetric across line $y = x$.

5a. $f(7) = 4; g(4) = 7$

5b. They might be inverse functions.

5c. $f(1) = -2; g(-2) = 5$

5d. They are *not* inverse functions, at least not over their entire domains and ranges.

5e. $f(x)$ for $x \geq 3$ and $g(x)$ for $x \geq -4$ are inverse functions.

7a. 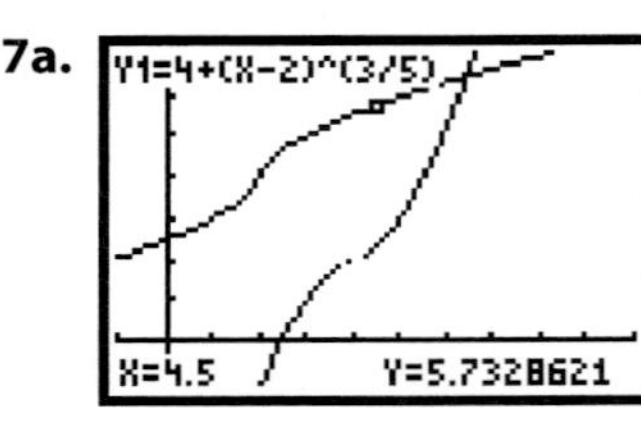

$[-1, 10, 1, -1, 7, 1]$

7b. The inverse function from 6b should be the same as the function drawn by the calculator.

7c. Find the composition of $f^{-1}(f(x))$. If it equals x, you have the correct inverse.

9a. i. $f^{-1}(x) = \frac{x + 140}{6.34}$

9a. ii. $f(f^{-1}(15.75)) = 15.75$

9a. iii. $f^{-1}(f(15.75)) = 15.75$

9a. iv. $f(f^{-1}(x)) = f^{-1}(f(x)) = x$

9b. i. $f^{-1}(x) = \frac{x - 32}{1.8}$

9b. ii. $f(f^{-1}(15.75)) = 15.75$

9b. iii. $f^{-1}(f(15.75)) = 15.75$

9b. iv. $f(f^{-1}(x)) = f^{-1}(f(x)) = x$

11a. $y = 100 - C$

11b. Solve $F = 1.8C + 32$ for C and substitute into $y = 100 - C$ to get $y = \frac{F - 212}{-1.8} = \frac{212 - F}{1.8}$.

13a. $c(x) = 7.18 + 3.98x$, where c is the cost and x is the number of thousand gallons.

13b. \$39.02

13c. $g(x) = \frac{x - 7.18}{3.98}$, where g is the number of thousands of gallons and x is the cost.

13d. 12,000 gal

13e. *Hint:* The compositions $g(c(x))$ and $c(g(x))$ should both be equivalent to x.

13f. about \$13

13g. *Hint:* The product of length, width, and height should be equivalent to the volume of water, in cubic inches, saved in a month.

15. *Hint:* Solve $12.6(b)^3 = 42.525$ to find the base. Then use the point-ratio form.

17. *Hint:* Consider a vertically oriented parabola and a horizontally oriented parabola.

LESSON 5.6

1a. $10^x = 1000$ **1b.** $5^x = 625$

1c. $7^x = \sqrt{7}$ **1d.** $8^x = 2$

1e. $5^x = \frac{1}{25}$ **1f.** $6^x = 1$

3a. $x = \log_{10} 0.001$; $x = -3$

3b. $x = \log_5 100$; $x \approx 2.8614$

3c. $x = \log_{35} 8$; $x \approx 0.5849$

3d. $x = \log_{0.4} 5$; $x \approx -1.7565$

3e. $x = \log_{0.8} 0.03$; $x \approx 15.7144$

3f. $x = \log_{17} 0.5$; $x \approx -0.2447$

5a. false; $x = \log_6 12$ **5b.** false; $2^x = 5$

5c. false; $x = \frac{\log 5.5}{\log 3}$ **5d.** false; $x = \log_3 7$

7a. 1980 **7b.** 13% **7c.** 5.6 yr

9a. $y = 88.7(1.0077)^x$ **9b.** 23 or 24 clicks

11a. $\hat{y} = \frac{38}{9}x - 8359.91$

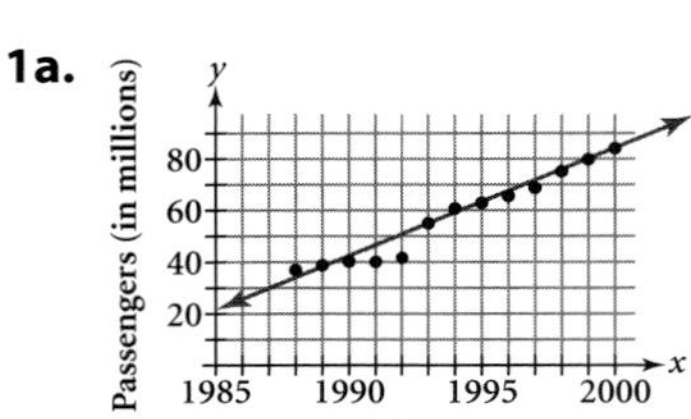

11b. 3.03, 0.71, −2.11, −6.43, −9.16, 0.02, 1.50, −0.52, −2.05, −3.17, −0.99, −0.51, −0.43

11c. 3.78 million riders. Most data are within 3.78 million of the predicted number.

11d. 126.8 million riders

13a. $y + 1 = x - 3$ or $y = x - 4$

13b. $y + 4 = (x + 5)^2$ or $y = (x + 5)^2 - 4$

13c. $y - 2 = |x + 6|$ or $y = |x + 6| + 2$

13d. $y - 7 = \sqrt{x - 2}$ or $y = \sqrt{x - 2} + 7$

15a.

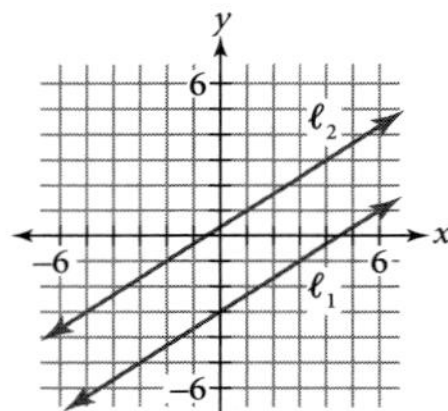

They are parallel.

15b. Possible answer: $A(0, -3)$; $P(1, 1)$; $Q(4, 3)$

15c. Possible answer: Translate 1 unit right and 4 units up. $2(x - 1) - 3(y - 4) = 9$.

15d. Possible answer: Translate 4 units right and 6 units up. $2(x - 4) - 3(y - 6) = 9$.

15e. *Hint:* Distribute and combine like terms. You should find that the equations are equivalent.

LESSON 5.7

1a. $g^h \cdot g^k$; product property of exponents

1b. $\log st$; product property of logarithms

1c. f^{w-v}; quotient property of exponents

1d. $\log h - \log k$; quotient property of logarithms

1e. j^{st}; power property of exponents

1f. $g\log b$; power property of logarithms

1g. $k^{m/n}$; definition of rational exponents

1h. $\log_u t$; change-of-base property

1i. w^{t+s}; product property of exponents

1j. $\frac{1}{p^h}$; definition of negative exponents

3a. $a \approx 1.763$

3b. $b \approx 1.3424$

3c. $c \approx 0.4210$

3d. $d \approx 2.6364$

3e. $e \approx 2.6364$

3f. $f \approx 0.4210$

3g. $c = f$ and $d = e$

3h. $\log\frac{a}{b}$

3i. When numbers with the same base are divided, the exponents are subtracted.

5a. true

5b. false; possible answer: $\log 5 + \log 3 = \log 15$

5c. true

5d. true

5e. false; possible answer: $\log 9 - \log 3 = \log 3$

5f. false; possible answer: $\log\sqrt{7} = \frac{1}{2}\log 7$

5g. false; possible answer: $\log 35 = \log 5 + \log 7$

5h. true

5i. false; possible answer: $\log 3 - \log 4 = \log\frac{3}{4}$

5j. true

7a. $y = 261.6(2^{x/12})$

7b.

Note	Frequency (Hz)	Note	Frequency (Hz)
C_4	261.6	G	392.0
C#	277.2	G#	415.3
D	293.6	A	440.0
D#	311.1	A#	466.1
E	329.6	B	493.8
F	349.2	C_5	523.2
F#	370.0		

9a. $y = 14.7(0.8022078)^x$

9b.

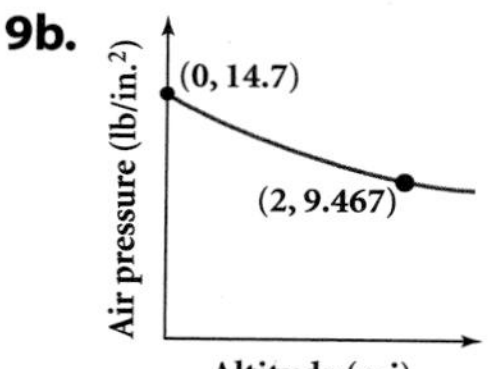

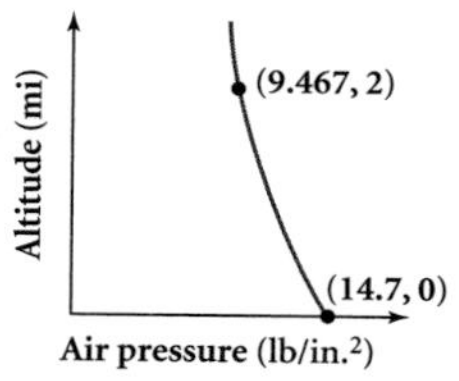

9c. $y = 8.91$ lb/in.²

9d. $x = 6.32$ mi

11. *Hint:* If more than one input value results in the same output value, then a function's inverse will not be a function. What does this mean about the graph of the function?

13a. The graph has been vertically stretched by a factor of 3, then translated to the right 1 unit and down 4 units.

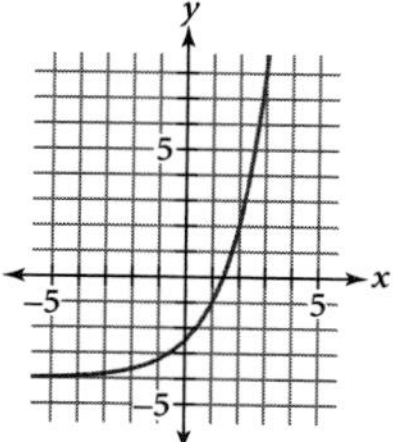

13b. The graph has been horizontally stretched by a factor of 3, reflected across the x-axis, and translated up 2 units.

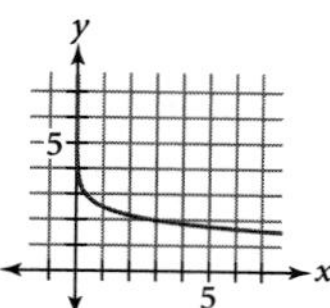

15a. Let h represent the length of time in hours, and let c represent the driver's cost in dollars. $c = 14h + 20$. The domain is the set of possible values of the number of hours, $h > 0$. The range is the set of possible values of the cost paid to the driver, $c > 20$.

15b. Let c represent the driver's cost in dollars, and let a represent the agency's charge in dollars. $a = 1.15c + 25$. The domain is the money paid to the driver if she had been booked directly, c. $c > 20$. The range is the amount charged by the agency, a. $a > 48$.

15c. $a = 1.15(14h + 20) + 25$, or $a = 16.1h + 48$

LESSON 5.8

1a. $\log(10^{n+p}) = \log((10^n)(10^p))$

$(n + p)\log 10 = \log 10^n + \log 10^p$

$(n + p)\log 10 = n\log 10 + p\log 10$

$(n + p)\log 10 = (n + p)\log 10$

1b. $\log\left(\frac{10^d}{10^e}\right) = \log(10^{d-e})$

$\log 10^d - \log 10^e = \log(10^{d-e})$

$d\log 10 - e\log 10 = (d - e)\log 10$

$(d - e)\log 10 = (d - e)\log 10$

3. about 195.9 mo or about 16 yr 4 mo

5a. $f(20) \approx 133.28$; After 20 days 133 games have been sold.

5b. $f(80) \approx 7969.17$; After 80 days 7969 games have been sold.

5c. $x = 72.09$; After 72 days 6000 games have been sold.

5d. $\frac{12000}{1+499(1.09)^{-x}} = 6000; 2 = 1 + 499(1.09)^{-x};$
$1 = 499(1.09)^{-x}; 0.002 = (1.09)^{-x};$
$\log(0.002) = \log(1.09)^{-x}; \log 0.002 = -x\log 1.09;$
$x = -\frac{\log 0.002}{\log 1.09} \approx 72.1$

5e.

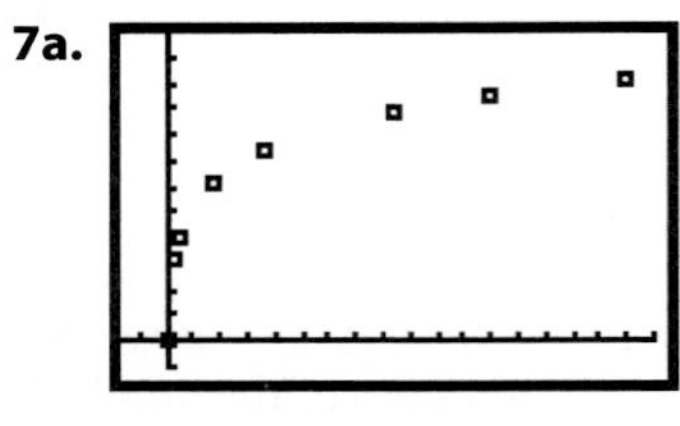

[0, 500, 100, 0, 15000, 1000]

Sample answer: The number of games sold starts out increasing slowly, then speeds up, and then slow down as everyone who wants the game has purchased one.

7a.

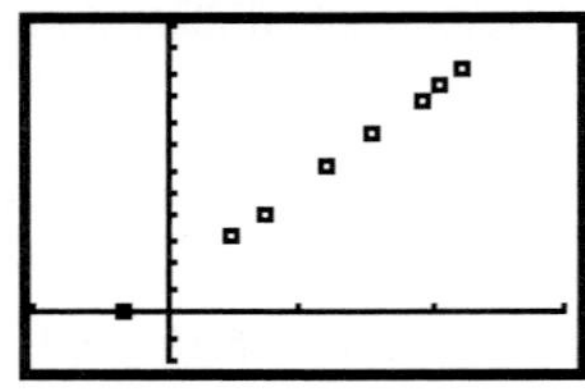

[−16, 180, 10, −5, 60, 5]

7b. $(\log x, y)$ is a linear graph.

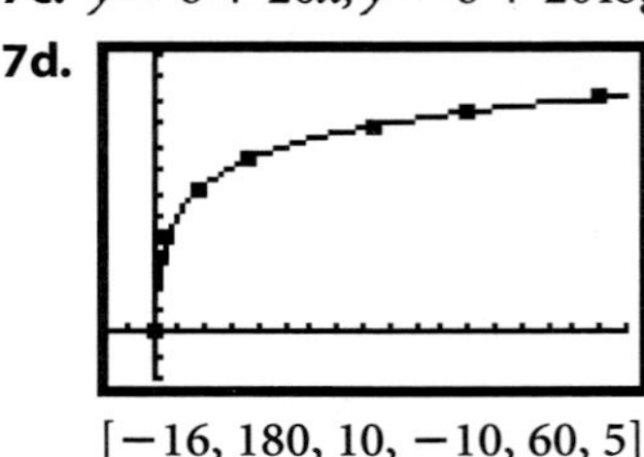

[−1, 3, 1, −10, 60, 5]

7c. $y = 6 + 20x; \hat{y} = 6 + 20\log x$

7d.

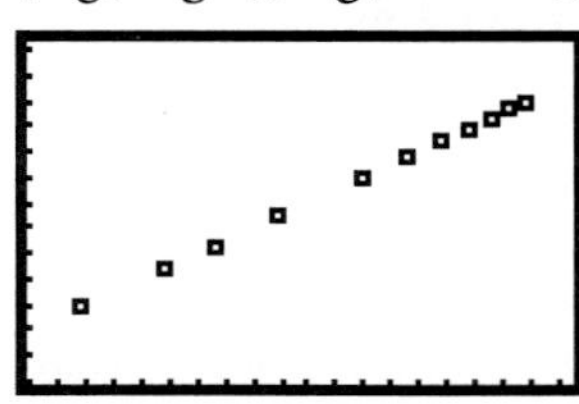

[−16, 180, 10, −10, 60, 5]

Sample answer: Yes; the graph shows that the equation is a good model for the data.

9a. The data are the most linear when viewed as (log(*height*), log(*distance*)).

[2.3, 4.2, 0.1, 1.5, 2.8, 0.1]

9b. $view = 3.589height^{0.49909}$

11a. $y = 18(\sqrt{2})^{x-4}, y = 144(\sqrt{2})^{x-10}$, or $y = 4.5(\sqrt{2})^x$

11b. $y = \frac{\log x - \log 18}{\log\sqrt{2}} + 4,$
$y = \frac{\log x - \log 144}{\log\sqrt{2}} + 10$, or $y = \frac{\log x - \log 4.5}{\log\sqrt{2}}$

13.

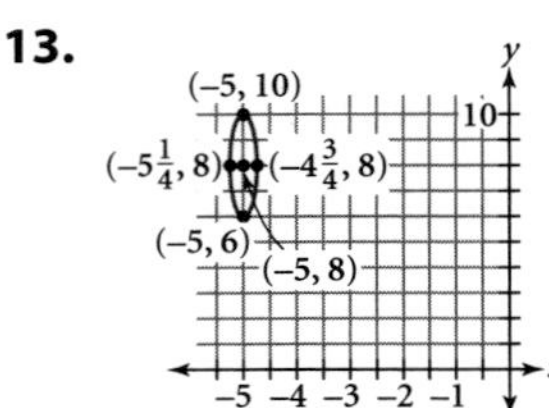

CHAPTER 5 REVIEW

1a. $\frac{1}{16}$ **1b.** $-\frac{1}{3}$ **1c.** 125 **1d.** 7 **1e.** $\frac{1}{4}$

1f. $\frac{27}{64}$ **1g.** −1 **1h.** 12 **1i.** 0.6

3a. $x = \frac{\log 28}{\log 4.7} \approx 2.153$

3b. $x = \pm\sqrt{\frac{\log 2209}{\log 4.7}} \approx \pm 2.231$

3c. $x = 2.9^{1/1.25} = 2.9^{0.8} \approx 2.344$

3d. $x = 3.1^{47} \approx 1.242 \times 10^{23}$

3e. $x = \left(\frac{101}{7}\right)^{1/2.4} \approx 3.041$

3f. $x = \frac{\log 18}{\log 1.065} \approx 45.897$

3g. $x = 10^{3.771} \approx 5902$ **3h.** $x = 47^{5/3} \approx 612$

5. about 39.9 h

7. $y = 5\left(\frac{32}{5}\right)^{(x-1)/6}$

9a.

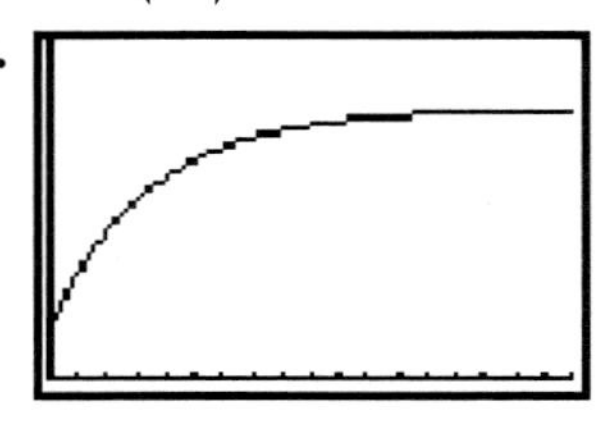

[0, 18, 1, 0, 125, 0]

9b. domain: $0 \leq x \leq 120$; range: $20 \leq y \leq 100$

9c. Vertically stretch by a factor of 80; reflect across the x-axis; vertically shift by 100.

9d. 55% of the average adult size

9e. about 4 years old

11a. approximately 37 sessions

11b. approximately 48 wpm

11c. Sample answer: It takes much longer to improve your typing speed as you reach higher levels. 60 wpm is a good typing speed, and very few people type more than 90 wpm, so $0 \le x \le 90$ is a reasonable domain.

CHAPTER 6 • CHAPTER 6 CHAPTER 6 • CHAPTER

LESSON 6.1

1a. 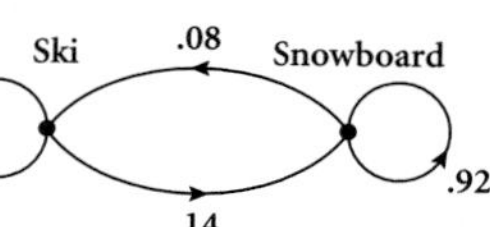

1b. $\begin{bmatrix} .86 & .14 \\ .08 & .92 \end{bmatrix}$

3. $\begin{bmatrix} .60 & .40 \\ .53 & .47 \end{bmatrix}$

5a. 20 girls and 25 boys **5b.** 18 boys

5c. 13 girls batted right-handed.

7a. 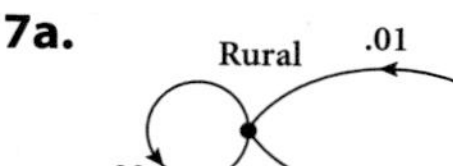

7b. 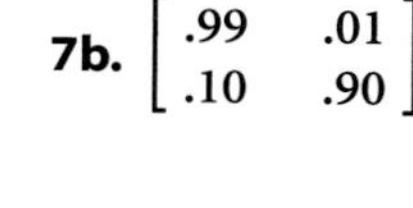
$\begin{bmatrix} .99 & .01 \\ .10 & .90 \end{bmatrix}$

7c. [16.74 8.26]; [17.3986 7.6014]

9a. 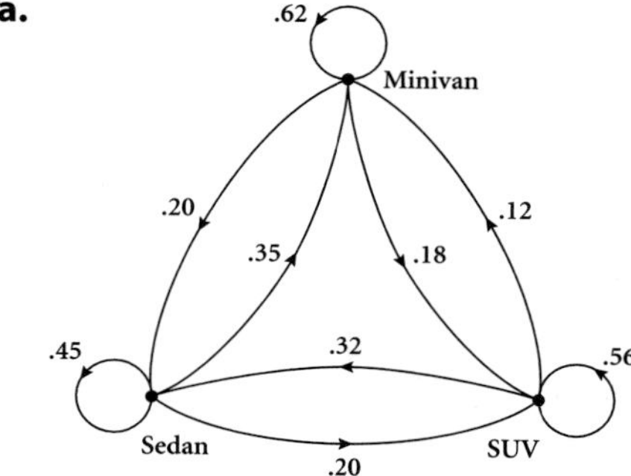

9b. $\begin{bmatrix} .62 & .20 & .18 \\ .35 & .45 & .20 \\ .12 & .32 & .56 \end{bmatrix}$

9c. The sum of each row is 1; percentages should sum to 100%.

11a. 5×5

11b. $m_{32} = 1$; there is one round-trip flight between City C and City B.

11c. City A has the most flights. From the graph, more paths have A as an endpoint than any other city. From the matrix, the sum of row 1 (or column 1) is greater than the sum of any other row (or column).

11d. 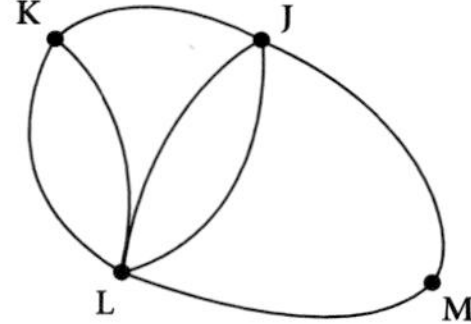

13. $7.4p + 4.7s = 100$

15a. Let x represent the year, and let y represent the number of subscribers.

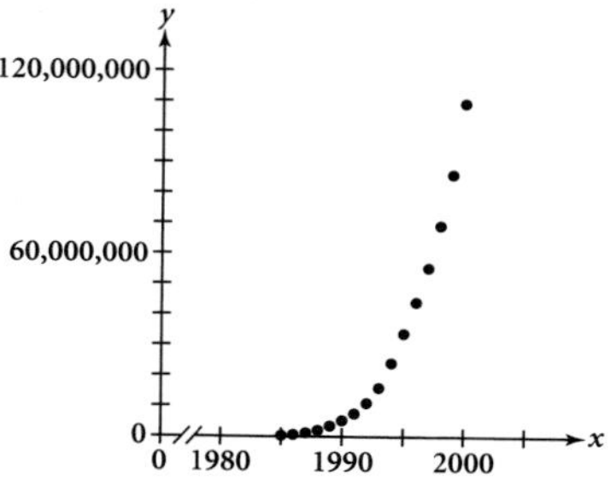

15b. possible answer: $\hat{y} = 1231000(1.44)^{x-1987}$

15c. About 420,782,749 subscribers. Explanations will vary.

LESSON 6.2

1. [196.85 43.15]; 197 students will choose ice cream, 43 will choose frozen yogurt.

3a. $\begin{bmatrix} 7 & 3 & 0 \\ -19 & -7 & 8 \\ 5 & 2 & -1 \end{bmatrix}$ **3b.** 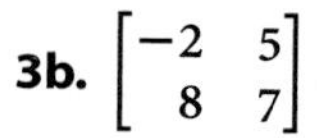
$\begin{bmatrix} -2 & 5 \\ 8 & 7 \end{bmatrix}$ **3c.** [13 29]

3d. not possible because the inside dimensions do not match

3e. $\begin{bmatrix} 4 & -1 \\ 4 & -2 \end{bmatrix}$

3f. not possible because the dimensions aren't the same

5a. 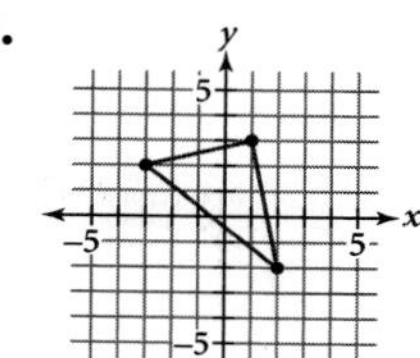

5b. $\begin{bmatrix} 3 & -1 & -2 \\ 2 & 3 & -2 \end{bmatrix}$

5c. 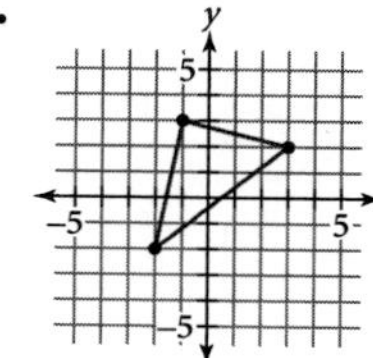

5d. The original triangle is reflected across the y-axis.

7a. 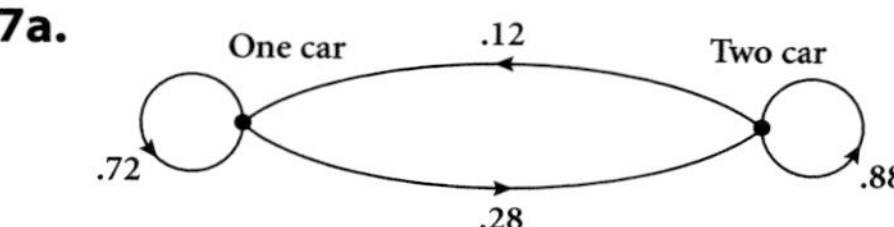

7b. [4800 4200]

7c. $\begin{bmatrix} .72 & .28 \\ .12 & .88 \end{bmatrix}$

7d. $[4800 \quad 4200]\begin{bmatrix} .72 & .28 \\ .12 & .88 \end{bmatrix} = [3960 \quad 5040]$

7e. $[3456 \quad 5544]$

9a. $a = 3, b = 4$ **9b.** $a = 7, b = 4$

11. The probability that the spider is in room 1 after four room changes is .375. The long-run probabilities for rooms 1, 2, and 3 are $[.\overline{3} \quad .\overline{3} \quad .\overline{3}]$.

13a. $\begin{bmatrix} 3 \\ 1 \\ 3 \\ 1 \\ 3 \\ 1 \\ 3 \\ 1 \\ 3 \\ 1 \\ 3 \\ 1 \end{bmatrix}$

13b. The first and last UPCs are valid.

13c. For the second code, the check digit should be 7. For the third code, the check digit should be 5.

15. $\overline{CD}$: $y = -3 + \frac{2}{3}(x - 1)$ or $y = -1 + \frac{2}{3}(x - 4)$;
$\overline{AB}$: $y = 2 + \frac{2}{3}(x + 2)$ or $y = 4 + \frac{2}{3}(x - 1)$;
$\overline{AD}$: $y = 2 - \frac{5}{3}(x + 2)$ or $y = -3 - \frac{5}{3}(x - 1)$;
$\overline{BC}$: $y = 4 - \frac{5}{3}(x - 1)$ or $y = -1 - \frac{5}{3}(x - 4)$

17. $x = 2, y = \frac{1}{2}, z = -3$

LESSON 6.3

1a. $\begin{cases} 2x + 5y = 8 \\ 4x - y = 6 \end{cases}$ **1b.** $\begin{cases} x - y + 2z = 3 \\ x + 2y - 3z = 1 \\ 2x + y - z = 2 \end{cases}$

3a. $\left[\begin{array}{ccc|c} 1 & -1 & 2 & 3 \\ 0 & 3 & -5 & -2 \\ 2 & 1 & -1 & 2 \end{array}\right]$ **3b.** $\left[\begin{array}{ccc|c} 1 & -1 & 2 & 3 \\ 1 & 2 & -3 & 1 \\ 0 & 3 & -5 & -4 \end{array}\right]$

5a. $\left[\begin{array}{ccc|c} 1 & 0 & 0 & -31 \\ 0 & 1 & 0 & 24 \\ 0 & 0 & 1 & -4 \end{array}\right]$ **5b.** $\left[\begin{array}{ccc|c} 1 & 0 & 0 & -1 \\ 0 & 1 & 0 & 1 \\ 0 & 0 & 1 & 0 \end{array}\right]$

5c. cannot be reduced to row-echelon form (dependent system)

5d. cannot be reduced to row-echelon form (inconsistent system)

7. *Hint:* Define variables for the three angle measures and write a system of three equations. The statement of the exercise should help you write two equations. For the third equation, recall that in a triangle the sum of the angle measures is 180°.

9. *Hint:* Create a system of three equations by substituting each pair of coordinates for x and y. Then solve the system for a, b, and c.

11a. first plan: \$14,600; second plan: \$13,100

11b. Let x represent the number of tickets sold, and let y represent the income in dollars; $y = 12500 + 0.6x$.

11c. $y = 6800 + 1.8x$

11d. more than 4750 tickets

11e. The company should choose the first plan if they expect to sell fewer than 4750 tickets and the second if they expect to sell more than 4750 tickets.

13. $\overline{AB}$: $y = 6 - \frac{2}{3}(x - 4)$ or $y = 4 + \frac{2}{3}(x - 1)$;
$\overline{BC}$: $y = 4 - \frac{2}{3}(x - 7)$ or $y = 6 - \frac{2}{3}(x - 4)$;
$\overline{CD}$: $y = 1 + 3(x - 6)$ or $y = 4 + 3(x - 7)$;
$\overline{DE}$: $y = 1$; $\overline{AE}$: $y = 4 - 3(x - 1)$ or $y = 1 - 3(x - 2)$

LESSON 6.4

1a. $\begin{bmatrix} 3 & 4 \\ 2 & -5 \end{bmatrix}\begin{bmatrix} x \\ y \end{bmatrix} = \begin{bmatrix} 11 \\ -8 \end{bmatrix}$

1b. $\begin{bmatrix} 1 & 2 & 1 \\ 3 & -4 & 5 \\ -2 & -8 & -3 \end{bmatrix}\begin{bmatrix} x \\ y \\ z \end{bmatrix} = \begin{bmatrix} 0 \\ -11 \\ 1 \end{bmatrix}$

1c. $\begin{bmatrix} 5.2 & 3.6 \\ -5.2 & 2 \end{bmatrix}\begin{bmatrix} x \\ y \end{bmatrix} = \begin{bmatrix} 7 \\ 8.2 \end{bmatrix}$

1d. $\begin{bmatrix} \frac{1}{4} & -\frac{2}{5} \\ \frac{3}{8} & \frac{2}{5} \end{bmatrix}\begin{bmatrix} x \\ y \end{bmatrix} = \begin{bmatrix} 3 \\ 2 \end{bmatrix}$

3a. $\begin{bmatrix} 1a + 5c & 1b + 5d \\ 6a + 2c & 6b + 2d \end{bmatrix} = \begin{bmatrix} -7 & 33 \\ 14 & -26 \end{bmatrix}$;
$\begin{bmatrix} a & b \\ c & d \end{bmatrix} = \begin{bmatrix} 3 & -7 \\ -2 & 8 \end{bmatrix}$

3b. $\begin{bmatrix} 1a + 5c & 1b + 5d \\ 6a + 2c & 6b + 2d \end{bmatrix} = \begin{bmatrix} 1 & 0 \\ 0 & 1 \end{bmatrix}$;
$\begin{bmatrix} a & b \\ c & d \end{bmatrix} = \begin{bmatrix} -\frac{1}{14} & \frac{5}{28} \\ \frac{3}{14} & -\frac{1}{28} \end{bmatrix}$

5a. $\begin{bmatrix} 4 & -3 \\ -5 & 4 \end{bmatrix}$

5b. $\begin{bmatrix} -\frac{1}{6} & \frac{2}{3} & \frac{1}{9} \\ \frac{1}{2} & -1 & 0 \\ 0 & 0 & \frac{1}{3} \end{bmatrix}$ or $\begin{bmatrix} -0.1\overline{6} & 0.\overline{6} & 0.\overline{1} \\ 0.5 & -1 & 0 \\ 0 & 0 & 0.\overline{3} \end{bmatrix}$

5c. $\begin{bmatrix} \frac{7}{5} & -\frac{3}{5} \\ -2 & 1 \end{bmatrix}$ or $\begin{bmatrix} 1.4 & -0.6 \\ -2 & 1 \end{bmatrix}$

5d. Inverse does not exist.

7a. Jolly rides cost $0.50, Adventure rides cost $0.85, and Thrill rides cost $1.50.

7b. $28.50

7c. Carey would have been better off buying a ticket book.

9. 20°, 50°, 110°

11. $x = 0.0016, y = 0.0126, z = 0.0110$

13a. $\begin{bmatrix} 4 & -3 \\ -5 & 4 \end{bmatrix}$

13b. $\begin{bmatrix} -\frac{5}{9} & \frac{13}{9} & \frac{1}{9} \\ \frac{1}{2} & -1 & 0 \\ -\frac{7}{6} & \frac{7}{3} & \frac{1}{3} \end{bmatrix}$ or

$\begin{bmatrix} -0.\overline{5} & 1.\overline{4} & 0.\overline{1} \\ 0.5 & -1 & 0 \\ -1.\overline{6} & 2.\overline{3} & 0.\overline{3} \end{bmatrix}$

15. *Hint:* You want to write a second equation that would result in the graph of the same line.

17a. $[A] = \begin{bmatrix} 0 & 2 & 0 & 1 \\ 2 & 0 & 1 & 0 \\ 0 & 1 & 0 & 1 \\ 1 & 0 & 1 & 0 \end{bmatrix}$

17b. It is 0 because there are zero roads connecting Murray to itself.

17c. The matrix has reflection symmetry across the main diagonal.

17d. 5; 10. The matrix sum is twice the number of roads; each road is counted twice in the matrix because it can be traveled in either direction.

17e. For example, if the road between Davis and Terre is one-way toward Davis, a_{34} changes from 1 to 0. The matrix is no longer symmetric.

LESSON 6.5

1a. $y < \frac{10 - 2x}{-5}$ or $y < -2 + 0.4x$

1b. $y < \frac{6 - 2x}{-12}$ or $y < -\frac{1}{2} + \frac{1}{6}x$

3a. $y < 2 - 0.5x$

3b. $y \geq 3 + 1.5x$

3c. $y > 1 - 0.75x$

3d. $y \leq 1.5 + 0.5x$

5.

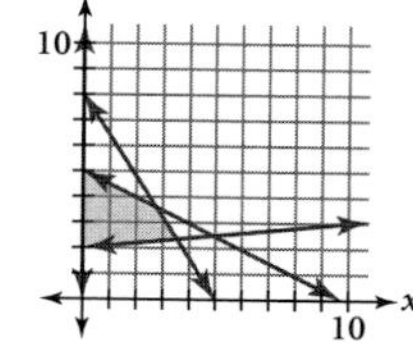

vertices: (0, 2), (0, 5), (2.752, 3.596), (3.529, 2.353)

7.

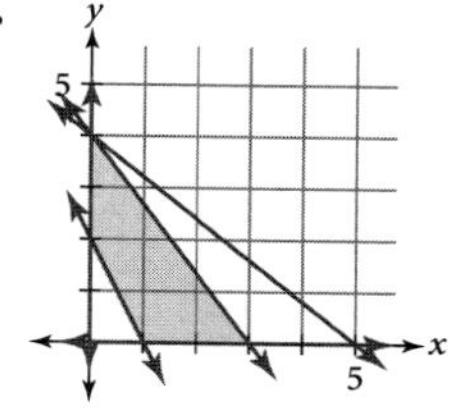

vertices: (0, 4), (3, 0), (1, 0), (0, 2)

9a. Let x represent length in inches, and let y represent width in inches.

$$\begin{cases} xy \geq 200 \\ xy \leq 300 \\ x + y \geq 33 \\ x + y \leq 40 \end{cases}$$

9b.

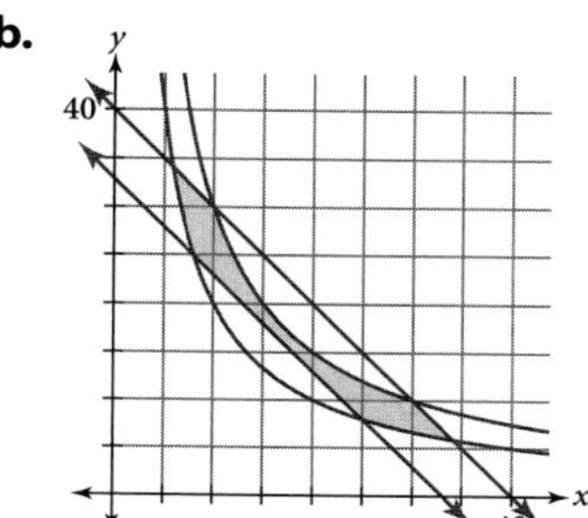

9c. i. no

9c. ii. yes

9c. iii. no

11a. $5x + 2y > 100$

11b. $y < 10$

11c. $x + y \leq 40$

11d. common sense: $x \geq 0, y \geq 0$

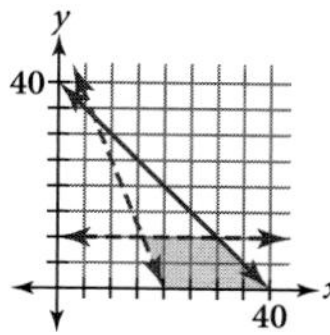

11e. (20, 0), (40, 0), (30, 10), (16, 10)

13. $a = 100, b \approx 0.7$

15a. 2 or 3 spores

15b. about 1,868,302 spores

Selected Answers

15c. $y = \dfrac{\log \dfrac{x}{2.68}}{\log 3.84}$

15d. after 14 hr 40 min

LESSON 6.6

1.

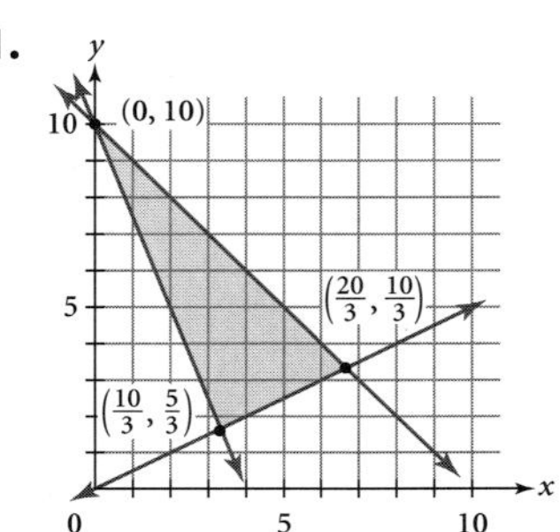

3.

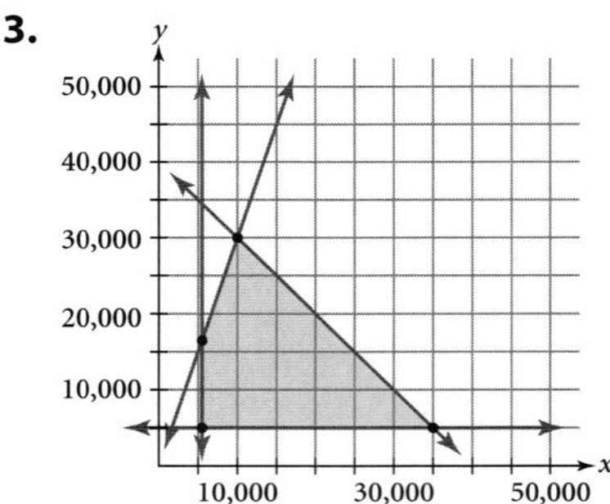

vertices: (5500, 5000), (5500, 16500), (10000, 30000), (35000, 5000); (10000, 30000); maximum: 3800

5a. possible answer:

$$\begin{cases} y \geq 7 \\ y \leq \frac{7}{5}(x - 3) + 6 \\ y \leq -\frac{7}{12}x + 13 \end{cases}$$

5b. possible answer:

$$\begin{cases} x \geq 0 \\ y \geq 7 \\ y \geq \frac{7}{5}(x - 3) + 6 \\ y \leq -\frac{7}{12}x + 13 \end{cases}$$

5c. possible answer:

$$\begin{cases} x \geq 0 \\ y \geq 0 \\ x \leq 11 \\ y \leq \frac{7}{5}(x - 3) + 6 \\ y \leq 7 \end{cases}$$

7. 5 radio minutes and 10 newspaper ads to reach a maximum of 155,000 people. This requires the assumption that people who listen to the radio are independent of people who read the newspaper, which is probably not realistic.

9. 3000 acres of coffee and 4500 acres of cocoa for a maximum total income of $289,800

11a. $x = -\frac{7}{11}, y = \frac{169}{11}$

11b. $x = -3.5, y = 74, z = 31$

13. $\begin{cases} x \geq 2 \\ y \leq 5 \\ x + y \geq 3 \\ 2x - y \leq 9 \end{cases}$

15. $y = -\left(\frac{x}{2}\right)^2 - \frac{3}{2}$ or $y = -\frac{1}{4}x^2 - \frac{3}{2}$

CHAPTER 6 REVIEW

1a. impossible because the dimensions are not the same

1b. $\begin{bmatrix} -4 & 7 \\ 1 & 2 \end{bmatrix}$

1c. $\begin{bmatrix} -12 & 4 & 8 \\ 8 & 12 & -8 \end{bmatrix}$

1d. $\begin{bmatrix} -3 & 1 & 2 \\ -11 & 11 & 6 \end{bmatrix}$

1e. impossible because the inside dimensions do not match

1f. $\begin{bmatrix} -7 & -5 & 6 \end{bmatrix}$

3a. $x = 2.5, y = 7$

3b. $x = 1.22, y = 6.9, z = 3.4$

5a. consistent and independent

5b. consistent and dependent

5c. inconsistent

5d. inconsistent

7. about 4.4 yr

9a. $\begin{bmatrix} .92 & .08 & 0 \\ .12 & .82 & .06 \\ 0 & .15 & .85 \end{bmatrix}$

9b. i. Mozart: 81; Picasso: 66; Hemingway: 63

9b. ii. Mozart: 82; Picasso: 70; Hemingway: 58

9b. iii. Mozart: 94; Picasso: 76; Hemingway: 40

11a. $a < 0; p < 0; d > 0$

11b. $a > 0; p > 0$; d cannot be determined

11c. $a > 0; p = 0; d < 0$

13. 20 students in second period, 18 students in third period, and 24 students in seventh period

15a. $x = 245$

15b. $x = 20$

15c. $x = -\frac{1}{2}$

15d. $x = \dfrac{\log\left(\frac{37000}{15}\right)}{\log 9.4} \approx 3.4858$

15e. $x = 21$

15f. $x = \dfrac{\log 342}{\log 36} \approx 1.6282$

17a. $y = 50(0.72)^{x-4}$ or $y = 25.92(0.72)^{x-6}$

17b. 0.72; decay

17c. approximately 186

17d. 0

19a. a translation right 5 units and down 2 units

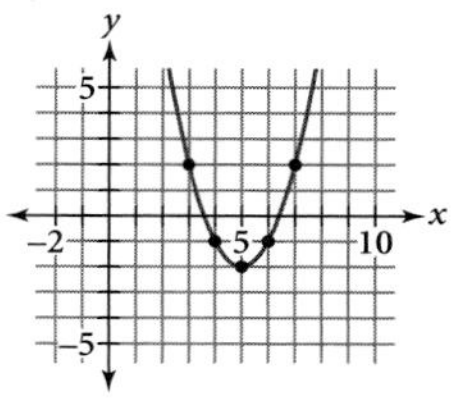

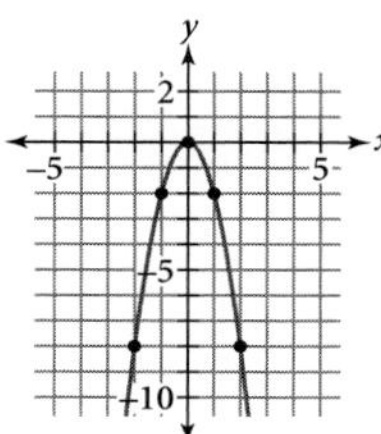

19b. a reflection across the x-axis and a vertical stretch by a factor of 2

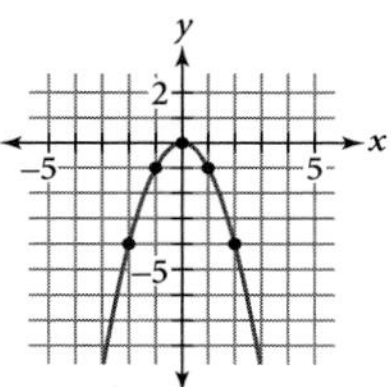

19c. $-1 \cdot [P] = \begin{bmatrix} 2 & 1 & 0 & -1 & -2 \\ -4 & -1 & 0 & -1 & -4 \end{bmatrix}$;

This is a reflection across the x-axis and a reflection across the y-axis. However, because the graph is symmetric with respect to the y-axis, a reflection over that axis does not change the graph.

19d. $[P] + \begin{bmatrix} -2 & -2 & -2 & -2 & -2 \\ 3 & 3 & 3 & 3 & 3 \end{bmatrix} =$

$\begin{bmatrix} -4 & -3 & -2 & -1 & 0 \\ 7 & 4 & 3 & 4 & 7 \end{bmatrix}$

CHAPTER 7 • CHAPTER 7 CHAPTER 7 • CHAPTER

LESSON 7.1

1a. 3 **1b.** 2 **1c.** 7 **1d.** 5

3a. no; {2.2, 2.6, 1.8, −0.2, −3.4}

3b. no; {0.007, 0.006, 0.008, 0.010}

3c. no; {150, 150, 150}

5a. $D_1 = \{2, 3, 4, 5, 6\}$; $D_2 = \{1, 1, 1, 1\}$; 2nd degree

5b. The polynomial is 2nd degree, and the D_2 values are constant.

5c. 4 points. You have to find the finite differences twice, so you need at least four data points to calculate two D_2 values that can be compared.

5d. $s = 0.5n^2 + 0.5n$; $s = 78$

5e. The pennies can be arranged to form triangles.

7a. i. $D_1 = \{15.1, 5.3, -4.5, -14.3, -24.1, -33.9\}$; $D_2 = \{-9.8, -9.8, -9.8, -9.8, -9.8\}$

7a. ii. $D_1 = \{59.1, 49.3, 39.5, 29.7, 19.9, 10.1\}$; $D_2 = \{-9.8, -9.8, -9.8, -9.8, -9.8\}$

7b. **i.** 2; **ii.** 2

7c. **i.** $h = -4.9t^2 + 20t + 80$; **ii.** $h = -4.9t^2 + 64t + 4$

9. Let x represent the energy level, and let y represent the maximum number of electrons; $y = 2x^2$.

11a. $x = 2.5$

11b. $x = 3$ or $x = -1$

11c. $x = \dfrac{\log 16}{\log 5} \approx 1.7227$

13. $\begin{cases} y \geq -\frac{1}{2}x + \frac{3}{2} \\ y \leq \frac{1}{2}x + \frac{9}{2} \\ y \leq -\frac{11}{6}x + \frac{97}{6} \end{cases}$

LESSON 7.2

1a. factored form and vertex form

1b. none of these forms

1c. factored form

1d. general form

3a. −1 and 2 **3b.** −3 and 2 **3c.** 2 and 5

5a. $y = x^2 - x - 2$

5b. $y = 0.5x^2 + 0.5x - 3$

5c. $y = -2x^2 + 14x - 20$

7a. $y = -0.5x^2 - hx - 0.5h^2 + 4$

7b. $y = ax^2 - 8ax + 16a$

7c. $y = ax^2 - 2ahx + ah^2 + k$

7d. $y = -0.5x^2 - (0.5r + 2)x - 2r$

7e. $y = ax^2 - 2ax - 8a$

7f. $y = ax^2 - a(r + s)x + ars$

9a. $y = (x + 2)(x - 1)$

9b. $y = -0.5(x + 2)(x - 3)$

9c. $y = \frac{1}{3}(x + 2)(x - 1)(x - 3)$

11a. lengths: 35, 30, 25, 20, 15; areas: 175, 300, 375, 400, 375

11b. $y = x(40 - x)$ or $y = -x^2 + 40x$

11c. 20 m; 400 m^2.

11d. 0 m and 40 m

13a. $12x^2 - 15x$ **13b.** $x^2 - 2x - 15$

13c. $x^2 - 49$ **13d.** $9x^2 - 6x + 1$

15a. $(x + 5)(x - 2)$ **15b.** $(x + 4)(x + 4)$

15c. $(x + 5)(x - 5)$

LESSON 7.3

1a. $(x - 5)^2$ **1b.** $\left(x + \frac{5}{2}\right)^2$

1c. $(2x - 3)^2$ or $4\left(x - \frac{3}{2}\right)^2$ **1d.** $(x - y)^2$

3a. $y = (x + 10)^2 - 6$ **3b.** $y = (x - 3.5)^2 + 3.75$

3c. $y = 6(x - 2)^2 + 123$ **3d.** $y = 5(x + 0.8)^2 - 3.2$

5. $(-4, 12)$

7a. Let x represent time in seconds, and let y represent height in meters; $y = -4.9(x - 1.1)(x - 4.7)$ or $y = -4.9x^2 + 28.42x - 25.333$.

7b. 28.42 m/s **7c.** 25.333 m

9. Let x represent time in seconds, and let y represent height in meters; $y = -4.9x^2 + 17.2x + 50$.

11a. $n = -2p + 100$ **11b.** $R(p) = -2p^2 + 100p$

11c. Vertex form: $R(p) = -2(p - 25)^2 + 1250$. The vertex is (25, 1250). This means that the maximum revenue is $1250 when the price is $25.

11d. between $15 and $35

13. $x = 2, x = -3$, or $x = \frac{1}{2}$

15a. Let x represent the year, and let y represent the number of endangered species.

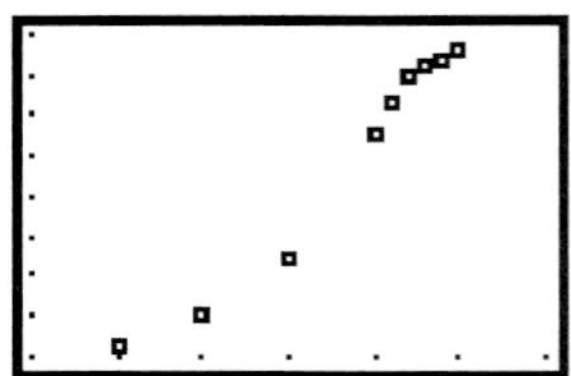

[1975, 2005, 5, 200, 1000, 100]

15b. $\hat{y} = 45.64x - 90289$

15c. approximately 1219 species in 2005; 3273 species in 2050

LESSON 7.4

1a. $x = 7.3$ or $x = -2.7$ **1b.** $x = -0.95$ or $x = -7.95$

1c. $x = 2$ or $x = -\frac{1}{2}$

3a. -0.102 **3b.** -5.898 **3c.** -0.243 **3d.** 8.243

5a. $y = (x - 1)(x - 5)$ **5b.** $y = (x + 2)(x - 9)$

5c. $y = 5(x + 1)(x + 1.4)$

7a. $y = a(x - 3)(x + 3)$ for $a \neq 0$

7b. $y = a(x - 4)\left(x + \frac{2}{5}\right)$ or $y = a(x - 4)(5x + 2)$ for $a \neq 0$

7c. $y = a(x - r_1)(x - r_2)$ for $a \neq 0$

9. *Hint:* When will the quadratic formula result in no real solutions?

11a. $y = -4x^2 - 6.8x + 49.2$

11b. 49.2 L **11c.** 2.76 min

13a. $x^2 + 14x + 49 = (x + 7)^2$

13b. $x^2 - 10x + 25 = (x - 5)^2$

13c. $x^2 + 3x + \frac{9}{4} = \left(x + \frac{3}{2}\right)^2$

13d. $2x^2 + 8x + 8 = 2(x^2 + 4x + 4) = 2(x + 2)^2$

15a. $y = 2x^2 - x - 15$ **15b.** $y = -2x^2 + 4x + 2$

17. $a = k = 52.08\overline{3}$ ft; $b = j = 33.\overline{3}$ ft; $c = i = 18.75$ ft; $d = h = 8.\overline{3}$ ft; $e = g = 2.08\overline{3}$ ft; $f = 0$; $229.1\overline{6}$ ft

LESSON 7.5

1a. $8 + 4i$ **1b.** 7

1c. $4 - 2i$ **1d.** $-2.56 - 0.61i$

3a. $5 + i$ **3b.** $-1 - 2i$

3c. $2 - 3i$ **3d.** $-2.35 + 2.71i$

5a.

5b.

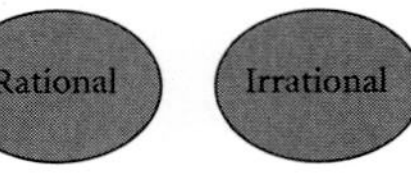

5c.

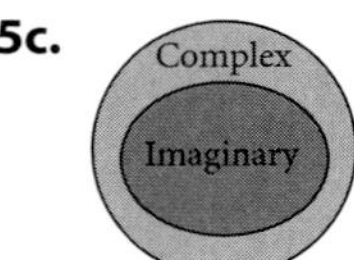

5d.

5e.

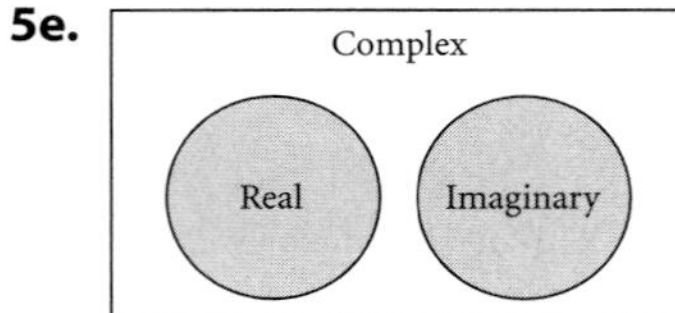

7a. $-i$ **7b.** 1 **7c.** i **7d.** -1

9. $0.2 + 1.6i$

11a. $y = x^2 - 2x - 15$ **11b.** $y = x^2 + 7x + 12.25$

11c. $y = x^2 + 25$ **11d.** $y = x^2 - 4x + 5$

13a. $x = (5 + \sqrt{34})i \approx 10.83i$ or $x = (5 - \sqrt{34})i \approx -0.83i$

13b. $x = 2i$ or $x = i$

13c. The coefficients of the quadratic equations are nonreal.

15a. 0, 0, 0, 0, 0, 0; remains constant at 0

15b. $0, i, -1 + i, -i, -1 + i, -i$; alternates between $-1 + i$ and $-i$

15c. $0, 1 - i, 1 - 3i, -7 - 7i, 1 + 97i, -9407 + 193i$; no recognizable pattern in these six terms

15d. $0, 0.2 + 0.2i, 0.2 + 0.28i, 0.1616 + 0.312i, 0.12877056 + 0.3008384i, 0.1260781142 + 0.2774782585i$; approaches $0.142120634 + 0.2794237653i$

17a. Let x represent the first integer, and let y represent the second integer.

$$\begin{cases} x > 0 \\ y > 0 \\ 3x + 4y < 30 \\ 2x < y + 5 \end{cases}$$

17b.

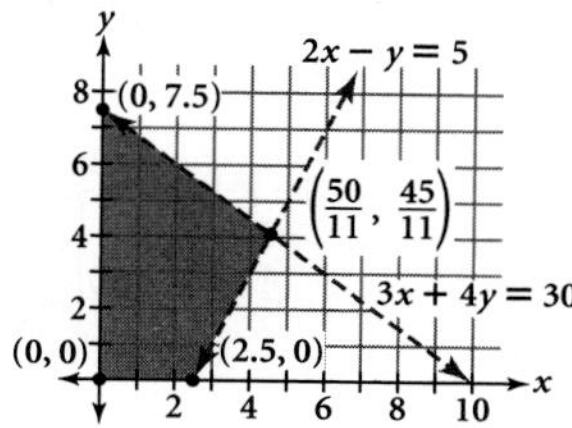

17c. (1, 1), (2, 1), (1, 2), (2, 2), (3, 2), (1, 3), (2, 3), (3, 3), (1, 4), (2, 4), (3, 4), (4, 4), (1, 5), (2, 5), (3, 5), (1, 6)

LESSON 7.6

1a. x-intercepts: $-1.5, -6$; y-intercept: -2.25

1b. x-intercept: 4; y-intercept: 48

1c. x-intercepts: $3, -2, -5$; y-intercept: 60

1d. x-intercepts: $-3, 3$; y-intercept: -135

3a. $y = x^2 - 10x + 24$ **3b.** $y = x^2 - 6x + 9$

3c. $y = x^3 - 64x$ **3d.** $y = 3x^3 + 15x^2 - 12x - 60$

5a. approximately 2.94 units; approximately 420 cubic units

5b. 5 and approximately 1.28

5c. The graph exists, but these x- and y-values make no physical sense for this context. If $x \geq 8$, there will be no box left after you take out two 8-unit square corners from the 16-unit width.

5d. The graph exists, but these x- and y-values make no physical sense for this context.

7a. sample answer:

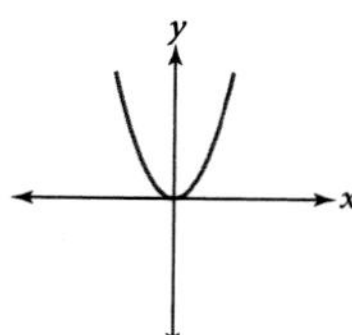

7b. sample answer:

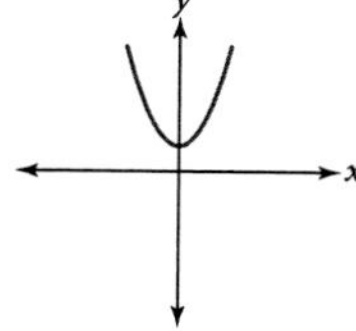

7c. not possible

7d. sample answer:

7e. sample answer:

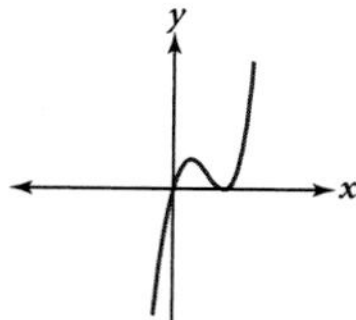

7f. not possible

9a. $(T + t)^2$ or $T^2 + 2Tt + t^2$

	T	t
T	TT	Tt
t	Tt	tt

9b. $(T + t)^2 = 1$ or $T^2 + 2Tt + t^2 = 1$

9c. $0.70 + t^2 = 1$

9d. $t \approx 0.548$ **9e.** $T \approx 0.452$

9f. $TT \approx 0.204$, or about 20% of the population

11. $y = 0.25(x + 2)^2 + 3$

13a. $f^{-1}(x) = \frac{3}{2}x - 5$

13b. $g^{-1}(x) = -3 + (x + 6)^{3/2}$

13c. $h^{-1}(x) = \log_2(7 - x)$

LESSON 7.7

1a. $x = -5, x = 3$, and $x = 7$

1b. $x = -6, x = -3, x = 2$, and $x = 6$

1c. $x = -5$ and $x = 2$

1d. $x = -5, x = -3, x = 1, x = 4$, and $x = 6$

3a. 3 **3b.** 4 **3c.** 2 **3d.** 5

5a. $y = a(x - 4)$ where $a \neq 0$

5b. $y = a(x - 4)^2$ where $a \neq 0$

5c. $y = a(x - 4)^3$ where $a \neq 0$; or $y = a(x - 4)(x - r_1)(x - r_2)$ where $a \neq 0$, and r_1 and r_2 are complex conjugates

7a. 4 **7b.** 5 **7c.** $y = -x(x + 5)^2(x + 1)(x - 4)$

9. The leading coefficient is equal to the y-intercept divided by the product of the zeros if the degree of the function is even, or the y-intercept divided by -1 times the product of the zeros if the degree of the function is odd.

11a. i. $y = (x + 5)^2(x + 2)(x - 1)$

11a. ii. $y = -(x + 5)^2(x + 2)(x - 1)$

11a. iii. $y = (x + 5)^2(x + 2)(x - 1)^2$

11a. iv. $y = -(x + 5)(x + 2)^3(x - 1)$

11b. i. $x = -5, x = -5, x = -2$, and $x = 1$

11b. ii. $x = -5, x = -5, x = -2$, and $x = 1$

11b. iii. $x = -5, x = -5, x = -2, x = 1$, and $x = 1$

11b. iv. $x = -5, x = -2, x = -2, x = -2$, and $x = 1$

13. *Hint:* A polynomial function of degree n will have at most $n - 1$ extreme values and n x-intercepts.

15. $3 - 5\sqrt{2}$; $0 = a(x^2 - 6x - 41)$ where $a \neq 0$

17a. $\begin{bmatrix} 4 & 9 \\ 2 & -3 \end{bmatrix}\begin{bmatrix} x \\ y \end{bmatrix} = \begin{bmatrix} 4 \\ 7 \end{bmatrix}$ $\quad \begin{bmatrix} x \\ y \end{bmatrix} = \begin{bmatrix} \frac{5}{2} \\ -\frac{2}{3} \end{bmatrix}$

17b. $\left[\begin{array}{cc|c} 4 & 9 & 4 \\ 2 & -3 & 7 \end{array}\right] \rightarrow \left[\begin{array}{cc|c} 1 & 0 & \frac{5}{2} \\ 0 & 1 & -\frac{2}{3} \end{array}\right]$

LESSON 7.8

1a. $3x^2 + 7x + 3$ **1b.** $6x^3 - 4x^2$

3a. $a = 12$ **3b.** $b = 2$ **3c.** $c = 7$ **3d.** $d = -4$

5. $\pm 15, \pm 5, \pm 3, \pm 1, \pm\frac{15}{2}, \pm\frac{5}{2}, \pm\frac{3}{2}, \pm\frac{1}{2}$

7a. $2(3i)^3 - (3i)^2 + 18(3i) - 9 =$
$-54i + 9 + 54i - 9 = 0$

7b. $x = -3i$ and $x = \frac{1}{2}$

9. $y = (x - 3)(x + 5)(2x - 1)$ or
$y = 2(x - 3)(x + 5)\left(x - \frac{1}{2}\right)$

11a. $f(x) = 0.00639x^{3/2}$ **11b.** $f^{-1}(x) \approx (156x)^{2/3}$

11c. 33 in. **11d.** about 176 ft

13a.

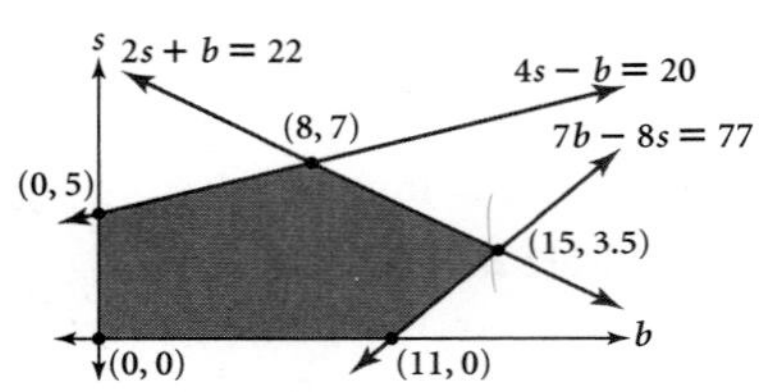

13b. 15 baseball caps and 3 sun hats; \$33

15a. $x = -3$ or $x = 1$ **15b.** $x = \frac{-3 \pm \sqrt{37}}{2}$

15c. $x = 1 \pm 2i$

CHAPTER 7 REVIEW

1a. $2(x - 2)(x - 3)$

1b. $(2x + 1)(x + 3)$ or $2(x + 0.5)(x + 3)$

1c. $x(x - 12)(x + 2)$

3. 1; 4; 10; $\frac{1}{6}n^3 - \frac{1}{2}n^2 + \frac{1}{3}n$

5a.

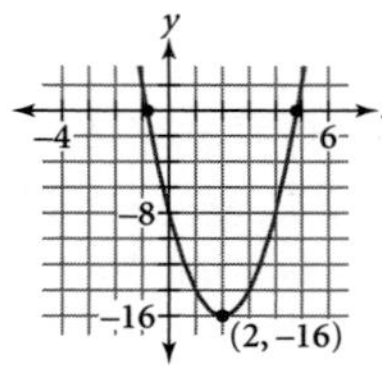

zeros: $x = -0.83$
and $x = 4.83$

5b.

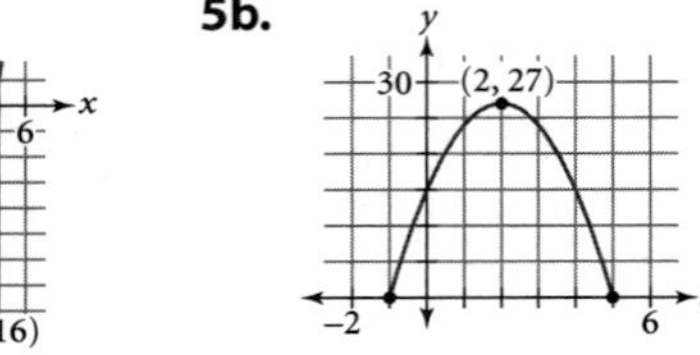

zeros: $x = -1$
and $x = 5$

5c.

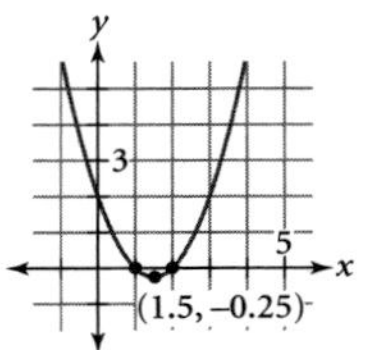

zeros: $x = 1$
and $x = 2$

5d.

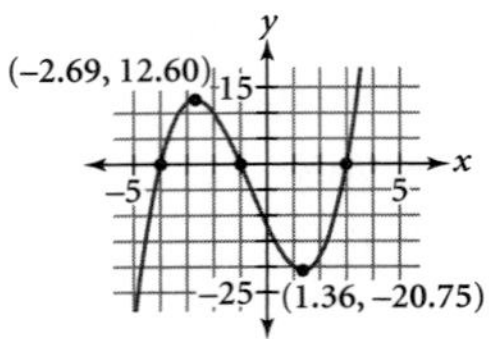

zeros: $x = -4$,
$x = -1$, and $x = 3$

5e.

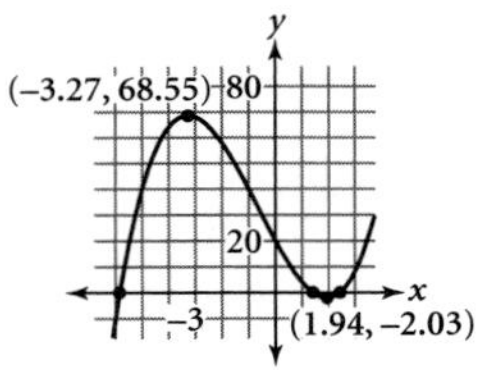

zeros: $x = -5.84$,
$x = 1.41$, and $x = 2.43$

5f.

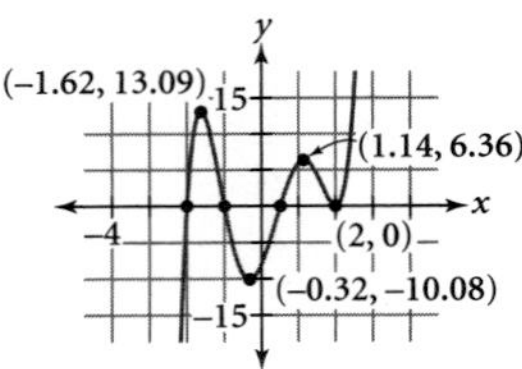

zeros: $x = -2$, $x = -1$,
$x = 0.5$, and $x = 2$

7. 18 in. by 18 in. by 36 in.

9a. $y = 0.5x^2 + 0.5x + 1$

9b. 16 pieces; 56 pieces

11a. $\pm 1, \pm 3, \pm 13, \pm 39, \pm\frac{1}{3}, \pm\frac{13}{3}$

11b. $x = -\frac{1}{3}$, $x = 3$, $x = 2 + 3i$, and $x = 2 - 3i$

13. $2x^2 + 4x + 3$

CHAPTER 8 • CHAPTER 8 CHAPTER 8 • CHAPTER

LESSON 8.1

1a.

t	x	y
−2	−7	−3
−1	−4	−1
0	−1	1
1	2	3
2	5	5

1b.

t	x	y
−2	−1	4
−1	0	1
0	1	0
1	2	1
2	3	4

1c.

t	x	y
−2	4	1
−1	1	2
0	0	3
1	1	4
2	4	5

1d.

t	x	y
−2	−3	0
−1	−2	1.73
0	−1	2
1	0	1.73
2	1	0

3a.

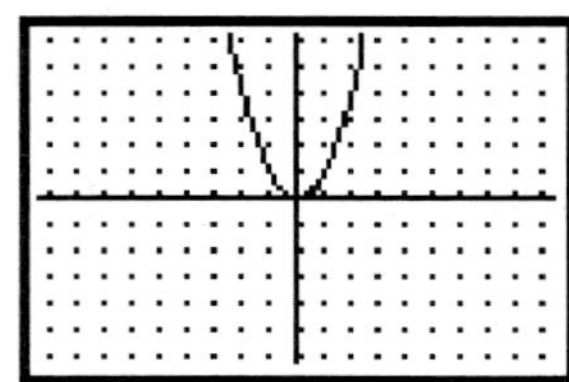

[−9.4, 9.4, 1, −6.2, 6.2, 1]

3b. The graph is translated right 2 units.

3c. The graph is translated down 3 units.

3d. The graph is translated right 5 units and up 2 units.

3e. The graph is translated horizontally a units and vertically b units.

5a. 15 s **5b.** 30 yd **5c.** -2 yd/s

5d. Sample answer: 65 yd is her starting position relative to the goal line, -2 yd/s is her velocity, and 50 yd is her position relative to the sideline.

5e. The graph simulation will produce the graphs pictured in the problem. A good window is [0, 100, 10, 0, 60, 10] with $0 \leq t \leq 15$.

5f. She crosses the 10-yard line after 27.5 s.

5g. $65 - 2t = 10$; 27.5 s

7a. The graph is reflected across the x-axis.

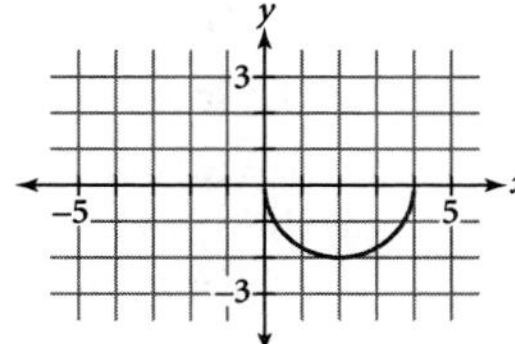

7b. The graph is reflected across the y-axis.

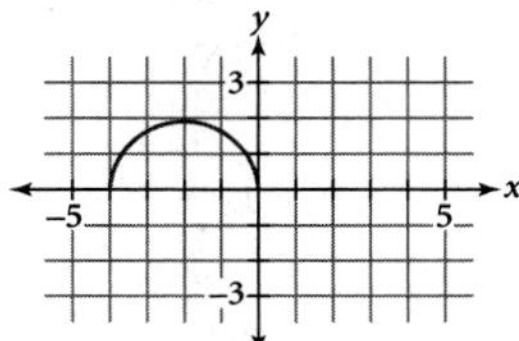

9a. $x = 0.4t$ and $y = 1$

9b. [0, 50, 5, 0, 3, 1]; $0 \leq t \leq 125$

9c. $x = 1.8(t - 100), y = 2$

9d. The tortoise will win.

9e. The tortoise takes 125 s and the hare takes approximately 28 s, but because he starts 100 s later, he finishes at 128 s.

11a.

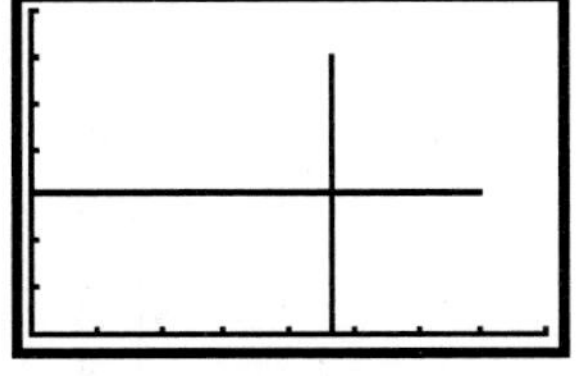

[0, 8, 1, 0, 7, 1]

11b. 1.4 m/s is the velocity of the first walker, 3.1 m is the vertical distance between the walkers when they start, 4.7 m is the horizontal distance between the walkers when they start, and 1.2 m/s is the velocity of the second walker.

11c. (4.7, 3.1)

11d. No, the first walker arrives at (4.7, 3.1) at 3.357 s, and the second walker arrives there at 2.583 s.

13. $(7, -3)$

15a. $2.5n^2 - 5.5n - 3$ **15b.** 887

17. $y = -2x^2 + 5x - 2$

LESSON 8.2

1a. $t = x - 1$ **1b.** $t = \frac{x+1}{3}$

1c. $t = \pm\sqrt{x}$ **1d.** $t = x + 1$

3a. $y = \frac{x+7}{2}$ **3b.** $y = \pm\sqrt{x} + 1$

3c. $y = \frac{2x-4}{3}$ **3d.** $y = 2(x+2)^2$

5.

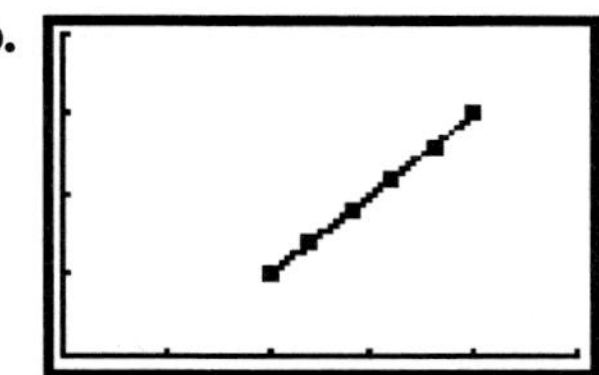

7. $-2.5 \leq t \leq 2.5$

9a. $x = 20 + 2t, y = 5 + t$

9b.

[0, 50, 10, 0, 20, 5]

$0 \leq t \leq 10$

The points lie on the line.

9c. $y = \frac{1}{2}x - 5$

9d. The slope of the line in 9c is the ratio of the y-slope over the x-slope in the parametric equations.

11a. $x = 1, y = 1.5t$

11b. $x = 1.1, y = 12 - 2.5t$

11c. possible answer: [0, 2, 1, 0, 12, 1]; $0 \leq t \leq 3$

11d.

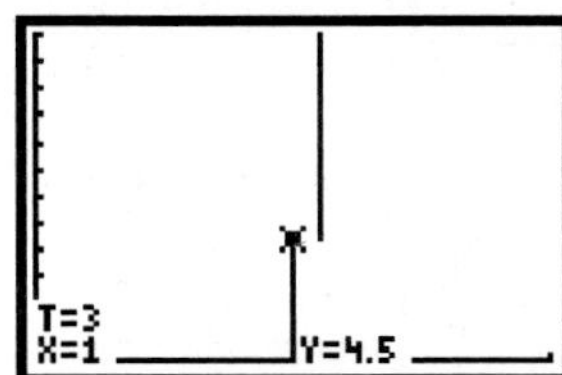

[0, 2, 1, 0, 12, 1]

$0 \leq t \leq 3$

They meet after hiking 3 h, when both are 4.5 mi north of the trailhead.

11e. $1.5t = 12 - 2.5t$; $t = 3$; substitute $t = 3$ into either y-equation to get $y = 4.5$.

13. $x = t^2, y = t$

15. $y = \left(\frac{2}{3}(x - 5) - 2\right) + 3$ or $y = \frac{2}{3}x - \frac{7}{3}$

LESSON 8.3

1. $\sin A = \frac{k}{j}$; $\sin B = \frac{h}{j}$;

$\sin^{-1}\left(\frac{k}{j}\right) = A$; $\sin^{-1}\left(\frac{h}{j}\right) = B$;

$\cos B = \frac{k}{j}$; $\cos A = \frac{h}{j}$;

$\cos^{-1}\left(\frac{k}{j}\right) = B$; $\cos^{-1}\left(\frac{h}{j}\right) = A$;

$\tan A = \frac{k}{h}$; $\tan B = \frac{h}{k}$;

$\tan^{-1}\left(\frac{k}{h}\right) = A$; $\tan^{-1}\left(\frac{h}{k}\right) = B$

3a. $a \approx 17.3$ **3b.** $b \approx 22.8$ **3c.** $c \approx 79.3$

5. 

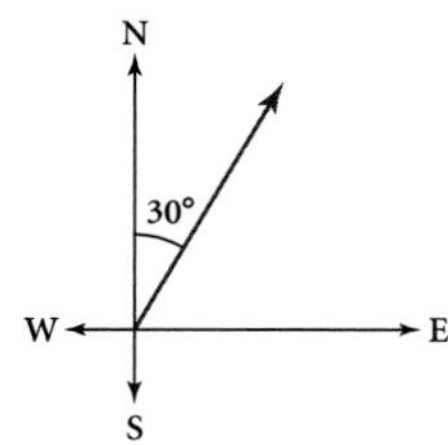

5a. 60°

5b.

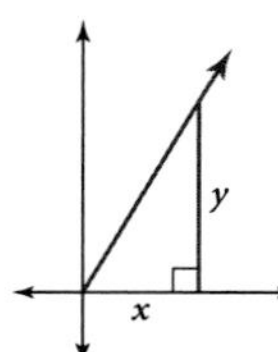

5c. 180 mi east, 311.8 mi north

7a.

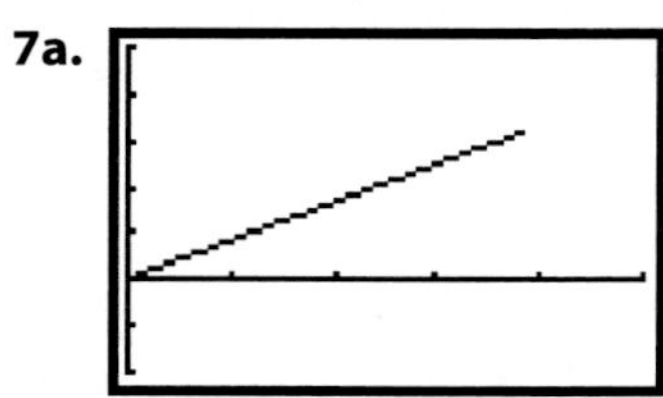

[0, 5, 1, −2, 5, 1]

$0 \leq t \leq 1$

7b. It is a segment 5 units long, at an angle of 40° above the x-axis.

7c. This is the value of the angle in the equations.

7d. It makes the segment 5 units long when $t = 1$; the graph becomes steeper, and the segment becomes shorter; the graph becomes shorter, but the slope is the same as it was originally.

9a.

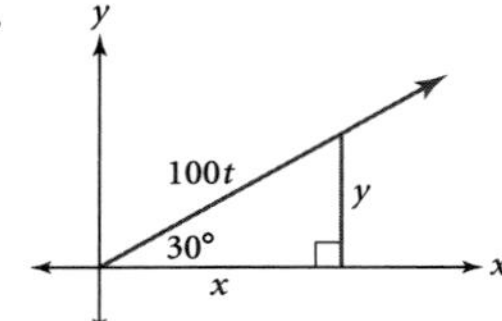

$x = 100t\cos 30°, y = 100t\sin 30°$

9b. $0 \leq t \leq 5$

9c. 100 represents the speed of the plane in miles per hour, t represents time in hours, 30° is the angle the plane is making with the x-axis, x is the horizontal position at any time, and y is the vertical position at any time.

11a.

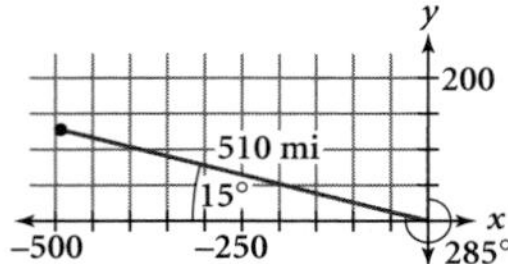

11b. 23.2 h **11c.** 492.6 mi west, 132.0 mi north

11d. The paths cross at approximately 480 mi west and 129 mi north of St. Petersburg. No, the ships do not collide because Tanker A reaches this point after 24.4 h and Tanker B reaches this point after 22.6 h.

13a. $y = 5 + \frac{3}{4}(x - 6)$ or $y = \frac{1}{2} + \frac{3}{4}x$

13b. $y = 5 + \frac{3(x - 6)}{4}$. They are the same equation.

15. $(x - 2.6)^2 + (y + 4.5)^2 = 12.96$

LESSON 8.4

1. $x = 10t\cos 30°, y = 10t\sin 30°$

3a.

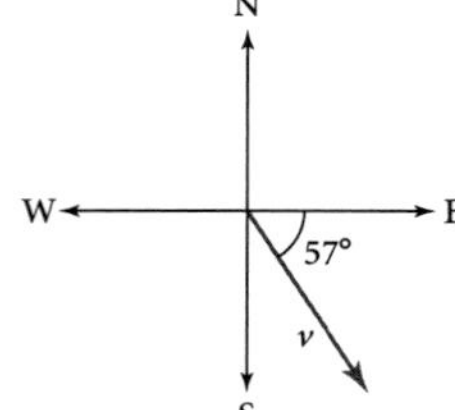

3b.

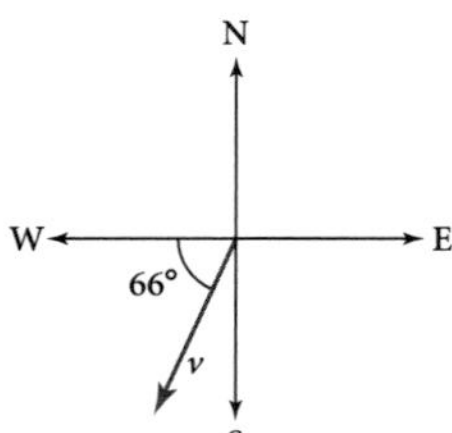

3c.

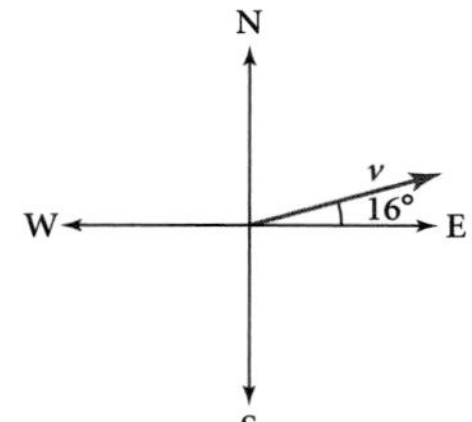

3d.

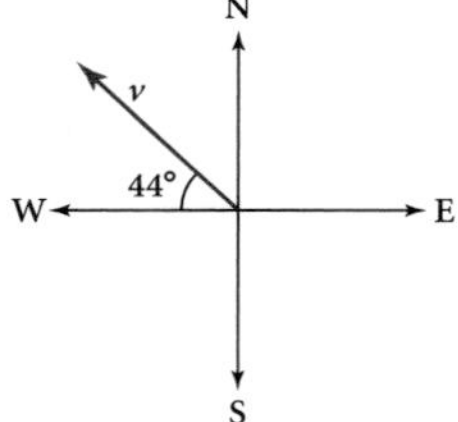

5a. $(-0.3, 0.5)$ **5b.** $x = -0.3 + 4t$

5c. $y = 0.5 - 7t$

5d.

$[-0.4, 0.1, 0.1, -0.1, 0.6, 0.1]$
$0 \le t \le 0.1$

5e. At 0.075 h (4.5 min), the boat lands 0.025 km (25 m) south of the dock.

5f. 0.605 km

7a. $y = -5t$ **7b.** $x = st$ **7c.** $s = 10$ mi/h

7d. 4.47 mi **7e.** 0.4 h **7f.** 11.18 mi/h

7g. 63.4°

9a. $y = -20t \sin 45°$ **9b.** $x = 20t \cos 45°$

9c. Both the plane's motion and the wind contribute to the actual path of the plane, so you add the x-contributions and add the y-contributions to form the final equations.

9d. possible answer: $[-1000, 0, 100, -100, 0, 10]$; $0 \le t \le 5$

9e. 4.24. It takes the plane 4.24 h to fly 1000 mi west.

9f. 60 mi

11a.

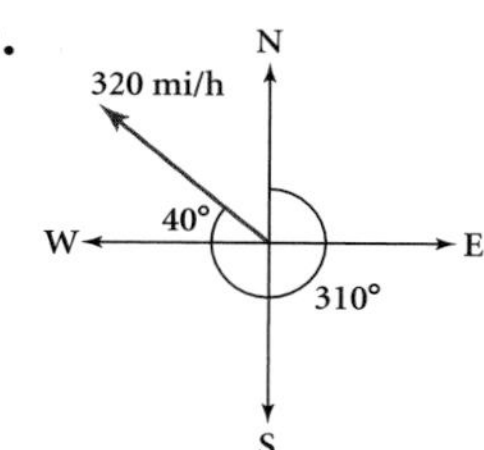

11b. $x = -320t \cos 40°, y = 320t \sin 40°$

11c.

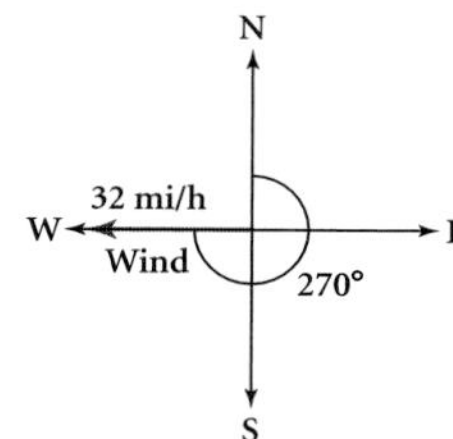

11d. $x = -32t, y = 0$

11e. $x = -320t \cos 40° - 32t, y = 320t \sin 40°$

11f. 1385.7 mi west and 1028.5 mi north

13a. x-component: $50 \cos 40° \approx 38.3$; y-component: $50 \sin 40° \approx 32.1$

13b. x-component: $90 \cos 140° \approx -68.9$; y-component: $90 \sin 140° \approx 57.9$

13c. x-component: -30.6; y-component: 90.0

13d. 95.1 N **13e.** 109° **13f.** 95.1 N at 289°

15a. two real, rational roots

15b. two real, irrational roots

15c. no real roots **15d.** one real, rational root

LESSON 8.5

1a. the Moon; centimeters and seconds

1b. right 400 cm and up 700 cm

1c. up-left **1d.** 50 cm/s

3a. $x = 2t, y = -4.9t^2 + 12$

3b. $-4.9t^2 + 12 = 0$

3c. 1.56 s, 3.13 m from the cliff

3d. possible answer: $[0, 4, 1, 0, 12, 1]$

5a. possible answer: $[0, 5, 1, 0, 4, 1], 0 \le t \le 1.5$

5b. *Hint:* Describe the initial angle, velocity, and position of the projectile. Be sure to include units, and state what planet the motion occurred on.

7a. $x = 83t \cos 0°, y = -4.9t^2 + 83t \sin 0° + 1.2$

7b. No; it will hit the ground 28.93 m before reaching the target.

7c. The angle must be between 2.44° and 3.43°.

7d. at least 217 m/s

9. 46 ft from the end of the cannon

11a. $x = 122t \cos 38°, y = -16t^2 + 122t \sin 38°$

11b. 451 ft **11c.** 378 ft

13a. $x = 2.3t + 4, y = 3.8t + 3$

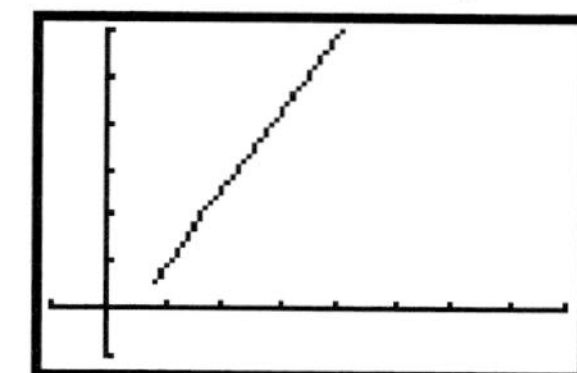

$[-5, 40, 5, -5, 30, 5]$

13b. 4.44 m/s on a bearing of 31°

15. $a(4x^3 + 8x^2 - 23x - 33) = 0$, where a is an integer, $a \ne 0$

LESSON 8.6

1. 9.7 cm

3. $X \approx 50.2°$ and $Z \approx 92.8°$

5a. $B = 25.5°$; $BC \approx 6.4$ cm; $AB \approx 8.35$ cm

5b. $J \approx 38.8°$; $L \approx 33.3°$; $KJ \approx 4.77$ cm

7a. 12.19 cm

7b. Because the triangle is isosceles, knowing the measure of one angle allows you to determine the measures of all three angles.

9. 2.5 km

11a. 41° **11b.** 70° **11c.** 0°

13a.

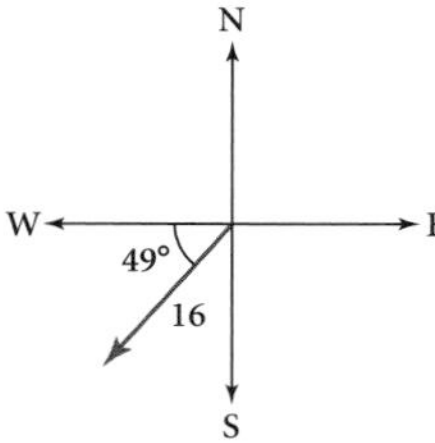

x-component: $12 \cos 78° \approx 2.5$;
y-component: $-12 \sin 78° \approx -11.7$

13b.

x-component: $-16 \cos 49° \approx -10.5$;
y-component: $-16 \sin 49° \approx -12.1$

15a. $26,376.31 **15b.** 20 years 11 months

LESSON 8.7

1. approximately 6.1 km

3a. $A \approx 41.4°$ **3b.** $b = 8$

5. 1659.8 mi

7. From point A, the underground chamber is at a 22° angle from the ground between A and B. From point B, the chamber is at a 120° angle from the ground. If the truck goes 1.5 km farther in the same direction, the chamber will be approximately 2.6 km directly beneath the truck.

9. 2.02 mi

11. 10.3 nautical mi

13. 1751 cm^2

CHAPTER 8 REVIEW

1a. $t = 3: x = -8, y = 0.5; t = 0: x = 1, y = 2;$ $t = -3: x = 10, y = -1$

1b. $y = \frac{6}{11}$ **1c.** $x = \frac{5}{2}$

1d. When $t = -1$, the y-value is undefined.

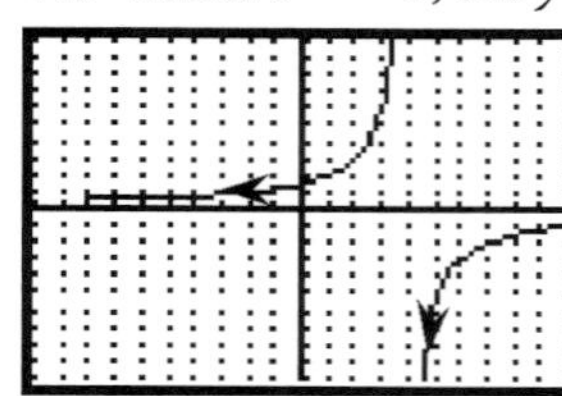

$[-10, 10, 1, -10, 10, 1]$

3a. $y = \frac{x + 7}{2}$. The graph is the same.

3b. $y = \pm\sqrt{x - 1} - 2$. The graph is the same except for the restrictions on t.

3c. $y = (2x - 1)^2$. The graph is the same. The values of t are restricted, but endpoints are not visible within the calculator screen given.

3d. $y = x^2 - 5$. The graph is the same, except the parametric equations will not allow for negative values for x.

5a. $A \approx 43°$ **5b.** $B \approx 28°$ **5c.** $c \approx 23.0$

5d. $d \approx 12.9$ **5e.** $e \approx 21.4$ **5f.** $f \approx 17.1$

7. 7.2 m

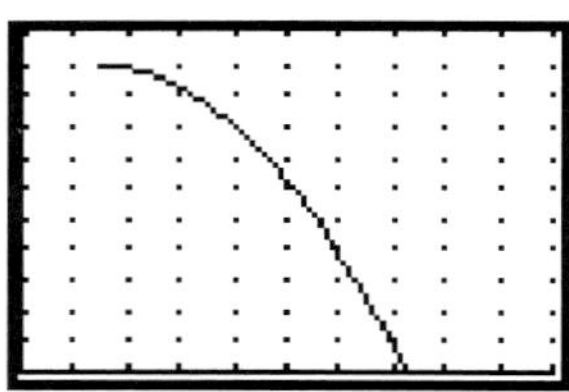

$[0, 10, 1, 0, 11, 1]$

9. She will miss it by 11.1 ft.

11a. $a \approx 7.8$ m, $c \approx 6.7$ m, $C = 42°$

11b. $A \approx 40°, b \approx 3.5$ cm, $C \approx 58°$

CHAPTER 9 • CHAPTER 9 CHAPTER 9 • CHAPTER

LESSON 9.1

1a. 10 units **1b.** $\sqrt{74}$ units

1c. $\sqrt{85}$ units **1d.** $\sqrt{81 + 4d^2}$ units

3. $x = -1 \pm \sqrt{2160}$ or $x = -1 \pm 12\sqrt{15}$

5. approximately 25.34 units

7. approximately between the points (2.5, 2.134) and (2.5, 3.866)

9a. $y = \sqrt{10^2 + x^2} + \sqrt{(20 - x)^2 + 13^2}$

9b. domain: $0 \leq x \leq 20$; range: $30 < y < 36$

9c. When the wire is fastened approximately 8.696 m from the 10 m pole, the minimum length is approximately 30.48 m.

11a. $d = \sqrt{(5 - x)^2 + (0.5x^2 + 4)^2}$

11b. approximately 6.02 units; approximately (0.92, 1.42)

13a–d.

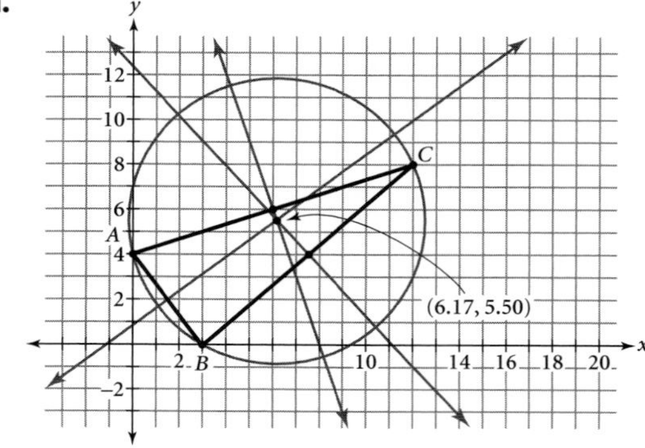

13b. All three perpendicular bisectors intersect at the same point. No, you could find the intersection by constructing only two perpendicular bisectors.

13c. Approximately (6.17, 5.50); this should agree with the answer to 12a.

13d. Regardless of which point is chosen, the circle passes through *A*, *B*, and *C*. Because the radius of the circle is constant, the distance from the recreation center to all three towns is the same.

15a. midpoint of $\overline{AB}$: (4.5, 1.5); midpoint of $\overline{BC}$: (2.5, 0); midpoint of $\overline{AC}$: (6, −3.5)

15b. median from *A* to $\overline{BC}$: $y = -0.\overline{36}x + 0.\overline{90}$ or $y = -\frac{4}{11}x + \frac{10}{11}$; median from *B* to $\overline{AC}$: $y = -1.7x + 6.7$; median from *C* to $\overline{AB}$: $y = 13x - 57$

15c. $(4.\overline{3}, -0.\overline{6})$ or $\left(4\frac{1}{3}, -\frac{2}{3}\right)$

17. approximately 44.6 nautical mi

19. $w = 74°, x = 50°$

LESSON 9.2

1a. center: (0, 0); radius: 2

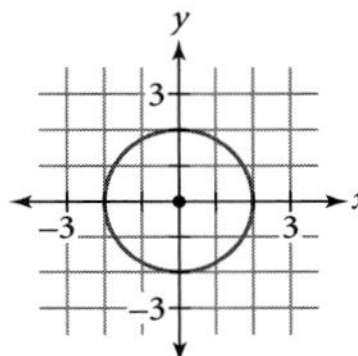

$y = \pm\sqrt{4 - x^2}$

1b. center: (3, 0); radius: 1

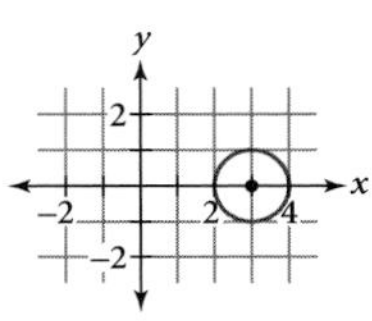

$y = \pm\sqrt{1 - (x - 3)^2}$

1c. center: (−1, 2); radius: 3

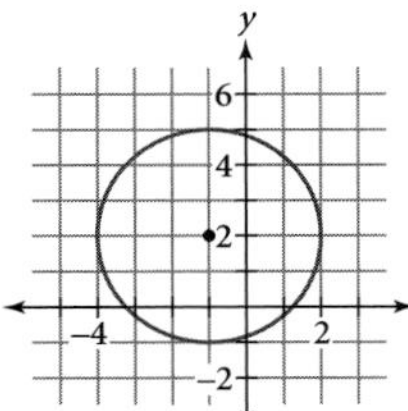

$y = \pm\sqrt{9 - (x + 1)^2} + 2$

1d. center: (0, 1.5); radius: 0.5

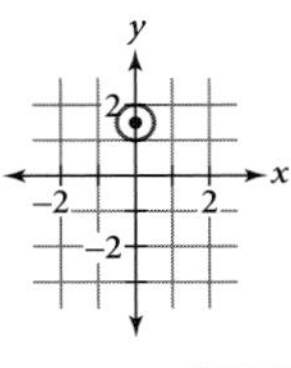

$y = \pm\sqrt{0.25 - x^2} + 1.5$

1e. center: (1, 2); radius: 2

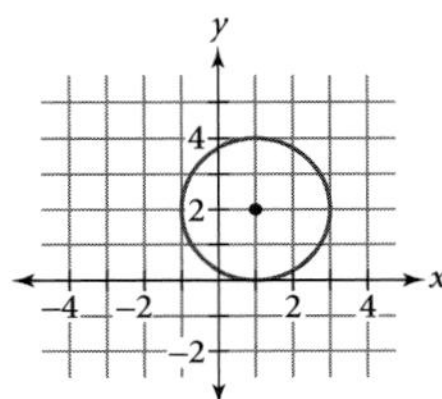

1f. center: (−3, 0); radius: 4

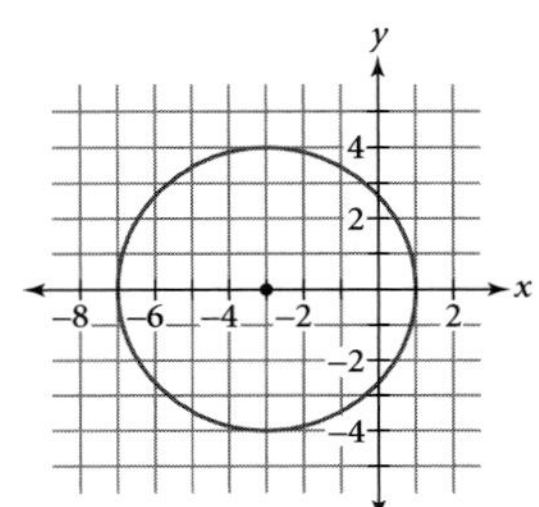

3a. $x = 5\cos t + 3, y = 5\sin t$

3b. $x = 3\cos t - 1, y = 3\sin t + 2$

3c. $x = 4\cos t + 2.5, y = 4\sin t + 0.75$

3d. $x = 0.5\cos t + 2.5, y = 0.5\sin t + 1.25$

5a. $x = 2\cos t, y = 2\sin t + 3$

5b. $x = 6\cos t - 1, y = 6\sin t + 2$

7a. $(\sqrt{27}, 0), (-\sqrt{27}, 0)$

7b. $(3, \sqrt{21}), (3, -\sqrt{21})$

7c. $(-1 + \sqrt{7}, 2), (-1 - \sqrt{7}, 2)$

7d. $(3 + \sqrt{27}, -1), (3 - \sqrt{27}, -1)$

9a. 1.0 m **9b.** 1.6 m

11a. 240 r/min **11b.** 18.6 mi/h **11c.** 6.3 mi/h

13. $y = -(x + 3)^2 + 2$

15. $y = 2x^2 - 24x + 117$

LESSON 9.3

1a. (1, 0.5) **1b.** $y = 8$ **1c.** (9, 2)

3a. focus: (0, 6); directrix: $y = 4$

3b. focus: (−1.75, −2); directrix: $x = -2.25$

3c. focus: (−3, 0); directrix: $y = 1$

3d. focus: (3.875, 0); directrix: $x = 4.125$

3e. focus: (−1, 5); directrix: $y = 1$

3f. focus: $\left(\frac{61}{12}, 0\right)$; directrix: $x = \frac{11}{12}$

5a. $x = t^2, y = t + 2$ **5b.** $x = t, y = -t^2 + 4$

5c. $x = 2t + 3, y = t^2 - 1$

5d. $x = -t^2 - 6, y = 3t + 2$

7. The path is parabolic. If you locate the rock at (0, 2) and the shoreline at $y = 0$, the equation is $y = \frac{1}{4}x^2 + 1$.

9. $y = \frac{1}{8}(x - 1)^2 + 1$

11a, c.

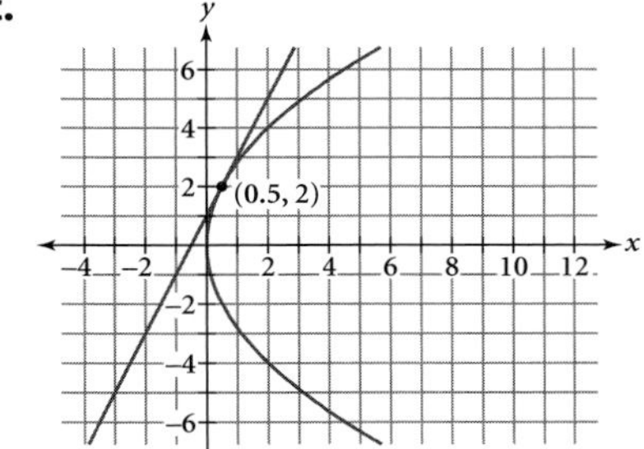

(0.5, 2); $m = 2$

11b. (2, 0)

11d.

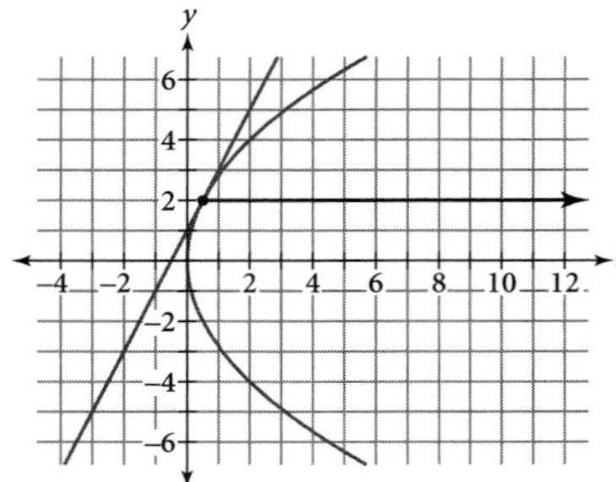

$m = 0$

11e.

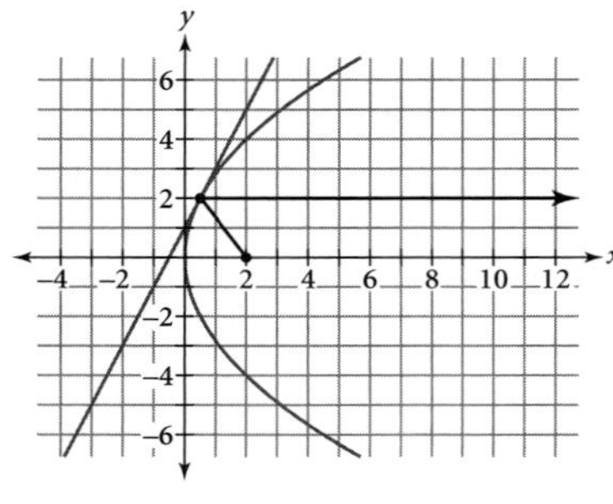

$m = -\frac{4}{3}$

11f. 63.4°; 63.4°; the angles are congruent.

13. $\frac{\sqrt{3}}{2}$; $\left(\pm\frac{\sqrt{2}}{2}, \frac{1}{2}\right)$

15a. $\pm 1, \pm 2, \pm 5, \pm 10, \pm\frac{1}{2}, \pm\frac{5}{2}$

15b. $\frac{1}{2}$ is the only rational root.

15c. $f(x) = (2x - 1)(x - 1 + 3i)(x - 1 - 3i)$

LESSON 9.4

1a. vertices: $(-2, 0)$ and $(2, 0)$; asymptotes: $y = \pm 2x$

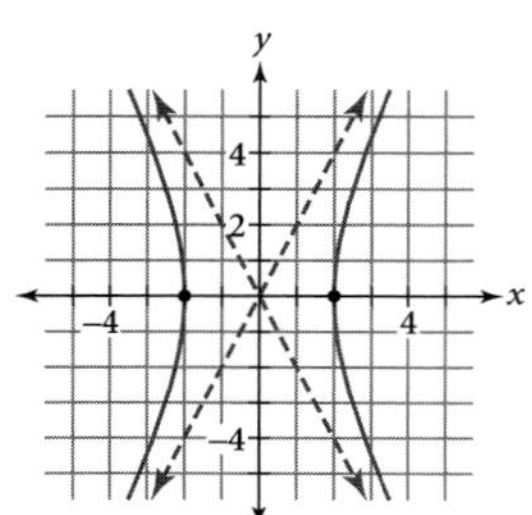

1b. vertices: $(2, -1)$ and $(2, -3)$; asymptotes: $y = \frac{1}{3}x - \frac{8}{3}$ and $y = -\frac{1}{3}x - \frac{4}{3}$

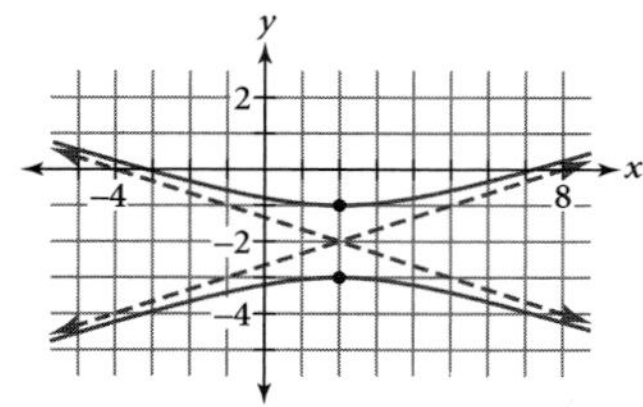

1c. vertices: $(1, 1)$ and $(7, 1)$; asymptotes: $y = x - 3$ and $y = -x + 5$

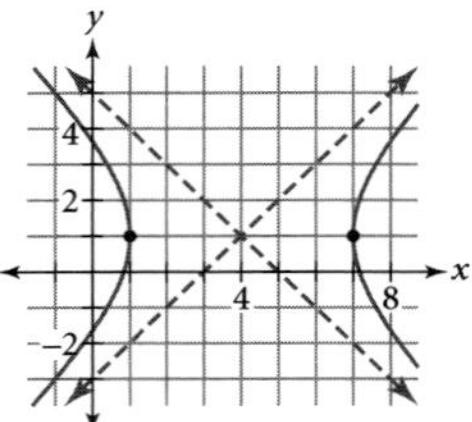

1d. vertices: $(-2, 1)$ and $(-2, -3)$; asymptotes: $y = \frac{2}{3}x + \frac{1}{3}$ and $y = -\frac{2}{3}x - \frac{7}{3}$

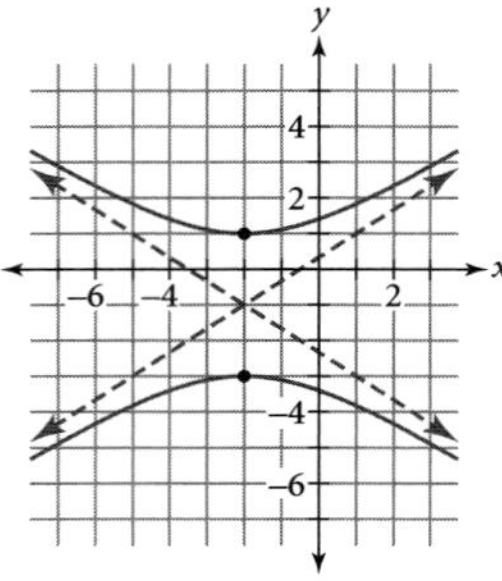

1e. vertices: $(-5, 3)$ and $(3, 3)$; asymptotes: $y = 0.5x + 3.5$ and $y = -0.5x + 2.5$

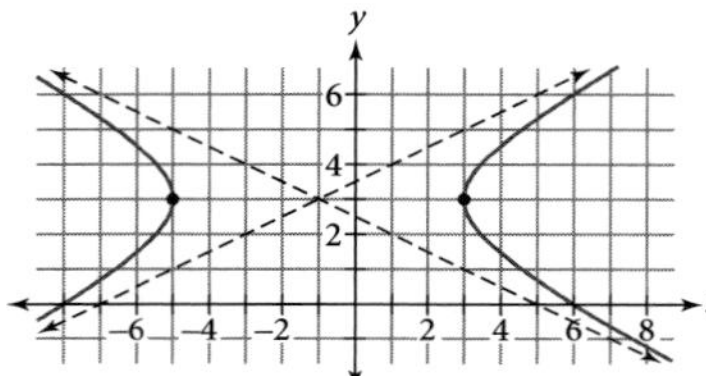

1f. vertices: $(3, 5)$ and $(3, -5)$; asymptotes: $y = \frac{5}{3}x - 5$ and $y = -\frac{5}{3}x + 5$

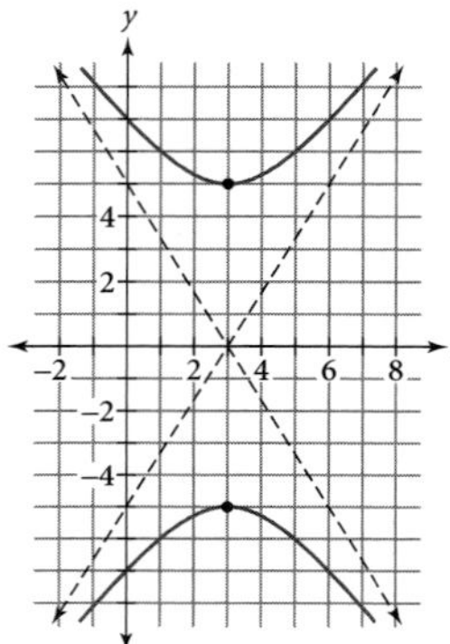

3a. $\left(\frac{x}{2}\right)^2 - \left(\frac{y}{1}\right)^2 = 1$ **3b.** $\left(\frac{y+3}{2}\right)^2 - \left(\frac{x-3}{2}\right)^2 = 1$

3c. $\left(\frac{x+2}{3}\right)^2 - \left(\frac{y-1}{4}\right)^2 = 1$

3d. $\left(\frac{y-1}{4}\right)^2 - \left(\frac{x+2}{3}\right)^2 = 1$

5a. $y = \pm 0.5x$ **5b.** $y = x - 6$ and $y = -x$

5c. $y = \frac{4}{3}x + \frac{11}{3}$ and $y = -\frac{4}{3}x - \frac{5}{3}$

5d. $y = \frac{4}{3}x + \frac{11}{3}$ and $y = -\frac{4}{3}x - \frac{5}{3}$

7. $\left(\frac{x-1}{5}\right)^2 - \left(\frac{y-1}{\sqrt{11}}\right)^2 = 1$

9a. possible answer: $\left(\frac{x-1}{2}\right)^2 - \left(\frac{y}{3}\right)^2 = 1$

9b. possible answer: $\left(\frac{y+2}{3}\right)^2 - \left(\frac{x+4.5}{2.5}\right)^2 = 1$

11a.

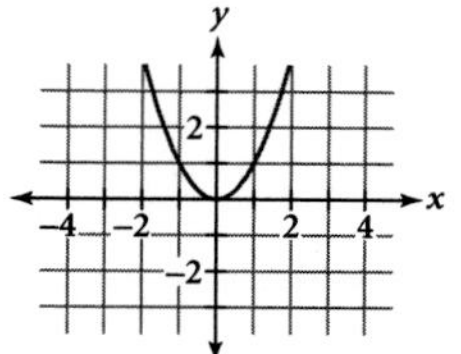

11b.

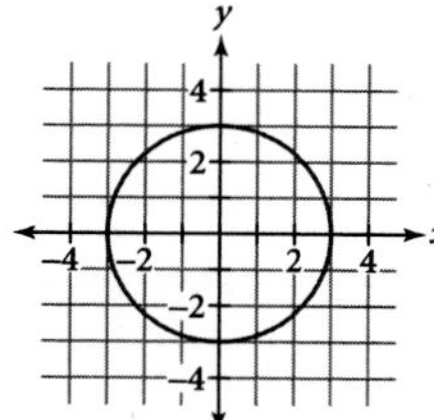

11c.

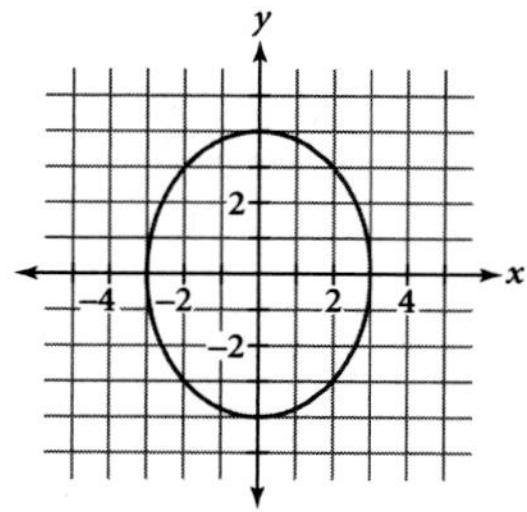

11d.

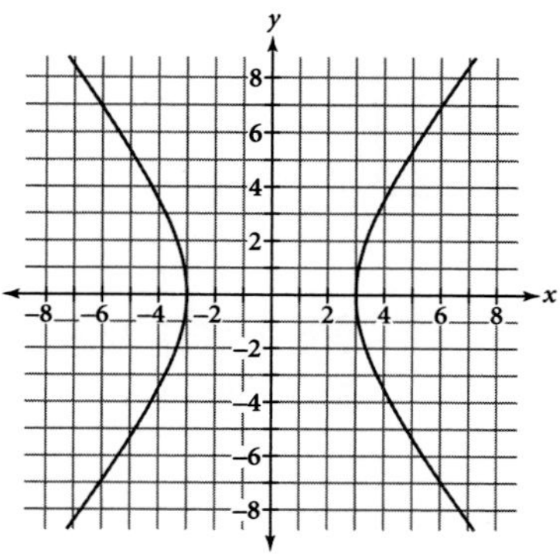

11e. The resulting shapes are a paraboloid, a sphere, an ellipsoid, and a hyperboloid.

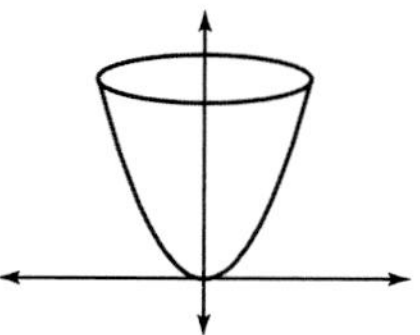

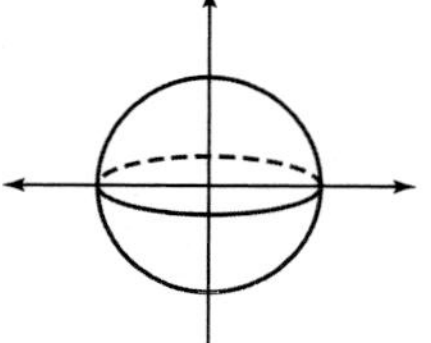

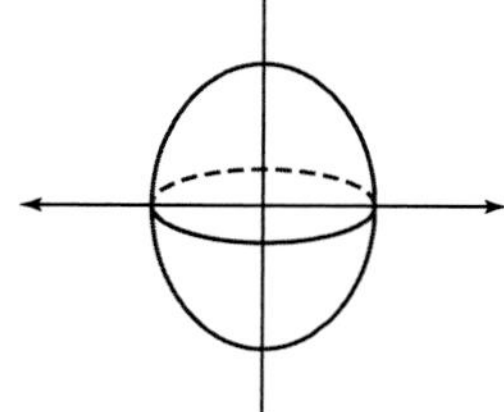

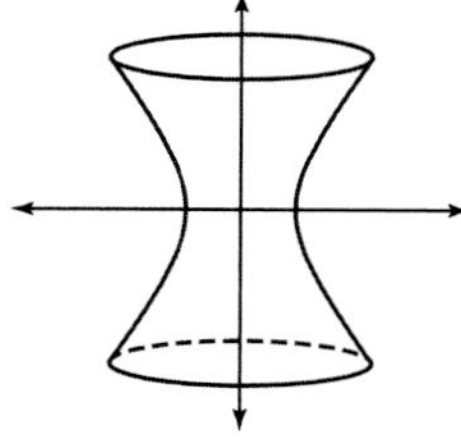

13. $0 = 4 - (x-3)^2$; $x = 1$ or $x = 5$

15a. possible answer: $y = -\frac{1}{8}(x-10)^2 + 17.5$

15b. approximately 18.5 ft or 1.5 ft

17a. $s = s_0\left(\frac{1}{2}\right)^{t/1620}$

17b. 326 g

17c. 13,331 yr

LESSON 9.5

1a. $x^2 + 14x - 9y + 148 = 0$

1b. $x^2 + 9y^2 - 14x + 198y + 1129 = 0$

1c. $x^2 + y^2 - 2x + 6y + 5 = 0$

1d. $9x^2 - 4y^2 - 36x - 24y - 36 = 0$

3a. $\left(\frac{y-5}{\sqrt{11}}\right)^2 - \left(\frac{x+4}{\sqrt{11}}\right)^2 = 1$; hyperbola

3b. $\left(\frac{x-3}{6}\right)^2 + \left(\frac{y-8}{\sqrt{72}}\right)^2 = 1$, or

$\left(\frac{x-3}{6}\right)^2 + \left(\frac{y-8}{6\sqrt{2}}\right)^2 = 1$; ellipse

3c. $\left(\frac{x+5}{\sqrt{5}}\right)^2 = \frac{(y-15.8)}{-3}$; parabola

3d. $(x+2)^2 + y^2 = 5.2$; circle

5a. $y = \frac{\pm\sqrt{400x^2 + 1600}}{-8}$ or $y = \mp\frac{5}{2}\sqrt{x^2+4}$

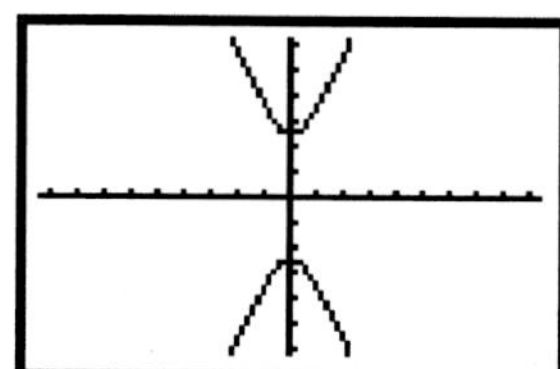

[−18.8, 18.8, 2, −12.4, 12.4, 2]

5b. $y = \frac{-16 \pm \sqrt{160x - 320}}{8}$ or

$y = \frac{-4 \pm \sqrt{10x - 20}}{2}$

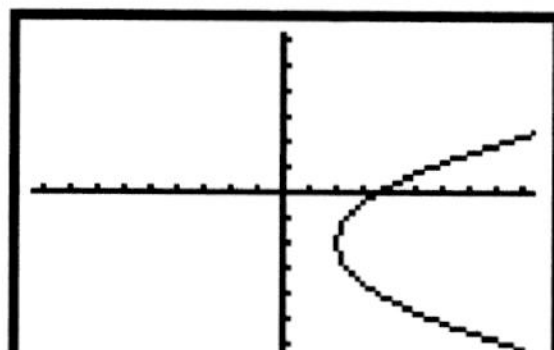

[−9.4, 9.4, 1, −6.2, 6.2, 1]

Selected Answers

5c. $y = \dfrac{8 \pm \sqrt{-64x^2 - 384x - 560}}{8}$

or $y = 1 \pm \dfrac{\sqrt{-16x^2 - 96x - 140}}{4}$

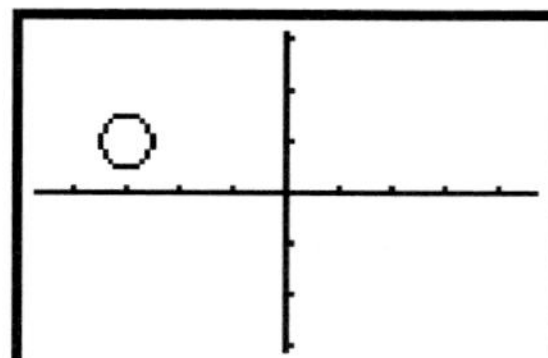

$[-4.7, 4.7, 1, -3.1, 3.1, 1]$

5d. $y = \dfrac{-20 \pm \sqrt{-60x^2 + 240x + 240}}{10}$

or $y = -2 \pm \dfrac{\sqrt{-15x^2 + 60x + 60}}{5}$

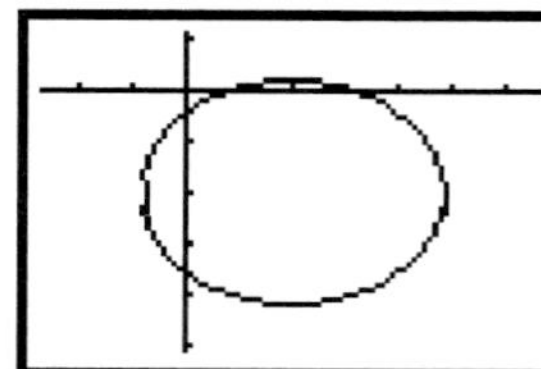

$[-2.7, 6.7, 1, -5.1, 1.1, 1]$

7. approximately 26.7 mi east and 13.7 mi north of the first station, or approximately 26.7 mi east and 13.7 mi south of the first station

9a, b. These constructions will result in a diagram similar to the one shown on page 532.

9c. $\triangle PAG$ is an isosceles triangle, so $PA = PG$. So $FP + GP$ remains constant because they sum to the radius.

9d. An ellipse. The sum of the distances to two points remains constant.

9e. Moving G within the circle creates other ellipses. The closer P is to G, the less eccentric the ellipse. Locations outside the circle produce hyperbolas.

11. $x^2 + y^2 = 11.52$

13a. $\left(-2, 5 + 2\sqrt{5}\right)$ and $\left(-2, 5 - 2\sqrt{5}\right)$

13b. $\left(1 + \frac{\sqrt{3}}{2}, -2\right)$ and $\left(1 - \frac{\sqrt{3}}{2}, -2\right)$

15. 113°

17. square, trapezoid, kite, triangle, pentagon

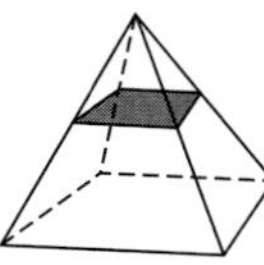
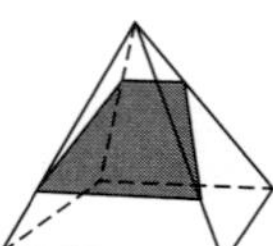
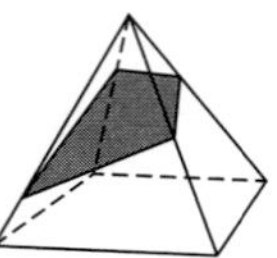
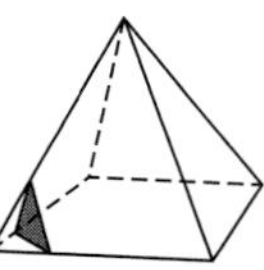
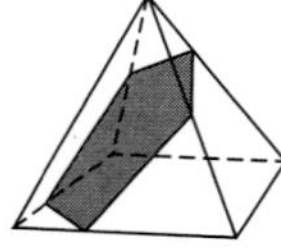

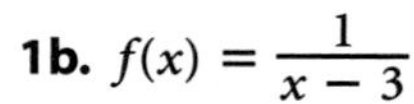

1a. $f(x) = \frac{1}{x} + 2$

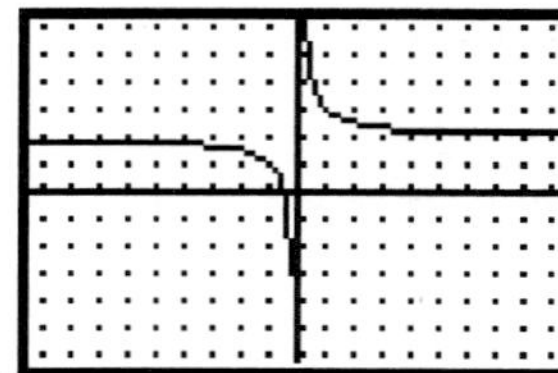

$[-9.4, 9.4, 1, -6.2, 6.2, 1]$

1b. $f(x) = \dfrac{1}{x - 3}$

$[-9.4, 9.4, 1, -6.2, 6.2, 1]$

1c. $f(x) = \dfrac{1}{x + 4} - 1$

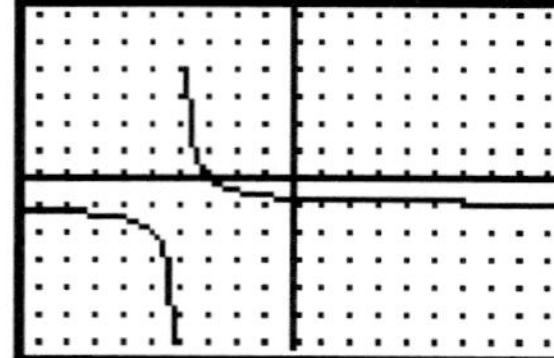

$[-9.4, 9.4, 1, -6.2, 6.2, 1]$

1d. $f(x) = 2\left(\frac{1}{x}\right)$ or $f(x) = \frac{2}{x}$

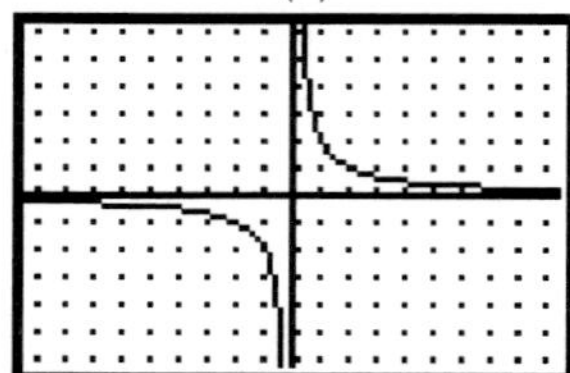

$[-9.4, 9.4, 1, -6.2, 6.2, 1]$

1e. $f(x) = 3\left(\frac{1}{x}\right) + 1$ or $f(x) = \frac{3}{x} + 1$

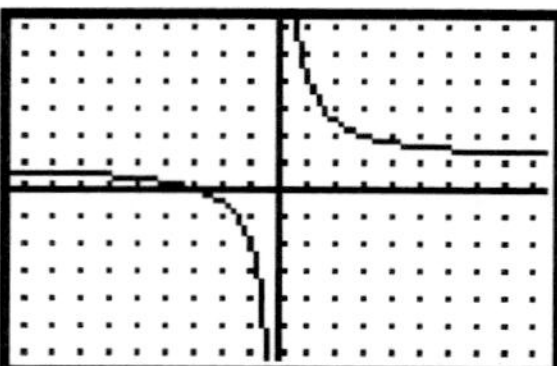

$[-9.4, 9.4, 1, -6.2, 6.2, 1]$

3a. $x = -4$

3b. $x = \frac{113}{18}$ or $x = 6.2\overline{7}$

3c. $x = 2.6$

3d. $x = -8.5$

5. 12 games

7a. 20.9 mL

7b. $f(x) = \dfrac{20.9 + x}{55 + x}$

7c. 39.72 mL

7d. The graph approaches $y = 1$.

9a. i. $y = 2 + \dfrac{-3}{x - 5}$

9a. ii. $y = 3 + \dfrac{2}{x + 3}$

9b. i. Stretch vertically by a factor of -3, and translate right 5 units and up 2 units.

9b. ii. Stretch vertically by a factor of 2, and translate left 3 units and up 3 units.

9c. i.

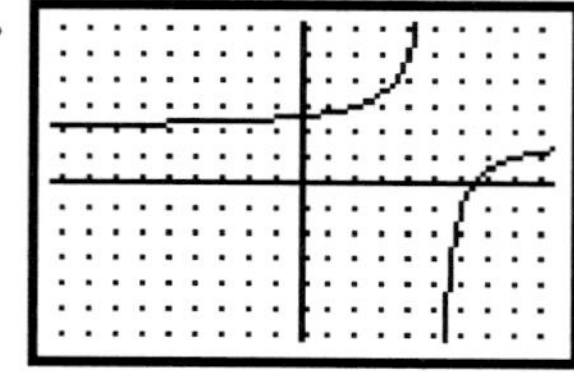

$[-9.4, 9.4, 1, -6.2, 6.2, 1]$

9c. ii.

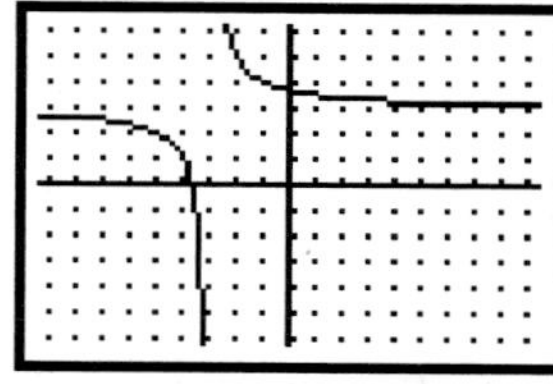

$[-9.4, 9.4, 1, -6.2, 6.2, 1]$

11a. a rotated hyperbola

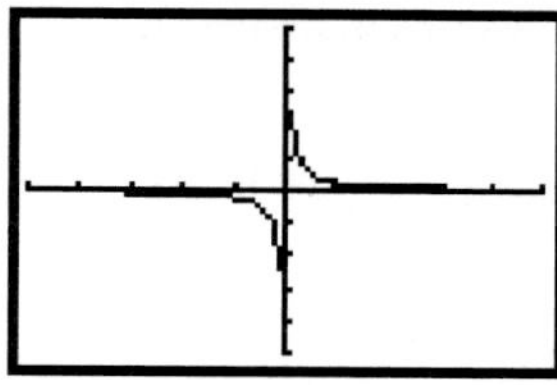

$[-5, 5, 1, -5, 5, 1]$

11b. The inverse variation function, $y = \frac{1}{x}$, can be converted to the form $xy = 1$, which is a conic section. Its graph is a rotated hyperbola.

11c. $xy - 3x - 2y + 5 = 0$; $A = 0, B = 1, C = 0, D = -3, E = -2, F = 5$

13. *Hint:* Graph $y = \frac{1}{x}$ and plot the foci $(\sqrt{2}, \sqrt{2})$ and $(-\sqrt{2}, -\sqrt{2})$. Measure the distance from both foci to points on the curve, and verify that the difference of the distances is constant.

15. $(x-2)^2 + (y+3)^2 = 16$

17a. 53° to the riverbank **17b.** 375 m

17c. $x = 5t\cos 37°, y = 5t\sin 37° - 3t$

19a. $b = \sqrt{3}, c = 2$ **19b.** $a = 1, c = \sqrt{2}$

19c. $b = \frac{1}{2}, c = 1$ **19d.** $a = \frac{\sqrt{2}}{2}, c = 1$

19e. $\frac{\sqrt{2}}{2} : \frac{\sqrt{2}}{2} : 1; \frac{1}{2} : \frac{\sqrt{3}}{2} : 1$

LESSON 9.7

1a. $\frac{(x+3)(x+4)}{(x+2)(x-2)}$ **1b.** $\frac{x(x-7)(x+2)}{(x+1)(x+1)}$

3a. $\frac{7x-7}{x-2}$ **3b.** $\frac{-7x+12}{2x-1}$

5a. $y = \frac{x+2}{x+2}$ **5b.** $y = \frac{-2(x-3)}{x-3}$

5c. $y = \frac{(x+2)(x+1)}{x+1}$

7a. vertical asymptote $x = 0$, slant asymptote $y = x - 2$

7b. vertical asymptote $x = 1$, slant asymptote $y = -2x + 3$

7c. hole at $x = 2$

7d. For 7a: $y = \frac{x^2 - 2x + 1}{x}$. The denominator is 0 and the numerator is nonzero when $x = 0$, so the vertical asymptote is $x = 0$.

For 7b: $y = \frac{-2x^2 + 5x - 1}{x - 1}$. The denominator is 0 and the numerator is nonzero when $x = 1$, so the vertical asymptote is $x = 1$.

For 7c: $y = \frac{3x-6}{x-2}$. A zero occurs once in both the numerator and denominator when $x = 2$. This causes a hole in the graph.

9. $y = \frac{-(x+2)(x-6)}{3(x-2)}$

11a. $x = 3 \pm \sqrt{2}$ **11b.** $x = \frac{3 \pm i\sqrt{7}}{2}$

13a.

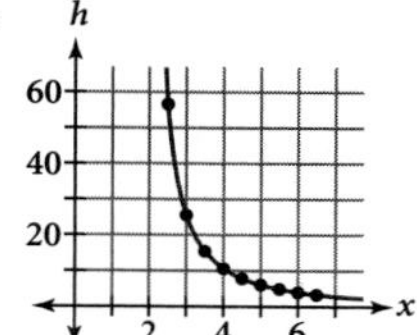

13b. The height gets larger as the radius gets smaller. The radius must be greater than 2.

13c. $V = \pi x^2 h - 4\pi h$ **13d.** $h = \frac{V}{\pi(x^2 - 4)}$

13e. approximately 400 units^3

15a. $83\frac{1}{3}$ g; approximately 17% almonds and 43% peanuts

15b. 50 g; approximately 27.3% almonds, 27.3% cashews, and 45.5% peanuts

LESSON 9.8

1a. $\frac{x(x+2)}{(x-2)(x+2)} = \frac{x}{x-2}$

1b. $\frac{(x-1)(x-4)}{(x+1)(x-1)} = \frac{x-4}{x+1}$

1c. $\frac{3x(x-2)}{(x-4)(x-2)} = \frac{3x}{x-4}$

1d. $\frac{(x+5)(x-2)}{(x+5)(x-5)} = \frac{x-2}{x-5}$

3a. $\frac{(2x-3)(x+1)}{(x+3)(x-2)(x-3)}$

3b. $\frac{-x^2+6}{(x+2)(x+3)(x-2)}$

3c. $\frac{2x^2-x+9}{(x-3)(x+2)(x+3)}$

3d. $\frac{2x^2-5x+6}{(x+1)(x-2)(x-1)}$

5a. $\frac{2(x-2)}{x+1}$ **5b.** 1

7a. $x = 3$ is a zero, because that value causes the numerator to be 0. The vertical asymptotes are $x = 2$ and $x = -2$, because these values make the denominator 0 and do not also make the numerator 0. The horizontal asymptote is $x = 0$, because this is the value that y approaches when $|x|$ is large.

7b.

9a. Answers will vary

9b. $-x^2 + xy - y = 0$; yes

9c. no

9d. not possible; no

9e. After reducing common factors, the degree of the numerator must be less than or equal to 2, and the degree of the denominator must be 1.

11a. $x = 3, y = 1$

11b. translation right 3 units and up 1 unit

11c. -2

11d. $y = 1 - \dfrac{2}{x-3}$ or $y = \dfrac{x-5}{x-3}$

11e. x-intercept: 5; y-intercept: $\frac{5}{3}$

13a. \$370.09

13b. \$382.82

13c. \$383.75

13d. \$383.99

CHAPTER 9 REVIEW

1a.

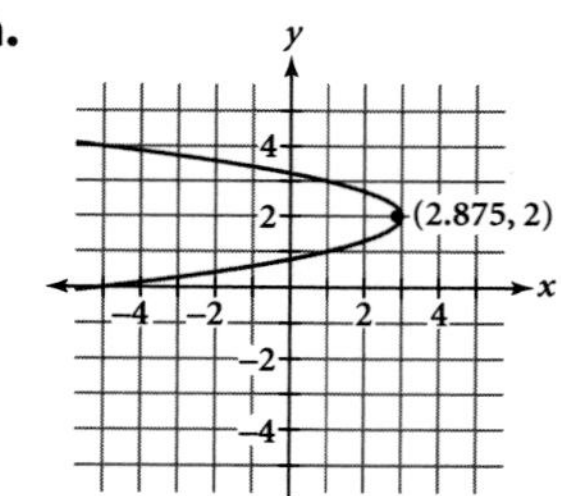

1b.

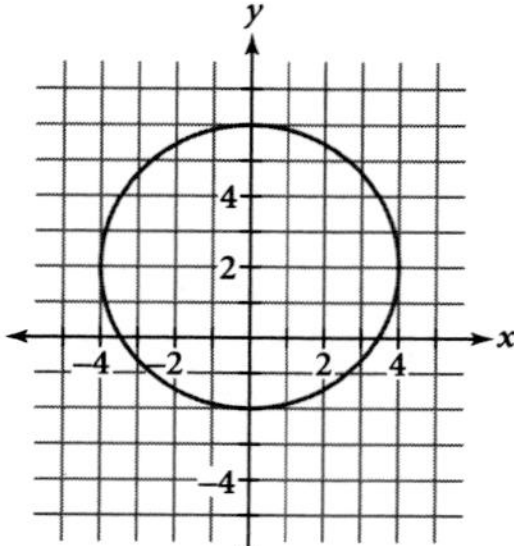

1c.

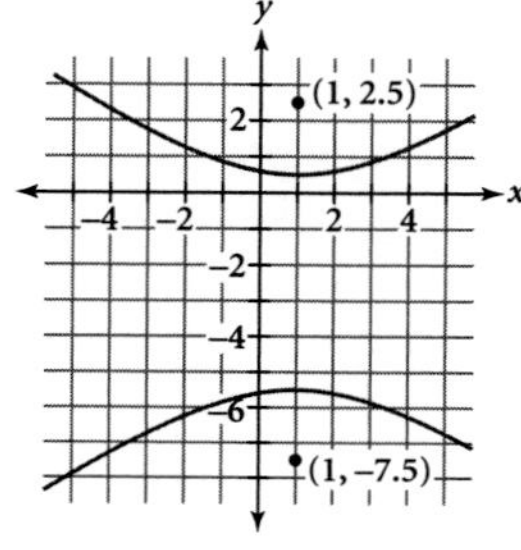

1d.

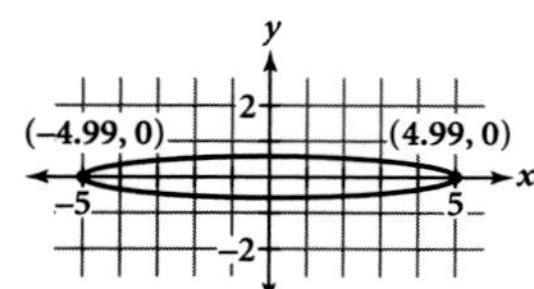

3a. $y = \pm 0.5x$

3b. $x^2 - 4y^2 - 4 = 0$

3c. $d = 0.5x - \sqrt{\dfrac{x^2}{4} - 1}$

3d. 1, 0.101, 0.050, 0.010; As x-values increase, the curve gets closer to the asymptote.

5. $(y - 4)^2 = \dfrac{x - 3}{0.25}$; vertex: (3, 4), focus: (4, 4), directrix: $x = 2$

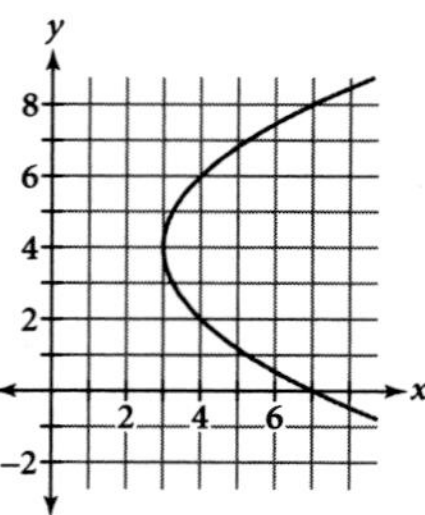

7a. $y = 1 + \dfrac{1}{x+2}$ or $y = \dfrac{x+3}{x+2}$

7b. $y = -4 + \dfrac{1}{x}$ or $y = \dfrac{-4x+1}{x}$

9. Multiply the numerator and denominator by the factor $(x + 3)$.

$$y = \frac{(2x - 14)(x + 3)}{(x - 5)(x + 3)}$$

11a. $\dfrac{3x^2 + 8x + 3}{(x - 2)(x + 1)(x + 2)}$

11b. $\dfrac{3x}{x + 1}$

11c. $\dfrac{(x + 1)^2(x - 1)}{x(x - 2)}$

13.

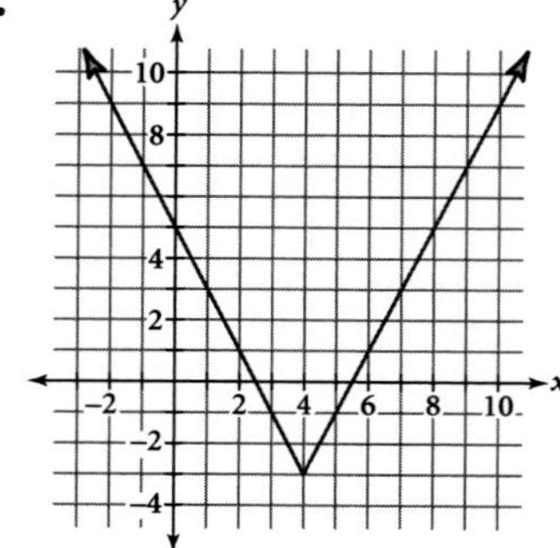

13a. $y = 2|x|$

13b. $y = 2|x - 4|$

13c. $y = 2|x - 4| - 3$

15a. Not possible. The number of columns in $[A]$ must match the number of rows in $[B]$.

15b. Not possible. To add matrices, they must have the same dimensions.

15c. $\begin{bmatrix} -3 & 1 \\ 1 & -5 \end{bmatrix}$ **15d.** $\begin{bmatrix} -2 & 6 \\ -10 & 0 \\ -7 & 3 \end{bmatrix}$

15e. $\begin{bmatrix} 5 & -3 \\ -1 & 9 \end{bmatrix}$

17a. 7.5 yd/s **17b.** 27.5°

17c. $x = 7.5t\cos 27.5°, y = 7.5t\sin 27.5°$

17d. $x = 100 - 7.5t\cos 27.5°, y = 7.5t\sin 27.5°$

17e. midfield (50, 26), after 7.5 s

19a. $\left(\frac{y}{5}\right)^2 - \left(\frac{x}{2}\right)^2 = 1$; hyperbola

19b. $(y + 2)^2 = \frac{(x - 2)}{\frac{2}{5}}$; parabola

19c. $(x + 3)^2 + (y - 1)^2 = \frac{1}{4}$; circle

19d. $\left(\frac{x - 2}{\sqrt{8}}\right)^2 + \left(\frac{y + 2}{\sqrt{4.8}}\right)^2 = 1$

or $\left(\frac{x - 2}{2\sqrt{2}}\right)^2 + \left(\frac{y + 2}{2\sqrt{1.2}}\right)^2 = 1$; ellipse

21a. $x \approx 1.64$ **21b.** $x \approx -0.66$

21c. $x = 15$ **21d.** $x \approx 2.57$

21e. $x \approx 17.78$ **21f.** $x = 3$

21g. $x = 2$ **21h.** $x = 495$

21i. $x \approx \pm 4.14$

23. Bases are home (0, 0), first (90, 0), second (90, 90), and third (0, 90).

Deanna: $x = 90, y = 28t + 12$

ball: $x = 125(t - 1.5)\cos 45°, y = 125(t - 1.5)\sin 45°$

Deanna reaches second base after 2.79 s, ball reaches second base after 2.52 s. Deanna is out.

CHAPTER 10

LESSON 10.1

1.

y, x, 300°, 60°, −0.866

approximately −0.866 m

3a. 2 **3b.** 4

5a. periodic, 180° **5b.** not periodic

5c. periodic, 90° **5d.** periodic, 180°

7. Quadrant I: $\cos\theta$ and $\sin\theta$ are positive;
Quadrant II: $\cos\theta$ is negative and $\sin\theta$ is positive;
Quadrant III: $\cos\theta$ and $\sin\theta$ are negative;
Quadrant IV: $\cos\theta$ is positive and $\sin\theta$ is negative.

9. $x = \{-270°, -90°, 90°, 270°\}$

11a. $\theta = -15°$ **11b.** $\theta = 125°$

11c. $\theta = -90°$ **11d.** $\theta = 48°$

13a. $\theta = 150°$ and $\theta = 210°$

13b. $\theta = 135°$ and $\theta = 225°$

13c. $\theta \approx 217°$ and $\theta \approx 323°$

13d. $\theta = 90°$

15a.

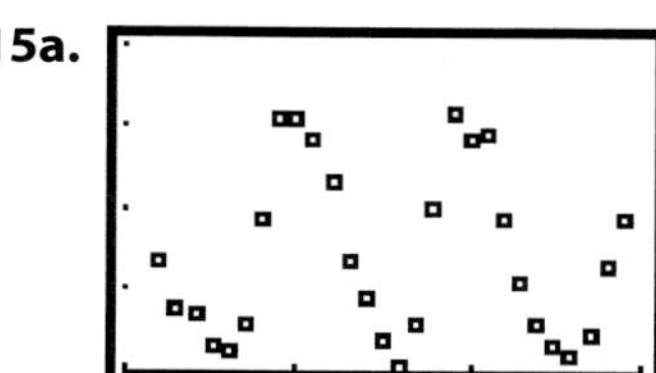

[1970, 2000, 10, 0, 200, 50]

The data are cyclical and appear to have a shape like a sine or cosine curve.

15b. 10–11 yr **15c.** 2001

17a. 43,200 s **17b.** 4.4 ft/s

19a. $\frac{3}{x - 4}$ **19b.** 2 **19c.** $\frac{2(3 + a)}{6 - a}$

LESSON 10.2

1a. $\frac{4\pi}{9}$ **1b.** $\frac{19\pi}{6}$ **1c.** −240° **1d.** 220°

1e. −135° **1f.** 540° **1g.** -5π **1h.** 150°

3a, b.

(0, 1), (1, 0), (−1, 0), (0, −1), $\left(\frac{1}{2}, \frac{\sqrt{3}}{2}\right)$, $\left(\frac{1}{\sqrt{2}}, \frac{1}{\sqrt{2}}\right)$, $\left(\frac{\sqrt{3}}{2}, \frac{1}{2}\right)$, $\left(-\frac{1}{2}, \frac{\sqrt{3}}{2}\right)$, $\left(-\frac{1}{\sqrt{2}}, \frac{1}{\sqrt{2}}\right)$, $\left(-\frac{\sqrt{3}}{2}, \frac{1}{2}\right)$, $\left(-\frac{\sqrt{3}}{2}, -\frac{1}{2}\right)$, $\left(-\frac{1}{\sqrt{2}}, -\frac{1}{\sqrt{2}}\right)$, $\left(-\frac{1}{2}, -\frac{\sqrt{3}}{2}\right)$, $\left(\frac{1}{2}, -\frac{\sqrt{3}}{2}\right)$, $\left(\frac{1}{\sqrt{2}}, -\frac{1}{\sqrt{2}}\right)$, $\left(\frac{\sqrt{3}}{2}, -\frac{1}{2}\right)$

A B C D E F G H I J K L M N

5. Less than; one rotation is 2π, which is more than 6.

7a, b.

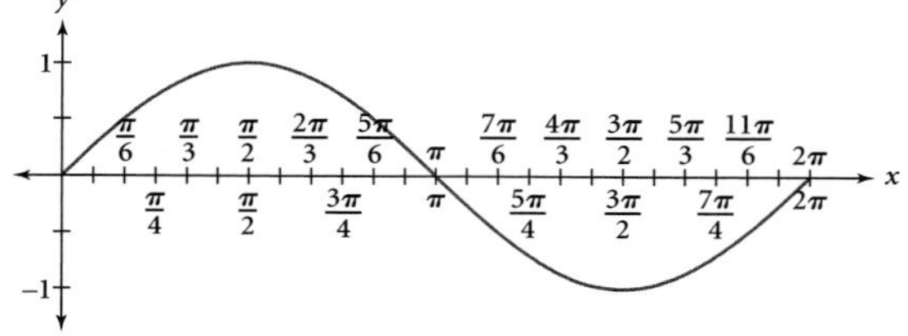

Selected Answers

7c. $\frac{\pi}{2}; \frac{3\pi}{2}$; 0, π, and 2π

9a. $\frac{3}{2}; \frac{3}{2}$ **9b.** $-2; -2$

9c. They are equal. **9d.** approximately 2.414

11a. $\frac{4\pi}{3}$ **11b.** $\frac{7\pi}{4}$ **11c.** $\frac{\pi}{3}$

13a. $A \approx 57.54 \text{ cm}^2$ **13b.** $\frac{A}{64\pi} = \frac{\frac{4\pi}{7}}{2\pi}$

13c. $A = 64\pi \cdot \frac{\frac{4\pi}{7}}{2\pi} \approx 57.54 \text{ cm}^2$

15a. 1037 mi **15b.** 61.17° **15c.** 2660 mi

17a. $y = -2(x + 1)^2$ **17b.** $y + 4 = (x - 2)^2$

17c. $y + 2 = \left|\frac{x + 1}{2}\right|$ **17d.** $-\frac{y - 2}{2} = |x - 3|$

19a. 18 cm **19b.** 169 cm

21. *Hint:* Construct $\overline{AP}$, $\overline{BP}$, and $\overline{CP}$. $\triangle APC$ is isosceles because $\overline{AP}$ and $\overline{CP}$ are radii of the same circle. $\angle ABP$ measures 90° because the angle is inscribed in a semicircle. Use these facts to prove that $\triangle ABP \cong \triangle CBP$.

LESSON 10.3

1a. $y = \sin x + 1$ **1b.** $y = \cos x - 2$

1c. $y = \sin x - 0.5$ **1d.** $y = -3\cos x$

1e. $y = -2\sin x$ **1f.** $y = 2\cos x + 1$

3a. The k-value vertically translates the graph of the function.

3b. The b-value vertically stretches or shrinks the graph of the function. The absolute value of b represents the amplitude. When b is negative, the curve is reflected across the x-axis.

3c. The a-value horizontally stretches or shrinks the graph of the function. It also determines the period with the relationship $2\pi a = \textit{period}$.

3d. The h-value horizontally translates the graph of the function. It represents the phase shift.

5. translate $y = \sin x$ left $\frac{\pi}{2}$ units

7a. Let x represent the number of days after a full moon (today), and let y represent the percentage of lit surface that is visible.

$y = 0.5 + 0.5\cos\left(\frac{2\pi x}{28}\right)$

7b. 72% **7c.** day 5

9. first row: 1; $\frac{\sqrt{3}}{2}$; $\frac{\sqrt{2}}{2}$; 0; $-\frac{\sqrt{2}}{2}$; -1; $-\frac{1}{2}$; $\frac{1}{2}$; $\frac{\sqrt{3}}{2}$;

second row: 0; $\frac{1}{2}$; $\frac{\sqrt{2}}{2}$; 1; $\frac{\sqrt{2}}{2}$; 0; $-\frac{\sqrt{3}}{2}$; $-\frac{\sqrt{3}}{2}$; $-\frac{1}{2}$;

third row: 0; $\frac{1}{\sqrt{3}}$; 1; undefined; -1; 0; $\sqrt{3}$; $-\sqrt{3}$; $-\frac{1}{\sqrt{3}}$

11a. $y = 1.5\cos 2\left(x + \frac{\pi}{2}\right)$

11b. $y = -3 + 2\sin 4\left(x - \frac{\pi}{4}\right)$

11c. $y = 3 + 2\cos\frac{x - \pi}{3}$

13a. 0.79 m **13b.** 0.74 m **13c.** 0.81 m

15. See below.

17a. i. $y = -\frac{2}{3}x + 4$

17a. ii. $y = \pm\sqrt{x + 4} - 2$

17a. iii. $y = \frac{\log(x + 8)}{\log 1.3} - 6$

17b. i.

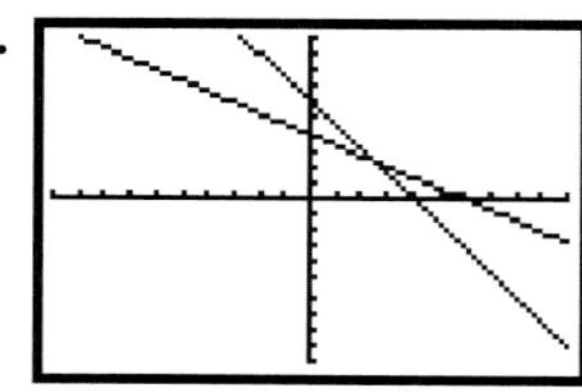

[−10, 10, 1, −10, 10, 1]

17b. ii.

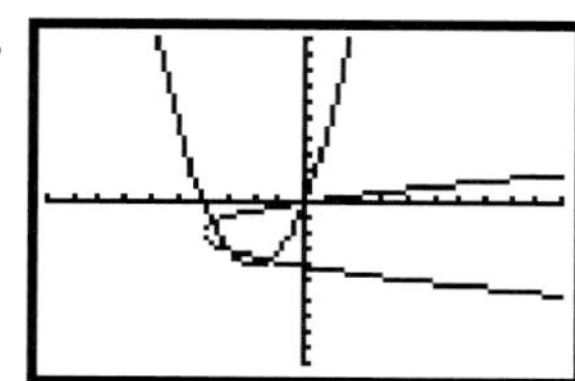

[−10, 10, 1, −10, 10, 1]

---

15. (*Lesson 10.3*)

Degrees	0°	15°	30°	45°	60°	75°	90°	105°	120°	135°	150°	165°	180°
Radians	0	$\frac{\pi}{12}$	$\frac{\pi}{6}$	$\frac{\pi}{4}$	$\frac{\pi}{3}$	$\frac{5\pi}{12}$	$\frac{\pi}{2}$	$\frac{7\pi}{12}$	$\frac{2\pi}{3}$	$\frac{3\pi}{4}$	$\frac{5\pi}{6}$	$\frac{11\pi}{12}$	π
Degrees	195°	210°	225°	240°	255°	270°	285°	300°	315°	330°	345°	360°	
Radians	$\frac{13\pi}{12}$	$\frac{7\pi}{6}$	$\frac{5\pi}{4}$	$\frac{4\pi}{3}$	$\frac{17\pi}{12}$	$\frac{3\pi}{2}$	$\frac{19\pi}{12}$	$\frac{5\pi}{3}$	$\frac{7\pi}{4}$	$\frac{11\pi}{6}$	$\frac{23\pi}{12}$	2π	

17b. iii.

$[-10, 10, 1, -10, 10, 1]$

17c. The inverses of i and iii are functions.

LESSON 10.4

1a. 27.8° and 0.49

1b. −14.3° and −0.25

1c. 144.2° and 2.52

1d. 11.3° and 0.20

3a–d. *Hint:* Graph $y = \sin x$ or $y = \cos x$ for $-2\pi \leq x \leq 2\pi$. Plot all points on the curve that have a y-value equal to the y-value of the expression on the right side of the equation. Then find the x-value at each of these points.

5. $-1 \leq \sin x \leq 1$. There is no angle whose sine is 1.28.

7a. $x \approx 0.485$ or $x \approx 2.656$

7b. $x \approx -2.517$ or $x \approx -3.766$

9. 106.9°

11a. *Hint:* Use your calculator.

11b. The domain is all real numbers. The range is $-\frac{\pi}{2} \leq x \leq \frac{\pi}{2}$. See graph for 11d.

11c. The function $y = \tan^{-1} x$ is the portion of $x = \tan y$, such that $-\frac{\pi}{2} < y < \frac{\pi}{2}$ (or $-90° < y < 90°$).

11d.

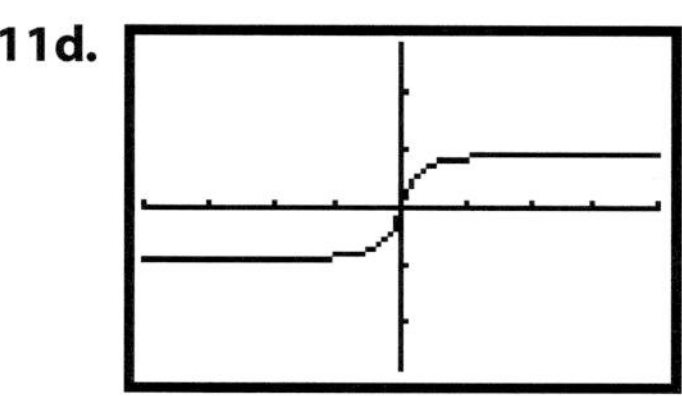

$[-20, 20, 5, -3\pi/2, 3\pi/2, \pi/2]$

13. 650°

15a. $8.0 \cdot 10^{-4}\ \text{W/m}^2$; $6.0 \cdot 10^{-4}\ \text{W/m}^2$

15b. $\theta = 45°$

15c. $\theta = 90°$

17a. $y = \tan \dfrac{x + \frac{\pi}{2}}{2}$

17a. $y = 1 - 0.5 \tan\left(x - \frac{\pi}{2}\right)$

19a. Ellipse with center at origin, horizontal major axis of length 6 units, and vertical minor axis of length 4 units. The parametric equations are $x = 3\cos t$ and $y = 2\sin t$.

19b. $\left(\frac{x+1}{3}\right)^2 + \left(\frac{y-2}{2}\right)^2 = 1$; $x = 3\cos t - 1$ and $y = 2\sin t + 2$

19c. approximately (1.9, 1.5) and (−2.9, 0.5)

19d. (1.92, 1.54) and (−2.92, 0.46)

LESSON 10.5

1a. $x = \left\{\frac{\pi}{3}, \frac{5\pi}{3}, \frac{7\pi}{3}, \frac{11\pi}{3}\right\}$

1b. $x = \left\{\frac{7\pi}{6}, \frac{11\pi}{6}, \frac{19\pi}{6}, \frac{23\pi}{6}\right\}$

3a. 5; 5

3b. 7; −2; 12; 7

3c. $\frac{11}{2\pi}$; 11

3d. 9; 9

5. $y = 1.2\sin\frac{2\pi t}{8} + 2$ or $y = 1.2\sin\frac{\pi t}{4} + 2$

7a. possible answer: $v = 155.6\sin(120\pi t)$

7b.

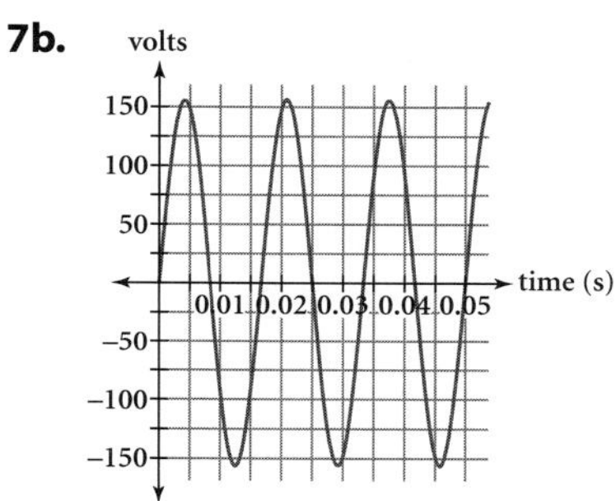

9a. $y_1 = -3\cos\left(\dfrac{2\pi(t + 0.17)}{\frac{2}{3}}\right)$, $y_2 = -4\cos\left(\dfrac{2\pi t}{\frac{2}{3}}\right)$

9b. at 0.2, 0.6, 0.9, 1.2, 1.6, 1.9 s

11a. about 9.6 h

11b. March 21 and September 21 or 22

13. Construct a circle and its diameter for the main rotating arm. Construct a circle with a fixed radius at each end of the diameter. Make a point on each of these two circles. Animate them and one endpoint of the diameter.

15. The sector has the larger area. The triangle's area is $10.8\ \text{cm}^2$; the sector's area is $12.5\ \text{cm}^2$.

17a. $\pm 1, \pm 5, \pm\frac{1}{2}, \pm\frac{5}{2}$

17b. $x = \frac{1}{2}$

17c. $x = \pm\sqrt{5}$

17d. $P(x) = 2\left(x - \frac{1}{2}\right)\left(x + \sqrt{5}\right)\left(x - \sqrt{5}\right)$

LESSON 10.6

1. Graph $y = \dfrac{1}{\tan x}$.

3. *Hint:* Use the distributive property to rewrite the left side of the equation. Use a reciprocal trigonometric identity to rewrite $\cot A$, then simplify. Use a Pythagorean identity to complete the proof.

5. A trigonometric equation may be true for some, all, or none of the defined values of the variable. A trigonometric identity is a trigonometric equation that is true for all defined values of the variable.

7a. *Hint:* Replace $\cos 2A$ with $\cos^2 A - \sin^2 A$. Rewrite $\cos^2 A$ using a Pythagorean identity. Then combine like terms.

7b. *Hint:* Replace $\cos 2A$ with $\cos^2 A - \sin^2 A$. Rewrite $\sin^2 A$ using a Pythagorean identity. Then combine like terms.

9a. $y = \sin x$ **9b.** $y = \cos x$ **9c.** $y = \cot x$

9d. $y = \cos x$ **9e.** $y = -\sin x$ **9f.** $y = -\tan x$

9g. $y = \sin x$ **9h.** $y = -\sin x$ **9i.** $y = \tan x$

11a–c. *Hint:* Use the reciprocal trigonometric identities to graph each equation on your calculator, with window $[0, 4\pi, \pi/2, -2, 2, 1]$.

13a. 2; undefined when θ equals 0 or π

13b. $3\cos\theta$; undefined when θ equals $0, \frac{\pi}{2}, \pi$, or $\frac{3\pi}{2}$

13c. $\tan^2\theta + \tan\theta$; undefined when θ equals $\frac{\pi}{2}$ or $\frac{3\pi}{2}$

13d. $\sec\theta$; undefined when θ equals $0, \frac{\pi}{2}, \pi, \frac{3\pi}{2}$, or 2π

15a. $1505.12

15b. another 15 years, or until he's 32

17a. $c(x) = \dfrac{60 + x}{100 + x}$

17b. $66\frac{2}{3}\%$

17c. 300 mL

17d.

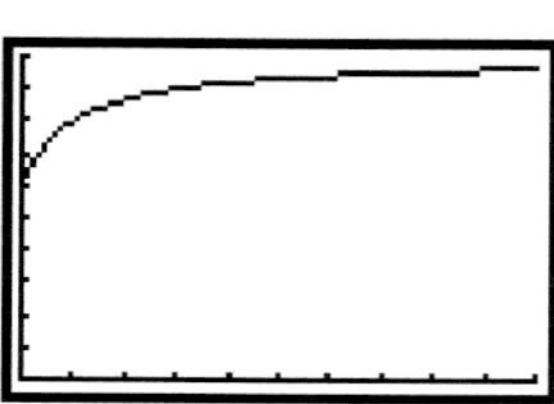

[0, 1000, 100, 0, 1, 0.1]

The asymptote is the line $y = 1$. The more pure medicine that is added the closer the concentration will get to 100%, but it will never actually become 100%.

17e. Use the diluting function to obtain concentrations less than 60%. Use the concentrating function to obtain concentrations greater than 60%.

LESSON 10.7

1a. not an identity **1b.** not an identity

1c. not an identity **1d.** not an identity

3a. $\cos 1.1$ **3b.** $\cos 2.8$

3c. $\sin 1.7$ **3d.** $\sin 0.7$

5. $\dfrac{4\sqrt{5}}{9}$

7. *Hint:* Begin by writing $\sin(A - B)$ as $\sin(A + (-B))$. Then use the sum identity given in Exercise 6. Next, use the identities $\cos(-x) = \cos x$ and $\sin(-x) = -\sin x$ to simplify further.

9. *Hint:* Begin by writing $\sin 2A$ as $\sin(A + A)$. Then use a sum identity to expand, and simplify by combining like terms.

11. *Hint:* Show that $\tan(A + B) \neq \tan A + \tan B$ by substituting values for A and B and evaluating. To find an identity for $\tan(A + B)$, first rewrite as $\frac{\sin(A + B)}{\cos(A + B)}$. Then use sum identities to expand. Divide both the numerator and denominator by $\cos A \cos B$, and rewrite each occurrence of $\frac{\sin\theta}{\cos\theta}$ as $\tan\theta$.

13a. *Hint:* Solve $\cos 2A = 1 - 2\sin^2 A$ for $\sin^2 A$.

13b. *Hint:* Solve $\cos 2A = 2\cos^2 A - 1$ for $\cos^2 A$.

15a. Period: $8\pi, 12\pi, 20\pi, 24\pi, 12\pi$

15b. The period is 2π multiplied by the least common multiple of a and b.

15c. 48π; multiply 2π by the least common multiple of 3, 4, and 8, which is 24.

17a. $x \approx -1.2361$ **17b.** $x \approx 1.1547$

17c. $x \approx 1.0141$ **17d.** $x = 0$

19a. Let x represent time in minutes, and let y represent height in meters above the surface of the water if it was calm.

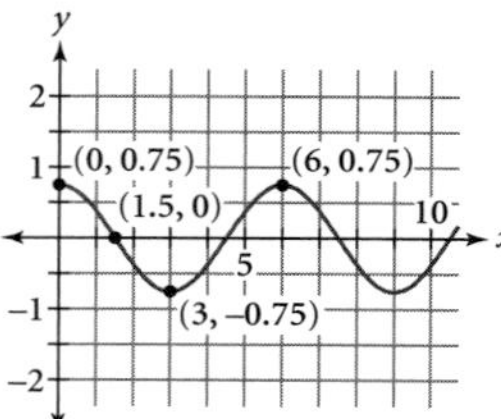

19b. $y = 0.75\cos\frac{\pi}{3}x$

19c. $y = 0.75\sin\left(\frac{\pi}{3}(x + 1.5)\right)$

CHAPTER 10 REVIEW

1a. I; 420°; $\frac{\pi}{3}$ **1b.** III; $\frac{10\pi}{3}$; 240°

1c. IV; −30°; $\frac{11\pi}{6}$ **1d.** IV; $\frac{7\pi}{4}$; −45°

3. Other equations are possible.

3a. period $= \frac{2\pi}{3}$; $y = -2\cos\left(3\left(x - \frac{2\pi}{3}\right)\right)$

3b. period $= \frac{\pi}{2}$; $y = 3\sin\left(4\left(x - \frac{\pi}{8}\right)\right)$

3c. period $= \pi$; $y = \csc\left(2\left(x + \frac{\pi}{4}\right)\right)$

3d. period $= \frac{\pi}{2}$; $y = \cot\left(2\left(x - \frac{\pi}{4}\right)\right) + 1$

5a. $y = -2\sin(2x) - 1$

5b. $y = \sin(0.5x) + 1.5$

5c. $y = 0.5\tan\left(x - \frac{\pi}{4}\right)$

5d. $y = 0.5\sec(2x)$

7. $\cos y = x$: domain: $-1 \leq x \leq 1$; range: all real numbers. $y = \cos^{-1} x$: domain: $-1 \leq x \leq 1$; range: $-\frac{\pi}{2} \leq y \leq \frac{\pi}{2}$

9. $y = -3\sin\left(\frac{x - \frac{\pi}{2}}{4}\right)$

11. 0.174 s, 0.659 s, 1.008 s, 1.492 s, 1.841 s, 2.325 s, 2.675 s

CHAPTER 11 • CHAPTER 11 CHAPTER 11 • CHAPTER

LESSON 11.1

1. $-3, -1.5, 0, 1.5, 3$; $u_1 = -3, d = 1.5$

3a. $3 + 4 + 5 + 6$; 18 **3b.** $-2 + 1 + 6$; 5

5. $S_{75} = 5700$

7a. $u_{46} = 229$

7b. $u_n = 5n - 1$, or $u_1 = 4$ and $u_n = u_{n-1} + 5$ where $n \geq 2$

7c. $S_{46} = 5359$

9a. 3, 6, 9, 12, 15, 18, 21, 24, 27, 30

9b. $u_1 = 3$ and $u_n = u_{n-1} + 3$ where $n \geq 2$

9c. 3384 cans **9d.** 13 rows with 15 cans left over

11. $S_x = x^2 + 64x$

13a. $u_1 = 4.9$ and $u_n = u_{n-1} + 9.8$ where $n \geq 2$

13b. $u_n = 9.8n - 4.9$ **13c.** 93.1 m **13d.** 490 m

13e. $S_n = 4.9n^2$ **13f.** approximately 8.2 s

15a. 576,443 people **15b.** 641,676 people

17a. $81, 27, 9, 3, 1, \frac{1}{3}$

17b. $u_1 = 81$ and $u_n = \frac{1}{3}u_{n-1}$ where $n \geq 2$

19a. $\frac{\sqrt{6} + \sqrt{2}}{4}$ **19b.** $\frac{\sqrt{6} - \sqrt{2}}{4}$

LESSON 11.2

1a. $0.4 + 0.04 + 0.004 + \cdots$

1b. $u_1 = 0.4, r = 0.1$

1c. $S = \frac{4}{9}$

3a. $0.123 + 0.000123 + 0.000000123 + \cdots$

3b. $u_1 = 0.123, r = 0.001$

3c. $S = \frac{123}{999} = \frac{41}{333}$

5. $u_1 = 32768$

7a. 96, 24, 6, 1.5, 0.375. 0.09375, 0.0234375, 0.005859375, 0.00146484375, 0.0003662109375

7b. $S_{10} \approx 128.000$

7c.

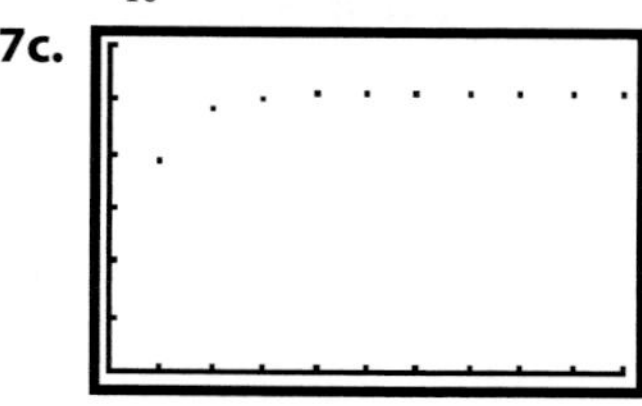

[0, 10, 1, 0, 150, 25]

7d. $S = 128$

9a. \$25,000,000 **9b.** \$62,500,000

9c. 2.5 **9d.** 44.4%

11a. $\sqrt{2}$ in. **11b.** 0.125 in.^{2}

11c. approximately 109.25 in.

11d. 128 in.^{2}

13. 88 gal

15a. \$56,625 **15b.** 43 wk

LESSON 11.3

1a. $u_1 = 12, r = 0.4, n = 8$

1b. $u_1 = 75, r = 1.2, n = 15$

1c. $u_1 = 40, r = 0.8, n = 20$

1d. $u_1 = 60, r = 2.5, n = 6$

3a. $S_5 = 92.224$ **3b.** $S_{15} \approx 99.952$ **3c.** $S_{25} \approx 99.999$

5a. 3069 **5b.** 22 **5c.** 2.8 **5d.** 0.95

7a. $S_{10} = 15.984375$

7b. $S_{20} \approx 15.99998474$

7c. $S_{30} \approx 15.99999999$

7d. They continue to increase, but by a smaller amount each time.

9a.i. 128 **9a.ii.** more than 9×10^{18}

9a.iii. 255 **9a.iv.** more than 1.8×10^{19}

9b. $\sum_{n=1}^{64} 2^{n-1}$

11a. 5, 15, 35, 75, 155, 315, 635

11b. No, they form a shifted geometric sequence.

11c. not possible

13a. $1 + 4 + 9 + 16 + 25 + 36 + 49 = 140$

13b. $9 + 16 + 25 + 36 + 49 = 135$

15. \$637.95

17. Yes. The long-run height is only 24 in.

CHAPTER 11 REVIEW

1a. $u_{128} = 511$ **1b.** $u_{40} = 159$

1c. $u_{20} = 79$ **1d.** $S_{20} = 820$

3a. 144; 1728; 20,736; 429,981,696

3b. $u_1 = 12$ and $u_n = 12\, u_{n-1}$ where $n \geq 2$

3c. $u_n = 12^n$ **3d.** approximately 1.2×10^{14}

5a. approximately 56.49 ft **5b.** 60 ft

7a. $S_{10} \approx 12.957$; $S_{40} \approx 13.333$

7b. $S_{10} \approx 170.478$; $S_{40} \approx 481571.531$

7c. $S_{10} = 40$; $S_{40} = 160$

7d. For $r = 0.7$ For $r = 1.3$

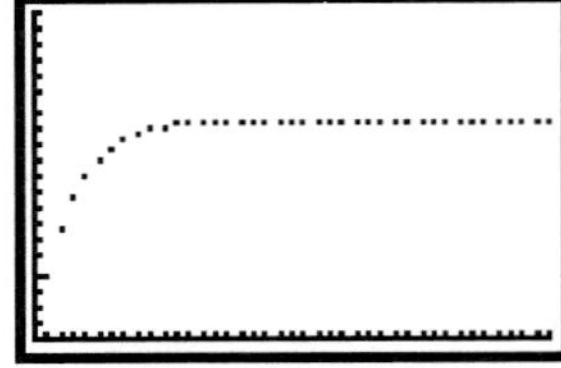

[0, 40, 1, 0, 20, 1]

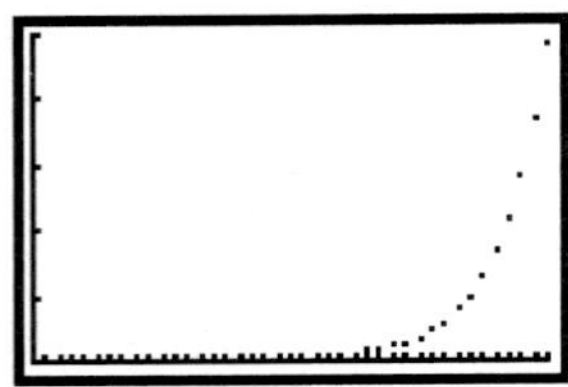

[0, 40, 1, 0, 500000, 100000]

For $r = 1$

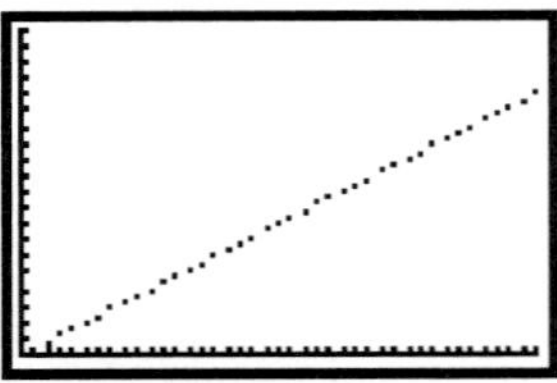

[0, 40, 1, 0, 200, 10]

7e. 0.7

CHAPTER 12 • CHAPTER 12 CHAPTER 12 • CHAPTER

LESSON 12.1

1a. $\frac{6}{15} = .4$ **1b.** $\frac{7}{15} \approx .467$ **1c.** $\frac{2}{15} \approx .133$

3a. $\frac{4}{14} \approx .286$ **3b.** $\frac{10}{14} \approx .714$ **3c.** $\frac{7.5}{14} \approx .536$

3d. $\frac{1.5}{14} \approx .107$ **3e.** $\frac{2}{14} \approx .143$

5a. experimental **5b.** theoretical

5c. experimental

7. *Hint:* Consider whether each of the integers 0–9 are equally likely. Each of the procedures has short-comings, but 7iii is the best method.

9a. 36

9b. 6; $\frac{1}{6} \approx .167$

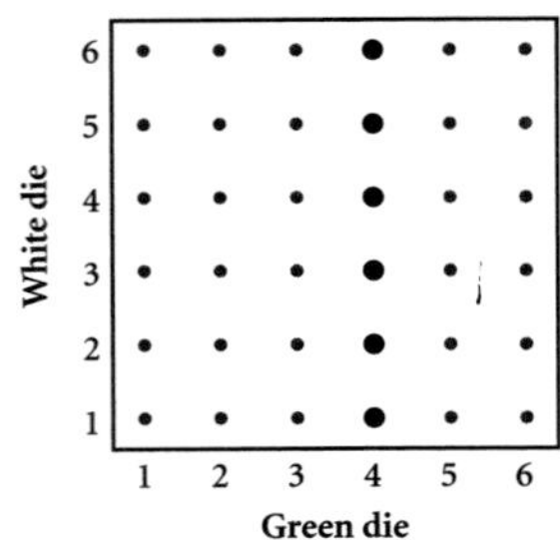

9c. 12; $\frac{12}{36} \approx .333$ **9d.** 3; $\frac{3}{36} \approx .083$

11a. 144 square units **11b.** 44 square units

11c. $\frac{44}{144}$ **11d.** $\frac{44}{144} \approx .306$

11e. $\frac{100}{144} \approx .694$ **11f.** 0; 0

13a. 270 **13b.** 1380

13c. $\frac{270}{1380} \approx .196$ **13d.** $\frac{1110}{1380} \approx .804$

15a. 53 pm, at point *C*

15b. 0 pm, at point *A*, the nucleus

15c. The probability starts at zero at the nucleus, increases and peaks at a distance of 53 pm, and then decreases quickly, then more slowly, but never reaches zero.

17. $\log\left(\frac{ac^2}{b}\right)$

19a.

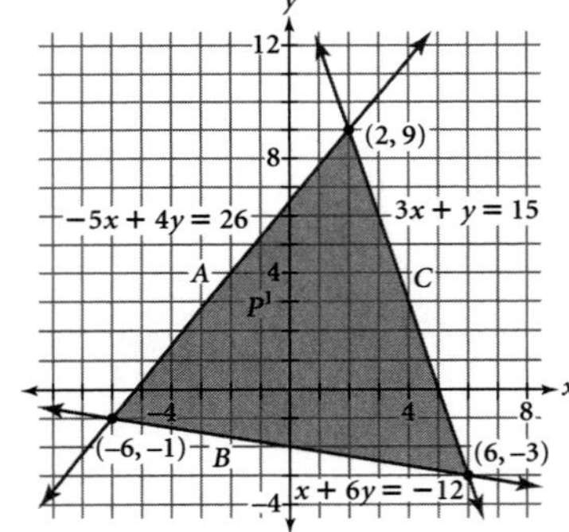

19b. (2, 9), (−6, −1), (6, −3)

19c. 68 square units

21a. Set i should have a larger standard deviation because the values are more spread out.

21b. **i.** $\bar{x} = 35, s \approx 22.3$; **ii.** $\bar{x} = 117, s \approx 3.5$

21c. The original values of $\bar{x}$ and s are multipied by 10.

21c. i. $\bar{x} = 350, s \approx 223.5$

21c. ii. $\bar{x} = 1170, s \approx 35.4$

21d. The original values of $\bar{x}$ are increased by 10, and the original values of s are unchanged.

21d. i. $\bar{x} = 45, s \approx 22.3$ **21d. ii.** $\bar{x} = 127, s \approx 3.5$

LESSON 12.2

1.

3. $P(\text{a}) = .7$; $P(\text{b}) = .3$; $P(\text{c}) = .18$; $P(\text{d}) = .4$; $P(\text{e}) = .8$; $P(\text{f}) = .2$; $P(\text{g}) = .08$

5. For the first choice, the probability of choosing a sophomore is $\frac{14}{21}$, and the probability of choosing a junior is $\frac{7}{21}$. Once the first student is chosen, the class total is reduced by 1 and either the junior or sophomore portion is reduced by 1.

7a. 24 **7b.** .25 **7c.** $\frac{2}{24} \approx .083$

7d. $\frac{1}{24} \approx .042$ **7e.** $\frac{23}{24} \approx .958$ **7f.** $\frac{12}{24} = .5$

9a. 4 **9b.** 8 **9c.** 16

9d. 32 **9e.** 1024 **9f.** 2^n

11a. $P(M3) = .45$; $P(G \mid M1) = .95$; $P(D \mid M2) = .08$; $P(G \mid M3) = .93$; $P(M1 \text{ and } D) = .01$; $P(M1 \text{ and } G) = .19$; $P(M2 \text{ and } D) = .028$; $P(M2 \text{ and } G) = .332$; $P(M3 \text{ and } D) = .0315$; $P(M3 \text{ and } G) = .4185$

11b. .08 **11c.** .0695 **11d.** .4029

13. $\frac{6}{16} = .375$

15a. 100,000 **15b.** 1,000,000,000

15c. 17,576,000 **15d.** 7,200,000

17a. $-3 + 2i$ **17b.** $2 + 24i$

17c. $\frac{18}{29} + \frac{16}{29}i$

19a. $\frac{50}{110} \approx .455$ **19b.** $\frac{120}{230} \approx .522$

LESSON 12.3

1. 10% of the students are sophomores and not in advanced algebra. 15% are sophomores in advanced algebra. 12% are in advanced algebra but are not sophomores. 63% are neither sophomores nor in advanced algebra.

3.

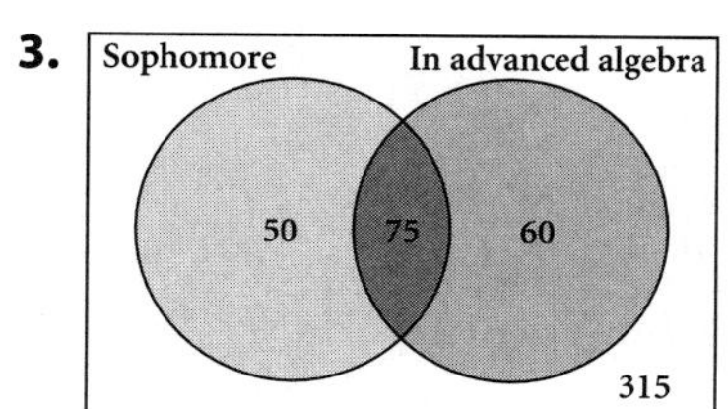

5a. Yes, because they do not overlap.

5b. No. $P(\text{A and B}) = 0$. This would be the same as $P(\text{A}) \cdot P(\text{B})$ if they were independent.

7a.

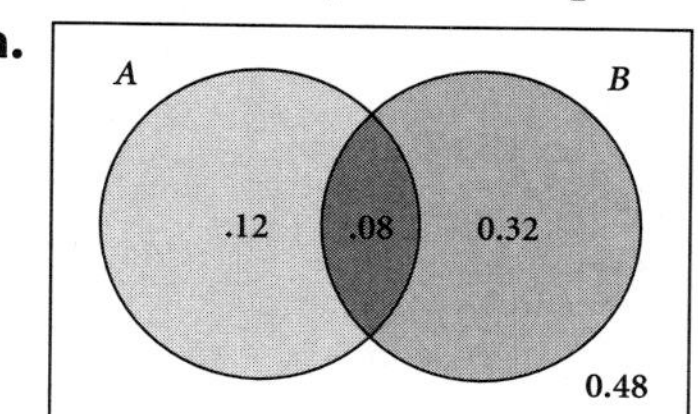

7b.i. .08 **7b.ii.** .60 **7b.iii.** .48

9.

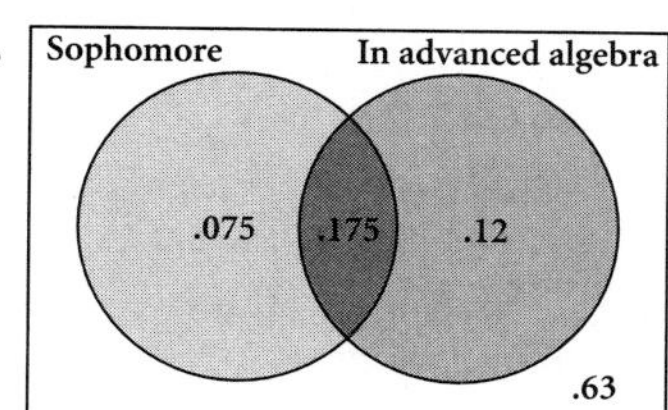

11a.

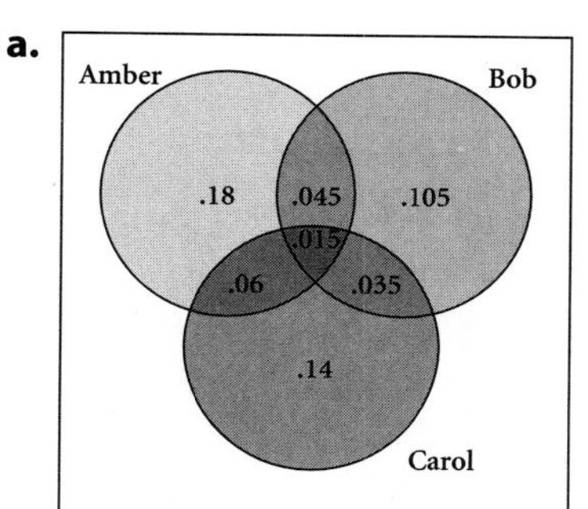

11b. .015 **11c.** .42

13. approximately 77

15a. $3\sqrt{2}$ **15b.** $3\sqrt{6}$ **15c.** $2xy^2\sqrt{15xy}$

LESSON 12.4

1a. Yes; the number of children will be an integer, and it is based on a random process.

1b. No; the length may be a non-integer.

1c. Yes; there will be an integer number of pieces of mail, and it is based on random processes of who sends mail when.

3a. approximately .068

3b. approximately .221

5a. Answers will vary. Theoretically, after 10 games Sly should get about 23 points, and Andy should get 21.

5b. Answers will vary. Theoretically, it should be close to .47.

5c.

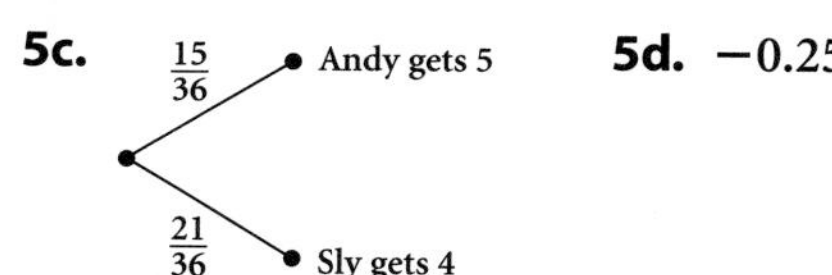

5d. -0.25

Selected Answers

5e. Answers will vary. One possible answer is 5 points for Sly if the sum of the dice is less than 8 and 7 points for Andy if the sum of the dice is greater than 7.

7a. \$25 **7b.** .67 **7c.** \$28.33

9a. .2 **9b.** .12

9c.

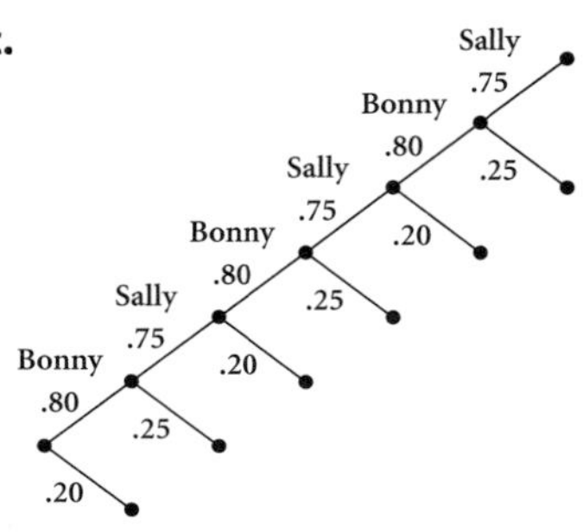

.072

9d. .392 **9e.** geometric; $u_1 = .20, r = .6$

9f. .476672 **9g.** .5

11a. .580

11b. 0; 0.312; 0.346; 0.192; 0.124; 0

11c. 0.974

11d. On average, the engineer should expect to find 0.974 defective radio in a sample of 5.

13. 1

15a.

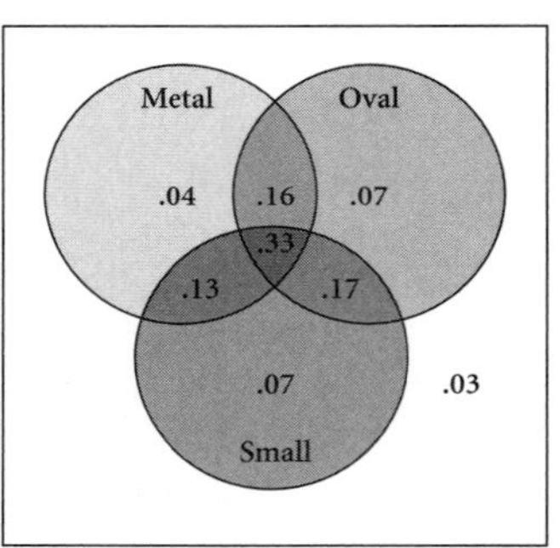

15b.

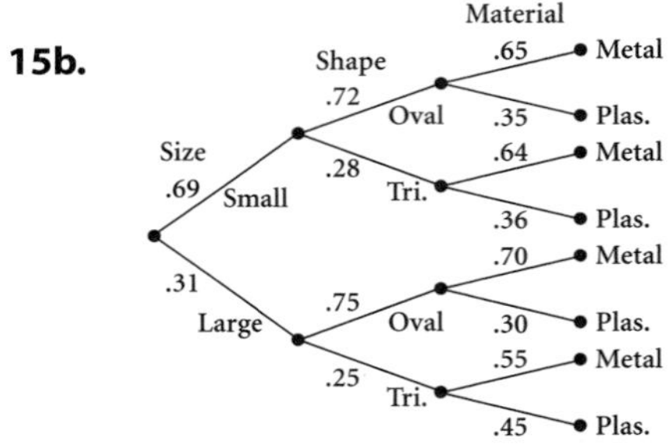

17. 44

LESSON 12.5

1a. Yes. Different arrangements of scoops are different.

1b. No. The order is not the same, so the arrangements should be counted separately if they are permutations.

1c. No. Repetition is not allowed in permutations.

1d. No. Repetition is not allowed in permutations.

3a. 210 **3b.** 5040

3c. $\frac{(n+2)!}{2}$ **3d.** $\frac{n!}{2}$

5a. 10000; $27.\overline{7}$ hr

5b. 100000; approximately 11.57 days

5c. 10

7. r factors

9a. 40,320 **9b.** 5040 **9c.** .125

9d. Sample answer: There are eight possible positions for Volume 5, all equally likely. So $P(5 \text{ in rightmost slot}) = \frac{1}{8} = .125$.

9e. .5; sample answer: there are four even-numbered books that can be in the rightmost position out of the eight books. So the probability of an even-numbered book being on the right is $\frac{4}{8}$ or .5.

9f. 1 **9g.** 40,319 **9h.** $\frac{1}{40320} \approx .000025$

11a. approximately .070 **11b.** approximately .005

11c. approximately .155 **11d.** \$3.20

13a. $\frac{30}{50} = .6$ **13b.** $\frac{16}{30} \approx .533$

15a. $\frac{1}{8} = .125$ **15b.** $\frac{3}{8} = .375$ **15c.** $\frac{1}{2} = .5$

17a. 41 **17b.** about 808.3 in.^{2}

LESSON 12.6

1a. 120 **1b.** 35 **1c.** 105 **1d.** 1

3a. $\frac{{}_7P_2}{2!} = {}_7C_2$ **3b.** $\frac{{}_7P_3}{3!} = {}_7C_3$

3c. $\frac{{}_7P_4}{4!} = {}_7C_4$ **3d.** $\frac{{}_7P_7}{7!} = {}_7C_7$

3e. $\frac{{}_nP_r}{r!} = {}_nC_r$

5. $n = 7$ and $r = 3$, or $n = 7$ and $r = 4$, or $n = 35$ and $r = 1$, or $n = 35$ and $r = 34$

7a. 35 **7b.** $\frac{20}{35} \approx .571$

9a. 4 **9b.** 8 **9c.** 16

9d. The sum of all possible combinations of n things is 2^n; $2^5 = 32$.

11a. 6 **11b.** 10 **11c.** 36

11d. ${}_nC_2 = \frac{n!}{2(n-2)!}$

13a. $x^2 + 2xy + y^2$

13b. $x^3 + 3x^2y + 3xy^2 + y^3$

13c. $x^4 + 4x^3y + 6x^2y^2 + 4xy^3 + y^4$

15a. .0194 is the probability that someone is healthy and tests positive.

15b. .02 is the probability that a healthy person tests positive.

15c. .0491 is the probability that a person tests positive.

15d. .395 is the probability that a person who tests positive is healthy.

17. approximately 19.5 m; approximately 26.2 m

LESSON 12.7

1a. x^{47} **1b.** $5{,}178{,}066{,}751x^{37}y^{10}$

1c. $62{,}891{,}499x^7y^{40}$ **1d.** $47xy^{46}$

3a. .299 **3b.** .795, .496 **3c.** .203, .502, .791

3d. Both the "at most" and "at least" numbers include the case of "exactly." For example, if "exactly" 5 birds (.165) is subtracted from "at least" 5 birds (.203), the result (.038) is the same as 1 − .962 ("at most" 5 birds).

3e. The probability that at least 5 birds survive is 20.3%.

5. $p < \frac{25}{33}$

7a. $x^4 + 4x^3y + 6x^2y^2 + 4xy^3 + y^4$

7b. $p^5 + 5p^4q + 10p^3q^2 + 10p^2q^3 + 5pq^4 + q^5$

7c. $8x^3 + 36x^2 + 54x + 27$

7d. $81x^4 - 432x^3 + 864x^2 - 768x + 256$

9a. .401 **9b.** .940

9c. $Y_1 = {}_{30}C_x(.97)^{30-x}(.03)^x$

9d. .940

11a. .000257 **11b.** .446 **11c.** .983

13. Answers will vary. This event will happen in 15.6% of trials.

15a. 2; 2.25; ≈ 2.370; ≈ 2.441

15b. $f(10) \approx 2.5937, f(100) \approx 2.7048, f(1000) \approx 2.7169, f(10000) \approx 2.7181$

15c. There is a long-run value of about 2.718.

17. 37.44 cm^2

19a. *Hint:* Graph data in the form (*distance, period*), (log (*distance*), *period*), (*distance*, log (*period*)), and (log (*distance*), log (*period*)), and identify which is the most linear. Find an equation to fit the most linear data you find, then substitute the appropriate variables (*distance*, *period*, log (*distance*), log (*period*)) for *x* and *y*, and solve for *y*. You should find that $period \approx distance^{1.50} \times 10^{-9.38}$.

19b. *Hint:* Substitute the period and distance values given in the table into your equation from 19a. Errors are most likely due to rounding.

19c. $period^2 = 10^{-18.76}\, distance^3$

CHAPTER 12 REVIEW

1. Answers will vary. You might number 10 chips or slips of paper and select one. You might look at a random-number table and select the first digit of each number. You could alter the program Generate to :Int 10Rand + 1.

3a. .5 **3b.** 17.765 square units

5a.

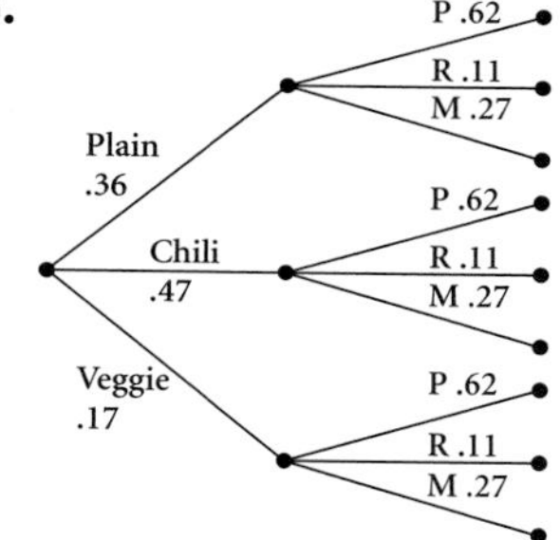

5b. .0517 **5c.** .8946 **5d.** .3501

7. 110.5

9. .044

LESSON 13.1

1. A: $\frac{1}{8}$; B: $\frac{1}{12}$; C: $\frac{1}{10}$; D: $\frac{1}{10}$

3. Answers will vary. A: $\sqrt{8} = 2\sqrt{2}$; B: $\sqrt{12} = 2\sqrt{3}$; C: 2.5; D: $3\frac{1}{3}$

5a.

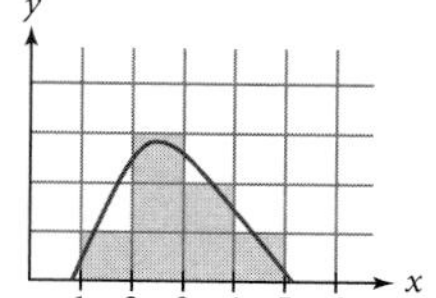

5b.

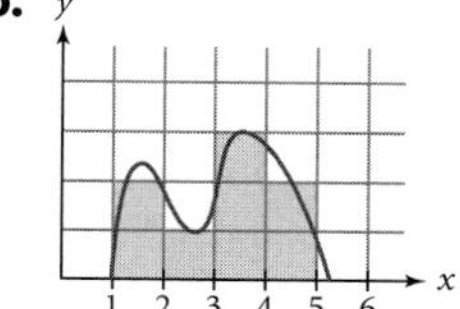

7a. true **7b.** true

7c. False; if the distribution is symmetric, then they can all be the same.

9. *Hint:* For 9a, create a random list of 100 numbers from 0 to 1, and store it in L1. Enter values of $(L1)^2$ in L2, and graph a histogram of these values. You may want to rerandomize L1 several times, and then generalize the shape of the histogram. See Calculator Notes 1L and 13D for help with these calculator functions. Use a similar process for 9b and 9c.

11. Answers will vary.

Selected Answers

13a.

x	0–3	3–6	6–9	9–12	12–15	15–18
$P(x)$	.015	.046	.062	.092	.2	.138

x	18–21	21–24	24–27	27–30	30–33
$P(x)$	.123	.154	.092	.062	.015

13b, d.

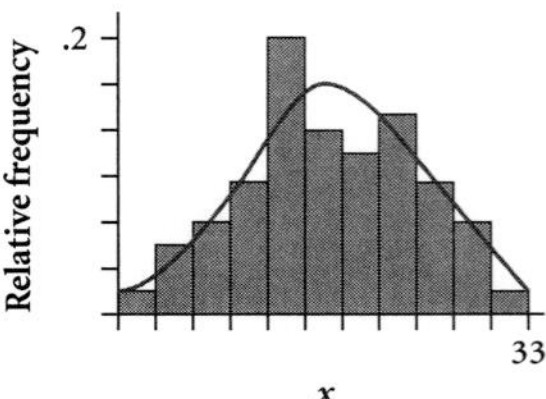

13c. 15–18 min

15. .022

17. QR is 0 when P overlaps R, then grows larger and larger without bound until P reaches the y-axis, at which point Q is undefined because $\overleftrightarrow{PO}$ and $\overleftrightarrow{RT}$ are parallel and do not intersect. As P moves through Quadrant II, QR decreases to 0. Then, as P moves through Quadrant III, QR increases, again without bound. When P reaches the y-axis, point Q is again undefined. As P moves through Quadrant IV, QR again decreases to 0. These patterns correspond to the zeros and vertical asymptotes of the graph in Exercise 16.

19. In all cases, the area remains the same. The relationship holds for all two-dimensional figures.

LESSON 13.2

1a. *Hint:* Enter the expressions as Y1 and Y2. Then graph or create a table of values, and confirm that they are the same.

1b. $y \approx .242$ and $n(x, 0, 1) \approx .242$

3a. $\mu = 18, \sigma \approx 2.5$

3b. $\mu = 10, \sigma \approx 0.8$

3c. $\mu \approx 68, \sigma \approx 6$

3d. $\mu \approx 0.47, \sigma \approx 0.12$

5.

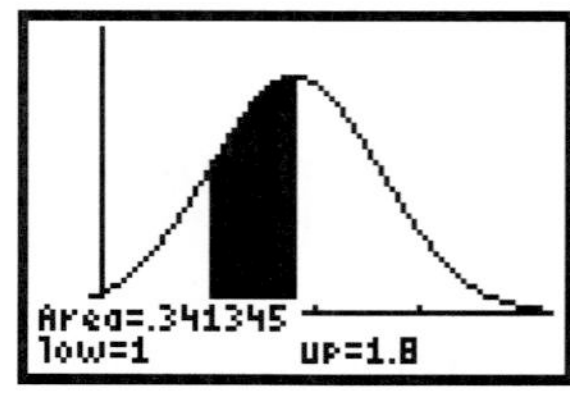

[−0.6, 4.2, 1, −0.1, 0.6, 0]

7a.

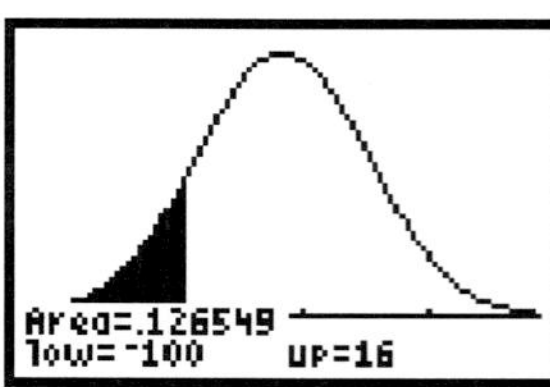

[14.7, 18.9, 1, −0.1, 0.6, 0]

7b. 12.7%. Sample answer: No, more than 10% of boxes do not meet minimum weight requirements.

9.

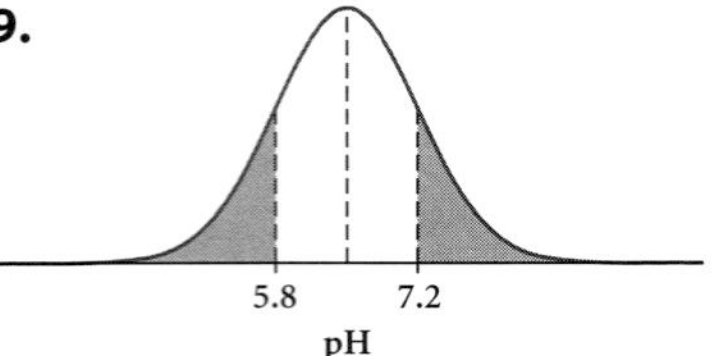

11a. $\mu = 79.1, \sigma \approx 7.49$

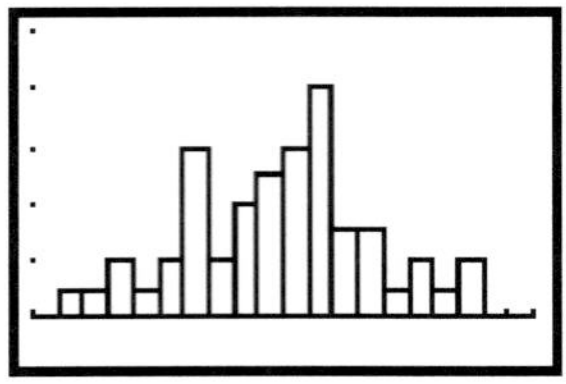

[60, 100, 2, −1, 10, 2]

11b. sample answer:

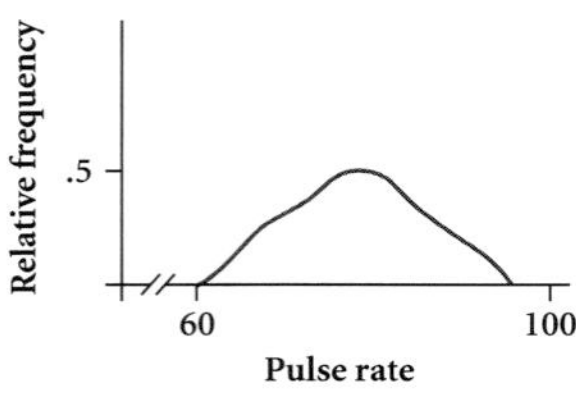

11c. $y = \frac{1}{7.49\sqrt{2\pi}}(\sqrt{e})^{-((x-79.1)/7.49)^2}$

11d. Answers will vary. The data do not appear to be normally distributed. They seem to be approximately symmetrically distributed with several peaks.

13a. *Hint:* Consider what the mean and standard deviation tell you about the distribution of test scores. Can you be sure which test is more difficult?

13b. the French exam, because it has the greatest standard deviation

13c. *Hint:* Determine how many standard deviations each student's score is from the mean. This will tell you how each student scored relative to other test-takers.

15. 25344

LESSON 13.3

1. *Hint:* See page 746.

3a. 122.6

3b. 129.8

3c. 131.96

3d. 123.8

5a. $z = 1.8$

5b. $z = -0.67$

5c. approximately .71

7a. (3.058, 3.142)

7b. (3.049, 3.151)

7c. (3.034, 3.166)

9a. decrease

9b. increase

9c. stay the same size

9d. increase

Selected Answers

11a. between 204.6 and 210.6 passengers

11b. .07

13a. $a = 0.0125$ **13b.** .6875

13c. .1875 **13d.** 0

13e. 0 **13f.** $18\frac{1}{3}$

15a. Let n represent the number of months, and let S_n represent the cumulated total.

Plan 1: $S_n = 398n + 2n^2$; Plan 2: $S_n = \frac{75(1 - 1.025^n)}{1 - 1.025}$

15b.

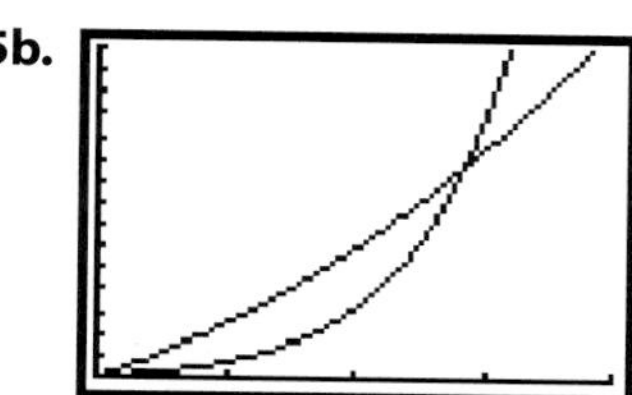

[0, 200, 50, 0, 150000, 10000]

15c. If you stay 11 years 9 months or less, choose Plan 2. If you stay longer, choose Plan 1.

LESSON 13.4

1a. 33.85% **1b.** 20.23%

1c. 10.56% **1d.** 0.6210%

3. 31.28%

5a. $224 < \mu < 236$

5b. $227.6 < \mu < 232.4$

5c. $228 < \mu < 232$

7. $s = 0.43$

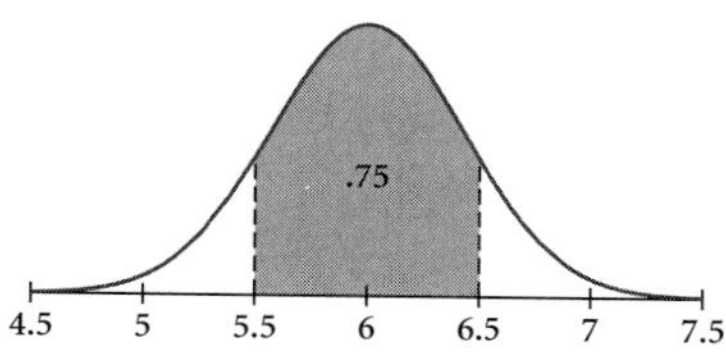

9a. 5 samples **9b.** $\bar{x} = 0.56$, $s = 0.20$

9c. approximately 0

9d. probably, because these results are highly unlikely if the site is contaminated

11. The graph appears to sit on a horizontal line. The graph is skewed; it doesn't have a line of symmetry.

13. $y = 4.53x + 12.98$; 6.2

LESSON 13.5

1a. .95 **1b.** −.95 **1c.** −.6 **1d.** .9

3a. −33 **3b.** 17; 4

3c. 6; 2.1213 **3d.** −.9723

3e. There is a strong negative correlation in the data.

3f. *Hint:* Do the points seem to decrease linearly?

5a. Correlation; weight gain probably has more to do with amount of physical activity than television ownership.

5b. Correlation; the age of the children may be the variable controlling both size of feet and reading ability.

5c. Correlation; the size of a fire may be the variable controlling both the number of firefighters and the length of time.

7. $r \approx .915$. There is a strong positive correlation between the number of students and the number of faculty.

9a. $r = -1$. This value of r implies perfect negative correlation, which is consistent with the plot.

9b. $r \approx .833$. This value of r implies strong positive correlation, but the plot suggests negative correlation with one outlier.

9c. $r = 0$. This value of r implies no correlation, but the plot suggests negative correlation with one outlier.

9d. Yes, one outlier can drastically affect the value of r.

13. possible answer: $y = -1.5x + 6$

15. 60 km/h

LESSON 13.6

1a. $\bar{x} = 1975$ **1b.** $\bar{y} = 40.15$ **1c.** $s_x = 18.71$

1d. $s_y = 8.17$ **1e.** $r \approx .9954$

3a. 0.3166, −0.2292, 0.1251, 0.1794, −1.3663, 0.9880

3b. 0.01365

3c. 0.1002, 0.0525, 0.0157, 0.0322, 1.8667, 0.9761

3d. 3.0435 **3e.** 0.8723

5a.

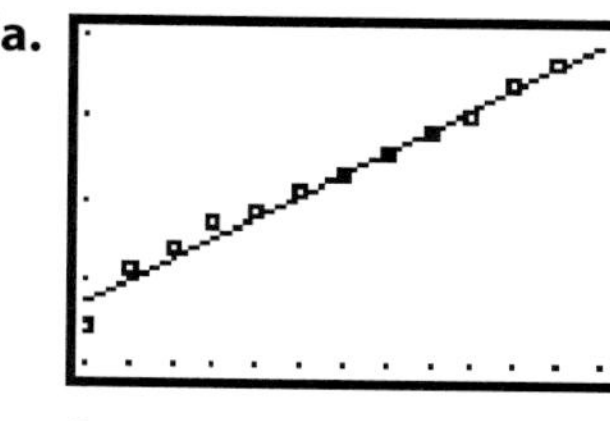

[1978, 1990, 1, 85, 105, 5]

$\hat{y} = 1.3115x - 2505.3782$

5b. 124.2 ppt

5c.

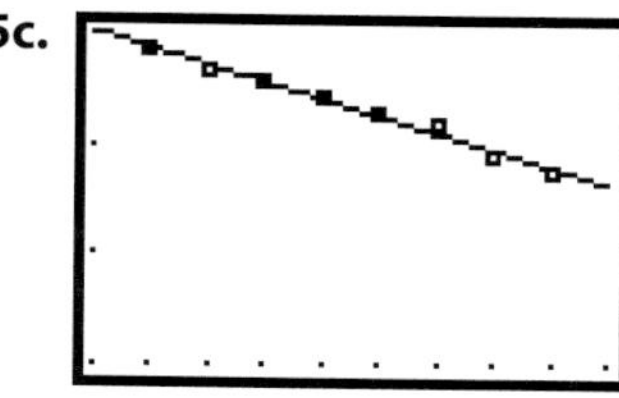

[1989, 1998, 1, 90, 105, 5]

$\hat{y} = -0.7714x + 1639.4179$

5d. 92.8 ppt. This is 31.4 ppt lower than the amount predicted in 5b.

7a. $\hat{y} = -1.212x + 110.2$

7b. possible answer: 10°N to 60°N

7c. The cities that appear not to follow the pattern are Denver, which is a high mountainous city; Mexico City, which is also a high mountainous city; Phoenix, which is in desert terrain; Quebec, which is subject to the Atlantic currents; and Vancouver, which is subject to the Pacific currents.

7d. Answers will vary.

9. *Hint:* You may want to consider how many points are used to calculate each line of fit, whether each is affected by outliers, and which is easier to calculate by hand.

11a. $y = 1000$ **11b.** $y = \dfrac{100}{\sqrt{x}}$

13. $y = -6(x - 1)(x + 2)(x + 5)$

15. The length will increase without bound.

LESSON 13.7

1a.

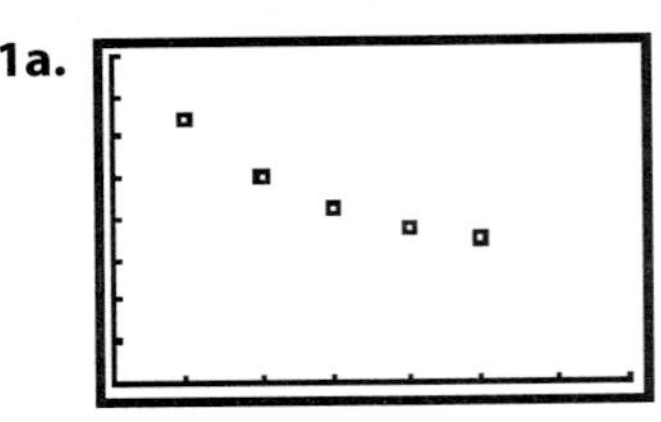

[0, 7, 1, 0, 80, 10]

1b.

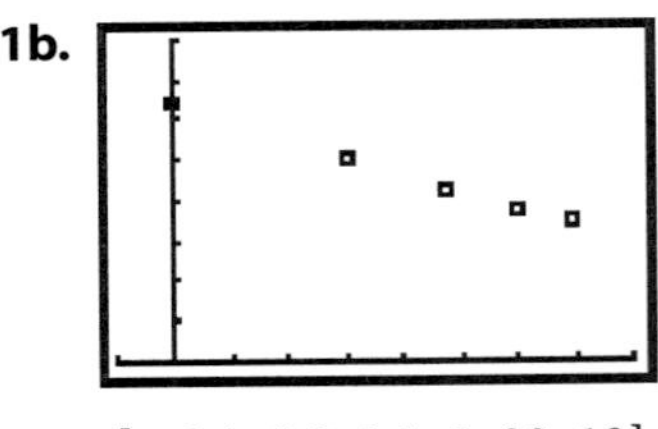

[−0.1, 0.8, 0.1, 0, 80, 10]

1c.

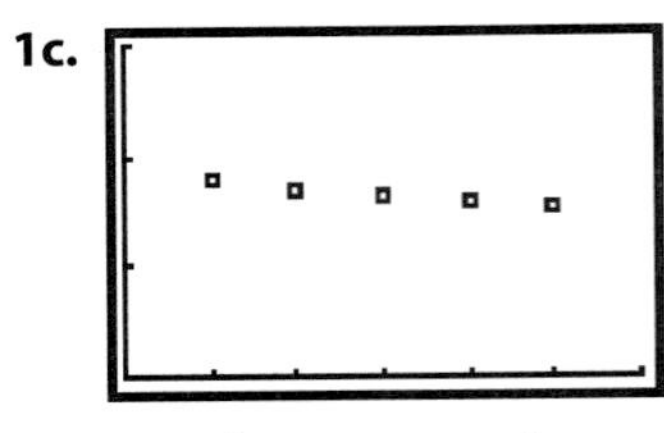

[0, 6, 1, 0, 3, 1]

1d.

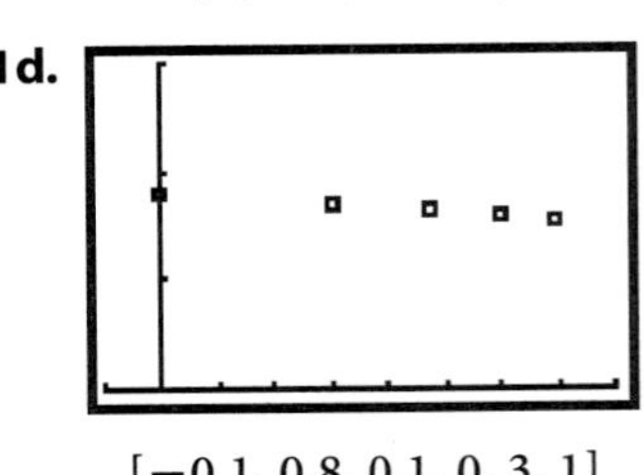

[−0.1, 0.8, 0.1, 0, 3, 1]

1e. It is difficult to tell visually. But $(\log x, \log y)$ has the strongest correlation coefficient, $r \approx -.99994$.

3a. $\hat{y} = 67.7 - 7.2x$

3b. $\hat{y} = 64 - 43.25\log x$

3c. $\hat{y} = 54.4 \cdot 0.592^x + 20$

3d. $\hat{y} = 46.33x^{-0.68076} + 20$

5a. $\hat{y} = -3.77x^3 + 14.13x^2 + 8.23x - 0.01$

5b. 0.079 **5c.** 12.52 m^3

5d. Because the root mean square is 0.079, you can expect the predicted volume to be within approximately 0.079 cubic meter of the true value.

7a. 4.2125 **7b.** 43.16875

7c. 6.28525 **7d.** .8544

7e. .90236; the cubic model is a better fit.

7f. $\hat{y} = -0.07925x + 8.175$; $R^2 \approx .582$. The values of R^2 and r^2 are equal for the linear model.

9a. 86.2 **9b.** 79.8 **9c.** 89.4

11a. approximately 1910

11b. approximately 847

11c. approximately 919

CHAPTER 13 REVIEW

1a. $0.5(20)(.1) = 1$ **1b.** $20 - 5\sqrt{6} \approx 7.75$

1c. .09 **1d.** $\dfrac{77}{300} \approx .257$

3a. $\bar{x} = 10.55$ lb; $s = 2.15$ lb

3b. 6.25 lb to 14.85 lb

5a.

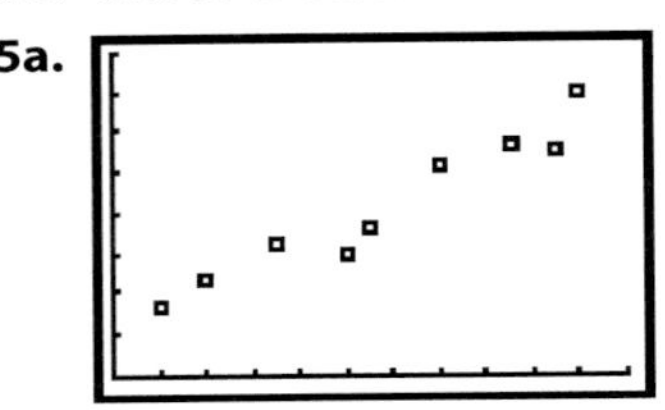

[0, 11, 1, 0, 80, 10]

5b. yes; $r \approx .965$, indicating a relationship that is close to linear

5c. $\hat{y} = 5.322x + 10.585$

5d. The rolling distance increases 5.322 in. for every additional inch of wheel diameter. The skateboard will skid approximately 10.585 in. even if it doesn't have any wheels.

5e. 7.5 in.

7. approximately .062

9a. hyperbola

9b. ellipse

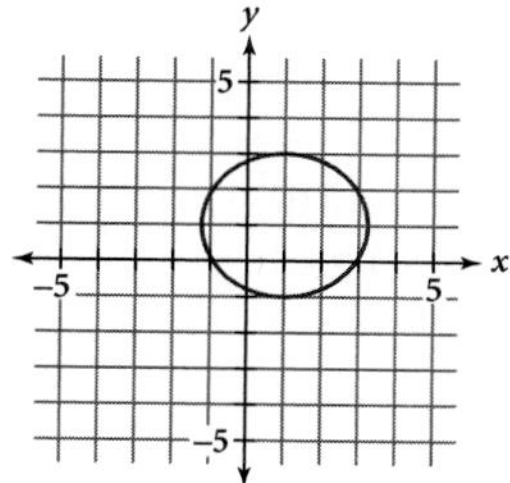

9c. parabola

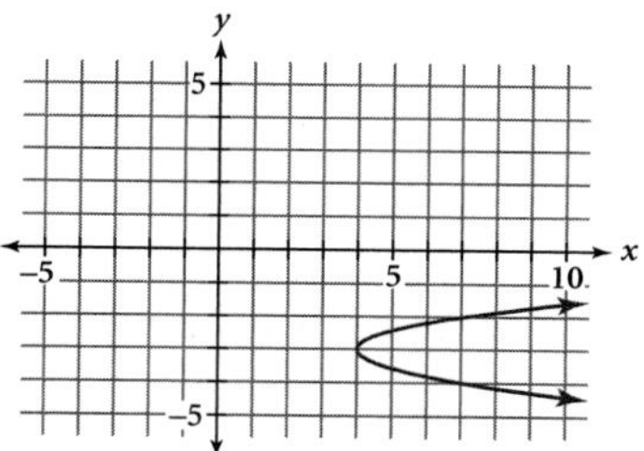

9d. hyperbola

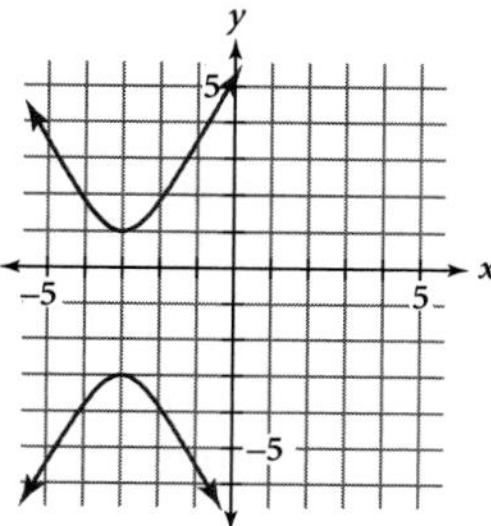

11a. $S_{12} = 144$ **11b.** $S_{20} = 400$ **11c.** $S_n = n^2$

13a. $y = -20x^2 + 332x$ **13b.** \$8.30; \$1377.80

15. Row 1: .72, .08; Row 2: .18, .02; Out of 100 people with the symptoms, the test will accurately confirm that 72 do not have the disease while mistakenly suggesting 8 do have the disease. The test will accurately indicate 18 do have the disease and make a mistake by suggesting 2 do not have the disease who actually have the disease.

16a. possible answer: 3.8% per year

16b. possible answer: $\hat{y} = 5.8(1 + 0.038)^{x-1970}$

16c. possible answer: 31.1 million

16d. The population predicted by the equation is much higher.

17a. seats versus cost: $r = .9493$; speed versus cost: $r = .8501$

17b. The number of seats is more strongly correlated to cost. Sample answer: The increase in number of seats will cause an increase in weight (both passengers and luggage) and thus cause an increase in the amount of fuel needed.

19a. $\frac{11\pi}{36}$ **19b.** approximately 3.84 cm

19c. approximately 7.68 cm^2

21a. (1, 4) **21b.** (−5.5, 0.5)

23a. domain: $x \geq \frac{3}{2}$; range: $y \geq 0$

23b. domain: any real number; range: $y \geq 0$

23c. $f(2) = 1$

23d. $x = \pm\sqrt{\frac{1}{3}}$ or $x \approx \pm 0.577$

23e. $g(f(3)) = 18$

23f. $f(g(x)) = \sqrt{12x^2 - 3}$

25a, b.

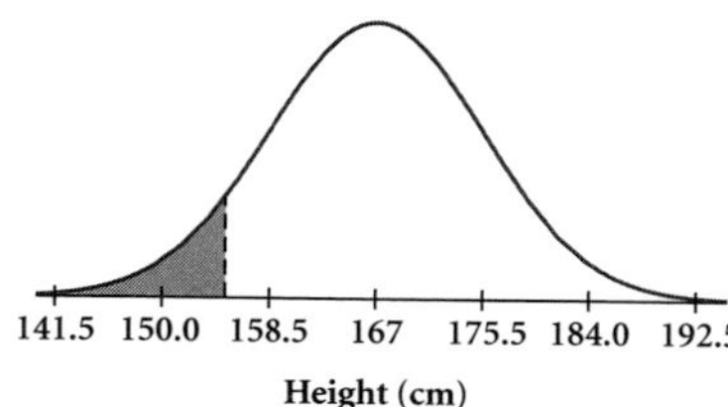

25c. approximately 7.9%

Glossary

The number in parentheses at the end of each definition gives the page where each word or phrase is first used in the text. Some words and phrases are introduced more than once, either because they have different applications in different chapters or because they first appeared within features such as Project or Take Another Look; in these cases, there may be multiple page numbers listed.

ambiguous case A situation in which more than one possible solution exists. (472)

amplitude Half the difference of the maximum and minimum values of a periodic function. (584)

angular speed The amount of rotation, or angle traveled, per unit of time. (577)

antilog The inverse function of a logarithm. (279)

arithmetic mean See **mean.**

arithmetic sequence A sequence in which each term after the starting term is equal to the sum of the previous term and a common difference. (31)

arithmetic series A sum of terms of an arithmetic sequence. (631)

asymptote A line that a graph approaches, but does not reach, as *x*- or *y*-values increase in the positive or negative direction. (516)

augmented matrix A matrix that represents a system of equations. The entries include a column for the coefficients of each variable and a final column for the constant terms. (318)

base The base of an exponential expression, b^x, is *b*. The base of a logarithmic expression, $\log_b x$, is *b*. (245)

bearing An angle measured clockwise from north. (439)

bin A column in a histogram that represents a certain interval of possible data values. (94)

binomial A polynomial with two terms. (360)

Binomial Theorem For any binomial $(p + q)$ and any positive integer *n*, the binomial expansion is $(p + q)^n = {}_nC_n p^n q^0 + {}_nC_{(n-1)} p^{n-1} q^1 + {}_nC_{(n-2)} p^{n-2} q^2 + \cdots + {}_nC_0 p^0 q^n$. (712)

bisection method A method of finding an *x*-intercept of a function by calculating successive midpoints of segments with endpoints above and below the zero. (417)

bivariate sampling The process of collecting data on two variables per case. (763)

Boolean algebra A system of logic that combines algebraic expressions with "and" (multiplication), "or" (addition), and "not" (negative) and produces results that are "true" (1) or "false" (0). (232)

box plot A one-variable data display that shows the five-number summary of a data set. (79)

box-and-whisker plot See **box plot.**

center (of a circle) See **circle.**

center (of an ellipse) The point midway between the foci of an ellipse. (501)

center (of a hyperbola) The point midway between the vertices of a hyperbola. (514)

Central Limit Theorem If several samples containing *n* data values are taken from a population, then the means of the samples form a distribution that is approximately normal, the population mean is approximately the mean of the distribution of sample means, and the standard deviation of the sample means is approximately the population's standard deviation divided by the square root of *n*. Each approximation is better for larger values of *n*. (753)

circle A locus of points in a plane that are located a constant distance, called the radius, from a fixed point, called the center. (447, 497, 498)

coefficient of determination (R^2) A measure of how well a given curve fits a set of nonlinear data. (786)

combination An arrangement of choices in which the order is unimportant. (704, 705)

common base property of equality For all real values of a, m, and n, if $a^n = a^m$, then $n = m$. (246)

common difference The constant difference between consecutive terms in an arithmetic sequence. (31)

common logarithm A logarithm with base 10, written $\log x$, which is shorthand for $\log_{10} x$. (274)

common ratio The constant ratio between consecutive terms in a geometric sequence. (33)

complements Two events that are mutually exclusive and make up all possible outcomes. (682)

completing the square A method of converting a quadratic equation from general form to vertex form. (380, 527)

complex conjugate A number whose product with a complex number produces a nonzero real number. The complex conjugate of $a + bi$ is $a - bi$. (391)

complex number A number with a real part and an imaginary part. A complex number can be written in the form $a + bi$, where a and b are real numbers and i is the imaginary unit, $\sqrt{-1}$. (391, 392)

complex plane A coordinate plane used for graphing complex numbers, where the horizontal axis is the real axis and the vertical axis is the imaginary axis. (394)

composition of functions The process of using the output of one function as the input of another function. The composition of f and g is written $f(g(x))$. (225)

compound event A sequence of simple events. (669)

compound interest Interest charged or received based on the sum of the original principal and accrued interest. (40)

conditional probability The probability of a particular dependent event, given the outcome of the event on which it depends. (672)

confidence interval A p% confidence interval is an interval about $\bar{x}$ in which you can be p% confident that the population mean, μ, lies. (748)

conic section Any curve that can be formed by the intersection of a plane and an infinite double cone. Circles, ellipses, parabolas, and hyperbolas are conic sections. (496)

conjugate pair A pair of complex numbers whose product is a nonzero real number. The complex numbers $a + bi$ and $a - bi$ form a conjugate pair. (391)

consistent (system) A system of equations that has at least one solution. (317)

constraint A limitation in a linear programming problem, represented by an inequality. (337)

continuous random variable A quantitative variable that can take on any value in an interval of real numbers. (724)

convergent series A series in which the terms of the sequence approach a long-run value, and the partial sums of the series approach a long-run value as the number of terms increases. (637)

correlation A linear relationship between two variables. (763)

correlation coefficient (*r*) A value between -1 and 1 that measures the strength and direction of a linear relationship between two variables. (763)

cosecant The reciprocal of the sine ratio. If A is an acute angle in a right triangle, then the cosecant of angle A is the ratio of the length of the hypotenuse to the length of the opposite leg, or $\csc A = \frac{hyp}{opp}$. See **trigonometric function.** (609)

cosine If A is an acute angle in a right triangle, then the cosine of angle A is the ratio of the length of the adjacent leg to the length of the hypotenuse, or $\cos A = \frac{adj}{hyp}$. See **trigonometric function.** (440)

cotangent The reciprocal of the tangent ratio. If A is an acute angle in a right triangle, then the cotangent of angle A is the ratio of the length of the adjacent leg to the length of the opposite leg, or $\cot A = \frac{adj}{opp}$. See **trigonometric function.** (609)

coterminal Describes angles in standard position that share the same terminal side. (569)

counting principle When there are n_1 ways to make a first choice, n_2 ways to make a second choice, n_3 ways to make a third choice, and so on, the product $n_1 \cdot n_2 \cdot n_3 \cdot \cdots$ represents the total number of different ways in which the entire sequence of choices can be made. (695)

cubic function A polynomial function of degree 3. (399)

curve straightening A technique used to determine whether a relationship is logarithmic, exponential, power, or none of these. See **linearizing.** (287)

cycloid The path traced by a fixed point on a circle as the circle rolls along a straight line. (628)

degree In a one-variable polynomial, the power of the term that has the greatest exponent. In a multivariable polynomial, the greatest sum of the powers in a single term. (360)

dependent (events) Events are dependent when the probability of occurrence of one event depends on the occurrence of the other. (672)

dependent (system) A system with infinitely many solutions. (317)

dependent variable A variable whose values depend on the values of another variable. (123)

determinant The difference of the products of the entries along the diagonals of a square matrix. For any 2×2 matrix $\begin{bmatrix} a & b \\ c & d \end{bmatrix}$, the determinant is $ad - bc$. (357)

deviation For a one-variable data set, the difference between a data value and some standard value, usually the mean. (87)

dilation A transformation that stretches or shrinks a function or graph both horizontally and vertically by the same scale factor. (309)

dimensions (of a matrix) The number of rows and columns in a matrix. A matrix with m rows and n columns has dimensions $m \times n$. (302)

directrix See **parabola.**

discontinuity A jump, break, or hole in the graph of a function. (185)

discrete graph A graph made of distinct, nonconnected points. (52)

discrete random variable A random variable that can take on only distinct (not continuous) values. (688)

distance formula The distance, d, between points (x_1, y_1) and (x_2, y_2), is given by the formula $d = \sqrt{(x_2 - x_1)^2 + (y_2 - y_1)^2}$. (489)

domain The set of input values for a relation. (123)

double root A value r is a double root of an equation $f(x) = 0$ if $(x - r)^2$ is a factor of $f(x)$. (409)

doubling time The time needed for an amount of a substance to double. (240)

e A transcendental number related to continuous growth, with a value of approximately 2.718. (293)

eccentricity A measure of how elongated an ellipse is. (502)

elimination A method for solving a system of equations that involves adding or subtracting multiples of the equations to eliminate a variable. (158)

ellipse A shape produced by stretching or shrinking a circle horizontally or vertically. The shape can be described as a locus of points in a plane for which the sum of the distances to two fixed points, called the foci, is constant. (217, 499, 500)

ellipsoid A three-dimensional shape formed by rotating an ellipse about one of its axes. (503)

end behavior The behavior of a function $y = f(x)$ for x-values that are large in absolute value. (405)

entry Each number in a matrix. The entry identified as a_{ij} is in row i and column j. (302)

even function A function that has the y-axis as a line of symmetry. For all values of x in the domain of an even function, $f(-x) = f(x)$. (235, 612)

event A specified set of outcomes. (659)

expanded form The form of a repeated multiplication expression in which every occurrence of each factor is shown. For example, $4^3 \cdot 5^2 = 4 \cdot 4 \cdot 4 \cdot 5 \cdot 5$. (245)

expansion An expression that is rewritten as a single polynomial. (711)

expected value An average value found by multiplying the value of each possible outcome by its probability, then summing all the products. (688, 689)

experimental probability A probability calculated based on trials and observations, given by the ratio of the number of occurrences of an event to the total number of trials. (659)

explanatory variable In statistics, the variable used to predict (or explain) the value of the response variable. (765)

explicit formula A formula that gives a direct relationship between two discrete quantities. A formula for a sequence that defines the *n*th term in relation to *n*, rather than the previous term(s). (114)

exponent The exponent of an exponential expression, b^x, is x. The exponent tells how many times the base, b, is a factor. (245)

exponential function A function with a variable in the exponent, typically used to model growth or decay. The general form of an exponential function is $y = ab^x$, where the coefficient, a, is the y-intercept and the base, b, is the ratio. (239, 240)

extraneous solution An invalid solution to an equation. Extraneous solutions are sometimes found when both sides of an equation are raised to a power. (206)

extrapolation Estimating a value that is outside the range of all other values given in a data set. (131)

extreme values Maximums and minimums. (405)

F

Factor Theorem If $P(r) = 0$, then r is a zero and $(x - r)$ is a factor of the polynomial function $y = P(x)$. This theorem is used to confirm that a number is a zero of a function. (413)

factored form The form $y = a(x - r_1)(x - r_2) \cdots (x - r_n)$ of a polynomial function, where $a \neq 0$. The values $r_1, r_2, \ldots, r_n$ are the zeros of the function, and a is the vertical scale factor. (370)

factorial For any integer n greater than 1, n factorial, written $n!$, is the product of all the consecutive integers from n decreasing to 1. (697)

fair Describes a coin that is equally likely to land heads or tails. Can also apply to dice and other objects. (657)

family of functions A group of functions with the same parent function. (194)

feasible region The set of points that is the solution to a system of inequalities. (337)

Fibonacci sequence The sequence of numbers 1, 1, 2, 3, 5, 8, . . . , each of which is the sum of the two previous terms. (37, 59)

finite A limited quantity. (630)

finite differences method A method of finding the degree of a polynomial that will model a set of data, by analyzing differences between data values corresponding to equally spaced values of the independent variable. (361)

first quartile (Q_1) The median of the values less than the median of a data set. (79)

five-number summary The minimum, first quartile, median, third quartile, and maximum of a one-variable data set. (79)

focus (plural **foci**) A fixed point or points used to define a conic section. See **ellipse, hyperbola,** and **parabola.**

fractal The geometric result of infinitely many applications of a recursive procedure or calculation. (32, 397)

frequency (of a data set) The number of times a value appears in a data set, or the number of values that fall in a particular interval. (94)

frequency (of a sinusoid) The number of cycles of a periodic function that can be completed in one unit of time. (602)

function A relation for which every value of the independent variable has at most one value of the dependent variable. (178)

function notation A notation that emphasizes the dependent relationship between the variables used in a function. The notation $y = f(x)$ indicates that values of the dependent variable, y, are explicitly defined in terms of the independent variable, x, by the function f. (178)

G

general form (of a polynomial) The form of a polynomial in which the terms are ordered such that the degrees of the terms decrease from left to right. (360)

general form (of a quadratic function) The form $y = ax^2 + bx + c$, where $a \neq 0$. (368)

general quadratic equation An equation in the form $Ax^2 + Bxy + Cy^2 + Dx + Ey + F = 0$, where A, B, and C do not all equal zero. (525)

general term The nth term, u_n, of a sequence. (29)

geometric probability A probability that is found by calculating a ratio of geometric characteristics, such as lengths or areas. (661)

geometric random variable A random variable that represents the number of trials needed to get the first success in a series of independent trials. (688)

geometric sequence A sequence in which each term is equal to the product of the previous term and a common ratio. (33)

geometric series A sum of terms of a geometric sequence. (637)

golden ratio The ratio of two numbers (larger to smaller) whose ratio to each other equals the ratio of their sum to the larger number. Or, the positive number whose square equals the sum of itself and 1. The number $\frac{1+\sqrt{5}}{2}$, or approximately 1.618, often represented with the lowercase Greek letter phi, ϕ. (60, 389)

golden rectangle A rectangle in which the ratio of the length to the width is the golden ratio. (60, 389)

greatest integer function The function $f(x) = [x]$ that returns the largest integer that is less than or equal to a real number, x. (155, 185)

H

half-life The time needed for an amount of a substance to decrease by one-half. (238)

histogram A one-variable data display that uses bins to show the distribution of values in a data set. (94)

hole A missing point in the graph of a relation. (544)

hyperbola A locus of points in a plane for which the difference of the distances to two fixed points, called the foci, is constant. (514, 518)

hyperboloid A three-dimensional shape formed by rotating a hyperbola about the line through its foci or about the perpendicular bisector of the segment connecting the foci. (496)

hypothesis testing The process of creating a hypothesis about one or more population parameters, and either rejecting the hypothesis or letting it stand, based on probabilities. (755)

I

identity An equation that is true for all values of the variables for which the expressions are defined. (609)

identity matrix The square matrix, symbolized by $[I]$, that does not alter the entries of a square matrix $[A]$ under multiplication. Matrix $[I]$ must have the same dimensions as matrix $[A]$, and it has entries of 1's along the main diagonal (from top left to bottom right) and 0's in all other entries. (327, 328)

image A graph of a function or point(s) that is the result of a transformation of an original function or point(s). (188)

imaginary axis See **complex plane.**

imaginary number A number that is the square root of a negative number. An imaginary number can be written in the form bi, where b is a real number ($b \neq 0$) and i is the imaginary unit, $\sqrt{-1}$. (391)

imaginary unit The imaginary unit, i, is defined by $i^2 = -1$ or $i = \sqrt{-1}$. (391)

inconsistent (system) A system of equations that has no solution. (317)

independent (events) Events are independent when the occurrence of one has no influence on the occurrence of the other. (671)

independent (system) A system of equations that has exactly one solution. (317)

independent variable A variable whose values are not based on the values of another variable. (123)

inequality A statement that one quantity is less than, less than or equal to, greater than, greater than or equal to, or not equal to another quantity. (336)

inference The use of results from a sample to draw conclusions about a population. (755)

infinite A quantity that is unending, or without bound. (637)

infinite geometric series A sum of infinitely many terms of a geometric sequence. (637)

inflection point A point where a curve changes between curving downward and curving upward. (739)

intercept form The form $y = a + bx$ of a linear equation, where a is the y-intercept and b is the slope. (121)

interpolation Estimating a value that is within the range of all other values given in a data set. (131)

interquartile range (*IQR*) A measure of spread for a one-variable data set that is the difference between the third quartile and the first quartile. (82)

inverse The relationship that reverses the independent and dependent variables of a relation. (268)

inverse matrix The matrix, symbolized by $[A]^{-1}$, that produces an identity matrix when multiplied by [A]. (327, 328)

inverse variation A relation in which the product of the independent and dependent variables is constant. An inverse variation relationship can be written in the form $xy = k$, or $y = \frac{k}{x}$. (537)

L

Law of Cosines For any triangle with angles A, B, and C, and sides of lengths a, b, and c (a is opposite $\angle A$, b is opposite $\angle B$, and c is opposite $\angle C$), these equalities are true: $a^2 = b^2 + c^2 - 2bc\cos A$, $b^2 = a^2 + c^2 - 2ac\cos B$, and $c^2 = a^2 + b^2 - 2ab\cos C$. (477)

Law of Sines For any triangle with angles A, B, and C, and sides of lengths a, b, and c (a is opposite $\angle A$, b is opposite $\angle B$, and c is opposite $\angle C$), these equalities are true: $\frac{\sin A}{a} = \frac{\sin B}{b} = \frac{\sin C}{c}$. (470)

least squares line A line of fit for which the sum of the squares of the residuals is as small as possible. (772)

limit A long-run value that a sequence or function approaches. The quantity associated with the point of stability in dynamic systems. (47)

line of fit A line used to model a set of two-variable data. (128)

line of symmetry A line that divides a figure or graph into mirror-image halves. (194)

linear In the shape of a line or represented by a line, or an algebraic expression or equation of degree 1. (52)

linear equation An equation characterized by a constant rate of change. The graph of a linear equation in two variables is a straight line. (114)

linear programming A method of modeling and solving a problem involving constraints that are represented by linear inequalities. (344)

linearizing A method of finding an equation to fit data by graphing points in the form $(\log x, y)$, $(x, \log y)$, or $(\log x, \log y)$, and looking for a linear relationship. (781)

local maximum A value of a function or graph that is greater than other nearby values. (405)

local minimum A value of a function or graph that is less than other nearby values. (405)

locus A set of points that fit a given condition. (490)

logarithm A value of a logarithmic function, abbreviated log. For $a > 0$ and $b > 0$, $\log_b a = x$ means that $a = b^x$. (274)

logarithm change-of-base property For $a > 0$ and $b > 0$, $\log_a x$ can be rewritten as $\frac{\log_b x}{\log_b a}$. (275, 282)

logarithmic function The logarithmic function $y = \log_b x$ is the inverse of $y = b^x$, where $b > 0$ and $b \neq 1$. (274)

Glossary

logistic function A function used to model a population that grows and eventually levels off at the maximum capacity supported by the environment. A logistic function has a variable growth rate that changes based on the size of the population. (67)

lurking variable A variable that is not included in an analysis but which could explain a relationship between the other variables being analyzed. (767)

M

major axis The longer dimension of an ellipse. Or the line segment with endpoints on the ellipse that has this dimension. (500)

matrix A rectangular array of numbers or expressions, enclosed in brackets. (300)

matrix addition The process of adding two or more matrices. To add matrices, you add corresponding entries. (313)

matrix multiplication The process of multiplying two matrices. The entry c_{ij} in the matrix $[C]$ that is the product of two matrices, $[A]$ and $[B]$, is the sum of the products of corresponding entries in row i of matrix $[A]$ and column j of matrix $[B]$. (313)

maximum The greatest value in a data set or the greatest value of a function or graph. (79, 373, 377)

mean ($\bar{x}$ or μ) A measure of central tendency for a one-variable data set, found by dividing the sum of all values by the number of values. For a probability distribution, the mean is the sum of each value of x times its probability, and it represents the x-coordinate of the centroid or balance point of the region. (78, 727)

measure of central tendency A single number used to summarize a one-variable data set, commonly the mean, median, or mode. (78)

median A measure of central tendency for a one-variable data set that is the middle value, or the mean of the two middle values, when the values are listed in order. For a probability distribution, the median is the number d such that the line $x = d$ divides the area into two parts of equal area. (78, 727)

median-median line A line of fit found by dividing a data set into three groups, finding three points $(M_1, M_2, \text{and } M_3)$ based on the median x-value and the median y-value for each group, and writing the equation that best fits these three points. (135, 137)

minimum The least value in a data set or the least value of a function or graph. (79, 373, 377)

minor axis The shorter dimension of an ellipse. Or the line segment with endpoints on the ellipse that has this dimension. (500)

mode A measure of central tendency for a one-variable data set that is the value(s) that occur most often. For a probability distribution, the mode is the value(s) of x at which the graph reaches its maximum value. (78, 727)

model A mathematical representation (sequence, expression, equation, or graph,) that closely fits a set of data. (52)

monomial A polynomial with one term. (360)

multiplicative identity The number 1 is the multiplicative identity because any number multiplied by 1 remains unchanged. (327)

multiplicative inverse Two numbers are multiplicative inverses, or reciprocals, if they multiply to 1. (327)

mutually exclusive (events) Two outcomes or events are mutually exclusive when they cannot both occur simultaneously. (679)

N

natural logarithm A logarithm with base e, written $\ln x$, which is shorthand for $\log_e x$. (293)

negative exponents For $a > 0$, and all real values of n, the expression a^{-n} is equivalent to $\frac{1}{a^n}$ and $\left(\frac{a}{b}\right)^{-n} = \left(\frac{b}{a}\right)^n$. (246, 282)

nonrigid transformation A transformation that produces an image that is not congruent to the original figure. Stretches, shrinks, and dilations are nonrigid transformations (unless the scale factor is 1 or -1). (211)

normal curve The graph of a normal distribution. (735)

normal distribution A symmetric bell-shaped distribution. The equation for a normal distribution with mean μ and standard deviation σ is $y = \frac{1}{\sigma\sqrt{2\pi}}\left(\sqrt{e}\right)^{-((x-\mu)/\sigma)^2}$. (735, 737)

null hypothesis A statement that a given hypothesis is not true. (755)

O

oblique (triangle) A triangle that does not contain a right angle. (468)

odd function A function that is symmetric about the origin. For all values of x in the domain of an odd function, $f(-x) = -f(x)$. (235, 612)

one-to-one function A function whose inverse is also a function. (268)

outcome A possible result of one trial of an experiment. (659)

outlier A value that stands apart from the bulk of the data. (89, 91)

P

parabola A locus of points in a plane that are equidistant from a fixed point, called the focus, and a fixed line, called the directrix. (194, 508, 510)

paraboloid A three-dimensional shape formed by rotating a parabola about its line of symmetry. (507)

parameter (in parametric equations) See **parametric equations.**

parameter (statistical) A number, such as the mean or standard deviation, that describes an entire population. (724)

parametric equations A pair of equations used to separately describe the x- and y-coordinates of a point as functions of a third variable, called the parameter. (424)

parent function The most basic form of a function. A parent function can be transformed to create a family of functions. (194)

partial sum A sum of a finite number of terms of a series. (630)

Pascal's triangle A triangular arrangement of numbers containing the coefficients of binomial expansions. The first and last numbers in each row are 1's, and each other number is the sum of the two numbers above it. (710)

percentile rank The percentage of values in a data set that are below a given value. (97)

perfect square A number that is equal to the square of an integer, or a polynomial that is equal to the square of another polynomial. (378)

period The time it takes for one complete cycle of a cyclical motion to take place. Also, the minimum amount of change of the independent variable needed for a pattern in a periodic function to repeat. (213, 566)

periodic function A function whose graph repeats at regular intervals. (566)

permutation An arrangement of choices in which the order is important. (697, 698)

phase shift The horizontal translation of a periodic graph. (584)

point-ratio form The form $y = y_1 \cdot b^{x-x_1}$ of an exponential function equation, where the curve passes through the point (x_1, y_1) and has ratio b. (254)

point-slope form The form $y = y_1 + b(x - x_1)$ of a linear equation, where (x_1, y_1) is a point on the line and b is the slope. (129)

polar coordinates A method of representing points in a plane with ordered pairs in the form (r, θ), where r is the distance of the point from the origin and θ is the angle of rotation of the point from the positive x-axis. (622)

polynomial A sum of terms containing a variable raised to different powers, often written in the form $a_nx^n + a_{n-1}x^{n-1} + \cdots + a_1x^1 + a_0$, where x is a variable, the exponents are nonnegative integers, and the coefficients are real numbers. (360)

polynomial function A function in which a polynomial expression is set equal to a second variable, such as y or $f(x)$. (360)

population A complete set of people or things being studied. (713, 724)

Glossary

power function A function that has a variable as the base. The general form of a power function is $y = ax^n$, where a and n are constants. (247)

power of a power property For $a > 0$, and all real values of m and n, $\left(a^m\right)^n$ is equivalent to a^{mn}. (246, 282)

power of a product property For $a > 0, b > 0$, and all real values of m, $(ab)^m$ is equivalent to $a^m b^m$. (246, 282)

power of a quotient property For $a > 0, b > 0$, and all real values of n, $\left(\frac{a}{b}\right)^n$ is equivalent to $\frac{a^n}{b^n}$. (246, 282)

power property of equality For all real values of a, b, and n, if $a = b$, then $a^n = b^n$. (246)

power property of logarithms For $a > 0, x > 0$, and $n > 0$, $\log_a x^n$ can be rewritten $n \log_a x$. (282)

principal The initial monetary balance of a loan, debt, or account. (40)

principal value The one solution to an inverse trigonometric function that is within the range for which the function is defined. (597)

probability distribution A continuous curve that shows the values and the approximate frequencies of the values of a continuous random variable for an infinite set of measurements. (725)

product property of exponents For $a > 0$ and $b > 0$, and all real values of m and n, the product $a^m \cdot a^n$ is equivalent to a^{m+n}. (246, 282)

product property of logarithms For $a > 0$, $x > 0$, and $y > 0$, $\log_a xy$ is equivalent to $\log_a x + \log_a y$. (282)

projectile motion The motion of an object that rises or falls under the influence of gravity. (377)

Q

quadratic curves The graph of a two-variable equation of degree 2. Circles, parabolas, ellipses, and hyperbolas are quadratic curves. (525)

quadratic formula If a quadratic equation is written in the form $ax^2 + bx + c = 0$, the solutions of the equation are given by the quadratic formula, $x = \frac{-b \pm \sqrt{b^2 - 4ac}}{2a}$. (386)

quadratic function A polynomial function of degree 2. Quadratic functions are in the family with parent function $y = x^2$. (194, 368)

quotient property of exponents For $a > 0$ and $b > 0$, and all real values of m and n, the quotient $\frac{a^m}{a^n}$ is equivalent to a^{m-n}. (246, 282)

quotient property of logarithms For $a > 0$, $x > 0$, and $y > 0$, the expression $\log_a\left(\frac{x}{y}\right)$ can be rewritten as $\log_a x - \log_a y$. (282)

R

radian An angle measure in which one full rotation is 2π radians. One radian is the measure of an arc, or the measure of the central angle that intercepts that arc, such that the arc's length is the same as the circle's radius. (574)

radical A square root symbol. (205)

radius See **circle.**

raised to the power A term used to connect the base and the exponent in an exponential expression. For example, in the expression b^x, the base, b, is raised to the power x. (245)

random number A number that is as likely to occur as any other number within a given set. (658)

random process A process in which no individual outcome is predictable. (656)

random sample A sample in which not only is each person (or thing) equally likely, but all groups of persons (or things) are also equally likely. (78, 756)

random variable A variable that takes on numerical values governed by a chance experiment. (688)

range (of a data set) A measure of spread for a one-variable data set that is the difference between the maximum and the minimum. (79)

range (of a relation) The set of output values of a relation. (123)

rational Describes a number or an expression that can be expressed as a fraction or ratio. (252)

rational exponent An exponent that can be written as a fraction. The expression $a^{m/n}$ can be rewritten as $\left(\sqrt[n]{a}\right)^m$ or $\sqrt[n]{a^m}$, for $a > 0$. (253, 282)

rational function A function that can be written as a quotient, $f(x) = \frac{p(x)}{q(x)}$, where $p(x)$ and $q(x)$ are polynomial expressions and $q(x)$ is of degree 1 or higher. (537)

Rational Root Theorem If the polynomial equation $P(x) = 0$ has rational roots, they are of the form $\frac{p}{q}$, where p is a factor of the constant term and q is a factor of the leading coefficient. (414)

real axis See **complex plane.**

recursion Applying a procedure repeatedly, starting with a number or geometric figure, to produce a sequence of numbers or figures. Each term or stage builds on the previous term or stage. (28)

recursive formula A starting value and a recursive rule for generating a sequence. (29)

recursive rule Defines the nth term of a sequence in relation to the previous term(s). (29)

reduced row-echelon form A matrix form in which each row is reduced to a 1 along the diagonal, and a solution, and the rest of the matrix entries are 0's. (318)

reference angle The acute angle between the terminal side of an angle in standard position and the x-axis. (567)

reference triangle A right triangle that is drawn connecting the terminal side of an angle in standard position to the x-axis. A reference triangle can be used to determine the trigonometric ratios of an angle. (567)

reflection A transformation that flips a graph across a line, creating a mirror image. (202, 220)

regression analysis The process of finding a model with which to make predictions about one variable based on values of another variable. (772)

relation Any relationship between two variables. (178)

relative frequency histogram A histogram in which the height of each bin shows proportions (or relative frequencies) instead of frequencies. (725)

residual For a two-variable data set, the difference between the y-value of a data point and the y-value predicted by the equation of fit. (142)

response variable In statistics, the outcome (dependent) variable that is predicted by the explanatory variable. (765)

rigid transformation A transformation that produces an image that is congruent to the original figure. Translations, reflections, and rotations are rigid transformations. (211)

root mean square error (s) A measure of spread for a two-variable data set, similar to standard deviation for a one-variable data set. It is calculated by the formula $s = \sqrt{\frac{\sum_{i=1}^{n}(y_i - \hat{y})^2}{n-2}}$. (145)

roots The solutions of an equation in the form $f(x) = 0$. (370)

row reduction method A method that transforms an augmented matrix into a solution matrix in reduced row-echelon form. (318)

S

sample A part of a population selected to represent the entire population. Sampling is the process of selecting and studying a sample from a population in order to make conjectures about the whole population. (713, 724)

scalar A real number, as opposed to a matrix or vector. (308)

scalar multiplication The process of multiplying a matrix by a scalar. To multiply a scalar by a matrix, you multiply the scalar by each value in the matrix. (308)

scale factor A number that determines the amount by which a graph is stretched or shrunk, either horizontally or vertically. (211)

secant The reciprocal of the cosine ratio. If A is an acute angle in a right triangle, the secant of angle A is the ratio of the length of the hypotenuse to the length of the adjacent leg, or $\sec A = \frac{hyp}{adj}$. See **trigonometric function.** (609)

sequence An ordered list of numbers. (29)

series A sum of terms of a sequence. (630)

shape (of a data set) Describes how the data are distributed relative to the position of a measure of central tendency. (80)

shifted geometric sequence A geometric sequence that includes an added term in the recursive rule. (47)

shrink A transformation that compresses a graph either horizontally or vertically. (209, 213, 220)

simple event An event consisting of just one outcome. A simple event can be represented by a single branch of a tree diagram. (669)

simple random sample See **random sample.**

simulation A procedure that uses a chance model to imitate a real situation. (659)

sine If A is an acute angle in a right triangle, then the sine of angle A is the ratio of the length of the opposite leg to the length of the hypotenuse, or $\sin A = \frac{opp}{hyp}$. See **trigonometric function.** (440)

sine wave A graph of a sinusoidal function. See **sinusoid.** (583)

sinusoid A function or graph for which $y = \sin x$ or $y = \cos x$ is the parent function. (583)

skewed (data) Data that are spread out more on one side of the center than on the other side. (80)

slope The steepness of a line or the rate of change of a linear relationship. If (x_1, y_1) and (x_2, y_2) are two points on a line, then the slope of the line is $\frac{y_2 - y_1}{x_2 - x_1}$, where $x_2 \neq x_1$. (115, 121)

spread The variability in numerical data. (85)

square root function The function that undoes squaring, giving only the positive square root (that is, the positive number that, when multiplied by itself, gives the input). The square root function is written $y = \sqrt{x}$. (201)

standard deviation (s) A measure of spread for a one-variable data set that uses squaring to eliminate the effect of the different signs of the individual deviations. It is the square root of the variance, or $s = \sqrt{\frac{\sum_{i=1}^{n}(x_i - \bar{x})^2}{n-1}}$. (88)

standard form (of a conic section) The form of an equation for a conic section that shows the transformations of the parent equation. (498, 499, 510, 518)

standard form (of a linear equation) The form $ax + by = c$ of a linear equation. (191)

standard normal distribution A normal distribution with mean 0 and standard deviation 1. (736)

standard position An angle positioned with one side on the positive x-axis. (567)

standardizing the variable The process of converting data values (x-values) to their images (z-values) when a normal distribution is transformed into the standard normal distribution. (746)

statistic A numerical measure of a data set or sample. (77)

statistics A collection of numerical measures, or the mathematical study of data collection and analysis. (77)

stem-and-leaf-plot A one-variable data display in which the left digit(s) of the data values, called the stems, are listed in a column on the left side of the plot, while the remaining digits, called the leaves, are listed in order to the right of the corresponding stem. (104)

step function A function whose graph consists of a series of horizontal lines. (185)

stretch A transformation that expands a graph either horizontally or vertically. (209, 213, 220)

substitution A method of solving a system of equations that involves solving one of the equations for one variable and substituting the resulting expression into the other equation. (153)

symmetric (data) Data that are balanced, or nearly so, about the center. (80)

synthetic division An abbreviated form of dividing a polynomial by a linear factor. (415, 416)

system of equations A set of two or more equations with the same variables that are solved or studied simultaneously. (151)

T

tangent If A is an acute angle in a right triangle, then the tangent of angle A is the ratio of the length of the opposite leg to the length of the adjacent leg, or $\tan A = \frac{opp}{adj}$. See **trigonometric function.** (440)

term (algebraic) An algebraic expression that represents only multiplication and division between variables and constants. (360)

term (of a sequence) Each number in a sequence. (29)

terminal side The side of an angle in standard position that is not on the positive x-axis. (567)

theoretical probability A probability calculated by analyzing a situation, rather than by performing an experiment, given by the ratio of the number of different ways an event can occur to the total number of equally likely outcomes possible. (659)

third quartile (Q_3) The median of the values greater than the median of a data set. (79)

transcendental number An irrational number that, when represented as a decimal, has infinitely many digits with no pattern, such as π or e, and is not the solution of a polynomial equation with integer coefficients. (293)

transformation A change in the size or position of a figure or graph. (194, 220)

transition diagram A diagram that shows how something changes from one time to the next. (300)

transition matrix A matrix whose entries are transition probabilities. (300)

translation A transformation that slides a figure or graph to a new position. (186, 188, 220)

tree diagram A diagram whose branches show the possible outcomes of an event, and sometimes probabilities. (668)

trigonometric function A periodic function that uses one of the trigonometric ratios to assign values to angles with any measure. (583)

trigonometric ratios The ratios of lengths of sides in a right triangle. The three primary trigonometric ratios are sine, cosine, and tangent. (439)

trigonometry The study of the relationships between the lengths of sides and the measures of angles in triangles. (439)

trinomial A polynomial with three terms. (360)

unit circle A circle with radius of one unit. The equation of a unit circle with center $(0, 0)$ is $x^2 + y^2 = 1$. (217)

unit hyperbola The parent equation for a hyperbola, $x^2 - y^2 = 1$ or $y^2 - x^2 = 1$. (515)

variance (s^2) A measure of spread for a one-variable data set that uses squaring to eliminate the effect of the different signs of the individual deviations. It is the sum of the squares of the deviations divided by one less than the number of values, or $s^2 = \frac{\sum_{i=1}^{n}(x_i - \bar{x})^2}{n-1}$. (88)

vector A quantity with both magnitude and direction. (455)

velocity A measure of speed and direction. Velocity can be either positive or negative. (426)

Venn diagram A diagram of overlapping circles that shows the relationships among members of different sets. (395)

vertex (of a conic section) The point or points where a conic section intersects the axis of symmetry that contains the focus or foci. (194, 514)

vertex (of a feasible region) A corner of a feasible region in a linear programming problem. (337)

vertex form The form $y = a(x - h)^2 + k$ of a quadratic function, where $a \neq 0$. The point (h, k) is the vertex of the parabola, and a is the vertical scale factor. (368)

zero exponent For all values of a except 0, $a^0 = 1$. (246)

zero-product property If the product of two or more factors equals zero, then at least one of the factors must equal zero. A property used to find the zeros of a function without graphing. (369)

zeros (of a function) The values of the independent variable (x-values) that make the corresponding values of the function ($f(x)$-values) equal to zero. Real zeros correspond to x-intercepts of the graph of a function. See **roots.** (369)

z-value The number of standard deviations that a given x-value lies from the mean in a normal distribution. (746)

Index

A

Index

B

C

D

E

F

G

H

Index

Index

M

N

O

P

Q

R

S

Index

Photo Credits

Abbreviations: top (*t*), middle (*m*), bottom (*b*), left (*l*), right (*r*)

Cover

Background and center image: NASA; all other images: Ken Karp Photography

Front Matter

v (*t*): Ken Karp Photography; **vi (*t*):** Ken Karp Photography; **vi (*b*):** Ken Karp Photography; **vii (*b*):** Ken Karp Photography; **ix (*t*):** Ken Karp Photography; **x (*t*):** Ken Karp Photography; **xi (*t*):** Ken Karp Photography; **xii:** Ken Karp Photography;

Chapter 0

1: Photograph by David Heald © The Solomon R. Guggenheim Foundation, New York; **3:** Michael Nicholson/Corbis; **4:** AP-Wide World Photos; **6:** Christie's Images; **7 (*t*):** Getty Images; **7 (*bm*):** Bodleian Library, Oxford, U.K. Copyright (MS Hunt. 214 Title Page); **11:** Christie's Images; **12:** Cheryl Fenton; **15:** Scala/Art Resource, NY; **16 (*t*):** Ken Karp Photography; **16 (*b*):** U.S. Genomics; **18:** Daniel Castor; **19:** Corbis; **20 (*b*):** © The New Yorker Cartoon Collection 2001 Jack Ziegler from *cartoonbank.com.* All Rights Reserved; **20 (*l*):** AFP/Corbis; **20 (*r*):** Reuters NewMedia/Corbis; **21:** Cheryl Fenton; **24:** NASA

Chapter 1

27: *Residual Light* by Anthony Discenza. Photos courtesy of the artist; **28 (*l*):** Sandro Vannini/Corbis; **28 (*r*):** Tom & Dee Ann McCarthy/Corbis; **30:** Owaki-Kulla/Corbis; **33:** Archive Photos/PictureQuest; **35:** Gary D. Landsman/Corbis; **36:** Ken Karp Photography; **37:** The Image Bank/Getty Images; **38:** Bohemia Nomad Picturemakers/Corbis; **39:** Ken Karp Photography; **39:** RF; **41:** Tom Collicott/Masterfile; **42:** Richard T. Nowitz/Science Source/Photo Researchers, Inc.; **43:** Bettmann/Corbis; **44:** Bob Krist/Corbis; **45 (*l*):** Duomo/Corbis; **45 (*r*):** Tom & Pat Leeson/DRK Photo; **46:** Ken Karp Photography; **47:** The Cleveland Memory Project; **48:** Tony Freeman/PhotoEdit/PictureQuest; **49:** RF; **50:** Cheryl Fenton; **52 (*t*):** Cheryl Fenton; **52 (*b*):** NOAA; **53:** Ken Smith/Scripps/DRK Photo; **57 (*t*):** Getty Images; **57 (*b*):** Paul Skelcher/Rainbow; **58:** Archivo Iconografico, S. A./Corbis; **59:** Lester Lefkowitz/Corbis; **63:** John Henley/Corbis; **64:** Stuart Westmorland/ Index Stock Imagery/PictureQuest; **65:** Ken Edward/Photo Researchers, Inc.; **67:** Lester Lefkowitz/Corbis; **70:** M. Harvey/DRK Photo; **72:** Galen Rowell/Corbis; **73:** Martha Bates/Stock Boston Inc./PictureQuest

Chapter 2

76: © 2003 Monika Sprüth Gallery/Artists Rights Society (ARS), New York/VG Bild-Kunst, Bonn; Courtesy of Monika Sprüth/ Philomene Magers, Cologne/Munich/Art Resource, NY; **77:** Laima Druskis/Stock, Boston Inc./PictureQuest; **80:** Ken Karp Photography; **81:** Ken Karp Photography; **82:** Getty Images; **83:** Corbis; **85 (*t*):** AP-Wide World Photos; **85 (*b*):** Ken Karp Photography; **86:** Ken Karp Photography; **87:** Photos courtesy of Lorraine Serena/Women Beyond Borders; **89:** NASA; **91:** Bohemian Nomad Picturemakers/ Corbis; **96:** Lester Lefkowitz/Corbis; **97 (*l*):** Gianni Dagli Orti/ Corbis; **97 (*r*):** Werner Forman Archive/Museum fur Volkerkunde, Berlin/Art Resource, NY; **98:** Chase Swift/Corbis; **101:** Ken Karp Photography; **102:** RF; **103:** Phillip James Corwin/Corbis; **105:** Bettmann/Corbis; **109 (*t*):** Reuters NewMedia Inc./Corbis; **109 (*b*):** NASA/NOAA; **110:** Getty Images

Chapter 3

113: Zaha Hadid Architects; **114:** Pablo Corral/Corbis; **115:** RF; **118:** Alan Schein Photography/Corbis; **119:** Dan Ackroyd & Heather Harvey; **121:** Gale Beery/Index Stock/PictureQuest; **122:** Ken Karp Photography; **125:** Deborah Davis/PhotoEdit/PictureQuest; **126:** Andre Jenny/Focus Group/PictureQuest; **129:** David Muench/Corbis; **130:** NASA; **131:** Chuck Savage/Corbis; **133:** Ken Karp Photography; **134:** Chuck Fishman/Contact Press Images/ PictureQuest; **137:** *Tourists on the Moon #2* by Yoshio Itagaki, 1998/Courtesy of the artist and Cristinerose Gallery, New York; **140:** Tim Wright/Corbis; **141:** Michael A. Dwyer/Stock Boston Inc./PictureQuest; **143:** Courtesy of the artist and The Project, NY; **145:** RF; **147:** Cheryl Fenton; **148:** Reuters NewMedia Inc./Corbis; **151:** *Green Mass,* I. Pereira, Gift of Leslie Bokor and Leslie Dame, Photograph © 2002 Board of Trustees, National Gallery of Art, Washington, 1950, oil on canvas; **155 (*t*):** AP-Wide World Photos; **155 (*bl*):** E. R. Degginger/Bruce Coleman Inc.; **155 (*br*):** E. R. Degginger/Bruce Coleman Inc.; **157:** Courtesy of the National Museum of the American Indian, Smithsonian Institution. Photo by R. A. Whiteside; **161 (*t*):** Ken Karp Photography; **161 (*b*):** E. R. Degginger/Bruce Coleman Inc.; **162 (*m*):** Burstein Collection/ Corbis; **162 (*mr*):** Dominique Berretty/Black Star Publishing/ PictureQuest; **166:** Jose Fuste Raga/Corbis

Chapter 4

171: Courtesy of the artist and Artemis Greenberg Van Doren Gallery, New York; **172:** Lorna Simpson, *Wigs (portfolio),* 1994, waterless lithograph on felt, 72″ × 162″ overall installed/Collection Walker Art Center, Minneapolis/T. B. Walker Acquisition Fund, 1995; **173:** DiMaggio/Kalish/Corbis; **174:** PEANUTS reprinted by permission of United Feature Syndicate, Inc.; **175:** Ellsworth Kelly, *Blue Green Curve,* 1972, Oil on canvas, 87-3/4 × 144-1/4 in. The Museum of Contemporary Art, Los Angeles, The Barry Lowen Collection; **177:** Douglas Kirkland/Corbis; **179:** Archivo Iconografico, S. A./ Corbis; **180:** Getty Images; **182:** David Bentley/Corbis; **183:** Robert Holmes/Corbis; **184:** Chris Chen/2c Management; **186 (*l*):** SIMPARCH, *Free Basin,* birch wood, metal supports, courtesy of SIMPARCH, installation view at the Wexner Center for the Arts, photo by Dick Loesch; **186 (*r*):** SIMPARCH, *Free Basin,* birch wood, metal supports, courtesy of SIMPARCH, installation view at the Wexner Center for the Arts, photo by Roman Sapecki; **187:** Ken Karp Photography; **188 (*m*):** Cheryl Fenton; **188 (*b*):** Danny Lehman/Corbis; **190:** Cheryl Fenton; **191:** © 2002 Eun-Ha Paek, stills from *L'Faux Episode 7* on *MilkyElephant.com;* **193 (*l*):** AP-Wide World Photos; **193 (*r*):** © Minnesota Historical Society/Corbis; **194 (*l*):** *Bessie's Blues* by Faith Ringgold © 1997, acrylic on canvas, 76″ × 79″, photo courtesy of the artist; **194 (*r*):** Phil Schermeister/Corbis; **196:** Getty Images; **197:** Bo Zaunders/Corbis; **199:** Robert Ginn/Index Stock Imagery/PictureQuest; **200:** © 1998 Jerry Lodriguss; **201:** Ken Karp Photography; **202:** James L. Amos/ Corbis; **203:** James A. Sugar/Corbis; **206:** Tony Freeman/PhotoEdit/ PictureQuest; **209:** Ken Karp Photography; **211:** Robert Lazzarini *payphone, 2002,* mixed media, 108 × 84.48 in. (274.3 × 213.4 × 121.9 cm) as installed in 2002 Biennial Exhibition, Whitney Museum of Art, New York (March 7–May 26, 2002); **212:** Archivo Iconografico, S. A. /Corbis; **216:** Bettmann/Corbis; **217:** Tom Nebbia/Corbis; **219:** Lester Lefkowitz/Corbis; **225:** AFP/Corbis; **227:** Ken Karp Photography; **235:** *Sense* oil on birch panel © 2002 Laura Domela, photo courtesy of the artist

Chapter 5

237: *Tree Mountain—A Living Time Capsule*—11,000 Trees, 11,000 People, 400 Years 1992–1996, Ylojarvi, Finland, (420 meters long × 270 meters wide × 28 meters high) © Agnes Denes. Photo courtesy of Agnes Denes; **238:** Roger Ressmeyer/Corbis; **241:** Buddy Mays/ Corbis; **243:** Clementine Gallery/Courtesy Heidi Steiger Collection; **244:** Bettmann/Corbis; **249:** Eric Kamischke; **252:** Paul Almasy/ Corbis; **254:** Franz-Marc Frei/Corbis; **255:** Reuters NewMedia Inc./ Corbis; **256:** Neal Preston/Corbis; **258 (*t*):** JPL/NASA; **258 (*b*):** Geoff Tompkinson/Photo Researchers, Inc.; **259:** Ruet Stephane/Corbis

Sygma; **260:** © 2002 Eames Office (*www.eamesoffice.com*); **263:** Ken Karp Photography; **264:** NASA; **269:** Alice Arnold/Retna Ltd.; **271:** Getty Images; **273:** Cheryl Fenton; **274:** Dr. Oyvind Hammer; **275:** Getty Images; **277 (*t*):** Tom Bean/Corbis; **277 (*b*):** Corbis; **278:** Getty Images; **279:** Bettmann/Corbis; **280:** Cheryl Fenton; **284:** Reuters NewMedia Inc./Corbis; **285:** Getty Images; **286:** Cheryl Fenton; **287:** Tom Stewart/Corbis; **289:** Ken Karp Photography; **290:** Bettmann/Corbis; **291:** Stock Portfolio-Stock Connection/ PictureQuest; **292:** Brownie Harris/Corbis; **294 (*m*):** Holt Confer/ Grant Heilman Photography; **294 (*mr*):** Grant Heilman Photography; **297:** H. Turvey/Photo Researchers, Inc.

Chapter 6

299: *Fragile* by Amy Stacey Curtis. Photos of *Fragile* © 2000 by Amy Stacey Curtis/*www.amystaceycurtis.com;* **300:** David Stoecklein/ Corbis; **301:** Ken Karp Photography; **303:** Karl Weatherly/Corbis; **304:** Corbis; **310:** Ken Karp Photography; **311:** Copyright Robert Silvers 2001 Photomosaics™. Photomosaics™ is the trademark of Runaway Technology, Inc. *www.photomosaic.com* U.S. Patent No. 6,137,498; **314:** Albright-Knox Art Gallery/Corbis; **315:** RF; **316 (*t*):** Blaine Harrington III/Corbis; **316 (*m*):** Thierry Cariou/Corbis; **318:** © Tate Gallery, London/Art Resource, NY © 2003 C. Herscovici, Brussels/Artists Rights Society (ARS), New York; **325 (*t*):** AP-Wide World Photos; **325 (*b*):** Mark Sadan; **332:** Lester Lefkowitz/Corbis; **334:** © The Nobel Foundation; **338:** Tom Stewart/Corbis; **340:** © Christie's Images/Corbis; **341 (*t*):** Melanie Einzig; **341 (*b*):** NASA; **342:** Graig Orsini/Index Stock Imagery/PictureQuest; **343:** Bettmann/Corbis; **344:** CNAC/ MNAM/Dist. Reunion des Musees Nationaux/Art Resource, NY, © 2003 Artists Rights Society (ARS), New York/ADAGP, Paris; **349 (*t*):** RF; **349 (*b*):** George D. Lepp/Corbis; **352:** © Christie's Images/Corbis; **353:** Anna Clopet/Corbis; **354:** Lowell Georgia/Corbis; **355 (*t*):** Masaaahiro Sano/Corbis; **355 (*b*):** Hulton-Deutsch Collection/ Corbis; **356:** Corbis

Chapter 7

359: *Things Fall Apart: 2001,* mixed media installation with vehicle; variable dimensions/San Francisco Museum of Modern Art, Accessions Committee Fund purchase © Sarah Sze; **361:** Getty Images; **363:** Ken Karp Photography; **364 (*l*):** Science Museum/ Science & Society Picture Library; **364 (*r*):** Science Museum/ Science & Society Picture Library; **366:** Ken Karp Photography; **367 (*m*):** Kevin Fleming/Corbis; **367 (*b*):** Ken Karp Photography; **368:** Mike Souther-Eye Ubiquitous/Corbis; **371 (*t*):** Elizabeth Catlett (American, b 1915), *Singing Their Songs,* 1992, Lithograph on paper (a.p.#6) 15-3/4 × 13-3/4 in. / National Museum of Women in the Arts, purchased with funds donated in memory of Florence Davis by her family, friends, and the NMWA Women's Committee; **371 (*b*):** Ken Karp Photography; **373:** Ken Karp Photography; **375 (*t*):** Michael Boys/Corbis; **375 (*m*):** Josiah Davidson/ PictureQuest; **377:** Scott T. Smith/Corbis; **378:** Ken Karp Photography; **380:** Christie's Images/Corbis; **381:** Wally McNamee/Corbis; **382:** Vadim Makarov; **383 (*m*):** Ken Karp Photography; **383 (*bl*):** The Granger Collection, New York City; **383 (*br*):** Bettmann/Corbis; **384 (*bl*):** A. H. Rider/Photo Researchers, Inc.; **384 (*br*):** Nigel J. Dennis/Photo Researchers, Inc.; **389:** © Jonathan Ferguson/Sunforge Studios; **391:** Bettmann/Corbis; **393:** Christie's Images/SuperStock; **396:** Digital Image © The Museum of Modern Art/Licensed by Scala/Art Resource, NY; **397 (*t*):** Mehau Kulyk/Photo Researchers, Inc.; **397 (*m*):** Hank Morgan/Photo Researchers, Inc.; **399:** Cornelia Parker *Mass (Colder Darker Matter),* 1997, charcoal, wire and black string, Collection of Phoenix Art Museum, Gift of Jan and Howard Hendler 2002.1; **400:** Ken Karp Photography; **403:** Children Beyond Borders/VSA Arts (*www.vsarts.org*); **405:** Karim Rashid Inc.; **408:** Courtesy of 303 Gallery, New York-Victoria Miro Gallery, London; **409:** Courtesy of the artist and Clifford-Smith Gallery, Boston. Photo courtesy of the artist; **411:** W. Perry Conway/Corbis; **412:** Mark Burnett/Photo Researchers; **421:** Owen Franken/Corbis

Chapter 8

423: Corey Rich/Coreyography LLC; **428:** Michael Prince/Corbis; **430 (*t*):** Stefano Bianchetti/Corbis; **430 (*b*):** David Lawrence/Corbis; **431:** Timothy Rodwell; **434:** Bettmann/Corbis; **436:** The Brett Weston Archive/Corbis; **437:** Nathan Benn/Corbis; **438:** Streano Havens-Stock Connection/PictureQuest; **443:** Roger Ressmeyer/Corbis; **448 (*t*):** Scala/Art Resource, NY; **448 (*b*):** Ken Karp Photography; **450:** Getty Images; **452:** Bettmann/Corbis; **454:** Keren Su/Corbis; **457:** Todd Gipstein/Corbis; **458:** Jose Luis Pelaez, Inc./Corbis; **460:** Ken Karp Photography; **463:** Ken Karp Photography; **464:** William James Warren/Corbis; **465 (*t*):** Getty Images; **465 (*b*):** Underwood & Underwood/Corbis; **466 (*t*):** Duomo/Corbis; **466 (*b*):** RF; **469:** James L. Amos/Corbis; **473:** Chabot Observatory; **474:** George Robinson-Stock Connection/PictureQuest; **476:** Jay Syverson/Corbis; **478:** Ken Karp Photography; **480:** Getty Images; **481 (*t*):** Bettmann/Corbis; **481 (*b*):** Johnny Crawford/The Image Works; **482:** © The New Yorker Collection from CartoonBank.com/Corbis; **484:** Digital Image © The Museum of Modern Art/Licensed by Scala/Art Resource, NY; **485:** Seguin Franck/Corbis Sygma

Chapter 9

487: Marion Brenner/Maya Lin Studio; **488:** Corbis; **491:** George Hall/Corbis; **492:** Curtis O'Shock/ImageState; **493:** RF; **494:** Scott Snibbe; **495:** Geoffrey Clements/Corbis; **496 (*tl*):** Reunion des Musees Nationaux/Art Resource, NY; © L&M Services B. V. Amsterdam 20030605; **496 (*tr*):** Archivo Iconografico, S. A./Corbis; **496 (*bl*):** Lee Snbider/Corbis; **496 (*br*):** St. Louis Science Center; **499 (*t*):** The Museum of Modern Art, Licensed by SCALA/Art Resource, NY; **499 (*b*):** Ken Karp Photography; **502:** Ken Karp Photography; **503:** Alan Schein Photography/Corbis; **505 (*t*):** Museum of Science and Industry, Chicago, Illinois; **505 (*b*):** Ed Eckstein/Corbis; **507 (*t*):** Paul Almasy/Corbis; **507 (*b*):** Michael Gadomski/Photo Researchers; **509:** Robert Landau/Corbis; **512:** Lee Foster/Bruce Coleman Inc.; **513:** RF; **514:** Fermi National Accelerator Laboratory; **518:** Ken Karp Photography; **521:** W. Cody/Corbis; **525:** Frank Zullo/Photo Researchers, Inc.; **526 (*t*):** Fermi National Accelerator Laboratory; **526 (*b*):** Fermi National Accelerator Laboratory; **528:** Christie's Images/Corbis; **533:** U.S. Coast Guard; **536:** Mary Sullivan; **537:** Ken Karp Photography; **542:** Cheryl Fenton; **549:** Robert Essel NYC/Corbis; **551:** Alinari/Art Resource, NY © 2003 Artists Rights Society (ARS) New York/Pro Litteris, Zurich; **556:** Cheryl Fenton; **560:** Julian Calder/Corbis

Chapter 10

564: Courtesy George Eastman House; **565:** Artwork photo by James Hart, Courtesy of Charlotte Jackson Fine Art, Santa Fe, NM, installation photo by Jorg Jakoby; **571:** Courtesy National Solar Observatory/Sacramento Peak; **572:** Lester Lefkowitz/Corbis; **573:** Courtesy of the artist and Hooks-Epstein Gallery, Houston, TX; **577:** RF; **579:** Bettmann/Corbis; **581:** RF; **582:** FOXTROT © Bill Amend. Reprinted with permission of UNIVERSAL PRESS SYNDICATE. All rights reserved; **583:** Corbis; **585:** Ken Karp Photography; **586 (*t*):** Burstein Collection/Corbis; **586 (*b*):** RF; **590:** Historical Picture Archive/Corbis; **592:** National Geographic/ Getty Images; **593:** Phil Degginger/Bruce Coleman Inc.; **599:** Ken Karp Photography; **601 (*l*):** Michael Busselle/Corbis; **601 (*r*):** NOAA/ Center for Operational Oceanographic Products and Services; **603:** Getty Images; **605:** Michael S. Yamashita/Corbis; **606:** Bettmann/ Corbis; **607:** Cedar Point Park; **613:** Scott Walking Adventures; **615:** Reuters NewMedia Inc./Corbis; **626:** Collection of the Artist, Courtesy of the Oakland Museum of California, photo by Michael Temperio

Chapter 11

629: Courtesy of the artist and Lehmann Maupin Gallery, New York; **630:** Binod Joshi/AP-Wide World Photos; **634:** Bettmann/Corbis; **635 (*t*):** Cheryl Fenton; **635 (*b*):** Joseph Sohm-Visions of America/ Corbis; **636:** Mark Langford-Index Stock Imagery/PictureQuest;

637: Ken Karp Photography; **639:** RF; **641:** Lester Lefkowitz/Corbis; **642 (*t*):** George D. Lepp/Corbis; **644:** Ken Karp Photography; **647:** Ali Meyer/Corbis; **648:** Ken Karp Photography; **651:** © Burstein Collection/Corbis/© Artists Rights Society (ARS) New York/ ADAGP, Paris; **652:** Lewis Kemper-Index Stock Imagery/PictureQuest

Chapter 12

655: Smithsonian American Art Museum, Washinton, D.C./Art Resource, NY: **656:** Mary Messenger-Stock Boston Inc./PictureQuest; **657 (*l*):** Roger Wood/Corbis; **657 (*r*):** National Museum of India, New Delhi/The Bridgeman Art Library; **661 (*t*):** RF; **662:** Royal Asiatic Society, London, UK/The Bridgeman Art Library; **673:** Ken Karp Photography; **675:** Ted Horowitz/Corbis; **676:** Bettmann/Corbis; **679:** Albright-Knox Art Gallery/Corbis; **680:** Tony Savino/The Image Works; **683:** Ken Karp Photography; **685:** RF; **687:** Francois Gohier/Photo Researchers, Inc.; **690:** Robert Young Pelton/Corbis; **691:** Mark C. Burnett-Stock Boston Inc./PictureQuest; **692:** Getty Images; **694 (*t*):** Cheryl Fenton; **694 (*b*):** Ken Karp Photography; **696:** Chris Rogers-Index Stock Imagery/PictureQuest; **697:** RF; **700:** Najlah Feanny/Corbis Saba; **701:** V & L/Photo Researchers, Inc.; **703:** Ken Karp Photography; **708:** RF; **709:** Academy of Natural Sciences of Philadelphia/Corbis; **712:** S. Charles Brown-Frank Lane Picture Agency/Corbis; **713:** Bob Daemmrich-Stock Boston Inc./ PictureQuest; **717:** Wolfgang Kaehler/Corbis; **720:** Pablo Corral/Corbis

Chapter 13

723: Naoki Okamoto/SuperStock; **724 (*t*):** Ken Karp Photography; **724 (*b*):** © Paul Ramirez Jonas, courtesy of the LFL Gallery, New York; **731 (*tl*):** Bettmann/Corbis; **731 (*tr*):** Jacques M. Chenet/Corbis; **731 (*b*):** Ken Karp Photography; **734:** Exhibit and photography by Shab Levy; **739:** Hulton-Deutsch Collection/Corbis; **740 (*bl*):** Cheryl Fenton; **740 (*br*):** Bettmann/Corbis; **742:** AP-Wide World Photos; **745 (*m*):** SuperStock; **745 (*b*):** Ken Karp Photography; **747:** Cheryl Fenton; **749:** P. Lahalle/Corbis; **750:** Phillip James Corwin/Corbis; **751:** Roger Ball/Corbis; **752:** Jane Sapinsky/Corbis; **754:** David Young-Wolff/PhotoEdit/PictureQuest; **755:** Dr. Yorgos Nikas/Photo Researchers, Inc.; **758:** Rob Rowan-Progressive Image/Corbis; **762:** Peter Steiner/Corbis; **763:** Jose Carrillo-Stock Boston Inc./ PictureQuest; **769:** Galen Rowell/Corbis; **770:** © Charles Matton, courtesy of Forum Gallery, New York; **772:** Bettmann/Corbis; **776:** NASA; **778:** Michael S. Yamashita/Corbis; **784:** Ken Karp Photography; **785:** RF; **786 (*bl*):** Bettmann/Corbis; **786 (*br*):** AFP/ Corbis; **787 (*mt*):** AP-Wide World Photos; **787 (*mb*):** Reuters NewMedia Inc./Corbis; **789:** Eric Perlman/Corbis; **791:** Getty Images; **792:** Jonathan T. Wright/Bruce Coleman Inc.; **793:** Corbis

Additional Answers

LESSON 0.1, PAGES 3, 5, 6

Investigation

A symbolic approach might work backward from the destination. The last part of the camel's trip will start at point B with maximum bananas he can carry, 1000.

3000 bananas	2000 bananas	1000 bananas	
0 miles z	A y	B x	1000 miles

The camel will travel x miles and end with $1000 - x$ bananas. To get 1000 bananas to point B, the camel will start with 2000 bananas at point A, make a round trip and a one-way trip of y miles each way ($3y$ miles), and end with $2000 - 3y$ bananas. $2000 - 3y = 1000$, so $y = 333\frac{1}{3}$ mi. To get 2000 bananas to point A, the camel start with 3000 bananas, make two round trips and a one-way trip of z miles each way, and end up with $3000 - 5z$ bananas. $3000 - 5z = 2000$, so $z = 200$. Total trip is $200 + 333\frac{1}{3} + x = 1000$ mi, so $x = 466\frac{2}{3}$ mi. He ends with $1000 - 467 = 533$ bananas, using drops at 200 miles and $533\frac{1}{3}$ miles from the beginning.

Exercises

7a.

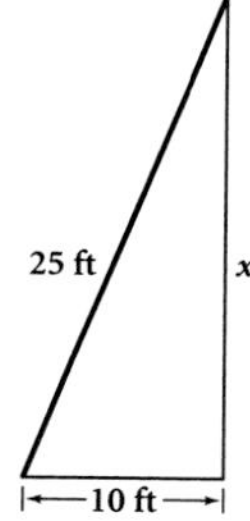

7b.

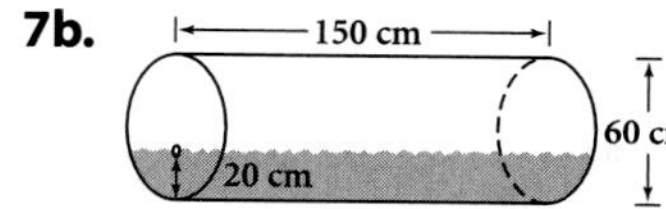

7c.

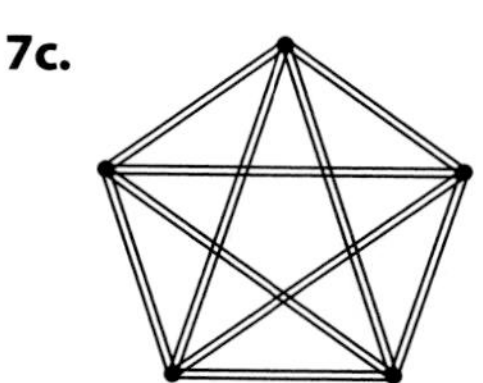

9a. Sample answer: Fill the 7-liter bucket; pour the contents into the 10-liter bucket; fill the 7-liter bucket again; pour 3 liters from the 7-liter bucket into the 10-liter bucket, completely filling the 10-liter bucket and leaving 4 liters in the 7-liter bucket; empty the 10-liter bucket; pour the 4 liters from the 7-liter bucket into the 10-liter bucket.

9b. Sample answer: Fill the 10-liter bucket; pour the contents into the 7-liter bucket, completely filling the 7-liter bucket and leaving 3 liters in the 10-liter bucket; empty the 7-liter bucket; pour the 3 liters from the 10-liter bucket into the 7-liter bucket. Fill the 10-liter bucket; pour 4 liters into the 7-liter bucket, completely filling the 7-liter bucket and leaving 6 liters in the 10-liter bucket; empty the 7-liter bucket. Pour the 6 liters from the 10-liter bucket into the 7-liter bucket. Fill the 10-liter bucket; pour 1 liter into the 7-liter bucket, completely filling the 7-liter bucket and leaving 9 liters in the 10-liter bucket. Empty the 7-liter bucket; pour 7 liters from the 10-liter bucket into the 7-liter bucket, completely filling the 7-liter bucket and leaving 2 liters in the 10-liter bucket.

10. (x by x) + (x by 2) + (3 by x) + (3 by 2)

The outer rectangle has length $(x + 2)$ and width $(x + 3)$, so the area is length times width, or $(x + 2)(x + 3)$. The areas of the inner rectangles are x^2, $2x$, $3x$, and 6. The sum of the areas of the inner rectangles is equal to the area of the whole outer rectangle, so $(x + 2)(x + 3) = x^2 + 2x + 3x + 6$.

11a. $x^2 + 4x + 7x + 28$

	x	4
x	x^2	$4x$
7	$7x$	28

11b. $x^2 + 5x + 5x + 25$

	x	5
x	x^2	$5x$
5	$5x$	25

11c. $xy + 2y + 6x + 12$

	x	2
y	xy	$2y$
6	$6x$	12

11d. $x^2 + 3x - x - 3$

	x	-1
x	x^2	$-1x$
3	$3x$	-3

12. Take the goat across and come back. Next, take the wolf across and bring the goat back. Next, take the cabbage across and come back. Last, take the goat across.

13a. $n + 3$, where n represents the number

13b. $v = m + 24.3$, where v represents Venus's distance from the Sun in millions of miles and m represents Mercury's distance from the Sun in millions of miles.

13c. $s = 2e$, where s represents the number of CDs owned by Seth and e represents the number of CDs owned by Erin.

LESSON 0.2, PAGES 10, 12

Problem 1

Step 1 Let A represent the number of adult chaperones. Let B represent the original number of boys. Let G represent the original number of girls.

Step 2

$$\begin{cases} \dfrac{A}{B+G} = \dfrac{1}{4} & \text{When Adam and Megan arrive.} \\ \dfrac{B+30}{G} = \dfrac{2}{1} & \text{When 30 more boys arrive.} \\ \dfrac{B+30}{G+30} = \dfrac{3}{4} & \text{When 30 more girls arrive.} \end{cases}$$

Step 3 $\dfrac{B+30}{G} = \dfrac{2}{1}$ $\qquad$ $\dfrac{B+30}{G+30} = \dfrac{3}{4}$

$B + 30 = 2G$ $\qquad$ $B + 30 = \frac{3}{4}(G + 30)$

$$2G = \frac{3}{4}(G + 30)$$

$$G = 18$$

$$B + 30 = 2G$$

$$B = 6$$

$$\frac{A}{B+G} = \frac{1}{4}$$

$$A = 6$$

Problem 2

Step 1 Let x represent the amount of money given to Abdul. Let $(8 - x)$ represent the amount of money given to Billy.

Step 2 A total of 80 pounds of tomatoes was used, so each person took home the equivalent of $\frac{80}{3}$, or $26\frac{2}{3}$, pounds. Because Abdul started with 50 pounds of tomatoes and took home only $26\frac{2}{3}$, he gave $50 - 26\frac{2}{3}$, or $23\frac{1}{3}$, pounds to Celia. Billy started with 30 pounds, so he gave Celia $30 - 26\frac{2}{3}$, or $3\frac{1}{3}$, pounds. The money should be divided such that the ratio of Abdul's money to Billy's money is proportional to the amount of tomatoes given to Celia.

$$\frac{x}{8-x} = \frac{23\frac{1}{3}}{3\frac{1}{3}}$$

Step 3 $\dfrac{x}{8-x} = \dfrac{23\frac{1}{3}}{3\frac{1}{3}}$

$$\frac{x}{8-x} = 7$$

$x = 7, \quad 8 - x = 1$

Problem 3

Step 1 Let a represent the average amount of cake for an adult. Let c represent the average amount of cake for a child.

Step 2 From the caterer's claim, you can write $20c = 15a$. The current party is represented by the expression $12c + 7a$, and this must be less than or equal to $20c$ or $15a$.

Step 3 $20c = 15a$

$c = 0.75a$

$12c + 7a = 12(0.75a) + 7a = 16a$

Exercises

10a. Let g represent the number of Georgian great-grandchildren, let f represent the number of Floridian great-grandchildren, let h represent the amount that each Georgian got from the will, let c represent the amount that each Floridian got from the will, and let d represent the amount that each great-grandchild eventually ended up with.

10b. $g + f = 36$, $h = c + 700$, $gh + fc = 206100$, $d = h - 175$, $36d = 206100$

10c. $g = 27, f = 9, h = 5900, c = 5200, d = 5725$

10d. There are 27 Georgian great-grandchildren and 9 Floridian great-grandchildren. According to the will, each great-grandchild living in Georgia received $5900 and each great-grandchild living in Florida received $5200. After the great-grandchildren evened it out, each received $5725.

11a. Draw a 45° angle, then subtract a 30° angle; $45° - 30° = 15°$

11b. Draw a 45° angle, then add a 30° angle; $45° + 30° = 75°$

11c. Draw a 45° angle, then add a 60° angle; $45° + 60° = 105°$

LESSON 0.3, PAGE 21

13a. $x^2 + 1x + 5x + 5$

	x	1
x	x^2	$1x$
5	$5x$	5

13b. $x^2 + 3x + 3x + 9$

	x	3
x	x^2	$3x$
3	$3x$	9

13c. $x^2 + 3x - 3x - 9$

	x	-3
x	x^2	$-3x$
3	$3x$	-9

14a.

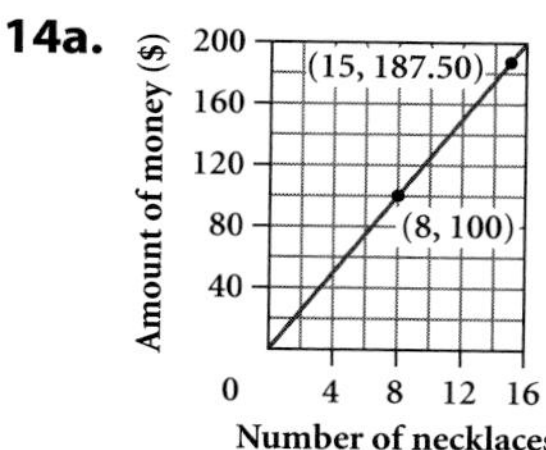

CHAPTER 0 REVIEW, PAGES 22, 24, 25

1. Sample answer: Fill the 5-liter bucket; pour 3 liters into the 3-liter bucket, leaving 2 liters in the 5-liter bucket; empty the 3-liter bucket; pour the remaining 2 liters from the 5-liter bucket into the 3-liter bucket. Fill the 5-liter bucket and pour 1 liter into the 3-liter bucket, completely filling the 3-liter bucket and leaving 4 liters in the 5-liter bucket.

2a. $x^2 + 3x + 4x + 12$

	x	4
x	x^2	$4x$
3	$3x$	12

2b. $2x^2 + 6x$

	x	3
$2x$	$2x^2$	$6x$

2c. $x^2 + 6x - 2x - 12$

	x	-2
x	x^2	$-2x$
6	$6x$	-12

2d. $2x^2 - 8x - 1x + 4$

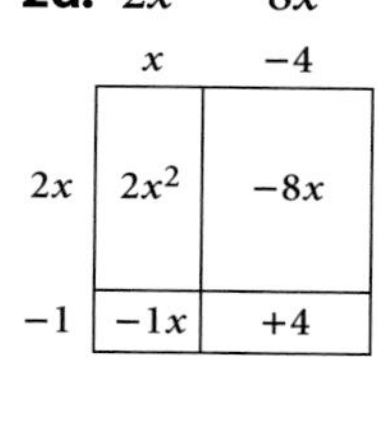

8a. Let w represent the mass in grams of a white block, and let r represent the mass in grams of a red block.

11a. $h = 0$. Before the ball is hit, it is on the ground.

11b. $h = 32$. Two seconds after being hit, the ball is 32 feet above the ground.

11c. $h = 0$. After three seconds, the ball lands on the ground.

14b. $1 \text{ mi} \cdot \frac{5280 \text{ ft}}{1 \text{ mi}} \cdot \frac{12 \text{ in.}}{1 \text{ ft}} \cdot \frac{2.54 \text{ cm}}{1 \text{ in.}} \cdot \frac{1 \text{ m}}{100 \text{ cm}} =$ 1609.344 m

15. See below.

LESSON 1.2, PAGE 39

Step 2 Sample answer:

Bounce number	Rebound height (m)
0	1.00
1	0.70
2	0.44
3	0.28
4	0.17
5	0.11
6	0.07

Step 3

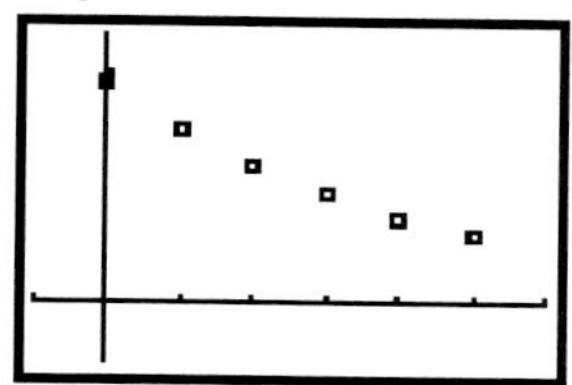

[−1, 6, 1, 0, 1, 1]

LESSON 1.3, PAGE 46

Step 5 The amount of medicine decreases sharply at first, then less and less as it levels off near 0 mL.

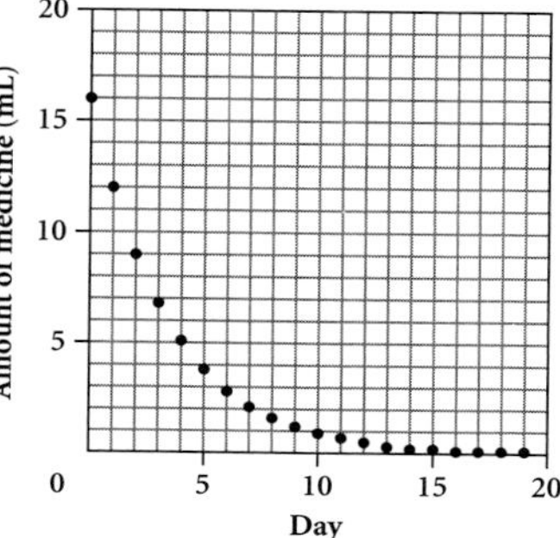

15. (*Chapter 0 Review*)

Sales Rep	Mr. Mendoza	Mr. Bell	Mrs. Plum
Client	Mr. Green	Ms. Phoung	Ms. Hunt
Location	Conference room	Convention hall	Lunch room
Time	9:00 A.M.	12:00 noon	3:00 P.M.

Step 6

Day	Amount of medicine (mL)
0	16
1	28
2	37
3	43.75
4	48.81

LESSON 1.4, PAGES 56, 57

6b.

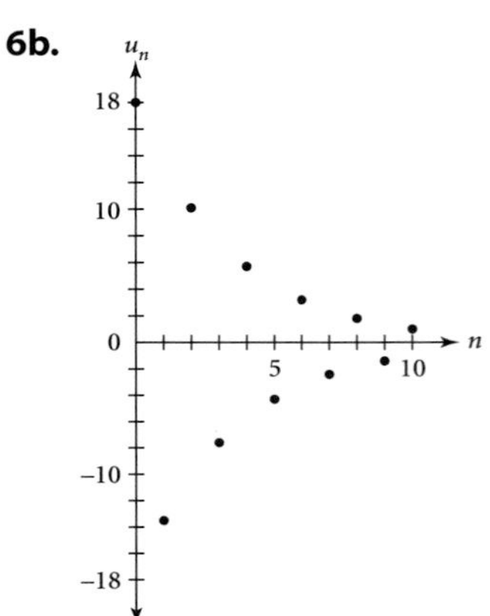

Because every term alternates signs, the graph is unique; each point alternates above or below the n-axis. The points above the n-axis create, however, a familiar geometric pattern, as do the points below the n-axis. If the points below the n-axis were reflected across the n-axis, you would have the graph of $u_0 = 18$ and $u_n = +0.75u_{n-1}$ where $n \geq 1$.

10a. approximately seven days

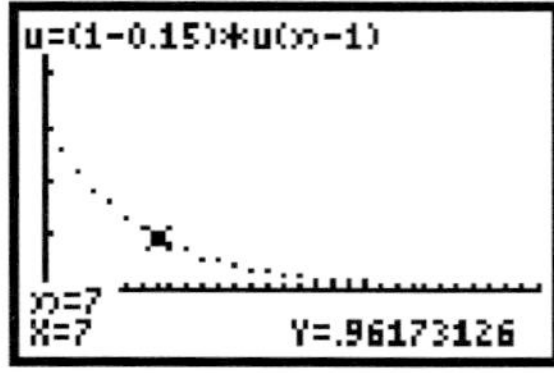

$[-1, 31, 1, -1, 5, 1]$

10b. increasing toward a long-run value of approximately 3.3 mg/L

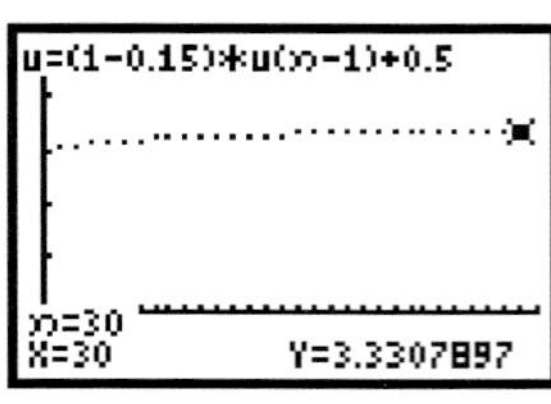

$[-1, 31, 1, -1, 5, 1]$

10c. decreasing toward a long-run value of approximately 0.67 mg/L

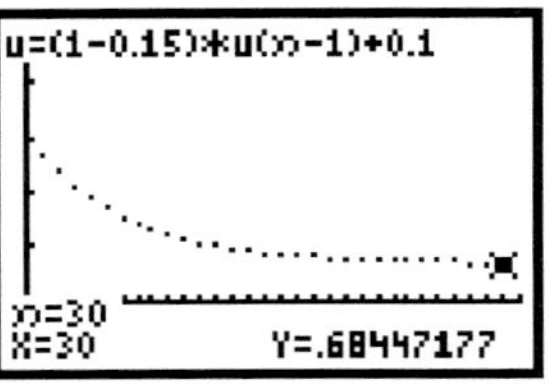

$[-1, 31, 1, -1, 5, 1]$

10d. approximately 0.225 mg/L

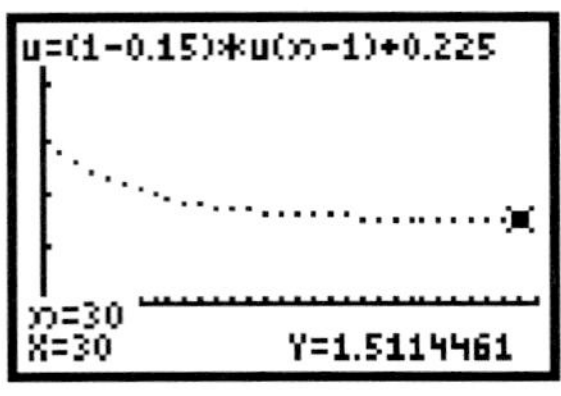

$[-1, 31, 1, -1, 5, 1]$

LESSON 1.5, PAGES 64, 66

1a. investment, because a deposit is added

2a. loan, because a payment is subtracted

2b. \$500 **2c.** \$25 **2d.** 4%

2e. quarterly (four times a year)

4a. $u_0 = 10000$ and $u_n = u_{n-1}\left(1 + \frac{0.10}{12}\right) - 300$ where $n \geq 1$

4b. $u_0 = 7000$ and $u_n = u_{n-1}\left(1 + \frac{0.1875}{12}\right) - 250$ where $n \geq 1$

4c. $u_0 = 8000$ and $u_n = u_{n-1}\left(1 + \frac{0.06}{4}\right) + 500$ where $n \geq 1$

4d. $u_0 = 0$ and $u_n = u_{n-1}\left(1 + \frac{0.070}{12}\right) + 100$ where $n \geq 1$

7d. The more frequently the interest is compounded, the more quickly the balance will grow. That is, after 10 years, an investment compounded daily will be greater than an investment compounded monthly, which will be greater than an investment compounded annually.

Project

Round number	Letters sent	Responded
1	200	12
2	2,400	144
3	28,800	1,728
4	345,600	20,736
5	4,147,200	248,832
6	49,766,400	2,985,984

LESSON 2.1, PAGE 80

Step 5 Students should see that the range of resting pulse rates is less than the range of exercise pulse rates. They might also compare respective values in the five-number summaries and generalize a percent increase in pulse rate from resting to exercise. Using the medians of the sample data sets, students might say that one's pulse rate should increase approximately 94% from resting to exercise $\left(\frac{140}{72} \approx 194\%\right)$.

LESSON 2.2, PAGE 93

18a. offensive team: $\bar{x} \approx 263.8$ lb, *median* $= 255$ lb; defensive team: $\bar{x} \approx 245.7$ lb, *median* $= 250$ lb

18b.

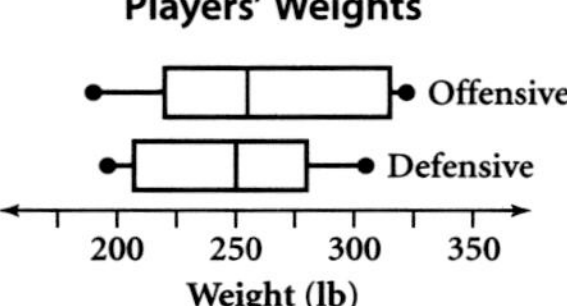

five-number summaries: offensive: 190, 220, 255, 315, 322; defensive: 196, 207, 250, 280, 305

Sample observations: The lightest players are on the offensive team. The offensive team has greater mean and median weights. The spread of the weights of the offensive team is greater than that of the defensive team. Over a quarter of the offensive players weigh more than any of the defensive players.

EXPLORATION, PAGE 107

1. Sample conjecture: Asian/Indian residents of Berkeley make more money than white residents. A summary table indicates that this is true, as the mean and median are both significantly higher for Asian/Indians than for whites. However, a histogram implies that Asian/Indians have virtually no income. This is because a histogram shows *number of people* in various income groups, and the population includes only 7 Asian/Indians compared to 329 whites.

2. Students might compare two different regions and find that one has a high percentage of population under 10 years old, and another has a high percentage over 70. The first community may decide to invest in day care and after school programs, while the second may choose to support a senior center.

CHAPTER 2 REVIEW, PAGE 111

8a.

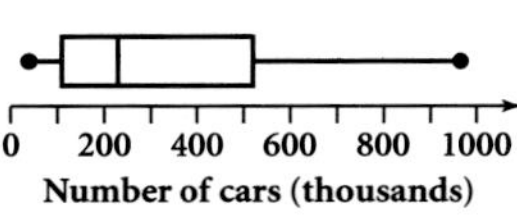

five-number summary: 39, 108, 228.5, 520, 965

8b.

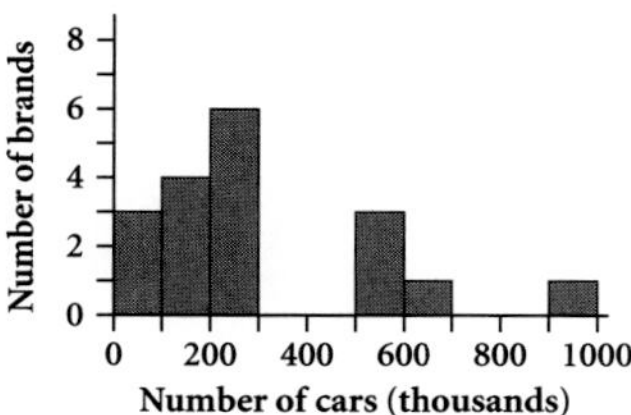

8c. The box plot will be shifted right, and some of the histogram's bins will change frequency as some brands fall into a different bin.

LESSON 3.1, PAGE 120

16. Answers will vary depending on bin width.

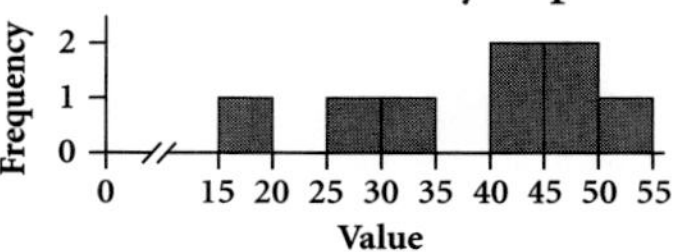

16a. The left whisker will be longer because the data are skewed left. The range will be from 19 to 51. The median will be around 42.

16b.

15 25 35 45 55

Data

LESSON 3.2, PAGE 122

Steps 1 and 2 Sample data:

Time (s) x	Distance (m) y
0.02	2.49462
0.04	2.467298
0.06	2.381489
0.08	2.337554
0.1	2.277556
0.12	2.216872
0.14	2.133946
0.16	2.046077
0.18	1.9534
0.2	1.85798
0.22	1.75762
0.24	1.65643
0.26	1.55429
0.28	1.45969
0.3	1.37168
0.32	1.29741
0.34	1.237
0.36	1.18908

Time (s) x	Distance (m) y
0.38	1.14803
0.4	1.11178
0.42	1.07801
0.44	1.04135
0.46	1.00016
0.48	0.95307
0.5	0.89870
0.52	0.83225
0.54	0.777
0.56	0.71692
0.58	0.64759
0.6	0.59597
0.62	0.54064
0.64	0.48544
0.66	0.43986
0.68	0.38879
0.7	0.35172
0.72	0.30737

Step 3 Answer for sample data:

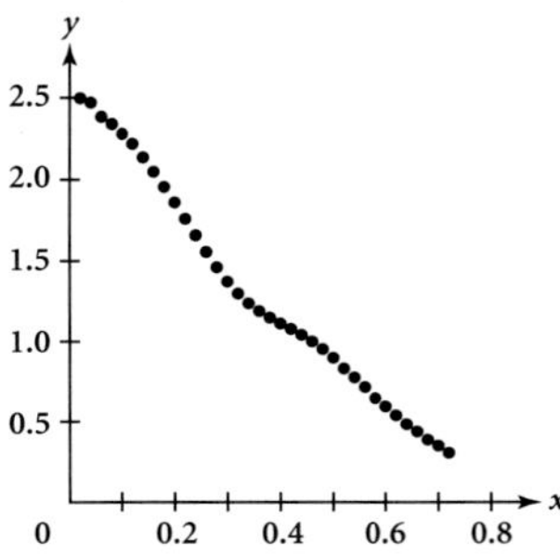

domain: $0.02 \leq x \leq 0.72$; range: $0.30 \leq y \leq 2.49$; The domain indicates the number of seconds the rocket is in motion. The range indicates the distance from the sensor.

Step 4 Possible answers for sample data:
$A(0.02, 2.49462)$, $B(0.18, 1.9534)$, $C(0.4, 1.11178)$, $D(0.7, 0.35172)$
slope between A and B: -3.3826
slope between A and C: -3.6391
slope between A and D: -3.1513
slope between B and C: -3.8255
slope between B and D: -3.0802
slope between C and D: -2.5335

LESSON 3.4, PAGES 138, 140

Step 1 Sample data:

Mass (g) x	Spring length (cm) y
50	5.0
60	5.5
70	6.0
80	6.3
90	6.8
100	7.1
110	7.5
120	7.7
130	8.1
140	8.5
150	8.8
160	9.2
170	9.5
180	9.9
190	10.3
200	10.7
210	11.3
220	11.4
230	11.9
240	12.4

Step 2

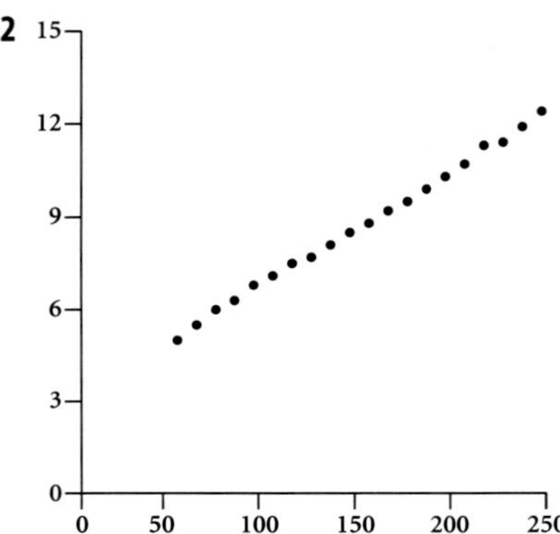

Step 3 $M_1(80, 6.3)$, $M_2(145, 8.65)$, $M_3(210, 11.3)$; equation of the line through M_1 and M_3 is approximately $y = 3.223 + 0.038x$; equation of the line through M_2 is approximately $y = 3.073 + 0.038x$; equation of median-median line is approximately $\hat{y} = 3.173 + 0.038x$.

Step 4

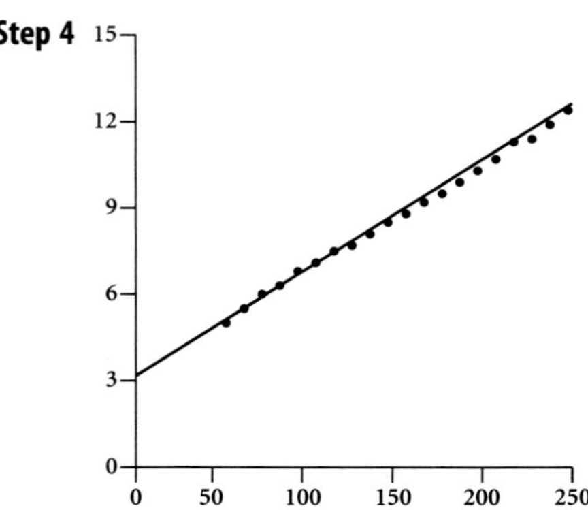

Step 5a If $x = 75$, then $\hat{y} = 3.173 + 0.038(75) = 6.023$; a mass of 75 g would stretch the spring approximately 6.0 cm. If $x = 175$, then $\hat{y} = 3.173 + 0.038(175) = 9.823$; a mass of 175 g would stretch the spring approximately 9.8 cm.

Step 5b When $x = 70$, $y = 6.0$ and $\hat{y} = 5.833$, a difference of 0.167; when $x = 90$, $y = 6.8$ and $\hat{y} = 6.593$, a difference of -0.207. Sample answer: The data may have been measured incorrectly.

Step 5e domain: $50 \leq x \leq 240$; range: $5 \leq y \leq 12.4$. The domain includes all the masses used and the range includes all the spring lengths measured.

Step 6 Sample answer: We learned that a spring stretches an equal amount as equal amounts of mass are added. By finding the median-median line, you can estimate the amount of stretch that will result from a given mass, or you can estimate the mass by measuring the length of the spring. We had difficulties getting exact measurements because the spring bounced and because it was hard to hold the ruler without bumping the spring.

11b. $M_1(1925, 17.1)$, $M_2(1928.5, 22.05)$, $M_3(1932, 23.3)$

11c. $\hat{D} = -1687.83 + 0.886t$

11d. For each additional year, the number of deaths by automobile increases by 0.886 per hundred thousand population.

11e. Answers might include the fact that the United States was in the Great Depression and fewer people were driving.

11f. It probably would not be a good idea to extrapolate because a lot has changed in the automotive industry in the past 75 years. Many safety features are now standard.

LESSON 3.5, PAGE 143

Step 1 Sample data:

From Detroit, MI (DTW) to	Time (min)	Distance (mi)
Cincinnati, OH (CVG)	64	229
Houston, TX (HOU)	189	1092
Los Angeles, CA (LAX)	288	1979
Memphis, TN (MEM)	104	610
Minneapolis/St. Paul, MN (MSP)	105	528
Phoenix, AZ (PHX)	248	1671
Louisville, KY (SDF)	67	306
San Francisco, CA (SFO)	303	2079

Step 2

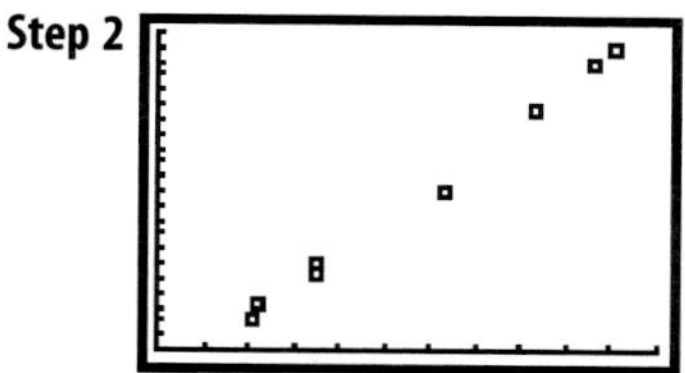

[0, 330, 30, 0, 2200, 100]

Step 3b The y-intercept represents the number of miles traveled at 0 minutes, approximately -235.1 mi for the sample data. The plane does not move backward. Instead, -235.1 represents the distance a plane would have traveled if it hadn't been sitting on the runway.

Step 3c The x-intercept is approximately 30.9. It represents the number of minutes the plane takes to take off and land.

EXPLORATION, PAGE 150

1. From the movable line, outliers are those points that have a vertical distance from the line far greater than the other points. From the residual plot, outliers are those residual points that have a vertical distance from the line $y = 0$ far greater than the other residuals. The residual plot usually makes it easier to identify outliers. Outliers are those points that have squares with area far greater than the other points. This is related to the other two approaches because the length of the side of each square is the vertical distance from the line, or the residual.

2. As the slope of the line of fit increases/decreases, the slope of the residual plot decreases/increases (inversely), but the residuals stay equidistant with respect to each other. As the y-intercept of the line moves up/down, the residual plot moves down/up (inversely). Since the residuals should have a sum approximately equal to zero, and be equally scattered positive and negative, students can adjust the line of fit by watching how the residual plot changes.

LESSON 3.7, PAGE 159

Step 3 Sample answer: $41x + 18y = -5$; the line passes through the same point of intersection.

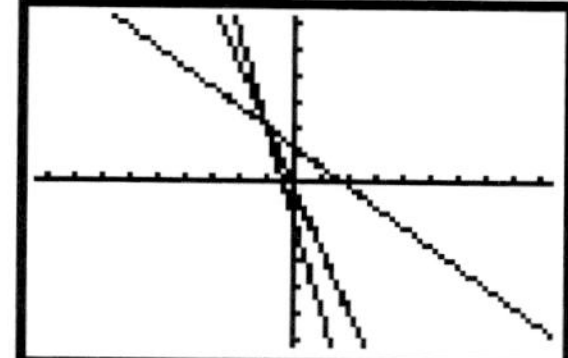

$[-9.4, 9.4, 1, -6.2, 6.2, 1]$

Step 5 $0x + 22y = 44$ or $y = 2$; the line passes through the same point of intersection.

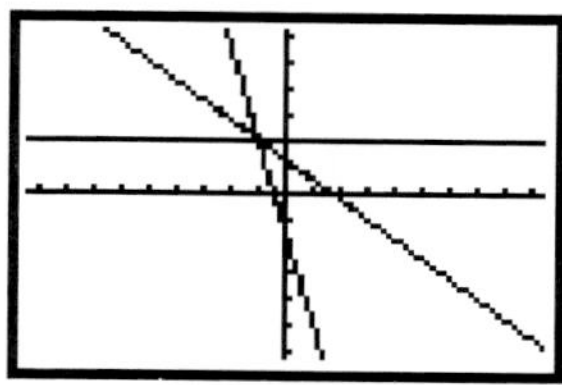

$[-9.4, 9.4, 1, -6.2, 6.2, 1]$

Step 7 Answers will vary. Students should also explore ways to eliminate y, thereby leaving a vertical line that represents the x-coordinate. In general, for the system

$$\begin{cases} Ax + By = C \\ Dx + Ey = F \end{cases}$$

Letting $M = \pm D$ and $N = \mp A$ will eliminate x and give the y-coordinate. Letting $M = \pm E$ and $N = \mp B$ will eliminate y and give the x-coordinate.

LESSON 4.1, PAGES 174, 176, 177

Part 1 Sample answer:

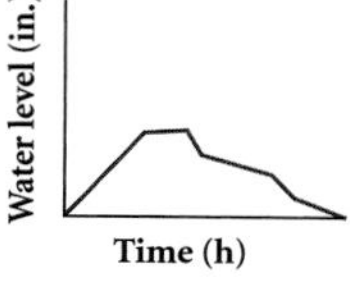

Part 2 Sample answer: Luis and Loretta have a small outdoor swimming pool. The children want to use the pool, but the water level is very low, so Luis turns on the hose and begins filling the pool at a constant rate. The children are restless and persuade Luis to increase the water flow and fill the pool faster. It fills at a faster constant rate than before. When the pool is completely full, he turns off the hose and the children are careful not to splash water out of the pool. After the children get out of the pool, he empties it. The water pours out

rapidly at first, then more slowly as there is less and less water left. He leaves just a little water in the bottom, which will slowly evaporate.

6a. Time in seconds is the independent variable; the height of the basketball in feet is the dependent variable.

Height (ft)
Time (s)

6b. The car's speed in miles per hour is the independent variable; the braking distance in feet is the dependent variable.

Braking distance (ft)
Speed (mi/h)

6c. Time in minutes is the independent variable; the drink's temperature in degrees Fahrenheit is the dependent variable.

Temperature (°F)
Time (min)

6d. Time in seconds is the independent variable; the acorn's speed in feet per second is the dependent variable.

Speed (ft/s)
Time (s)

6e. Time in minutes is the independent variable; your height above the ground in feet is the dependent variable.

Height (ft)
Time (min)

7c. Foot length in inches is the independent variable; shoe size is the dependent variable. The graph will be a series of discontinuous horizontal segments because shoe sizes are discrete.

Shoe size
Foot length (in.)

7d. Time in hours is the independent variable; distance in miles is the dependent variable. The graph will be continuous because distance is changing continuously over time.

Distance (mi)
Time (h)

7e. The day of the month is the independent variable; the maximum temperature in degrees Fahrenheit is the dependent variable. The graph will be discrete points because there is just one temperature reading per day.

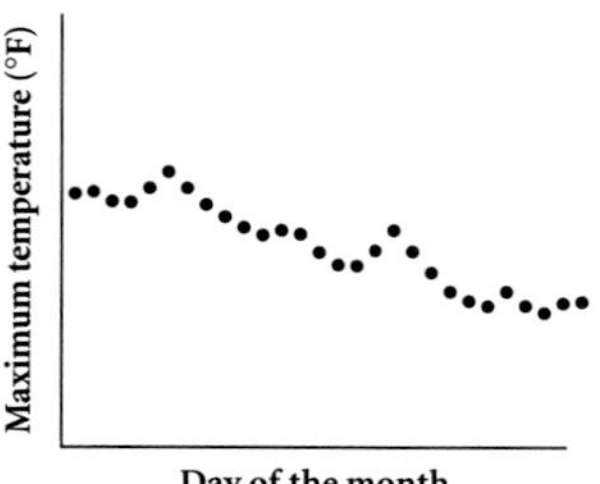

8. Sample answer: The cost of parking your car at a lot that charges a certain fixed price for up to an hour, and then half as much for each additional hour or fraction thereof.

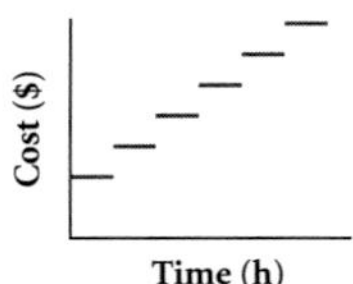

LESSON 4.5, PAGE 201

Step 1a

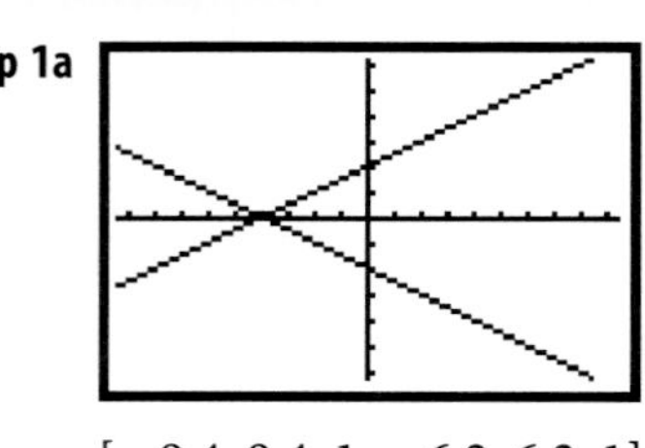

[−9.4, 9.4, 1, −6.2, 6.2, 1]

Step 1b

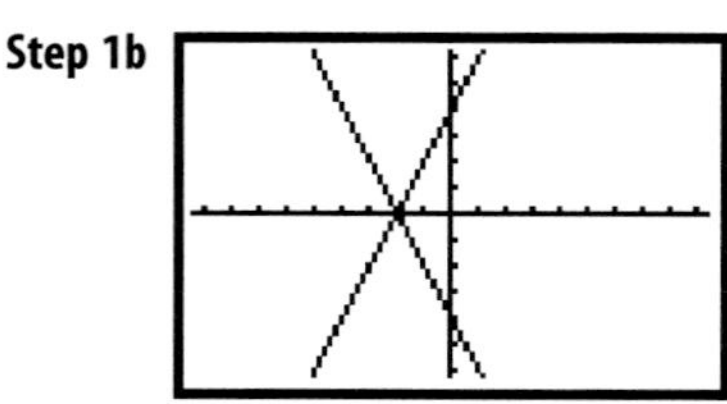

[−9.4, 9.4, 1, −6.2, 6.2, 1]

Step 1c

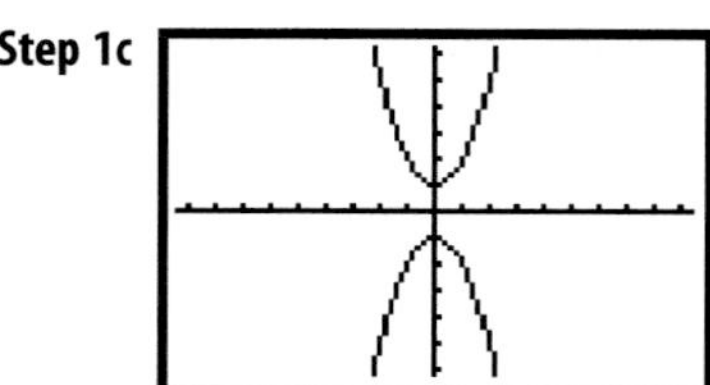

[−9.4, 9.4, 1, −6.2, 6.2, 1]

Step 2a

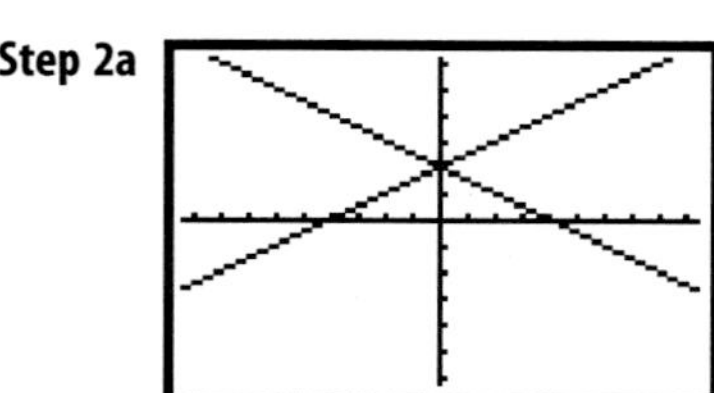

[−9.4, 9.4, 1, −6.2, 6.2, 1]

Step 2b

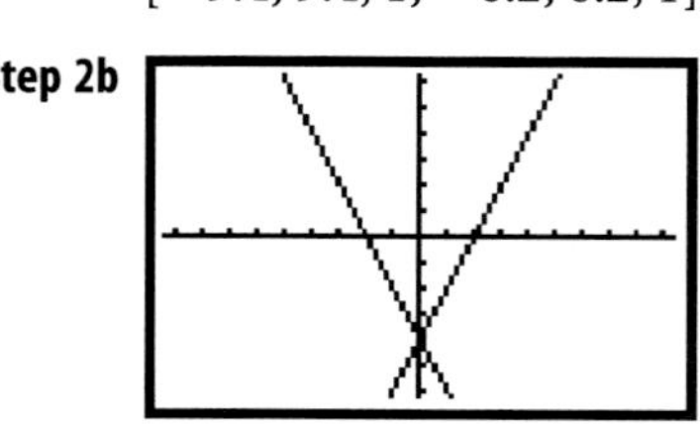

[−9.4, 9.4, 1, −6.2, 6.2, 1]

EXPLORATION, PAGE 208

Question 2 Possible answer: To rotate the image from the first to the third quadrant, use two reflections; one negates the x-coordinate, and the other negates the y-coordinate. To rotate the image from the first to the second or fourth quadrant, reflect across the line $y = x$ (interchanging the coordinates), then reflect across one axis (negating one coordinate).

LESSON 4.6, PAGES 215, 216

10a.

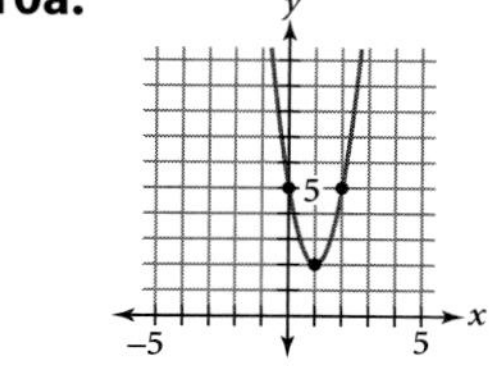

10b.

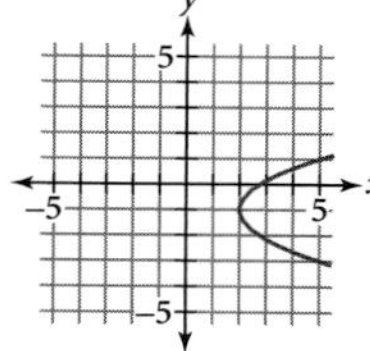

10c.

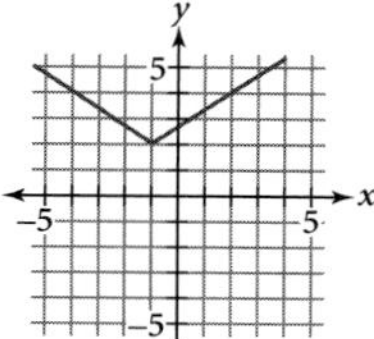

11a.

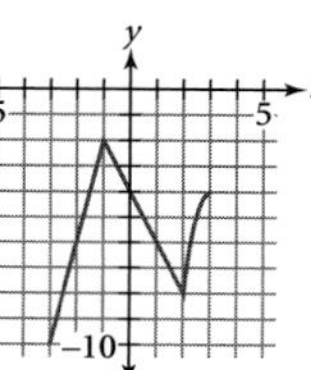

11b.

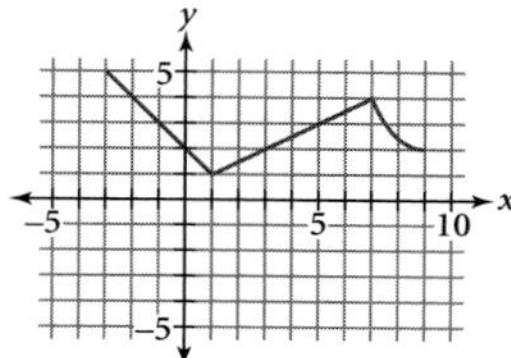

11c.

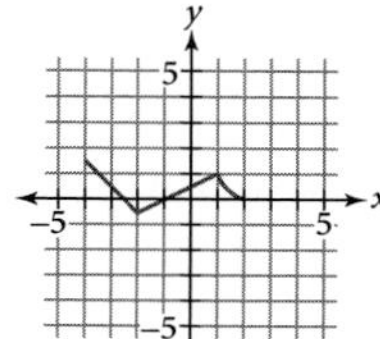

14a.

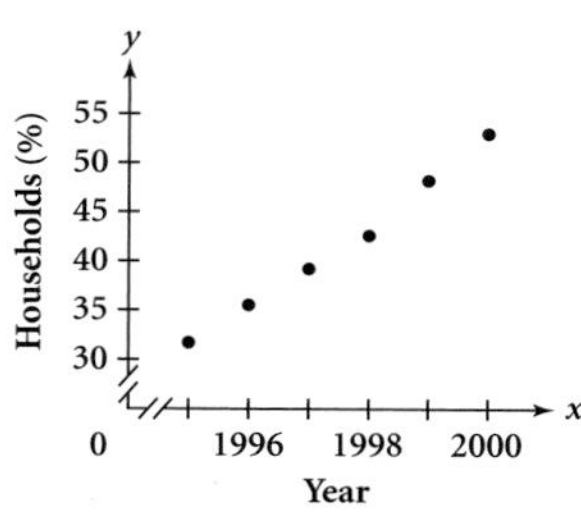

LESSON 4.7, PAGES 224

15b. $y = -3x + 1$ **15c.** $y = 3x - 1$

$y = -3x + 1$ $y = 3x + 1$

$y = 3x - 1$ $y = 3x + 1$

CHAPTER 4 REVIEW, PAGE 233

1. Sample answer: For a time there are no pops. Then the popping rate slowly increases. When the popping reaches a furious intensity, it seems to level out. Then the number of pops per second drops quickly until the last pop is heard.

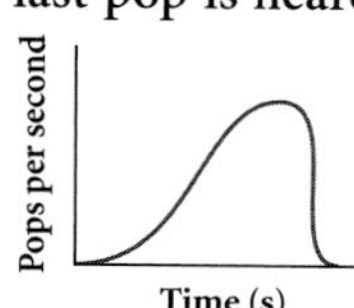

3a.

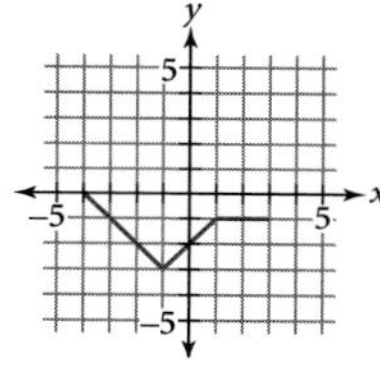

3b.

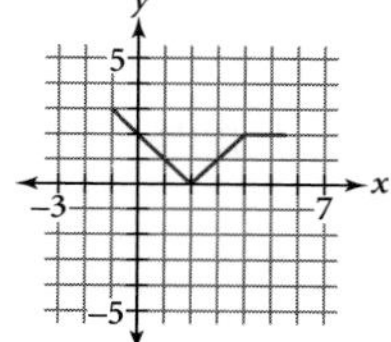

3c.

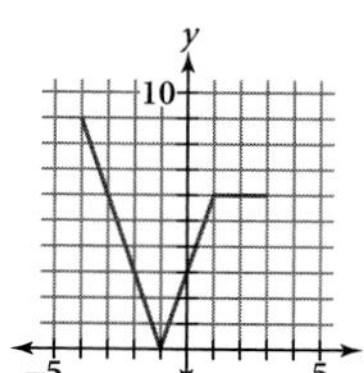

3d.

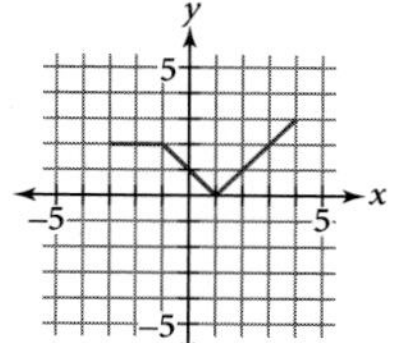

LESSON 5.1, PAGES 238, 241

Step 1 Sample answer: Assume there are 30 students in the class. The following sample data was used in obtaining sample answers for all steps of this investigation:

(0, 30)	(5, 12)	(10, 5)	(1, 26)	(6, 11)
(11, 5)	(2, 19)	(7, 9)	(12, 2)	(3, 17)
(8, 8)	(4, 14)	(9, 8)		

Step 2

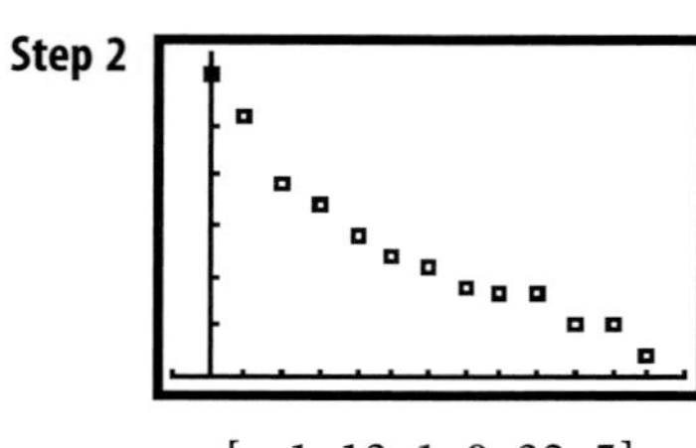

[−1, 13, 1, 0, 32, 5]

The values for the number standing do not have a common difference, so look at their ratios instead:

$\frac{26}{30} \approx 0.867, \frac{19}{26} \approx 0.731, \frac{17}{19} \approx 0.895, \frac{14}{17} = 0.824,$
$\frac{12}{14} \approx 0.857, \frac{11}{12} = 0.917, \frac{9}{11} \approx 0.818, \frac{8}{9} \approx 0.889,$
$\frac{8}{8} = 1, \frac{5}{8} = 0.625, \frac{5}{5} = 1, \frac{2}{5} = 0.4$

Average these 12 ratios to obtain $r \approx 0.8186$.

Recursive formula:
$u_0 = 30$
$u_n = 0.8186 \cdot u_{n-1}$ where $n \geq 1$

Step 6 In a radioactive sample, a certain fraction of the atoms undergo radioactive decay within each period of time. This activity simulates radioactive decay because the number of people who sit down after each roll of the dice represents the atoms that have undergone decay. Rolling a 1 represents one atom that undergoes radioactive decay.

7a–d.

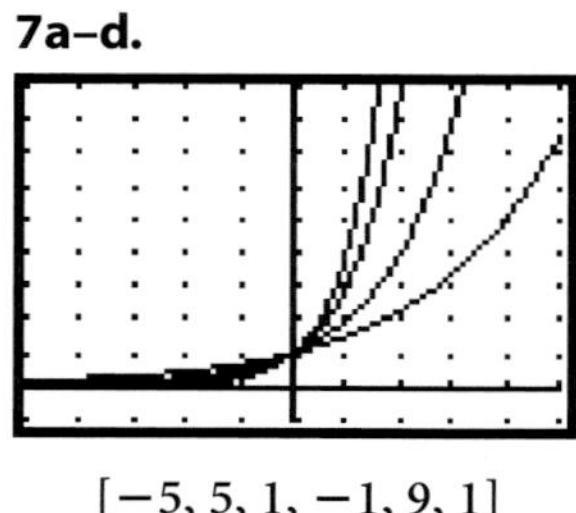

[−5, 5, 1, −1, 9, 1]

7e. As the base increases, the graph becomes steeper. The curves all intersect the y-axis at (0, 1).

7f. The graph of $y = 6^x$ should be the steepest of all of these. It will contain the points (0, 1) and (1, 6).

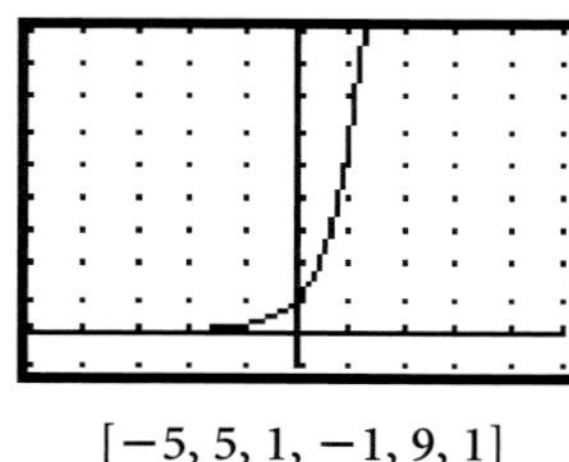

[−5, 5, 1, −1, 9, 1]

LESSON 5.2, PAGES 245, 249

Step 1a $2^3 \cdot 2^4 = (2 \cdot 2 \cdot 2) \cdot (2 \cdot 2 \cdot 2 \cdot 2) = 2^7$

Step 1b $x^5 \cdot x^{12} = (x \cdot x \cdot x \cdot x \cdot x) \cdot (x \cdot x \cdot x \cdot x \cdot x \cdot x \cdot x \cdot x \cdot x \cdot x \cdot x \cdot x) = x^{17}$

Step 1c $10^2 \cdot 10^5 = (10 \cdot 10) \cdot (10 \cdot 10 \cdot 10 \cdot 10 \cdot 10) = 10^7$

Step 3a $\frac{4^5}{4^2} = \frac{4 \cdot 4 \cdot 4 \cdot \cancel{4} \cdot \cancel{4}}{\cancel{4} \cdot \cancel{4}} = 4^3$

Step 3b $\frac{x^8}{x^6} = \frac{\cancel{x} \cdot \cancel{x} \cdot \cancel{x} \cdot \cancel{x} \cdot \cancel{x} \cdot \cancel{x} \cdot x \cdot x}{\cancel{x} \cdot \cancel{x} \cdot \cancel{x} \cdot \cancel{x} \cdot \cancel{x} \cdot \cancel{x}} = x^2$

Step 3c See below.

Step 5a $\frac{2^3}{2^4} = \frac{\cancel{2} \cdot \cancel{2} \cdot \cancel{2}}{2 \cdot \cancel{2} \cdot \cancel{2} \cdot \cancel{2}} = \frac{1}{2^1}$

Step 5b $\frac{4^5}{4^7} = \frac{\cancel{4} \cdot \cancel{4} \cdot \cancel{4} \cdot \cancel{4} \cdot \cancel{4}}{4 \cdot 4 \cdot \cancel{4} \cdot \cancel{4} \cdot \cancel{4} \cdot \cancel{4} \cdot \cancel{4}} = \frac{1}{4^2}$

Step 5c $\frac{x^3}{x^8} = \frac{\cancel{x} \cdot \cancel{x} \cdot \cancel{x}}{x \cdot x \cdot x \cdot x \cdot x \cdot \cancel{x} \cdot \cancel{x} \cdot \cancel{x}} = \frac{1}{x^5}$

Step 8 sample answer: $(2^3)^4 = (2^3)(2^3)(2^3)(2^3) = 2^{3+3+3+3} = 2^{12}$

$(a^n)^m = a^{nm}$

Step 9 sample answer: $(2 \cdot 3)^3 = (2 \cdot 3)(2 \cdot 3)(2 \cdot 3) = 2 \cdot 2 \cdot 2 \cdot 3 \cdot 3 \cdot 3 = 2^3 \cdot 3^3$

$(a \cdot b)^n = a^n b^n$

Step 10 Sample answer: $\frac{x^3}{x^3} = \frac{\cancel{x} \cdot \cancel{x} \cdot \cancel{x}}{\cancel{x} \cdot \cancel{x} \cdot \cancel{x}} = 1$, but, by the property from Step 4, $\frac{x^3}{x^3} = x^{3-3} = x^0$.

9g. Sample answer: The graph of $y = x^7$ will fall in the first and third quadrants, will be narrower than $y = x^3$ or $y = x^5$, and will pass through (0, 0), (1, 1), (−1, −1), (2, 128), and (−2, −128).

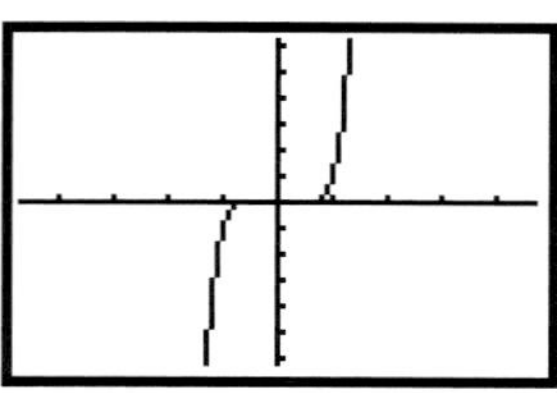

[−4.7, 4.7, 1, −6.2, 6.2, 1]

Step 3c *(Lesson 5.2)*

$$\frac{(0.94)^{15}}{(0.94)^5} = \frac{\cancel{(0.94)}\cancel{(0.94)}\cancel{(0.94)}\cancel{(0.94)}\cancel{(0.94)}(0.94)(0.94)(0.94)(0.94)(0.94)(0.94)(0.94)(0.94)(0.94)(0.94)}{\cancel{(0.94)}\cancel{(0.94)}\cancel{(0.94)}\cancel{(0.94)}\cancel{(0.94)}} = (0.94)^{10}$$

LESSON 5.5, PAGE 266

Step 1

i.

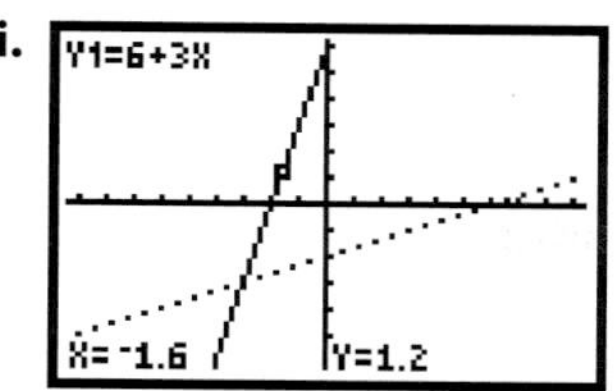

$[-9.4, 9.4, 1, -6.2, 6.2, 1]$

ii.

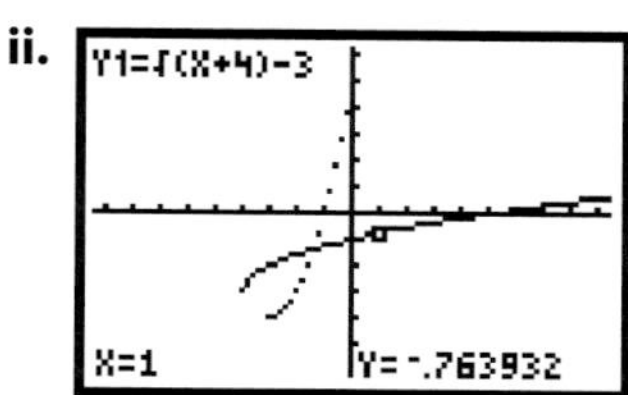

$[-9.4, 9.4, 1, -6.2, 6.2, 1]$

iii.

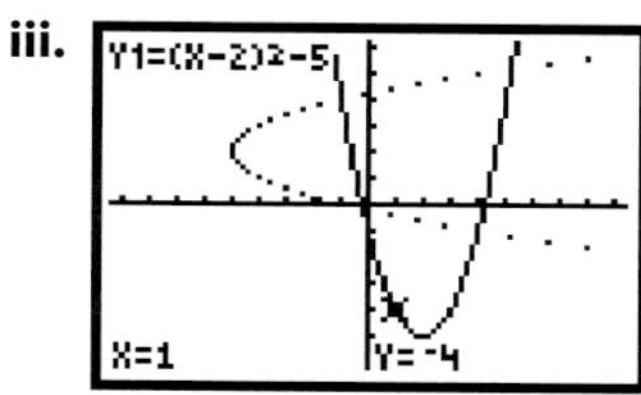

$[-9.4, 9.4, 1, -6.2, 6.2, 1]$

iv.

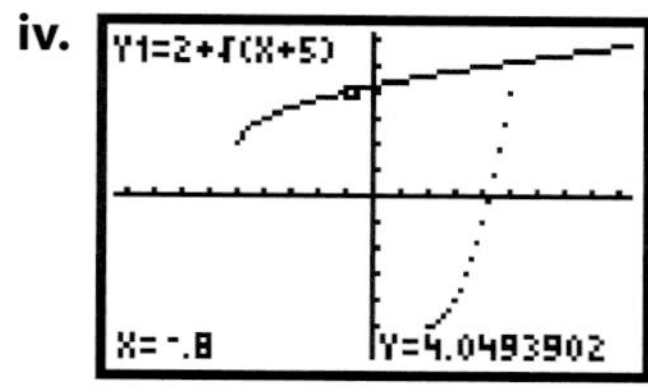

$[-9.4, 9.4, 1, -6.2, 6.2, 1]$

v.

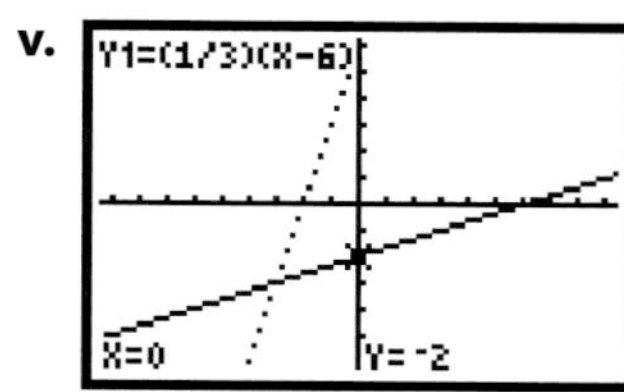

$[-9.4, 9.4, 1, -6.2, 6.2, 1]$

vi.

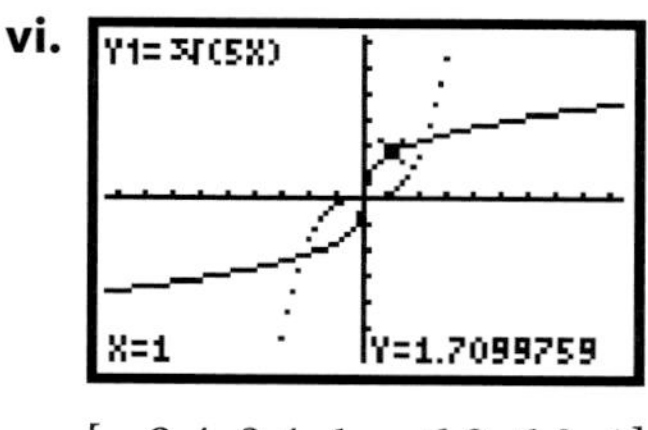

$[-9.4, 9.4, 1, -6.2, 6.2, 1]$

LESSON 5.6, PAGE 273

Steps 1 and 2 For all values of x, $\log(10^x) = x$.

X	Y1	Y2
1	10	1
1.25	17.783	1.25
1.5	31.623	1.5
1.75	56.234	1.75
2	100	2
2.25	177.83	2.25
2.5	316.23	2.5
X=1		

LESSON 5.7, PAGE 281

Step 4 Sample answer: The numbers are placed on a slide rule so that their base-10 (common) logarithms form a linear scale. This means, for example, that the distance between $10^{0.4}(\approx 2.51)$ and $10^{0.5}(\approx 3.16)$ will be the same as the distance between $10^{0.5}$ and $10^{0.6}(\approx 3.98)$. To form a logarithmic scale for a slide rule, start out with a linear scale from 0 to 1. For each number between 0 and 1 that is a multiple of 0.1, use your calculator to find the common antilog of that number, that is, raise 10 to that power. Write each resulting number directly above the exponent you used to obtain it. For greater accuracy, subdivide the linear scale further.

Step 5 Sample answer: If you "add" 2 and 3 in the same way on a slide rule, you will get 6. It appears that you are actually multiplying 2 and 3 rather than adding them. This happens because you are using logarithmic scales and are really adding the common logs of the numbers, which are the exponents to which 10 must be raised to get the numbers. The multiplication rule of exponents says that you multiply two numbers with the same base by adding their exponents. Other pairs of numbers also show that you are multiplying the numbers.

Step 6 Sample answers:

a. Place 1 over 3. Look under 3 on the top ruler. The result will be 9.

b. If you place 1 over 5, you will not be able to find the product because 7 will run off the slide rule. However, you can extend your slide rule to the right and to the left. One slide rule length to the right represents 100. The answer is 35.

c. Place 1 over 2.5. Look under 3.5 on the top ruler. The result is 8.75. This shows that $2.5 \cdot 3.5 = 8.75$.

d. From Step 6c, $2.5 \cdot 3.5 = 8.75$. Because $25 = 10 \cdot 2.5$ and $35 = 10 \cdot 3.5$, it follows that $25 \cdot 35 = 100 \cdot 8.75 = 875$. (You could also extend both slide rules.)

Step 9 Sample answers:

a. Place 2 above 10. Read the number below 1, which is 5.

b. Place 3.5 above 2.5. You will need to extend the lower slide rule to the left to read the number that appears below 1, which is approximately 0.71.

c. Same method and answer as Step 6b.

d. Extend the bottom ruler to the right. Place 5 over 18 and read the number below 1, which is 3.6.

LESSON 5.8, PAGES 289, 291

Step 4 sample data:

Time (s)	Temperature (°F)
0	89.8143
30	86.7953
60	83.2372
90	80.7256
120	78.7182
150	77.0818
180	75.9116
210	74.7286
240	73.8714
270	73.1955
300	72.7045
330	72.2136
360	71.8864
390	71.5571
420	71.3857
450	71.2143
480	71.2143
510	71.2143
540	71.2143
570	71.0429
600	71.0429

L1	L2	L3 3
0	89.814	1.2745
30	86.795	1.1985
60	83.237	1.0877
90	80.726	.98792
120	78.718	.88752
150	77.082	.78403
180	75.912	.69122

L3 ="log(L2-71)"

Delete repeated values at the end of the list to create a better logarithm graph.

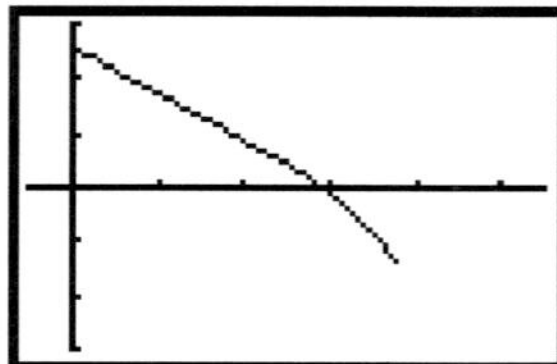

[−60, 600, 120, −1.5, 1.5, 0.5]

Step 5 The median-median line for the sample data in Step 4 is $\hat{y} = -0.004x + 1.364$.

Substitute $\log(y - 71)$ for y and t for x, and solve for y. $y = 71 + 23.121(0.991)^x$. The temperature limit is 71°; the approximate change between the original temperature and the limit is 23.121, and 0.991 is the percentage of this change that occurs each second.

1a. $\log(10^{n+p}) = \log((10^n)(10^p))$

$(n + p)\log 10 = \log 10^n + \log 10^p$

$(n + p)\log 10 = n\log 10 + p\log 10$

$(n + p)\log 10 = (n + p)\log 10$

Because the logarithm of the left side equals the logarithm of the right, the left and right sides are equal. Or, because $\log(10^{n+p}) = \log((10^n)(10^p))$, $10^{n+p} = (10^n)(10^p)$.

1b. $\log\left(\frac{10^d}{10^e}\right) = \log(10^{d-e})$

$\log 10^d - \log 10^e = \log(10^{d-e})$

$d\log 10 - e\log 10 = (d - e)\log 10$

$(d - e)\log 10 = (d - e)\log 10$

Because the logarithm of the left side equals the logarithm of the right, the left and right sides are equal. Or, because $\log\left(\frac{10^d}{10^e}\right) = \log(10^{d-e})$, $\frac{10^d}{10^e} = 10^{d-e}$

8a. Let x represent time in minutes, and let y represent tempeature in degrees Fahrenheit.

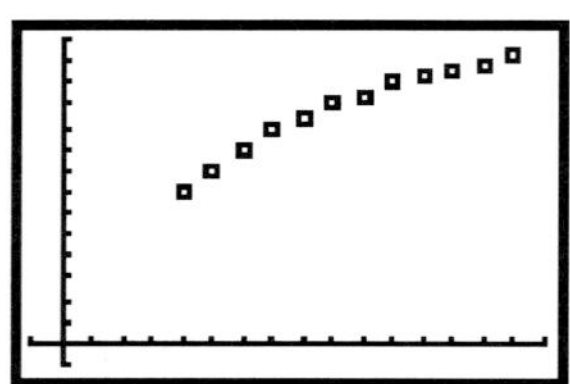

[−2, 32, 2, −5, 70, 5]

8b. Because the curve is both reflected and translated, first graph points in the form $(x, -y)$. Then translate the points up so that the data approach a long-run value of zero. Then graph points in the form $(x, \log(-y + 74))$, which appears to be linear.

The median-median line for these altered data is $\log(-y + 74) = 1.823 - 0.0298x$. Solving for y gives the equation $\hat{y} = 74 - 10^{1.823-0.0298x}$, or $\hat{y} = 74 - 66.53(0.9337)^x$.

9a. The data are the most linear when viewed as (log(*height*), log(*distance*)).

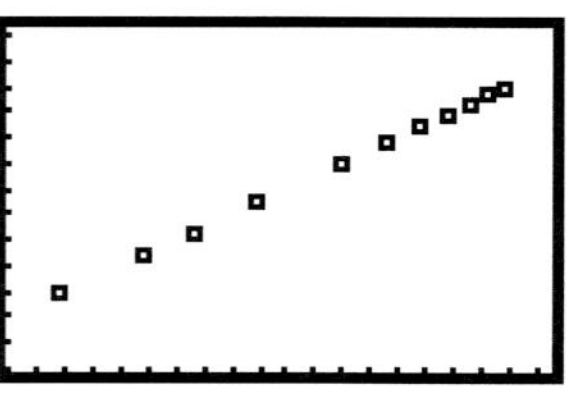

[2.3, 4.2, 0.1, 1.5, 2.8, 0.1]

9b. The median-median line equation for these altered data is $\hat{y} = 0.555 + 0.49909x$. Or, in terms of the original data, $\log(\textit{distance}) = 0.555 + 0.49909 \log(\textit{height})$. Solving for *distance* gives the equation $y = 10^{0.555+0.49909 \log x}$, $y = 10^{0.555} \cdot 10^{0.49909 \log x}$, $y = 3.589(10^{\log x})^{0.49909}$, or $y = 3.589x^{0.49909}$.

LESSON 6.2, PAGE 317

14a. i. consistent and independent

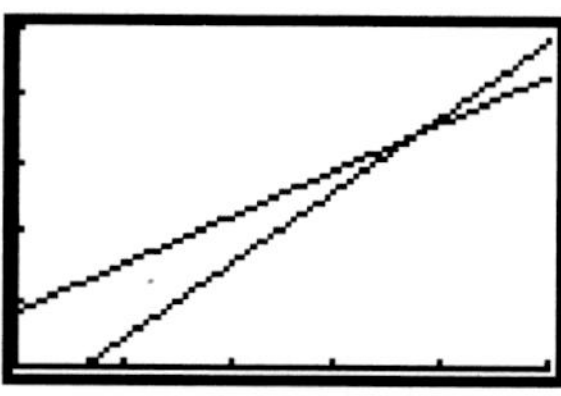

[0, 50, 10, 0, 50, 10]

14a. ii. inconsistent

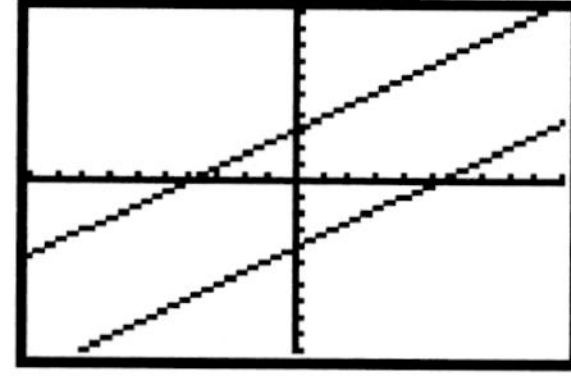

[−10, 10, 1, −10, 10, 1]

14a. iii. inconsistent

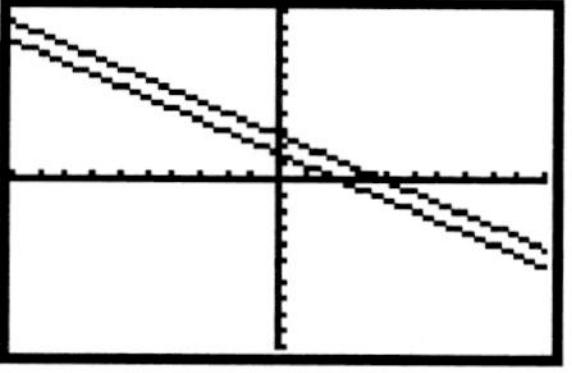

[−10, 10, 1, −10, 10, 1]

14a. iv. consistent and independent

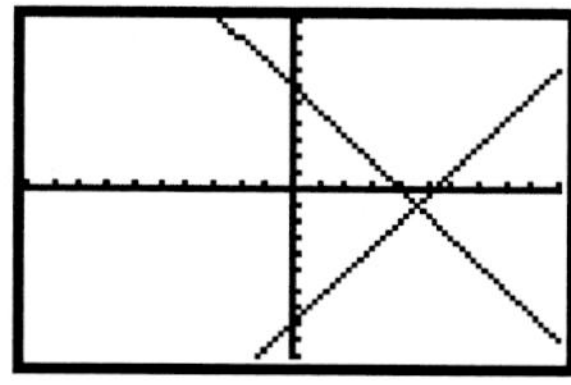

[−10, 10, 1, −10, 10, 1]

14a. v. inconsistent

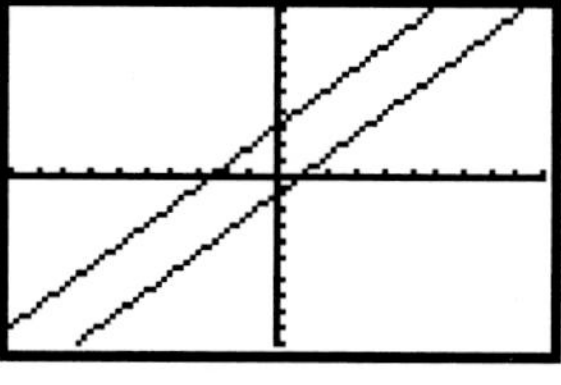

[−10, 10, 1, −10, 10, 1]

14a. vi. consistent and dependent

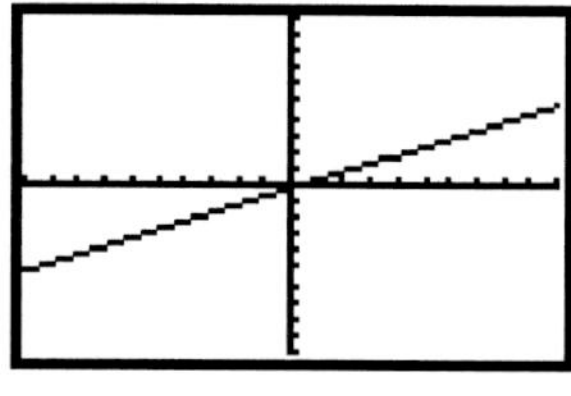

[−10, 10, 1, −10, 10, 1]

14a. vii. consistent and dependent

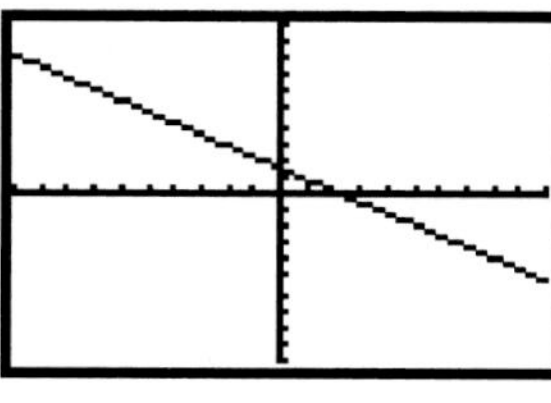

[−10, 10, 1, −10, 10, 1]

14a. viii. consistent and independent

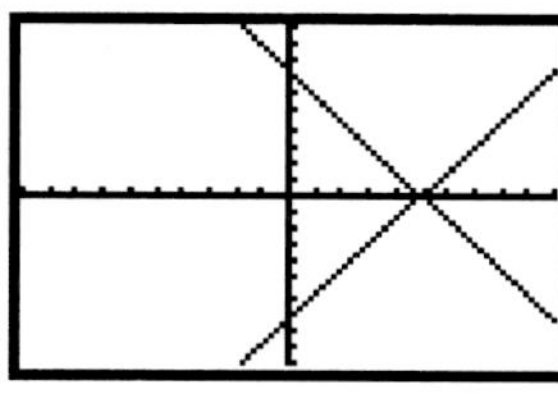

[−10, 10, 1, −10, 10, 1]

14a. ix. consistent and dependent

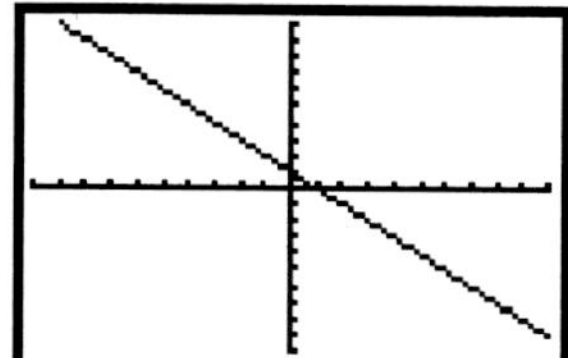

[−10, 10, 1, −10, 10, 1]

LESSON 6.5, PAGE 336

Step 1

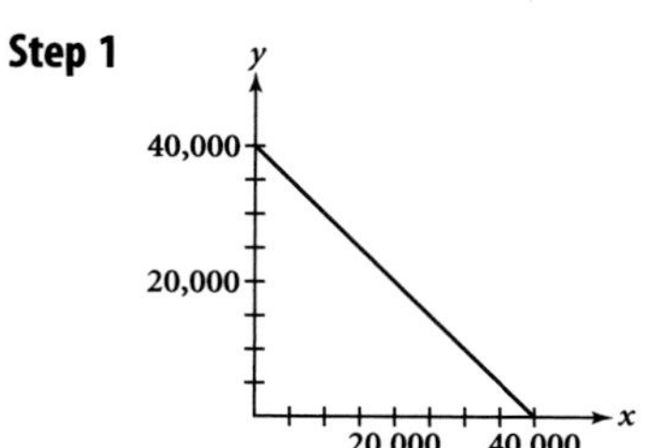

LESSON 6.6, PAGE 345

Step 2
$$\begin{cases} 0.5x + y \leq 8 & \text{Pottery-wheel hours constraint} \\ 3x + 18y \leq 60 & \text{Kiln hours constraint} \\ x \geq 6 & \text{At least 6 unglazed} \\ x \geq 0 & \text{Common sense} \\ y \geq 0 & \text{Common sense} \end{cases}$$

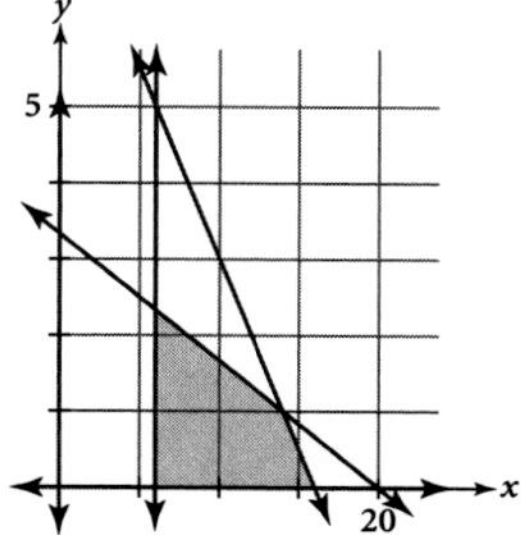

CHAPTER 6 REVIEW, PAGE 351

1a. impossible because the dimensions are not the same

1b. $\begin{bmatrix} -4 & 7 \\ 1 & 2 \end{bmatrix}$

1c. $\begin{bmatrix} -12 & 4 & 8 \\ 8 & 12 & -8 \end{bmatrix}$

1d. $\begin{bmatrix} -3 & 1 & 2 \\ -11 & 11 & 6 \end{bmatrix}$

Additional Answers

1e. impossible because the inside dimensions do not match

1f. $[-7 \quad -5 \quad 6]$

2a. $\begin{bmatrix} 0.8 & -0.6 \\ 0.2 & -0.4 \end{bmatrix}$

2b. $\begin{bmatrix} -\frac{3}{85} & \frac{16}{85} & -\frac{2}{85} \\ \frac{18}{85} & -\frac{11}{85} & \frac{12}{85} \\ -\frac{32}{85} & \frac{29}{85} & \frac{7}{85} \end{bmatrix}$

or $\begin{bmatrix} -0.0353 & 0.1882 & -0.0235 \\ 0.2118 & -0.1294 & 0.1412 \\ -0.3765 & 0.3412 & 0.0824 \end{bmatrix}$

2c. does not exist

2d. $\begin{bmatrix} -\frac{5}{56} & \frac{1}{7} & \frac{1}{8} \\ -\frac{3}{56} & \frac{2}{7} & -\frac{1}{8} \\ -\frac{29}{56} & \frac{3}{7} & \frac{1}{8} \end{bmatrix}$

LESSON 7.1, PAGE 363

Steps 1 and 2 sample data:

Time (s) x	Height (m) y
0.00	2.000
0.05	1.988
0.10	1.951
0.15	1.890
0.20	1.804
0.25	1.694
0.30	1.559
0.35	1.400
0.40	1.216
0.45	1.008

D_1	D_2
−0.012	
−0.037	−0.025
−0.061	−0.024
−0.086	−0.025
−0.110	−0.024
−0.135	−0.025
−0.159	−0.024
−0.184	−0.025
−0.208	−0.024

LESSON 7.2, PAGE 372

Step 2 sample data (unadjusted for starting line):

Time (s)	Distance from motion sensor (m)
0.2	0.143
0.4	0.145
0.6	0.143
0.8	0.316
1.0	1.046
1.2	1.720
1.4	2.321
1.6	2.857
1.8	3.325
2.0	3.731
2.2	4.070
2.4	4.341
2.6	4.548
2.8	4.688
3.0	4.756

Time (s)	Distance from motion sensor (m)
3.2	4.757
3.4	4.693
3.6	4.562
3.8	4.371
4.0	4.119
4.2	3.809
4.4	3.438
4.6	3.010
4.8	2.528
5.0	1.993
5.2	1.397
5.4	0.761
5.6	0.101
5.8	0.074
6.0	0.081

Step 3 sample data (adjusted for starting line):

Time (s) x	Distance from line (m), y
0.2	−0.357
0.4	−0.355
0.6	−0.357
0.8	−0.184
1.0	0.546
1.2	1.220
1.4	1.821
1.6	2.357
1.8	2.825
2.0	3.231
2.2	3.570
2.4	3.841
2.6	4.048
2.8	4.188
3.0	4.256

Time (s) x	Distance from line (m), y
3.2	4.257
3.4	4.193
3.6	4.062
3.8	3.871
4.0	3.619
4.2	3.309
4.4	2.938
4.6	2.510
4.8	2.028
5.0	1.493
5.2	0.897
5.4	0.261
5.6	−0.399
5.8	−0.426
6.0	−0.419

Step 4 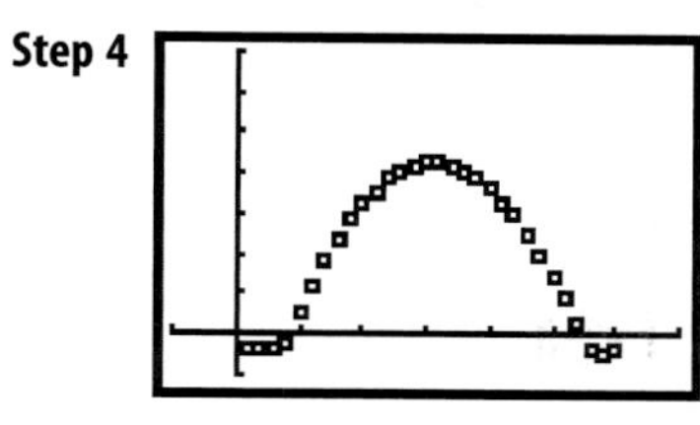

[−1, 7, 1, −1, 7, 1]

The shape of the graph is parabolic. A quadratic function would model these data. Neglecting the first and last couple of points (when the can started and stopped), the second differences, D_2, are almost constant around −0.06, which implies that a quadratic model is appropriate.

Step 8 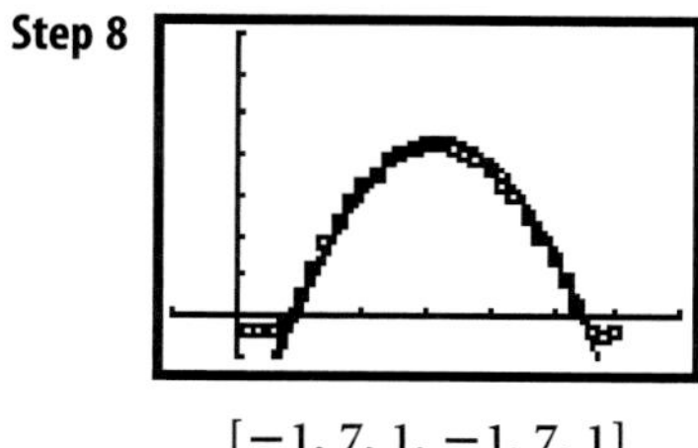

[−1, 7, 1, −1, 7, 1]

You would use the vertex form when you know the vertex and at least one other point by which to determine the scale factor. You would use the general form when you have any three points. You would use the factored form when you know the *x*-intercepts and at least one other point by which to determine the scale factor.

LESSON 7.5, PAGE 395

5c. 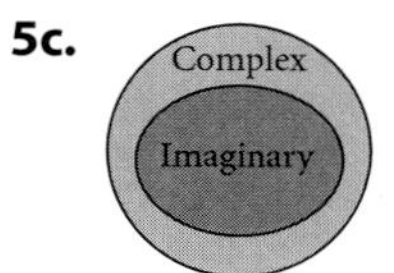

5d. 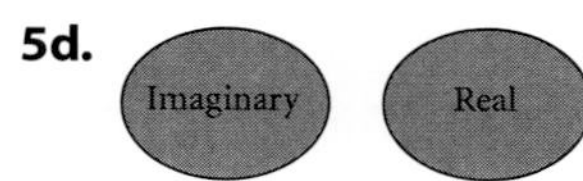

8. 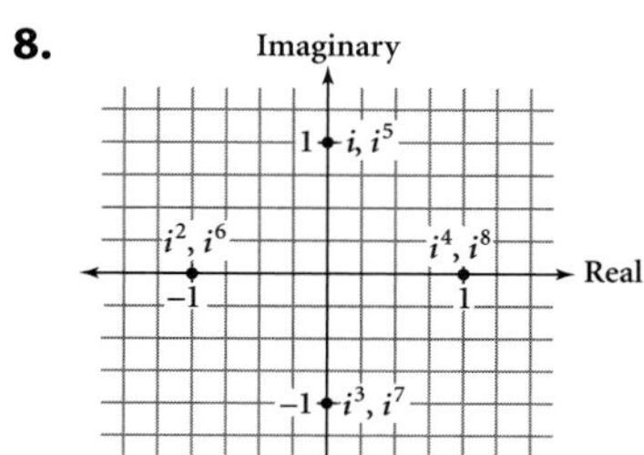

Each multiplication by *i* rotates another 90° counterclockwise. They all correspond to 1, *i*, −1, or −*i*; $i^{17} = i$.

LESSON 7.7, PAGES 406, 409

Investigation

These answers assume that the piece of notebook paper is 21.5-by-28 cm or 8.5-by-11 in. Answers will vary if paper with different dimensions is used.

sample data:

Distance along bottom (base of triangle) (cm) x	Height of triangle (cm)	Area (cm²) y
0.0	10.8	0
2.0	10.7	11
4.0	10.4	21
6.0	9.9	30
8.0	9.3	37
10.0	8.4	42
12.0	7.4	44
14.0	6.2	43
16.0	4.8	38
18.0	3.2	29
20.0	1.4	14
21.5	0	0

polynomial function: $y = \frac{1}{2}x\left(\frac{462.25 - x^2}{43}\right)$ or $y = \frac{1}{86}x(21.5 - x)(21.5 + x)$ or $y = -\frac{1}{86}x^3 + \frac{43}{8}x$

[−5, 25, 5, −10, 50, 10]

Maximum: approximately (12.4, 44.5); when *x* is approximately 12.4 cm, the area is maximized at approximately 44.5 cm².

Exercises

6a. 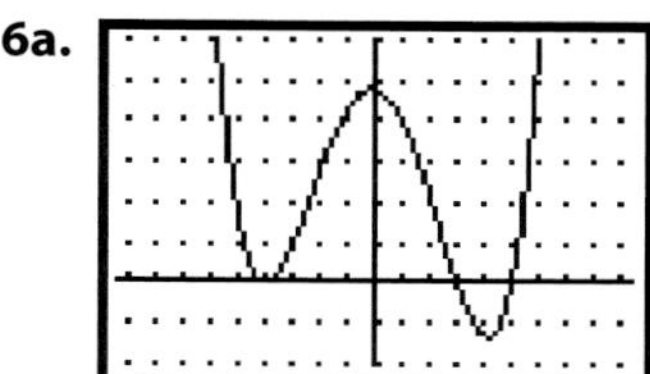

[−9.4, 9.4, 1, −200, 600, 100]

6b. 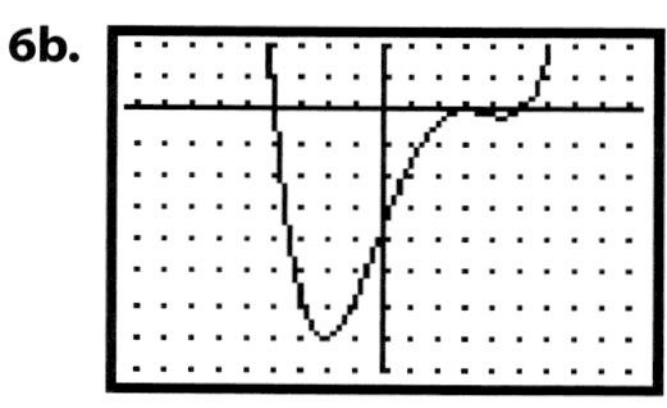

[−9.4, 9.4, 1, −800, 200, 100]

6c.

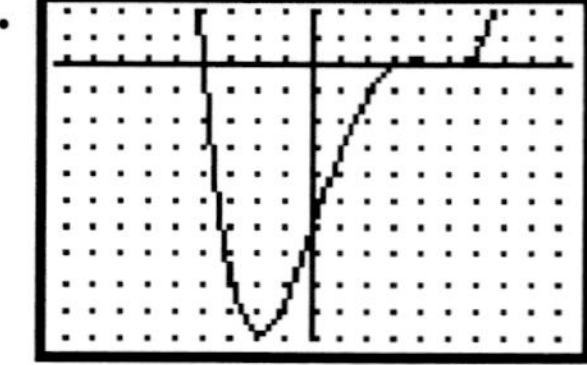

[−9.4, 9.4, 1, −1000, 200, 100]

6d.

[−9.4, 9.4, 1, −2000, 500, 500]

6e.

[−9.4, 9.4, 1, −2000, 2500, 500]

6f.

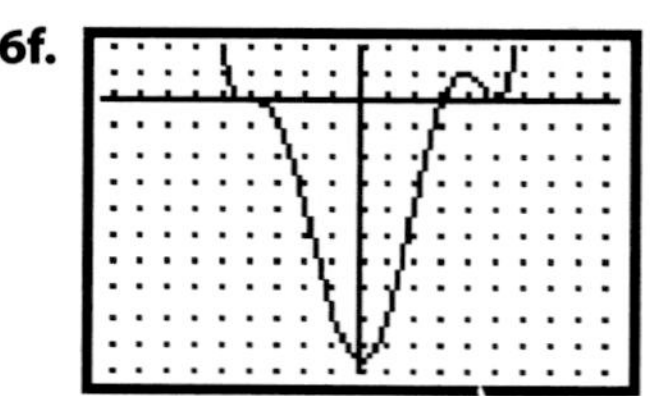

[−9.4, 9.4, 1, −10000, 2000, 1000]

CHAPTER 7 REVIEW, PAGE 419

4a. vertex form; general form: $y = 2x^2 - 8x - 8$; factored form:

$$y = 2\left(x - \left(2 + 2\sqrt{2}\right)\right)\left(x - \left(2 - 2\sqrt{2}\right)\right)$$

4b. factored form; general form: $y = -3x^2 + 12x + 15$; vertex form: $y = -3(x - 2)^2 + 27$

4c. general form; factored form: $y = (x + 2)(x + 1)$; vertex form: $y = (x + 1.5)^2 - 0.25$

4d. factored form; general form: $y = x^3 + 2x^2 - 11x - 12$; no vertex form for cubic equations

4e. general form; factored form:

$$y = 2\left(x - \frac{-5 + \sqrt{73}}{4}\right)\left(x - \frac{-5 - \sqrt{73}}{4}\right);$$

vertex form: $y = 2(x + 1.25)^2 - 9.125$

4f. vertex form; general form: $y = -x^2 - 14x - 51$; factored form:

$$y = -\left(x - \left(-7 + i\sqrt{2}\right)\right)\left(x - \left(-7 - i\sqrt{2}\right)\right)$$

5a.

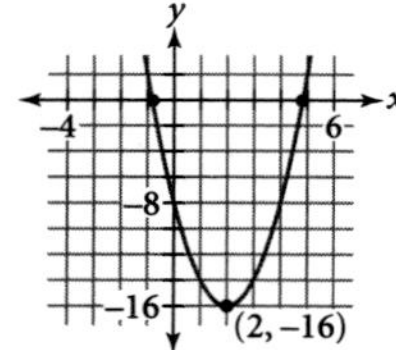

zeros: $x = -0.83$ and $x = 4.83$

5b.

zeros: $x = -1$ and $x = 5$

5c.

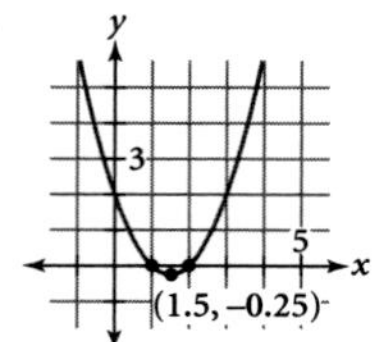

zeros: $x = 1$ and $x = 2$

5d.

zeros: $x = -4$, $x = -1$, and $x = 3$

5e.

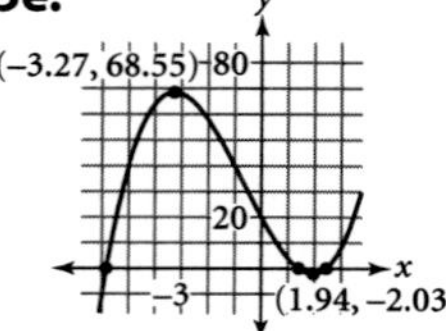

zeros: $x = -5.84$, $x = 1.41$, and $x = 2.43$

5f.

zeros: $x = -2$, $x = -1$, $x = 0.5$, and $x = 2$

LESSON 8.1, PAGES 426, 427, 428

Step 1a $22t = 900$; 40.9 h

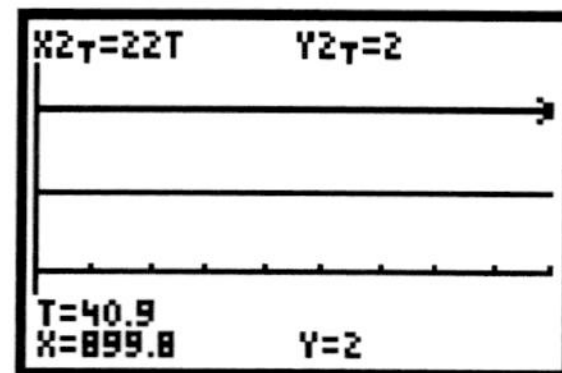

[0, 900, 100, −1, 3, 1]
$0 \le t \le 50$

Step 1b $x = 18 \cdot 40.9$; 736.2 mi east of Corpus Christi

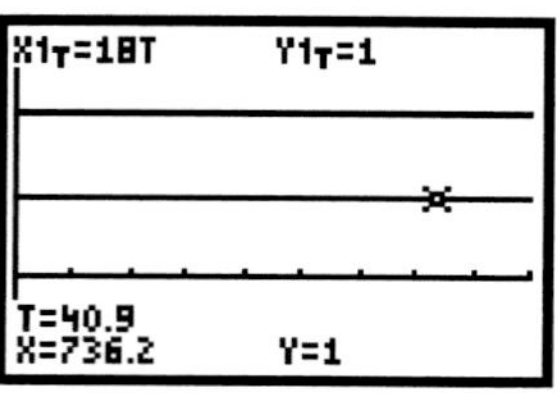

[0, 900, 100, −1, 3, 1]
$0 \le t \le 50$

Step 1c $18t + 82 = 22t$; 20.5 h

X2T=22T Y2T=2
T=20.5
X=451 Y=2

[0, 900, 100, −1, 3, 1]
$0 \le t \le 50$

X1T=18T Y1T=1
T=20.5
X=369 Y=1

[0, 900, 100, −1, 3, 1]
$0 \le t \le 50$

Step 1d $22t - 18t < 60$; $t < 15$; during the first 15 h

X1T=18T Y1T=1
T=15
X=270 Y=1

[0, 900, 100, −1, 3, 1]
$0 \le t \le 50$

X2T=22T Y2T=2
T=15
X=330 Y=2

[0, 900, 100, −1, 3, 1]
$0 \le t \le 50$

1a.

t	x	y
−2	−7	−3
−1	−4	−1
0	−1	1
1	2	3
2	5	5

1b.

t	x	y
−2	−1	4
−1	0	1
0	1	0
1	2	1
2	3	4

1c.

t	x	y
−2	4	1
−1	1	2
0	0	3
1	1	4
2	4	5

1d.

t	x	y
−2	−3	0
−1	−2	1.73
0	−1	2
1	0	1.73
2	1	0

2a.

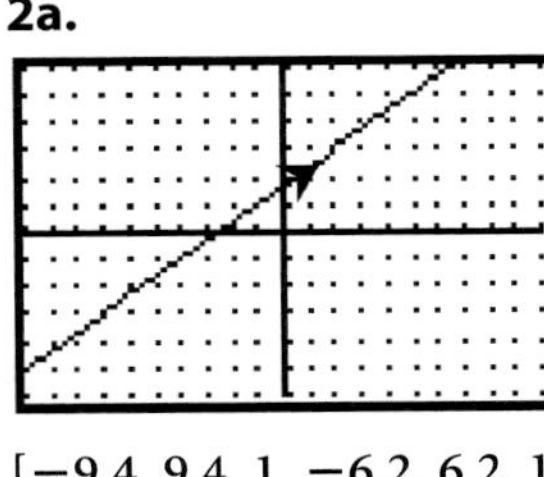

[−9.4, 9.4, 1, −6.2, 6.2, 1]
$-3 \le t \le 2.5$

2b.

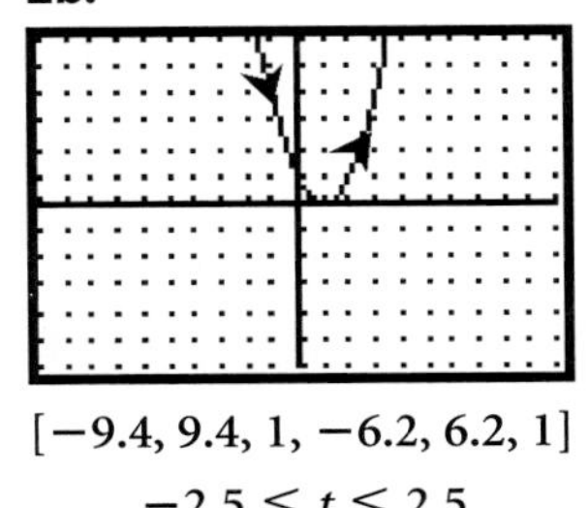

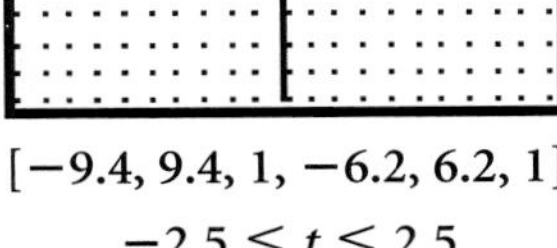

[−9.4, 9.4, 1, −6.2, 6.2, 1]
$-2.5 \le t \le 2.5$

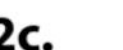

2c.

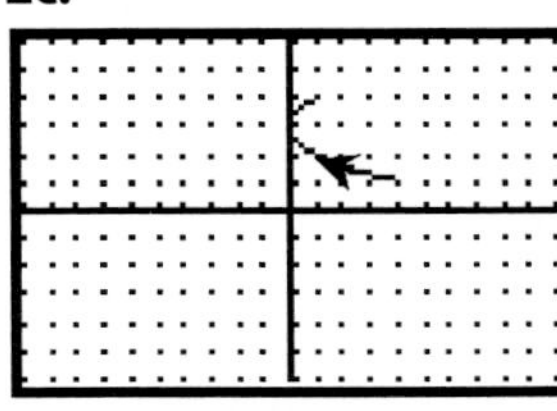

[−9.4, 9.4, 1, −6.2, 6.2, 1]

2d.

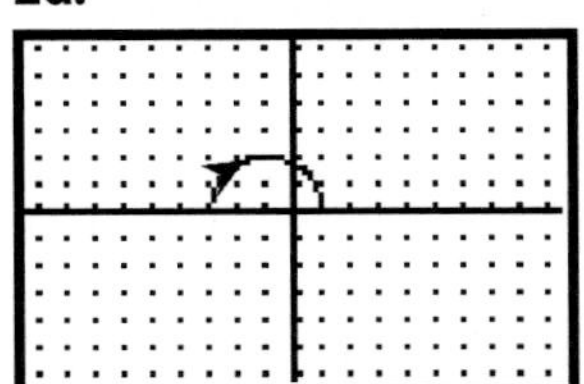

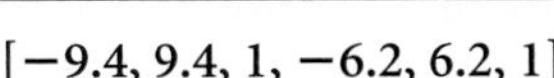

[−9.4, 9.4, 1, −6.2, 6.2, 1]

3a.

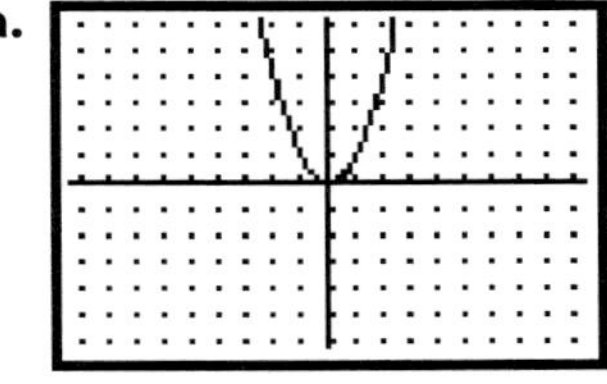

[−9.4, 9.4, 1, −6.2, 6.2, 1]

3b. The graph is translated right 2 units.

[−9.4, 9.4, 1, −6.2, 6.2, 1]

3c. The graph is translated down 3 units.

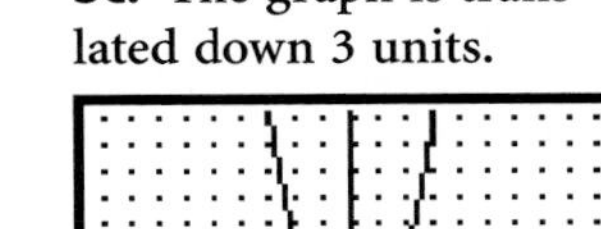

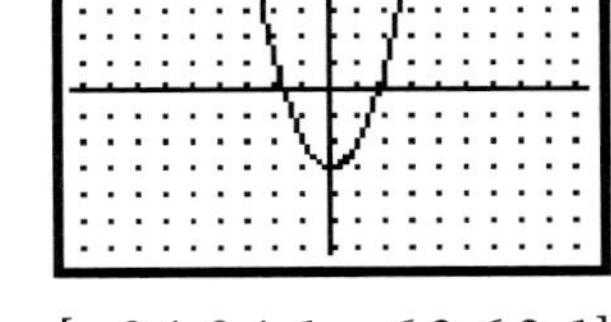

[−9.4, 9.4, 1, −6.2, 6.2, 1]

4f. The 3 stretches the graph vertically, the 2 translates it right 2 units, and the 4 being subtracted translates it down 4 units.

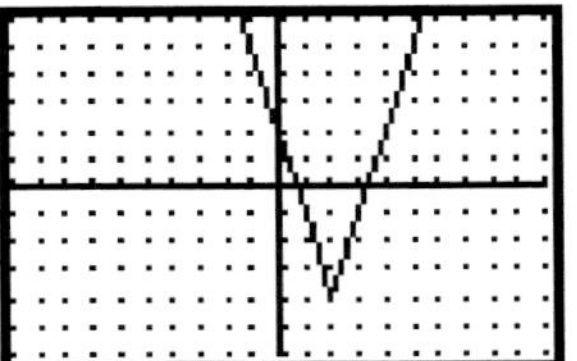

[−9.4, 9.4, 1, −6.2, 6.2, 1]

5f.

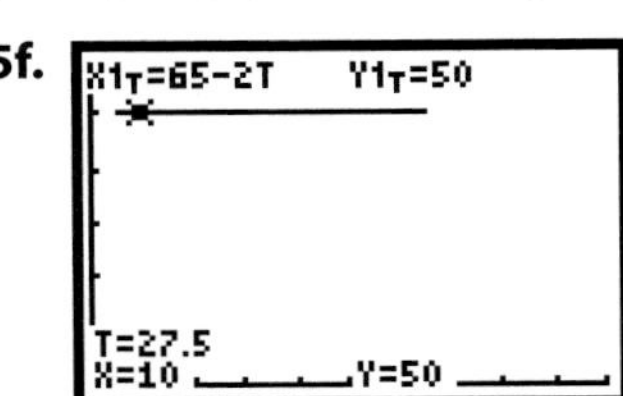

[0, 100, 10, 0, 65, 10]
$0 \le t \le 30$

She crosses the 10-yard line after 27.5 s.

Step 2 Sample data: A complete data set is available on the Calculator Programs and Data CD. If students are not able to download data sets to their calculators, use this condensed data set. The sample answers given in Steps 3 and 4 are based on the full data set. If students use the condensed data, answers will be slightly different.

t	x	y
0.1	0.95	2.50
0.6	1.00	2.47
1.1	1.10	2.39
1.6	1.19	2.38
2.1	1.26	2.32
2.6	1.36	2.25
3.1	1.43	2.21
3.6	1.50	2.12
4.1	1.62	2.11
4.6	1.71	2.02
5.0	1.78	1.95

14d. Tanker A: $x = 18t$, $y = 1$; Tanker B: $x = 900 - 22t$, $y = 2$; they are within 50 mi of each other for $21.25 \le t \le 23.75$.

after 10 h

[0, 900, 100, −1, 3, 1]

after 20 h

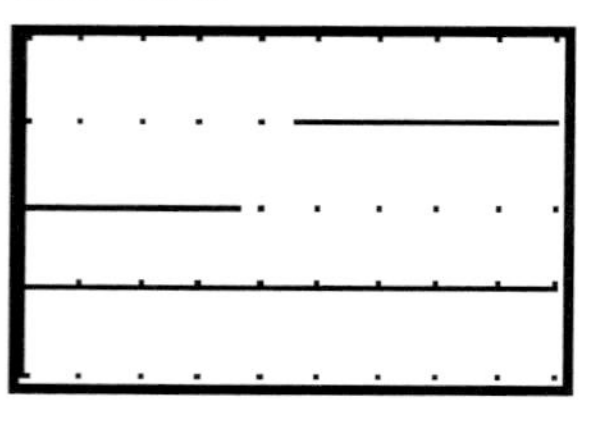

[0, 900, 100, −1, 3, 1]

after 30 h

[0, 900, 100, −1, 3, 1]

16d.

[−10, 10, 1, −10, 10, 1]

Step 3

Time (s)	Boat A		Boat B		Boat C	
t	x	y	x	y	x	y
0	0	10	25	5	5	0
1	7	10	24	5	8	4
2	14	10	23	5	11	8
3	21	10	22	5	14	12

3a.

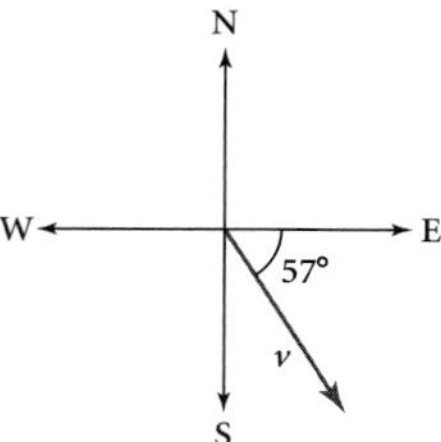

3b.

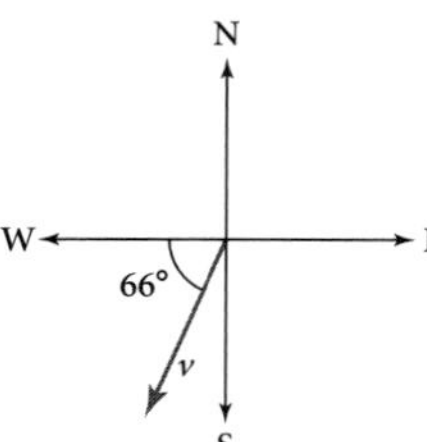

3c.

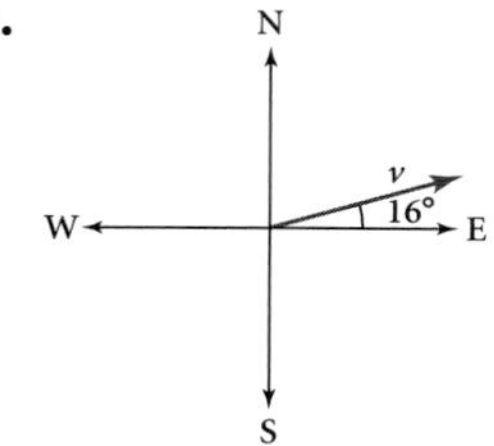

3d.

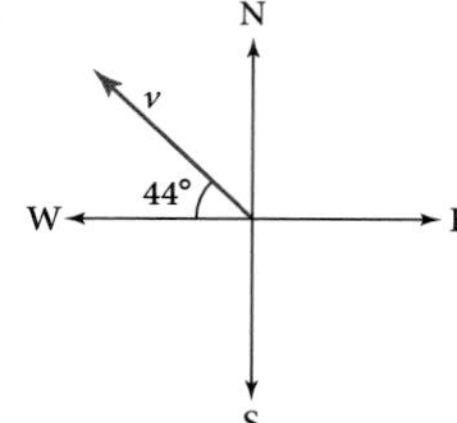

16b. $\left[\begin{array}{cc|c} 5 & -3 & -1 \\ 2 & 4 & 5 \end{array}\right] \xrightarrow{\frac{1}{5}R_1 \to R_1} \left[\begin{array}{cc|c} 1 & -\frac{3}{5} & -\frac{1}{5} \\ 2 & 4 & 5 \end{array}\right]$

$\xrightarrow{-2R_1 + R_2 \to R_2} \left[\begin{array}{cc|c} 1 & -\frac{3}{5} & -\frac{1}{5} \\ 0 & \frac{26}{5} & \frac{27}{5} \end{array}\right] \xrightarrow{\frac{5}{26}R_2 \to R_2} \left[\begin{array}{cc|c} 1 & -\frac{3}{5} & -\frac{1}{5} \\ 0 & 1 & \frac{27}{26} \end{array}\right]$

$\xrightarrow{\frac{3}{5}R_2 + R_1 \to R_1} \left[\begin{array}{cc|c} 1 & 0 & \frac{11}{26} \\ 0 & 1 & \frac{27}{26} \end{array}\right]$

1d. When $t = -1$, the y-value is undefined.

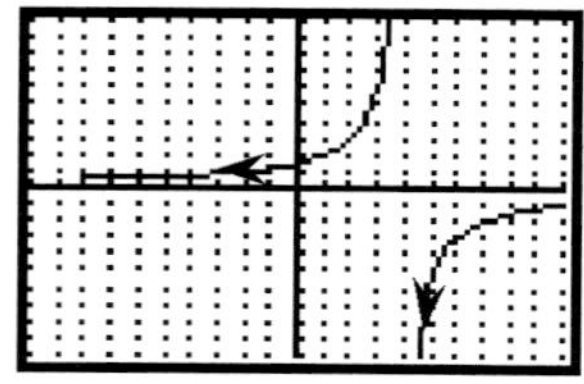

[−10, 10, 1, −10, 10, 1]

LESSON 9.1, PAGE 488

Step 2 Sample answer: These values of AC and CB were calculated using the Pythagorean Theorem. Students may also measure the lengths.

x (m)	AC (m)	CB (m)	$AC + CB$ (m)
0	5	21.19	26.19
2	5.39	19.31	24.70
4	6.40	17.46	23.86
6	7.81	15.65	23.46
8	9.43	13.89	23.33
10	11.18	12.21	23.39
12	13	10.63	23.63
14	14.87	9.22	24.09
16	16.76	8.06	24.82
18	18.68	7.28	25.96
20	20.62	7	27.62

Step 3 Using the table of data from Step 2, the best location for point C is 8 m from the end of the pool. The minimum distance by this method is approximately 23.33 m.

Using the Pythagorean Theorem to write the equation $y = \sqrt{x^2 + 5^2} + \sqrt{(20 - x)^2 + 7^2}$, where y represents the sum $AC + CB$, and finding the minimum of the function, the best location for point C is approximately 8.33 m. The minimum distance by this method is approximately 23.32 m.

Although the function $y = \sqrt{x^2 + 5^2} + \sqrt{(20 - x)^2 + 7^2}$ has a definite minimum, there is a range of x-values, approximately $7.7 \le x \le 9.0$, that result in paths that differ by less than 0.01 m.

Step 4

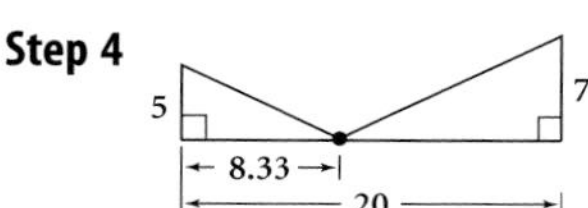

Step 5

x (m)	Time for AC (s)	Time for CB (s)	Total time (s)
0	4.17	52.98	57.15
2	4.49	48.28	52.77
4	5.34	43.65	48.99
6	6.51	39.13	45.64
8	7.86	34.73	42.59
10	9.32	30.53	39.85
12	10.83	26.58	37.41
14	12.39	23.05	35.44
16	13.97	20.15	34.12
18	15.57	18.20	33.77
20	17.18	17.50	34.68

LESSON 9.2, PAGE 503

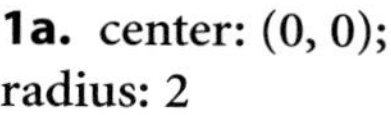

1a. center: (0, 0); radius: 2

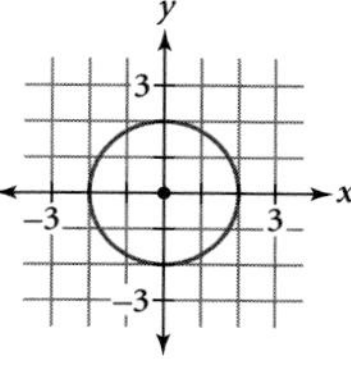

$y = \pm\sqrt{4 - x^2}$

1b. center: (3, 0); radius: 1

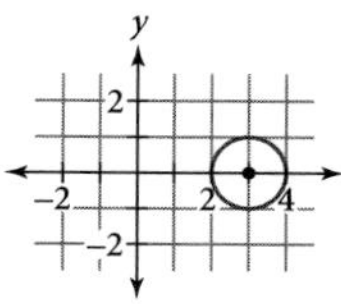

$y = \pm\sqrt{1 - (x - 3)^2}$

1c. center: (−1, 2); radius: 3

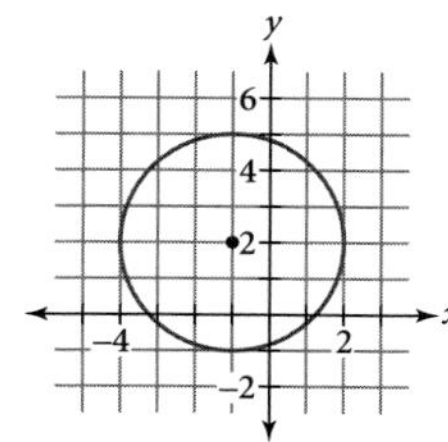

$y = \pm\sqrt{9 - (x + 1)^2} + 2$

1d. center: (0, 1.5); radius: 0.5

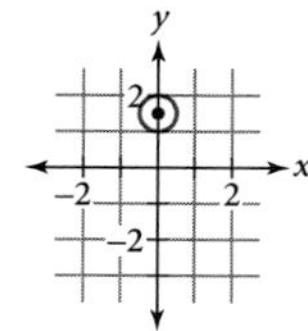

$y = \pm\sqrt{0.25 - x^2} + 1.5$

1e. center: (1, 2); radius: 2

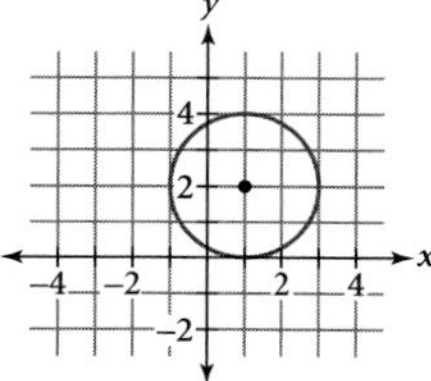

1f. center: (−3, 0); radius: 4

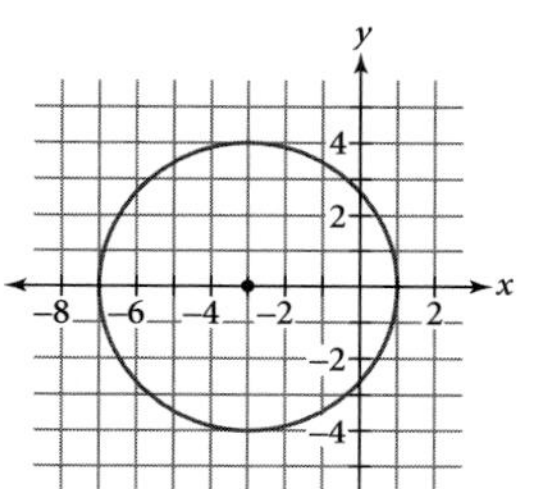

4a. endpoints: (2, 0), (−2, 0), (0, 4), (0, −4)

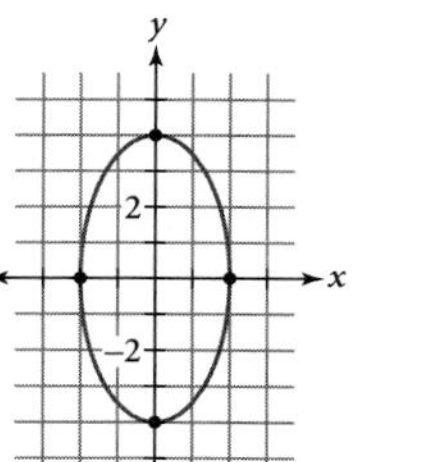

4b. endpoints: (5, −2), (−1, −2), (2, −1), (2, −3)

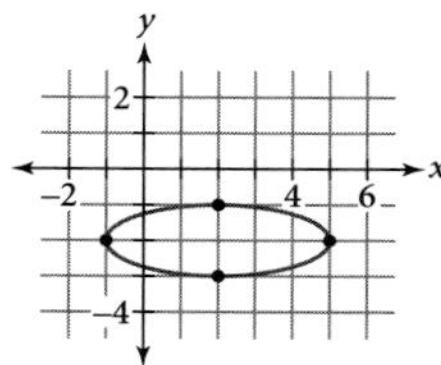

4c. Endpoints: (1, 1), (7, 1), (4, 4), (4, −2). Endpoints may vary because graph is a circle.

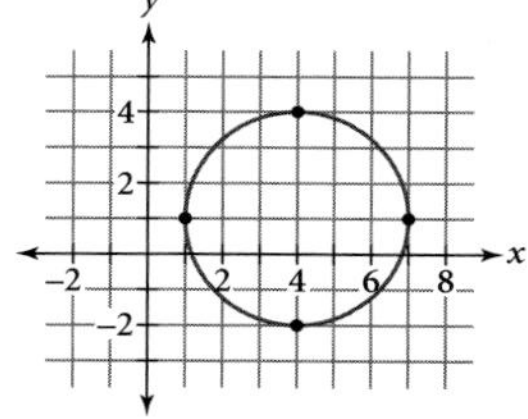

Additional Answers

4d. endpoints: $(-5, -1)$, $(1, -1)$, $(-2, 1)$, $(-2, -3)$

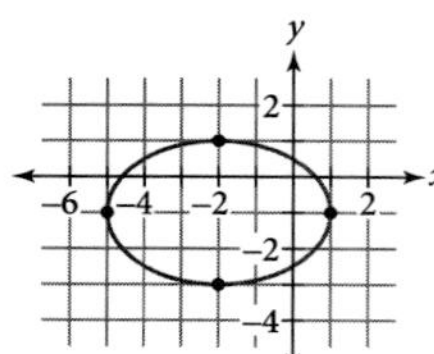

4e. endpoints: $(-5, 3)$, $(3, 3)$, $(-1, 5)$, $(-1, 1)$

4f. endpoints: $(0, 0)$, $(6, 0)$, $(3, 5)$, $(3, -5)$

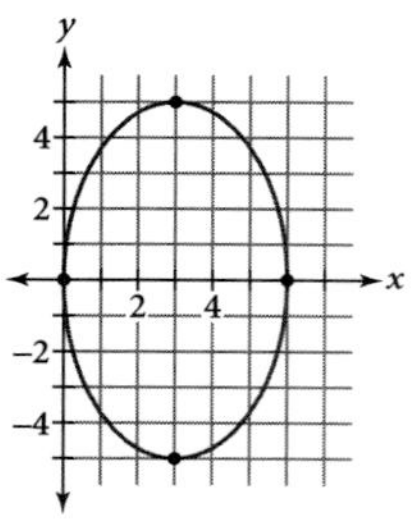

LESSON 9.3, PAGE 511

2a. line of symmetry: $x = 0$

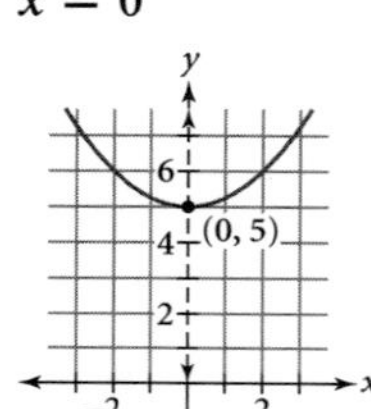

2b. line of symmetry: $y = -2$

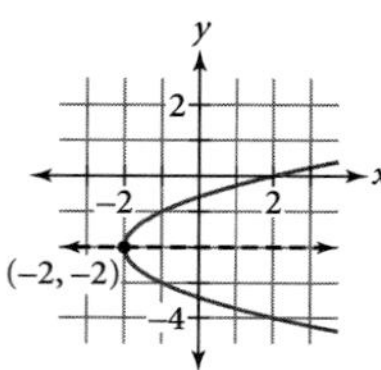

2c. line of symmetry: $x = -3$

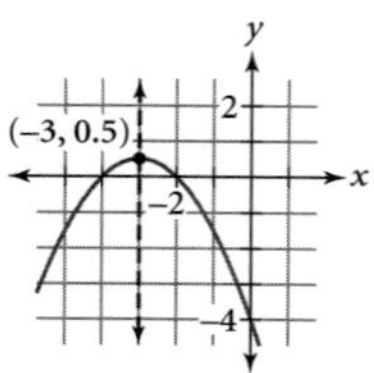

2d. line of symmetry: $y = 0$

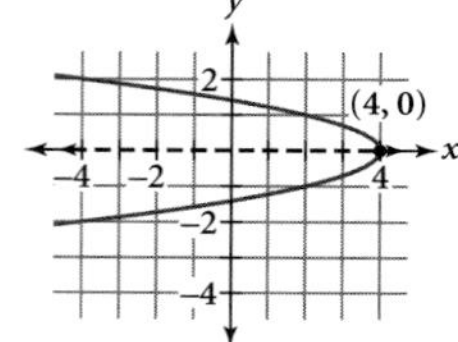

2e. line of symmetry: $x = -1$

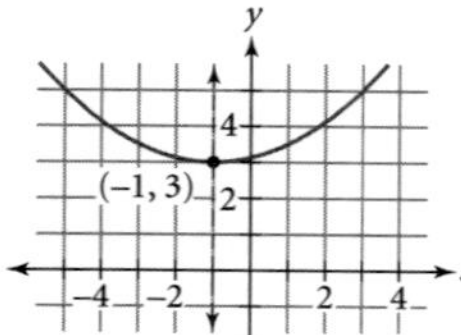

2f. line of symmetry: $y = 0$

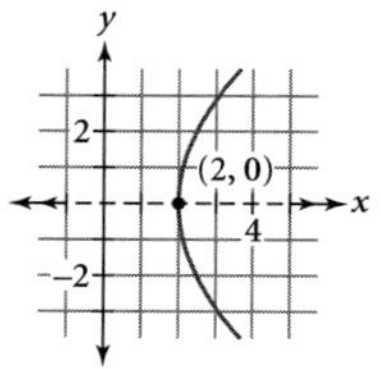

LESSON 9.4, PAGES 518, 520, 521, 522

Step 1 sample data:

Time (s)	Distance (m)	Time (s)	Distance (m)
0	5.000	3.8	0.926
0.2	4.720	4.0	0.966
0.4	4.381	4.2	1.056
0.6	4.016	4.4	1.240
0.8	3.688	4.6	1.387
1.0	3.558	4.8	1.568
1.2	3.302	5.0	1.673
1.4	3.078	5.2	1.978
1.6	2.709	5.4	2.251
1.8	2.410	5.6	2.478
2.0	2.249	5.8	2.748
2.2	1.969	6.0	3.099
2.4	1.770	6.2	3.284
2.6	1.605	6.4	3.533
2.8	1.525	6.6	3.820
3.0	1.291	6.8	4.116
3.2	1.022	7.0	4.379
3.4	0.901	7.2	4.695
3.6	0.882	7.4	4.955

Graph of the data:

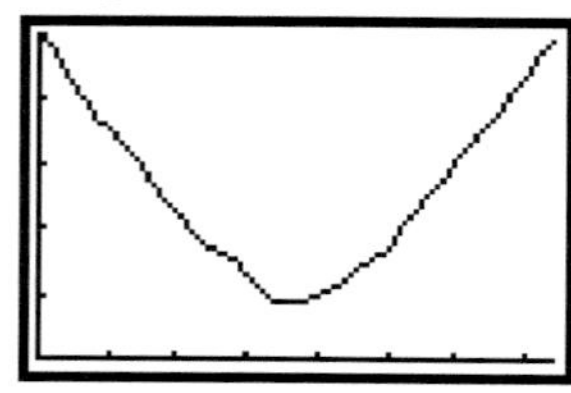

[0, 7.4, 1, 0, 5, 1]

1a. vertices: $(-2, 0)$ and $(2, 0)$; asymptotes: $y = \pm 2x$

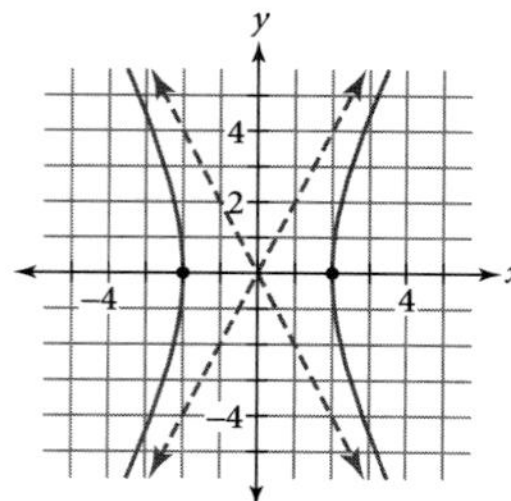

1b. vertices: (2, −1) and (2, −3); asymptotes: $y = \frac{1}{3}x - \frac{8}{3}$ and $y = -\frac{1}{3}x - \frac{4}{3}$

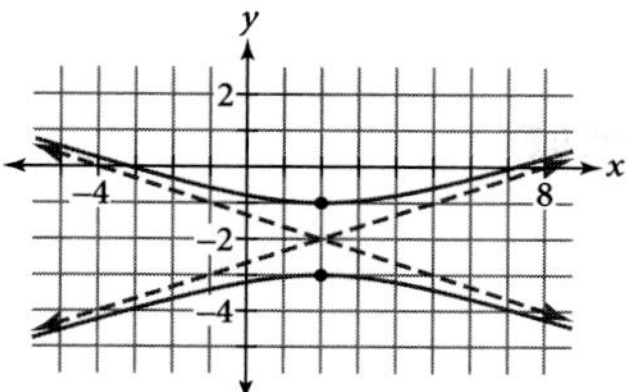

1c. vertices: (1, 1) and (7, 1); asymptotes: $y = x - 3$ and $y = -x + 5$

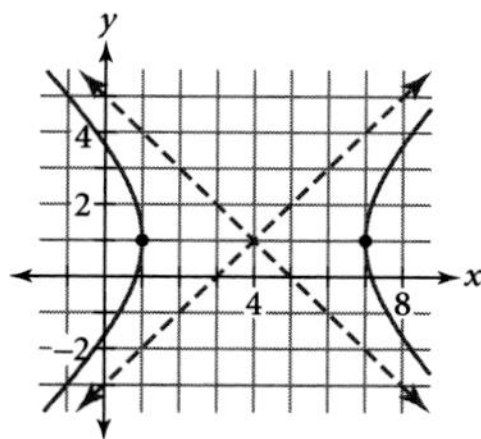

1d. vertices: (−2, 1) and (−2, −3); asymptotes: $y = \frac{2}{3}x + \frac{1}{3}$ and $y = -\frac{2}{3}x - \frac{7}{3}$

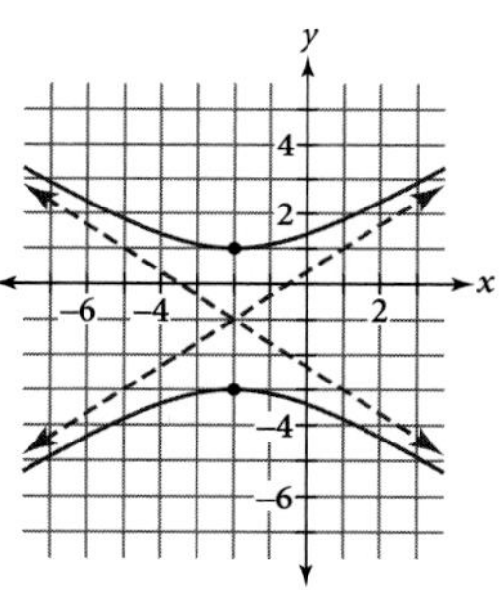

1e. vertices: (−5, 3) and (3, 3); asymptotes: $y = 0.5x + 3.5$ and $y = -0.5x + 2.5$

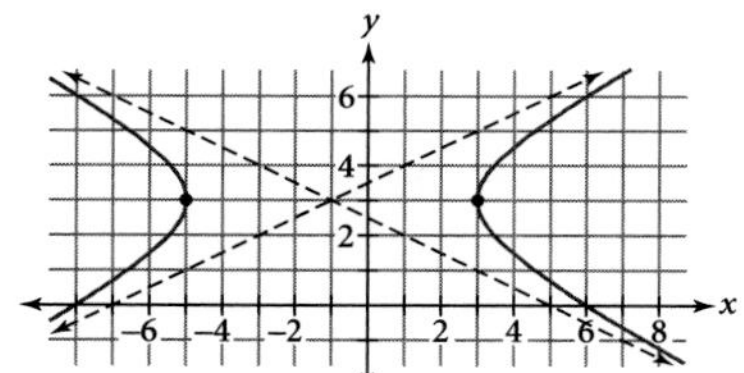

1f. vertices: (3, 5) and (3, −5); asymptotes: $y = \frac{5}{3}x - 5$ and $y = -\frac{5}{3}x + 5$

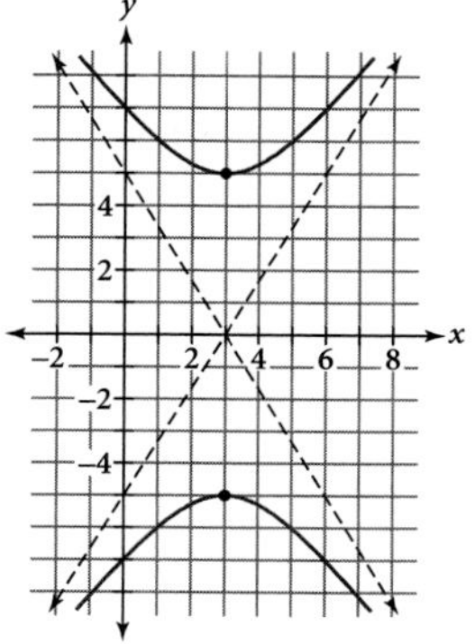

11a.

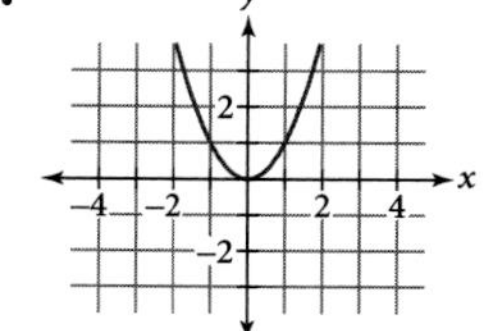

11b.

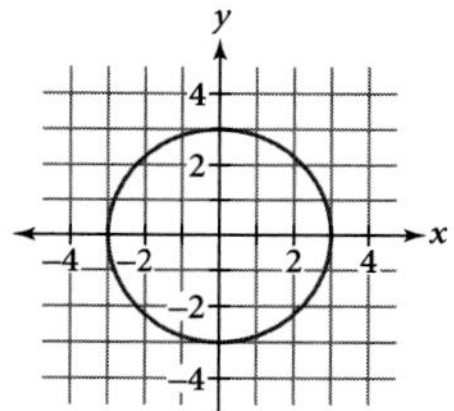

11c.

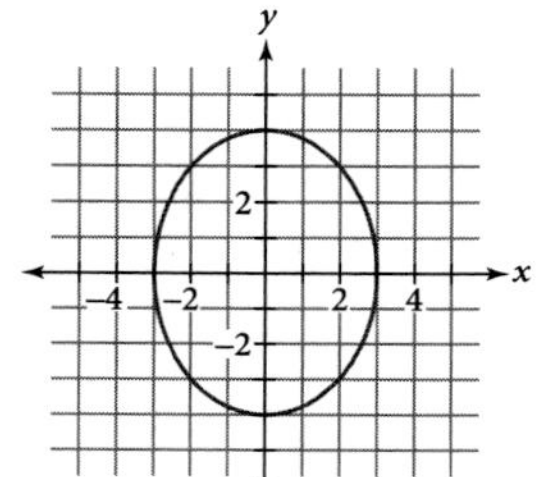

11d.

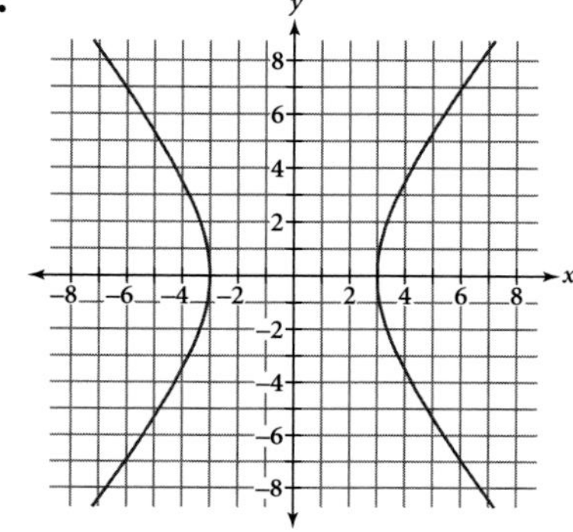

Additional Answers

11e. The resulting shapes are a paraboloid, a sphere, an ellipsoid, and a hyperboloid, although students will probably give a description of each figure rather than the proper name.

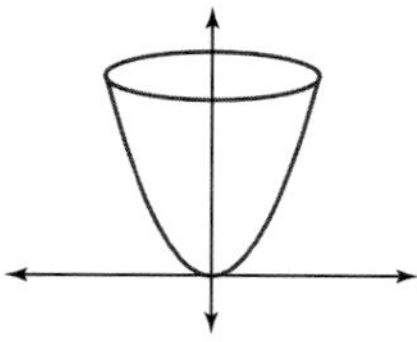
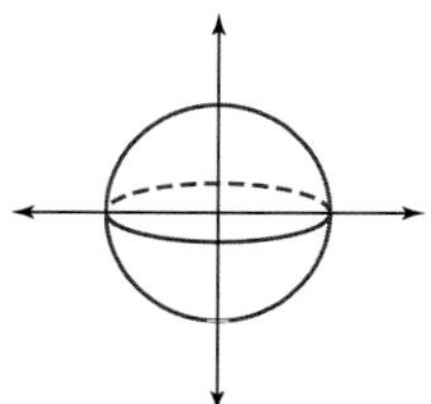
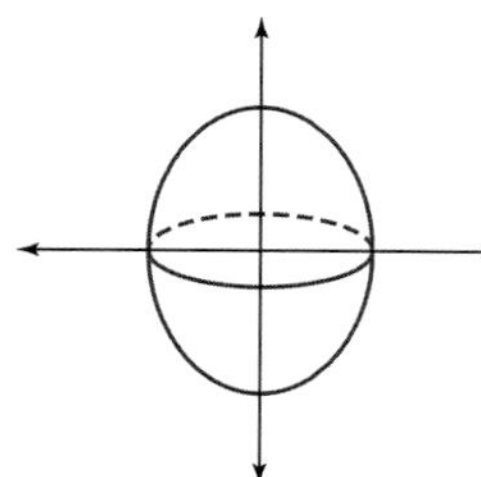
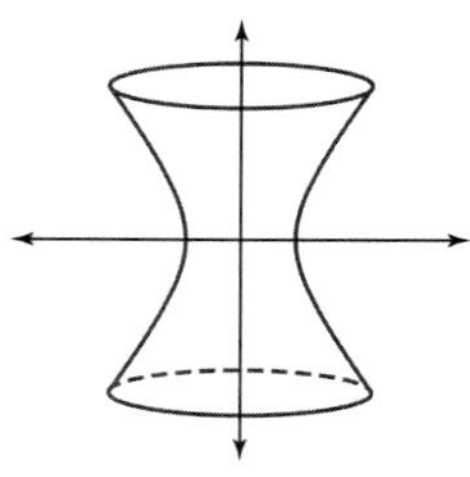

14. $\left(\frac{x - 11900000}{57900000}\right)^2 + \left(\frac{y}{56700000}\right)^2 = 1$

16a. vertex: $(-1, -2)$; focus: $(-1, -2.25)$; directrix: $y = -1.75$

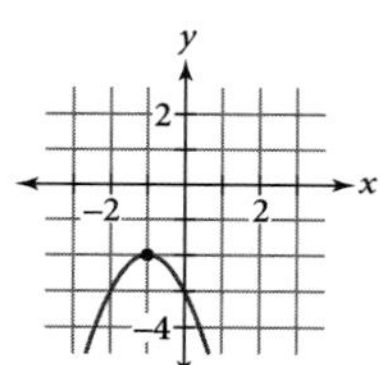

16b. vertex: $(3, 0.5)$; focus: $(3, 1)$; directrix: $y = 0$

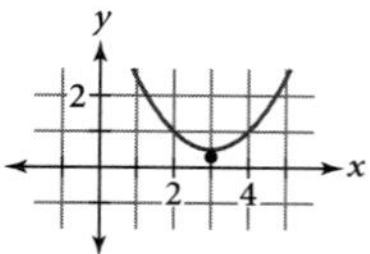

16c. vertex: $(-6, 0)$; focus: $(-5.5, 0)$; directrix: $x = -6.5$

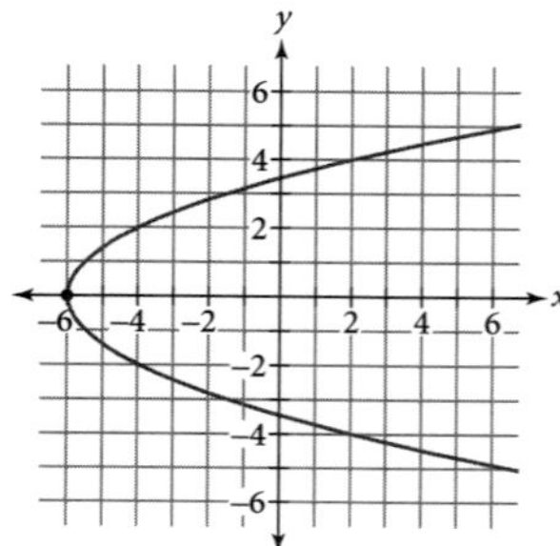

EXPLORATION, PAGE 524

Step 7 The trace is an ellipse. Because the sum $AC + CB$ remains constant as point C moves, the intersections trace the locus of points for which the sum of the distances from two fixed points, F_1 and F_2, is constant.

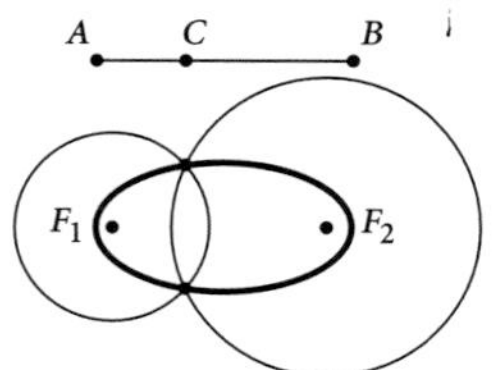

Step 9

1. As the foci move farther apart, the minor axis of an ellipse becomes shorter and the major axis becomes longer. When the distance between the foci is greater than AB, an ellipse no longer exists. When the foci are both at the same point, you have a circle.

3. Construct a line (directrix) and focus (F). Construct $\overline{FB}$ to any point B on the directrix. Construct the midpoint, A, of $\overline{FB}$ and then the perpendicular line through the midpoint. Construct the line perpendicular to the directrix through point B. Construct the intersection, P, of the perpendicular bisector and the perpendicular. (Optional: Construct $\overline{FP}$.) Select points P and B to construct the locus. Because the construction produces congruent right triangles, $PF = PB$, so point P is equidistant from the focus and the directrix, and the locus is a parabola.

4. Possible construction: Construct a line. On the line, construct $\overline{AB}$ and point C outside $\overline{AB}$. Construct $\overline{AC}$ and $\overline{BC}$. Now follow Steps 4, 5, 6, and 9 of the ellipse instructions in the activity.

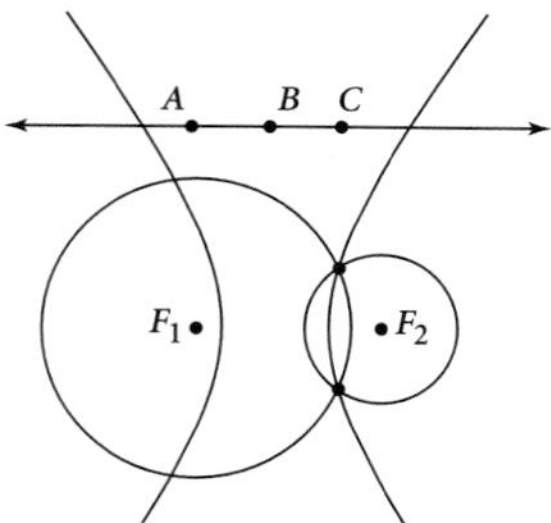

LESSON 9.5, PAGES 531, 533

5a. $y = \dfrac{\pm\sqrt{400x^2 + 1600}}{-8}$ or $y = \mp\frac{5}{2}\sqrt{x^2 + 4}$

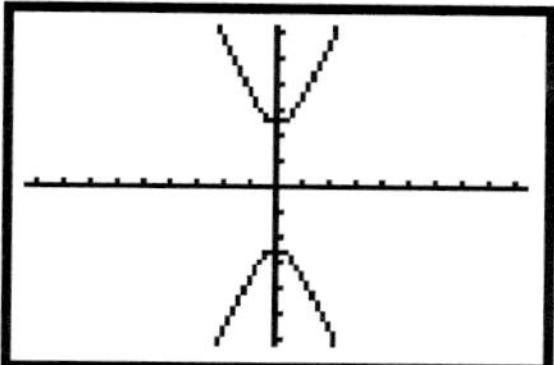

[−18.8, 18.8, 2, −12.4, 12.4, 2]

5b. $y = \dfrac{-16 \pm \sqrt{160x - 320}}{8}$ or

$y = \dfrac{-4 \pm \sqrt{10x - 20}}{2}$

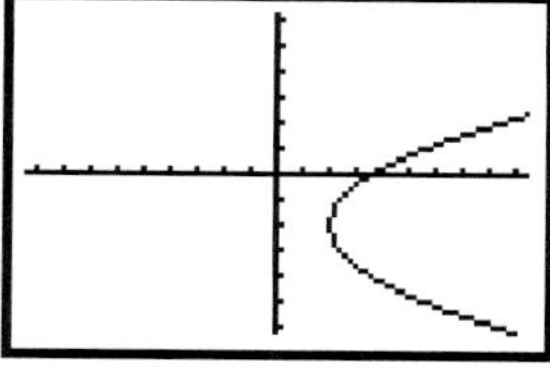

[−9.4, 9.4, 1, −6.2, 6.2, 1]

5c. $y = \dfrac{8 \pm \sqrt{-64x^2 - 384x - 560}}{8}$

or $y = 1 \pm \dfrac{\sqrt{-16x^2 - 96x - 140}}{4}$

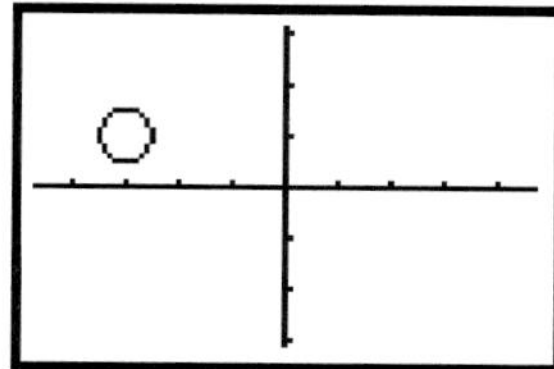

[−4.7, 4.7, 1, −3.1, 3.1, 1]

5d. $y = \dfrac{-20 \pm \sqrt{-60x^2 + 240x + 240}}{10}$

or $y = -2 \pm \dfrac{\sqrt{-15x^2 + 60x + 60}}{5}$

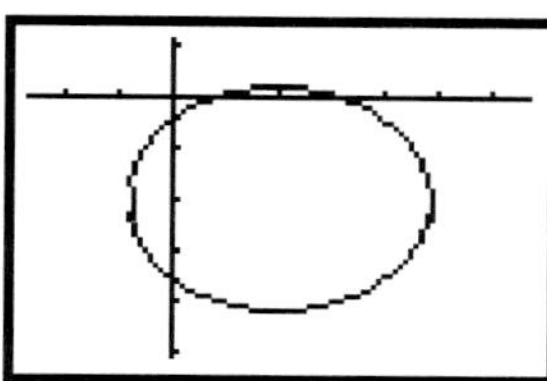

[−2.7, 6.7, 1, −5.1, 1.1, 1]

6a. $\left(\frac{3}{4}, \frac{73}{16}\right)$ or (0.75, 4.5625)

6b. (1.5, 0.5), (1.5, −0.5), (−1.5, 0.5), (−1.5, −0.5)

6c. (1.177, −1.240), (−1.177, −1.240), (2.767, −5.160), (−2.767, −5.160)

12. $y = -\frac{7}{24}x^2 - \frac{17}{12}x + 9$ or $x = 1.75y^2 - 25y + 83.25$

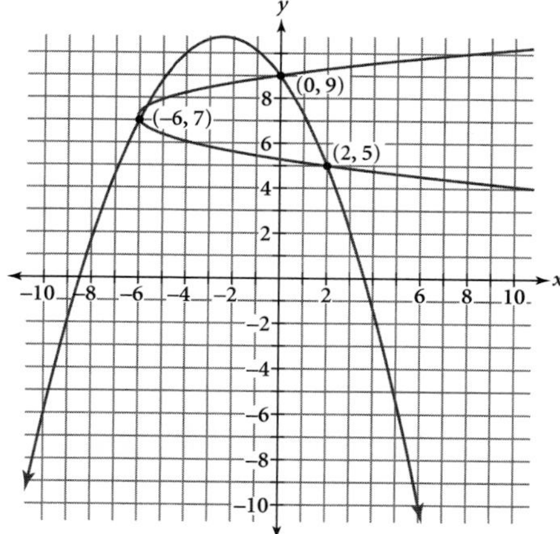

EXPLORATION, PAGE 535

2. $x = -2.1t^2 - 3.5t - 2.1$, $y = 2.1t^2 - 3.5t + 2.1$

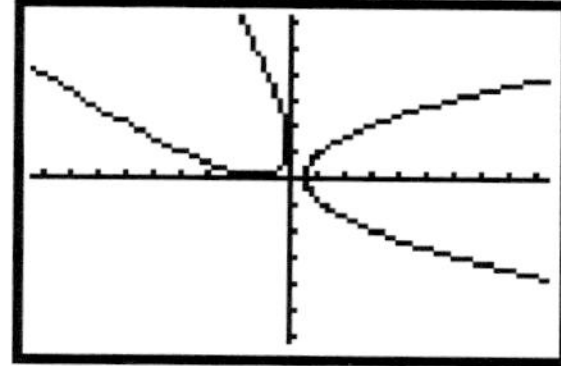

[−47, 47, 5, −31, 31, 5]

$-5 \leq t \leq 5$

3. $y = \frac{1}{2x}$. Replace x with $(x\cos\theta - y\sin\theta)$ and y with $(x\sin\theta + y\cos\theta)$ and substitute −45° for θ.

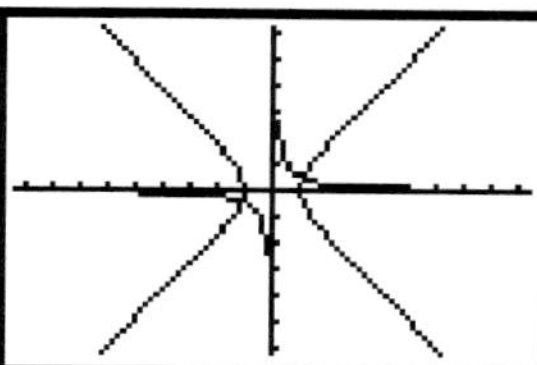

[−9.4, 9.4, 1, −6.2, 6.2, 1]

4a. Sample answer: A vertically oriented hyperbola with vertices (0, 1) and (0, −1) and asymptotes $y = \pm x$; the standard form of the equation for this hyperbola is $y^2 - x^2 = 1$.

4b. the graph of the hyperbola $y^2 - x^2 = 1$ rotated 50° counterclockwise about the origin

4c. 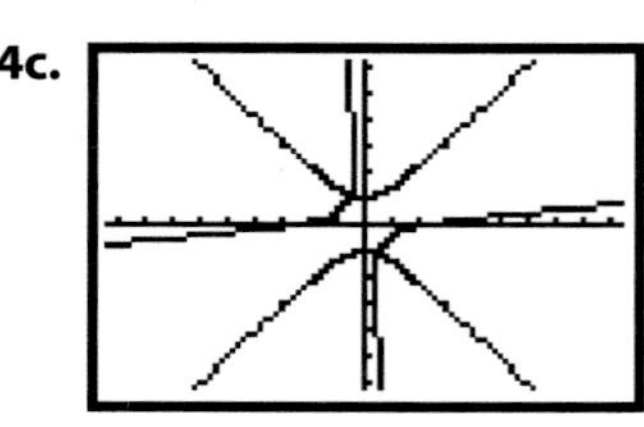

$[-9.4, 9.4, 1, -6.2, 6.2, 1]$

$0 \le t \le 360$

Extension

$x_1 = 2\cos t$ and $y_1 = 2\sin t$, with t-min $= 90°$, t-max $= 450°$, and t-step $= 120°$;
$x_2 = 0.5x_1 \cos 60° - 0.5y_1 \sin 60°$ and
$y_2 = 0.5x_1 \sin 60° + 0.5y_1 \cos 60°$

LESSON 9.6, PAGES 537, 540

Step 1 sample data:

Length (cm) x	Mass (number of pennies) y
16	6
16	5
15	7
15	6
14	6
13	7
13	6
12	8
12	7
11	8
10	9
9	10
8	11
7	13
6	16

1a. $f(x) = \frac{1}{x} + 2$

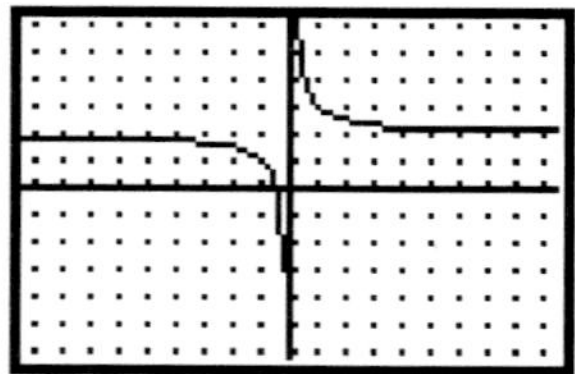

$[-9.4, 9.4, 1, -6.2, 6.2, 1]$

1b. $f(x) = \frac{1}{x - 3}$

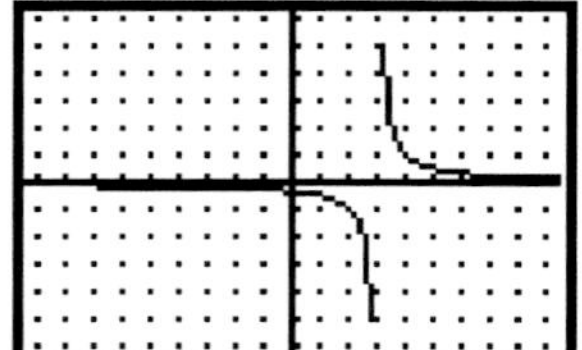

$[-9.4, 9.4, 1, -6.2, 6.2, 1]$

1c. $f(x) = \frac{1}{x + 4} - 1$

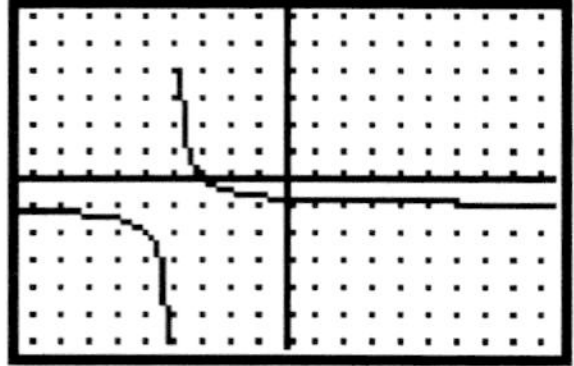

$[-9.4, 9.4, 1, -6.2, 6.2, 1]$

1d. $f(x) = 2\left(\frac{1}{x}\right)$ or $f(x) = \frac{2}{x}$

$[-9.4, 9.4, 1, -6.2, 6.2, 1]$

1e. $f(x) = 3\left(\frac{1}{x}\right) + 1$ or $f(x) = \frac{3}{x} + 1$

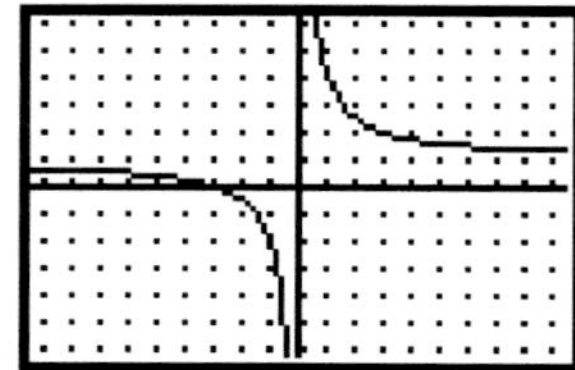

$[-9.4, 9.4, 1, -6.2, 6.2, 1]$

LESSON 9.7, PAGE 548

4a. 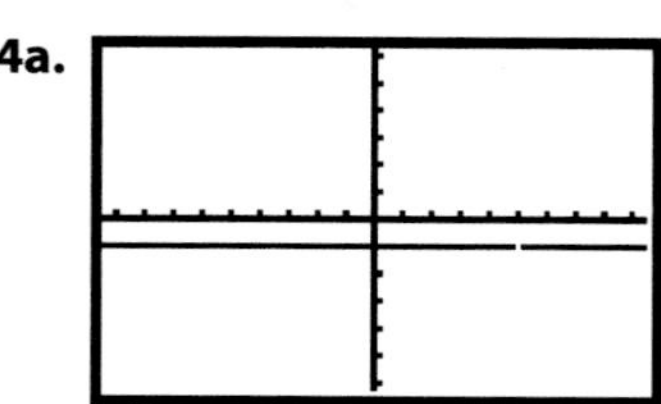

$[-9.4, 9.4, 1, -6.2, 6.2. 1]$

hole at $x = 5$

4b.

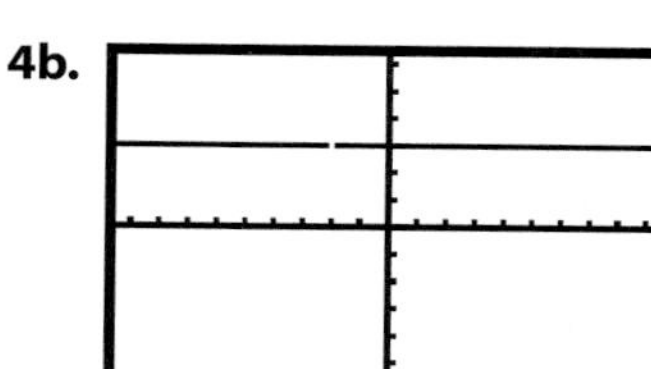

[−9.4, 9.4, 1, −6.2, 6.2. 1]

hole at $x = -2$

4c.

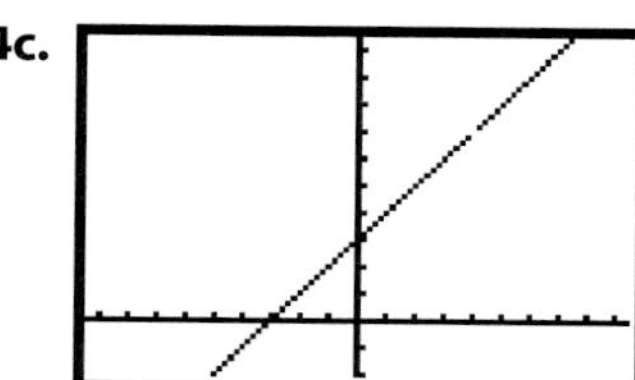

[−9.4, 9.4, 1, −2, 10.4]

hole at $x = 4$

5a. $y = \dfrac{x + 2}{x + 2}$

5b. $y = \dfrac{-2(x - 3)}{x - 3}$

5c. $y = \dfrac{(x + 2)(x + 1)}{x + 1}$

CHAPTER 9 REVIEW, PAGE 558

1a.

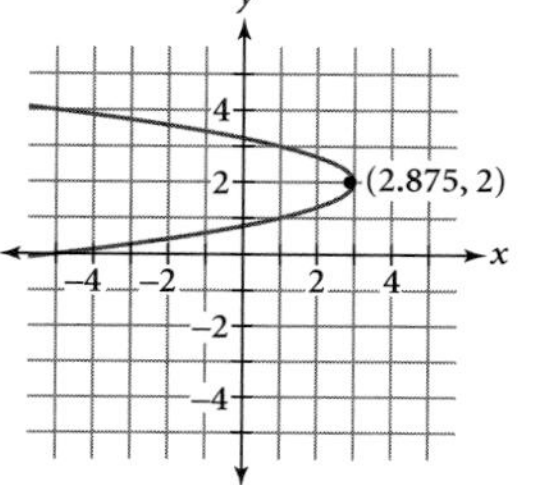

1b.

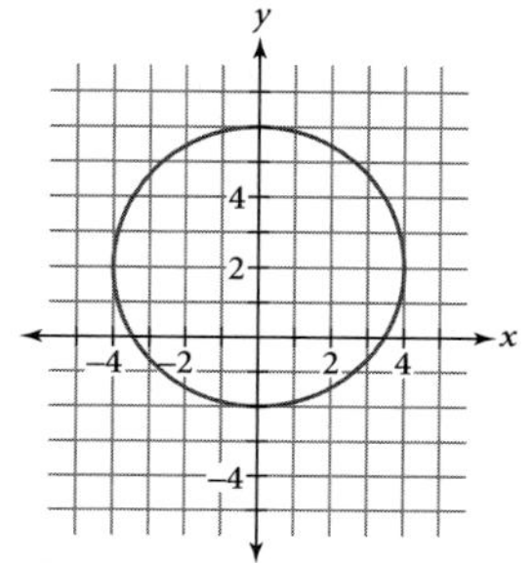

1c.

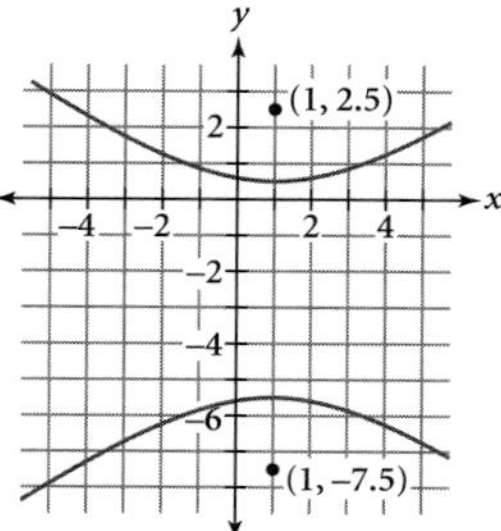

1d.

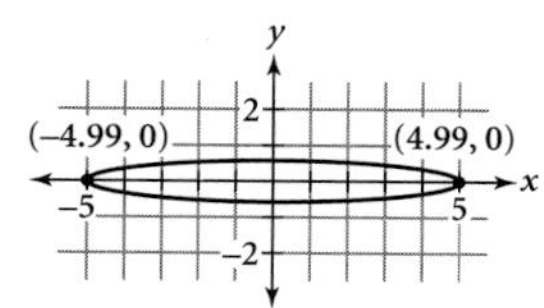

LESSON 10.1, PAGES 569, 571

2b. −0.8387; cos 147° = −cos 33°; reference angle 33°

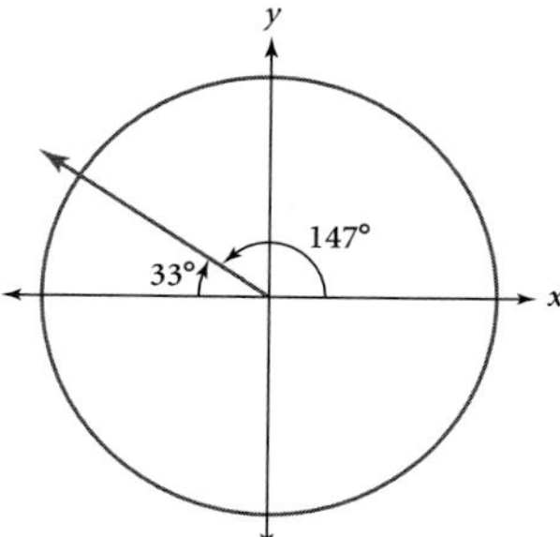

2c. −0.9848; sin 280° = −sin 80°; reference angle 80°

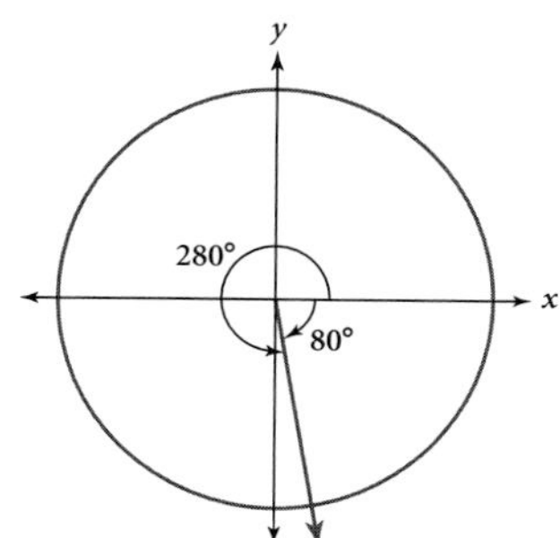

2d. 0.6428; cos 310° = cos 50°; reference angle 50°

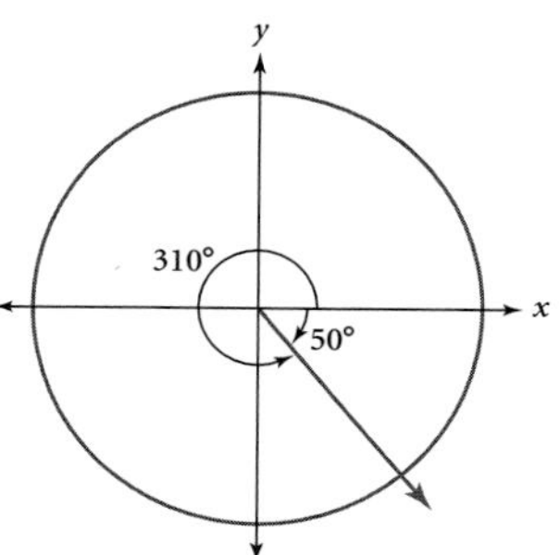

2e. −0.7314; sin (−47°) = −sin 47°; reference angle 47°

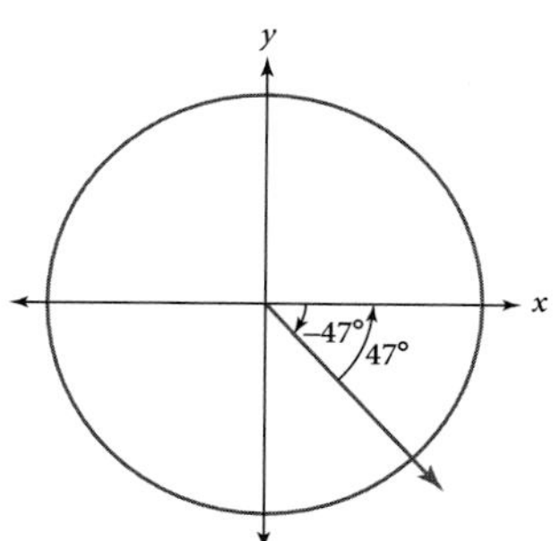

14.

θ	$\sin\theta$	$\cos\theta$	$\tan\theta$	$\frac{\sin\theta}{\cos\theta}$
0°	0	1	0	0
30°	0.5	0.866	0.577	0.577
60°	0.866	0.5	1.732	1.732
90°	1	0	undefined	undefined
120°	0.866	−0.5	−1.732	−1.732
150°	0.5	−0.866	−0.577	−0.577
180°	0	−1	0	0
210°	−0.5	−0.866	0.577	0.577
240°	−0.866	−0.5	1.732	1.732
270°	−1	0	undefined	undefined
300°	−0.866	0.5	−1.732	−1.732
330°	−0.5	0.866	−0.577	−0.577
360°	0	1	0	0

The values of $\tan\theta$ are equivalent to the ratio $\frac{\sin\theta}{\cos\theta}$.

$$\frac{\sin\theta}{\cos\theta} = \frac{\frac{\text{opposite}}{\text{hypotenuse}}}{\frac{\text{adjacent}}{\text{hypotenuse}}} = \frac{\text{opposite}}{\text{hypotenuse}} \cdot \frac{\text{hypotenuse}}{\text{adjacent}} =$$

$$\frac{\text{opposite}}{\text{adjacent}} = \tan\theta$$

LESSON 10.3, PAGES 585, 593

Investigation
sample data: See below.

17b. i.

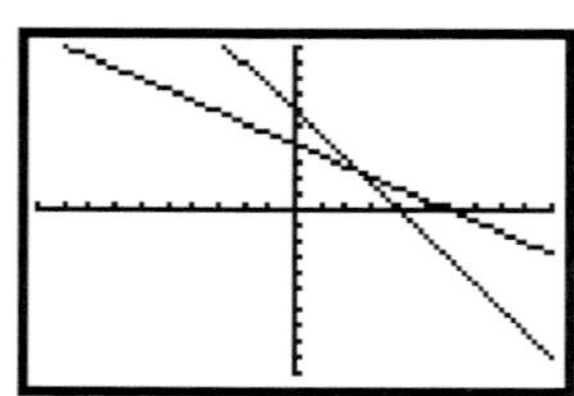

[−10, 10, 1, −10, 10, 1]

17b. ii.

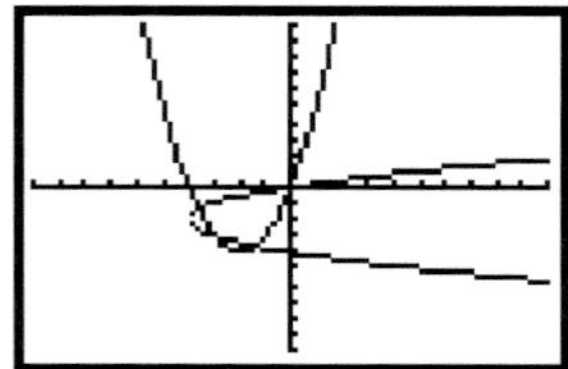

[−10, 10, 1, −10, 10, 1]

17b. iii.

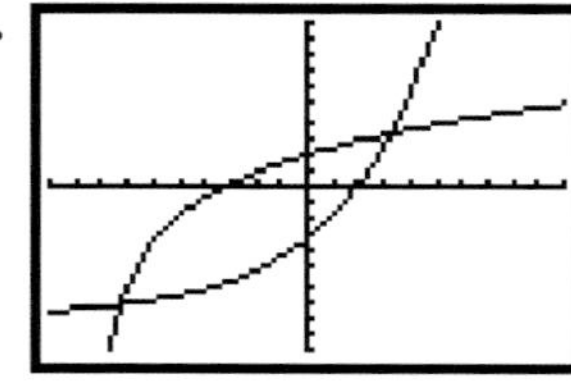

[−10, 10, 1, −10, 10, 1]

LESSON 10.4, PAGE 598

4a.

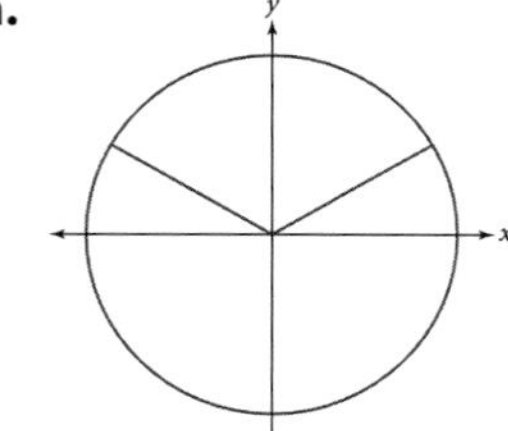

4b.

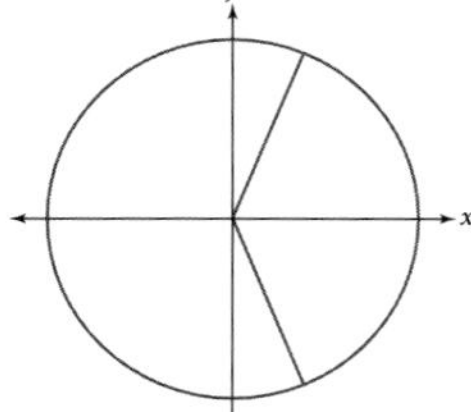

4c.

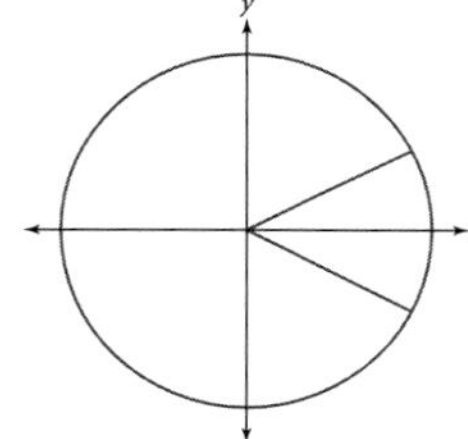

4d.

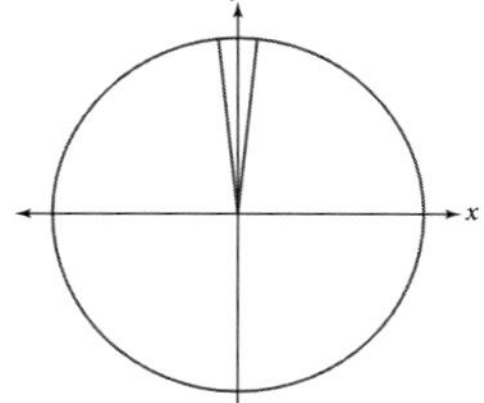

Investigation *(Lesson 10.3)*

Time (s)	Distance (m)	Time (s)	Distance (m)	Time (s)	Distance (m)	Time (s)	Distance (m)
0.05	0.900	0.55	0.749	1.05	0.766	1.55	0.889
0.10	0.903	0.60	0.730	1.10	0.786	1.60	0.879
0.15	0.899	0.65	0.714	1.15	0.809	1.65	0.863
0.20	0.888	0.70	0.704	1.20	0.830	1.70	0.844
0.25	0.873	0.75	0.698	1.25	0.850	1.75	0.824
0.30	0.855	0.80	0.697	1.30	0.867	1.80	0.802
0.35	0.836	0.85	0.702	1.35	0.881	1.85	0.779
0.40	0.814	0.90	0.712	1.40	0.891	1.90	0.760
0.45	0.791	0.95	0.727	1.45	0.894	1.95	0.740
0.50	0.768	1.00	0.745	1.50	0.894	2.00	0.724

LESSON 10.5, PAGE 603

Step 2 sample data:

Time (s)	Height (m)	Time (s)	Height (m)
0	0.561397	1.66656	0.581991
0.05376	0.563182	1.72032	0.607665
0.10752	0.578284	1.77408	0.630044
0.16128	0.604919	1.82784	0.665192
0.21504	0.639792	1.8816	0.699241
0.2688	0.673841	1.93536	0.720659
0.32256	0.699653	1.98912	0.731917
0.37632	0.71805	2.04288	0.728622
0.43008	0.724229	2.09664	0.715167
0.48384	0.719698	2.1504	0.687845
0.5376	0.729446	2.20416	0.664505
0.59136	0.701163	2.25792	0.631417
0.64512	0.632653	2.31168	0.607391
0.69888	0.603409	2.36544	0.592975
0.75264	0.576362	2.4192	0.586934
0.8064	0.564005	2.47296	0.592837
0.86016	0.587071	2.52672	0.609038
0.91392	0.597093	2.58048	0.632104
0.96768	0.640204	2.63424	0.657778
1.02144	0.668624	2.688	0.682628
1.0752	0.705831	2.74176	0.702261
1.12896	0.729308	2.79552	0.713794
1.18272	0.741253	2.84928	0.714206
1.23648	0.738919	2.90304	0.705419
1.29024	0.724366	2.9568	0.690454
1.344	0.695946	3.01056	0.667938
1.39776	0.656954	3.06432	0.64144
1.45152	0.620983	3.11808	0.618374
1.50528	0.587895	3.17184	0.60588
1.55904	0.567712	3.2256	0.597505
1.6128	0.5673	3.27936	0.597917

LESSON 10.6, PAGES 610, 611, 612

Step 1

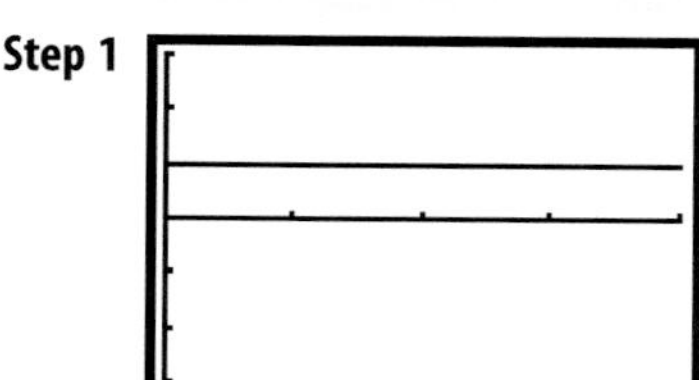

$[0, 2\pi, \pi/2, -3, 3, 1]$

$\sin^2 x + \cos^2 x = 1$

Step 2 By the Pythagorean Theorem, the sum of the squares of the right triangle's legs' lengths equals the square of the hypotenuse's length. For this right triangle, that means $(\sin A)^2 + (\cos A)^2 = 1$, or $\sin^2 A + \cos^2 A = 1$.

Step 3 In a unit circle with a reference triangle, $\sin x$ and $\cos x$ are the lengths of the legs of the right triangle, and 1 is the length of the hypotenuse. So, $\sin^2 x + \cos^2 x = 1$ is similar to $a^2 + b^2 = c^2$, the Pythagorean Theorem.

Step 5 $\frac{\sin^2 x}{\cos^2 x} + 1 = \frac{1}{\cos^2 x}$, or $\tan^2 x + 1 = \sec^2 x$

Proof:

$\tan^2 x + 1 \stackrel{?}{=} \sec^2 x$	Original equation.
$(\tan x)^2 + 1 \stackrel{?}{=} \sec^2 x$	$\tan^2 x$ means $(\tan x)^2$.
$\left(\frac{\sin x}{\cos x}\right)^2 + 1 \stackrel{?}{=} \sec^2 x$	Identity for $\tan x$.
$\frac{(\sin x)^2}{(\cos x)^2} + \frac{(\cos x)^2}{(\cos x)^2} \stackrel{?}{=} \sec^2 x$	Find a common denominator.
$\frac{(\sin x)^2 + (\cos x)^2}{(\cos x)^2} \stackrel{?}{=} \sec^2 x$	Add.
$\frac{1}{(\cos x)^2} \stackrel{?}{=} \sec^2 x$	Pythagorean identity.
$\left(\frac{1}{\cos x}\right)^2 \stackrel{?}{=} \sec^2 x$	Consider 1 to be 1^2. Then you can rewrite $\frac{1^2}{(\cos x)^2}$ as $\left(\frac{1}{\cos x}\right)^2$.
$(\sec x)^2 \stackrel{?}{=} \sec^2 x$	Reciprocal identity.
$\sec^2 x = \sec^2 x$	$\sec^2 x$ means $(\sec x)^2$.

Step 6

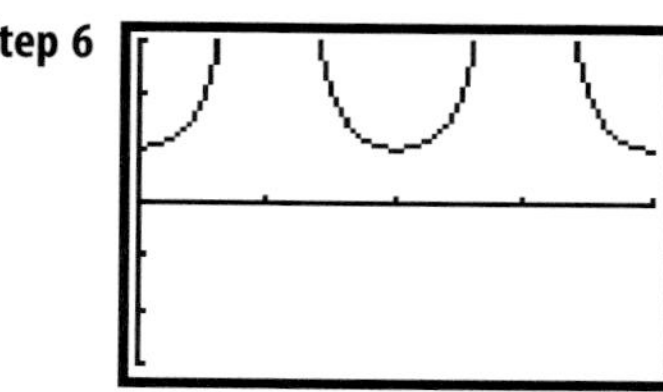

$[0, 2\pi, \pi/2, -3, 3, 1]$

The domain values are undefined when $\cos x = 0$, or when $x = \frac{\pi}{2} + \pi n$ or $x = 90° + 180°n$ where n is an integer.

Step 7 $1 + \dfrac{\cos^2 x}{\sin^2 x} = \dfrac{1}{\sin^2 x}$, or $1 + \cot^2 x = \csc^2 x$

Proof:	
$1 + \cot^2 x \stackrel{?}{=} \csc^2 x$	Original equation.
$1 + (\cot x)^2 \stackrel{?}{=} \csc^2 x$	$\cot^2 x$ means $(\cot x)^2$.
$1 + \left(\dfrac{\cos x}{\sin x}\right)^2 \stackrel{?}{=} \csc^2 x$	Identity for $\cot x$.
$\dfrac{(\sin x)^2}{(\sin x)^2} + \dfrac{(\cos x)^2}{(\sin x)^2} \stackrel{?}{=} \csc^2 x$	Find a common denominator.
$\dfrac{(\sin x)^2 + (\cos x)^2}{(\sin x)^2} \stackrel{?}{=} \csc^2 x$	Add.
$\dfrac{1}{(\sin x)^2} \stackrel{?}{=} \csc^2 x$	Pythagorean identity.
$\left(\dfrac{1}{\sin x}\right)^2 \stackrel{?}{=} \csc^2 x$	Consider 1 to be 1^2. Then rewrite $\frac{1^2}{(\sin x)^2}$ as $\left(\frac{1}{\sin x}\right)^2$.
$(\csc x)^2 \stackrel{?}{=} \csc^2 x$	Reciprocal identity.
$\csc^2 x = \csc^2 x$	$\csc^2 x$ means $(\csc x)^2$.

Step 8

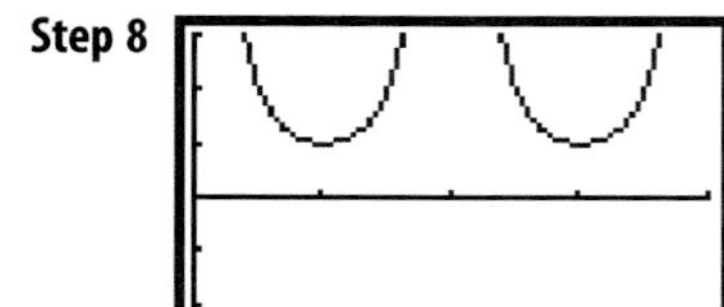

$[0, 2\pi, \pi/2, -3, 3, 1]$

The domain values are undefined when $\sin x = 0$, or when $x = \pi n$ or $x = 180°n$ where n is an integer.

3. Proof:

$\tan x(\cot x + \tan x) \stackrel{?}{=} \sec^2 x$	Original equation.
$\tan x \cot x + (\tan x)^2 \stackrel{?}{=} \sec^2 x$	Distribute.
$\tan x \cdot \dfrac{1}{\tan x} + \tan^2 x \stackrel{?}{=} \sec^2 x$	Reciprocal identity.
$1 + \tan^2 x \stackrel{?}{=} \sec^2 x$	Reduce.
$\sec^2 x = \sec^2 x$	Pythagorean identity.

11a.

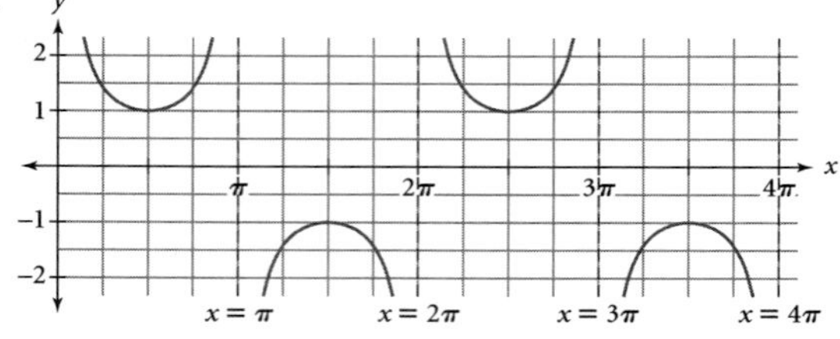

11b.

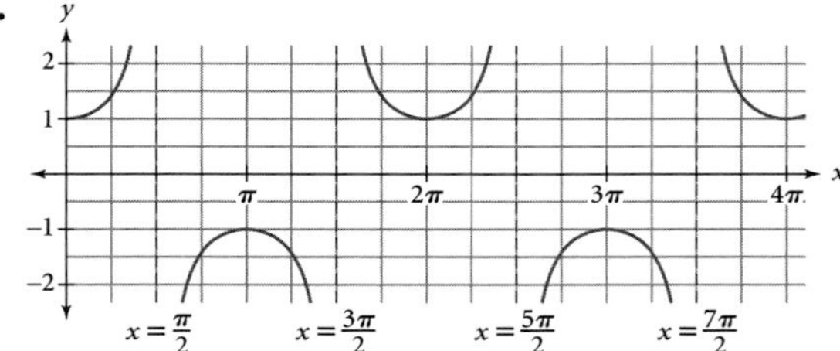

11c.

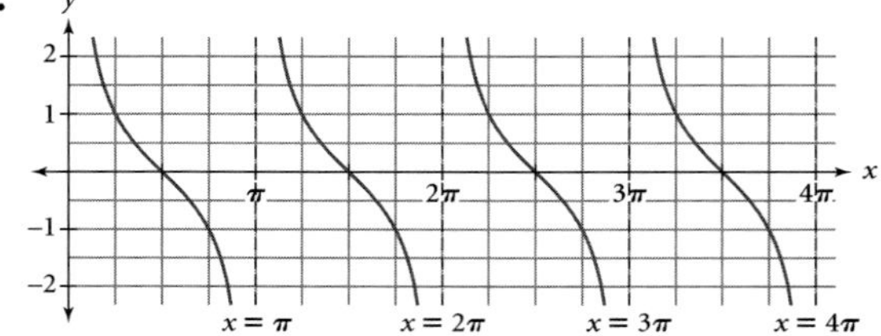

LESSON 10.7, PAGES 616, 617, 620

Step 1 sample data for a single G-392 Hz tuning fork:

Time (s) x	Pressure y	Time (s) x	Pressure y
0	2.6569	0.0105	2.76435
0.0005	2.79853	0.011	2.79976
0.001	2.78022	0.0115	2.663
0.0015	2.62759	0.012	2.57143
0.002	2.55433	0.0125	2.61661
0.0025	2.65568	0.013	2.75824
0.003	2.79487	0.0135	2.79731
0.0035	2.78999	0.014	2.67888
0.004	2.63614	0.0145	2.57021
0.0045	2.558	0.015	2.60806
0.005	2.64225	0.0155	2.75214
0.0055	2.7851	0.016	2.79853
0.006	2.78877	0.0165	2.69597
0.0065	2.64713	0.017	2.56777
0.007	2.56288	0.0175	2.60684
0.0075	2.63736	0.018	2.73626
0.008	2.779	0.0185	2.81075
0.0085	2.78877	0.019	2.70208
0.009	2.6569	0.0195	2.57753
0.0095	2.55678	0.02	2.59341
0.01	2.63248		

sample data for a single C-256 Hz tuning fork:

Time (s) x	Pressure y	Time (s) x	Pressure y
0	2.63542	0.0105	2.70862
0.0005	2.60602	0.011	2.67934
0.001	2.63542	0.0115	2.60602
0.0015	2.67934	0.012	2.63542
0.002	2.76718	0.0125	2.65006
0.0025	2.76718	0.013	2.70862
0.003	2.72326	0.0135	2.7379
0.0035	2.60602	0.014	2.72326
0.004	2.59138	0.0145	2.70862
0.0045	2.65006	0.015	2.63542
0.005	2.65006	0.0155	2.62066
0.0055	2.72326	0.016	2.59138
0.006	2.7379	0.0165	2.6647
0.0065	2.76718	0.017	2.75254
0.007	2.69398	0.0175	2.79658
0.0075	2.65006	0.018	2.72326
0.008	2.57674	0.0185	2.63542
0.0085	2.63542	0.019	2.62066
0.009	2.6647	0.0195	2.63542
0.0095	2.75254	0.02	2.62066
0.01	2.7379		

Step 2 sample data for the combination of G and C tuning forks:

Time (s) x	Pressure y	Time (s) x	Pressure y
0	2.44078	0.0105	2.67155
0.0005	2.46154	0.011	2.81807
0.001	2.69841	0.0115	2.83883
0.0015	2.83761	0.012	2.6105
0.002	2.75946	0.0125	2.41026
0.0025	2.63614	0.013	2.48718
0.003	2.67033	0.0135	2.78999
0.0035	2.78266	0.014	2.98657
0.004	2.77656	0.0145	2.8486
0.0045	2.57021	0.015	2.57143
0.005	2.43346	0.0155	2.47497
0.0055	2.56166	0.016	2.62515
0.006	2.86569	0.0165	2.7619
0.0065	2.99023	0.017	2.70574
0.007	2.78266	0.0175	2.58608
0.0075	2.49939	0.018	2.66056
0.008	2.45299	0.0185	2.84249
0.0085	2.65568	0.019	2.89255
0.009	2.80098	0.0195	2.67399
0.0095	2.73626	0.02	2.42857
0.01	2.61172		

Step 3 sample data for a tin whistle:

Time (s) x	Pressure y	Time (s) x	Pressure y
0	2.5409	0.0105	2.75092
0.0005	2.73871	0.011	2.66911
0.001	2.78022	0.0115	2.54701
0.0015	2.59096	0.012	2.74481
0.002	2.71673	0.0125	2.77411
0.0025	2.84005	0.013	2.59096
0.003	2.62149	0.0135	2.71429
0.0035	2.62027	0.014	2.85226
0.004	2.77045	0.0145	2.62393
0.0045	2.63492	0.015	2.60806
0.005	2.51893	0.0155	2.77411
0.0055	2.74725	0.016	2.62759
0.006	2.71429	0.0165	2.53236
0.0065	2.57021	0.017	2.73993
0.007	2.72772	0.0175	2.7094
0.0075	2.82662	0.018	2.56777
0.008	2.61538	0.0185	2.7326
0.0085	2.68132	0.019	2.83761
0.009	2.81807	0.0195	2.60806
0.0095	2.61538	0.02	2.66667
0.01	2.54945		

Graph for a tin whistle:

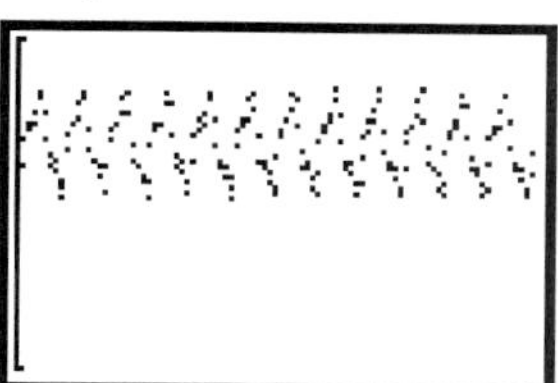

[0, 0.02, 1, 2, 3, 1]

Because this graphing window shows approximately 12 periods, the fundamental frequency is $\frac{0.02}{12}$, or approximately 0.0017 s.

6. Proof:

$$\sin(A + B) \stackrel{?}{=} \sin A \cos B + \cos A \sin B$$

$$\cos\left(\frac{\pi}{2} - (A + B)\right) \stackrel{?}{=} \sin A \cos B + \cos A \sin B$$

$$\cos\left(\left(\frac{\pi}{2} - A\right) - B\right) \stackrel{?}{=} \sin A \cos B + \cos A \sin B$$

$$\cos\left(\frac{\pi}{2} - A\right)\cos B + \sin\left(\frac{\pi}{2} - A\right)\sin B \stackrel{?}{=} \sin A \cos B + \cos A \sin B$$

$$\sin A \cos B + \cos A \sin B = \sin A \cos B + \cos A \sin B$$

7. Proof:

$$\sin(A - B) \stackrel{?}{=} \sin A \cos B - \cos A \sin B$$
$$\sin(A + (-B)) \stackrel{?}{=} \sin A \cos B - \cos A \sin B$$
$$\sin A \cos(-B) + \cos A \sin(-B) \stackrel{?}{=} \sin A \cos B - \cos A \sin B$$
$$\sin A \cos B + \cos A(-\sin B) \stackrel{?}{=} \sin A \cos B - \cos A \sin B$$
$$\sin A \cos B - \cos A \sin B = \sin A \cos B - \cos A \sin B$$

8. Proof:

$$\sin 2A \stackrel{?}{=} 2 \sin A \cos A$$
$$\sin(A + A) \stackrel{?}{=} 2 \sin A \cos A$$
$$\sin A \cos A + \cos A \sin A \stackrel{?}{=} 2 \sin A \cos A$$
$$2 \sin A \cos A = 2 \sin A \cos A$$

9. Proof:

$$\cos(2A) \stackrel{?}{=} \cos^2 A - \sin^2 A$$
$$\cos(A + A) \stackrel{?}{=} \cos^2 A - \sin^2 A$$
$$\cos A \cos A - \sin A \sin A \stackrel{?}{=} \cos^2 A - \sin^2 A$$
$$\cos^2 A - \sin^2 A = \cos^2 A - \sin^2 A$$

LESSON 11.1, PAGE 632

Step 2

n	S_n	D_1	D_2
1	5		
		9	
2	14		4
		13	
3	27		4
		17	
4	44		4
		21	
5	65		4
		25	
6	90		4
		29	
7	119		4
		33	
8	152		4
		37	
9	189		4
		41	
10	230		

degree: 2; $S_n = 2n^2 + 3n$

Step 4 sample answers:

First term u_1	Common difference d	Partial sum S_n
4	4	$S_n = 2n^2 + 2n$
4	5	$S_n = 2.5n^2 + 1.5n$
4	6	$S_n = 3n^2 + n$
5	4	$S_n = 2n^2 + 3n$
5	5	$S_n = 2.5n^2 + 2.5n$
5	6	$S_n = 3n^2 + 2n$
6	4	$S_n = 2n^2 + 4n$
6	5	$S_n = 2.5n^2 + 3.5n$
6	6	$S_n = 3n^2 + 3n$

LESSON 11.2, PAGE 641

7c.

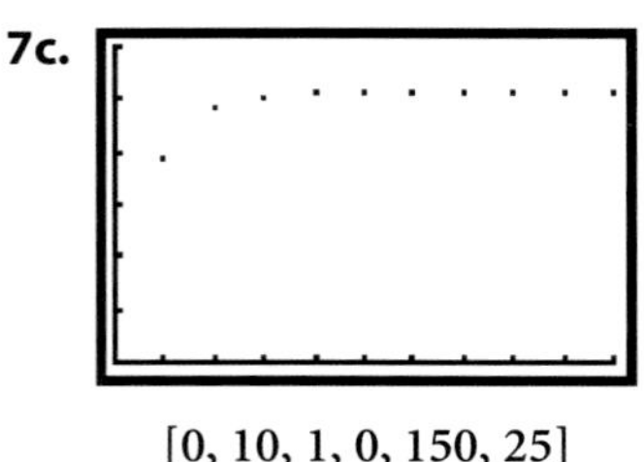

[0, 10, 1, 0, 150, 25]

LESSON 11.3, PAGE 645

Step 2

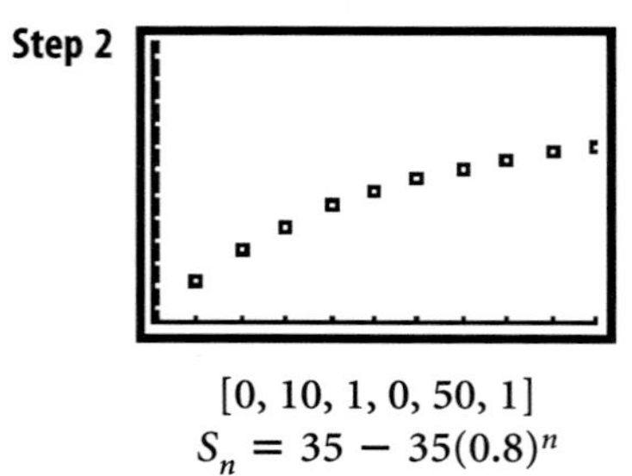

[0, 10, 1, 0, 50, 1]
$S_n = 35 - 35(0.8)^n$

EXPLORATION, PAGE 666

Step 2 Sample answer: To determine where the center of a coin must land for a successful outcome, first subtract the coin diameter from the square side length. If the result is negative, it is impossible to have a successful coin toss. Otherwise, the result tells you that the center of the coin must fall within a square of that side length, centered in a grid square. For example, for a penny with diameter 19 mm, and grid of side length 20 mm, the center of the coin must fall within a 1 mm × 1 mm square in the center of a grid square. The area of this square is 1 mm², and the total area of the square is 400 mm². Results for each combination are given in the table below. For the fourth type of grid paper, consider that the side length of a grid square is 40 mm, with 2.5 mm added on each end, for a total side length of 45 mm.

Step 2, 3

	20 mm grid	30 mm grid	40 mm grid	40 mm grid with 5 mm lines
Penny	$\frac{1}{400} = .0025$	$\frac{121}{900} \approx .134$	$\frac{441}{1600} \approx .276$	$\frac{441}{2025} \approx .218$
Nickel	$\frac{0}{400} = 0$	$\frac{81}{900} = .09$	$\frac{361}{1600} \approx .226$	$\frac{361}{2025} \approx .178$
Dime	$\frac{4}{400} = .01$	$\frac{144}{900} = .16$	$\frac{484}{1600} = .3025$	$\frac{484}{2025} \approx .239$
Quarter	$\frac{0}{400} = 0$	$\frac{36}{900} \approx .04$	$\frac{256}{1600} = .16$	$\frac{256}{2025} \approx .126$

LESSON 12.2, PAGE 669

Step 2

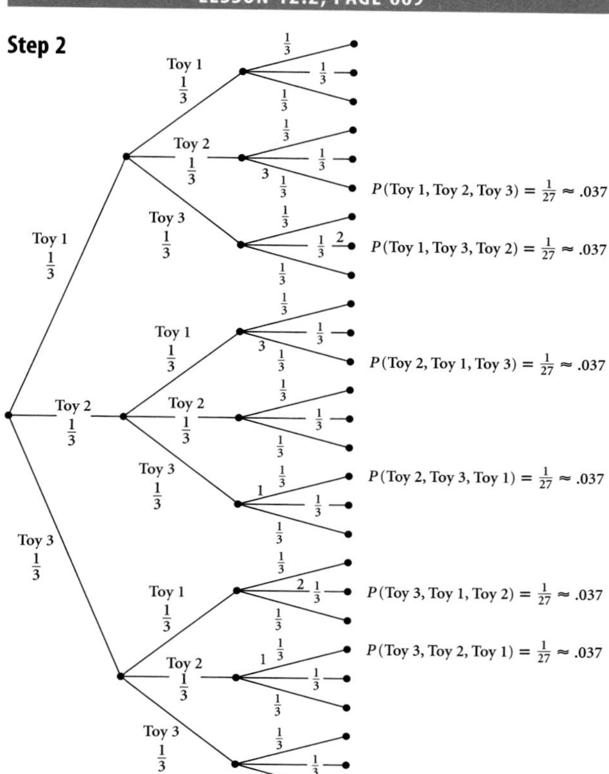

$P(\text{all possible paths}) = 1$;

$P(\text{highlighted paths}) = \frac{6}{27} \approx .222$

EXPLORATION, PAGES 677, 678

Step 3 There should be approximately the same number of each outcome, so the bins should be approximately even.

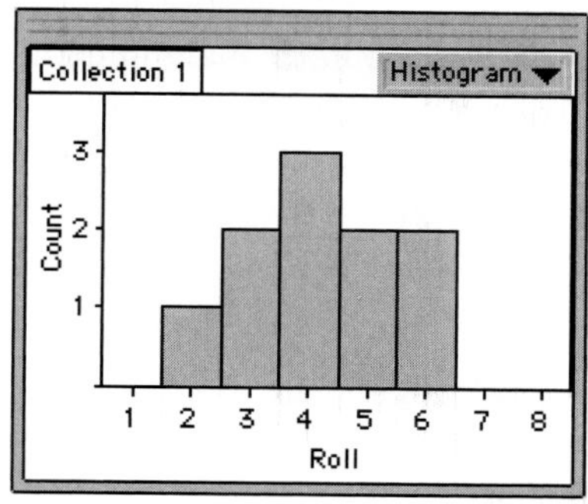

There ended up being no 1's and an uneven number of 2's and 4's.

Step 7 The bins are somewhat more even, although there is still a lot of difference in the heights of the bins. Compared to the histogram for 10 cases, the histogram for 100 cases shows that some 1's were rolled and that 4 is no longer the mode.

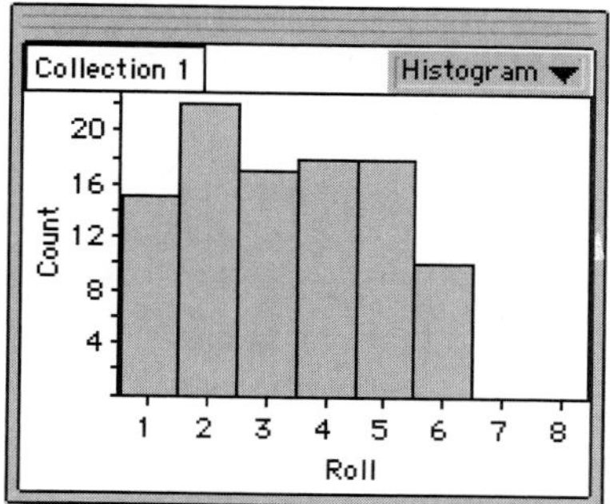

Step 8 The mode is 2, and the range is approximately 12. The random generator does not seem to favor one number, because when you rerandomize the results are very different each time.

Step 9 The bins should be more even.

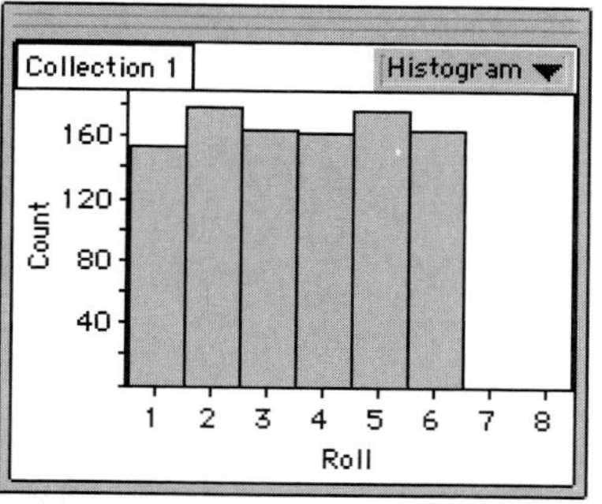

The mode is 2 and the range is approximately 30, because the number of occurences varies from about 150 to about 180. The random generator does not seem to favor one number.

LESSON 12.7, PAGE 718

18a. The experimental probabilities are likely to be different from .5 and .5. In this sample simulation, $P(\text{H}) = .6$ and $P(\text{T}) = .4$.

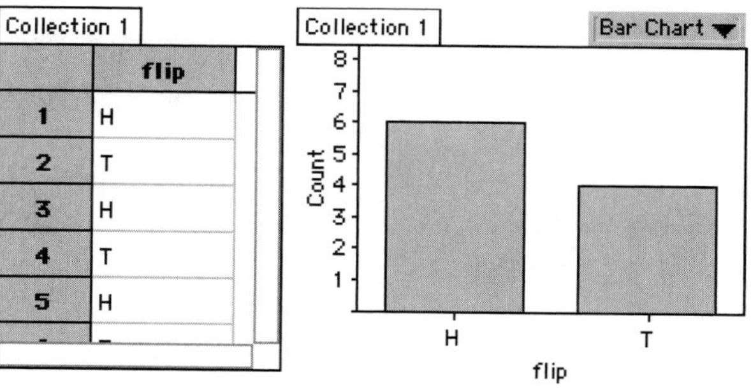

18b. The experimental probabilities should be closer to .5 and .5, but are likely to not yet be exact. In this sample simulation, $P(\text{H}) = .49$ and $P(\text{T}) = .51$.

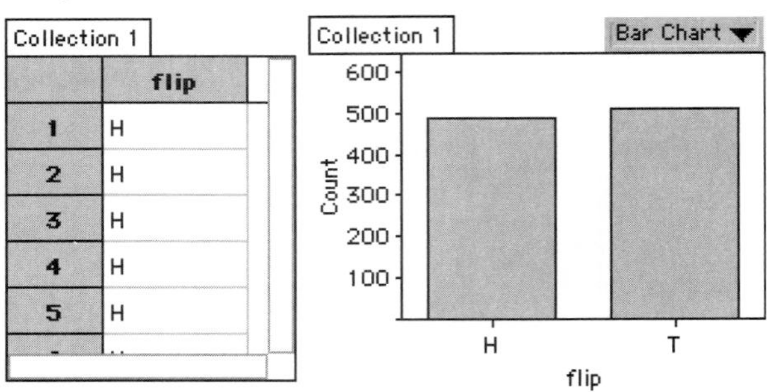

18c. You create an unfair coin by defining **randomPick** with more heads to choose from. For example, **randomPick("H","H","H","T")** would make the experimental probability of heads approximately .75.

LESSON 13.1, PAGES 725, 729

Step 3

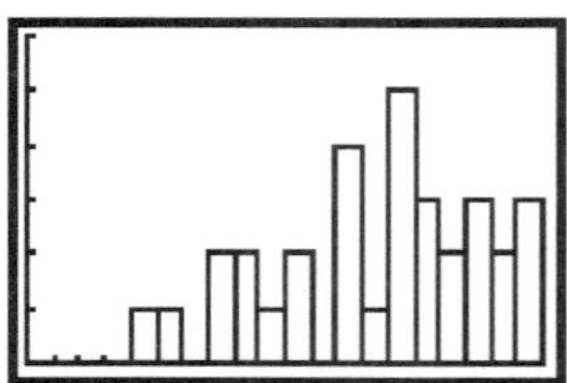

[0, 20, 1, 0, 0.1875, 0.03125]

6b. Sample answer: mode = 4.5, median ≈ 4

8. Solutions will vary. General shapes are shown below.

8a.

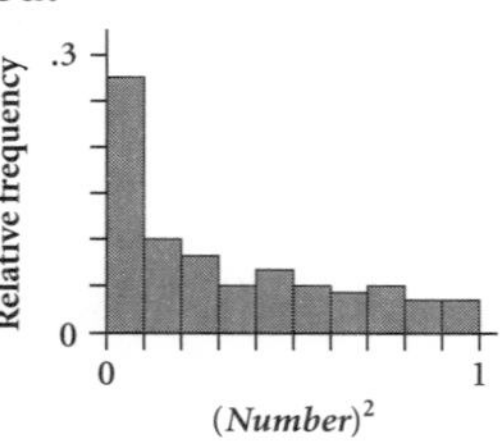

The range is 0 to 1. If you square a number less than 1, the result is smaller than the original number.

8b.

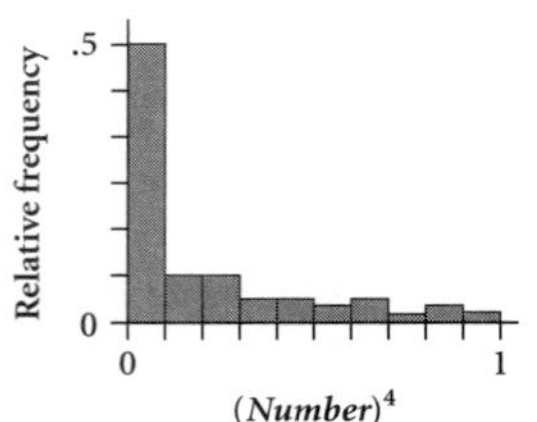

Raising numbers between 0 and 1 to the power of 4 gives even smaller results, but they remain between 0 and 1.

8c.

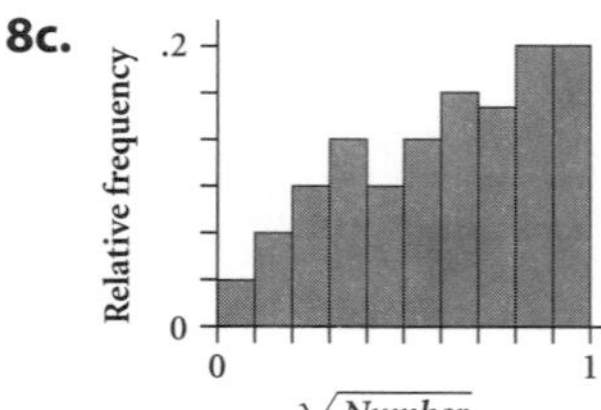

Taking square roots of numbers between 0 and 1 gives larger results, but still never larger than 1.

9a. Sample histograms for 100 trials.

[0, 1, 0.1, −0.1, 0.4, 0.1]

9b.

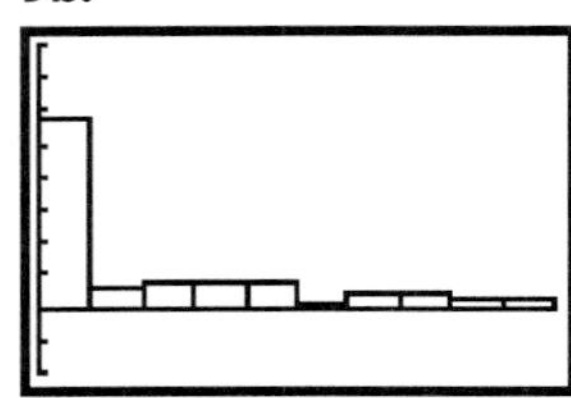

[0, 1, 0.1, −0.1, 0.4, 0.1]

9c.

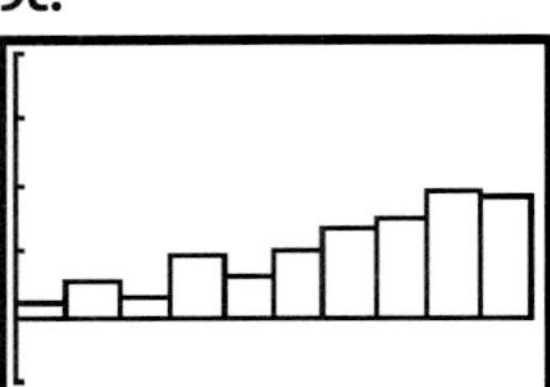

[0, 1, 0.1, −0.1, 0.4, 0.1]

10a. possible answer:

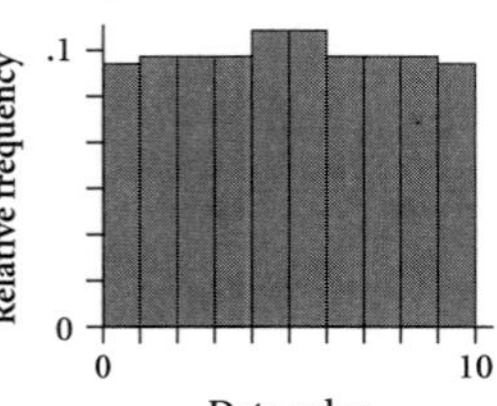

10b. possible answer:

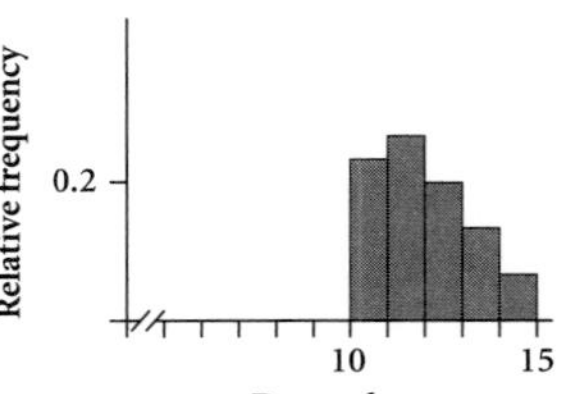

LESSON 13.2, PAGES 734, 741

Step 2

Heads (x)	0	1	2	3	4	5	6	7
$P(x)$	.000	.000	.003	.014	.042	.092	.153	.196

Heads (x)	8	9	10	11	12	13	14	15
$P(x)$	.196	.153	.092	.042	.014	.003	.000	.000

The sum is the total of the probabilities of all different outcomes, 1.

Step 3

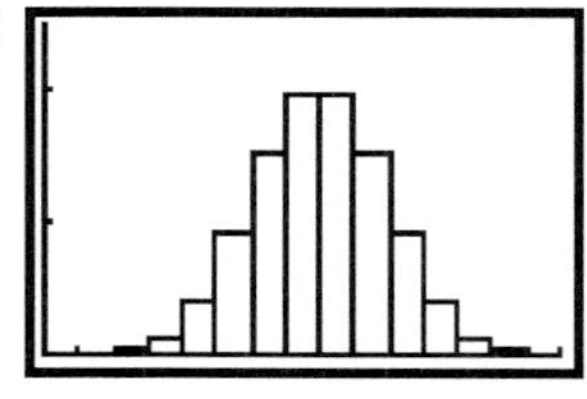

[0, 15, 1, 0, 0.25, 0.1]

The histogram is mound-shaped and symmetric. The maximum value is .196 at $x = 7$ and $x = 8$, and the minimum value is 0 at $x = 0$, $x = 1$, $x = 14$, and $x = 15$.

7a.

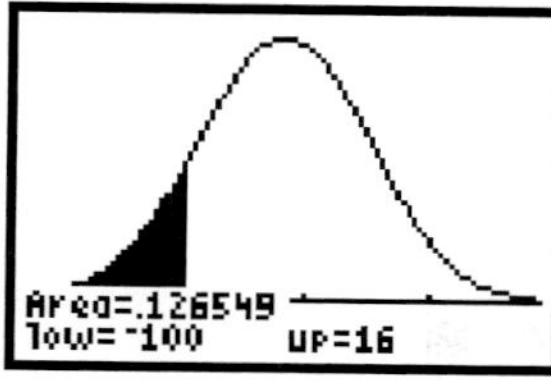

[14.7, 18.9, 1, −0.1, 0.6, 0]

7b. 12.7%. Sample answer: Not acceptable; more than 10% of boxes do not meet minimum weight requirements.

8a. Guess-and-check will provide a mean of about 12.96 oz so that the region with leftmost endpoint of 12 provides an area of 0.90.

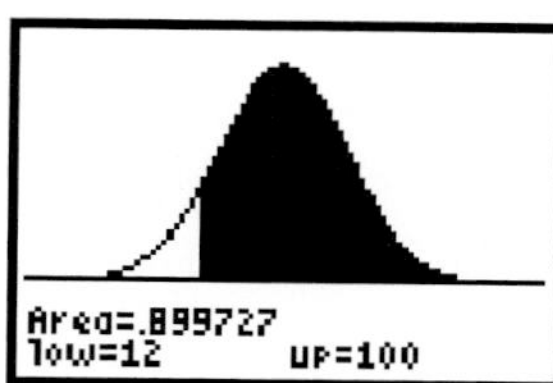

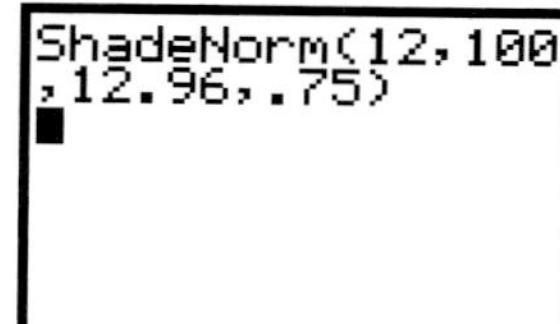

8b.

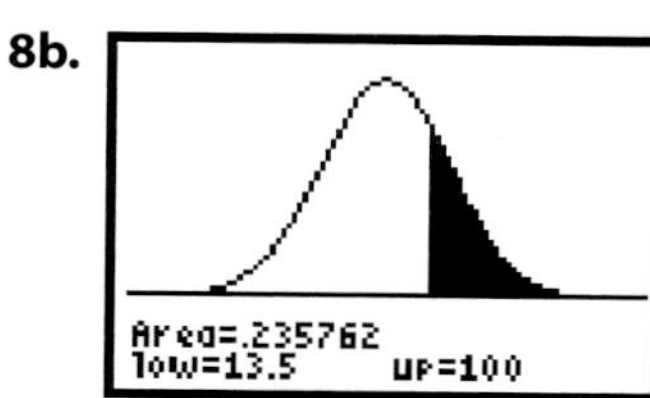

$N(13.5, 20, 12.96, 0.75) \approx 0.24 = 24\%$

11a. $\mu = 79.1, \sigma \approx 7.49$

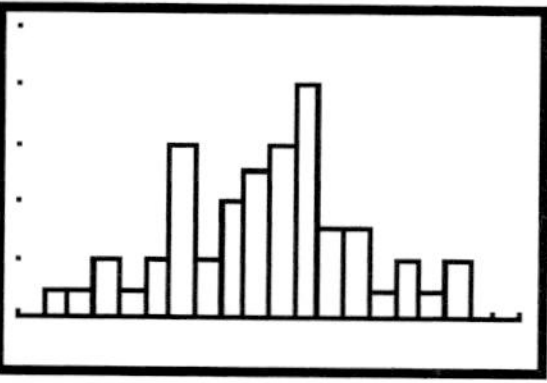

[60, 100, 2, −1, 10, 2]

11b. sample answer:

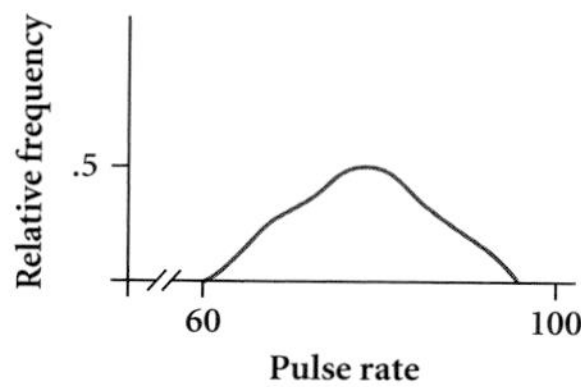

11c. $y = \frac{1}{7.49\sqrt{2\pi}}\left(\sqrt{e}\right)^{-((x-79.1)/7.49)^2}$

11d. Answers will vary. The data do not appear to be normally distributed. They seem to be approximately symmetrically distributed with several peaks.

EXPLORATION, PAGE 761

Step 3 possible answer:

p	2.5th percentile	97.5th percentile	Is a result of 53% probable?	Is a result of 78% probable?
0	0	0	no	no
.1	4	20	no	no
.2	10	32	no	no
.3	18	46	no	no
.4	26	52	no	no
.5	36	64	yes	no
.6	46	74	yes	no
.7	58	80	no	yes
.8	70	92	no	yes
.9	80	98	no	no
1	100	100	no	no

Step 4

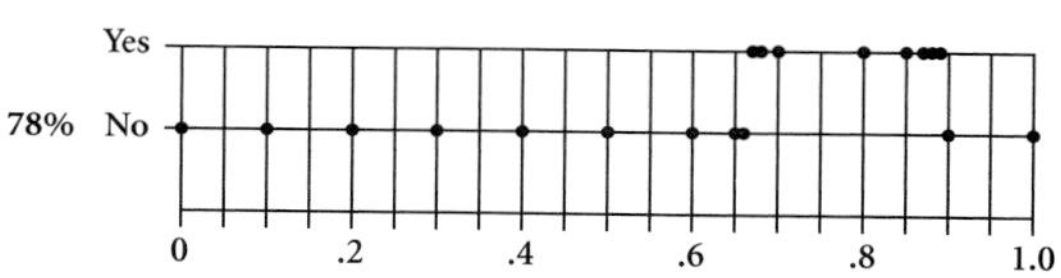

Step 5 A result of 53% is probable for p-values between .42 and .66. A result of 78% is probable for p-values between .67 and .89.

Additional Answers

LESSON 13.5, PAGE 764

Step 3 sample data:

Student #	Question 1	Question 2	Question 3	Question 4	Question 5
1	0	120	60	100	3
2	20	120	90	200	4
3	80	65	80	140	6
4	55	20	220	260	5
5	10	20	155	200	4
6	15	0	145	200	4
7	90	10	80	150	6
8	215	10	0	60	6
9	100	0	140	150	6
10	60	30	120	105	5
11	65	0	120	150	6
12	10	60	300	360	4
13	120	0	0	45	6
14	30	45	285	90	4
15	40	60	150	190	4
16	0	85	150	75	3
17	0	180	30	30	4
18	80	0	0	0	6
19	90	20	0	0	6
20	45	10	180	285	5
21	10	120	0	90	4
22	40	30	100	115	5
23	0	0	360	60	5
24	30	50	45	90	5
25	60	20	30	90	6
26	45	20	30	45	5
27	20	105	20	60	4
28	0	90	0	120	4
29	50	40	0	90	5
30	40	10	0	45	4

LESSON 13.6, PAGE 773

Step 1 Sample data:

Student number	Hand span	Foot length	Length of little finger	Height	Length of cubit	Length of lower leg	Length of upper arm	Width of thumbnail
1	18.5	23.5	6	159	41.6	47	31	1.2
2	21.2	26	6.5	170	42	48	36	1.3
3	20.8	25.8	6.2	173	44.2	49.5	36.2	1.3
4	20.4	24.5	6.1	164	42.1	48.5	34	1.3
5	18.1	23	5.9	155	39.5	46	30.2	1.2
6	22	28.4	6.5	189	47.5	52.2	40.5	1.4
7	20.5	29	6.4	191	47.9	52.6	41	1.4
8	20.7	26.2	6.2	175	46	51	34	1.3
9	20.5	25	6.1	168	44	50	35.4	1.2
10	19.2	24.1	5.9	158	43.5	48	33.6	1.1

LESSON 13.7, PAGE 784

Step 4 exponential; root mean square error is approximately 1.595

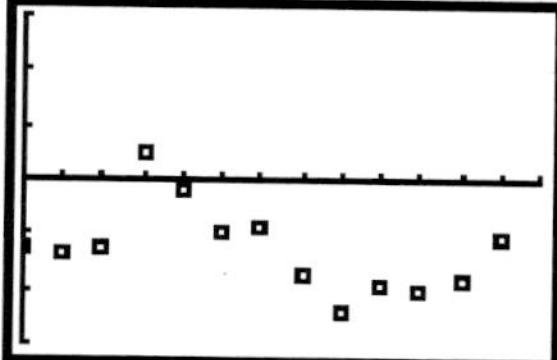

[0, 130, 10, −3, 3, 1]

quadratic; root mean square error is approximately 1.095

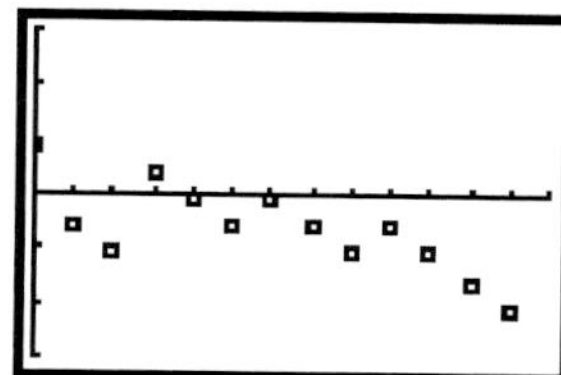

[0, 130, 10, −3, 3, 1]

cubic; root mean square error is approximately 1.422

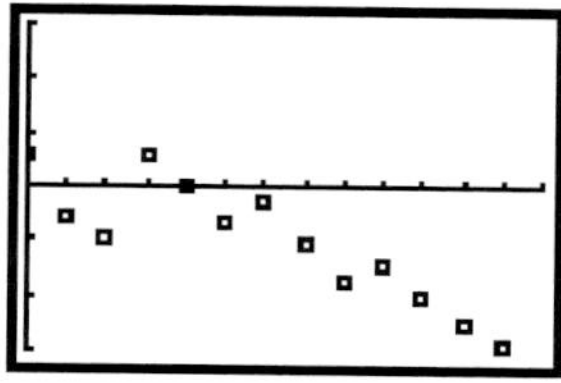

[0, 130, 10, −3, 3, 1]

Step 5 The quadratic curve is best. It has the least root mean square error and presents less of a pattern in the residuals than the other models.

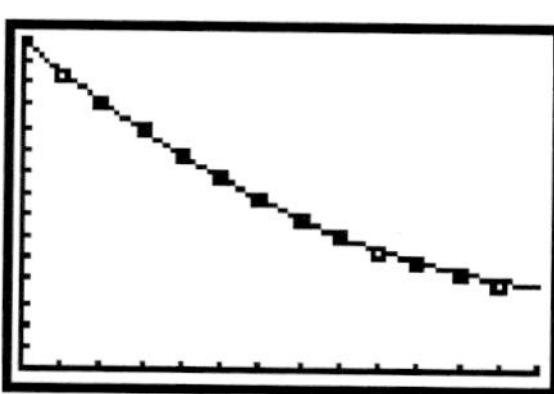

[0, 130, 10, 0, 150, 10]

1a.

[0, 7, 1, 0, 80, 10]

1b.

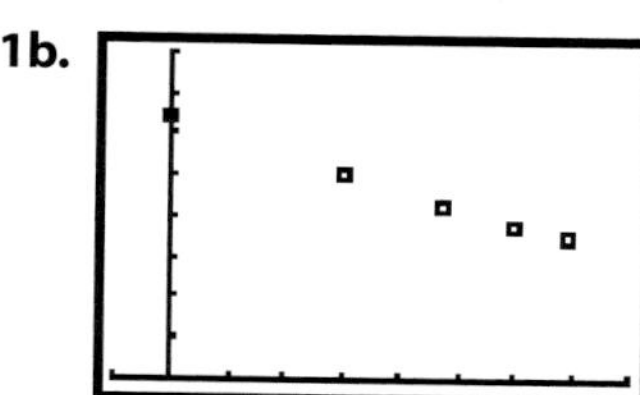

[−0.1, 0.8, 0.1, 0, 80, 10]

1c.

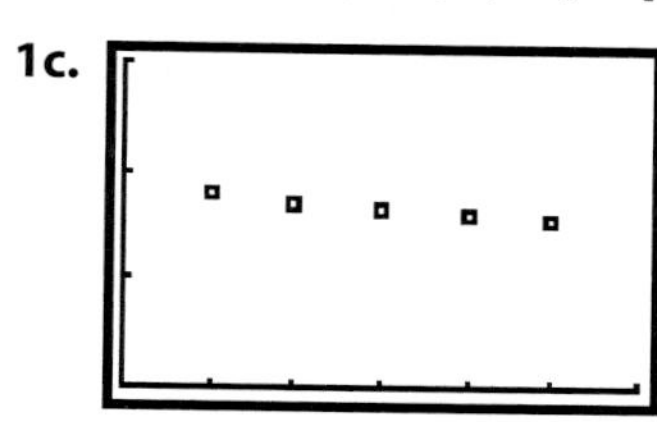

[0, 6, 1, 0, 3, 1]

1d.

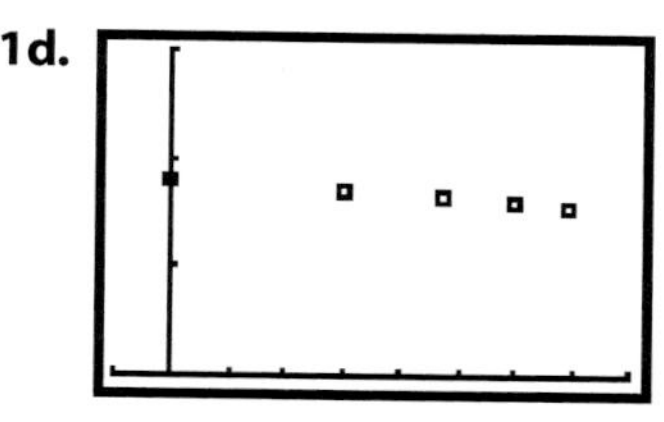

[−0.1, 0.8, 0.1, 0, 3, 1]